Petroleum Geology of Northwest Europe: Proceedings of the 5th Conference

Volume 2

Petroleum Geology of Northwest Europe: Proceedings of the 5th Conference

held at the Barbican Centre, London, 26–29 October 1997

Volume 2

edited by

A. J. Fleet
The Natural History Museum, London

and

S. A. R. Boldy
Amerada Hess Norge A/S, Oslo

with

S. D. Burley	BG Technology, Loughborough
R.E. Dunay	Mobil North Sea Limited, London
S. S. Flint	University of Liverpool
S. I. Fraser	Amerada Hess Ltd, London
A. Hurst	University of Aberdeen
H. D. Johnson	Imperial College, London
B. Levell	Petroleum Development Oman, Muscat
J. W. Munns	Oil and Gas Division, UK Department of Trade and Industry
P. M. Shannon	University College, Dublin
A. M. Spencer	Statoil, Stavanger
M. Thompson	BP Exploration Operating Company Ltd, Uxbridge
J. R. Underhill	University of Edinburgh

1999

Published by

The Geological Society

London

THE GEOLOGICAL SOCIETY

The Geological Society of London was founded in 1807 and is the oldest geological society in the world. It received its Royal Charter in 1825 for the purpose of 'investigating the mineral structure of the Earth' and is now Britain's national society for geology. Both a learned society and a professional body, the Geological Society is recognized by the Department of Trade and Industry (DTI) as the chartering authority for geoscience, able to award Chartered Geologist status upon appropriately qualified Fellows. The Society has a membership of 8600, of whom about 1500 live outside the UK.

Fellowship of the Society is open to persons holding a recognized honours degree in geology or a cognate subject and who have at least two years' relevant postgraduate experience, or not less than six years' relevant experience in geology or a cognate subject. A Fellow with a minimum of five years' relevant postgraduate experience in the practice of geology may apply for chartered status. Successful applicants are entitled to use the designatory postnominal CGeol (Chartered Geologist). Fellows of the Society may use the letters FGS. Other grades of membership are available to members not yet qualifying for Fellowship.

The Society has its own Publishing House based in Bath, UK. It produces the Society's international journals, books and maps, and is the European distributor for publications of the American Association of Petroleum Geologists (AAPG), the Society for Sedimentary Geology (SEPM) and the Geological Society of America (GSA). Members of the Society can buy books at considerable discounts. The Publishing House has an online bookshop (*http://bookshop.geolsoc.org.uk http://bookshop.geolsoc.org.uk*).

Further information on Society membership may be obtained from the Membership Services Manager, The Geological Society, Burlington House, Piccadilly, London W1V 0JU (E-mail: *enquiries@geolsoc.org.uk*; tel: +44 (0)171 434 9944).

The Society's Web Site can be found at *http://www.geolsoc.org.uk/*. The Society is a Registered Charity, number 210161.

Published by The Geological Society from:
The Geological Society Publishing House
Unit 7, Brassmill Enterprise Centre
Brassmill Lane
Bath BA1 3JN
UK
Orders: Tel. +44 (0)1225 445046
Fax +44 (0)1225 442836)
Online bookshop: *http://bookshop.geolsoc.org.uk*

First published 1999

The publishers make no representation, express or implied, with regard to the accuracy of the information contained in this book and cannot accept any legal responsibility for any errors or omissions that may be made.

British Library Cataloguing in Publication Data
A catalogue record for this book is available from the British Library.

ISBN 1-86239-039-8

Distributors

USA
AAPG Bookstore
PO Box 979
Tulsa
OK 74101-0979
USA
(*Orders*: Tel. +1 918 584-2555
Fax +1 918 560-2652
Email bookstore@aapg.org)

Australia
Australian Mineral Foundation Bookshop
63 Conyngham Street
Glenside
South Australia 5065
Australia
(*Orders*: Tel. +61 88 379-0444
Fax +61 88 379-4634
Email bookshop@amf.com.au)

India
Affiliated East-West Press PVT Ltd
G-1/16 Ansari Road, Daryaganj,
New Delhi 110 002
India
(*Orders*: Tel. +91 11 327-9113
Fax +91 11 326-0538)

Japan
Kanda Book Trading Co.
Cityhouse Tama 204
Tsurumaki 1-3-10
Tama-shi
Tokyo 206-0034
Japan
(*Orders*: Tel. +81 (0)423 57-7650
Fax +81 (0)423 57-7651)

Typeset by Aarontype Ltd, Easton, Bristol BS5 0HE, UK

Printed by Alden Press, Osney Mead, Oxford OX2 0EF, UK

Contents

VOLUME 2

The Carboniferous of the Southern North Sea

Introduction and review 727
R. E. Dunay and S. S. Flint

Reservoirs of the Dinantian (Lower Carboniferous) play of the Southern North Sea 729
J. R. Maynard and R. E. Dunay

Regional corelation of Westphalian sandbodies onshore UK: implications for reservoirs in the Southern North Sea 747
J. F. Aitken, D. G. Quirk and P. D. Guion

Continent-scale sequence stratigraphy of the Namurian, Upper Carboniferous and its applications to reservoir prediction 757
S. Davies, G. Hampson, S. Flint and T. Elliott

Incised valley fill sandstone bodies in Upper Carboniferous fluvio-deltaic strata: recognition and reservoir characterization of Southern North Sea analogues 771
G. J. Hampson, S. J. Davies, T. Elliott, S. S. Flint and H. Stollhofen

Structural analysis of 3D seismic data, using the correlation attribute: a case study – Carboniferous of the Southern North Sea (UK) 789
S. Birrell and J. Courtier

'NW European Gas Atlas' – new implications for the Carboniferous gas plays in the western part of the Southern Permian Basin 799
P. Gerling, M. C. Geluk, F. Kockel, A. Lokhorst, G. K. Lott and R. A. Nicholson

The Trent Gas Field: correlation and reservoir quality within a complex Carboniferous stratigraphy 809
P. T. O'Mara, M. Merryweather, M. Stockwell and M. M. Bowler

Jurassic subtle traps

Introduction and review 825
S. A. R. Boldy and S. I. Fraser

Controls on Late Jurassic, subtle sand distribution in the Tampen Spur area, Northern North Sea 827
N. H. Dawers, A. M. Berge, K-O Häger, C. Puigdefabregas and J. R. Underhill

Sequence stratigraphy and sedimentary history of the Humber Group (Late Jurassic–Ryazanian) in the Outer Moray Firth (UKCS, North Sea) 839
D. Kadolsky, S. J. Johansen and S. Duxbury

Downthrown closures of the Outer Moray Firth 861
B. A. Moseley

Controls on Upper Jurassic sediment distribution in the Durward–Dauntless area, UK Blocks 21/11, 21/16 879
S. A. Stewart, S. I. Fraser, J. A. Cartwright, J. A. Clark and H. D. Johnson

Upper Jurassic basin axial turbidites within the Gertrud Graben, Danish Central Graben 897
E. S. Rasmussen, A-M. Jepsen and K. G. Maver

Chalk renaissance

Introduction and review 909
S. A. R. Boldy

Chalk exploration, the search for a subtle trap 911
N. P. Bramwell, G. Caillet, L. Meciani, N. C. Judge, M. Green and P. Adam

The capabilities and challenges of the seismic method in chalk exploration 939
J. K. Anderson

Influence of syn-depositional faulting on thickness variations in chalk reservoirs – Valhall and Hod fields 949
C. L. Farmer and O. I. Barkved

Exploration and appraisal of the South Arne Field, Danish North Sea 959
D. S. Mackertich and D. R. G. Goulding

Banff Field, UK Central Graben – evaluation of a steeply dipping, fractured chalk reservoir 975
N. Evans, P. Rorison and G. Sykes

High pressure/high temperature plays

Introduction and review 991
B. Levell

A subsurface perspective on ETAP – an integrated development of seven Central North Sea fields 993
J. Pooler and M. Amory

The Elgin and Franklin fields: UK Blocks 22/30c, 22/30b and 29/5b 1007
J. Lasocki, J-M. Guemene, A. Hedayati, C. Legorjus and W. M. Page

Shearwater prospect development: a high pressure/high temperature challenge 1021
J. F. Blehaut, F. van Beek, C. Billeau, J. K. Gause, S. Kimminau, A. Paardekam, N. Radcliffe, R. Rademaker, L. Storms, B. J. Welsh and A. Wittemann

Structural development and trap formation in the Central North Sea HP/HT play 1029
D. E. Helgeson

Integrated field development and reservoir management

Introduction and review 1037
S. S. Flint and H. D. Johnson

The Brent Field: improving subsurface characterization for late field life management 1039
S. James, D. Pronk, F. Abbots, V. Ward, A. van Dierendonck and D. Stevens

Application of 3D visualization and VSP for horizontal well positioning – 9/13a-N1 case history, Nevis Field, UKCS 1051
A. J. Dickson, G. C. Bingham, G. C. Stylianides, H. W. A. Thompson and N. A. Way

Tern Field development: a marriage of new technologies for business benefit 1063
R. C. Black, H. J. Poelen, M. J. Roberts and S. E. Roddy

Integrating sequence stratigraphy in field development and reservoir management – the Telford Field 1075
R. M. Syms, D. F. Savory, C. J. Ward, C. C. Ebdon and A. Griffin

Fulmar: a mature field revisited 1089
P. Spaak, J. Almond, S. Salahudin, Z. Mohd Salleh and O. Tosun

Reservoir characterization in the Captain Field: integration of horizontal and vertical well data 1101
P. T. S. Rose

Britannia Field, UK Central North Sea: modelling heterogeneity in unusual deep-water deposits 1115
L. S. Jones, S. W. Garrett, M. Macleod, M. Guy, P. J. Condon and L. Notman

Innovation and risk management in a small subsea-tieback: Arkwright Field, Central North Sea, UK 1125
J. D. Kantorowicz, I. J. Andrews, S. Dhanani, M. Gillis, C. Jennings, P. J. Lumsden, G. Orr, R. W. Simm and J. Williams

The reservoir development of the Fife Field 1135
S. Currie, S. Gowland, A. Taylor and M. Woodward

Ekofisk Field redevelopment: improved reservoir management through cross-discipline technology and integration of three dimensional models 1147
S. C. Key, B. Agarwal, G. V. Søiland and H. H. Nielsen

Reservoir management of the Wytch Farm Oil Field, Dorset, UK: providing options for growth into later field life 1157
A. J. C. Hogg, I. J. Evans, P. F. Harrison, T. Meling, G. S. Smith, S. D. Thompson and G. F. T. Watts

Reservoir studies

Introduction and review 1175
A. Hurst

Characterization of fault zones in the Gullfaks Field for reservoir modelling 1177
G. Yielding, J. A. Øverland and G. Byberg

High resolution zonation within a tide-dominated deltaic reservoir: the Middle Jurassic Beryl Formation, Beryl Field, UKCS 1187
G. Maxwell, A. Hartley and J. Crane

Capturing reservoir heterogeneity in a sand-rich submarine fan, Miller Field 1199
C. R. Garland, P. Haughton, R. F. King and T. P. Moulds

Integrated reservoir characterization and uncertainty analysis, Heidrun Field, Norway 1209
T. Olsen, K. J. Rosvoll, J. M. Kjærefjord, D. M. Arnesen, C. Sandsdalen, S. H. Jørgenvåg, V. Langlais and K. E. Svela

An integrated approach to hydrocarbon emplacement in chalk, Norwegian North Sea Central Graben 1221
I. E. I. Øxnevad and M. S. G. Taylor

Applications of geophysical technology

Introduction and review 1233
J. W. Munns

Strathspey vertical-cable seismic survey: a North Sea first 1235
P. E. Leach

Faroes Large Aperture Research Experiment (FLARE): imaging through basalt 1243
R. S. White, J. Fruehn, K. R. Richardson, E. Cullen, W. Kirk, J. R. Smallwood and C. Latkiewicz

Exploring the Shetland–Faeroes Basin using wide-angle seismic technology 1253
P. J. Barton, S. Hughes, C. Zelt and R. Masotti

Three-component 3D borehole profile imaging program on Ekofisk Field 1255
H. H. Nielsen, J. Dangerfield, S. C. Key, G. V. Søiland and L. Berg

Rock physics and quantitative wavelet estimation for seismic interpretation: Tertiary North Sea 1265
R. W. Simm, S. Xu and R. E. White

Seismic inversion as a vehicle for integration of geophysical, geological and petrophysical information for reservoir characterization: some North Sea examples 1271
J. J. M. Buiting and M. Bacon

Predicting sandbody distribution and porosity for Callovian to late Oxfordian succession; Block 9/13 UKCS: an integrated approach 1281
M. Wood, G. Bingham and P. Mitchell

A, B AVO cross plotting and its application in Greenland and the Barents Sea 1289
E. S. Isaacson and D. B. Neff

Applications of the coherency cube in the UKCS 1299
M. J. Hughes, S. Dhanani, R. K. Frimpong, M. Gainski, N. L. Haskell, R. P. Heath, J. D. Kantorowicz, P. M. Maguire and S. E. Nissen

Basin modelling applications in reducing risk and maximizing reserves

Introduction and review 1309
S. D. Burley and I. C. Scotchman

Charge and overpressure modelling in the North Sea: multi-dimensional modelling and uncertainty analysis 1313
M. R. Giles, S. L. Indrelid, N. J. Kusznir, A. Loopik, J. A. Meijerink, J. McNutt, P. Dijkstra, W. Heidug, J. Toth, M. Willis, K. Rutten, B. Elsinga, P. Huysse, P. Riviere, H. Bürgisser and E. Rowley

Hydrocarbon systems modelling of the Norwegian Central Graben fairway trend 1325
M. S. G. Taylor, A. LeRoy and M. Førland

Diagenetic porosity creation in an overpressured graben 1339
R. S. Haszeldine, M. Wilkinson, D. Darby, C. I. Macaulay, G. D. Couples, A. E. Fallick, C. G. Fleming, R. N. T. Stewart and G. McAulay

The Jurassic petroleum system of the West of Britain Atlantic margin – an integration of tectonics, geochemistry and basin modelling 1351
A. J. Holmes, C. E. Griffith and I. C. Scotchman

Petroleum systems analysis of the Paleocene play in the West of Shetland area 1367
R. Jowitt, A. Hindle, D. Jones and P. Rose

Oil and gas migration in the Sherwood Sandstone of the East Irish Sea Basin 1383
G. Cowan, S. D. Burley, A. N. Hoey, P. Holloway, P. Bermingham, N. Beveridge, M. Hamborg and O. Sylta

Appendix: a list of common abbreviations xiii

Index xv

VOLUME 1

Conference Organizing Committee xii

Conference Technical Committee xii

Sponsoring Bodies xii

Foreword xiii
Jim Brooks

General Introduction xiv
A. J. Fleet and S. A. R. Boldy

Regional syntheses, tectono-stratigraphic analyses and structural studies

Introduction and review 3
J. R. Underhill

Palaeozoic to Tertiary rift and basin dynamics: mid-Norway to the Bay of Biscay – a new context for hydrocarbon prospectivity in the deep water frontier 7
D. G Roberts, M. Thompson, B. Mitchener, J. Hossack, S. Carmichael and H-M Bjørnseth

Principal tectonic events in the evolution of the northwest European Atlantic margin 41
A. G. Doré, E. R. Lundin, L. N. Jensen, Ø. Birkeland, P. E. Eliassen and C. Fichler

The evolution of the Central North Sea Rift 63
D. Erratt, G. M. Thomas and G. R. T. Wall

Evolution of extensional styles at the southern termination of the Nordland Ridge, mid-Norway: a response to variations in coupling above Triassic salt 83
R. Pascoe, R. Hooper, K. Storhaug and H. Harper

Processes and products of footwall degradation, northern Brent Field, Northern North Sea 91
A. E. McLeod and J. R. Underhill

The Zeta Structure: a footwall degradation complex formed by gravity sliding on the western margin of the Tampen Spur, Northern North Sea 107
M. Berger and A. M. Roberts

The origin and genesis of major Jurassic unconformities within the triple junction area of the North Sea, UK 117
R. J. Davies, D. O'Donnell, P. N. Bentham, J. P. C. Gibson, M. R. Curry, R. E. Dunay and J. R. Maynard

Tectono-stratigraphic development of the southern part of UKCS Quadrant 15 (eastern Witch Ground Graben): implications for the Mesozoic–Tertiary evolution of the Central North Sea Basin 133
G. Jones, P. Rorison, R. Frost, R. Knipe and J. Colleran

Middle Oxfordian to Volgian sequence stratigraphy of the Greater Shearwater area 153
J. M. Jeremiah and P. H. Nicholson

Laramide events: Mid North Sea High (UK Quadrants 38 & 39) 171
H. Johnson, M. F. Quinn, J. Bulat and D. Long

Impact of salt on the structure of the Central North Sea hydrocarbon fairways 179
S. A. Stewart and J. A. Clark

Rift–raft tectonics: examples of gravitational tectonics from the Zechstein basins of northwest Europe 201
J. Penge, J. W. Munns, B. Taylor and T. M. F. Windle

4D evolution of segmented strike-slip fault systems: applications to NW Europe 215
T. Dooley, K. McClay and M. Bonora

Atlantic margin: offshore Norway to offshore Ireland

Introduction and review 229
P. M. Shannon and A. M. Spencer

Petroleum systems of the Atlantic margin of northwest Europe 231
A. M. Spencer, Ø. Birkeland, G. Ø. Knag and R. Fredsted

Structural elements and petroleum geology of the Norwegian sector of the northern Barents Sea 247
P. Grogan, A.-M. Østvedt-Ghazi, G. B. Larssen, B. Fotland, K. Nyberg, S. Dahlgren and T. Eidvin

The prospectivity of the Voring and Møre basins on the Norwegian Sea continental margin 261
H. Brekke, S. Dahlgren, B. Nyland and C. Magnus

The first deepwater well in Norway and its implications for the Upper Cretaceous Play, Vøring Basin 275
J. E. Kittilsen, R. R. Olsen, R. F. Marten, E. K. Hansen and R. R. Hollingsworth

Techniques used in the exploration of turbidite reservoirs in a frontier setting – Helland Hansen licence, Vøring Basin, offshore mid Norway 281
F. Sanchez-Ferrer, S. D. James, B. Lak and A. M. Evans

Cenozoic development of the Norwegian margin 60–64°N: sequences and sedimentary response to variable basin physiography and tectonic setting 293
O. J. Martinsen, F. Bøen, M. A. Charnock, G. Mangerud and A. Nøttvedt

Oil seepage onshore West Greenland: evidence of multiple source rocks and oil mixing 305
J. A. Bojesen-Koefoed, F. G. Christiansen, H. P. Nytoft and A. K. Pedersen

West Greenland versus Vøring Basin: comparison of two deepwater frontier exploration plays 315
R. B. Aram

Cretaceous (post-Valanginian) sedimentation and rift events in NE Greenland (71–77°N) 325
A. G. Whitham, S. P. Price, A. M. Koraini and S. R. A. Kelly

Sandstone wedges of the Cretaceous–Lower Tertiary Kangerlussuaq Basin, East Greenland – outcrop analogues to the offshore North Atlantic 337
M. Larsen, L. Hamberg, S. Olaussen, T. Preuss and L. Stemmerik

Early Tertiary heat flow along the UK Atlantic margin and adjacent areas 349
P. F. Green, I. R. Duddy, K. A. Hegarty and R. J. Bray

Evidence for pre-Cretaceous rifting in the Rockall Trough: a quantitative analysis using plate tectonic modelling 359
J. Cole and J. Peachey

Evidence for pre-Cretaceous rifting in the Rockall Trough: an analysis using quantitative 2D structural/stratigraphic modelling 371
P. A. Nadin, M. A. Houchen and N. J. Kusznir

The regional geology and exploration potential of the NE Rockall Basin 379
P. Waddams and T. Cordingley

The Northeast Rockall Basin and its significance in the evolution of the Rockall–Faeroes/East Greenland rift system 391
M. P. Tate, C. D. Dodd and N. T. Grant

The structural and stratigraphic framework of the Irish Rockall Trough 407
S. Corfield, N. Murphy and S. Parker

Structural setting, geological development and basin modelling in the Rockall Trough 421
P. M. Shannon, A. W. B. Jacob, B. M. O'Reilly, F. Hauser, P. W. Readman and J. Makris

Petroleum geology of the Irish Rockall Trough – a frontier challenge 433
A. Walsh, G. Knag, M. Morris, H. Quinquis, P. Tricker, C. Bird and S. Bower

Structural evolution of the Slyne Trough 445
P. N. Dancer, S. T. Algar and I. R. Wilson

The structural evolution of the Erris Trough, offshore northwest Ireland, and implications for hydrocarbon generation 455
T. J. Chapman, T. M. Broks, D. V. Corcoran, L. A. Duncan and P. N. Dancer

Jurassic non-marine source rocks and oils of the Porcupine Basin and other North Atlantic margin basins 471
P. Butterworth, A. Holba, S. Hertig, W. Hughes and C. Atkinson

Comparative Jurassic and Cretaceous tectono-stratigraphy and reservoir development in the Jeanne d'Arc and Porcupine basins 487
B. P. J. Williams, P. M. Shannon and I. K. Sinclair

Sedimentary basins and petroleum systems offshore Newfoundland and Labrador 501
N. R. DeSilva

The Hibernia Oilfield – effects of episodic tectonism on structural character and reservoir compartmentalization 517
I. K. Sinclair, J. E. Evans, E. A. Albrechtsons and L. J. Sydora

Atlantic margin: Faeroe–Shetland

Introduction and review 531
B. Levell and M. Thompson

Rifting and the development of the Faeroe–Shetland Basin 533
K. Dean, K. McLachlan and A. Chambers

Palaeogene magmatism in the Faeroe–Shetland Basin: influences on uplift history and sedimentation 545
P. H. Naylor, B. R. Bell, D. W. Jolley, P. Durnall and R. Fredsted

Stratigraphic relationships of the Lower Tertiary of the Faeroe Basalt Plateau and the Faeroe–Shetland Basin 559
L. Kiørboe

Early Tertiary magmatism in the offshore NW UK margin and surrounds 573
J. D. Ritchie, R. W. Gatliff and P. C. Richards

The thermal impact of Paleocene magmatic underplating in the Faeroe–Shetland–Rockall region 585
P. D. Clift

Reconciling gravity and seismic data in the Faeroe–Shetland Basin, West of Shetland 595
W. Ashcroft, A. Hurst and C. J. Morgan

The importance of fluid pressures and migration to the hydrocarbon prospectivity of the Faeroe–Shetland White Zone 601
J. E. Iliffe, A. G. Robertson, G. H. F. Ward, C. Wynn, S. D. M. Pead and N. Cameron

Hydrocarbon migration history, West of Shetland: integrated fluid inclusion and fission track studies 613
J. Parnell, P. F. Carey, P. Green and W. Duncan

Reservoir quality and petrophysical evaluation of Paleocene sandstones in the West of Shetland area 627
M. Sullivan, T. Coombes, P. Imbert and C. Ahadamach-Demars

Anisotropy and amplitude versus offset: a case history from the West of Shetlands 635
R. W. Margesson and C. H. Sondergeld

The Paleocene deepwater sandstone play West of Shetland 645
E. Lamers and S. M. M. Carmichael

The Turonian play in the Faeroe–Shetland Basin 661
N. Grant, A. Bouma and A. McIntyre

The Foinaven Field: managing reservoir development uncertainty prior to start-up 675
M. M. Cooper, A. C. Evans, D. J. Lynch, G. Neville and T. Newley

The Schiehallion development 683
H. M. Leach, N. Herbert, A. Los and R. L. Smith

Solan, Strathmore and the back basin play, West of Shetland 693
R. Herries, R. Poddubiuk and P. Wilcockson

The Victory gas field, West of Shetland 713
M. W. Goodchild, K. L. Henry, R. J. Hinkley and S. W. Imbus

Appendix: a list of common abbreviations xv

Index xvii

The Carboniferous of the Southern North Sea

The Carboniferous of the Southern North Sea

Introduction and review

R. E. DUNAY[1] and S. S. FLINT[2]

[1] *Mobil North Sea, Ltd, 3 Clements Inn, London WC2A 2EB, UK*
[2] *University of Liverpool, Department of Earth Sciences, Brownlow Street, Liverpool L69 3BX, UK*

The prospectivity of the Carboniferous of NW Europe has occupied explorationists since the early oil discoveries made in the Carboniferous of the East Midlands of England and the early gas discoveries made in the uppermost Carboniferous of the Ems Graben in western Germany. Much effort, particularly in the past twenty years, has been expended in increasing proven reserves in the Carboniferous. Results, however, have been mixed. At the last 'Petroleum Geology of NW Europe' Conference, held in April 1992 (Parker 1993), of the seven Carboniferous papers presented, only one discovered hydrocarbon accumulation, the Caister Field (Block 44/23a), with gas-bearing Westphalian A and B reservoir horizons, was described in detail. The remaining papers dealt principally with regional play aspects of the Carboniferous and the development of sedimentological and structural models.

Although five years separate this volume from that of the 1992 conference, most of the papers presented here likewise basically cover regional or technological developments. In regard to the Lower Carboniferous, **Maynard & Dunay** discuss two potential Visean clastic reservoirs. The Lower Carboniferous is a principal target in the northern quadrants of the Southern North Sea and remains essentially a frontier play. One of the principal problems in more actively explored Westphalian fluvio–deltaic reservoir sands is sandbody correlation and the prediction of reservoir connectivity. This is discussed by **Aitken *et al.***, who integrate a dataset to model reservoir continuity, and by **Davies *et al.*** who consider continental-scale sequence stratigraphy. **Hampson *et al.*** record incised valley fills in the onshore Upper Carboniferous. The recognition of this model aids in the prediction of reservoir behaviour in offshore Upper Carboniferous reservoirs. Seismic imaging and correlation of the Carboniferous is the subject of the contribution by **Birrell and Courtier**.

The remaining two papers are studies of proven accumulations, both in Namurian to Westphalian sandstone reservoirs. **Gerling *et al.*** discuss the *NW European Gas Atlas* and its implications for the gas plays of the Permian Basin. **O'Mara *et al.*** discuss the structural and sedimentological setting of the Trent Field, a Marsdenian and Westphalian A gas field, located principally in UK Block 43/24.

The major challenges of the Carboniferous are represented in this section. The principal problems of predicting reservoir quality and continuity remain, as does the recognition of intra Carboniferous seals. The papers presented here illustrate the attempts to address some of these problems. With the continuation of such work, perhaps more proven Carboniferous hydrocarbon accumulations, hopefully including some big discoveries, will be presented at the next conference on the Petroleum Geology of NW Europe.

References

PARKER, J. R. (ed.) 1993. *Petroleum Geology of Northwest Europe: Proceedings of the 4th Conference*. Geological Society, London.

DUNAY, R. E.. & FLINT, S. S. 1999. The Carboniferous of the Southern North Sea. *In*: FLEET, A. J. & BOLDY, S. A. R. (eds) *Petroleum Geology of Northwest Europe: Proceedings of the 5th Conference*, 727.

Reservoirs of the Dinantian (Lower Carboniferous) play of the Southern North Sea

J. R. MAYNARD[1] and R. E. DUNAY[2]

[1] *Mobil North Sea Ltd, Grampian House, Union Row, Aberdeen AB10 1SA, UK (e-mail james_r_maynard@email.mobil.com)*
[2] *Mobil North Sea Ltd, Mobil Court, 3 Clements Inn, London WC2A 2EB, UK*

Abatract: Critical to the successful exploitation of the northern margin of the Southern Gas Basin is the development of the Lower Carboniferous (Dinantian, Viséan) play. Whilst the exploration for intra-Carboniferous traps has been unsuccessful, the presence of large Base Permian evaporite sealed closures still holds opportunities. The discovery of hydrocarbons within one of these closures on the edge of the traditional gas basin suggests that migration of gas from Westphalian and Namurian coals and shales has occurred. Thus in this area, the primary remaining risk is the presence and distribution of reservoir. Two potential reservoirs are examined in the subsurface, the Fell Sandstone Formation and the Whitby Member. Onshore analogue data has been combined with the sparse offshore data to explore the distribution of these sandstones. The Fell Sandstone Formation was deposited at a time of high sediment supply resulting in a thick (300 m) succession of fluvial sandstones whose distribution is closely linked to the accommodation space developed in the hanging walls of contemporaneous faults. The Whitby Member (thickness 30 m) was deposited at a time of lower sediment supply which enabled relative sea-level changes to control the vertical distribution of sandstone bodies. It demonstrates some of the features which suggest it could infill a palaeovalley. If active faulting continued throughout this time then a similar hanging wall concentration of sandbodies, as is seen in the Fell Sandstone Formation, could be expected.

The Dinantian play is one of the last plays to be exploited in the Southern North Sea (SNS). This is primarily because of its position on the northern limit of the Gas Basin where problems of migration and seal are significant. Until relatively recently little hard data has existed on the potential reservoirs within this succession, their presence having been inferred through seismic interpretation and onshore analogues. In this paper we discuss two potential reservoirs discovered offshore with respect to depositional models and their importance to the petroleum potential of the Dinantian play. Firstly the Asbian to Holkerian Fell Sandstone Formation which onshore in Northumberland is in excess of 300 m thick (Turner *et al.* 1993). This reservoir, if filled with hydrocarbons in the large relief closures observed on the northern margin of the SNS would provide significant economic volumes of gas. The second reservoir is Asbian in age and herein named the Whitby Member.

The stratigraphic nomenclature used here is from Knox and is shown in Fig. 1, correlated to the onshore UK stratigraphy. The onshore stratigraphy is from George *et al.* (1976) which has recently been updated and modified by Riley (1993). Problems exist when attempting high resolution biostratigraphic correlation because current type palynological zonations are not always consistent with the micro fauna (Riley pers comm) which suggests some palaeoenvironmental control of palynomorphs. However, the succession can be divided lithostratigraphically which is fairly reliable at a low resolution and palynology provides a broad zonation scheme; in addition some limestones (marine flooding surfaces) act as marker beds onshore and these can be used locally for correlation offshore. A more detailed correlation of significant onshore exposures and the wells used in this study is given in Fig. 2.

The upper boundary of the Scremerston Formation, which contains sandstone, silt, mudstone and coal cycles, is taken at the basal Yoredale limestone bed (Cameron 1993). The Scremerston sandstones, as with the informally named Whitby Member, most likely represent fluvial deposits. These sands have significant reservoir potential, and are broadly Asbian in age. The lower Scremertson boundary is taken after Cameron (1993) on the sudden transition to the massive sandstone facies of the Fell Sandstone Formation.

Because of the massive nature of the underlying Fell Sandstone Formation, fossil recovery is relatively poor and age determination imprecise. The biostratigraphic evidence, however, supports a broadly lower Asbian to possibly Holkerian age determination. The lower boundary is defined at the abrupt transition to the dolomites, mudstones, and tight sandstones of the Cementstone Group, which ranges from Chadian to Courceyan in age.

The Scremerston/Fell Sandstone sedimentary package can be traced eastward into the Dutch sector of the North Sea. The two formations are undifferentiated in the Dutch sector and are combined into the Elleboog Formation (Boogaert & Knowe 1993).

Dinantian palaeogeographic reconstructions of northwest Europe (Maynard *et al.* 1997) show the basin to be developed along an east–west trend to the north of the impending Variscan orogen. The reconstruction places the northern margin of the SNS at the northern margin of the basin proximal to the highland source terrains of the Caledonian and Fenno–Scandinavian areas. The SNS subcrop map (Fig. 3) illustrates the preservation of Carboniferous beneath the Base Permian unconformity and shows the east–west preservation of Dinantian strata which constrains the present-day play area.

The southerly part of the Dinantian is primarily the site of carbonate sediment accumulation, with deepwater deposits fringing the carbonate ramps. The centre of the basin was the site of rifting. This caused deepening and the development of basinal, black, marine shales such as are present intercalated with the southerly-derived flysch of the Culm in Germany. In Scotland, northern England and the Mid-North Sea High (MNSH) clastic depositional systems were sourced from the northeast and concentrated down the axis of the strike-slip (NE–SW) lineaments, possibly including the Midland Valley.

MAYNARD, J. R. & DUNAY, R. E. 1999. Reservoirs of the Dinantian (Lower Carboniferous) play of the Southern North Sea. *In*: FLEET, A. J. & BOLDY, S. A. R. (eds) *Petroleum Geology of Northwest Europe: Proceedings of the 5th Conference*, 729–745. © Petroleum Geology '86 Ltd. Published by the Geological Society, London.

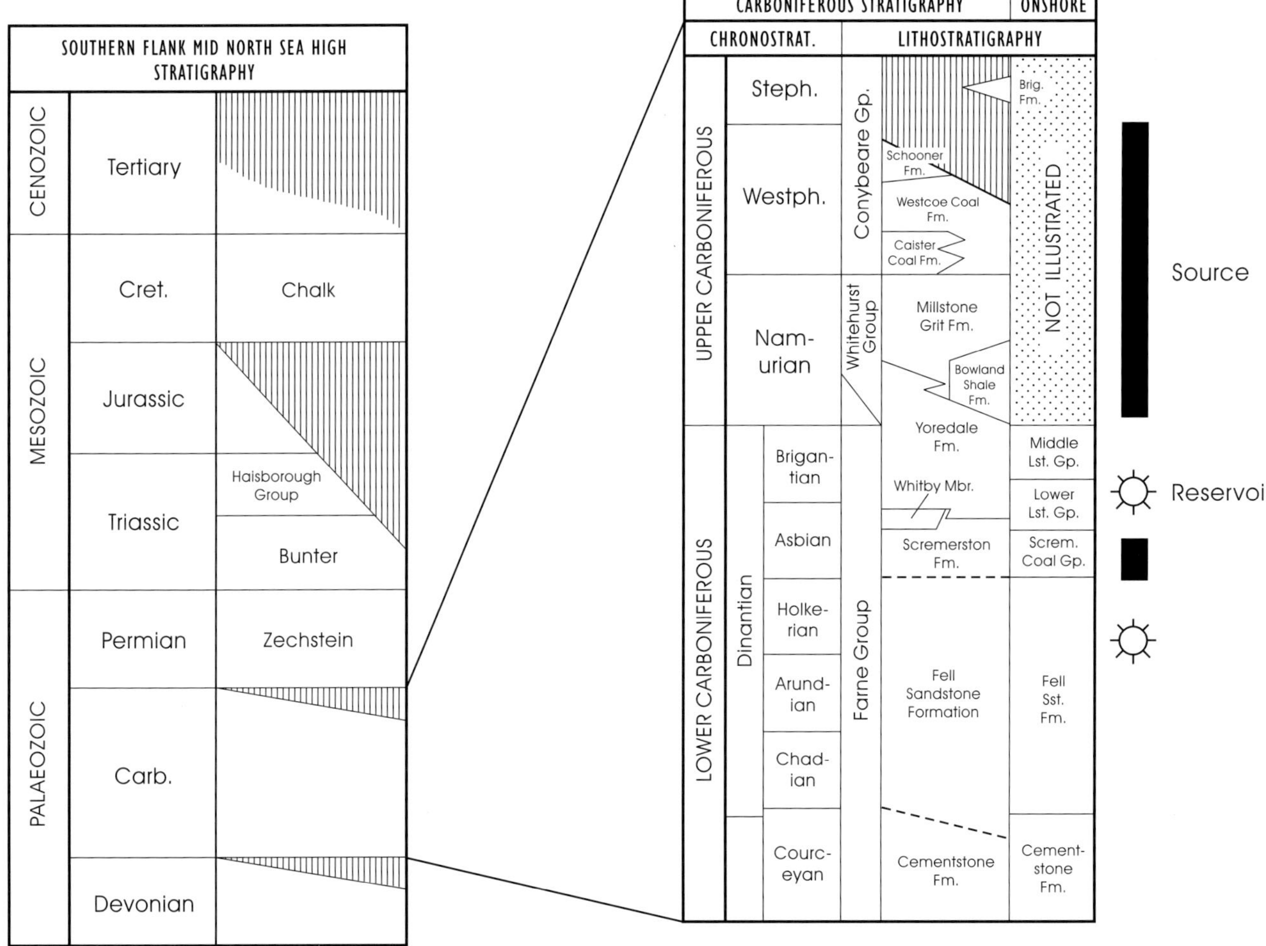

Fig. 1. The stratigraphic framework for the Southern North Sea adopted in this study based on Cameron (1993).

Faulting was coincident with the volcanic activity present in the Midland Valley at this time. A fluvio–deltaic system prograded through these rift basins filling the topographic lows and forming the Fell Sandstone Formation. On the margins of this system, Yoredale facies sediments were formed consisting of cyclic deposits of marine carbonates and shales and fluvio–deltaic sands.

Dataset

All relevant released wells in the UK Quadrants 41, 42, 43 and 44 and adjacent onshore areas were utilized in this study. In addition, a number of other unreleased wells were also included. The location of the released wells is shown on Fig. 9.

Many 2D regional seismic surveys have been employed of both proprietary and non-proprietary origin, to map at a number of different levels within the Carboniferous. The quality of much of the data is moderate to poor in the study area and correlations across major faults are extremely uncertain. A certain amount of seismic facies mapping was undertaken in support of the gravity interpretation. This exercise resulted in both a depth map of top Carboniferous and a map of the subcrop of Carboniferous strata to the Base Permian (Figs 3 and 4).

Potential field data (back-stripped gravity data) were critical for the identification of pre-Carboniferous structure because the poor quality of the seismic data precluded mapping the basement structure in all but the northern most part of the study area (Quads 36–38). The post Carboniferous gravity effects were removed by mapping and modelling the gravity field of the overlying strata. This was then subtracted from the residual bouger data to give an estimate of the gravity response of the pre-Permian section.

The adjacent onshore Lower Carboniferous succession is well studied and the subsurface is well constrained by seismic, drilling and outcrop information. Reservoir analogue information is drawn from onshore outcrop of the Fell Sandstone Formation (Hodgson & Gardiner 1971; Turner *et al.* 1993) which occurs in northern England and a sandstone which outcrops in one of the best exposed cliff sections of Upper Dinantian age in the UK, that of the Asbian/Brigantian Redshin Quarry Sandstone Formation. This sandstone is exposed in 5 km of cliffs to the north of Berwick Upon Tweed, Northumberland (Gardiner 1985). This data has been used by many authors in support of the SNS subsurface model (Leeder & Hardman 1990; Collinson *et al.* 1993; Hollywood & Whorlow 1993). Our study relies upon much of this prior work which we have modified in respect of our more localized focus.

Regional structural synthesis

A structural configuration of the Carboniferous Basin may be reconstructed using the present-day depth to Top Carboniferous, the interpreted gravity and the Carboniferous subcrop to Base Permian. Because of the poor quality of seismic in all but the northernmost part of the area, it is not possible to say with

Fig. 2. A detailed Dinantian onshore to offshore correlation focused on the late Dinantian with example onshore exposures indicated. Note that limestones have been used to map the successions onshore. Their frequency is variable and although a few prominent marker beds can be readily traced around, this probably excludes them from use as good marker beds for regional offshore correlations without the support of very precise biostratigraphy.

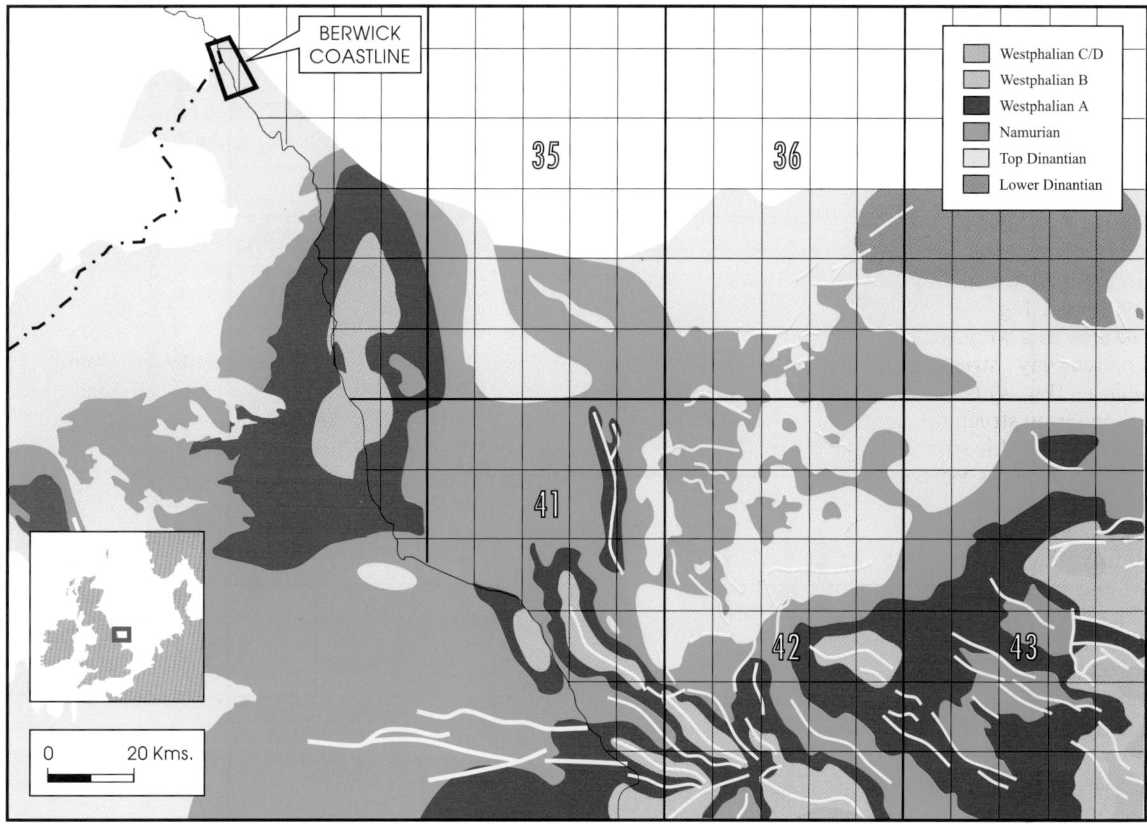

Fig. 3. The Carboniferous subcrop to the Base Permian unconformity in the northern part of the Southern North Sea. The Dinantian play area coincides with the preservation of the Dinantian sediments at subcrop to the overlying Permian Zechstein evaporites which form the most efficient top seal.

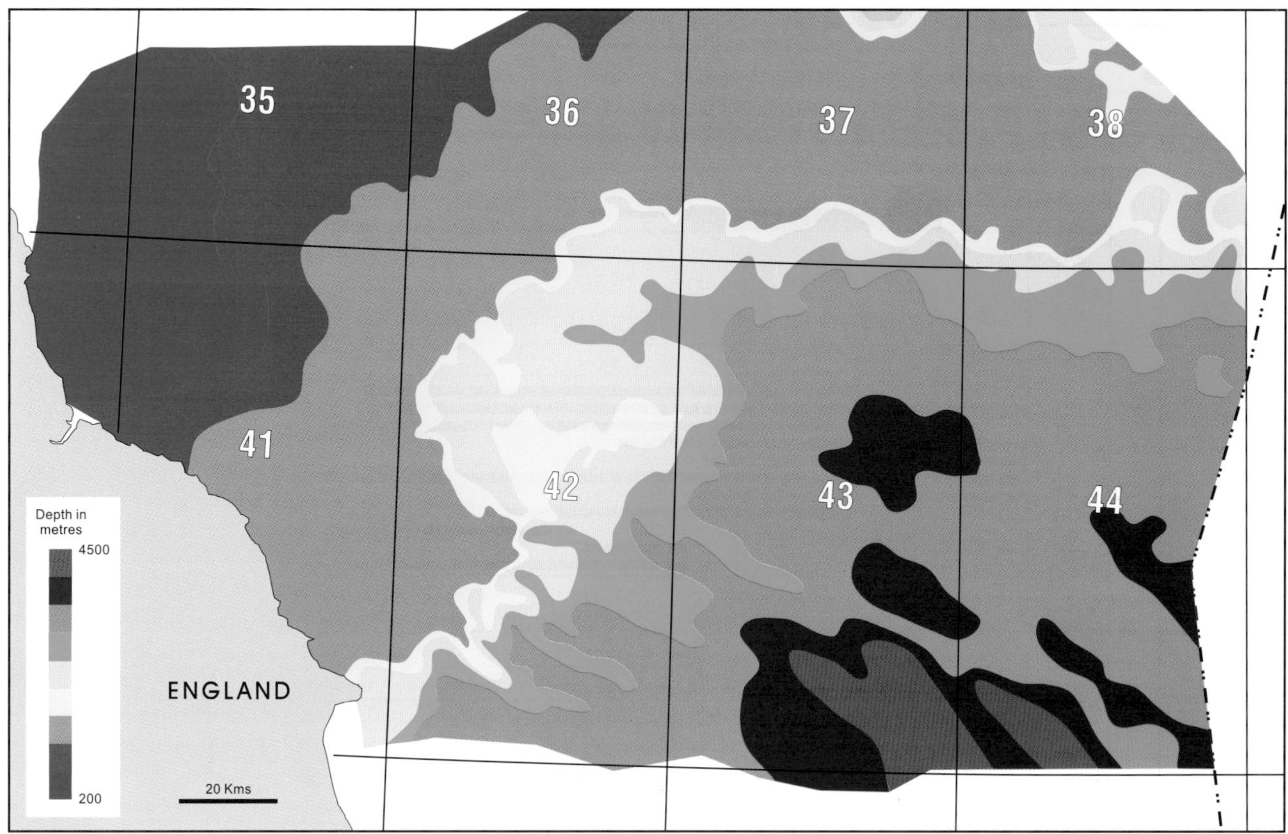

Fig. 4. Depth map to the Top Carboniferous. This map illustrates some of the more obvious large structures which occur within the play area.

certainty which faults were active during the late Dinantian. In general, fluvial sand bodies in active tectonic regions tend to migrate into the footwalls of faults (Leeder 1993) so an understanding of the orientation and position of any such faults would in theory give a indication of likely fluvial sandbody concentration. In the northern area and in the onshore, the data do suggest syn-depositional faults which would support active faulting further south in areas with poorer data. Thus the margins of the reconstructed basins could reasonably be defined by active normal faults. A review of the tectonic framework of the time is given in Maynard *et al.* (1997) and Fig. 5 shows the palaeogeography for the European area as a whole.

The present-day structural configuration of the Top Carboniferous (Fig. 4) is a composite of the various syn- and post-Carboniferous structural events. The structure of the east–west trending MNSH is seen to dip to the south into the Sole Pit and Silverpit basins via a structural 'terrace' in the west. The dominant structural trends are the NW–SE Gas Basin trend with a NE–SW offset trend. These trends are possibly inherited from the Variscan orogeny (late Carboniferous/early Permian) and later Tertiary events. It is not possible to tell how much of this structure is influenced by earlier fault trends in the main basin although on the MNSH major Carboniferous influencing faults are observed on seismic. The prominent structural terrace is probably inherited from the early Carboniferous, and influenced sedimentation as an intra-basinal high through to the late Permian. To the west the Carboniferous structure has been significantly inverted by the later Tertiary structuration along the Solepit–Dowsing axis.

The interpretation of back-stripped gravity is shown in Fig. 6. The map shows a block and basin structure in the SNS, with some of the blocks being underpinned by granites. The map is broadly similar to that produced by (Collinson *et al.* 1993) and is comparable to the 'block and basin' half-graben structures observed onshore (Fraser & Gawthorpe 1990). The map interpretation shows a series of basins in the northern part of the SNS which are orientated east–west as an extension of the trend seen in northern England. To the south the basins take on the NW–SE gas basin trend which is thought to reflect the deep crustal structure inherited from the assembly of the continental crust in the area (Matte 1986). A north–south component is also visible in the west with relative structural lows connecting the various basins in the SNS with the Northumberland Basin by an offshore extension of the Cleveland/Stainmore Basin.

The SNS pre-Permian subcrop map (Fig. 3) demonstrates an amalgam of many features seen in the gravity data and the depth structure. Late Carboniferous structural events are overprinted on earlier sites of Carboniferous basins. The MNSH is clearly seen with the oldest subcrop and the east–west and north–south trends are seen in this area. To the south the NW–SE gas basin trend and NE–SW offset trend are visible.

A schematic well correlation depicts the broad facies belts developed in the late Dinantian from the platform area of the MNSH into the basins to the south (Fig. 7). Very few wells have penetrated this age of sediments in the Solepit or Silverpit basins, however those that have indicate that an argillaceous distal facies is present.

Wells on the southern flank of the MNSH, such as Well 43/2-1, have interbedded limestones and sandstones of the Cementstone Formation overlain by the thickly (>300 m) developed high net to gross (>90%) sandstones of the fluvial Fell Sandstone Formation. These in turn are overlain by the cyclic deposits of marine shales, limestones, coals, silts and fluvial sandstones which are broadly known as a Yoredale 'facies assemblage'. These comprise the coal-rich Scremerston Formation and the coal-poor Yoredale Formation. These lithological units are seen all along the southern MNSH flanks into the Dutch sector of the SNS. Passing off the flanks of the MNSH into the northern Gas Basin, the Yoredale and

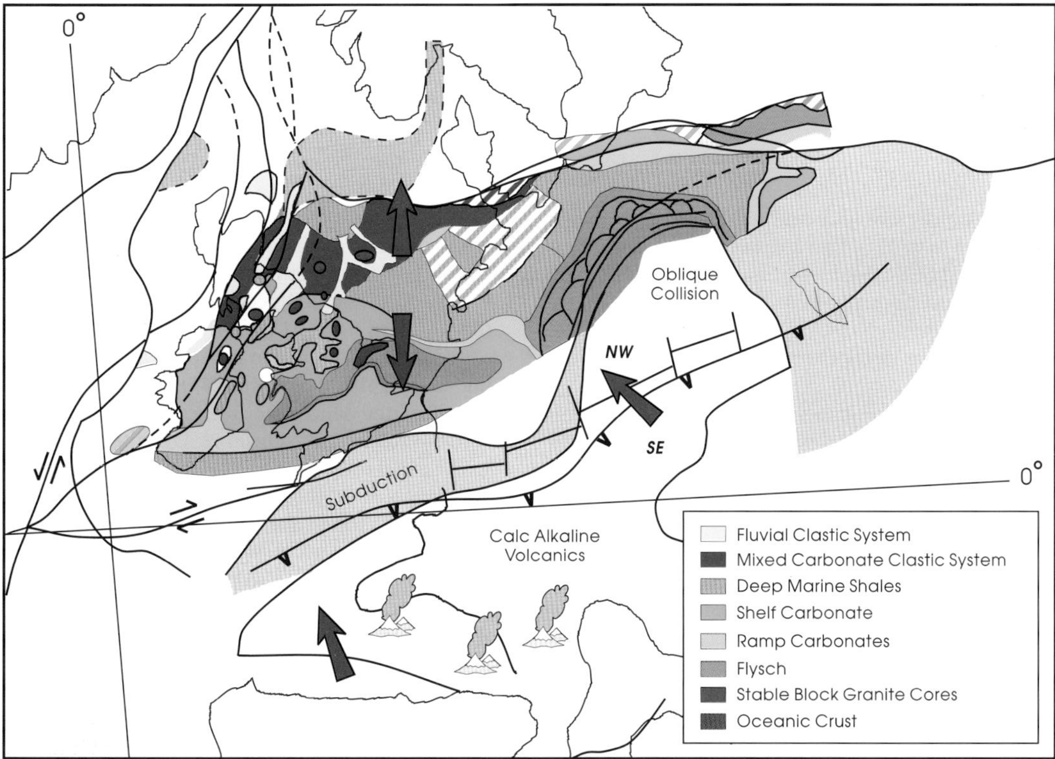

Fig. 5. Holkerian/Asbian regional European palaeogeography. The northwesterly oblique closure of the Rheic ocean occurs to the south of the area of interest which lies on the northern margin of an epicontinental seaway, dominated by an extensive carbonate platform and dark shale deposition. Major drainage systems sourced from the north empty coarse clastics into the region which is now the northern Southern North Sea.

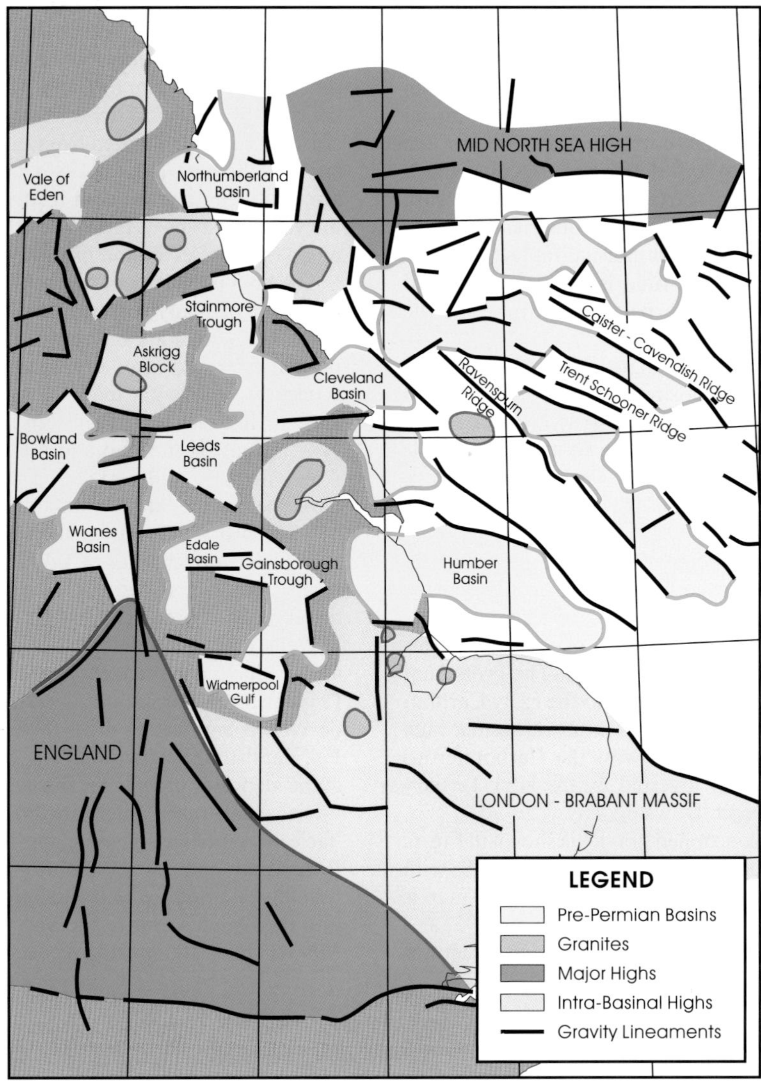

Fig. 6. An interpretation of the major Carboniferous depocentres in the Southern North Sea and the adjacent onshore UK. This interpretation is derived from back-stripped gravity data and illustrates the highs and half-grabens into which Dinantian sediments were deposited. Note the east–west orientation of basins in the northern part of the Southern North Sea.

Scremerston formations pass into marine shales with occasional thin limestones (e.g. 43/17-2). The exact age correlatives of the units below the Yoredale Formation are unknown because the deepest penetrations within the basin are only to the Brigantian; however, it is reasonable to assume that a similar transition to more distal facies occurs within the Fell Sandstone Formation.

Passing westward into the structurally higher Cleveland Basin, Yoredale facies of the Yoredale and Scremerston formations are again developed up-dip from correlative marine shales. The Fell Sandstone Formation also feathers into many thinner units decreasing the net : gross of the unit. This feathering may betray an affinity to the cyclic Yoredale facies developed in the overlying formations. Further north in the Northumberland/Tweed basins the Fell Sandstone Formation returns to its full net : gross as in the east and is of similar thickness. The barrier of the palaeohigh formed by the Askrigg/Alton blocks and the un-named granite in northern Quad 41 helps restrict sediment supply to the Cleveland Basin by diverting sediment westward. The presence of the Namurian age Bowland Shale Formation helps define the deepest parts of the Dinantian Basins. The organic-rich marine shales were deposited by an end Dinantian transgression that is seen to onlap the basin margins and pass laterally into the Millstone Grit Formation of the Namurian. Sandstones of inferred deep water mass flows are also present in this central area.

The late Dinantian fluvial sandstones within this area vary from well developed occurrences (≈300 m, 90% net : gross) of the southern flank of the MNSH to the east (Quad 43 and 44) to the basinal absence to the south and the transitional feathering seen in the west (Quad 41). Prediction of the quality and extent of the sandstone in these areas becomes an important component of risk. Onshore UK the occurrence of younger Yoredale fluvial sandstones coincides with the presence and lateral extent of the Fell Sandstone Formation.

The sandstones are derived from the a northerly province which is consistent with the data collected offshore (Fig. 13) and suggests a source somewhere to the north of the MNSH. Sandstones probably followed fault-controlled lows through the MNSH to be deposited as an alluvial plain on the southern margin. The limited well evidence suggests that in areas of a steeper gradient in the east (Quad 44) the sandstone was of more limited basinal extent whilst areas of lesser gradient such as on the structural terrace in Quad 42 allowed the sandstones to extend further basinward (e.g. Well 42/15a-2). This evidence of basinal change is tentatively supported in this terrace area by a change in seismic facies within the Fell Sandstone Formation and overlying Scremerston/Yoredale

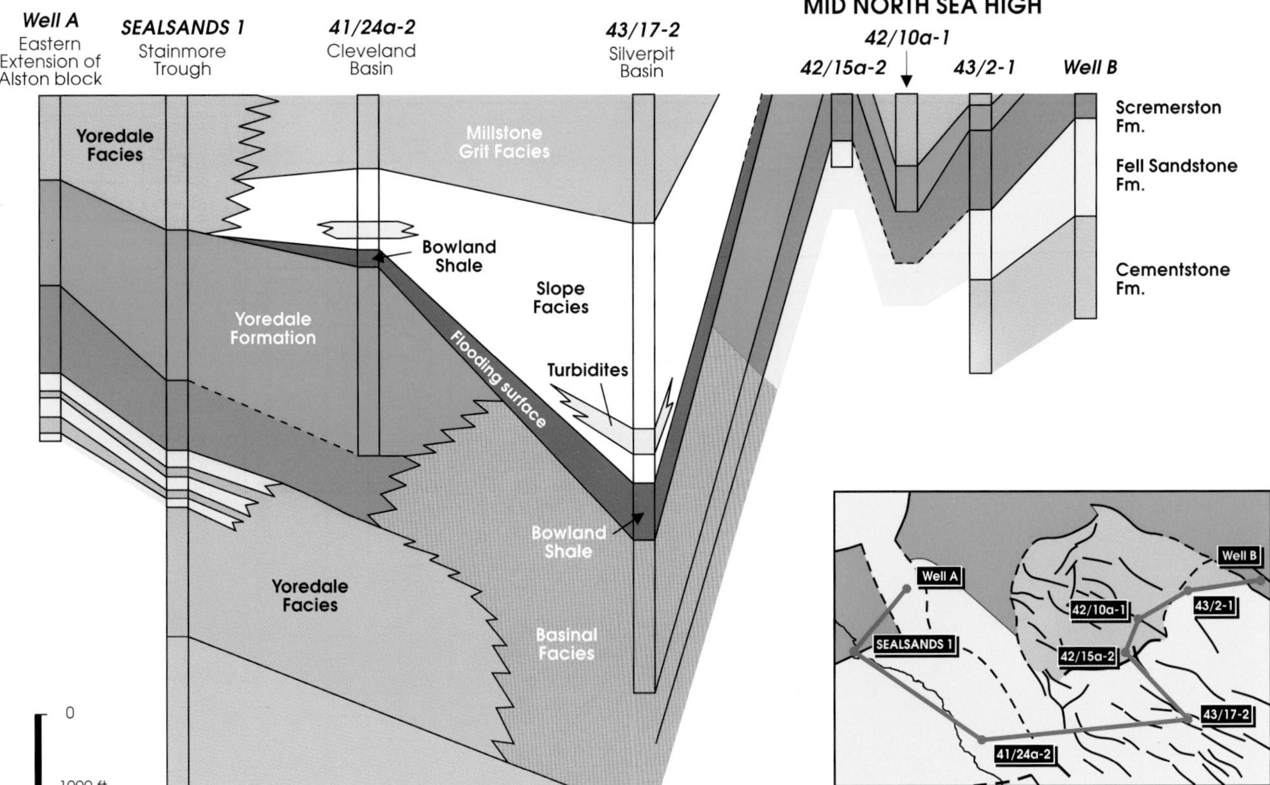

Fig. 7. A regional well correlation of the Dinantian in the northern Southern North Sea summarizing what is known from well penetration about the lateral facies variations west to east (approximately a distance of 150 km) and north to south (about 50 km) over the basin margin.

formations off the edge of the structural terrace. However, it must be said that only the character on the terrace can be calibrated by well data.

Potential reservoirs

Fell Sandstone Formation

The Fell Sandstone Formation is a unit that has been recorded in many wells in the SNS but no known core exists. However, a well from the southern flank of the MNSH does benefit from an almost complete FMS and NMR tool coverage which provides us with a wealth of data on reservoir character and quality.

Offshore, the Fell Sandstone Formation is encountered in Wells 42/10a-1, 42/15a-2, 43/2-1, 44/2-1, as well as in a further four confidential wells and in many wells to the east in the Dutch sector of the SNS.

Figure 8 shows a 75 km west to east correlation of the Dinantian in four wells in the UK SNS. The section is orientated perpendicular to depositional dip. The blocky log signature of the Fell Sandstone Formation is shown underlying the cyclic Yoredale facies of the Scremerston Formation with its prominent thinner fluvial sandstones. The sandstone in these wells is between 250 and 425 m thick with a high net : gross (>85%). Prominent shale breaks of 5–10 m are apparent and some of these in the upper parts of the sandstone have yielded marine acritarchs suggesting that the depositional mechanism may be related to the overlying marine/non marine Yoredale facies. These shale breaks, as in the onshore (see later discussion), may be laterally extensive and form major permeability barriers within the greater sandstone body (macro form).

One well has complete FMS data coverage of the sandstone. This micro-resistivity tool can only resolve electrical conductivity contrasts to a few tens of millimetres at best but that is sufficient to resolve clay drapes on foresets and in burrows and so reveal some of the sedimentary structures. In general the sandstone is cross-bedded with set sizes of a few tens of centimetres. No burrowing can be discerned and few pebble lags are seen, although as a result of washouts causing image deterioration over some parts of the hole, these features cannot be entirely excluded. In general the interpretation is consistent with features seen onshore. This strongly suggests that the onshore sedimentological model of a series of stacked fluvial bodies described by Turner *et al.* (1993) is valid for the offshore.

Figure 9 illustrates the palaeogeographical reconstruction of the Fell Sandstone Formation. The reconstruction complements the correlations discussed earlier illustrating the known and inferred distribution of the sandstone. The slope and basinal deposits shown offshore remain speculative because of the lack of deep drilling.

Correlative carbonates of both basinal and platform facies are known from onshore UK.

Porosity and permeability measurements are derived from wireline log analysis because no direct core measurements are available. Data come from conventional porosity determinations utilizing logs such as the neutron and density and from newer logs as produced by nuclear magnetic resonance (NMR) tools.

Porosity versus depth of maximum burial plots for the Fell Sandstone Formation from SNS wells show a definite trend of decreasing porosity with depth. A minimum porosity is reached at a maximum burial depth of between 13 000–14 000 ft SS (subsea).

Little is known about the petrology of the Fell Sandstone Formation offshore as the only available samples are from cuttings and disturbed percussion sidewall cores. The sandstone is a fine-grained, quartz arenite which has undergone feldspar dissolution to create secondary porosity. In some

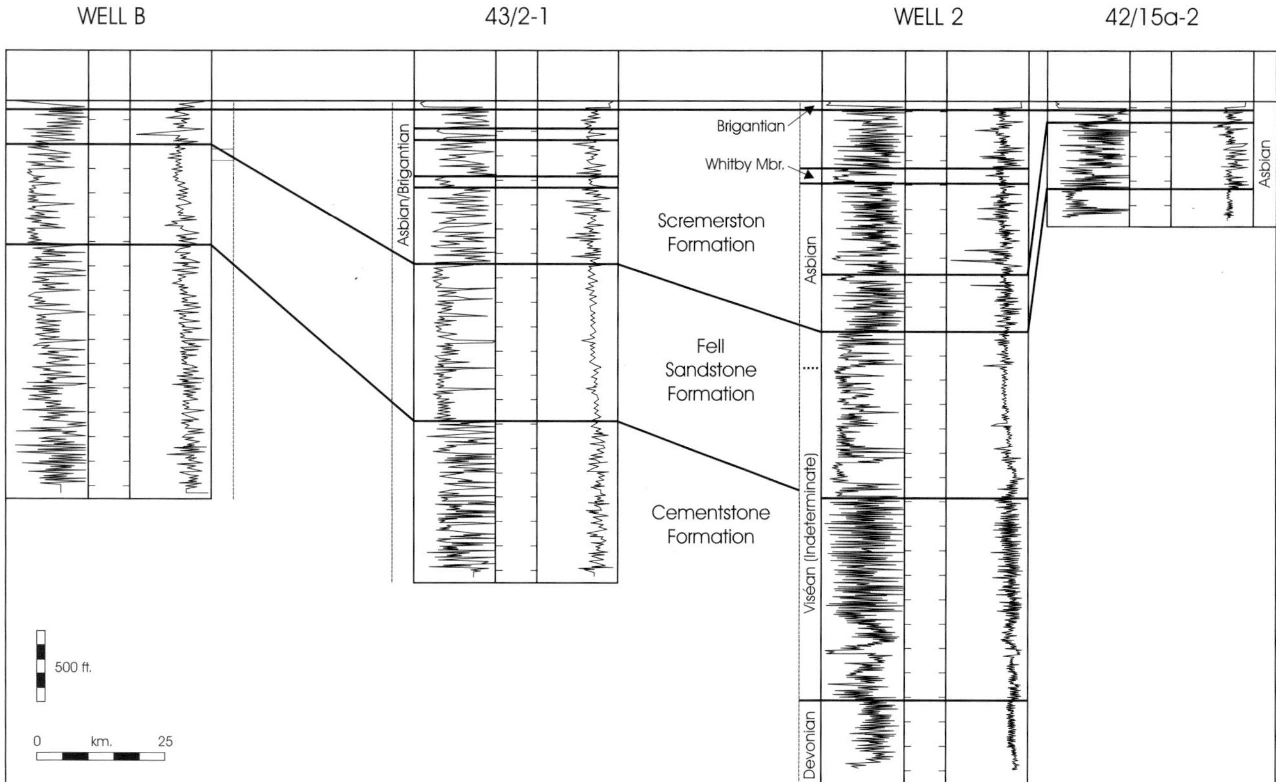

Fig. 8. A depositional strike parallel correlation (east to west) of the Fell Sandstone Formation along the southern flank of the Mid-North Sea High.

areas on the flanks of the MNSH the porosity reaches a maximum of 26%. Some authigenic clays such as illite and kaolinite have been deposited, reducing permeability. The main authigenic component is quartz which forms euhedral overgrowths on quartz grains.

The following is a brief summary of the sedimentology and occurrence of the onshore Fell Sandstone Formation, a full review is given in Turner *et al.* (1993).

Onshore, the Fell Sandstone Formation is over 300 m thick and comprises a stacked succession of fluvial sandstones separated by a number of laterally persistent claystone partings (Turner *et al.* 1993). These sandstones vary from 10 to 70 m thickness.Very little of the volume is comprised of overbank fines. Water production/aquifer pressure data show that these claystones are significant vertical barriers. Some sandbodies remain in communication despite these baffling data, whilst others are isolated. The sandstones consist predominantly of fine–medium-grained tabular cross-bedded sandstones. Minor channels are observed in some outcrops although large scale channel forms are not easily discerned nor are lateral/downstream accretion units. The sandstone units are sharp based and show minor local incision into the under-lying thin shales, when mapped out they are laterally extensive over many kilometres (many mapped around Berwick in excess of 5 km) although they do exhibit a lensoid form perpendicular to the palaeo-current direction. The facies assemblages have been interpreted to have been deposited by rivers in shallow, low sinuosity, braided streams. Palaeocurrents suggest a south-westerly transport direction.

The interpretation of the Fell Sandstone Formation as discrete bodies in the hanging walls of the main half-graben faults of the Tweed and Northumberland basins (Turner *et al.* 1993), would imply that the sandstone as a whole is not sheet-like. Offshore data cannot directly support or refute this assumption, but the Fell Sandstone Formation maintains a thickness of an average 330 m with very gradual thickness changes over the northern Quad 42–43 area (approximately 100 km). This would tend to suggest a more sheet-like geometry, although sampling in this area is sparse.

The Fell Sandstone Formation onshore can be traced for at least 70 km in basinward (SSW) extent from its northernmost outcrop near Berwick-upon-Tweed (Fig. 2). It does, however, eventually thin and pass laterally into deltaic facies which feather out around Bewcastle to the southwest.

Whitby Member, Scremerston Formation

The Whitby Member forms a thin sandstone within the Asbian section in at least three unreleased SNS wells and is thought to be typical of many of the Scremerston Formation/Yoredale Formation equivalent sandstones. The study of it is aided in the subsurface as it occurs within a distinctive seismic triplet on the studied dataset. The sandstone is cored in one well and imaged by FMS in another SNS well. Additional data are derived from a superb onshore exposure of a roughly age-equivalent sand-stone which is exposed on the coast of Northumberland and shows many of the features seen in the more limited offshore dataset.

Figure 10 shows a correlation between those wells containing the Whitby Member. The correlation is aided by good seismic and biostratigraphical (palynological, micro and macro palaeontological) data, from core and sidewall cores in Wells 2 and 3 and by seismic, palynological and regional limestone correlation to Well 1. The sandstone is a bipartite body which appears to have an erosive base with respect to the underlying shales and marine limestone horizon.

Palynological analysis has been undertaken on the Whitby Member in Wells 2 and 3. The sections have similar palynofloral assemblages, including *Schulzospora campyloptera*, *Tripartites vetustus*, *Kraueselisporites echinatus*, *Triquitrites marginatus*, *Rotaspora fracta*, and *Raistrickia nigra* (N. Turner, BGS confidential report). The pollen assemblages indicate affinities with the VF Miospore zone, suggesting a Brigantian to late Asbian age. However, detailed macro and micro faunal

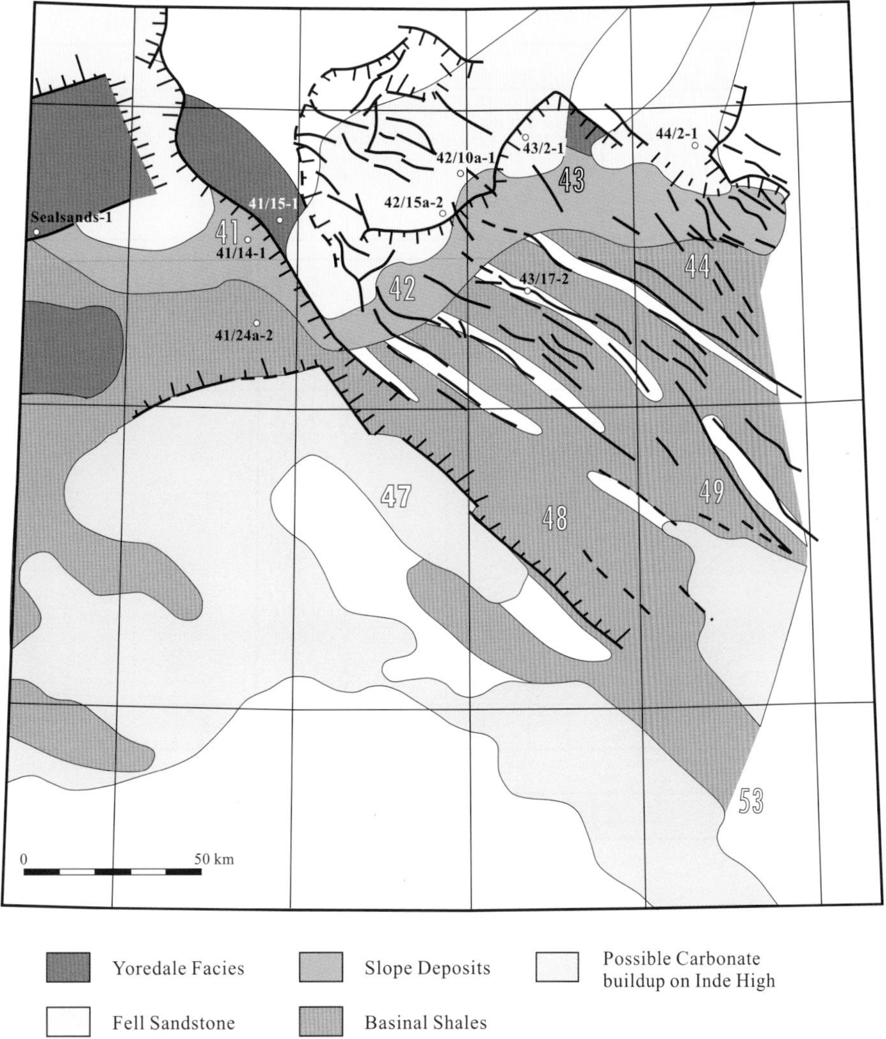

Fig. 9. Palaeogeography of the Fell Sandstone Formation in the area of interest compiled from well data and seismic facies. The Fell is fed through the lows formed by faulting onto the margins of the seaway, forming a 'fringe' to the northern part of the basin. It is thought to feather out basinward.

analyses undertaken on core in the overlying Scremerston section in Well 3 yielded *Howchinia* sp., *Neoarchaediscus* sp., *Saccamminopsis* sp. and *Koninckopora inflata* (N. Riley, BGS confidential report). This assemblage indicates that the Asbian–Brigantian boundary lies above the Whitby Sandstone, and that the Whitby Member itself is Asbian, (probably late Asbian) in age.

Core of the upper leaf of the Whitby Member in Well 2 shows a fine to granular-grained micaceous sandstone with normally graded beds (<1 m) which stack in fining upward units (Fig. 11). Planar cross-bedding, low angle lamination with current ripples are dominant. Bed bases are erosive with granule lags and mud rip-up clasts. Foresets are locally mud draped. The sandstone is interpreted as a stacked succession of fluvial channels. The sandstone erosively overlies a dark grey mudstone with pyritized bivalves which suggests a marine origin. Underlying these are sediments which have undergone pedogenesis.

FMS image logs from Well 3 clearly show many similar features seen in the core from Well 2. An interpretation is shown in Fig. 13. The upper leaf is about 10 m thick and comprises at least 2 overall fining-up units. Each unit has an irregular, erosive or loaded base with clay rip-up clasts and small rounded pebbles. Cross-bedding and planar lamination dominate but ripple lamination cannot be clearly resolved. Internal erosion at bed boundaries is common especially where coincident with foresets. The upper leaf grades into fines with bioturbation and is interpreted as channel abandonment.

The lower leaf is some 20 m thick and the base of the sand rests sharply on laminated clay. At least two channel fills can be interpreted and their bases are bounded by pebble channel lags. Numerous internal scour surfaces are present. Beds reach a maximum of 2.5 m, suggesting some large-scale in-channel dune forms which, as in the core foresets, can be picked out by their clay drapes. The top of the lower sand grades into fines with an overlying thin coal (<25 cm).

The interval between the upper and lower sand leaves is dominated by fines with some intercalated coarser material. This unit may represent the marine interval seen in core from the Well 2 and/or overbank fines.

Palaeocurrent data from foresets was collated to derive two rose diagrams for the upper and lower parts of the sands. The upper sand shows a wide spread in orientations around a SSW direction whilst the lower sand shows a southerly direction with a narrower spread. The differences in palaeocurrent orientation may be a result of differences in sinuosity of the channels from the two leaves. Sinuosity may be relatively higher in the upper leaf, given the greater range of palaeoflow direction.

The Whitby Member consists of stacked fluvial channels which are dominantly planar cross-bedded with numerous

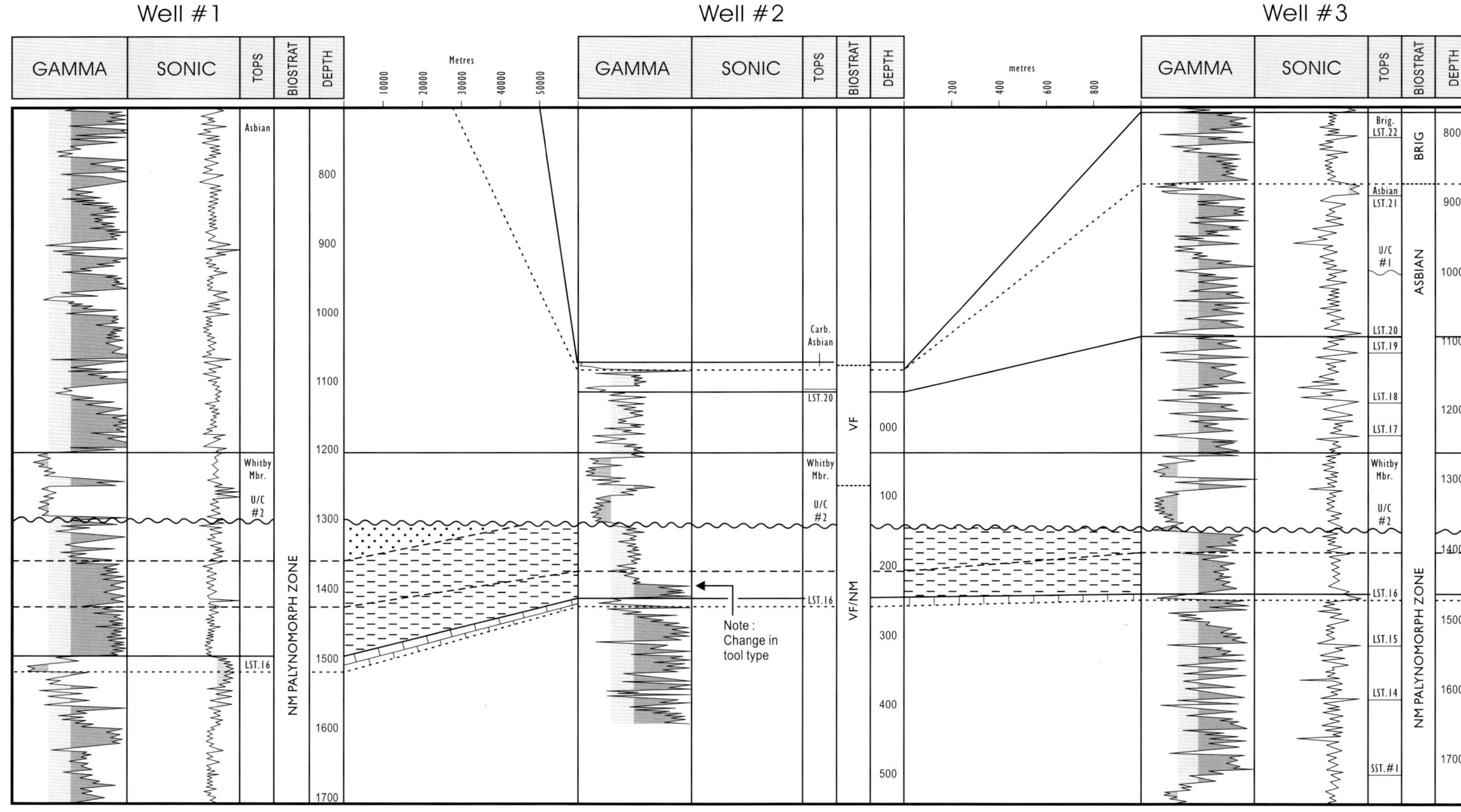

Fig. 10. Correlation of the late Asbian Whitby Sandstone Member (depth in feet. An excellent log correlation is seen between these three confidential wells. The two at the left are over 50 km apart. The succession immediately below the sandstone to the underlying limestone has a distinct wireline signature which shows some incision which is at least equal to the thickness of the stacked channel sandstones (note jump in GR in Well 2 at 250 ft because of a change of tool type). For details of palynological zonation see Maynard *et al.* (1997).

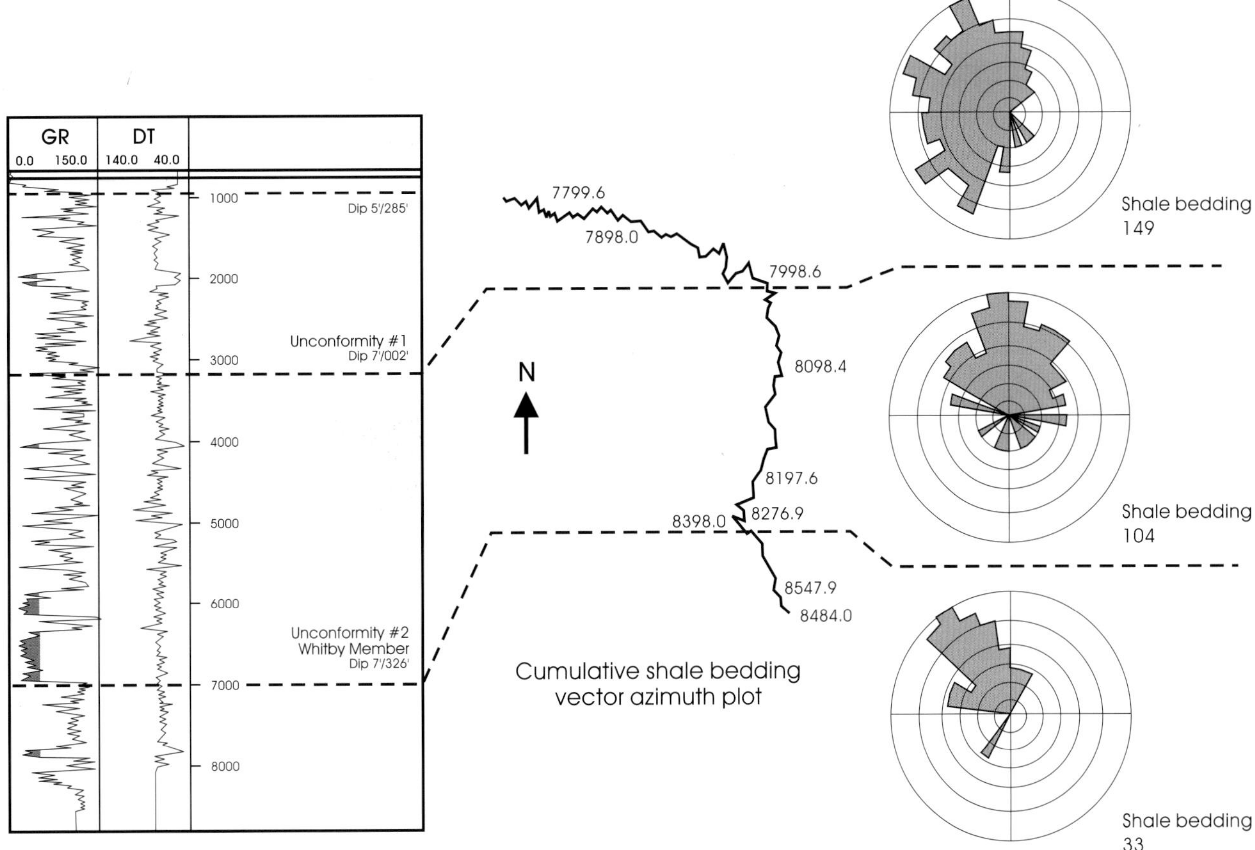

Fig. 11. Two unconformities can be recognized from a dip azimuth vector plot of shale bedding from interpreted FMS data from Well 3. The upper unconformity occurs at the uppermost of a series of thick mature palaeosols which may mark a sequence boundary represented by an interfluve. The lowermost is associated with the base of the Whitby Member and is interpreted as the erosive surface of a palaeovalley and is thus also a potential sequence boundary.

scour surfaces. They are interpreted as a component of a sheet like braided fluvial sandstone because of their lateral persistence (>60 km).

Some noticeable differences exist between Wells 2 and 3. Firstly in Well 2, the lower sandstone is thinner and the upper sandstone is thicker whilst the overall sand body thickness remains constant which suggests some degree of depositionally inherited accommodation. Secondly, the amount of incision on the base of the sandstone is some 12 m over a distance of about 1 km based on the thickness of the underlying shales to the limestone bed (40 m incision between Wells 1 and 3). This incision may point to the erosive surface being a candidate sequence boundary with the sandstone infilling a palaeovalley. In addition the shale dip azimuth plot from Well 3 shows changes in dip direction at the base of the sandstone which strongly suggests that an unconformity is present (Fig. 12). A second unconformity is seen higher in the section at the top of a series of thick palaeosols; this may be a candidate for an interfluve to a younger palaeovalley. The extensive nature of this body and its sheet like geometry can usefully be compared to geometries seen in the Namurian where sandstones such as the Rough Rock exhibit similar geometry (Maynard 1992; Davies *et al.* 1999)

The upper part of the Whitby Member was analysed in detail. The sandstone is a moderately sorted, medium to coarse-grained quartz-arenite but would have originally contained feldspar and been defined as a sub-arkose. Silty clay drapes and micaceous coaly planes are also seen in thin-section. The detrital grains are mostly quartz with minor muscovite mica. Very little matrix is present within the channel facies. Authigenic minerals are dominated by quartz and kaolinite. Local occurrences of haematite are located in sediments at the top of the channel (minor ferroan dolomite and illite is rare). Kaolinite is very abundant (5–10%) and occurs as aggregates of booklets within pores which are occasionally oil stained and as large composite aggregates where the kaolinite has replaced grains. Quartz is also abundant (5–10%) and occurs as overgrowths to the detrital grains, occluding primary porosity. The ferroan dolomite (<5%) is less abundant and, where present, infills the secondary porosity.

There is evidence from shale grains that a significant period of leaching occurred. The leaching could have been caused by meteoric water (during the Permian uplift) and has removed both quartz and feldspars. It may also have lead to the formation of kaolinite. This form of leaching may have produced the hematite minerals as well as enhancing the secondary porosity.

Porosity and permeability values from available cores from Yoredale facies within Wells 2 and 3 were classified by facies and plotted in Fig. 14. The channel sandstones of the Whitby Member have the highest permeabilities and porosities with measured porosity from 8–18% (average 13.3%) and permeabilities from 0.4 to 120 mD (arith. mean 23.3 mD, geom. mean 11.8 mD). This confirms that the sandstone is of moderate reservoir quality, although it is better when compared to many other Carboniferous sandstones of younger age. A comparison of the log-derived NMR porosity–permeability plot from the Whitby Member is shown in Fig. 15 with the measured data superimposed.

The type section for the onshore analogue of the Whitby Member is located at Redshin Quarry, Spittal, Northumberland (British National Grid Reference: NU 016 504). This sandstone forms a spectacular coastal exposure in the cliffs

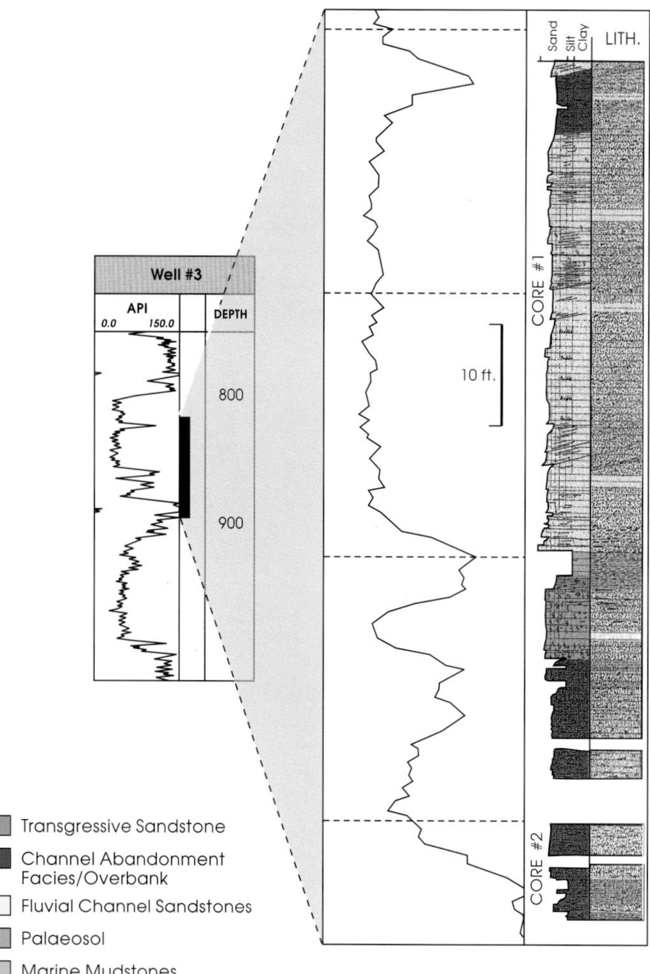

Fig. 12. Core description from Well 2 through the upper leaf of the Whitby Sandstone Member (scale in feet). Note the core is deviated at approximately 60° from vertical.

to the north of Berwick-upon-Tweed in Northumberland (Gardiner 1985). This sandstone is late Asbian (Lower Limestone Group = Yoredale Formation; N. Riley, BGS confidential report) in age and is possibly time-equivalent to the Whitby Member. To the south of the town, along the Spittal foreshore, a section from the Scremerston Coal Group through the Redshin Quarry Sandstone can be examined in detail.

Photo-mosaic images were taken along the cliffs to the north of Berwick and the architectural elements of the fluvial sands were interpreted. Figs 16 and 17 illustrate part of this mosaic with an interpretation. The sandbody shows several similarities to the Whitby Sandstone. There are two 'leaves' or sandbodies separated by a shale break. They both have sharp contacts with the underlying units. The lower sandstone is underlain by the marine Dun Limestone. The lower leaf is dominated by planar cross-bedding with very little channel scour whilst the upper leaf is planar cross-bedded with trough cross-bedding. Channels and both lateral and down-stream accretion elements are observed. The upper leaf shows laterally persistent shale beds often draping channel scours; some are possibly palaeosols (because of their red mottled coloration). This contrasts with the lower leaf in which laterally impersistent shale layers can be observed. The sandstone maintains a thickness of 30 m over the entire lateral extent of outcrop (≈9 km) and extends inland up to 60 km (Gardiner 1985) and therefore has a sheet-like geometry.

The sandbody is interpreted as a braided, fluvial sheet system. Several similar sandstones exist within the Yoredale cyclothems exposed in the cliffs to the south of Spittal and these in turn have common features with many of the very extensive sands seen in other parts of the Carboniferous (Namurian; Maynard 1992; Church & Gawthorpe 1994; Hampson *et al.* 1996; Wignall & Maynard 1996). An important observation with respect to the reservoir quality of the sandstone is that the mesoscale architecture (channel elements etc.) is different to the macroscale architecture (sheet geometry of the sand) in the sense that the channels often appear to be lined with fines which could greatly affect production.

Stratigraphic model

The succession within the Dinantian is dominated by cyclicity and it would be possible to apply a simplistic sequence stratigraphic breakdown to the succession given a precise biostratigraphical framework. At present this precise biostratigraphical framework does not exist even onshore (Riley pers. comm. 1996) and offshore the data are sparse.

The depositional environment above the Fell Sandstone Formation is essentially one of a cyclic fluvio–deltaic clastic to marine carbonate interplay. Figure 18 shows the conceptual facies development through time for a typical Yoredale Cyclothem. Initially, during highstand, small mouth bars prograde into shallow marine waters. A deltaic plain is established of low gradient with a high suspended bedload fluvial system embedded in fine-grained overbank fines. Ribbon-like, high

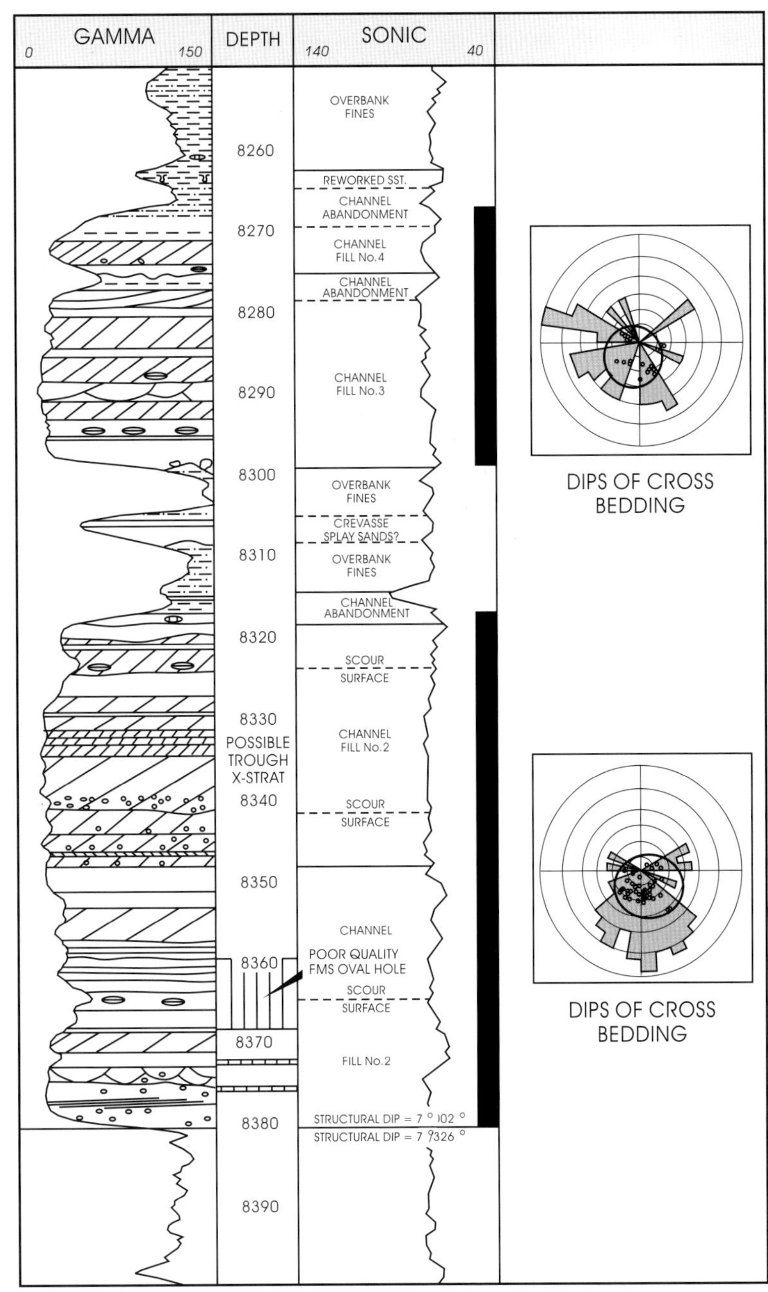

Fig. 13. An interpretation of the FMS image over the Whitby Sandstone Member from Well 3 (scale in feet).

sinuosity, low connectivity sandbodies result. Some limited coal development is seen with lacustrine facies. Relative sea-level fall (plus increased climatic run-off associated with an adjacent sediment source) brings the possibility of emplacing a braided sheet-like fluvial system which incises into underlying deposits. Mature soils develop on terraces and interfluves. Transgression of the sea drowns the underlying deposits and eventually results in the development of bioclastic limestones with very little terrigenous material. These limestones could be considered as containing the maximum flooding surface.

In this model, the Whitby Member fluvial sandstone would be placed within the palaeovalley. The Whitby Member does show considerable incision at its base over the distance of several tens of kilometres, which lends support to regional basal incision. At this time, no evidence can be presented for correlative interfluve surfaces because of the lack of high resolution biostratigraphic control in other wells. In addition, the stacked nature of channels within the sandbody and their scale relative to this incision also supports the palaeovalley interpretation. It is thus likely but not fully demonstrated that the sandstones form incised valley fills (Zaitlin *et al.* 1994).

The Fell Sandstone Formation is clearly different from the overlying Scremerston and Yoredale formations with less marine influence and a significantly higher net sand content. The thickness and facies distributions have been interpreted by Turner *et al.* (1993) as structurally controlled. In this model the highest net : gross facies occurs in the hanging walls of predominantly east–west trending Devonian–early Carboniferous tilted fault blocks while the lowest net : gross successions occur on the footwalls. Locally, transfer zones act as depocentres for thick sand development. This model assumes axial drainage from the east and northeast which is supported by palaeocurrents in the onshore. Offshore palaeocurrent analysis is broadly in agreement with the onshore data. This drainage along with the fault-constrained deposition may

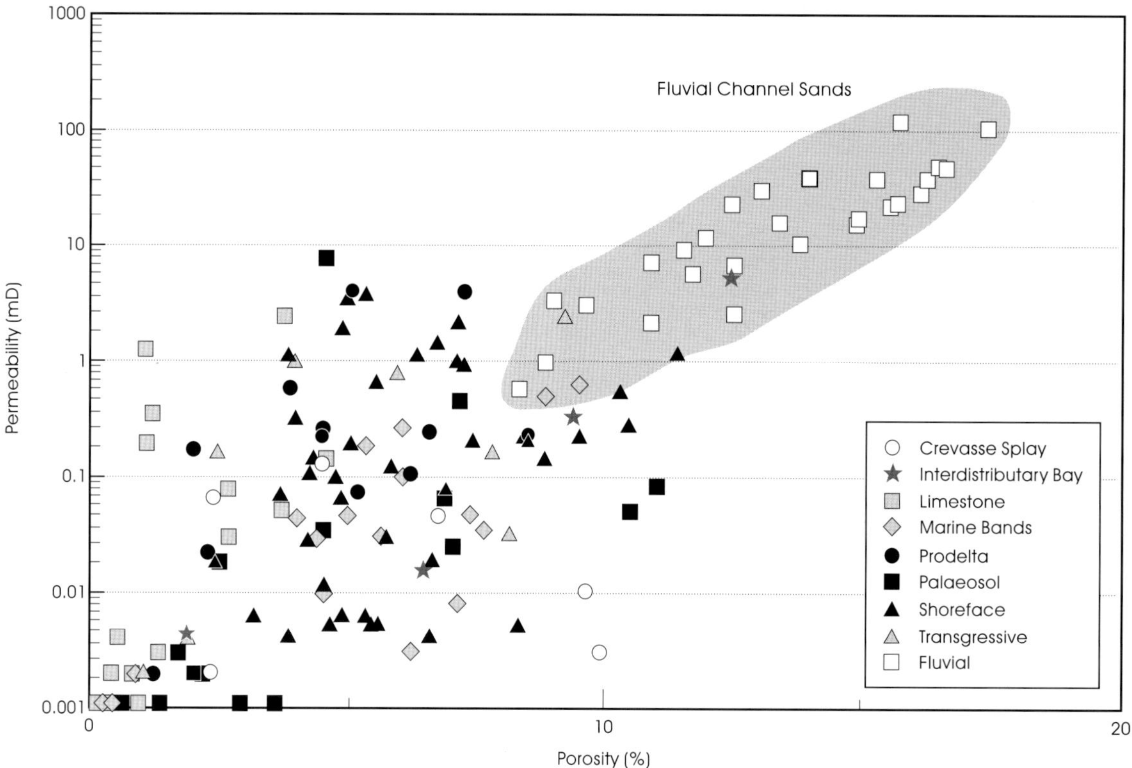

Fig 14. Measured core porosity versus permeability for all facies from the late Dinantian. The fluvial channel facies are highlighted.

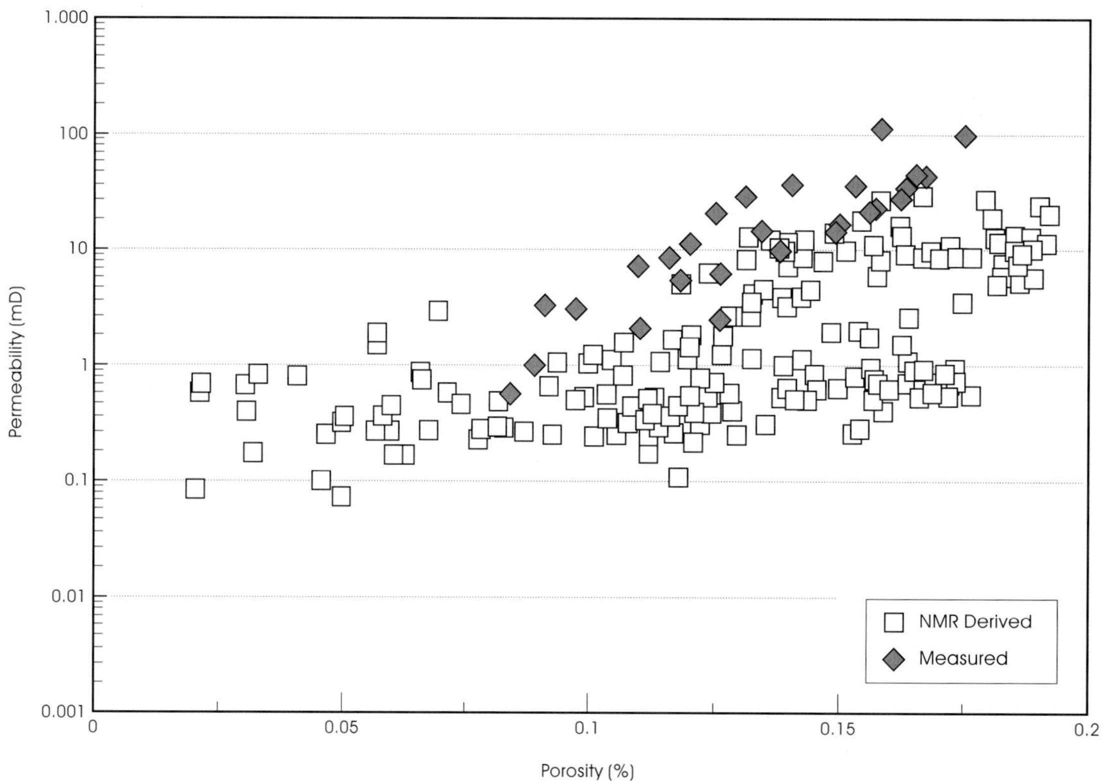

Fig 15. Measured and log-derived (NMR) porosity–permeability plot for the Whitby Sandstone Member.

explain the east–west persistence of the Fell Sandstone Formation (Turner *et al.* 1993). As discussed above, the offshore data tend toward a uniform sheet-like occurrence over Quadrants 42 and 43 which does not fully support this model. There is evidence for a degree of cyclicity within the multiple-stacked channel sandbodies that occur within the Fell Sandstone Formation offshore as discussed above. This cyclicity could be caused by relative base-level changes whose sedimentary expression is largely being overwhelmed by the large sediment supply into the hanging walls of faults. The active subsidence would allow a great degree of sediment aggradation reducing or preventing sediment by-pass.

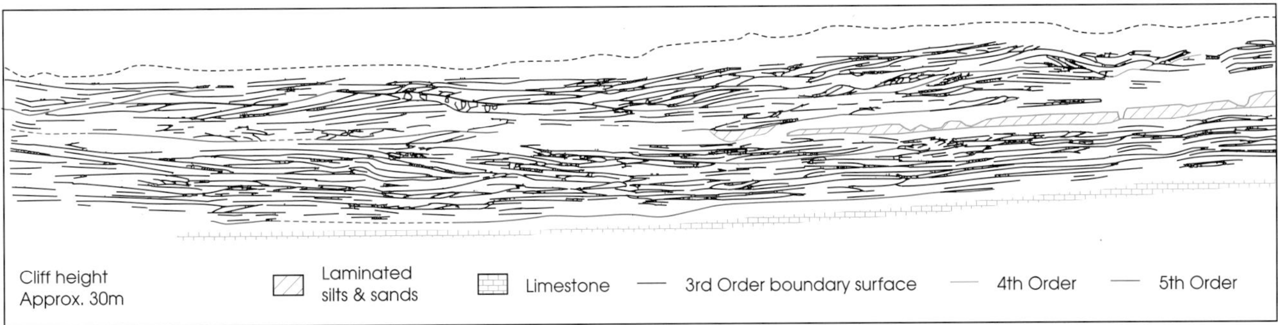

Fig. 16. Onshore exposure of the Redshin Quarry Sandstone in the cliffs to the north of Berwick Upon Tweed, Northumberland. With line interpretation of the large scale sedimentary features. Note the contrast between the upper and lower parts of the sandbody (details in text).

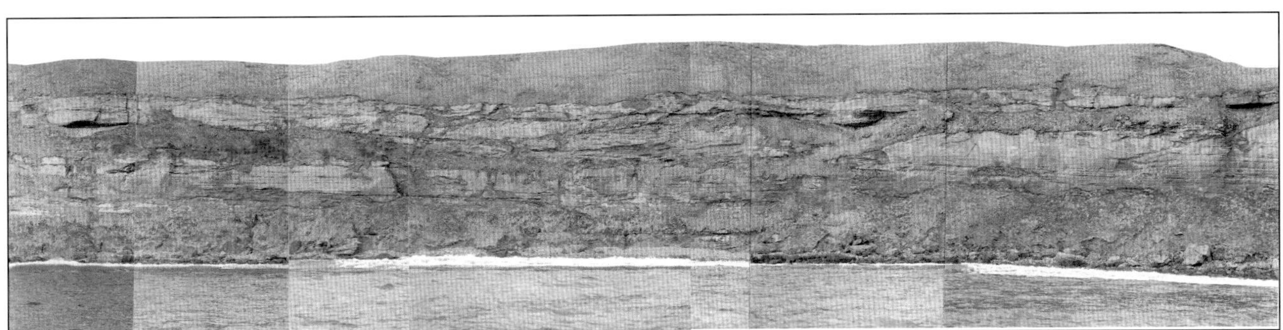

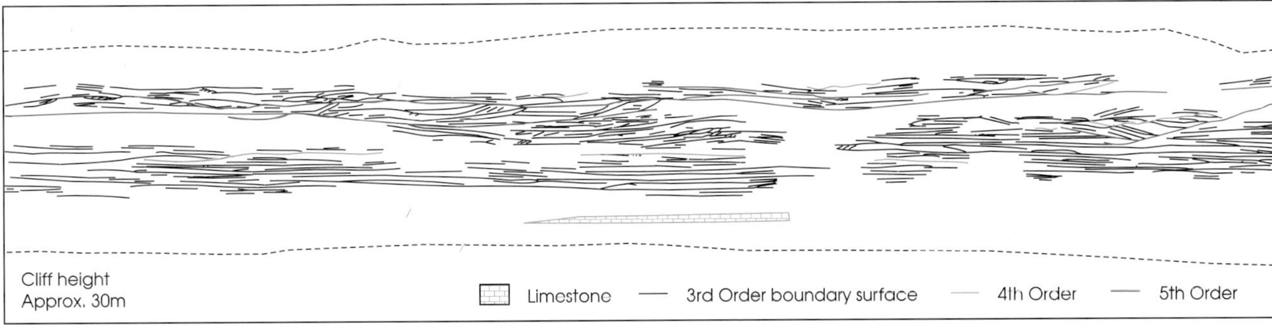

Fig. 17. Onshore exposure of the Redshin Quarry Sandstone in the cliffs to the north of Berwick Upon Tweed, Northumberland. With line interpretation of the large scale sedimentary features and bounding surface hierarchy.

Implications for the petroleum system

Many potential reservoirs exist within the Dinantian subcrop of the northern part of the SNS which at their best display good reservoir characteristics. The geographical spread of the sandstones mean that there is an excellent chance of the bit encountering these potential reservoirs.

Although the offshore evidence supports a sheet-like geometry for the Dinantian reservoirs, the examination of the onshore shows that over a large scale >10 km the distribution of sandstone is potentially more complex. A sheet-like geometric model is probably fairly reliable at the exploration phase but once a discovery has been made then the geometry of the sandbody becomes critical.

In the sections above we have explored two potentially contrasting models, Turner *et al.* (1993) structural model and a palaeovalley or potential incised valley fill (IVF) model. Both models result in compartmented reservoirs although the

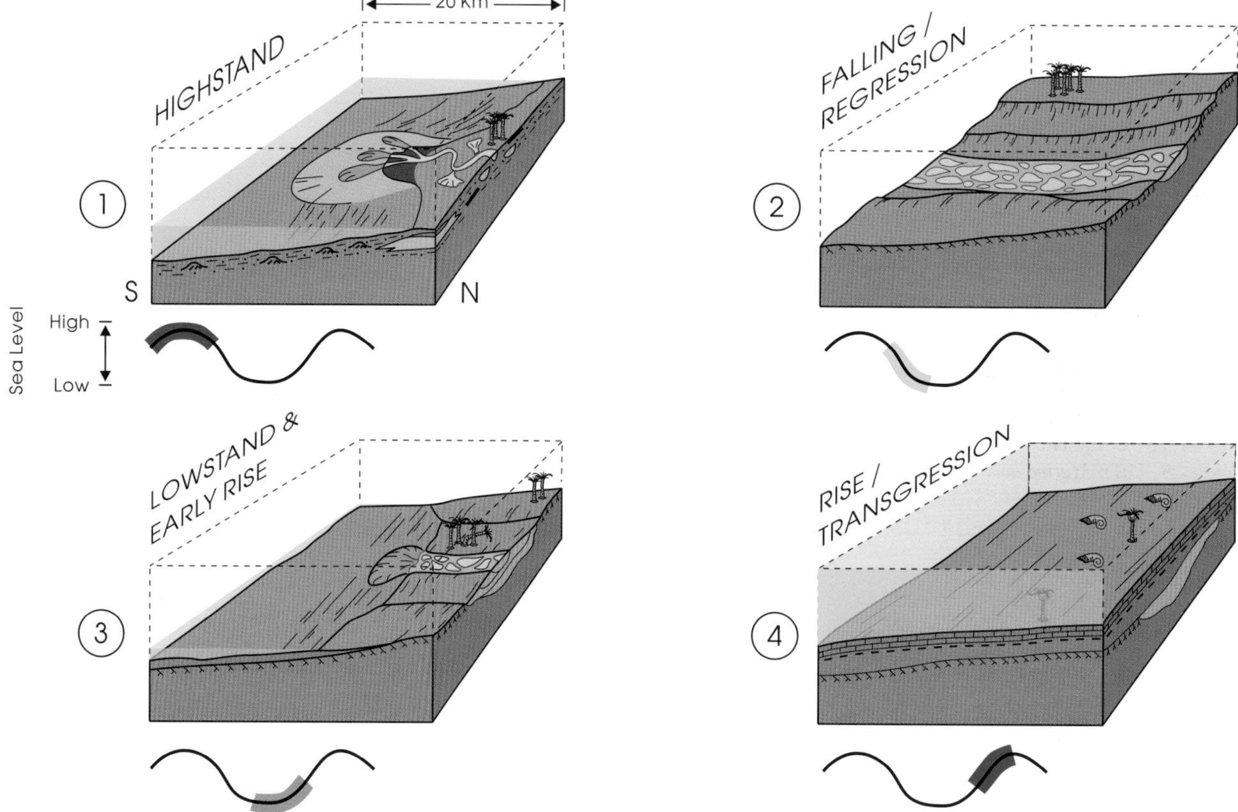

Fig. 18. A sequence stratigraphic explanation for the development of a Yoredale cyclothem and the associated sandbodies.

Turner *et al.* (1993) model would involve fault control on basin drainage which could result in localized vertical aggradation. This hypothesis is supported in the recent and modern sedimentary record where drainage basins and fluvial deposition is strongly influenced by active faults (Leeder 1993; Leeder *et al.* 1996). Thus recognition of syndepositional faults would greatly aid the explorationist. The incised valley fill model also restricts the sandbody to a palaeovalley whose limits although potentially fault-controlled are not as well defined. The reality is that both models are probably valid and end members of the system with the same controls with high frequency relative sea-level changes being superimposed on a topography/bathymetry controlled by active fault/passive (hanging wall compaction) subsidence influenced the site of palaeovalleys. The difference is the rate and magnitude of the sediment supply. In the Holkerian to early Asbian (Fell Sandstone Formation) the sediment supply was large, swamping the accommodation space developed by rise in sea-level and hanging wall subsidence. The Asbian to Brigantian (Yoredale and Scremerston Formations), in contrast, was a time of less sediment supply, allowing sediment starvation and the development of marginal marine carbonate facies.

The maximum depth of burial has an important control on porosity preservation within the reservoir. Thus any potential reservoir intervals which occur toward the southern part of the area, where deep burial during the Mesozoic has occurred, will have a lower quality. In addition to porosity the productivity of any reservoir will be affected by the architecture of the sandbody. The onshore analogues show that the macro-scale geometry of a 'sheet-like' sandstone like the Fell Sandstone Formation is complex with potentially isolated lensoid bodies within the thicker whole. The available evidence shows that these bodies although isolated still have significant net cross sectional area and potential volume (cross-section 5000 m by 10–70 m; Turner *et al.* 1993). The exposed Redshin Quarry Sandstone, although extensive as a macroscale body (15 m by 10 000 m), also shows a complex mesoscale geometry within its macroscale sheet-like upper leaf. These channel forms and downstream/lateral accretion units are juxtaposed with potential reservoir baffles in the form of claystone/palaeosol partings and could significantly alter well bore drainage and performance.

One gas discovery has been made in the offshore in Block 42/15 where a poor quality Dinantian reservoir within a large Base Zechstein closure has been charged by the adjacent mature Westphalian and Namurian source horizons. However the occurrence of these source beds needs to be near the potential reservoirs to minimise potential tortuous migration pathways. This requires prospects to be toward the south of the area near the Westphalian/Namurian subcrop.

The lack of a thick intra-Carboniferous top seal due to the nature of Yoredale deposition is noted as well as within the laterally extensive palaeovalleys/channel systems. Thus to lower the risk reservoirs should subcrop the sealing Permian Zechstein evaporites.

Drilling offshore has proven a number of potential reservoirs within the Dinantian which have good reservoir characteristics including some high net : gross successions. Critical to any risk analysis is how far south into the former basins these sands may extend and how their reservoir characteristics alter with the transition to basinal facies. As can be seen above there is a delicate balance between reservoir quality, presence, hydrocarbon charge and seal, which makes for a high risk but potentially rewarding play.

Thanks to summer student H. Griffiths. Colleagues at Mobil, P. Bentham, A. Holmes, G. Butcher, J. Gibson, M. Evans and some ex colleagues; P. Harrison and P. Young. Also thanks to T. Good of the Genetic Units Project, Heriot Watt University for provision of the coastal photographs and N. Riley from the BGS for useful discussions in the field. Thanks to our reviewers P. O'Mara and S. Davies whose suggestions were gratefully recieved. BHP and Total Oil Marine are thanked for permission to publish.

References

BOOGAERT, H. A. & KNOWE, W. F. P. 1993. Stratigraphic nomenclature of The Netherlands. *Mededelingen Rijks Geologische Dienst*, **50**, 1–20.

CAMERON, T. D. J. 1993. *In*: KNOX, R. W. O.'B. & CORDEY, W. G. (eds) *Lithostratigraphic Nomenclature of the UK North Sea, Part 5, Carboniferous and Devonian of the Southern North Sea*. BGS/UKOOA publication.

CHURCH, K. D. & GAWTHORPE, R. L. 1994. High resolution sequence stratigraphy of the late Namurian in the Widmerpool Gulf (East Midlands, UK). *Marine and Petroleum Geology*, **11**, 528–544.

COLLINSON, J. D., JONES, C. M., BLACKBOURN, G. A., BESLY, B. M., ARCHARD, G. M. & MCMAHON, A. H. 1993. Carboniferous depositional systems of the Southern North Sea. *In*: PARKER, J. R. (ed.) *Petroleum Geology of Northwest Europe: Proceedings of the 4th Conference*. The Geological Society, London, 677–687.

DAVIES, S., HAMPSON, G., FLINT, S. S., TREVOR ELLIOTT, T., ATKINSON, C. 1999. Continental scale sequence stratigraphy of the Upper Carboniferous and its application to reservoir prediction. *In*: FLEET, A. J. & BOLDY, S. A. R. (eds) *Petroleum Geology of Northwest Europe: Proceedings of the 5th Conference*. Geological Society, London, 757–770.

FRASER, A. J. & GAWTHORPE, R. L. 1990. Tectono-stratigraphic development and hydrocarbon habitat of the Carboniferous in Northern England. *In*: HARDMAN, F. P. & BROOKS, J. (eds) *Tectonic Events Responsible for Britains Oil and Gas Reserves*. Geological Society, London, Special Publications, **55**, 49–86.

GEORGE, T. N., JOHNSTON, G. A. L., MITCHELL, M., PRENTICE, J. E., RAMSBOTTOM, W. H. C., SEVASTOPULO, G. D. & WILSON, R. B. 1976. *A correlation of Dinantian rocks in the British Isles*. Geological Society, London, Special Report, **7**, 87pp.

GARDINER, A. R. 1985. *Sedimentological Studies of the Scremerston Coal and Lower Limestone Groups in the Northumberland Basin*. PhD Thesis, University of Leeds.

HAMPSON, G. J, ELLIOTT, T., FLINT, S. S. 1996. Critical application of high resolution sequence stratigraphic concepts to the Rough Rock Group (Upper Carboniferous) of northern England. *In*: HOWELL, J. A. & AITKIN, J. F. (eds) *High Resolution Sequence Stratigraphy: Innovation and Applications*, Geological Society, London, Special Publications, **104**, 221–246.

HODGSON, A. V. & GARDINER, M. D. 1971. An investigation of the aquifer potential of the Fell Sandstone of Northumberland. *Quarterly Journal of Engineering Geology*, **4**, 91–109.

HOLLYWOOD, J. M. & WHORLOW, C. V. 1993. Structural development and hydrocarbon occurrence of the Carboniferous in the UK Southern North Sea Basin. *In*: PARKER, J. R. (ed.) *Petroleum Geology of Northwest Europe: Proceedings of the 4th Conference*. Geological Society, London, 689–696.

LEEDER, M. R. 1993. Tectonic controls upon drainage development, river channel migration and alluvial architecture: implications for hydrocarbon reservoir development and characterization. *In*: NORTH, C. P. & PROSSER, D. J. (eds) *Characterisation of Fluvial and Aeolian Reservoirs*. Geological Society, London, Special Publications, **73**, 7–22.

—— & HARDMAN, M. 1990. Carboniferous geology of the Southern North Sea Basin and controls on hydrocarbon prospectivity. *In*: HARDMAN, F. P. & BROOKS, J. (eds). *Tectonic Events Responsible for Britains Oil and Gas Reserves*. Geological Society, London, Special Publications, **55**, 87–106.

——, MACK, G. H., PEAKALL, J. & SALYARDS, S. L. 1996. First quantitative test of alluvial stratigraphic models: Southern Rio Grande rift, New Mexico. *Geology*, **24**, 87–90.

MATTE, P. 1986. Tectonics and plate tectonics model for the Variscan belt of Europe. *Tectonophysics*, **126**, 329–374.

MAYNARD, J. R. 1992. The sequence stratigraphy of the Upper Yeadonian of northern England. *Marine and Petroleum Geology*, **9**, 197–207.

——, HOFMANN, W., DUNAY, R. E., BENTHAM, P. N., DEAN, K. P. & WATSON, I. 1997. The Carboniferous Basin of North Western Europe: the development of a petroleum system. *Petroluem Geoscience*, **3**, 97–115.

RILEY, N. J. 1993. Dinantian (Lower Carboniferous) biostratigraphy and chronostratigraphy in the British Isles. *Journal of the Geological Society, London*, **150**, 427–446.

TURNER, B. R., YOUNGER, B. R. & FORDHAM, C. E. 1993. Fell Sandstone Group lithostratigraphy south-west of Berwick-upon-Tweed: implications for the regional development of the Fell Sandstone. *Proceedings of the Yorkshire Geological Society*, **49**, 269–281.

WIGNALL, P. B. & MAYNARD, J. R. 1996. High resolution sequence stratigraphy in the early Marsdenian (Namurian, Carboniferous) of the central Pennines and adjacent areas. *Proceedings of the Yorkshire Geological Society*, **51**, 127–140.

ZAITLIN, B. A., DALRYMPLE, R. W. & BOYD, R. 1994. The stratigraphic organisation of incised valley systems associated with relative sea-level change. *In*: DALRYMPLE, R. W., BOYD, R. & ZAITLIN, B. A. (eds) *Incised Valley Systems: Origin and Sedimentary Sequences*. Tulsa, SEPM, 46–60.

Regional correlation of Westphalian sandbodies onshore UK: implications for reservoirs in the Southern North Sea

J. F. AITKEN,[1] D. G. QUIRK and P. D. GUION

Geology Department (BMS), Oxford Brookes University, Gipsy Lane, Headington, Oxford OX3 0BP, UK

[1] *Present address: BG plc, Gas Research and Technology Centre, Ashby Rd, Loughborough LE11 3GR, UK*

Abstract: An extensive and closely-spaced seismic and well dataset from coal and hydrocarbon exploration in the East Pennine Coalfield and the East Midlands Oilfield has enabled the detailed subsurface correlation and mapping of major Westphalian A to C sandbodies. Maximum flooding surfaces are represented by marine bands which are faunal concentrate condensed horizons. The large fluvial sandbodies do not show characteristics of incized valley fills. The remoteness of the study area from the sea during deposition meant that eustatic changes are less significant than other factors. The interplay of tectonics, climate and autocyclic processes was responsible for exceedingly complex sequences in terms of both lateral and vertical organization, and it is difficult to isolate the relative importance of the various mechanisms controlling sedimentation.

Closely spaced onshore borehole data and outcrop studies have been used to model reservoir characteristics and continuity offshore in the Southern North Sea, where well spacing is far greater. Architectural variability and 3D geometry of onshore sandbodies can be used as an analogue for Southern North Sea reservoirs. Geometric data from 20 mapped onshore sandbodies illustrates a relationship between sandbody width and thickness, with 90% of channel sandbodies being less than 25 km in width and less than 40 m in thickness. A remarkable similarity exists between the sand distribution onshore UK and Westphalian reservoir intervals in the Southern North Sea. Sandbodies onshore and offshore show comparable thicknesses (up to 100 m) and widths (up to 30 km). Additionally, the sandbodies do not display incised bases, as is also typical of all the main Westphalian reservoir targets in the Southern North Sea.

The Westphalian of the Southern North Sea has become an important target for gas exploration (Leeder & Hardman 1990; Collinson *et al.* 1993; Ritchie & Pratsides 1993; Quirk & Aitken 1997) and oil is produced onshore from the Westphalian in the East Midlands Oilfield (Kent 1985; Fraser & Gawthorpe 1990; Fraser *et al.* 1990). Despite their importance, Westphalian reservoirs tend to be difficult to locate and develop and are highly complicated in terms of their internal architecture.

This paper examines the geometry of major onshore UK Westphalian channel sandbodies as analogues to similar subsurface reservoirs, particularly within the Southern North Sea and investigates the controls on their development. The study area of *c.* 14 000 km^2, equivalent to 56 blocks in the UK sector of the North Sea, encompassing the East Pennine Coalfield and the East Midland Oilfield (Fig. 1), lies east of the Pennines and is bounded to the west by the outcrop of the Westphalian which dips gently eastwards beneath a Permian and Mesozoic cover.

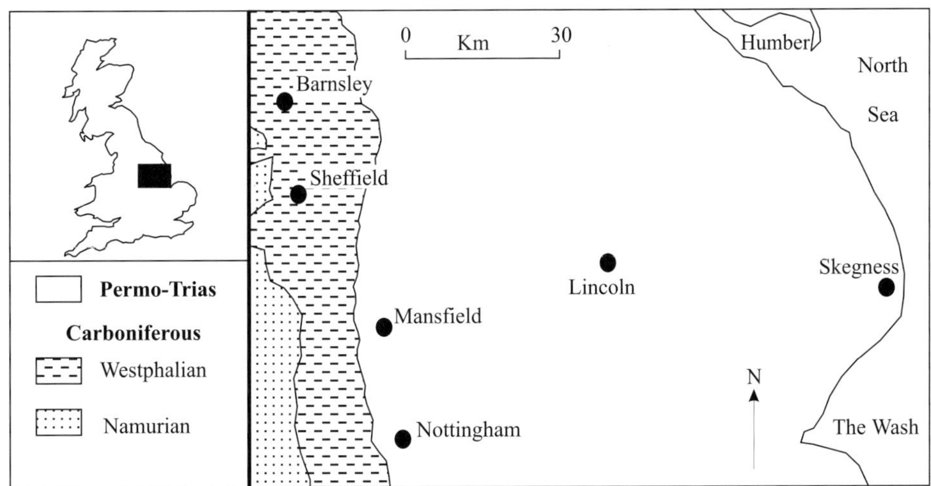

Fig. 1. Location of the study area in the east Pennines and east Midlands.

Aitken, J. F., Quirk, D. G. & Guion, P. D. 1999. Regional correlation of Westphalian sandbodies onshore UK: implications for reservoirs in the Southern North Sea. *In*: Fleet, A. J. & Boldy, S. A. R. (eds) *Petroleum Geology of Northwest Europe: Proceedings of the 5th Conference*, 747–756.

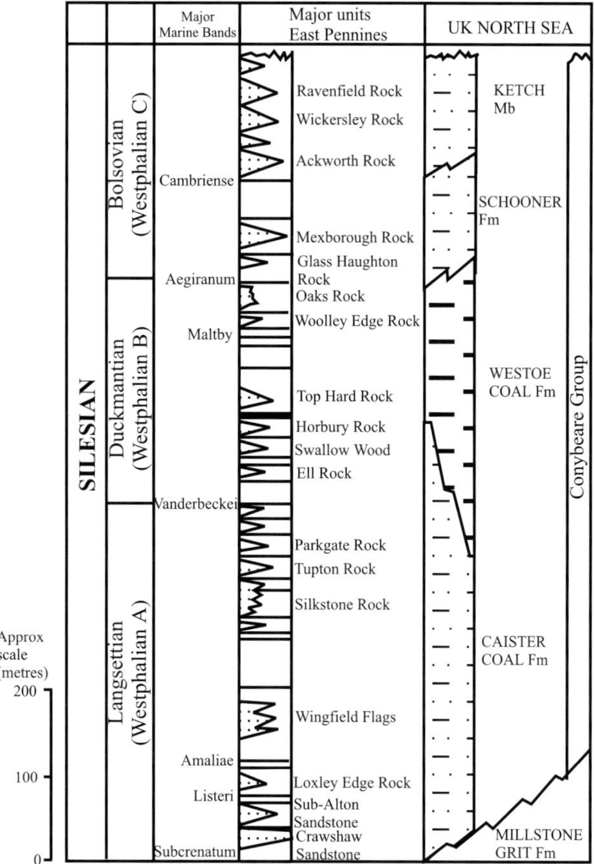

Fig. 2. Generalized stratigraphy of the Westphalian A–C of the east Pennines and the Southern North Sea, showing main seams, marine bands and major channel sandbodies (modified after Guion *et al.* 1995*a*).

The study area is relatively undisturbed tectonically and contains a number of stratigraphic markers, particularly coal seams and marine bands, which reliably constrain the vertical and lateral extent and internal organization of the sandbodies. The stratigraphic interval studied extends from the Silkstone Rock and its correlatives in the middle Westphalian A (Langsettian), below which there is little penetration in coal exploration wells, to the Ackworth Rock which lies above the Cambriense Marine Band in the middle Westphalian C (Bolsovian) (Fig. 2). Although a considerable number of sandstones occur above this level and form important reservoirs in the Southern North Sea, the angular nature of the unconformity at the base of the Permian onshore has meant that upper Westphalian C sandbodies are only intermittently preserved.

Dataset

This study is based on over 1000 colliery shaft and coal exploration borehole records and hydrocarbon exploration and production wells supplemented with details from relatively limited outcrop. Additional borehole and shaft sections were extracted from Wilcockson (1950) and the relevant Geological Survey memoirs. The most reliable sedimentological data was obtained from descriptive core logs; most coal exploration wells are fully cored through the coal-bearing Westphalian. Many of the records, especially from the west of the study area, are old and lithologies are recorded in colloquial mining terminology (e.g. Wilcockson 1950). Consequently, seam correlation is difficult and detailed facies interpretations are not always possible. Farther to the east, however, the records are more recent, seams are correlated accurately and lithological descriptions contain enough detail to interpret facies. The close spacing of coal mine shaft and exploration boreholes (of the order of hundreds of metres) allows more detailed mapping of sandbodies than is possible with widely-spaced hydrocarbon exploration wells of the Southern North Sea.

The borehole data have been supplemented with several hundred kilometres of 2D seismic data. However, most of these data occur in the coastal area between the Wash and the Humber (Fig. 1), with only a few lines farther inland.

Facies

The Westphalian deposits of central and northern England have been extensively studied (Elliott 1968; Fielding 1984*a*, *b*; Guion 1984, 1987; Haszeldine 1984; many of which have been summarized by Guion & Fielding 1988). However, many of the detailed facies are difficult to identify in borehole data, therefore, Guion *et al.* (1995*a*) established a simplified facies scheme that enables more consistent recognition of facies. This scheme is followed here and summarized in Table 1 and Fig. 3. The sandbodies under discussion all fall into the major channel facies of Guion *et al.* (1995*a*), which corresponds to the washout sandstone facies of Elliott (1968) and the major distributary channel facies of Fielding (1984*b*) and Guion & Fielding (1988). In the study area, the channel facies are commonly associated with overbank facies of Guion *et al.* (1995*a*).

Westphalian fluvial sandbodies

Following the expansion of exploration into the Carboniferous play in the Southern North Sea, research into analogue Westphalian sandbodies onshore has increased. Ritchie & Pratsides (1993) suggested that the Caister sandstones may represent incised valley fills cut during relative sea-level lowstand, but Quirk (1997) regards most offshore Westphalian sandbodies to be sheet-like in extent and rarely displaying significant erosion at their bases and he suggests that these sandbodies were aggradational. Mijnssen (1997) has modelled sandbody connectivity in the Barren Red Measures of the Schooner Field and concluded that sandbody connectivity is the key geological factor influencing reservoir behaviour because of low net-to-gross ratios. In addition, channel orientation has the largest impact on connected gas initially in place (Mijnssen 1997). In the onshore UK, Guion *et al.* (1995*b*) examined the Silkstone Rock (Westphalian A) in detail and concluded that it is an aggradational channel system whose development was controlled by upstream switching of the channel system associated with overall basinal and compactional subsidence. Rippon (1997) has produced summary maps of orientations of a hierarchy of channel systems throughout the coalfields of mainland Britain from the Westphalian A to B. This work illustrated that for the Pennine Basin, flow was mainly from the west and northwest and Rippon argued that the sandbodies are not confined to incised valleys but proposes, similarly to Guion *et al.* (1995*b*), that the sandbodies represent aggradational systems. In the present study the majority of major sandbodies are similar and will be illustrated with a single typical example, the lower Westphalian C Mexborough Rock (Fig. 2).

Mexborough Rock

The Mexborough Rock is a multi-leaved, composite sandbody which occurs in the lower Westphalian C (Fig. 2) between the Edmondia marine band and the Shafton Coal which lies beneath the Shafton Marine Band (Fig. 4). Within this interval lies the Main '*Estheria*' Band, which acts as a marker horizon

Table 1. Facies associations and characteristics of the major facies of the Westphalian coal-bearing deposits of the Pennine Basin (after Guion *et al.* 1995*a*)

Facies associations and facies	Lithology	Sedimentary structures	Geometry	Fossils
Pedogenic				
Mire (mainly coal)	Coal, impure coal	Lamination, banding	Extensive sheets, greater than 0.1 m thick; may split or die out laterally	Plant remains
Palaeosol (mainly seat earth)	Grey to white, brown/cream or red claystone, siltstone or sandstone depending on substrate and drainage conditions. Thin impure coals	Irregular laminations disturbed by rootlets, or lamination totally destroyed. Common mottling. Abundant polished ('listric') surfaces, siderite nodules, sphaerosiderite or iron oxides, depending on drainage conditions	Generally extensive sheets	*In situ* rootlets, *Stigmaria*, *Calamites* roots in some palaeosols
Marine				
	Dark grey to black fissile carbonaceous claystone	Well-developed thin lamination, sometimes massive	Extensive sheets	Marine goniatites, bivalves, brachiopods, gastropods, crinoids, bryozoa, forams, *Lingula*, *Orbiculoidea*, plant fragments, trace fossils
Lake fill				
Lacustrine	Medium grey to black claystone or siltstone, carbonaceous mudstone, cannel, boghead, coal	Flat lamination, rare sandy laminae and scours	Sheet-like	Non-marine bivalves, fish, ostracods, *Spirobis*, plant fragments, trace fossils
Lacustrine delta (a) distal	Siltstones, interlaminated siltstone/sandstone forming upward-coarsening sequences	Flat lamination, current-and wave-ripple cross-lamination, climbing ripples, backflow ripples, ripple form sets, soft sediment deformation	Sheet-like to lobate deposits occur distally and beneath proximal lacustrine delta deposits, generally shows upward-coarsening above lacustrine deposits	Trace fossils, plant debris, rare non-marine bivalves
(b) proximal	Sandstone, interlaminated sandstone/siltstone, forming upward-coarsening sequences	Current-ripple cross-lamination, cross-bedding at top of sequences, climbing ripples, wave-ripple cross-lamination, occasional trough-like scour surfaces, flat lamination, ripple form sets, backflow ripples, soft sediment deformation	Lobate to sheet-like deposits up to about 10 km across and 8 m thick, with gradational or sharp bases, forming upward-coarsening sequences above distal lacustrine delta	Plant debris, trace fossils
Channel				
Major channel	Thick, erosively based sandstone bodies, often with horizons of breccia of conglomerate. Subordinate siltstone and clay	Erosion surfaces, trough and planar cross-bedding, inclined heterolithic surfaces, ripple- and cross-lamination, soft sediment deformation	Elongate belts, typically 1–20 km wide, 10s of km long, greater than 8 m thickness	Plant fragments and debris, often abundant, rare trace fossils
Minor channel	Sandstone, siltstone, claystone, typically heterolithic, breccia, conglomerate; very variable	Erosion surfaces, ripple cross-lamination, trough and planar cross-bedding, inclined heterolithic surfaces, flat lamination, soft sediment deformation, bank collapse deposits	Elongate belts, typically up to 1 km wide, several km long, up to 8 m thick	Plant fragments and debris, often abundant, rare trace fossils
Near-channel				
Overbank	Siltstone, claystone; sometimes interbedded sandstone	Massive or weakly laminated siltstone, passing distally into laminated claystone. Occasionally interbedded siltstone/sandstone with low dips away from adjacent channel	Elongate belts adjacent and parallel to channel margins	Abundant plant leaves and stems, *in situ* trees
Crevasse splay	Sharp-based sandstones interbedded with siltstones and claystones	Current-ripple cross-lamination, flat lamination, cross-bedding, wave rippled tops	Lobate deposits adjacent to channels. Individual splays generally <1 m thick, often vertically stacked. Thin distally away from channel	Plant debris, *Pelecypodichnus* escape shafts

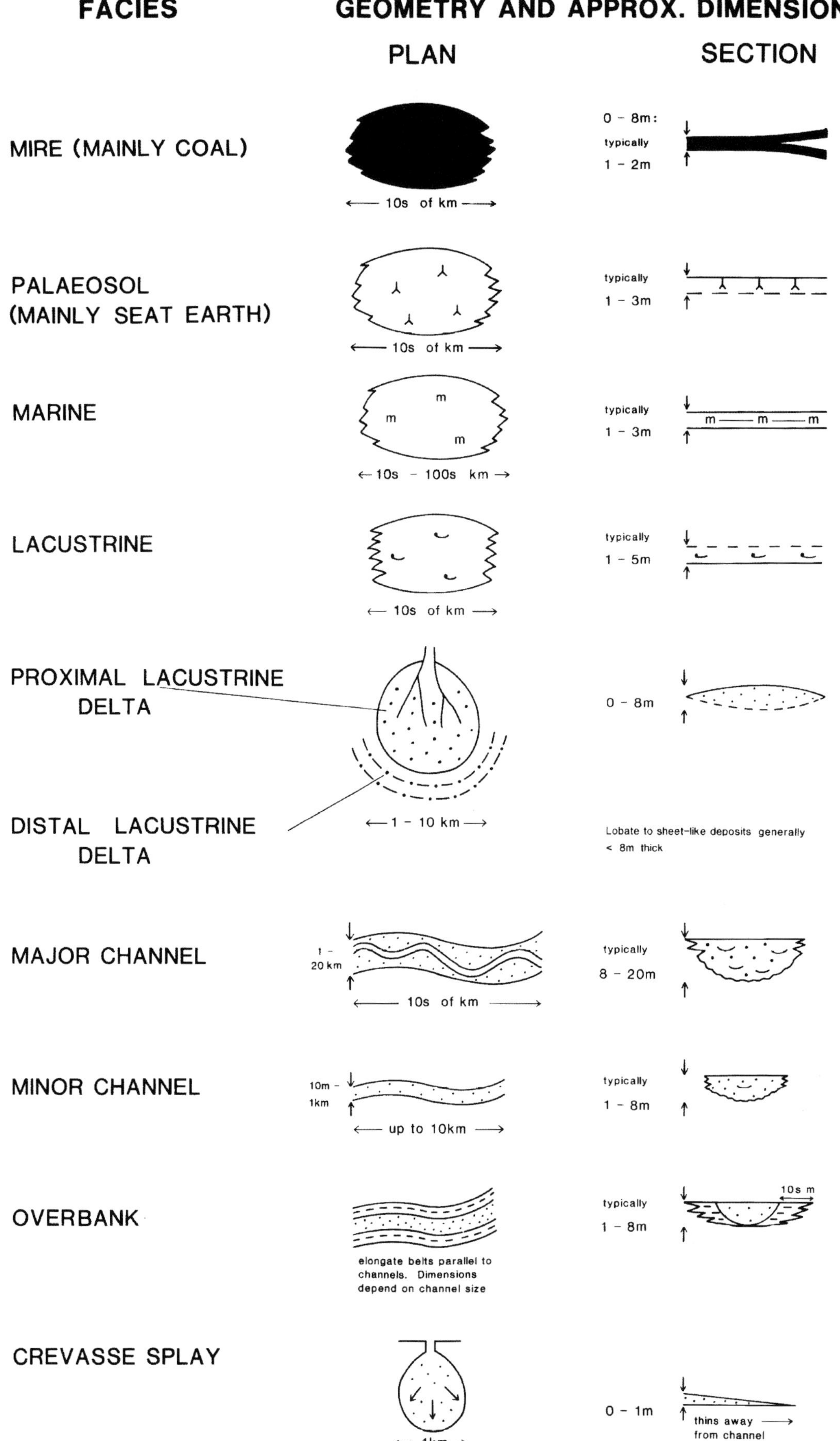

Fig. 3. Schematic representation of the geometry and approximate vertical and lateral extent of the major facies of the coal-bearing Westphalian of the Pennine Basin (after Guion *et al.* 1995*a*).

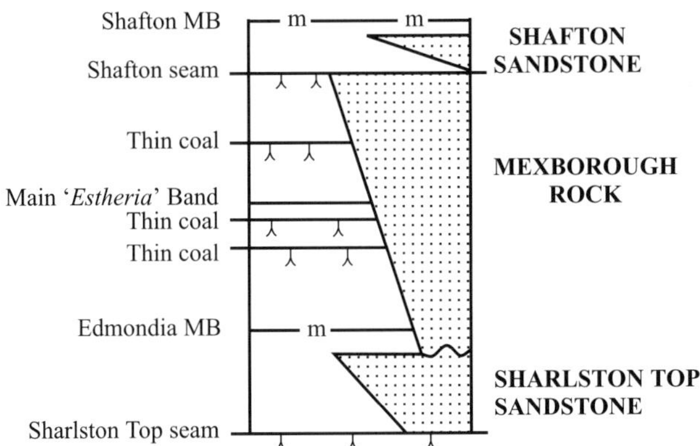

Fig. 4. Generalized stratigraphic section for the Mexborough Rock interval.

and is indicative of brackish water conditions. Where the upper leaves of the Mexborough Rock are present the Main '*Estheria*' Band is absent. Locally, a second sandbody occurs beneath the Edmondia Marine Band which rests on the Sharlston Top (or High Main) seam, and is here informally termed the Sharlston Top sandstone (Fig. 4). Where the Edmondia Marine Band is absent the Mexborough Rock appears to be erosionally merged with the Sharlston Top sandstone creating an anomalously thick sandbody.

An isopach map of gross sand thickness is shown in Fig. 5 in which most of the Mexborough rock is interpreted to consist of major channel facies. The base of the Mexborough rock is always taken as the base of the first major sandstone above the Edmondia Marine Band, but the upper surface of the sandstone is diachronous with respect to thin coal horizons (Fig. 4). The isopachs show that a sandstone belt, commonly of the order of 30–40 m in thickness, but locally exceeding 60 m thick where merged with the underlying Sharlston Top sandstone, extends from east to west for at least 80 km (Fig.5). Sandstone thicknesses of greater than 10 m generally correspond to major channel facies. It is interesting to note that the Mexborough Rock crosses the Gainsborough Trough (one of the major Dinantian extensional lineaments) and that the thickest development of sand is to the south of the trough (Fig. 5). A minor sand lobe, generally less than 15 m thick but locally exceeding 20 m, extends southwestwards from the main body of the Mexborough Rock (Fig. 5). Beyond the margins of the Mexborough Rock thin sandstones occur interbedded with variably rooted siltstone and mudstone with thin coal seams. These thin sandstones disappear at *c.* 15 km from the margin of the main sandbody and are replaced by more or less continuous siltstone/mudstone/thin coal successions (Fig. 6).

At outcrop, in the Sheffield and Barnsley districts, J. I. Chisholm (pers. comm. 1997) has recorded palaeo-flows trending towards the north and west. In the outcrop area the Mexborough rock comprises well-sorted, fine- to medium-grained pale grey sandstone, but locally it is reddened beneath the Permian unconformity. Three main facies occur at outcrop, namely trough cross-bedded sandstone, massive sandstone and laminated, very fine-grained sandstone and siltstone. Trough

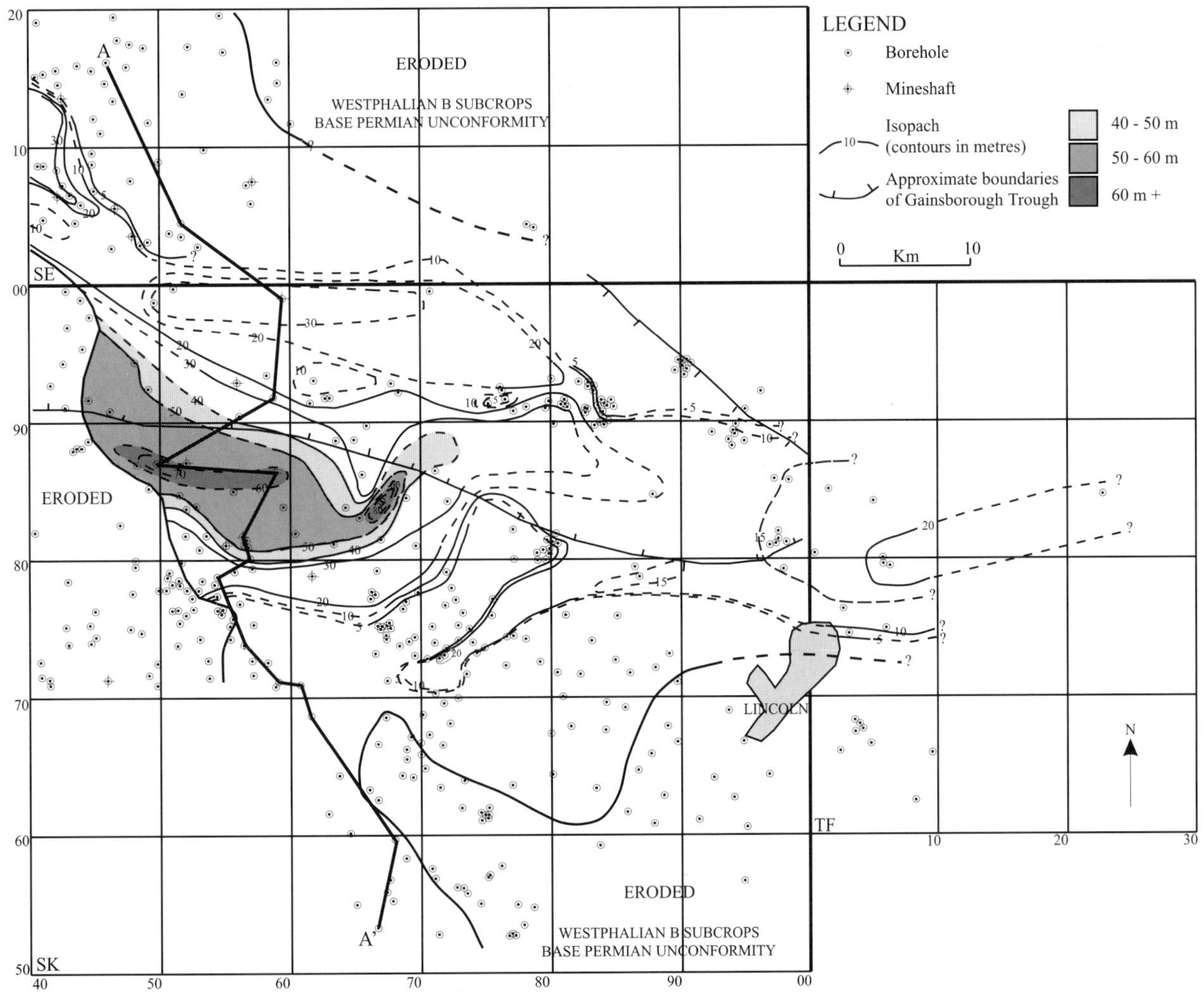

Fig. 5. Isopach map of gross sandstone comprising the Mexborough Rock, contoured assuming sandbody continuity. A–A′ line of section illustrated in Fig. 6.

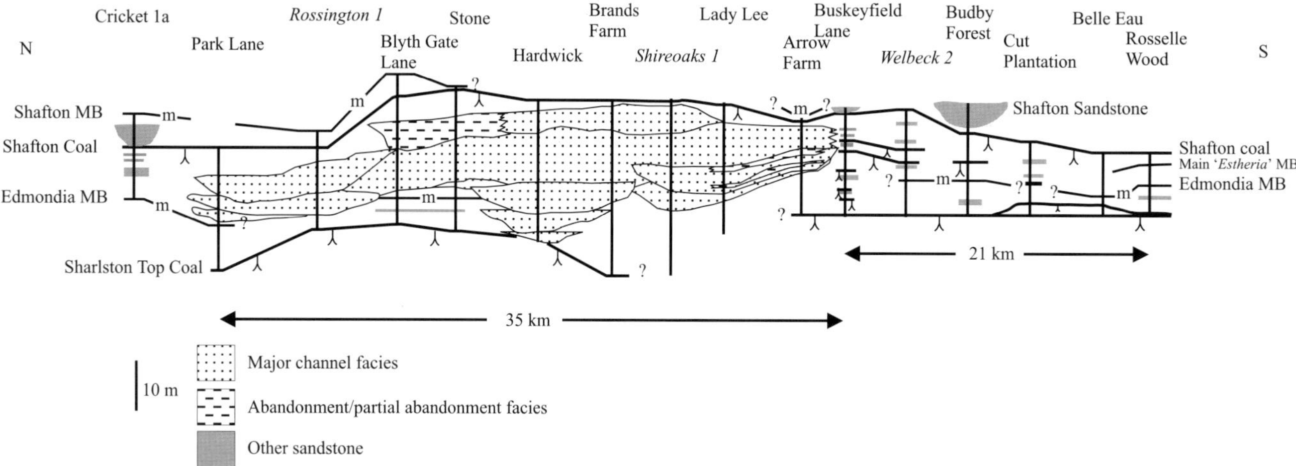

Fig. 6. Diagrammatic cross-section showing interpreted facies of the Mexborough Rock based on colliery shaft records (italics) and coal exploration boreholes. For location of section see Fig. 5.

cross-bedding is the dominant sedimentary structure, occurring in sets between 0.2 and 1.5 m in thickness and co-sets at least 6 m thick. Massive sandstone occurs locally, where it can be the dominant feature in individual outcrops, occurring both as relatively flat-based sheets and within small-scale channel-forms. This massive sandstone shows indistinct parallel lamination at its margins and sometimes passes upward into indistinctly rippled top surfaces and contains abundant large plant stems. Laminated fine-grained facies occur as thin units less than 0.5 m in thickness, which may extend laterally for several hundred metres.

Interpretation. The Mexborough Rock is clearly a multi-storey, fluvial sandbody flowing from the east towards the northwest. Trough cross-bedded sandstone was deposited by the migration of 3D dune forms in a sandy braided system (Cant & Walker 1978; Haszeldine & Anderton 1980). Massive sandstone facies were probably deposited by hyper-concentrated flows with rapid flow deceleration such that little reworking occurred. Such flows could have been triggered by large flood events or alternatively as the result of channel bank collapse and the entrainment of the sediment as a subaqueous mass flow (Turner & Monro 1987). Laminated fine-grained facies are interpreted to have been deposited in shallow water over pre-existing bar forms during waning flow when coarser-grained material was not in motion. The sand lobe that extends southwesterly from the main body of the Mexborough Rock (Fig. 4) is equivalent to the minor channel/lacustrine delta complex of Guion *et al.* (1995*a*) and may represent failed avulsion. The interbedded sandstone and siltstone facies adjacent to the Mexborough Rock correspond to the overbank facies of Guion *et al.* (1995*a*). It is not possible to conclusively prove that these overbank deposits are contemporaneous with the Mexborough Rock because the necessary data is unavailable. However, two similar sandbodies, namely the Glass Houghton Rock (Westphalian C) and the Silkstone Rock (Westphalian A) have both been shown to be associated with contemporaneous overbank deposits by Bedrock (1985) and Guion *et al.* (1995*b*), respectively. In both of these examples, coal seam splitting and an increase in ash content occurs towards the sandbodies suggesting periodic clastic input into the mires. The most probable mechanism for these observations is overbank flooding from an active contemporaneous channel system. The occurrence of failed avulsion deposits and overbank sediments intimately associated with the Mexborough Rock imply that the channels which deposited the Mexborough Rock were not confined to incised channel belts, but that they were actively aggrading.

The fact that the Mexborough Rock cuts across the southern margin of the Gainsborough Trough (Fig. 5) implies that the bounding faults to this graben had ceased activity by Westphalian C times. Quirk & Aitken (1997) similarly showed that syn-sedimentary fault movement was insignificant during the Westphalian in the northern part of the Southern North Sea.

Controls on deposition of Westphalian sandbodies

The occurrence of basin-wide stratigraphic markers in the form of coal seams and marine bands implies that allocyclic controls were significant within the studied strata. A low gradient alluvial–paralic setting including shallow marine, minor delta, coastal plain, fluvial channel and associated overbank environments is envisaged for the coal-bearing deposits of the UK Westphalian (e.g. Guion *et al.* 1995*a*). Glacio–eustatic sea level changes of several tens of metres, resulting from the numerous glaciations of Gondwanaland, would be expected to have had dramatic effects on such a low lying area. Indeed, the deposits of eustatic sea level rises are present in the form of faunal concentrate marine bands, interpreted as maximum flooding surfaces. It is therefore surprising that evidence for falls in relative sea level are generally not observed.

The predominant background sedimentation within the Westphalian in the study area was fine-grained silt and mud. Consequently, inputs of sand in the form of major channel sandbodies is significant and implies an external control on their origin.

It is probable that the Westphalian in the UK was deposited many hundreds, if not thousands, of kilometres from the sea. Subsidence rates in the Late Carboniferous were high (e.g. Leeder & McMahon 1988), and with new radiometric data which remove up to 10 Ma from Silesian time (Claoué-Long *et al.* 1995; Riley *et al.* 1995), far higher than previously thought. They would have been capable of generating large volumes of accommodation space. Hence, the combined effects of distance from the sea and high subsidence rates would probably mean that falls in eustatic sea level could have little impact. Creation of accommodation space by eustatic rises in sea level would have been accentuated by high subsidence rates. An icehouse climatic regime persisted throughout the Upper Carboniferous, but the sediments in the UK were deposited in the equatorial belt where the climate would have remained more or less constant. However, during glacial episodes, the mountains in the hinterland, many hundreds or thousands of kilometres north of the study area, may have

(a)

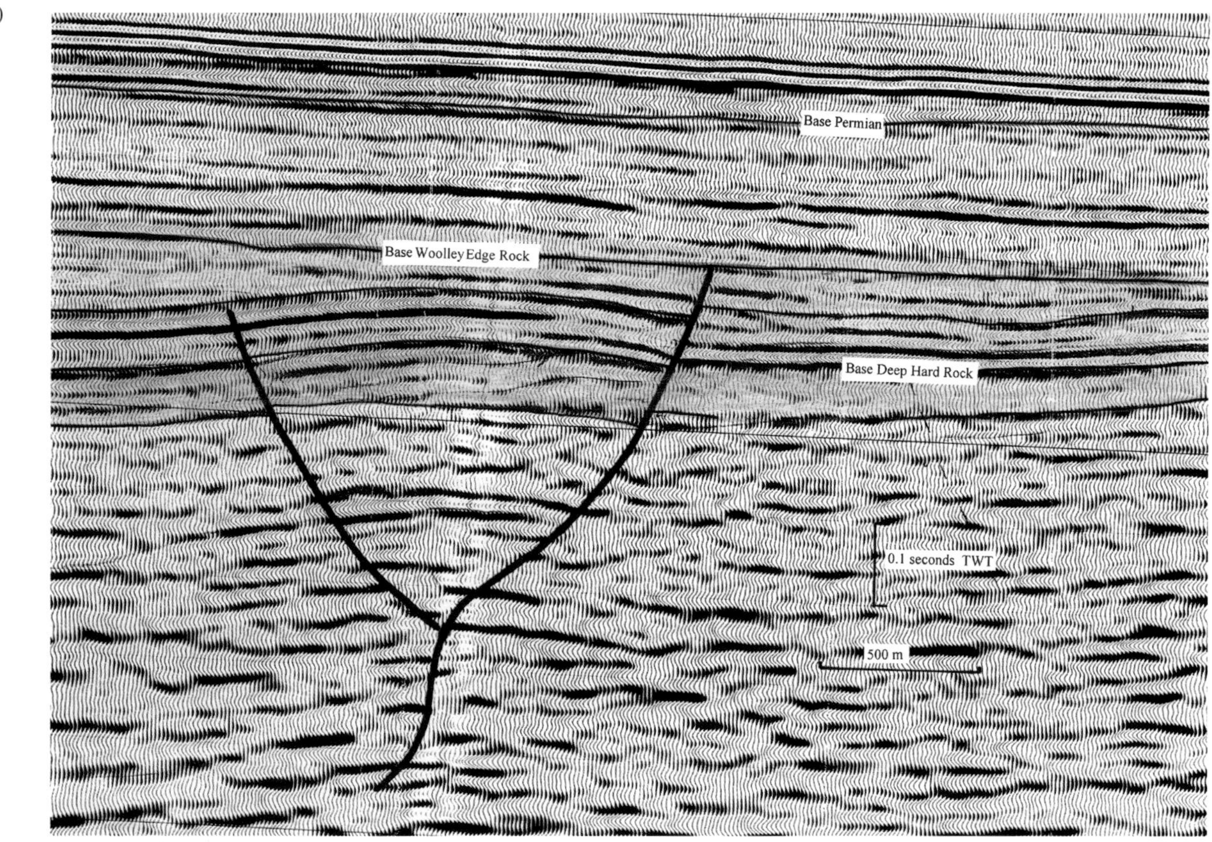

(b)

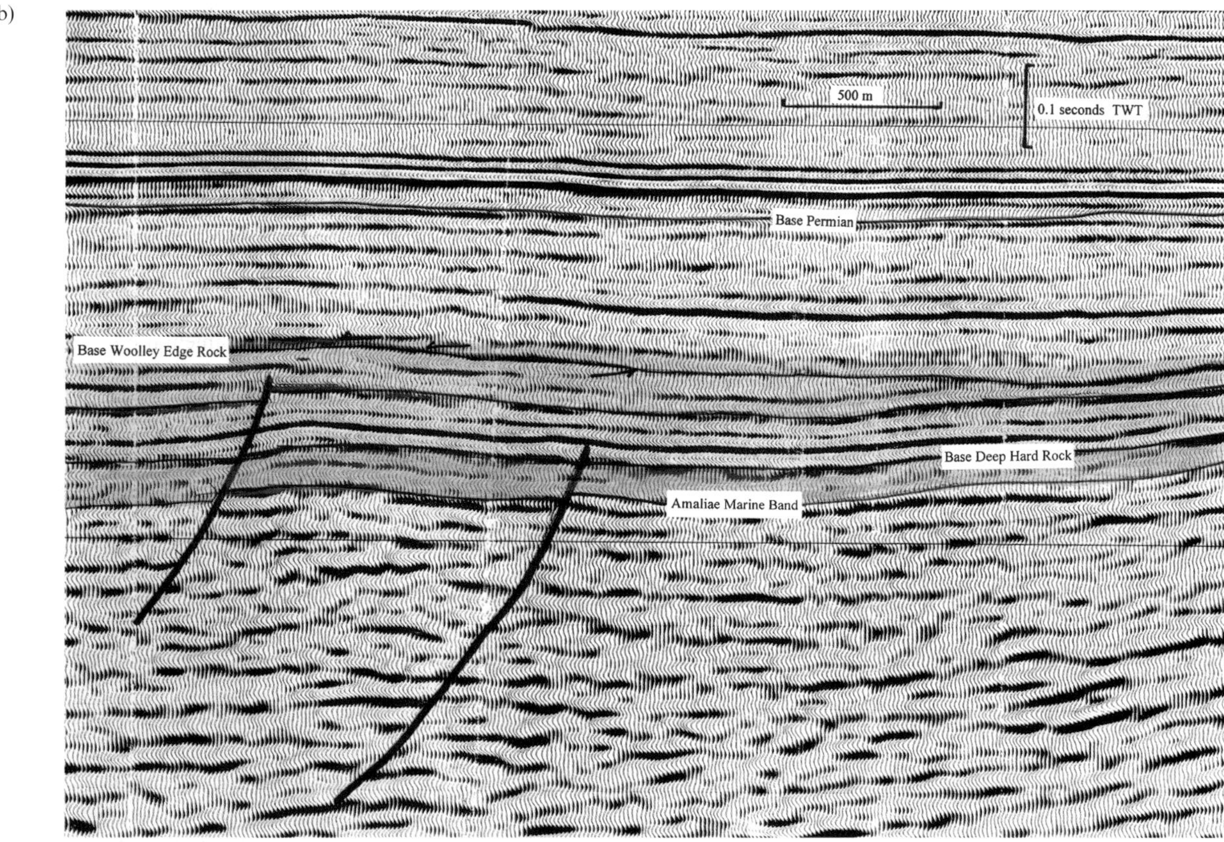

Fig. 7. Seismic sections from the East Midlands Oil Field showing four picks, namely, from the bottom, the lower Westphalian A Amaliae marine band; the base of the upper Westphalian A Deep Hard Rock; an upper Westphalian A or lower Westphalian B reflection, possibly equivalent to the Vanderbeckei Marine Band, and finally the base of the Woolley Edge Rock. (**a**) To show the termination of faults at the base of the Woolley Edge Rock. (**b**) To show the incision at the base of the Woolley Edge Rock (see text for details).

experienced local glaciation, with large volumes of sediment and water being released during episodes of glacial melt. It is postulated that such events may have given rise to the aggradational fluvial packages.

Although the Mexborough Rock is apparently unaffected by faults bounding the Gainsborough Trough, both extrabasinal and intrabasinal tectonic activity had an affect on other sandbodies. This is most clearly illustrated by the upper Westphalian B Woolley Edge Rock (Fig. 2). The Woolley Edge Rock contrasts markedly with underlying Westphalian A and B sandbodies in terms of its grain size and its palaeoflow directions. Westphalian A and B sandbodies are typically fine-grained and deposited by flows towards the east (Rippon 1997), whereas the Woolley Edge Rock comprises medium- to coarse-grained, pebbly sandstone with palaeoflow directions from the north and east. Overlying Westphalian B and Westphalian C sandbodies are also medium- to coarse-grained and display palaeocurrents flowing to the west and northwest. Figure 7 illustrates sections of two seismic lines from the East Midlands Oil Field. Four picks have been highlighted on the lines, namely, from bottom to top: the lower Westphalian A, Amaliae marine band; the base of the upper Westphalian A Deep Hard Rock; an upper Westphalian A or lower Westphalian B reflection, possibly equivalent to the Vanderbeckei Marine Band, and finally the base of the Woolley Edge Rock. Figure 7(a) shows that faults terminate at the base of the Woolley Edge Rock and Fig. 7(b) shows that the base of the Woolley Edge Rock has truncated at least two seismic loops, indicating some 50 m of erosion. Thus a tectonic event is indicated which was accompanied by intra-Westphalian erosion and a significant switch in source area and sediment type.

At a smaller scale, facies distributions are autocyclic in origin, being influenced by compactional control of palaeotopography (Guion *et al.* 1995*b*). The overall successions produced are exceedingly complex both in their lateral and vertical distribution and it is difficult to isolate the relative importance of the various mechanisms controlling sedimentation.

Sequence stratigraphic interpretations within the Upper Carboniferous have largely been aimed at the Namurian (e.g. Maynard 1992; Church & Gawthorpe 1994; Hampson *et al.* 1996, 1997; Jones & Chisholm 1997) where there is a greater marine influence than in the Westphalian. Fewer attempts have been made to apply sequence stratigraphic concepts to the Westphalian (e.g. Hartley 1993; Quirk 1993, 1997) as many of the features typical of Mesozoic and Cenozoic sequences are missing probably due to a greater influence of subsidence, sediment supply, discharge and remoteness from the sea. Nonetheless, Quirk (1997) has developed a seismic-scale model for Westphalian sequences in the northern part of the Southern North Sea involving widespread fluvial aggradation during transgression.

Implications for the Southern North Sea

The definition of reservoir architecture involves two tasks; firstly to establish the geometry of the sandstone bodies that comprise potential reservoirs; and secondly to define heterogeneities and potential permeability barriers. Both of these tasks benefit from analogue studies. Westphalian sandbodies onshore UK are used here as analogues for similar age reservoirs in the Southern North Sea. Thus, for example, information about the length and width of onshore sand bodies can be used to estimate the lateral extent of similar thickness reservoirs in the offshore.

For each mapped onshore sandbody a number of widths were measured and plotted against the maximum thickness measured in any well at that cross-section. No attempt was made to further subdivide the data into zones of different reservoir quality as in many cases this information was not available. However, a certain amount of interpretation was required to discriminate between different sandbodies. For example, intervals where sandbodies were anomalously thick were excluded as these were believed to result from the amalgamation of more than one sandbody. Figure 8 is a display of width/thickness data based on the mapping of 20 sandbodies. It shows that there is a relationship between channel width and thickness, with the maximum width being approximately 30 km and the maximum thickness approximately 50 m (but up to 100 m in thickness where sandbodies are amalgamated). In addition, the geometric data illustrates that 90% of channel sandbodies are less than 25 km in width and less than 40 m in thickness.

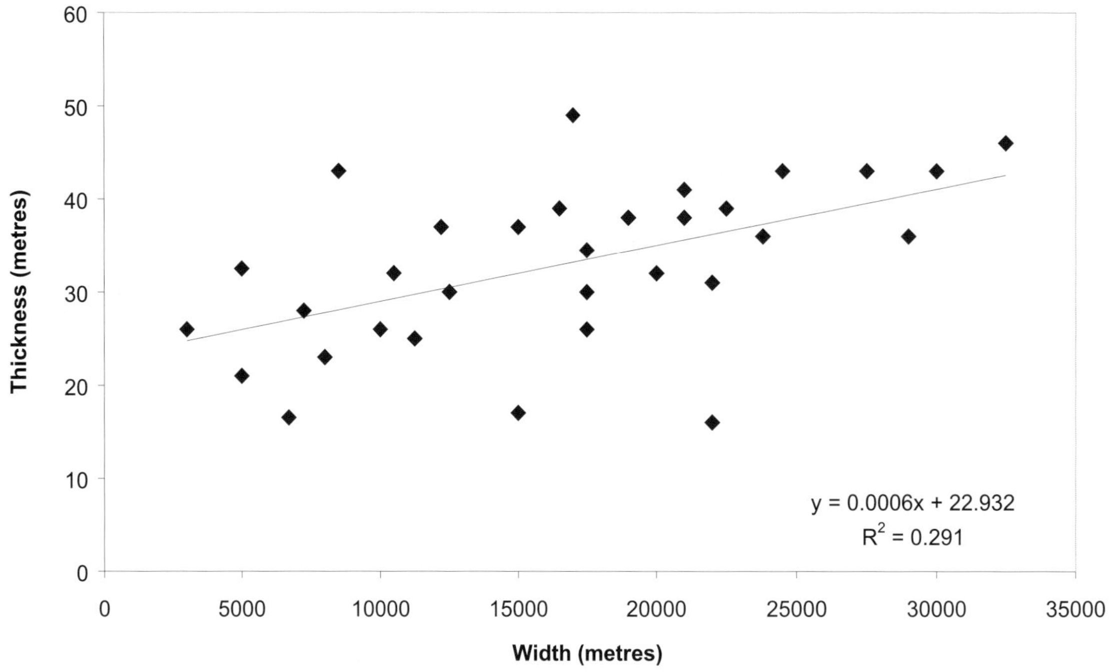

Fig. 8. Width/thickness graph for 20 Westphalian major sandbodies.

A remarkable similarity exists between the sand distribution in the Mexborough Rock (Fig. 5) and other onshore major Westphalian sandbodies, and an early Westphalian B reservoir interval mapped by Quirk (1997) in the Southern North Sea (fig. 6 in Quirk 1997). The sandbodies show comparable thicknesses (up to 100 m) and widths (up to 40 km in the offshore); in addition, the sandbodies do not display incised bases, as is also typical of all the main Westphalian reservoir targets in the Southern North Sea (Quirk 1993, 1997). Using the onshore analogues it would appear that reservoir intervals greater than 30 m in thickness will extend for more than 10 km perpendicular to palaeoflow (Fig. 8). In addition there is a probability of approximately 35% of penetrating a relatively poor reservoir zone within the main channel belt. The Mexborough Rock typically contains numerous fine-grained horizons which are interpreted as partial abandonment channel reaches. These are commonly difficult to correlate, especially at offshore development well spacings and form potential baffles of up to several hundred metres in extent (Fig. 6).

Conclusions

Major channel sandbodies in the Westphalian, onshore UK have dimensions comparable to incized valley fills but are not characteristic of incized valley fills because:

(1) they do not appear to be incized;
(2) generally, only single composite sandbodies occur at any one stratigraphic level, rather than a number separated by discrete interfluve surfaces;
(3) the sandbodies are mainly of composite origin, comprising a number of discrete and temporally separated major alluvial systems, stacked to form a single composite sandbody;
(4) contemporaneous overbank deposits are associated with the sandbodies.

It is argued that the development of these sandbodies was controlled by a combination of distance from the sea, high subsidence rates, climate effects in the hinterland and local autocyclic processes. Seismic data show erosional truncation (50–60 m) at the base of the Woolley Edge Rock associated with faults which terminate at the unconformity, indicating that tectonic effects have had an influence at other times.

Geometric data from 20 mapped sandbodies illustrates a relationship between channel width and thickness, with 90% of channel sandbodies being less than 25 km in width and less than 40 m in thickness. A remarkable similarity exists between the sand distribution onshore UK and Westphalian reservoir intervals in the Southern North Sea. Sandbodies onshore and offshore show comparable thicknesses (up to 100 m) and widths (up to 30–40 km). Additionally, the sandbodies do not display incised bases, as is typical of many of the main Westphalian reservoir targets in the Southern North Sea.

The research of which this forms a part was funded by Oxford Brookes University. We are grateful to Candecca Resources Ltd (in particular A. Hodge), BP Exploration Operating Company Ltd (in particular A. Fraser), Schlumberger Geo-Quest and the staff at the National Geosciences Data Centre at the BGS, Keyworth, for providing data. I. Chisholm is thanked for showing us the outcrop and providing his palaeocurrent data from the Mexborough Rock.

References

BEDROCK, M. 1985. *Sedimentology of some Westphalian C sequences in the Yorkshire Coalfield.* PhD Thesis, Imperial College, University of London.

CANT, D. J. & WALKER, R. G. 1978. Fluvial processes and facies sequences in the sandy braided South Saskatchewan River, Canada. *Sedimentology*, **25**, 625–648.

CHURCH, K. D. & GAWTHORPE, R. L. 1994. High resolution sequence stratigraphy of the late Namurian in the Widmerpool Gulf (East Midlands, UK). *Marine and Petroleum Geology*, **11**, 528–544.

CLAOUÉ-LONG, J. C., COMPSTON, W., ROBERTS, J. & FANNING, C. M. 1995. Two Carboniferous ages: a comparison of SHRIMP zircon dating with conventional zircon ages and $^{40}Ar/^{39}Ar$ analysis. *In*: BERGGREN, W. A., KENT, D. V., AUBREY, M-P. & HARDENBOL, J. (eds) *Geochronology, Time Scales and Global Stratigraphic Correlation.* SEPM (Society for Sedimentary Geology), Special Publications, **54**, 3–21.

COLLINSON, J. D., JONES, C. M., BLACKBOURN, G. A., BESLY, B. M., ARCHARD, G. M. & MCMAHON, A. H. 1993. Carboniferous depositional systems of the Southern North Sea. *In*: PARKER, J. R. (ed.) *Petroleum Geology of Northwest Europe: Proceedings of the 4th Conference.* Geological Society, London, 677–687.

ELLIOTT, R. E. 1968. Facies, sedimentation successions and cyclothems in the productive Coal Measures in the east Midlands, Great Britain. *Mercian Geologist*, **2**, 351–372.

FIELDING, C. R. 1984*a*. Upper delta plain lacustrine and fluviolacustrine facies from the Westphalian of the Durham Coalfield. *Sedimentology*, **31**, 547–567.

——1984*b*. A coal depositional model for the Durham Coal Measures of, N. E. England. *Journal of the Geological Society, London*, **141**, 919–931.

FRASER, A. J. & GAWTHORPE, R. L. 1990. Tectono-stratigraphic development and hydrocarbon habitat of the Carboniferous in Northern England. *In*: HARDMAN, R. F. P. & BROOKS, J. (eds) *Tectonic Events Responsible for Britain's Oil and Gas Reserves.* Geological Society, London, Special Publications, **55**, 49–86.

——, NASH, R. P., STEELE, R. P & EBDON, C. C. 1990. A regional assessment of the intra-Carboniferous play of Northern England. *In*: BROOKS, J. (ed.) *Classic Petroleum Provinces.* Geological Society, London, Special Publications, **50**, 417–440.

GUION, P. D. 1984. Crevasse splay deposits and roof rock quality in the Threequarters Seam (Carboniferous) in the East Midlands Coalfield. *In*: RAHMANI, R. A. & FLORES, R. M. (eds) *Sedimentology of Coal and Coal-Bearing Sequences.* International Association of Sedimentologists, Special Publications, **7**, 291–308.

——1987. The influence of a palaeochannel on seam thickness in the Coal Measures of Derbyshire, England. *International Journal of Coal Geology*, **7**, 269–299.

—— & FIELDING, C. R. 1988. Westphalian A and B sedimentation in the Pennine Basin, UK. *In*: BESLY, B. M. & KELLING, G. (eds) *Sedimentation in a Synorogenic Basin Complex: the Upper Carboniferous of NW Europe.* Blackie, Glasgow, 153–177.

——, FULTON, I. M. & JONES, N. S. 1995*a*. Sedimentary facies of the coal-bearing Westphalian A and B north of the Wales-Brabant High. *In*: WHATELEY, M. K. G. & SPEARS, D. A. (eds) *European Coal Geology.* Geological Society, London, Special Publications, **82**, 45–78.

——, BANKS, N. L. & RIPPON, J. H. 1995*b*. The Silkstone Rock (Westphalian A) from the east Pennines, England: implications for sandbody genesis. *Journal of the Geological Society, London*, **152**, 819–832.

HAMPSON, G. J., ELLIOTT, T. & DAVIES, S. J. 1997. The application of sequence stratigraphy to Upper Carboniferous fluvio-deltaic strata of the onshore UK and Ireland: implications for the Southern North Sea. *Journal of the Geological Society, London*, **154**, 719–733.

——, —— & FLINT, S. S. 1996. Critical application of high resolution sequence stratigraphic concepts to the Rough rock Group (Upper Carboniferous) of northern England. *In*: HOWELL, J. H. & AITKEN, J. F. (eds) *High Resolution Sequence Stratigraphy: Innovations and Applications.* Geological Society, London, Special Publications, **104**, 221–246.

HARTLEY, A. 1993. A depositional model for the Mid-Westphalian A to late Westphalian B Coal Measures of South Wales. *Journal of the Geological Society, London*, **150**, 1121–1136.

HASZELDINE, R. S. 1984. Muddy deltas in freshwater lakes and tectonism in the Upper Carboniferous coalfield of, N.E. England. *Sedimentology*, **31**, 811–822

—— & ANDERTON, R. 1980. A braidplain facies model for the Westphalian B Coal Measures of north-east England. *Nature*, **284**, 51–53.

JONES, C. M. & CHISHOLM, J. I. 1997. The Roaches and Ashover Grits: sequence stratigraphic interpretation of a 'turbidite-fronted delta' system. *Geological Journal*, **32**, 45–68.

KENT, P. E. 1985. UK onshore oil exploration 1930–1964. *Marine and Petroleum Geology*, **2**, 56–64.

LEEDER, M. R. & Hardman. M. 1990. Carboniferous geology of the Southern North Sea Basin and controls on hydrocarbon prospectivity. *In*: HARDMAN, R. F. P. & BROOKS, J. (eds) *Tectonic Events Responsible for Britain's Oil and Gas Reserves*. Geological Society, London, Special Publications, **55**, 87–105.

—— & MCMAHON, A. H. 1988. Upper Carboniferous (Silesian) basin subsidence in northern Britain. *In*: BESLY, B. M. & KELLING, G. (eds) *Sedimentation in a Synorogenic Basin Complex the Upper Carboniferous of North-West Europe*. Blackie, Glasgow, 43–52.

MAYNARD, J. R. 1992. Sequence stratigraphy of the Upper Yeadonian of northern England. *Marine and Petroleum Geology*, **9** 197–207.

MIJNSSEN, F. C. J. 1997. Modelling of sandbody connectivity in the Schooner Field. *In*: Ziegler, K., TURNER, P. & DAINES, S. R. (eds) *Petroleum Geology of the Southern North Sea: Future Potential*. Geological Society, London, Special Publications, **123**, 169–180.

QUIRK, D. G. 1993. Interpreting the Upper Carboniferous of the Dutch Cleaver Bank High. *In*: PARKER, J. R. (ed.) *Petroleum Geology of Northwest Europe: Proceedings of the 4th Conference*. Geological Society, London, 697–706.

——1997. Sequence stratigraphy of the Westphalian in the northern part of the Southern North Sea. *In*: ZIEGLER, K., TURNER, P. & DAINES, S. R. (eds) *Petroleum Geology of the Southern North Sea: Future Potential*. Geological Society, London, Special Publications, **123**, 153–168.

—— & AITKEN, J. F. 1997. The structure of the Westphalian in the northern part of the Southern North Sea. *In*: ZIEGLER, K., TURNER, P. & DAINES, S. R. (eds) *Petroleum Geology of the Southern North Sea: Future Potential*. Geological Society, London, Special Publications, **123**, 143–152.

RILEY, N. J., CLAOUÉ-LONG, J., HIGGINS, A. C., OWENS, B., SPEARS, A., TAYLOR, L. & VARKER, W. J. 1995. Geochronometry and geochemistry of the European mid-Carboniferous boundary global stratotype proposal, Stonehead Beck, North Yorkshire, UK. *Annales de la Société géologique de Belgique*, **116**, 275–289.

RIPPON, J. 1997. Sand body orientation, palaeoslope analysis and basin fill implications in the Westphalian A–C of Great Britain. *Journal of the Geological Society, London*, **153**, 881–900.

RITCHIE, J. S. & PRATSIDES, P. 1993. The Caister Fields, Block 44/23a, UK North Sea. *In*: PARKER, J. R. (ed.) *Petroleum Geology of Northwest Europe: Proceedings of the 4th Conference*. Geological Society, London, 759–769.

TURNER, B. R. & MONRO, M. 1987. Channel formation and migration by mass-flow processes in the Lower Carboniferous Fell Sandstone Group, northeast England. *Sedimentology*, **34**, 1107–1122.

WILCOCKSON, W. H. 1950. *Sections of Strata of the Coal Measures of Yorkshire* (3rd edn). Midland Institution of Mining Engineers.

Continental-scale sequence stratigraphy of the Namurian, Upper Carboniferous and its applications to reservoir prediction

S. DAVIES,[1,2] G. HAMPSON,[1,3] S. FLINT[1] and T. ELLIOTT[1]

[1] *Department of Earth Sciences, Jane Herdman Laboratories, University of Liverpool, Brownlow Street, Liverpool, L69 3 BX, UK*
[2] *Present address: Department of Geology, University of Leicester, University Road, Leicester LE1 7RH, UK*
[3] *Present address: T. H. Huxley School of Environment, Earth Science and Engineering, Imperial College of Science, Technology and Medicine, Prince Consort Road, London SW7 2BP, UK*

Abstract: The search for Upper Carboniferous reservoirs can be aided by the development of a chronostratigraphic framework combining detailed sedimentological information with a template using the diagnostic ammonoid-bearing marine bands from onshore analogues derived from European, American and Canadian basins. Analysing Namurian successions constrains key sand-prone intervals, which include the upper Kinderscoutian, lower Marsdenian and top Yeadonian, from a number of depositional settings. A controversial issue for the Upper Carboniferous is the relative importance of high frequency and high magnitude glacio–eustatic sea-level fluctuations as a driving mechanism in the development of basin fill over the controls exerted through the prevailing tectonic regime, climate and sediment supply. The recognition and characterization of time-equivalent sea-level rises and, with greater significance for hydrocarbon exploration, sea-level falls, from a number of European basins attests to their influence. Candidate reservoirs can be constrained at various temporal resolutions and may also be restricted geographically. Significant candidate reservoirs include multistorey fluvial incised valley fills and deepwater sand-rich successions. The most productive onshore reservoirs are coarse-grained/conglomeratic fluvial intervals located in the base of incised valleys where a significant proportion of the subsequent valley fill is fine-grained estuarine sediments. There is potential for large hydrocarbon reservoirs within sand-rich deep water successions but their occurrence in tectonically complex or deeply buried areas has thus far precluded their exploitation. A chronostratigraphic framework established for the UK and Ireland can be applied to European basins and, in a more limited sense, to North America, where marine horizons can be matched. The application of this framework to the subsurface lies in the recognition of key candidate reservoirs and their likely occurrence, both geographically and temporally.

Established ideas concerning Upper Carboniferous stratigraphy have been re-evaluated with the advent of sequence stratigraphy highlighting the importance of fluctuations in relative sea-level on the development of basin fill successions (Maynard 1992; Martinsen 1993; Davies & Elliott 1996; Hampson 1995; Martinsen *et al.* 1995; Hampson *et al.* 1997). This approach has been applied to Namurian successions in foreland and intramontane basins along major orogenic belts and their adjacent cratonic basins across the Euramerican province (as defined by Calder & Gibling 1994). These basins extended from southern equatorial through northern, temperate regions and were sourced from both northern upland areas and from the rising mountain belt created as southern Gondwana collided with the northern Laurussia (Fig. 1). Throughout this period, a large ice mass developed across the southern hemisphere continent of Gondwana (Veevers & Powell 1987). The marine bands used for correlation in the Carboniferous basins of Euramerica are widely accepted to represent flooding events related to fluctuating ice volume (Ramsbottom 1977; Veevers & Powell 1987). Revisions to absolute age dates derived from Namurian strata emphasize the high frequency of these sea-level changes. Previous periodicity estimates of 120 000 a (Maynard & Leeder 1992) have been revised to 65 000 a using the most recent dates which reduce the Chokierian–Yeadonian from 4 Ma (Hess & Lippolt 1986) to 1.6 Ma (Jones 1995; Riley *et al.* 1995).

The significance of a sequence stratigraphic approach for the prediction of hydrocarbon reservoirs has been emphasized by several authors. The existence of sequence boundaries, representing high frequency and high magnitude sea-level falls and associated reservoir sandstone bodies have been established in the onshore Carboniferous successions of both UK and Ireland. The prospective reservoirs fall into two main groups (Fig. 2): (a) the multi-storey fluvial systems including valley fills and sheet-like bodies which are the most volumetrically important and widely exploited and; (b) those of potential significance but are not currently exploited. Prospective reservoirs in this second group include: (i) turbidites; (ii) mouth bar sandstones; (iii) tidally influenced sandstones and; (iv) shoreface sandstones.

A number of further questions remain: (i) are these reservoirs stratigraphically constrained?; (ii) can a framework of sea-level falls established for the UK and Ireland be applied outside the core UK/Ireland area?; (iii) what are the characters of sequences developed in time-equivalent successions from other Euramerican Carboniferous basins?; (iv) what is the resolution of correlations established?; and (v) what does this information elicit for the prediction of Carboniferous reservoirs in the sub-surface?

Chronostratigraphic and sequence stratigraphic framework

Carboniferous successions are generally constrained by a high resolution biostratigraphy provided by an ammonoid

Davies, S., Hampson, G., Flint, S. & Elliott, T. 1999. Continental-scale sequence stratigraphy of the Namurian, Upper Carboniferous and its applications to reservoir prediction. *In*: Fleet, A. J. & Boldy, S. A. R. (eds) *Petroleum Geology of Northwest Europe: Proceedings of the 5th Conference*, 757–770.

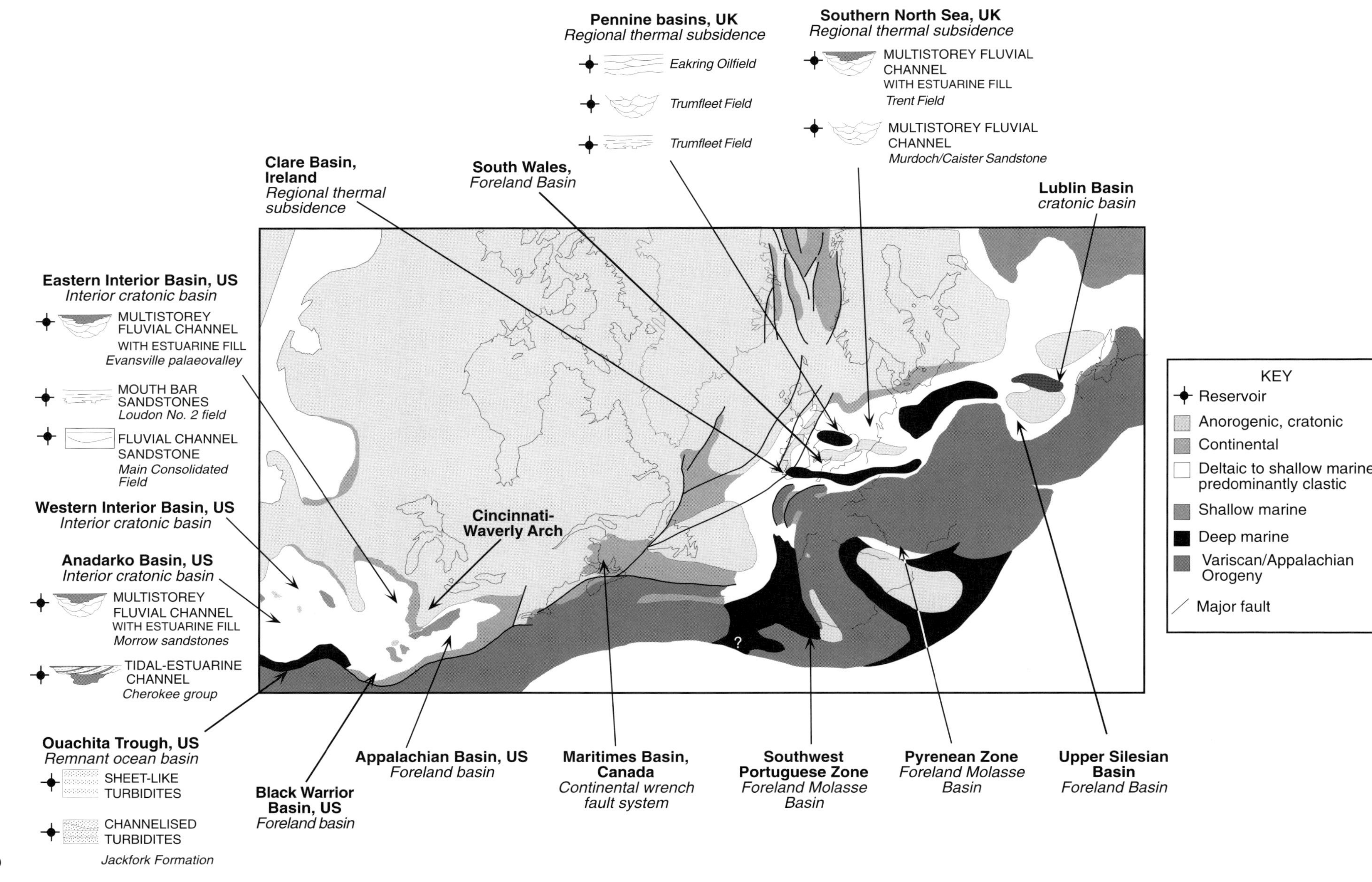

Fig. 1. (**a**) Summary of the main Carboniferous basins across the Euramerican province (*sensu.* Calder & Gibling 1994) and their primary tectonic regime. The palaeogeographical map is redrawn from Ziegler (1989). Some of the main Namurian/Lower Westphalian hydrocarbon reservoirs are illustrated. (**b**) UK map outlining sub-basins discussed in the text.

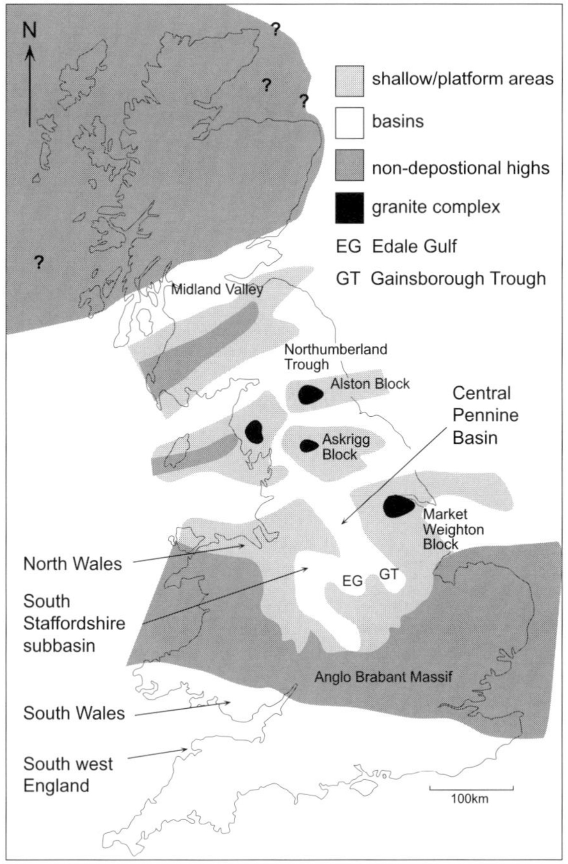

Fig. 1. (*continued*).

stratigraphy. This biostratigraphic framework enables geographically isolated basins from different structural settings to be directly compared. Using this framework (Fig. 3), it is possible to produce accurate palaeoenvironmental and palaeogeographical reconstructions of strata that are considered to be genetically related within time slices. The initial premise for predicting the occurrence of Upper Carboniferous reservoirs is to consider several co-eval basin fill successions in a chronostratigraphic framework and identify a number of promising stratigraphically defined sand fairways. Subsequently, the type of sandstone, extent, architecture and vertical character can be considered in the context of an individual basin. Twenty-one Namurian sedimentary successions from a range of basins and sub-basins with relatively complete sedimentological and stratigraphic records are included but the figure is not intended to be exhaustive.

Successions from the UK and Irish basins provide the most comprehensive databases available. Forty-six index ammonoid horizons are currently recognized in the UK Pennine basins (Riley *et al.* 1995; Fig. 3) and this framework is employed in this paper as the 'core' biostratigraphy. It is assumed that this UK biostratigraphy is the most complete record of marine bands bearing diagnostic thick-shelled ammonoids (Ramsbottom *et al.* 1979). A number of problems exist for the application of this biostratigraphic framework outside the UK/Ireland Carboniferous. For example, the ammonoid identifications from a range of specialists may not be standard. In addition, not all the index ammonoids may be found or indeed occur in all basins and the biostratigraphic division of sedimentary successions may vary in resolution (e.g. in the Polish Lublin Basin, Kotas 1995). In summarizing the biostratigraphic framework, a hierarchy of marine bands can be defined (Fig. 3) within any given succession: (i) those with fauna identified as the index marine bands (i.e. R1b2); (ii) those that can be identified to the zone level (i.e. R1b); and (iii) marine bands which can be classified to the stage (R1). Marine band 'equivalents' identified using characteristic faunal assemblages may identify horizons on resolutions from (i) to (iii) within the hierarchy.

Severe problems are encountered where marine fauna are entirely absent and successions cannot easily be correlated between basins. This correlation problem is most significant in the Upper Carboniferous successions in the Maritimes area, Canada. The palynological zones used in Europe cannot yet be correlated with the key stratigraphic taxa in the predominantly non-marine Namurian to Westphalian successions in Eastern Canada. Ongoing work should ultimately resolve some of the main stage boundaries and enable the Canadian successions to be included in a global framework (Utting & McLean, pers. comm. 1997).

The recognition of sea-level falls can be made at the highest resolution in the greatest number of basins during the Kinderscoutian–Yeadonian using the biostratigraphic framework (Fig. 3). Temporally restricted, geographically widespread periods of reservoir development can be demonstrated in the Kinderscoutian, Marsdenian, and Yeadonian stages as the framework can be extended with confidence beyond the UK–Irish sector. In addition, the representatives of sea-level falls can be documented, and correlated within and between basins. A number of prospective Carboniferous sandstone reservoir types can be defined. The range of depositional settings, systems tracts and typical dimensions are defined using the onshore database available from a number of Euramerican basins. The sedimentology, stratigraphy, significance and geographic occurrence of these prospective reservoirs is discussed in the context of the chronostratigraphic framework using goniatite marine bands. Although all reservoir types are illustrated, only a much more limited number, predominantly major fluvial sandstones, are currently exploited in the search for hydrocarbons (Fig. 1).

In the Kinderscoutian to Yeadonian time interval, sea-level falls are predominantly recognized as erosional surfaces at the base of multi-storey fluvial systems and by their lateral correlatives, interfluves (discussed in detail in Hampson *et al.* 1997). Multi-storey sandstone bodies are the most volumetrically significant Upper Carboniferous reservoir type (Fig. 1). Many, though not all, are interpreted in the literature as incised valley fills or sheet-like multi-storey sandstone bodies developed following major sea-level falls, and recording increasing accommodation space during the subsequent sea-level rise. Upper Carboniferous multi-storey sandstones documented in the literature are represented by a range of vertical and lateral dimensions (Fig. 4).

The timing, controlling factors and character of the major fluvial systems from the Namurian and Lower Westphalian in Euramerican basins

The tectonic evolution of an individual basin determines the long-term subsidence and uplift history onto which sediment supply changes, eustatic fluctuations and climatic influences are superimposed. A detailed history and comparison of tectonic regimes operating throughout the Namurian and early Westphalian places the operating depositional systems in context. The examples discussed (Figs 1 and 3) comprise four main categories: (i) major foreland basins developed along the main suture zones (Appalachian Basin, Rheno–Hercynian region comprising South Wales through the Ruhr and into Poland); (ii) extensional to thermally subsiding provinces (Ireland, northern England, Belgium); (iii) cratonic basins (Eastern Interior Basin USA, Anadarko Basin, Lublin Basin); and (iv) strike-slip provinces (Maritimes Basin).

Candidate Reservoir Sandbody	Lateral continuity	Sequence Stratigraphic Significance	Key examples
multistorey fluvial channels	Varies between 1 km and 60 km (see Fig.)	Late lowstand to early rise in sea-level following a significant fall	Numerous: , Kilkee Sandstone, Namurian; Farewell Rock, Namurian
multistorey sheet-like sandstone	Up to 70 km	Late lowstand to early rise in sea level following a significant fall	Numerous: Rough Rock, Yeadonian
sand-dominated turbidite deposits	100's of metres - kms	predominantly lowstand deposits	Ross Sandstone Formation, Alportian; Shale Grit, Kinderscoutian; Jackfork Formation, Kinderscoutian/Yeadonian
sand-dominated turbidite deposits -channelized	channelized turbidites few hundred metres	predominantly lowstand deposits	
sand-poor turbidites and deep marine sediments	few 100 metres exposed	predominantly lowstand deposits	Brejeira Formation, Namurian; Crackington Formation, Westphalian
mouthbar	Variable (see examples)	a) Top of prograding lowstand wedge; b) within highstand	a) 4-5 km, Kinderscoutian Ireland; b) 25 km Breathitt Formation, Westphalian B
shoreface	several 10's of km along strike but rare in the Carboniferous	top of the transgressive systems tract	Kinderscoutian, Ireland & UK
tidally-influenced sandstones	potentially 10's of km	lowstand	Hazel Patch Sandstone,Kentucky, Westphalian A
floodplain sandstones	n/a	high base level	Joggins Formation, Namurian/Westphalian, Canada
palaeosols	Variable depends on stratigraphic significance. Could be kms	mature, palaeosols may represent an interfluve to an incised valley fill	interfluve Kilkee Sandstone, Farewell Rock
meandering fluvial (lateral accretion)	Limited <1 km	Highstand systems tract	e.g. highstand sandstones from the Breathitt Formation
fluvial channels	Variable; <200 m	depends on context	Joggins Formation, Namurian/Westphalian, Canada
estuarine	kms -10's of km	early transgressive systems tract	Upper Kinderscout Grit, Namurian
tidal-estuarine	10's of km	early transgressive systems tract	Pine Creek Sandstone, Westphalian;

Fig. 2. Comprehensive listing of candidate Carboniferous sandbodies with candidate reservoirs illustrated.

Smaller predominantly deepwater molasse basins include the Southwest Portuguese Zone (Oliveira 1990), the Cantabrian, and Pyrenean basins (Devolve *et al.* 1993). Finally, remnant ocean basins are represented by the Ouachita Trough which received sediment derived from both a northern shelf region and axial systems in the main Appalachian basin.

The Appalachian Basin, US

The Appalachian Basin formed following collision along the southern and eastern margins of Laurasia. From Late Devonian to Early Carboniferous times, the basin was starved of terrigenous sediment and dominated by marine depositional environments (Tankard 1986) during a period of high global sea-level (Ross & Ross 1985). The forebulge, a long-lived feature, formed a margin to the Appalachian Basin (Cincinnati–Waverley Arch Complex, Fig. 1). From the earliest mid Namurian, shallow and broad subsidence followed renewed thin skinned thrusting onto the thick and thermally mature continental margin, with a rigid lithoshpere (Tankard 1986).

A basinwide unconformity developed across the Appalachian Basin in the mid-Namurian. The unconformity is most pronounced along the margins. Along the western edge of the basin, Westphalian sediments overlie the Viséan–lower Namurian sediments (Chesnut 1994). In the depocentre, successions are either conformable (Englund 1979) or have a minimal time gap (equivalent to the Chokierian and Alportian, Beuthin 1994).

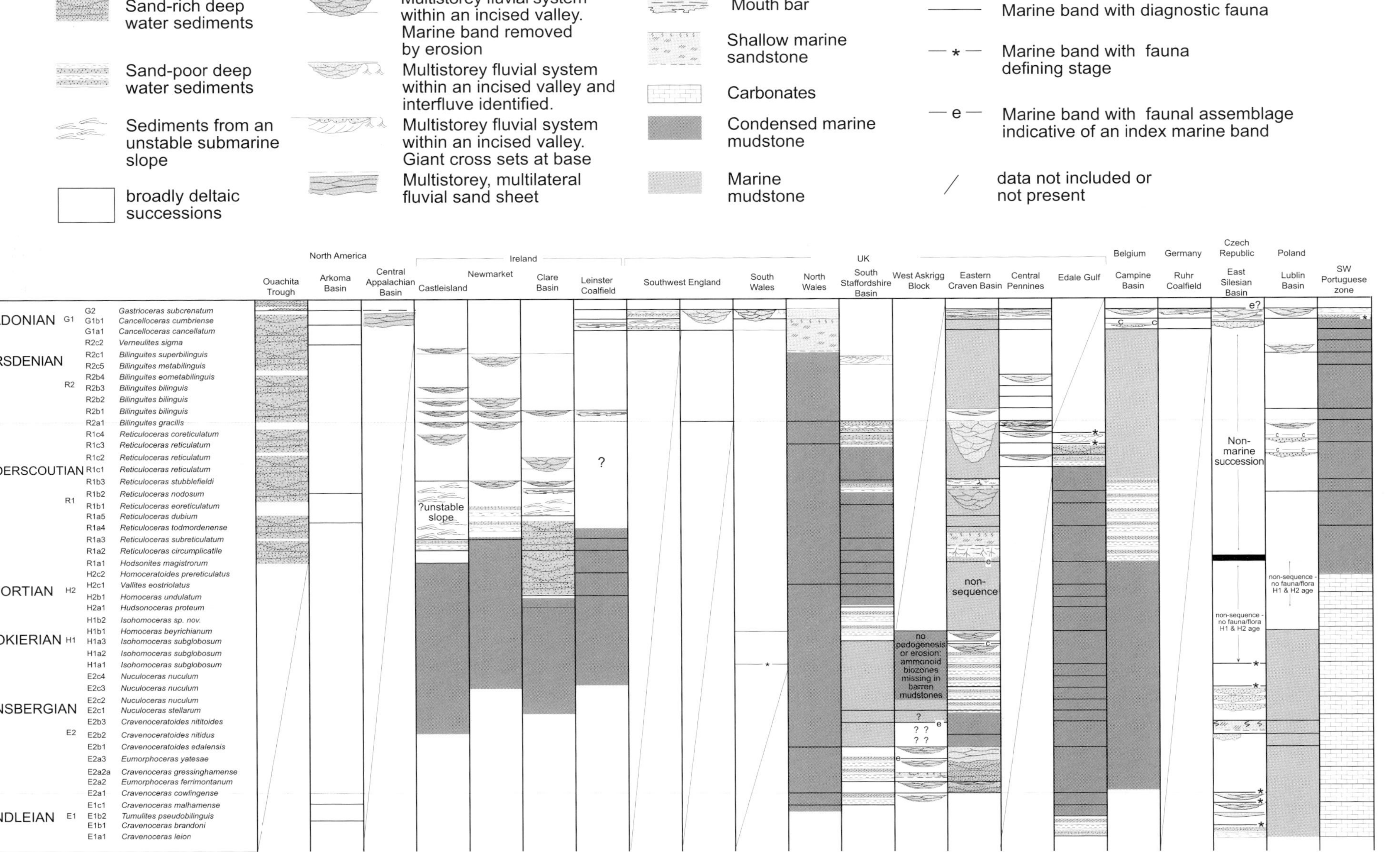

Fig. 3. Marine band correlation for 18 basins and sub-basins from the Euramerican Province. The representations of successions from individual basins is as accurate as possible. Unless otherwise stated sandbodies are exact representations of units present in the succession. The figure is discussed in more detail in the text. Sources of information: Ouachita Trough (Shanmugam & Moiola 1985), Arkoma Basin (Saunders & Ramsbottom 1993). Ireland: Castleisland, Newmarket and Leinster Coalfield, (Higgs 1986), Clare Basin Arnsbergian–Alportian (Braithwaite 1994), Alportian to Kinderscoutian turbidites (Collinson *et al.* 1991), Kinderscoutian to Marsdenian deltaics (Pulham 1987). UK: southwest England deepwater (Eagar & Xu Li 1993), deltaics (Eager & Xu Li 1993); north Wales, south Staffordshire Basin (Pendleian to Kinderscoutian: Aitkenhead *et al.* 1985, Davies & McLean 1996; Marsdenian: Jones & Chisholm 1997), West Askrigg Block (Martinsen 1993; Brandon *et al.* 1995; own unpublished data); Eastern Craven Basin (Brandon *et al.* 1995, Davies & McLean 1996); Central Pennines (Pendleian to basal Kinderscoutian; Stevenson & Gaunt 1971, Aitkenhead & Riley 1996, Davies & Mclean 1996, Marsdenian; Wignall & Maynard 1996, Yeadonian; Hampson *et al.* 1996, Waters *et al.* 1996). Belgium: Campine Basin (Langanaeker & Dusar 1992). Germany: Ruhr Coalfield (Hampson unpublished data). Czech Republic: East Silesian Basin (Kotas 1995). Poland: Lublin Basin (Porzycki & Zdanowski 1995.). Portugal: SW Zone (Oliveira 1990).

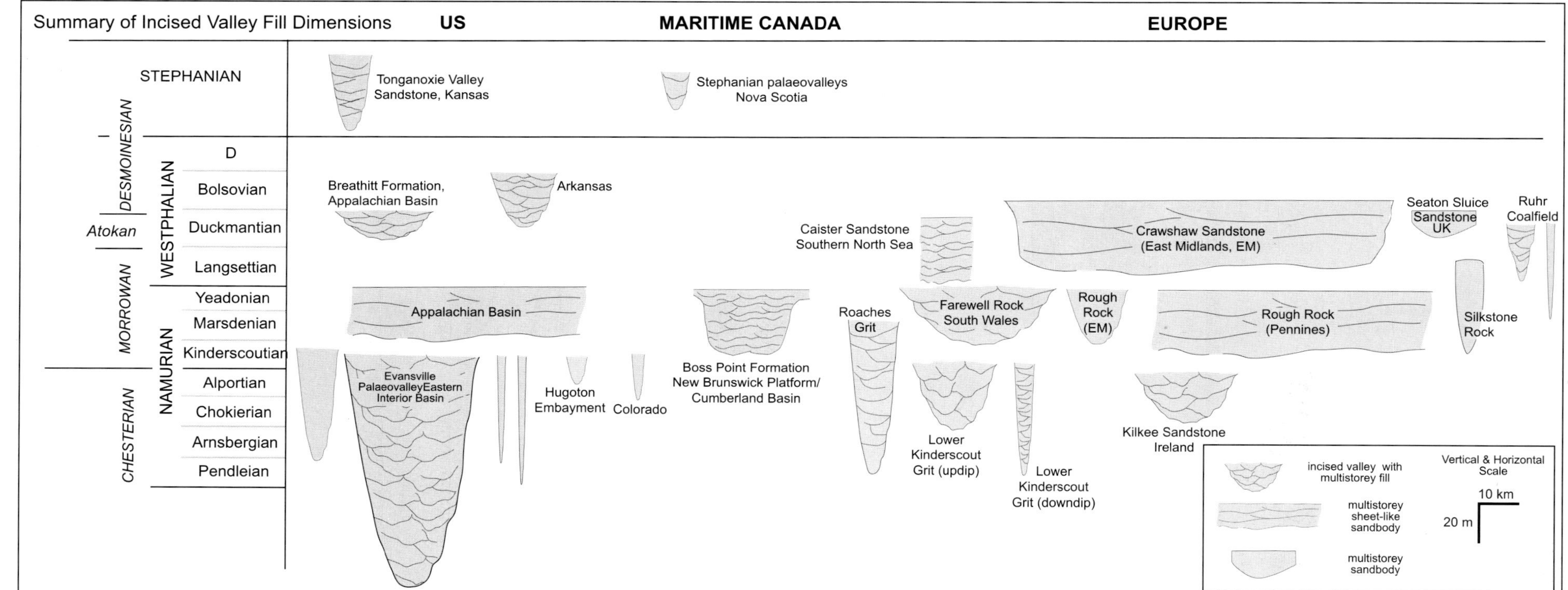

Fig. 4. Summary of the vertical and lateral dimensions of fluvial sandbodies including incised valley fills and multistorey sheet-like sand bodies. Kinderscoutian (or equivalent): Evansville Palaeovalley, Eastern Interior Basin, (Bristol & Howard 1974; Howard & Whitaker 1988), Colorado (unnamed Krystinik & Blakeney 1990), Lower Kinderscout Grit (Hampson 1997), Kilkee Sandstone (Pulham 1989). Marsdenian: Roaches Grit (Jones & Chisholm 1997). Yeadonian: Appalachian Basin (Chesnut 1994; Archer & Greb 1996), Farewell Rock, South Wales (Hampson *et al.* 1997), Rough Rock, East Midlands (Church & Gawthorpe 1994), Rough Rock, Pennine Basin (Bristow 1988, Hampson *et al.* 1997). Langsettian: Crawshaw Sandstone (Church & Gawthorpe 1994). Duckmantian: Breathitt Formation Valleys (pers. comm. Aitken & Flint 1995), Silkstone Rock (Guion *et al.* 1995), Seaton Sluice Sandstone (Rippon 1996), Caister Sandstone, Southern North Sea (Ritchie & Pratsides 1993). Bolsovian: Mexborough Rock (Aitken 1997), Hartshorne Sandstone (Houseknecht 1983). Stephanian: Tonganoxie Valley Sandstone, Kansas (Feldman *et al.* 1995), Brora Coal Valley Fill, Nova Scotia (Gibling & Wightman 1994).

Both a eustatic sea-level fall and tectonic mechanism have been proposed for this basinwide unconformity. A broadly co-eval eustatic sea-level fall in the upper Pendleian–Arnsbergian is suggested from biological evidence. In deeper water successions across Euramerica a reduction in ammonoid diversity (Saunders & Ramsbottom 1986; Riley *et al.* 1995) and extinctions in shelf sequences (Saunders & Ramsbottom 1986) have been interpreted to result from a global fall sea-level fall. A mid-Carboniferous period of major oceanic overturn also relates to this regression (Raymond *et al.* 1989). As a comparison, the entire Persian Gulf was completely exposed during the Pleistocene lowstand and fluvial channels incised into a subaerial surface (Kassler 1973). Marginal uplift associated with advance of the orogenic thrust wedge (Quinlan & Beaumont 1984; Tankard 1986) has been postulated as a primary cause of a regional unconformity developed across the basin although some of the fluvial systems have southwesterly-directed palaeodrainage which is not consistent with a marginal uplift (Beuthin 1994).

The unconformity is observed in both the outcrop and subsurface and is represented by scours, channels, palaeokarst surfaces and incised valleys (Chesnut 1994). Above the unconformity surface major, axial fluvial systems draining mature source regions in the Canadian Shield and flowing to the south ('Lee Sandstones' of Archer & Greb 1995) occur in the central Appalachian Basin. This predominance of early Namurian to Westphalian A axial fluvial systems, forming major sandstone belts, reflects an initially underfilled foreland basin (Sengor 1995). The rising orogenic mountain belt to the east was not a major source region during this time.

These axial systems are represented by sheet-like sandstone bodies, with a vertical preserved thicknesses of 30–40 m, that exceed 40 km width and can be traced laterally for up to 90 km (Fig. 4). The margins of these bodies are generally poorly constrained and/or defined and interfluves are not identified. The basal surfaces of these sandbodies have demonstrable relief and have been documented to erode through underlying marine bands. These wide 'sand-belts' are most common in the Appalachian Basin and were deposits by predominantly low sinuousity systems (Archer & Greb 1995). The location of these sand-belts shifts laterally with time, progressively onlapping the western basin margin as the focus of subsidence moves in response to the advance of the thrust load (Chesnut 1994).

During 'lowstand' periods the coastline may be 1000 km from depositional sites and the headwaters some 3700 km from the coast (Archer & Greb 1995). Although these sand-belts are considered to lie at great distances from the palaeoshoreline, an upper, estuarine component is commonly present. This component comprises a fine-grained to heterolithic interval with trace fossils indicative of brackish conditions (Archer & Greb 1995). This estuarine component contrasts with the heterolithic fill created by the decrease in stream power and fluvial abandonment, more common in younger valley systems in the Appalachian Basins and within valley fills in the UK and Ireland.

Marine transgressions during the Namurian and early Westphalian were from the south, via the Black Warrior Basin and southern Appalachian basins (Chesnut 1994). Fine-grained shales containing marine fauna and trace fossils were deposited during marine flooding. These basinwide horizons separate the fluvial sandstone bodies (Chesnut 1994). Marine shales in successions from the later Westphalian have characteristic faunal assemblages which are used to correlate these flooding surfaces with marine bands in the North Sea (Riley & Turner 1995). However, the Namurian and Lower Westphalian marine bands cannot yet be correlated at such a high resolution.

In the Appalachian Basin, some significant falls in sea-level are represented by the abrupt introduction of shallow water sandstones above offshore sediments. A fine-grained marine succession underlying the last major, Westphalian-aged axial system, is abruptly overlain by a wave-influenced outer estuarine/shallow shelf deposition which shallows upwards into an intertidal sand flat. The unit is represented by a quartz-rich sandstone unit which is sharp based with a few metres of regional relief. The interval varies in thickness, from 15–40 m, contains abundant marine trace fossils and mud drapes over bi-directional ripples (e.g. the Hazel Patch Sandstone, Greb & Chesnut 1996). The base of this unit represents a marked and regional basinward shift in facies present across a large area of the basin but with very different reservoir characteristics compared to the fluvial systems. The quartz-rich mineralogy would improve the porosity and permeability characteristics although mud drapes would act as potential baffles to fluid migrations.

Above the final, late Westphalian A, axial system the basin was filled by predominantly shallow-water fluvio–deltaic sediments (Chesnut 1994). Westward flowing, low sinuosity streams with complex dendritic and sheet form geometries (Davies *et al.* 1992) were sourced from the rising orogenic mountains. Above erosion surfaces these multistorey fluvial sandstone bodies are characterized by fine- to coarse-grained sandstones with unidirectional trough cross beds, and minor planar tabular cross beds, and correlate laterally to interfluves. The upper portion of these channel complexes are characterized by a range of deposits including siltstone-draped, lateral accretion surfaces, representing an increase in sinuosity and interbedded fine-grained and heterolithic sediments deposited during abandonment of the fluvial system. More rarely, burrowed sigmoidal cross-beds are present, representing a tidal influence in the late stages of valley filling. The sandstone bodies extend laterally for 5–25 km and are 10 to 15 m thick (Aitken & Flint 1995).

The Appalachian Basin continued to subside in response to the advancing orogen and changes in accommodation space were closely allied to and modified by fluctuations in sea-level. Reduced accommodation space during periods of low sea-level promoted incision and the development of these multistorey systems. Single storey fluvial distributaries, however, are associated with periods of higher accommodation development (Aitken & Flint 1995). Thin, high sinuosity fluvial channels occur within the transgressive and highstand systems tract (Fig. 2; Aitken & Flint 1994). The highstand fluvial channels are sandstone filled and amalgamated whereas in the transgressive systems tract isolated fluvial channels occur with heterolithic fills and increased evidence for tidal influence (Aitken & Flint 1995).

Mouth bars from the Westphalian Breathitt Group of the Appalachian Basin may have a lateral extent at least equivalent to or greater than the interpreted incised valleys. Although individual mouth bars may only be exposed for up to 5 km along depositional strike (Aitken & Flint 1995), these prograding systems coalesce and reach 60 m in thickness. Internally the mouthbars are characterized by rhythmically bedded sandstones and siltstones with evidence for tidal influence. The mouth bars are interpreted to occur within the highstand systems tract and represent the return of clastic sedimentation as the rate of sea-level rise decreases (Aitken & Flint 1994). The heterolithic nature of these coalesced mouth-bars would produce a low quality reservoir despite being areally extensive.

In summary, the largest fluvial systems in the Appalachian Basin occur in the upper Namurian to lower Westphalian. Smaller palaeovalleys characterize the later Westphalian. The fill character is predominantly fluvial but an estuarine component may occur. The upper storeys in the later Westphalian valleys may be filled with fine-grained sediments generated by either abandonment of the fluvial system or development of an estuary.

The Eastern Interior Basin, US

The Eastern Interior Basin, lying to the west of the Waverly–Cinncinati Arch is one of four major intracratonic basins in North America (Klein 1995). The Carboniferous is the last of three periods characterized by widespread intracratonic basin subsidence which were associated with major orogenic events (Willard & Klein 1990). A period of relatively slow, predominantly thermal, subsidence during the later Devonian (Klein 1995) was succeeded by an increase in subsidence rate and magnitude in the Early Carboniferous (Heidlauf *et al.* 1986). Collision on the eastern margin of the Appalachian Basin resulted in regional compressive stresses with thrust loading producing flexural stresses which were transmitted through the lithosphere (Craddock & van der Plujim 1989). The increased lithospheric rigidity, which produced broad, shallow subsidence in the Central Appalachian Basin, also favoured the lithospheric transmission of stresses. This lateral stress transmission was associated with strike slip faulting in the Eastern Interior Basin (Nelson 1990*a, b*) and reactivated pre-existing structures, focusing subsidence along older trends.

A network of valleys mark an unconformity in the mid-Namurian. A range of valley dimensions are represented but relatively narrow valleys, 2–3 km in width, predominate and are documented to incise to depths down to 60 m (Howard & Whitaker 1988; Archer & Greb 1995). Major trunk river systems in the same basin are represented by the largest palaeovalley dimensions at 20–32 km wide and 100–120 m deep (Evansville palaeovalley, Fig. 4; Bristol & Howard 1974). These valleys were incised into the underlying siltstone, sandstone and limestone lithologies of the Lower Namurian. The limestones may locally prevent erosion and interfluve areas are created (Bristol & Howard 1974) but where incision can occur, fluvial systems will erode down to the next barrier. Flat bottomed valleys formed when limestone intervals act as a barrier and prevent erosion (Bristol & Howard 1974; Archer & Greb 1995). The majority of valleys are therefore narrow and deeply incised, except where extensively terraced, e.g. the Evansville palaeovalley, creating a much wider and deeper valley.

Coarse-grained, fluvial sediments constitute only a minor component of the valley fill from the Eastern Interior Basin. The valley fills are dominated by finer-grained lithologies and low-quality reservoir sands. The basal gravel conglomerates are up to 13 m thick, with no fine-grained overbank deposits preserved, and extend up to 5 km along the palaeovalley (Howard & Whitaker 1988). Valleys located in the south-eastern part of the basin clearly show fining upward trends (Greb 1989). Bipartite fills are characteristic of a number of valleys in Carboniferous basins. Namurian-age valleys from the Colorado area (Fig. 4), also have coarse-grained basal storeys and are overlain by the deposits of heterolithic meandering channels and/or estuarine sediments (Krystinik & Blakeney 1990). In the Stephanian Tonganoxie palaeovalley, Indiana, (Feldman *et al.* 1995 and Fig. 4), only the basal portion, 2–18 m thick, is a coarse-grained, variably conglomeratic, braided fluvial deposit. The bulk of the valley fill comprises estuarine fine-grained sediments and isolated estuarine sandstones channels.

Reactivation of Precambrian faults produced uplift on the eastern margin of the Eastern Interior Basin (Shrake 1991) and the location of palaeovalleys is controlled by these fault zones (Greb 1989). The documented southwest palaeoflow in these valleys parallels the bounding faults and some channelling occurs across the uplifted blocks (Greb 1989). In contrast, valleys cross fold axes with only very limited diversion in the northern part of the basin. Therefore the cutting of palaeovalleys relates to a base-level fall which exposed the low-lying coastal shelf present in the Viséan and Lower Namurian. The location of this drainage system is controlled by pre-existing structures (Greb 1989). The climate during this time was predominantly semi-arid whereas in the hinterland source areas the climate may have been much more seasonal.

The Ouachita Basin, US

The river systems identified in the Eastern Interior and Appalachian Basin contributed to deposition in the Ouachita Trough, a remnant ocean basin (Chesnut 1994). Turbidites and other submarine sediment gravity deposits were fed from the large deltaic and fluvial systems derived from the orogenic belt. Longitudinal transport was predominant along the asymmetric basin. Palaeocurrent data indicate SW flowing rivers and neodynium isotope characteristics confirm that Ouachita turbidites were sourced from the Canadian shield with a more minor source from the rising mountain belt (Gleason *et al.* 1994). Approximately 10 km of Viséan to Westphalian B deep water sediments were deposited in the Ouachita Trough. The ocean basin began closing in the Devonian to lowest Carboniferous and by early Westphalian A the remnant ocean basin had been subducted (Houseknecht 1986).

Diagnostic fauna have not been recovered from deepwater Jackfork Sandstone successions from the Ouachita trough (Shanmugam & Moiola 1988) despite abundant marine trace fossil assemblages and condensed fine-grained intervals. The absence of key fauna-bearing horizons hinders attempts to correlate successions within the basin and importantly to correlate up-depositional dip into the fluvio–deltaics. Although the succession is known to contain gas reserves (Shirley 1997) a number of detrimental factors reduce their reservoir potential, including high burial depths and the structurally complex plays close to the Appalachian orogenic belt.

The European Basin

The Wales–London–Brabant High extended from Ireland across central England into Europe (Fig. 1b). This palaeogeographical barrier separated the Rhenohercynian Zone from a 'Northern Shelf', a region comprising Ireland, northern England (the 'Pennine Basin'), the Southern North Sea (UK and Dutch sectors) and the Campine Basin (Belgium). Back-arc extension to the north of the subduction zone, from the late Devonian to early Carboniferous, created a series of half-graben whose orientation was strongly influenced by inherited Caledonian structures (Leeder 1988). Variscan structures are dominated by NE–SW trends in the west of the region in contrast to the NW–SE trends in the east. Dinantian subsidence, bathymetry and sedimentary facies distribution were controlled by these sub-basins during this syn-rift stage. Late Caledonian granites form the cores of the Askrigg and Alston blocks which were buoyant and relatively high areas throughout much of the Carboniferous.

By the early Namurian, thermal subsidence replaced active rifting north of the Wales–London–Brabant High (Leeder & McMahon 1988; Fraser & Gawthorpe 1990). However, subsidence rates may have actually continued to be high and the thickness of deposited sediment cannot be accounted for by post-rift thermal subsidence (Haszeldine 1989; Waters *et al.* 1994). The new radiometric dates reduce the amount of time available for deposition and reinforce the high frequency character of sequences developed in the Carboniferous (Jones 1995; Riley *et al.* 1995). Even without continuing tectonic movement, the relict Dinantian bathymetry and compaction of the fine-grain dominated basin fill ensured Namurian sedimentation continued to be influenced by the fault-bounded blocks and basins established in the Dinantian. The influence of the blocks and basins diminished through the Namurian and into the Westphalian.

In the Craven/northern Pennine basins, the first major fluvial bodies occurred in the uppermost Pendleian. The local erosional relief of up to 15 m is visible at outcrop over distances of a few hundred metres or more. Much greater regional relief, generally around 30 to 40 m, over distances of several kilometres can be documented where correlative interfluves are identified (authors own unpublished data). Revised correlations and recognition of new faunal horizons (Brandon *et al.* 1995) suggest turbidites occur broadly down depositional dip from these fluvial systems (Baines 1977; Sims 1988). Lower Namurian, shallow marine sandstones are geographically restricted to the more marginal areas of the Pennine Basin such as near the Askrigg Block. These sandstones may extend laterally for a few kilometres and are extensively wave reworked. Marine fauna and marine trace fossils are abundant in these sandstones (Arthurton *et al.* 1988).

Further south in the Southern Pennine and North Wales basins, condensed shale successions represent deposition from the basal Namurian through to the Alportian or even Kinderscoutian. Thick successions of turbidite sandstones deposited at this time were confined to individual sub-basins and during relatively short periods of time, usually encompassing 3–4 marine bands (Walker 1996).

Onshore UK and Ireland, Namurian-age incised valleys generally range from 10–30 km wide representing regional-scale erosion associated sea-level fall. The Yeadonian Rough Rock from the central area of the Pennine Basin East Midlands is an exception. The Rough Rock has a more sheet-like appearance, is 80–90 km in width and correlative interfluves have yet to be determined. The system is interpreted as a multi-storey, multilateral sand sheets present in the main Pennine Basins (Bristow 1988, 1993). The Westphalian A Crawshaw Sandstone in the East Midlands is also laterally extensive, *c.* 70 km wide but has well defined margins and documented interfluves which suggest a valley fill origin (Fig. 4). The Crawshaw Sandstone is the final representative of this style of fluvial deposition from the onshore with subsequent fluvial systems predominantly characterized by less laterally extensive sandstone bodies developed on the low-lying coastal plain.

The most commonly preserved thickness of these palaeovalleys is 25–35 m. A very limited number of examples exceed these vertical dimensions; incision of up to 80 m is associated with the Marsdenian Roaches Grit (Jones & Chisholm 1997; Figs 3 and 4) and the Pule Hill Grit (Wignall & Maynard 1996).

The character and internal architecture of Carboniferous incised valleys and sand sheets have been discussed in detail by Hampson *et al.* (1997). In summary, the majority of valleys are filled by 6–10 m thick channel members present above a composite basal erosion surfaces commonly with intraformational conglomerates. Lateral accretion is rare and fine-grained sediments, including channel margin, channel plug and in-channel bank failure deposits, are preserved in laterally restricted lenses. Valley fill successions comprise 95% sand and do not fine upward. Although an upward increase in spacing of erosion surfaces represents increased channel preservation, other vertical changes in fluvial architecture are weakly developed. In general, the low sinuosity systems did not evolve through time. Many valleys are capped by a rooted sandstone, prior to marine flooding, which implies that these valleys fill to emergence (cf. Hampson *et al.* 1997). The Farewell Rock is an exception to this fill style where decreasing grain-size, decreasing cross-bed co-set thickness and increasing thickness of current-ripple cross-lamination intervals in channel members are typical (Hampson *et al.* 1997). This represents a decrease in stream power following a decrease in channel slope as sea-level rises. An upper fine-grained fill which can be traced across the valley for 40 km is interpreted as a siltstone-dominated channel plug and bay-head delta. A rooted horizon, prior to the main flooding surface, demonstrates that the valley still filled to emergence.

Distributary channels overlying mouth bars are interpreted from the Rough Rock flags (Myers & Bristow 1989) and beneath the Roaches Grit (Jones & Chisholm 1997). These channels are characterized by channelized, cross-bedded coarse-grained sandstones and can be distinguished from the lowstand/early transgressive multistorey, multilateral sandstone bodies by their more limited lateral extent.

In general, other sandstone bodies, including mouth bar, tidal and shoreface sandstones (Fig. 2), would be poor reservoirs, because of low porosities and permeabilities related to grainsize and poor sorting. The presence of fines in these poorly sorted sandstones promotes the growth of authigenic clay cements, including illite and kaolinite (Cowan 1989). Fine-grained baffles and/or limited lateral extent also reduce reservoir potential. Mouth bar sandbodies from Carboniferous basins are rarely promising reservoir plays and are not confined to a single systems tract. In the Kinderscoutian of the Clare Basin, Ireland mouth bars extend laterally for between 3 and 6 km (Pulham 1987, 1989). At their most proximal location with respect to the fluvial distributaries, 12 m thick mouth bars are characterized by erosive-based, cross-stratified sandstone beds modified by wave action, and can be demonstrated to pass laterally into siltstones away from sediment input points.

The Maritime Basin, Canada

The Maritimes Basin is located between the USA and European provinces and is part of the Euramerican Province (Calder & Gibling 1994). The early tectonic evolution of the Maritime Basin, Canada was associated with post-tectonic extension following the Acadian orogeny (mid-Devonian to Viséan). The extension resulted in magmatic underplating beneath the Cobequid Highlands (Piper *et al.* 1993). This phase was succeeded by reactivation of regional strike-slip faults in the upper Namurian to Stephanian evolution (Langdon & Hall 1994). This latter phase has been interpreted to represent thermal subsidence, but subsidence rates derived from offshore wells show a very rapid increase in subsidence in the late Namurian. The Viséan to early Namurian is characterized by subsidence rates of between 40–60 m Ma^{-1} which increase to 100–130 m Ma^{-1} in the late Namurian through early Westphalian which suggests active subsidence (Rehill 1996, Gibling pers. comm. 1997). There is evidence for syndepositional motion on transcurrent faults across the Maritimes Basin and syn- and post-depositional halokinesis is important (Gibling 1995). In the SW Maritimes Basin (Cumberland Basin) episodes of rapid basin subsidence/source area uplift and increased conglomeratic alluvial fan development resulting from strike-slip movements alternate with periods of slower regional subsidence resulting from transpressional flexure (Ryan *et al.* 1987).

In the Maritimes area, in common with northern Ireland, Scotland, the Barents Sea area and the Urals, earliest Namurian sedimentation was characterized by thick carbonate–evaporite–red bed cycles interpreted as marine, marginal marine and inland sabkha horizons with the Maritimes reflecting an increasingly enclosed basin. Gradually, lacustrine conditions were established in eastern areas of the basin (Crawford 1995) whereas in more westerly areas, sedimentation was dominated by alluvial fans and thick successions of fine-grained red beds.

After the last dated, fully marine interval, the exact age of successions in the Maritimes Basin remain in debate; however, recent work defines the non-marine Boss Point Formation as Namurian (Utting pers. comm. 1998). In the Boss Point Formation, multistorey fluvial systems extend laterally for up to 12 km and have a preserved thickness of 15–90 m, although the average thickness is 38 m with up to 15 m of regional relief

(Browne & Plint 1994; Fig. 4). These systems were major low sinuosity, braided systems and are dominated by alternations of conglomerate or pebbly sandstone and trough cross-bedded sandstone with no overall upward fining or preservation of abandoned channel plugs and levees (Browne & Plint 1994). Occasionally there is a transition into planar-laminated sandstone and into ripple cross-laminated sandstone. The individual sandstone bodies are overlain by lacustrine mudstones which represent rapid low energy flooding of the braidplain.

The Joggins Formation (top Namurian, Utting pers. comm. 1998) overlies the Boss Point Formation and represents a major change in depositional environment. These younger fluvial systems can be multistorey but are characterized by higher sinuosity, ephemeral systems, where lateral and downstream accretion is common. The sandstone bodies are heterolithic in character, generally fine upwards and reach a maximum of 10 m in thickness (Fig. 2). The fluvial intervals extend laterally for 150 m or less and are encased in thick, fine-dominated floodplain successions (Davies & Gibling 1998). These small areally restricted sandstone bodies also characterize the Westphalian where individual compound channel bodies are up to 12.5 m thick and extend laterally for between 30 to 80 m (Rust *et al.* 1984). Numerous flooding surfaces including lacustrine limestones (with possible marine influence, Archer *et al.* 1995) and coal intervals split the succession into discrete packages.

The transition to greater subsidence rates at the end of the Namurian coupled with a possible change in sediment calibre promotes the development of single storey fluvial bodies in a high accommodation regime during deposition of the Joggins Formation. The high magnitude, high frequency sea-level fluctuations have been demonstrated to be an important driving force in Carboniferous basins from the US and Europe when co-eval falls produced fluvial incision in tectonically diverse basins (Hampson *et al.* 1997 and this paper). However, the Joggins Formation differs significantly from this pattern since a hierarchy of numerous flooding events can be identified but there is no evidence for significant falls in base level.

Controls on dimensions and fill characteristics of Namurian and Lower Westphalian palaeovalleys

Glacioeustatically driven sea-level fluctuations would have been the same magnitude and frequency across the Euramerican province and could have exerted a fundamental control on the creation of palaeovalleys from basins in a range of tectonic settings. However, basin-specific controls would have influenced valley location, incision depths, dimensions and fill characteristics. Comparisons of UK incised valley systems with those from North America highlight many differences.

The narrowest valleys are stratigraphically located in the mid-Namurian. The smallest Lower Namurian palaeovalleys of the illustrated examples occur in Colorado (Fig. 4; Krystinik & Blakeney 1990). The narrow, deep valleys present at the Mississippian–Pennsylvanian unconformity in the US, are much less abundant from the onshore UK and Irish Carboniferous where late Dinantian rifting fragmented the carbonate margin. The carbonate margin remained intact in the US basins providing a low-relief topography which was subsequently incised. This feature is one of the clearest differences in palaeovalley style between the US and the UK. In the UK, incision into the underlying limestone is documented on the Alston and Askrigg blocks (Fig. 1b; Dunham & Wilson 1985) where laterally restricted valleys do exist (Brandon *et al.* 1995, Davies unpublished data). Most are likely to be stratigraphically restricted to the Arnsbergian and geographically limited to the blocks (Dunham & Wilson 1985; Brandon *et al.* 1995).

Dimensions of temporally equivalent valley systems in disparate basins are similar. The dimensions of 'Lee Sandstones' in the Appalachian Basin (Archer & Greb 1995) are comparable to Namurian multi-storey sand-belts of the Rough Rock in the UK Pennine Basin (Bristow 1988, 1993; Hampson *et al.* 1996). These Upper Namurian/basal Westphalian sandstone bodies are broadly time-equivalent although correlation at the highest resolution has yet be established (Fig. 2). The lateral extent over tens of kilometres and similar preserved thickness may be the result of the comparable subsidence rates and similar substrate character. In both the Appalachian and Central Pennine basins, the fluvial systems were forced out into the basin, by a fall in sea-level, and cut down into underling deltaics but were then able to expand across a broad low plain. Archer & Greb (1995) related these laterally extensive palaeovalleys to their position within the basin, whereas the narrower valleys were confined to areas on the margins of the basin (described as a 'shelf') where narrower and potentially deeper incision through underling successions occurred. This contrast is also observed in the Pennine basin where narrower 'Rough Rock equivalent' valleys are confined to the more slowly subsiding East Midlands platform (Church & Gawthorpe 1994).

The internal characteristics of large-scale sandstone belts and valley fills from the US and UK appear to differ. The entirely fluvial Rough Rock contrasts with the Appalachian examples where fine-grained sediments with features indicating estuarine conditions are an important component. Examples of fine-grained fills of the UK palaeovalleys (e.g. Hampson *et al.* 1997) are predominantly represented by fluvial abandonment facies such as bay fills and overbank deposits which do not appear to be influenced by the marine system. The effects of rising sea-level on the entirely fluvial valley fills are reflected by an upwards increase in the spacing of erosion surfaces. There are a few onshore UK examples of marine influenced fine-grained fills within palaeovalleys (Elliott & Davies 1994; Wignall & Maynard 1996; Hampson *et al.* 1997). Greb & Archer (1995) note that that even in more proximal valley systems there is an upper estuarine component to the valley fill.

It is possible that exposed sections through the Rough Rock and other UK and Irish palaeovalleys represent more proximal sections, in comparison with those examples chosen from the US, or that the sand-rich valleys are preferentially exposed. Alternative interpretations include that a high sediment supply to the UK valleys was sufficient fill the valleys to emergence prior to the next flooding event. In contrast the sediment supply to the Appalachian Basin was not high enough to fill the valleys prior to the next rise in sea-level. The valleys were then back-filled with marine-influenced sediments.

The late Namurian/Westphalian A was a time of overall sea-level low (Ross & Ross 1985) compared either to the underlying Mississippian or the subsequent Pennsylvanian (Westphalian B through Stephanian). An overall rise in sea-level must have accompanied the break-up of the Gondwanan ice sheet during the late Westphalian and Stephanian (Gonzalez-Bonorino & Eyles 1995). Examples of Stephanian palaeovalleys, such as the 41 m deep Tonganoxie Valley (Feldman *et al.* 1995), suggest that high magnitude sea-level falls were still relatively important though perhaps not of the order of those earlier in the succession.

The role of changing sea-level is much more controversial in European Westphalian successions as marine incursions became fewer and the marine connection to the open ocean became more tenuous, although deep water deposition continued into the Westphalian D in southwest Portugal (Perreira pers. com. 1996) and until at least Westphalian C in southwest England. In the Westphalian and Stephanian of the Maritimes Basin, foraminifera characteristic of coastal settings are abundant in successions overlying non-marine, fluvial sandstones (Gibling & Wightman 1994; Archer *et al.* 1995).

Conclusions

Upper Carboniferous reservoir development in the Euramerican province is controlled by a combination of eustatic sea-level, sediment supply, initial basin bathymetry, spatial subsidence patterns and subsidence history. Various stratigraphic levels are characterized by different balances of these external controls.

The chronostratigraphic framework constructed using goniatite marine bands defines stratigraphic intervals where potential reservoir sandstone bodies are predominant. The resolution of these intervals is dependent upon the occurrence of important marine bands and every marine band may not be recognized from all basins. Onshore analogues from basins across the Euramerican province can be used to rank the stratigraphy in terms of the most likely reservoir prospects.

The highest biostratigraphic resolution can be achieved in the greatest number of basins during the Upper Kinderscoutian, the Marsdenian and the Yeadonian. The erosional unconformites beneath multistorey fluvial sandbodies have been demonstrated to be time equivalent. This provides very clear evidence of an overriding glacio–eustatic sea-level control on timing of incision, and demonstrates that eustatic sea-level lowstands are the primary driving force in sand-prone reservoir development.

A summary of incised valleys fills and multistorey sand sheet demonstrates the restriction of multistorey, multilateral sand sheets to the Upper Namurian/Basal Westphalian A and the variation in lateral and vertical dimensions. Many of these Upper Namurian/Basal Westphalian A fluvial sandbodies are of the greatest lateral extent, 70 to 90 km, and with a general vertical thickness of 25–35 m.

These sand sheets are not, however, necessarily the best reservoirs. The Kinderscoutian contains a number of sand-rich units and good reservoirs occur at this level in some of the North American basins particularly where incision occurs into the underlying Late Dinantian. Analogues in the US, suggest that the best reservoirs producing oil and gas are to be found in these small, deep palaeovalleys containing a relatively thin, coarse-grained basal fluvial component and the remainder of the valley fill comprising an estuarine mud-dominated succession and minor fine-grained estuarine/tidal sandstones. These reservoirs are economically viable because they exist onshore, at relatively shallow depths (<1500 m) and can be easily identified by a high density drilling programme. The most similar valleys to those analogues in the US would be located in the upper Dinantian and, in northern England, lower Namurian Yoredale type successions. Similar sized reservoirs discovered in the Southern North Sea (Maynard pers. comm. 1997) are not yet economically viable.

The Marsdenian contains several promising sand-rich intervals, with predominantly multistorey fluvial systems recorded, within a number of European basins (Fig. 3) but stratigraphic control outside Europe is poor and even within the UK, the study of the Marsdenian has been relatively limited (Wignall & Maynard 1996). The remainder of the Upper Carboniferous is characterized by fluvial systems with a range of dimensions which are never more than 30 km width.

The predominant tectonic regime within each basin had a fundamental control on the important valley positioning, lateral extent and palaeoflow. The reservoir type and geometry are subsequently controlled by basin topography and spatial variations in subsidence, i.e. incised valleys vs fluvial sheet complexes. Spatial variations in subsidence may account for differences in lateral extent of co-eval sandbodies, e.g. the Rough Rock of the Pennine Basin and the East Midlands area, where narrower valleys form where subsidence rates are lower. Temporal variations in subsidence, e.g. the major increase in subsidence from the Namurian into the Westphalian, influence the development of candidate reservoirs. High subsidence regimes promote isolated fluvial bodies as in the Canadian Maritimes basin. Single storey fluvial systems may also be restricted to the transgressive and highstand systems tracts (e.g. Westphalian, Appalachian Basin).

In general terms, viewing the data from North America and Europe (Fig. 4), incised valley fills and multistorey sandstone sheets reach maximum dimensions around the uppermost Namurian/basal Westphalian. Into the upper Westphalian and Stephanian in the US and Canada, there is a pronounced change to smaller valley fills. In the Southern North Sea. The different types of fluvial sandstone bodies increase into the Westphalian B, although reservoir potential may decrease as a result of greater heterogeneity within the succession. Coarse sandstone bodies with suitable mineralogies, e.g. the Caister Sandstone and the sheet sandstone systems of the Schooner and Ketch fields (Besly 1998) are important reservoirs, although less laterally extensive than some of the Namurian analogues.

The authors would like to thank ARCO UK Ltd for funding this research at the University of Liverpool. J. Maynard and A. Hartley are thanked for thorough and thought-provoking reviews.

References

Aitken, J. F. & Flint, S. S. 1994. High frequency sequences and the nature of incised valley fills in fluvial systems of the Breathitt Group (Pennsylvanian) Appalachian Foreland Basin, Eastern Kentucky. *In:* Boyd, R., Dalrymple, R. W. & Zaitlin, B. (eds) *Incised Valley Systems: Origin and Sedimentary Sequences*. Society of Economic Palaeontologists and Mineralogists, Special Publications, **51**, 353–368.

—— & ——1995. The application of high-resolution sequence stratigraphy to fluvial systems: a case study from the Breathitt Group, eastern Kentucky, USA. *Sedimentology*, **42**, 3–30.

Aitkenhead, N., Chisholm, J. H. & Stevenson, I. P. 1985. *Geology of the country around Buxton, Leek and Bakewell: Sheet 111.* British Geological Survey: England and Wales.

—— & Riley, N. J. 1996. Kinderscoutian and Marsdenian successions in the Bradup and Hag Farm boreholes, near Ilkley, west Yorkshire. *Proceedings of the Yorkshire Geological Society*, **51**, 115–126.

Archer, A. W. & Greb, S. F. 1995. An Amazon-scale drainage system in the Early Pennsylvanian of Central North America. *Journal of Geology*, **103**, 611–628.

——, Calder, J. H., Gibling, M. R., Naylor, R. N., Reid, D. R. & Wightman, W. G. 1995. Trace fossils and agglutinated foraminifera as indicators of marine environments in the classic Carboniferous section at Joggins, Nova Scotia, Canada. *Canadian Journal of Earth Sciences* **32**, 2027–2039.

Arthurton, R. S., Johnson, E. W. & Mundy, D. J. C. 1988. *Geology around the country of Settle: Memoir for the 1:50 000 geological sheet 60*. British Geological Survey: England and Wales.

Baines, J. G. 1977. *The Stratigraphy and Sedimentology of the Skipton Moor Grits (Namurian A) and their Lateral Equivalents*. PhD thesis, University of Keele.

Besly, B. M. 1998. Carboniferous. *In*: Glennie, K. W. (ed.) *Petroleum Geology of the North Sea: Basic Concepts and Recent Advances*. Blackwell Science, Oxford, 104–136.

Beuthin, J. D. 1994. A sub-Pennsylvanian palaeovalley in the Central Appalachian Basin and its implications for tectonic and eustatic controls on the origin of the regional Mississippian–Pennsylvanian. *In*: Denninson, J. M. & Ettensohn, F. R. (eds) *Tectonic and Eustatic Controls on Sedimentary Cycles. Concepts in palaeontology and sedimentology 4*. Society of Economic Palaeontologists and Sedimentologists (Society for Sedimentary Geologists), 107–120.

Braithwaite, K. 1994. Stratigraphy of a Mid-Carboniferous section at Inishcorker, Ireland. *Annales de la Societé geologique de Belgique*, **T116**, 209–219.

BRANDON, A., RILEY, N. J., WILSON, A. A. & ELLISON, R. A. 1995. Three new early Namurian (E1c–E2a) marine bands in central and northern England, UK, and their bearing on correlations with the Askrigg Block. *Proceedings of the Yorkshire Geological Society*, **50**, 333–355.

BRISTOL, H. M. & HOWARD, R. H. 1974. Sub-Pennsylvanian valleys in the Chesterian surface of the Illinois Basin and related Chesterian slump blocks. *Geological Society of America Special Publications*, **148**, 315–335.

BRISTOW, C. S. 1988. Controls on the sedimentation of the Rough Rock Group (Namurian) from the Pennine Basin of Northern England. *In*: BESLY, B. M & KELLING, G. (eds) *Sedimentation in a Synorogenic Basin Complex: the Upper Carboniferous of Northwest Europe*. Blackie, 114–131.

——1993. Sedimentology of the Rough Rock a Carboniferous braided river sheet sandstone in Northern England. *In*: BEST, J. L. & BRISTOW, C. S. (eds) *Braided Rivers*. Geological Society, London, Special Publications, **75**, 291–304.

BROWNE, G. H. & PLINT, A. G. 1994. Alternating braidplain and lacustrine deposition in a strike-slip setting: the Pennsylvanian Boss Point Formation of the Cumberland Basin, Maritime Canada. *Journal of Sedimentary Research*, **B64**, 40–59.

CALDER, J. H., & GIBLING, M. R. 1994. The Euramerican Coal Province: controls on Late Paleozoic peat accumulation. *Palaeogeography, Palaeoclimatology, Palaeoecology*, **106**, 1–21.

CHESNUT, D. R. 1994. Eustatic and tectonic controls on deposition of the Lower and Middle Pennsylvanian strata of the Central Appalachian Basin. *In*: DENNISON, J. M. & ETTENSOHN, F. R. (eds) *Tectonic and Eustatic Controls on Sedimentary Cycles. Concepts in sedimentology and palaeontology* 4. Society of Economic Palaeontologists and Sedimentologists (Society for Sedimentary Geologists), 51–64.

CHURCH, K. D. &, GAWTHORPE, R. L. 1994. High resolution sequence stratigraphy of the late Namurian in the Widmerpool Gulf (East Midlands, UK). *Marine and Petroleum Geology*, **11**, 528–544.

COLLINSON, J. D., MARTINSEN, O., BAKKEN, B. & KLOSTER, A. 1991. Early fill of the Western Irish Namurian Basin: a complex relationship between turbidites and deltas. *Basin Research*, **3**, 223–242.

COWAN, G. 1989. Diagenesis of Upper Carboniferous sandstones: Southern North Sea Basin. *In*: WHATELEY, M. K. G. & PICKERING, K. T. (eds) *Deltas: Sites and Traps for Fossil Fuels*. Geological Society, London, Special Publications, **41**, 57–73.

CRADDOCK, J. P. & VAN DER PLUJIM, B. A. 1989. Late Palaeozoic deformation of the cratonic carbonate cover of eastern North America. *Geology*, **17**, 416–419.

CRAWFORD, T. L. 1995. Carbonates and associated sedimentary rocks of the Upper Viséan to Namurian Mabou Group, Cape Breton Island, Nova Scotia: evidence for lacustrine deposition. *Atlantic Geology*, **31**, 167–182.

DAVIES, H., BURN, M., BUDDING, M. C. & WILLIAMS, H. 1992. High resolution sequence stratigraphic analysis of fluvio-deltaic cyclothems: the Pennsylvanian Breathitt Group, east Kentucky. *In*: *American Association of Petroleum Geologists 1992 Annual Convention Programme*, 27.

DAVIES, S. J. & ELLIOTT, T. 1996. Spectral gamma ray characterization of high resolution sequence stratigraphy: examples from Upper Carboniferous fluvio-deltaic systems, County Clare, Ireland. *In*: HOWELL, J. A. & AITKEN, J. F. (eds) *High Resolution Sequence Stratigraphy: Innovations and Applications*. Geological Society, London, Special Publications, **104**, 25–35.

—— & MCLEAN, D. 1996. Spectral gamma ray and palynological characterisation of marine bands in the Kinderscoutian (Namurian, late Carboniferous) of the Pennine Basin. *Proceedings of the Yorkshire Geological Society*, **51**, 103–114.

—— & GIBLING, M. R. 1998. Evolution of an Upper Carboniferous non-marine succession in a high accommodation setting, Maritimes Basin, Canada. *In*: *American Association of Petroleum Geologists, Annual Conference*, Salt Lake City, Utah, US.

DEVOLVE, J.-J., SOUQUET, P., VACHARD, D., PERRET, M. & AGUIRRE, P. 1993. Characterisation of a Carboniferous foreland Basin in the Pyrenees, facies, timing, of synsedimentary tectonism. *Comptes Rendus de l'Academie Sciences des Paris Serie II*, **316**(7), 959–966.

DUNHAM, K. C. & WILSON, A. A. 1985. *Geology of the Northern Pennine Orefield: Volume 2, Stainmore to Craven*. British Geological Survey: England and Wales.

EAGAR, R. M. C. & XU LI. 1993. A revision of the biostratigraphy of the Late Namurian-Early Westphalian of Westward Ho! North Devon. *Proceedings of the Geologists Association*, **104**, 161–179.

ELLIOTT, T. & DAVIES, S. J. 1994. *High Resolution Sequence Stratigraphy of an Upper Carboniferous Basin-Fill Succession, County Clare, Western Ireland, Fieldtrip B2*. Liverpool, UK.

ENGLUND, K. J. 1979. Mississippian System and lower series of the Pennsylvanian System in the proposed Pennsylvanian System stratotype area. *In*: ENGLUND, K. J., ARNDT, H. H. & HENRY, T. W. (eds) *Proposed Pennsylvanian System Stratotype, Virginia and West Virginia* The America Geological Institute, Selected guidebook series **1**, 69–72.

FELDMAN, H. R., GIBLING, M. R., ARCHER, A. W. WIGHTMAN, W. G. & LANIER, W. P. 1995. Stratigraphic architecture of the Tonganoxie palaeovalley fill (Lower Virgillian) in Northeastern Kansas. *American Association of Petroleum Geologists Bulletin*, **79**, 1019–1043.

FRASER, A. J. & GAWTHORPE, R. L. 1990. Tectono-stratigraphic development and hydrocarbon habitat of the Carboniferous in Northern England. *In*: HARDMAN, R. F. P. & BROOKS, J. (eds) *Tectonic Events Responsible for Britain's Oil and Gas Reserves*. Geological Society, London, Special Publications, **55**, 49–86.

GIBLING, M. R. 1995. Upper Paleozoic rocks, Nova Scotia. *In*: WILLIAMS, H. (ed.) *Geology of the Appalachian–Caledonian Orogen in Canada and Greenland*. Geological Survey of Canada, Geology of Canada, **6**, 493–523.

—— & WIGHTMAN, W. G. 1994. Paleovalleys and protozoan assemblages in a Late Carboniferous cyclothem, Sydney Basin, Nova Scotia. *Sedimentology*, **41**, 699–719.

GLEASON, J. D., PATCHETT, P. D., DICKINSON, W. R. & RUIZ, J. 1994. Nd isotopes link Ouachita turbidites to Appalachian sources. *Geology*, **22**, 347–350.

GONZALEZ-BONORINO, G. & EYLES, N. 1995. Inverse relation between ice extent and the late Paleozoic glacial record of Gondwana. *Geology*, **23**, 1015–1018.

GREB, S. F. 1989. A sub-rectangular paleovalley system, Caseyville Formation, Eastern Interior Basin, Western Kentucky. *Southeastern Geology*, **30**, 59–74.

—— & ARCHER, A. W. 1995. Rhythmic sedimentation in a mixed tide and wave deposit, Hazel patch sandstone (Lower Pennsylvanian), eastern Kentucky coal field. *Journal of Sedimentary Research*, **B65**, 96–106.

—— & CHESNUT, D. R. 1996. Lower and Lower Middle Pennsylvanian fluvial to estuarine deposition, Central Appalachian Basin – effects of eustasy tectonics and climate. *Geological Society of America Bulletin*, **108**, 303–317.

GUION, P. D., BANKS, N. L. & RIPPON, J. H. 1995. The Silkstone Rock (Westphalian A) from the east Pennines, England: implications for sand body genesis. *Journal of the Geological Society, London*, **152**, 819–832.

HAMPSON, G. J. 1995. Discrimination of regionally-extensive coals in the Upper Carboniferous of the Pennine Basin, U.K. using high-resolution sequence stratigraphic concepts. *In*: WHATELEY, M. K. G. & SPEARS, D. A. (eds) *European Coal Geology*. Geological Society, London, Special Publications, **82**, 79–97.

——1997. A sequence stratigraphic model for deposition of the Lower Kinderscout Delta, an Upper Carboniferous turbidite-fronted delta. *Proceedings of the Yorkshire Geological Society*, **51**, 273–296.

——, ELLIOTT, T. & FLINT, S. S. 1996. Critical application of high resolution sequence stratigraphic concepts to the Rough Rock Group (Upper Carboniferous) of northern England. *In*: HOWELL, J. A. & AITKEN, J. F. (eds) *High Resolution Sequence Stratigraphy: Innovations and Applications*. Geological Society, London, Special Publications, **104**, 221–246

——, —— & DAVIES, S. J. 1997. The application of sequence stratigraphy to Upper Carboniferous fluvio–deltaic strata of the onshore UK and Ireland: implications for the southern North Sea. *Journal of the Geological Society, London*, **154**, 719–733.

HASZELDINE, R. S. 1989. Evidence against crustal stretching, north–south tension and Hercynian collision, forming British Carboniferous basins. *In*: ARTHURTON, R. S. (eds) *The Role of Tectonics in Devonian and Carboniferous Sedimentation in the British Isles*. Yorkshire Geological Society Occasional Publication, **6**, 25–33.

HEIDLAUF, D. T., HSUI, A. T. & KLEIN, G. D. 1986. Tectonic subsidence analysis of the Illinois Basin. *Journal of Geology*, **94**, 779–794.

HESS, J. C. & LIPPOLT, H. J. 1986. $^{40}Ar/^{39}Ar$ ages of tonstein and tuff sanidines: new calibration points for the improvement of the Upper Carboniferous time scale. *Isotope Geoscience*, **59**, 143–154.

HIGGS, K. 1986. The stratigraphy of the Namurian Rocks of the Leinster coalfield. *Geological Survey of Ireland, Bulletin*, **3**, 257–276.

HOUSEKNECHT, D. W. 1986. Evolution from passive margin to foreland basin; the Atoka Formation of the Arkoma basin, south-central USA. *In*: ALLEN, P. A. & HOMEWOOD, P. (eds) *Foreland Basins*. Special Publication of the International Association of Sedimentologists, **8**, 327–345.

HOWARD, R. H. & WHITAKER, S. T. 1988. Hydrocarbon accumulation in a palaeovalley at Mississippian-Pennsylvanian unconformity near Hardinville, Crawford county, Illinois: a model paleogeomorphic trap. *Illinois Petroleum*, **129**, 1–26.

JONES, P. J. 1995. *Timescales, 5-Carboniferous*. Australian Geological Survey Organisation.

JONES, C. M. & CHISHOLM, J. I. 1997. The Roaches and Ashover Grits: sequence stratigraphic interpretation of a 'turbidite-fronted' delta. *Geological Journal*, **32**, 45–68.

KASSLER, P. 1973. The structural and geomorphic evolution of the Persian Gulf. *In*: PARKER, B. H. (ed.) *The Persian Gulf*. Springer-Verlag, Berlin, 11–32.

KLEIN, G. D. 1995. Intracratonic basins. *In*: INGERSOLL, R. V. & BUSBY, C. J. (eds) *Tectonics of Sedimentary Basins*. Blackwells, 459–478

KOTAS, A. 1995. Moravian–Silesian–Cracovian region. *In*: ZDANOWSKI, A. & ZAKOWA, H. (eds) *The Carboniferous System in Poland*. Warszawa, 17–19.

KRYSTINIK, L. F. & BLAKENEY, B. A. 1994. Sedimentology of the upper Morrow Formation in eastern Colorado and western Kansas. *In*: SONNEBERG, S. A. & SHANNON, L. T. (eds) *Morrow Sandstones of Southeast Colorado and Adjacent Areas*. Rocky Mountain Association of Geologists, Denver, 37–50.

LANGDON, G. S. & HALL, J. 1994. Devonian and Carboniferous tectonics and basin deformation in the Cabot Strait Area, Eastern Canada. *American Association of Petroleum Geologists Bulletin*, **78**, 1748–1774.

LANGENAEKER, V. & DUSAR, M. 1992. Subsurface facies analysis of the Namurian and earliest Westphalian in the western part of the Campine Basin (N Belgium). *Geologie en Mijnbouw*, **71**, 161–172.

LEEDER, M. R. 1988. Devono-Carboniferous river systems and sediment dispersal from the orogenic belts and cratons of NW Europe. *In*: HARRIS, A. L. & FETTES, D. J. (eds) *The Caledonian–Appalachian Orogen*. Geological Society, London, Special Publications, **38**, 549–558.

—— & MCMAHON, A. 1988. Upper Carboniferous (Silesian) basin subsidence in northern Britain. *In*: BESLEY, B. M & KELLING, G. (eds) *Sedimentation in a Synorogenic Basin Complex: the Upper Carboniferous of Northwest Europe*. Blackie, Glasgow, 43–52.

MARTINSEN, O. J. 1993. Namurian (late Carboniferous) depositional systems of the Craven–Askrigg area, northern England: implications for sequence-stratigraphic models. *In*: POSAMENTIER, H. W., SUMMERHAYES, C. P., HAQ, B. U. & ALLEN, G. P. (eds) *Sequence Stratigraphy and Facies Associations*. International Association of Sedimentologists, Special Publication, **18**, 247–281.

——, COLLINSON, J. D. & HOLDSWORTH, B. K. 1995. Millstone Grit cyclicity revisited, II: sequence stratigraphy and sedimentary responses to changes in relative sea-level. *In*: PLINT, A. G. (ed.) *Sedimentary Facies Analysis*. International Association of Sedimentologists, Special Publications, **22**, 305–331.

MAYNARD, J. R. 1992. Sequence stratigraphy of Upper Yeadonian of Northern England. *Marine and Petroleum Geology*, **9**, 197–207.

—— & LEEDER, M. R. 1992. On the periodicity and magnitude of Late Carboniferous glacio-eustatic sea-level changes. *Journal of the Geological Society, London*, **149**, 303–311.

MYERS, K. J. & BRISTOW, C. S. 1989. Detailed sedimentology and gamma-ray log characteristics of a Namurian deltaic succession II: gamma ray logging. *In*: WHATELEY, M. K. & PICKERING, K. T. (eds) *Deltas: Sites and Traps for Fossil Fuels*. Geological Society, London, Special Publications, **41**, 81–88.

NELSON, W. J. 1990*a*. Comment on 'Major Proterozoic basement features of the eastern mid-continent of North America revealed by recent COCORP profiling'. *Geology*, **18**, 378–379.

——1990*b*. Structural styles of the Illinois Basin. *In*: LEIGHTON, M. W., KOLATA, D. R., OLTZ, D. F. & EIDEL, J. J. (eds) *Interior Cratonic Basins. American Association of Petroleum Geologists Memoirs*, **51**, 209–243.

OLIVEIRA, J. T. 1990. Part VI: South Portuguese Zone; Chapter 2, Stratigraphy and synsedimentary tectonism. *In*: DALLMEYER, R. D. & MARTINEZ GARCIA, E. (eds) *Pre-Mesozoic Geology of Iberia*. Springer-Verlag, 334–347.

PIPER, D. J. W., DE-PIPER, G. & LONCAREVIC, B. D. 1993. Devonian–Carboniferous igneous intrusions and their deformation, Cobequid Highlands, Nova Scotia. *Atlantic Geology*, **29**, 219–232.

PORZYCKI, J. & ZDANOWSKI, A. 1995. Southeastern Poland (Lublin Carboniferous Basin). *In*: ZDANOWSKI, A. & ZAKOWA, H. (eds) *The Carboniferous System in Poland*. Polish Geological Institute, Warszawa, 100–102.

PULHAM, A. J. 1987. *Depositional and Syn-Sedimentary Deformation Processes in Namurian Deltaic sequences of West County Clare, Ireland*. PhD thesis, University of Wales, Swansea.

——1989. Controls on internal structure and architecture of sandstone bodies within Upper Carboniferous fluvial-dominated deltas, County Clare, Western Ireland. *In*: WHATELEY, M. K. G. & PICKERING, K. T. (eds) *Deltas: Sites and Traps for Fossils Fuels*. Geological Society, London, Special Publications, **41**, 179–203.

QUINLAN, G. M. & BEAUMONT, C. 1984. Appalachian thrusting, lithospheric flexure and the Paleozoic stratigraphy of the eastern interior of North America. *Canadian Journal of Earth Sciences*, **21**, 973–996.

RAMSBOTTOM, W. H. C. 1977. Major cycles of transgression and regression (mesothems) in the Namurian. *Proceedings of the Yorkshire Geological Society*, **41**, 261–291.

——, CALVER, M. A., EAGAR, R. M. C., HODSON, F., HOLLIDAY, D. W., STUBBLEFIELD, C. J. & WILSON, R. B. 1979. *A Correlation of Silesian Rocks in the British Isles*. The Geological Society, London.

RAYMOND, A., KELLEY, P. H. & LUTKEN, C. B. 1989. Polar glaciers and life at the equator: the history of Dinantian and Namurian (Carboniferous) climate. *Geology*, **17**, 408–411.

REHILL, T. A. 1996. *Late Carboniferous Nonmarine Sequence Stratigraphy and Petroleum Geology of the Central Maritimes Basin, Eastern Canada*. Unpublished PhD thesis, Dalhousie University, Halifax, NS.

RILEY, N. J., CLAOUÉ-LONG, J. C., HIGGINS, A. C., OWEN, B., SPEARS, A., TAYLOR, L. & VARKER, W. J. 1995. Geochronometry and geochemistry of the European mid-Carboniferous boundary global stratotype proposal, Stonehead Beck, North Yorkshire, UK. *Annales de la Société Géologique de Belgique*, **T116**, 275–289.

—— & TURNER., N. 1995. The correlation of mid-Westphalian marine bands between the central Appalachian Basin (USA) and the United Kingdom. *The XIII International Congress on the Carboniferous and Permian*, Krakow, Poland, 122.

RIPPON, J. H. 1996. Sand body orientation, palaeoslope analysis and basin-fill implications in the Westphalian A–C of Great Britain. *Journal of the Geological Society, London*, **153**, 881–900.

RITCHIE, J. S. & PRATSIDES, P. 1993. The Caister Fields, Block 44/23a, UK North Sea. *In*: PARKER, J. R. (eds) *Petroleum Geology of Northwest Europe: Proceedings of the 4th Conference*. The Geological Society, London, 759–769.

ROSS, C. A. & ROSS, J. R. P. 1985. Late Palaeozoic depositional sequences are synchronous and worldwide. *Geology*, **13**, 194–197.

RUST, B. R., GIBLING, M. R. & LEGUN, A. S. 1984. Coal deposition in an anastomosing fluvial system: the Pennsylvanian Cumberland Group south of Joggins, Nova Scotia, Canada. *In*: RAHOVEN, R. A. & FLORES, R. M. (eds) *Sedimentology of Coal and Coal-bearing Sequences*. International Association of Sedimentologists, *Special Publications*, **7**, 105–120.

RYAN, R. J., CALDER, J. H., DONOHOE, H. V. & NAYLOR, R. 1987. Late Paleozoic sedimentation and basin development adjacent to the Cobequid Highlands Massif, Eastern Canada. *In*: BEAUMONT, C. & TANKARD, A. J. (eds) *Sedimentary Basins and Basin-Forming Mechanisms*. Canadian Society of Petroleum Geologists Memoirs, **12**, 311–317.

SAUNDERS, W. B. & RAMSBOTTOM, W. H. C. 1986. The mid-Carboniferous eustatic event. *Geology* **14**, 208–212.

—— & ——1993. Re-evaluation of two early Pennsylvanian (middle Namurian) Ammonoids and their bearing on Mid-Carboniferous correlations. *Journal of Palaeontology*, **67**, 993–999.

SENGOR, A. M. C. 1995. Sedimentation and tectonics of fossil rifts. *In*: INGERSOLL, R. V. & BUSBY, C. J. (eds) *Tectonics of Sedimentary Basins*. Blackwells, 53–118.

SHANMUGAM, G. & MOIOLA, R. J. 1988. Submarine fans: characteristics, models, classification and reservoir potential. *Earth Science Reviews*, **24**, 383–428.

SHIRLEY, K. 1997. Headlines gone, but activity goes on; Oklahoma's Arkoma Basin remains busy. *American Association of Petroleum Geologists, Explorer*, **May**, 14–15.

SHRAKE, D. L. 1991. Pre-Mount Simon basin under the Cinncinati Arch. *Geology*, **19**, 139–142.

SIMS, A. D. 1988. *The Evolution of a Sand-Rich Basin Fill Sequence*. PhD thesis, University of Leeds.

STEVENSON, I. P. & GAUNT, G. D. 1971. *Memoir for geological sheet 99: Geology of the country around Chapel-en-le-Frith*. British Geological Survey: England and Wales.

TANKARD, A. H. 1986. On the depositional response to thrusting and lithospheric flexure: examples from the Appalachian and Rocky Mountain basins. *In*: ALLEN, P. A. & HOMEWOOD, P. (eds) *Foreland Basins*. International Association of Sedimentologists,-Special Publication, **8**, 369–362.

VEEVERS, J. J. & POWELL, C. M. 1987. Late Palaeozoic glacial episodes in Gondwanaland reflected in transgressive–regressive depositional sequences in Euramerica. *Bulletin of the Geological Society of America*, **98**, 475–487.

WALKER, R. G. 1966. Shale Grit and Grindslow Shales: transition from turbidite to shallow water sediments in the Upper Carboniferous of northern England. *Journal of Sedimentary Petrology*, **36**, 90–114.

WATERS, C. N., GLOVER, B. W. & POWELL, J. H. 1994. Structural synthesis of S Staffordshire, UK: implications for the Variscan evolution of the Pennine Basin. *Journal of the Geological Society, London*, **151**, 697–713.

——, AITKENHEAD, N., JONES, N. S. & CHISHOLM, J. I. 1996. Late Carboniferous stratigraphy and sedimentology of the Bradford area and its implications for the regional geology of Northern England. *Proceedings of the Yorkshire Geological Society*, **51**, 87–102.

WIGNALL, P. B. & MAYNARD., J. R. 1996. High-resolution sequence stratigraphy in the early Marsdenian (Namurian, Carboniferous) of the central Pennines and adjacent areas. *Proceedings of the Yorkshire Geological Society*, **51**, 127–140.

WILLARD, G. A. & KLEIN, G. D. 1990. Tectonic subsidence history of the central Appalachian basin and its influence on Pennsylvanian coal deposition. *Southeastern Geology*, **30**, 217–239.

ZIEGLER, P. A. 1989. *Evolution of Laurussia: A Study in Late Palaeozoic Plate Tectonics*. Kluwer Academic Press, Dordrecht.

Incised valley fill sandstone bodies in Upper Carboniferous fluvio–deltaic strata: recognition and reservoir characterization of Southern North Sea analogues

G. J. HAMPSON,[1,2], S. J. DAVIES,[1,3] T. ELLIOTT,[1] S. S. FLINT and H. STOLLHOFEN[4]

[1] *STRAT Group, Department of Earth Sciences, University of Liverpool, Liverpool, UK*
[2] *Present address: T. H. Huxley School of Environment, Earth Science and Engineering, Imperial College, London, UK*
[3] *Present address: Department of Geology, University of Leicester, University Road, Leicester LE1 7RH, UK*
[4] *Institut für Geologie, Universität Würzburg, Germany*

Abstract: Multistorey fluvial sandstone bodies in Upper Carboniferous fluvio–deltaic strata are proven reservoirs in the Southern North Sea. Several of these bodies have been interpreted as incised valley fills. Analogous valley fill sandstone bodies have been studied in outcrop and subsurface datasets from Upper Carboniferous successions in the onshore UK and Germany. Using techniques and tools applicable to Southern North Sea datasets, we review the diagnostic criteria of these valley fills: (1) stratigraphic context, characterized by deep erosion into underlying strata, lateral correlation to an interfluve surface and intimate association with an initial flooding surface in overlying strata; (2) basinward facies shift at the base of the sandstone body; (3) erosion of underlying time markers; and (4) distinctive internal architecture, which reflects increasing accommodation space during valley filling.

Several features of onshore valley fill sandstones have been characterized in order to constrain the properties of analogous valley fill reservoirs in the Southern North Sea. (1) Valley geometry and extent. Studied onshore valley fills generally have a uniform thickness of 20–25 m, thickening locally to 30–45 m, and widths of 5–25 km. A small number of valley fills, associated with turbidite-fronted deltas, thicken to 50–80m in the 2–5 km adjacent to their mouths. Sheet-like fluvial sandstones overlying sequence boundaries have thicknesses comparable to conventional valley fills, but exceed 35–70 km in width. (2) Valley connectivity; typically, valley fills occur as discrete sandstone bodies, but they may amalgamate laterally, to form sheet-like sandstones, and vertically, producing thick (up to 200 m) sand-prone stratigraphic packages. The internal geometry of these sand-prone packages is complex. (3) Valley fill character. Valley fills generally lack an overall fining-upwards trend and are dominated by coarse- to medium-grained sandstone of low-sinuosity (braided?) fluvial facies throughout. Where present, fine-grained facies are preferentially preserved in the upper part of a valley fill. (4) Detrital mineralogy and provenance. At least some valley fill sandstones exhibit a different composition and provenance to surrounding strata. Such valley fill sandstones are likely to be anomalously feldspathic in the Southern North Sea.

During the last 15 years, considerable gas reserves have been discovered in Upper Carboniferous rocks in the Southern North Sea (Besly 1998). The main reservoirs in this succession are multistorey fluvial sandstone bodies. The correlation and distribution of these sandstone bodies have presented persistent exploration problems (Besly 1998). In recent years these issues have been addressed with some success using sequence stratigraphy. Correlation in Upper Carboniferous strata relies on the identification and characterization of condensed, highly fossiliferous shale layers, referred to as marine bands, which can be characterized in the subsurface using a combination of geochemistry, spectral gamma-ray logging and conventional biostratigraphic techniques (Leeder *et al.* 1990; Hollywood & Whorlow 1993). However, Upper Carboniferous stratigraphy may be resolved at a finer scale by the application of sequence stratigraphy, which provides a template for the recognition and correlation of additional transgressive surfaces and widespread surfaces of erosion and emergence (sequence boundaries) in between the marine bands (e.g. Church & Gawthorpe 1994; Davies & Elliott 1996; Hampson *et al.* 1997). The resulting improvement in stratigraphic resolution has aided correlation at both exploration and production scales (e.g. Quirk 1993; Ritchie & Pratsides 1993), but further application of sequence stratigraphy as a tool for reservoir characterization has been largely under-utilized. Major erosively-based sandstone bodies within Upper Carboniferous fluvio–deltaic strata have traditionally been interpreted as the deposits of fluvial systems that were an integral part of the depositional system, for example as distributary channels in a delta system (e.g. Elliott 1976, Haszeldine & Anderton 1980; Pulham 1989). More recently, some of these sandstone bodies have been re-interpreted to lie within incised fluvial valleys at sequence boundaries (Ritchie & Pratsides 1993; O'Mara *et al.* 1999). These two contrasting interpretations imply significant differences in sandstone body character, which may determine their behaviour as hydrocarbon reservoirs.

The character of multistorey fluvial sandstone reservoirs in the Upper Carboniferous of the Southern North Sea is strongly influenced by primary depositional factors, which can be addressed using sequence stratigraphy. Case histories from several fields have highlighted these factors and associated production issues:

(1) The extent, thickness and connectivity of multistorey fluvial sandstone reservoirs varies between fields and laterally within a single field (e.g. the Trent Field, O'Mara *et al.* 1999). This variability reflects the valley fill or non-valley fill origin of such bodies and, in the case of the former, the three dimensional morphology of the valley system.
(2) Multistorey fluvial sandstone reservoirs generally exhibit little internal variation in net : gross and reservoir quality (e.g. the Caister and Murdoch sandstones; Ritchie &

HAMPSON, G. J., DAVIES, S. J., ELLIOTT, T., FLINT, S. S. & STOLLHOFEN, H. 1999. Incised valley fill sandstone bodies in Upper Carboniferous fluvio–deltaic strata: recognition and reservoir characterization of Southern North Sea analogues. *In*: FLEET, A. J. & BOLDY, S. A. R. (eds) *Petroleum Geology of Northwest Europe: Proceedings of the 5th Conference*, 771–788.

Pratsides 1993, McLean & Murray 1996). However, facies heterogeneity does compartmentalize the Trent Sandstone reservoir, in which the facies architecture displays an incised valley fill signature (O'Mara *et al.* 1999).

(3) Reservoir quality in multistorey fluvial sandstone reservoirs reflects a complicated diagenetic history, with the result that virtually all observed porosity is secondary in origin (Cowan 1989, Leeder & Hardman 1990). Despite this, the generation and retention of secondary porosity is partly controlled by grain size and detrital mineralogy (Hawkins 1978; Cowan 1989). In particular, feldspar degradation to kaolinite during early burial may result in low porosity and permeability in some reservoirs (e.g. the lower Trent Sandstone; O'Mara *et al.* 1999). Such variations in detrital mineralogy reflect an allocyclic control(s) on provenance.

The aims of this paper are threefold: (1) to briefly review criteria for recognizing incised valley fill deposits in Upper Carboniferous fluvio–deltaic strata; (2) to describe and interpret the character and variability of incised valley fill sandstones documented in the onshore Upper Carboniferous succession; and (3) to use these complexes as analogues in addressing reservoir characterization issues in the Southern North Sea.

Geological setting

During Upper Carboniferous times, the Southern North Sea formed part of a vast depositional area which covered large parts of North America and northwest Europe (Fig. 1). This depositional area was created by foreland loading by the southward-lying Variscan mountain chain, combined with a component of extensional, intracratonic rifting and thermal sag (Leeder 1988). In detail, the depositional area comprised a number of interconnected basins with different subsidence rates and sediment thicknesses (Fig. 1). In the context of adjoining

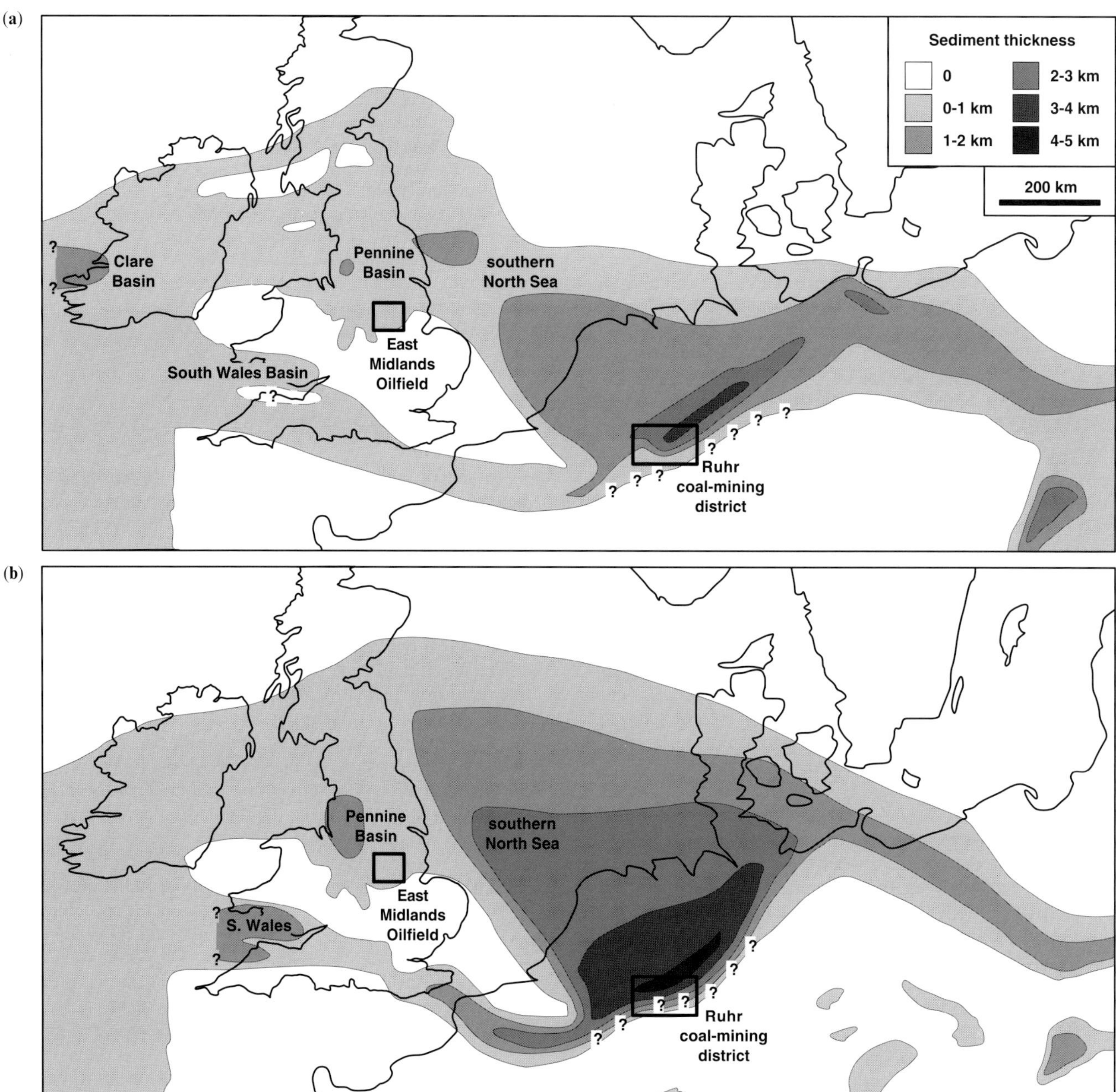

Fig. 1. Isopach maps of the Variscan depositional area in northwest Europe during (**a**) the Namurian and (**b**) the Westphalian, compiled from Calver (1969), Thomas (1974), Guion & Fielding (1988), Leeder & Hardman (1990), Drozdzewski (1993) and Quirk & Aitken (1997). The Southern North Sea and study areas discussed in this paper are shown.

areas, the Southern North Sea subsided at an intermediate rate, higher than the East Midlands and Pennine Basin and lower than the Ruhr District, northwest Germany (Fig. 1).

Climate within the Variscan depositional area remained uniform throughout Namurian and Westphalian A–B times, as western Europe lay within a broad non-seasonal, humid, equatorial climatic belt (e.g. Leeder 1988). However, the climate became more arid during the late Westphalian, as recorded by the occurrence of primary red beds in many basins.

Basins in the Variscan depositional area are traditionally regarded as freshwater, with the marine bands recording episodic connection to an open ocean during sea-level highstands (e.g. Holdsworth & Collinson 1988; Martinsen *et al.* 1995). However, the issues of basin salinity and geographical proximity to the co-eval marine ocean remain somewhat contentious (e.g. Hampson *et al.* 1997). For example, the Southern North Sea succession contains clear evidence for tidal activity (e.g. O'Mara *et al.* 1999), which is generally absent in adjoining onshore areas, including the Pennine Basin and the Ruhr District. This evidence suggests that the Southern North Sea probably occupied a more seaward position.

Despite differences in tectonic subsidence and proximity to the co-eval ocean, each of the basins in the Variscan depositional area exhibits a similar fill succession (Collinson 1988, Fig. 2). The earliest basin fill comprises deep water mudstones which are thickest in the basin depocentre. Sandstone deposition first occurred within a turbidite-fronted delta succession, which infilled the inherited bathymetry within a particular basin or sub-basin. Overlying deposits comprise sheet deltas which reflect the establishment of widespread shallow water conditions. These basin fill components contain numerous marine bands and together comprise the Millstone Grit (Fig. 2). Shallow water deltas in the Millstone Grit grade upwards into the Coal Measures, which comprise delta plain deposits containing abundant coal seams and few marine bands (Fig. 2). Coal seams are less common in the Upper Coal Measures (Westphalian C/D). Within the southern part of the Variscan depositional area (e.g. in South Wales and the Ruhr District) there is a relatively abrupt change to a more alluvial depositional style around the Westphalian B/C boundary. The Upper Coal Measures here are dominated by lithic sandstones derived from the southward-lying Variscan thrust front (e.g. Heard 1922; Frank *et al.* 1992).

In this paper we consider multistorey fluvial complexes within turbidite-fronted deltas, sheet deltas and delta plain deposits in the Namurian and Westphalian A successions of the onshore UK and Germany. Specific complexes are taken from outcrop exposures in South Wales (the Farewell Rock) and northern England (the Lower Kinderscout Grit and Rough Rock) and subsurface datasets from the East Midlands oil field (the Rough Rock and Crawshaw Sandstone) and the coal mining area of the Ruhr District, northwest Germany (the Westphalian A Coal Measures, including the Präsident Sandstone and 'Albert 3 Sandstone').

Multistorey fluvial complexes and incised valley fills

Thick, sandstone-dominated, multistorey fluvial complexes are common in the Upper Carboniferous strata of northwest Europe and North America. Traditionally these complexes have been regarded as an integral part of the depositional system represented by surrounding deposits. In this interpretation, channel members were stacked to form multistorey bodies as a result of autocyclic channel avulsion or river channel aggradation. The laterally restricted character of some multistorey complexes suggests that river channel-belts were confined by an additional feature, such as active faults (e.g. Fielding 1984) or thick, cohesive peat deposits (e.g. Guion *et al.* 1995). Local thickening of major fluvial complexes has been attributed to deep local scouring (e.g. Rippon 1996). Laterally extensive, sheet-like multistorey complexes suggest fluvial deposition in wider, non-confined channel-belts, possibly fluvial braidplains (e.g. Bristow 1988, 1993). Although each of the above mechanisms for producing thick, multistorey sandstone bodies implies a subtly different fluvial architecture, they all infer that the fluvial sandstones are genetically linked to lateral and underlying deposits.

In recent years, many of the multistorey fluvial complexes have been re-evaluated as the fill deposits of incised fluvial valleys cut in response to a relative fall in sea-level (Maynard 1992; Aitken & Flint 1994; Church & Gawthorpe 1994; Davies & Elliott 1996; Hampson *et al.* 1996, 1997; Jones & Chisholm 1997). The base of such a valley represents an unconformity of widespread extent across which there is no genetic link in facies, termed a sequence boundary. Incised valleys form when rivers erode down to a lowered base level, produced as relative

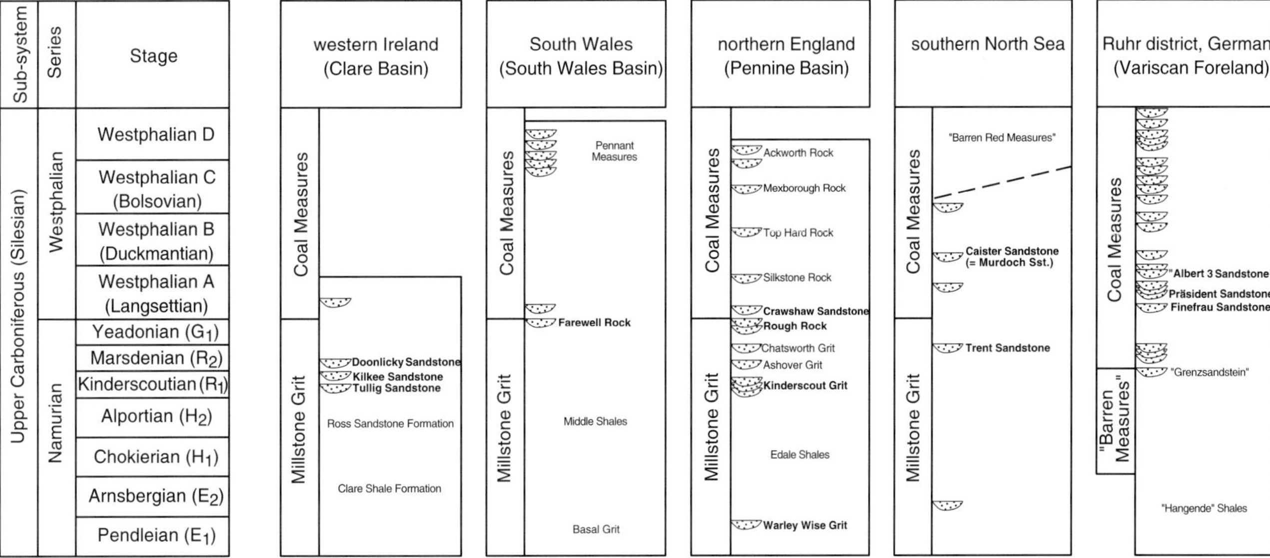

Fig. 2. Schematic lithostratigraphic columns through the Upper Carboniferous basin fill successions in western Ireland, South Wales, northern England, the Southern North Sea and the Ruhr District, northwest Germany, showing major fluvial sandstone complexes. Complexes discussed in this paper are highlighted in bold type.

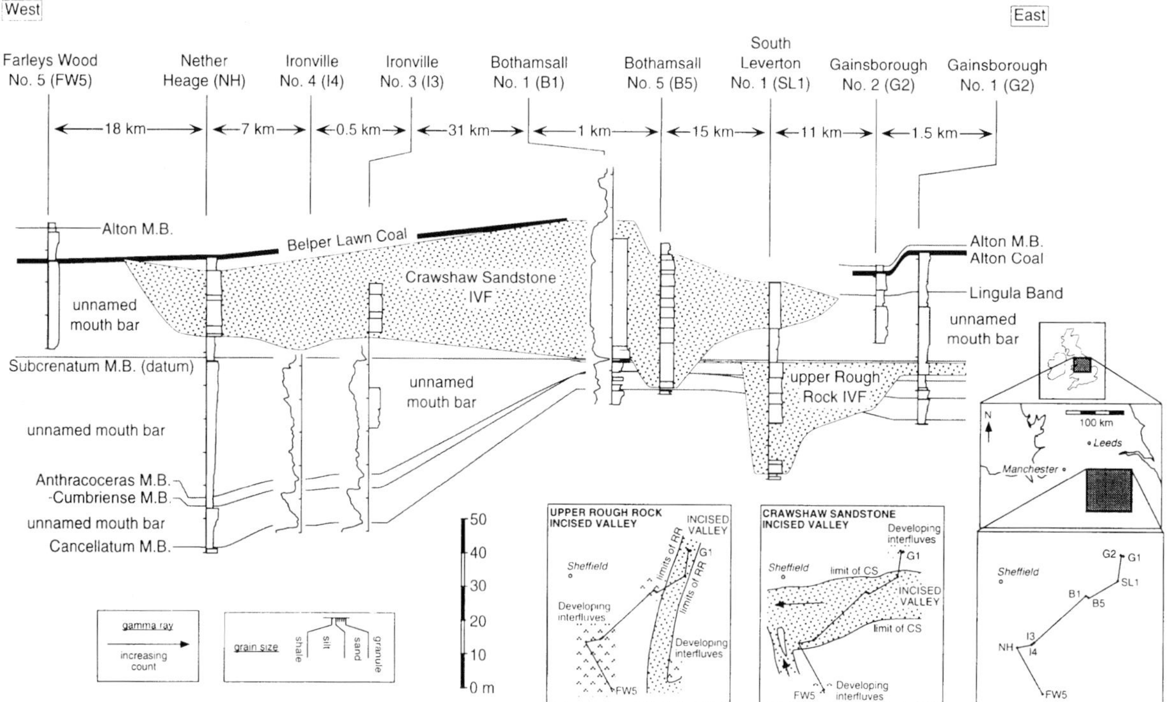

Fig. 3. Depositional strike cross-section through the Rough Rock Group and lowermost Coal Measures on the East Midlands Shelf bordering the Pennine Basin, northern England. The erosional bases of the Crawshaw Sandstone and upper Rough Rock incised-valley fills remove several marine bands. Gamma-ray logs and grain size profiles are shown to the left and right of logged sections, respectively. The locations of the correlation panel, logged sections and mean palaeocurrents are shown on the inset maps. Additional palaeogeographical data shown on these maps are taken from Church & Gawthorpe (1994) for the Rough Rock and Guion & Fielding (1988) for the Crawshaw Sandstone.

Fig. 4. Multistorey fluvial sandstone complex exposed in the Rauen–Witten Quarry, Ruhr District, northwest Germany. Concave-upwards erosion surfaces within the complex define the base of individual channel fill storeys. The complex has large (*c.* 6 m) basal erosional relief and lies directly on the Hinnebeck (Sigma) Marine Band, demonstrating an abrupt shallowing in water depth associated with a basinward shift in facies. The complex is approximately 30 m thick.

sea-level falls (Posamentier & Vail 1988), and they are cut by the headward (up-dip) migration of a knick-point from the break in slope at the exposed highstand shoreline (Koss *et al.* 1994; Leeder & Stewart 1996). Such valleys are generally cut only by large, high-discharge rivers (Berryhill *et al.* 1987; Leeder & Stewart 1996). Incised valleys are filled as base level rises, reflecting a relative rise in sea-level (Posamentier & Vail 1988).

Recognition of incised valley fills

Four criteria enable incised valley fills to be distinguished from multistorey fluvial complexes produced by other mechanisms in Upper Carboniferous strata. These criteria are described briefly below, and readers are referred to Hampson *et al.* (1997) for a fuller discussion.

(1) Stratigraphic context. The base of an incised valley is a regionally extensive, high-relief erosional surface that correlates laterally to an interfluve, a terrace-like, hiatal surface that formed beyond the valley margins (e.g. the Rough Rock and Crawshaw Sandstone, Fig. 3). The extent and relief of the valley erosion surface are more widespread than the erosional bases of individual channels within the valley (e.g. Fig. 4). Also, the valley erosion surface corresponds to an overlying trangressive flooding surface (the initial flooding surface), which may be represented by a regionally extensive coal seam in landward areas (e.g. the Belper Lawn Coal, Fig. 3; Aitken 1994, Hampson *et al.* 1996).

(2) Basinward facies shift. Facies associations in the valley fill differ radically from the underlying associations, reflecting a 'basinward shift in facies' as the fluvial system was forced into the basin during a sea-level fall. This facies shift may be accompanied by evidence for an abrupt shallowing of water depth (e.g. Fig. 4) and/or an increase in fluvial gradient, in response to a lowered fluvial base level. Typically, channel fill members within the valley fill are distinct in grain size, scale and overall facies character from deposits preserved beneath and between the valleys.

(3) Missing time markers. Erosion at the base of an incised valley may remove preceding systems tracts and marine bands (e.g. the Rough Rock and Crawshaw Sandstone; Fig. 3), thereby producing a recognizable time-gap. These strata are preserved beneath valley interfluves.

(4) Internal architecture. Incised valleys have a distinctive internal architecture, which records a trend of increasing accommodation space as relative sea-level rose during valley infilling. Increasing accommodation space may be evident from increasing preservation of channel fill and fine-grained members upwards (e.g. the Farewell Rock; Fig. 5), or changes in the character of the fluvial system (e.g. from low to high sinuosity, or an increase in tidal influence). This trend culminates in the initial flooding surface, which forms when sediment flux is outpaced by the rate of accommodation space increase.

Characteristics of Upper Carboniferous incised valley fill complexes in onshore areas

Comparison of documented Upper Carboniferous incised valley fill sandstones reveals considerable variation in their extent, geometry and connectivity (e.g. Davies *et al.* 1999). This variability is discussed below and summarized in Fig. 6. In contrast, the fill style of the incised valleys is relatively uniform (Hampson *et al.* 1997).

Valley extent and geometry

High magnitude erosional relief at the base of a valley is most clearly evident where an interfluve palaeosol occurs at one or both margins of a complex and a regionally extensive coal seam or transgressive surface overlies both the correlative palaeosol and the complex (e.g. the Rough Rock and Crawshaw Sandstone; Fig. 3; see also Church & Gawthorpe 1994). These valley fill sandstone bodies have a mean thickness of 20–25 m over much of their extent, with a maximum thickness of 30–45 m locally (Fig. 6). The width of such sandstones is more variable (5–25 km; Fig. 6), giving rise to width-to-maximum depth ratios of between 1:150 and 1:625. These width and thickness values lie comfortably within the range of such data for incised valleys as a whole (Reynolds 1996), in contrast to the discrete, isolated fluvial channels and mouth bars occurring beneath incised valleys, which are up to 15 m thick and vary from several hundred metres to 2–3 km in width (Elliott & Davies 1994; Hampson *et al.* 1997). In subsurface data from the Westphalian A Coal Measures of northwest Germany, valley fill sandstones can be mapped as linear features with a relatively uniform thickness (*c.* 20–25 m), steep sides and flat bases (e.g. the 'Albert 3 Sandstone', Fig. 7). The flat-based character of such valley fills is often evident at the local scale of a single outcrop, although localized areas of deep (30–45 m) erosional scour are observed adjacent to valley margins and at points where valley fill sandstones amalgamate laterally (e.g. the 'Albert 3 Sandstone'; Fig. 7). By analogy with modern river valleys, the former are interpreted as deep scour pools caused by lateral flow constriction against valley margins (e.g. Schumm & Etheridge 1994), while the latter may represent scour pools at valley confluences (e.g. Best 1988; Bristow *et al.* 1993).

In a few cases, valley fill sandstones thicken considerably from 20–30 m to 50–80 m over a distance of *c.* 2–5 km, towards, and immediately up-stream of, the mouth of the valley (e.g. the Lower Kinderscout Grit; Fig. 8; Hampson 1997; see also the Roaches/Ashover Grit, Jones & Chisholm 1997). These deep, basinward portions of the valleys are infilled by giant (10–40 m thick), downcurrent-thickening foresets of lobate geometry (giant foresets *sensu* Hampson 1997) which are interpreted as the deposits of either side-attached fluvial bars (McCabe 1977, Jones & Chisholm 1997) or Gilbert-type deltas (Collinson 1968; Hampson 1997). To date, such valleys have been documented only within the context of turbidite-fronted deltas with steep submarine slopes. Each valley is inferred to have eroded up-stream from the top of the submarine slope (Jones & Chisholm 1997). We speculate that the steep gradient at the top of the submarine slope may have facilitated the headward, upstream erosion of anomalously deep incised valleys during periods of sea-level fall.

Extensive sheet-like sandstone bodies are documented at some stratigraphic levels. These bodies are similar in mean and maximum thickness to the valley fills described above (10–30m and 20–45 m, respectively), but exceed 35–70 km in width (Fig. 6). Their width-to-maximum depth ratios exceed 1:1000. In some cases, these sheet-like bodies erode through underlying marine bands and correlate laterally to interfluve palaeosols, demonstrating a valley fill origin (e.g. the Farewell Rock; Fig. 9). In other cases, where data density is sufficiently high to allow detailed mapping of such bodies, they comprise several, steep-walled and flat-based bodies which are laterally amalgamated, rather than a single sheet (e.g. the Präsident Sandstone; Fig. 10). This morphology appears to define several coalesced river valley networks which dissect a single floodplain surface. Exceptionally deep erosional scour (30–45 m) is observed locally in discrete patches scattered throughout such sheet-like valley fill complexes (e.g the Präsident Sandstone; Fig. 10) and these patches may represent valley confluence

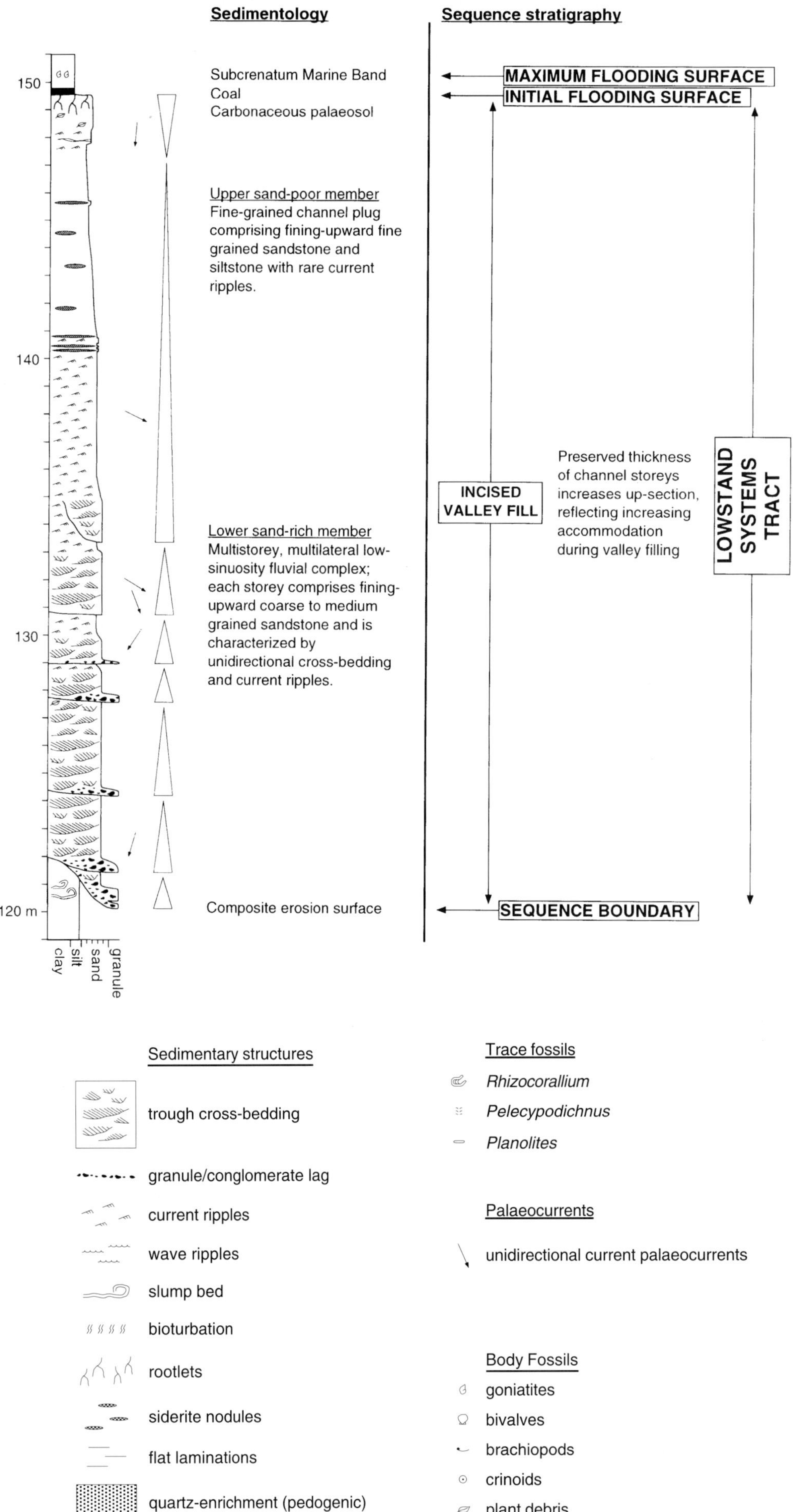

Fig. 5. Detailed sedimentary log through the Farewell Rock at Amroth, South Wales showing sedimentology, mean palaeocurrents, facies and sequence stratigraphic interpretations. Fining-upward fluvial successions, denoted by triangles, are interpreted as preserved remnants of channel-fill members.

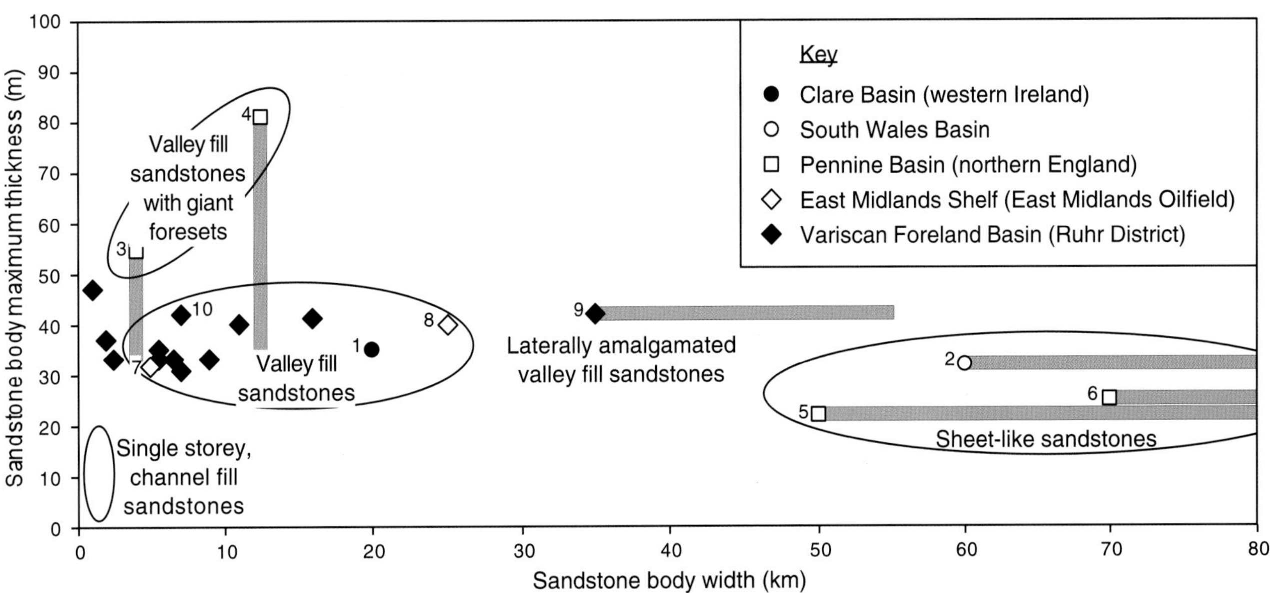

Fig. 6. Width versus maximum depth for studied multistorey fluvial sandstone bodies in onshore successions. Sandstone bodies are coded according to palaeogeographical location. Three distinct fields are recognized: valley fill sandstones, valley fill sandstones with giant foresets and sheet-like sandstones. Valley fill sandstones with giant foresets thicken considerably near their mouths. This down-dip thickening is represented within a grey bar for each data point. Measured widths for sheet-like sandstones are minimum values, and larger potential widths are represented by grey bars. Individual sandstone bodies referred to in the text are numbered as followed: 1 = Kilkee Sandstone, 2 = Farewell Rock, 3 = Lower Kinderscout Grit body LKG8, 4 = Ashover/Roaches Grit (after Jones & Chisholm 1997), 5 = lower leaf of the Rough Rock, 6 = upper leaf of the Rough Rock, 7 = Rough Rock, 8 = Crawshaw Sandstone, 9 = Präsident Sandstone, 10 = 'Albert 3 Sandstone'.

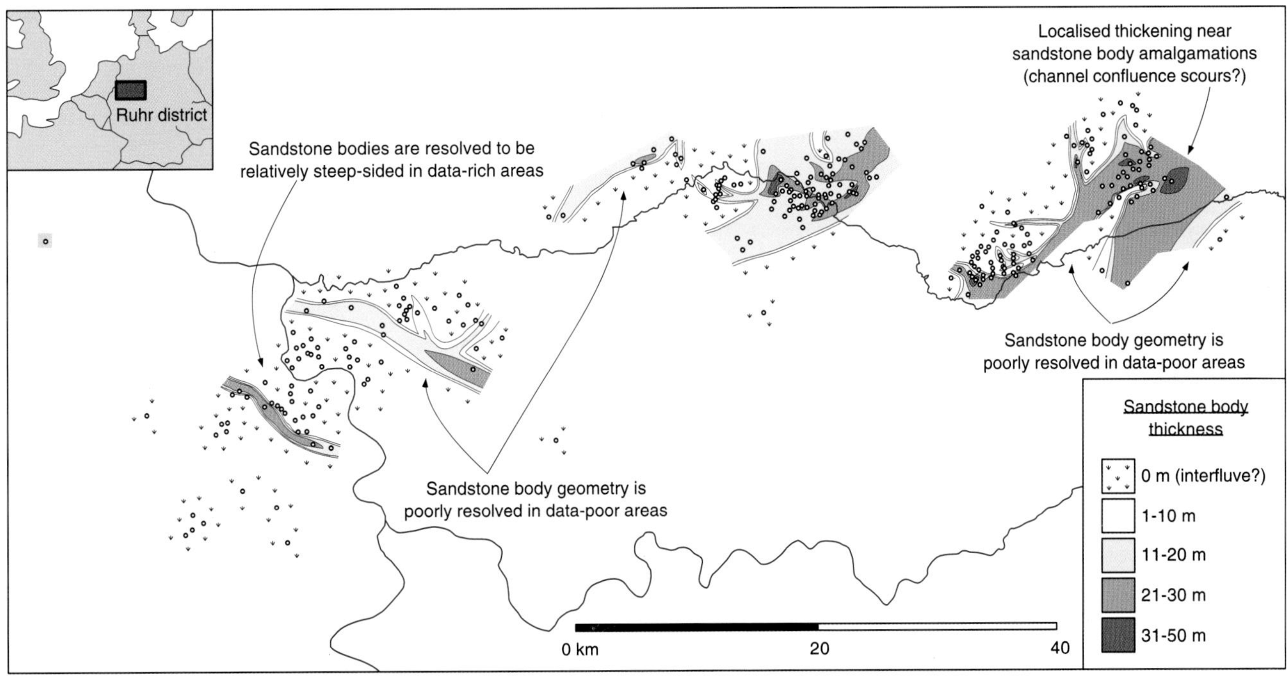

Fig. 7. Isopach map of the valley fill sandstone complex below the Albert 3 Seam in the Ruhr District, northwest Germany (here termed the 'Albert 3 Sandstone'). Data points are cored exploration boreholes for coal-mining, which are shown as open circles. The complex erodes into a widespread marine delta front succession throughout the mapped area. Regional palaeoslope was towards the northwest. Note the occurrence of deep (>30 m), localized erosional scours adjacent to valley margins and near valley confluences.

scour pools in a fluvial braidplain. Where the margins and internal thickness variations of a sheet-like body are more poorly defined, a valley fill interpretation is more problematic (e.g. see conflicting interpretations of the Rough Rock, central Pennines, in Bristow 1988; Maynard 1992; Hampson *et al.* 1996). Nevertheless, sheet-like bodies of non-valley origin generally occur above sequence boundaries and record slowly increasing accommodation space (Davies *et al.* 1999). Such sheet-like bodies may represent fluvial braidplains formed as a result of a relative sea-level fall.

Valley connectivity

As discussed earlier, there is evidence from their lateral thickness variations and geometries that some sheet-like sandstones may represent several, laterally amalgamated valley fill networks (e.g. the Präsident Sandstone; Fig. 10). The connectivity of discrete valley fill bodies is high in such stratigraphic intervals. However, valley fill networks developed at different stratigraphic levels are rarely amalgamated vertically, despite deep erosion into underlying strata at their bases (e.g. the

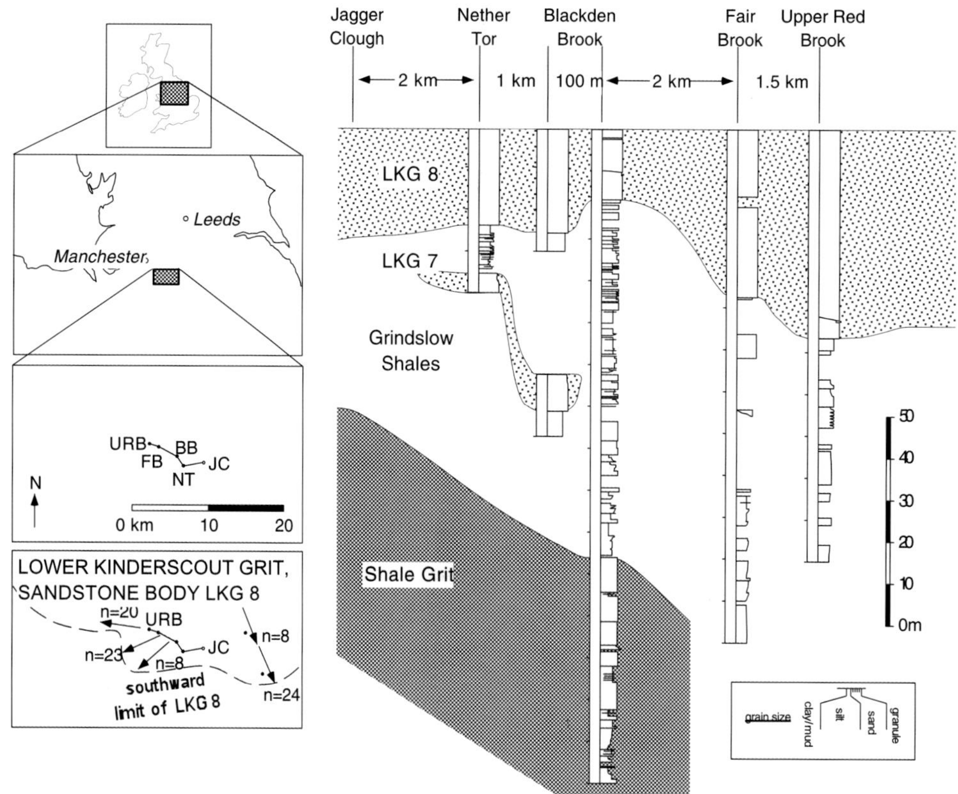

Fig. 8. Depositional dip cross-section through the Lower Kinderscout Grit in the Edale Gulf, Pennine Basin. This correlation framework is based on logged sections combined with a re-interpretation of sections described in BGS Memoirs (Stevenson & Gaunt 1970). Sandstone body LKG 8 is of Gilbert-type delta origin (Collinson 1968; Hampson 1997) and thickens to the west, down depositional dip. The nature of sandstone body LKG7 is unclear. The Grindslow Shales represent a submarine slope association, while the Shale Grit comprise deep water turbidite sandstones (Collinson 1969). The locations of the correlation panel, selected logged sections and mean palaeocurrents are shown on the inset map. Key and abbreviations as for Fig. 3.

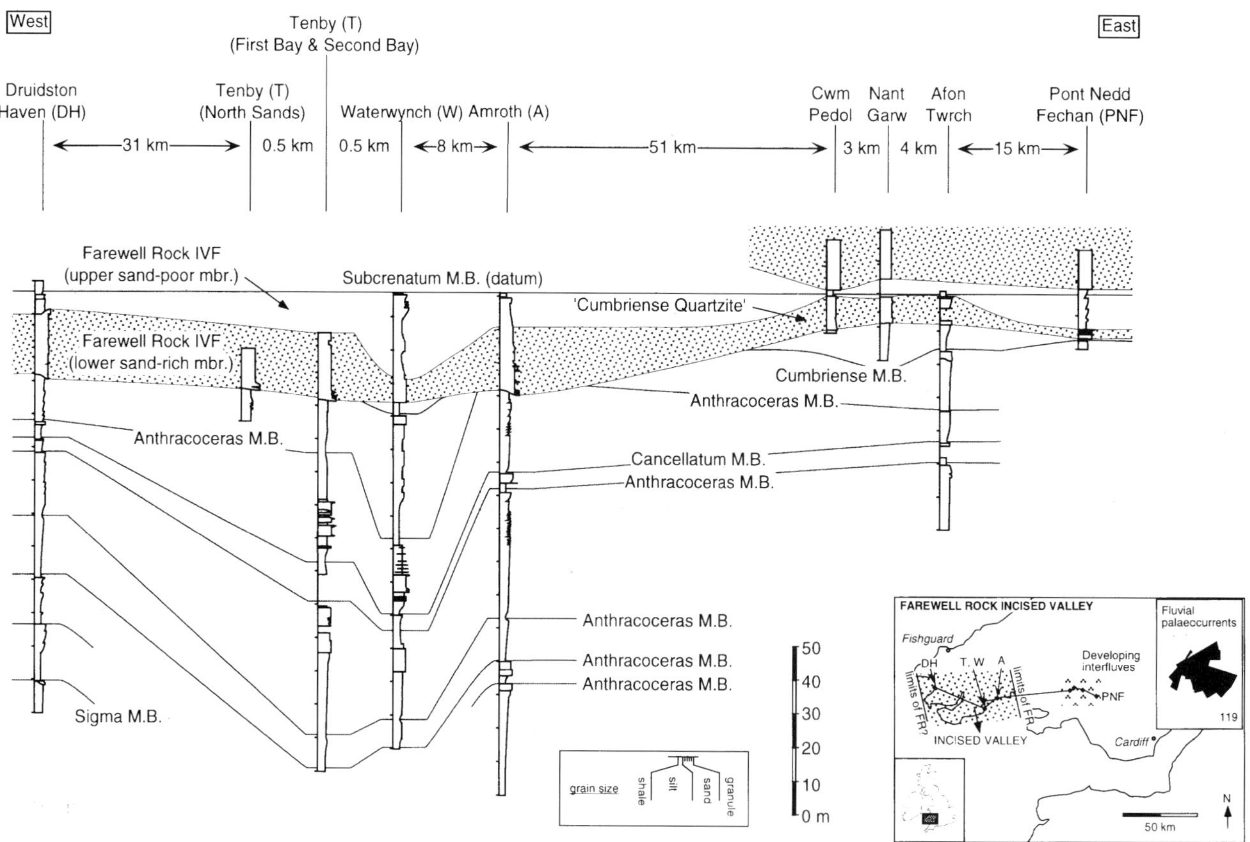

Fig. 9. Depositional strike cross-section through the Farewell Rock and underlying strata ('Middle Shales') in South Wales. The erosional base of the Farewell Rock incised valley fill is associated with an angular unconformity which removes the Cumbriense and Anthracoceras Marine Bands. The Farewell Rock incised valley fill comprises a lower sand-rich member and an upper sand-poor member (see text for details). The locations of the correlation panel, selected logged sections (including the Amroth section shown in Fig. 5) and mean palaeocurrents are shown on the inset map. Key and abbreviations as for Fig. 3.

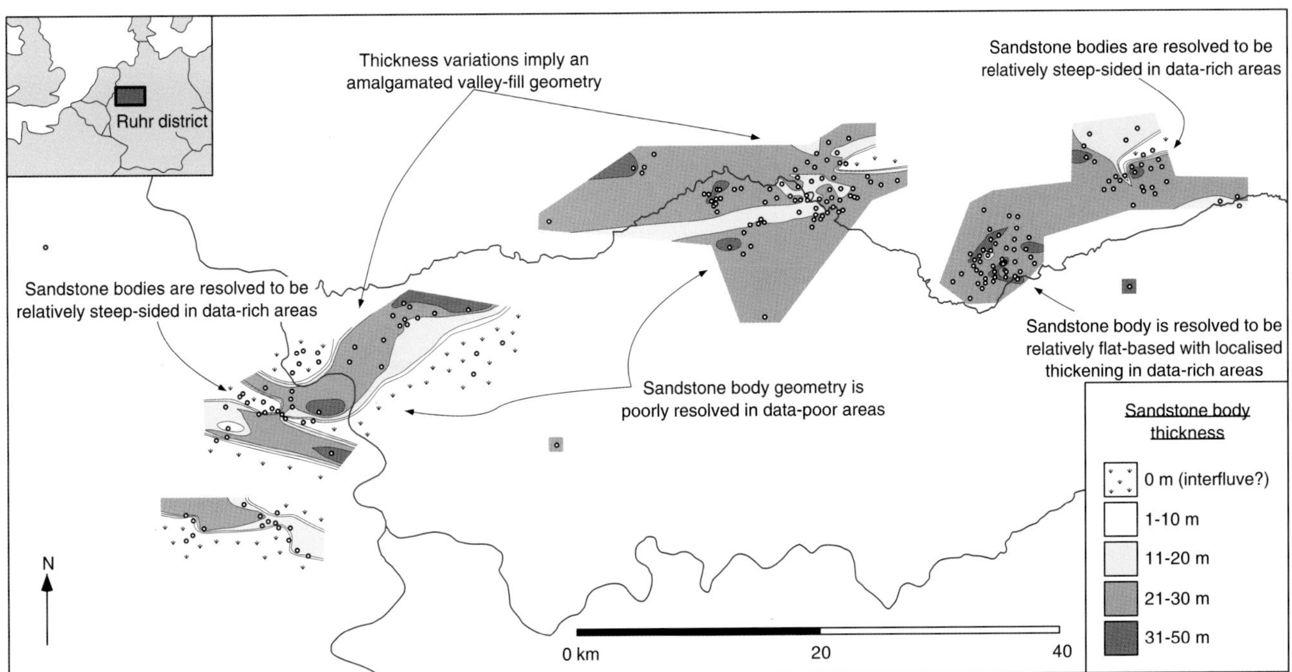

Fig. 10. Isopach map of the Präsident Sandstone sheet-like fluvial sandstone complex, which lies below the Johann Seam in the Ruhr District, northwest Germany. Data points are cored exploration boreholes for coal mining, which are shown as open circles. The fluvial complex erodes into a widespread lacustrine delta front succession throughout the mapped area. Regional palaeoslope was towards the northwest. Note that deep (>30 m), localized erosional scours appear to be scattered throughout the extent of the complex.

Rough Rock and Crawshaw Sandstone, Fig. 3). This poor vertical connectivity is even noted in strata dominated by valley fill sandstones (e.g. the middle Bochum Measures (Upper Westphalian A), central Ruhr District, Fig. 11). Where observed, vertical amalgamation of different valley fill bodies is attributed to deep local erosion. The greatest degree of vertical amalgamation is observed in the Kinderscout Grit, which forms a pebbly, sandstone-dominated interval up to 250 m thick in northern England. This interval contains at least three incised valley networks developed at different stratigraphic levels (the Upper Kinderscout Grit and Lower Kinderscout Grit bodies LKG6 and LKG8 in Fig. 12; Hampson 1997). The lowest two valleys (LKG6 and LKG8) are characterized by deep local erosional scours, particularly near the valley mouths (e.g. Fig. 8), and their infill successions contain giant (*c.* 10 m thick) cross-beds of fluvial and Gilbert-type deltaic origin (Collinson 1968; McCabe 1977; Hampson 1997). Over much of their extent, valley fill sandstones in the Kinderscout Grit are separated by mudstone-dominated, coal-bearing intervals, some containing marine bands (Fig. 12). However, local thickening and amalgamation of the valley fill sandstones, combined with erosion into underlying sandstone bodies, greatly complicates sandstone body geometries and connectivities, such that the Kinderscout Grit may locally comprise a single sandstone body over 200 m thick (e.g. at Torside Clough in Fig. 12).

Valley fill character

Documented Upper Carboniferous incised valley fills are invariably sandstone-dominated throughout, as are sheet-like sandstones. Each has a multistorey character, comprising several, vertically and laterally stacked channel-fill bodies with erosive bases. Individual channel-fill bodies average 6–10 m thickness, but may be up to 15 m thick (Hampson *et al.* 1997) or 30 m thick, where giant cross-beds are present (e.g. the Lower Kinderscout Grit; McCabe 1977; Hampson 1997).

Individual channel fill successions are dominated by unidirectional, current-produced structures. Typically, these comprise decimetre- to metre-scale trough and/or tabular cross-beds that grade upwards into current-ripple cross-lamination. The base of each storey is defined by a prominent erosion surface which cuts into, and commonly through, current-ripple cross-laminated facies at the top of the underlying channel fill succession, resulting in erosional amalgamation of channel fill successions (Fig. 5). Lateral accretion surfaces are rare, but some channel fill members contain downcurrent-dipping cross-strata which are interpreted to represent dune migration down the lee side of in-channel bar macroforms (e.g. Bristow 1988, 1993). The scarcity of lateral accretion surfaces and occasional presence of in-channel macroforms implies that each channel fill member was deposited in a low sinuosity channel that was possibly braided at low river stage. A few fluvial complexes (e.g. the Lower Kinderscout Grit) contain channel fill members with giant (*c.* 10 m thick) cross-beds with complex internal architectures which are localized in extent ('giant cross-beds' *sensu* Hampson 1997). These cross-beds are interpreted as deep fluvial scour-and-fill structures (McCabe 1977; Hampson 1997). Giant cross-beds with simpler, Gilbert-style geometries ('giant foresets' *sensu* Hampson 1997) occur exclusively at valley mouths and are interpreted as coarse-grained deltas (Collinson 1968, Hampson 1997).

The preserved thickness of individual channel fill bodies generally increases upwards within each valley fill complex (Fig. 5), suggesting that valleys were infilled as accommodation space gradually increased during the early stages of relative sea-level rise (Hampson *et al.* 1997). Despite this motif of increasing accommodation space, the complexes commonly lack an overall fining upwards trend (e.g. the Präsident Sandstone; Fig. 13). Fine-grained facies comprising channel margin, channel plug or in-channel bank failure deposits are restricted to locally preserved lenses which rarely exceed more than a few tens of metres laterally (e.g. Pulham 1989). Overbank or floodplain deposits have generally not been recognized in those valley fill complexes studied, implying that they had a low preservation potential as channels switched location within the complex. Consequently, the sandstone

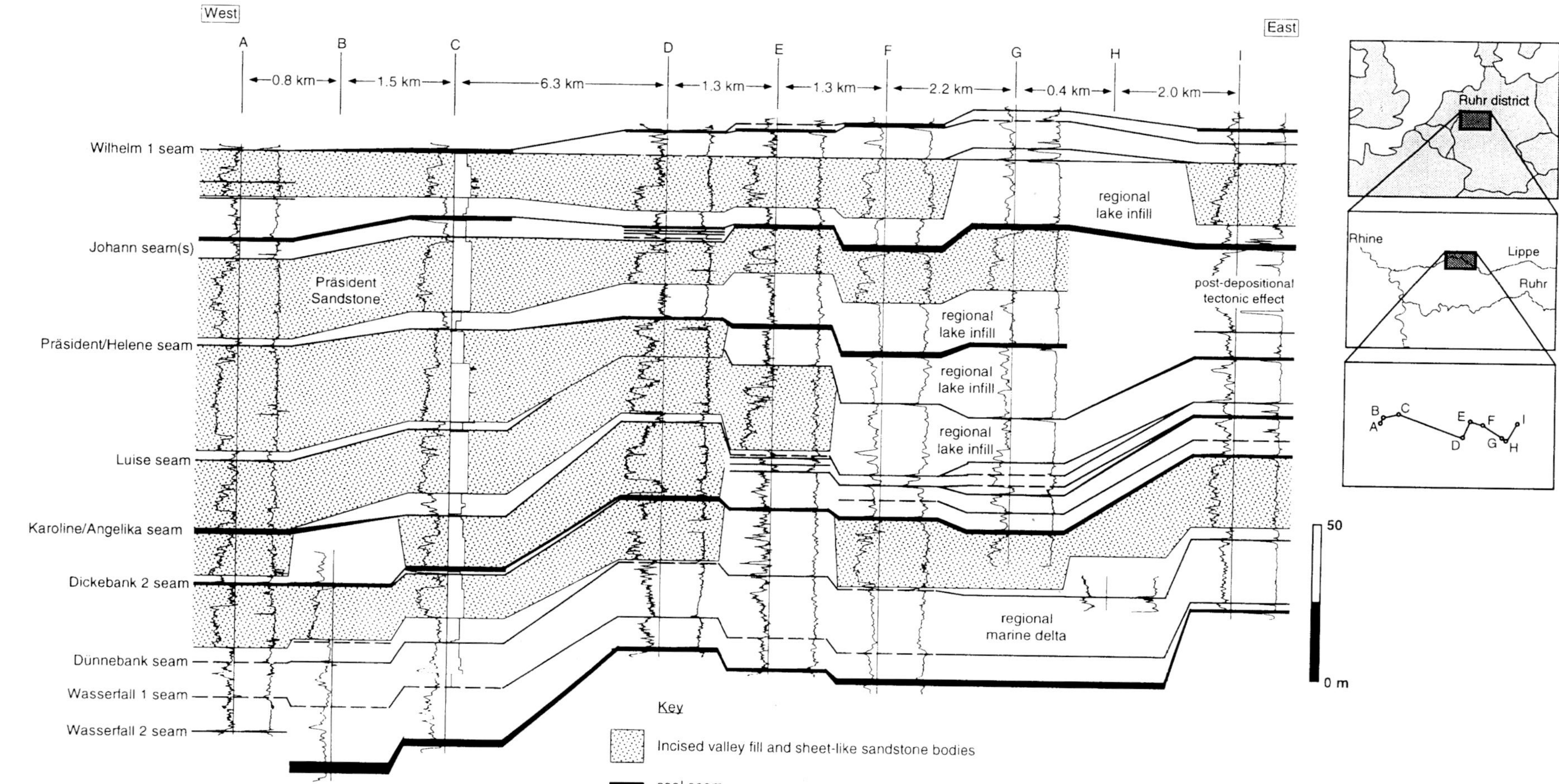

Fig. 11. Correlation panel through the middle Bochum Measures (Upper Westphalian A), central Ruhr District, between the Wilhelm and Wasserfall coal seam groups. Gamma ray and compensated density logs are shown on the left and right of each logged section, respectively. The locations of the correlation panel and cores are shown on the inset maps.

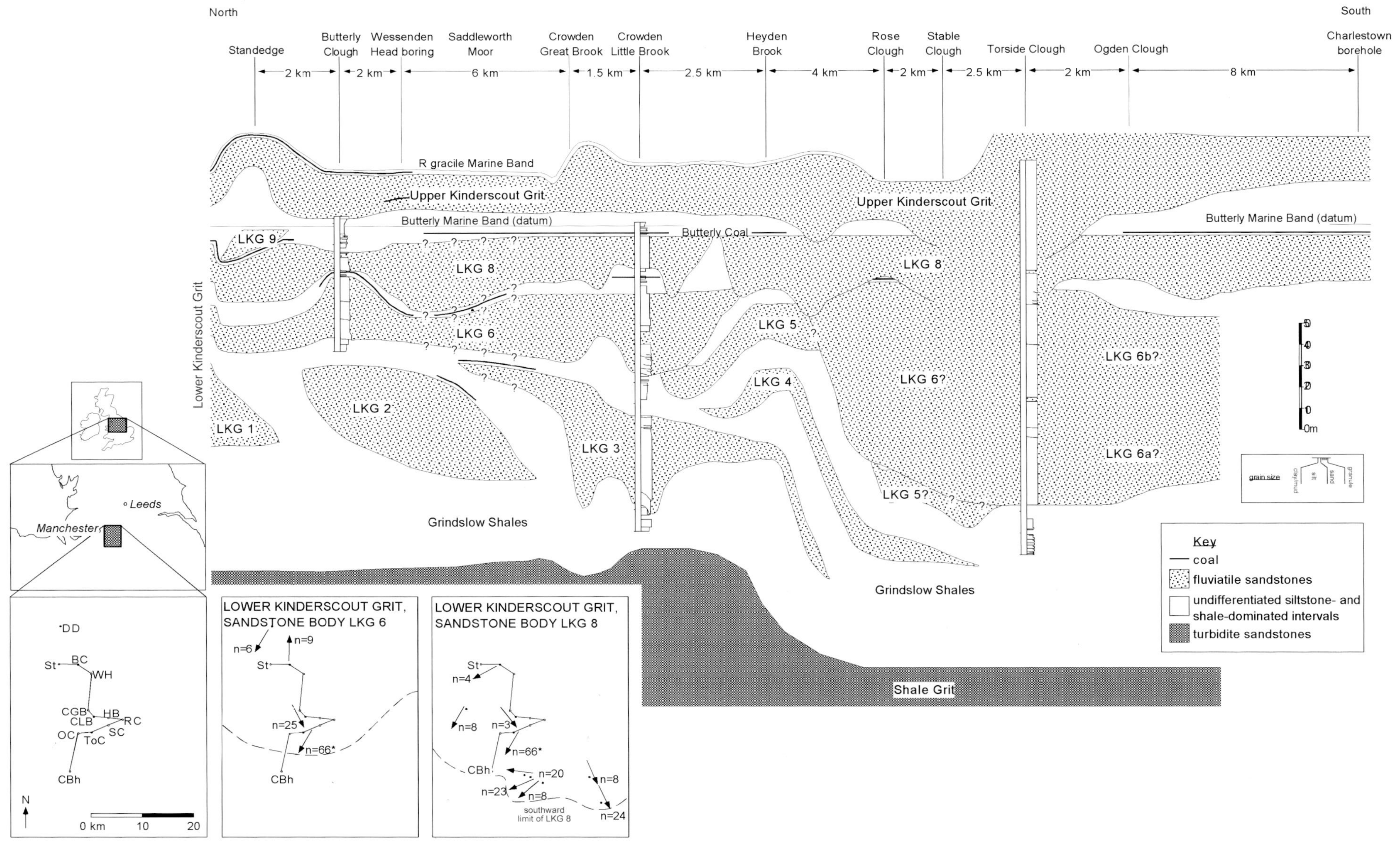

Fig. 12. Depositional dip cross-section through the Lower Kinderscout Grit in the Huddersfield Sub-basin and Edale Gulf, Pennine Basin. This correlation framework is based on logged sections combined with a re-interpretation of sections describd in BGS Memoirs (Wray *et al.* 1930; Bromehead *et al.* 1933; Stephens *et al.* 1953; Smith *et al.* 1967; Stevenson & Gaunt 1970) and maps (British Geological Survey 1977, 1978*a*, *b*, 1980). Sandstone bodies LKG 8, LKG 9 and the Upper Kinderscout Grit contain only fluvial deposits, whereas LKG 6 is of mixed fluvial and Gilbert-type delta origin (Hampson 1997). The nature of sandstone bodies LKG1–5 is unclear. The Grindslow Shales represent a submarine slope association, while the Shale Grit comprise deepwater turbidite sandstones (Collinson 1969). The locations of the correlation panel, selected logged sections and mean palaeocurrents are shown on the inset map. Key and abbreviations as for Fig. 3.

content of the complexes is generally greater than 95%. The uniform, sand-rich character of the valley fill complexes is also evident in gamma-ray logs, which are typically uniform and blocky with moderate radioactivity values (<100 API units; Fig. 13). Siltstone intervals and mudclast lags are represented by 'spikes' of high radioactivity (100–160 API units). Similar gamma-ray profiles are obtained from outcrop exposures of the complexes (Myers & Bristow 1989, Davies & Elliott 1996). Changes in the internal architecture of the channel fill members within each complex are also weakly developed, indicating that the fluvial systems changed little through time. Tidally influenced deposits are invariably absent in the studied valley fill complexes, reflecting the apparent lack of strong tides in the European Upper Carboniferous basins.

In all studied examples, the valley fill complexes are capped by a palaeosol horizon, either locally or regionally (e.g. the Rough Rock and Crawshaw Sandstone, East Midlands and the Farewell Rock, south Wales; Figs 3, 5 and 9). This palaeosol directly underlies the initial flooding surface at the top of the complex and indicates that the valleys were filled to emergence prior to transgression. Valley filling during a period of increasing accommodation requires a relatively high sediment flux, which most likely contributed to fluvial systems remaining sand-rich and, possibly, braided throughout valley infilling.

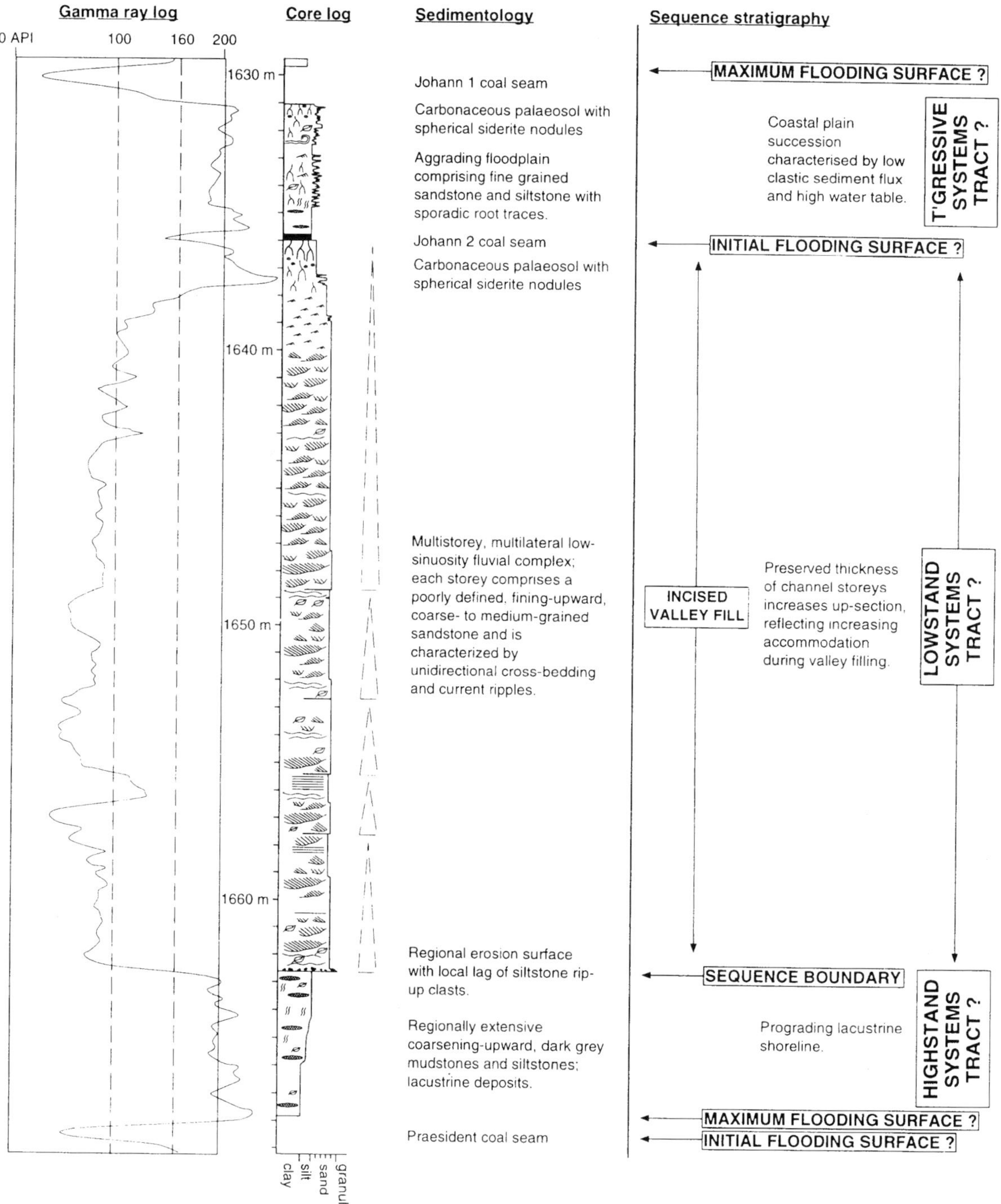

Fig. 13. Gamma-ray and core logs through the Präsident Sandstone. Note that the Präsident Sandstone lacks a clear overall fining-upward trend, in contrast to the Farewell Rock (Fig. 5). Poorly-defined fining-upward cycles up to 5 m thick, denoted by dashed triangles, are interpreted as single storey channel fill members. Laterally, the sandstone correlates to a single palaeosol. The location of the cored section is shown on Figure 11 (well C). Key and abbreviations as for Fig. 5.

One exception to the sandstone filled incised valleys is the Farewell Rock (South Wales), in which the upper 10–25 m comprise siltstones, deposited largely from suspension, that can be traced laterally for approximately 40 km (Figs 5 and 9). In the Farewell Rock complex, the upward increase in the preservation of channel fill members is accompanied by: (1) decreasing average grain size; (2) decreasing cross-bed coset thickness; and (3) increasing thickness of current ripple cross-laminated intervals in successive channel fill members (Fig. 5). These changes record decreasing stream power through time, probably in response to decreasing channel slope as relative sea-level rose. This trend culminated in the deposition of the upper unit of the Farewell Rock, interpreted as a siltstone-dominated channel plug and bay-head delta succession (Hampson 1995).

Detrital mineralogy and provenance of valley fill sandstones

Although relatively little systematic analysis has been carried out on the composition of incised valley fill sandstones in onshore areas, there is some evidence from several basins for changes in provenance at the sequence boundaries which define their bases. For example, Kinderscoutian valley fill sandstones in western Ireland are associated with an abrupt increase in quartz and heavy minerals, with no corresponding increase in K-feldspar. Consequently, these incised valley fills are characterized by relatively high Th/K ratios (>6), reflecting the low proportion of potassium-bearing minerals in relation to underlying and overlying deposits here (Table 1 and Fig. 14; Davies & Elliott 1996). This change in mineralogical composition reflects a different provenance for the incised valley fill sandstones.

A comparable change is observed across the base of the sheet-like Rough Rock sandstone complex in the Pennine Basin, although sandstones in this basin have a very different mineralogy and provenance to those in western Ireland (Table 1 and Fig. 14; Myers & Bristow 1989). Sandstones in the Pennine Basin and Southern North Sea are dominantly subarkosic and were derived from the northward-lying Scottish–Scandinavian Caledonides (Gilligan 1920, Drewery *et al.* 1987), with minor locally-derived sandstones from the southward-lying London–Brabant Massif (Holdsworth 1963). The Rough Rock contains an anomalously high proportion of fresh K-feldspars, which is detected as a low Th/K ratio (3–5; Table 1) on spectral gamma ray logs (Myers & Bristow 1989).

In the northwestern Pennine Basin (Rossendale Sub-basin), the Rough Rock comprises two discrete sandstone bodies separated by the Sand Rock Mine Coal. The lower body has been interpreted as a separate incised valley fill confined to the Rossendale Sub-basin, with its non-regional extent reflecting a possible tectonically forced, or enhanced, origin (Hampson *et al.* 1996). The lower Rough Rock sandstone is underlain by the Haslingden Flags, which have an anomalous, western provenance characterized by greenish-grey lithic clasts and reworked Ordovician and Devonian palynomorphs (McLean & Chisholm 1996). The influx of this westerly-derived clastic material immediately below the lower Rough Rock sandstone supports the interpretation of a tectonically enhanced sequence boundary at the base of the latter.

Valley fill and sheet-like sandstones of similarly pebbly character and immature, feldspathic composition to the Rough Rock are noted at several other stratigraphic levels in the Pennine Basin, including the Warley Wise Grit Formation (formerly the Skipton Moor Grits) and Kinderscout Grit (Reading 1964). These sandstone complexes may exhibit low Th/K ratios similar to the Rough Rock. This inference is confirmed by preliminary data from the Upper Kinderscout Grit. The immature, feldspathic composition of these sandstones and the abundance of lithic clasts within them imply that they underwent less chemical weathering in the source area and/or during subsequent transport into the Pennine Basin. This reduction in chemical weathering may be attributed to either tectonic uplift and subsequent unroofing of fresh granitic sources in the Scottish–Scandinavian hinterland or to climate and/or drainage run-off changes in this area. These abrupt influxes of coarse-grained sandstone are documented at the same stratigraphic intervals in a number of other basins (Davies *et al.* 1999). The mechanism(s) which caused these influxes appear to have operated over longer time scales (*c.* 1 Ma) than the high-frequency glacio–eustatic sea-level fluctuations which drove river incision (65–100 ka, Hampson *et al.* 1997). An equivalent situation is envisaged for the Farewell Rock in the South Wales Basin, which was derived from a local, northerly source not represented in the underlying Middle Shales, implying possible rejuvenation of Caledonian structures near the northern basin margin (George 1982). This sheet-like incised valley complex is also associated with an angular unconformity at its base, which represents a tectonically enhanced sequence boundary (Fig. 9).

Sandstones in the Westphalian A Coal Measures succession of the Ruhr District were derived from a heterogeneous, mainly metamorphic and granitic source area, probably from the Scandinavian–Baltic Shield (Hedeman & Teichmüller 1971). Palaeocurrents in these sandstones are oriented towards the southwest (Hedeman & Teichmüller 1971; Jankowski *et al.*

Table 1. Mean total radioactivity (cps), potassium (%K), uranium (ppm U) and thorium (ppm Th) contents, and Th/K and Th/U ratios for selected Upper Carboniferous fluvial sandstones.

	n	Mineralogy	cps mean ± sd	%K mean ± sd	ppm U mean ± sd	ppm Th mean ± sd	Th/K mean ± sd	Th/U mean ± sd
Kinderscoutian, western Ireland								
Tullig sandstone (fluvial incised valley fill)	83	2–5% feldspar	44.0 ± 9.7	1.09 ± 0.44	1.88 ± 0.57	9.0 ± 2.5	8.4 ± 1.4	5.03 ± 0.82
Kilkee sandstone (fluvial incised valley fill)	14		39.0 ± 6.2	1.06 ± 0.35	2.42 ± 0.60	11.2 ± 2.6	11.3 ± 3.9	4.68 ± 0.69
mouth bar sandstones			44.0 ± 13.6	1.80 ± 0.37	3.18 ± 0.76	12.4 ± 2.9	6.9 ± 1.1	4.63 ± 1.16
wave-reworked sandstones			15.7 ± 2.0	0.23 ± 0.05	1.00 ± 0.21	2.5 ± 20.8	11.1 ± 1.9	2.52 ± 0.48
Yeadonian, northern England								
Rough Rock (sheet-like fluvial sandstone)	81	12–14% K-feldspar	39 ± 6.1	1.59 ± 0.24	1.1 ± 0.4	6.0 ± 1.3	3.8 ± 0.8	
Rough Rock Flags (mouth bar sandstones)	102		49 ± 12	1.53 ± 0.20	2.0 ± 0.7	9.8 ± 3.7	6.5 ± 2.7	

Data for the Yeadonian of northern England are from Myers & Bristow (1989). n = number of samples, cps = counts per second, sd = standard deviation.

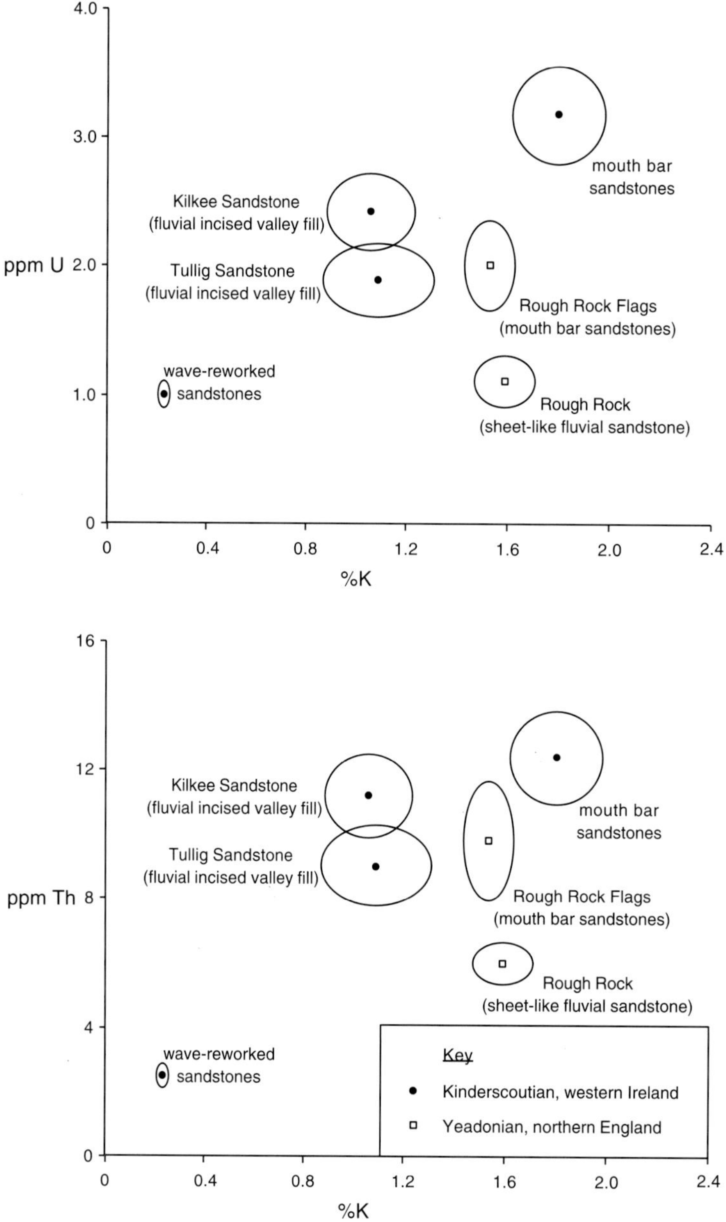

Fig. 14. (**a**) U–K and (**b**) Th–K cross-plots for selected fluviatile sandstones in the Kinderscoutian strata of western Ireland and Yeadonian strata of northern England. The latter dataset is from Myers & Bristow (1989). Each data point represents a mean value, and the axes of the surrounding ellipse have a length of one standard deviation (see Table 1). Note that incised valley fill and sheet-like fluvial sandstones plot distinctly from underlying and overlying mouth bar and wave-reworked sandstones in both datasets (see text for details).

1993). As in the Pennine Basin, several incised valley fill and sheet-like sandstones in this succession are anomalously pebbly and contain compositionally immature clasts. For example, the 'Albert 3 Sandstone' valley fill (Fig. 7) contains pebbles of quartz porphyry (Scherp 1956) and the sheet-like Finefrau Sandstone contains clasts of quartzite, metamorphosed sandstone and granitic cataclasite of both normal and alkaline composition (Scherp 1956). The influx of these anomolous clasts may reflect either tectonic or climatic changes in the hinterland. In addition, some valley fill and sheet-like sandstone bodies also bear clasts cannibalized from the earlier, and southward-lying, fill of the Variscan Foreland Basin (Hedeman & Teichmüller 1971): the 'Albert 3 Sandstone' contains clasts of reworked Namurian sandstone (Scherp 1956) and the Finefrau Sandstone contains clasts of reworked pyrite and Devonian Limestone (Schaub 1956; Stadler 1985).). These southerly-derived sandstones do not appear to exhibit anomalous palaeoflow patterns, but instead contain regional palaeocurrents oriented towards the southwest. The introduction of these reworked clasts has been attributed to uplift and erosion of older parts of the basin fill, driven by the northward movement of Variscan thrust front (e.g. Jankowski *et al.* 1993). Continuation of this process in the Ruhr district resulted in the predominantly lithic composition of Westphalian C–D sandstones, which were derived from a similar, southerly source (Hedeman & Teichmüller 1971; Jankowski *et al.* 1993).

Onshore incised valley fill sandstones as analogues for offshore fluvial and estuarine reservoirs

'Classical' features of incised valleys, such as erosional truncation of underlying strata at valley bases and onlap of fill deposits onto valley margins (Mitchum *et al.* 1977), are described only rarely in seismic data from the Upper Carboniferous strata of the Southern North Sea (e.g. Evans *et al.*

1992). Evans *et al.* (1992) use such features, where present, to define discrete, laterally confined sandstone bodies of comparable dimensions to valley fill complexes mapped in onshore areas (e.g. the 'Albert 3 Sandstone', Ruhr District; Fig. 7). However, most available seismic data is too poor in quality to reliably pick such features (e.g. Quirk 1993, 1997), and the interpretation of valley fills must rely on alternative criteria (e.g. Ritchie & Pratsides 1993, O'Mara *et al.* 1999). The criteria for recognition of incised valley fills, summarized in this paper, are based on sedimentology, facies analysis, biostratigraphy and gamma-ray logs, which are traditional tools generally available to geologists working Upper Carboniferous plays in the Southern North Sea. Accordingly, these criteria can be used to assess offshore fluvial and reservoirs as incised valley fills.

In core and wireline logs, multistorey fluvial sandstone reservoirs in the Upper Carboniferous succession of the Southern North Sea are generally similar in thickness, sand content, facies and stratigraphic context to incised valley fill and sheet-like sandstones documented in onshore areas (e.g. Collinson *et al.* 1993; Ritchie & Pratsides 1993; McLean & Murray 1996; Besly 1998). These similarities suggest that onshore valley fills are appropriate analogues for some fluvial and estuarine reservoirs in the Southern North Sea.

Reservoir extent and thickness

Most proven reservoirs exhibit uniform thickness (30–40 m) over distances of 5–10 km across individual fields (e.g. the Caister and Murdoch Sandstones; Ritchie & Pratsides 1993; McLean & Murray 1996), although a valley fill geometry may be apparent over a larger area (e.g. the Trent Sandstone, O'Mara *et al.* 1999). The extent and locally uniform thickness of these reservoirs are consistent with valley fill dimensions and thickness variations documented in onshore areas (Figs 6, 7 and 10).

Using onshore valley fill analogues, several further characteristics may be predicted for offshore valley fill reservoirs. Valley fill reservoirs will be deeply erosive with steep sides, such that a thick (30–40 m) reservoir sandstone may pinch out laterally over several hundred metres. Further, the orientation, width and extent of valley fill sandstone bodies cannot be accurately predicted using facies trends in underlying and laterally adjacent rocks, which are genetically unrelated, within a single field. Instead, regional mapping of valley fill sandstone bodies through several blocks will provide a more complete view of valley and reservoir trends in a specific field, especially where relatively high-resolution seismic data can be integrated into these maps. Interfluve palaeosols at valley margins may, in some instances, possess distinctive sedimentological and spectral gamma-ray characteristics which further aids the prediction of valley fill reservoirs laterally (Davies & Elliott 1996; Hampson *et al.* 1997).

Sheet-like sandstones are also likely to occur within the offshore Upper Carboniferous succession. The stratigraphic distribution of these sandstones onshore is poorly understood (Davies *et al.* 1999), although we note that two of the three examples described in this paper (the Rough Rock, Pennine Basin, and the Farewell Rock, South Wales Basin) are associated with an influx of extrabasinal material, probably driven by tectonic reorganizations in the source area.

Reservoir connectivity

Valley fill reservoir complexes are likely to be capped by regionally extensive coals and widespread, non-rooted mudstones of condensed, lacustrine or marine character. These mudstones may form stratigraphic seals. However, in some stratigraphic intervals in the onshore succession, these mudstones are cut out by overlying valley fills, resulting in thick, locally amalgamated sandstones with complex geometries (e.g. the Kinderscout Grit, Fig. 12). To date, such intervals have only been documented in onshore areas within turbidite-fronted delta successions. Similar amalgamated valley fills may be present in the Southern North Sea, in intervals containing exceptionally deep valleys (50–80 m; Fig. 6) at several, closely-spaced stratigraphic levels. If present, amalgamated valley fill reservoirs may retain pockets of unswept oil and gas, depending on detailed reservoir geometry and structural dip.

Internal facies variation within reservoirs

The uniformly coarse-grained, sandstone-dominated character of most proven reservoirs (e.g. the Caister and Murdoch Sandstones; Ritchie & Pratsides 1993; McLean & Murray 1996) corresponds well to that of onshore valley fills, which generally exhibit a high net:gross ratio (>0.95) and low-sinuosity (braided?) fluvial facies style throughout, with fine-grained units of limited lateral continuity (several tens of metres). However, the internal facies architecture of valley fill and multistorey fluvial sandstones influences the quality of some reservoirs in the onshore East Midlands Oilfield (e.g. Hawkins 1978; Rothwell & Quinn 1987; Storey & Nash 1993) and may also affect some offshore reservoirs. Where valley fill reservoirs are not uniformly coarse-grained throughout, we anticipate that fine-grained facies representing the preserved tops of individual channel fill units will be more common towards the top of the reservoir. For example, a relatively fine-grained, tidally-influenced interval near the top of the Trent Sandstone valley fill is documented in the Trent Field (O'Mara *et al.* 1999). This fine-grained interval is directly analogous to the upper, fine-grained member of the onshore Farewell Rock valley fill (Figs 5 and 9), because its deposition and preservation reflects increasing accommodation space, sufficient to outpace coarse-grained sediment flux, near the top of a valley fill body.

Detrital mineralogy

Upper Carboniferous sandstones in the Southern North Sea are derived from a mixed plutonic igneous and metamorphic source area in the Scottish-Scandinavian Caledonides, similar to that which supplied sand to the Pennine Basin (Cowan 1989). Accordingly, the sandstones are mainly subarkosic. Some valley fill sandstones in the onshore Pennine Basin succession are notably more feldspathic, and we anticipate that some offshore valley fill reservoirs will have a similar composition. Despite comprising coarse-grained facies, these reservoirs may have unusually low reservoir quality, reflecting pore occlusion by the degradation of feldspar to kaolinite during early burial (e.g. the lower Trent Sandstone; O'Mara *et al.* 1999). Feldspathic valley fill and sheet-like sandstones in the Pennine Basin succession (e.g. the Skipton Moor Grits, Kinderscout Grit and Rough Rock; Reading 1964) are associated with abrupt influxes of pebby sandstone, driven by a low-frequency (*c.* 1 Ma) allocyclic mechanism(s). Consequently, the stratigraphic intervals containing such major, feldspathic sandstone bodies may be predicted via correlation from the Southern North Sea into adjacent onshore areas (Hampson *et al.* 1997; Davies *et al.* 1999).

Conclusions

A substantial number of major fluvial sandstone complexes in Upper Carboniferous fluvio-deltaic strata, including reservoir sandstones in the Southern North Sea, have recently been re-interpreted as incised valley fills. We review criteria for the recognition of incised valley fill deposits using sedimentology, facies analysis, biostratigraphy and gamma-ray logs in onshore examples. These criteria are equally applicable to Upper Carboniferous fluvial reservoirs in the Southern North Sea, where comparable data are available.

Incised valley fill deposits studied in onshore Upper Carboniferous strata are generally similar in thickness, net:gross, facies and stratigraphic context to fluvial and estuarine valley fills in time-equivalent strata in the Southern North Sea. Additional characteristics of valley fill sandstones are documented in onshore areas, enhancing their use as analogues for offshore valley fill reservoirs.

(1) Valley geometry and extent. Incised valley fills exhibit a uniform thickness of 20–25 m over much of their extent, increasing to 30–45 m locally, and widths of 5–25 km, giving width-to-maximum depth ratios between 1:150 and 1:625. A subset of valley fills, which to date have been documented only in turbidite-fronted deltas, thicken considerably, to 50–80 m, in the 2–5 km adjacent to their mouths. Sheet-like fluvial sandstones overlying sequence boundaries have thicknesses comparable to conventional valley fills, but exceed 35–70 km in width, giving width-to-maximum depth ratios of at least 1:1000. The width and orientation of analogous valley fills can rarely be determined within an area of similar size to a Southern North Sea field, but may be ascertained by regional mapping over a larger area.

(2) Valley connectivity. Valley fills are generally present as discrete sandstone bodies, but they may be amalgamated laterally, thereby forming sheet-like sandstones, and vertically, producing thick (up to 200 m) sand-prone stratigraphic packages. Such sand-prone strata exhibit complex internal geometries in which shale layers capping individual valley fills may persist over several tens or hundreds of square kilometres.

(3) Valley fill character. Valley fills are typically dominated by coarse- to medium-grained sandstone of low-sinuosity (braided?) fluvial facies throughout, lacking an overall fining-upwards trend. Where present, fine-grained facies are preferentially preserved in the upper part of a valley fill.

(4) Detrital mineralogy and provenance. At least some valley fill sandstones are of different composition and provenance to surrounding strata, such that they may be differentiated using spectral gamma ray logs. In the Southern North Sea, such valley fill sandstones are likely to be anomalously coarse-grained and feldspathic, although their reservoir quality may be unusually low as a result of feldspar degradation to kaolinite during early burial.

The authors would like to thank A. D. Reynolds and A. Schultz for their constructive reviews. We gratefully acknowledge Ruhrkohle AG and Montan Consulting for permission to publish subsurface data from the Ruhr district. The work summarized in this paper was funded by NERC and the Royal Society European Science Exchange Programme (G. J. H.), Conoco and Arco (S. J. D., T. E. and S. S. F.).

References

AITKEN, J. F. 1994. Coal in a sequence stratigraphic framework. *Geoscientist*, **4**(5), 9–12.

——& FLINT, S. S. 1994. High-frequency sequences and the nature of incised-valley fills in fluvial systems of the Breathitt Group (Pennsylvanian), Appalachian Foreland Basin, eastern Kentucky. *In:* DALRYMPLE, R. W., BOYD, R. & ZAITLIN, B. A. (eds) *Incised-valley systems: origin and sedimentary sequences*. Society of Economic Paleontologists and Mineralogists, Special Publications, **51**, 353–368.

BERRYHILL, H. L., SUTER, J. R. & HARDIN, N. S. 1987. Seismic models of late Quaternary facies and structure, northern Gulf of Mexico. *American Association of Petroleum Geologists, Studies in Geology*, **23**.

BESLY, B. M. 1998. Carboniferous. *In:* GLENNIE, K. W. (ed.) *Introduction to the Petroleum Geology of the North Sea* (4th edn). Blackwell, Oxford.

BEST, J. L. 1988. Sediment transport and bed morphology at river channel confluences. *Sedimentology*, **35**, 481–498.

BRISTOW, C. S. 1988. Controls on the sedimentation of the Rough Rock Group (Namurian) from the Pennine Basin of northern England. *In:* BESLY, B. M. & KELLING, G. (eds) *Sedimentation in a Synorogenic Basin Complex: the Upper Carboniferous of Northwest Europe*. Blackie, Glasgow, 114–131.

——1993. Sedimentology of the Rough Rock: a Carboniferous braided river sheet sandstone in northern England. *In:* BEST, J. L. & BRISTOW, C. S. (eds) *Braided Rivers*. Geological Society of London, Special Publication, **75**, 291–304.

——, C. S., BEST, J. L. & ROY, A. G. 1993. Morphology and facies models of channel confluences. *In:* MARZO, M. & PUIGDEFABREGAS, C. (eds) *Alluvial Sedimentation*. International Association of Sedimentologists, Special Publication, **17**, 91–100.

British Geological Survey 1977. *Chapel-en-le-Frith*. 1:50 000 series Geological Sheet **99** (England and Wales).

——1978*a*. *Huddersfield*. 1:50 000 series Geological Sheet **77** (England and Wales).

——1978*b*. *Buxton*. 1:50 000 series Geological Sheet **111** (England and Wales).

——1980. *Glossop*. 1:50 000 series Geological Sheet **86** (England and Wales).

BROMEHEAD, C. E. N., EDWARDS, W. N., WRAY, D. A. & STEPHENS, J. V. 1933. *The geology of the country around Holmfirth and Glossop*. Geological Survey Memoir, England and Wales, Sheet **86**.

CALVER, M. A. 1969. Westphalian of Britain. *Compte rendu du sixième Congrès International de Stratigraphie et de Géologie du Carbonifère*, Sheffield 1967, **1**, 233–254.

CHURCH, K. D. & GAWTHORPE, R. L. 1994. High resolution sequence stratigraphy of the late Namurian in the Widmerpool Gulf (East Midlands, UK). *Marine and Petroleum Geology*, **11**, 528–544.

COLLINSON, J. D. 1968. Deltaic sedimentation units in the Upper Carboniferous of northern England. *Sedimentology*, **10**, 233–254.

——1969. The sedimentology of the Grindslow Shales and the Kinderscout Grit: a deltaic complex in the Namurian of northern England. *Journal of Sedimentary Petrology*, **39** 194–221.

——1988. Controls on Namurian sedimentation in the Central Province Basins of northern England. *In*: BESLY, B. M. & KELLING, G. (eds) *Sedimentation in a Synorogenic Basin Complex: the Upper Carboniferous of Northwest Europe*. Blackie, Glasgow, 85–101.

——, JONES, C. M., BLACKBOURN, G. A., BESLY, B. M., ARCHARD, G. M. & MCMAHON, A. H. 1993. Carboniferous depositional systems of the Southern North Sea. *In:* PARKER, J. R. (ed.) *Petroleum Geology of Northwest Europe: Proceedings of the 4th Conference*. Geological Society of London, 677–687.

COWAN, G. 1989. Diagenesis of Upper Carboniferous sandstones: southern North Sea Basin. *In:* WHATELEY, M. K. G. & PICKERING, K. T. (eds) *Deltas: Sites and Traps for Fossil Fuels*. Geological Society of London, Special Publication, **41**, 57–73.

DAVIES, S. J. & ELLIOTT, T. 1996. Spectral gamma ray characterisation of high resolution sequence stratigraphy: examples from Upper Carboniferous fluvio–deltaic systems. *In:* HOWELL, J. A. & AITKEN, J. F. (eds) *High Resolution Sequence Stratigraphy: Innovations and Applications*. Geological Society, London, Special Publications, **104**, 25–35.

——, HAMPSON, G. J., FLINT, S. S., & ELLIOTT, T. 1999. Continent-scale sequence stratigraphy of the Upper Carboniferous and its applications to reservoir prediction. *In*: FLEET A. J. & BOLDY, S. A. R. (ed.) *Petroleum Geology of Northwest Europe: Proceedings of the 5th Conference*. Geological Society, London, 757–770.

DREWERY, S., CLIFF, R. A. & LEEDER, M. R. 1987. Provenance of Carboniferous sandstones from U-Pb dating of detrital zircons. *Nature*, **325**, 50–53.

DROZDZEWSKI, G. 1993. The Ruhr Coal Basin (Germany): structural evolution of an autochthonous foreland basin. *International Journal of Coal Geology*, **22**, 231–250.

ELLIOTT, T. 1976. Upper Carboniferous sedimentary cycles produced by river-dominated elongate deltas. *Journal of the Geological Society of London*, **132** 199–208.

—— & DAVIES, S. J. 1994. High resolution sequence stratigraphy of an Upper Carboniferous basin-fill succession, County Clare, western Ireland. *High resolution sequence stratigraphy: innovations and applications, Fieldtrip B2 guidebook, Liverpool.*

EVANS, D. J., MENEILLY, A. & BROWN, G. 1992. Seismic facies analysis of Westphalian sequences of the southern North Sea. *Marine and Petroleum Geology*, **9**, 578–589.

FIELDING, C. R. 1984. A coal depositional model for the Durham Coal Measures of NE England. *Journal of the Geological Society of London*, **141**, 919–931.

FRANK, F., ZINKERNAJEL, U. & FÜCHTBAUER, H. 1992. *Sources of the Upper Carboniferous Sandstones in North-western Germany*. Deutsche Wissenschaftliche Gessellschaft für Erdol, Erdgas und Kohle E.V., Report 384-8.

GEORGE, G. T. 1982. Sedimentology of the Upper Sandstone Group (Namurian G1) in south-west Dyfed: a case study. *In:* BASSETT, M. G. (eds) *Geological Excursions in Dyfed, Southwest Wales*. National Museum of Wales, 203–214.

GILLIGAN, A. 1920. The petrography of the Millstone Grit series of Yorkshire. *Quarterly Journal of the Geological Society*, **75**, 251–294.

GUION, P. D. & FIELDING, C. R. 1988. Westphalian A and B sedimentation in the Pennine Basin, UK. *In*: BESLY, B. M. & KELLING, G. (eds) *Sedimentation in a synorogenic basin Complex: the Upper Carboniferous of northwest Europe*. Blackie, Glasgow, 153–177.

——, BANKS, N. L. & RIPPON, J. H. 1995. The Silkstone Rock (Westphalian A) from the east Pennines, England: implications for sand body genesis. *Journal of the Geological Society, London*, **152**, 819–832.

HAMPSON, G. J. 1995. *Incised Valley Fills and Sequence Stratigraphy of Selected Carboniferous Delta Systems in the UK*. PhD Thesis, University of Liverpool, UK.

——1997. A sequence stratigraphic model for deposition of the Lower Kinderscout Delta, an Upper Carboniferous turbidite-fronted delta. *Proceedings of the Yorkshire Geological Society*, **51**, 273–296.

——, ELLIOTT, T. & FLINT, S. S. 1996. Critical application of high resolution sequence stratigraphic concepts to the Rough Rock Group (Upper Carboniferous) of northern England. *In:* HOWELL, J. A. & AITKEN, J. F. (eds) *High Resolution Sequence Stratigraphy: Innovations and Applications*. Geological Society, London, Special Publications, **104**, 221–246.

——, ELLIOTT, T. & DAVIES, S. J. 1997. The application of sequence stratigraphy to Upper Carboniferous fluvio-deltaic strata of the onshore UK and Ireland: implications for the southern North Sea. *Journal of the Geological Society, London*, **147**, 719–735.

HASZELDINE, R. S. & ANDERTON, R. 1980. A braidplain facies model for the Westphalian B Coal Measures of north-east England. *Nature*, **284**, 51–53.

HAWKINS, P. J. 1978. Relationship between diagenesis, porosity reduction and oil emplacement in late Carboniferous sandstone reservoirs, Bothamsall Oilfield, East Midlands. *Journal of the Geological Society of London*, **135**, 7–24.

HEARD, A. 1922. The petrology of the Pennant Series. *Geological Magazine*, **59**, 83–92.

HEDEMAN, H.-A. & TEICHMÜLLER, R. 1971. The palaeogeographical development of the Upper Carboniferous. *Fortschritte in der Geologie von Rheinland und Westfalen*, **19**, 132–145.

HOLDSWORTH, B. K. 1963. Prefluvial, autogeosynclinal sedimentation in the Namurian of the southern Central Province. *Nature*, **199**, 133–135.

—— & COLLINSON, J. D. 1988. Millstone Grit cyclicity revisited. *In:* BESLY, B. M. & KELLING, G. (eds) *Sedimentation in a Synorogenic Basin Complex: the Upper Carboniferous of Northwest Europe*. Blackie, Glasgow, 132–152.

HOLLYWOOD, J. M. & WHORLOW, C. V. 1993. Structural development and hydrocarbon occurrence of the Carboniferous in the UK Southern North Sea Basin. *In:* PARKER, J. R. (ed.) *Petroleum Geology of Northwest Europe: Proceedings of the 4th Conference*. Geological Society of London, 689–696.

JANKOWSKI, B., DAVID, F. & SELTER, V. 1993. Facies complexes of the Upper Carboniferous in north-west Germany and their structural implications. *In:* GAYER, R. A., GRIELING, R. O. & VOGEL, A. K. (eds) *Rhenohercynian and Subvariscan fold belts*. Vieweg, Wiesbaden, 139–158.

JONES, C. M. & CHISHOLM, J. I. 1997. The Roaches and Ashover Grits: sequence stratigraphic interpretation of a 'Turbidite-Fronted Delta' system. *Geological Journal*, **32**, 45–68.

KOSS, J. E., ETHERIDGE, F. G. & SCHUMM, S. A. 1994. An experimental study of the effects of base-level change on fluvial, coastal plain and shelf systems. *Journal of Sedimentary Research*, **B64**, 90–98.

LEEDER, M. R. 1988. Recent developments in Carboniferous geology: a critical review with implications for the British Isles and northwest Europe. *Proceedings of the Geologists' Association*, **99**, 73–100.

—— & HARDMAN, M. 1990. Carboniferous geology of the Southern North Sea Basin and controls on hydrocarbon prospectivity. *In*: HARDMAN, R. F. P. & BROOKS, J. (eds) *Tectonic Events Responsible for Britain's Oil and Gas Reserves*. Geological Society, London, Special Publications, **55**, 87–105.

—— & STEWART, M. D. 1996. Fluvial incision and sequence stratigraphy: alluvial responses to relative sea-level fall and their detection in the geological record. *In:* HESSELBO, S. P. & PARKINSON, N. D. (eds) *Sequence Stratigraphy in British geology*. Geological Society, London, Special Publications, **103**, 25–39.

RAISWELL, R., AL-BIATTY, H., MCMAHON, A. & HARDMAN, M. 1990. Carboniferous stratigraphy, sedimentation and correlation of well 48/3-3 in the southern North Sea Basin: integrated use of palynology, natural gamma/sonic logs and carbon/sulphur geochemistry. *Journal of the Geological Society, London*, **147**, 287–300.

MARTINSEN, O. J., COLLINSON, J. D. & HOLDSWORTH, B. K. 1995. Millstone Grit cyclicity revisited, II: sequence stratigraphy and sedimentary responses to changes of relative sea-level. *In:* PLINT, A. G. (eds) *Sedimentary Facies Analysis*. International Association of Sedimentologists, Special Publications, **22**, 305–327.

MAYNARD, J. R. 1992. Sequence stratigraphy of the Upper Yeadonian of northern England. *Marine and Petroleum Geology*, **9**, 197–207.

MCCABE, P. J. 1977. Deep distributary channels and giant bedforms in the Upper Carboniferous of the central Pennines, northern England. *Sedimentology*, **24**, 271–290.

MCLEAN, D. & CHISHOLM, J. I. 1996. Reworked palynomorphs as provenance indicators in the Yeadonian of the Pennine Basin. *Proceedings of the Yorkshire Geological Society*, **51**, 141–151.

—— & MURRAY, I. 1996. Subsurface correlation of Carboniferous coal seams and inter-seam sediments using palynology: application to exploration for coalbed methane. *In*: GAYER, R. & HARRIS, I. (eds) *Coalbed Methane and Coal Geology*. Geological Society of London, Special Publications, **109**, 315–324.

MITCHUM, R. M., VAIL, P. R. & SANGREE, J. B. 1977. Stratigraphic interpretation of seismic reflection patterns in depositional sequences. *In:* PAYTON, C. E. (ed.) *Seismic Stratigraphy – Applications to Hydrocarbon Exploration*, American Association of Petroleum Geologists, Memoir, **26**, 117–133.

MYERS, K. J. & BRISTOW, C. S. 1989. Detailed sedimentology and gamma-ray log characteristics of a Namurian deltaic succession II: gamma ray logging. *In:* WHATELEY, M. K. G. & PICKERING, K. T. (eds) *Deltas: Sites and Traps for Fossil Fuels*. Geological Society of London, Special Publications, **41**, 81–88.

O'MARA, P., MERRYWEATHER, M., STOCKWELL, M. & BOWLER, M. M. 1999. The Trent gas field: correlation and reservior quality within a complex Carboniferous stratigraphy. *In*: FLEET, A. J. & BOLDY, S. A. R. *Petroleum Geology of Northwest Europe. Proceedings of the 5th Conference*. Geological Society, London, 809–821.

POSAMENTIER, H. W. & VAIL, P. R. 1988. Eustatic controls on clastic deposition II – sequence and systems tract models. *In:* WILGUS, C. K., HASTINGS, B. S., KENDALL, C. G. S. C., POSAMENTIER, H. W., ROSS, C. A. & VAN WAGONER, J. C. (eds) *Sea-level Changes – an Integrated Approach*, Society of Economic Paleontologists and Mineralogists, Special Publications, **42**, 125–154.

PULHAM, A. J. 1989. Controls on internal structure and architecture of sandstone bodies within Upper Carboniferous fluvial-dominated deltas, County Clare, western Ireland. *In:* WHATELEY, M. K. G. & PICKERING, K. T. (eds), *Deltas: Sites and Traps for Fossil fuels.* Geological Society, London, Special Publications, **41**, 179–203.

QUIRK, D. G. 1993. Interpreting the Upper Carboniferous of the Dutch Cleaver Bank High. *In:* PARKER, J. R. (ed.) *Petroleum Geology of Northwest Europe: Proceedings of the 4th Conference.* Geological Society, London, 697–706.

——1997. Sequence stratigraphy of the Westphalian in the northern part of the southern North Sea. *In*: ZIEGLER, K., TURNER, P. & DAINES, S. R. (eds), *Petroleum Geology of the Southern North Sea: Future Potential.* Geological Society, London, Special Publication, **123**, 153–168.

—— & AITKEN, J. F. 1997. The structure of the Westphalian in the northern part of the southern North Sea. *In*: ZIEGLER, K., TURNER, P. & DAINES, S. R. (eds), *Petroleum Geology of the Southern North Sea: Future Potential.* Geological Society, London, Special Publications, **123**, 143–152.

READING, H. G. 1964. A review of the factors affecting sedimentation of the Millstone Grit (Namurian) in the Central Pennines. *In:* VAN STRAATEN, L. M. J. U. (eds) *Deltaic and Shallow Marine Deposits.* Elsevier, Amsterdam, 340–346.

REYNOLDS, A. D. 1996. Paralic successions. *In:* EMERY, D. & MYERS, K. J. (eds) *Sequence Stratigraphy.* Blackwell Science, Oxford, 134–177.

RIPPON, J. H. 1996. Sand body orientation, palaeoslope analysis and basin-fill implications in the Westphalian A–C of Great Britain. *Journal of the Geological Society, London*, **153**, 881–900.

RITCHIE, J. S. & PRATSIDES, P. 1993. The Caister Fields, Block 44/23a, UK North Sea. *In:* PARKER, J. R. (ed.), *Petroleum geology of Northwest Europe: Proceedings of the 4th Conference.* Geological Society, London, 219–225.

ROTHWELL, N. R. & QUINN, P. 1987. The Welton Oilfield. *In:* BROOKS, J. & GLENNIE, K. (eds) *Petroleum Geology of Northwest Europe.* Graham & Trotman, London, 181–189.

SCHAUB, H. 1956. Devonkalk-Gerölle im Finefrau-Konglomerat südwestlich Duisburg. *Zeitschrift deutsche Geologische Gesellschaft*, **107**, 83–86.

SCHERP, A. 1956. Zur petrographie des Finefrau-Konglomerates bei Essen und einiger anderer geröllführender Sandsteine des Ruhrkarbons. *Neues Jahrbuch für Geologie und Paläontologie,* Monatshefte 1956, 240–244.

SCHUMM, S. A. & ETHERIDGE, F. G. 1994. Origin, evolution and morphology of fluvial valleys. *In:* DALRYMPLE, R. W., BOYD, R. & ZAITLIN, B. A. (eds) *Incised-Valley Systems: Origin and Sedimentary Sequences.* Society of Economic Paleontologists and Mineralogists, Special Publications, **51**, 11–25.

SMITH, E. G., RHYS, G. H. & EDEN, R. A. 1967. *The Geology of the Country Around Chesterfield, Matlock and Mansfield.* Geological Survey Memoir, England and Wales, Sheet **112**.

STADLER, G. 1985. Schwefelkiesgerölle in Konglomeratlagen des Ruhrkarbons (Iron sulphide pebbles in conglomeratic beds of the Ruhr Carboniferous). *Fortschritte in der Geologie von Rheinland und Westfalen*, **33**, 119–127.

STEPHENS, J. V., MITCHELL, G. H. & EDWARDS, W. 1953. *The geology of the country between Bradford and Skipton.* Geological Survey Memoir, England and Wales, Sheet **69**.

STEVENSON, I. P. & GAUNT, G. D. 1970. *The geology of the country around Chapel-en-le-Frith.* Geological Survey Memoir, England and Wales, Sheet **99**.

STOREY, B. & NASH 1993. The Eakring Dukeswood oil field: an unconventional technique to describe a field's geology. *In:* PARKER, J. R. (ed.) *Petroleum Geology of Northwest Europe: Proceedings of the 4th Conference.* Geological Society, London, 1527–1537.

THOMAS, L. P. 1974. The Westphalian (Coal Measures) in South Wales. *In*: OWEN, T. R. (ed.) *The Upper Palaeozoic and Post-Palaeozoic Rocks of Wales.* University of Wales, Cardiff, 133–160.

WRAY, D. A., STEPHENS, J. V., EDWARDS, W. N. & BROMEHEAD, C. E. N. 1930. *The geology of the country round Huddersfield and Halifax.* Geological Survey Memoir, England and Wales, Sheet **77**.

Structural analysis of 3D seismic data, using the correlation attribute: a case study – Carboniferous of the Southern North Sea (UK)

S. BIRRELL[1] and J. COURTIER[2]

[1] *Granite Rock Limited, 1 St Swithin Row, Aberdeen AB10 6DL, UK*
[2] *Conoco (UK) Limited*

Abstract: With the advent of a new seismic attribute, generically termed correlation, interpreters have a non-specialist tool which enables decisions to be made on structural and stratigraphic patterns within a 3D dataset. The process behind the attribute may appear to be black box technology, however, the resultant data are straightforward and enable the interpreters to make their own conclusions about the seismic information presented. Correlation data are simply a quantified comparison of adjacent seismic traces. The value to be unlocked from this attribute lies in rapid delineation of fault and stratigraphic patterns. This requires a revised approach to the interpretation workflow, involving analysis of the correlation attribute volume during primary stages of any 3D-interpretation project. Using a technique termed 'ribbon interpretation', correlation data are analysed for information relating to lineaments and data inconsistencies. The identification of features using ribbons, which are short 2 point segments, can then be stacked and filtered by the interpreter to give direct information on faulting and stratigraphic features. The filtered ribbon data are then progressed through to horizon interpretation, where they can be integrated to provide a more robust structural or stratigraphic solution. Application of the ribbon interpretation technique within the mature environment of the structurally complex, Carboniferous play (UK SNS) (Fig. 1) has allowed faster and better results across exploration, appraisal and production scenarios.

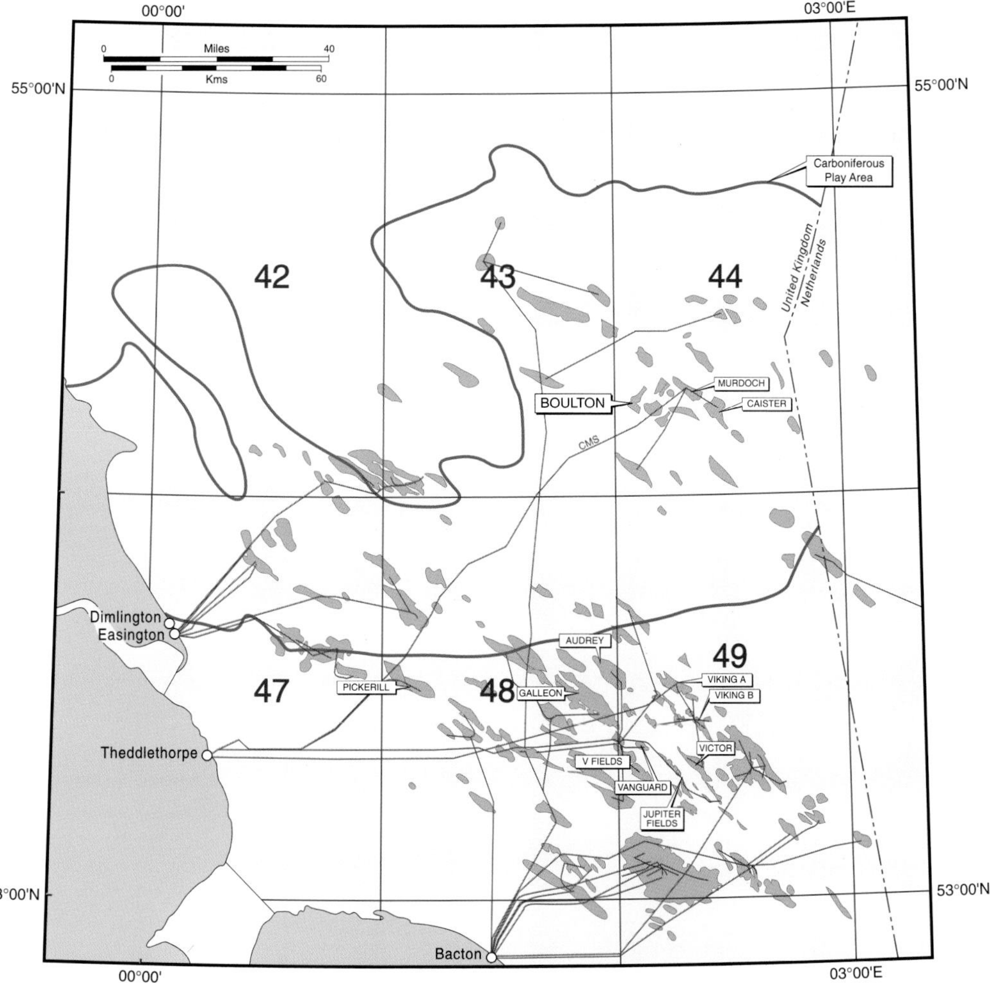

Fig. 1. Location map for the Carboniferous play of the UK SNS.

BIRRELL, S. & COURTIER, J. 1999. Structural analysis of 3D seismic data, using the correlation attribute: a case study – Carboniferous of the Southern North Sea (UK). *In*: FLEET, A. J. & BOLDY, S. A. R. (eds) *Petroleum Geology of Northwest Europe: Proceedings of the 5th Conference*, 789–797.

Over the past two years, a new seismic attribute has been introduced to the hydrocarbon exploration industry. The correlation attribute, as it can be generically termed, simplifies our seismic datasets and allows interpreters to make their own decisions about what structural and stratigraphic information the 3D seismic data are presenting (Fig. 2).

Correlation data, in layman's terms, are a quantification of the comparison or difference between adjacent seismic traces. The attribute can then be scaled or filtered to enhance the display of the data.

The value to be unlocked from this attribute lies in rapid delineation of fault and stratigraphic patterns prior to interpretation of a 3D dataset. This requires a revised approach to the interpretation workflow, whereby pretty wallpaper is converted into powerful information for the exploration and drilling decision making process. This paper presents a revised interpretation workflow integrating correlation data, using a unique technique termed 'ribbon interpretation'.

Using case studies from the Carboniferous of the UKCS Southern North Sea (Fig. 1), an area that appears to provide excellent results from correlation processing, the paper illustrates the new workflow approach and ribbon technique, while also presenting the benefits and pitfalls associated with this seismic attribute.

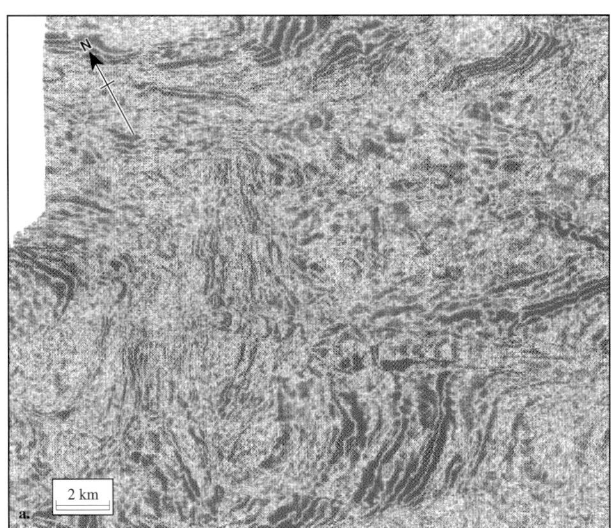

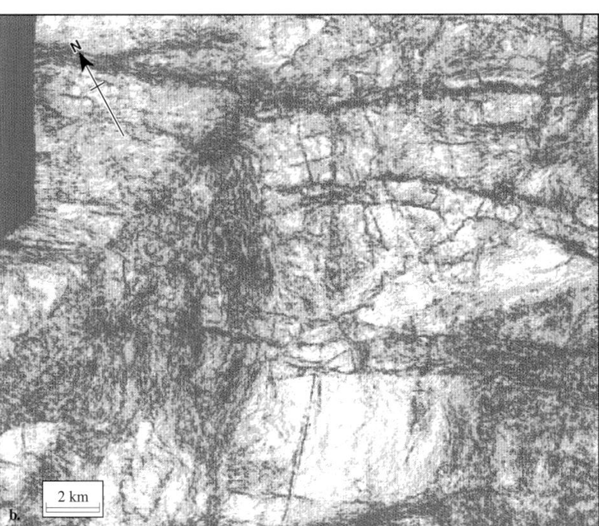

Fig. 2. Comparison between amplitude and correlation timeslice through regional Carboniferous section.

3D Seismic interpretation workflow procedures

Commonly used interpretation workflow

The modal procedures for 3D seismic interpretation involve the use of a single conventional amplitude representation of 3D data. The central column, coloured orange, of Fig. 3 illustrates a typical seismic interpretation workflow.

It is accepted that subsequent to, and occasionally in parallel with interpretation, post-stack processing may be undertaken to provide specialist datasets for improved imaging and complex attribute extraction.

However, the results of specialist processing tend to be integrated with the interpretation flow at the end of a project, thereby proving more of an additional verification than an influence on the primary interpretation (Fig. 3; pink flow). Within the main workflow, horizon, structural and stratigraphic recognition runs concurrently with horizon and fault interpretation. In many cases, seismic event termination is the defining criteria for both.

Even with the use of timeslicing, intelligent event tracking algorithms and 3D visualization, the definition of surfaces and faults is undertaken using incremental 2D interpretation, a time consuming technique and one that will not always provide the most robust solution. Lapses in concentration, poor data zones and bad 'crossline' imaging will all contribute to 'interpretation busts' or ambiguities, while interpreter bias within the process can lead to unintentional application of inappropriate structural models.

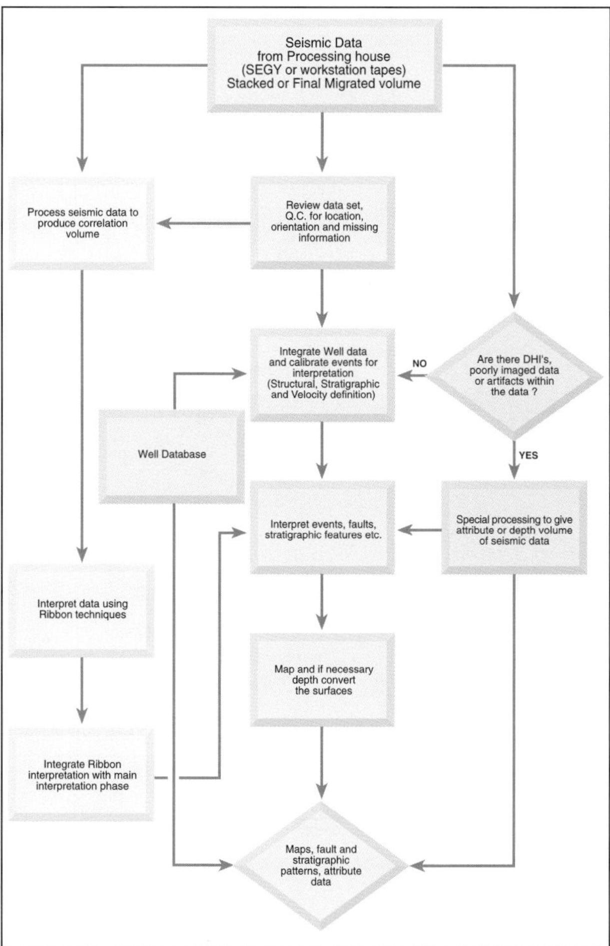

Fig. 3. 3D seismic interpretation workflow.

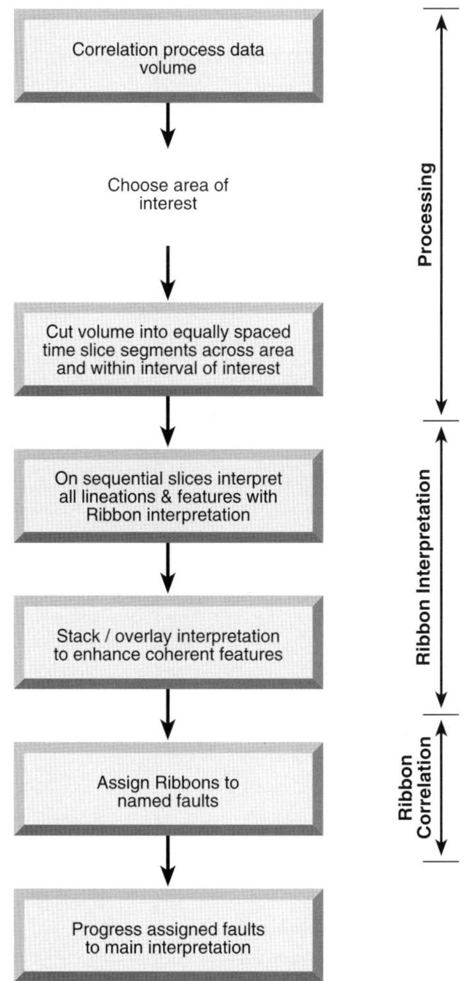

Fig. 4. Ribbon interpretation and correlation techniques.

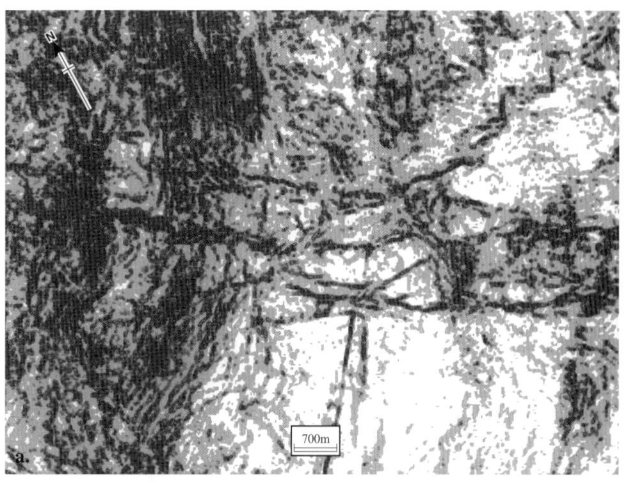

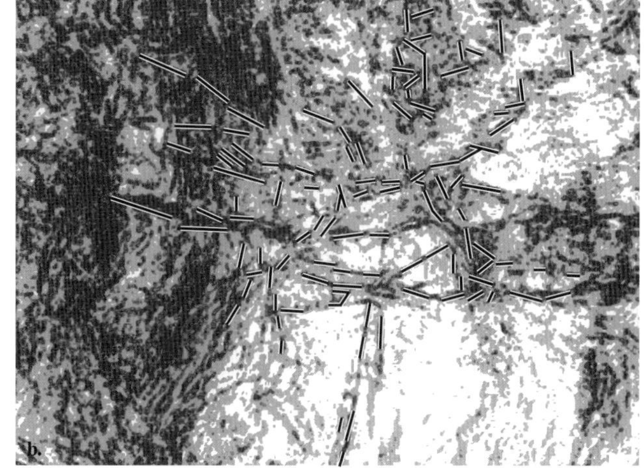

Fig. 5. Illustration of ribbon interpretation on a correlation attribute timeslice.

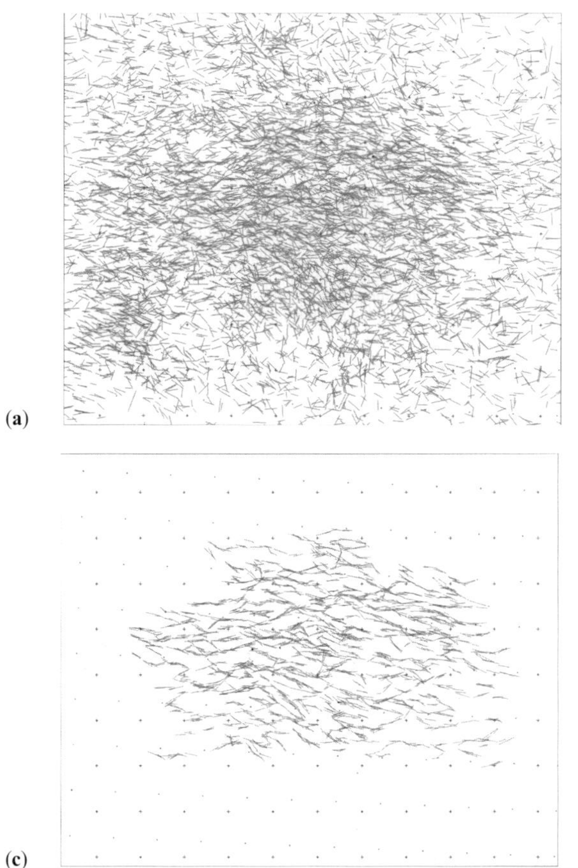

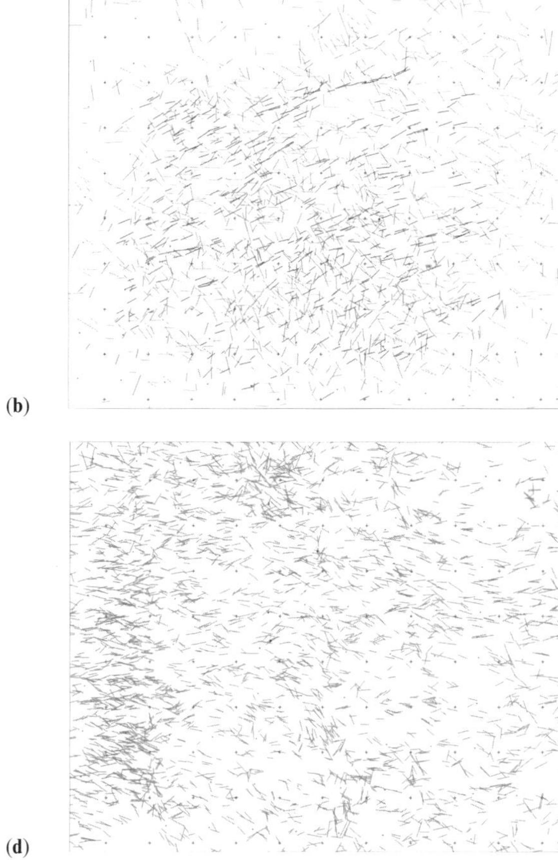

Fig. 6. Ribbon correlation sequence.

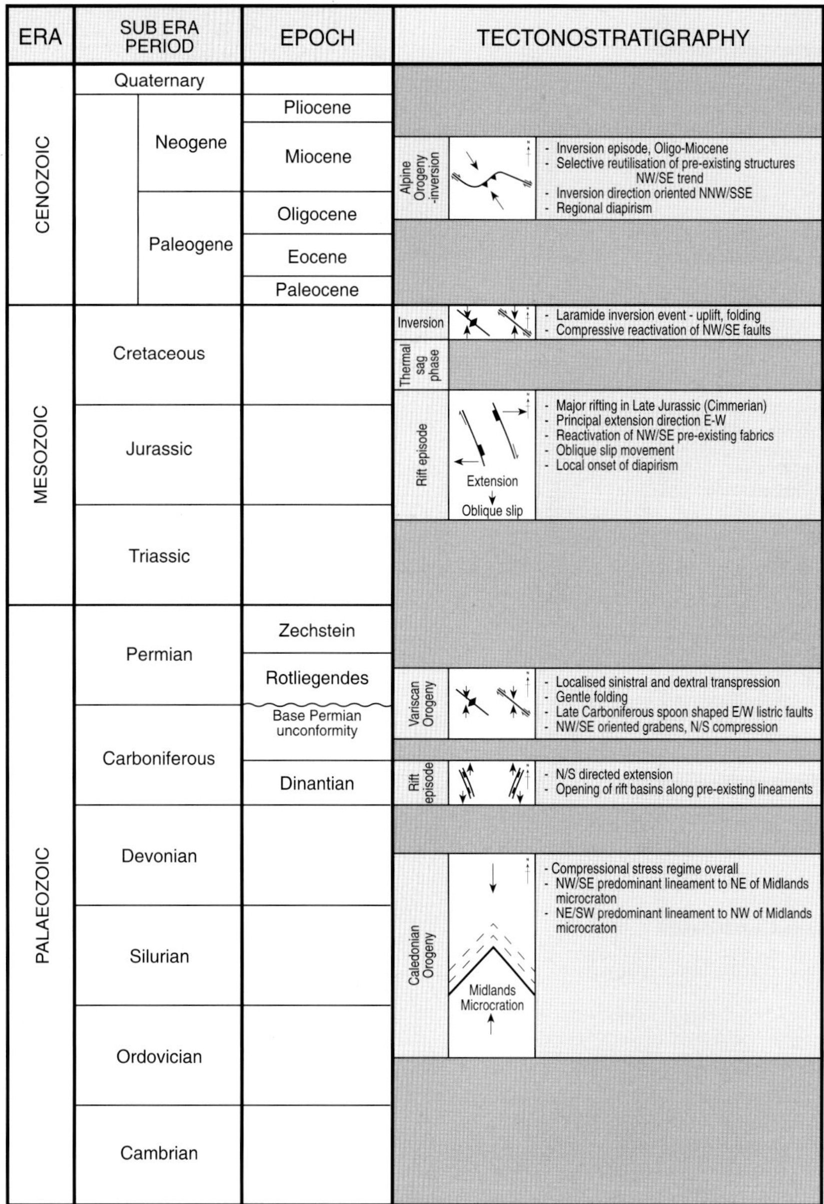

Fig. 7. Tectono-stratigraphic summary chart, after Van Hoorn 1987.

Revised interpretation workflow

Use of correlation processed data, in conjunction with an innovative interpretation technique, allows us to improve the robustness of interpretation models and provide higher quality results within a faster time frame. Most benefit can be gained by interpreting correlation data at the outset of any project, as a precursor to the horizon interpretation. This allows the interpreted product from the correlation volume to be integral with and an influence on subsequent interpretation (Fig. 3; green flow).

Interpretation of the correlation data is possible prior to any horizon picking or well-to-seismic calibration of the dataset, and this is achieved using a technique termed ribbon interpretation. The revised workflow for any 3D interpretation project should therefore include processing and interpretation of a correlation volume prior to horizon picking (Fig. 3; green flow).

Ribbon interpretation and correlation techniques

The ribbon correlation and interpretation techniques allow the interpreter to convert information held within the correlation volume into a useful form of data that can be integrated with the conventional process of fault and surface interpretation. The techniques should be viewed as fundamental and not specialist to the interpretation workflow.

How, and when should this stage of interpretation be undertaken? It should be carried out as a precursor to event and structure picking, thus ensuring that there is no prior interpretation bias applied to the data. What the interpreter is doing is looking at the 'raw' information contained within the 3D seismic volume and interpreting this.

Figure 4 shows the suggested workflow when using ribbon interpretation and correlation. The first phase is carried out using sequential timeslice layers, created from the 3D correlation volume (Fig. 2). The technique relies on the same principles as CMP stacking to discriminate between real features (signal) and artifacts (noise). The optimal timeslice increment for interpretation can be calculated as a function of: (1) dominant frequency of data across target interval; (2) features required to be enhanced. However, it has been observed that timeslice increments should be set at no less than half the period of the target interval wavelet for optimal results. This may equate to between 2 and 4 samples, depending on the data. Each timeslice

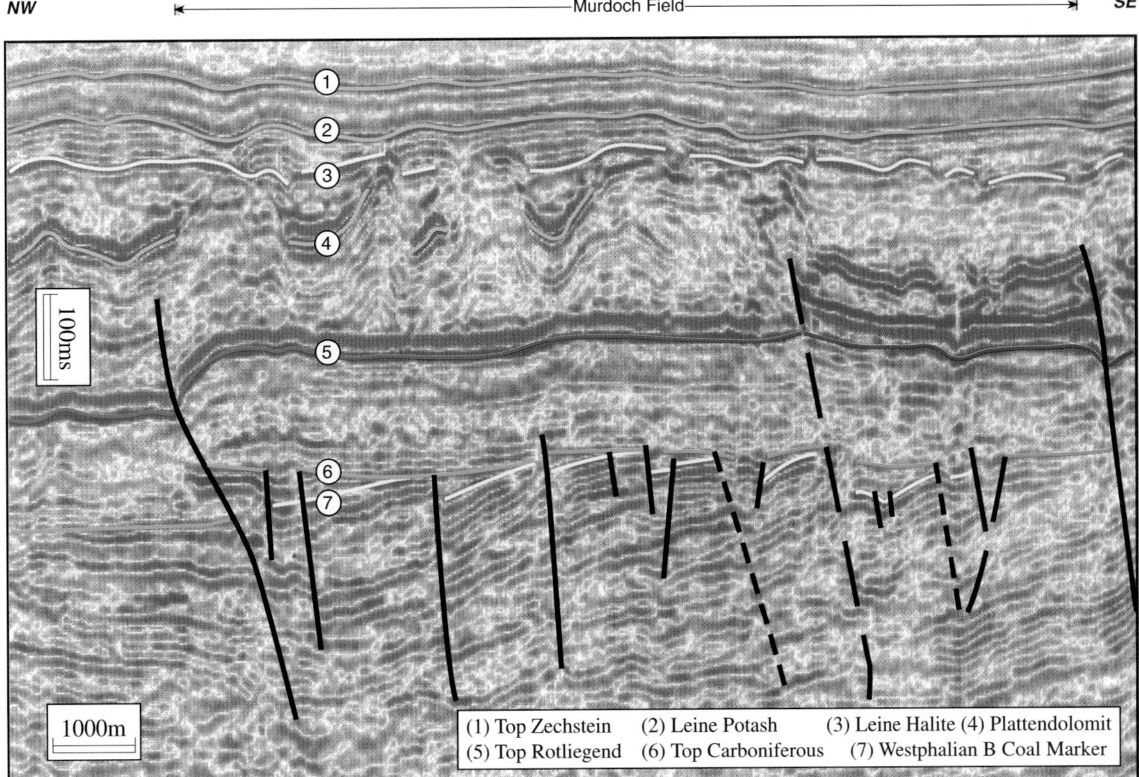

Fig. 8. NW–SE seismic section across the Murdoch Field, showing internal faulting.

is analysed for features and patterns, and each of these discontinuities should then be picked with short two-point ribbon segments (Fig. 5). Note, at this stage that the interpreter may be inclined to pre-suppose the origin of a given feature; however, this should be avoided and all features picked. Discrimination on the basis of noise, stratigraphic features, artifacts etc. can be carried out during the subsequent correlation phase. Each subsequent or previous timeslice should be interpreted in the same manner, across the target interval. From a data management perspective, it is advisable to assign all ribbons within a given timeslice a representative name, for example 'T2400cx' or 'T2400r'.

At completion of this first phase, all interpreted ribbons should be stacked and viewed, either in a suitable map view (Fig. 6) or on a representative timeslice. Major trends within the data will be immediately obvious. These trends will tend to represent the large scale features, which would have been easily identifiable on the conventional data. However, behind the main trends, and captured within the ribbon data lies more subtle information relating to reservoir-scale faulting and less obvious stratigraphic features.

If at this stage there are no obvious trends observed in the data, it will appear that the interpreter is faced with a pile of 'spaghetti'. This is an understandable perception, however; through the subsequent manual filtering stages it will be possible to extract important information from this dataset.

The ribbon correlation stage involves re-assigning recognizable and coherent trends, within the data, as coherent fault or stratigraphic features. Figure 6 defines how this process is undertaken. As the major and then secondary trends are removed from the 'spaghetti', subsidiary trends will become apparent. The trends may be coherent noise, subcrop patterns or secondary faulting, and they can be correctly calibrated through cross-reference with the original seismic volume.

The interpreter is now at the decision point of the revised workflow (Fig. 3). At this stage he or she is able to:

(1) create a fault pattern from the re-assigned ribbons which can then be carried through to mapping, fault analysis, or for use in reservoir simulation models;
(2) progress the ribbon information into the conventional phase of interpretation.

The existence of the assigned fault ribbons will provide the following benefits: improved 3D correlation of fault features; better event termination definition; and instant 3D verification of fault pattern correlation. This will in turn provide a final interpretation product which can be assigned a higher degree of confidence, and on a pro-rata basis will have been carried out in a much faster time frame than using a conventional interpretation workflow.

Pitfalls and benefits of using correlation data

The use of correlation attribute data should not be viewed as a panacea to solve the problems of poor seismic data and bad interpretation, but as an extra tool to allow the interpreter to find a solution to the structural and stratigraphic complexities of thc 3D scismic data. Some of the clear pitfalls of the data and techniques presented in this paper can be outlined as follows:

(1) poor seismic data (i.e. low S : N), will generally result in poor correlation data;
(2) correlation data cannot discriminate between coherent noise, faulting or stratigraphic features, this must be undertaken by the interpreter; however, the techniques presented in this paper should simplify the process;
(3) the output from the correlation processing sequence is sensitive to processing parameter selection, and care should be taken at this stage to understand the quality of your data and what are the objectives of the processing;
(4) the use of correlation data, and any interpretation techniques applied to it, should not be viewed as a replacement

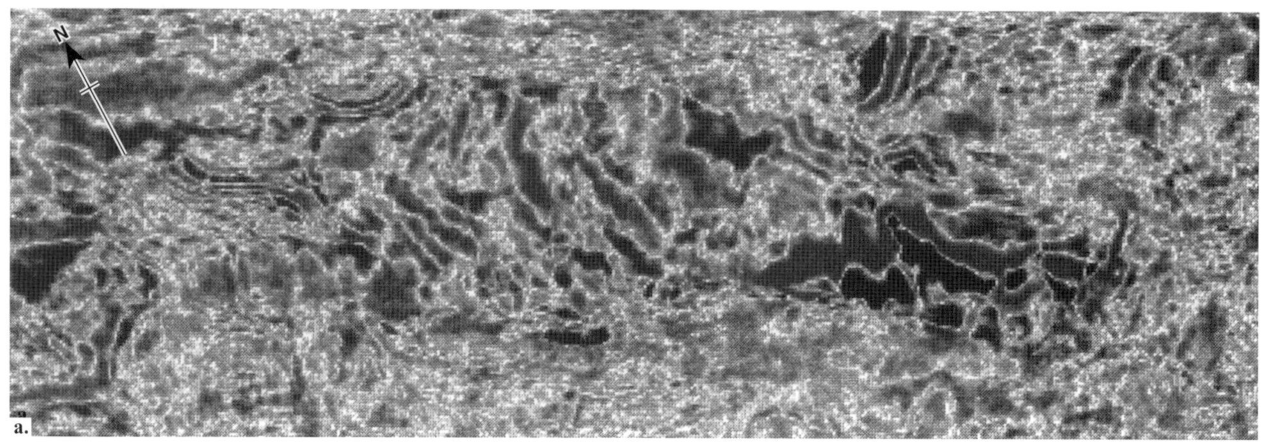

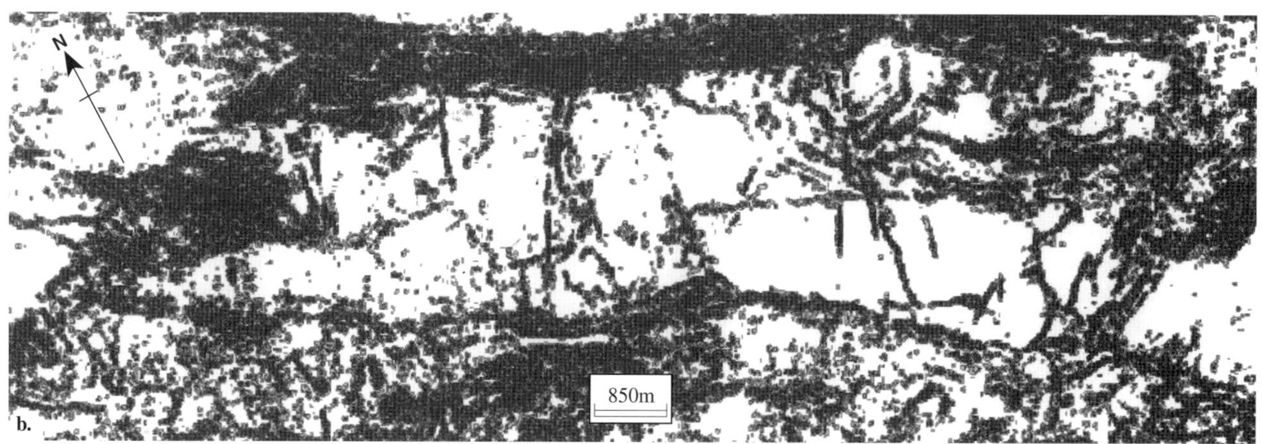

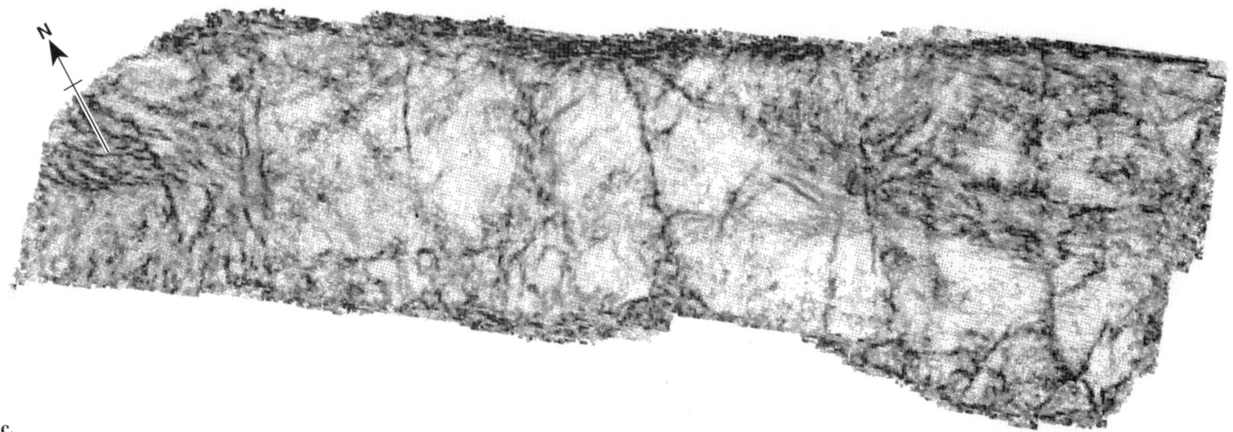

Fig. 9. Comparison between (a) amplitude, (b) correlation and (c) attribute extraction displays, across the Murdoch Field.

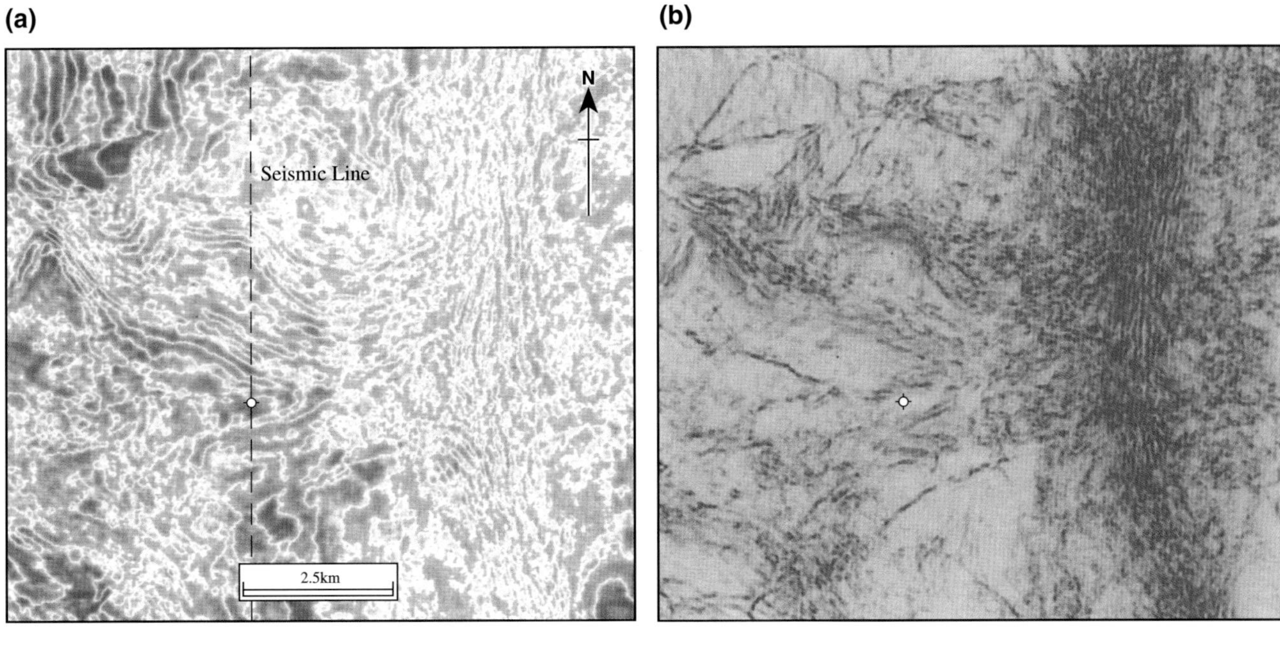

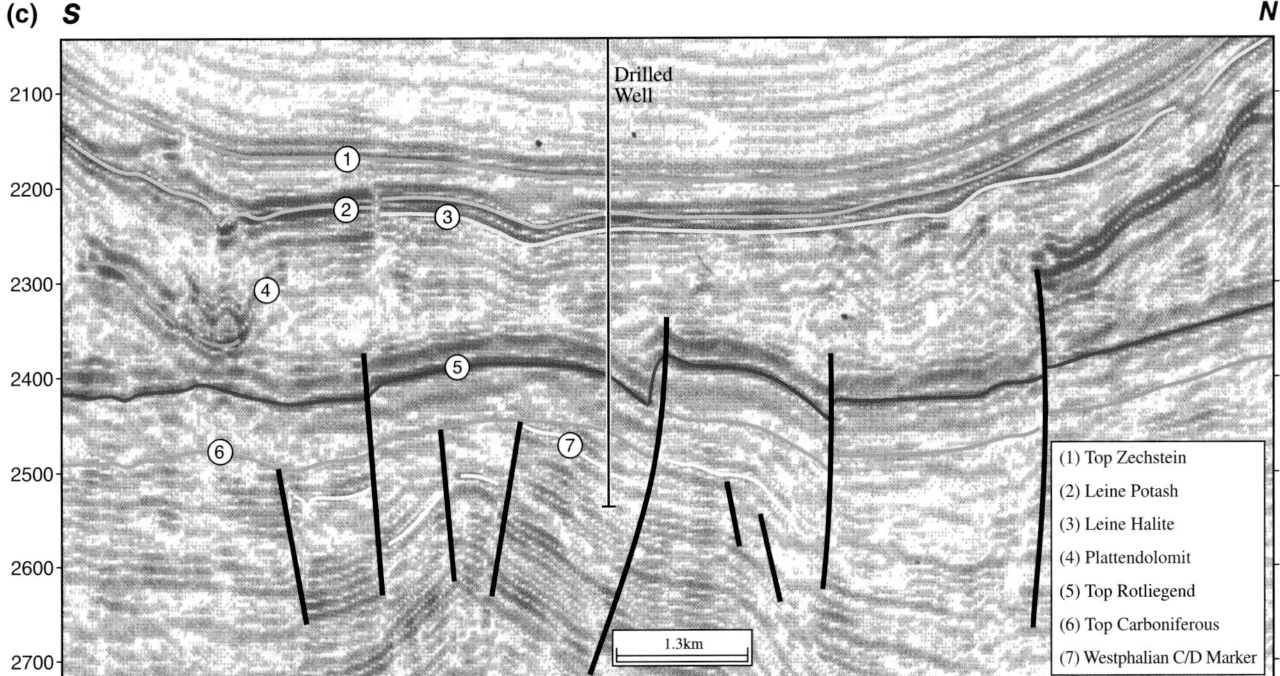

Fig. 10. Comparison between (**a**) amplitude and (**b**) correlation data used for well planning examples, and (**c**) seismic line (see (**a**)) showing well positions.

for detailed seismic interpretation; on the contrary, interpreters should view correlation data and interpretation as the precursive stage to all interpretation projects.

That said, there are many benefits in using correlation data; for example:

(1) unlike current 3D interpretation techniques, there is no bias built into the interpretation, and this is one of the overriding advantages over other interpretation techniques;
(2) the data provide higher lateral resolution of structural and stratigraphic features than conventional seismic data;
(3) it helps avoid miscorrelation of faults during structural interpretation;
(4) ribbon techniques allow a better 3D solution to fault and stratigraphic interpretation on 3D data;
(5) use of correlation data can save time and money during a project.

Case study

The Carboniferous of the UK Southern North Sea

The Carboniferous play of the Southern North Sea can be viewed as structurally complex, where prospectivity is determined through the identification of valid structural traps, within which there exists a viable reservoir. The Carboniferous strata have undergone polyphase deformation (Fig. 7, after Van Hoorn 1987; Arthur 1993; Glennie 1990; Bartholomew *et al.* 1993) with present-day structures manifesting characteristics of extensional, compressional and lateral movement.

Arguably, as a mature basin with mature plays, one of the keys to unlocking the residual value from existing Southern North Sea fields and additional prospectivity is understanding fault distribution and compartmentalization. Correlation processing and subsequent interpretation using ribbon techniques

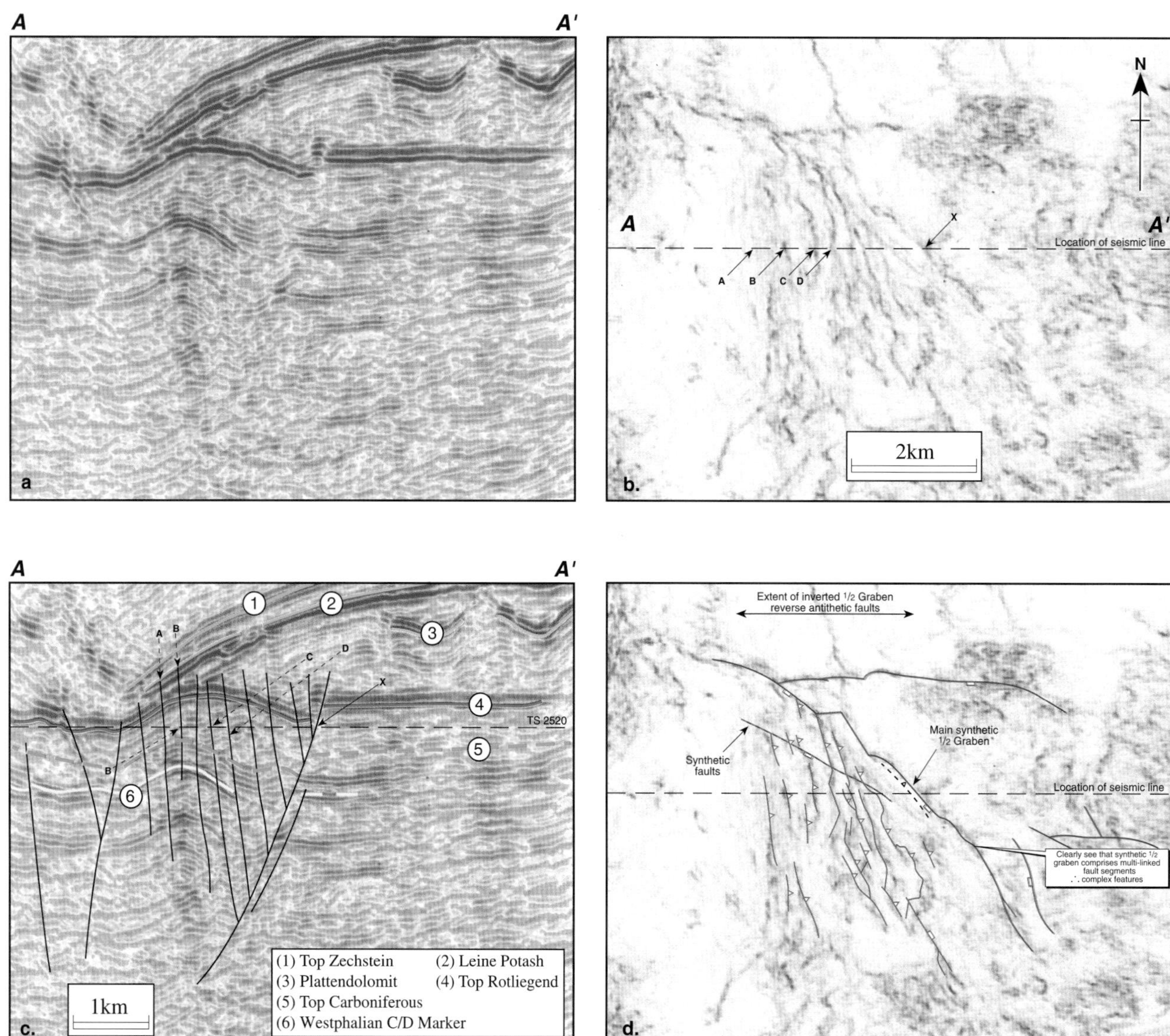

Fig. 11. Illustration of fault interpretation and correlation of complex structure, using continuity attribute.

provides a very efficient tool to solve the problems within the Carboniferous. 3D seismic data across the Carboniferous play area (Fig. 1) respond very well to correlation processing.

Regional fault and play interpretation

In comparison, correlation processing provides high resolution imaging of fault patterns when used as an alternative to amplitude data (Fig. 2). This allows for a more effective and accurate mapping of regional trends and play distribution. With the enhanced fault framework, structural analysis can be undertaken faster and with increased confidence.

Fault pattern verification for fault seal analysis studies within a producing field

The Murdoch Field, Block 44/22a, discovered in 1984, has been in production for 5 years. There are five exploration wells penetrating the reservoir and six production wells. The field, defined externally by large scale inverted and reverse faults trending NW–SE, is internally compartmentalized by extensional faulting, dominantly NE–SW trending (Fig. 8). The reservoir for the field is the Westphalian B Murdoch Sandstone, which has a near constant thickness across the structure of approximately 38 m. The thin nature of the reservoir means that even small faults may cause complete offset of the reservoir leading to compartmentalization. Using correlation-processed seismic data, the fault pattern across the field was reviewed and updated. The resulting improved fault pattern was then analysed to understand sealing and reservoir offset potential. Subsequent integration with dynamic data, from the production wells, allowed a better understanding of discrete flow units. Figure 9 shows a comparison between an amplitude and correlation timeslice and an attribute extraction along the top reservoir seismic event. From this we can see that the correlation slice and extracted attribute give significantly better imaging of the structural pattern over Murdoch when compared to the amplitude slice. However, the correlation timeslice has been used to help map the reservoir in the Murdoch Field, as opposed to the attribute extraction which is a product of the interpretation.

Re-mapping for well planning purposes

Preparation for well planning and refinement of reserves related to drilling locations requires a very detailed definition of faulting. Using correlation processing and ribbon interpretation at the outset of a project provides the data to upgrade fault interpretation at any time throughout the project evaluation and appraisal. Figure 10 shows the comparison between an amplitude and correlation slice across an area already drilled, but with a second well planned. In this instance it is important to understand the structural relationship between the first well and the planned second well. Figure 11 shows the results of the ribbon interpretation and correlation on the vertical seismic data.

In addition, in developing the structural pattern controlling prospectivity, correlation data allow clear information upon which to base the fault pattern. For example, Fig. 11 shows a series of vertical seismic and time-slice sections, these have been interpreted to show a complex inversion feature. Although not necessarily unique, the interpretation makes use of real information from the seismic data, made readily visible through the use of correlation, and interpreted using ribbons. The lucid interpretation has allowed the interpreter to enhance their understanding of the mapped structure, and therefore assess the risks associated with it.

Conclusions

The Carboniferous of the UK Southern North Sea gives very good results when processed for the correlation attribute. The particular structural problems of fault pattern, sealing potential and compartmentalization, manifested within the Carboniferous play, can be successfully addressed using correlation attributes, ribbon interpretation and correlation.

However, the correlation attribute should not be used as a specialist tool but as a tool fundamental to the interpretation sequence when dealing with exploration, appraisal or development issues.

The value of the correlation attribute is best accessed through a revised interpretation workflow which includes ribbon interpretation and correlation. The correlation attribute is not a substitute for skilled interpretation, but is an additional tool which provides results with a higher confidence and in a quicker time frame.

The authors wish to thank Conoco (UK) Ltd management and colleagues for their kind provision of data, assistance and discussions, and J. Ashbridge who was instrumental in developing the technique and improving the text for the manuscript. We are also grateful to Conoco's partners who gave permission to use data over their interests.

References

ARTHUR, T. J. 1993. Mesozoic structural evolution of the UK Southern North Sea: insights from analysis of fault systems. *In*: PARKER, J. R. (ed.) *Petroleum Geology of Northwest Europe: Proceedings of the 4th Conference*. Geological Society, London, 1269–1279.

BARTHOLOMEW, J. B. *et al.* 1993. Regional structural evolution of the North Sea: oblique slip and the reactivation of basement lineaments. *In*: PARKER, J. R. (ed.) *Petroleum Geology of Northwest Europe: Proceedings of the 4th Conference*. Geological Society, London, 1109–1122.

GLENNIE, K. W. 1990. Chapter 2; Outline of the North Sea history and structural framework. *In*: GLENNIE, K. W. (ed.) *Introduction to the Petroleum Geology of the North Sea*. Blackwell, Oxford, 34–77.

VAN HOORN, B. 1987. Structural evolution, timing and tectonic style of the Sole Pit inversion. *Tectonophysics*, **137**, 239–284.

'NW European Gas Atlas' – new implications for the Carboniferous gas plays in the western part of the Southern Permian Basin

P. GERLING,[1] M. C. GELUK,[2] F. KOCKEL,[1] A. LOKHORST,[2] G. K. LOTT[3] and R. A. NICHOLSON[3]

[1] *Bundesanstalt für Geowissenschaften und Rohstoffe (BGR), Stilleweg 2, 30655 Hannover, Germany*
[2] *Nederlands Instituut voor Toegepaste Geowetenschappen TNO (NITG-TNO), PO Box 80015, 3508 TA Utrecht, The Netherlands*
[3] *British Geological Survey, Keyworth, Nottingham, NG12 5GG, UK*

Abstract: The 'Northwest European Gas Atlas' comprises maps on characteristics (e.g. molecular and isotopic compositions) of natural gases in northwest European gas fields, on the distribution and facies of source and reservoir rocks, on maturities, and other relevant geological information. The mapped area includes the entire Southern Permian Basin from the Southern North Sea to central Poland. Palaeozoic source rocks in the Dinantian, Namurian and Westphalian have been identified in the western part of the Southern Permian Basin. They contain kerogens of marine (Type I and II) and continental origin with TOC contents as high as 12%.

There are two Carboniferous production provinces in this area: C1 in the Southern North Sea and C2 in the area along the border between The Netherlands and Germany. The natural gas in most of the C1 production province has methane contents of more than 80%; in most of the C2 province even more than 85%. Nitrogen is the second most abundant constituent in both provinces. Carbon dioxide plays a significant role only locally in the areas of intrusive rocks. Isotope data show that the source of the natural gases in the C2 province is a terrestrial rock (Westphalian). In the C1 province, the gases are of mixed origin: a low maturity terrestrial source rock (Westphalian) and a more mature marine source rock (?Namurian).

Oil and gas have been produced from the northwest European onshore and offshore areas for several decades, but so far little has been done on an international basis to compare gas composition of different gas fields, or to relate gas composition with provenance. Natural gas, consisting predominantly of methane with varying amounts of the higher homologues (ethane, propane, etc.), is often also combined with non-hydrocarbons such as nitrogen, carbon dioxide and hydrogen sulphide.

Considerable data on gas composition are available, to a lesser extent in the published literature and to a much greater extent in both company records and the archives of the national Geological Surveys. In a joint project, representatives of the Geological Surveys of Denmark, Germany, Great Britain, The Netherlands, and Poland have compiled a comprehensive overview of the composition and isotopic ratios of the natural gases in the Southern Permian Basin. The aim was to construct a series of regional maps, not to present details of specific fields.

The product of this study is the 'Northwest European Gas Atlas' (Lokhorst 1998), in which 28 contour maps are used to show the regional distribution of hydrocarbon gas components, their physical parameters, such as calorific values and densities, and the distribution of the noncombustibles CO_2, and N_2. These distribution maps are presented for four reservoir horizons: Carboniferous, Rotliegend, Zechstein and post-Zechstein. Fifteen up-to-date geological maps, important for understanding the petroleum geology, show the distribution and/or facies of source rocks, reservoir rocks, maturities, and other geological features considered relevant (e.g. salt structures and intrusives). Finally, 64 diagnostic cross plots – 4 for each of the 16 production provinces – of various isotopic ratios provide information on the genesis of the natural gases.

The final database (derived from commercial data and 200 in-house gas analyses) consists of 939 datasets, comprising data on the composition of the gases (methane, ethane, propane, butane, pentane, nitrogen, carbon dioxide, and hydrogen sulphide), and 516 datasets containing isotope data.

This paper summarizes the results of the 'Northwest European Gas Atlas' Project with regard to the Carboniferous gas reservoirs in the western part of the Southern Permian Basin. This paper focuses on these reservoirs because the data indicate that the pre-Westphalian sediments have a significant hydrocarbon potential.

An overview of the distribution of the composition of the natural gases follows a brief discussion of the source rocks, the occurrence of Carboniferous reservoirs and their structural setting. Finally, the origin of the gases is discussed on the basis of their molecular and isotopic composition. This is done by comparing two production provinces, one in the Southern North Sea and one in the area along the border between The Netherlands and Germany.

Source rocks

Important Palaeozoic source rocks have been identified in Dinantian, Namurian and Westphalian sediments (Lokhorst 1998). The Dinantian basin was delineated by the Mid North Sea–Ringkøbing–Fyn High to the north and the London–Brabant Massif to the south. In the northernmost areas, sediments were deposited in a fluvial/deltaic to shallow-marine setting. Most of the study area is underlain by an extensive carbonate platform, stretching from the UK to NW Germany. Intra-platform basins are known from central England (e.g. Northumberland, Stainmore, Cleveland and Widmerpool basins), but they may well exist in other places in the study area. Their existence has, however, not been proved by drilling. In Dinantian times, a starved basin developed in western Germany. It was filled from the south with flysch sediments. The southern margin of this trough is characterized by

GERLING, P., GELUK, M. C., KOCKEL, F., LOKHORST, A., LOTT, G. K. & NICHOLSON, R. A. 1999. 'NW European Gas Atlas' – new implications for the Carboniferous gas plays in the western part of the Southern Permian Basin. *In*: FLEET, A. J. & BOLDY, S. A. R. (eds) *Petroleum Geology of Northwest Europe: Proceedings of the 5th Conference*, 799–808.

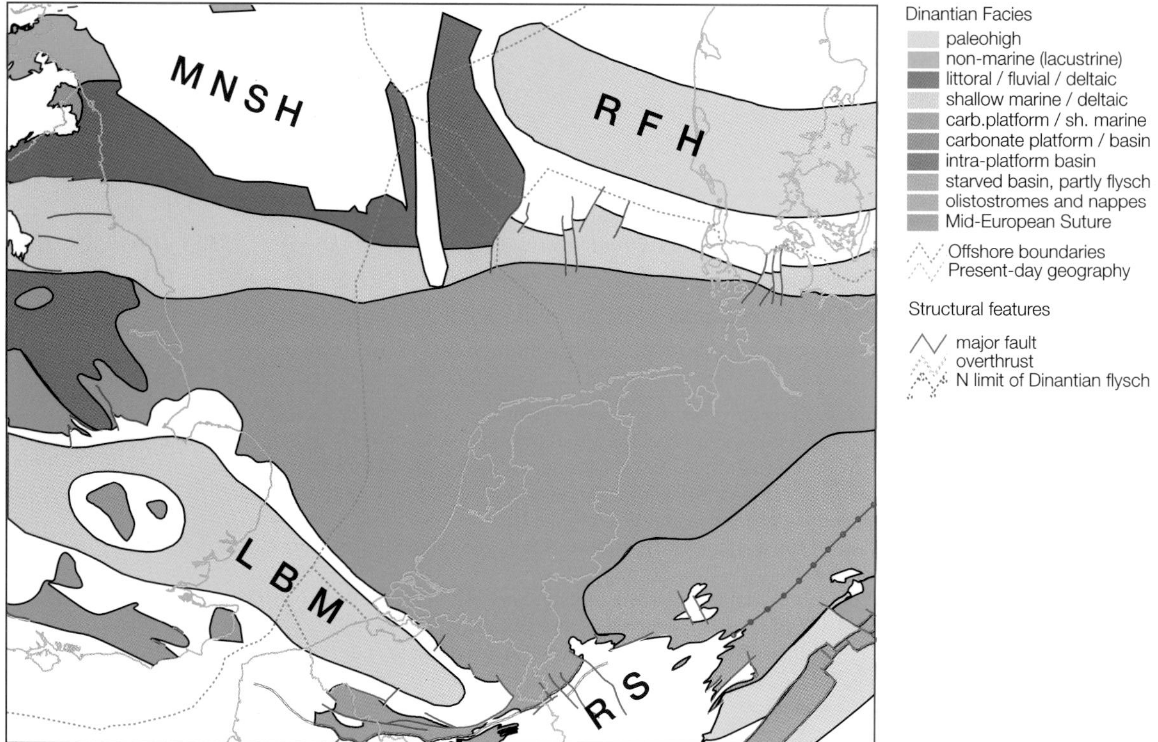

Fig. 1. Dinantian distribution and facies. LBM = London–Brabant Massif; MNSH = Mid North Sea High; RFH = Ringkøbing Fyn High; RS = Rheinische Schiefergebirge.

olistostromes and nappes. Dinantian source rocks (Fig. 1) occur in three different facies. In the north, they comprise deltaic, coal-bearing sediments of the Farne Group (Yoredale facies) in the northern part of the Cleaver Bank High. Organic matter is of Type III kerogen, with total organic carbon (TOC) contents between 0.89 and 1.87%. In the intra-platform basins, source rocks may be of marine (Types I + II) or continental origin (Type III). In SW England, and parts of NW Germany (Rheinische Schiefergebirge, Harz Mountains) source rocks occur in the starved basin facies (Culm facies). This is represented by black shales, siliceous carbonates, siliceous shales and dark mudstones. The thickness can reach 600 m, but is generally much less. Organic material is of kerogen Types I and II with TOC contents between 0.5 and 12%.

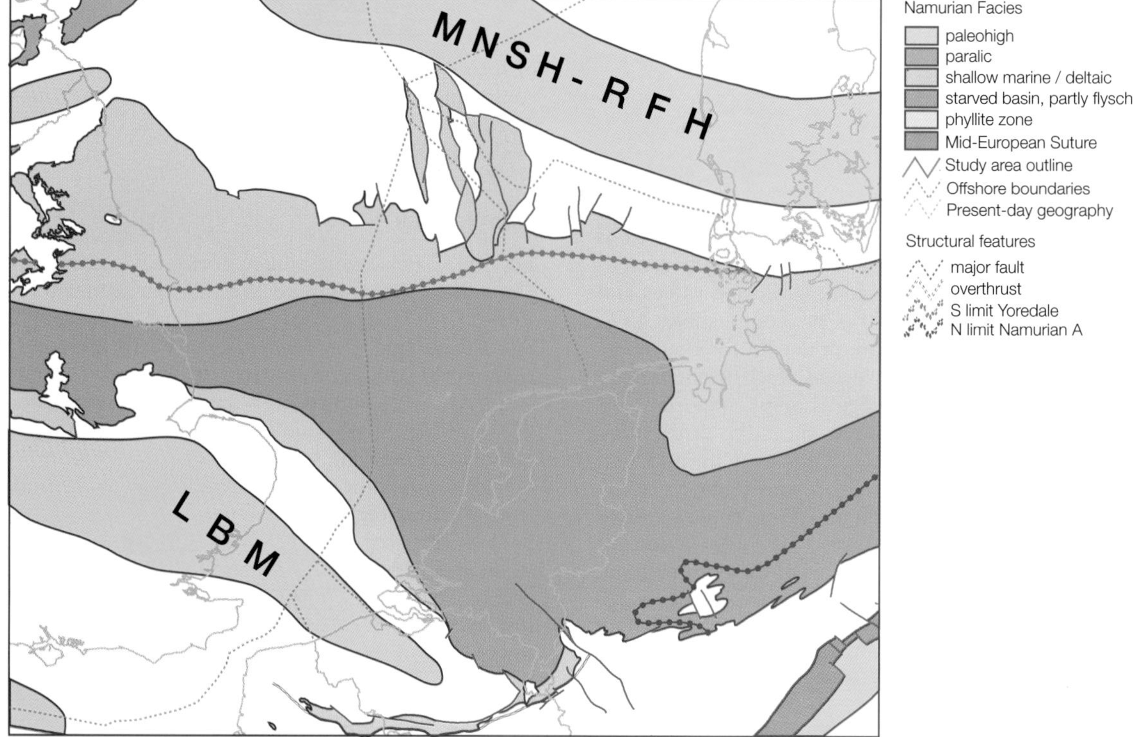

Fig. 2. Namurian A–B distribution and facies. LBM = London–Brabant Massif; MNSH = Mid North Sea High; RFH = Ringkøbing Fyn High.

The Namurian A–B was deposited essentially in the same basin as the Dinantian (Fig. 2). Two main facies have been identified in the study area, a shallow-marine/deltaic facies fringing the margins of the Namurian basin and a starved facies in the central part. The deltaic facies (Yoredale facies) has Type III source rocks with TOC contents of up to 2%. Most of the study area is underlain by basal Namurian marine shales (Bowland Shale/Geverik Member/Hangende Alaunschiefer), with excellent source-rock characteristics. TOC values range from 2% up to almost 60% with Type I and II kerogen. In the upper part of the Namurian, Coal Measures prevail in the Millstone Grit Formation and in the Stolberg and Sprockhoevel formations, with Type III kerogen and TOC contents as high as 5.4%.

Westphalian Coal Measures are widely accepted as the most important source rock in the area. Coal seams range up into the mid-Westphalian C with sediments containing up to 5% coal. In the West Netherlands Basin, the occurrence of marine source rocks with Type I and II kerogen has been reported (De Jager *et al.* 1996).

Carboniferous reservoirs and structural setting

Carboniferous gas fields in the western part of the Southern Permian Basin occur in two areas, namely the Southern North Sea and contiguous onshore UK, and the area along the border between The Netherlands and NW Germany. These two areas will be referred to hereafter as C1 and C2, respectively.

The Carboniferous play in the C1 area has been prominent only since the application of 3D seismics in exploration since the mid 1980s (Bailey *et al.* 1993; Besly *et al.* 1993; Maynard *et al.* 1997). An important trigger has been the better understanding of the complexity of the Carboniferous structures (Hollywood & Whorlow 1993). Most discoveries are in UK Quadrants 43, 44, 48 and 49, and the Dutch Blocks D, E and K. The Silverpit Claystone provides the seal for these fields (Bailey *et al.* 1993).

Sandstone reservoirs occur in area C1 at several stratigraphic intervals:

(i) Dinantian sandstones (Fell Sandstone) south of the Mid North Sea High;
(ii) Namurian (Millstone Grit Formation) (e.g. Trent Field);
(iii) Lower Westphalian B (Caister Sandstone/Murdoch Sandstone/Botney Member) (e.g. Caister, Murdoch, and D12-FA fields);
(iv) Westphalian C/D (Ketch Mb/Hospital Ground Formation) (e.g. Ketch Field and E13–1);

Basal Rotliegend sandstones may occur in association with all the above reservoirs. Published data indicate that gas fields occur in different structural settings:

(i) basal Zechstein closures coinciding with Carboniferous fault-bounded anticlines (e.g. the Caister Field) (Ritchie & Pratsides 1993);
(ii) half-graben filled with a thick succession of Westphalian C to possibly Stephanian sediments (Hollywood & Whorlow 1993).

Carboniferous discoveries in the C2 area date from the 1950s to 1970s. Reservoirs onshore in The Netherlands occur mainly in Upper Westphalian C to Stephanian strata, and in Germany in Westphalian A to D (NLfB 1997). Zechstein evaporites form the seal for the reservoirs. Traps are formed by fault-bounded basal Zechstein highs. The Rotliegend is generally absent or very thin in this area (NITG-TNO 1998).

Maturity

Maturity values for the top of the pre-Permian (Fig. 3) in area C1 fall predominantly between 1.0 and 1.5% random vitrinite reflectance (R_r). Areas of low maturity, ranging from 0.6 to 1.0% R_r, include the Central Netherlands High, Mid North Sea High, Cleaver Bank High, the East Midlands Shelf and the southern part of the Sole Pit Basin. The highest maturities, between 1.0 and 2.0% R_r, occur beneath the inverted Mesozoic basins (Broad Fourteens Basin, Central North Sea graben, Cleveland Basin, Sole Pit Basin; Fig. 3). Area C2 shows an eastward increase in maturity from around 0.8% to values well above 2.0% in the vicinity of magmatic intrusions, reaching as high as 3.0 to 6.0% R_r.

Distribution of gas components

The geochemical signatures of natural gases can provide information about the genesis of the gases, for example, whether they are of bacterial origin or have been thermally generated, as well as about the types of precursor kerogen. Additionally, gas mixtures from different sources, or altered gases, can often be identified (e.g. Schoell 1983; Whiticar 1990). Inter- or intra-reservoir correlation, determination of hydrocarbon source potential, migration pathways, and input into basin analysis models are among the immediate applications of geochemical information obtained from natural gases. All these applications are based on the fact that there are significant and predictable compositional variations between the various gas types.

The regional distribution of gas constituents or physical gas parameters provides valuable information about the natural gas quality. For this project it was decided to map methane (CH_4), nitrogen (N_2), carbon dioxide (CO_2), the gas composition methane/(ethane + propane) [$C_1/(C_2+C_3)$], stable carbon isotope ratios of methane ($\delta^{13}CH_4$), calorific values, and gas densities.

The differences in gas composition between the two Carboniferous production provinces C1 and C2 are illustrated in Figs 4–6. The information shown on these maps is based on 21 producing wells from reservoirs in the C1 production province and 24 wells from 21 gas fields in the C2 province.

Methane is the predominant gas in almost the entire production area of the provinces described here (Fig. 4). Nearly all Carboniferous gas fields in production province C1 contain more than 80% methane. Only over the Cleaver Bank High does the CH_4 content fall below 80%. Most of the gas reservoirs in province C2 contain more than 85% methane. These reservoirs form a NW–SE trending area accompanied on both sides by areas with significantly lower methane concentrations. Just to the NE of this area is the depocentre of the Southern Permian Basin, where the main source rocks, the Westphalian coals, are relatively deeply buried, and so have any potential. On the southwest side, the Upper Cretaceous Bramsche–Vlotho–Uchte intrusive and its apophyses have, to a large extent, locally influenced maturity (cf. Fig. 3) and caused a dramatic decline in the methane-generating potential of the Westphalian coal seams. Additionally, the gas in these reservoirs is contaminated by CO_2 originating from the thermal alteration of carbonates (e.g. Boigk & Stahl 1970) and by intrusion-related nitrogen, most probably from the deeper crust or the mantle, as inferred by Gerling *et al.* (1997).

Elevated nitrogen concentrations ($N_2 > 10\%$) occur locally (Fig. 5). The ratio of nitrogen to methane may have a genetic basis, i.e. a decrease in methane-generating potential coincides with an increase in nitrogen-generating potential in coaly organic matter (e.g. Krooss *et al.* 1993). Conversely, the spatial distribution of Upper Cretaceous intrusives in NW Germany appears to coincide with high nitrogen contents in the surrounding reservoirs, suggesting derivation of the nitrogen from the intrusives. This explanation may also be valid for gas fields on the Cleaver Bank High.

Carbon dioxide is the third most abundant gas component in the reservoirs, and creates a severe problem for field

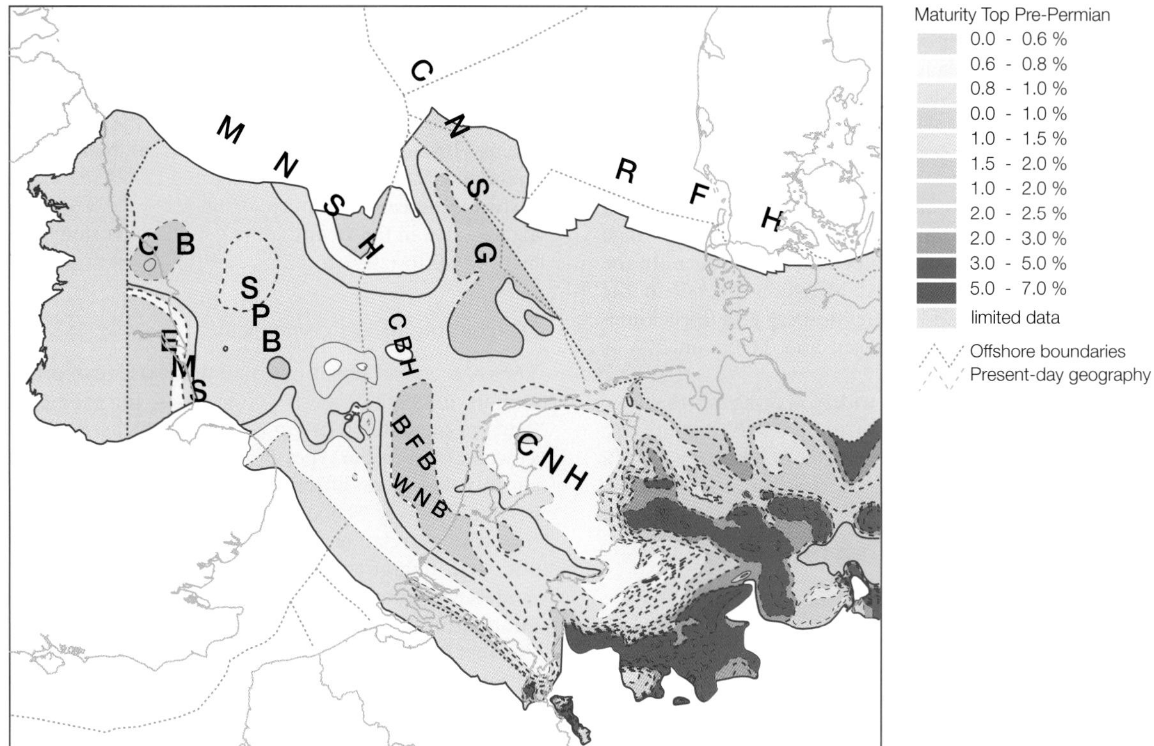

Fig. 3. Vitrinite reflectance map (Rr) (top pre-Permian). BFB = Broad Fourteens Basin; CB = Cleveland Basin; CBH = Cleaver Bank High; CNH = Central Netherlands High; CNSG = Central North Sea Graben; EMS = East Midland Shelf; MNSH = Mid North Sea High; RFH = Ringkøbing Fyn High; SPB = Sole Pit Basin; WNB = West Netherlands Basin.

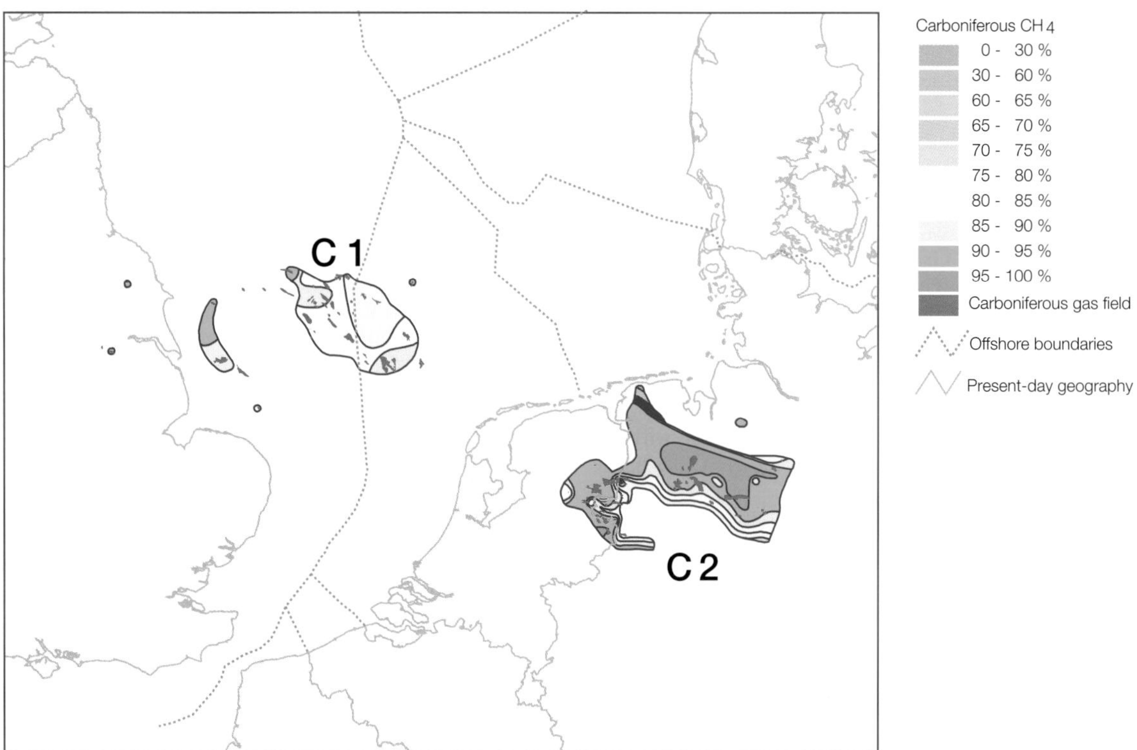

Fig. 4. Methane content of Carboniferous reservoirs. C1: Southern North Sea Carboniferous production province; C2: Carboniferous production province along the border between The Netherlands and Germany.

development. CO_2 contents usually range between 0 and 5%, although isolated higher concentrations do occur (Fig. 6). In contrast to the low maturity areas, the CO_2 contents at the Cleaver Bank High are relatively high, i.e. more than 1% in almost the entire mapped area, and occasionally exceeding 5%. These relatively high carbon dioxide concentrations could have originated from magmatic exhalations or thermal alteration of carbonates in the deeper crust, for example. Evidence for this is given by gravity and magnetic anomalies in this area (Lee *et al.* 1993). However, it remains uncertain whether these

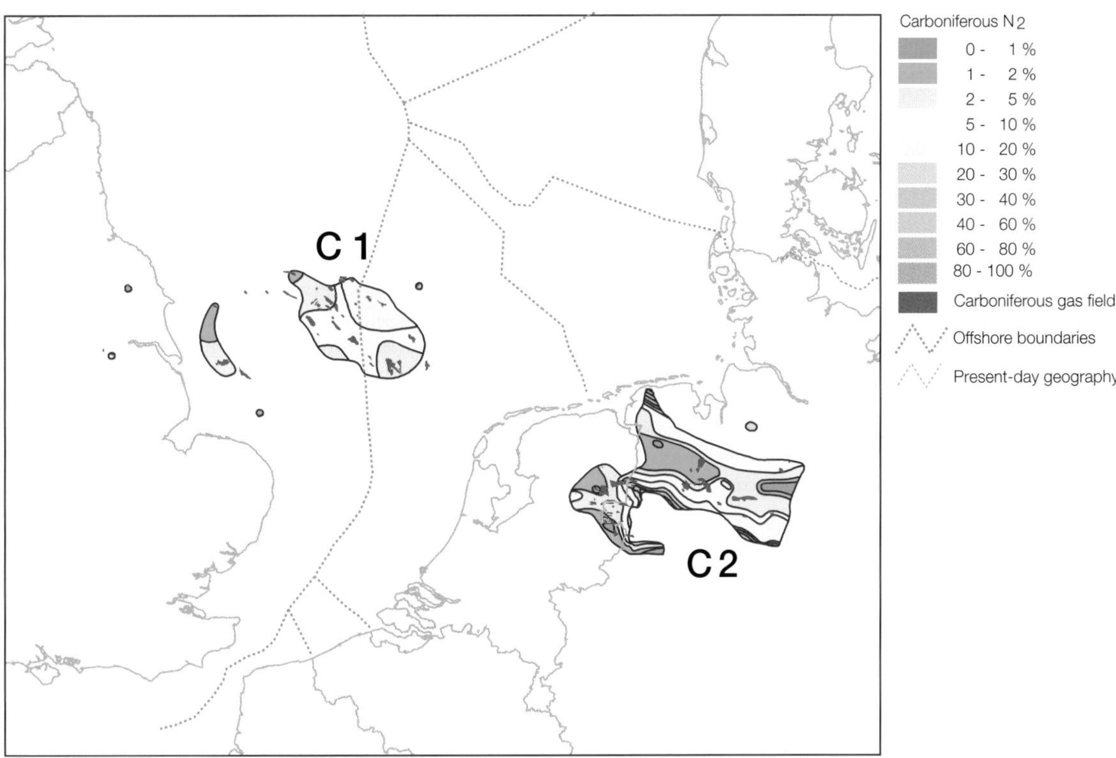

Fig. 5. Nitrogen content of Carboniferous reservoirs. C1: Southern North Sea Carboniferous production province; C2: Carboniferous production province along the border between The Netherlands and Germany.

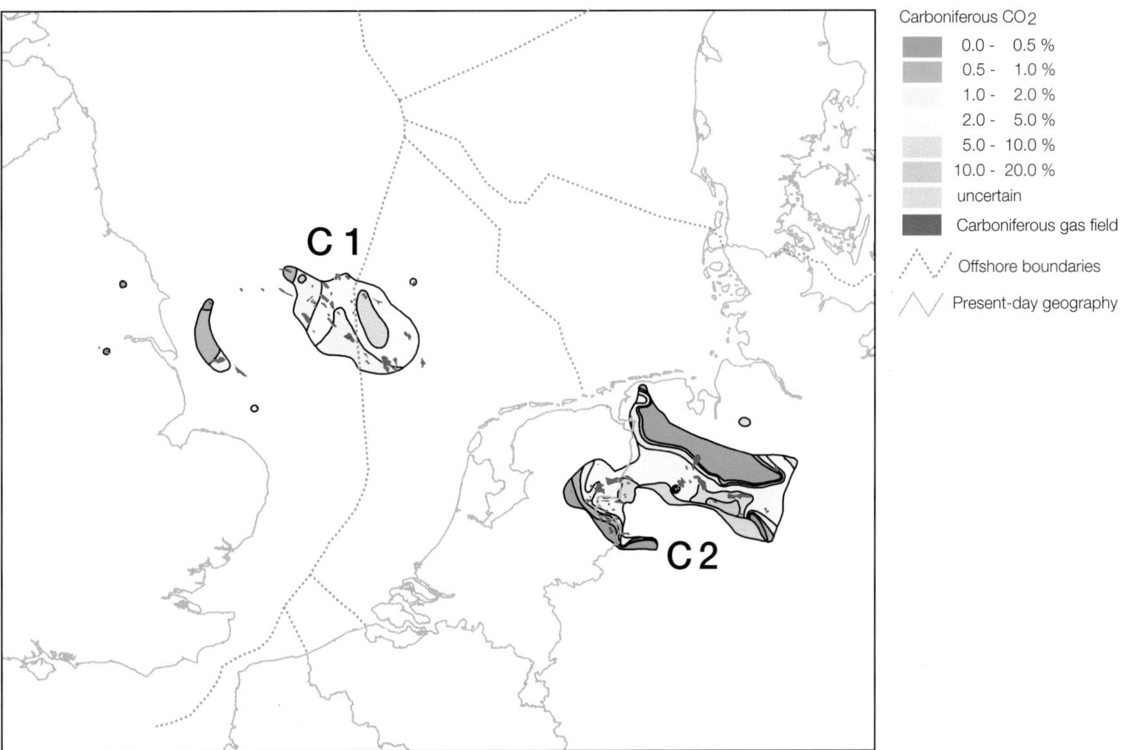

Fig. 6. Carbon dioxide content of Carboniferous reservoirs. C1: Southern North Sea Carboniferous production province; C2: Carboniferous production province along the border between The Netherlands and Germany.

indications coincide with elevated maturities in the area of the Cleaver Bank High. In NW Germany and eastern Netherlands, the CO_2 contents in reservoir gases correlate well with the maturity map. Concentrations are below 1% in areas with maturities below 1.5% vitrinite reflectance. Conversely, the Upper Cretaceous intrusives are clearly marked by high carbon dioxide contents, locally more than 10%.

The Bernard parameter $C_1/(C_2+C_3)$ (Bernard *et al.* 1976) on a molecular basis, reflects the maturity of the source rocks. In areas with high source-rock maturities, such as are found near the Bramsche–Vlotho–Uchte intrusive in NW Germany, reservoirs contain dry natural gases ($C_1/(C_2+C_3)>75$), whereas the reservoirs further away (in both production provinces) contain mostly wet gases with $C_1/(C_2+C_3)<25$.

Stable carbon isotope ratios of gaseous hydrocarbons are influenced by the type and maturity of the source rock. The methane data for the Carboniferous reservoirs, again, seem to reflect the maturity of the Carboniferous precursor materials (cf. Fig 3). $\delta^{13}CH_4$ values in reservoirs around the Upper Cretaceous intrusives in NW Germany are more positive (indicating more abundant ^{13}C) than −33‰, and in most cases are even higher than −27‰, indicating a rather high maturity of the precursor material. In the area of the Cleaver Bank High, however, these values are always lower than −33‰, thus indicating a lower source-rock maturity. Although this is in agreement with the maturity map, this conclusion must be viewed with caution since this interpretation does not take into account differences in source-rock type. Calorific values of reservoir gases, calculated from gas compositions, are given in $MJ\,m^{-3}$. Contaminants such as N_2 or CO_2 have a negative effect and consequently reduce the value. Additionally, the molecular composition of gaseous hydrocarbons is the most important parameter for determining the calorific value. Particularly high concentrations of higher alkanes lead to significant increases in the calorific value. Values lie between 30 and 44 $MJ\,m^{-3}$ in both areas. In NW Germany and eastern Netherlands, with a coincidentally increasing Bernard parameter, nitrogen and carbon dioxide contents reduce the calorific values towards the intrusives. At the Cleaver Bank High and the surrounding area, calorific values decrease from SW to NE, thus reflecting the increasing dryness of the gas and the increasing contaminant content.

Gas density is a complex parameter calculated from all gas components in the reservoir. Each contaminant contributes to the density as much as the higher alkanes. Hence, a wet gas and a gas containing significant contaminants would have similar high densities. Only dry hydrocarbon gases without significant amounts of contaminants have gas densities as low as 0.50–0.55; such values occur in parts of NW Germany. Further to the west, densities in eastern Netherlands are as high as 0.60, even reaching 0.65–0.70, but this increase is only caused by the presence of wet gases. At the Cleaver Bank High and in the surrounding reservoirs, densities are always greater than 0.55, being between 0.65 and 0.70 in the greater part of the area, and locally more than 0.75. Here, the combination of wet hydrocarbon gas and the presence of contaminants is responsible for these higher values.

Gas origin: information from molecular and isotopic compositions

A genetic characterization of reservoir gases can be of considerable assistance in understanding and describing the specific conditions that developed in a production province. Moreover, this information may be very useful when comparing different production provinces. The approach used here focuses on methane and nitrogen which, together with carbon dioxide, are the predominant natural gas components. The genetic decoding of carbon dioxide is problematic (because of an overlap of various genetic or secondary processes such as decarboxylation, dissociation of carbonates, thermochemical sulphate reduction, magmatic exhalation) and has, therefore, not been included in these considerations. Ethane has been included from the minor gas constituents because it provides significant additional information about the type and maturity of a gas-producing source rock.

Gaseous hydrocarbons

The genesis of gaseous hydrocarbons can be interpreted by using, for example, the Bernard diagram (Bernard *et al.* 1976; Faber & Stahl 1984), in which the molecular gas ratio $C_1/(C_2+C_3)$ is plotted against the stable carbon isotope ratio for methane. This combination is particularly suitable for distinguishing gases with a large range in the relative amount of C_{2+} hydrocarbons. The plot permits bacterially generated methane to be distinguished from thermogenic hydrocarbon gases, with a further distinction between thermogenic gases from marine and terrestrial source rocks.

A Bernard diagram for Carboniferous reservoir gases from the C1 production province is shown in Fig. 7a. The gases have $C_1/(C_2+C_3)$ ratios between 8 and 45 and $\delta^{13}C_1$ values between −44 and −30‰, clearly indicating thermogenic origin from a marine precursor. Two exceptions are the gases with the most negative and the most positive isotope ratios (both from the UK sector of the production province). These two ratios indicate a typical oil-associated gas, in the first case and gas from a terrestrial precursor material, in the second.

Gases from reservoirs in the C2 production province have $C_1/(C_2+C_3)$ ratios of between 11 and 315, and $\delta^{13}C_1$ values between −32 and −22‰ (Fig. 7a). The gases display, with their synchronous increase in carbon isotope ratios and gas ratios, an almost ideal maturity trend. All of these gases seem to derive from a terrestrial precursor, although the 'driest' and the 'wettest' gases lie outside the area of coal-derived gases.

The gases from province C2 were generated from Westphalian coals, whereas the Carboniferous gases from the C1 province are of mixed origin: a low maturity terrestrial source rock (Westphalian) and a more mature marine source rock (?Namurian). For comparison, Fig. 7b shows the data for the Rotliegend gas fields (R1 and R2, corresponding to the C1 area, and R3, corresponding to the C2 area). It can be seen that the Rotliegend natural gases show the same differences as the gases in the Carboniferous fields.

The combination of stable carbon isotope ratios of methane and ethane allows the type and maturity of the gas-producing source rock to be estimated. Based on the pioneering work of Stahl (1968) and Stahl & Carey (1975) showing empirical relationships between the maturity of source rocks (vitrinite reflectance, R_r) and the isotopic composition of the related gaseous hydrocarbons, several researchers (e.g. Sundberg & Bennett 1983; James 1983, Ping & Xu 1986, Schütze & Mühle 1986, Faber 1987, Chung *et al.* 1988; Galimov 1988; Berner 1989; Zhang & Feng 1990; Clayton 1991; Berner *et al.* 1992) have proposed methods for application of carbon isotopes of gases to hydrocarbon exploration. The advantages and disadvantages of the individual models are discussed elsewhere (Berner & Faber 1993).

In Fig. 8 the methane/ethane maturity lines proposed by Berner & Faber (1996) have been used which allow adjustment to kerogen compositions. The figure shows the methane/ethane maturity lines for sapropelic and terrestrial organic matter. Values of −23‰ and −29‰ have been chosen for the carbon isotope ratios of the terrestrial and sapropelic gas precursors. If a hydrocarbon gas contains only cogenetic methane and ethane from one of these source rocks, the corresponding pair of values should plot on or near a maturity line, indicating the maturity of the source rock.

However, the gas in natural gas deposits very often has not been generated solely from a single source rock, but contains components from one or more other source rocks. Isotope data for such mixed gases do not generally plot on a maturity line. In the case of gases from just two sources, which (to our current knowledge) is very common in natural gas reservoirs, carbon isotope data for methane and ethane of the mixed gas can be calculated using simple algorithms, including the molecular ratios of the mixed gases. Considering variable source types and maturities, 'mixing corridors' can be established for the two gases. These are presented in Fig. 8:

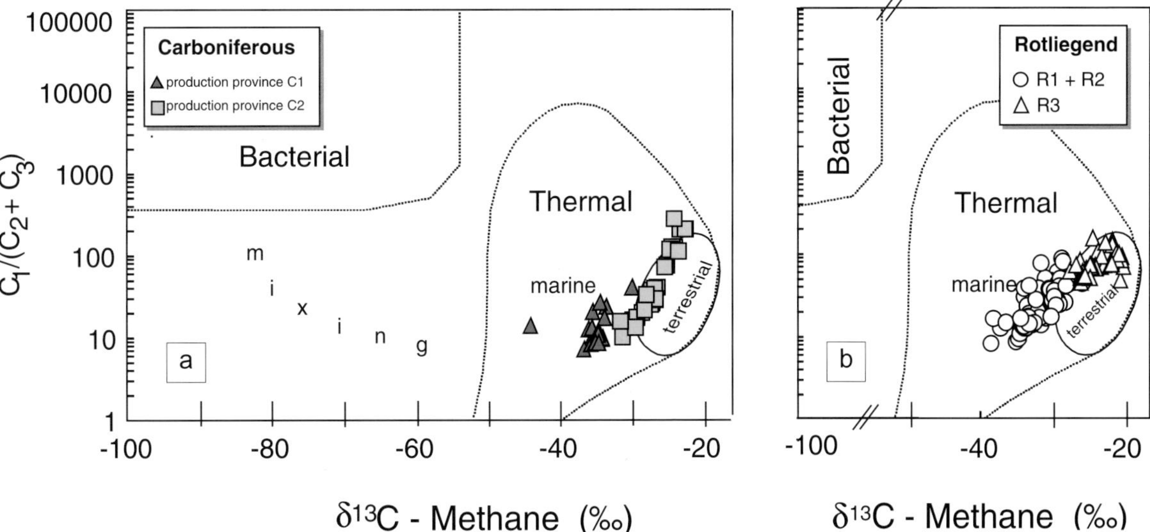

Fig. 7. (**a**) Gases from Carboniferous reservoirs in the Southern North Sea and onshore UK (production province C1) seem to originate from marine source rocks, whereas those from NW Germany and eastern Netherlands (production province C2) are more likely generated from Westphalian coals. (**b**) Data for Rotliegend gas fields substantiate the interpretation.

(i) If the gas is a mixture of dry gas from a terrestrial precursor and wet gas from a sapropelic precursor, it always lies within the 'corridor' above the maturity lines for the two source rocks;

(ii) If the gas is a mixture of a gas from a rather low maturity terrestrial source with a dry gas from sapropelic organic matter with a higher maturity, it lies in the 'mixing corridor' below the maturity lines for the two source rocks.

Application of these considerations to these reservoir data has stimulated new interpretations of the data from the two Carboniferous production provinces C1 and C2 (Fig. 9a).

Gas from the C1 production province has $\delta^{13}C_{CH_4}$ values between −44 and −30‰ and $\delta^{13}C_{C_2H_6}$ values between −30 and −21‰. Most of the data clearly indicate a mixture of gas from a predominantly marine source with a maturity of about 1.5–2% R_r with a minor amount of gas from a terrestrial source of lower maturity. Only the UK gas with the most positive $\delta^{13}C_{CH_4}$ value seems to contain a higher proportion of gas from a terrestrial source. The most negative $\delta^{13}C_{CH_4}$ value indicates the presence of palaeobacterial methane, which is fairly common in oil-associated gases.

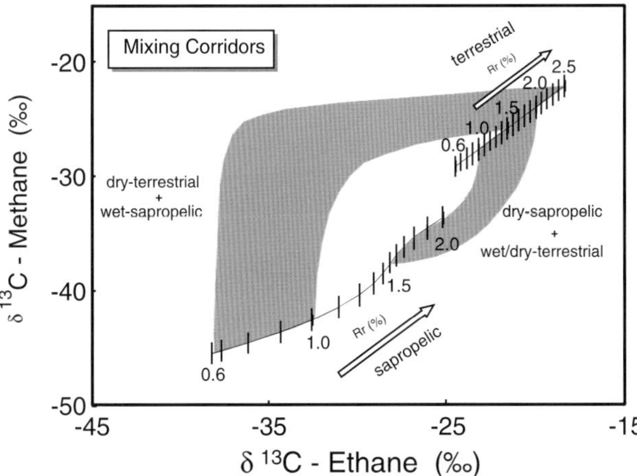

Fig. 8. Stable carbon isotope ratios for methane and ethane permit estimation of the type and maturity of gas-generating source rocks. Kerogen-related maturity lines can be fitted to data for specific source rocks. Mixtures of gases from different source rocks can be interpreted using the molecular and isotopic compositions of the mixed gases (after Berner & Faber 1988).

Most gases from the C2 production province have $\delta^{13}C_{CH_4}$ values between −32 and −22‰ and $\delta^{13}C_{C_2H_6}$ values between −28 and −22‰, indicating a mixture of gases from a predominantly terrestrial source with maturity values up to 2% R_r and (in some cases) a minor amount of gas from a lower maturity marine source. The latter source is assumed to be organic matter in the Zechstein 2 cycle (Stassfurt Carbonate).

For comparison, Fig. 9b shows the corresponding data for the Rotliegend gas fields (R1 and R2 ≈ C1, and R3 ≈ C2). It can be seen that the Rotliegend natural gases show the same differences as the gases in the Carboniferous fields.

The conclusions drawn from Fig. 9 support the conclusions drawn from Fig. 7 that most of the hydrocarbon gases from the C1 production province could have been generated from marine organic matter. We believe that pre-Westphalian marine shales, e.g. in sediments, such as the Bowland Shales in the Lower Namurian, may be potential source rocks. The other components of these gas mixtures were generated in the Westphalian coal seams, which are the main source rock in production province C2.

Nitrogen

The genetic interpretation of nitrogen is based on isotopic and molecular nitrogen data from pyrolysis experiments on coaly organic matter and also on isotope–geochemical measurements of autochthonous Zechstein gases (Fig. 10, after Gerling *et al.* 1997). It is of note that differences in the isotopic ratios allow nitrogen from a marine source rock to be distinguished from nitrogen derived from terrestrial precursor materials.

The database for gases from the C1 production province is rather small. However, the data for all five gases (N_2 contents of 0.2–21%, $\delta^{15}N$ values between 5 and 13‰) indicate a mixture of nitrogen from both a terrestrial and a marine source. The gas with the highest nitrogen content has the highest percentage of nitrogen from the marine precursor, which must be pre-Westphalian if the methane and nitrogen are cogenetic.

The gases from the C2 production province (N_2 contents of 0.7–20%, $\delta^{15}N$ values between −3 and 16‰) can be clearly divided into two groups with $\delta^{15}N$ values ≥5‰ and with $\delta^{15}N$

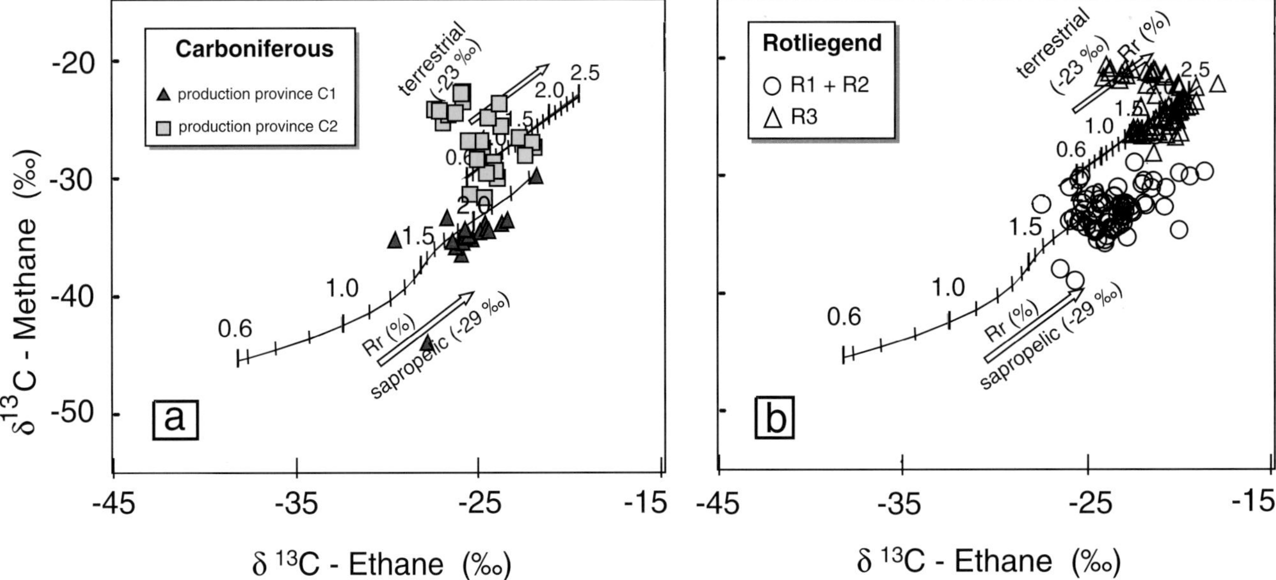

Fig. 9. (**a**) C1 gases obviously originated from marine organic matter of relatively high maturity (~1.5–2.0% R_r), whereas those from production province C2 were generated from terrestrial source materials. The maturity of the latter gases vary in a broad range up to 2% R_r. Mixture with gas from a lower-maturity marine source is observed for several C2 gases (cf. Fig. 7). (**b**) Data for Rotliegend gas fields substantiate the interpretation.

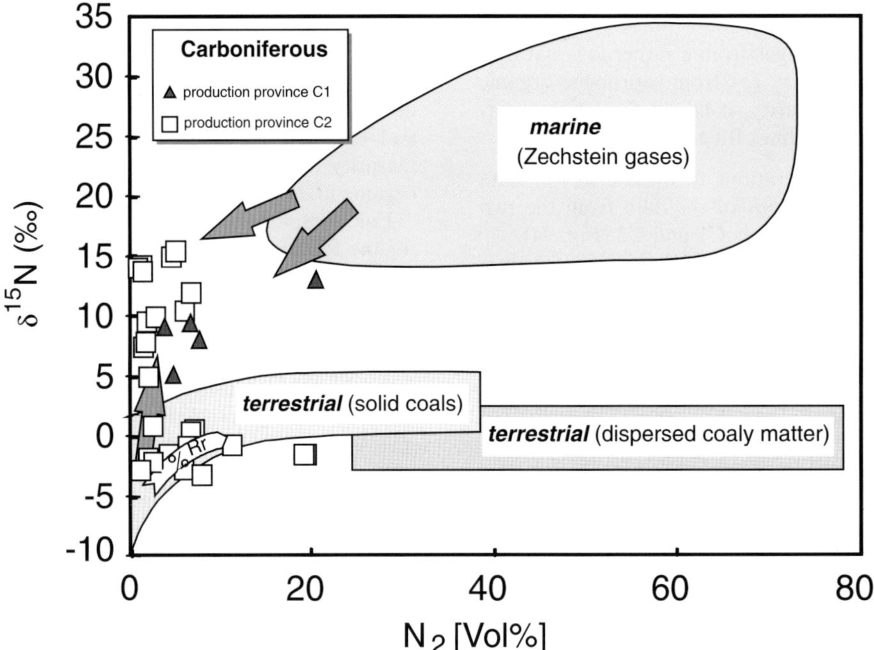

Fig. 10. Nitrogen gases are differentiated into two groups. Those with $\delta^{15}N > 5$‰ indicating a mixture of terrestrial (probably Westphalian) and marine sources. The marine source for the C1 gases is believed to be a Namurian sediment, whereas that of the C2 gases is a Zechstein sediment (Stassfurt Carbonate). Gases with $\delta^{15}N < 1$ are only derived from Westphalian coals.

values <1‰. The first group is clearly a mixture of nitrogen from both a terrestrial (Westphalian) and a marine source (Zechstein), whereas the nitrogen of the latter group seems to derive from terrestrial organic matter only. Since these gases are from reservoirs close to the igneous intrusive of Bramsche–Vlotho–Uchte, gas from the deep crust or mantle (cf. Gerling *et al.* 1997) should also be considered.

In summary, all gases from the C1 production province and some natural gases from production province C2 contain nitrogen from several sources, with a significant proportion from marine source rocks. It is inferred that in C1 gases, this nitrogen derives from pre-Westphalian source rocks, whereas the 'marine nitrogen' in the C2 gases either derives from organic matter in Zechstein sediments or is related to intrusives. This interpretation is in agreement with the statements made earlier concerning the gaseous hydrocarbons.

Conclusions

The 'NW European Gas Atlas' provides a comprehensive overview of the geochemical and geological setting of the Southern Permian Basin, and for the first time makes it possible to compare reservoir contents of large-scale petroleum-bearing units. An understanding of the composition of gases and the close relationship between geological history, source rock composition and hydrocarbon gas generation provide new conclusions that will be of significant help in evaluating the regional or local hydrocarbon potential in the area of investigation.

The following conclusions can be drawn for the Carboniferous gas plays in the western part of the Southern Permian Basin:

(i) isotopic data for different gases ($\delta^{15}N$, $\delta^{13}C_1$, $\delta^{13}C_2$) are a prerequisite for an understanding of the origin of natural gases and their components;
(ii) analysis of the isotopic data indicates that the gases in Carboniferous reservoirs in the Southern North Sea originate from two different source rocks: a relatively low-maturity terrestrial source, most likely the Westphalian Coal Measures, and a higher maturity marine source, perhaps the organic-rich Namurian shales;
(iii) analysis of the isotopic data also indicates that the gases in Carboniferous reservoirs in NW Germany and eastern Netherlands originate from terrestrial Westphalian source rocks only; in view of the higher coalification of the area, deeper source rocks of marine origin are likely to be overmature;
(iv) the nitrogen in several of the Southern North Sea gas fields is inferred to be a mixture of gas from both marine and terrestrial source rocks. This is in line with earlier statements concerning the gaseous hydrocarbons. Unfortunately, it is impossible to determine the proportions of gases in the mixture because the end members are missing.

On the basis of these conclusions, it is strongly recommended that the occurrence, distribution, and gas-generation potential of pre-Westphalian source rocks should be investigated in greater detail.

The 'NW European Gas Atlas' Project has been carried out under contract No. JOU2-CT93-0295 and ERBCIPD-CT94-0502 of the European Union. We would like to express our thanks to the numerous oil companies who are active in the area for permission to use their gas analysis data. We also wish to thank our colleagues for their contribution to the maps shown here: J. V. M. Brugge, L. Diapari, J. Heckers, W. J. J. Fermont, K. Adlam and F. B. Rispens.

References

BAILEY, J. B., ARBIN, P., DAFFINOTI, O., GIBSON, P. & RITCHIE, J. S. 1993. Permo-Carboniferous plays in the Silver Pit Basin. *In*: PARKER, J. R. (ed.) *Petroleum Geology of Northwest Europe: Proceedings of the 4th Conference*. Geological Society, London, 707–715.

BERNARD, B. B., BROOKS, J. M. & SACKETTT, W. M. 1976. Natural gas seepage in the Gulf of Mexico. *Earth and Planetary Science Letters*, **31**, 45–54.

BERNER, U. 1989. Entwicklung und Anwendung empirischer Modelle für die Kohlenstoffisotopenvariationen in Mischungen thermogener Erdgase. Ph.D. Thesis Techn, University Clausthal, 162pp.

—— & Faber, E. 1988. Maturity related mixing model for methane, ethane and propane, based on carbon isotopes. *Organic Geochemistry*, **13**, 67–72.

—— & ——1993. *Zusammenführung und Weiterentwicklung isotopengeochemischer Methoden in der Exploration von Kohlenwasserstoffen. BGR-Report 112 083*, 48pp, Federal Institute Geoscience National Resources, Hannover.

—— & ——1996. Empirical carbon isotope/maturity relationships for gases from algal kerogens and terrigenous organic matter, based on dry, open-system pyrolysis. *Organic Geochemistry*, **24**, 947–955.

——, —— & STAHL, W. 1992. Mathematical simulation of carbon isotopic fractionation between huminitic coals and related methane. *Chemical Geology*, **94**, 315–319.

BESLY, B. M., BURDLEY, S. D. & TURNER, P. 1993. The late Carboniferous 'Barren Red Play' of the Silver Pit area, Southern North Sea. *In*: PARKER, J. R. (ed.) *Petroleum Geology of Northwest Europe: Proceedings of the 4th Conference*. Geological Society, London, 727–740.

BOIGK, H. & STAHL, W. 1970. Zum Problem der Entstehung nordwestdeutscher Erdgaslagerstätten. *Erdöl und Kohle, Erdgas, Petrochemie vereinigt mit Brennstoff-Chemie*, **23**, 325–333.

CHUNG, H. M., GORMLEY, J. R. & SQUIRES, R. M. 1988. Origin of gaseous hydrocarbons in subsurface environments: Theoretical considerations of carbon isotope distributions. *Chemical Geology*, **71**, 97–103.

CLAYTON, C. 1991. Carbon isotope fractionation during natural gas generation from kerogen. *Marine and Petroleum Geology*, **8**, 232–240.

DE JAGER, J., DOYLE, M. A., GRANTHAM, P. J. & MABILLARD, J. E. 1996. Hydrocarbon habitat of the West Netherlands Basin. *In*: RONDEEL, H. E., BATJES, D. A. J. & NIEUWENHUIS, W. H. (eds) *Geology of Gas and Oil under the Netherlands*, 191–211.

FABER E. 1987. Zur Isotopengeochemie gasförmiger Kohlenwasserstoffe. *Erdöl, Erdgas, Kohle*, **103**, 210–218.

—— & STAHL, W. J. 1984. Geochemical surface exploration for hydrocarbons in the North Sea. *AAPG Bulletin*, **68**, 363–386.

GALIMOV, E. 1988. Sources and mechanisms of formation of gaseous hydrocarbons in sedimentary rocks. *Chemical Geology*, **71**, 77–95.

GERLING, P., IDIZ, E., EVERLIEN, G. & SOHNS, E. 1997. New aspects on the origin of nitrogen in natural gas in northern Germany. *Geologisches Jahrbuch*, **D103**, 65–84.

HOLLYWOOD, J. M. & WHORLOW, C. V. 1993. Structural development and hydrocarbon occurrence of the Carboniferous in the UK Southern North Sea Basin. *In*: PARKER, J. R. (ed.) *Petroleum Geology of Northwest Europe: Proceedings of the 4th Conference*. Geological Society, London, 689–696.

JAMES, A. 1983. Correlation of natural gas by use of carbon isotope distribution between hydrocarbon components. *American Association of Petroleum Geologists Bulletin*, **67**, 1176–1191.

KROOSS, B., LEYTHAEUSER, D. & LILLACK, H. 1993. Nitrogen-rich natural gases – Qualitative and quantitative aspects of natural gas accumulation in reservoirs. *Erdöl und Kohle, Erdgas, Petrochemie vereinigt mit Brennstoff-Chemie*, **46**, 271–276.

LEE, M. K., PHARAOH, T. C., WILLIAMSON, J. P., GREEN, C. A. & DE VOS, W. 1993. Evidence on the deep structure of the Anglo-Brabant Massif from gravity and magnetic data. *Geological Magazine*, **130**(5), 575–582.

LOKHORST, A. (ed.) 1998. *Northwest European Gas Atlas – Composition and Isotope Ratios of Natural Gases*. NITG-TNO, Haarlem.

MAYNARD, J. R., HOFMANN, W., DUNAY, R. E., BENTHAM, P. N., DEAN, K. P. & WATSON, I. 1997. The Carboniferous of western Europe: the development of a petroleum system. *Petroleum Geoscience*, **3**, 97–115.

NITG-TNO 1998. *Explanation to map sheet X, Almelo–Winterswijk. Geological Atlas of the Subsurface of the Netherlands*, 142pp, Haarlem.

NLFB. 1997. *Erdöl und Erdgas in der Bundesrepublik Deutschland*. 51pp, Hannover.

PING, S. & XU, Y. 1986. Continental sediments in China. *Academia Sinica*, 185 199.

RITCHIE, J. S. & PRATSIDES, P. 1993. The Caister Fields, Block 44/23a, UK North Sea. *In*: PARKER, J. R. (ed.) *Petroleum Geology of Northwest Europe: Proceedings of the 4th Conference*. Geological Society, London, 759–769.

SCHOELL, M. 1983. Genetic characterization of natural gases. *American Association of Petroleum Geologists Bulletin*, **67**, 2225–2238.

SCHÜTZE, H. & MÜHLE, K. 1986. How to get relations between bedrocks and $\delta^{13}C$ values of methane and ethane in natural gases. *Proceedings of the 4th Meeting Isotopes in Nature, Leipzig* 1986, 589–603. Zentralinstitut für Isotopen- und Strahlenforschung, Leipzig.

STAHL, W. J. 1968. *Kohlenstoff-Isotopenanalysen zur Klärung der Herkunft norddeutscher Erdgase*. PhD Thesis Techno, University Clausthal, 107pp.

—— & CAREY, JR. B. D. 1975. Source-rock identification by isotope analyses of natural gases from fields in the Val Verde and the Delaware Basins, West Texas. *Chemical Geology*, **16**, 257–267.

SUNDBERG, K. R. & BENNETT, C. R. 1983. Carbon isotope paleothermometry of natural gas. *Advances in Organic Geochemistry*, **1981**, 769–774.

WHITICAR, M. J. 1990. A geochemical perspective of natural gas and atmosperic methane. *Organic Geochemistry*, **16**, 531–547.

ZHANG, Y. G. & FENG, X. Z. 1990. Catalytic versus noncatalytic degradation of organic matter related to its gas productivity. *In*: ITTEKKOT, V., KEMPE, S., MICHAELIS, W. & SPITZY, A. (eds) *Facets of Modern Biogeochemistry*, 402–415, Springer, Berlin.

The Trent Gas Field: correlation and reservoir quality within a complex Carboniferous stratigraphy

P. T. O'MARA, M. MERRYWEATHER, M. STOCKWELL and M. M. BOWLER

ARCO British Limited, London Square, Cross Lanes, Guildford, Surrey, GU1 1UE, UK (e-mail: pomara@is.arco.com)

Abstract: The Trent Field gas accumulation in the UKCS (United Kingdom Continental Shelf) Southern Gas Basin is reservoired in Carboniferous age sediments. It is contained within a NW–SE trending base Permian structural feature that straddles Blocks 43/24a, 43/23 and 43/25. The proven reserves within the core area lie solely within the 43/24a block. Field appraisal and development encountered three main areas of complexity: structure, reservoir continuity and reservoir property variations.

The 20 km long base Permian feature is controlled by NW–SE trending post-Rotliegendes reverse faults which produced a positive inversion. Antithetic faults to these reverse faults also occur within the structure. A second WSW–ENE normal fault trend comparmentalizes the field, and is also thought to have influenced sedimentation during Carboniferous times. Similar fault-influenced deposition is documented at equivalent times in the UK onshore. Ultimately this structural complexity controls the Carboniferous subcrop, which is seen to increase in age from late to early Westphalian A, in a southeasterly direction, although dramatic changes can occur on a more local scale in some fault compartments.

The Trent Field accumulation is contained within an interval ranging in age from Marsdenian to early Westphalian A. It encompasses a number of facies associations in delta top and lower delta plain environments, which vary rapidly both vertically and laterally. Reservoir facies include incised valley-fills, transgressive reworked sandstones and distributary channels, which vary markedly in their lateral extent. Reservoir quality of these facies ranges from very poor to excellent and is controlled primarily by the depositional environment in which grain size and sediment maturity are the most important factors.

The Trent Gas Field lies within Block 43/24a, to the west of the producing Carboniferous gas fields of Quadrant 44, south of the Triassic Bunter gas fields Esmond, Forbes, Gordon and northeast of the Rotliegendes gas fields of Quadrant 43, 47, 48 and 49. It is located 120 km off the Yorkshire coast in average water depths of 49 m (Fig. 1). The accumulation is contained within a faulted base Permian feature which straddles Blocks 43/24a, 43/23 and 43/25. This structure covers an area of 75 km^2 although the producible reserves are only located in the central core area of 43/24a. Marsdenian (Millstone Grit Formation) and Westphalian A (Caister Coal Formation) aged sandstones form the reservoir for the gas and are hereafter informally termed the Trent Sandstone (upper and lower) and Westphalian A distributary channel sandstone respectively. The production mechanism is by natural depletion. The field is operated from ARCO's onshore operations room at Great Yarmouth using an unmanned platform. Gas is currently being evacuated via the Eagles Transport System into the Amoco terminal at Bacton.

The structure has been delineated by four exploration/appraisal wells (Fig. 2). A further three development wells were pre-drilled prior to jacket installation in July 1996, a fourth was required post hook-up. First gas production was on 11th November 1996.

Exploration and delineation history

The licensees in Block 43/24a are:

- ARCO British Limited (Operator) 61.25%
- Talisman Energy (UK) Limited 20.0%
- Atlantic Richfield (St James') Limited 18.75%

The block was awarded to ARCO in 1989 as part of the 11th round of licensing. Mandatory 50% relinquishment was made in July 1997.

The structure defined at base Permian level was first tested in 1985 by the British Gas Well 43/25-1 which flowed at less than 1 million square cubic feet of gas per day ($\times 10^6$ SCFG(D)) from Westphalian A sandstones (Table 1). In 1990 ARCO drilled 43/24-1 and encountered a gas bearing Carboniferous section over 330 m thick with a gross reservoir interval of 37 m. This well tested 34×10^6 SCFG(D) from the Trent Sandstone. Well 43/24-2 was drilled 3.5 km to the southeast, along the crest of the structure and in early 1992 encountered water bearing Trent Sandstone but a highly permeable Westphalian A distributary channel sandstone in the gas leg. The well tested at 29×10^6 SCFG(D).

In mid 1992 the Chevron 43/23 group drilled Well 43/23-2 at the northwestern end of the structural closure. The well encountered a tight gas bearing Millstone Grit section which failed to flow at measurable rates on test. An extensive 3D seismic survey was acquired by the 43/24 group in early 1993. During the first quarter of 1993 Well 43/24-3 was drilled 4.0 km to the southeast of 43/24-2 and encountered several gas bearing horizons within the Millstone Grit and Caister Coal formations. It tested 33×10^6 SCFG(D) from the former reservoir and 19×10^6 SCFG(D) from the latter.

The fourth Well 43/24-4 was drilled from the 43/24-1 location in late 1993 to the western flank of the 43/24 structure. It failed to encounter any reservoir quality sandstones within the sections encountered by the previous wells. An older aged interval was found to be gas bearing, but the well was suspended untested.

Development drilling

Four development wells were drilled across the Trent structure from a platform located at the 43/24-1 location (Fig. 3).

The first development well 43/24-P1 was a 1.2 km step out to the south of 43/24-1. The well encountered a thick,

O'Mara, P. T., Merryweather, M., Stockwell, M. & Bowler, M. M. 1999. The Trent Gas Field: correlation and reservoir quality within a complex Carboniferous stratigraphy. *In*: Fleet, A. J. & Boldy, S. A. R. (eds) *Petroleum Geology of Northwest Europe: Proceedings of the 5th Conference*, 809–821. © Petroleum Geology '86 Ltd. Published by the Geological Society, London.

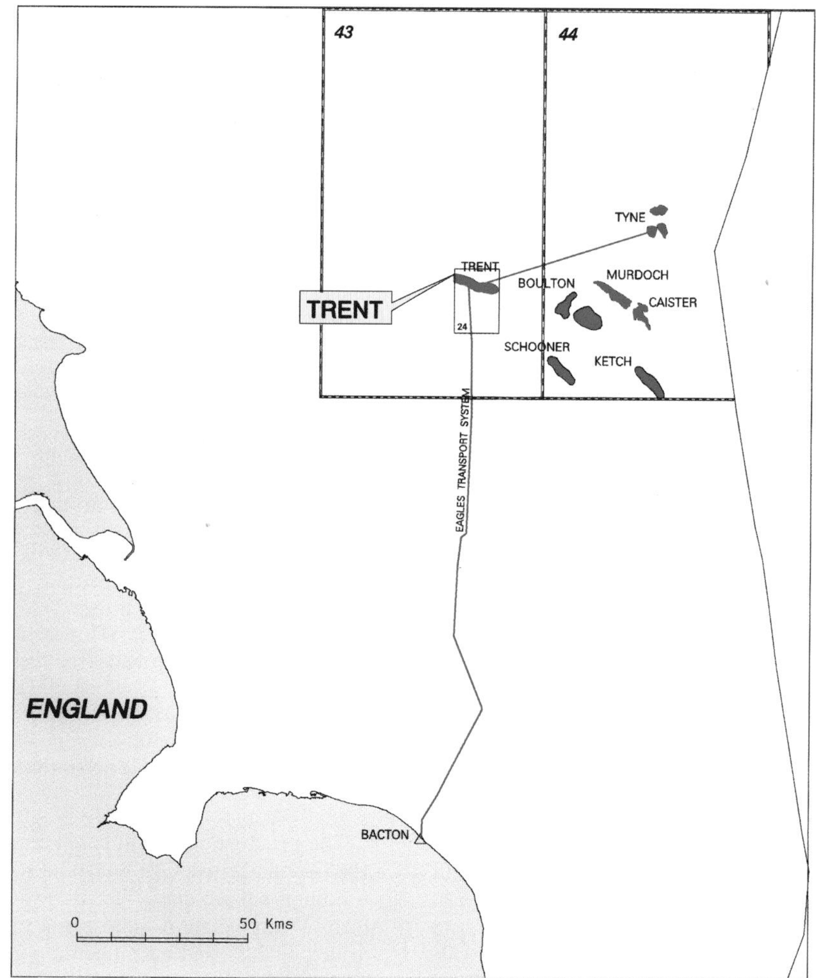

Fig. 1. Location Map of Trent Gas Field, showing transport route to the Amoco Bacton terminal via the ETS pipeline.

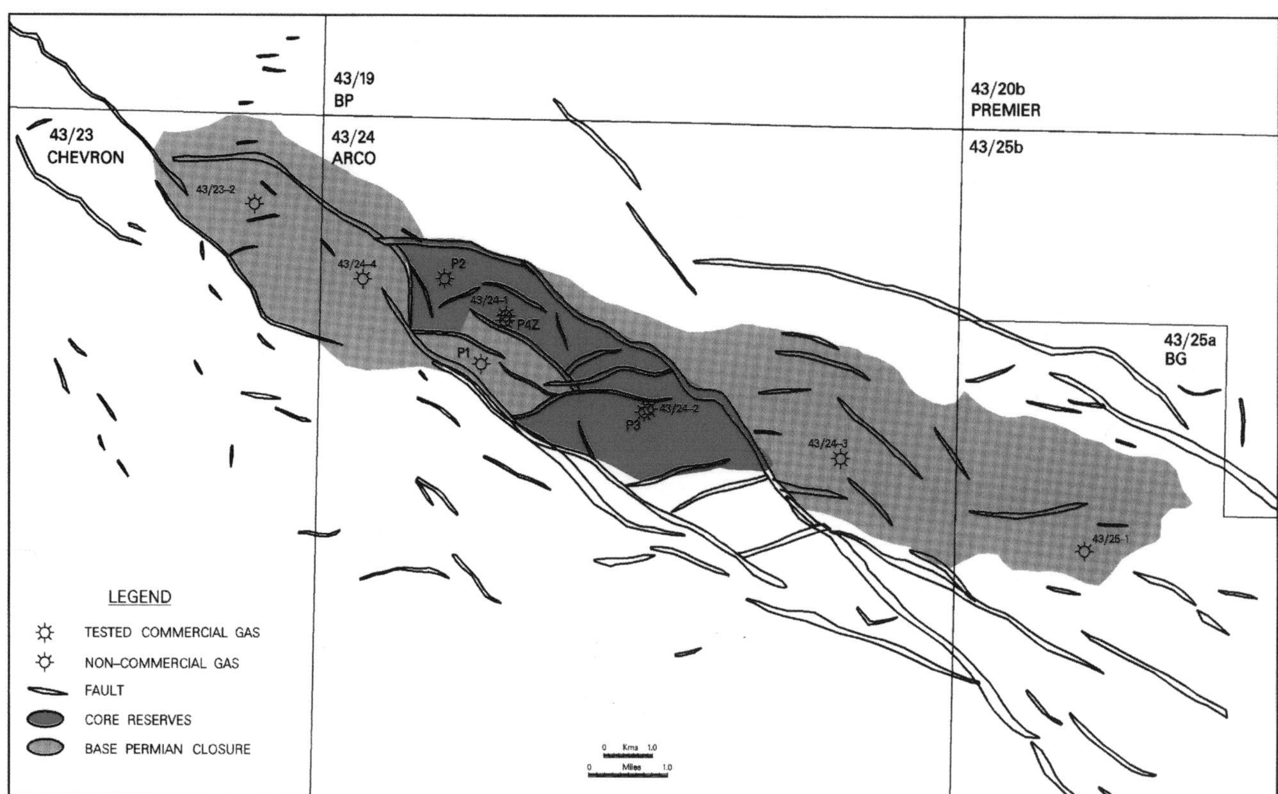

Fig. 2. Trent Gas Field accumulation map showing locations of exploration/delineation and development wells. The core development area is highlighted in red. The extent of the base Permian closure is highlighted in orange.

Table 1. A summary of Trent Field well results from exploration and development drilling. Note 43/24-P3 and 43/24-P4z are not included because they are twins of 43/24-2 and 43/24-1, respectively

Well	Year	Test interval	Flow rate ($\times 10^6$ SCFG(D))
43/25-1	1985	Westphalian A Distributary Channel	0.5
43/24-1	1990	Upper and lower Trent Sandstone combined	35
43/24-2	1992	Westphalian A Distributary Channel	29
43/23-2	1992	Upper and lower Trent Sandstone combined	0.5
43/24-3	1993	Westphalian A Distributary Channel	19
		Upper and lower Trent Sandstone combined	31
43/24-4	1993	Untested	
43/24-P1	1995	Untested	
43/24-P2	1995	Lower Trent Sandstone	0.5
		Upper Trent Sandstone	33

down-faulted Caister Coal Formation section which did not contain any reservoir quality sandstones and was plugged and abandoned in August 1995.

The second development well, 43/24-P2, a 1.4 km step out to the west northwest of 43/24-1 encountered a reservoir section of reduced thickness and reservoir quality. It tested at 33×10^6 SCFG(D) from the Trent Sandstone in October 1995. In light of these developing well results, the development programme was modified. The 43/24-P3 well twinned the 43/24-2 well at bottom hole location. The development plan had included re-use of the 43/24-1 well but mechanical problems meant that a sidetrack, 43/24-P4z, was required. This well twinned the 43/24-1 well.

Field stratigraphy and geological history

The field stratigraphy of the Trent area is typical of Quadrants 43 and 44 of the Southern Gas Basin. The stratigraphic nomenclature used here is from Cameron (1993) (Fig. 4).

The oldest rocks penetrated by the Trent wells are basinal shales of the Bowland Shale Formation. Rapid basin subsidence and repeated progradation of the Millstone Grit Formation deltaic complexes allowed the accommodation of a thick Namurian sequence with up to 900 m of interbedded sandstones and shales (Fig. 5). Sedimentation patterns and sedimentary input were controlled by east–west extensional faulting. By middle Namurian times, this repeated progradation allowed the establishment of a lower delta plain which was periodically inundated by open marine conditions depositing marine bands, although considerably larger areas experienced brackish conditions. Incised valleys cut into the top of these deltaic complexes during episodes of relative sea-level fall providing reservoir sandstones throughout the Namurian. One of the youngest of these is the Trent Sandstone. During the middle Westphalian A there was a gradual transition from lower delta plain to upper delta plain/coastal alluvial plain. Distributary channel-fills associated with this facies association are reservoir targets in the Trent area and were penetrated in 44/24-P1 and in the eastern area of the Trent structure (43/25-1).

During the late Carboniferous the Southern North Sea occupied part of an intracratonic foreland area to the north of the Hercynian orogenic front. The main compressional Hercynian structural styles include broad open folds and minor wrench-related normal and reverse faults. The faults have two trends; a predominant WNW–ESE direction and a NE–SW trend. Within the Trent area these structural trends are clearly evident together with east–west orientated normal faults. Rejuvenation of these faults has occurred during the Triassic, Mesozoic and Tertiary and often masks the original extent of Hercynian movements.

The basin was then subjected to extensive erosion caused by Hercynoid collision, producing basin inversion and resulting in a pronounced regional unconformity at the base of the Permian. At least 1000 m of upper Carboniferous sediment were stripped off the Trent area at this time. The subcrop of the Carboniferous in the Trent area becomes progressively younger eastwards. The 43/25-1 well demonstrates a middle Westphalian A (Caister Coal Formation) subcrop, whereas, in the crestal areas the subcrop is earliest Westphalian A and possibly Namurian. Local variations in subcrop are also noted in some down-faulted blocks such as at the 43/24-P1 locality.

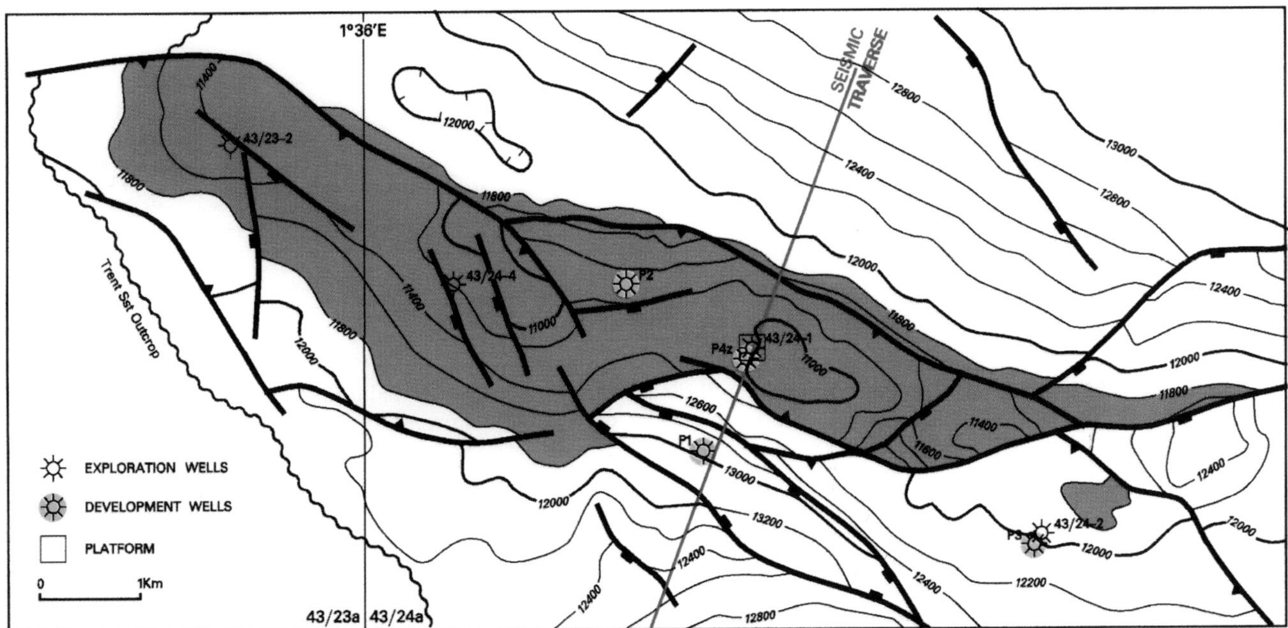

Fig. 3. Top Trent Sandstone depth map. Exploration/delineation and development wells are shown at top reservoir location. Contours are in feet.

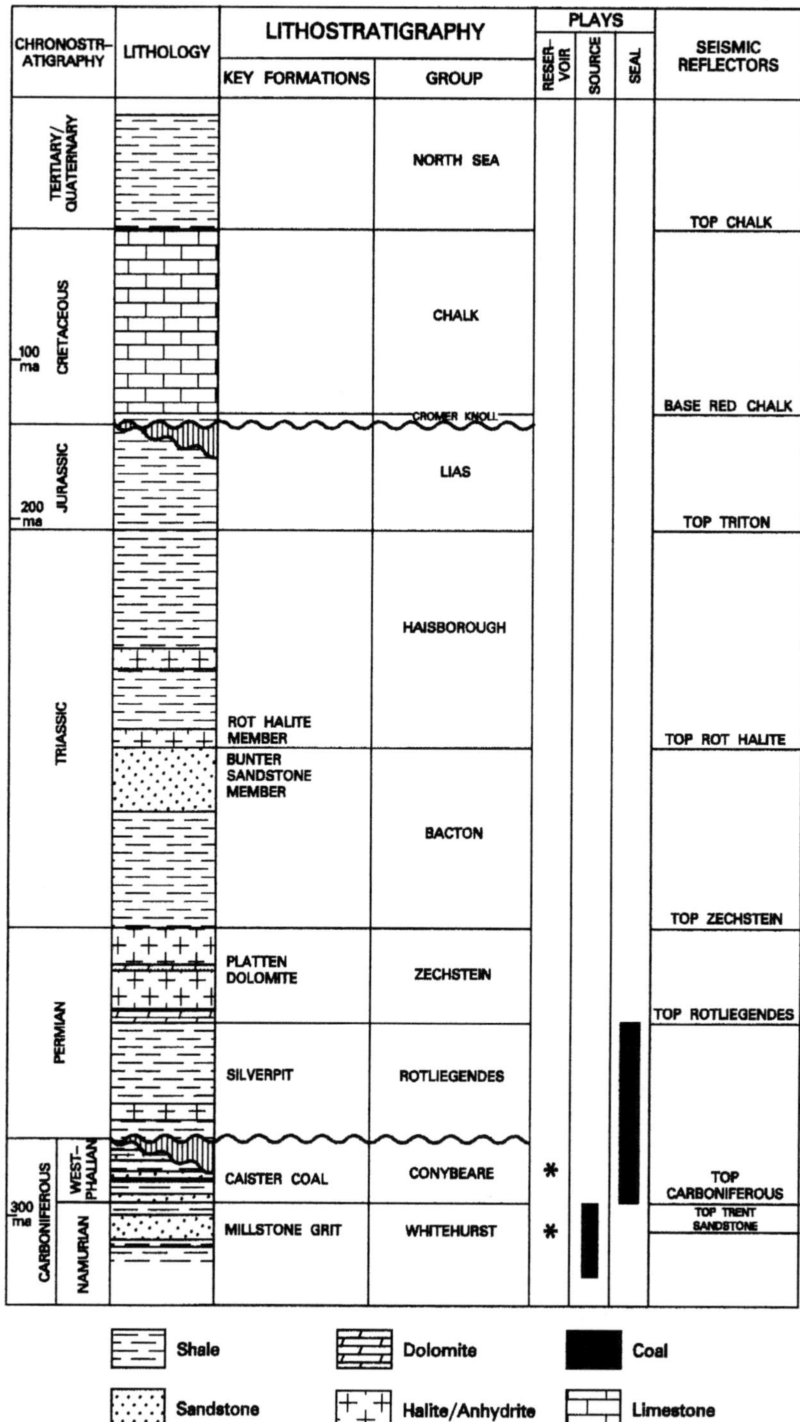

Fig. 4. Generalized Trent stratigraphy, showing seismic reflectors, key lithostratigraphic and chronostratigraphic units. It also shows the positions of the source, reservoir and seal units.

As a consequence of regional extension, a new Hercynian foreland basin developed during the Permian. Within this basin, in the early Permian (Rotliegendes Group), 370 m of reddish lacustrine shales, which represent the lateral equivalents to the Rotliegendes Leman sandstones, were deposited to the south of the area. These sediments also include discrete halite beds (halites A–E) and contribute to the regional top seal for the Trent Field gas accumulation and other Carboniferous gas fields.

The late Permian (Zechstein Group) in the Trent area consists of four cycles of evaporitic sediments (ZI–ZIV). The control on deposition of these sediments appears to have been eustatic variation in sea level (Taylor 1990). They comprise carbonate–anhydrite–halite–potash cycles that represent a deepening trend with progressive increase in water depth, upwards. The restriction of the marine basin is thought to be accentuated by the influence of a barrier which cut off open marine conditions to the north. The depositional thickness of the Zechstein is unknown but may have been much more than the 250 m encountered in the Trent area. Subsequent halokinesis results in the present day thickness of the interval being highly variable.

During Trent Field drilling, a number of problems were encountered throughout the Permian section including: twisting

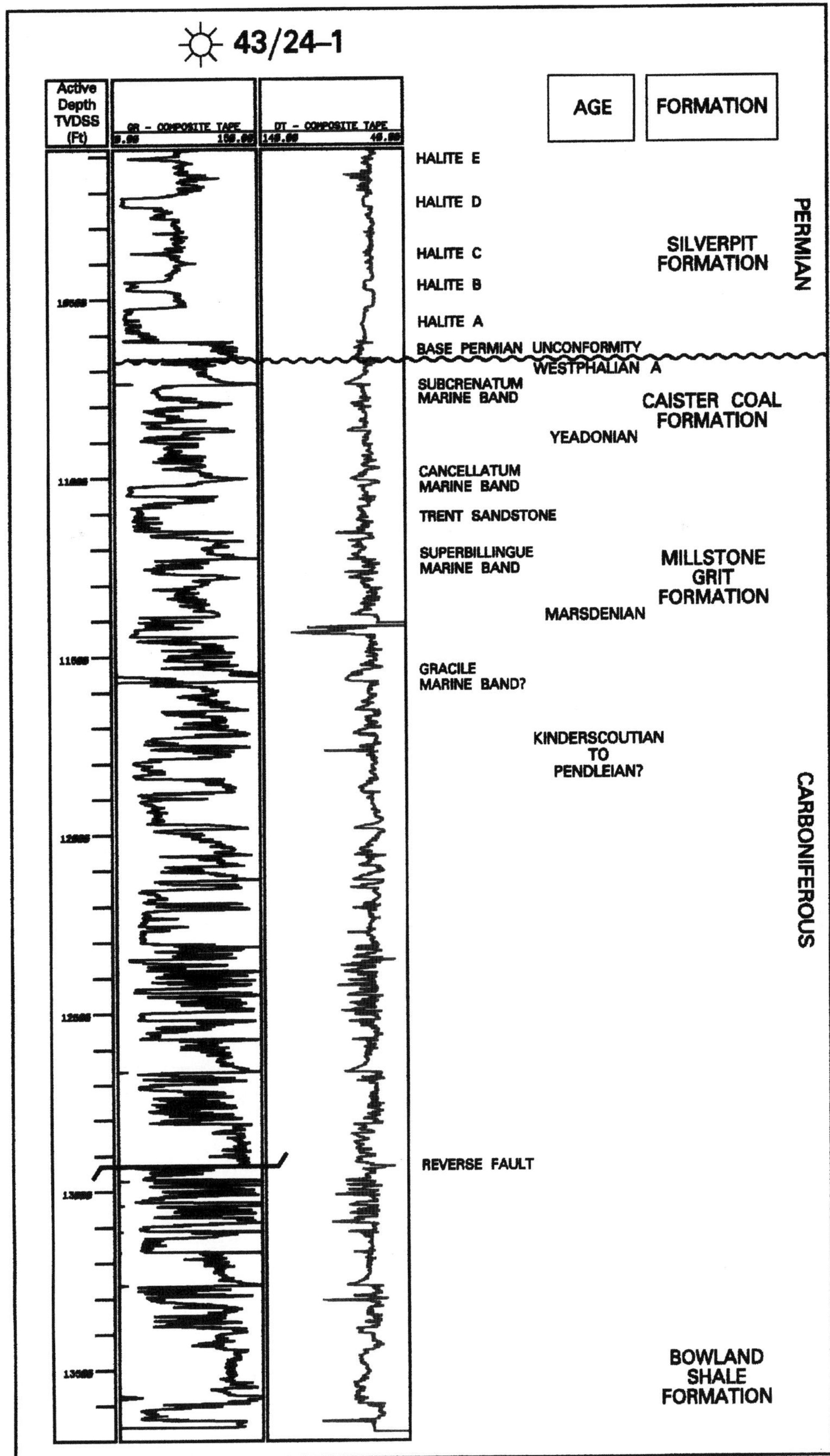

Fig. 5. 43/24-1 well log, showing the presence of halites in the base of the Permian sequence, a reverse fault in the basal Millstone Grit section and the Bowland Shale section in the lower parts of the well.

off and differential sticking in the halites and anhydrite sections; kicks of overpressured gas and brine in the dolomite sections which have serious implications for well control; and casing collapse following halite movement.

Extensional tectonics in a continental setting throughout the Triassic influenced sedimentation and generated graben areas in which up to 1340 m of Triassic sandstones, shales and halites accumulated. The first phase of Zechstein halokinesis commenced late in the Triassic and was probably triggered by early fault movements as evidenced by the formation of pillow structures in response to sediment loading (Cameron *et al.* 1992). The Lower Jurassic is represented by 520 m of Liassic sediments which overlie the Triassic across Trent. The Middle and Upper Jurassic sediments were stripped off at the base Cimmerian unconformity. Rapid subsidence resumed in the Early Cretaceous with the deposition of 32 m of condensed mudstone dominated facies, represented by the Cromer Knoll Group, that onlaps the Cimmerian unconformity surface. A major global rise in sea level in the late Cretaceous led to the drowning of the sediment source areas and permitted the widespread deposition of the Chalk Group which exceeds 520 m in thickness (Haq *et al.* 1987). Seismic evidence suggests that salt movement re-commenced during Cenomanian times and that many faults movements were reversed within the pre-Zechstein section resulting from regional compression within the Hercynian basement.

Early Tertiary sedimentation marked a change from the Cretaceous carbonate-dominated sediments to predominantly clastic deposition which continued until the Miocene. Alpine movements in the Oligo–Miocene resulted in the final phase of basin inversion and renewed halokinesis. In Block 43/24 these movements culminated in continued reversal of faults of the pre-Zechstein section. The mid-Tertiary unconformity marks the cessation of these movements and the resumption of subsidence with associated clastic sedimentation. Up to 275 m of Tertiary claystone is present in the Trent wells.

Geophysics

In 1993 a 320 km^2 proprietary 3D seismic survey was acquired and processed. This survey covered the entire Base Permian closure and extended over the northern portions of Blocks 43/23, 43/24 and 43/25. In 1994 the whole 3D seismic volume was post-stack depth migrated with the primary objective of increasing resolution within the Carboniferous section and improving fault definition in the pre-Zechstein.

To fully understand the hydrocarbon system and define the relationship between the reservoir units and the overlying seal, eight seismic horizons were interpreted:

- Top Chalk
- Base Red Chalk
- Top Triton Anhydrite
- Top Rot Halite
- Top Zechstein
- Top Rotliegendes
- Base Permian
- Top Trent Sandstone

Overall the quality of the 3D seismic data is good leading to an unambiguous interpretation of the overburden horizons down to the Top Rotliegendes. The base Permian reflector has been interpreted with a relatively high degree of confidence although synthetic seismograms generated for the wells indicate that the picked event corresponds to the bottom of the lowermost halite unit in the basal part of the Rotliegendes Group, and not to the true top of the Carboniferous. Development well drilling has also demonstrated that these basal Rotliegendes Group halite units have flowed and are seen to thicken on the downthrown side of base Permian faults.

Data quality in the Carboniferous is variable. On account of poor reflectivity within the Westphalian A and Namurian sequences and the overall low signal to noise ratio over the Trent Field structure itself, interpretation of intra-Carboniferous seismic events and fault delineation is problematic. The top of the Trent Sandstone corresponds to a relatively low amplitude seismic event. Where this event is constrained by well control there is a high level of confidence in the interpretation but this diminishes away from the wells and is significantly reduced in fault compartments where no wells have been drilled. Uncertainties in the correlation of Carboniferous seismic events across faults were demonstrated by the first development well, 43/24-P1, which showed that the most appropriate seismic correlation away from the 43/24-1 well into the 43/24-P1 location was incorrect (Fig. 6). 43/24-P1 encountered a much younger Carboniferous section than predicted and failed to reach the Trent Sandstone reservoir.

Depth conversion

Depth structure maps were generated using a vertical layer cake time to depth conversion method with the layers defined by the eight interpreted seismic horizons. For the majority of the layers the velocities were calculated using best fit relationships between interval velocity and mid-point depth from surrounding well data. The exception to this was the Lower Triassic and the Zechstein layers where a thickness versus two way travel time function was used. Depth conversion sensitivities were performed but showed the base Permian closure to be a robust structural feature, the size and relief of which did not change significantly when different depth conversion functions were applied.

Source rocks

Thermal maturity data for the Trent and key offset wells indicate that the Caister Coal and Millstone Grit Formations (Fig. 4) source-rock facies (coals and carbonaceous mudstones) immediately underlying the Permian have crossed the oil generation threshold and are between the peak oil and peak gas generation thresholds. They have poor to good total organic carbon (TOC). In Well 43/25-1 sediments towards the base of the well have poor residual potential to source gas because of their high levels of maturation.

In adjacent synclines to the Trent inversion structure, additional gas-prone Carboniferous source rocks are present within preserved sections of Caister Coal and Westoe Coal Formations. They are either generating at present or have generated significant amounts of gaseous hydrocarbons from the abundant mudstones and coals within the sections.

In light of these data sources for the Trent Field, gas is not perceived to be a major risk as the area lies within the main mature gas basin. The sections containing the source rocks would have reached peak gas maturity from the Cretaceous to the present day. Migration routes to the Trent area are short, and combine both horizontal and vertical paths. Gas is likely to have migrated into the structure via the major faults which bound and compartmentalize the structure.

Trap

At base Permian a large 20 km elongate structure is mapped with a closing contour which coincides with the observed gas water contact (GWC) in the wells at 3590 m (11 780 ft) true vertical depth sub sea (TVDSS). This closure trends NW–SE across the northern part of 43/24a and extends westwards into 43/23a and eastwards into 43/25a (Fig. 2). Maximum relief on the base Permian structure approaches 365 m (1200 ft) and occurs in the area of the 43/24-1 well (Fig. 7). The base Permian

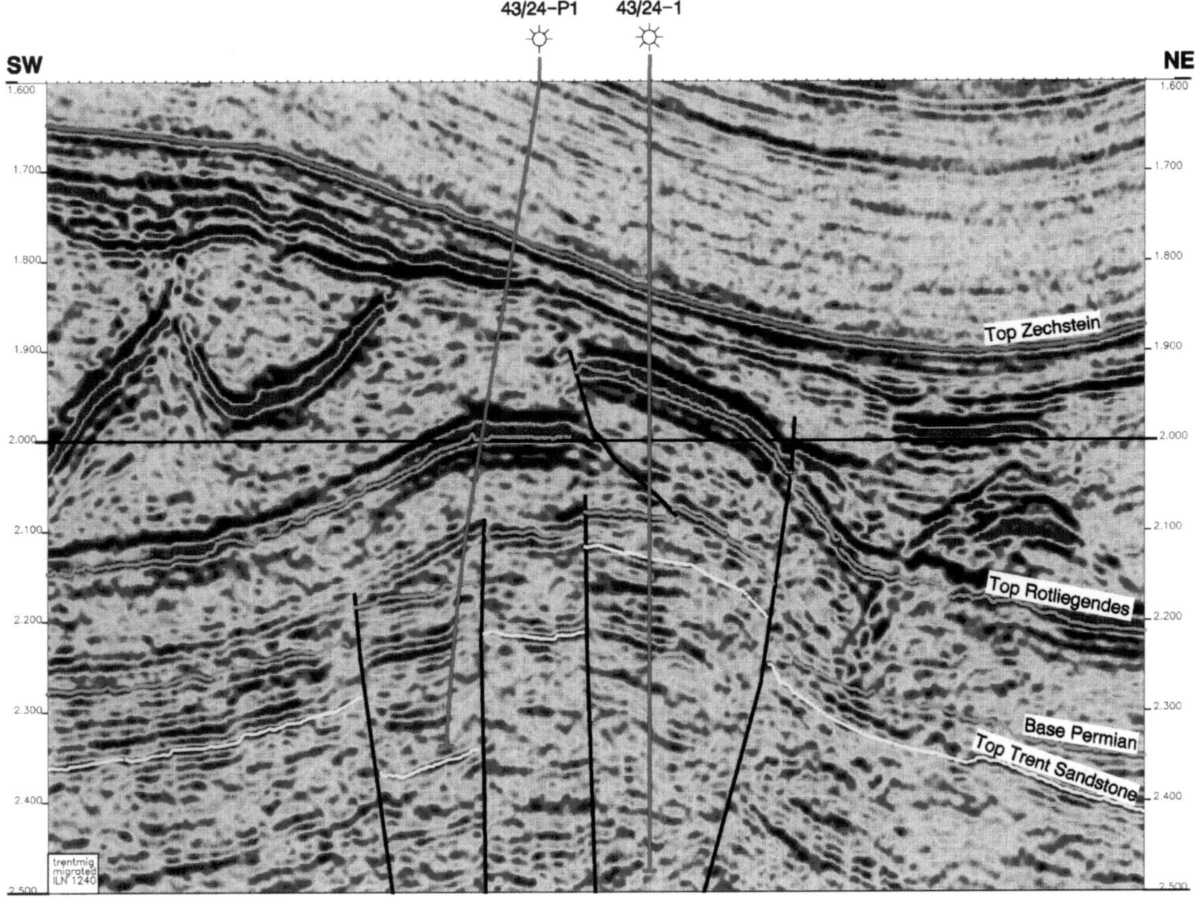

Fig. 6. Seismic cross-section across the Trent Field structure orientated in a north–south direction. Position of the line is shown on Fig. 3.

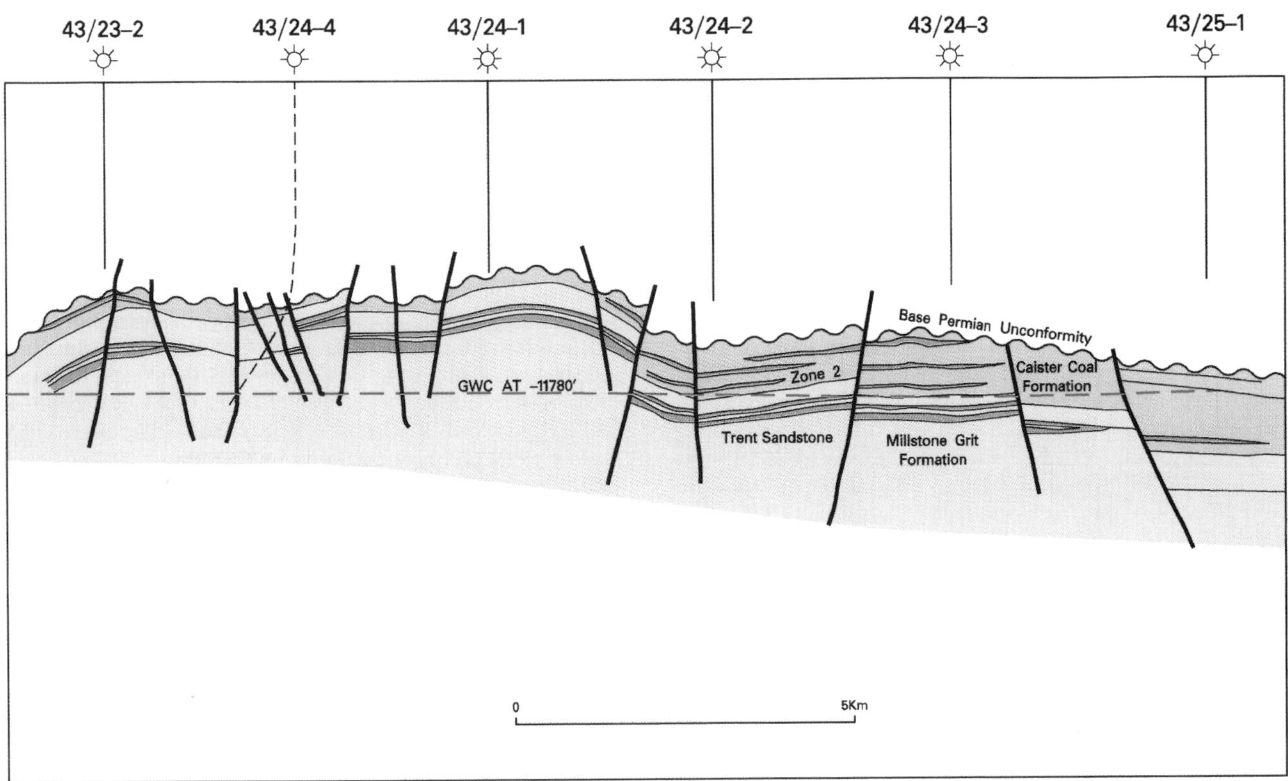

Fig. 7. Geoseismic cross-section along strike of the Trent Gas Field through the exploration and appraisal wells (see Fig. 2 for location of wells). Note the position of the GWC relative to the major stratigraphic units, the Trent Sandstone and Base Permian unconformity. Zone 2 equates to the Westphalian A distributary channel sandstone reservoir (see also Fig. 9).

structure is dominated by a series of en echelon NW–SE trending reverse faults which have been responsible for producing the positive inversion feature.

On the Top Trent Sandstone map a smaller 10 km elongate NW–SE trending closure is mapped with a closing contour down to the GWC of 3590 m TVDSS (11 780 ft). Again the main faults mapped are the NW–SE trending reverse faults and an antithetic set with the same trend. In addition, a second WSW–ENE trend of mainly normal faults are interpreted which divide the Trent Field into separate compartments and may have acted as a control on Carboniferous sedimentation.

Reservoir

Reservoir correlation

Traditionally, correlation of the Carboniferous section of the Southern Gas Basin has tended to rely upon the use of relatively low resolution palynostratigraphy, because the repetitive and cyclic nature of the succession renders lithostratigraphical correlation unsuitable. This was combined with inferred marine band stratigraphy based on wireline log response. Despite the vast improvements in palynostratigraphic correlation techniques in recent years, Namurian palynomorphs are still prone to excessive reworking, caving and poor quality assemblages from both depositional and mechanical causes. The main advances in palynostratigraphic correlation schemes are within the coal-bearing Caister Coal and Westoe Coal formations. Thus a different approach was a pre-requisite for accurate correlation.

The key was the recognition of 'golden spike' or definitive time lines from the detailed evaluation of marine bands. In the late Namurian in the onshore UK sections, the subdivision based on key ammonoid species is well documented (Collinson 1969, 1976; Holdsworth & Collinson 1988; Ramsbottom 1969). Each marine band is named after the type species often unique to that marine band, although in the identification of certain marine bands assemblages must be used. This onshore marine band stratigraphy for the late Namurian and Westphalian A was applied to the Trent Field and has proved invaluable for stratigraphic correlation (Fig. 8). The unequivocal identification of the marine band by its constituent macrofauna can only be performed on whole core or rotary sidewall cores. Additionally it relies on the marine band sufficiently developing its ammonoid phase which requires marine salinity.

The marine band stratigraphy has proved to be the key to the high (90%) confidence level in well correlation achieved for the Marsdenian to lower Westphalian A interval within the core area of the Trent Field. This interval contains all the reservoir zones encountered in the Trent Field to date. Beyond the limits of macrofaunal control confidence levels in well correlation are significantly lower and rely upon lithostratigraphy together with less well constrained palynostratigraphy.

The macrofaunal evidence identified from the section to date comes from 43/24-2, 43/24-3, 43/24-4, 43/24-P1 and 43/24-P2, (Riley BGS pers. comm.). Marine bands from the lower Westphalian A (Amaliae) to the Marsdenian (*Bilinguites bilinguis*) have been identified. Correlation from 43/24-4, 43/24-P2 and 43/24-2 via 43/24-1 is supported by the recovery of *Bilingites superbilingue* and *Verneulites sigma* from 43/24-4 and 43/24-2 immediately below the Trent sandstone (Fig. 9). The unit which consists of two distinct sandbodies is effectively bracketed by the occurrence of *Cancelloceras cancellatum* overlying the sandstone in 43/24-P2, which can be correlated to a similar flooding event in 42/24-4 also yielding *C. cancellatum*. These two marine band occurrences suggest that both the upper and lower Trent Sandstones onshore equivalent would be the Chatsworth Grit (Fig. 8). Evidence for correlation of the Westphalian A interval comes from marine macrofauna in 43/24-2 and 43/24-P2 and non-marine bivalves in 43/24-P1.

The succession in 43/24-4 appears anomalous because of a reduction in thickness of the upper Marsdenian interval combined with a lack of reservoir quality sandstone. The marine bands which bracket the sandstone in other wells are present but there is no accompanying sandstone; this evidence strongly suggests an interfluve or channel by-pass area. Initially a fault was postulated to explain the absence of the Trent Sandstone, but there is no evidence of a fault in the *C. cancellatum* to *B. superbilingue* interval, which was cored in this well and was shown to contain the Trent Sandstone in well 43/24-P2, 0.5 km to the west. A fault was, however, located in core above the *C. cancellatum* marine band. There was no exposure surface or palaeosol at this locality, which would mark an interfluvial sequence boundary *sensu*; Hampson *et al.* (1996). However, Church & Gawthorpe (1994) also did not note a palaeosol in core beneath the *Gastrioceras subcrenatum* marine band in the Wilds Bridge 1 Borehole.

It is noted from the well correlation that cycle thickness does not change significantly across the Trent area except for around the 43/24-4 well suggesting that the area of channel by-pass may have been more long lived than for one cycle (Fig. 9). The interfluve area between 43/24-4 and 43/24-P2 in the west is mirrored in the east by the section between 43/24-3 and 43/25-1, where 43/25-1 also probably represents an interfluve. Such well correlations have been used to estimate channel widths and suggest that the onshore analogues are more akin to the Chatsworth Grit in the East Midlands area (see Church & Gawthorpe 1994, for discussion and fig. 5) than the more intensely studied Rough Rock of the Pennine Basin (Hampson 1995; Hampson *et al.* 1996, 1997).

Geological model

Upper Carboniferous depositional model

The geological model for the Trent Field is one of sedimentation in a low lying delta front and delta plain setting. The overall Millstone Grit depositional sequence is dominated by an initial basinal and delta slope infill of the pre-existing Dinantian basin-and-block topography. Repetitive progradation of fluvio–deltaic systems derived from the north and northeast and prograding to the south and southwest followed. The upper part of the Millstone Grit and the lower part of the Caister Coal Formation is typified by delta top and lower delta plain sediments, respectively.

Recent advances in sequence stratigraphic techniques have led to a re-evaluation of fluvio–deltaic strata within the Upper Carboniferous. The cyclicity and basin-wide extent of high frequency sequences has been demonstrated, particularly from the late Namurian (Hampson *et al.* 1997). There is abundant evidence of high magnitude (60 ± 15 m; Crowley & Baum 1991) glacio–eustatic fluctuations (reviews by Ramsbottom 1977; Holdsworth & Collinson 1988; Leeder 1988; Maynard & Leeder 1992). These fluctuations are thought to be climatically controlled and have been attributed to ice sheet growth (sea-level fall) and rapid melt out (sea-level rise). They have a dominant 100 kKa periodicity thereby relating them to 4th order cycles of relative sea-level change (Church & Gawthorpe 1994). Such fluctuations are also thought to partly control the surface area available for weathering and consequent sediment flux derived from fluvial run-off and are considered to have been sufficient to account for observed changes in facies and sediment supply within the late Namurian (Hampson *et al.* 1997).

Reservoir characterization

The detailed chronostratigraphic correlation framework constructed above, based on the integration of comparative marine

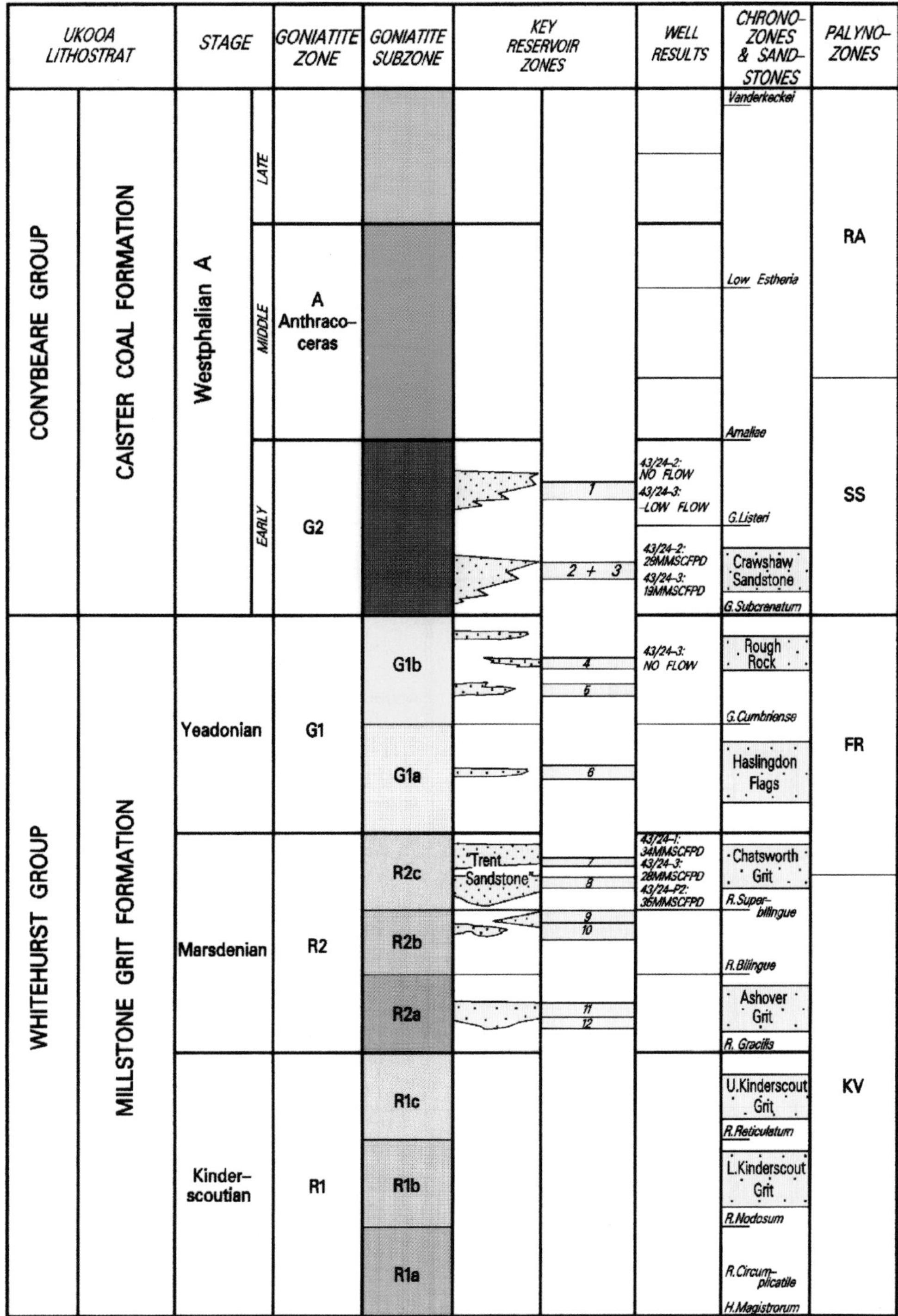

Fig. 8. Detailed Silesian zonation scheme for the Trent Sandstone interval showing the positions of the major reservoir units and important marine bands.

band stratigraphy, lithostratigraphy, sequence stratigraphy and palynostratigraphy is used along with core and log data from Trent and key offset wells to define three key reservoir facies (Fig. 9): incised valley fills; distributary channels; and transgressive reworked sandstones; and distributary channels.

Incised valley fills (IVF). Lowstand deposits comprise major multistorey, braided fluvial sandstone complexes interpreted as incised valley fills (Hampson *et al.* 1997). They overlie sequence boundaries which are identified as widespread deeply eroded surfaces which can be correlated between individual basins. A sequence boundary is known from the UK Pennine Basin beneath the Chatsworth Grit unit (O'Beirne 1994) and its regional extent and high degree of incision (+40 m) is confirmed by its identification in the Trent Field area. Fluvial deposits within incised valley fills have a sheet-like geometry in the Pennine Basin (i.e. Rough Rock; Hampson 1995; Hampson *et al.* 1996, 1997) but are more laterally confined on the East Midlands shelf which underwent contemporaneous minor active extensive tectonism (Hampson *et al.* 1996).

The lower Trent Sandstone is interpreted to be deposited in a similar setting and comprises a 20–30 m thick multistorey, coarse-grained, pebbly, fluvial deposit back-filling an incised valley (Figs 9 and 10). It is the product of high energy, braided channel systems, depositing a series of stacked and erosive barforms aligned sub-parallel to the prevailing palaeocurrent

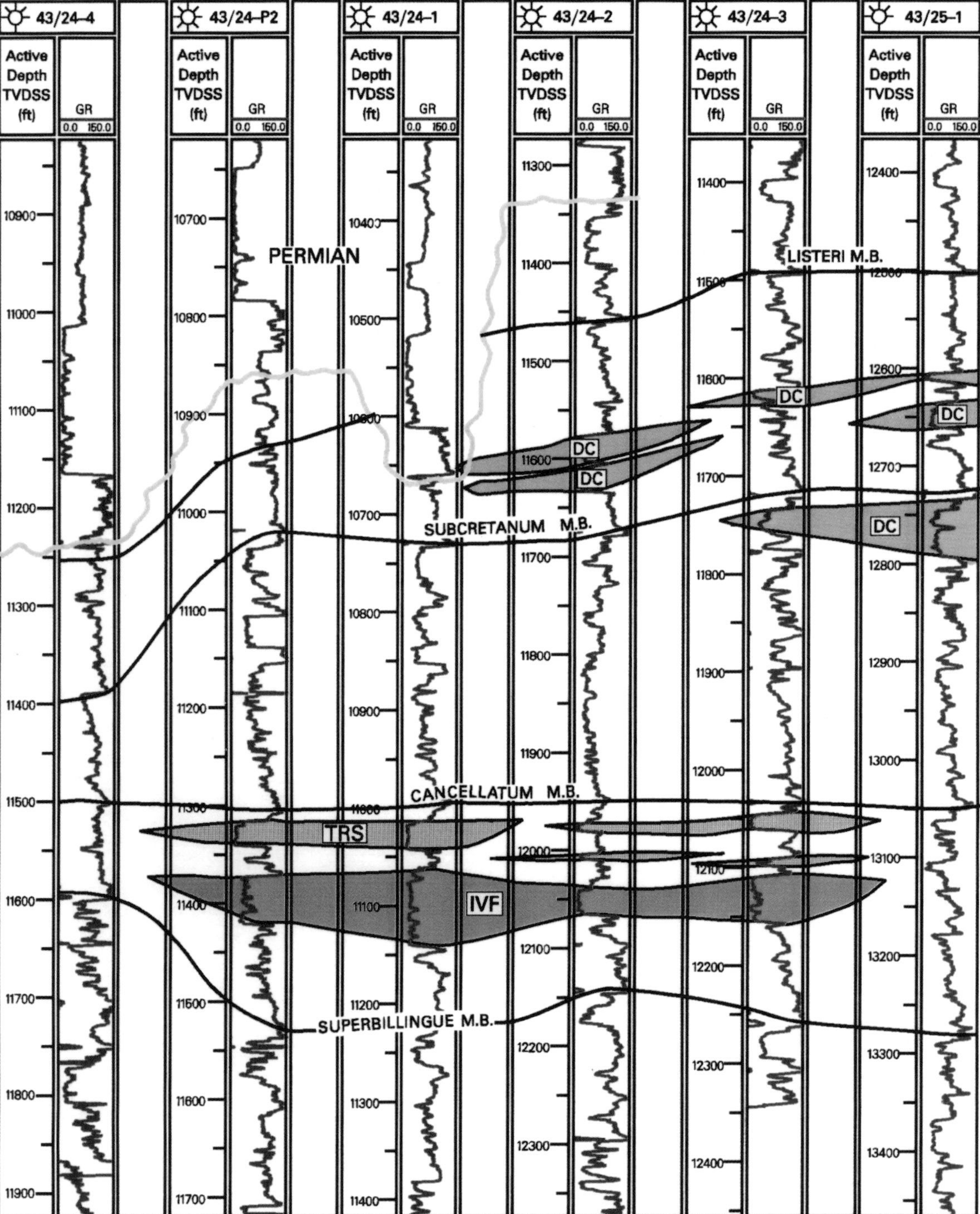

Fig. 9. Well correlation of the Trent area showing lateral continuity of the reservoir units and major marine horizons. Cross-section is flattened on the *Cancelloceras cancellatum* marine band.

(NE–SW). Shale content is low and interbar connectivity is thought to be excellent. The well correlations suggest the Trent valley system was laterally confined, similar to systems on the East Midlands shelf (Church & Gawthorpe 1994; Hampson *et al.* 1996, 1997).

Incised valley-fills have correlative interfluvial sediments which are palaeosols. A correlative interfluvial palaeosol to the widely correlatable sequence boundary beneath the Rough Rock (Hampson *et al.* 1996) occurs in core in Well 43/24-4 underlying the inferred position of the *G. subcrenatum* marine band (Fig. 9). However, there is no significant palaeosol development at the correlative horizon to the Trent Sandstone incised valley in the 43/24-4 well where the sandstone is not present. Thus it is proposed that the character of the interfluvial palaeosols is variable, reflecting variations in substrate, maturity and transgressive overprint.

Transgressive reworked sandstones (TRS). Transgressive deposits are thin within most sequences, typified by condensed sediments including marine bands, because sediment accumulation rates failed to keep pace with increasing rates of accommodation space creation (Church & Gawthorpe 1994). However, during late lowstand and early transgressive times the limited developments of new accommodation space in certain instances led to multiple, poorly developed and restricted flooding events and/or incision surfaces that may be

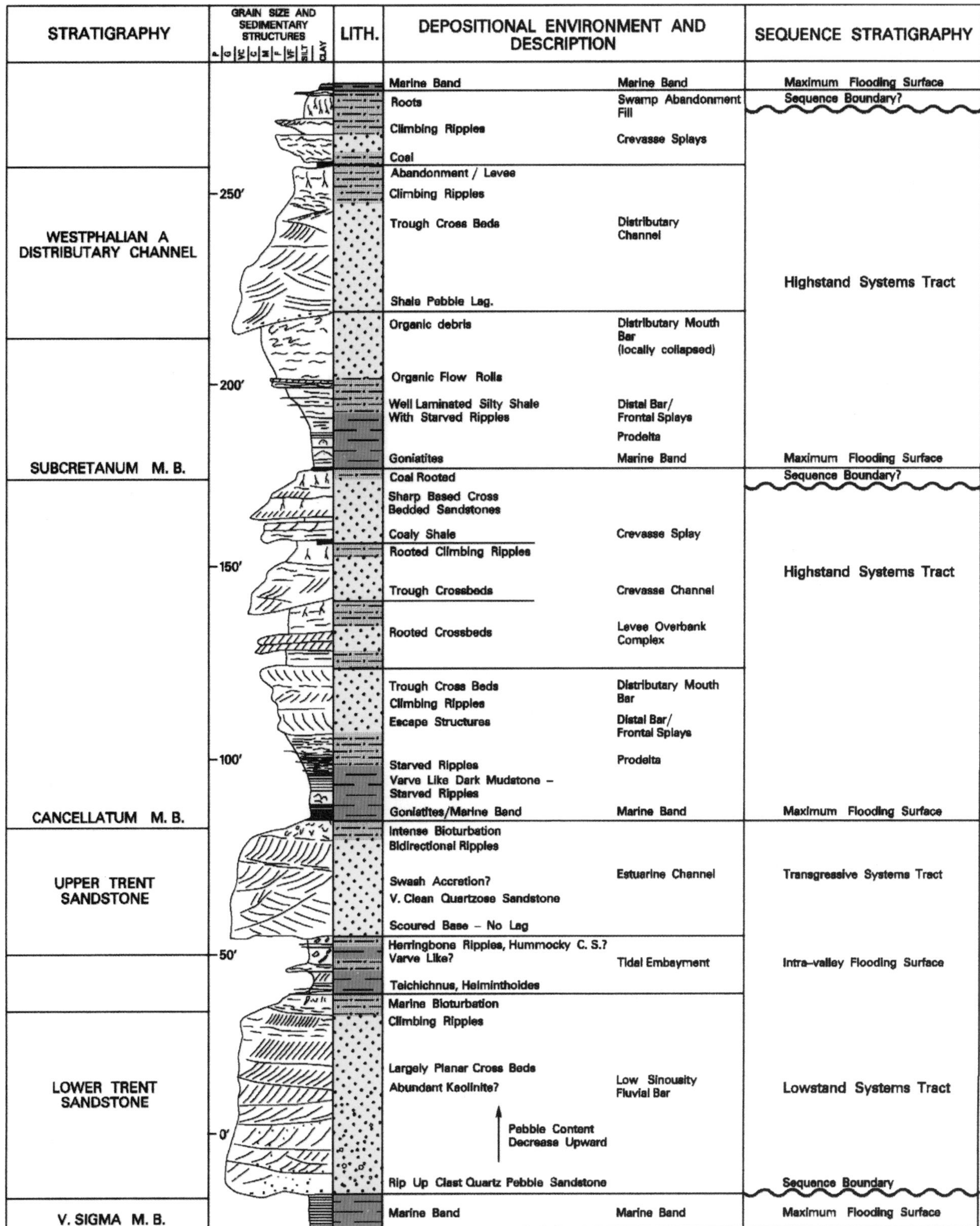

Fig. 10. Summary of depositional environments from the Trent wells based of core description from a number wells.

restricted to the incised valley itself. These produced complex compound incised valley fills (Zaitland *et al.* 1994). If sediment flux is insufficient during fluvial deposition to fill the valley, significant marine reworking may take place during marine transgression. This occurs prior to the maximum flooding surface and marine band that marks the maximum extent of transgression and complete filling of the valley. The *C. cancellatum* marine band marks the complete infilling of the Trent Sandstone incised valley and overlaps the valley sides onto the interfluve areas as in the case of Well 43/24-4.

Where incised valleys are not completely filled with fluvial sediments, the marine reworking of the underlying fluvial sand produces high quality reservoir in various channelized and non-channelized tidal–estuarine environments. The upper Trent sandstone is interpreted to be part of one such trans-gressive wedge that formed prior to marine band deposition, and represents an estuarine/tidal channel complex formed during the late stage filling of the valley. It is underlain by a marine influenced interval which represents a flooding surface restricted to the valley (Figs 9 and 10). The lower Breathitt Group of the Central Appalachian Basin, Kentucky, as mapped by ARCO, provides very good analogues for such incised valleys and accompanying tidal sandstones (O'Mara 1997).

Distributary channels (DC). Highstand deposits are characterized by point sourced lobate deltas prograding into the basin depositing pro-delta shales, low sinuosity distributary channels, distributary mouth bars, crevasse splays and interdistributary bay mudstones in a delta front to lower delta plain environment. The reservoirs deposited in such environments differ from those formed in incised valley fills in that they comprise simple barforms, that form strongly linear bodies of limited lateral extent (Fig. 9). Channels are single storeys of approximately 10 m thick with incision restricted to that of the normal hydraulic process of a low sinuosity stream (≈5 m). The channel lag deposits in such channels generally comprise mudstone rip-up clasts and reworked siderite pebbles representative of surrounding flood plain material (Fig. 10). This is in direct comparison to incised valley fill lags which comprise thick conglomeratic units with abundant exotic detrital clasts. Petrographically the sandstones are immature containing a higher lithic component than both incised valley fills or transgressive reworked sandstones.

The Caister Coal Formation, overlying the *G. subcrenatum* marine band marks a change in depositional style to lower delta plain and the prevalence of distributary channel sandstones therein.

Reservoir quality

Reservoir quality in the Trent wells ranges from very poor to excellent and is controlled by depositional environment (Table 2). Grain size and sediment maturity (both textural and mineralogical) are the most influential factors.

Incised valley fill fluvial sediments from coarse- to fine-grained sub-arkosic sandstones are of poor to moderate quality with permeabilities from 0.5–130 millidarcies (mD). This is controlled by grain size and kaolinite content (after the dissolution of feldspar). The coarser grained portion is better quality, whereas kaolinite inhibits both permeability and porosity in the finer grained portion.

Low sinuosity distributary channel sandstone are medium- to fine-grained and of moderate quality, with permeabilities ranging from 1–420 mD. They are predominantly quartz-rich, with a lithic portion, that along with the fine-grained nature, reduces porosity and permeability.

Tidal/estuarine channel sandstones are predominantly medium-grained, quartzose sandstones. They form the best quality reservoirs with permeabilities of 100–320 mD. Feldspar and clay minerals may have been removed by tidal reworking: such cleaning-up of sandstones within the Namurian has been noted in shallow marine environments (Percival 1992).

Porosity variation is less extreme with most reservoir facies within the range of 6–15%. Porosity is dominated by relatively ineffective microporosity, especially in incised valley fill sediments where kaolinite is evident.

Table 2. A summary of reservoir properties from the main reservoir facies encountered in the Trent Field area

	Transgressive reworked sandstones (upper Trent)	Incised valley-fills (lower Trent)	Distributary channel (Westphalian A)
Net : Gross	0.48–0.98	0.58–0.9	0.7–0.92
Average porosity (%)	8–13	4–12	4.7–12.8
Water saturation (%)	<8	<22	<25
Average permeability (mD)	100–320	≈1(0.01–60)	50–160
Thickness (m)	<10	<30	<33
Storativity (%)	≈30	<60	≈5

Conclusions

An integrated approach of chronostratigraphic and lithostratigraphic techniques has led to a high degree of confidence in the correlation framework which has provided a detailed facies model for the Trent Gas Field. The key to the framework is a number of key stratigraphic markers (goniatites) derived from core and SWC material and a facies scheme developed from core description and key analogue sections. This has allowed for an improved understanding of reservoir facies and their continuity within the Millstone Grit Formation. Also it has led to a realization that, additional to IVF reservoir targets, are TRS, which are important in the commercial success of the Namurian play in the Southern North Sea. The direct and co-eval analogue (Chatsworth Grit) is the best analogue, it has a number of important differences to other, more extensively studied sections in the late Namurian. Reservoir property variations are shown to be directly controlled by depositional facies; consequently the accuracy of the facies model will be critical in future development well planning and long-term reservoir management.

Thanks to all the members of the Trent and Tyne development team both past and present. Special appreciation is extended to N. Riley from the BGS for his evaluation of the Trent macrofauna. Also thanks to Collinson Jones Consulting Ltd for their early Trent reports. D. Jordan is thanked for his detailed core descriptions. D. Cooper, A. Spencer and T. England are thanked for their useful comments on the first draft. Arco British Ltd and Talisman Energy (UK) Ltd are thanked for permission to publish. The constructive comments of reviewers S. Flint and R. Dunay as well as input from S. Davies are noted.

References

CAMERON, T. D. J. 1993. Part 5, Carboniferous and Devonian of the Southern North Sea. *In:* KNOX, R. W. O'B. & CORDEY, W. G. (eds) *Lithostratigraphic Nomenclature of the UK North Sea.* British Geological Survey, Nottingham, UK.

——, CROSBY, A., BALSON, P. S., JEFFERY, D. H., LOTT, G. K., BULAT, J. & HARRISON, D. J. 1992. *United Kingdom offshore regional report: the geology of the Southern North Sea.* HMSO London for the British Geological Survey.

CHURCH, K. D. & GAWTHORPE, R. L. 1994. High resolution sequence stratigraphy of the late Namurian in the Widmerpool Gulf (East Midlands, UK). *Marine and Petroleum Geology*, **11**, 528–544.

COLLINSON, J. D. 1969. The sedimentology of the Grindslow Shales and the Kinderscout Grit: a deltaic complex in the Namurian of northern England. *Journal of Sedimentary Petrology*, **39,** 194–221.

——1976. Deltaic evolution during basin fill – Namurian of Central Pennine Basin, England. *American Association of Petroleum Geologists Bulletin*, **60**, 659.

CROWLEY, K. D. & BAUM, S. K. 1991. Estimating Carboniferous sea-level fluctuations from Gondwanan ice extent. *Geology*, **19**, 975–977.

HAMPSON, G. 1995. Discrimination of regionally extensive coals in the Upper Carboniferous of the Pennine Basin, UK using high resolution sequence stratigraphic concepts. *In:* WHATELY, M. K. G. & SPEARS., D. A. (eds) *European Coal Geology*. Geological Society Special Publications, **82**, 79–97.

——, ELLIOT, T. & DAVIES, S. J. 1997. The application of sequence stratigraphy to Upper Carboniferous fluvio–deltaic strata of the onshore UK and Ireland: implications for the southern North Sea. *Journal of the Geological Society, London*, **154**, 719–733.

——, —— & FLINT, S. S. 1996. Critical application of high resolution sequence stratigraphic concepts to the Rough Rock Group (Upper Carboniferous) of northern England. *In*: HOWELL, J. A. & AITKEN, J. F. (eds) *High Resolution Sequence Stratigraphy: Innovations and Applications*. Geological Society, London, Special Publications, **104**, 221–246.

HAQ, B. U., HARDENBOL, J. & VAIL, P. R. 1987. Chronology of fluctuating sea-levels since the Triassic. *Science*, **235**, 1156–1167.

HOLDSWORTH, B. K. & COLLINSON, J. D. 1988. Millstone Grit cyclicity revisited. *In:* BESLY, B. M. & KELLING, G. (eds) *Sedimentation in a Syn-orogenic Basin Complex*. Blackie, Glasgow, 132–152.

LEEDER, M. R. 1988. Recent developments in Carboniferous geology: a critical review with implications for the British Isles and northwest Europe. *Proceedings of the Geologists Association*, **99**, 73–100.

MAYNARD, J. R. & LEEDER, M. R. 1992. On the periodicity and magnitude of Late Carboniferous glacio–eustatic sea level change. *Journal of the Geological Society, London*, **148**, 805–808.

O'BEIRNE, A. 1994. The progradation of a delta during transgression: from the Namurian of the Central Province, England. *In*: JOHNSON, S. A. (ed.) *High Resolution Sequence Stratigraphy: Innovations and Applications*. Abstract. University of Liverpool. 389–391.

O'MARA, P. T. 1997. *Reservoir analogues of South Central Kentucky*. Unpublished Confidential Report for ARCO British Ltd.

PERCIVAL, C. J. 1992. The Harthope Gannister – a transgressive barrier-island to shallow-marine sand-ridge from the Namurian of Northern England. *Journal of Sedimentary Petrology*, **62**, 442–454.

RAMSBOTTOM, W. H. C. 1969. The Namurian of Britain. *Comptes Rendues, 6ième Congrés International Stratigraphie Géologie du Carbonifère (Sheffield 1967)*, 71–77.

——1977. Major cycles of transgression and regression (mesothems) in the Namurian. *Proceedings of the Yorkshire Geological Society*, **41**, 261–291.

TAYLOR, J. C. M. 1990. Upper Permian – Zechstein. *In*: GLENNIE, K. W. (ed.) *Introduction to the Petroleum Geology of the North Sea (3rd Edition)*. Blackwell Scientific Publications.

ZAITLAND, B. A. DALRYMPLE, R. W. & BOYD, R. 1994. The stratigraphic organization of incised valley systems associated with relative sea level change. *In*: DALRYMPLE, R., BOYD, R. & ZAITLAND, B. A. (eds) *Incised Valley Systems: Origin and Sedimentary Sequences*. Tulsa SEPM, 46–60.

Jurassic subtle traps

Jurassic subtle traps

Introduction and review

S. A. R. BOLDY[1] AND S. I. FRASER[2]

[1] *Amerada Hess Norge A/S, Langkaien 1, 0150 Oslo, Norway*
[2] *Amerada Hess Limited, 33 Grosvenor Place, London SW1, UK*

In reviewing the Jurassic papers in the Proceedings of the 4th Conference on the 'Petroleum Geology of Northwest Europe' Fraser (1993) drew attention to the fact that over 50% of the reserves in the UK sector of the Northern and Central North Sea were contained in the Jurassic (Cordey 1993). Fraser went on to state that '... the Jurassic probably contains the majority of the undiscovered reserves in the North Sea basin in subtle structural and stratigraphic traps, many of which may only be defined using novel interpretation techniques, such as sequence stratigraphy, in concert with 3D seismic interpretation'. The regional and field specific use of detailed lithostratigraphy, biostratigraphy and chronostratigraphy was demonstrated by a variety of workers, in particular from BP and Exxon, to provide a basis for a rigorous and systematic approach to understanding the stratigraphic evolution of North Sea Jurassic basin fill processes. The 1992, 4th Barbican Conference dedicated several sessions to the Jurassic alone, entitled 'The Jurassic: from regional models to field development; the impact of sequence stratigraphy on hydrocarbon geology,' and the purpose of the Jurassic session at the 5th Conference was to review our current thinking on these concepts and their application to successful hydrocarbon exploration.

The underlying assumption is that virtually all of the economic Jurassic four-way dip and up-thrown fault closures in the North Sea have been drilled. The search for additional reserves in the Jurassic must therefore target more subtle features such as:

(i) downthrown fault closures;
(ii) stratigraphic traps;
(iii) untested sequences identified from 3D seismic and high resolution sequence stratigraphic studies; and
(iv) synclinal areas of Jurassic section, containing resedimented Jurassic sands.

The first paper by **Dawers *et al.*** outlines how 3D seismic has been used to unravel the complex nature of hanging wall traps and the distribution of spatially and temporally discontinuous syn-rift reservoir facies. The research is focused on the area to the east of the Statfjord Field, in the Norwegian sector of the Northern North Sea, where the extensive 3D coverage and well data are available over both footwall and hanging wall locations. The role of fault linkage and growth as a factor in controlling sediment dispersal within extensional regimes is examined in depth by the authors who relate the resultant evolution of intra-Draupne stratigraphic units to the interaction of en-echelon fault segments. The work concludes that within the shallow marine deposits encountered to date there exists a strong stratigraphic element. The discoveries and future potential in this area lie in reservoir targets dominated by laterally restricted reservoir sands: the products of localized crestal erosion of the major tilted fault blocks.

Kadolsky *et al.* show how detailed high resolution sequence stratigraphy, along with structural analysis from 3D seismic interpretation, has been used to predict the distribution of the Upper Jurassic syn-rift sands of the Outer Moray Firth and to highlight the potential for stratigraphic traps. The transgressive and regressive over-stepping of a complex fault controlled topography is documented and related to two phases of active extension of the basin. Facies patterns and sequence architectures are controlled by the orientation of active faults which dictate the spatial evolution of coastal plain and shoreface facies of the Late Oxfordian–Kimmeridgian, to the dominantly mass flow deposits and basinal channel facies of the Volgian–Rayazanian. Contemporaneous sequences are described and the potential for significant lowstand prospectivity is clearly highlighted.

Remaining in the Outer Moray Firth, **Moseley** discusses the variation in the nature of downthrown hanging wall traps and through comparing successful and unsuccessful cases, outlines a novel ranking system for such prospects. On closer examination of the tests to date, it becomes apparent that critical to the success of these targets is the nature of the sedimentary units within the footwall to the traps, the timing of fault movement and the nature of lateral seal capacity, which allows a more pragmatic classification of potential downthrown trap prospectivity in fault bonded terrace locations.

Moving still further south in the North Sea, **Stewart *et al.*** describe the use of 3D seismic and detailed stratigraphic sequence correlation in pursuing sub-seismic resolution. Late Jurassic shallow marine Fulmar age sands onto the western flanks of the Central Graben. Subtle interplay of pre-existing topographic relief and the complex transgression of a valley/hill network reveals the difficulties in predicting the distribution of sands within this shelfal setting. The distribution and orientation of Zechstein salt walls and drainage networks combine to generate accommodation space which may be connected or isolated from coarse clastic sediment source areas. Preservation of reservoir facies relies on a combination of factors which conspire to complicate the geological model for the West Central Shelf. However, a comprehensive dataset from the greater Durward and Dauntless area has enabled the reconstruction of the depositional substrate and, with the integration of sequence relationships, has allowed a more refined predictive template for ongoing exploration activity in analogue settings.

The final paper by **Rasmussen *et al.***, continues the move southward, and describes the use of well data and seismic inversion studies to search for Late Jurassic turbidite sands in the depocentres within the Danish sector of the Central Graben. Tantalizing well results from more grabenal locations suggest that reservoir quality basinal lowstand facies are developed down-dip from the current well locations. Seismic anomalies provide encouraging evidence for the presence of coarse clastics within the axis of the basin and seismic inversion studies confirm the interpretation that turbidites are potentially developed axially. Certainly, flanking structural

BOLDY, S. A. R. & FRASER, S. I. 1999. Jurassic subtle traps: introduction and review. *In*: FLEET, A. J. & BOLDY, S. A. R. (eds) *Petroleum Geology of Northwest Europe: Proceedings of the 5th Conference*, 825–826.

highs provide ample sediment source, however, the play which is unassessed remains relatively high risk.

Hanging wall traps for Jurassic sands have been known to be an important play in the North Sea, particularly for syn-rift Upper Jurassic sands, since the discovery of the Brae trend in 1975. Nevertheless, this play continues to be important with new discoveries being made and this can be expected to continue. The search for true stratigraphic traps in the Jurassic depocentres of the North Sea remains in its infancy, despite the attention of 3D seismic interpreters and sequence stratigraphers. These prospects will usually be deep and therefore expensive to drill, as well as being inherently risky. Purely stratigraphic prospectivity within the grabenal areas of the Central North Sea and Moray Firth remain relatively unassessed. Despite the almost blanket coverage of 3D data and the realization that sequence stratigraphic models predict the development of basinal facies of reservoir quality, it is likely that these prospects will only be pursued aggressively when sands can be predicted confidently by the seismic data volume. Clearly, seismic inversion studies inspire further confidence that the prediction of basinal sands is a possibility. However, well calibration is essential for refinement of any earth model. Hence a dilemma exists where limited basinal well information results in poor seismic model definition (the majority of well penetrations, >90%, are drilled on the flanks of the basin). Until such time as when the economic drivers, be they price or capacity related, are considerably stronger, the prospect of drilling high risk, expensive deep exploration wells on nebulus stratigraphic closures is remote.

References

Cordey, W. G. 1993. Jurassic exploration history: a look at the past and the future. *In*: Parker, J. R. (ed.) *Petroleum Geology of Northwest Europe: Proceedings of the 4th Conference*. Geological Society, London, 195–198.

Fraser, A. J. 1993. The Jurassic: from regional models to field development; the impact of sequence stratigraphy on hydrocarbon geology. *In*: Parker, J. R. (ed.) *Petroleum Geology of Northwest Europe: Proceedings of the 4th Conference*. Geological Society, London, 191–194.

Controls on Late Jurassic, subtle sand distribution in the Tampen Spur area, Northern North Sea

N. H. DAWERS,[1] A. M. BERGE,[2] K.-O. HÄGER,[2] C. PUIGDEFABREGAS[2] and J. R. UNDERHILL[1]

[1] *Department of Geology and Geophysics, University of Edinburgh, Grant Institute, The King's Buildings, West Mains Road, Edinburgh EH9 3JW, UK (e-mail: nancye.dawers@glg.ed.ac.uk)*

[2] *Norsk Hydro Research Centre, Sandsliveien 90, N-5020 Bergen, Norway*

Abstract: The role of fault growth and linkage is an important, but poorly understood, factor in controlling the distribution of sediments within extensional settings. Tectonostratigraphic analysis of the Statfjord East fault system, located in the East Shetland Basin of the Northern North Sea, demonstrates the importance of Late Jurassic normal faulting in controlling the nature of subtle, hanging wall traps. Wells in Norwegian Block 34/7 have penetrated prospective sandstone reservoirs that correlate with several thin, but seismically resolvable, units within syn-rift sediments of the Statfjord East hanging wall. Detailed 3D seismic interpretation and mapping of amplitude anomalies in Block 34/7 and the adjacent part of Block 33/9 reveal a number of spatially discontinuous stratigraphic units within the Late Jurassic, syn-rift Draupne Formation. These depositional units are spatially related to sub-basins, which are controlled by interaction and linkage of several en echelon fault segments. The main control on the distribution of local depocentres is the along-strike displacement variation associated with fault propagation by segment linkage. A close association between sandstone occurrence and structural position, suggests a model in which shoreline migration is controlled by the dynamics of fault lengthening through time.

The development of subtle hydrocarbon traps during rift basin evolution has gained wide recognition in recent years (e.g. Gabrielsen *et al.* 1995; Nøttvedt *et al.* 1995), and is becoming an increasingly important focus for exploration in the mature North Sea province. The effects of variable footwall uplift and hanging wall subsidence patterns associated with evolving normal faults predict a variety of syn-rift reservoir facies (e.g. Leeder & Gawthorpe 1987), including dip-slope deposits, footwall degradation complexes along large, active fault scarps (Underhill *et al.* 1997; McLeod & Underhill 1999), focused clastic deposits associated with fault relay zones (e.g. Gawthorpe & Hurst 1993) and basin floor fans (Partington *et al.* 1993).

In spite of the recent interest in syn-rift successions, the spatial and temporal evolution of normal faulting and the effects on the stratigraphic development of rift basins remain poorly understood. Much work has focused on kinematic models of fault block rotation (e.g. Roberts *et al.* 1993*a*). While such models predict some of the overall stratigraphic features of half-graben rift basins, they do not incorporate variations that arise from the lateral and vertical propagation of normal faults, and are thus of limited use in predicting facies on a local scale.

This paper discusses controls on subtle syn-rift traps, developed in the Upper Jurassic of the Northern North Sea, focusing on the spatial and temporal relationships between syn-rift stratigraphy and normal faulting in the Statfjord East area of the East Shetland Basin. The Statfjord East structure and associated syn-rift deposits are representative of many Late Jurassic half-graben in the North Sea. Moreover, the area is well-suited to the study of marine rift basin development, in that 3D seismic data and well data are available for both footwall and hanging wall locations.

Geological setting

The Statfjord East area is located near the UK–Norwegian boundary in the East Shetland Basin of the Northern North Sea, in a region known as the Tampen Spur (Fig. 1). A series of large, rotated fault blocks characterizes the Tampen Spur, with the footwall crests of these blocks creating some of the largest structural traps within the Brent Province, such as the Statfjord, Statfjord East, Murchison, Snorre and Gullfaks petroleum fields (Fig. 1). These east-dipping normal faults result from extension during the Middle Jurassic through Early Cretaceous (e.g. Kirk 1980; Nyberg 1987; Lee & Hwang 1993; Rattey & Hayward 1993), which overprints and to some extent reactivates earlier Permo-Triassic rift structures (Færseth 1996). Estimates of Late Jurassic–Early Cretaceous extensional strain in this area range from roughly 10% to 20% (Yielding 1990; Roberts *et al.* 1993*b*; Rouby *et al.* 1996).

Figure 2 summarizes the stratigraphy of the Tampen Spur. The onset of Jurassic rifting is marked by the drowning of the Brent delta system, followed by the deposition of Upper Bajocian–Oxfordian mudstones of the Heather Formation. The Draupne Formation, known as the Kimmeridge Clay Formation in UK nomenclature, forms an important syn-rift wedge of Late Oxfordian–Ryazanian age between the Heather Formation and the carbonates of the Cretaceous Cromer Knoll Group.

The syn-rift stratigraphy of the southwestern part of Norwegian Block 34/7 is of particular interest here. Well results from Block 34/7 indicate the presence of prospective sandstone reservoirs in the Upper Jurassic Draupne Formation. Solli (1995) delineated the 'Snorre-H' trap as a prospective stratigraphic trap lying within the syn-rift Draupne Formation, situated in the hanging wall of the Statfjord East

DAWERS, N. H., BERGE, A. M., HÄGER, K.-O., PUIGDEFABREGAS, C. & UNDERHILL, J. R. 1999. Controls on Late Jurassic, subtle sand distribution in the Tampen Spur area, Northern North Sea. *In*: FLEET, A. J. & BOLDY, S. A. R. (eds) *Petroleum Geology of Northwest Europe: Proceedings of the 5th Conference*, 827–838.

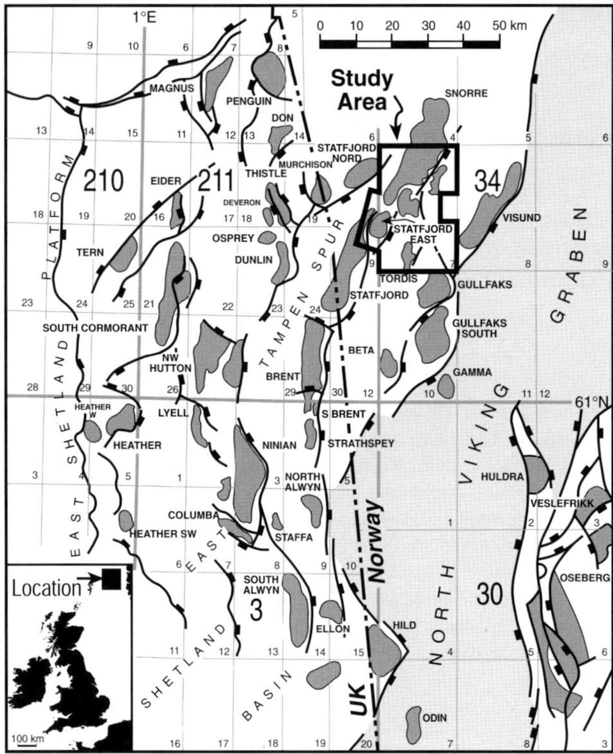

Fig. 1. Location map for the East Shetland Basin and surrounding area, showing major oil fields (shaded regions) associated with large, tilted fault blocks. The study area is outlined; it comprises Norwegian Block 34/7 and the adjacent Statfjord East area in Block 33/9.

Ma*	Period*		Stage*	Formation	Group	
	Cret.		Valanginian		Cromer Knoll	Post-Rift Subsidence
140			Berriasian / Ryazanian†			
	Jurassic	Late	Volgian	Draupne / Kimmeridge Clay	Viking / Humber	Rifting
150			Tithonian / Kimmeridgian			
			Oxfordian			
			Callovian	Heather		
160		Middle	Bathonian			
170			Bajocian	Tarbert, Ness, Etive	Brent	
			Aalenian	Rannoch, Broom		
180		Early	Toarcian	Drake	Dunlin	
190			Pliensbachian	Burton, Cook		Post-Rift Subsidence
200			Sinemurian	Amundsen		
			Hettangian	Nansen, Statfjord	Banks	
210	Triassic		Rhaetian			

Fig. 2. Stratigraphic framework for the Tampen Spur region. This study focuses on the syn-rift Upper Jurassic Viking Group, known in the UK sector as the Humber Group. *Timescale from Harland *et al.* (1990). †Stage definitions used here are those based on Boreal faunas.

fault and down-flank from the footwall of the Inner Snorre fault (Fig. 3). These sandstones are interpreted to reflect large-scale erosion of the footwall of the Inner Snorre fault, which was exposed above sea-level during the formation of the Viking Graben in the Late Jurassic (e.g. Dahl & Solli 1993; Solli 1995). In the hanging wall of the nearby Murchison fault of the Statfjord North field, Upper Jurassic sands known as the Munin sands, have been found in the syn-rift structural lows (Haram *et al.* 1990; Barnes *et al.* 1992; Wood & Schwartzbard 1994). The geological model proposed by Dahl and Solli (1993) and Solli (1995) predicts dip-slope deposition in a coastal marine gulf setting, along with submarine and talus fans occurring along degrading fault scarps.

Datasets

Four 3D seismic surveys were interpreted: e86, sg9201, ge83 and sg8431. These surveys have considerable overlap, covering

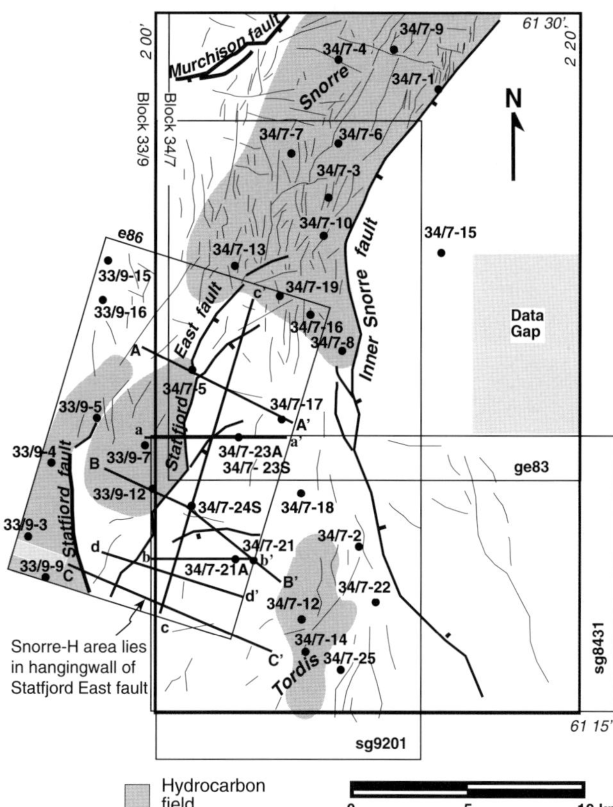

Fig. 3. Fault map showing the general structural framework of the Statfjord East/Snorre-H area. The Statfjord East Fault, located in the e86 survey, is made up of several NE-striking segments. Cross-section A–A′, B–B′ and C–C′ are shown in Fig. 4, and seismic sections along a–a′, b–b′, c–c′ and d–d′ are shown in Fig. 9. Also shown are the outlines of the 3D surveys (full-fold data areas) and wells used in this study. Inline, CDP spacing for the surveys are: e86 – 18.75, 12.5 m; sg9201 – 12.5, 12.5m; sg8431 – 25, 12.5 m; and ge83 – 50, 25 m.

nearly all of Block 34/7 and part of Block 33/9 (Fig. 3). This paper focuses on the e86 and sg9201 surveys because they are the most relevant to the Statfjord East/Snorre-H area. The e86 and sg9201 surveys have closer inline and CDP spacings than the other older surveys (see Fig. 3 caption), are of good quality, and stratigraphic reflections and faults are well imaged. For the purposes of this paper, the seismic interpretation has not been depth converted.

The wells used in this study to constrain the seismic interpretation are shown on Fig. 3. These include the Snorre-H wells (34/7-21, -21A, -23A, -23S, -24S), which are located in the hanging wall of the Statfjord East fault, as well as those located on the Snorre and Statfjord East footwalls (Fig. 3). Although the 3D seismic datasets are assumed to be zero-phase, horizons were defined at trace positions (i.e. peak, trough, zero-crossing) that tie most closely to the formation tops provided from Norsk Hydro's database.

Biostratigraphic zonation, well correlation and facies analysis of cored intervals of sand-prone upper Draupne were carried out at the Norsk Hydro Research Centre in order to assess the syn-rift play potential of the Snorre fault block (Nøttvedt *et al.* in press). These results, which are also described in Häger & Smelror (1997), are incorporated here in order to develop a model of the structural and stratigraphic evolution of the area.

General observations

Figure 4 illustrates the overall geometry of the Statfjord East half-graben. The syn-rift deposits of the Statfjord East Basin

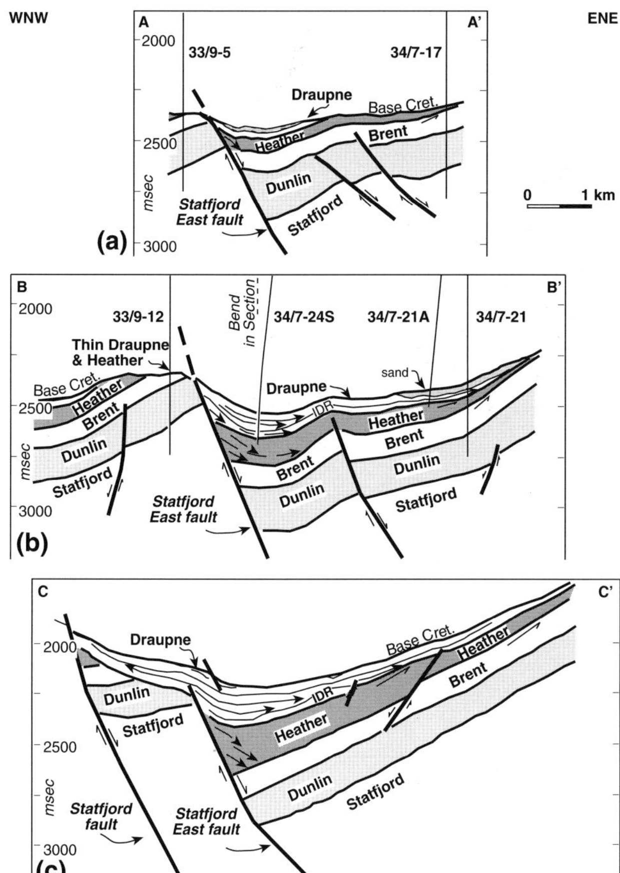

Fig. 4. Cross-sectional geometries of the Statfjord East footwall and hanging wall: (**a**) northern, (**b**) central, and (**c**) southern parts of the Statfjord East area; see Fig. 3 for locations. Note the thickness changes of the syn-rift sequence overlying the Brent Group, especially in the central and southern sections (b and c). IDR refers to a prominent Intra-Draupne reflection.

comprise a westward thickening wedge, with an overall synclinal shape. The Tarbert Formation, which forms the youngest formation of the Brent Group, is thought to mark the onset of Jurassic rifting in this part of the Northern North Sea (e.g. Yielding *et al.* 1992; Underhill *et al.* 1997), but for the purposes of this study, Top Brent is the earliest syn-rift surface mapped (Figs. 4 and 5a).

The top of the syn-rift sequence is marked by a prominent Base Cretaceous seismic event, which is generally referred to as an unconformity in spite of the fact that in some basinal settings there is no stratigraphic omission (e.g. Rawson & Riley 1982; Rattey & Hayward 1993). This regional seismic marker results from a sharp acoustic impedance contrast between carbonates of the Lower Cretaceous Cromer Knoll Group and underlying formations. Although this reflector is of early Cretaceous age in the Northern North Sea (e.g. Rawson & Riley 1982; Rattey & Hayward 1993), it is referred to here as the Base Cretaceous Event (BCE) (Fig. 5b).

Two other horizons of regional or semi-regional extent were mapped within the syn-rift interval. The top Heather Formation/base Draupne Formation is marked by a sharp acoustic impedance contrast. Along the eastern margin of the Statfjord East Basin, Top Heather has been truncated by the BCE, as shown in Figs 4a and b. The Heather Formation is observed to thicken westward towards the main fault structures, particularly in the southern part of the basin (Figs 4b and c). In Wells 33/9-12 and 33/9-7 on the Statfjord East footwall, the Heather Formation is present, but too thin to be seismically resolvable (Fig. 4b). However, a top Heather/base Draupne reflector can be mapped locally down-flank from the Statfjord East footwall crest, in the area between Wells 33/9-5 and 33/9-7 (Figs 4b and 5c).

A prominent reflector within the Draupne Formation was mapped over part of the study area (Fig. 5d); it divides the Draupne into a lower, relatively homogeneous seismic unit, and a more heterogeneous upper unit. This horizon is restricted to the deeper parts of the Statfjord East Basin (Figs 4b, c and 5d). We refer to it here as the Intra-Draupne reflector.

Geometry of the Statfjord East fault and main syn-rift units

The general structural framework is illustrated by the dip-azimuth map of the BCE horizon (Fig. 6). The fault pattern is dominated by large NE- to NNE-striking faults that are delineated in Fig. 6 by the dark shading on easterly-facing escarpments. Also observed are numerous, but less important, N–S and WNW-striking faults.

The Statfjord East fault system is comprised of a series of NE-striking, left-stepping, en echelon fault segments that are linked by northerly-striking segments (Fig. 3). At the Top Brent level the en echelon nature of the Statfjord East fault is particularly clear (Fig. 5a). The NE-striking en echelon segments define a series of sub-basins along the Statfjord East hanging wall. The sub-basins are evident in the maps of the Top Heather Formation (Fig. 5c) and Top Brent Group (Fig. 5a), and in thickness variations shown in Fig. 7.

The variation in thickness of the Heather Formation is shown in Fig. 7a. An east-northeast striking fault, located south of Well 34/7-24S, separates a pronounced depocentre near the south edge of the study area from a less pronounced depocentre near 34/7-24S. Thickness variations for the lower part of the Draupne, i.e. the portion between the Intra-Draupne reflector and the top of Heather Formation, are shown in Fig. 7b. The lower part of the Draupne Formation is also thickest in local depocentres along the southern part of the fault, with an additional depocentre evident along a segment west of the 34/7-23 wells. Figure 7c shows the variations in the upper Draupne. In the north, upper Draupne does not appear to drape the Statfjord East Fault; however, in the southern part of the area the upper Draupne is deposited across the fault, where it blankets part of the degraded portion of the footwall (Figs 4c and 7c).

Stratigraphy of the Draupne Formation

One of the primary objectives of this work is to understand the nature of the Upper Jurassic, syn-rift Draupne Formation. Within this interval, a number of distinct internal Draupne reflectors are observed, including the base of the sands in the upper part of the Draupne. Before focusing on the seismic nature of the Draupne Formation, we first summarize the results of stratigraphic analyses of Wells 34/7-21, 34/7-21A, 34/7-23A, 34/7-23S and 34/7-24S. The palynological zonation, assessment of reworking, and facies descriptions are further outlined in Häger & Smelror (1997) and Nøttvedt *et al.* (in press).

Stratigraphic architecture

The results of the core studies for wells 34/7-21, 34/7-21A, 34/7-23A and 34/7-23S are shown in Fig. 8. The Draupne Formation consists of a lower shale unit, which, in wells -21, -21A, -23A and 23S passes gradually into the coarsening-upward sand-prone upper Draupne. The lower shale is a thinly laminated black shale with little evidence of bioturbation. It contains thinly interbedded shelly carbonate, pyrite laminae

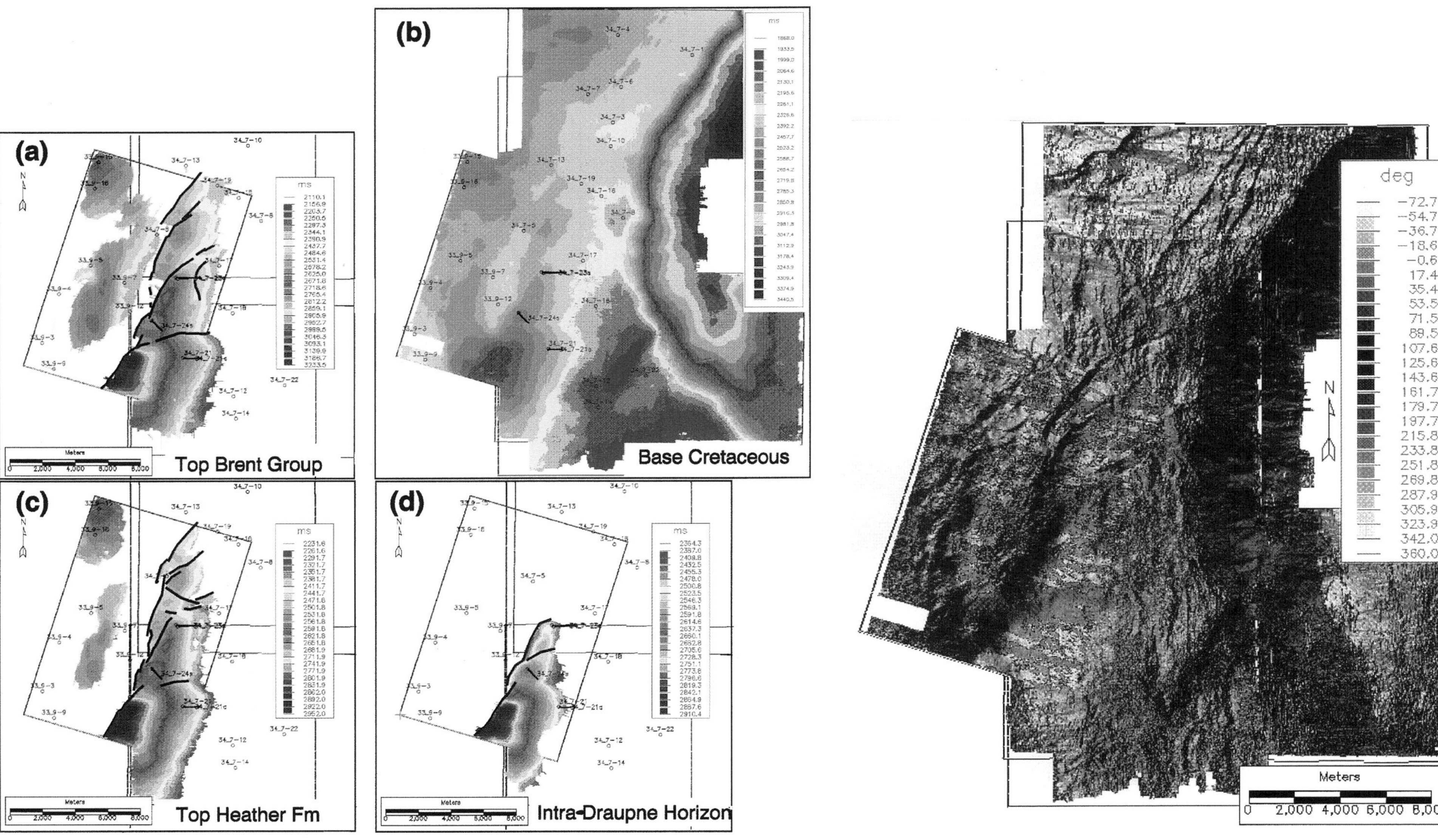

Fig. 5. Time-structure maps of (**a**) Top Brent; (**b**) Base Cretaceous; (**c**) Top Heather; and (**d**) the Intra-Draupne reflector. These horizons have been interpreted on every second inline and every tenth crossline, except for top Brent, which was interpreted on every tenth inline and crossline.

Fig. 6. Dip-azimuth map of the auto-tracked Base Cretaceous map, with the greyscale simulating illumination from the northwest.

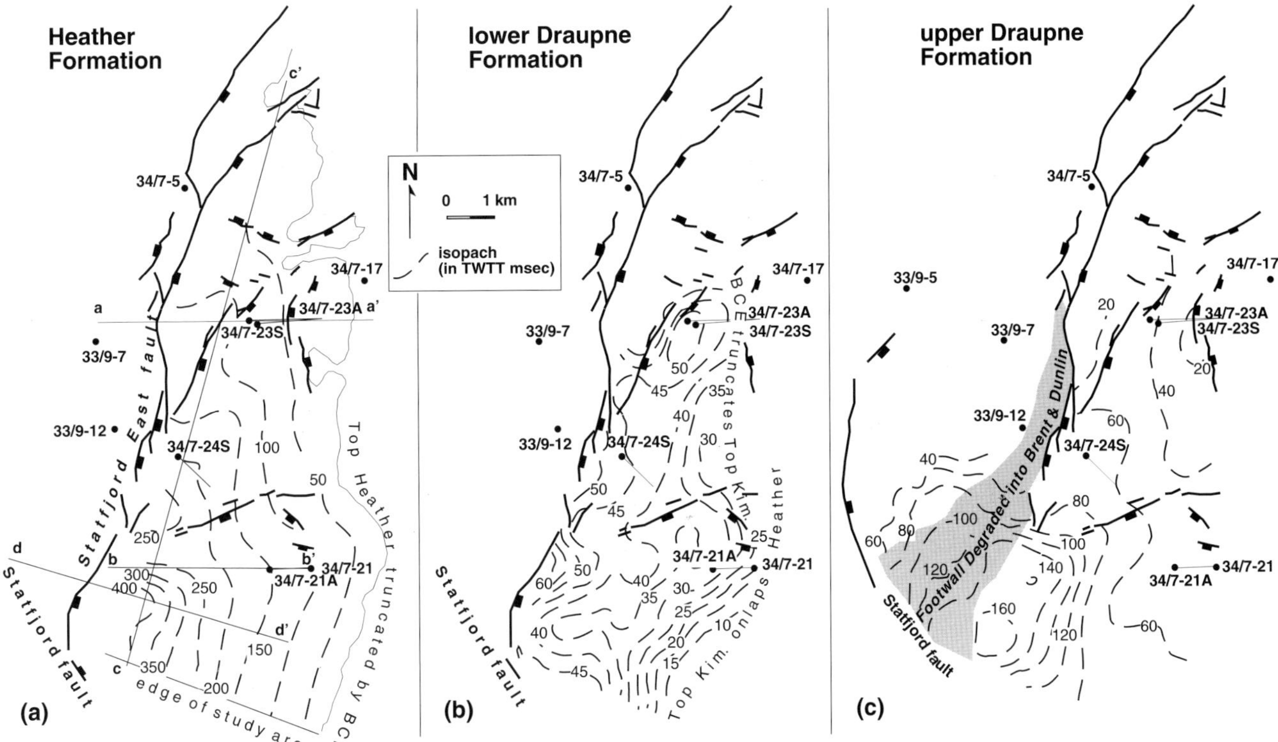

Fig. 7. Isopachs of the main syn-rift units: (**a**) the Heather Formation; (**b**) lower part of the Draupne Formation, i.e. below the Intra-Draupne reflector; (**c**) upper part of the Draupne Formation, i.e. above the Intra-Draupne reflector. Seismic sections a–a′, b–b′, c–c′ and d–d′ in part (a) are shown in Fig. 9.

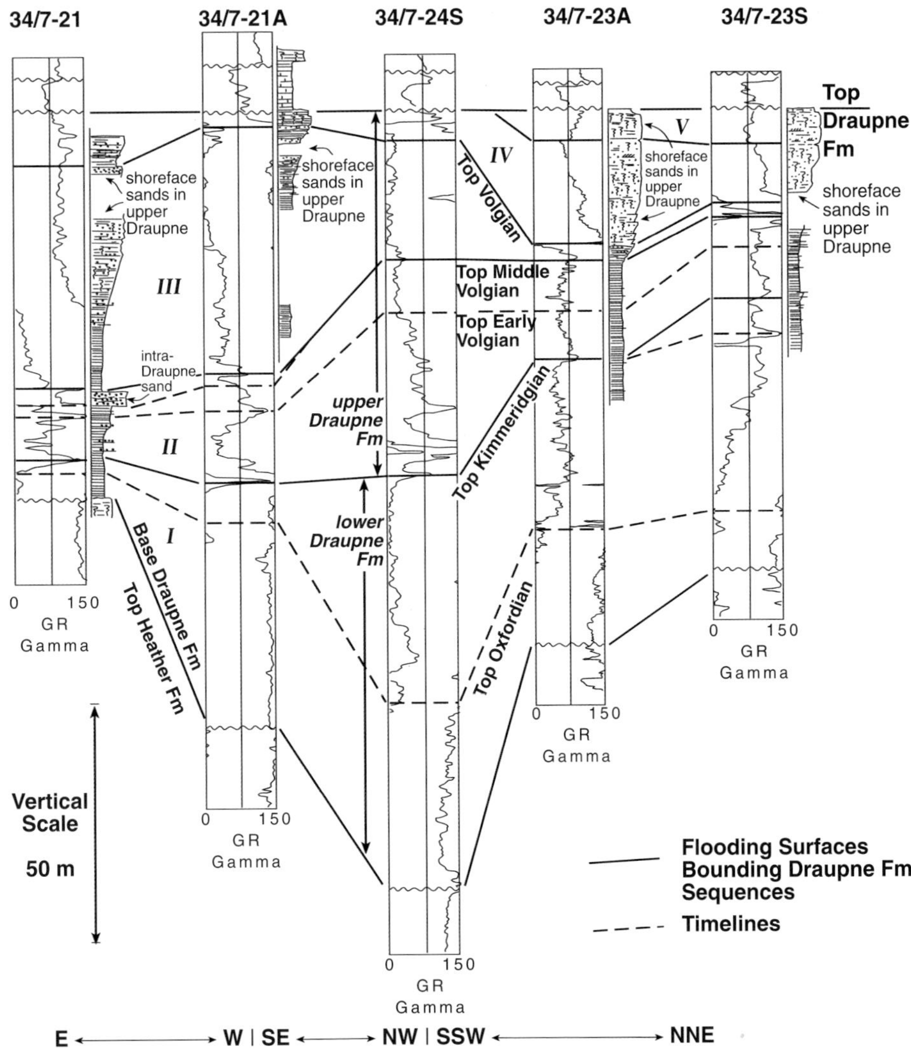

Fig. 8. Correlation panel for the Snorre-H wells, showing the gamma response and summary of sedimentological data. Also shown are the key surfaces that bound stratigraphic sequences I–V. See text for discussion.

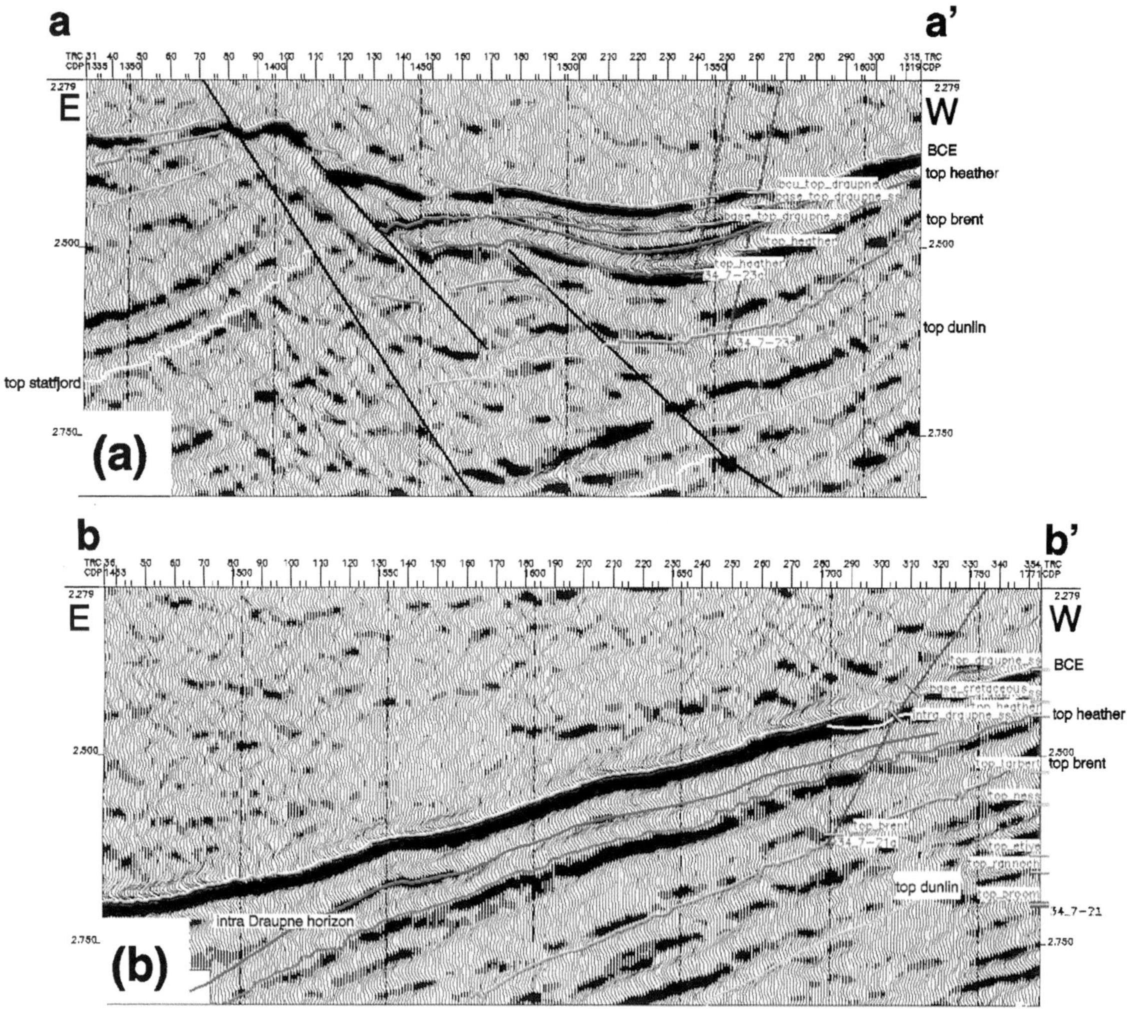

Fig. 9. Seismic sections, from the e86 survey, across the Snorre-H Basin; see Figs 3 and 7a for location. (**a**) Traverse through Wells 34/7-23A and -23S, showing the base of the upper Draupne sand in pink. (**b**) Traverse through Wells 34/7-21A and -21, showing the base of the intra-Draupne sand in yellow. (**c**) An along-strike crossline through Wells 34/7-24S and -23A. Note that the intrabasinal highs are associated with the NE-striking splays of the Statfjord East fault system. These control thickness variations within the syn-rift sequence. The southernmost splay was more important during Heather deposition, whereas the ones toward the north were more important during Draupne deposition. (**d**) Inline 170 showing the Statfjord fault (left) and Statfjord East fault (right). Several internal reflectors overlie the top Kimmeridgian horizon, shown in red; the lower ones onlap top Kimmeridgian, whereas the uppermost ones appear to drape a degraded portion of the Statfjord East footwall, which has been displaced by the Statfjord fault.

and nodules, belemnites, and frequent small-scale slumping and syndepositional faulting. Above the lower shale in Well 34/7-21, an interbedded sand unit, referred to as the intra Draupne sand on Fig. 8, contains mud clasts and coal debris and is thought to represent a submarine channel deposit.

The upper Draupne sandstone observed in Wells 34/7-21, -21A, -23A and -23S, is characterized by centimetres to decimetres thick units of fine- to medium-grained, micaceous, ripple-laminated and cross-laminated sand. Bioturbation decreases upward, where horizontal laminae and low-angle cross beds characterize the upper part. Facies interpretation points to these sediments being deposited in a shallow marine shelf to shoreline environment of linear progradational character. The shallowing-upward sequence of upper Draupne sandstone is capped by the unconformable carbonates of the Cromer Knoll Group.

The Snorre-H wells represent a fairly complete succession from the Upper Bajocian through Kimmeridgian (Häger & Smelror 1997). In Well 34/7-21, minor stratigraphic breaks may be present in the mid Callovian and mid Oxfordian, and in the late Early–early mid Volgian. The late mid Volgian–Late Volgian and Late Ryazanian intervals are present, but the transition from mid to Late Volgian is not well defined. Well 34/7-21A, which is deviated ~600 m westward, shows a similar succession, but with some differences in the late Early–mid Volgian. The upper Draupne sand deposition is observed in Well 34/7-21 to be mainly of Late Volgian age, with the upper few metres of Ryazanian age. In Wells 34/7-23A and -23S, however, it is mostly of Ryazanian age, with only the lowermost part being of Late Volgian age. Well 34/7-24S encountered no sand, but has a succession that is very similar in age to Wells -21 and -21A, i.e. mainly Upper Volgian shales with an overlying uppermost Ryazanian shale.

Several episodes of reworking are evident in the Snorre-H wells (Häger & Smelror 1997). Minor amounts of dinoflagellates reworked from the Brent Group first appear in the Late Callovian–Early Oxfordian. Reworking of Brent/Dunlin taxa increased markedly in the Kimmeridgian and continued into the Late Volgian. In Ryazanian times, taxa from the Draupne, Heather and Brent formations are reworked.

Also shown in Fig. 8 are key correlation surfaces. Flooding surfaces bounding five Draupne Formation sequences were defined on the basis of sedimentological data from cored intervals. Some of these surfaces were also found to correspond

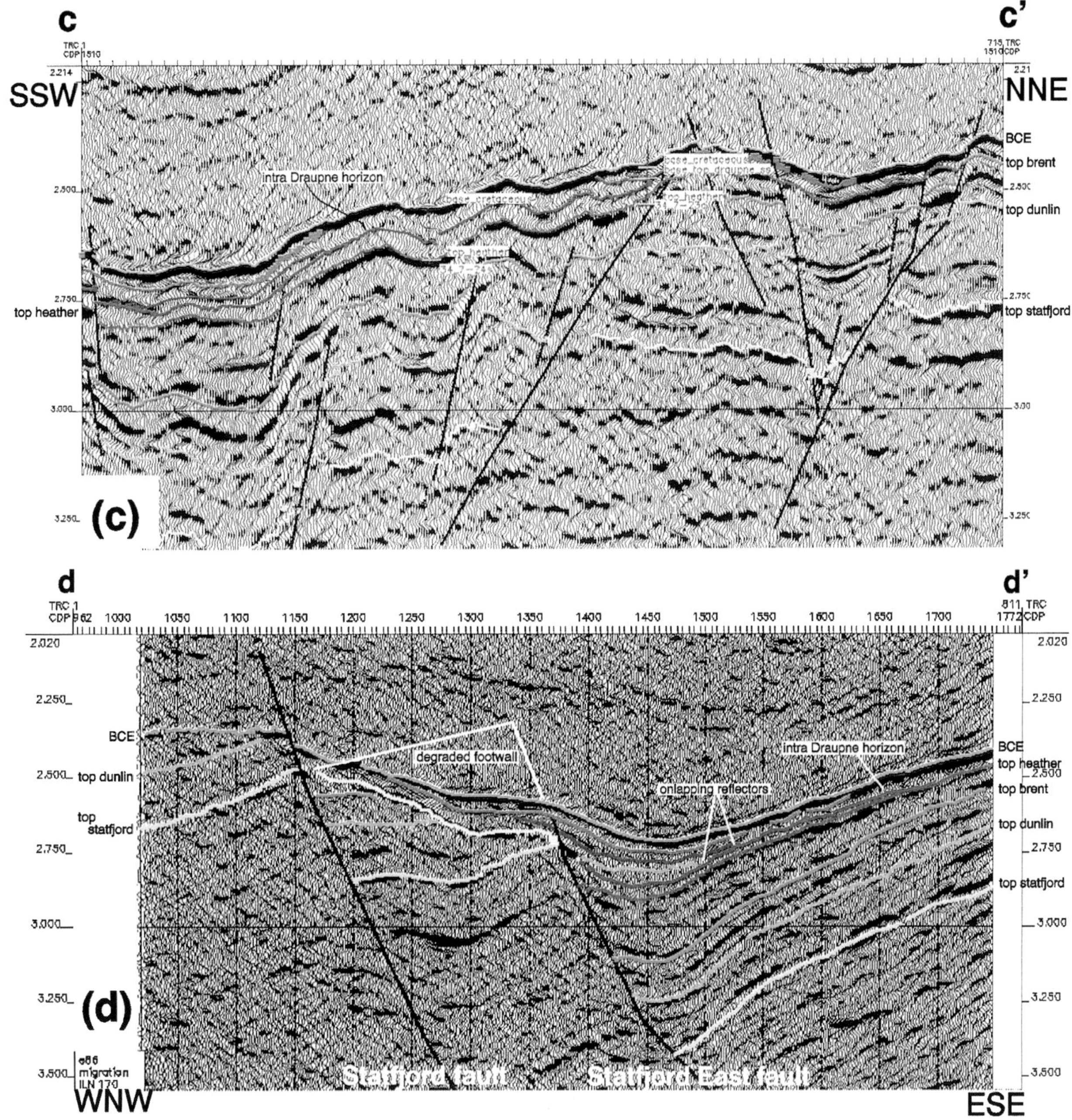

Fig. 9. (*continued*).

to biostratigraphically-defined timelines. Where core data were absent, these correlation surfaces were interpreted from gamma logs. On a gross scale, the Draupne Formation is comprised of two main sediment packages referred to here, informally, as lower and upper Draupne (Fig. 8). These packages are divided by a flooding surface, which corresponds to the top Kimmeridgian timeline, and is characterized by small-scale slumping and syn-sedimentary faulting. The lower Draupne package, sequence I on Fig. 8, consists of laminated shale, which is thicker in the vicinity of the Statfjord East fault (Well 34/7-24S) and thinner towards the east, where it onlaps the tilted Top Heather surface (Well 34/7-21). Four sequences, II–V on Fig. 8, are distinguished within the upper Draupne Formation. The onset of sand deposition occurs within sequence II. Sequences III and IV correspond to progradational shoreline wedges, whose thickness and location we later relate to compartmentalization of the basin by segments of the Statfjord East fault. Sequence III, of Late Volgian age, is thickest in the vicinity of the Wells 34/7-21, 34/7-21A and 34/7-24S, where in Wells 34/7-21 and 34/7-21A it encompasses all but the uppermost part of the upper Draupne sand. In the vicinity of Wells 34/7-23A and 34/7-23S, however, sequence III is only represented by the lowermost part of the upper Draupne sand. Sequence IV, of Ryazanian age, is thickest in the Wells 34/7-23A and 34/7-23S and thins south and eastward. A thin capping of transgressive sands in Wells 34/7-23A and 34/7-23S defines sequence V.

Seismic nature of the Draupne Formation

As mentioned earlier, the Draupne Formation can be defined seismically as consisting of a lower unit and an upper unit, separated by an Intra-Draupne reflector. The lower part of the Draupne Formation is relatively homogeneous in its seismic character, whereas the overlying unit can be further differentiated into a number of spatially discontinuous units.

Figure 9 shows several traverses through the Snorre-H wells described earlier. The base of the upper Draupne sandstone is observed to be seismically resolvable in Wells 34/7-23S and 34/7-23A (Fig. 9a). The sand appears on seismic data as a lobe-like feature lying immediately below the BCE. In Wells 34/7-21 and 34/7-21A, a reflector is observed to correlate with the position of the intra Draupne sandstone (Fig. 9b). Thus, the intra- and upper sands are not seismically distinguishable here, but a lobate feature can be mapped northward and southward from Wells 34/7-21 and 34/7-21A, which is interpreted to contain both sand units.

The Intra-Draupne reflector lies below the base of both the upper and intra Draupne sandstones (Figs 9a and b). Although the reflector is difficult to resolve at well 34/7-21, in Wells 34/7-24S, -21A, -23A and -23S it corresponds approximately to the top of sequence I, i.e. the top Kimmeridgian time-line. However, it must be noted that in the 34/7-23 wells, the Intra-Draupne reflector may climb up within the Volgian, possibly because of sub-seismic lateral facies changes. Given the relatively homogeneous seismic character of the interval between the Intra-Draupne reflector and the Top Heather, this interval is interpreted as the shale-dominated lower Draupne Formation. Small basinward-dipping faults are frequently observed along the top of sequence I on the hanging wall dip-slope. As can be seen in Figs 7b and 9b, the lower Draupne shale thickens westwards, with several local depocentres developed along segments of the Statfjord East fault (Fig. 7b).

The Intra-Draupne reflector is observed to onlap the Top Heather along the hanging wall dip-slope in the southern part of the Snorre-H Basin. However, along the eastern edge of the sub-basin near Wells 34/7-23S and -23A, it has been truncated by the BCE (Fig. 9a). This is thought to be related to a small fault near these wells, which uplifted the Intra-Draupne reflector on its footwall.

Figure 9c shows an along-strike traverse through the Statfjord East Basin. Like the Heather Formation, the Draupne Formation is observed to thicken towards the south, reaching a maximum thickness near the edge of the e86 survey. The salient feature of the along-strike basin geometry is the presence of intrabasin highs associated with the northeast striking fault segments (Fig. 9c). These features have a fold-like nature in cross-section and are similar to structures that Schlische (1995) has related to slip variations along segmented normal faults. Note that, in general, the thickness variations in the syn-rift succession are less pronounced across the fault segments located in the northern part of the basin.

The internal seismic character of the upper Draupne Formation in the deepest part of the basin consists of several stacked reflectors that onlap the top Kimmeridgian surface (or the Intra-Draupne reflector), both transverse and longitudinally to the basin axis (Figs 9c and d). These are in turn overlain by internal reflections that are truncated by the BCE (Figs 9c and d). The Statfjord East footwall immediately adjacent to this area has been degraded down through Brent/Dunlin levels (Fig. 9d). This suggests that the deeper internal reflectors observed in this part of the Snorre-H Basin are related to processes of scarp degradation. Based on the biostratigraphic zonation for sequences observed in Wells 34/7-24S, -21 and -21A, the degradation is thought to have occurred during Late Kimmeridgian–Volgian times. The reflections that overlie the stacked reflectors are more continuous and over-step the degraded Statfjord East footwall. In Well 33/9-12, located just north of the most intensely degraded footwall area, a thin drape of Draupne Formation shale is present. Although the interval sampled does not contain clear age indicators, the shale here is assigned an age of ?mid Volgian-?Ryazanian, based on general lithology, facies and log breaks. This suggests that this portion of the footwall had become tectonically inactive and drowned during the deposition of the upper Draupne Formation.

Inferences from seismic attributes

In areas where the BCE is underlain by upper Draupne sand, i.e. near Wells 34/7-23A, -23S, -21 and -21A, the intensity of this normally prominent seismic event is observed to decrease. In other words, the acoustic impedance contrast between the Cromer Knoll Group carbonate and Draupne sandstone is slightly less than the impedance contrast between the carbonate and shale (e.g. Hansen *et al.* 1994). Therefore, there is the potential to discriminate the Draupne sandstones using the seismic attributes of the BCE. In order to investigate this possibility, a number of different seismic attribute maps, using various measures of amplitude and various window widths, were made for the autotracked interpretation of the BCE reflector in the e86 dataset.

Figure 10a shows the spatial variation of the RMS amplitude within a window from 4 ms above the BCE to 24 ms below. The yellow areas correspond to low amplitudes and the blue areas correspond to higher amplitudes. Note that upper Draupne sand occurrence in Wells 34/7-21, -21A, -23A and -23S corresponds to low amplitudes. The areal extent of the interpretation of the base of the sand, which is resolvable in seismic sections (Figs 9a and b), is shown on the attribute map (Fig. 10a). The interpretation of the sand extent correlates well with the areas of low amplitude observed in the seismic attribute map; because of this we are able to interpret this map in terms of seismic facies. A mapped horseshoe-shaped feature to the NNW of Wells 34/7-23A and -23S is interpreted as an extension of the sand unit observed in those wells. An amplitude anomaly located between Wells 34/7-23A, -23S and -24S is interpreted as an extension of the sand of Wells 34/7-21 and -21A. A traverse across this anomaly is shown in Fig. 10b. We interpret the upper Draupne sand lobe observed in Wells 34/7-23A and -23S as lying structurally higher than this amplitude anomaly, and shaling out across one of the intrabasinal faults. Figure 11 summarizes the key elements of the seismic interpretation, including the distribution of subtle, upper Draupne Formation sands based on the seismic attributes of the BCE.

Discussion

Stratigraphic evolution

The seismic interpretation and well results described earlier suggest the following stratigraphic evolution for the area.

The early stage of syn-rift evolution is reflected in the nature of the Heather Formation. The Heather Formation was deposited across footwall crests, including the Statfjord East area discussed here, and the Statfjord and Visund footwalls (Roberts *et al.* 1993a; Færseth *et al.* 1995, respectively). In places where the Heather Formation has been drilled, it is not known to contain significant sandstones. Thus there appears to be little evidence of significant footwall islands during the Late Bajocian through Oxfordian times. Nevertheless, spatial variability in rates of faulting is evident in thickness variations of the Heather Formation, such as that observed here. Although regional-scale variation in Heather Formation thickness may in part be erosional, such as on footwall crests, the thickness variation observed in the Snorre-H Basin is interpreted as representing relatively high rates of displacement along only the southernmost part of the Statfjord East fault system during this interval.

The shale-dominated lower part of the Draupne Formation, i.e. sequence I, represents sediment starved, under-filled conditions (Nøttvedt *et al.* in press), suggesting that sediment supply could not keep pace with the rate of fault-controlled subsidence, as seen in many rift settings (e.g. Prosser 1993). The thickness variation in the lower Draupne of the Snorre-H

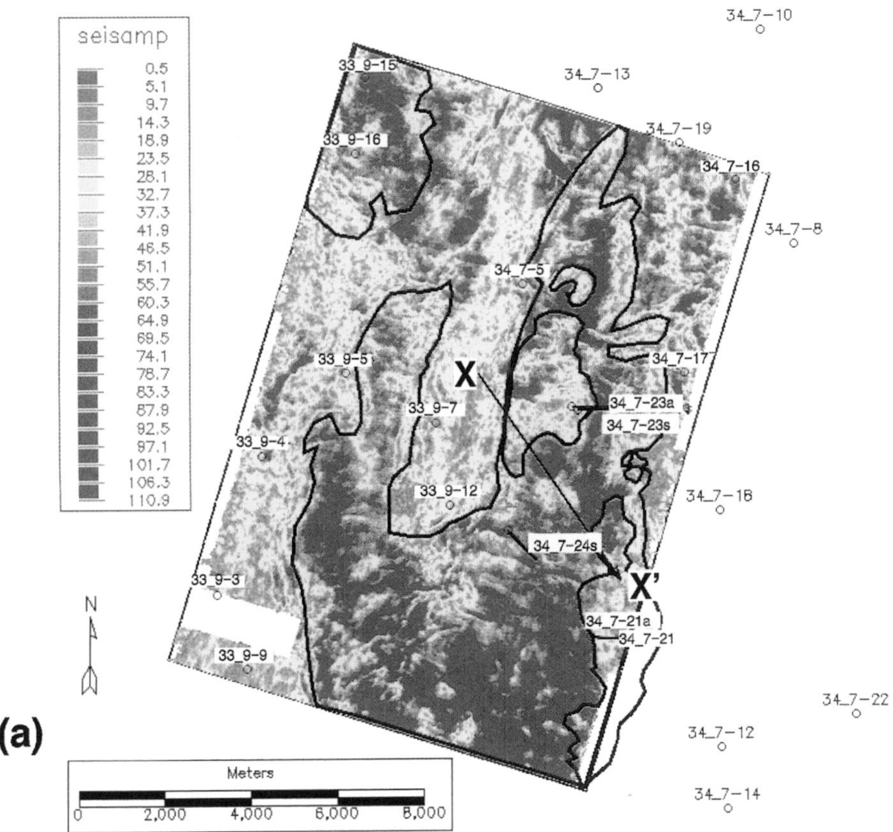

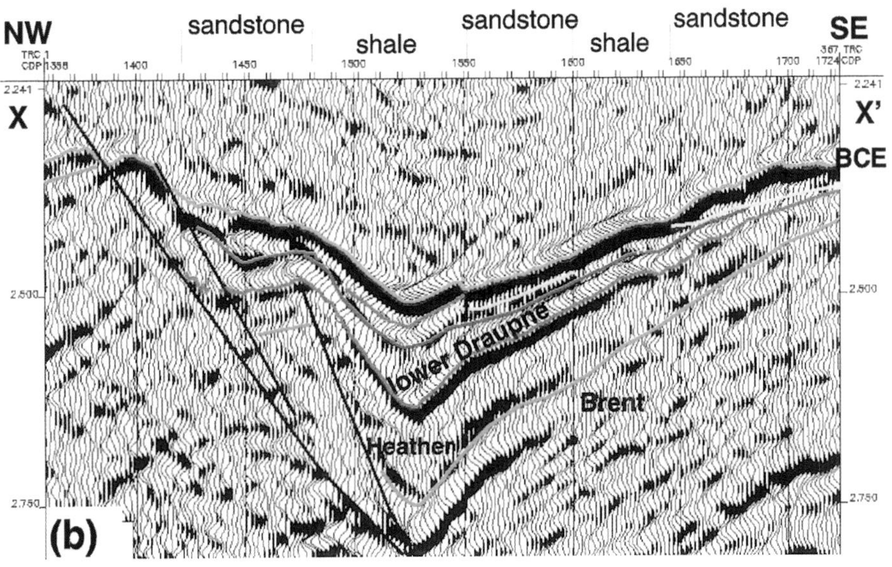

Fig. 10. (**a**) Spatial variation in the GeoQuest IESX seismic attribute calculation of RMS amplitude for the BCE. This map was calculated using a window extending from 4 ms above the BCE to 24 ms below. Outlined are the extent of Draupne Formation subcrop, and the upper Draupne sand lobes mapped in the vicinity of Wells 34/7-23A, -23S, -21 and -21A. Note that there are a number of localized amplitude anomalies that may represent subtle, thin sands that are not readily observed in seismic sections. (**b**) Seismic traverse showing interpretation of several amplitude anomalies (see part (a) for location of traverse).

Basin indicates that the Statfjord East fault system consisted of three active fault segments during Kimmeridgian times, extending from the southern part of the study area northward to the vicinity of Wells 34/7-23A and -23S. Slumps and synsedimentary faults observed in Well 34/7-21 and minor, basinward dipping faults that are observed seismically on the top of sequence I suggest increased tilting of the hanging wall dipslope, caused by increased fault displacement rates.

Biostratigraphic evidence of reworking suggests that erosion of Brent Group sediments had begun by Kimmeridgian times (Häger & Smelror 1997). However, the shale-prone nature of the lower Draupne Formation may be taken to indicate that erosion of Heather Formation on the emerging footwalls was the major contributor to the lower Draupne sediments.

The upper Draupne succession is marked by an influx of sand into the Snorre-H Basin during the Early and mid

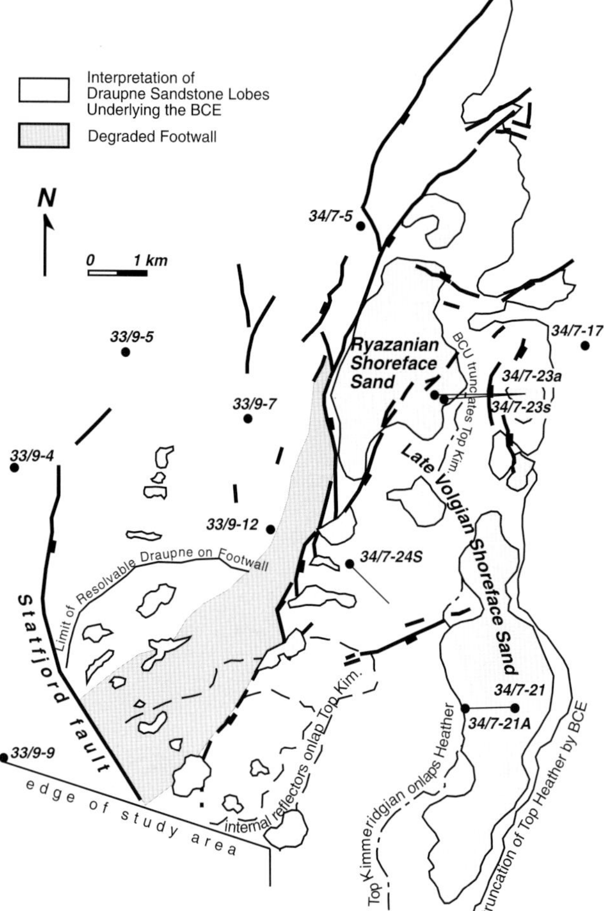

Fig. 11. Map showing the interpreted areal extent of the upper Draupne sands.

Volgian; this is evidenced by the intra Draupne sand observed in Well 34/7-21, which is interpreted as a forced regressive event (Nøttvedt *et al.* in press). The degradation of the southern part of the Statfjord East footwall, and the deposition of gravitationally-deposited debris are interpreted, to have occurred primarily in Volgian times. The Upper Volgian is characterized by the shoreface succession, which is interpreted as an arcuate belt along the hanging wall dip-slope, extending from south of Wells 34/7-21 and -21A northward to the area between Wells 34/7-24S and -23S/-23A. The degraded footwall area extending from Well 33/9-12 southward became drowned during the Late Volgian, probably as a result of displacement along the northern part of the Statfjord fault, which overlaps the southern part of the Statfjord East fault.

During the Ryazanian, we interpret a northward migration of the fault-controlled Snorre-H embayment, with sequences IV and V prograding across the sub-basin north of Wells 34/7-23A and -23S. This was followed by a cessation in normal faulting and largely passive-infilling during most of the Early Cretaceous.

Faulting

The spatial and temporal relationships observed in the syn-rift sediments of the Snorre-H Basin show that fault growth through segment linkage is an important factor in basin development. This is illustrated by the thickness variations shown in Fig. 7b and in the interpretation of the shoreline pattern, shown in Figs 11 and 12. In particular, we observe an active depocentre in the southwestern part of Block 34/7 during the deposition of the Heather Formation, followed by a series of active, fault-controlled depocentres developing in the Kimmeridgian, during the deposition of the lower Draupne Formation shale.

The pattern of northward migration of faulting is again evident in the position of the Late Volgian and Ryazanian shoreface deposits, which are found from both the seismic interpretation and the biostratigraphy, to young towards the north. The position of the Ryazanian sand lobe appears to have been controlled by the formation and linkage with an en echelon fault segment located east of Wells 33/9-7 and 33/9-5 (Fig. 12). The persistence of the deepest depocentre in the southern part of the basin probably results from interaction with the Statfjord fault. The Statfjord and the Statfjord East faults are thought to coalesce just south of the study area (Nyberg 1987).

In conventional terms, the Draupne Formation sequences – particularly those of Kimmeridgian through Early Volgian age – exhibit characteristics of 'rift climax' depositional systems, which correspond to times of maximum displacement rates on the border fault system (Prosser 1993). The present study suggests that structural nature of the 'rift climax' is that of an interacting array of en echelon fault segments. Studies of the displacement geometries along overlapping, en echelon normal fault segments suggest that this pattern of basin development is not unusual (e.g. Schlische & Anders 1996). Gawthorpe *et al.* (1994) discuss a number of neotectonic examples of segmented half-graben that exhibit high rates of displacement in segment centres relative to segment tips. Although, this general pattern of displacement rate variation is expected to be observed even along a single, isolated fault, a number of studies have shown that interacting en echelon fault segments are characterized by locally enhanced slip (e.g. Dawers & Anders 1995; Willemse *et al.* 1996). This implies that abrupt increases in displacement rates should correspond to times of fault interaction and linkage.

Sediment dispersal

Segmented fault geometries are frequently observed to influence the pattern of sediment dispersal, as well as influencing the facies architecture. In particular, relay ramps between overlapping fault segments may provide a route for sediments from the adjacent eroding footwall to enter the basin (Gawthorpe & Hurst 1993; Underhill 1994; Gawthorpe *et al.* 1997). In the case discussed here this is clearly a possible scenario, indeed some of the more subtle patterns observed in the seismic attribute map shown in Fig. 10a may be footwall-derived. However, as implied in the model of Dahl & Solli (1993), the most significant source of sediment is expected to have been the large Snorre footwall. In general, the extensive area of a footwall dip-slope results in this being the major source of basin sediments (Gawthorpe *et al.* 1994).

Conclusions

Several conclusions are drawn from this study:

(1) Detailed 3D seismic interpretation of the syn-rift Draupne Formation on the Statfjord East hanging wall, integrated with results of core studies, show that subtle shoreface sands can be distinguished using seismic attribute maps of the Base Cretaceous seismic event. Sands may also occur with the Draupne in the deepest depocentre, adjacent to a deeply degraded portion of the footwall.

(2) Facies geometry and distribution is related to the segmented nature of the fault system. Shale deposition in the lower part of Draupne was controlled by increased accommodation rates associated with the development of a

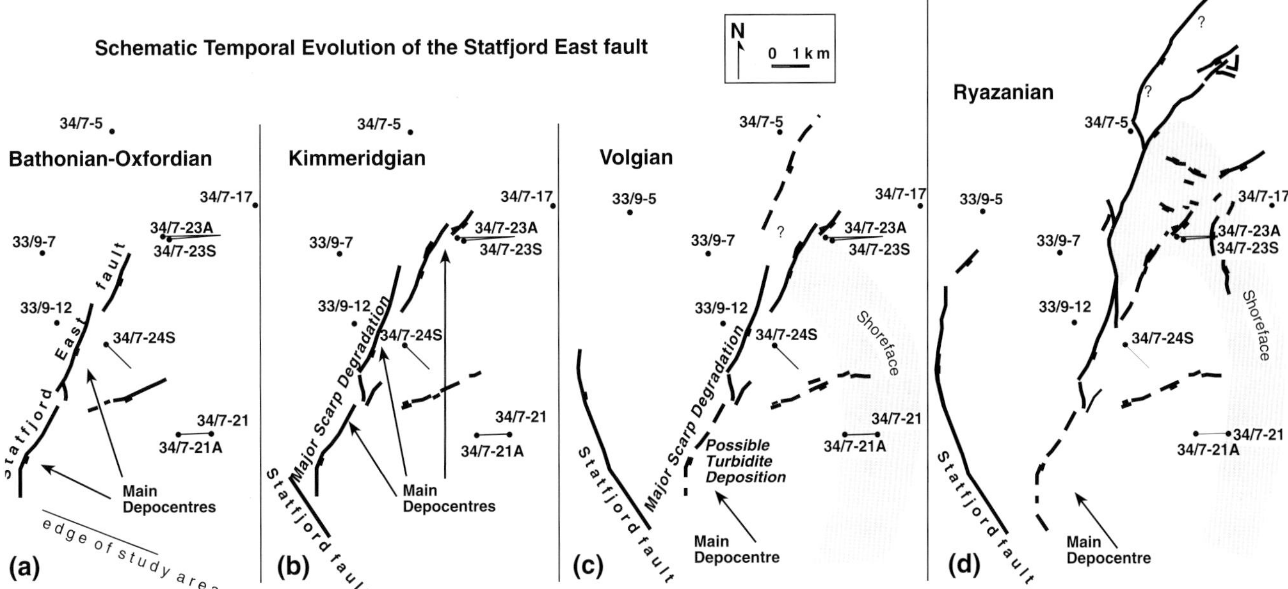

Fig. 12. Schematic diagram showing the temporal evolution of the Statfjord East fault, from the time of (**a**) Heather Formation deposition, through (**b**) the time of lower Draupne shale deposition, and then in (**c**) and (**d**), times of upper Draupne sand deposition.

series of fault-controlled sub-basins. The upper Draupne shoreface sands record a northward migration of the shoreline in Early Ryazanian times, which is interpreted to have resulted from the northward growth of the fault system by linkage of en echelon fault segments.

(3) The rift climax phase of basin development is characterized by a highly segmented fault structure.

Note added in revision

Since this paper was written, three new wells have been drilled in Norwegian Block 34/7. These have proven sands in the upper Draupne Formation, validating our interpretation of the seismic attribute map.

This work was funded by Norsk Hydro and by a Natural Environmental Research Council (NERC) award (no. GR3/R9521) to JRU, under the Realising Our Potential Award (ROPA) scheme. Seismic interpretation was carried out using Schlumberger GeoQuest IESX software, at facilities in Edinburgh funded by the Centre for Marine and Petroleum Technology (formerly PSTI), Norsk Hydro, Shell Expro, and Esso (UK) Ltd. We thank G. Mangerud and P. Skott for their efforts in releasing data; R. Jordan and R. Helland for their help in the transmittal of well data; A. Nøttvedt, T. Dreyer, R. Færseth, A. O. Eide, G. Mangerud, P. Skott, S. Gupta and A. McLeod for discussions; G. White for help with figures, and C.-L. Lau for computer support. A. Nøttvedt, S. Fraser and S. Boldy provided helpful reviews.

References

Barnes, K. R., Sneddon, J. N. & McAdow, D. 1992. Integrated exploration search for additional Upper Jurassic prospectivity in the North Viking graben, Norwegian North Sea. *American Association of Petroleum Geologists and Society of Economic Paleontologists and Mineralogists, Annual Meeting Abstracts*, 6.

Dahl, N. & Solli, T. 1993. The structural evolution of the Snorre Field and surrounding areas. *In*: Parker, J. R. (ed.) *Petroleum Geology of Northwest Europe: Proceedings of the 4th Conference*. Geological Society, London, 1159–1166.

Dawers, N. H. & Anders, M. H. 1995. Displacement–length scaling and fault linkage. *Journal of Structural Geology*, **17**, 607–614.

Færseth, R. B. 1996. Interaction of Permo-Triassic and Jurassic extensional fault-blocks during the development of the northern North Sea. *Journal of the Geological Society, London*, **153**, 931–944.

——, Sjøblom, T. S., Steel, R. J., Liljedahl, T., Sauar, B. E. & Tjelland, T. 1995. Tectonic controls on Bathonian–Volgian synrift successions on the Visund fault block, northern North Sea. *In*: Steel, R. J. *et al.* (eds) *Sequence Stratigraphy on the Northwest European Margin*. NPF Special Publications, Elsevier, Amsterdam, **5**, 325–346.

Gabrielsen, R. H., Steel, R. J. & Nøttvedt, A. 1995. Subtle traps in extensional terranes: a model with reference to the North Sea. *Petroleum Geoscience*, **1**, 223–235.

Gawthorpe, R. L. & Hurst, J. M. 1993. Transfer zones in extensional basins: their structural style and influence on drainage development and stratigraphy. *Journal of the Geological Society, London*, **150**, 1137–1152.

——, Fraser, A. J. & Collier, R. E. Ll. 1994. Sequence stratigraphy in active extensional basins: Implications for the interpretation of ancient basin fills. *Marine and Petroleum Geology*, **11**, 642–658.

——, Sharp, I., Underhill, J. & Gupta, S. 1997. Linked sequence stratigraphic and structural evolution of propagating normal faults. *Geology*, **25**, 795–798.

Häger, K.-O. & Smelror, M. 1997. Reworking of dinocysts as a means of obtaining useful geological information: a study of the Upper Jurassic Draupne Formation in the Tampen area, Norwegian North Sea. *American Association of Stratigraphic Palynologists, Annual Meeting Abstracts*, **20**.

Hansen, P. A., Lowden, D. J. & Paulsen, J. 1994. 3D Seismic inversion to explore for Upper Jurassic sands, North Viking Graben. *European Association of Exploration Geophysicists 56th Meeting Abstracts*, **BO18**.

Haram, L., Johannessen, E. P., Syrstad, E. & Renshaw, D. K. 1990. A subtle Upper Jurassic stratigraphic trap in the northern North Sea: An exploration case history. *European Association of Petroleum Geologists, Annual Meeting Abstracts*, **E6**.

Harland, W. B., Armstrong, R. L., Cox, A. V., Craig, L. E., Smith, A. G. & Smith, D. G. 1990. *A Geologic Time Scale 1989*. Cambridge University Press, New York.

Kirk, R. H. 1980. Statfjord Field – a North Sea giant. *In*: Halbouty, M. T. (ed.) Giant Oil and Gas Fields of the Decade 169–1978. *American Association of Petroleum Geologists Memoirs*, **30**, 95–116.

LEE, M. J. & HWANG, Y. J. 1993. Tectonic evolution and structural styles of the East Shetland Basin. *In*: PARKER, J. R. (ed.) *Petroleum Geology of Northwest Europe: Proceedings of the 4th Conference*. Geological Society, London, 1137–1149.

LEEDER, M. R. & GAWTHORPE, R. L. 1987. Sedimentary models for extensional tilt-block/half-graben basins. *In*: COWARD, M. P., DEWEY, J. F. & HANCOCK, P. L. (eds) *Continental Extensional Tectonics*. Geological Society, London, Special Publications, **28**, 139–152.

MCLEOD, A. & UNDERHILL, J. R. 1999. Processes and products of footwall degradation, northern Brent Field, northern North Sea. *In*: FLEET, A. J. & BOLDY, S. A. R. (eds) *Petroleum Geology of Northwest Europe: Proceedings of the 5th Conference*. Geological Society, London, 91–106.

NYBERG, I. T. 1987. Statfjord Øst. *In*: SPENCER, A. M., CAMPBELL, C. J., HANSLIEN, S. H., HOLTER, E., NELSON, P. H. H., NYSÆTHER, E. & ORMAASEN, E. G. (eds) *Geology of the Norwegian Oil and Gas Fields*. Graham & Trotman, London, 351–362.

NØTTVEDT, A., GABRIELSEN, R. H. & STEEL, R. J. 1995. Tectonostratigraphy and sedimentary architecture of rift basins, with reference to the northern North Sea. *Marine and Petroleum Geology*, **12**, 889–901.

——, BERGE, A. M., DAWERS, N. H., FAERSETH, R. B., HÄGER, K. *et al.* in press. Syn-rift evolutions and resulting play models in the Snorre-H area, northern North Sea. *In*: NØTTVEDT, A. *et al.* (eds) *Dynamics of the Norwegian Margin*. Geological Society, London, Special Publication.

PARTINGTON, M. A., MITCHENER, B. C., MILTON, N. J. & FRASER, A. J. 1993. Genetic sequence stratigraphy for the North Sea Late Jurassic and Early Cretaceous: distribution and prediction of Kimmeridgian–Late Ryazanian reservoirs in the North Sea and adjacent areas. *In*: PARKER, J. R. (ed.) *Petroleum Geology of Northwest Europe: Proceedings of the 4th Conference*. Geological Society, London, 347–370.

PROSSER, S. 1993. Rift-related linked depositional systems and their seismic expression. *In*: WILLIAMS, G. D. & DOBBS, A. (eds) *Tectonics and Seismic Sequence Stratigraphy*. Geological Society, London, Special Publications, **71**, 35–66.

RATTEY, R. P. & HAYWARD, A. B. 1993. Sequence stratigraphy of a failed rift system: The middle Jurassic to early Cretaceous basin evolution of the Central and Northern North Sea. *In*: PARKER, J. R. (ed.) *Petroleum Geology of Northwest Europe: Proceedings of the 4th Conference*. Geological Society, London, 215–249.

RAWSON, P. F. & RILEY, L. A. 1982. Latest Jurassic–Early Cretaceous events and the 'Late Cimmerian unconformity' in the North Sea area. *Bulletin of the American Association of Petroleum Geologists*, **66**, 2628–2648.

ROBERTS, A. M., YIELDING, G. & BADLEY, M. E. 1993*a*. Tectonic and bathymetric controls on stratigraphic sequences within an evolving half-graben. *In*: WILLIAMS, G. D. & DOBBS, A. (eds) *Tectonics and Seismic Sequence Stratigraphy*. Geological Society, London, Special Publications, **71**, 87–121.

——, ——, KUSZNIR, N. J., WALKER, I. & DORN-LOPEZ, D. 1993*b*. Mesozoic extension in the North Sea: constraints from flexural backstripping, forward modelling and fault populations. *In*: PARKER, J. R. (ed.) *Petroleum Geology of Northwest Europe: Proceedings of the 4th Conference*. Geological Society, London, 1123–1136.

ROUBY, D., FOSSEN, H. & COBBOLD, P. R. 1996. Extension, displacement, and block rotation in the larger Gullfaks area, northern North Sea: determined from map view restoration. *Bulletin of the American Association of Petroleum Geologists*, **80**, 875–890.

SCHLISCHE, R. W. 1995. Geometry and origin of fault-related folds in extensional settings. *Bulletin of the American Association of Petroleum Geologists*, **79**, 1661–1678.

—— & ANDERS, M. H. 1996. Stratigraphic effects and tectonic implications of the growth of normal faults and extensional basins. *In*: BERATAN, K. K. (ed.) *Reconstructing the History of Basin and Range Extension Using Sedimentology and Stratigraphy*. Geological Society of America, Boulder, Colorado, Special Papers, **33**, 183–203.

SOLLI, T. 1995. Upper Jurassic play concept – an integrated study in Block 34/7, Norway. *First Break*, **13**, 21–30.

UNDERHILL, J. R. 1994. Discussion on palaeoecology and sedimentology across a Jurassic fault scarp, NE Scotland. *Journal of the Geological Society*, London, **151**, 729–731.

——, SAWYER, M. J., HODGSON, P., SHALLCROSS, M. D. & GAWTHORPE, R. L. 1997. Implications of fault scarp degradation for Brent Group prospectivity, Ninian Field, Northern North Sea. *Bulletin of the American Association of Petroleum Geologists*, **81**, 99–1022.

WILLEMSE, E. J. M., POLLARD, D. D. & AYDIN, A. 1996. Three-dimensional analyses of slip distributions on normal fault arrays with consequences for fault scaling. *Journal of Structural Geology*, **18**, 295–309.

WOOD, J. & SCHWARTZBARD, A. E. 1994. Upper Jurassic lowstand and highstand systems tracts on the dip slope of Snorre–Vigdis–Tordis megafootwall. *European Association of Petroleum Geologists, 6th Conference Abstracts*, **CO43**.

YIELDING, G. 1990. Footwall uplift associated with Late Jurassic normal faulting in the northern North Sea. *Journal of the Geological Society, London*, **147**, 219–222.

——, BADLEY, M. E. & ROBERTS, A. M. 1992. The structural evolution of the Brent Province. *In*: HASZELDINE, R. S., GILES, M. R. & BROWN, S. (eds) *Geology of the Brent Group*. Geological Society, London, Special Publications, **61**, 27–43.

Sequence stratigraphy and sedimentary history of the Humber Group (Late Jurassic–Ryazanian) in the Outer Moray Firth (UKCS, North Sea)

D. KADOLSKY,[1] S. J. JOHANSEN[2] and S. DUXBURY[3]

[1] *Texaco Ltd, 1 Westferry Circus, Canary Wharf, London E14 4HA, Great Britain (e-mail: kadold@texaco.com)*

[2] *Texaco Inc., Exploration and Production Technology Department, 3901 Briarpark, Houston, Texas 77042, USA*

[3] *Duxbury Stratigraphic Consultants, 4 Coldstone Avenue, Kingswells, Aberdeen AB15 8TT, UK*

Abstract: The Humber Group in the Outer Moray Firth is an onlapping sedimentary succession of Late Oxfordian to Ryazanian age, recording a trend of continuously rising relative sea-level. Nineteen subordinate transgressive–regressive cycles ('sequences') have been identified in the numerous wells in the area. The identification of these sedimentary units throughout the study area is indispensable for the interpretation of its sedimentary history, and hence for the ability to predict the possibility of subtle stratigraphic traps. Transgression began during the Late Oxfordian in the North Buchan Graben and culminated in the Early Ryazanian, when only parts of the Halibut Horst and the Fladen Ground Spur remained exposed. Mapping of the onlap reveals the drowning from the south of a significant topographic relief, which was further enhanced by syndepositional rifting. Three structural grains affected sedimentation: (1) E–W (possibly a repeated reactivation of pre-Late Jurassic faults, e.g. North Halibut Graben: pre-Late Oxfordian to Middle Volgian); (2) NE–SW (e.g. Theta Graben: Late Oxfordian to Early Kimmeridgian; Highlander–Piper Ridge: Kimmeridgian to Mid-Volgian); (3) NW–SE (e.g. Witch Ground Graben: Early Volgian to Ryazanian). Sedimentation was initially dominated by coastal plain and shoreface facies of marine-dominated deltas and estuaries (Piper Formation *s.l.*), sourced mainly from the Fladen Ground Spur. From deposition of the upper Piper Formation onwards, intra-rift horsts, particularly the Halibut Horst, were also important sand sources. Deltaic systems back-stepped toward the basin flanks when accommodation space generation began to exceed sediment supply. Increased rifting in Early Volgian times triggered large-scale mass flow deposition from the Halibut Horst and from the East Piper High. Back-stepping shoreface systems continued their progressive onlap of the basin margins. Lowstand systems tracts in the individual sequences were muted by the overpowering long-term transgression, and significant mass flow deposits were not primarily controlled by the collapse of constructional highstand shelf margins. Instead, long-term tectonic uplift of specific areas sourced basin-margin submarine fan systems, typically confined to half graben on the flanks of the basin (e.g. Claymore sands), and basin-floor submarine channel systems in the core of the Witch Ground Graben (e.g. Galley sands). The potential for subtle stratigraphic traps is greatest in these turbiditic sandbodies where their boundaries are abrupt, as a result of channeling in self-constructed levees, or confinement by fault-induced seafloor topography.

In the Moray Firth hydrocarbon province, approximately 5.9×10^9 barrels of oil equivalent recoverable reserves have been discovered to date (updated from David 1996). Some 53% of this volume is trapped in sandstone reservoirs of the Humber Group in the Outer Moray Firth (OMF) (map, Fig. 1a).These sandstones have been deposited in estuarine to shoreface settings (mainly Piper Formation *s.l.*) and as mass flow sands within the Kimmeridge Clay Formation (e.g. Claymore Sand, Galley Sand), which is the source rock for almost all hydrocarbon accumulations in this area.

David (1996) shows that, although the Moray Firth is a mature exploration province, additional potential exists as the discovery rate has not levelled out. From an analysis of Jurassic discoveries by depositional setting and trap type, David (1996) concludes that:

(i) hanging wall traps hold more future potential than footwall or anticlinal traps (as this trap type tend to be recognized and drilled first), both in shelfal and basinal sands;
(ii) purely stratigraphic traps in basinal sands may have the largest potential, as very little hydrocarbon has thus far been discovered in such settings. Turbiditic sands in the Kimmeridge Clay Formation would, moreover, be interbedded with the source rock.

Successful exploration for such stratigraphic traps requires the availability of seismic that images the potential reservoirs, and of a detailed biostratigraphic and sequence stratigraphic framework, within which the palaeogeography of the various sand dispersal systems can be reconstructed. Such frameworks were proposed by Partington *et al.* (1993*a*, *b*), Harker & Rieuf (1996) and Stephen & Davies (1998). A sequence stratigraphic analysis of 102 wells (including development wells) drilled on Blocks 14/20, 15/16 and adjacent areas (Johansen *et al.* 1995, unpublished company report) showed that refinements and modifications to these schemes were necessary. As a consequence, a new biostratigraphic and a sequence stratigraphic framework was developed, which is described by Duxbury *et al.* (1999) (Fig. 2). This paper outlines the depositional history of the Humber Group in the Outer Moray Firth (OMF) within this newly established framework, and a predictive model for the distribution of mass flow sands within the area.

KADOLSKY, D., JOHANSEN, S. J. & DUXBURY, S. 1999. Sequence stratigraphy and sedimentary history of the Humber Group (Late Jurassic–Ryazanian) in the Outer Moray Firth (UKCS, North Sea). *In*: FLEET, A. J. & BOLDY, S. A. R. (eds) *Petroleum Geology of Northwest Europe: Proceedings of the 5th Conference*, 839–860.

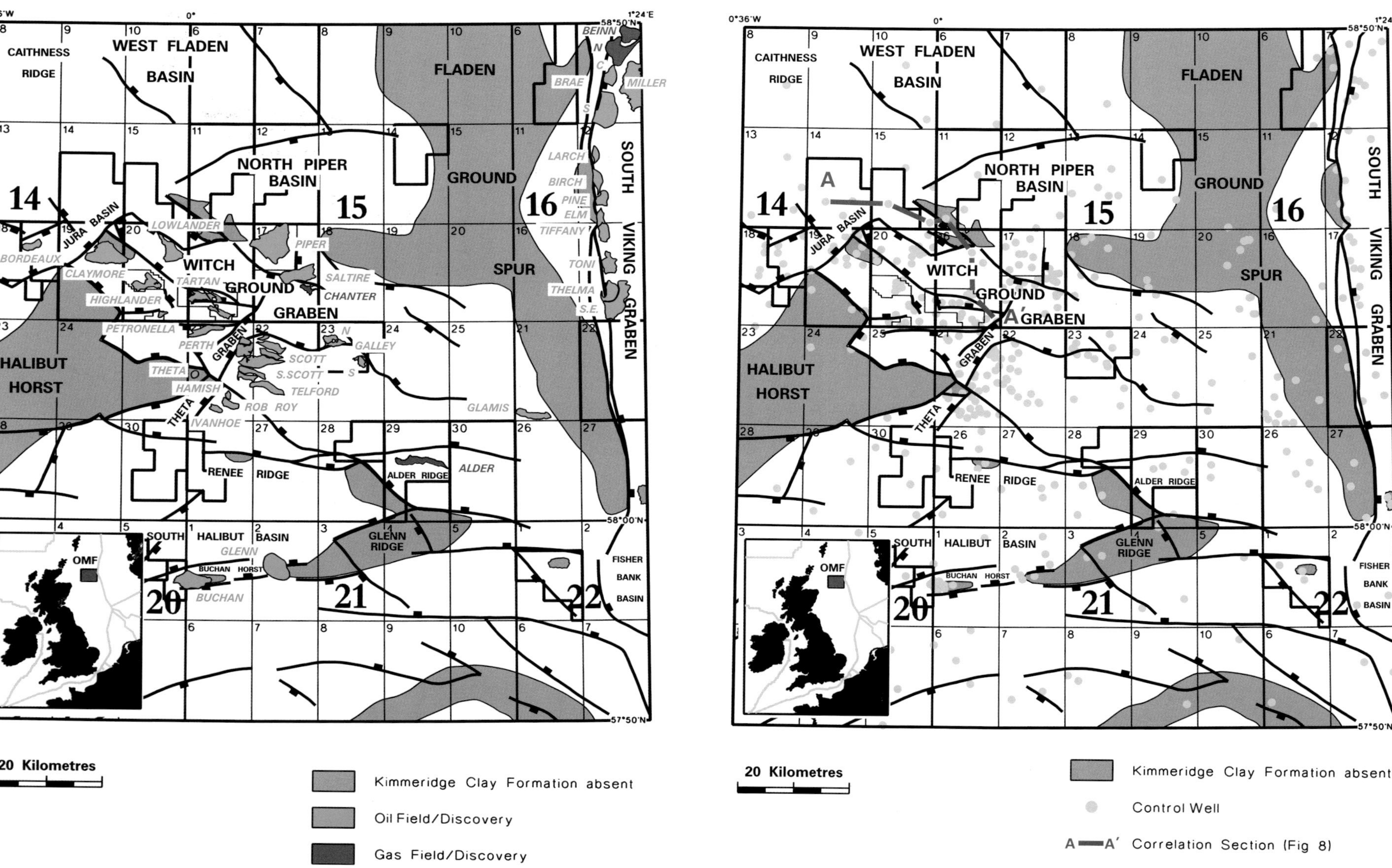

Fig. 1. Location maps. **(a)** Jurassic and pre-Jurassic hydrocarbon fields and discoveries and principal structural features. **(b)** Study wells.

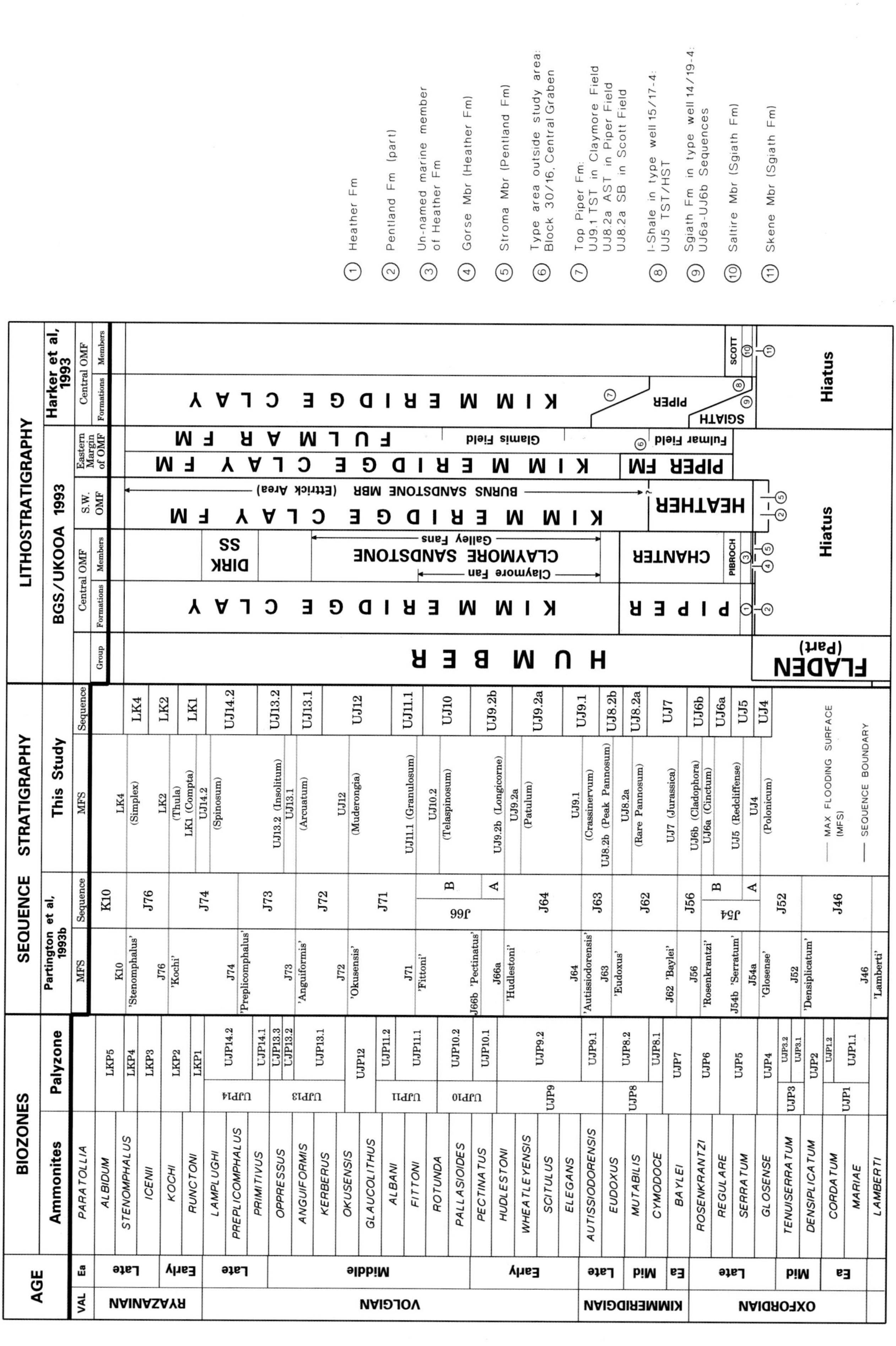

AGE: Stage	AGE: Substage	BIOZONES: Ammonites	BIOZONES: Palyzone	SEQUENCE STRATIGRAPHY: Partington et al, 1993b MFS	Partington et al, 1993b Sequence	This Study MFS	This Study Sequence
VAL	Ea	PARATOLLIA					
RYAZANIAN	Late	ALBIDUM	LKP5	K10 'Stenomphalus'	K10	LK4 (Simplex)	
		STENOMPHALUS	LKP4				LK4
		ICENII	LKP3	J76 'Kochi'	J76	LK2 (Thula)	LK2
	Early	KOCHI	LKP2				
		RUNCTONI	LKP1			LK1 (Compta)	LK1
VOLGIAN	Late	LAMPLUGHI	UJP14: UJP14.2		J74	UJ14.2 (Spinosum)	UJ14.2
		PREPLICOMPHALUS		J74 'Preplicomphalus'			
		PRIMITIVUS	UJP14.1		J73		
	Middle	OPPRESSUS	UJP13: UJP13.3, UJP13.2			UJ13.2 (Insolitum)	UJ13.2
		ANGUIFORMIS	UJP13.1	J73 'Anguiformis'	J72	UJ13.1 (Arcuatum)	UJ13.1
		KERBERUS					
		OKUSENSIS	UJP12	J72 'Okusensis'		UJ12 (Muderongia)	UJ12
		GLAUCOLITHUS			J71		
		ALBANI	UJP11: UJP11.2				
		FITTONI	UJP11.1	J71 'Fittoni'		UJ11.1 (Granulosum)	UJ11.1
		ROTUNDA	UJP10: UJP10.2		J66 B	UJ10.2 (Telaspinosum)	UJ10
		PALLASIOIDES					
	Early	PECTINATUS	UJP10.1	J66b 'Pectinatus'			
		HUDLESTONI	UJP9: UJP9.2	J66a 'Hudlestoni'	J66 A	UJ9.2b (Longicorne)	UJ9.2b
		WHEATLEYENSIS			J64	UJ9.2a (Patulum)	UJ9.2a
		SCITULUS					
		ELEGANS		J64 'Autissiodorensis'			
KIMMERIDGIAN	Late	AUTISSIODORENSIS	UJP9.1		J63	UJ9.1 (Crassinervum)	UJ9.1
		EUDOXUS	UJP8: UJP8.2	J63 'Eudoxus'		UJ8.2b (Peak Pannosum)	UJ8.2b
	Mid	MUTABILIS			J62	UJ8.2a (Rare Pannosum)	UJ8.2a
		CYMODOCE	UJP8.1				
	Ea	BAYLEI	UJP7	J62 'Baylei'		UJ7 (Jurassica)	UJ7
OXFORDIAN	Late	ROSENKRANTZI	UJP6	J56 'Rosenkrantzi'	J56	UJ6b (Cladophora)	UJ6b
		REGULARE	UJP5		J54 B	UJ6a (Cinctum)	UJ6a
		SERRATUM		J54b 'Serratum'		UJ5 (Redcliffense)	UJ5
		GLOSENSE	UJP4	J54a 'Glosense'	J54 A	UJ4 (Polonicum)	UJ4
	Mid	TENUISERRATUM	UJP3: UJP3.2		J52		
		DENSIPLICATUM	UJP3.1; UJP2	J52 'Densiplicatum'			
	Ea	CORDATUM	UJP1: UJP1.2		J46		
		MARIAE	UJP1.1				
		LAMBERTI		J46 'Lamberti'			

— MAX FLOODING SURFACE (MFS)

— SEQUENCE BOUNDARY

LITHOSTRATIGRAPHY

	BGS/UKOOA 1993: Group	Central OMF: Formations	Central OMF: Members	S.W. OMF	Eastern Margin of OMF	Harker et al, 1993: Central OMF Formations	Central OMF Members
Upper	HUMBER	KIMMERIDGE CLAY	DIRK SS; CLAYMORE SANDSTONE (Claymore Fan; Galley Fans)	KIMMERIDGE CLAY FM; BURNS SANDSTONE MBR (Ettrick Area)	FULMAR FM (Glamis Field); KIMMERIDGE CLAY FM	KIMMERIDGE CLAY	
Lower		PIPER ① ②	CHANTER; PIBROCH ③ ④ ⑤	HEATHER ② ⑤	PIPER FM; Fulmar Field ⑥	PIPER ⑦; SGIATH ⑨ ⑧	SCOTT ⑩ ⑪
Base	FLADEN (Part)	Hiatus				Hiatus	

① Heather Fm

② Pentland Fm (part)

③ Un-named marine member of Heather Fm

④ Gorse Mbr (Heather Fm)

⑤ Stroma Mbr (Pentland Fm)

⑥ Type area outside study area: Block 30/16, Central Graben

⑦ Top Piper Fm: UJ9.1 TST in Claymore Field; UJ8.2a AST in Piper Field; UJ8.2a SB in Scott Field

⑧ I-Shale in type well 15/17-4: UJ5 TST/HST

⑨ Sgiath Fm in type well 14/19-4: UJ6a-UJ6b Sequences

⑩ Saltire Mbr (Sgiath Fm)

⑪ Skene Mbr (Sgiath Fm)

Fig. 2. Relationship of the sequence stratigraphic scheme and the dinocyst biozonation used here to the sequences of Partington *et al.* (1993*b*), to ammonite zones (after Partington *et al.* 1993*b*) and to recently published lithostratigraphic subdivisions of the Humber Group.

Data used

The dataset for the present study comprises new biostratigraphic analyses of 78 wells on Blocks 14/20, 15/16, 15/23 and 15/29 and selected additional wells elsewhere in the OMF. All other wells in the OMF were interpreted on the basis of already available reports and log data. In total, approximately 500 wells in the entire OMF were included in the final study (map, Fig. 1b).

Numerous publications treat various aspects of Humber Group geology in the OMF. A list of papers providing stratigraphical and sedimentological information about individual fields is provided by Duxbury *et al.* (1999). Regional treatments of the Humber Group are given by Turner *et al.* (1984), Andrews & Brown (1987), Boldy & Brealey (1990), Boote & Gustav (1987), Hallsworth *et al.* (1996), Harker *et al.* (1987, 1993), O'Driscoll *et al.* (1990) and Richards *et al.* (1993). A sequence stratigraphic approach has been taken in more recent studies including Harker & Rieuf (1996), Carruthers *et al.* (1996), Davies *et al.* 1996, Stephen & Davies 1998, Davies *et al.* (1999). Previously published palaeogeographical maps put the OMF into a more regional context (Rattey & Hayward 1993; Harker & Rieuf 1996). While these papers have been consulted, all interpretations have been made from raw log, biostratigraphic and sedimentological data.

Recognition and nomenclature of sequences and their systems tracts

Nineteen transgressive–regressive depositional episodes (sequences) are recognized in the Humber Group of the OMF (Fig. 2); they are formally defined and described by Duxbury *et al.* (1999). The basis for the sequence definition is the recognition of transgressive–regressive cycles in shoreface settings.

Such cycles are present in the OMF from the UJ4 (Late Oxfordian) to LK2 (Early Ryazanian) Sequences. For most of the cycles the sedimentology and biostratigraphy had been studied from core material. In addition, first-hand analysis of mass flow sand sections in deep-water settings have allowed a parallel sequence stratigraphic subdivision of the UJP8.2–LK4 (Late Kimmeridgian to Ryazanian) interval. The frequency of depositional episodes in the shoreface and in the deep-water environments was found to be directly comparable, suggesting the applicability of a unified sequence subdivision in these different environments.

For reference, the relationship of the new sequence stratigraphic subdivision with recently published lithostratigraphic frameworks is also given in Fig. 2. Rapid lateral facies changes in the OMF have resulted in diachronous boundaries of most lithostratigraphic units, rendering them essentially terms for broad facies belts.

Systems tracts

Our sequence stratigraphic nomenclature for shore-zone sediments such as the Piper Formation (*s.l.*) is modified from the system originally proposed by Van Wagoner *et al.* (1990) and Van Wagoner (1991) for high-frequency sequences developed in deltaic deposits of North America.

(i) Sequence boundaries (SB) are erosive surfaces cut into marine shorefaces, delta front deposits, or significantly older rocks, and are inferred to have formed when relative base-level was low.
(ii) Aggradational systems tract (AST). Estuarine fill and coastal plain units with evidence of mixed tidal, fluvial, and quiet-water deposition commonly occur above the SBs; Van Wagoner (1991) interpreted these as incised valley-fill units and assigned them to the lowstand systems tract (LST) (see below). Here these are termed aggradational systems tracts (AST), because they record aggradation of the lower delta plain (or coastal plain) during rising base-level.
(iii) Ravinement surface (RS). The marine transgressive surface at the base of the transgressive systems tracts (TST). Where an AST is present, the RS forms its top; where the AST is absent, it coincides with the SB.
(iv) Transgressive systems tract (TST). Marine sediments between the ravinement surface (RS) and the overlying maximum flooding surface (MFS), recording a rise in sea-level.
(v) Maximum flooding surface (MFS). The surface of maximum coastal onlap, recognized by the deepest marine, most clastic-starved sediments
(vi) Highstand systems tract (HST). The regressive coastline deposits between the MFS and the next SB.

Discussion

There are good reasons for modifying the Van Wagoner *et al.* (1990) nomenclature. Sydow & Roberts (1994) documented that the 'highstand systems tract' of many deltaic deposits may actually be deposited during falling sea-level and lowstand time. This is expected in sequences such as the Upper Jurassic of the OMF, where the total package is strongly transgressive and Type I sequence boundaries are therefore rare. The LST of Van Wagoner *et al.* (1990) then is not the true lowstand deposit, but forms during coastal transgression and so might rightfully belong in the TST. However, we have split the coastal plain/valley fill aggradational units (AST) from the clearly transgressive marine units (TST) because of their different sedimentology and reservoir properties. As Sydow & Roberts (1994) noted, the up-dip equivalents of true highstand deposits may be thin erosional remnants of marine and fluvial valley fill units; their preservation potential in the sedimentary record is not good.

Basinal settings

Nomenclature for the deeper marine gravity flow deposits of the Humber Group is more straightforward than in coastal settings. Maximum flooding surfaces are recognized as organic-rich horizons recording algal and diatom bloom periods and clastic starvation of the basin interior. Turbiditic influxes of siliciclastics are conventionally interpreted to form during relative lowstands and are termed lowstand systems tracts (LST). This terminology has been maintained here, although no evidence has been found to suggest that sediment supply was so great during Humber deposition that the depositional systems constructed a prograding shelf/slope break. Humber Group turbiditic deposits appear to originate from fault terraces located between uplifting and subsiding fault-bound areas, and thus forming narrow shelves on which shore-zone sands could temporarily accumulate.

New sequence terminology

In this paper, sequences, their component systems tracts (LST, AST, TST, HST) and surfaces (SB, RS, MFS) are named after the dinocyst zonal age of the maximum flooding surface. The dinocyst zonation of Duxbury Stratigraphic Consultants (Duxbury *et al.* 1999) has been applied; as an alternative, sequence names based on key dinocysts are proposed (Fig. 2).

The use of dinocyst zones allows accurate age dating, without the uncertainty and possible confusion in translating dinocyst ages to ammonite biozones, as is current practice. For a full description of this approach, and for the definition and well examples of the individual sequences, see Duxbury *et al.* (1999).

A comment on the representation of fossil names in print is here required: a species name consists of a genus name and the species epithet; the latter is always rendered in lower case (international codes of botanical and zoological nomenclature). The entire species name is by convention often given in italics, as in this publication series. However, a fossil name forming part of a lithostratigraphical term is no longer subject to the nomenclature codes, i.e. it is not rendered in italics, and it is not to be changed when the species on which it is based changes its name for taxonomic reasons (Holland *et al.* 1978); further, for expedience we may quote it without its genus name. Sequence stratigraphic terms apply to rocks, and hence are considered lithostratigraphic terminology in this context.

In many cases a sequence boundary lies within a continuous sand package, and it proves more practical to treat the sand package as a single unit. Such units are referred to as 'depositional episodes', and correspond to the genetic sequence *sensu* Galloway (1989). They comprise the interval from one MFS to the next one, i.e. across a sequence boundary. Such units are described by their bounding MFSs, with the earlier one named first, eg. Episode UJ8.2a MFS–UJ8.2b MFS.

Structural setting

The study area (Fig. 1) comprises the larger part of the Jurassic basin of the OMF, which is an irregular elongate basin

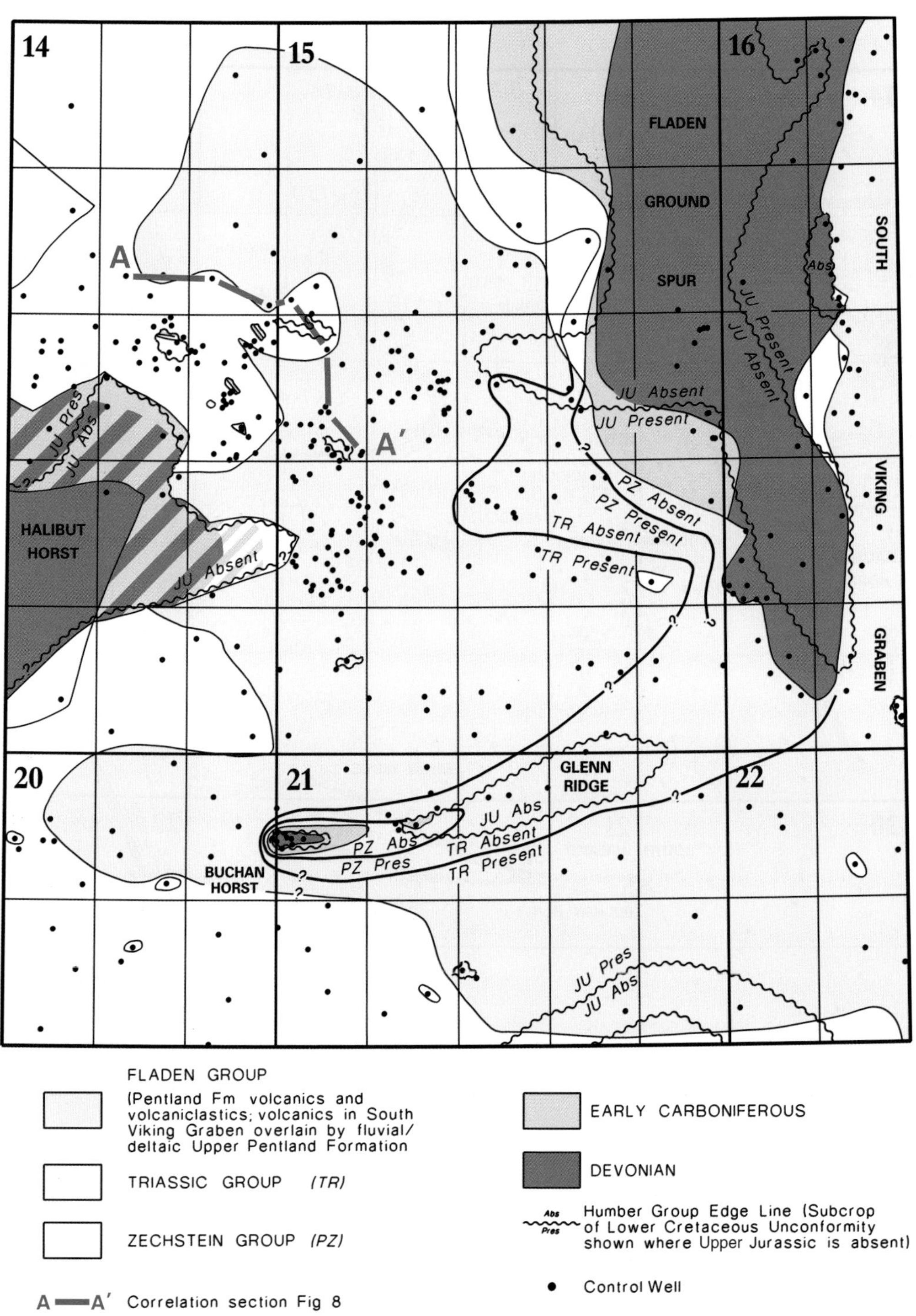

Fig. 3. The subcrop of the Humber Group.

trending NNW–SSE. The basin is bounded on the east by the Fladen Ground Spur and on the west by the Halibut Horst. The southern boundary is defined by the Buchan Horst and the Glenn Ridge. In the southwest, it is continuous with the Southern Moray Firth Basin.

The subcrop of the Humber Group (Fig. 3) and the Humber Group onlap map (Fig. 4) illustrate the general basin topography; major faults that were active during the later part of Humber Group deposition are plotted on Figs 1 and 7.

A number of E–W and NE–SW structural trends cross the basin. Many of these features obliquely intersect major NW–SE orientated normal faults and partition the Outer Moray Firth into sub-basins. These cross-basinal features possibly had complex histories of dip-slip and strike-slip movement that accommodated differential rift extension under changing stress regimes. The reconstruction of syndepositional topography is essential for the understanding of the depositional history and the origin of reservoir sands. The most significant structures are discussed below.

The Fladen Ground Spur was a persistent structural high before and throughout the Late Jurassic, as shown by subcrop and onlap maps. Zechstein facies (Well 16/16b-2) shows that it was a positive feature already in Permian times, and extensive exposures of Carboniferous and Devonian sand-rich formations were major sediment sources during Humber Group deposition.

The syndepositional significance of the Halibut Horst is less evident because of modifications by post-depositional uplift and erosion. Boldy & Brealey (1990) and Hibbert & Mackertich (1993) advocated a significant post-Piper Formation uplift and quote the truncated remnant of the basal Humber Group in Well 15/21-1 as evidence. Early Cretaceous uplift in southern

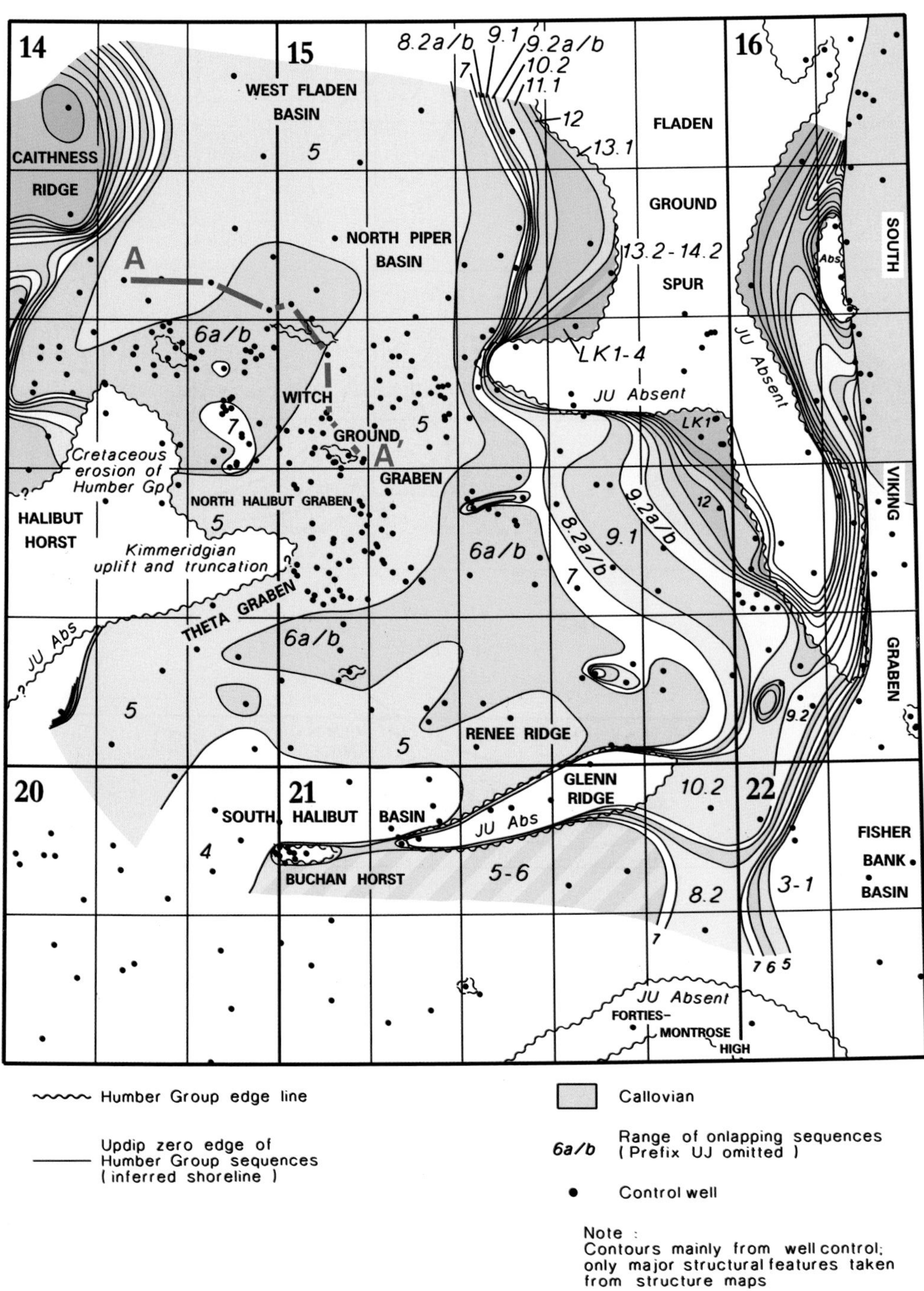

Fig. 4. The onlap of the Humber Group sequences.

Blocks 14/18 and 14/19 and shedding of large amounts of Early Cretaceous mass flow clastics (Scapa sands) is also well established (O'Driscoll *et al.* 1990). The predominant E–W structural grain of the easternmost part of the Halibut Horst is thus of post-Piper (post Early Kimmeridgian) age; onlap mapping (Fig. 4) suggests the probable presence of an earlier SSW–NNE trending high from the southern margin of the Halibut Horst to the Caithness Ridge in the north.

The Glenn Ridge–Buchan Horst trend is a WSW–ENE trending high in the southern part of the study area. The Glenn Ridge was part of a pre-Middle Jurassic positive feature, as the Pentland Formation rests on Zechstein or Carboniferous. On the Glenn Ridge these formations remain buried under subaerial volcanic rocks of the Glenn eruption centre (Smith & Ritchie 1993).

The Theta Graben is an important NE–SW trending rift basin, centred in Block 15/21 adjacent to the Halibut Horst. The West Claymore Basin in Blocks 14/18 and 14/19 and its extension to the NE into the West Fladen Basin (Figs 4, 5 and 6) has the same structural grain and forms a shallower parallel rift. The West Claymore Basin offsets the NW–SE trending Witch Ground Graben.

A structural sill developed between the West Claymore West Fladen basins in the NW and the Theta Graben/North Halibut

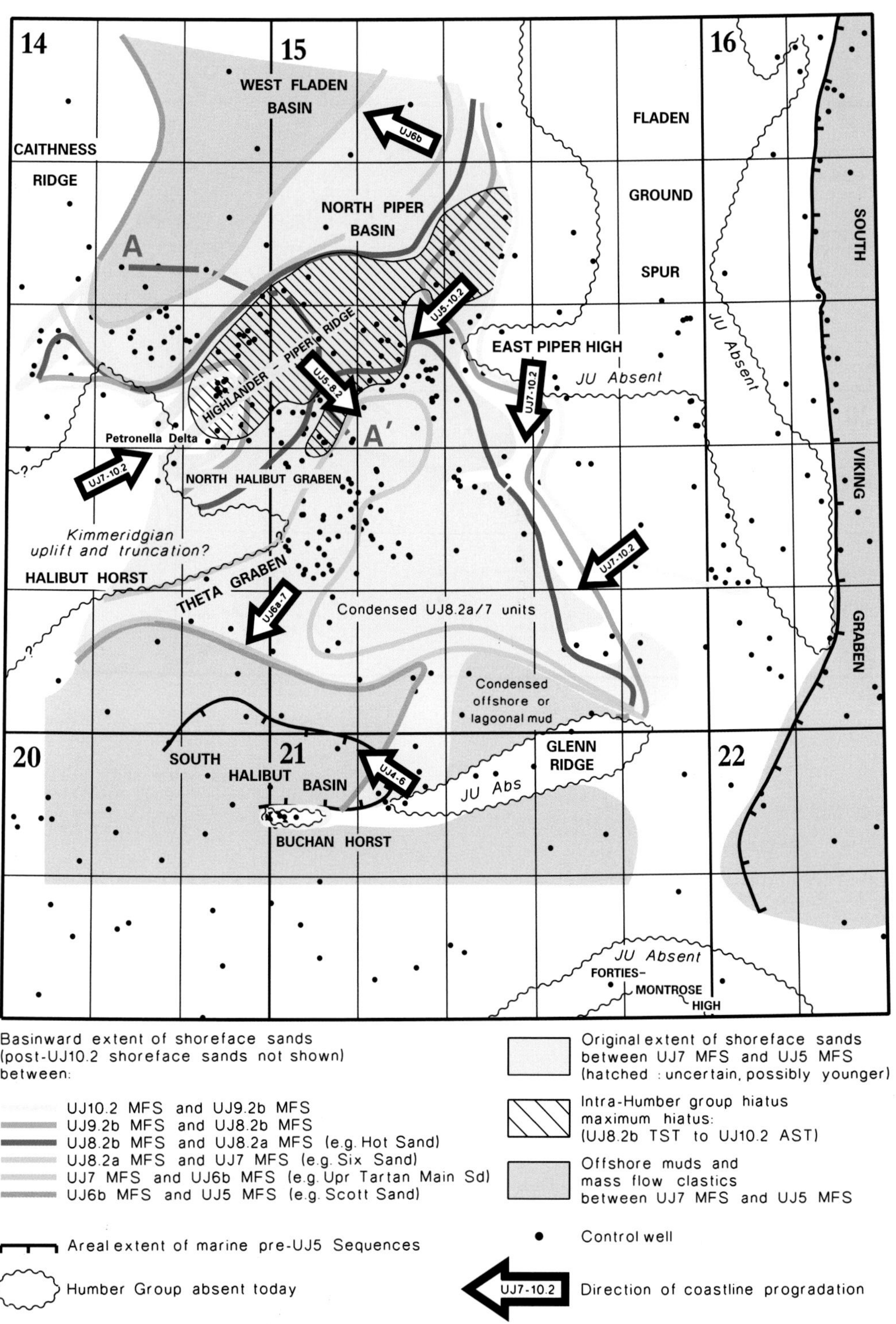

Fig. 5. The basinward extent of shallow marine sands of the lower Humber Group sequences.

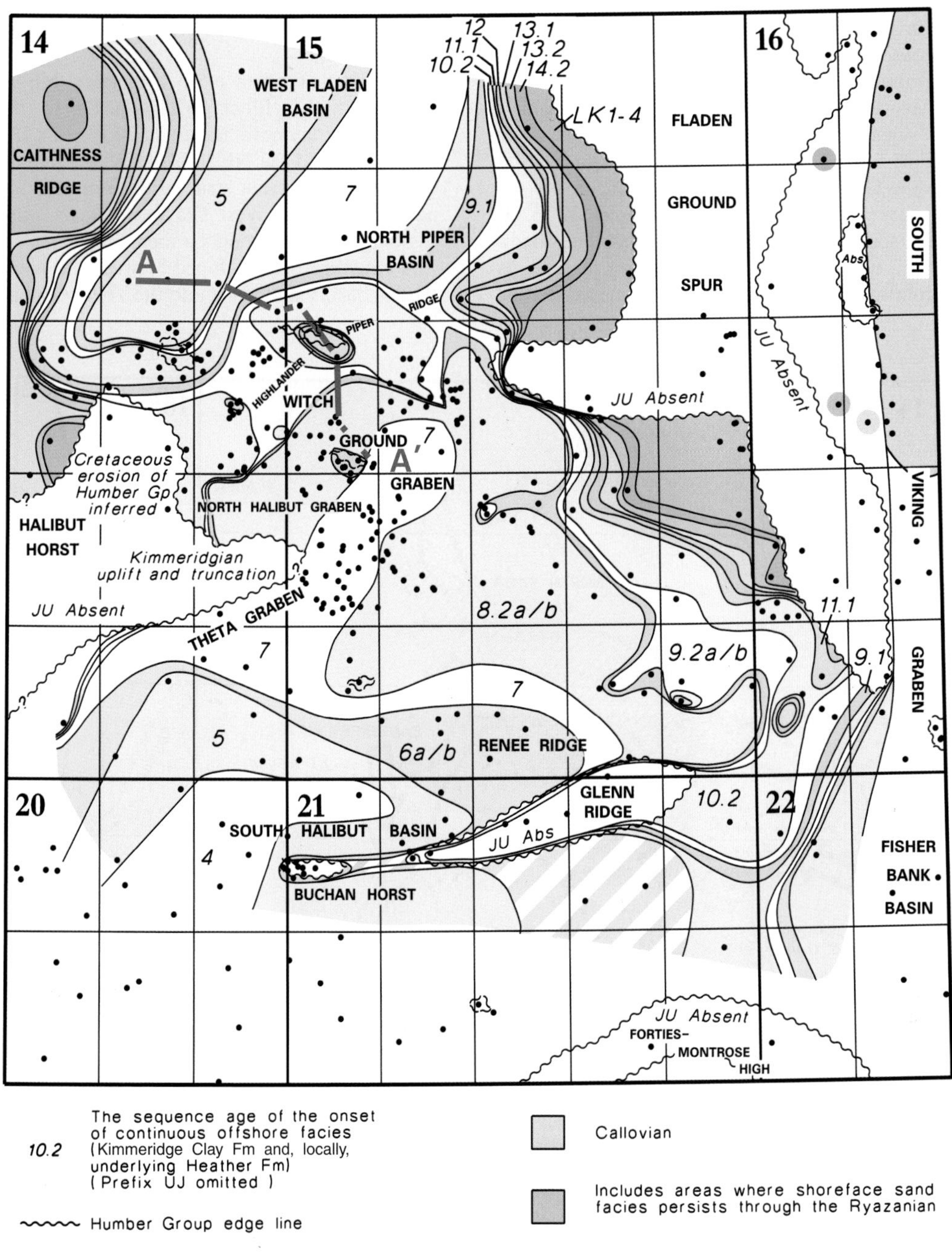

Fig. 6. The age of the onset of continuous offshore mud facies (i.e. of the base of the Kimmeridge Clay Formation or, where present, of the underlying Heather Formation).

Graben in the SE, and this is referred to here as the 'Highlander–Piper Ridge'. It extends from the Halibut Horst across Block 14/20 toward long-persistent positive features in southern Block 15/11 (already apparent in the subcrop distribution, Fig. 3, and best illustrated by the Kimmeridge Clay Formation onlap, Fig. 6). Here it is joined by the Piper Field fault terrace (Block 15/17), which appears to be a westerly extension of the E–W trending 'East Piper High'.

E–W trending structural lineaments affecting sedimentation are also evident in the distribution of the western margin of the Pentland Formation subcrop, and in the lower Humber Group in the North Halibut Graben and its extensions to the east. Here the Late Oxfordian to Early Kimmeridgian interval from the UJ5 to the UJ7 sequence is very thick; the graben is flanked in the north by the Petronella Ridge, which is onlapped by only a thin UJ6–7 sand, and to the south by the Halibut Spur, on which the Piper *s.l.* Formation was eroded (Boldy & Brealey 1990); further east, the Telford Ridge and the Galley Central High are also evident as positive features during Piper Formation *s.l.* (UJ5–UJ7) times.

Depositional history of the Humber Group sequences

Four maps and a section summarize aspects of the Humber Group sedimentary developments:

(i) Fig. 4: the onlap of the sequences;
(ii) Fig. 5: the basinward extent of shallow marine sands of the sequences;
(iii) Fig. 6: the age of the onset of persistent offshore mud facies, i.e. the age of the base of the Kimmeridge Clay Formation or, where present, of the Heather Formation;

(iv) Fig. 7: the distribution of Kimmeridgian to Ryazanian mass flow sands;
(v) Fig. 8: a correlation section across the Highlander-Piper Ridge.

UJ4 (Polonicum) Sequence

The oldest sequence recognized, the UJ4 (Polonicum) Sequence, is present in the SW part of the study area (Fig.4) and consists mainly of mudstones. Sands do locally occur, e.g in the aggrading systems tract (AST) of Well 20/5b-2, and in the highstand systems tract (HST) of Well 21/1-5ST. Complete transgressive–regressive sandy developments are present in Wells 21/2-1 and -5, interpreted to be at the eastern end of an embayment. All sands are of very limited lateral extent and occur in the vicinity of the Buchan Horst with its outcrop of Early Carboniferous and Devonian sandstones, which is the most likely source.

Several authors date this unit in Well 20/5b-2 as Callovian to Early Oxfordian (Carruthers *et al.* 1996; Davies *et al.* 1996; Harker & Rieuf 1996; Stephen & Davies 1998). However, although dinocysts of this age have been reported in one out of three contractor biostratigraphy reports prepared for this well (Davies *et al.* 1996, fig. 12), a re-examination of the original palynological preparations did not confirm the presence of any pre-Late Oxfordian marker species. Moreover, none are reported from Wells 20/5-3, -4, 21/1-5ST and 15/26-5, which have a succession similar to, and on log readily correlatable with, 20/5b-2. Indeed, on the basis of available biostratigraphic data the entire South Halibut Basin experienced its first marine transgression not earlier than in the UJ4 Sequence. The preceding UJ3.1 Sequence (Middle Oxfordian) extended no further east than the Ross Field (Blocks 13/28, 13/29), and Callovian to Early Oxfordian sequences are restricted to an area of the Inner Moray Firth even further west. Previous palaeogeographical and tectonic conclusions for the Callovian and Early Oxfordian of the North Buchan Basin area thus have to be reconsidered.

In the West Fladen Basin the earliest part of the Humber Group is an association of fluvial channel sands, interchannel mudstones and coals (Fig. 8, Well 14/14a-2). Marine microplankton appears only in the uppermost part of this unit, suggesting the presence of the UJ5 and possibly UJ4 Sequence here. The onset of this fluvial regime can only be dated as post-Middle Jurassic by means of the terrestrial palynomorph assemblages in 14/14a-2. Hence the presence of the UJ4 Sequence and of even older Oxfordian sequences in non-marine facies is possible. Sediments of such fluvial and other non-marine to marginally marine coastal plain facies constitute the Sgiath Formation, although its age in the type Well 14/19-4 is interpreted as that of the UJ6a and UJ6b sequences. The 'younging' of the Sgiath facies reflects the time shift in facies zones expected during continued transgression.

Dramatic changes in the thickness of the fluvial succession of the West Fladen Basin suggest infill of incised valleys over an unconformity with great relief. The UJP4 marine microplankton occurrences in the upper part of this unit may reflect marine incursions into bay or estuarine settings during a marine highstand.

Interval UJ5 SB–UJ5 MFS

Sequence UJ5 (Redcliffense) (mid-Late Oxfordian) covered a large part of the OMF basin. Southeast of the Highlander–Piper Ridge, it has a well developed AST typically beginning with a coal seam, followed by laminated lagoonal mudstones (Skene Member); these mudstones bear initially a freshwater or slightly brackish microflora, which may gradually or suddenly become marine and diverse. This increase in salinity occurs below the ravinement surface (RS), and so represents marine waters invading lower coastal plain bays or estuaries. The transgressive systems tract (TST) is developed as a sandy, thoroughly bioturbated, fining-upward mudstone (Saltire Member).

In the West Fladen Basin, thin mudstones with brackish UJP5 age dinocyst associations occur in the upper part of the fluvial unit mentioned previously. They are the up-dip estuarine equivalent of the marine sequences present in Piper Field and further south.

The UJ5 depositional episode may comprise two transgressive–regressive episodes, but this requires further study of key well sections. The younger unit of the two is here consistently referred to as UJ5, and the older one as 'UJ5a', where it has been tentatively recognized.

In Piper Field the I-Shale may be the UJ5 highstand and the M-Shale the 'UJ5a' highstand. Depositionally up-dip, e.g. in the Tartan Field, the 'UJ5a' episode may be equivalent to the early marine ingression into the previously almost freshwater lagoonal shales of the Skene Member. In the North Buchan Basin the two episodes are developed as thick offshore mud sections.

Episodes UJ5 MFS–UJ6a MFS–UJ6b MFS

The interval from the UJ5 MFS to the UJ6b MFS (late Late Oxfordian) is combined in Figs 5–6, as the consistent subdivision is often difficult. Biostratigraphically, the UJP5 dinocyst zone is distinguished from the UJP6 zone by the highest presence of *Stephanelytron redcliffense*, which is infrequent and may be overlooked, particularly in older studies. The UJ6a and UJ6b sequences are in a single dinocyst zone and hence difficult to differentiate biostratigraphically.

The two episodes are well developed in the NW–SE striking Theta Graben trend, in Block 15/21 and in Wells 15/16b-22 and 15/17-9. This area formed a depocentre in which the UJ6a and UJ6b Sequences developed ASTs in a massive clean estuarine sand facies, forming important reservoir rocks. Outside the depocentre the distinction of the two episodes is hampered as one highstand is often less well developed than the other, or eroded, or not present due to up-dip pinch-out. Even in an area with dense well control and relatively good biostratigraphic and sedimentological data, such as the Tartan Field, analysis of the dataset has not resulted in an unequivocal interpretation. Fig. 8 shows a preferred interpretation of Wells 15/16b-20 and -22.

In the Piper Field the UJ6a and UJ6b highstands are identified with the E-Shale and D-Shale, respectively, of the Piper reservoir zonation, forming relatively thin but laterally continuous sequences. In the southern parts of Blocks 15/22 and 15/21, the UJ6b highstand is the very thick 'Mid-Shale' unit, and the thin UJ6a highstand is usually removed by erosion at the UJ6b Sequence Boundary, resulting in amalgamation of the UJ6a and UJ6b ASTs in this area. Only Wells 15/21a-22 and 31 show both highstands.

The sands above the UJ5 MFS are the earliest regionally extensive sand units in the OMF Humber Group; the Scott Sand, and the Lower Sand in the Tartan Field are examples. A Fladen Ground Spur source has been suggested by O'Driscoll *et al.* (1990) for most of these sandstones, which are quartzarenitic and hence differ from the younger feldspathic sands surrounding the Halibut Horst. These wave-dominated deltaic systems prograded southwards towards the North Buchan Graben, where they grade into thick offshore muds. Minor mass flow sands of UJP 6 age in Wells 14/30b-3, 15/26b-5 and 21/1–5ST may be delta-front slumps from the prograding UJ6b sands.

The NNE–SSW striking sand 'bridge' in Blocks 21/2 and 15/27 appears to have been a shoreface complex which joined

(a)

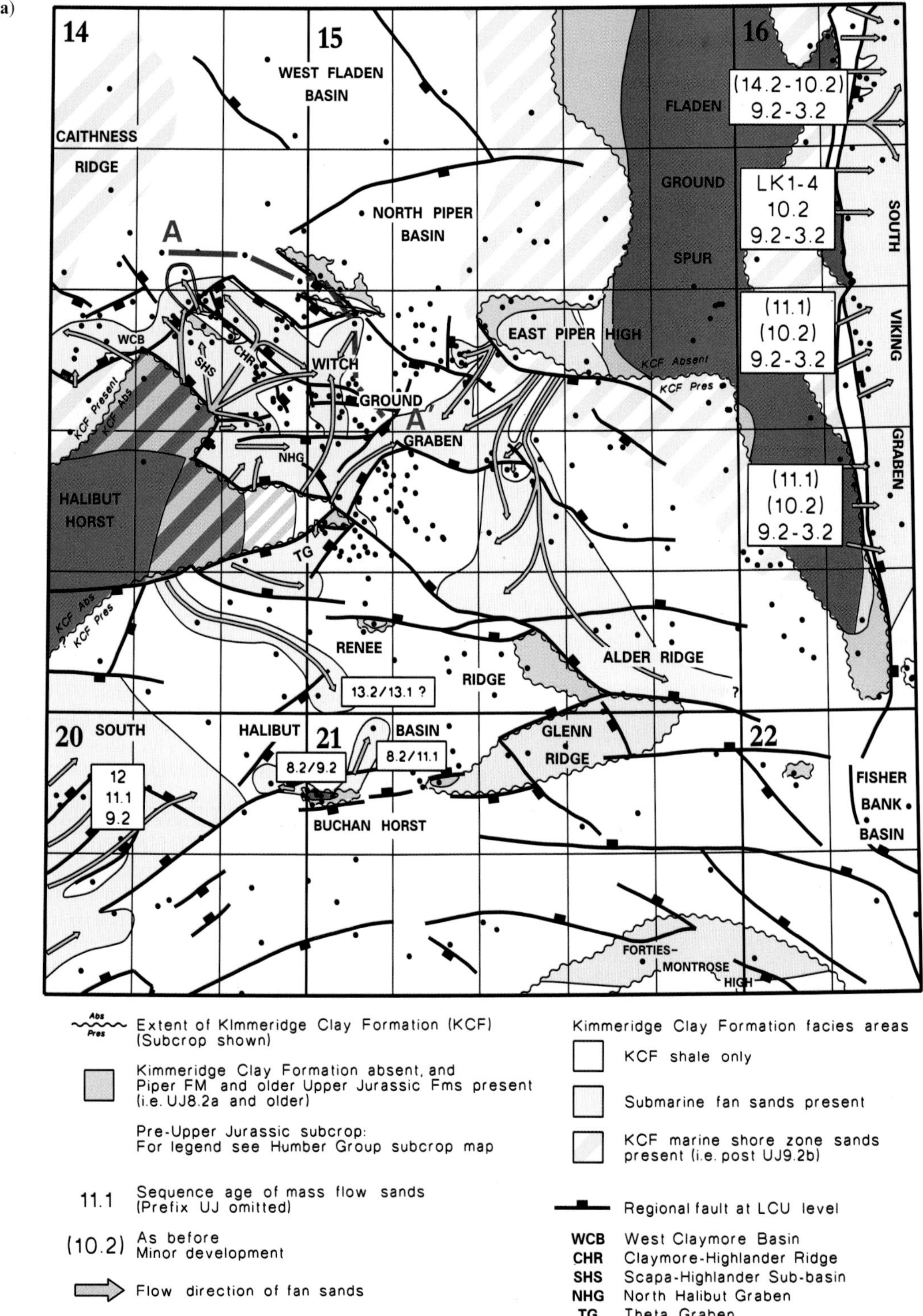

Fig. 7. The distribution of Kimmeridgian to Ryazanian mass flow sands. (**a**) Overview. (**b**) Detail map of the Witch Ground Graben and its surroundings.

sands being sourced from the Buchan Horst with those sands sourced from the north. A muddy backwater appears to have been present on Block 15/28; thin UJ5-6 shales are present, and sand starvation may have occurred because of the diversion of the main progradation to the SW and limited input from the Fladen Ground Spur immediately to the ENE.

In the western part of the West Fladen Basin the UJ6 Sequences are represented by marine mudstones. These are very thin in Well 14/14a-2 (Fig. 8) and thicken to the NE, e.g. Well 14/10-1. Farther to the east (in Wells 15/6-1, 15/7-1 and 15/11a-4), they grade into alternations of channelized sands and mudstones with marine microplankton, interpreted as lagoonal and estuarine deposits. They border the N–S trending Fladen Ground Spur, which was the most likely sand source.

Further southeast, on Block 14/19 and similarly in Well 14/15a-4 (Fig. 8) a thin coastal plain association of freshwater and marine mudstones, fluvial and marine sands and a coal seam is present (Sgiath Formation, type Well 14/19-4). Two marine horizons are present, here interpreted as the coastal plain expressions of the UJ6a and UJ6b highstands.

(b)

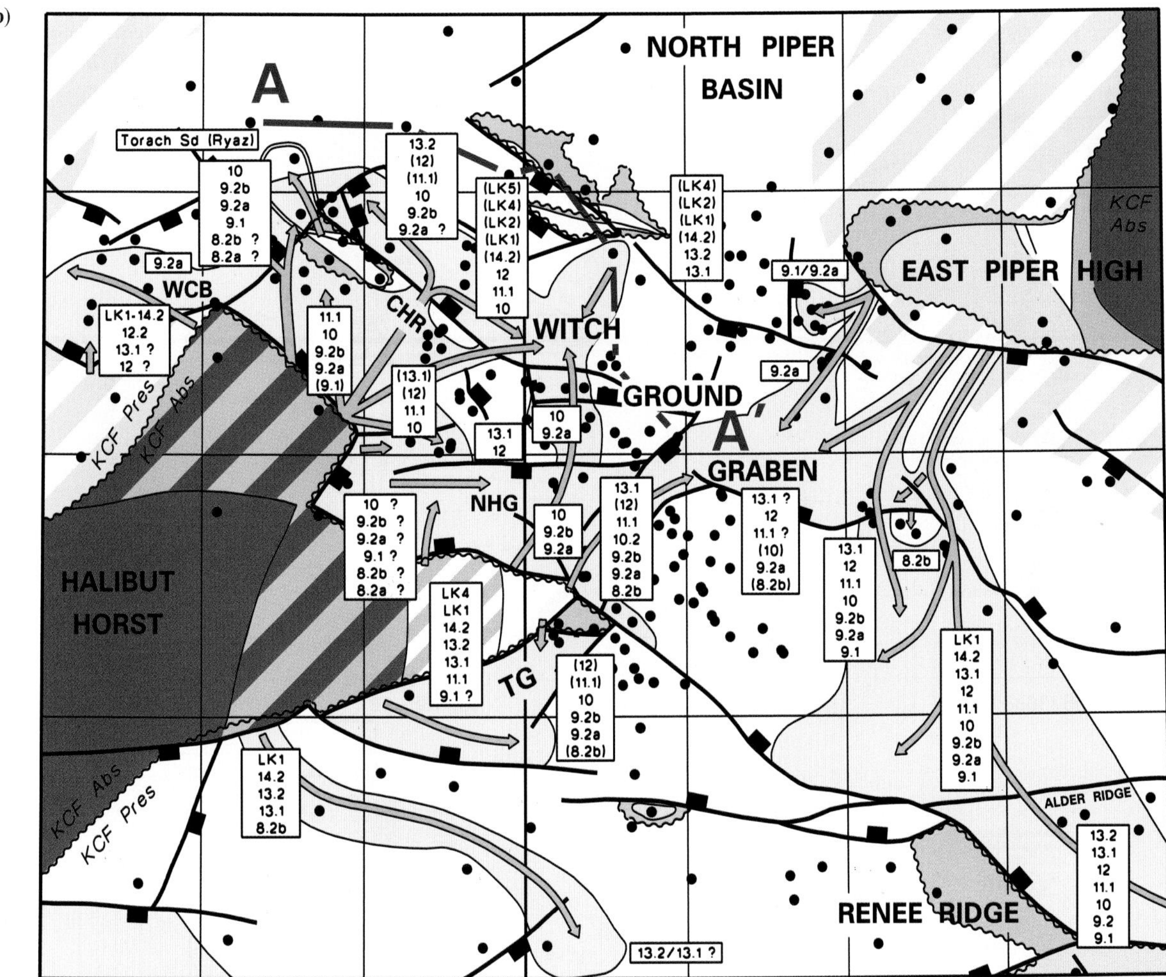

Fig. 7. (*continued*).

The influx of large quantities of sand contrasts with the sedimentation prior to the UJ5 MFS, which is essentially argillaceous, except for the basal fluvial sandy unit in the West Fladen Basin. Enhanced relief related to rifting is one possible cause, as subsidence of the NE–SW trending Theta Graben is evident on Scott Sand isopachs (O'Driscoll *et al.* 1990) and intraformational bevelling on structural highs is evident within the Tartan Field. This could have been accompanied by uplift of adjacent parts of the Fladen Ground Spur, enhancing the topographical relief and reorganizing fluvial drainage systems.

In a Saltire Field well in Block 15/17, a 10 m thick mass flow deposit of Pentland Formation pebbles in a sandy matrix was encountered in core, situated between UJ5 and UJ6a highstand mudstones; its origin was probably an active fault scarp at the western end of the East Piper High, which was to become an important area of origin for mass flow sands and volcanic pebbles from Sequence UJ9.1 onwards. The E–W trending North Halibut Graben was simultaneously active; a thick UJ5–UJ7 interval was deposited, which contrasts with the very thin development of the UJ6 Sequences and absence of UJ5 on the Petronella Ridge adjacent to the north and on parts of the Telford Ridge to the south.

Episode UJ6b MFS–UJ7 MFS

The interval from the UJ6b MFS to the UJ7 MFS is exemplified by the 'upper reservoir unit' of the Scott, Rob Roy and Ivanhoe fields (cf. Duxbury *et al.* 1999). In the Piper Field the interval from the D-Shale to the C-Shale is interpreted to represent this interval. The southward extent of the sands is similar to that of the preceeding sequences, but thickness and grain size have decreased. A shoreface connection to the Glenn Ridge is no longer recognized.

The absence from Tartan Field of the UJ6b MFS and HST (but not the UJ6b AST, cf. Wells 15/16b-20 and -22 in Fig. 8) is controlled by uplift of the western shoulder of the Theta Graben. The UJ7 Sequence begins with a well-developed ravinement surface and a thin and rapidly fining upward TST, suggesting a significant transgression. Concentrations of UJP6 microflora in the UJ7 TST in Wells 15/16-12, -9 and -21 hint at reworking of UJ6b highstand sediments.

In Block 14/20, one thin TST/HST of UJP6 age is usually present at the base of the Piper Formation *s.l.*, which could be interpreted as part of either the UJ6a or UJ6b sequence. In Block 14/19 the thin but regularly layered paralic Sgiath Formation has two horizons with marine microfossils, here interpreted as the UJ6a and 6b highstands. The overlying UJ7 TST has a marked ravinement surface, and again reworked UJP6 dinocysts are recorded here.

In the eastern West Fladen Basin a thick, well developed UJ6b highstand shale grades into a thick wave-dominated sandy HST, e.g. in Wells 15/6-1 and 15/11a-4, prograding from east to west. Depositionally up-dip, in Well 15/7-1, the highstand shale pases laterally into a probable shaly estuarine unit, and the regularly coarsening-upward sand into a more irregular tidal flat or coastal plain sand. Depositionally down-dip, e.g. in Wells 14/10-1 and -2, the unit has graded into thin offshore mudstones.

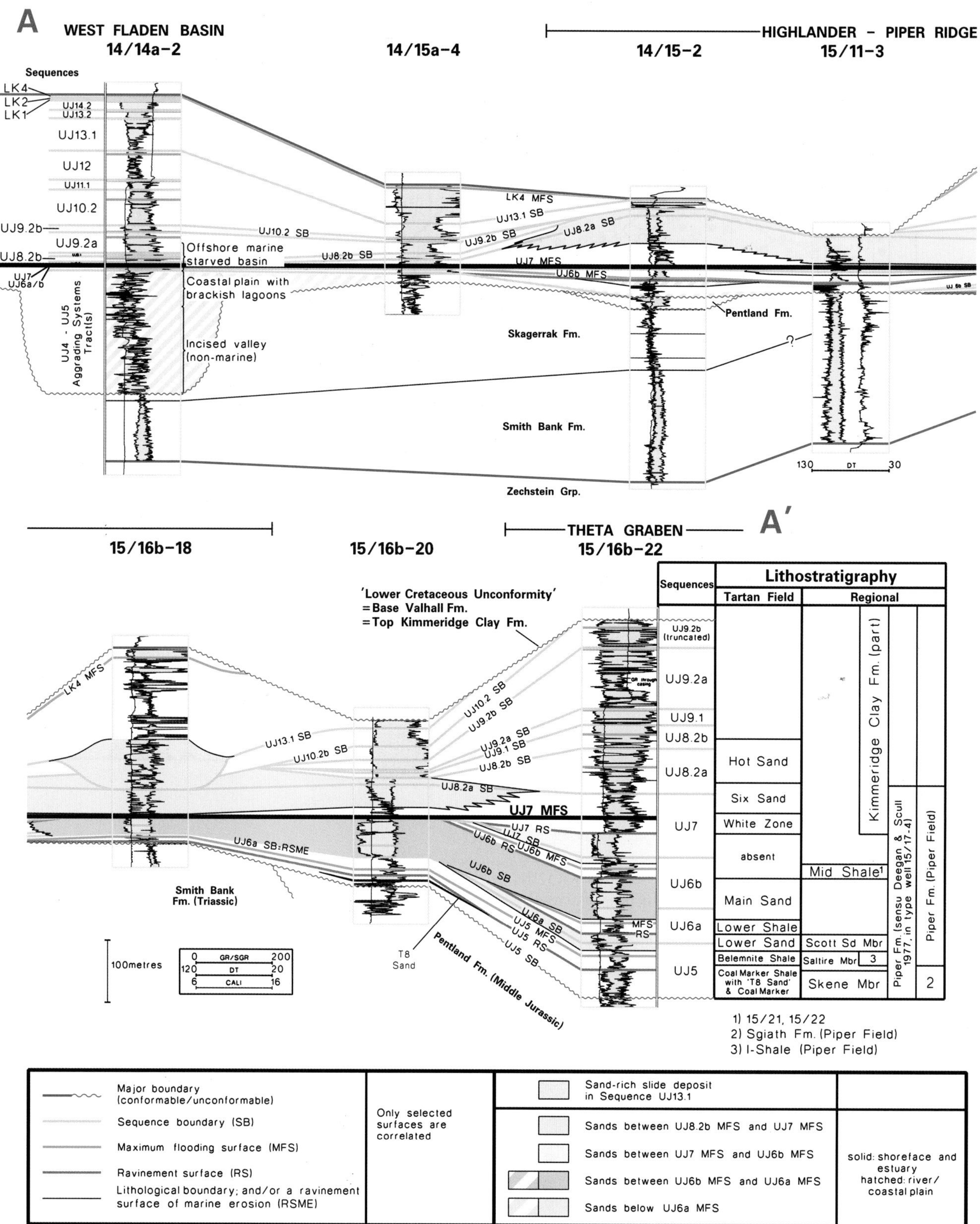

Fig. 8. A correlation section across the Highlander–Piper Ridge.

Episodes UJ7 MFS–UJ8.2a MFS–UJ8.2b MFS

A major reorganization of the depositional systems occurred at the UJ7 MFS (Early Kimmeridgian), reflecting changing tectonic activity. The UJ7 MFS to UJ8.2b MFS episodes (Early to Middle Kimmeridgian) record the encroachment of a large fan-delta into southern Block 14/20 (near the Petronella Field), sourced from the Halibut Horst. This fan-delta system passed eastwards into the wave-dominated shoreface and tidal pass complex of the 'Six Sand' in NW Tartan Field in the UJ7–UJ8.2a episode. The overlying UJ8.2a–UJ8.2b MFS episode in the Tartan Field is an offshore marine sand ('Hot Sand'). Both of these units grade towards the SE, in the Theta Graben, into offshore muds (15/16b-22, Fig. 8). The SE Tartan area, intervening between the Theta Graben and NW Tartan, was the uplifted graben shoulder at this time, and as a consequence the two units experienced reduced sedimentation and even non-deposition in lower shoreface to offshore environments.

East of the Theta Graben, e.g. in Well 15/23-6A, a sandy upper/lower shoreface TST/HST couplet is developed in the UJ8.2a Sequence, as the basin rose to the Fladen Ground Spur.

Northeast of the Petronella fan-delta system, the distal margins of the fan-delta merged with a coarse-grained to pebbly sandstone complex deposited in mesotidal shoreface or tidal pass systems that fringed small exposed horst blocks on Block 14/20. These outcrops of Carboniferous may have provided the very coarse to pebble-sized quartz grains encountered in the Highlander and Lowlander fields. The thickest development of this sand was encountered in Well 14/20b-H3Z of the Highlander Field, where 175 m (573 ft) of homogeneous coarse-grained sandstone occurs.

The UJ7 to UJ8.2b sands extend from Block 14/20 to the southern part of 15/11 and the NW of Block 15/18 (Wells -1, -4 and -5). They are probably also present in the southern part of 15/12 , where massive clean sands occur, but biostratigraphic control is poor.

The sands of Block 14/20 have previously been considered as Piper Formation *s.l.* equivalents, i.e. corresponding to the UJ5 to UJ7 sequences (Waddams & Clark 1991; Whitehead & Pinnock 1991; McCants & Burley 1996). But new palynology from several wells in Block 14/20 show that the UJ5 sequence is absent, the UJ6 sequences are thin, and the principal transgression is the UJ7 highstand (instead of UJ6a or 6b), necessitating the redating of an overlying, more subtle grain size decrease as the UJ8.2a highstand. No younger sand units than the UJ8.2b AST occur in the reservoir interval of the Highlander and Lowlander fields, while in the southern part of Block 14/20, closer to the Petronella fan delta apex, UJP6 to UJP10 (Late Oxfordian to Early Volgian) dates were obtained from the sands (Wells 14/20-1, -11, -16).

In the Piper Field, the C-Shale may represent the UJ7 highstand. The overlying C-Sand is a thin, clean coarse lag deposit, interpreted as a UJ8.2a AST (upper Six Sand equivalent). The overlying Unit IV, often removed at the Base Kimmeridge Clay unconformity, is a fining-upward argillaceous sand probably of the UJ8.2a TST. After this time, tectonic uplift on the Piper fault block, as well as in the SE corner of the Tartan Field, resulted in submarine erosion and condensation or non-deposition of this and the following sequences (cf. Duxbury *et al.* 1999, fig. 6).

To the south, the distribution of offshore muds reflects the continuing infill of the Theta Graben. The earliest mass flow sands, sourced from the Halibut Horst, appear in the UJ8.2a episode in the North Halibut Graben. Block 15/22 exhibits lower shoreface clastic starvation above the UJ7MFS, followed by thin offshore muds. A coast-parallel zone of cleaner sands stretches from Block 15/23 to 15/30. Thin mass flow deposits appear in the Central Galley area (Wells 15/23-1 and 7) in the upper episode, possibly related to tilting of the Central Galley High.

The thick sands in Blocks 14/20, 15/11, 15/12 and 15/18 form a 'sand bridge' between the Halibut Horst and the Fladen Ground Spur. These two highs and the above-mentioned small horsts in Block 14/20 were the sand sources. The up-dip depositional environment of this area relative to the SE and NW reflects the topographic elevation of the Highlander–Piper Ridge during this period. After the deposition of the UJ8.2b AST, a hiatus developed along the ridge crest (Highlander, Lowlander, southern 15/11). The absence of significant erosion, as well as of deposition, suggests a gentle and limited topographic elevation of this sill, which became successively submerged from the Early Volgian (UJ9.2b sequence) onwards.

To the NW of this ridge, in Claymore Field, the interval consists of thin, extensively burrowed, very argillaceous and very fine-grained sandstone, which could either be lower shoreface sandstones or burrowed distal flood-tidal delta deposits (cf. Harker *et al.* 1987, fig. 4: 'Piper Formation'). The facies transition from coarse sandstone on Block 14/20 to thin burrowed muddy sandstone occurs across a few km and can be traced in a NE–SW direction from Blocks 14/19 to 15/11 along the Highlander–Piper Ridge. In the West Fladen Basin (Well 14/14a-2, Fig. 8) the interval is a thin marine shale.

The UJ8.2b transgression produced a further increase in water depth; examples are wells 15/16-6, 9 in west Tartan and 15/23-6A in Galley, where no more shoreface sands occur above this MFS. By contrast, the Highlander–Piper Ridge was not flooded: in Petronella only a minor grain size fluctuation is recorded, and in Highlander and Lowlander a hiatus is developed between the coarse sands of the UJ8.2b AST and the overlying Kimmeridge Clay. In Claymore, the UJ8.2b transgression is similarly developed as a minor grain size fluctuation in the above-mentioned lower shoreface sands.

The UJ8.2b (Peak Pannosum) MFS is the 'Eudoxus MFS' of Partington *et al.* (1993*a*, *b*). These authors considered this a 'tectonically enhanced MFS'. Also, it is often considered to be coincident with the base of the Kimmeridge Clay Formation. In the study area, however, a major tectonic reorganization occurred earlier, in Sequence UJ7 (Early Kimmeridgian), when the locus of Piper sand deposition shifted from the trend of the Piper–Rob Roy–Scott fields to the localized fan-deltas and tidal pass systems of the 'Supra-Piper', or Six Sand–Hot Sand and their coarse equivalents in Block 14/20. A prominent flooding surface formed across the entire sedimentation area, while erosion began on the Halibut Horst and on small horst blocks in Block 14/20.

The age of the base of the Kimmeridge Clay varies widely across the study area (Fig. 5), although this facies change from shoreface to offshore occurred in the UJ8.2a or 8.2b sequences over a comparatively larger area than is the case in other sequences. In the Southern and Inner Moray Firth basins, where facies is more basinal than in the OMF, the change from offshore muds with relatively low gamma ray radioactivity (GR) (Heather Formation, cf. Fig. 2) to the high GR facies of the Kimmeridge Clay Formation occurs in the UJ8.2a to UJ8.2b sequences, accompanied by the disappearance of calcareous foraminifera.

The amount of coastal onlap by the UJ8.2a and UJ8.2b sequences (Fig. 4) is, however, quite limited. The wide distribution of the facies changes could be caused by a basinwide change in water circulation leading to the dysaerobic Kimmeridge Clay facies. In the OMF, the relatively large area in which the change from shoreface to offshore muds in Kimmeridge Clay facies occurred in the UJ8.2a to UJ8.2b Sequences coincides approximately with the area of Piper Formation *s.l.* (sequences UJ5 to UJ7) deposition, i.e. with the flooding of a relatively low relief area. Topographic relief would not have been much accentuated by the Theta Graben rifting, as sediment supply kept pace in the UJ6a/b sequences. When this area was flooded, and provided that a certain water depth was required to turn deposition into dysaerobic muds, then the surpassing of this water depth would cause the facies change over the entire flat area, regardless of the magnitude of the required increase in water depth.

The strong diachroneity of the onset of offshore mud facies in the Kimmeridge Clay Formation (Fig. 5) is controlled by three principal factors:

(1) the timing of onlap onto the basin margins, coupled with the duration of initial shoreface facies;
(2) the relationship between clastics supply and relative sea-level rise (the early onset of offshore muds in the West Fladen Basin and in the South Halibut Basin is related to the lack of clastics input here;
(3) the uplift of the Highlander–Piper Ridge and the north-western Theta Graben shoulder which caused a local hiatus (Base Kimmeridge Clay unconformity).

Episodes UJ8.2b MFS–UJ9.1 MFS–UJ9.2a MFS–UJ9.2b MFS

The interval from the UJ8.2b MFS to the UJ9.2b MFS is discussed as one, as a reliable distinction of the sequences was not always possible and their sedimentary histories are similar.

On the east flank of the OMF Basin, extensive shoreface sands of the UJ9.2a and 9.2b sequences provide the reservoir of the Glamis Field in Block 16/21, terminating with the UJ10.2 TST. On the west flank of the OMF Basin, a relatively complete section of shallow marine sandstone is known only from the Petronella Field (Wells 14/20-1 and 11).

Along the Highlander–Piper Ridge in Blocks 14/20, 15/11, 15/16 and 15/17, a hiatus between the Piper Formation and the Kimmeridge Clay Formation approximates this interval. The onlap record of the Kimmeridge Clay Formation on the Highlander–Piper Ridge constrains the timing of Witch Ground Graben rifting, which introduced a NW–SE trend bisecting the Highlander–Piper High (Figs 5 and 6). Inside the Witch Ground Graben, in the Lowlander area, the onlap occurred in the UJ9.2b sequence, while on both graben shoulders it is dated as UJ10.2 (Well 14/20b-29 on the northern shoulder, Highlander wells on the southern shoulder). The entire Kimmeridge Clay Formation is only 12 m thick in Well 14/20b-29, but it is a virtually complete record, indicating sediment condensation on this submarine high. In contrast, the equivalent interval is 30 times thicker in Lowlander, just 2 km to the SW but on the down-thrown side of the Witch Ground Graben bounding fault.

Well 15/16b-18 (Fig. 8) was drilled on the southern flank of the Highlander–Piper Ridge. It contains a UJ7–UJ8.2a AST sand ('Six Sand') which is abruptly overlain by probable mass flow deposits and interbedded with hemipelagic shales which contain a mixture of Middle to Late Volgian (UJP13.1 and younger) and reworked Late Oxfordian (UJP6–7) forms. This suggests that this section of the Highlander–Piper High was an active high throughout most of the Volgian, while other sections (Witch Ground Graben, SE Scapa basin) had been downfaulted in NW–SE trending graben structures. In the Piper Field, to the east, the biostratigraphic data are poor but suggest onlap by the UJ10.2 sequence. No gap is evident in Saltire Field, but adjacent highs in Blocks 15/12 and 15/13 have a poorly dated hiatus.

A lesser amount of uplift is also perceptible on the Theta Graben shoulders. On the northwestern shoulder, Well 15/16b-21 records a basal Kimmeridge Clay Formation unit of UJP9.1 age which onlaps the UJ8.2a AST of the underlying Piper Formation. In southeast Tartan field, the Kimmeridge Clay Formation onlap has been dated to UJP 9.1, and the UJ7 and 8.2a sequences show submarine condensation. On the southeastern shoulder, in Block 15/21, the UJ7 and UJ8.2a sequences are also condensed (Fig. 5).

In summary, the contiguous Highlander–Piper Ridge remained emergent up to UJP9.2 times, when it was dissected in Block 14/20 by the incipient Witch Ground Graben. The SW portion (Highlander, Petronella Fields) and the NE portion (Piper Field) were flooded by the UJ10.2 highstand, while the middle sector (northern Block 15/16, southern Block 15/11) may have stayed high until the UJ13.1 highstand. During the UJ7 to 8.2b sequences, uplift occurred also on the shoulders of the Theta Graben.

The UJ9.1 to 9.2b interval saw the initiation of large-scale mass flow deposition in the entire region (Fig. 7). The nearly simultaneous onset in different grabens, and with different source areas indicates the beginning of a major rifting phase, consistent with the date of the dissection and partial submersion of the Highlander–Piper Ridge within UJP9.2.

Shallow marine facies of the UJ10.2 to LK4 sequences

After the flooding of the Highlander–Piper Ridge by the UJ10.2 highstand, shallow marine sands were restricted to coast-parallel zones along the margin of the Fladen Ground Spur, and along a north–south trend from the Halibut Horst to the Caithness Ridge. All have in common that the fining- and coarsening-upward cycles are subtle and the sedimentation rate was often slow, as evidenced by the thinness and presence of glauconite. Compared to the previous sequences, a lack of shoreface progradation as a result of reduced sediment supply is evident. Knowledge of these sands is sparse, but first-hand core sedimentology and biostratigraphy of Wells 15/14a-3 and 15/25b-1A enabled extrapolations to other wells.

In Blocks 15/18 and 15/19, a transition can be observed from relatively thick dysaerobic Kimmeridge Clay sections in the south into thick argillaceous very fine-grained burrowed sandstone sections in the north. In Well 15/18a-7, a 226 m (741 ft) thick section of burrowed, mostly very fine-grained and argillaceous sand is dated UJP8.2 to UJP12; only 4 km down-dip, in Well 15/18a-6, the co-eval interval is developed as 148 m (485 ft) of black shale. Likewise, in Well 15/19-5 a thick sand section appears to be a Kimmeridge Clay equivalent, whereas in Well 15/19-4, 5 km to the SSW, much shalier, but still burrowed sands of UJP8.2 age grade into younger mudstones. These grain size and biofacies relationships provide evidence for a southward slope, in agreement with the flow directions of the Galley turbidites, inferred from other lines of evidence (see later).

Adjacent to the South Viking Graben, shallow marine sands start to onlap the intermediate fault platforms from palyzone UJP10 onwards, and on sparse available biostratigraphy this onlap coincides with a marked reduction or even cessation of mass flow processes in the Brae facies belt (Figs 4 and 7).

Mass flow sands of the UJ9.1 to LK4 sequences

The distribution of these is given in Fig. 7. Combining of these sequences is possible because of the apparent near-constancy of source areas and of broad fan outlines over much of their age ranges. Fan outlines have been mapped from well control and these show the extent of clean sands (GR <80 API units) of more than 3.3 m (10 ft) thickness per sequence. The following discussion proceeds from west to east and then to the south.

The Claymore 'Fan'

The Claymore Sands are fan deposits with the main feeder in the vicinity of Well 14/19-27. This well encountered 1095 m (3592 ft) of continuous sands in fault contact with the Lower Carboniferous. Sparse records of UJP11–13 palynomorphs occur in the middle of the sand section, and of Early Hauterivian indicators in the higher part. A core of 2.5 m (8.3 ft) in the Middle Volgian section showed coarse to very coarse subarkoses with mudclasts, carbonaceous debris and granitic rock fragments. The composition of the detritus suggests erosion of the South Halibut Granite, and of the Devonian and Carboniferous formations covering it.

In Claymore, the earliest mass flow sands are interbedded with black shales in the UJ9.1, 9.2a and 9.2b sequences. These are overlain by a thick fine to very fine-grained subarkosic sand section with very few shale beds, assigned to the UJ10.2 and UJ11.1 sequences. A UJ10.2 highstand deposit is absent, but a UJ11.1 highstand shale terminates the deposition of the Claymore Sands. Maher & Harker (1987) and Harker *et al.* (1991) subdivide the sands into earlier 'Low Gamma Ray Sands' (UJ9.1 to 10.2 sequences), overlain by the 'High Gamma Ray Sands' (UJ11.1 sequence). The difference signifies a change to more fine-grained and thinner bedded units, although in both units the GR is high, owing to the K-feldspar content, the presence of clay laminae and grains, and of organic matter.

Thickness distribution indicates ponding against the NW–SE trending Claymore–Highlander Ridge, a large tilted fault block with a crest along its NE edge. Sand thicknesses are greatest adjacent to the basin margin faults, with more than 535 m (1754 ft, base not reached) present in Well 14/19-9. In the UJ11.1 sands of this well, bioturbation is observed in core. These sands are continuous with the Main Claymore Field sands to the north, which on the basis of extensive core coverage are interpreted as turbiditic (without bioturbation). Thus Well 14/19-9 appears to be located in the shallow marine topset sector of a fan delta, while the main Claymore reservoir sands were emplaced by turbiditic flows further down-dip, in the foreset sector.

In a down-dip direction to the northwest, the Claymore sands grade rapidly into non-reservoir silty sands and argillaceous silts. Even further down-dip, correlative shales are interbedded with discrete beds of clean sands, e.g. Well 14/19-24 and in the Witch Ground Graben. These sands are interpreted as basinal turbidites originating from the Claymore fan delta. They reached the Witch Ground Graben via the West Claymore Basin and/or by spilling across topographic lows between the Claymore and Highlander fields.

The topset sector of the Claymore fan delta appears to have extended in an easterly direction as far as the Petronella area, as shallow marine sands as young as Sequence UJ10.2 have been encountered. The lesser thickness here is a function of the accommodation space on the E–W trending Petronella ridge. A much greater sand thickness is encountered in the North Halibut Graben south of Petronella, e.g. 927 m in Well 14/24-2. The emergence of the Highlander–Piper Ridge prevented this fan delta from spreading further northeast, but the onset of Witch Ground Graben rifting in sequence UJ9.2b times created accommodation space and a seafloor slope here. Smaller fan systems began to downlap onto the graben floor, as in Well 14/20b-24, in which turbidite sands of UJP9.2 age lie directly on non-marine UJ8.2b AST sands.

The Petronella Delta was onlapped by Kimmeridge Clay Formation during the UJ10.2 highstand. In the following UJ11.1 sequence, more distal 'High GR Sands' were deposited on the Claymore Fan, but cleaner and coarser turbidite sands now began to onlap the Highlander Field (Hot Lens Equivalents of Whitehead & Pinnock 1991) and also entered the Witch Ground Graben. These sands probably spilled across structural lows that bound the Highlander Field to the NW and SE. A regional tilt in an easterly direction may have caused these changes. A palaeoslope in an easterly direction is also suggested by the eastward fining and thinning of the overlying 'Kimm Silt', the down-dip equivalent of massive shoreface sands further west, in Blocks 14/17, 14/12 and 14/11. The 'Kimm Silt' unit of Wells 14/18-3 and 14/19-2 is illustrated by Andrews & Brown (1987, fig. 6) as a 'Mid-Volgian Sand/ Silt Unit'.

In the UJ12 sequence, turbidite deposition ceased in the area of the Claymore Field, but a massive turbidite sand is present in the Petronella Field, the distal equivalents of which are developed in tigerstripe facies in the Highlander Field. Thereafter, turbidite deposition ceased also at Well 14/20, although coarse mass flow sands continued to be deposited in more proximal positions such as in Well 14/19-27.

A new episode of mass flow sand deposition occurred in the UJ14.2 to LK4 interval (Late Volgian to Ryazanian) in the Witch Ground Graben. The sands encountered in Lowlander are, however, thin-bedded and distal; the only place where local sand source rocks were exposed during this interval was the Halibut Horst, and flow through the previously discussed low, northwest of the Highlander Field is envisaged. In the West Claymore Basin, localized mass flow sands were again deposited, as shown by a local sand in Well 14/18b-12, and the more substantial 'Torach Sand' in the northwest area of the Claymore Field, which extends as far north as Well 14/14a-3. The distribution of the Torach Sand suggests an origin on the Claymore Horst, and redeposition of Claymore Sands is envisaged.

The North Halibut Graben and the Tartan Field

The North Halibut Graben is a deep E–W trending graben of Late Jurassic age in the northern parts of Blocks 14/25 and 15/21. Well 14/24-2 penetrated 927 m of coarse sands at its up-dip western end which suggests that it could have been filled by straight eastward transport throughout the entire Late Jurassic. However, no well penetrations in this graben exist on Block 14/25.

In Block 15/21, discrete episodes of mass flow sands have been identified during the UJ8.2b, 9.2a, 9.2b and 10.2 sequences. The UJ8.2b mass flow sands are localized, while the UJ9.2a–UJ10.2 sands are thicker and more widespread.

Their ages correspond with those of the West Tartan mass flows (Hot Lens B: UJ9.2a; Spiculitic Sand (stringers) UJ9.2b; Hot Lens A: UJ10.2), which are, however, much thinner and located in tectonically less subsided positions. The ages of the Tartan mass flows would be compatible with an origin from the Highlander–Piper Ridge which was exposed until the UJ10.2 highstand; however only the lower units, the 'Hot Lens B' and the 'Spiculitic Sand' Members, have coarse quartz grains which are prevalent in the Highlander sands; hence they may indeed be derived from there. The overlying more voluminous 'Hot Lens A' Member is fine-grained. For want of other suitable contemporaneous sources, the Hot Lens A sands have to be derived from the Halibut Horst; hence a NNW flow direction across the main active faults is postulated. This assumes that sediment supply kept pace with subsidence in the North Halibut Graben, resulting in a much greater thickness of sediment being deposited here than on the Tartan structure, which was reached by the overflow. In west Tartan an approximately north–south trending low area is indicated by the Kimmeridge Clay isochore. This may imply continuing subsidence along the Theta Graben trend, or (more likely) the expression of topographic relief created in pre-UJP8.2 times.

The Theta Graben

The continuing presence of this structure as an effective topographic feature is underlined by the observation that none of the turbidite sands deposited in this graben reached the adjacent high structures to the east, where the Scott, Telford, Ivanhoe and Rob Roy fields are situated, with the possible exception of a few thin sand beds. Their lack of correlatability suggests, however, the alternative possibility that at least some of them are Neptunean dykes, which have repeatedly been encountered elsewhere in cores in the Kimmeridge Clay Formation.

The eastern end of the Halibut Horst, termed the Halibut Spur, dissects the Theta Graben (Boldy & Brealey 1990; Hibbert & Mackertich 1993). It was uplifted from approximately UJP8.2 times onwards, and is the most likely sand source of the UJ8.2 turbidites observed. As the northern part of the Theta Graben intersects with the newly formed North Halibut Graben, the turbidites in this intersection should be attributed to the latter.

The SW end of the Theta Graben is intersected by another ENE–SSW trending graben formed adjacent to the southern margin of the Halibut Horst. Here, in Wells 14/25a-2AZ and 14/29-1, the UJ9.2 to 11.1 mass flows fade out, and a markedly younger episode of mass flow deposition, from UJ13.1 to LK4, is evident. A very elongate 'fan' is postulated to account for the presence of a UJ13.1 or 13.2 turbidite sand in Well 15/26b-5.

The Saltire–Chanter fans

In the Saltire, Chanter and Westray fields (SE sector of Block 15/17), a single unit of massive clean quartzose sands, probably of UJP9.2 age, provides an important reservoir unit. Slightly different ages for the Saltire and Chanter mass flows have been postulated (Casey *et al.* 1993). This is consistent with the discontinuous sand distribution between the Saltire and Chanter fields, although available biostratigraphical evidence is inconclusive. The Chanter sand has also been encountered in Wells 15/17-8A and 15/17-24, giving a very elongate north–south trending distribution. The Chanter and Saltire sands may be redeposited Piper (*s.l.*) Formation coastline sands reworked from the East Piper High, when it started to rise in response to Witch Ground Graben rifting. Wells near the western edge of the East Piper High indicate that:

(i) the 'Piper Field-style' cycles of relatively thin transgressive, regressive and aggrading sands grade eastward into massive, thick, coarse, channelized proximal sands, penetrated only in one of the most eastern wells, 15/17-22Z (Casey *et al.* 1993);
(ii) the hiatus at the top of the Piper Formation grades eastward again into sedimentary continuity, with thick shallow marine sands of post-Piper ages being present in Wells 15/12-1 and -2, 15/18-1, -4 and -5.

These preserved examples suggest that east of the Highlander–Piper Ridge in Block 15/17, outside the area affected by uplift, potentially thick shoreface and coastal plain sands of post-Piper age (post UJ7) may have been deposited on top of Piper *s.s.* sands, which would all have been available for redeposition.

The cessation of sand flow after just one sequence may be a consequence of the flooding in UJ10.2 times of the Piper Ridge and those marginal parts of the East Piper High which sourced the Chanter and Saltire mass flows. The rise of the East Piper High continued, however, but resulted in supply only to the Galley systems further east; therefore a regional eastward tilt causing a diversion of flows should be considered.

The Galley–Alder 'fan' systems

In Block 15/23, two separate fan systems are interpreted to be present:

(i) in North Galley (Wells 15/23-4A and 9), a quartzarenitic sand system partially ponded against the E–W trending Galley Ridge, but was able to cross it (Wells 15/23-5 and -8), eroding the subcrop down to the Pentland Formation;
(ii) in South Galley (Wells 15/23-2 and 12), high-density turbidites prevail, which are rich in pebbles and cobbles of mainly Pentland volcanic rocks in a quartzarenite matrix. This depositional system extended down-current to the SE, where, in Well 15/29-3, thick sands with grain sizes up to coarse to granule grade are still present. Up-current, conglomerates are interpreted in Well 15/23a-11, which penetrated a channel incised down to the Pentland volcanics. Although the flow is inferred to have been from the north, no trace of arenaceous turbidites is seen in nearby Well 15/23-6A, confirming that there was little or no overbank deposition, suggesting a deeply incised channel here.

The conglomerates cored in Well 15/23a-12 provide unique evidence as to the source of the clastics. Approximately 90% of the pebble and cobble-sized material is derived from Pentland Formation volcanics. Of the remaining pebble population, well rounded quartz pebbles are most frequent, which can be derived from Devonian and Carboniferous sandstones; subordinate clasts are derived from Carboniferous sandstones, Piper Formation shelly calcareous mudstones, Kimmeridge Clay Formation siltstones and shales, and Zechstein dolomites. The only potential source area where all of these formations crop out is the E–W trending high in the northern part of Blocks 15/18 and 15/19, here termed the East Piper High. The Fladen Ground Spur proper is ruled out for want of the volcanics, and the Glenn Ridge could only have provided volcanics; however, the wells nearest to it, in Block 15/29, encountered only quartz sand.

The mixing of clasts of different formations, and the presence of huge amounts of quartz sand containing variable, but sometimes high, amounts of marine shells (bivalves, brachiopods and belemnites) points to the presence of a shallow marine shelf on the East Piper High. Erosion of the Pentland Formation outcropping on this High provided the volcanic pebbles, while the large amounts of quartz sand were derived from the erosion of the sand-rich Carboniferous and Devonian formations outcropping further east on the Fladen Ground Spur. Wave action improved the sorting of these sands, and mixed them with contemporaneous shells and with the Pentland Formation pebbles. Such a nearshore sand with volcanics pebbles is preserved in a core from Well 15/24-2, close to Galley.

Volumetrically, the stripping of the East Piper High of a previously deposited Piper Formation would not provide the quantities of sand known to be present in the system, even if the aforementioned thickening of the Piper Formation *s.l.* to the east of Block 15/17 is considered. For example, Well 15/29-3 still has 317 m (1039 ft) of net sand, and this thickness may even double down-dip in the undrilled syncline to the south. The source area must have been relatively small: the eastern part of Block 15/19, the western part of Block 15/20 and adjacent areas to the north may have drained onto shelves on the East Piper High. To maintain a continuous supply of sediment from the UJ9.2a to the UJ13.1 sequence, a continuous rise of the source area is required. Sand supply was terminated simultaneously in both Galley systems in the UJ13.1 sequence. Cessation of uplift of the East Piper High is the inferred cause.

Sand-rich mass flows resumed in South Galley during the UJ14.2 and LK1 sequence times, when the much more restricted 'Dirk Sand' Member (Richards *et al.* 1993) was deposited. Again an origin from the East Piper High is inferred.

The inferred overall S–SE flow direction appears to parallel the margin of the Fladen Ground Spur, i.e. the flows appear to flow along-slope instead of down-slope, which would be to the W. However, the abundance of Pentland volcanics in South Galley definitely excludes a more easterly origin; moreover, a southward slope is indicated by the facies change of the Kimmeridge Clay Formation seen between Wells 15/19-4 and 5, and 15/18a-6 and 7 (see earlier). The ability to cross the crests of synsedimentary rising fault blocks and even incise them (Wells 15/23-5, -8, -11 and 15/29-8) suggests a relatively high overall seafloor slope to the south to provide the necessary kinetic energy.

The furthest SE continuation of the South Galley system is uncertain, as the southern extension of the Fladen Ground Spur and the Alder Ridge were probably topographic highs, and the available well control in this area shows no trace of sands; possibly the available accommodation space in the deep low between the Glenn Ridge and the Alder Ridge accommodated all mass flows. The mapped maximum Kimmeridge Clay thickness in this low is more than 914 m (3000 ft), and if the net : gross ratio of 75% seen in Well 15/29-3 is maintained, >686 m (2250 ft) of net sand could be accommodated here.

The Galley systems show clear evidence of channelization (Clark pers. comm.). This was achieved by the flows constructing their own levees. Outside the sand-rich channel systems low-density turbidites, representing levee and spillover deposits, are recognizable over wide distances. Reservoir-grade sands are, however, not developed in this environment, and the boundaries of the sand-rich channel systems are well defined.

Table 1. Comparison of Galley and South Viking Graben fan systems

	Galley	South Viking Graben
Onset of mass flows	UJ9.2a	approx. UJ3.2
Cessation of principal mass flow deposition	UJ13.1	UJ11.1 (more variable in the N)
Predominant large clasts	Pentland Fm	Devonian
Predominant reworked palynomorphs	Carboniferous	Permo-Triassic
Fault scarp breccias	not known	present
Source area	East Piper High	Fladen Ground Spur
Orientation and length of source area	E–W, <30 km	N–S, >75 km

A comparison between the Galley and the South Viking Graben fan systems show significant differences (Table 1) (South Viking Graben after Turner *et al.* 1987, Cherry 1993, and in-house data).

The Brae Formation is related to the much earlier formation of the South Viking Graben. Much steeper slopes may have existed than in the Galley source area, to account for the large volume of redeposited clasts and the presence of fault scarp breccias. However, disintegration of sandstones and winnowing by shoreface processes were also active on a large-scale along the margin of the South Viking Graben. By contrast, the Galley systems are related to the Witch Ground Graben rifting; the uplift of the E–W trending source area is contemporaneous with uplift of parts of the Halibut Horst (which at least also partly trends E–W).

The Buchan 'Fans'

Localized mass flow sands are present in Wells 20/5b-2 and 21/1a-12 near the Buchan Horst. Their age is poorly constrained, but they are most likely older than adjacent 'fans' in Well 15/26b-5 and in the Ettrick area. They may be mass flows from the Buchan Horst, where remnants of presumed shoreface sands as young as UJP11 have been encountered.

The Ettrick 'Fans'

The Ettrick sands are widespread in the SW of the mapped area, where the South Halibut Horst and the Buchan Graben meet. Their ages are based on sparse biostratigraphic data, and on Partington *et al.* (1993*a*). Their origin is thought to be the Petershead Ridge, further to the SW.

Discussion

Sand provenance

The principal sand-bearing formations in the study area are the Devonian ('Old Red Sandstone') and the Lower Carboniferous formations. Lower Permian (Rotliegend) red-bed clastics may locally be present, but they cannot be distinguished with certainty from the similar barren Devonian red-beds and are, on Figs 3 and 7, amalgamated with them. Only these formations contain quartz pebbles, which are also encountered in Humber Group sandstones. The Lower Carboniferous formations usually contain palynomorphs which are commonly reworked into Humber Group sandstones. The Triassic formations could only have provided fine to very fine-grained sand; the Zechstein and Fladen groups are almost completely free of quartz sand in the study area. Another probable clastics source is the large South Halibut granite (Andrews *et al.* 1990), subcropping west of the study area (cf. Fig. 3) in the centre of the Halibut Horst and in parts of the adjacent South Moray Firth Basin.

In order to determine the origin of the Humber Group sands, the onlap and subcrop maps (Figs 4 and 3), the inferred direction of shore progradation of the Piper Formation *s.l.* sequences (Fig. 6) and the flow directions of the younger mass flow sands (Fig. 7) have been analysed. Much of this has been already discussed in the preceding section; a summarizing discussion is set out below.

Fladen Ground Spur

The Fladen Ground Spur must have provided the clastics both of the Brae fans in the South Viking Graben, and of the shore zone sands of the Piper Formation *s.l.* Relative to the amounts of clastics provided, the potential source areas were relatively small. High topographic elevation of parts of the Fladen Ground Spur is postulated to account for the quantities and the presence of coarse fractions shedded from it.

It is tempting to postulate an alternative sediment influx from much larger high areas on the East Shetlands Platform to the north and to regard the fluvial sands of the Sgiath Formation in the northern OMF as evidence for such an influx. However, the time equivalents of the sand-bearing Piper Formation sequences (from the UJ5 HST to the UJ8.2a AST) in the West Fladen Basin are thin offshore muds, indicating a lack of clastics influx at this time. The fluvial sands were time-equivalents of the coals and clays of the Skene Member (UJ5 AST), i.e. they did not even reach a large part of the area covered by the Piper Formation sands. Moreover, the inferred westward palaeoslope of the Fladen Ground Spur would have caused drainage systems to be directed westwards instead of southwards. Evidence for the westward palaeoslope of the Fladen Ground Spur flank includes: (1) the onlap pattern of the Humber Group sequences and the age of change-over to Kimmeridge Clay facies (Figs 4 and 5); (2) the direction of progradation of the UJ6b HST in the West Fladen Basin (see earlier description) from east to west; and (3) the presence of a fluvial sand package in Well 15/13b-5, which is interpreted as an up-dip equivalent of upper shoreface Piper sands in Wells 15/13-1 and -3, which are comparable with the Piper sands in Piper Field itself. Previous interpretations of the age of this sand as Middle Jurassic were probably based on an incorrect understanding of the biostratigraphical significance of non-marine palynomorphs.

Halibut Horst

Because of the close spatial association of feldspathic shore zone and mass flow sands with the Halibut Horst, these sands are considered to be derived from the latter (O'Driscoll *et al.* 1990). Jurassic onlap suggests that it was indeed a contemporaneous high area, although Early Cretaceous uplift and erosion also occurred. It is probable that the South Halibut granite in the centre of the Halibut Horst contributed arkosic detritus. Alternatively, rapid erosion of arkosic sands of Carboniferous and Devonian formations may have preserved their feldspar content when the detritus was redeposited as second cycle sediment. Heavy mineral studies in the vicinity of the eastern end of the Halibut Horst (Hallsworth *et al.* 1996) suggest that most sandstones were derived from Palaeozoic sediments. A granitic source contributed only some clastics to the mass flow sands of the Theta Graben, but granitic rock fragments were described from Well 14/19-27.

The Halibut Horst extends approximately 110 km in an E–W direction and 20 km in a N–S direction, and is interpreted as having shed clastics from almost all its margins. Similar to the Fladen Ground Spur, a strong topographic relief is postulated to account for the amount of erosion and the presence of coarse fractions.

East Piper High

During the deposition of the Galley Sands, basaltic rocks of the Pentland Formation cropped out only on the East Piper High, which therefore is the only possible source of the basalt pebbles in the Galley Sands of the South Galley Field. Coastal erosion created these pebbles, while longshore drift accumulated quartz sand and lesser amounts of pebbles from other outcropping formations on narrow fault-bound shelves on the East Piper High. Periodic uplift then caused these clastics to be redeposited in the Galley fan systems. The source area for these sands appears to be approximately the same as for the preceding Piper sands.

General characteristics of sand source areas

Not every contemporaneous topographic high area was a significant contributor of clastics during Humber Group sedimentation. The influxes from the southern Fladen Ground Spur, the East Shetlands Platform and the Caithness Ridge are remarkably limited. Special conditions, such as particularly high topographic relief in selected areas, which would most likely be tectonically induced, are invoked. The source areas are typically long-lived, suggesting long-term uplift against a background of basinwide subsidence throughout the Late Jurassic and Ryazanian.

Timing of tectonic activity

The timing of tectonic phases affecting sedimentation patterns can be summarized as follows:

E–W trends. Rifting began in the pre-UJ5 and may have lasted to approximately UJ11.1, but as the E–W trend in these areas intersects with the NE–SW trend of the Theta Graben, the temporal relationship between these two cannot always be distinguished with certainty.

In the Inner Moray Firth, E–W trending faults affect Early Oxfordian (UJ1) onlap, and it is conceivable that the timing in the OMF was similar, i.e. E–W faulting occurred at a time without a sedimentary record. E–W trends are present in the Triassic isopachs in Block 14/19, and in the distribution of the Pentland Formation along its westerly margin. While this could be attributable to rifting and erosion during the hiatus between Pentland Formation and Humber Group, the WSW–ENE trending Glenn Ridge was already a positive feature before the Middle Jurassic, which here onlaps Early Carboniferous formations. Similarly, in the detritus shed from the E–W trending Halibut Horst, no Pentland volcanics material has been recognized, again suggesting the possibility of pre-Middle Jurassic faulting.

In the North Halibut Graben and in the North Buchan Graben, the presence and thickness of the earliest Humber Group sequences, UJ5 and UJ6a–b, appears to be controlled by the E–W trend of these lows. Possibly the Petronella Ridge in Block 14/20 and the Renee Ridge in Blocks 14/30 and 15/26 acted as the rising graben shoulders.The SW–NE striking Theta Graben intersects these grabens, and from well data alone, it cannot be distinguished whether later subsidence in the sparsely drilled parts of these structures was controlled by E–W or SW–NE striking rifts. In the more densely drilled Blocks 15/16, 15/21 and 15/22, the Theta Graben clearly emerges as the depositional centre during the Late Oxfordian.

Younger episodes of E–W faulting appear to have affected the SE Halibut Spur and the East Piper High. Boldy & Brealey (1990) conclude that the Piper Formation (Sequences UJ5 to UJ7) was originally deposited on the SE Halibut Spur which only rose in post-Piper times, possibly from the UJ8.2b sequence onwards, when the first turbidite sands were shed into the Theta Graben.

The East Piper High was an active provider of clastics for the Saltire, Chanter and/or Galley fans from Sequence UJ9.1 to UJ13.1 and again in sequences UJ14.2 and LK1. Active uplift is the most likely cause, removing previously deposited thick shore zone sands, of which truncated remnants have been preserved in Wells 15/18-1, -4 and -5.

SW–NE (Theta Graben) trend. The Theta Graben was active from the Late Oxfordian (UJ5) to the Early Kimmeridgian (UJ7); similarly the West Fladen Basin (from Block 14/18 to 14/10) was active from Oxfordian (pre-UJ5) to UJ7 and possibly later. The onset of sand supply from the Fladen Ground Spur from the UJ5 HST onwards may reflect uplift related to this rifting phase. Also related is the gentle uplift of the Highlander–Piper Ridge (SW–NE), which separates the Theta Graben and the West Fladen Basin.

Uplift of the Halibut Horst may have begun (or rather, resumed) in the UJ7 sequence (Early Kimmeridgian), as shoreface progradation from this high to the SE is first observed in the UJ7 HST. The structural alignment of this uplift is not recognizable from well control, but may be related to the emergence of the Highlander–Piper Ridge mentioned earlier.

NW–SE (Witch Ground Graben) trend. Rifting may have commenced during Sequence UJ9.1 times as this is the age of the onset of minor mass flow deposits. It became more intensive from the UJ9.2 sequences onwards, as indicated by the simultaneous onset of siginificant mass flows from multiple sources, and the flooding of the rift segment of the Highlander–Piper Ridge in the UJ9.2b sequence, and continued into the Ryazanian and later Cretaceous.

Basin floor fans, eustasy and tectonics.

In a strongly transgressive regime, type I sequence boundaries that Vail *et al.* (1977*a*, *b*) recognized in strongly progradational shelf-edge systems are not likely to form. The development of basinal mass flow fan systems is unlikely to reflect the collapse of constructional highstand shelf edges in such a setting. In a sediment-deficient synrift environment, shelf edges are strongly controlled by structure, and do not contain the large volumes of unconsolidated sediment that the constructional shelf edges of passive margin or foreland basin systems commonly have. Instead, delta platforms that can serve as point sources for major mass flow systems form where structural controls focus fluvial input, often for extended periods of time.

The size of these delta platforms may be modest because of the limited drainage catchments in the source terranes and because of the relatively steep slopes upon which they are built. Linear mass flow systems will also develop along the fault scarps. The essential factor to form mass flow deposits is the relative lowering of the erosional base-level, which in a synrift environment may be achieved by uplift of the graben shoulders, and need not be strongly controlled by eustatic sea-level. In the OMF Basin, the origin of extensive mass flow deposits has been traced to two fault-bound highs, which appear to have been consistently uplifted during the Late Jurassic and the Early Cretaceous, viz. the Halibut Horst and the East Piper High.

Characteristics of mass flow sand distribution in the OMF rift basin

The Halibut Horst, as a fault-bound intrarift horst block, generally had very narrow fault-defined shelves that served as linear sources for slope–apron systems, similar to the Brae systems on the eastern margin of the Fladen Ground Spur. The Halibut Horst was flanked by deep grabens or half-grabens, viz. the Theta Graben, the North Halibut Graben, the Scapa–Highlander Sub-basin and the West Claymore Basin. These served as large sediment sinks for the slope–apron systems, resulting in large sediment thicknesses, but limited areal spread.

North of the Halibut Horst was the Halibut shelf, a platform area that separated it from the Caithness Ridge. Platform areas on rift system margins commonly serve as entry points for sediments, and it is no surprise that this margin of the OMF had voluminous mass flow deposits throughout the Late Jurassic and into the Cretaceous. In places, topographic focusing of fluvial systems may have provided large point sources, such as at the structural juncture of the Halibut shelf and the Halibut Horst, on the southern half of Block 14/19 (This area is presently more elevated than the platform further east, and devoid of Humber Group as a result of Early Cretaceous uplift). The Petronella fan delta may have resulted from this postulated focused flow, and its submarine extensions sourced the Claymore Fan systems that filled the Scapa–Highlander Basin. These systems may have resembled Mutti Type II systems, with confined channel systems passing rapidly down-dip into unconfined lobes and ultimately distal lobe fringes.

The reconstruction of sediment source areas and mass flow sand distribution leads to the conclusion that mass flows in many cases crossed tectonically active fault block crests. This was achieved in two different ways:

(1) Sub-basins surrounding the Halibut Horst were generally underfilled, but there were areas where the sediment supply was so great that it filled the developing topography to the level of structural sills, allowing turbidite flows to proceed deeper into the centre of the OMF. This may be the case in the southern Scapa–Highlander Basin, where smaller submarine fans are interpreted to have entered the Witch Ground Graben while the Highlander area was being onlapped by gravity flows from the Halibut Horst. Likewise, northward flows from the Halibut Spur may have filled the North Halibut Graben and crossed into the west Tartan area (Hot Lens A, UJ10.2 sequence) and possibly into the Witch Ground Graben.
(2) The Galley fans behaved in a similar manner, but they also incised their major channels into the crests, so that turbidites were in contact with the Humber Group subcrop. A higher topographic energy than in the systems originating on the Halibut Horst is envisaged in the Galley systems.

Two types of fan systems have been recognized in the OMF:

(1) Fan deltas, namely the Claymore–Petronella system. This displays greatest thickness adjacent to the fault scarp which separates it from the clastics source. Burrowed shallow marine sands (Well 14/19-9, and Petronella Field) are in spatial continuity with sands deposited by gravity flow processes, such as the Main Area Claymore reservoir sand. The grain size within this fan decreases rapidly, from coarse in Well 14/19-27 to fine/very fine in the main Claymore area, to predominantly silt in the West Claymore Basin. A very limited relief has to be assumed to account for this rapid loss of transport energy. At a greater distance from the Claymore fan delta in the West Claymore Basin and in the Witch Ground Graben, channelized turbidites of the same age (UJ9.1 to UJ11.1) occur, which originated from the fan delta.
(2) Submarine fans, e.g. the Galley fans. These are high and low density turbidite fans which are typically channelized. Erosion at the channel base is usually limited, and the levees are constructive, built by overbank deposition of finer fractions. Good reservoir quality occurs within the clean blocky channel sands, while levee deposits tend to have modest to no reservoir properties. As a result of channelization and near-constancy of sediment source areas, the area of sand occurrence is very well defined (Fig. 9), even though in individual sequences the channel axes may be offset against each other. A consequence of this is that towards the fan margins a lesser number of sequences with reservoir sands exists than in the centre. Between individual channels, hydraulic discontinuity may exist, for example between Galley Wells 15/23-4B and -9 (Duxbury *et al.* 1999, fig. 12), although they are imbedded in levee deposits containing thin-bedded sands.

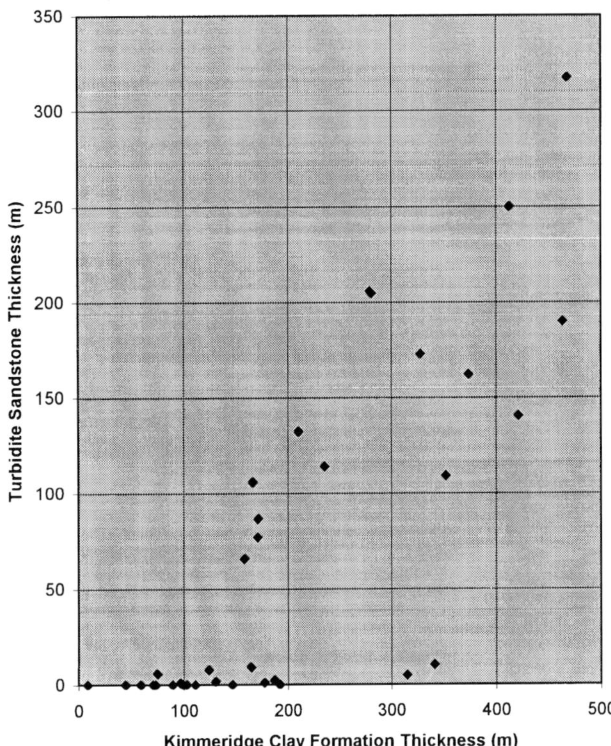

Fig. 9. Total thickness of Kimmeridge Clay Formation (Sequences UJ8.2a to LK4) vs submarine fan sand gross thickness in the Galley Fan and its surroundings.

The well-defined side boundaries of sand-rich channelized fans are conducive to the formation of combined stratigraphic–structural traps. The ponding of unconfined flows against topographical highs could lead to the formation of purely stratigraphical traps. In addition to geological modelling, seismic imaging is required for a recognition of such exploration prospects.

'Tectonically enhanced maximum flooding surfaces?'

Partington *et al.* (1993*a*) defined 'tectonically enhanced maximum flooding surfaces' (TEMFS) as 'three-dimensional reorganization events', which 'drown footwalls, switch off deposition of coarse clastics in both the basin centre and marginal areas, and lead to major reorganization of both the basinal and shelfal palaeogeographies'. The authors recognized the following TEMFSs in the North Sea:

'Eudoxus' [=UJ8.2b]; 'Fittoni' [=UJ11.1]; and 'Anguiformis' [=UJ13.1].

We consider this a useful concept to describe basin-restricted tectonic events but would differ on several specific observations: Partington *et al.*'s fig. 4 (1993*a*) shows four Tartan well logs intended to illustrate the Eudoxus TEMFS and the facies change between footwall and hanging wall deposition. However, the correlated horizon is the UJ9.2b MFS, and the wells are located on one fault block, without a synsedimentary fault intervening between them. The thinning from west to east of

Table 2. Age range of the Claymore and Galley mass flow sands

	Partington *et al.*	this paper
Claymore	UJ8.2b–UJ11.1	UJ9.1–UJ11.1
Galley	UJ11.1–UJ13.1	UJ9.1–UJ13.1

the Hot Sand (UJ8.2a to UJ8.2b interval) is caused by a transition from lower shoreface to offshore environment, while in the following sequences a gentle uplift of the eastern area causes a lowering of sedimentation rates, including a bypass by the 'Hot Lens B' and 'Hot Lens A' turbidite sands. The claim that 'the proposed TEMFSs constrain most, if not all, of the deep marine fan systems observed in the North Sea Late Jurassic' can only be confirmed for the Claymore Sands. Our datings of significant submarine fans compare (as in Table 2; sequence nomenclature standardized according to Fig. 2).

Thus, in the Galley fan, as well as in the Burns Sand Member (Richards *et al.* 1993) of the Inner Moray Firth, the UJ11.1 ('Fittoni') MFS lies within the fan sands.

In the study area, major tectonic reorganizations occurred:

(1) During sequence UJ5 (mid-Late Oxfordian), when Theta Graben rifting started and topographic reactivation triggered the sand supply forming the Piper Formation;
(2) During sequence UJ7 (Early Kimmeridgian), when the locus of Piper sand deposition shifted from the trend of the Piper–Rob Roy–Scott fields, to the localized fan-deltas and tidal pass systems of the 'Supra–Piper', or Six Sand–Hot Sand and their coarse equivalents on Block 14/20. A prominent flooding surface formed across the entire sedimentation area, while erosion began on the Halibut Horst and on small horst blocks on Block 14/20.
(3) Within sequences UJ9.1 to 9.2b (Early Volgian), when the Witch Ground Graben was initiated. This coincides with the onset of significant submarine fan activity.
(4) During the UJ 13.1 to 13.2 sequences, when submarine fan deposition ceased in Galley, in the Highlander Area and locally in the Inner Moray Firth. A North Sea wide facies change occurred in the UJ13.2 sequence, when a period of 'Hot Shale' facies lasting to the LK4 sequence began. This is a North Sea wide event, distinguished as the 'Mandal Formation' by Vollset & Doré (1984), and the 'Derwent Member' of the Kimmeridge Clay Formation plus a restricted 'Mandal Formation' by Price *et al.* (1993).

Conclusions

(1) The potential for subtle stratigraphic traps clearly exists in the OMF Basin, as multiple sand sources and multiple sand dispersal systems existed in probably every sequence. A range of depositional environments, from coastal plain to deep basinal, developed both in a vertical sense (due to continuing deepening of the basin during Humber Group deposition) and in a horizontal one (simultaneous occurrence of shore zone and basinal environments within the same sequence). Changes in the orientation of faulting affected the sand distribution more than the sand sourcing areas. Prograding and aggrading shore zone sands originally blanketed a large part of the OMF (Piper Fm) and appear thus of limited potential to form stratigraphic traps. However, the mass flow sands within the Kimmeridge Clay Formation are much more limited in their spatial distribution as a result of the existence of only a limited number of sourcing points, the confinement in leveed channels, and further confinement by seafloor topography which in turn was influenced by syn-sedimentary faulting. The complex pattern resulting from the interplay of all variables cannot be resolved from well control alone; seismic imaging is clearly required for successful further exploration.

(2) A detailed biostratigraphic and sequence stratigraphic framework is indispensable to this end. Interpretational errors can be introduced alone by the application of an inadequate framework. Previously published accounts of the sedimentary history propose a lesser number of transgressions, and as a result they unite separate highstand events. For example, the 'I-Shale' transgression of Harker *et al.* (1987, 1993) is now interpreted as the UJ5 highstand in the Piper Field, but as the UJ6b highstand in the Scott Field and as the UJ7 highstand in the Claymore Field. As the 'I-Shale' forms the base of the Piper Formation as defined by Harker *et al.* (1987), this formation is, against the intentions of the authors, rather diachronous (Fig. 2). Harker & Rieuf (1996) do not distinguish the UJ4 and UJ5 transgressions, and as a result they describe a 'glosense' (i.e. UJ4) transgression in a large area of the OMF, which is not supported by biostratigraphic evidence. In an early stage of this study the UJ9.1 and UJ9.2a sequences were not recognized which resulted in the hiatus between the shore-zone sands and the base of the Kimmeridge Clay Formation not being recognized on the Highlander–Piper Ridge.

(3) In this study, sequence stratigraphic methods and terminology were applied, although the Humber Group is essentially a syn-rift sediment, in which eustatic effects (if any) may be masked by tectonic effects. The working hypothesis used was that relative sea-level changes, regardless of their cause, should produce similar sedimentary responses. This is evident in shore zone environments, where transgressive and regressive successions can be easily identified and interpreted in terms of AST, TST and HST. Tectonically-induced local unconformities, however, contribute to the complexities of reservoir architecture. An example is the disappearance of the UJ6b TST to UJ7 AST interval between Wells 15/16b-22 and 20, cf. Fig. 8), while over-and underlying units seemed to be continuous.

(4) In basinal settings, the application of sequence stratigraphy to syn-rift turbiditic sections requires a widening of concepts. The mass flow deposits are not related to the collapse and erosion of constructional highstand shelf deposits during eustatic sea-level lowstands, but are related to rifting processes. Base-level lowering was primarily achieved by tectonic uplift (against a background of overall basin subsidence), while rifting continuously created accommodation space and slope of the sea-floor. The strong control on the basin morphology by fault activity resulted in a relative constancy in areal distribution and longevity of fan complexes. Sediment source areas and depositional shelves were often very restricted. In the Claymore area, fan deltas may have graded directly into fault apron fans with limited lateral extent. In the Galley systems, thick, sand-rich levee-complexes of up to 40 km down-current extension were sourced from relatively small outcrop areas. Strong topographic relief in both the outcrop area and along the flow paths of the channel/levee complexes is invoked to provide the required volumes of redeposited clastics and the energy to transport pebble- and even cobble-sized material as far south as South Galley.

This study was only made possible by building on the work of many geoscientists who have worked this area over the past 25 or so years. In particular the Texaco in-house biostratigraphic work of K.-H. Georgi and J. Lund (undertaken until 1988 at Deutsche Texaco AG, Wietze, Germany) deserves to be mentioned. D. O'Driscoll and N. Clark (Texaco) and two referees provided constructive criticism. We thank Amerada Hess Limited for permitting publication of presently unreleased well data, and the Texaco management for permission to publish this study.

The interpretations expressed in this article are the opinions of the authors. The regional synopsis was carried out by D. Kadolsky; methodical aspects of sequence stratigraphy and the evaluation of the Piper *s.l.* sedimentology (with focus on Blocks 14/20 and 15/16) by S. J. Johansen; biostratigraphic analyses and biozone identifications by S. Duxbury.

References

ANDREWS, I. J. & Brown, S. 1987. Stratigraphic evolution of the Jurassic, Moray Firth. *In*: BROOKS, J. & GLENNIE, K. (eds) *Petroleum Geology of North West Europe*. Graham & Trotman, London, 785–795.

——, LONG, D., RICHARDS, P. C., THOMSON, A. R., BROWN, S., CHESHER, J. A.and MCCORMAC, M. 1990. *United Kingdom Offshore Regional Report: the Geology of the Moray Firth*. British Geological Survey, HMSO, London, 1–96.

BOLDY, S. A. R. & BREALEY, S. 1990. Timing, nature and sedimentary result of Jurassic tectonism in the Outer Moray Firth. *In*: HARDMAN, R. F. P. & BROOKS, J. (eds) *Tectonic Events Responsible for Britain's Oil and Gas Reserves*. Geological Society, London, Special Publications, **55**, 259–279.

BOOTE, D. R. D. & GUSTAV, S. H. 1987. Evolving depositional systems within an active rift, Witch Ground Graben, North Sea. *In*: BROOKS, J. & GLENNIE, K. (eds) *Petroleum Geology of North West Europe*. Graham & Trotman, London, 819–833.

CARRUTHERS, A., MCKIE, T., PRICE, J., DYER, R., WILLIAMS, G. & WATSON, P. 1996. The application of sequence stratigraphy to the understanding of Late Jurassic turbidite plays in the Central North Sea, UKCS. *In*: HURST, A. *et al.* (eds) *Geology of the Humber Group: Central Graben and Moray Firth, UKCS*. Geological Society, London, Special Publications, **114**, 29–45.

CASEY, B. J., ROMANI, R. S. & SCHMITT, R. H. 1993. Appraisal geology of the Saltire Field, Witch Ground Graben, North Sea. *In*: PARKER, J. R. (ed.) *Petroleum Geology of Northwest Europe: Proceedings of the 4th Conference*. The Geological Society, London, 507–517.

CHERRY, S. T. J. 1993. The interaction of structure and sedimentary process controlling deposition of the Upper Jurassic Brae Formation Conglomerate, Block 16/17, North Sea. *In*: PARKER, J. R. (ed.) *Petroleum Geology of Northwest Europe: Proceedings of the 4th Conference*. The Geological Society, London, 387–400.

DAVID, M. J. 1996. History of hydrocarbon exploration in the Moray Firth. *In*: HURST, A. *et al.* (eds) *Geology of the Humber Group: Central Graben and Moray Firth, UKCS*. Geological Society, London, Special Publications, **114**, 47–80.

DAVIES, R. J., O'DONNELL, D., BENTHAM, P. N., GIBSON, J. P. C., CURRY, M. R. & DUNAY, R. E. 1999. The origin and genesis of major Jurassic unconformities within the triple junction area of the North Sea, UK. *In*: FLEET, A. J. & BOLDY, S. A. R. (eds) *Petroleum Geology of Northwest Europe. Proceedings of the 5th Conference*. Geological Society, London, 117–131.

——, STEPHEN, K. J. & UNDERHILL, J. R. 1996. A re-evaluation of Middle and Upper Jurassic stratigraphy and the flooding history of the Moray Firth Rift System, North Sea. *In*: HURST, A. *et al.* (eds) *Geology of the Humber Group: Central Graben and Moray Firth, UKCS*. Geological Society, London, Special Publications, **114,** 81–108.

DUXBURY, S., KADOLSKY, D. & JOHANSEN, S. 1999. Sequence stratigraphic subdivision of the Humber Group in the Outer Moray Firth Area (UKCS, North Sea). *In*: JONES, R. & SIMMONS, M. (eds) *Biostratigraphy in Production and Development Geology*. Geological Society, London, Special Publications, **152**.

GALLOWAY, W. E. 1989. Genetic stratigraphic sequences in basin analysis I: architecture and genesis of flooding surface bounded depositional units. *American Association of Petroleum Geologists Bulletin*, **73**, 125–142.

HALLSWORTH, C., MORTON, A. C. & DORE, G. 1996. Contrasting mineralogy of Upper Jurassic sandstones in the Outer Moray Firth, North Sea: implications for the evolution of sediment dispersal patterns. *In*: HURST, A. *et al.* (eds) *Geology of the Humber Group: Central Graben and Moray Firth, UKCS*. Geological Society, London, Special Publications, **114**, 131–144.

HARKER, S. D. & RIEUF, M. 1996. Genetic stratigraphy and sandstone distribution of the Moray Firth Humber Group (Upper Jurassic). *In*: HURST, A. *et al.* (eds) *Geology of the Humber Group: Central Graben and Moray Firth, UKCS*. Geological Society, London, Special Publications, **114**, 109–130.

——, GUSTAV, S. H. & RILEY, L. A. 1987. Triassic to Cenomanian stratigraphy of the Witch Ground Graben. *In*: BROOKS, J. & GLENNIE, K. (eds) *Petroleum Geology of Northwest Europe*. Graham & Trotman, London, 809–818.

——, GREEN, S. C. H. & ROMANI, R. S. 1991. The Claymore Field, Block 14/19, UK North Sea. *In*:, ABBOTTS, I. L. (ed.) *United Kingdom Oil and Gas Fields, 25 Years Commemorative Volume*. Geological Society, London, Memoirs, **14**, 269–278.

——, MANTEL, K. A., MORTON, D. J. & RILEY, L. A. 1993. The stratigraphy of Oxfordian–Kimmeridgian (Late Jurassic) reservoir sandstones in the Witch Ground Graben, United Kingdom North Sea. *American Association of Petroleum Geologists Bulletin*, **77**(10), 1693–1709.

HIBBERT, M. J. & MACKERTICH, D. S. 1993. The structural evolution of the eastern end of the Halibut Horst, Block 15/21, Outer Moray Firth, UK North Sea. *In*: PARKER, J. R. (ed.) *Petroleum Geology of Northwest Europe: Proceedings of the 4th Conference*. The Geological Society, London, 1179–1188.

HOLLAND, C. H. *et al.* 1978. *A Guide to Stratigraphical Procedure*. Geological Society of London Special Report, **11**, 1–18.

MAHER, C. E. & HARKER, S. D. 1987. Claymore oil field. *In*: BROOKS, J. & GLENNIE, K. (eds) *Petroleum Geology of North West Europe*. Graham & Trotman, London, 835–845.

MCCANTS, C. Y. & BURLEY, S. 1996, Reservoir architecture and diagenesis in downthrown fault block plays: the Lowlander Prospect of Block 14/20, Witch Ground Graben, Outer Moray Firth, UK North Sea. *In*: HURST, A. *et al.* (eds) *Geology of the Humber Group: Central Graben and Moray Firth, UKCS*. Geological Society, London, Special Publications, **114**, 251–285.

O'DRISCOLL, D., HINDLE, A. D. & LONG, D. C. 1990. The structural controls on Upper Jurassic and Lower Cretaceous reservoir sandstones in the Witch Ground Graben, UK North Sea. *In*: HARDMAN, R. F. P. & BROOKS, J. (eds) *Tectonic Events Responsible for Britain's Oil and Gas Reserves*. Geological Society, London, Special Publications, **55**, 299–323.

PARTINGTON, M. A., MITCHENER, B. C., MILTON, N. J. & FRASER, A. J. 1993*a*. Genetic sequence stratigraphy for the North Sea Late Jurassic and Early Cretaceous: distribution and prediction of Kimmeridgian–Late Ryazanian reservoirs in the North Sea and adjacent areas. *In*: PARKER, J. R. (ed.) *Petroleum Geology of Northwest Europe: Proceedings of the 4th Conference*. The Geological Society, London, 347–370.

——, COPESTAKE, P., MITCHENER, B. C. & UNDERHILL, J. R. 1993*b*. Biostratigraphic calibration of genetic stratigraphic sequences in the Jurassic–lowermost Cretaceous (Hettangian to Ryazanian) of the North Sea and adjacent areas. *In*: PARKER, J. R. (ed.) *Petroleum Geology of Northwest Europe: Proceedings of the 4th Conference*. The Geological Society, London, 371–386.

PRICE, J., DYER, R., GOODALL, I., MCKIE, T., WATSON, P. & WILLIAMS, G. 1993. Effective stratigraphical subdivision of the Humber Group and the Late Jurassic evolution of the UK Central Graben. *In*: PARKER, J. R. (ed.) *Petroleum Geology of Northwest Europe: Proceedings of the 4th Conference*. The Geological Society, London, 443–458.

RATTEY, R. P. & HAYWARD, A. P. 1993. Sequence stratigraphy of a failed rift system: the Middle Jurassic to Early Cretaceous basin evolution of the Central and Northern North Sea. *In*: PARKER, J. R. (ed.) *Petroleum Geology of Northwest Europe: Proceedings of the 4th Conference*. The Geological Society, London, 215–249.

RICHARDS, P. C., LOTT, G. K., JOHNSON, H., KNOX, R. W. O'B. & RIDING, J. B. 1993. *Lithostratigraphic nomenclature of the U.K. North Sea. 3. Jurassic of the Central and Northern North Sea*. British Geological Survey and UKOOA, Keyworth, Nottingham.

SMITH, K. & RITCHIE, J. D. 1993. Jurassic volcanic centres in the Central North Sea. *In*: PARKER, J. R. (ed.) *Petroleum Geology of Northwest Europe: Proceedings of the 4th Conference*. The Geological Society, London, 519–517.

STEPHEN, K. J. & DAVIES, R. J. 1998. Documentation of Jurassic sedimentary cycles from the Moray Firth Basin, UK North Sea. *In*: GRACIANSKY, P. C. DE, HARDENBOL, J., JACQUIN, T., FARLEY, M. & VAIL, P. R. (eds) *Mesozoic–Cenozoic Sequence Stratigraphy of European Basins*. SEPM Special Publications, **60**, 485–510.

SYDOW, J. & ROBERTS, H. H. 1994. Stratigraphic framework of a late Pleistocene shelf-edge delta, northeast Gulf of Mexico. *American Association of Petroleum Geologists Bulletin*, **78**, 1276–1312.

TURNER, C. C., COHEN, J. M., CONNELL, E. R. & COOPER, D. M. 1987. A depositional model for the South Brae oilfield. *In*: BROOKS, J. & GLENNIE, K. (eds) *Petroleum Geology of North West Europe*. Graham & Trotman, London, 853–864.

——, RICHARDS, P. C., SWALLOW, J. L. & GRIMSHAW, S. P. 1984. Upper Jurassic sedimentary facies in the Central Outer Moray Firth Basin, North Sea. *Marine and Petroleum Geology*, **1**, 105–117.

VAIL, P. R., MITCHUM, R. M. JR & THOMPSON, S. III 1977*a*. Seismic stratigraphy and global changes of sea level, part 3: relative changes of sea level from coastal onlap. *In*: *Seismic Stratigraphy – Applications to Hydrocarbon Exploration*. American Association of Petroleum Geologists Memoirs, **26**, 63–81.

——, —— & ——1977*b*. Seismic stratigraphy and global changes of sea level, part 4: global cycles of relative changes of sea level. *In*: PAYTON, C. E. (eds) *Seismic Stratigraphy – Applications to Hydrocarbon Exploration*. American Association of Petroleum Geologists Memoirs, **26**, 83–97.

VAN WAGONER, J. C. 1991. High-frequency sequence stratigraphy and facies architecture of the Sego Sandstone in the Book Cliffs of western Colorado and Eastern Utah. *In*: VAN WAGONER, J. C., JONES, C. R., TAYLOR, D. R. *et al.* (eds) *Sequence Stratigraphy Applications to Shelf Sandstone Reservoirs – AAPG Field Conference Guidebook*. American Association of Petroleum Geologists.

——, MITCHUM, R. M., CAMPION, K. M. & RAHMANIAN, V. D. 1990. Siliciclastic sequence stratigraphy in well logs, cores, and outcrops. *In*: *Methods in Exploration Series*, **7**. The American Association of Petroleum Geologists.

VOLLSET, J. & DORÉ, A. G. 1984. A revised Triassic and Jurassic lithostratigraphic nomenclature for the Norwegian North Sea. *NPD Bulletin*, **3**, Norwegian Petroleum Directorate, Stavanger, 1–53.

WADDAMS, P. & CLARK, N. M. 1991, The Petronella Field, Block 14/20b, UK North Sea. *In*: ABBOTTS, I. L. (ed.) *United Kingdon Oil and Gas Fields, 25 Years Commemorative Volume*. Geological Society, London, Memoirs, **14**, 353–360.

WHITEHEAD, M. & PINNOCK, S. J. 1991. The Highlander Field, Block 14/20b, UK North Sea. *In*: ABBOTTS, I. L. (ed.) *United Kingdom Oil and Gas Fields, 25 Years Commemorative Volume*. Geological Society, London, Memoirs, **14**, 323–329.

Downthrown closures of the Outer Moray Firth

B. A. MOSELEY

Amerada Hess Limited, 33 Grosvenor Place, London SW1X 7HY, UK
(e-mail: bryan.moseley@hess.com)

Abstract: In the Outer Moray Firth area of the UK Continental Shelf, some 3×10^9 BBL of recoverable hydrocarbons have been discovered. The reservoir rocks are primarily shallow marine (Piper) and deep marine (Claymore) sands of Late Jurassic age, with subordinate amounts of hydrocarbons contained in Lower Cretaceous sandstones. The major fields include Piper, Scott, Claymore and Tartan. Whilst these are principally classical tilted fault block footwall traps, all except Piper have elements of downthrown, hanging wall trapping that add significantly to the reserve base. Several other fields and discoveries, including Scapa, Saltire, Perth, and Lowlander are entirely dependent upon downthrown fault closure.

A number of exploration wells drilled on valid downthrown terraces have, however, proved dry, apparently a result of lateral fault seal failure. An examination of the success and failure cases suggests that the critical factors controlling the trap integrity in this area are the geology and geometry of the sediments in the footwall, the timing of fault movement and the nature of the depositional system in the hanging wall. These appear to be more important than the more commonly used shale smear or gouge criteria. Consideration of these factors has allowed the construction of a ranking system for downthrown Mesozoic prospects.

The Outer Moray Firth (OMF) is one of the United Kingdom's most prolific hydrocarbon producing areas (Fig. 1). Although commercial accumulations are found in horizons which range in age from the Devonian to the Eocene, by far the greater portion of the reserves occur in Upper Jurassic and Lower Cretaceous sandstones (David 1996). Major producing fields include Piper, Claymore, Tartan and Scott, which have cumulative reserves in excess of 2×10^6 BBL. Smaller fields include Ivanhoe/Rob Roy, Iona (formerly South Piper), Saltire and Chanter, and discoveries awaiting development include Lowlander and Perth. The fields are located both in upthrown traps on the graben flanks and in downthrown traps towards

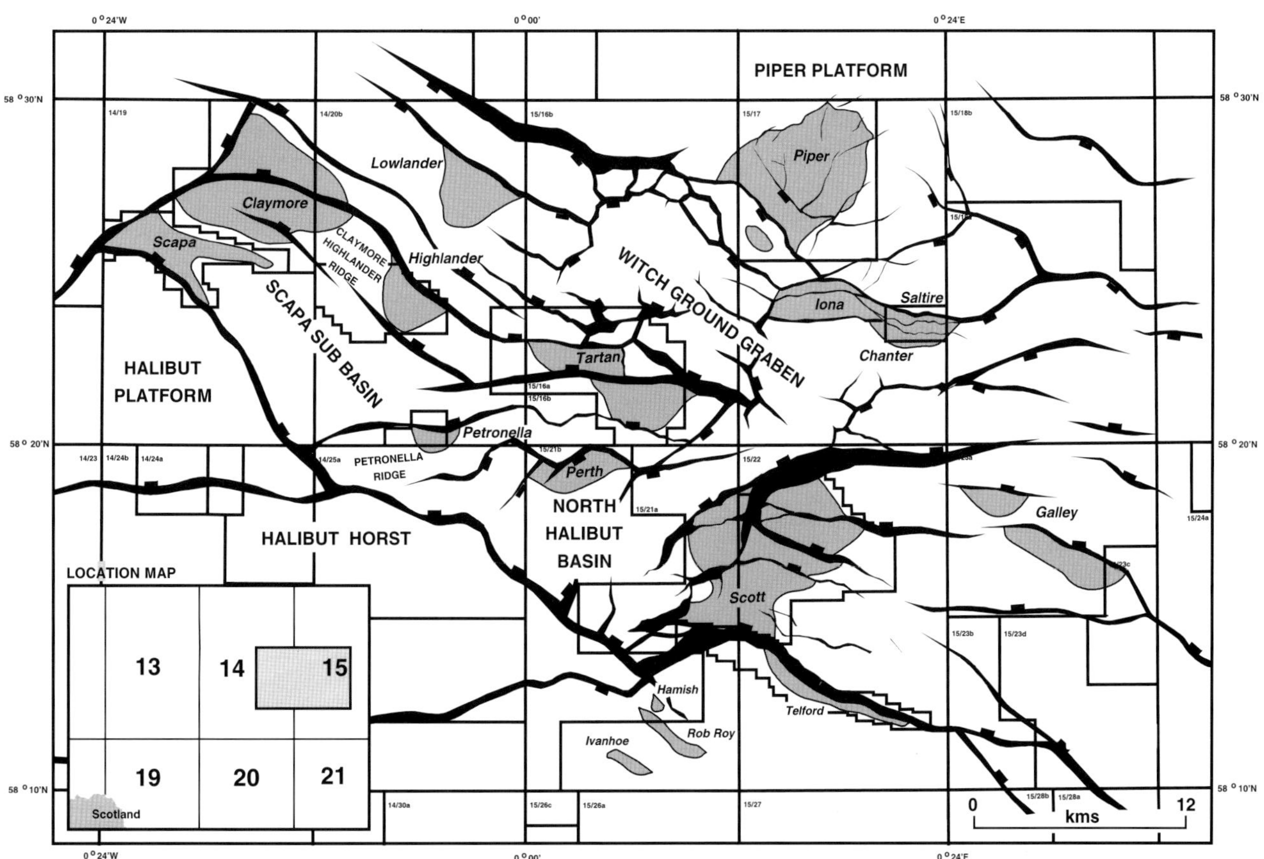

Fig. 1. Simplified structural elements and principal oil fields, Outer Moray Firth area.

MOSELEY, B. A. 1999. Downthrown closures of the Outer Moray Firth. *In*: FLEET, A. J. & BOLDY, S. A. R. (eds) *Petroleum Geology of Northwest Europe: Proceedings of the 5th Conference*, 861–878.

the graben axes (Fig. 1). An element of downthrown closure is important in many of the above, ranging from entirely downthrown traps (e.g. Chanter, Lowlander) to incremental reserves from a downthrown element (e.g. Tartan, Scott).

A review published after the first round of discoveries suggested that the success rate for downthrown closures was similar to that for upthrown closures, and that in general faults with a throw of greater than 2500 ft were likely to seal (Hindle 1989). Faults of substantially less throw have, however, subsequently proved to be sealing (see 'Scott Area', this paper), but a number of exploration wells since drilled on fault terraces downthrown by similar amounts have proved dry. Although other reasons such as lack of source or poor quality reservoir are the probable causes for some disappointments, several can clearly be assigned to trap failure. This paper attempts to address the issues of trap integrity rather than those of reservoir quality and sourcing, and, by comparing success and failure cases in the OMF, rationalize the risks associated with different trap geometries.

Reservoir geology

In the broadest terms, the Upper Jurassic and Lower Cretaceous reservoirs of the OMF can be divided between pre-rift deltaic and shallow marine deposits of the Piper (*sensu lato*) Formation and syn- to post-rift deeper marine gravity flow deposits of the Claymore and Galley Members of the Kimmeridge Clay Formation, and the Scapa Member of the Valhall Formation (Fig. 2). Following the period of Middle Jurassic volcanic activity which saw the deposition of the Rattray Formation (Smith & Ritchie 1993), active faulting on SSW–NNE trends, probably associated with post-volcanic subsidence (Underhill & Partington 1993), controlled Piper deposition and preservation from the mid Oxfordian. Unless otherwise stated, the term 'Piper' is used in this paper in its broadest sense, namely to include all the pre-rift deltaic and shallow marine sands deposited from the mid Oxfordian to the late Kimmeridgian. The Witch Ground Graben was formed during the major rifting episode which commenced in the late Kimmeridgian and continued into the Volgian, concurrent with the *eudoxus* transgression. The dominant fault orientation switched to NW–SE (Boldy & Brealey 1990). Erosion of fault block crests resulted in the deposition of the Claymore, Galley and Scapa Members in the graben axes. Apart, therefore, from the eroded crests the Piper can be considered for exploration purposes as a sheet sand deposit. The gravity flow deposits, however, show a strong structural control on their deposition (Casey *et al.* 1993).

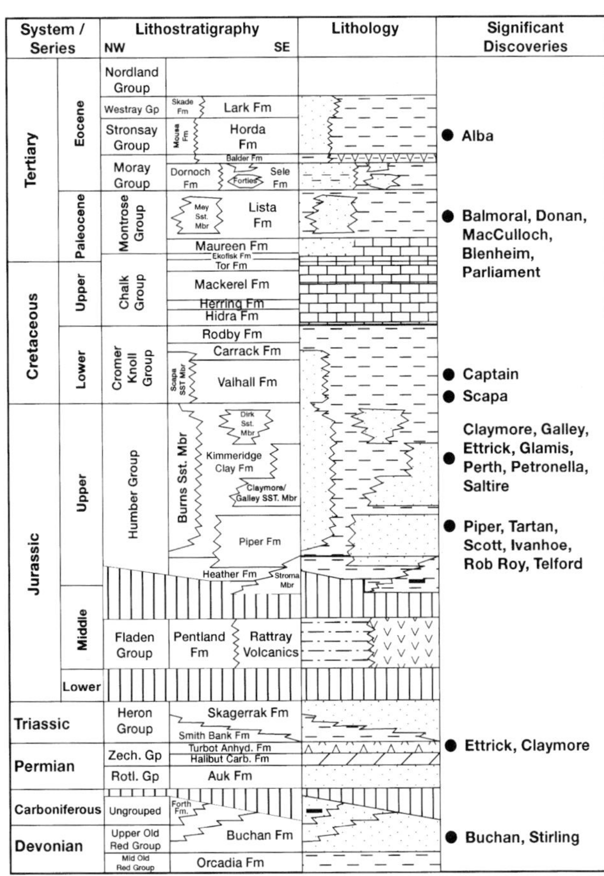

Fig. 2. Simplified stratigraphic column, Outer Moray Firth area (after David 1996).

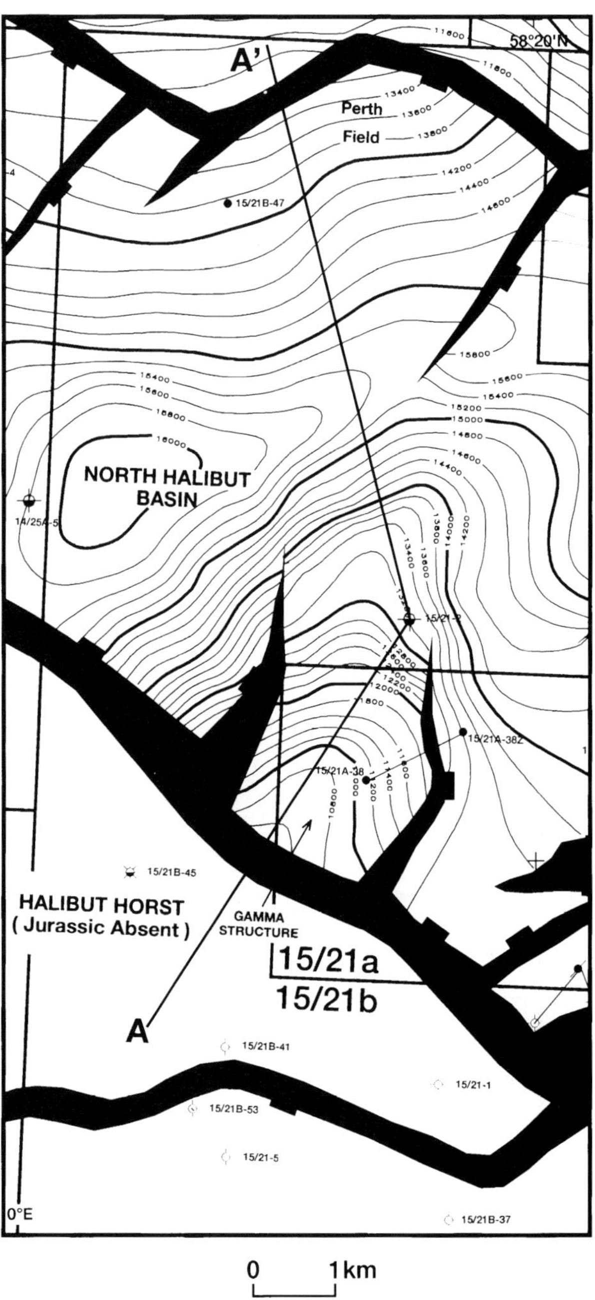

Fig. 3. North Halibut Basin: simplified near Top Piper depth structure map.

Fault seals

A number of fault seal mechanisms have been proposed by various authors. These include the formation of a clay shear zone along the fault plane (Weber *et al.* 1978) which can be defined in terms of smear potential, gouge ratio and smear factor (Yielding *et al.* 1997); diagenesis (McCants & Burley 1996); and cataclasis (Knipe 1992). With the possible exception of the various clay smear ratios, however, the prediction of the probability of a particular fault sealing has been notably problematic. Regardless of the mechanism of the seal, the effects can be considered in terms of seal or breach across the fault plane (cross-fault seal), and seal or breach up the fault plane (fault plane seal).

Outer Moray Firth: case studies

North Halibut Basin (Block 15/21)

The North Halibut Basin is an east–west trending half-graben (Figs 1 & 3), with its southern margin formed by a large down-to-the-north fault against the Halibut Horst, and its northern margin dipping down from the Petronella–Tartan Ridge. The graben fill dates from the Late Kimmeridgian to the Early Cretaceous, and shows classic growth sequences in the south which wedge out to the north and onlap the ridge (Fig. 4). The syn-rift Upper Jurassic interval comprises organic-rich claystones of the Kimmeridge Clay Formation (currently at peak oil maturity) with interbedded sandstones. These latter were largely derived from the Halibut Horst, and evidence from recent exploration drilling has given unequivocal evidence of its unroofing during the Late Jurassic. A series of conglomeratic fans have been penetrated along the northern margin of both the Halibut Horst and the Halibut Platform to the northwest by (among others) Wells 14/19-26, -27 and 14/24a-2. Finer-grained sand flows moved further out into the basin, pinching out on its dip slope and infilling the remnant rift topography. The post-early Ryazanian to latest Hauterivian Lower Cretaceous sequence shows a continuation of the same sedimentation pattern, albeit in a mixed carbonate–clastic system. Where tightly cemented by reprecipitated carbonate and undisturbed by later fault movement, the conglomerates can form an effective lateral seal to a downthrown trap.

The Perth Field, discovered by Well 15/21b-47 in 1992, is downthrown from the northern margin of the basin (Fig. 3). The reservoir comprises intra-Kimmeridge Clay marine gravity flow sands of latest Kimmeridgian to middle Volgian age. The field is dip closed to the south, with an east–west rollover at top reservoir level providing both closure and a focus for oil migration. Subtle fault-controlled submarine topography appears to have diverted the sand flows to the northeast, and an element of stratigraphic trapping is therefore important to the west. The northern limit appears to be either pinchout before, or onlap against, a southerly dipping fault stepping down from the Petronella–Tartan Ridge (Figs 3 & 4). An oil column of approximately 1000 ft has been proven by Well 15/21b-47 and the subsequent sidetrack, 15/21b-47Z.

On the southern flank of the basin a large northerly plunging inversion anticline (the Gamma Structure) which abuts the Halibut Horst has been penetrated by two wells, 15/21-2 and 15/21a-38 (Fig. 3). Well 15/21-2 was drilled in 1975 in a location 3 km north of the horst and penetrated a thick intra-Kimmeridge Clay sandstone sequence of late Kimmeridgian–mid/late Volgian age. Although shows were recorded through much of the interval, wireline log-derived oil saturations were in the order of 20–40%. It appears that the shows represent palaeocolumns which have leaked, probably as a result of late movement on the fault separating the structure from the

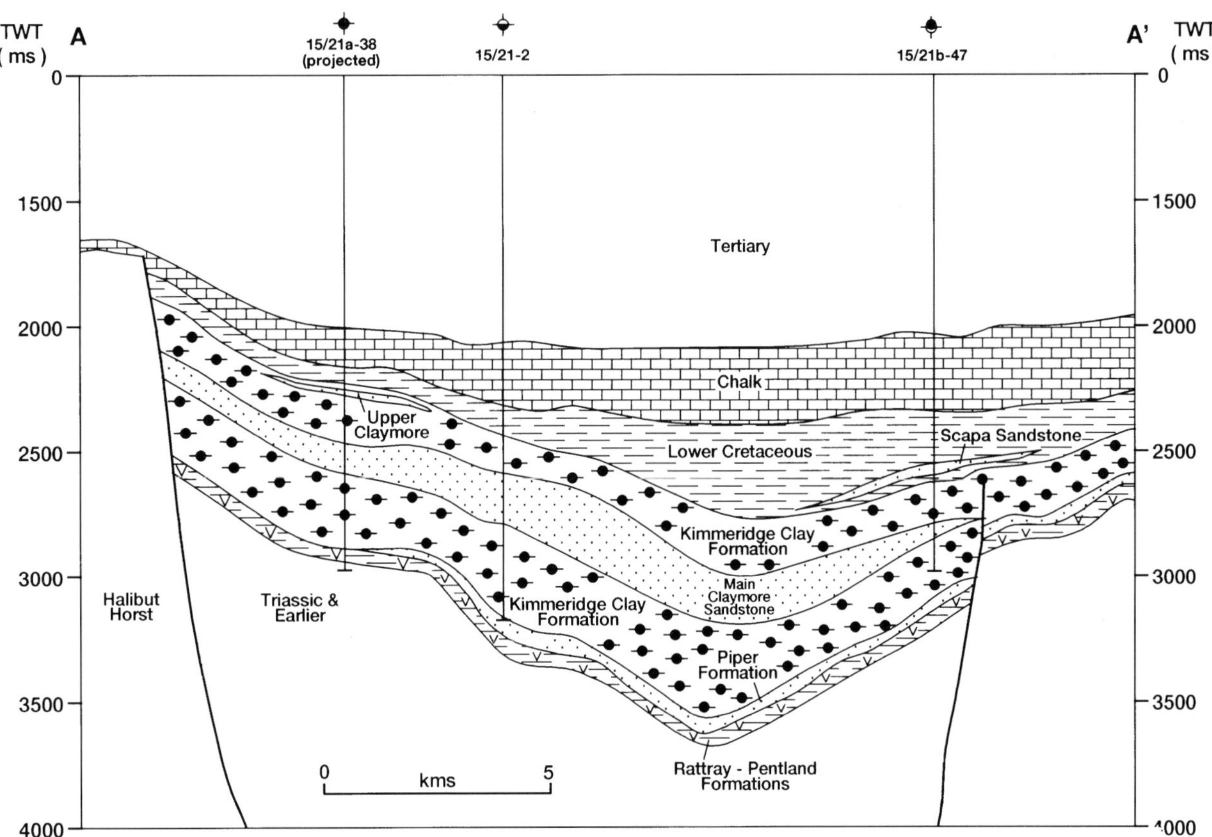

Fig. 4. North Halibut Basin: geoseismic section A–A′.

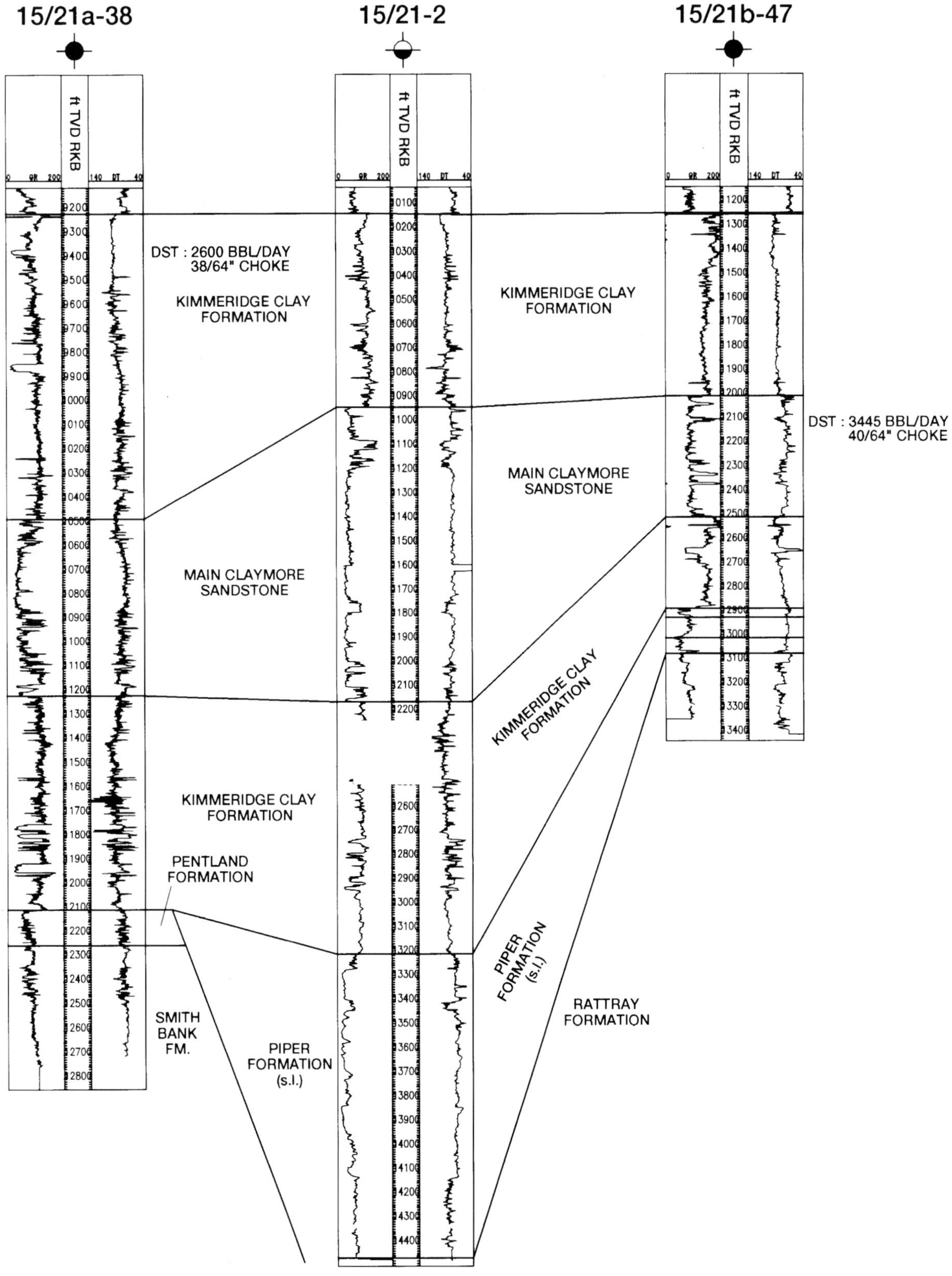

Fig. 5. North Halibut Basin: lithostratigraphic well correlation.

Halibut Horst. Well 14/24a-3 penetrated the Carboniferous core of the horst at −4864 ft beneath a 104 ft veneer of Chalk. Modern 3D seismic data confirm that the horst has been moving until at least the early Eocene (Hibbert & Mackertich 1993), and the form of the horst is reflected by present-day bathymetry. The situation can be contrasted with the downthrown lateral (southwestern) seal to the Scapa Field (McGann *et al.* 1991), against the relatively stable Halibut Platform which is a Devonian fault block, itself downthrown to the north of the horst proper. Additionally, the high carbonate content of the

Lower Cretaceous gravity flow system has created a 500 m wide halo of tightly cemented fault-scarp conglomerates which enhance the seal (Harker & Chermak 1992).

Well 15/21a-38 (and 38Z) was drilled into the flank of the anticline south-southeast of 15/21-2. Again a thick water-bearing 'Main Claymore' sand package was penetrated within the Kimmeridge Clay, correlative in age with that encountered by 15/21-2. A 20 ft oil-bearing unit was, however, found above the Main Claymore, and was tested at 2660 BOPD on a 38/64″ choke (Fig. 5). The probable explanation is that the 'Main' unit is in communication with the similar sands of 15/21-2 and hydrocarbons have migrated up into the Tertiary via the horst bounding fault (indicating a fault plane breach) and then dispersed, whereas the oil in the upper sand is stratigraphically trapped. This is a pattern seen elsewhere in the area (see Well 15/16b-18, below). A small Eocene discovery above the horst was made by Well 15/21b-45 (Fig. 3).

The western part of the Halibut Horst in Block 15/21 is formed by a Forth Formation succession of unknown but potentially great thickness, consisting of interbedded sandstones, claystones and coals of Visean to Namurian age. Although of poor reservoir quality, the sandstones have sufficient porosity and permeability to act as an effective leakage route in the case of a cross-fault breach (Fig. 6). The combination of downthrown pre-rift (Piper) sandstone reservoir juxtaposed against Carboniferous in the footwall forms a high risk target, but a sand-prone syn-rift section is also potentially high risk if combined with late fault movement adjacent to the sand input point.

The North Halibut Graben therefore contains both success and failure cases for syn-rift reservoirs, the former illustrated by the onlap or pinch-out trap of the Perth Field and the stratigraphic trap of the 'Upper' Claymore in well 15/21a-38,

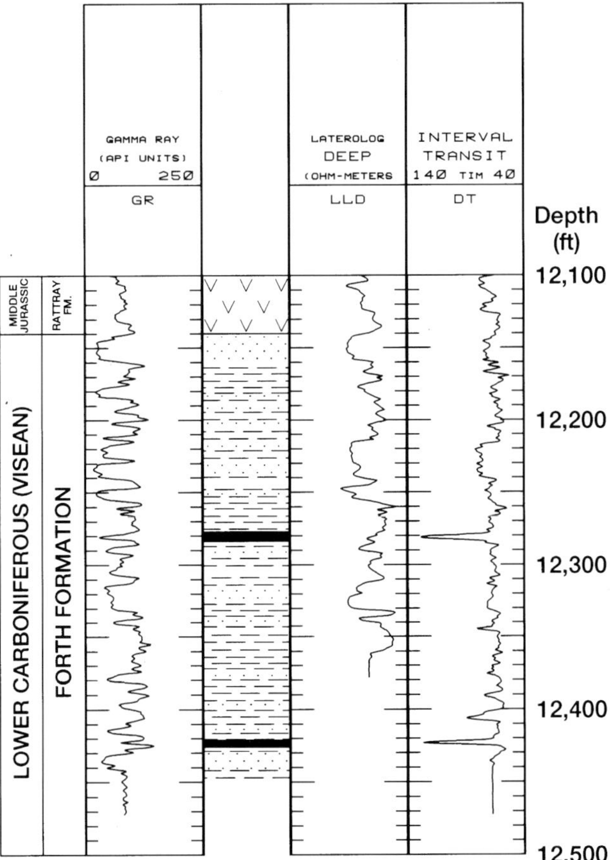

Fig. 6. North Halibut Basin: typical Carboniferous lithology and wireline log section, Well 15/21a-7.

and the latter by the lateral seal failure of the 'Main' Claymore Gamma Structure against the Halibut Horst bounding fault.

South Piper area (Block 15/17)

The Chanter, Saltire and Iona fields lie to the south of the Piper Field (Fig. 7). They contain both pre-rift and syn-rift reservoirs, and consist of blocks faulted down from the Piper Platform. Published data (Schmitt 1991; Casey *et al.* 1993) indicate that these fields are primarily simple juxtaposition traps, in which the reservoir horizons are downthrown against impermeable Middle Jurassic volcanics or Triassic claystones. Although characterized by complex internal faulting, the published 2D sections suggest that the ultimate original oil–water contact (OOWC) in each block was controlled by the juxtaposition of hanging wall reservoir against porous and permeable (Zechstein or Carboniferous) units in the footwall (Fig. 8). This is at the point where a shale smear mechanism might be expected to be at its most effective, suggesting that this is not an important seal mechanism, and that a cross-fault breach occurs as soon as porous lithologies are juxtaposed by the major terrace extensional faults. A probable transfer fault within the Chanter Field which juxtaposes Piper sand against Piper sand does separate differing oil–water contacts (Casey *et al.* 1993).

Notable partial successes and failures include Piper Field Block III; the terrace to the southeast of Piper Field; and the terrace penetrated by Well 15/16b-18. Piper Field Block III is a downthrown terrace located to the southwest of the Piper platform (Fig. 7). Although in areal terms it had the potential to contain large reserves had its bounding faults been sealing, when drilled by Well 15/17-7 (Fig. 9) the OOWC was found to be limited to the area of a four-way dip closure on the terrace (Schmitt & Gordon 1991). Similarly, the terrace separating Piper Field from Saltire Field was found to be dry when penetrated by Wells 15/17-19 and -20. Again this indicates a juxtaposition failure and lack of effective cross-fault seal (Figs 7 & 8).

Well 15/16b-18 was drilled by Texaco in 1988 on a terrace downthrown to the southwest of the Piper Platform and targeted both Galley and Piper sands. No independent four-way dip closure was present on the terrace, and the prospect therefore relied on cross-fault seal for success (Figs 7 & 10). The well found a Piper section immediately underlying a 'Lower' Galley section of mid to late Volgian age which was water bearing, but also a thin (25 ft) oil-bearing 'Upper' Galley section of late Volgian to early Ryazanian age (Fig. 11). RFT data indicate that the Piper and 'Lower' Galley units are acting as one pressure system and have been depleted, probably by production from the Piper Field. This implies pressure connection between the downthrown and upthrown Piper aquifers, probably through the footwall Carboniferous against which the water bearing sections are juxtaposed. No shows were seen, implying that fault seals were and always have been ineffective. Pressure data in the 'Upper' Galley, however, show this to be overpressured, implying a stratigraphic seal with no connection to the Piper aquifer (Fig. 12). The position is very similar to that encountered by 15/21a-38 (see earlier).

The South Piper area demonstrates the efficacy of downthrown juxtaposition traps for Upper Jurassic reservoirs, but also the high risks involved in reliance on cross-fault seals to close a prospect in which potential reservoir units are juxtaposed across major extensional faults.

Tartan area (Block 15/16)

The Tartan Field consists of two fault blocks, South Tartan (upthrown) and North Tartan (downthrown, Fig. 13). The reservoir is largely (pre-rift) Piper sands, but the distinctive

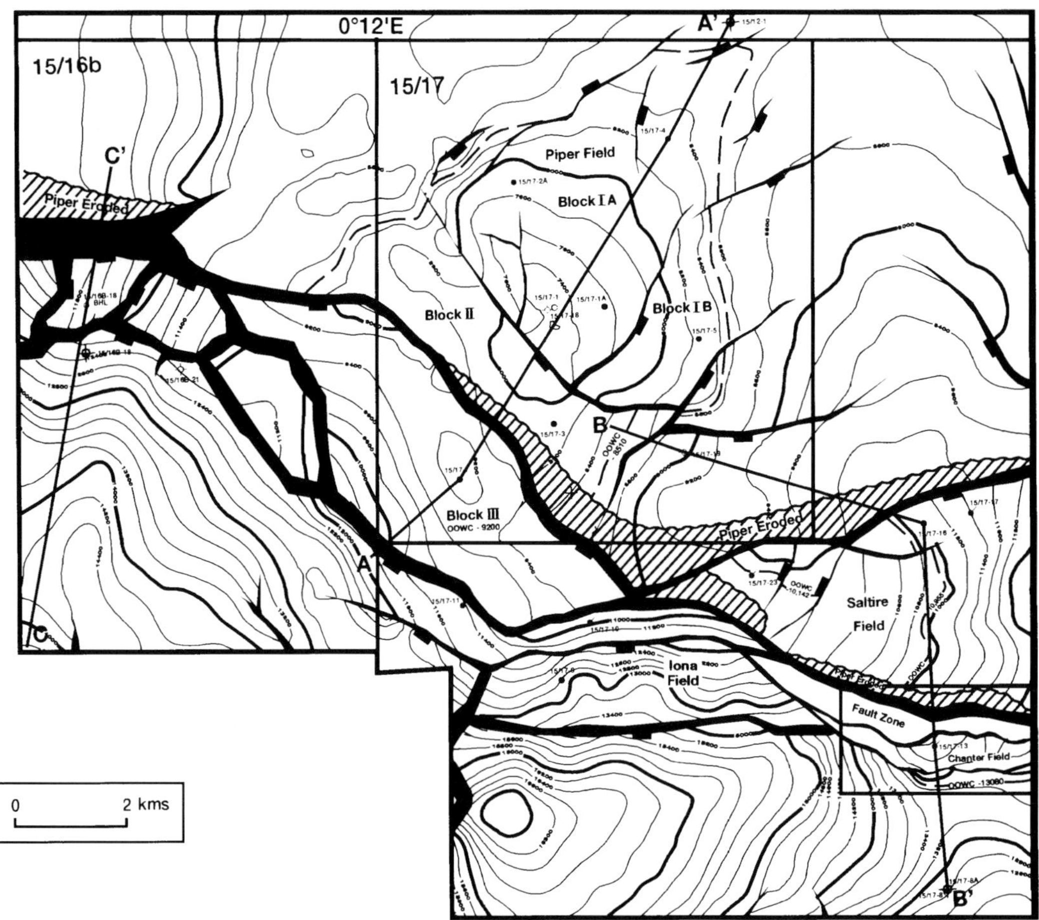

Fig. 7. Piper area: simplified near Top Piper depth structure map (after Schmitt 1991; Schmitt & Gordon 1991; Casey *et al.* 1993).

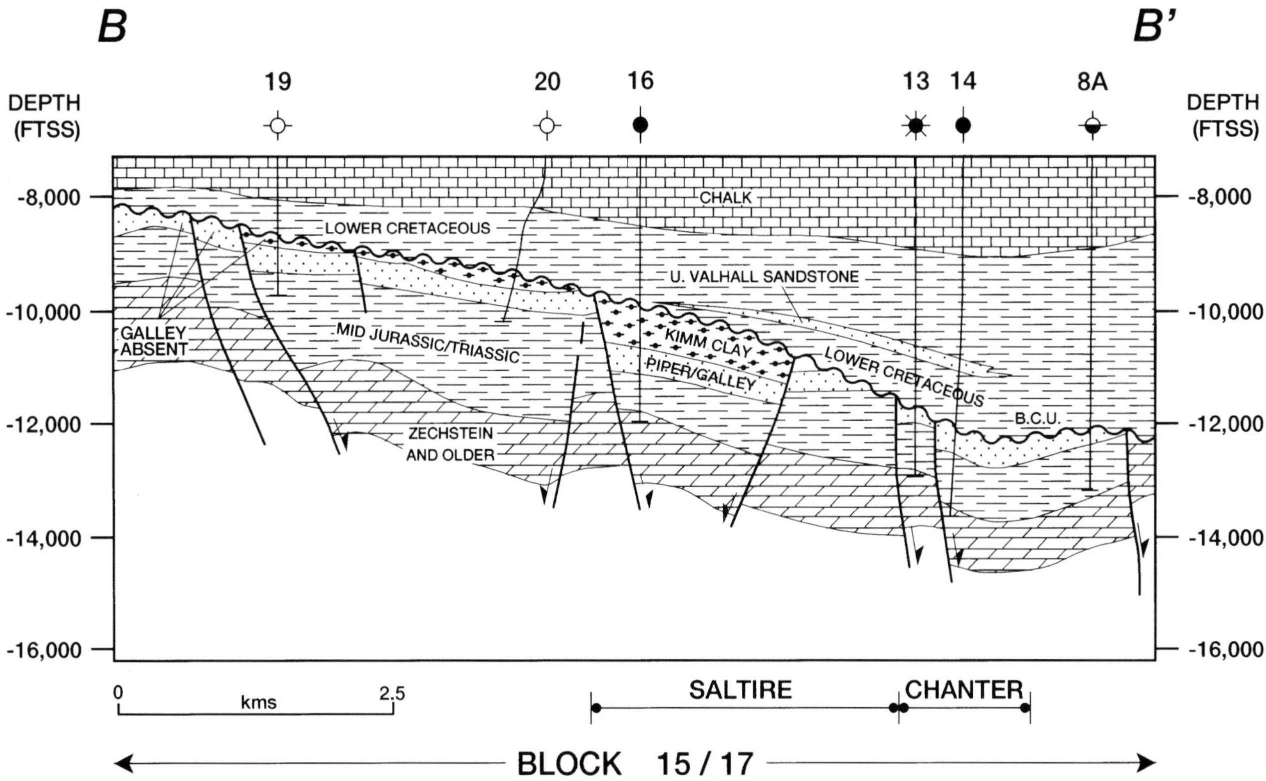

Fig. 8. Piper area: geoseismic section B–B′ from Piper Field to Chanter Field (after Casey *et al.* 1993).

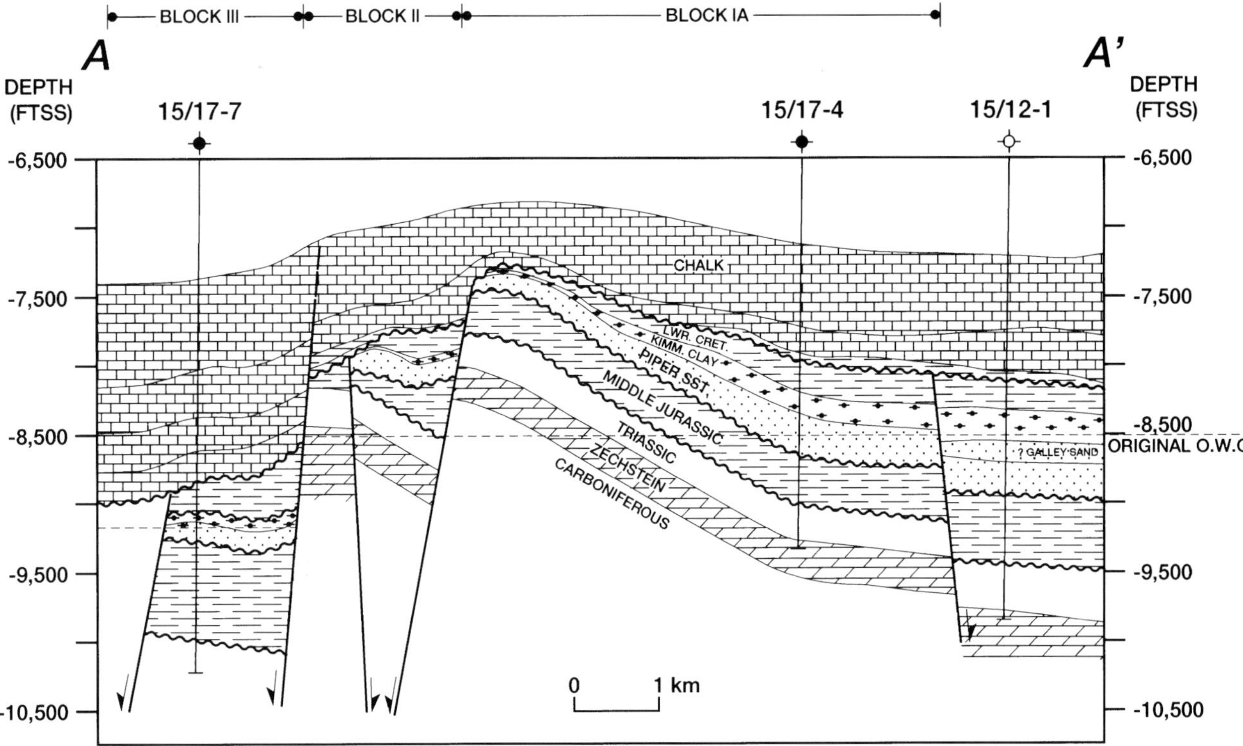

Fig. 9. Piper area: geoseismic section A–A′ (after Schmitt & Gordon 1991).

'Hot Sand' and 'Hot Lens' reservoir units characteristic of the Tartan area (Coward *et al.* 1991) mark early submarine gravity flow deposition in conditions of increasing anoxia.

Whilst the structure of the upthrown block is that of a conventional rotated fault block, the downthrown block lies in an area of poor quality seismic, particularly at its western end. It is clear, however, that a significant element of downthrown trapping exists, in excess of any four-way dip closure on the terrace. The geometry of the fault blocks is notable, with a marked southerly dip from North Tartan into the South Tartan bounding fault, complemented by southerly dip on the South Tartan block (Fig. 14).

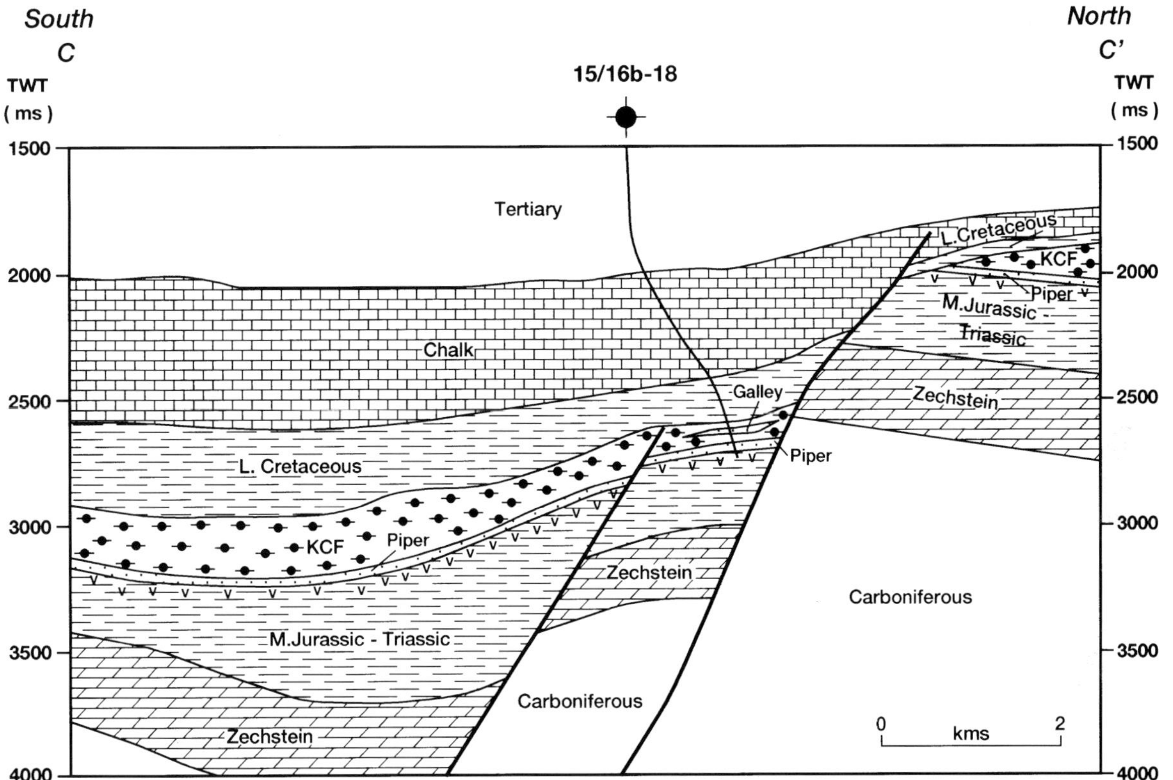

Fig. 10. Piper area: geoseismic section C–C′.

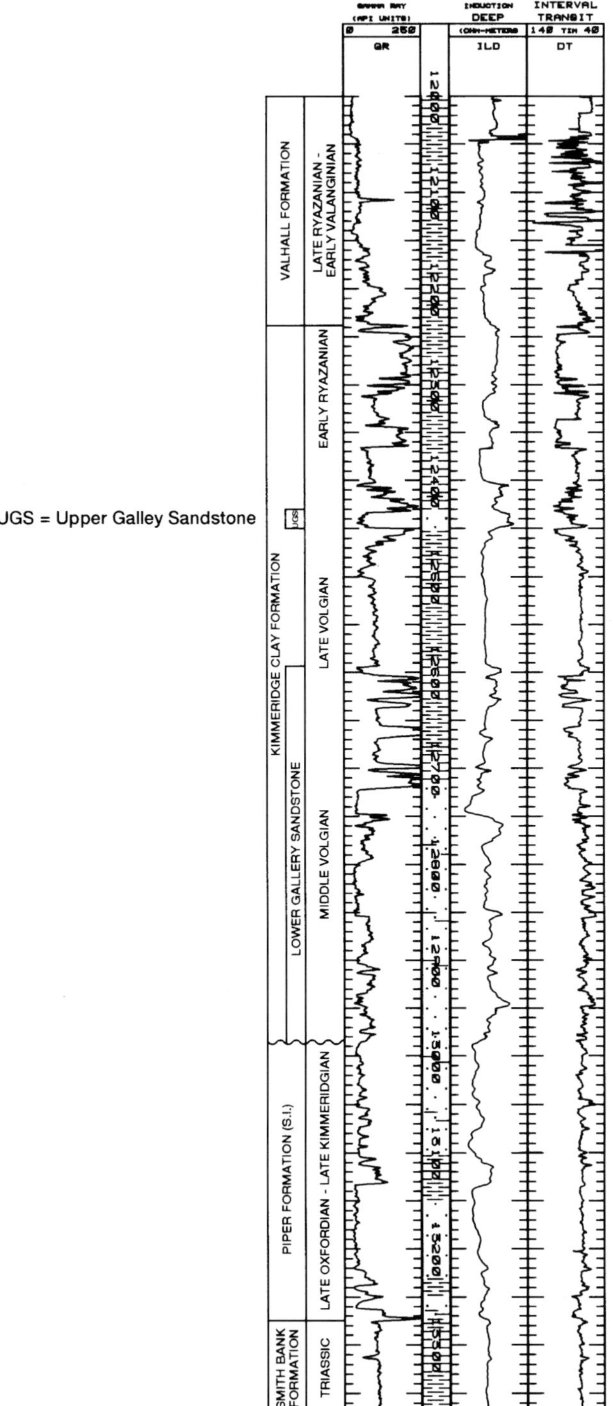

Fig. 11. Piper area: Well 15/16b-18 wireline log.

Well 15/21b-20 was drilled in 1991 to test a separate downthrown closure, which relied on cross-fault seal to trap (Figs 13 & 15). The well found fair quality Piper sands with oil shows, but RFT data indicated a water gradient substantially overpressured (*c.* 1000 psi) from North Tartan (Fig. 16). The terrace dips up to the west, where it is juxtaposed with Carboniferous in a further comparatively flat-lying fault block. No significant dip reversal is seen across this fault. The palaeocolumn suggests either that the well penetrated an active migration route (perhaps unlikely in view of the strength of the shows), or that a weak cross-fault seal has breached. The current pressure regime indicates a pressure barrier exists up-dip from the well. A dynamic charge-and-breach system can be envisaged for situations of weak fault seal.

A similar situation was encountered by Well 15/26b-22, targeted at Piper sands and drilled in 1995 on the Beta North East (BNE) Terrace southeast of Tartan (Figs 13 & 17). The prospect was downthrown some 1200 ft from the Tartan block and relied on the bounding faults to seal. Once again good oil shows were found in a thick and fair quality Piper section, but log and pressure data showed the reservoir to be water saturated. The pressure data showed some overpressure (*c.* 300 psi), but in marked contrast to Well 15/16b-18 did not show any aquifer depletion from Tartan production. The Piper section is juxtaposed against Carboniferous in the footwall, with dip continuity across the fault to the north. In contrast to the Gamma area in Block 15/21, substantial late movement on the Tartan Ridge is not shown by the seismic. Although there has clearly been some Late Cretaceous–Early Tertiary inversion (Fig. 15), the thick layer of Chalk, together with underlying thinner sequences of Lower Cretaceous and Kimmeridge Clay, cover the Tartan Ridge and form the top seal for the Tartan Field.

Some 3.5 km to the east, Well 15/16-16 was drilled in 1982 as a Tartan injector down dip from Well 15/16-4A (Fig. 18). It penetrated the Tartan oil–water contact (OWC) at −10 328 ft, 50 ft below the top of a 269 ft interval of Piper sandstone. Following a section of Middle Jurassic volcanics and Triassic claystone, a Carboniferous oil column was also encountered (probably below a faulted contact) and tested at 760 BOPD (Coward *et al.* 1991). Although the Jurassic reservoir had been slightly depleted by initial Tartan production, the Carboniferous reservoir was at virgin pressure (Fig. 16). A proprietary oil typing study (carried out for Amerada Hess and Texaco) has shown the Jurassic oil from 15/16b-22 to be virtually identical to the Carboniferous oil from 15/16b-16. This close similarity is unusual: the Jurassic oil from Tartan is rather different, although still clearly derived from a Kimmeridge Clay source, as is the oil from both the Jurassic and Carboniferous in Well 15/21a-7. The oil from the Perth Field is different again. A common source facies for the 15/16b-16 Carboniferous and the 15/16b-22 Jurassic oils is therefore strongly suggested, as is a cross-fault breach allowing a direct up-dip migration path from the BNE Terrace to the Carboniferous below Tartan (Fig. 18).

The Tartan area clearly demonstrates the risks involved in drilling downthrown terraces where Piper sands are juxtaposed to Carboniferous clastics with no footwall counter dip (BNE), but also shows the rewards of bold exploration in an area of structural complexity and poor quality seismic data (North Tartan).

Lowlander area (Block 14/20)

The Lowlander Field lies in the northern part of Block 14/20b (Fig. 1) and is unusual in the Moray Firth in that it is a successful pre-rift downthrown trap with no corresponding field up-dip. The Piper sands have been subjected to extensive burial-related diagenesis associated with faulting (McCants & Burley 1996). The structural expression at Base Cretaceous level is an anticlinal nose extending southwest from a synthetic fault adjacent to the northern Witch Ground Graben bounding fault, but at Top Piper level a number of fault blocks are present (Fig. 19). The trap is provided by three-way dip closure, together with presumed cross-fault seal against the Carboniferous in the footwall. The field is overpressured by *c.* 900 psi.

The radial pattern of the fault blocks is notable, mirroring the overlying Base Cretaceous nose. There is some evidence that the faults between the blocks are sealing, resulting in slightly different OWCs between them. Marked dip reversal between the hanging wall and the footwall is also seen (Fig. 20).

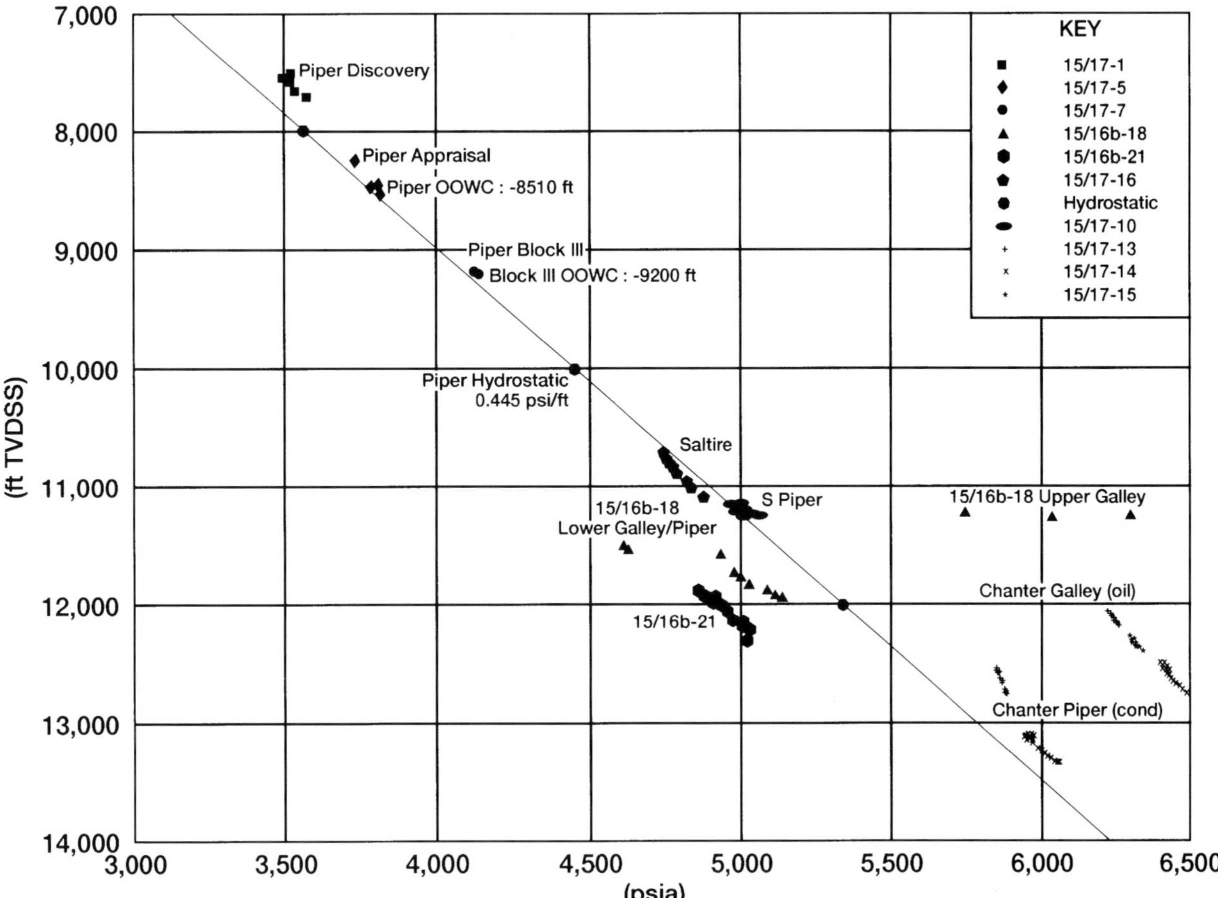

Fig. 12. Piper area: RFT pressure data.

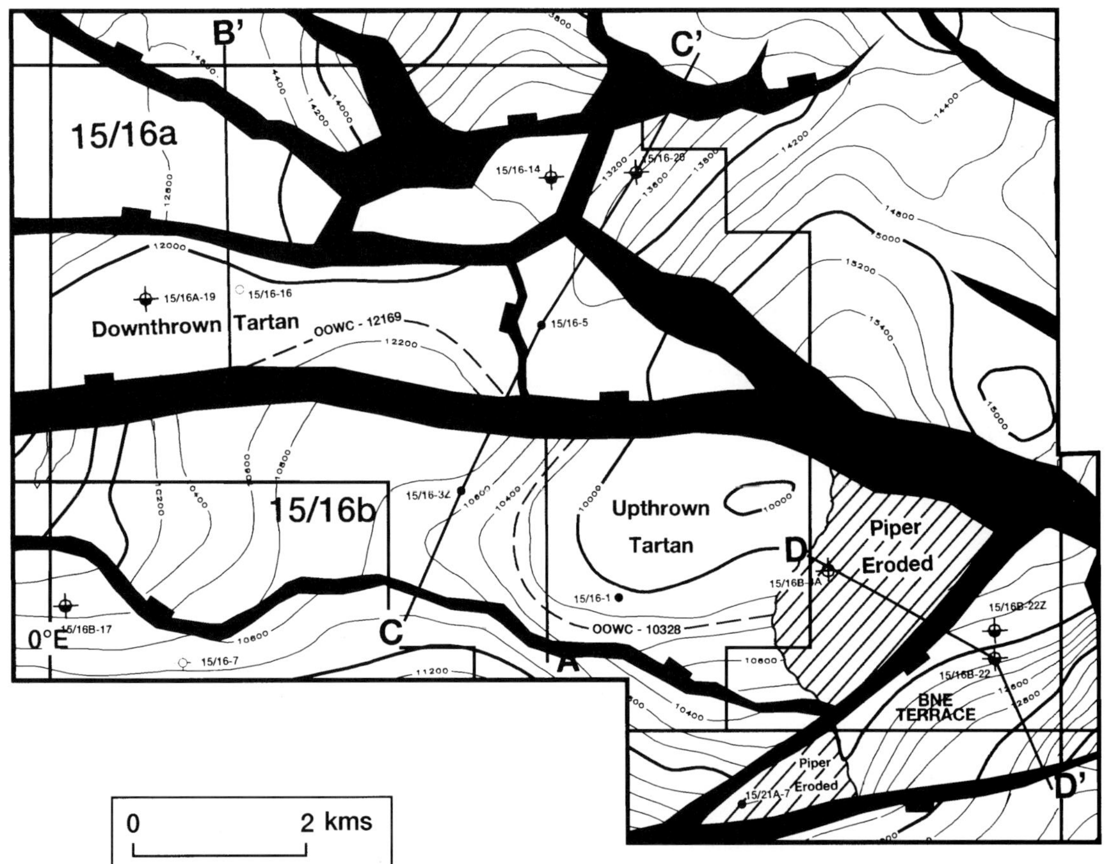

Fig. 13. Tartan area: simplified near Top Piper depth structure map (after Coward *et al.* 1991).

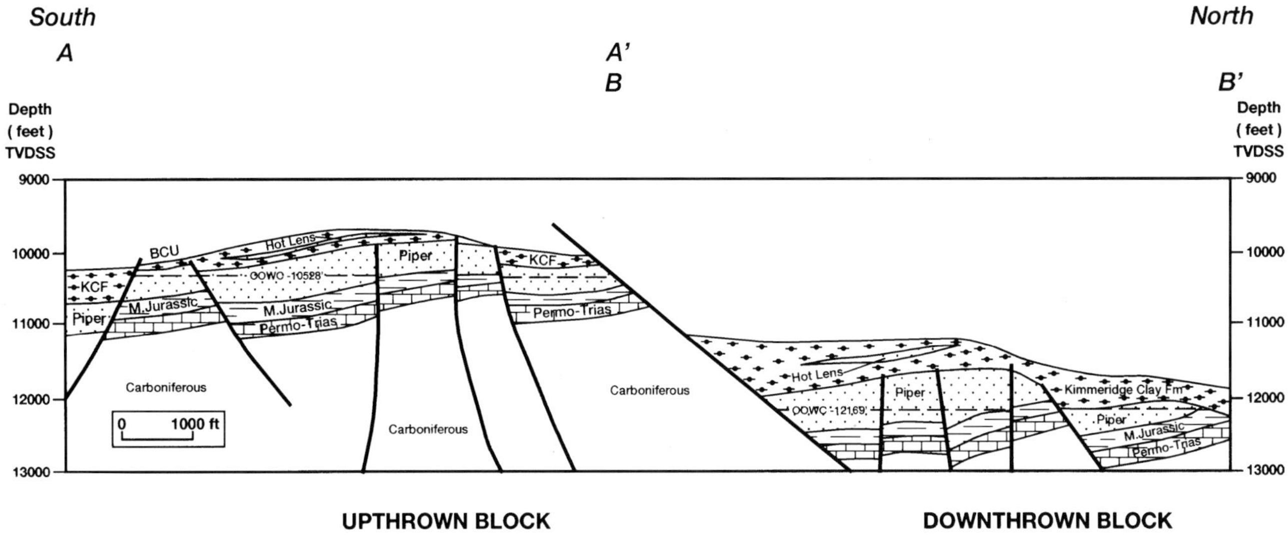

Fig. 14. Tartan area: composite geoseismic section A–A′, B–B′ (after Coward *et al.* 1991).

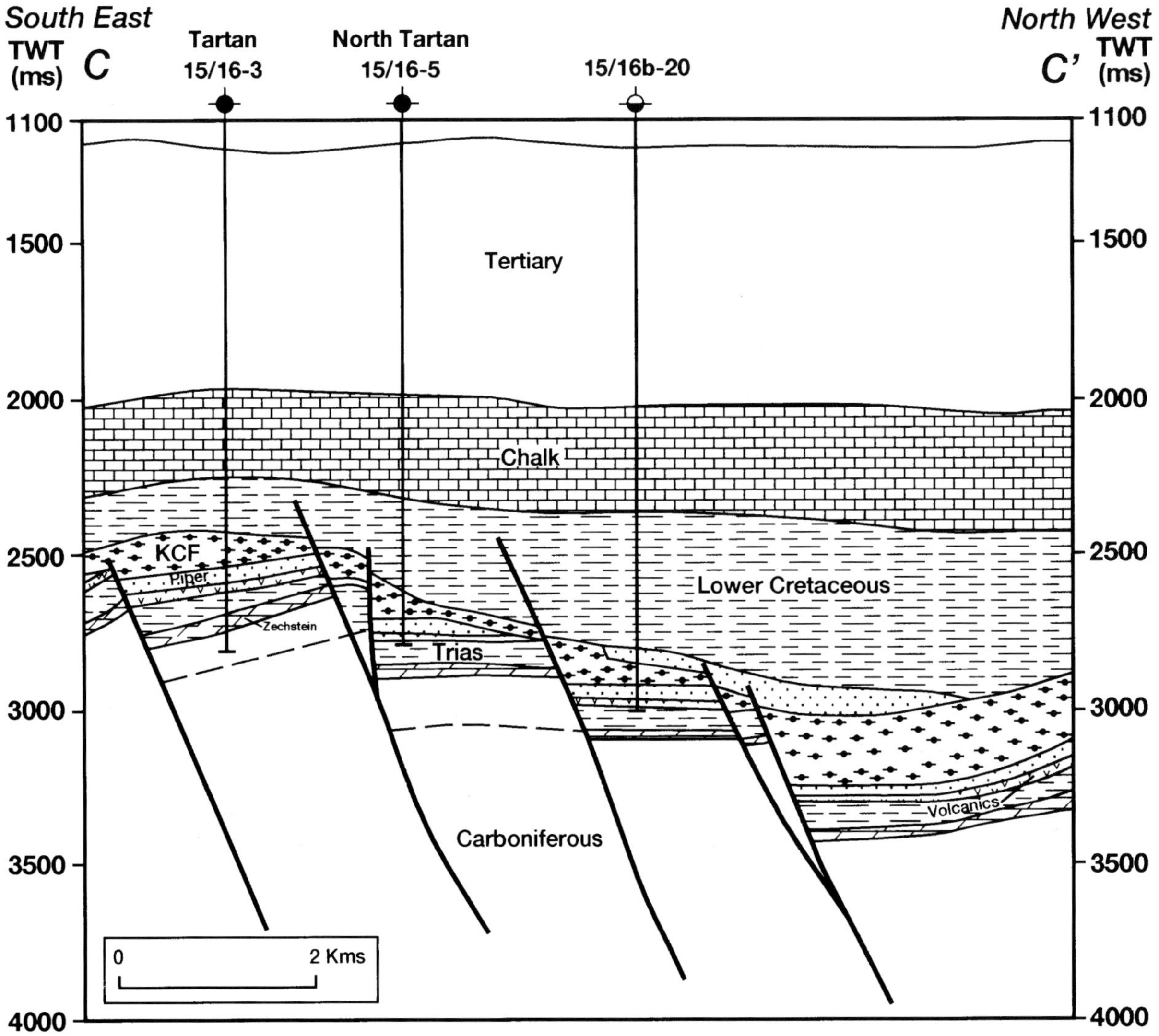

Fig. 15. Northeast Tartan area: geoseismic section C–C′.

Scott area (Blocks 15/21–15/22)

The Scott Field consists of a series of rotated fault blocks and detached relay ramps at the intersection of the North Halibut Basin and the Witch Ground Graben (Fig. 1), with the reservoir being Piper sands. The fault blocks are arranged radially around the crestal area (Fig. 21), in a more complete example of the Lowlander geometry, with marked counter dip seen between the blocks. Pressure variations show many of the faults to be sealing. As might be expected of an intra-basinal

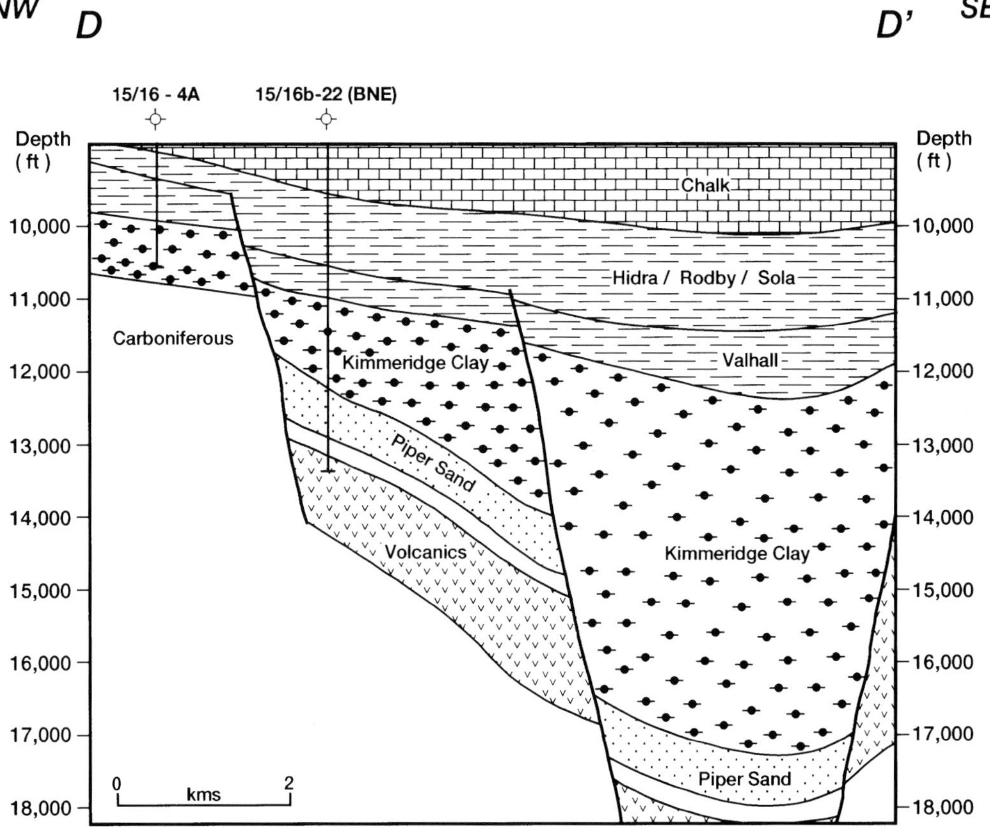

Fig. 16. Southeast Tartan area: geoseismic section D–D′. Note dip continuity across northwestern fault.

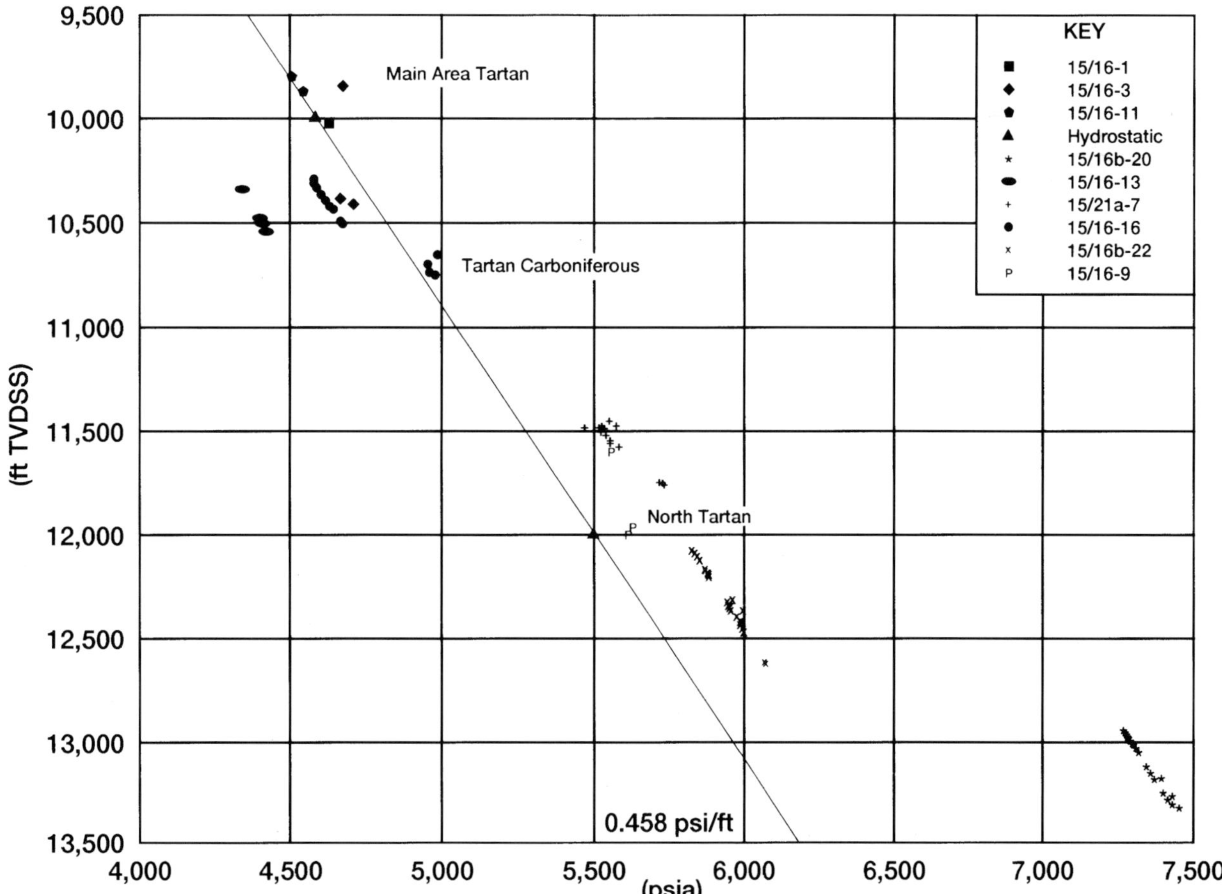

Fig. 17. Tartan area: RFT pressure data.

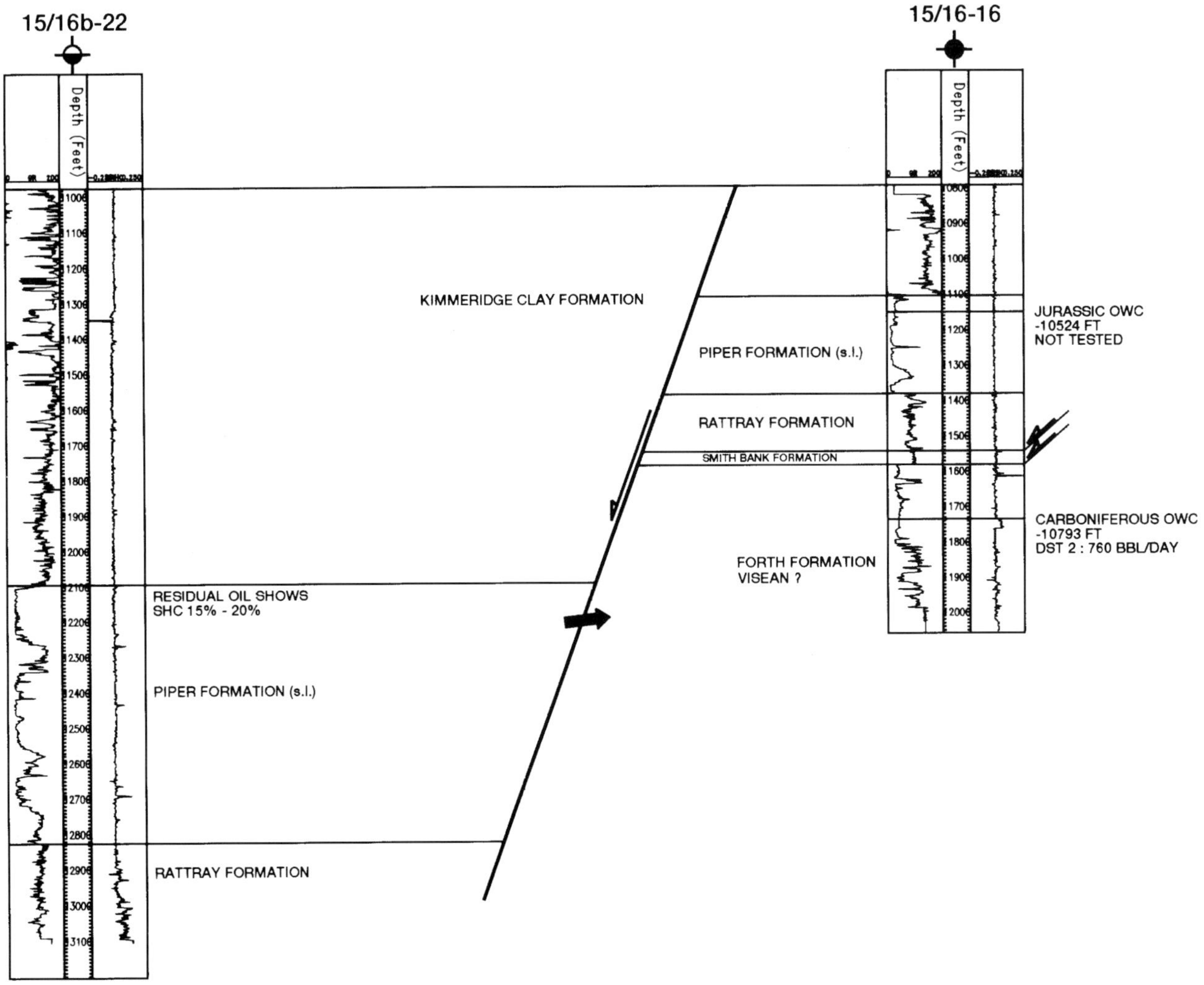

Fig. 18. Southeast Tartan area: well correlation 15/16b-16–15/16b-22.

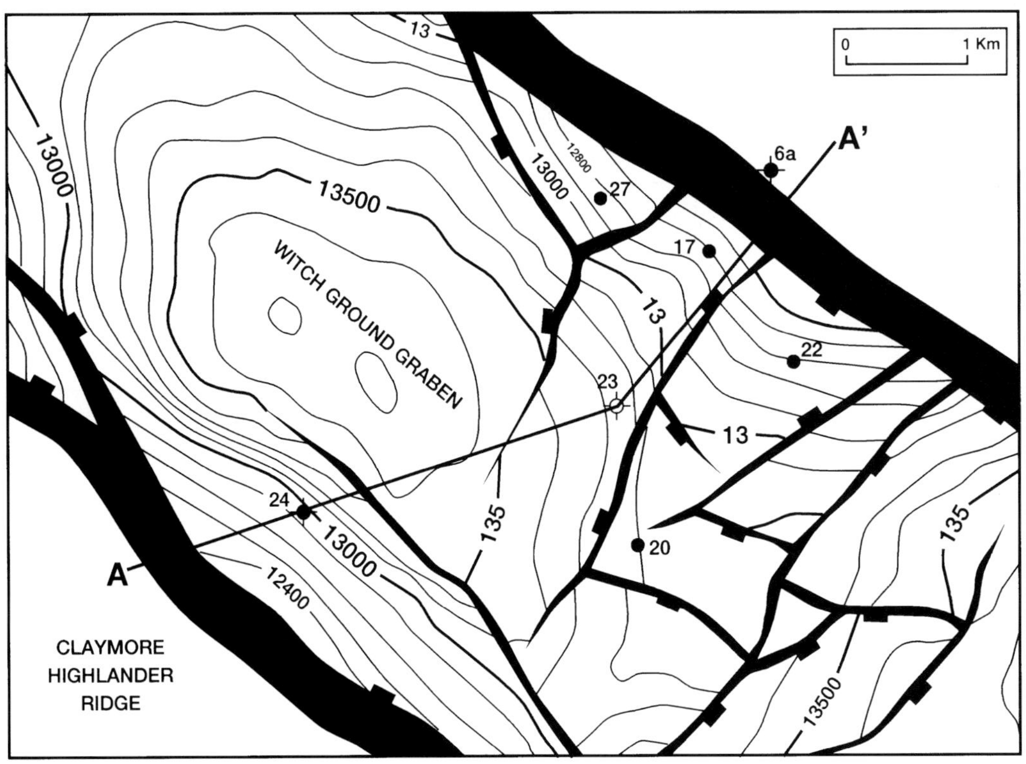

Fig. 19. Lowlander area: simplified near Top Piper depth structure map (after McCants & Burley 1996).

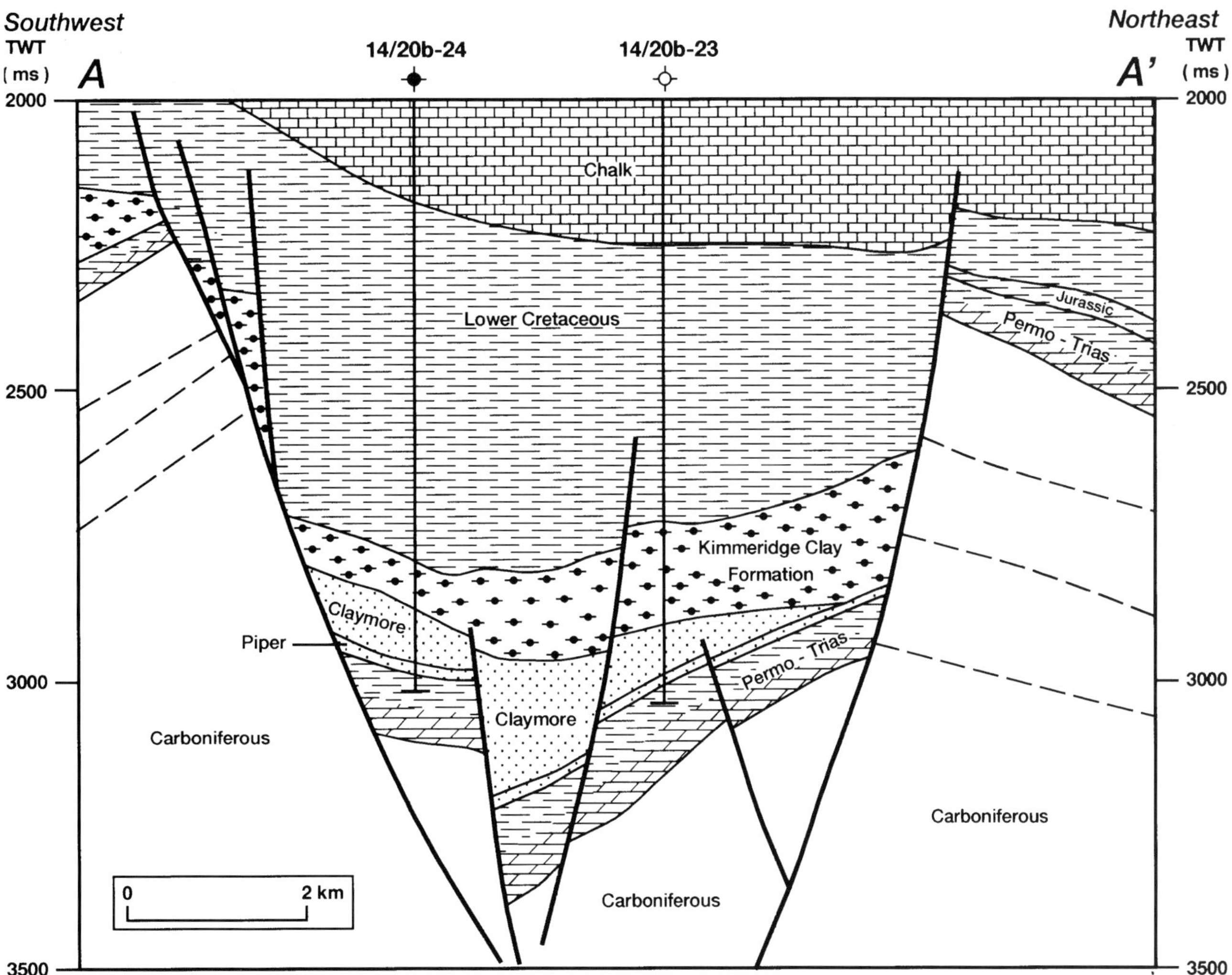

Fig. 20. Lowlander area: geoseismic section A–A′. Note dip reversal on northern flank from Jurassic in hanging wall to Carboniferous in footwall.

high of great vertical relief, the field is significantly overpressured. Block I is *c.* 3000 psi above hydrostatic, Blocks II and IV 150 and 200 psi higher, respectively and Block III nearly 500 psi higher again (Fig. 22). Each block shows a different OOWC. Hydrocarbon migration patterns have also been complex, with differing contacts between the Scott and Piper (*s.s.*) sands even in the same Block. The deepest contacts are thrown below the Top Carboniferous seismic pick (Fig. 23), and therefore cross-fault seal may be an important contributor to the compartmentalization of the field. An alternative view is that there is no cross-fault seal. Carboniferous sands in the footwall, where juxtaposed to Piper in the hanging wall, may be oil-bearing and in the same pressure regime. In this case the top seal would be provided by the juxtaposition of Kimmeridge Clay (hanging wall) and Carboniferous, Permo-Triassic or Middle Jurassic impermeable strata (footwall). The Carboniferous has not yet been penetrated in a crestal position in the field area.

The South Scott structure, downthrown some 2000 ft from the Telford Ridge, also benefits from marked footwall counter-dip. Here the hanging wall pre-rift sands are unequivocally thrown against footwall Palaeozoic, again assumed to be Carboniferous. The pressure regime is the same as Block I.

On an intermediate terrace system lying between the Halibut Horst spur to the south and the deep Scott terraces to the north lies the Sigma area of small fault blocks downthrown from the horst. The Sigma ‘C’ discovery was made by Well 15/21b-51, drilled in 1993 on a Piper nose extending north from the horst, and in addition to poor quality but oil-bearing Claymore Sandstone, an oil column was encountered in the Piper. Later appraisal drilling (by Well 15/21b-52 and its sidetracks) was disappointing, and in conjunction with improved seismic data showed the accumulation to be restricted to a four-way dip closure on the terrace. Again the horst bounding faults had been shown to leak, and the potentially large fault-trapped upside was absent.

The Scott area illustrates a variety of success and failure cases, but particularly highlights the dip relationships between fault blocks which can aid the formation of highly effective fault seals.

Other examples

North Claymore Field and Scapa Field (Block 14/19, Fig. 1) are both Lower Cretaceous Scapa (syn- to post-rift) sandstone reservoirs laid down in a mixed carbonate–clastic system. North Claymore is a structural nose downthrown to the north of the Main Claymore fault block, with three-way dip closure to the north, east and west, and fault closure to the south (Harker *et al.* 1991). The southern seal has not been penetrated and it is uncertain whether it is a fault plane seal or a tight (carbonate cemented) fault scarp conglomerate analogous to the southwest boundary of the Scapa Field. A thick Carboniferous section was penetrated by Well 14/19-2, and this proved that the Main Claymore OOWC continued from the Mesozoic into the Palaeozoic section. In Scapa, closure is downthrown to the

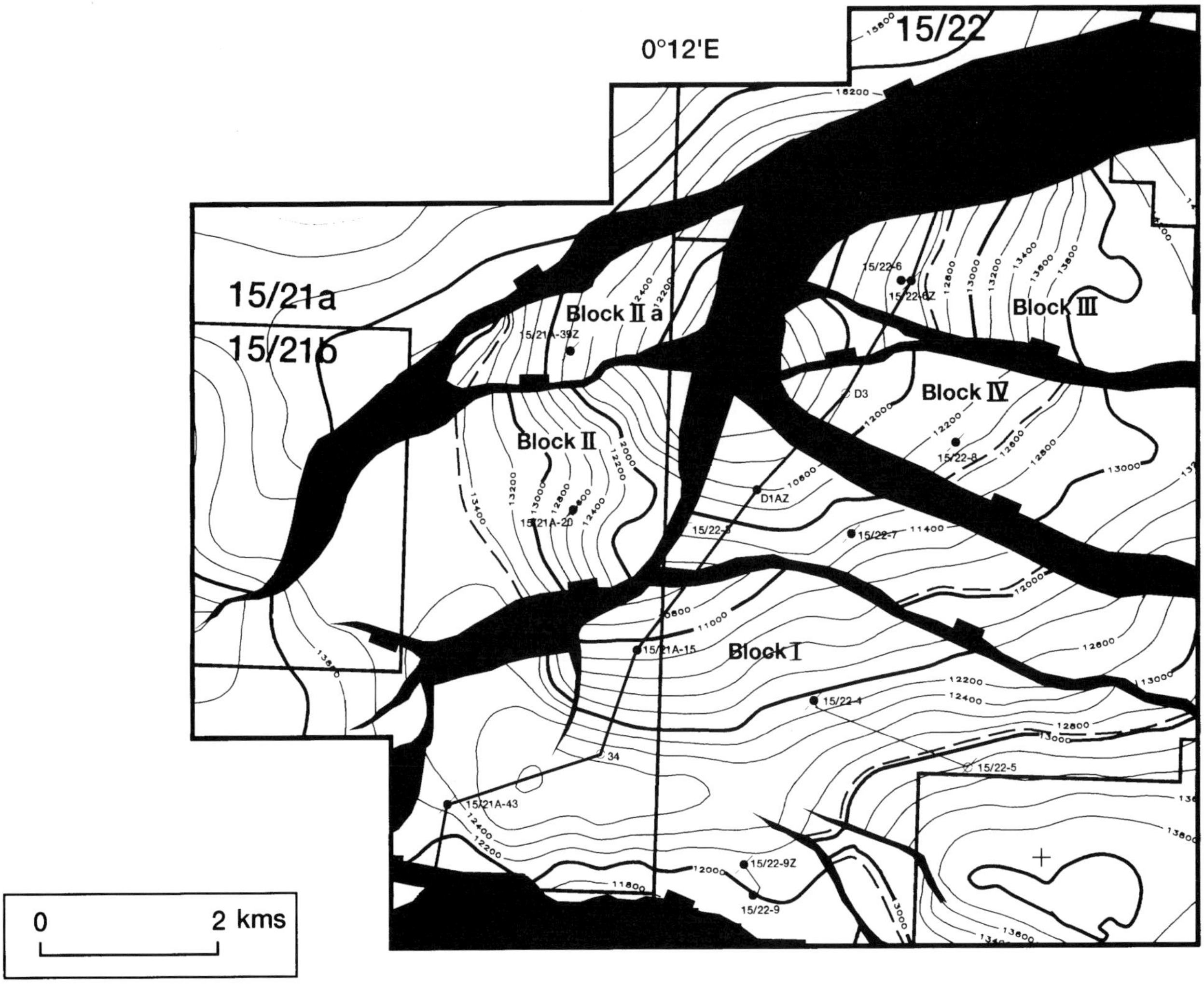

Fig. 21. Scott area: simplified near Top Piper depth structure map.

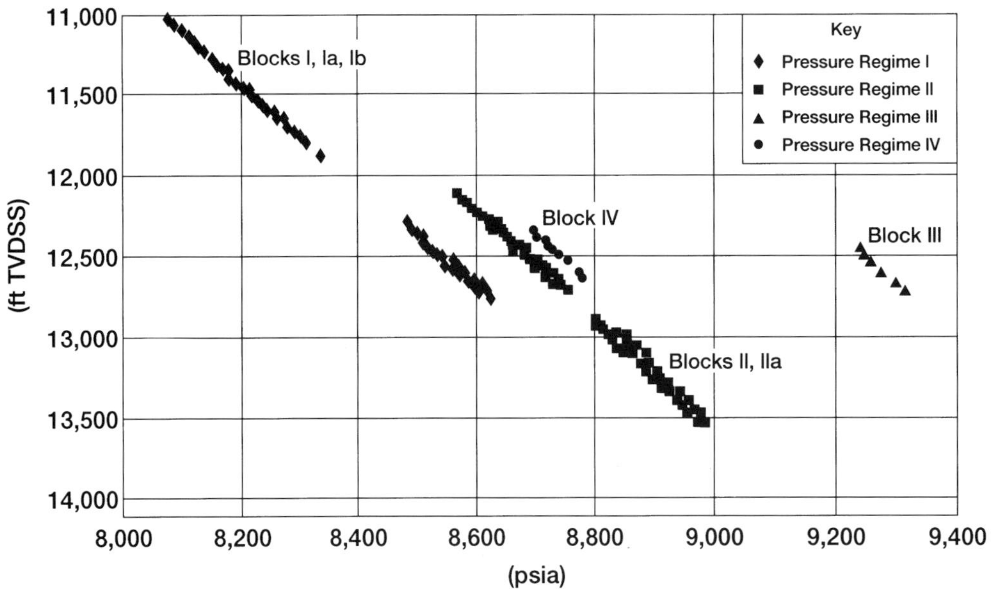

Fig. 22. Scott area: RFT pressure data.

southwest, upthrown to the northwest, stratigraphic to the northeast and dip to the southeast (Harker & Chermak 1992).

The Galley Field (Block 15/23a, Fig. 1) consists of a central fault block capped by deeply eroded Piper sands, with the erosional deposits from the Piper laid down as intra-Kimmeridge Clay gravity flows in two downthrown areas to the north and southeast of the main block. It is unclear whether the downthrown areas are sealed by stratigraphic, juxtaposition or fault seal trapping, but remains another example of a successful downthrown syn-rift play.

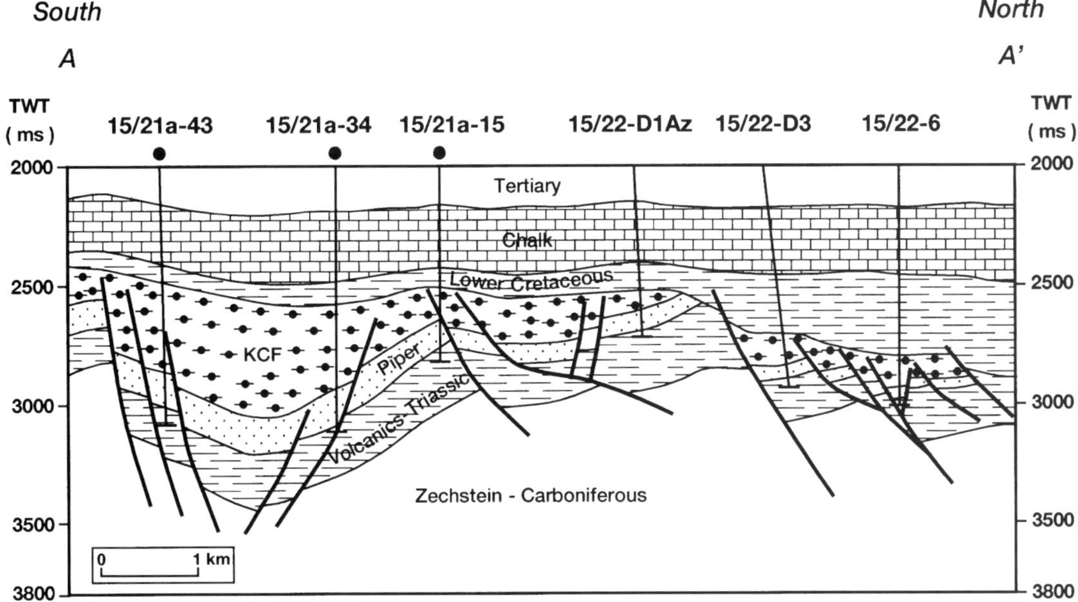

Fig. 23. Scott area: geoseismic section A–A′.

Reservoir and fault relationships

Examination of the potential reservoir, seal and leak units highlights the point that pre-rift units will almost inevitably be juxtaposed to the fault plane or zone (Fig. 24). A hanging wall pre-rift trap will therefore rely entirely on cross-fault seal when it is juxtaposed to porous and permeable lithology in the footwall if no trapping geometry exists in the footwall. This is not so with syn- and post-rift hanging wall traps. A variety of up-dip seal mechanisms may be effective in addition to the fault plane seal, notably tight fault scarp conglomerates, and up-dip pinch-out caused by a number of factors. These include sand bypass, axial sand deposition, or gravity flows distal to their input point losing energy as they climb a basin slope. It might be expected that syn- and post-rift hanging wall traps are more likely to be successful than pre-rift traps, and this appears to be confirmed by the statistics (David 1996).

A number of trap geometries are illustrated in Fig. 25. The simplest type of downthrown trap is the juxtaposition trap (Fig. 25a), exemplified by the fields south of Piper. In this case both fault plane seal and cross-fault seal are effective. The geometry of the footwall is irrelevant, as the lateral seal is provided by impermeable Permian to Middle Jurassic lithologies. In the case of cross-fault breach and juxtaposed permeable units, the footwall geometry is crucial to providing an effective seal (Fig. 25b). This is a point easy to miss when the

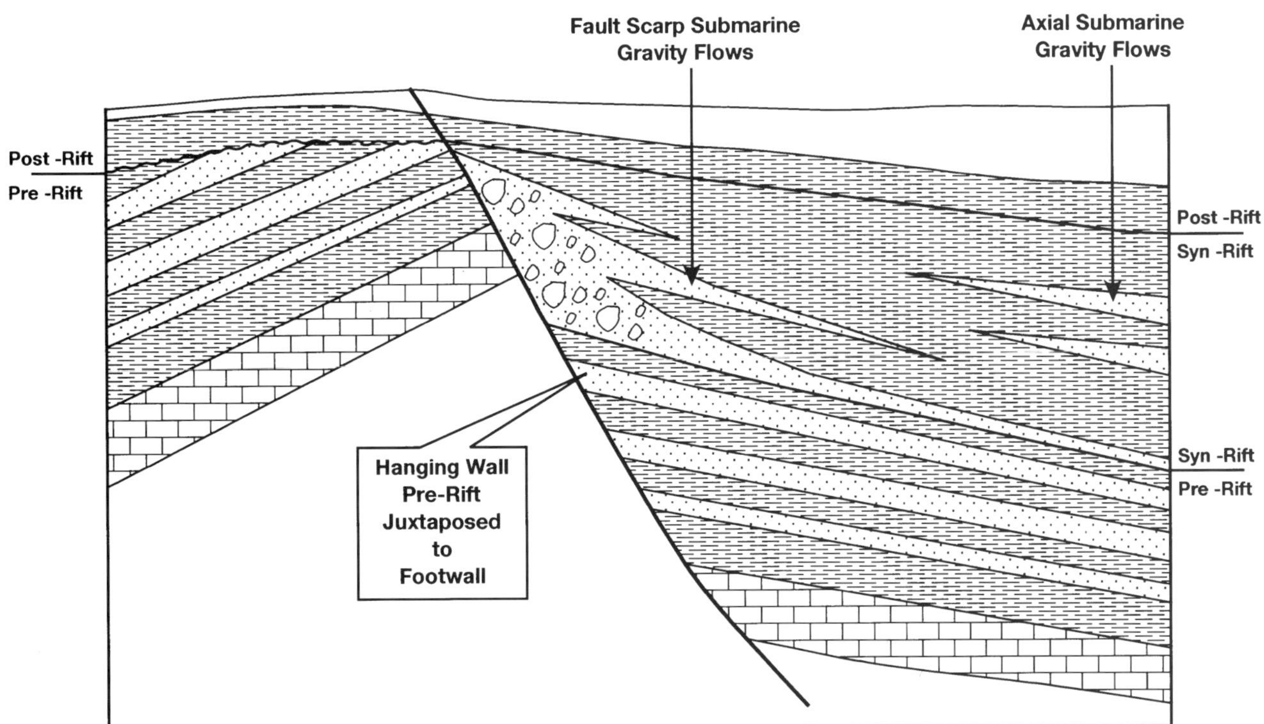

Fig. 24. Relationship of reservoir units to fault plane.

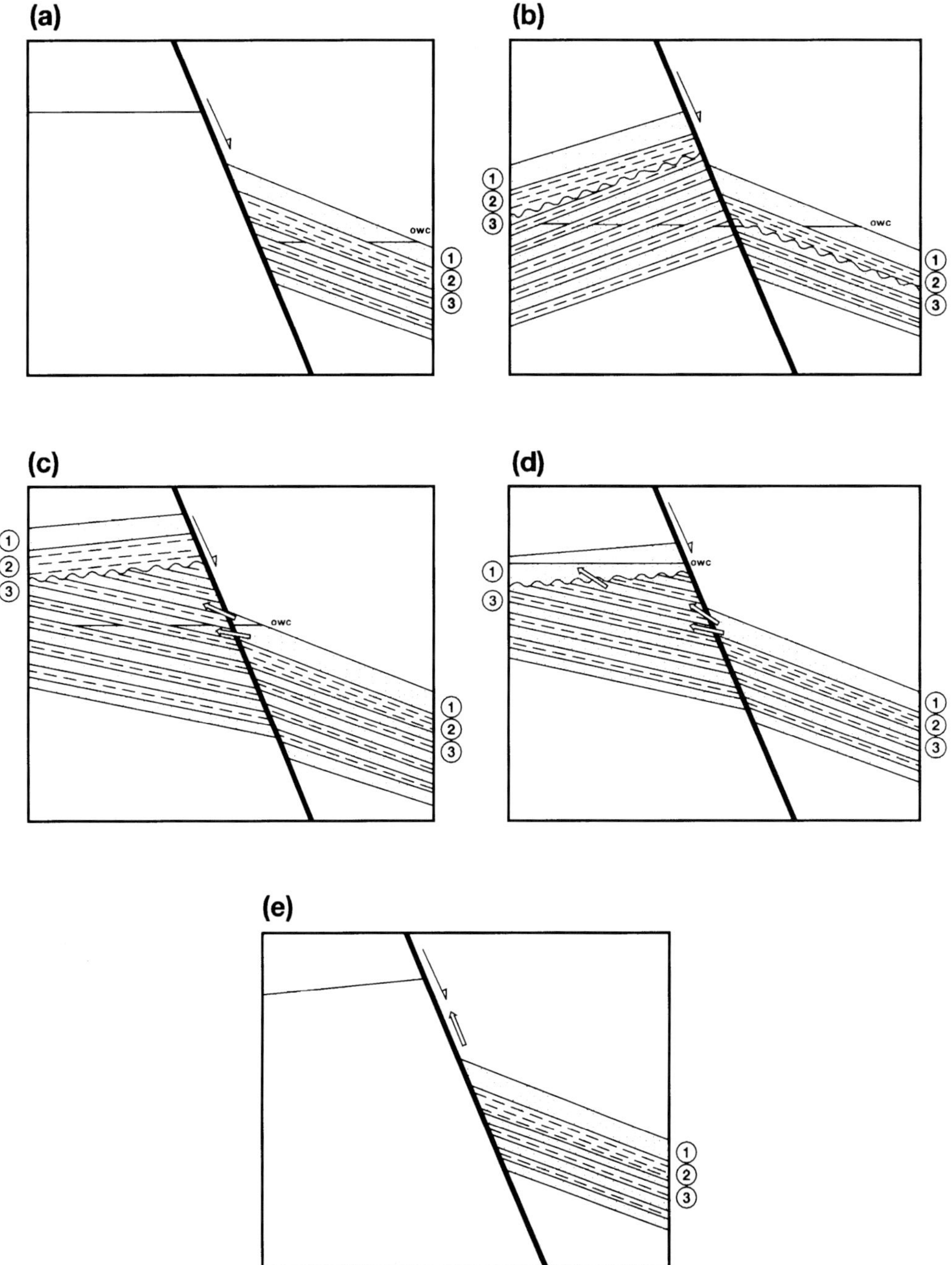

Fig. 25. Down-thrown trapping geometry. (**a**) Fault-plane seal and cross-fault seal. Footwall geometry is irrelevant. In the Outer Moray Firth, Unit 1 corresponds to Piper Formation, Unit 2 to impermeable units (i.e. Rattray Formation, Smith Bank Formation, Turbot Formation), and Unit 3 to Forth Formation. The overlying unit is Kimmeridge Clay Formation (regional source and seal). (**b**) Fault-plane seal, cross-fault breach. Little or no angular unconformity at the top of Unit 3 results in faulted four-way dip closure. A variation, with the same geometry would be fault-plane seal and cross-fault seal, with the latter forming before hydrocarbon migration and not disrupted thereafter; in this case, hydrocarbons would be restricted to the hanging wall block. The footwall geometry, dipping down from the fault, appears to be crucial for this trap type to be effective in the Outer Moray Firth. (**c**) Fault-plane seal, cross-fault breach. The large angular unconformity at the top of Unit 3 forms a combined structural and stratigraphic trap. Footwall Unit 1 could also be hydrocarbon bearing, charged via a different migration pathway. (**d**) Fault-plane seal, cross-fault breach. Unit 2 is eroded out allowing migration from Unit 3 to Unit 1 across the angular unconformity. (**e**) Fault-plane breach. Hydrocarbons migrate up the fault plane to shallower traps.

sediments in the footwall and hanging wall are of very different ages, and especially when data quality is often sufficiently poor to hinder accurate footwall mapping. Even where data quality is good, the rhythmic nature of Carboniferous sedimentation means correlation across faults can be very difficult. In this case, the trap geometry represents a simple four way dip and/or fault closed structure, but with (in the OMF) Jurassic sands on one side of the structure and Carboniferous sands on the other. Where such geometry exists, leakage from the structure can take place both up the fault plane if the fault moves and breaches the topseal, and also when the ultimate structural spill point (in the hanging wall or footwall) is reached. In reality, the Carboniferous is itself likely to be highly faulted and compartmentalized, and successful tests have often shown depletion (e.g. Well 15/21a-7). This situation is an 'end member' of a range of possible sealing systems (Allen 1989). A variation is where both cross-fault seal and fault-plane seal are present, and although potential reservoir units are present in the footwall they are not hydrocarbon bearing. Again, footwall counter dip seems to be required for an effective trap (i.e. Lowlander), possibly because of the effects of lithostatic loading (see later). No successful examples have been identified which lack this crucial feature. Intermediate situations are well known within both gas (e.g. Indefatigable) and oil (e.g. Fulmar) fields, where hydrocarbons are reservoired in similar age sands on both sides of a fault but with differing fluid contacts and (often) pressure regimes (Johnson *et al.* 1986; Pearson 1991).

Where no counter dip is present in the older levels in the footwall, a cross-fault breach will allow oil to migrate up-dip from the hanging wall (Fig. 25c). A 'Top Piper' structure map would give no hint of such a situation. A trap can still be formed by an impermeable topseal (i.e. Wells 15/16-16 and -22). Where no such topseal is present, hydrocarbons will continue to migrate vertically (Fig. 25d). Finally, a fault-plane breach (Fig. 25e) will allow the structure to empty into shallower levels (i.e. Wells 15/21-2 and 15/21a-38).

Several wells in the OMF have proven oil in good quality reservoir on a downthrown terrace, but restricted to an upthrown trapping element; the larger reserve case which would have resulted from effective cross-fault seals was not found (see Piper Block III, Well 15/17-7, above). Other wells have discovered residual oil shows in good quality reservoir. These presumably represent palaeotraps, where the lateral seal has failed and the moveable oil has escaped either up or across the fault plane (see North Halibut Graben Well 15/21–2 and Tartan area Wells 15/16b-16 and -22, earlier). The abundance of the oil shows in these wells make the alternative explanation, which is that they lie on a oil migration path, unlikely. This type of situation is the clearest indication of trap failure, and allows other reasons for failure such as poor quality reservoir or lack of effective source or migration route to be discounted. Different mechanisms are probably responsible for these failures. Significant late movement on the Halibut Horst bounding fault is probably responsible for the trap failure of 15/21-2. In contrast, the 15/16b-16 and 15/16b-22 structures do not show significant late movement, but lack footwall counter-dip, and may be examples of breached weak seals.

An additional and intriguing element to the downthrown trap conundrum is the fault block configuration. Seismic data quality over North Tartan is too poor for unambiguous mapping, but the remaining two successful examples where Piper sands are faulted against Carboniferous (Lowlander and Scott) show a radial arrangement of fault blocks (Figs 19 & 21). This may enhance the effectiveness of both cross-fault and fault-plane seals. The component of vertical stress (from the lithostatic load) orthogonal to the fault blocks results in compression across the fault (Fig. 26), and this may result in an intrinsically better seal. In three dimensions, the radial layout would behave as a lens focusing the lithostatic load onto the faults within the structure. This model predicts that the greater the lithostatic loading (depth), the greater the potential for effective fault seal. In practical exploration terms a maximum depth limit would be imposed by diagenetic destruction of the reservoir. There is some evidence to support the model, as the fault seal traps which have proved successful in the Moray Firth lie in the comparatively narrow depth range of approximately 9000 ft to 14 000 ft. This appears to mark the upper and lower limits of effective fault seal and effective reservoir, respectively. Little if any work has been published on the effect of fault block geometry on seal effectiveness, and it is a question which clearly merits more research. A major assumption is that the fault block behaves as a unit, and that dip changes deep in the block (e.g. in the case of a large unconformity at Top Carboniferous) have little impact. At least two mechanisms have been suggested for the formation of fault

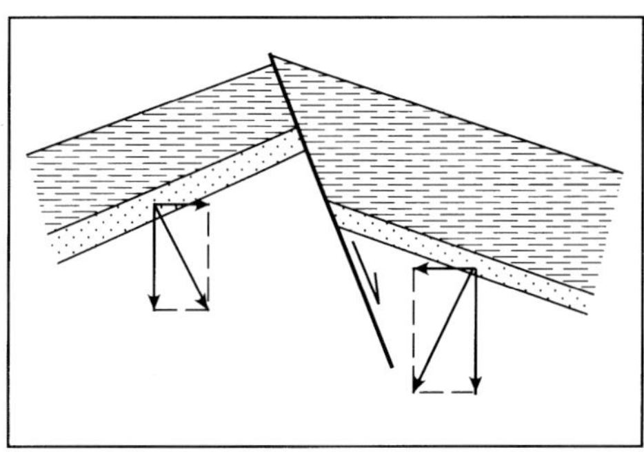

Fig. 26. An intrinsically better seal?

block geometry showing footwall counter dip. The first involves the breaching of a relay ramp between two offset extensional faults; the zone of the relay ramp will retain its inherited dip when it forms an independent terrace with continuing extension (S. Stewart 1997, pers. comm.). The second involves ductile drape over an extensional fault. Concerns about space problems with this type of geometry therefore appear to be unfounded.

Conclusions

In the light of the above observations, a risking sequence for downthrown Mesozoic prospects in the OMF which do not show evidence of Tertiary fault movement and breaching can be drawn up, as follows :

Fault juxtaposition geology F'wall/H'wall	Footwall counter-dip	Fault block arrangement	Risk	Successful examples
Carboniferous/Piper	No	Terrace	Very High	None
Carboniferous/Piper	Yes	Terrace?	High?	N Tartan[1]
Carboniferous/Piper	Yes	Radial	Medium	Scott Lowlander
Carboniferous/Syn-rift	[2]	[2]	Medium	Perth 15/16b-18 15/21b-38 N Claymore
Impermeable[3]/ Pre- or syn-rift	NR	NR	Low	Chanter Saltire Iona

[1] Poor seismic data quality restricts accurate mapping and trap definition.
[2] Stratigraphic trapping elements, and the nature of the depositional system, are likely to be as important as structural elements in the syn-rift case.
[3] Zechstein evaporites/Triassic claystones/Middle Jurassic volcanics.
NR: Not relevant for juxtaposition trap.

It appears that the prime factors controlling the integrity of a downthrown pre-rift trap are the geology of the footwall (permeable or impermeable) where it abuts the hanging wall reservoir; counter dip in the footwall; the fault block configuration (radial or terrace); the depth of burial; and the timing of the last significant fault movement. Clay smear might be expected to play an important role when sediments of a similar age are juxtaposed early in the lithification process, when clays remain ductile; the mechanism appears to be less important in the OMF, where this is often not the case. Syn-rift traps are more likely to be successful as more potential trapping mechanisms may be effective. These include stratigraphic pinch-outs either distal to a sediment input point, or caused by axial sand deposition or sand bypass, and tight fault scarp conglomerates. A good working hypothesis about the sand depositional system is therefore essential. Concentrating on the fault plane as the principal sealing mechanism may be misleading, as the trap geometry will be defined by the geometry of the sediments on both side of the fault plane if there is a cross-fault breach. The dynamic breach-and-seal nature of 'weak' fault seals (those formed without the benefit of footwall counter dip or a radial fault block layout) is shown by the existence of overpressured dry holes which nevertheless have palaeo-oil columns.

I would like to thank the management and many colleagues at Amerada and partner companies for their interest and support during the preparation of this paper, but particularly S. Boldy and M. Attree for much encouragement and constructive criticism; A. Hewett of Kerr McGee for stimulating debate on the variations in the trap geometry of downthrown closures; S. Stewart for several very useful discussions; and M. Leishmann and A. Raymond for sedimentological and geochemical input, respectively. Regional mapping was carried out by A. Law. Permission to publish was granted by Texaco, Kerr McGee, Deminex, Premier, Amoco, Enterprise and Mobil. E. Navarro and E. Hollett of AHL drafted the figures. The views expressed in this paper are those of the author, and not necessarily those of Amerada Hess or its partners.

References

ALLEN, U. A. 1989. Model for Hydrocarbon Migration and Entrapment Within Faulted Structures. *American Association of Petroleum Geologists Bulletin*, **73**(7), 803–811.

BOLDY, S. A. R. & BREALEY, S. 1990. Timing, nature and sedimentary result of Jurassic tectonism in the Outer Moray Firth. *In*: HARDMAN, R. F. P. & BROOKS, J. (eds) *Tectonic Events Responsible for Britain's Oil and Gas Reserves*. Geological Society, London, Special Publications, **55**, 259–279.

CASEY, B. J., ROMANI, R. S. & SCHMITT, R. H. 1993. Appraisal geology of the Saltire Field, Witch Ground Graben, North Sea. *In*: PARKER, J. R. (ed.) *Petroleum Geology of Northwest Europe: Proceedings of the 4th Conference*. Geological Society, London, 507–517.

COWARD, R. N., CLARK, N. M. & PINNOCK, S. J. 1991. The Tartan Field, Block 15/16, UK North Sea. *In*: ABBOTTS, I. L. (ed.) *United Kingdom Oil and Gas Fields, 25 Years Commemorative Volume*. Geological Society, London, Memoirs, **14**, 377–384.

DAVID, M. J. 1996. History of hydrocarbon exploration in the Moray Firth. *In*: HURST, A., JOHNSON, H., BURLEY, S. D., CANHAM, A. C. & MACKERTICH, D. S. (eds) *Geology of the Humber Group: Central Graben and Moray Firth, UKCS*. Geological Society, London, Special Publications, **114**, 47–80.

HARKER, S. D. & CHERMAK, A. 1992. Detection and prediction of Lower Cretaceous sandstone distribution in the Scapa Field, North Sea. *In*: HARDMAN, R. F. P (ed.) *Exploration Britain: Geological Insights for the Next Decade*. Geological Society, London, Special Publications, **67**, 221–246.

——, GREEN, S. C. & ROMANI, R. S. 1991. The Claymore Field, Block 14/19, UK North Sea. *In*: ABBOTTS, I. L. (ed.) *United Kingdom Oil and Gas Fields, 25 Years Commemorative Volume*. Geological Society, London, Memoirs, **14**, 269–278.

HIBBERT, M. J. & MACKERTICH, D. S. 1993. The structural evolution of the eastern end of the Halibut Horst, Block 15/21, Outer Moray Firth, UK North Sea. *In*: PARKER, J. R. (ed.) *Petroleum Geology of Northwest Europe: Proceedings of the Fourth Conference*. Geological Society, London, 1179–1188.

HINDLE, A. D. 1989. Downthrown traps of the NW Witch Ground Graben, UK North Sea. *Journal of Petroleum Geology*, **12**(4), 405–418.

JOHNSON, H. D., MACKAY, T. A. & STEWART, D. J. 1986. The Fulmar Oil-field (Central North Sea): geological aspects of its discovery, appraisal and development. *Marine and Petroleum Geology*, **3**, 99–125.

KNIPE, R. J. 1992. Faulting processes and fault seal. *In*: LARSEN, R. M., BREKKE, H., LARSEN, B. T. & TALLERAAS, E. (eds) *Structural and Tectonic Modelling and its Application to Petroleum Geology*. NPF Special Publications, **1**, 325–342.

MCCANTS, C. Y. & BURLEY, S. D. 1996. Reservoir architecture and diagenesis in downthrown fault block plays: the Lowlander Prospect of Block 14/20b, Witch Ground Graben, Outer Moray Firth, UK North Sea. *In*: HURST, A. *et al.* (eds) *Geology of the Humber Group: Central Graben and Moray Firth, UKCS*. Geological Society, London, Special Publications, **114**, 251–285.

MCGANN, G. J., GREEN, S. C. H., HARKER, S. D. & ROMANI, R. S. 1991. The Scapa Field, Block 14/19, UK North Sea. *In* : ABBOTTS, I. L. (ed.) *United Kingdom Oil and Gas Fields, 25 Years Commemorative Volume*. Geological Society, London, Memoirs, **14**, 369–376.

PEARSON, J. F. S. 1991. The Indefatigable Field, Blocks 49/18, 49/19, 49,23, 49/24, UK North Sea. *In*: ABBOTTS, I. L. (ed.) *United Kingdom Oil and Gas Fields, 25 Years Commemorative Volume*. Geological Society, London, Memoirs, **14**, 443–450.

SMITH, K. & RITCHIE, J. D. 1993. Jurassic volcanic centres in the Central North Sea. *In*: PARKER, J. R. (ed.) *Petroleum Geology of Northwest Europe: Proceedings of the 4th Conference*. Geological Society, London, 519–531.

SCHMITT, H. R. H. 1991. The Chanter Field, Block 15/17, UK North Sea. *In*: ABBOTTS, I. L. (ed.) *United Kingdom Oil and Gas Fields, 25 Years Commemorative Volume*. Geological Society, London, Memoirs, **14**, 261–268.

SCHMITT, H. R. & GORDON, A. F. 1991. The Piper Field, Block 15/17, UK North Sea. *In*: ABBOTTS, I. L. (ed.) *United Kingdom Oil and Gas Fields, 25 Years Commemorative Volume*. Geological Society, London, Memoirs, **14**, 361–368.

UNDERHILL, J. R. & PARTINGTON, M. A. 1993. Jurassic thermal doming and deflation in the North Sea: implications of the sequence stratigraphic evidence. *In*: PARKER, J. R. (ed.) *Petroleum Geology of Northwest Europe: Proceedings of the 4th Conference*. Geological Society, London, 337–345.

YIELDING, G., FREEMAN, B. & NEEDHAM, D. T. 1997. Quantitative fault seal prediction. *American Association of Petroleum Geologists Bulletin*, **81**, 897–917.

WEBER, K. J., MANDL, G., PILAAR, W. F., LEHNER, F. & PRECIOUS, R. G. 1978. The role of faults in hydrocarbon migration and trapping in Nigerian growth fault structures. *Offshore Technology Conference*, **10**, 3356, 2643–2653.

Controls on Upper Jurassic sediment distribution in the Durward–Dauntless area, UK Blocks 21/11, 21/16

S. A. STEWART,[1] S. I. FRASER,[1] J. A. CARTWRIGHT,[2] J. A. CLARK[2] and H. D. JOHNSON[2]

[1] *Amerada Hess Ltd, 33 Grosvenor Place, London SW1X 7HY*
[2] *T. H. Huxley School of Environment, Earth Science and Engineering, Imperial College, London SW7 2BP*

Abstract: The Upper Jurassic shallow marine Fulmar sands are widespread in the West Central Graben but have an increasingly irregular distribution when traced westwards across the West Central Shelf (Western Platform). This is strikingly illustrated in the Durward and Dauntless fields (Blocks 21/11 and 21/16), located 20 km west of Kittiwake, where several exploration, appraisal and development wells failed to find the Fulmar sands objective. The main aim of this paper is to offer an explanation for this irregular sand distribution in the Durward/Dauntless area.

This study represents an integrated analysis of the thin (50–250 ft) Upper Jurassic succession (equivalent to the Fulmar and Kimmeridge Clay formations) based on around 90 wells and a sub-regional 3D seismic dataset, which covers most of the West Central Shelf. A combination of sedimentological, biostratigraphical and well log criteria has been used to define up to nine genetic depositional sequences bounded by regionally correlatable maximum flooding surfaces. This stratigraphic framework provides a linkage between the previously unpublished Durward–Dauntless area and the Kittiwake Field. Typical 'Fulmar sands' facies are restricted to the Kimmeridgian in this area and occur in up to five depositional sequences, which extend from the Base Jurassic unconformity (earliest Kimmeridgian) up to the *eudoxus* and *autissiodorensis* maximum flooding surfaces (mfs) (latest Kimmeridgian). These sequences display marked lateral facies changes from sand to mud, while stratal patterns and thickness variations indicate onlap against earlier deposits. This is in striking contrast to the younger mud-dominated depositional sequences (Volgian to Ryazanian), which display complex local subsidence patterns bearing little relationship to Fulmar sand isopach patterns within the Kimmeridgian.

The 3D seismic data have enabled mapping of the Base Cretaceous, Top Zechstein Salt and Top Basement (pre-Zechstein), but is unable to directly resolve the thin Upper Jurassic interval. However, these data have enabled a regional structural/stratigraphic model to be developed, particularly in relation to the effects of the nature and rate of accommodation space creation. Conclusions derived from the 3D seismic interpretations have been integrated with those from the well-based sequence stratigraphic studies.

The resulting geological model for the Upper Jurassic concludes that Fulmar sand distribution was largely controlled by pre-existing topography, which had evolved during a significant period of (late Triassic–pre Upper Jurassic) subaerial exposure. This topography was critical in controlling highstand sand distribution and its ultimate preservation potential. The importance of pre-Upper Jurassic topography in determining accommodation space became secondary to dissolution of the Zechstein during the suspension-dominated sedimentation of the Volgian and Lower Cretaceous. These local controls vary on a kilometre scale and are superimposed upon the longer wavelength control of regional eastwards dip, which evolved from the *cymodoce* mfs until the Albian and caused a general westwards onlap of Upper Jurassic and early Cretaceous successions across the West Central Shelf.

The model suggests that 3D topographic reconstruction of the pre-Jurassic substrate is the single most critical factor in predicting Fulmar reservoir distribution on the transgressed surface of the West Central Shelf.

The Upper Jurassic shallow marine Fulmar sands are one of the most important hydrocarbon reservoirs in the Central North Sea (CNS), but predicting their distribution has often been problematic throughout the basin, especially on the West Central Shelf (WCS). To date, 75 exploration wells on the WCS have yielded the following fields: Gannet West (now called Guillemot A; Armstrong *et al.* 1987), Kittiwake (Glennie & Armstrong 1991), Mallard, Teal, South Teal, Durward and Dauntless. Durward and Dauntless were discovered in 1993 and 1994, respectively.

This paper summarizes the geological model which has been developed to account for the irregular Fulmar sand distribution in and around the Durward/Dauntless fields (Blocks 21/16 & 21/11), close to the currently defined western limit of Fulmar sands on the WCS (Fig. 1). Existing models demonstrate that pre- and post-Fulmar geology must be considered, in addition to the sedimentology of the Fulmar itself, in order to develop a model which successfully accounts for the distribution of reservoir, hydrocarbons and traps within this fairway (Johnson *et al.* 1986; Hodgson *et al.* 1992; Høiland *et al.* 1993; Penge *et al.* 1993; Wakefield *et al.* 1993; Martin & Pollard 1996; Veldkamp *et al.* 1996). Hence this paper also includes key aspects of Triassic and Cretaceous/Tertiary geology.

One of the principal problems in defining Fulmar sand distribution on the WCS is that the Fulmar isopach (*c.* 0–200 ft) is often at, or below, the limit of seismic resolution (as is the overlying Kimmeridge Clay Formation – KCF), and so is not directly mappable on the widespread (1500 km^2) 3D seismic data. However, the seismic data do constrain the relationship between the Jurassic and the underlying geology. This

STEWART, S. A., FRASER, S. I., CARTWRIGHT, J. A., CLARK, J. A. & JOHNSON, H. D. 1999. Controls on Upper Jurassic sediment distribution in the Durward–Dauntless area, UK Blocks 21/11, 21/16. *In*: FLEET, A. J. & BOLDY, S. A. R. (eds) *Petroleum Geology of Northwest Europe: Proceedings of the 5th Conference*, 879–896.

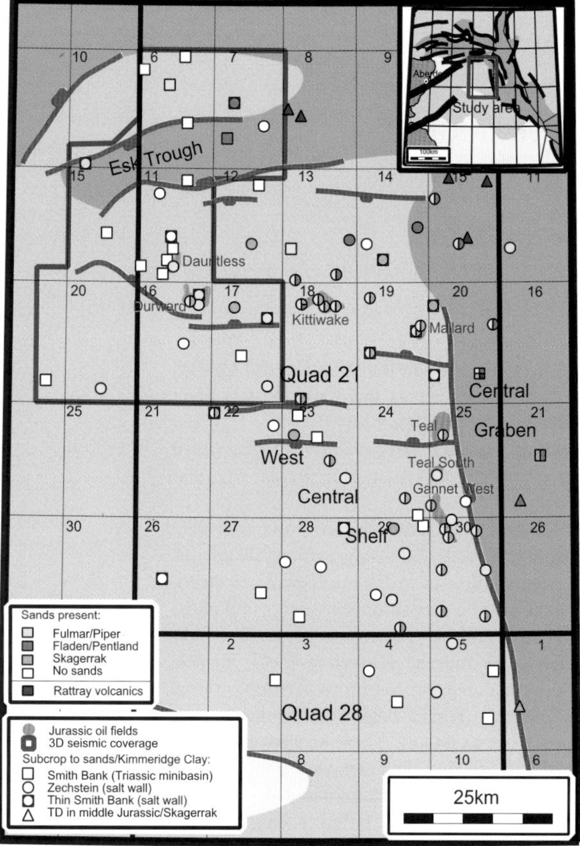

Fig. 1. Location of West Central Shelf relative to the Central Graben and Moray Firth. Dark blue shading indicates deep, basement-controlled graben; prominent basement faults are grey. The 'Esk Trough' is the most southerly Moray Firth basement graben. Licence block numbers are labelled. Well symbol shape indicates the subcrop lithology to the sands/KCF (Kimmeridge Clay Formation), indicating whether the well was drilled on a pod/minibasin or an interpod/salt high. Well symbol colour indicates the age of sand present, if any.

study combines all available WCS wells and the regional 3D seismic data to develop a new geological model to predict the distribution of the Fulmar sands on the WCS. The model presented here is based on log correlations across Kittiwake and Durward/Dauntless combined with the gross morphology of key sediment packages derived from 3D seismic coverage.

Geological setting

Sand penetrations on the WCS

Around 90 well penetrations of Skagerrak (Triassic; Goldsmith *et al.* 1995), Middle Jurassic (Pentland Formation) and Upper Jurassic (Fulmar Formation) sands on the WCS and West Central Graben have been used to define the stratigraphic framework in this study (Fig. 1). A compilation of Mesozoic sand versus substrate lithology (Fig. 1) shows that the reservoirs of the WCS are invariably associated with a salt substrate, while adjacent Triassic (Smith Bank Formation) – cored 'highs' are covered only by marine muds of the KCF and Cromer Knoll Group. These observations raise the question of whether the sands were once present as a regional sheet, which was eroded prior to KCF deposition, or whether they were originally deposited only in irregular, topographically-controlled 'lows,' such as in salt-cored 'valleys', or in incised fluvial valleys cut into Triassic shales. Many published models, taking the well control at face value, implicitly assume the latter case (e.g. Wakefield *et al.* 1993). However, uneroded outliers of an originally regional shallow marine sand sheet on top of Triassic sediment pods would be economically important in the WCS Fulmar fairway, so this possibility should also be critically considered.

Depositional setting of the Fulmar shallow marine sands

Depositional models for the Fulmar sands favour a shallow marine shoreface to shallow shelf setting, with deposition occurring during a period of overall coastal retrogradation (e.g. Johnson *et al.* 1986; Gowland 1996; Howell *et al.* 1996). Despite a paucity of primary sedimentary structures, facies interpretations suggest a wave/storm-dominated shelf/shoreface depositional system, supported by the occasional preservation of storm-generated event beds. These interpretations have been augmented by detailed ichnofacies studies, aimed at providing independent constraints on palaeobathymetry and substrate-related conditions (e.g. Martin & Pollard 1996) and offering a higher resolution stratigraphic framework (e.g. Taylor & Gawthorpe 1993). Ichnofacies have been used to constrain water depth (e.g. Lockley *et al.* 1987; Ekdale 1988) leading to the successful use of trace fossil assemblages as palaeobathymetric indicators, particularly in shallow marine successions (see Frey *et al.* 1990, for full discussion). In the Fulmar sands, ichnofacies have been used to predict the nature of the substrate, prevalent energy regime, rates of deposition, salinity and oxygen levels (Howell *et al.* 1996). Ichnofacies have also underpinned interpretation of the Fulmar sands as an aggrading facies succession of shallow marine sands, implying that accommodation space filled by the Fulmar was evolving with time (Wakefield *et al.* 1993; Martin & Pollard 1996). In this context, the interpretation of a typical cored Fulmar well from the Durward/Dauntless area is considered.

Well 21/11-4 encountered *c.* 180 ft of Fulmar sand, which is pervasively burrowed, mainly by *Ophiomorpha*, and lacks diagnostic primary sedimentary structures. The paucity of facies associations consistent with deposition in 'transition zone' environments suggests that the sands are high energy shallow marine shoreface deposits with a dominantly aggradational sandbody architecture. The sands are interpreted as a series of amalgamated lower and middle shoreface sands and are predicted to have a sheet-like geometry with only very gradual (km–100s km) lateral facies variation (Gowland 1996).

Initial efforts to reconcile the dominantly *Ophiomorpha* burrowed sands with the aggradational nature of this sandbody resulted in a geological model based upon syn-Fulmar accommodation space creation (e.g. Wakefield *et al.* 1993). This model incorporated the possible misconception that a high energy shoreface remained throughout deposition at a consistent water depth to maintain the *Ophiomorpha*-dominated sand substrate. However, *Ophiomorpha* occurs over a wide range of sandy nearshore depositional environments, which have significantly different hydrodynamic regimes, salinity profiles and oxygen concentrations. (e.g. Pollard *et al.* 1993; Anderson & Droser, 1998). Hence, the predominance of the burrow-form *Ophiomorpha* need not indicate uniform palaeobathymetry.

Stratigraphic framework

The Jurassic section encountered in Kittiwake (21/17 & 18) is some 250 ft thicker than that in the contemporaneous Durward/Dauntless sections. The Kittiwake field lies *c.* 15 km east of Blocks 21/11 and 21/16 and oil-bearing Fulmar sands have been extensively cored. The Kittiwake sections yield a detailed stratigraphic architecture for the Upper Jurassic section on the WCS, which can be tested against, and used to resolve, the relatively attenuated sections found in the Durward/Dauntless wells.

Key candidate stratal surfaces were sampled for calibration in Kittiwake area Wells 21/18-2, 21/18-3, 21/18-5 and 21/18-6 with additional data from 21/17-3 and 21/17-4. In the Durward/Dauntless area, Wells 21/11-4, 21/16-1, 21/16-2, 21/16-3, and 21/16-4 were sampled. Using a combination of sedimentological, biostratigraphical and wireline log criteria, surfaces for genetic sequence stratigraphic correlation (*sensu* Galloway 1989) were identified. Additional candidate flooding surfaces are recognized which bound genetically related sediments where no biostratigraphically resolvable stratigraphic breaks occur. These surfaces correspond to the boundary between intervals displaying an overall upward increase in gamma ray response (retrograding unit) and the onset of the succeeding upward 'cleaning' of the gamma ray signature (prograding unit) (e.g. Partington *et al.* 1993*a*). These zones of maximum log response correspond to the most distal facies, or marine condensed sections (Loutit *et al.* 1988), and are widely interpreted as maximum flooding surfaces (mfs; e.g. Posamentier *et al.* 1988). The position of the most proximal facies within the progradational genetic unit is referred to here as the surface of maximum regression (mrs), equivalent to the maximum extent of progradation (e.g. Milton 1993). The correlation between the sequence framework employed here and other stratigraphic schemes is shown on Fig. 2.

Sequence stratigraphy

Up to ten genetic sequences have been defined by several correlatable maximum flooding surfaces in the Late Oxfordian to Ryazanian section (Figs 3 & 4). The stratigraphic envelope bounding these genetic sequences is defined by an erosional surface at its base (Base Jurassic unconformity) and by a minor sequence boundary at its top (Top Kimmeridge Clay Formation). The top surface corresponds to the boundary between the *stenomphalus* and *albidum* (PK2–PK3) ammonite zones and is of intra-Late Ryazanian age (Fig. 2; Rattey & Hayward

CHRONOSTRATIGRAPHY					BIOSTRATIGRAPHY		
PERIOD		AGE / STAGE			AMMONITE ZONES	PALYNOLOGICAL ZONES BIOSTRAT Ltd	MICROPALEONTOLOGY MICROSTRATIGRAPHIC SERVICES Ltd
CRETACEOUS	EARLY	VAL.(pars)		early	par	E. pharo PK4	
		RYAZANIAN		late	alb	D. spinosum PK3	
					sten		
					icenii	G.sp A Davey PK2	
				early	kochi	R. thula PK1	
					runct		
JURASSIC	LATE	VOLGIAN late	PORTLANDIAN	late	lamp	G. virgula PJ44	
					pre	G. gigas acme PJ43	
					prim		
		VOLGIAN middle		early	opp	E. polyplacophorum PJ42 b / a	
					ang	C. panneum PJ41 / S. jurassica PJ40	
					kerb	M. simplex PJ39	
					oku	M. simplex acme PJ38 c	
					gla	b	
					alb	a	
			KIMMERIDGIAN SENSU ANGLICO	late	fitt	O. patulum PJ37 d	
					rot	c	
					pall	b	
		VOLGIAN early			pect	a	
				'mid'	hud	O. patulum 'acme' PJ36	
					wheat	C. longicorne PJ35	
					scit	P. pannosum PJ34	
					eleg		
		KIMMERIDGIAN SENSU GALLICO		early	aut	E. luridum PJ33 b	
					eud	a	
					mut		
					cym	G. jurassica PJ32	
					bay	S. crystallinum PJ31	LJM7
		OXFORDIAN		late	ros	S. crystallinum acme PJ30	LJM8
					reg	E. galeritum PJ29	
					serr	E. galeritum acme PJ28 b / a	
					glos	C. polonicum PJ27	
				middle	ten	R. aemula PJ26	LJM9
					den	R. aemula acme PJ25	LJM10
				early	cord	W. fimbriata PJ24	LJM11
					mar	S. vestitum acme PJ23	

SEQUENCE STRATIGRAPHY					
Ma	PARTINGTON et al., 1993a	THIS STUDY DURWARD / DAUNTLESS	THIS STUDY KITTIWAKE		stratal surface
	K10			top-Kimmeridge-Clay-Formation	sb
129	J76	DDGU10	KGU9		
130	J74			lamplughi-PJ44	mfs
132	J73	DDGU9	KGU8	oppresus	mfs
		DDGU8		anguiformis	mfs
134	J72	DDGU7		kerberus	mfs
135	J71	DDGU6			
136	J66b	DDGU5	KGU7	fittoni-PJ37(c;d)	mfs
137	J66a (J65)	DDGU4		pectinatus-PJ37a	mfs
138	J64	DDGU3	KGU6	hudlestoni PJ36	mfs
				top Fulmar Formation	
140	J63	DDGU2c	KGU5	autissiodorensis-PJ33b	mfs
141	J62	DDGU2b	KGU4	eudoxus-PJ33a	mfs
		DDGU2a	KGU3	mutabilis PJ32/33a	mfs
			KGU2		mfs
		DDGU1	KGU1	cymodoce-PJ32	mfs
145	J56			Base Jurassic unconformity	sb
146	J54b				
147	J54a				
148	J52				
149	J46				

Fig. 2. Correlation between the genetic sequence stratigraphic framework employed here and other sequence stratigraphic, biostratigraphic and chronostratigraphic schemes. KGU: Kittiwake genetic unit. DDGU: Durward/Dauntless area genetic unit. sb: Sequence boundary. mfs: Maximum flooding surface.

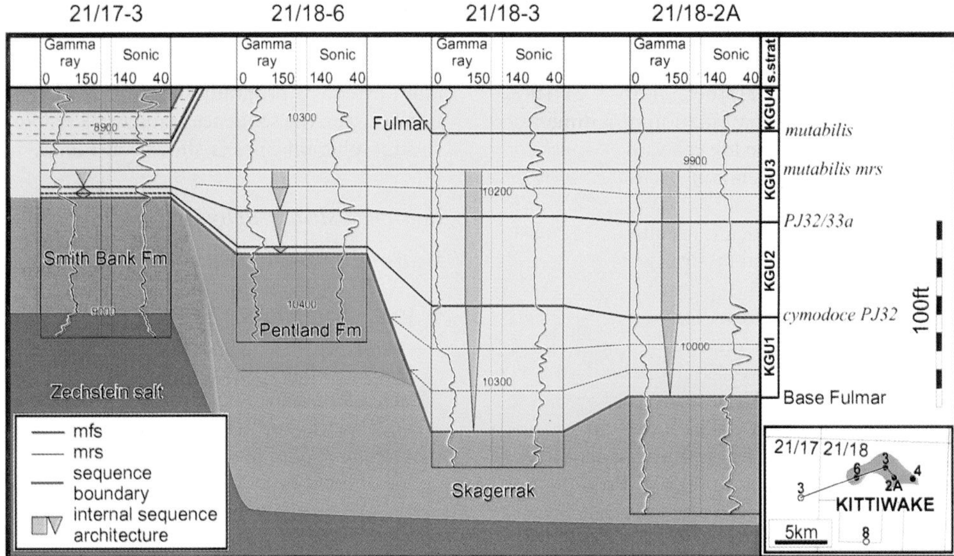

Fig. 3. Fulmar sequence variations, Kittiwake; flattened on the *mutabilis* mrs. We interpret the thickness variations in the pre-*mutabilis* sequences as representing onlap fill; see text for discussion.

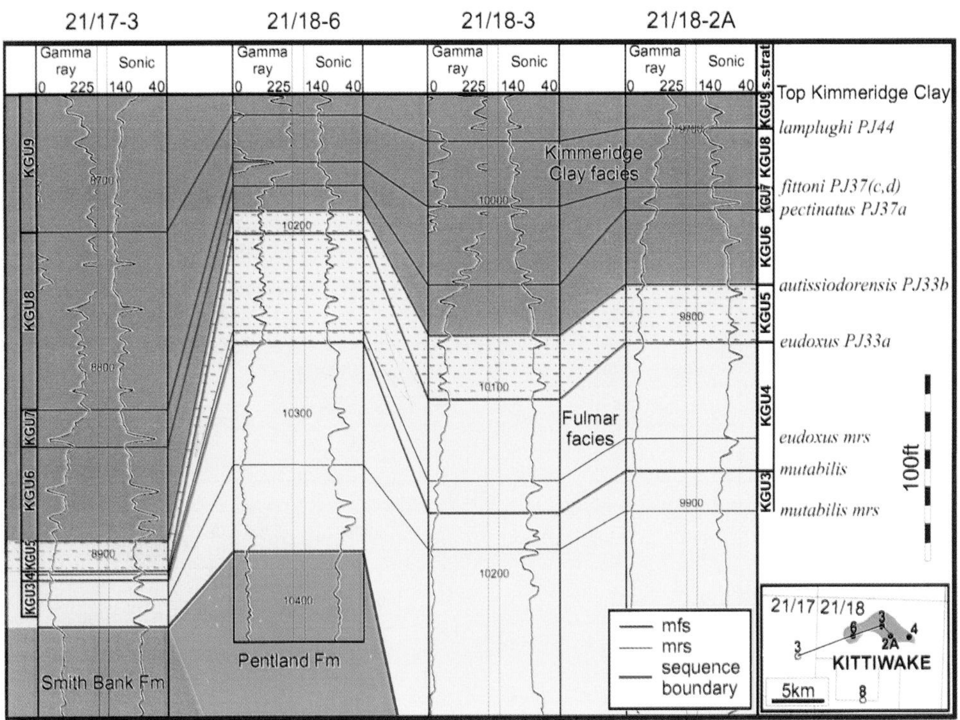

Fig. 4. Intra-Kimmeridge Clay Formation and Fulmar sequence thickness variations, Kittiwake. Section flattened on top Kimmeridge Clay Formation.

1993). The prominent maximum flooding surfaces used here for correlation (tied to ammonite nomenclature where possible) are *cymodoce* (PJ32), (PJ32/33a), *mutabilis*, *eudoxus* (PJ33a), *autissiodorensis* (PJ33b), *pectinatus* (PJ37a), *fittoni* (PJ37d) and *lamplughi* (PJ44).

Sequence stratigraphic well correlation – Kittiwake. The nine genetic sequences in the Kittiwake area are labelled KGU1-9 (Fig. 2). Flattening key Kittiwake wells on the *mutabilis* mrs (Fig. 3), highlights the geometry and nature of lateral facies and thickness variations in sequences KGU1-3. The *cymodoce* PJ32 mfs is recognizable in all wells and can be traced westwards towards Blocks 21/11 and 21/16. This mfs bounds the first major sand package in Wells 21/18-2A and 21/18-3 and, although highly condensed, is present at the base of the Jurassic section in Wells 21/18-6 and 21/17-3 to the west. The sequence architecture within KGU1 consists of an overall 'progradational', cleaning upward profile. The KGU2 sequence consists of a dominantly aggradational sand package in Wells 21/18-3 and 21/18-2A (Fig. 3). In contrast, time equivalent facies architectures in Wells 21/18-6 and 21/17-3 are dominated by thin progradational stacking patterns (Fig. 3). KGU3 sequence architectures in Wells 21/18-2A, 21/18-3 and 21/18-6 are generally aggradational.

Contemporaneous depositional sequences in Blocks 21/16 and 21/11 (labelled DDGU1-10; Fig. 2) are dominated by high energy shallow marine shoreface sands, with little evidence for distal shoreface or offshore transition silts and muds. The changes in sequence stacking reflect the availability of accommodation space with aggrading genetic units representing accommodation space availability during high stand deposition (e.g. Gawthorpe *et al.* 1994). Between the Base Fulmar unconformity surface and the *mutablis* mrs, prograding units reflect a basin physiography with limited accommodation potential and the resultant dominantly offlapping stratal geometries are associated with minor incision and local sequence boundary development. Overall, the sequences thin westwards and define a pinchout geometry. Where accommodation volume was limited, stratigraphic thinning was accomplished by deposition of only the upper section of each successive genetic unit. Younger genetic units are more consistent in thickness and this onlap–fill relationship can be accounted for by the gradual reduction of accommodation space potential as sediments infill pre-existing topography. No obvious divergent stratal relationships are evident below the *mutabilis* mrs, with only the youngest parts of the genetic stratigraphic sequences defining a back-stepping architecture. This suggests that topography existed prior to deposition of 'Fulmar' facies.

The west–east correlation of surfaces broadly defines a clinoform geometry with up-dip terminations of stratal surfaces defining landward onlap with apparent progressive coastal encroachment. The progressive landward encroachment of proximal marine sediments within each genetic stratigraphic unit indicates the development of slight regional tilt to the east. In this part of the WCS, progressive coastal onlap culminates in the widely documented *eudoxus* mfs sea-level maximum, which occurs throughout the Central North Sea (e.g. Donovan *et al.* 1993; Milton 1993; Partington *et al.* 1993*b*; Underhill & Partington 1993; Carruthers *et al.* 1996; Davies *et al.* 1996; Harker & Rieuf 1996).

Wells flattened on the top Kimmeridge Clay Formation illustrate Kimmeridge clay facies distribution in the Kittiwake area (Fig. 4). Significant genetic sequence thickness variations occur above the prominent *pectinatus* mfs from west to east (Fig. 4). Genetic units above the *pectinatus* mfs are opposite to the trend observed in the pre-*eudoxus* genetic stratigraphic units, where sections dramatically thin westwards. For example, Well 21/17-3 has an expanded shelfal mudstone facies section in relation to Wells 21/18-6 and 21/18-2A, which both have a condensed, but complete, time equivalent stratigraphic section. Stratal thickening of these offshore shelf mud-dominated sequences suggests a different mechanism for generating accommodation volume compared with that of the older genetic units.

In addition, the preservation of stratally thickened sequence architectures infers a syn-depositional component to accommodation volume creation.

Sequence stratigraphic well correlation – Durward/Dauntless. There are ten genetic sequences in the Durward/Dauntless area, labelled DDGU1-10 (Fig. 2). The majority of well penetrations encounter 50–200 ft of Upper Jurassic sediments, which are dominated by mudstone facies. A key issue is the stratigraphic age relationship between 'Fulmar' facies found in the Durward/Dauntless area and those penetrated in Blocks 21/17 and 21/18.

Between the Base Fulmar Unconformity and the Top Kimmeridge Clay Formation nine mfs define the ten genetic stratigraphic sequences. The prominent mfs (provisionally tied to the nearest ammonite zones) used for correlation are *cymodoce* (PJ32), *autissiodorensis* (PJ33b), *hudelstoni* (PJ36), *pectinatus* (PJ37a), *fittoni* (PJ37d), *kerberus*, *anguiformis*, *opressus* and *lamplughi* (PJ44). Most of these are common to the surfaces documented in Blocks 21/17 & 21/18 with the exception of those flooding surfaces which are resolved locally in expanded stratigraphic sections and where more detailed sampling has permitted greater resolution, for example PJ32/33a, *mutabilis*, *eudoxus* PJ33a (lower sections in Kittiwake) – and *hudelstoni*, *kerberus*, *anguiformis* and *oppressus* (upper section in Durward/Dauntless).

A projected west–east section from Dauntless to Durward, flattened on the *autissiodorensis* mrs (Fig. 5), enables comparison with the Fulmar sands in Kittiwake (Fig. 3). The *cymodoce* PJ32 mfs is present in all of the wells in both areas, constraining the age of the oldest Fulmar sands, which equates to the base of palynozone PJ32 and the boundary between the J56/J62 depositional sequence of Partington *et al.* (1993*a*) (Fig. 2). The sands were deposited over a maximum time period of around 1 Ma, corresponding to a rate of relative sea-level rise of 0.3m/1000 year. The DDGU1 sequence shows lateral thickness variations, pinch-out geometries and internal sequence stacking pattern contrasts. Where accommodation volume is present, dominantly aggradational successions were deposited. This is observed in both Wells 21/11-4 and 21/16-2, whereas in Wells 21/16-1 and 21/16-3, progradational sequence stacking combined with much reduced thickness implies more limited accommodation space availability. Maximum reservoir sandbody development and deposition occurs in sequence DDGU2. Increased accommodation volume resulted from a rise in relative sea-level associated with the *eudoxus* and *autissiodorensis* marine trangressions. Sequence thickening is generally achieved in this area by onlap infill of a pre-existing topography, with only the youngest parts of the genetic sequence deposited when accommodation space was limited. The sequence stratigraphic stacking patterns appear very consistent between the Durward/Dauntless and Kittiwake areas, with high quality reservoir sand development confined to Kimmeridgian strata (*sensu* gallico). The age of the youngest sands in the Durward/Dauntless area (*autissiodorensis* mfs) is younger than at Kittiwake, which is consistent with the retrogradational nature of sandbody deposition as the coastal/shoreface sand belt moved progressively westwards in response to rising relative sea-level and eastwards regional tilt.

Implications of correlation between Wells 21/11-4 and 21/16-4. The interval between the Base Cretaceous 'unconformity' (conformable with the top of the Jurassic in this part of the WCS) and Top Zechstein reflectors in these two wells is similar in thickness and seismic character (Fig. 6). Over 280 ft of Upper Jurassic section is present in each case, but the facies are markedly different. Genetic sequence correlation between Wells 21/11-4, 21/16-4 and 21/17-3 (Fig. 6) based on previous geological models would have required the basal section preserved in Well 21/16-4 (pre-*autissiodorensis* mfs lower shoreface to offshore transition zone muds) to be younger than any shallow marine shelf sand facies encountered locally (Wakefield *et al.* 1993). However, the well correlation in this study (Fig. 6) demonstrates that: (1) contemporaneous shoreface and offshore facies were being deposited sub-regionally; and (2) accommodation volume existed prior to the *autissiodorensis* marine transgression.

Genetic sequences within the Kimmeridge Clay Formation are expanded. As with the internal sequence character in Kittiwake trend wells (Fig. 4), a complete post-*autissiodorensis* mfs stratigraphic section is preserved with no obvious lateral pinch-out of genetic units. Stratal thickening is achieved by divergence and the expanded genetic units are interpreted here as infilling syn-depositionally generated accommodation volume.

The genetic architectures in these wells reflect two contrasting processes of accommodation infill: (1) lateral pinch-out of stratal surfaces with infill of accommodation space via onlap of progressively younger genetic units, which dominates pre-*autissiodorensis* times (i.e. 'Fulmar' deposition); and (2) divergent growth sequences of Kimmeridge Clay facies into increasing accommodation space, which is more characteristic of post-*autissiodorensis* mfs stratigraphy.

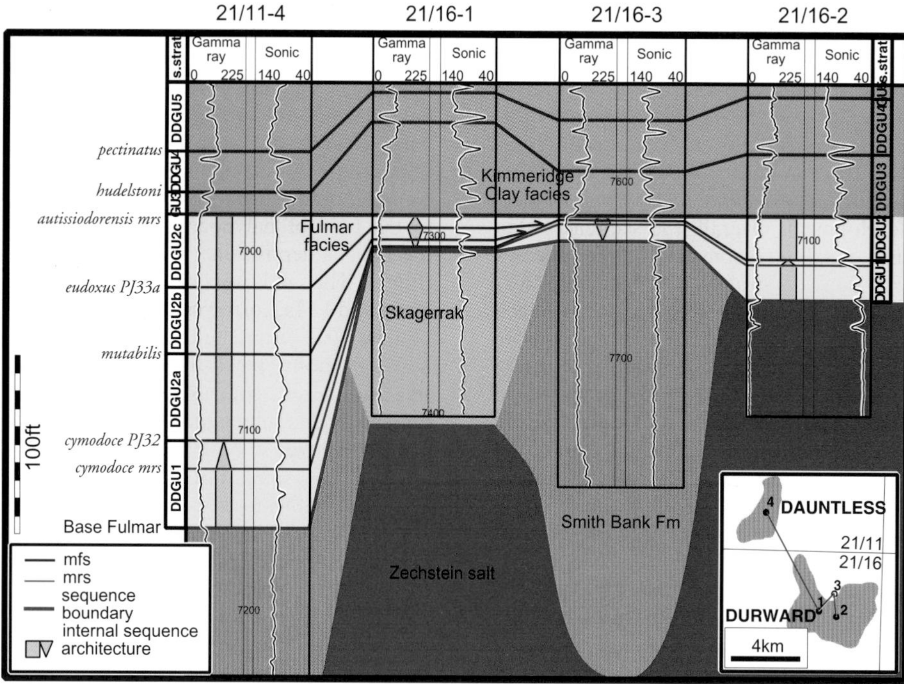

Fig. 5. Fulmar sequence variations, Durward/Dauntless exploration wells. Section flattened on *autissiodorensis* mrs.

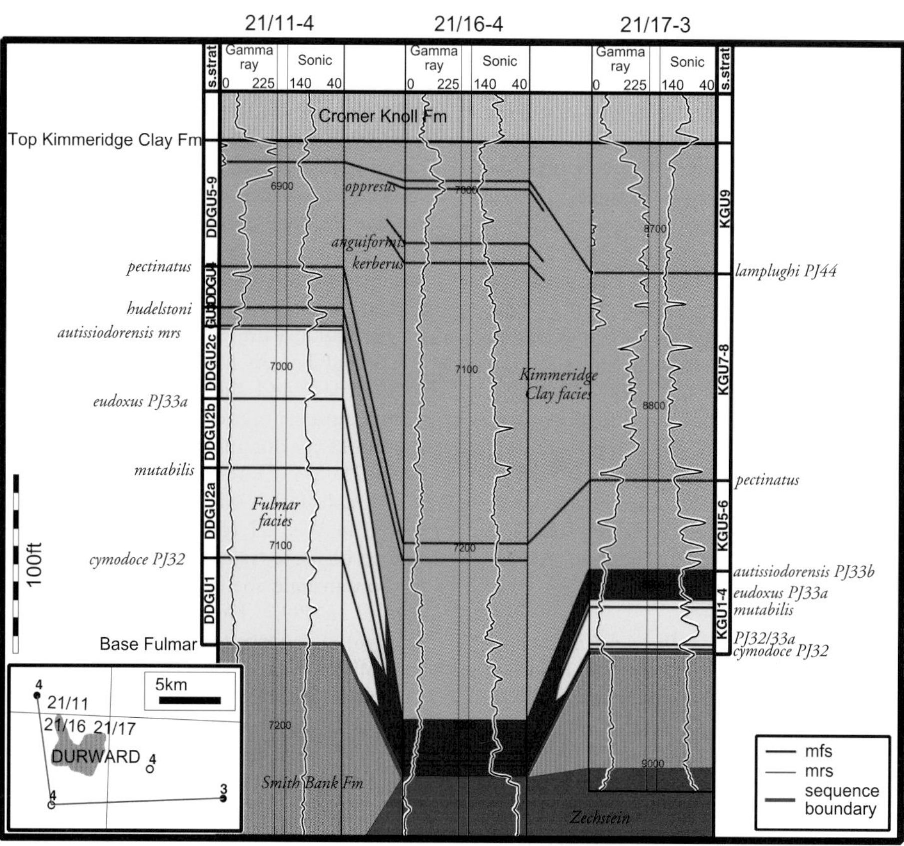

Fig. 6. Comparison of 21/11-4 with exploration wells drilled on salt highs 21/16-4 and 21/17-3. Pre-*autissiodorensis* section in 21/16-4 is a mudstone equivalent of the sands in 21/11-4 and 21/17-3. The Kimmeridge Clay Formation in the salt high wells is expanded relative to 21/11-4.

Development well control – Durward/Dauntless. In the Dauntless Field, Well 21/11-C2 is drilled several hundred metres northwest of Well 21/11-4. Figure 7 illustrates the stratal architecture between those wells and two further wells drilled structurally higher on an adjacent Smith Bank pod. Only the youngest part of the genetic unit defined by *eudoxus* PJ33a mfs and *autissiodorensis* mfs is present in Well 21/11-C2 (Fig. 7). Progressive onlap of all pre-*pectinatus* genetic units onto the depositional surface is apparent, implying that the pre-existing topography controlling accommodation space persisted into the time of KCF deposition. Indeed, Well 21/11-2 drilled on the crest of the same sediment pod, encountered only 15 ft of hot shale between the Cromer Knoll and Smith Bank sediments (Fig. 7).

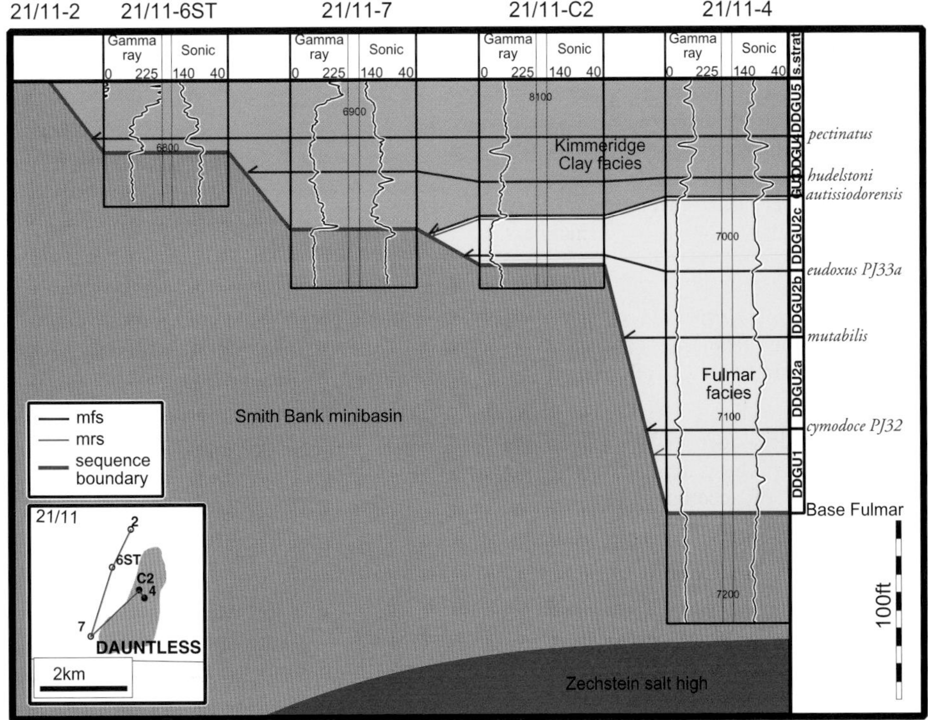

Fig. 7. Comparison between exploration Well 21/11-4, development Well 21/11-C2 and exploration Wells 21/11-7 and 21/11-6A drilled higher on the same Triassic pod illustrating loss of the Fulmar sands and Kimmeridge Clay Formation from the base up. Well 21/11-2, drilled on the very crest of this Triassic pod, contains no pre-*pectinatus* strata. These relationships are interpreted here as onlap fill.

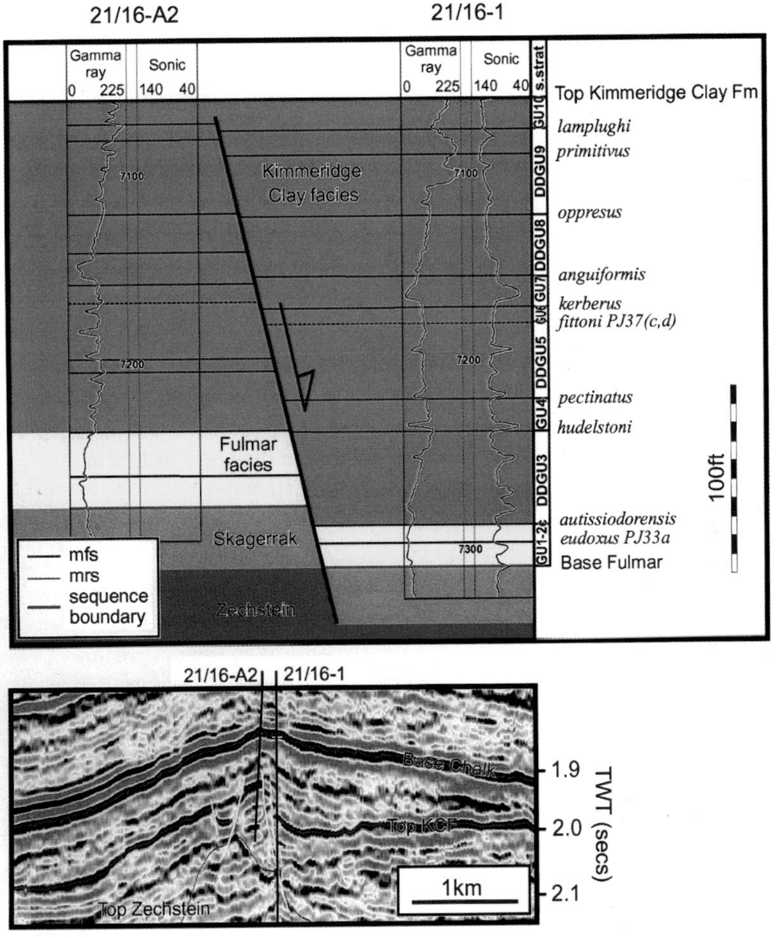

Fig. 8. Comparison between exploration Well 21/16-1 and development Well 21/16-A2. These wells are drilled on either side of a seismically resolvable fault offsetting the top Jurassic; the section is flattened on top Jurassic. Thickening of the Kimmeridge Clay Formation across the fault is apparent in most of the genetic sequences, suggesting that movement across the fault began in the Upper Jurassic. Note that in contrast the Fulmar Formation does not thicken towards the downthrown side of the fault.

In the Durward Field, Wells 21/16-1 and 21/16-A2 are drilled 180 m apart on the downthrown and upthrown sides, respectively, of a fault which has a 50 ft throw at top Jurassic level. The Fulmar section is slightly thicker on the upthrown side of the fault, but the KCF section thickens across the fault into the hanging wall in most of the genetic units (Fig. 8). It is acknowledged that the Fulmar section could be tectonically thinned in Well 21/16-1. However, this correlation suggests that, regardless of whether the fault affected Fulmar thickness, it was active during KCF times.

Sequence stratigraphic conclusions (Kittiwake and Durward/Dauntless). The main conclusions from the sequence stratigraphic panels generated in this study are as follows:

(1) Nine mfs divide the Late Oxfordian to Ryazanian stratigraphy into around ten genetic sequences, which display a variety of sequence stacking patterns related to different mechanisms and magnitudes of accommodation volume development.
(2) The *cymodoce* mfs constrains the age of the oldest sands within both the Kittiwake and Durward/Dauntless trend wells, inferring that no significant regional tilt existed at this time.
(3) The *eudoxus/autissiodorensis* mfs (i.e. DDGU2c/KGU5) separate two distinct phases of accommodation space infill.
(4) Pre-*eudoxus/autissiodorensis* mfs stratigraphy is characterized by: lateral thickness variations and pinch-out geometries of sand-dominated shoreface facies; mudstone facies occurring as distal, lateral time equivalents of the shoreface sands; stratigraphic architecture dominated by onlap and coastal retrogradation with younger genetic stratigraphic units progressively preserved during overall marine transgression; genetic unit thickness variability reduced with time, implying a gradual decay of the topographically-enhanced accommodation volume.
(5) Post-*eudoxus/autissiodorensis* mfs stratigraphy is characterized by: lateral thickness variations within individual genetic sequences, each dominated by open marine pelagic/hemipelagic sediments; thinned, condensed sequences preserving complete stratigraphic sections; thicker, expanded genetic sequences displaying stratal divergence and thickening across faults, which root on to salt highs; accommodation volume development related to syn-depositional processes, which appear to become increasingly important during marine transgression.

Seismic interpretation and regional evaluation

3D seismic data cover most of the WCS and are generally of sufficient quality to map the Base Cretaceous, Top Salt and Top Basement. Unfortunately, the Jurassic section tends to be close to, or below, the limit of seismic resolution. However, the seismic data have been used to consider the geological evolution of the WCS from a regional perspective, yielding conclusions for incorporation into the geological model, which are additional to those derived from the well-based sequence stratigraphic studies discussed earlier.

Lower Triassic minibasin (pod) geometry

The most striking aspect of the pre-Cretaceous geology of the WCS is a ubiquitous development of salt 'walls' and intervening sediment minibasins (Fig. 9). The sediment minibasins have previously been termed 'pods' and 'rafts' (e.g. Hodgson *et al.* 1992; Penge *et al.* 1993); the term 'minibasin' is used here following recent studies of similar structures in the Gulf of Mexico (e.g. Rowan & Weimer 1998). The minibasins subsided into the Zechstein salt, which had an initial thickness of *c.* 1 km in this area (Smith *et al.* 1993). The minibasins are filled with

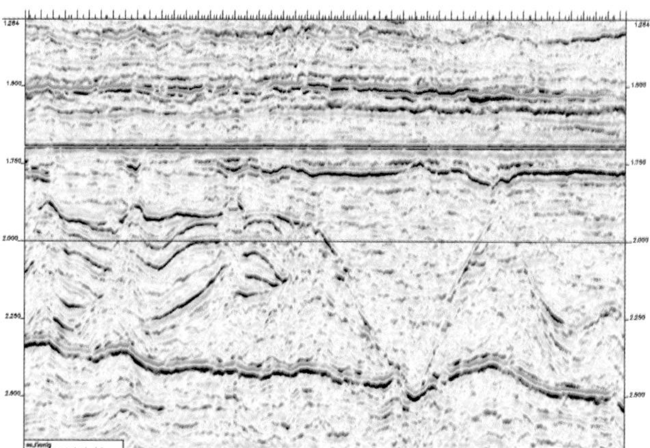

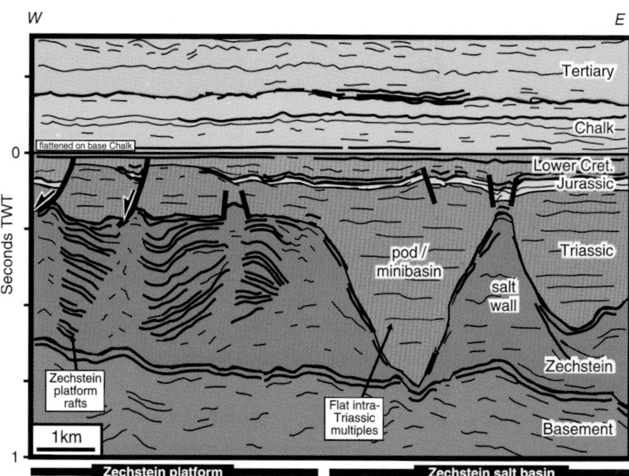

Fig. 9. Seismic section and geoseismic interpretation showing the architecture of minibasins and salt highs which underlie the thin Jurassic section. The relatively thick 'salt' interval at the west end of the section is part of the Zechstein platform and contains carbonate and sulphate interbeds, and was not prone to redistribution in the Triassic (Clark *et al.* 1998).

lower Triassic Smith Bank shale and are characterized by the following features (Fig. 10).

(1) Generally linear geometries, although blob-like and dendritic examples can be found. Typical dimensions are in the order of a few kilometres wide, around ten kilometres long and in the order of 1.5 km thick. The trend, where discernable, is northeast–southwest. Several intersecting linear trends are present, with the salt wall network mirroring the geometry of the minibasin system.

(2) Pockmarks caused by salt chimneys, which are usually circular in plan view and are narrower than the salt walls. These salt chimneys form the roots of circular faults which are elements of a pervasive fault system offsetting the Top Jurassic but not the Top Lower Cretaceous (described later).

(3) The location and trend of the salt walls and minibasins are unrelated to basement faults as a result of structural detachment in the Zechstein salt (e.g. Hospers *et al.* 1988; Penge *et al.* 1993). Faults at basement level are usually an order of magnitude smaller in throw than the typical minibasin thickness.

(4) The geometry of the salt high/minibasin system is very similar to that produced in analogue models of thin-skinned extension (Guglielmo *et al.* 1997).

(5) The Smith Bank shales are seismically transparent, as is the adjacent Zechstein halite. The internal geometry of the minibasins is, therefore, unknown and on seismic data they are characterized by multiples generated by the overlying

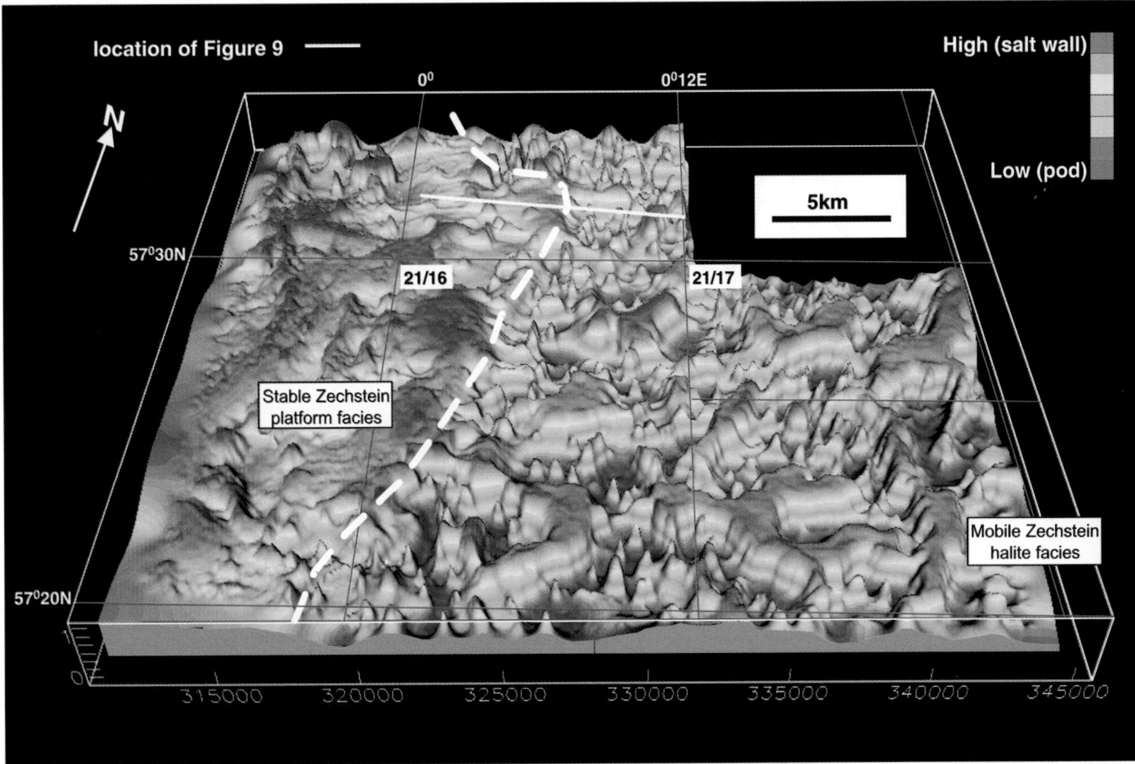

Fig. 10. 3D perspective view from the south, lit from the southwest, of a surface representing the proportion of Triassic relative to Zechstein (surface = Triassic isochore/[Triassic + Zechstein isochore]). x-axis scale in metres. The proportional surface is displayed rather than the isochore or depth surfaces to exclude the effects of late faults and regional tilt. Red corresponds to high salt proportion (salt high), blue to high Triassic proportion (minibasin). Dashed line represents the edge of the tectonically stable Zechstein 'platform' facies (see also Fig. 9) and corresponds to the limits of pronounced Triassic minibasin subsidence.

Chalk/Base Cretaceous reflectors (these multiples can be misinterpreted as onlap fill).

(6) The bottoms of the minibasins invariably rest on top of mechanical basement, usually the Top Rotliegend. Well control shows that the mid to late Triassic Skagerrak sands lie on top of the adjacent salt, suggesting that minibasin subsidence was completed by mid-Triassic times.

Significance of the base Upper Jurassic unconformity

The cessation in the production of minibasin accommodation space was governed by the rate of minibasin subsidence and the original thickness of the Zechstein isopach. Smith *et al.* (1993) note that the Skagerrak fluvial systems were forming synchronously: (1) on salt highs upon the platforms which flank the WCG (such as the WCS), suggesting that minibasin subsidence was complete in these locations; and (2) on top of Smith Bank shale within the minibasins of the basin centre, suggesting ongoing minibasin subsidence in the WCG. They attribute this to thickening of the Zechstein isopach towards the basin centre (now the Central Graben; their figs 4 & 5). Wakefield *et al.* (1993) point out that cored Skagerrak on the WCS can be heavily fractured in comparison with the overlying Jurassic sands and they suggest that the Skagerrak now occurs in down-faulted outliers, which are remnants of an originally more extensive fluvial system. However, Wakefield *et al.* (1993) do not suggest that the Skagerrak was originally sheet-like on the WCS. Instead, they recognized that minibasin grounding occurred prior to Skagerrak deposition in this area and suggested that differential subaerial erosion led to topography characterized by palaeovalleys centred on salt highs in the Middle and Upper Triassic (see also Penge *et al.* 1993).

The subaerial exposure signified by the fluvial middle to late Triassic facies marks the onset of a period of differential erosion of the grounded minibasin system which lasted until Upper Jurassic transgression. This represents a period of approximately 80 Ma punctuated only by a marginal marine, fluvio-estuarine incursion, which left a minor Middle Jurassic outlier in the Kittiwake area (Well 21/18-6; Wakefield *et al.* 1993). Very little published data on the geomorphology of eroded, inactive minibasin systems are available to substantiate this aspect of geological models for the Upper Jurassic of the WCS.

Where the Upper Jurassic sequence is thick enough to be resolved on seismic data, it commonly displays geometries which can be interpreted as onlap on to palaeovalley flanks (Smith Bank 'hillsides' – Fig. 11; Wakefield *et al.* 1993).

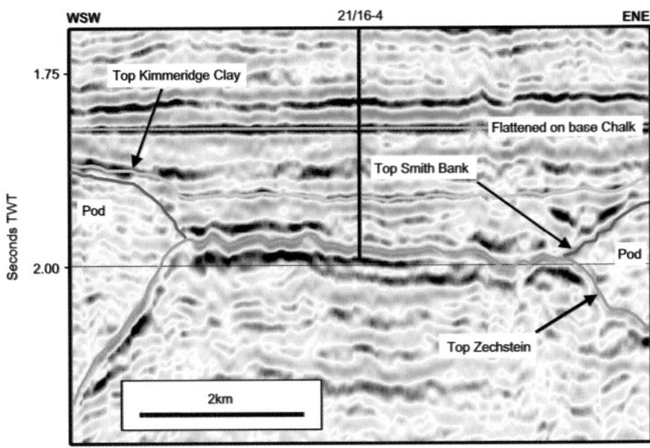

Fig. 11. Section through the salt high drilled by 21/16-4 showing thickening of the Jurassic sequence towards the salt high from the adjacent Triassic minibasins/pods. The majority of the Jurassic section in this thick is KCF.

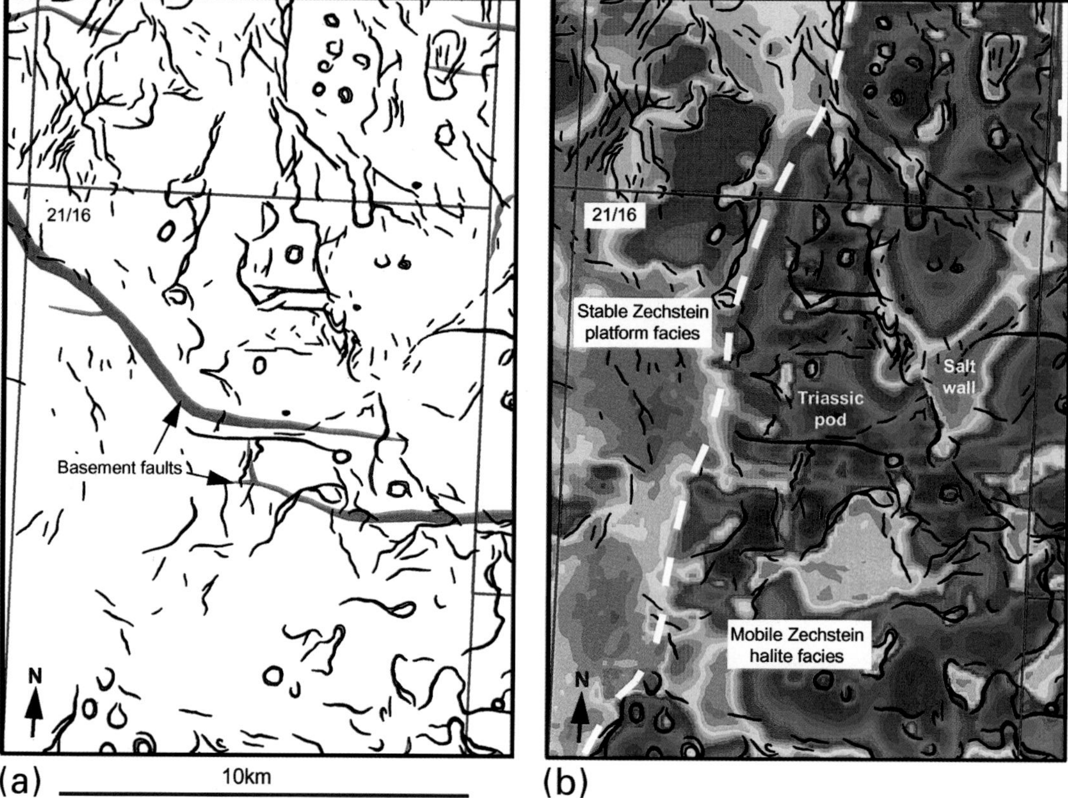

Fig. 12. Comparison of the fault system mapped at Base Cretaceous level with basement faults (**a**) and the salt architecture (**b**). There is no relationship between the Base Cretaceous faults and the basement structures, but a strong correspondence between the Base Cretaceous faults and the location and geometry of the salt.

Late Jurassic faulting – evidence for salt dissolution?

In the Block 21/16 area a complex array of minor faults offsets the Upper Jurassic (the Base Chalk is unfaulted). This fault system is described in more detail by Clark *et al.* (1999), from which this summary has been drawn. The fault population in plan view displays a spectrum of shapes varying from linear to circular. Fault lengths range from 200–300 m to 5 km, the strongly curved/circular faults vary in diameter from 100 to 1000 m and the maximum displacement on the largest faults is in the order of 100 m (exceeding the maximum Fulmar sand thickness recorded in this area). Fault orientations are apparently random and display no correlation with basement fault structures (Fig. 12a). The well control has shown that these faults were active in the Volgian (Fig. 8). Decompaction of the KCF suggests that only a minor proportion of the observed thickening of the Cromer Knoll Group across these faults is a result of compaction of the KCF (Fig. 13), implying that active faulting continued into the Lower Cretaceous (Wakefield *et al.* 1993; Dickinson 1996).

The following observations regarding the fault system can be made:

(1) There is a strong link between this Upper Jurassic fault pattern and the structure of the top Zechstein surface (Fig. 12b). The faults invariably overlie salt highs (i.e. where the salt was near base level and therefore subject to groundwater circulation) and the plan view shape of the fault is often seen to reflect that of the underlying salt high. Circular faults overlie salt chimneys and linear faults root on to the salt walls.

(2) The faults die out downwards in the Zechstein salt.

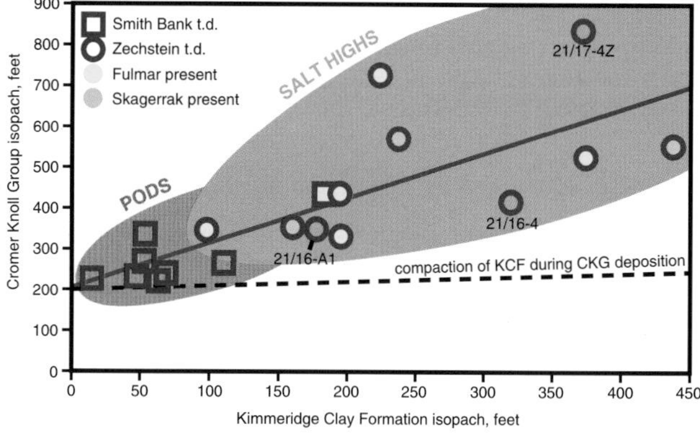

Fig. 13. Graph of Cromer Knoll Group (lower Cretaceous) thickness plotted against Kimmeridge Clay Formation thickness as encountered in 19 exploration wells in Blocks 21/11, 21/12, 21/16 and 21/17. There is a reasonable relationship between Cromer Knoll and KCF thickness. The decompaction trend shows the thickness of Cromer Knoll predicted from compaction of the KCF (assuming that an additional 200 ft of Cromer Knoll Group sediment was deposited as a result of regional subsidence), implying that accommodation space creation in Cromer Knoll times was dominated by other mechanisms and that the fault array mapped at base Cretaceous was active into the lower Cretaceous. The data points also define two relatively distinct fields corresponding to pods and salt highs (the lithology at well total depth is indicated by squares vs circles), showing that more accommodation space was being generated on the salt highs relative to the adjacent pods in KCF and Cromer Knoll Group times. The data points also indicate whether sand was present; the anomalous wells are discussed in the text.

(3) The sense of displacement on these faults is always down towards the salt high.
(4) The faults are similar to documented examples of structures associated with salt dissolution (review by Johnson 1997; 3D seismic example of karst in Hardage *et al.* 1996).

The variety of geometries and orientations of the faults and the presence of circular faults in particular rules out regional extension as a causal mechanism. In conclusion, it would appear that salt dissolution is the most likely mechanism to have generated the late Jurassic/early Cretaceous fault system in this area.

Conclusions from well & seismic data

The well-based sequence stratigraphy and the seismic-based regional geological evaluation both conclude that pre-Fulmar topography was a key factor in determining Fulmar sand distribution. This contrasts with the view that the intimate relationship between Fulmar presence and salt highs is indicative of syn-Fulmar salt dissolution-dominated accommodation space development (Wakefield *et al.* 1993).

In contrast, several inter-related controls potentially play a role in determining KCF distribution and thickness. Of the list of possible accommodation space controls, those which do not appear to find a place in the model offered here are thin-skinned extension, basement faulting and 'random, spontaneous' salt movements. In contrast, salt dissolution, differential compaction and ultimately (certainly by Cromer Knoll times), regional tilt are significant. The importance of both palaeotopography and salt dissolution in governing accommodation space is also noted in the salt valley–sediment minibasin system of the South Oman Salt Basin, which is closely analogous to the WCS (Heward 1990). Relative variations in the significance of these controls from Fulmar to Cromer Knoll times underpin the geological model and are discussed later.

Geological model for the Mesozoic in the 21/16, 21/11 area

Fulmar sand source

The majority of sediment supplied to the WCS and WCG was probably provided by fluvial systems draining the extensive stable platform areas to the west and southwest (Johnson *et al.* 1986; Howell *et al.* 1996). Sediment supply may have been localized within fault transfer zones on the WCG margin (e.g. Roberts *et al.* 1990) while coastal erosion of intra-basinal highs may have provided more limited amounts of sediment (Rattay & Hayward 1993; Stewart 1993; Dickinson 1996).

The most favoured sediment source rocks are the Triassic Skagerrak sands, which are thought to have been sourced from the Scandian shield (Jeans *et al.* 1993) as well as eastern Scotland. The most proximal Triassic to the Grampian High, that in the Forth Approaches Basin, has significant net sand including coarse fractions which are rare in the WCS (e.g. Well 26/8-1).

Heavy mineral analyses show that the Fulmar of the WCS has the same mineralogical characteristics as the local Skagerrak sands (low monazite, high chrome spinel, high apatite; Hallsworth, 1994). The grain size of the Fulmar is, however, often coarser than that of locally preserved Skagerrak sands. The Fulmar heavy mineral signature appears to show source area variability across the CNS and often appears to be dominantly locally sourced. The Fulmar of the WCS is most likely reworked Skagerrak from the extensive up-dip source areas to the west (e.g. Forth Approaches Basin) and, to a much lesser extent, from existing *in-situ* valley fills (e.g. Wakefield *et al.* 1993).

The inferred wave/storm-dominated processes would have been effective in promoting considerable lateral sediment transportation (10s–100s km) and the development of laterally extensive sandy coastal/shoreface zones parallel to depositional strike (e.g. Gowland 1996). These were partly fault controlled in the WCG (Howell *et al.* 1996). The uniformity of facies characteristics implies that depositional processes were relatively uniform, both spatially and temporally, even though the geometry of the preserved sandbodies is highly variable. For example, Fulmar shoreface deposits of the WCG, which trend parallel to the gross shoreline orientation, are identical in terms of their facies to the so-called incised valley fills of the WCS (e.g. Wakefield *et al.* 1993), which trend perpendicular to shoreline strike. This suggests that the type of accommodation space, its rate of creation and its subsequent preservation are more important in controlling sand distribution than the actual depositional environment. These possible controls are discussed in the following sections.

Topography – 2D considerations

To illustrate some of the effects of the interplay between topographic evolution and sediment distribution on the WCS, the evolution of an idealized valley fill through time is first considered in a simple 2D model (Fig. 14a, b). Several factors work against the valley being filled in a simple layer-cake manner, as shown in Fig. 14a, b. Firstly, topography of the valley floor itself may not be absolutely flat because of stratigraphic heterogeneities within the underlying Zechstein (Gatliff *et al.* 1994). Intra-salt rafts of carbonate/sulphate/shale would be added to the residual cap rock during lower Triassic diapirism and salt dissolution. Any resulting local cap rock thicks would form positive features on the valley floor as a result of differential erosion. Positive topographic features result from this process in recently exposed salt basins (Fig. 15a, b). Secondly, there is the possibility of an irregular topographic infill by pre-Fulmar sediments, such as Skagerrak and more rarely Middle Jurassic Pentland fluvial/esturine sediments (Fig. 1).

The pre-Fulmar fill of salt-floored valleys is not ubiquitous, for two reasons. Firstly, there was a long period between Skagerrak deposition and the Upper Jurassic, during which subaerial erosion (e.g. during the Middle Jurassic) would have removed some of the Skagerrak fill. Secondly, under certain circumstances 3D topographic control could have prevented the original deposition of the Skagerrak. For example, isolated basin-like salt valleys are less likely to have been accessed by fluvial systems than, say, a location at the intersection of two valleys. This important topographic issue is considered more fully in the next section with reference to the Fulmar.

The combination of Permian outliers forming positive features on the valley floors with a partial fill of pre-Fulmar fluvial sediments means that a more realistic 2D geological model can be constructed reflecting the geological evolution of the area in the 80 Ma period prior to Fulmar deposition (Fig. 14c, d). This model accounts for the variation in pre-KCF stratigraphy on the Durward East salt high drilled by Wells 21/16-2, 21/16-A1 and 21/16-A1Z (Fig. 14c, d).

Topography – 3D considerations

Aspects of the control of irregular topography on the distribution of fluvial and shallow marine sediments can be visualized by considering the contrasting likelihoods of sand reaching an isolated, basin-shaped hollow completely surrounded by low hills with that of sand arriving at the intersection of linear valleys which are well-connected to the sand source area. The latter could be a connection through: (1) an estuary with a shallow marine shelf; or (2) linkage with an up-dip highland

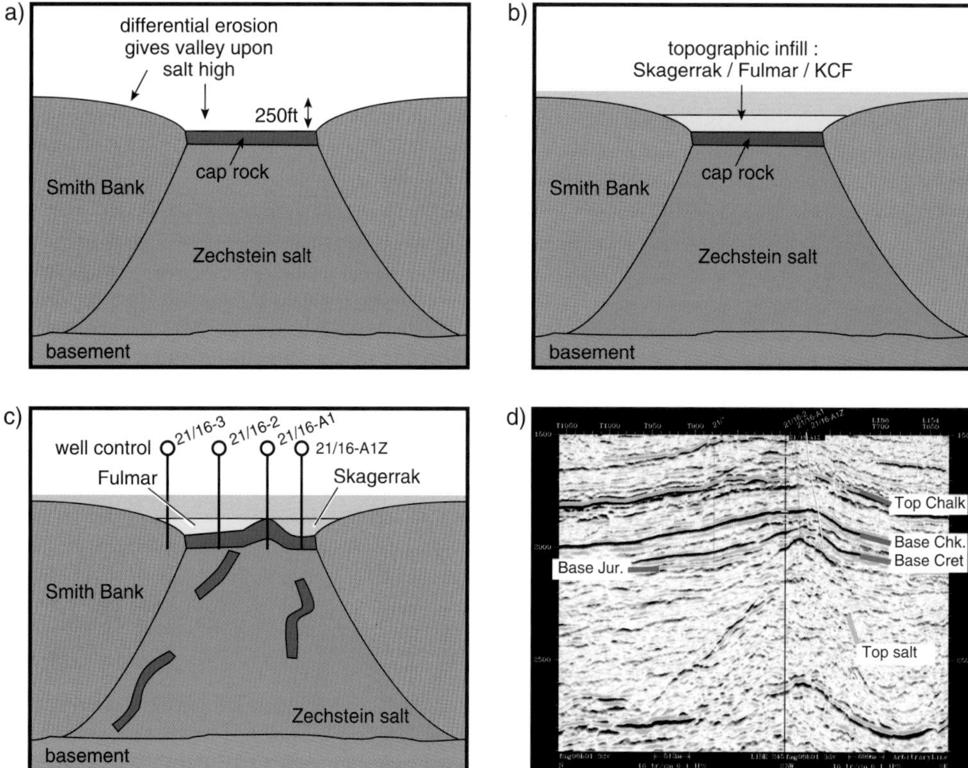

Fig. 14. The geology of a salt valley considered in 2D, taking into account pre-Upper Jurassic erosion and depositional events. (**a**) Differential erosion of the salt relative to adjacent grounded Triassic minibasins in the period Late Triassic–Late Jurassic. (**b**) Simple undifferentiated sand fill of the valley. This sand/salt relationship characterizes most published models of Fulmar distribution. (**c**) Possible valley fill architecture taking into account differential erosion of the Zechstein itself which could lead to minor hills on the valley floor resulting from the presence of allochthonous interbeds; and Skagerrak sands which may have been partially eroded in the Early/Middle Jurassic to give outliers which are onlapped by the Fulmar sands. (**d**) Section through Durward East showing valley topography. The stratigraphy encountered by each well corresponds with that shown schematically in (c).

area through a fluvial drainage network. A connectivity parameter can be defined which expresses the degree of isolation of a given valley or location. This parameter is a measure of how likely sand transport processes could access that location; the better the connection, the more likely that location would be to receive sand during a highstand. This parameter can only be estimated from good 3D seismic control. In addition to this aspect of the influence of topography on Upper Jurassic shallow marine sand transport and deposition, it is also necessary to consider preservation potential. The latter is particularly sensitive since third order highstand–lowstand downward shifts could lead to erosion of highstand sands below sequence boundaries. Preservation potential during lowstands is better the more enclosed, or less well connected a given location is. Preservation potential and connectivity are opposing parameters from the point of view of Fulmar presence and illustrate why an irregular topography subject to transgression punctuated by lowstands will accrue shallow marine sands only in those locations which are well-connected enough to receive sands but not sufficiently 'open' to lose them again during lowstands.

The various cases are illustrated in Fig. 16. It is implicit in this argument that the topography in question has a similar relief to the elevation range of the third order eustatic fluctuations, otherwise the sediment transport processes associated with the shallow marine highstands (e.g. tides/longshore drift) would be insensitive to the transgressed topography. Well control in the Block 21/16 area shows the thickness variations in the Jurassic section between the centre of the Triassic pods (palaeohill tops, e.g. Well 21/11-2) and the adjacent valley floors (e.g. Well 21/16-2) to be in the order of 200 ft. This represents the possible range in topographic elevations in the 21/16 area at the onset of Fulmar deposition. The highstand marked by the *cymodoce* mfs extended westwards from the graben margin by at least 2 blocks, a distance of some 25 km. Given the slope gradients of *c.* 0.1° on modern shallow marine shelves (Johnson & Baldwin 1996), a relative sea-level rise in the order of 100 ft is envisaged to have occurred between the Base Fulmar unconformity and the sea-level maximum in *cymodoce* times. This is comparable with the relief of hills in the 21/16 area preserved below the Base Jurassic Unconformity (Fig. 11).

When considered in 3D through time, the topographical component of the geological model for the Upper Jurassic can account for nearly all of the KCF subcrop geology (Permian evaporites/Permian evaporite interbeds/Smith Bank/Skagerrak/Fulmar). However, an integrated geological model for the Upper Jurassic of the 21/16, 21/11 area needs to take into account the other geological controls mentioned earlier, most notably salt dissolution.

Salt dissolution

In addition to the dissolution-related fault system, sequence thickness variations within the KCF have been demonstrated to be random, only sharing a similar final overall thickness of the KCF which appears to loosely reflect subcrop geology (Fig. 13). The thickest KCF sections on the WCS tend to be those overlying salt highs (e.g. Wells 21/16-4, 21/17-3, 21/12-1; Fig. 13). A significant role for salt dissolution during KCF times has already been argued with respect to the Volgian/Ryazanian

(a)

(b)

Fig. 15. Photographs of salt valley topographies in the Paradox Basin, Utah. (**a**) Valley occupying the crest of Salt Valley Anticline, looking SE. Salt underlies the low, subdued topography lying north of the sandstone escarpment; this salt is the crest of a salt wall. The escarpment represents the youngest units in the sediment pod adjacent to the salt wall. Minor hills rising above the valley floor result from differential erosion of carbonate interbeds which have been brought to the surface by a combination of halokinesis and exhumation. (**b**) Topography at top salt resulting from differential erosion of the Paradox Formation in Sinbad Valley. These highs would give local thins or zones of sand absence were the valley now to be filled with a sheet sand system.

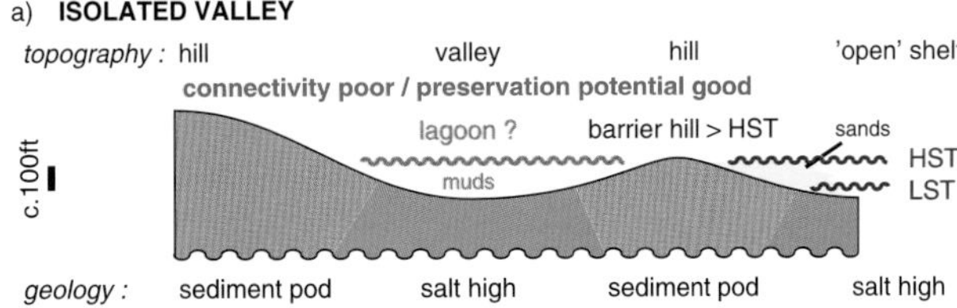

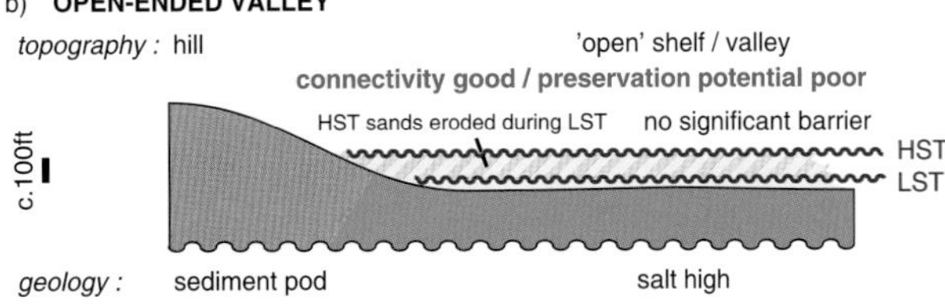

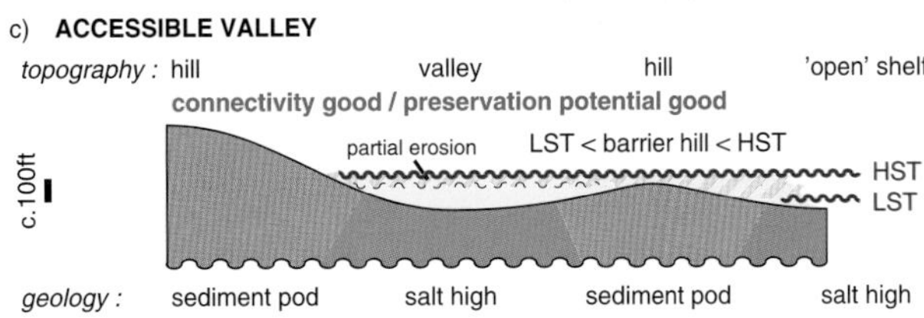

Fig. 16. Sedimentation in a salt valley taking account of 3D topography, showing the effect of the 'openness' of the valley (height of the lowest barrier hill between that valley and the sand-bearing marine system) versus the amplitude of third order eustatic fluctuations. (**a**) Case when valley is completely enclosed by hills which are sufficient to prevent sand input. Occasional inundation might result in the deposition of thin sands and silts. This situation represents excellent preservation potential, but a poor degree of connectivity to the open marine shelf. (**b**) The other extreme, where an open-ended, well connected valley will receive highstand sands, but these may be stripped back out of the valley during the following lowstand. (**c**) An intermediate case where highstand sands spill into the accommodation space within the valley but are preserved by the barrier hill during the following lowstand.

fault array and salt dissolution conveniently accounts for the variation in sequence thickness within the KCF. There is no reason why dissolution-controlled accommodation space should evolve at the same rate above each salt high, as the amount of Zechstein cap rock varies spatially. However, as the shaley KCF and Cromer Knoll sequences built up, they would gradually inhibit groundwater circulation, eventually cutting off the dissolution process. With the KCF and Cromer Knoll sediments being lithologically similar, one might expect salt dissolution to stop once a uniform thickness of cover shales had developed.

Accepting the importance of salt dissolution in controlling KCF thickness, a key question then becomes why should salt dissolution not have been the dominant process on the WCS earlier, during Fulmar deposition ? The following reasons are offered.

(1) The most significant issue is that a major change in sediment transport mechanism occurs at the onset of KCF deposition. Skagerrak and Fulmar sand transport consisted of bedload sediment movement (e.g. by fluvial and/or shallow marine currents) while the KCF and Cromer Knoll are characterized by a major pelagic component, involving suspended sediment deposition. The main implication of the latter is that topography ceases to be a significant control.

(2) The duration of highstands such as the *cymodoce* event in the Block 21/16 area is poorly constrained. Although the Fulmar Formation is generally considered to represent a considerable timespan (over 10 Ma, e.g. Donovan *et al.* 1993), the amount of time during Fulmar deposition that the 21/16 area was submerged (*cymodoce–autissiodorensis*) was only in the order of 1.5 Ma (we cite half of the actual timespan of Partington *et al.* (1993*a*) to take into account lowstands when subaerial conditions may have been present). During Kimmeridge Clay deposition, however (*autissiodorensis–stenomphalus*), the 21/16 area was permanently submerged and therefore subject to continuous dissolution for a period of approximately 12 Ma (Fig. 2; Partington *et al.* 1993*a*), significantly longer than the period of Fulmar deposition. Hence the amount of accommodation space produced by salt dissolution in Fulmar times may have been significantly less than that produced in KCF times, commensurate with the respective times of marine inundation. This does not refute a role for salt dissolution in amplifying accommodation space in Fulmar times, but underlines the possibility of an overriding influence of pre-existing topography on Fulmar sand distribution.

Summary of geological controls

The geological model for the 21/16, 21/11 area is characterized by a progressive evolution in the dominant controlling process from pre-existing topography during Skagerrak and Fulmar times (Fig. 17), through salt dissolution in the Volgian and, subsequently, to differential compaction and regional tilt in the Lower Cretaceous (Fig. 18). This model builds upon earlier versions featuring the variance of several parameters through time, in this case emphasizing the role of pre-existing topography during Fulmar deposition and restricting the importance of salt dissolution to the period of KCF and Cromer Knoll Group deposition (cf. Høiland *et al.* 1993; Wakefield *et al.* 1993).

Tertiary folding – significance and mechanism

The Durward, Gannet West and Kittiwake fields all have significant reserves within salt-cored four way dip closure. These closures are members of an array of salt-detached folds which evolved on the WCS in the Eocene–Oligocene – their age is constrained by growth sequences on the fold flanks (Glennie & Armstrong, 1991). Other examples are the salt highs drilled by Wells 21/12-1 and 21/22-1, and several others which remain undrilled. These folds are significant in that they invariably nucleate above the salt highs, which had previously controlled the Mesozoic sand fairways. Where present, these folds change the trap style in the sand fairways from stratigraphic pinch-out to lower risk four-way dip closure.

The folds resulted from the upward movement of the salt highs. However, since the minibasins were already grounded, regional shortening rather than renewed minibasin subsidence is the most likely driving mechanism. Regional shortening can be thick-skinned (basement involved) or thin-skinned (confined to the post-salt sequence). Top basement is relatively unfaulted in the WCS, with reverse faults being particulary rare. In addition, a lack of correspondence between basement and cover fault locations and trends has already been noted. Eocene–Oligocene thick-skinned shortening/inversion is therefore ruled out as the responsible mechanism. In contrast, a major detached down-to-the-basin extensional fault array has been mapped around the periphery of the WCS (Bishop 1996; Buchanan *et al.* 1996; Stewart 1996). Growth sequences in the hanging walls of these faults are Eocene–Oligocene in age, and the system is probably related to increasing easterly regional tilt in the late Paleocene (Stewart 1996). The WCS Tertiary fold-belt evolved to accommodate extension across the WCS peripheral graben system (Stewart 1996).

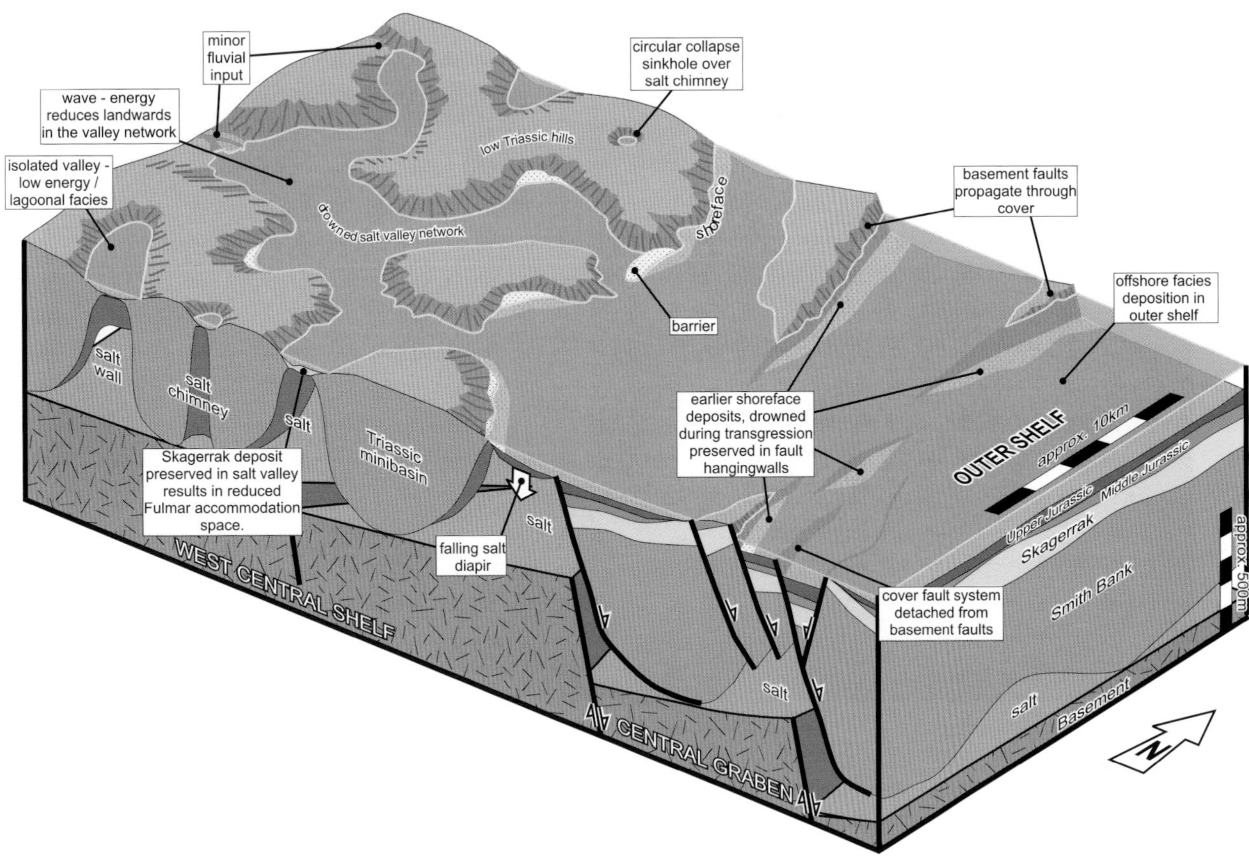

Fig. 17. Idealized snapshot of WCS palaeogeography based on the geological model discussed in the text, showing possible Fulmar facies distribution with respect to local geological controls during an Upper Jurassic highstand.

Conclusions

This study attempts to predict the distribution of sub-seismic sands by integrating a high resolution, well-based sequence stratigraphic analysis with sub-regional 3D seismic data. Sand prediction is achieved indirectly by evaluating the seismically resolvable geological controls on the sand deposition and preservation, which represents an extension of previous work on this problem in the WCS (e.g. Wakefield *et al.* 1993). Recognition of the importance of topography of the eroded minibasin/salt high system in relation to the role of salt dissolution has provided an explanation of wells which were anomalous in the context of previous models (e.g. thick Upper Jurassic yet no Fulmar on some salt highs). A fortunate corollary of interpreting topography as the major control on sand distribution, as opposed to syn-depositional salt dissolution, is that the predictive aspect of the geological model is more robust (providing there is enough sand in the system to fill available accommodation space). This is because the topography of the eroded minibasin system reflects differential erosion of salt relative to the surrounding sediments. In contrast, models relying principally on salt dissolution require prediction of absolute variations in salt dissolution during the period of Fulmar deposition, which is a virtually impossible task knowing only the salt isopach at the present day.

CONTROLS ON ACCOMMODATION VOLUME (West Central Shelf)	Salt movement	Dissolution / faulting	Pre-existing topography	Differential compaction	Regional tilt
scale	1-2km	1-2km	1-2km	1-2km	10-100km
importance	low high	low high	low high	low high	low high
Chalk					
Cromer Knoll Group					
Upper Jurassic: Kimmeridge Clay Formation					
Upper Jurassic: Fulmar sands					
Skagerrak / Middle Jurassic					
Smith Bank Formation					

Fig. 18. Geological model depicted in terms of variation in relative importance of controls on accommodation space generation in the Durward/Dauntless area from Smith Bank (Lower Triassic) to Chalk (Upper Cretaceous) times.

Parameters quantifying key 3D aspects of the topography of the surface transgressed in the Upper Jurassic have been defined. With the mapped 3D geometry of the salt high/Smith Bank minibasin network on the WCS acting as a proxy for topography (Fig. 19), undrilled zones of Upper Jurassic accommodation space can be risked for Fulmar reservoir in terms of sand access (connectivity) and sand preservation through lowstands (preservation potential) (compare Figs 16, 17 & 19). Although application of these parameters remains subjective, this predictive approach to Fulmar and Skagerrak distribution represents a possible step forward from previous models of sand distribution on the WCS. This model may be also be applicable to other marginal areas and intra-basinal highs in the CNS (such as the Forties–Montrose and Jæren highs) although it is recognized that basement faulting was a significant additional factor within the Central Graben itself.

The following companies are thanked for releasing seismic, wireline and biostratigraphic data: Amerada Hess Ltd, British Borneo North Sea Ltd, D. Bailey of Biostrat Ltd, DSM Energy (UK) Ltd, Saga

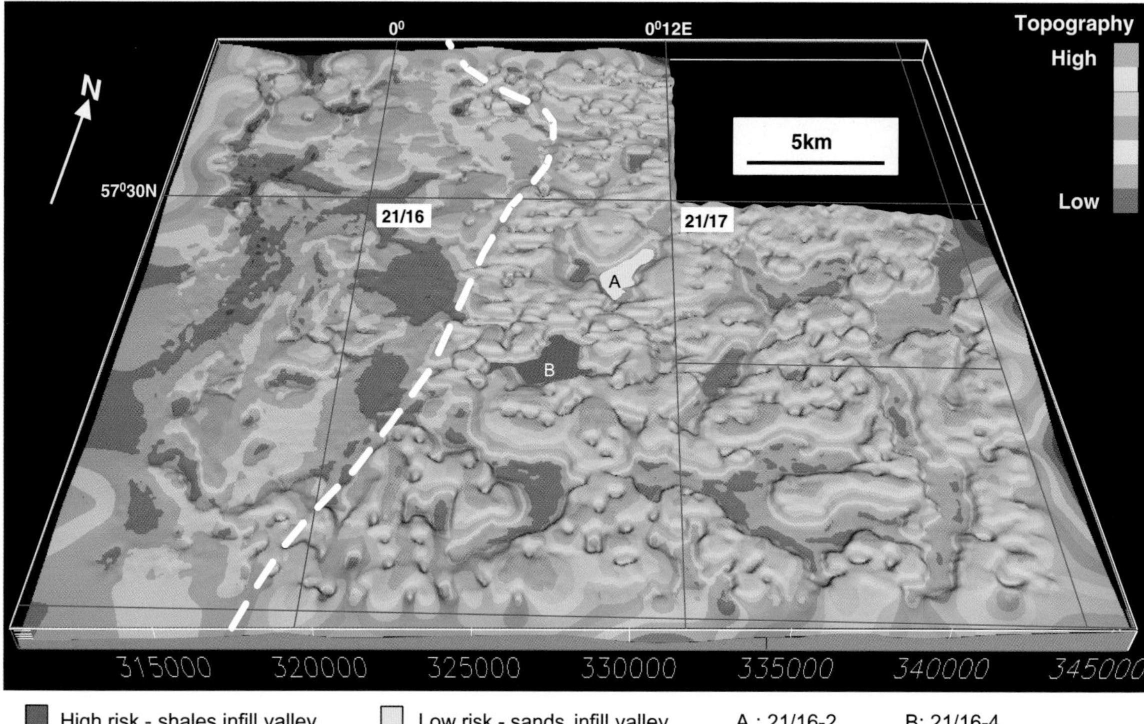

Fig. 19. Representation of pre-Upper Jurassic topography obtained by inverting the salt geometry surface shown in Fig. 10, i.e. 'topography' = 1 − (Triassic isochore/[Triassic + Zechstein isochore]). The surface gives an impression of valley connectivity and preservation potential and these ideas can be used to rank zones of accommodation space with respect to sand presence. Examples of known sand presence/absence based on well control are annotated. The apparently low area in the west is an artifact of this method resulting from the presence of significant thicknesses of Zechstein platform strata preserving a thick 'salt' isochore.

Petroleum UK Ltd and Seafield Resources plc. D. Kelsey and the Central team at Amerada Hess are thanked for support and technical discussion during this study. The manuscript benefitted from a thorough review by J. Price. F. Nimmo is thanked for programming a decompaction algorithm. J. Clark acknowledges PhD sponsorship from Amerada Hess Ltd. The views expressed here are solely those of the authors and not necessarily those of Amerada Hess or any of the other companies listed above.

References

ANDERSON, B. G. & DROSER, M. L. 1998. Ichnofacies and geometric configurations of *Ophiomorpha* within a sequence stratigraphic framework: an example from the Upper Cretaceous US western interior. *Sedimentology*, **45**, 379–396.

ARMSTRONG, L. A., TEN HAVE, A. & JOHNSON, H. D. 1987. The geology of the Gannet fields, Central North Sea, UK sector. *In*: BROOKS, J. & GLENNIE, K. (eds) *Petroleum Geology of North West Europe*, Graham & Trotman, London, 533–548.

BISHOP, D. J. 1996. Regional distribution and geometry of salt diapirs and supra-Zechstein Group faults in the western and central North Sea. *Marine & Petroleum Geology*, **13**, 355–364.

BUCHANAN, P. G., BISHOP, D. J. & HOOD, D. N. 1996. Development of salt-related structures in the Central North Sea: results from section balancing. *In*: ALSOP, G. I., BLUNDELL, D. J. & DAVISON, I. (eds) *Salt Tectonics*. Geological Society, London, Special Publications, **100**, 111–128.

CARRUTHERS, A., MCKIE, T., PRICE, J., DYER, R., WILLIAMS, G. & WATSON, P. 1996. The application of sequence stratigraphy to the understanding of Late Jurassic turbidite plays in the Central North Sea, UKCS. *In*: HURST, A., JOHNSON, H. D., BURLEY, S. D., CANHAM, A. C. & MACKERTICH, D. S. (eds) *Geology of the Humber Group: Central Graben and Moray Firth, UKCS*. Geological Society, London, Special Publications, **114**, 29–45.

CLARK, J. A., CARTWRIGHT, J. A. & STEWART, S. A. 1999. Mesozoic dissolution tectonics on the West Central Shelf, UK Central North Sea. *Marine and Petroleum Geology*, **16**, 283–300.

——, STEWART, S. A. & CARTWRIGHT, J. A. 1998. Evolution of the NW margin of the North Permian Basin, UK North Sea. *Journal of the Geological Society, London*, **155**, 663–676.

DAVIES, R. J., STEPHEN, K. J. & UNDERHILL, J. R. 1996. A re-evaluation of Middle and Upper Jurassic stratigraphy and the flooding history of the Moray Firth Rift System, North Sea. *In*: HURST, A., JOHNSON, H. D., BURLEY, S. D., CANHAM, A. C. & MACKERTICH, D. S. (eds) *Geology of the Humber Group: Central Graben and Moray Firth, UKCS*. Geological Society, London, Special Publications, **114**, 81–108.

DICKINSON, B. 1996. The Puffin field: the appraisal of a complex HP–HT gas–condensate accumulation. *In*: HURST, A., JOHNSON, H. D., BURLEY, S. D., CANHAM, A. C. & MACKERTICH, D. S. (eds) *Geology of the Humber Group: Central Graben and Moray Firth, UKCS*. Geological Society, London, Special Publications, **114**, 299–327.

DONOVAN, A. D., DJAKIC, A. W., IOANNIDES, N. S., GARFIELD, T. R. & JONES, C. R. 1993. Sequence stratigraphic control on Middle and Upper Jurassic reservoir distribution within the UK Central North Sea. *In*: PARKER, J. R. (ed.) *Petroleum Geology of Northwest Europe: Proceedings of the 4th Conference*. Geological Society, London, 251–269.

EKDALE, A. A. 1988. Pitfalls of palaeobathymetric interpretations based on trace fossil assemblages. *Palaios*, **3**, 464–472.

FREY, R. W., PEMBERTON, G. & SAUNDERS, T. D. A. 1990. Ichnofacies and bathymetry: a passive relationship. *Journal of Palaeontology*, **64**, 155–158.

GALLOWAY, W. E. 1989. Genetic stratigraphic sequences in basin analysis I: architecture and genesis of flooding surface bounded depositional units. *American Association of Petroleum Geologists Bulletin*, **69**, 125–142.

GATLIFF, R. W., RICHARDS, P. C., SMITH, K., GRAHAM, C. C., MCCORMAC, M., SMITH, N. J. P., LONG, D., CAMERON, T. D. J., EVANS, D., STEVENSON, A. G., BULAT, J. & RITCHIE, J. D. 1994. *United Kingdom Offshore Regional Report: the Geology of the Central North Sea*. London, HMSO for the British Geological Survey.

GAWTHORPE, R. L., FRASER, A. J. & COLLIER, R. 1994. Sequence Stratigraphy in active extensional basins: implications for the interpretation of ancient basin fills. *Marine and Petroleum Geology*, **11**, 642–658.

GLENNIE, K. W. & ARMSTRONG, L. A. 1991. The Kittiwake Field, Block 21/18, UK North Sea. *In*: ABBOTTS, I. L. (ed.) *United Kingdom Oil and Gas Fields, 25 Years Commemorative Volume*. Geological Society, London, Memoirs, **14**, 339–345.

GOLDSMITH, P. J., RICH, B. & STANDRING, J. 1995. Triassic correlation and stratigraphy in the south Central Graben, UK North Sea. *In*: BOLDY, S. A. R. (ed.) *Permian and Triassic Rifting in Northwest Europe*, Geological Society, London, Special Publications, **91**, 123–143.

GOWLAND, S. 1996. Facies characteristics and depositional models of highly bioturbated shallow marine siliciclastic strata: an example from the Fulmar Formation (Late Jurassic), UK Central North Sea. *In*: HURST, A., JOHNSON, H. D., BURLEY, S. D., CANHAM, A. C. & MACKERTICH, D. S. (eds) *Geology of the Humber Group: Central Graben and Moray Firth, UKCS*. Geological Society, London, Special Publications, **114**, 185–214.

GUGLIELMO, G., JACKSON, M. P. A. & VENDEVILLE, B. C. 1997. Three dimensional visualization of salt walls and associated fault systems. *American Association of Petroleum Geologists Bulletin*, **81**, 46–61.

HALLSWORTH, C. R. 1994. *Heavy mineral suites from Triassic and Jurassic sandstones in Quadrant 21: implications for provenance*. British Geological Survey Technical Report WH/94/213C.

HARDAGE, B. A., CARR, D. L., LANCASTER, D. E., SIMMONS, J. L., ELPHICK, R. Y., PENDLETON, V. M. & JOHNS, R. A. 1996. 3-D seismic evidence of the effects of carbonate karst collapse on overlying clastic stratigraphy and reservoir compartmentalisation. *Geophysics*, **61**, 1336–1350.

HARKER, S. D. & RIEUF, M. 1996. Genetic stratigraphy and sandstone distribution of the Moray Firth Humber Group (Upper Jurassic). *In*: HURST, A., JOHNSON, H. D., BURLEY, S. D., CANHAM, A. C. & MACKERTICH, D. S. (eds) *Geology of the Humber Group: Central Graben and Moray Firth, UKCS*. Geological Society, London, Special Publications, **114**, 109–130.

HEWARD, A. P. 1990. Salt removal and sedimentation in Southern Oman. *In*: ROBERTSON, A. H. F., SEARLE, M. P. & RIES, A. C. (eds) *The Geology and Tectonics of the Oman Region*. Geological Society, London, Special Publications, **49**, 637–652.

HODGSON, N. A., FARNSWORTH, J. & FRASER, A. J. 1992. Salt-related tectonics, sedimentation and hydrocarbon plays in the Central Graben, North Sea, UKCS. *In*: HARDMAN, R. F. P. (ed.) *Exploration Britain: Geological Insights for the Next Decade*. Geological Society, London, Special Publications, **67**, 31–63.

HØILAND, O., KRISTENSEN, J. & MONSEN, T. 1993. Mesozoic evolution of the Jæren High area, Norwegian Central North Sea. *In*: PARKER, J. R. (ed.) *Petroleum Geology of Northwest Europe: Proceedings of the 4th Conference*. The Geological Society, London, 1189–1195.

HOSPERS, J., RATHORE, J. S., JIANHUA, F., FINNSTRØM, E. G. & HOLTHE, J. 1988. Salt tectonics in the Norwegian–Danish Basin. *Tectonophysics*, **149**, 35–60

HOWELL, J. A., FLINT, S. S. & HUNT, C. 1996. Sedimentological aspects of the Humber Group (Upper Jurassic) of the South Central Graben, UK North Sea. *Sedimentology*, **43**, 89–114.

JEANS, C. V., REED, S. J. B. & XING, M. 1993. Heavy mineral stratigraphy in the UK Trias: Western Approaches, onshore England and the Central North Sea. *In*: PARKER, J. R. (ed.) *Petroleum Geology of Northwest Europe: Proceedings of the 4th Conference*. Geological Society, London, 609–624.

JOHNSON, H. D., MACKAY, T. A. & STEWART, D. J. 1986. The Fulmar oil field (central North Sea): geological aspects of its discovery, appraisal and development. *Marine & Petroleum Geology*, **3**, 99–125.

—— & BALDWIN, C. T. 1996. Shallow clastic seas. *In*: READING, H. G. Sedimentary environments: Processes, facies and stratigraphy (3rd edition). Blackwell Science, Oxford, 232–280.

JOHNSON, K. S. 1997. Evaporite karst in the United States. *Carbonates and Evaporites*, **12**, 2–14.

LOCKLEY, M. G., RINDSBERG, A. K. & ZEILER, R. M. 1987. The Palaeoenvironmental significance of the nearshore Curvolithus ichnofacies. *Palaios*, **2**, 255–262.

LOUTIT, T. S., HARDENBOL, J., VAIL, P. R. & BAUM, G. R. 1988. Condensed sections: the key to age dating and correlation of continental margin sequences. *In*: WILGUS, C. K., HASTINGS, B. S., KENDALL, C. G. C., POSAMENTIER, H. W., ROSS, C. A. & VAN WAGONER, J. C. (eds) *Sea Level Changes: an Integrated Approach*. Society of Economic Palaeontologists and Mineralogists, Special Publications, **42**, 183–216.

MARTIN, M. A. & POLLARD, J. E. 1996. The role of trace fossil (ichnofabric) analysis in the development of depositional models for the Upper Jurassic Fulmar Formation of the Kittiwake field (Quadrant 21 UKCS). *In*: HURST, A., JOHNSON, H. D., BURLEY, S. D., CANHAM, A. C. & MACKERTICH, D. S. (eds) *Geology of the Humber Group: Central Graben and Moray Firth, UKCS*. Geological Society, London, Special Publications, **114**, 163–183.

MILTON, N. 1993. Evolving depositional geometries in the North Sea Jurassic rift. *In*: PARKER, J. R. (ed.) *Petroleum Geology of Northwest Europe: Proceedings of the 4th Conference*. Geological Society, London, 425–442.

PARTINGTON, M. A., COPESTAKE, P., MITCHENER, B. C. & UNDERHILL, J. R. 1993*a*. Biostratigraphic correlation of genetic stratigraphic sequences in the Jurassic-lowermost Cretaceous (Hettangian to Ryazanian) of the North Sea and adjacent areas. *In*: PARKER, J. R. (ed.) *Petroleum Geology of Northwest Europe: Proceedings of the 4th Conference*. Geological Society, London, 371–386.

——, MITCHENER, B. C., MILTON, N. J. & FRASER, A. J. 1993*b*. Genetic sequence stratigraphy for the North Sea Late Jurassic and Early Cretaceous: distribution and prediction of Kimmeridgian-late Ryazanian reservoirs in the North Sea and adjacent areas. *In*: PARKER, J. R. (ed.) *Petroleum Geology of Northwest Europe: Proceedings of the 4th Conference*. Geological Society, London, 347–370.

PENGE, J., TAYLOR, B., HUCKERBY, J. A. & MUNNS, J. W. 1993. Extension and salt tectonics in the East Central Graben. *In*: PARKER, J. R. (ed.) *Petroleum Geology of Northwest Europe: Proceedings of the 4th Conference*. Geological Society, London, 1197–1209.

POLLARD, J. E., GOLDRING, R. & BUCK, S. G. 1993. Ichnofabrics containing *Ophiomorpha*: significance in shallow-water facies interpretation. *Journal of the Geological Society, London*, **150**, 149–164.

POSAMENTIER, H. W., JERVEY, M. T. & VAIL, P. R. 1988. Eustatic controls on clastic deposition–conceptual framework. *In*: WILGUS, C. K., HASTINGS, B. S., KENDALL, C. G. C., POSAMENTIER, H. W., ROSS, C. A. & VAN WAGONER, J. C. (eds) *Sea Level Changes: an Integrated Approach*. Society of Economic Palaeontologists and Mineralogists, Special Publications, **42**, 109–124.

RATTEY, R. P. & HAYWARD, A. B. 1993. Sequence stratigraphy of a failed rift system: The Middle Jurassic to Early Cretaceous basin evolution of the Central and Northern North Sea. *In*: PARKER, J. R. (ed.) *Petroleum Geology of Northwest Europe: Proceedings of the 4th Conference*. Geological Society, London, 215–249.

ROBERTS, A. M., PRICE, J. D. & SVAVA OLSEN, T. 1990. Late Jurassic half-graben control on the siting and structure of hydrocarbon accumulations: UK/ Norwegian Central Graben. *In*: HARDMAN, R. F. P. & BROOKS, J. (eds) *Tectonic Events Responsible for Britain's Oil and Gas Reserves*. Geological Society, London, Special Publications, **55**, 229–257.

ROWAN, M. G. & WEIMER, P. 1998. Salt–sediment interaction, Northern Green Canyon and Ewing Bank (Offshore Louisiana), Northern Gulf of Mexico. *American Association of Petroleum Geologists Bulletin*, **82**, 1055–1082.

SMITH, R. I., HODGSON, N. & FULTON, M. 1993. Salt control on Triassic reservoir distribution, UKCS Central North Sea. *In*: PARKER, J. R. (ed.) *Petroleum Geology of Northwest Europe: Proceedings of the 4th Conference*. Geological Society, London, 547–557.

STEWART, I. J. 1993. Structural controls in the Late Jurassic age shelf system, Ula trend, Norwegian North Sea. *In*: PARKER, J. R. (ed.) *Petroleum Geology of Northwest Europe: Proceedings of the 4th Conference*. Geological Society, London, 469–483.

STEWART, S. A. 1996. Tertiary extensional fault systems on the western margin of the North Sea Basin. *Petroleum Geoscience*, **2**, 167–176.

TAYLOR, A. M & GAWTHORPE, R. L. 1993. Application of sequence stratigraphy and trace fossil analysis to reservoir description: examples from the Jurassic of the North Sea. *In*: PARKER, J. R. (ed.) *Petroleum Geology of Northwest Europe: Proceedings of the 4th Conference*. Geological Society, London, 317–335.

UNDERHILL, J. R. & PARTINGTON, M. A. 1993. Jurassic thermal doming and deflation in the North Sea: implications of the sequence stratigraphic evidence. *In*: PARKER, J. R. (ed.) *Petroleum Geology of Northwest Europe: Proceedings of the 4th Conference*. Geological Society, London, 337–345.

VELDKAMP, J. J., GAILLARD, M. G., JONKERS, H. A. & LEVELL, B. K. 1996. A Kimmeridgian time-slice through the Humber Group of the central North Sea: a test of sequence stratigraphic records. *In*: HURST, A., JOHNSON, H. D., BURLEY, S. D., CANHAM, A. C. & MACKERTICH, D. S. (eds) *Geology of the Humber Group: Central Graben and Moray Firth, UKCS*. Geological Society, London, Special Publications, **114**, 1–28.

WAKEFIELD, L. L., DROSTE, H., GILES, M. R. & JANSSEN, R. 1993. Late Jurassic plays along the western margin of the Central Graben. *In*: PARKER, J. R. (ed.) *Petroleum Geology of Northwest Europe: Proceedings of the 4th Conference*. The Geological Society, London, 459–468.

Upper Jurassic basin axial turbidites within the Gertrud Graben, Danish Central Graben

E. S. RASMUSSEN,[1] A.-M. JEPSEN[2] and K. G. MAVER[2]

[1] *Geological Survey of Denmark and Greenland, Thoravej 8, DK-2400 Copenhagen NV, Denmark*
[2] *Ødegaard A/S, Kroghsgade 1, DK-2100 Copenhagen Ø, Denmark*

Abstract: For more than twenty years, the Jurassic succession in the Danish Central Graben has been subject to intense exploration for hydrocarbons. Approximately 43 wild-cats have been drilled and most of these tested structural traps located on footwall crests. The reservoirs encountered were Middle and Upper Jurassic sandstones deposited mainly in nearshore depositional environments. Some of these wells penetrated thin turbidites of Late Jurassic to Early Cretaceous age. Within the Gertrud Graben distinct seismic anomalies indicate the presence of basin floor turbidites, which can be correlated to fan fringe turbidites encountered in the Jeppe-1, Gwen-2 and Mona-1 wells. Seismic inversion provides additional evidence of sandstone deposits in the zone characterized by high acoustic impedance. The turbidites are located within the axial zone of the NW– SE trending Gertrud Graben. Southward the turbidites pinch out gradually; the northern limit of the deposits (in Norwegian territory) is unknown. The deposition of the turbidites is interpreted to be associated with a lowstand of sea-level when conditions were favourable for deposition of coarse-grained deposits in basinal areas. The sediments were probably sourced from an area to the north. Basin axial turbidites are well-known phenomena in various basins. They are not always associated with structural closures and consequently constitute a high risk exploration target. However, in mature basins such as the Danish Central Graben this type of play should be considered in future exploration.

The deposition of gravity flows in graben structures occurs within topographic lows. Some of these may, during later structural activity, get displaced and become a part of a structural closure in which accumulation of hydrocarbons may occur. This kind of play is well known and forms major hydrocarbon accumulations in the North Sea region, e.g. Abbotts (1991). Some gravity deposits remain unexplored because of their setting within lows in which structural closures can rarely be defined. However, several processes related to deposition of gravity flows, e.g. detachment of lobes or isolation of major fans after active deposition, may form stratigraphic traps. Within the Gertrud Graben, seismic anomalies characterized by high amplitude reflections within an otherwise transparent reflection pattern have been recognized. The zone with high amplitude reflections correlates with thin turbidites with oil shows encountered in the Jeppe-1 well. The turbiditic sandstone succession has a gross thickness of 25 m and a net : gross of 75%, with porosity up to 10%. The presence of oil shows in the thin turbiditic sandstones in the Jeppe-1 well, drilled on a footwall crest, suggests the possibility of thicker sandstones in the basinal areas.

The aim of this study is to map the distribution of the seismic anomalies by performing seismic inversion. Seismic inversion is used to derive acoustic impedance as a lithology indicator and to establish a geological model which can be used to predict the lithology and architecture of the depositional system.

Geological setting

The Danish Central Graben evolved as a major east-dipping graben from the Callovian in the late Middle Jurassic to the mid-Valanginian in the Early Cretaceous. The development was characterized by a combination of fault controlled subsidence and salt tectonics (Andersen *et al.* 1982; Møller 1986). Three extensional tectonic pulses have been recognized. The first pulse spans the Callovian and Oxfordian: it was dominated by subsidence along the Coffee–Soil Fault and by N–S trending faulting within the graben area. The second pulse occurred during the Early Volgian times. Subsidence was concentrated along new NNW–SSE striking faults and an increase in the influence of salt movements was associated with this phase. The third pulse, during the Valanginian, was characterized by distinct fault-block rotation, especially in the northern part of the graben. Local thrusting has also been recognized during this phase, e.g. the Gert High (Rasmussen 1995; Møller & Rasmussen in press).

The Gertrud Graben evolved as an eastward tilted half-graben during the second pulse of extension in the Volgian (Søderstrøm *et al.* 1991; Gowers *et al.* 1993; Rasmussen 1995; Møller & Rasmussen in press). The graben is bounded towards the north and east by the Sørvestlandet High and Piggvar Terrace/Mandal High, respectively and by the Gert High towards the west (Fig. 1). During the Late Kimmeridgian, when the graben was a part of a major plateau (including the Piggvar Terrace and the Heno Plateau towards the south), the area was filled by nearshore sandstones of the Heno Formation (Fig. 2). During the rotation of the Gertrud Graben, pelagic fine-grained mudstones of the Farsund Formation were deposited. Within the marine Farsund Formation, organic-rich and sand-rich turbidites were laid down as passive rift fill in topographic lows formed during the main tilting. This deposition of the turbidites occurred during the Late Volgian and Ryazanian (Andsbjerg & Dybkjær in press) (Fig. 2). The Sørvestlandet High and the Mandal High formed major source areas of sandy nearshore deposits redistributed as gravity flow deposits during the Late Jurassic, e.g. the Ula Formation (Vollset & Doré 1984). The turbidites penetrated in the Jeppe-1 well are interpreted as being associated with prograding lowstand deposits (Johannessen *et al.* 1996). The depositional environment was characterized by deposition of organic-rich mudstones with intercalation of sandy and silty turbidites and by sand-rich debris flow in a starved basin (Ineson *et al.* in press). The third tectonic pulse, which

Rasmussen, E. S, Jepsen, A.-M. & Maver, K. G. 1999. Upper Jurassic basin axial turbidites within the Gertrud Graben, Danish Central Graben. *In*: Fleet, A. J. & Boldy, S. A. R. (eds) *Petroleum Geology of Northwest Europe: Proceedings of the 5th Conference*, 897–906.

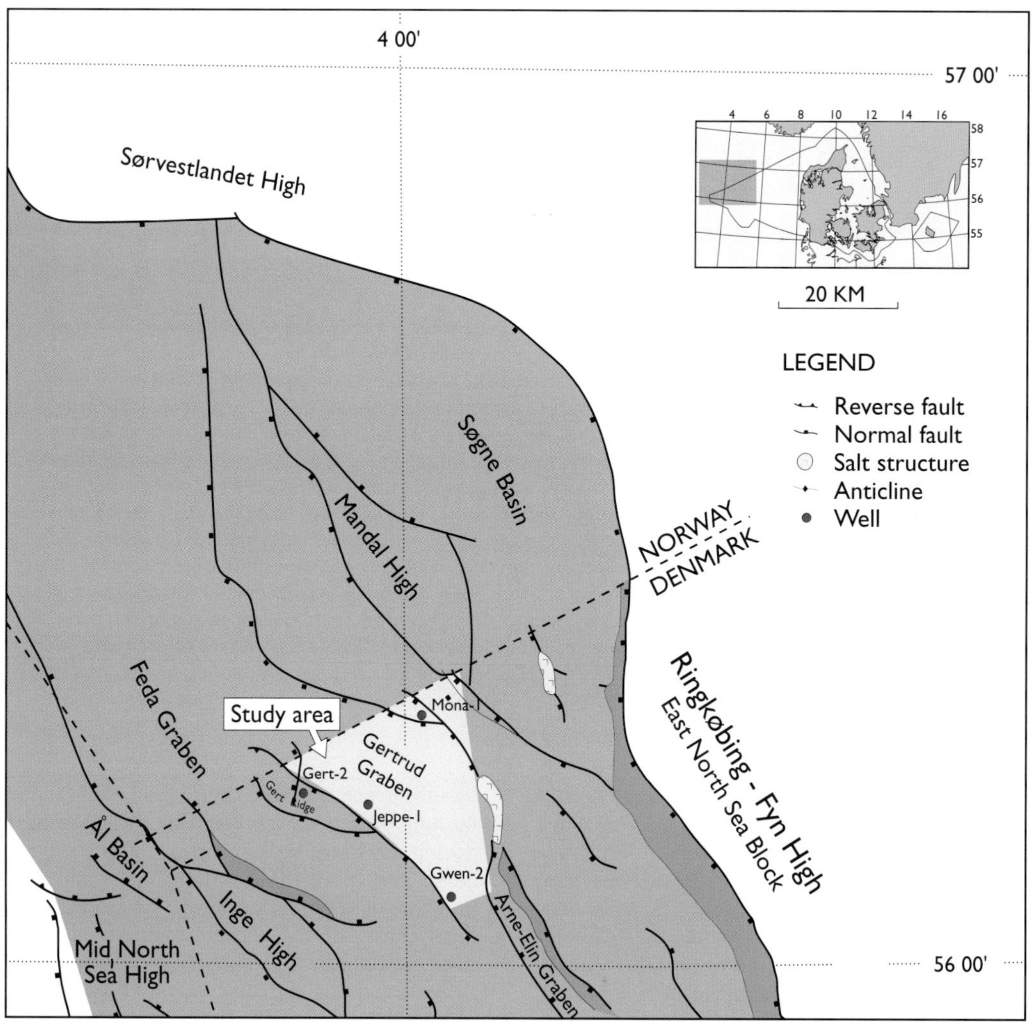

Fig. 1. Structural elements of the Danish and Norwegian Central Graben. The location of study area and wells used in the study are shown. Partly based on Gowers *et al.* (1993).

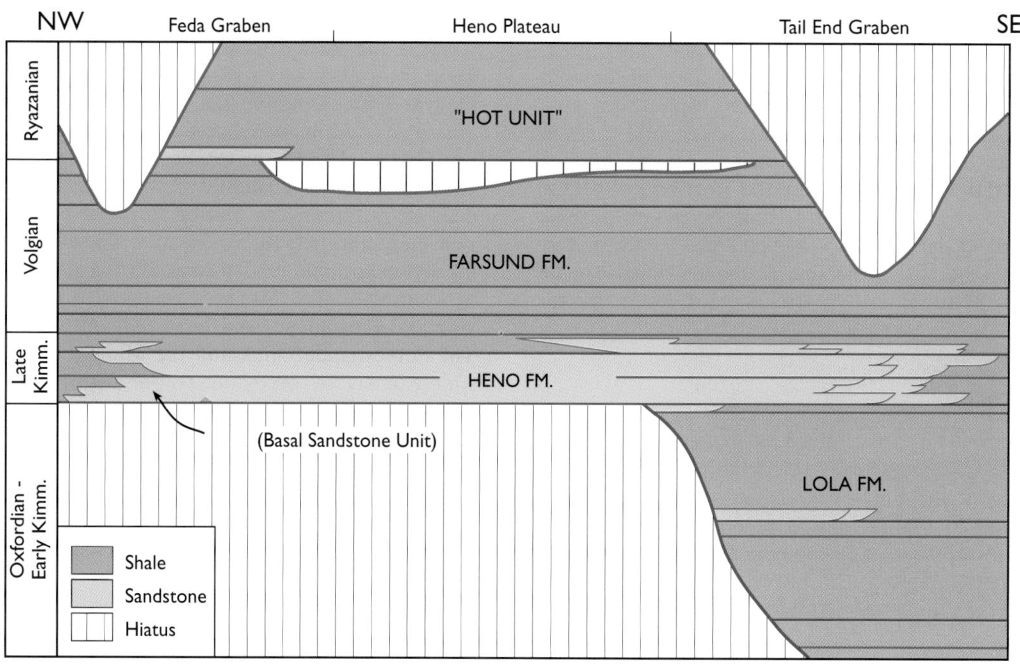

Fig. 2. Stratigraphic column of the Feda Graben, the Heno Plateau and the Tail End Graben. Based on Andsbjerg and Dybkjær (in press.) and Bergan *et al.* (1989)

terminated the extensional tectonic regime of the graben, segmented the Gertrud Graben into minor rotated fault blocks. The graben was strongly inverted during the Cretaceous and early Palaeogene at the boundary fault towards the Mandal High (Vejbæk & Andersen 1986). Minor inversion also occurred along fault planes within the graben.

Methodology

The CGD85, NP85, and NH86 seismic surveys formed the database for the study giving a spacing density of less than 1.5 km. The CGD85 and NP85 datasets were reprocessed in 1996 yielding good quality data. The quality of the NH86 is generally poor, but a few reprocessed lines show high resolution within the Jurassic succession. Well velocity surveys from Jeppe-1, Gwen-2, Mona-1, and Gert- 2 formed the basis for seismic to well correlation. Petrophysical logs from these wells and a cored section from the Jeppe-1 well formed the basis for the establishment of the depositional model.

In order to establish a detailed subsurface model, inversion of the post-stack seismic data was performed. Seismic inversion can enhance subsurface resolution by removing the effect of the wavelet; and by estimating acoustic impedance, a direct correlation with the well logs is made possible, thereby enabling a consistent interpretation.

The ISIS seismic inversion is a globally optimized and multi-trace method based on a simulated annealing. Neither well logs nor a detailed starting model is used to constrain the inversion directly. The seismic is thus faithful to the seismic data and the final results may therefore be evaluated by comparison with the well logs algorithm (Maver & Rasmussen 1995).

Seismic study

Seismic facies analysis

On the seismic section in Fig. 3 the upper part of the Farsund Formation is shown at the Jeppe-1 well and the extension eastwards into the Gertrud Graben. The turbidite succession penetrated in the well and the interpreted continuation into the graben is shown in yellow.

Two seismic facies have been recognized within this part of the Farsund Formation (Figs 3 and 4). The general seismic reflection pattern, characterized by a transparent reflection pattern, is referred to as Facies A in Fig. 3. The upper boundary of Facies A, beneath the Lower Cretaceous deposits, is sharp and characterized by a very distinct peak, reflecting a marked decrease in acoustic impedance within the Farsund Formation from the Lower Cretaceous succession. Facies A dominates in the Farsund Formation, but locally in the uppermost part a high amplitude and parallel reflection pattern can be recognized; this is referred to as Facies B (Figs 3 and 4). At the upper boundary of Facies B, the transition from the Lower Cretaceous deposits is less distinct. The strong peak reflection at this boundary is less evident and the polarity is often reversed (Fig. 5). Thus, the boundary is represented by a trough.

Results of the seismic inversion

The derived depth-to-time calibrated Jeppe-1 acoustic impedance log has been used to estimate a wavelet. The synthetic traces, derived by convolving a well-derived wavelet and the reflectivity log, show a reasonable correlation with the seismic data at the Jeppe-1 well location (Fig. 6). This indicates that

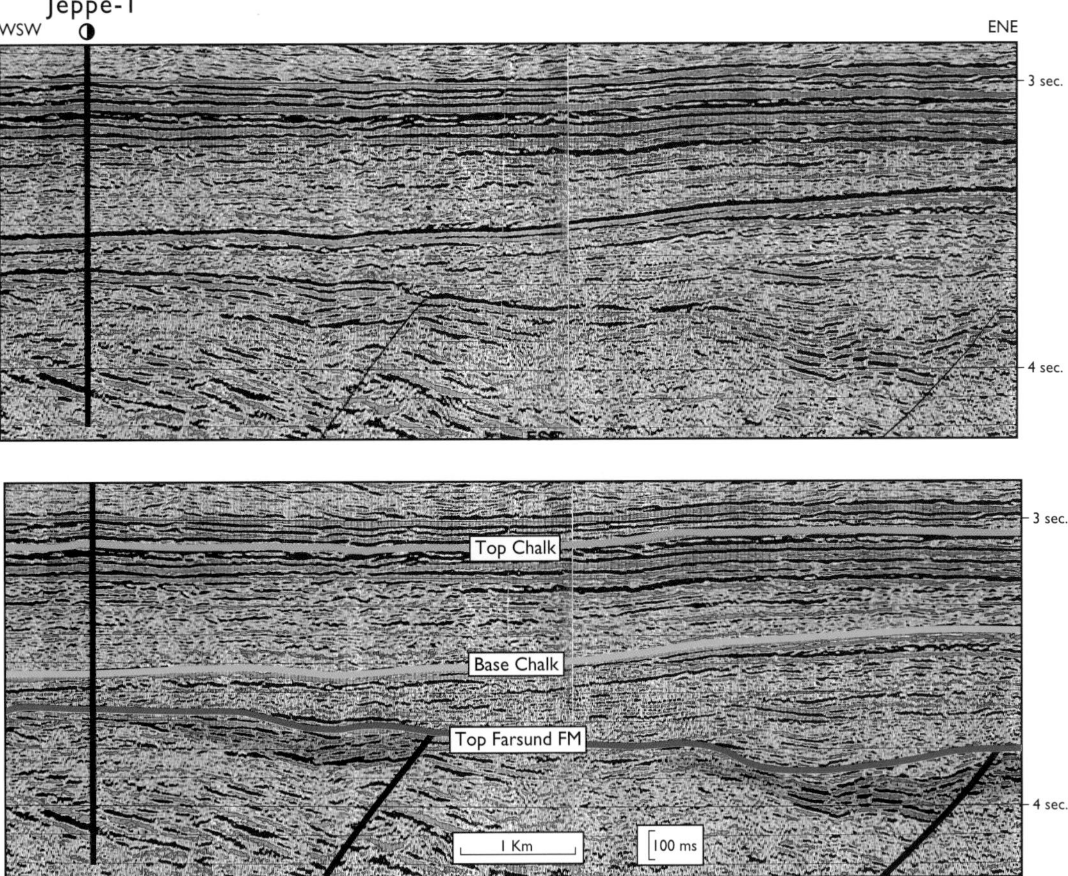

Fig. 3. Seismic cross-section from the western part of the Gertrud Graben showing the seismic anomalies within the Farsund Formation. The high amplitude seismic reflection pattern is prominently developed in the eastern part; to the right in the figure at 4.0 s TWT. See Fig. 5 for location of the seismic section.

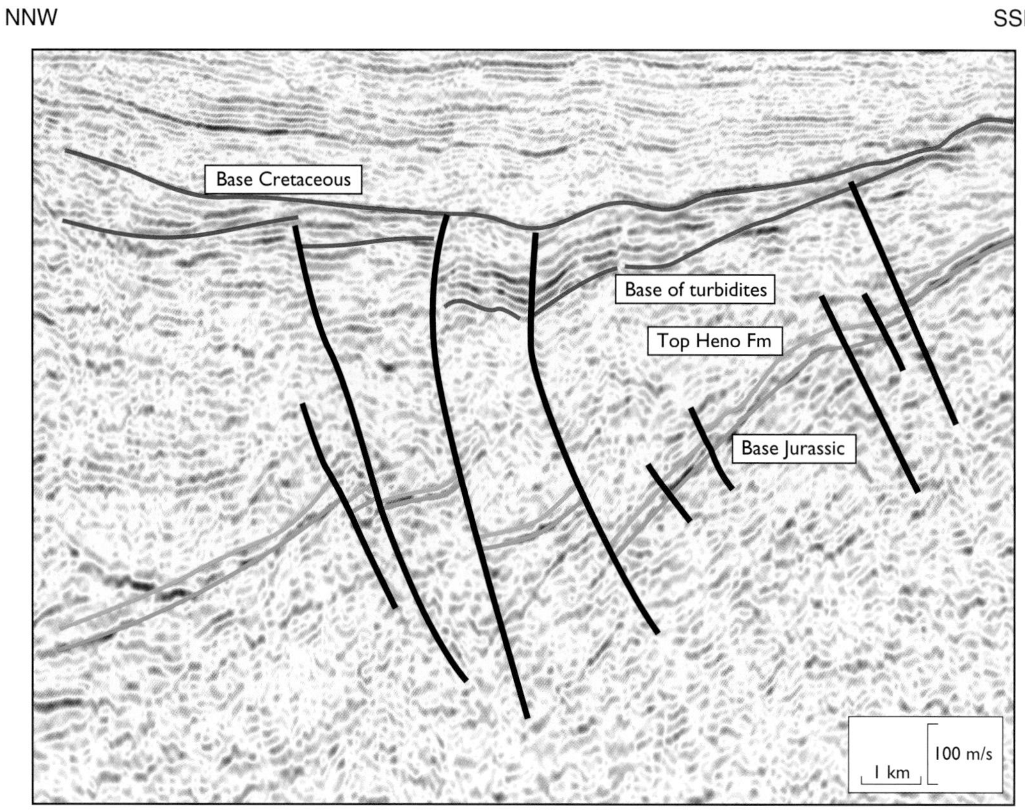

Fig. 4. Seismic strike-section perpendicular to the seismic section shown in Fig. 3. The high amplitude seismic reflection pattern can easily be recognized in the uppermost part of the Farsund Formation. Note that the seismic amplitude anomaly is only preserved on the hanging wall block. See Fig. 5 for location of the seismic section. Seismic courtesy Danpec A/S, geoteam A/S, and Nopec International A/S.

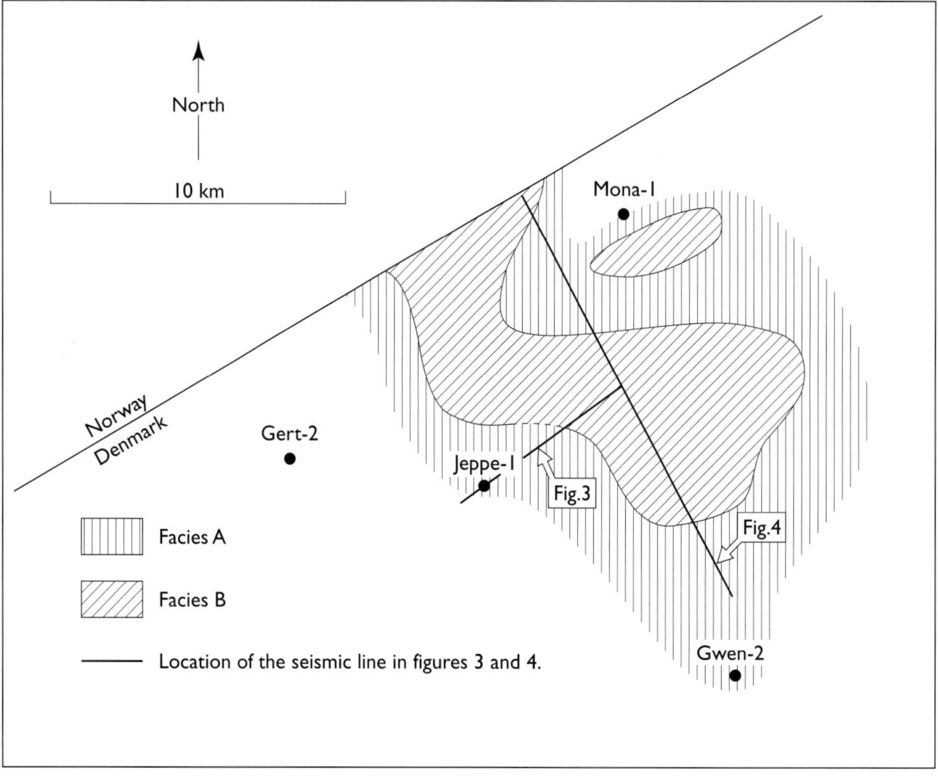

Fig. 5. Subcrop map of the Valanginian unconformity (Top Farsund Formation) showing the distribution of Facies A and B within the Gertrud Graben.

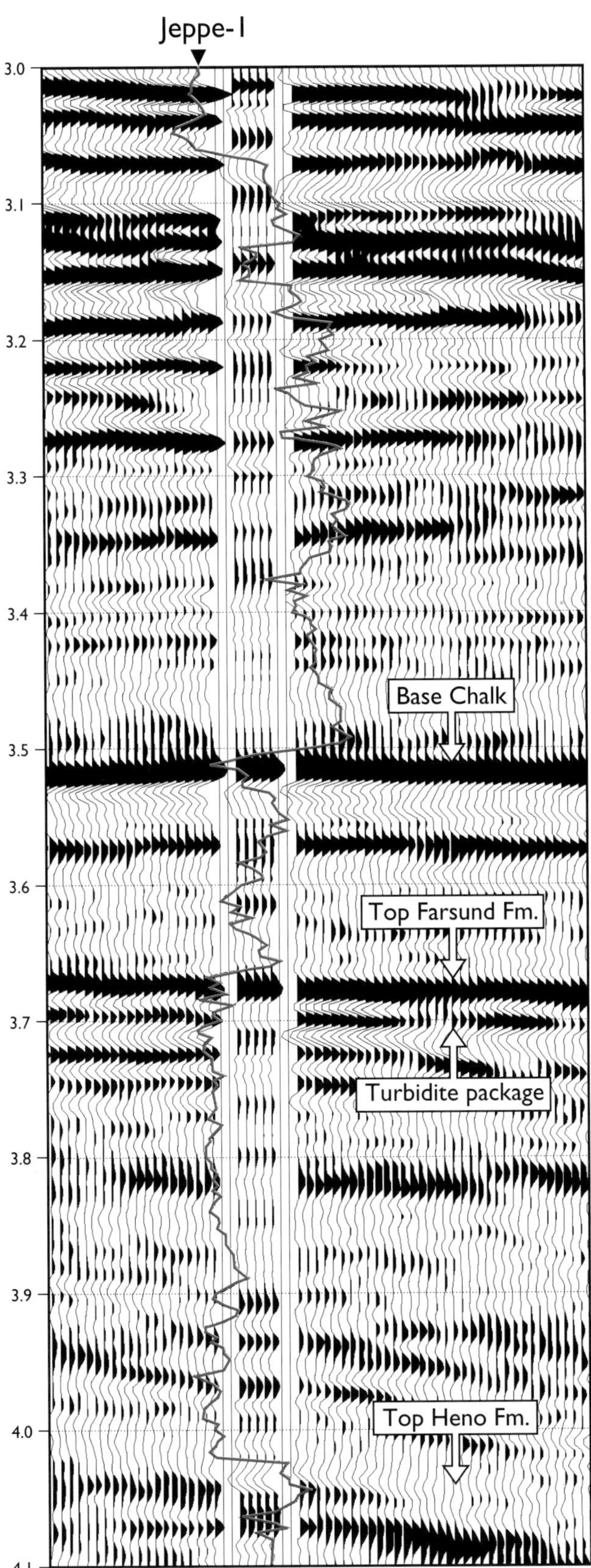

Fig. 6. Synthetic traces derived by convolving the chosen wavelet with the Jeppe-1 reflectivity log and inserted into the seismic section at the well location. The Jeppe-1 acoustic impedance log is plotted at the well location.

the wavelet is representative of the seismic data and may be used to invert the 2D seismic section. Two key seismic horizons were used to derive a low-frequency model that compensates for the information not present in the seismic data. The low-frequency model was generated by low-pass filtering the acoustic impedance log and extrapolating the log along the seismic horizons.

The seismic inversion was performed by using the wavelet and the low-frequency model. The seismic inversion result at the well location shows a fairly good correlation with the acoustic impedance log (see Fig. 7). This indicates that the acoustic impedance result may present a valid subsurface model as the seismic inversion is not constrained directly by the well log. Furthermore, the low-frequency model only introduces limited information into the seismic inversion, so to evaluate the influence of the low-frequency model, an inversion not utilizing this model was carried out (Fig. 8).

In those zones where the correlation between the acoustic impedance log and the acoustic impedance section is not optimal, this is attributed to the quality of the seismic data. As the well logs in general seem to be of good quality, incoherent noise, and multiples present in the seismic data are regarded as the source of errors in the acoustic impedance section.

At the well location (Fig. 7), sandy intervals are represented by high acoustic impedance of approximately 8.7×10^6 $kg\,m^{-2}\,s^{-1}$, whereas acoustic impedance of approximately $6.8\times10^6\,kg\,m^{-2}\,s^{-1}$seems to characterize the fine-grained pelagic deposits of the Farsund Formation. This seems to indicate that sandstones deposited within the Farsund Formation are represented by higher acoustic impedance and therefore provides a tool for an interpretation of the seismic Facies B. At the location of the seismic Facies B, the seismic inversion indicates a series of high acoustic impedance units characterized by features with a concave upwards base and scattered lensoidal features (Fig. 8). These features show the highest acoustic impedance values within the central part, approximately $8.7 \times 10^6\,kg\,m^{-2}\,s^{-1}$, with values gradually decreasing away from the centre. One interpretation of this could be clean sandstones interbedded in shales, e.g. channelized sandstones (see later).

Forward modelling was carried out to test a realistic sedimentological model in order to predict the lithology of the depositional system characterized by the high acoustic impedance pattern. According to Johannessen *et al.* (1996) and Ineson *et al.* (in press), turbidites and debris flows of similar age were penetrated in the Jeppe-1 well (Fig. 9). Thin classical Bouma sequences interbedded in the mudstones infer fan fringe deposition of a basin axial fan complex. A sedimentological analogue for the succession could consequently be stacked, mainly channelized sandstones deposited in a submarine fan complex. To test this interpretation, forward modelling was carried out to simulate a channel (Fig. 10) and this way compared with the acoustic impedance result. An interval velocity of the sandstone succession should be approximately $3400\,ms^{-1}$ for this model. The interval velocities of the thin turbidites encountered in the Jeppe-1 well were distinctly higher, approximately $3800\,ms^{-1}$ to $4000\,ms^{-1}$. Thin turbidites from the Mona-1 well northeast of the study area reach interval velocities of $3600\,ms^{-1}$ and consequently the assumed interval velocity used in the modelling is low. However, in the Miller Field of the UK sector, similar thin calcite cemented turbidites of channel margin deposition have interval velocities of approx. $4000\,ms^{-1}$ and higher (Garland 1993). The correlatable channel sandstones of the Miller Field vary in interval velocities between approximately $3400\,ms^{-1}$ and $3600\,ms^{-1}$. The sandstone showing the best reservoir quality, a low density sandstone at the upper part of the reservoir, has interval velocities below $3400\,ms^{-1}$ (Garland 1993). Since sandstones

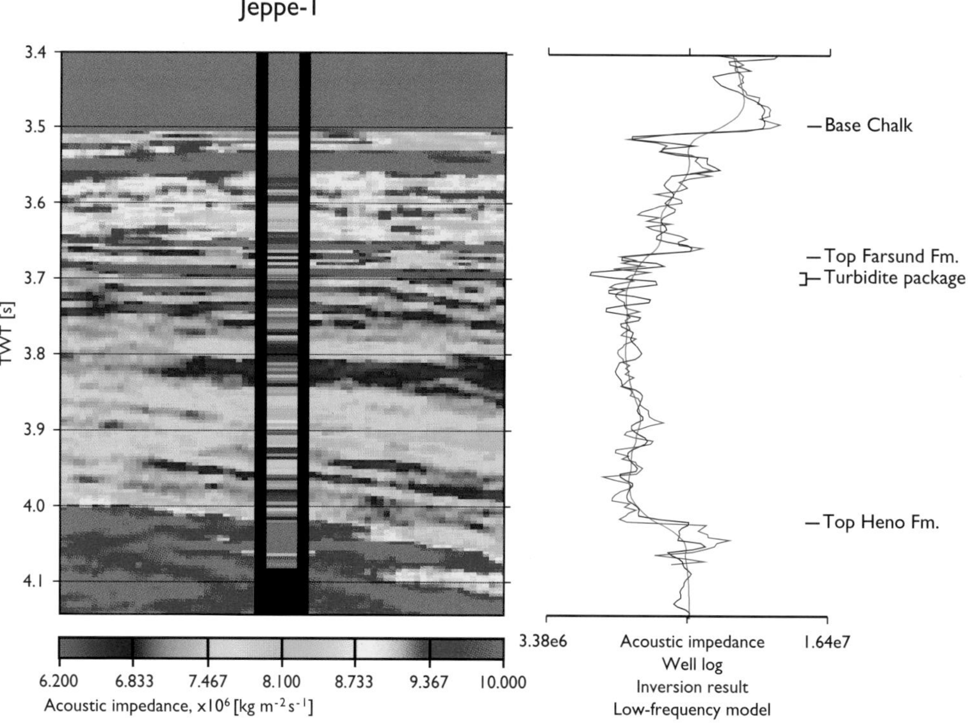

Fig. 7. Acoustic impedance log for Jeppe-1 inserted into the final acoustic impedance result (left). Comparison of acoustic impedance log, acoustic impedance result and low-frequency model for Jeppe-1 (right).

with high velocities may represent poor reservoir quality, use of the assumed interval velocities of the forward modelling seems reasonable. Alternatively, models resulting in the same seismic reflection pattern could be silty channelized deposits; this of course constitutes a significant risk in the model.

Sedimentological model

Several studies of the Upper Jurassic succession in the Danish Central Graben have demonstrated thin turbidites in the uppermost part of the Farsund Formation (Johannessen *et al.* 1996; Andsbjerg & Dybkjær 1997; Ineson in press), particularly within the Late Volgian–Ryazanian time interval. These turbidites have been interpreted as being part of prograding lowstand or transgressive systems tracts (Johannessen *et al.* 1996; Andsbjerg & Dybkjær 1997). They are best developed close to the master fault of the Tail End Graben and in the Gertrud and Arne–Elin graben.

In the Jeppe-1 well, situated on a footwall crest within the Gertrud Graben, sand-rich gravity flow deposits of latest Late Volgian and Ryzanian age were penetrated. These include sediments deposited from cohesive debris flows and turbulent flows (Bouma Tab). The cored section in the Jeppe-1 well shows both poorly sorted, matrix-rich and matrix-poor coarse- to fine-grained sandstones (Fig. 11). The mud-poor sandstones are rare and characterized by sharp, flat or scoured bases and may be parallel-laminated and normally graded. Contorted sand-mudstone units up to 50 cm in thickness are common. These turbidites are in association with thin sand–mud turbidites, interpreted as being a part of overbank deposits and record slumping and debris flows that may be the result of instability of a channel levee system, or may be related to slope instability associated with the evolving Gert High. Thin sand-rich turbidites of similar age have also been encountered in the Mona-1 and Gwen-2 wells (Andsbjerg & Dybkjær 1997) located on the eastern and southern flanks of the graben, respectively. In a sequence stratigraphic framework these gravity flow deposits are referred to as a prograding lowstand complex. Results of the seismic mapping indicate that deposition of channelized sandstones took place within the axial part of the Gertrud Graben, whilst thin turbidites interbedded with mudstones accumulated in the marginal areas and on footwall crests. This setting is somewhat similar to that inferred for the Namurian Pendle Grits of northern England. These are thought to have been deposited on the highly rugose floor of a relatively young extensional basin (Collinson 1988; Collinson pers. comm.). In some sections, the base of the Pendle Grits shows a gradual thickening upwards from basinal mudstones, suggesting gradual progradation and onlap on the footwall high, whilst nearby sections show thick, amalgamated channelized sandstones lying directly on basinal mudstones, a likely result of high-density flows being confined in hanging wall depressions. During Volgian and Ryazanian times the Gertrud Graben was an eastward dipping half-graben bounded by a major master fault towards the Mandal High; the graben was, however, also under the influence of salt movements that resulted in a more saucer-shaped basin configuration. Consequently, deposition of gravity deposits was concentrated in the central part of the Gertrud Graben as basin axial deposits. The source area for the turbidites is likely to have been the Sørvestlandet High towards the north and northeast, but the Mandal High and the Søgne Basin towards the west are also potential source areas. A major hiatus representing the period between the Middle Volgian and Ryazanian in the Søgne Basin indicates that this area was exposed for erosion during deposition of the latest Late Volgian and Ryazanian deposits in the Gertrud Graben, thus representing another potential sediment source area. In these areas, Upper Jurassic shallow marine and shelf sands may have been reworked to form the source of deep marine fan complexes in the adjacent depocentres (e.g. Ula Formation).

The seismic study presented here suggests that sandstones were confined either within channels, or formed channel–levee

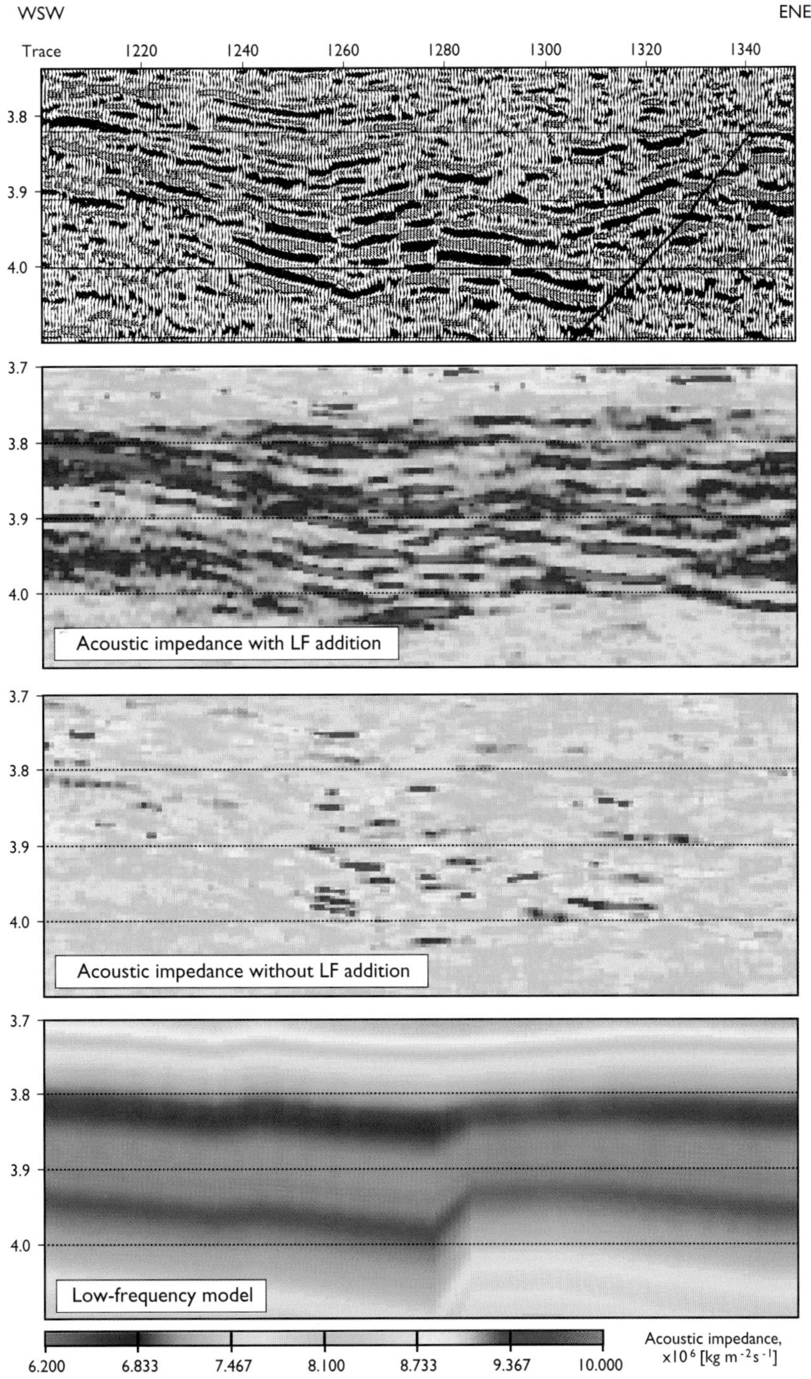

Fig. 8. Part of the seismic section from Fig. 3 and the corresponding acoustic impedance result with the low-frequency model, without the low-frequency model, and the derived low-frequency model.

systems. The interpreted size of the individual channel fill sandstones is about 200 m wide and up to 40 m thick (Fig. 8). In places a stacked organization is interpreted. However, often they seem to be randomly distributed, indicating frequent shifting of transport routes. The overall coarsening upward trend of the lowstand succession penetrated in the Jeppe-1 well indicates a prograding fan system deposited in the depression formed during the early Volgian rift pulse. The depositional environment was anoxic and in marginal settings, distal to the postulated axial fan system, was dominated by deposition of organic-rich muds either as hemipelagic sediments or mud turbidites (Ineson in press). The inferred depositional environment is shown in Fig. 12.

Discussion

The prediction of the lithological setting within the Gertrud Graben is based on the seismic study which is associated with a number of uncertainties: resolution of the seismic data, ambiguity of the acoustic impedance data, and the specified values used to simulate sand-rich turbidites in the forward seismic modelling study.

From the acoustic impedance section, it is possible to see some high acoustic impedance units at trace 1260–1320 m (Fig. 8), which are interpreted as sandstone layers. A main uncertainty associated with these results is the fact that any acoustic impedance only represents the product of the velocity

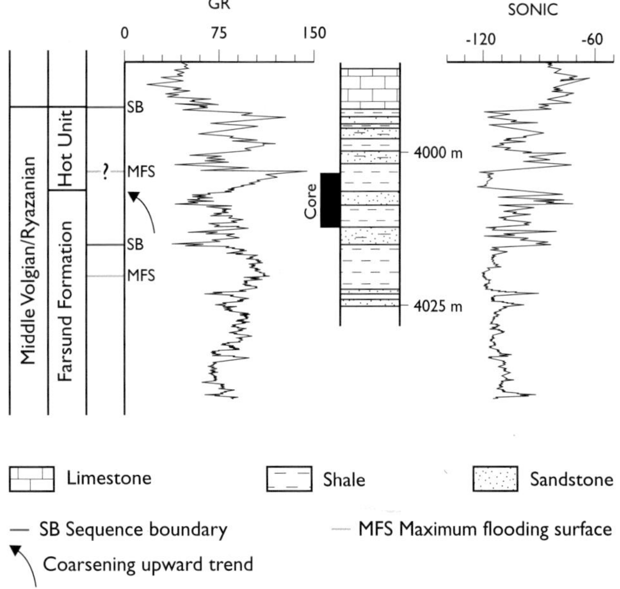

Fig. 9. Lithological log of the turbiditic succession in the Jeppe-1 well.

and density of the individual unit. A valid interpretation may therefore only be performed by comparing the acoustic impedance data with well log information and by setting up a plausible geological model. As the thickness of the individual units are close to the seismic resolution limit where the upper and lower interface cannot be resolved, both the acoustic impedance and layer thickness may be distorted. In addition, the units may also be stacked, resulting in a complex seismic interference pattern which does not allow for identification of the individual units. In this case, the specific reflection pattern from a possible suite of sandbodies has been modelled (Fig. 10). Though the seismic reflection pattern is indicative of large contrasts in acoustic impedance and though some ambiguity surrounds the actual shape, the basic interpretation of sandbodies seems valid. The high amplitude reflection pattern, as seen on the seismic, is not expected to represent thin layers of sandstones with high impedance, as seen at the well location (Fig. 7). This is based on the modelling study which indicates that the thin layers of sandstones with high acoustic impedance are represented by a low amplitude seismic reflection pattern (Fig. 10). Therefore, the size and geometry of the features indicate that relative thick layers of a similar lithology, e.g. sandstone, are responsible for the reflection pattern.

Both limestone stringers and siltstone may be associated with the modelled acoustic impedance data. This ambiguity constitutes a high exploration risk. Limestone stringers are very frequent in the lower part of the Farsund Formation, Upper Kimmeridgian to Lower Volgian succession (Andsbjerg pers. comm.), but they are very rare in the section of interest of this study which concentrates on the Upper Volgian to Ryazanian interval, as is shown by the cores from the Jeppe-1 well, which contain no such stringers, either limestone or dolomite (Andersen pers. comm.). Therefore, it seems unlikely that the high amplitude reflection pattern mapped within the Gertrud Graben represents a seismic response from limestone stringers. The interpretation of sandstones, as responsible for the seismic anomaly within the Gertrud Graben, is supported by the penetrated sand-rich gravity deposits encountered in the Jeppe-1 well which seem to thicken into the graben. The results of the seismic inversion, indicating moderate impedance contrasts, are consistent with such an interpretation, although siltstones might give a similar response.

If sand-rich turbidites were deposited here it was in association with the organic-rich part of the Farsund Formation (Hot Unit). The presence of an excellent source rock, probably within the peak oil generation window, makes this play concept interesting.

Conclusion

A seismic study of the Gertrud Graben reveals that basin axial turbidites were possibly deposited during the Late Jurassic. The turbidites are predicted on the basis of a number of criteria: a high amplitude reflection pattern which can be correlated with turbidites encountered in the Jeppe-1 well and acoustic impedance results from the seismic inversion which are able to predict the acoustic impedance well log. A valid and unbiased subsurface model has therefore been derived which indicates the presence of high impedance layers away from the well. These layers have been mapped and seem to be located within the central part of the Gertrud Graben following a NW–SE trend.

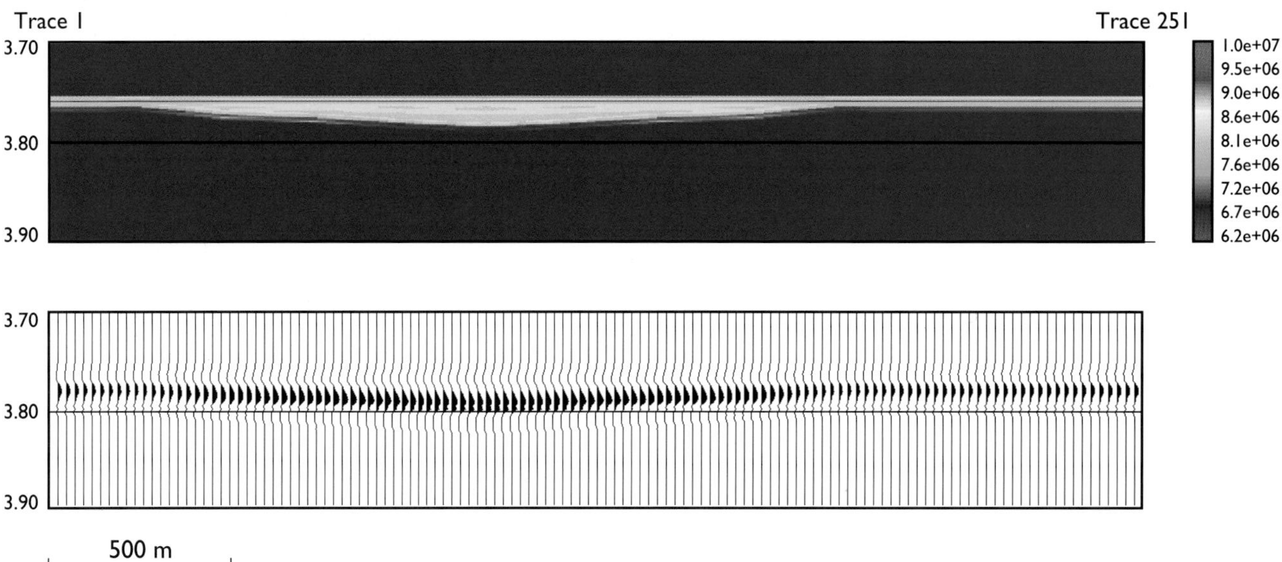

Fig. 10. Results of the forward modelling of a channel and the resulting reflection pattern. The acoustic impedance is comparable with the results of the inversion of the seismic data.

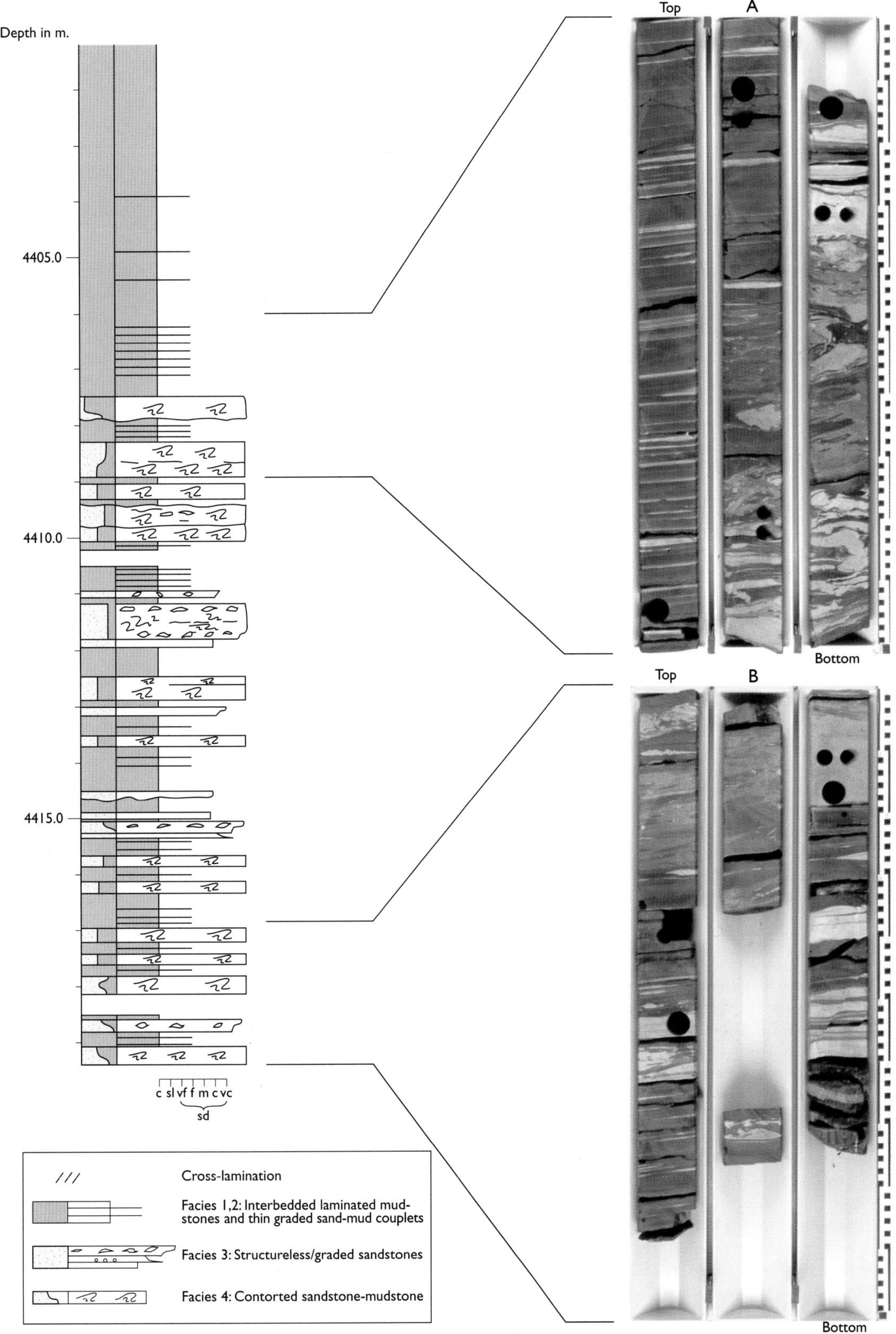

Fig. 11. Sedimentological log from the cored section in the Jeppe-1 well and two photographs of Core A; 4406.93–4408.90 and core B; 4416.93–4419.40. Core A illustrates the structureless sandstones and contorted sandstone–mudstone units interbedded with cross-laminated sandstone beds. Core B shows the contorted sandstone–mudstone units. In the upper part of the log the boundary between the generally thickening upward succession and the organic-rich muddy Hot Units can be seen. Modified from Ineson (in press).

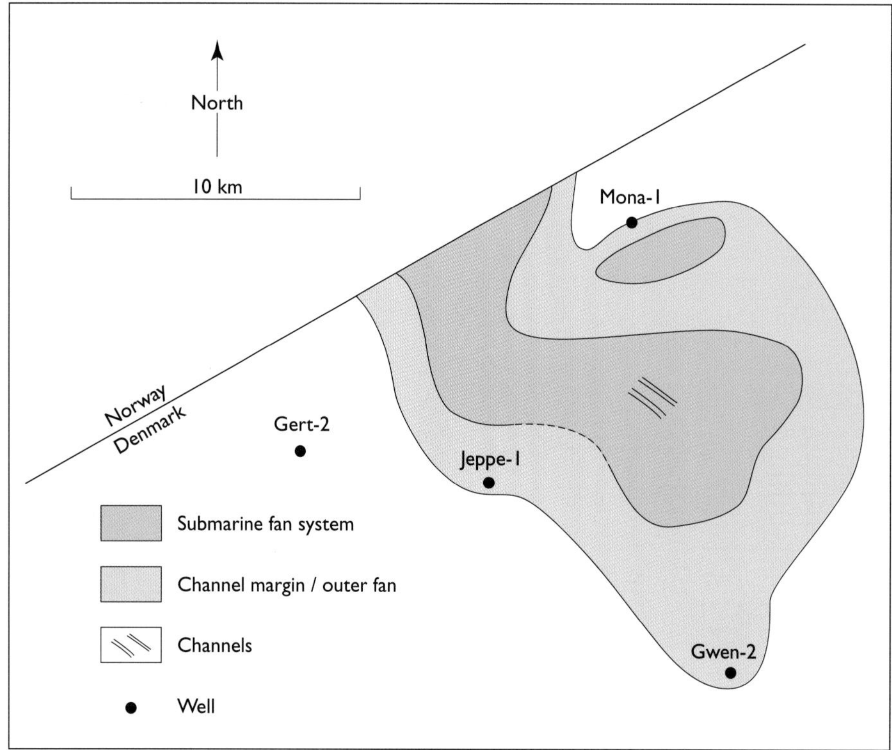

Fig. 12. Depositional model for the fan deposits within the Gertrud Graben based on well information and this study.

The authors would like to thank S. Fraser and an anonymous reviewer for constructive comments and S. Boldy for the editorial work. J. Ineson is acknowledge for fruitful discussions on the depositional environment of the turbidites penetrated in the Jeppe-1 well. The project was financially supported by the Danish Ministry of Energy under the Danish Energy Research and Development Program 1996. Danpec A/S, geoteam A/S, and Nopec International A/S are thanked for permission to publish the seismic data. The article has been published with the permission of the Geological Survey of Denmark and Greenland. S. Sølberg, G. Nicolaisen and J. Halskov, GEUS drew the figures and V. Salby, Ødegaard A/S has proofread the manuscript .

References

ABBOTTS, I. L. 1991. *United Kingdom oil and gas fields 25 years commemorative volume*. The Geological Society Memoirs, **14**, 573.

ANDERSEN, C., OLSEN, J. C., MICHELSEN, O. & NYGAARD, E. 1982. Structural outline and development. *In*: MICHELSEN, O. (ed.) *Geology of the Danish Central Graben*. Geolocial Survey of Denmark, Series B, **8**, 9–26.

ANDSBJERG, J. & DYBKJÆR, K. 1997. Jurassic sequence stratigraphy of the Danish Central Graben. *In*: ANDSBJERG J. (ed.) *Sedimentology and Sequence Stratigraphy of Middle Jurassic Deposits; Danish and Norwegian Central Graben*. Unpublished PhD thesis, University of Copenhagen.

BERGAN, M., TØRUDBAKKEN, B. & WANDÅS, B. 1989. Lithostratigrapic correlation of Upper Jurassic sandstones within the Norwegian Central Graben: Sedimentological and tectonic implications. *In*: COLLINSON, J. D. (ed.) *Correlation in Hydrocarbon Exploration. Norwegian Petroleum Society*. Graham & Trotman, London, 243–251.

COLLINSON, J. C. 1988. Controls on Namurian sedimentation in the Central Province of northern England. *In:* BESLY, B. M. & KELLING, G. (eds) *Sedimentation in a Synorogenic Basin Complex, the Upper Carboniferous of Northwest Europe*. Blackie, Glasgow, 85–101.

GARLAND, C. R. 1993. Miller Field: reservoir stratigraphy and its impact on development. *In*: PARKER, J. R. (ed.) *Petroleum Geology of Northwest Europe*: *Proceedings of the 4th Conference*. Geological Society, London, 401–414.

GOWERS, M. B., HOLTAR, E. & SWENSON, E. 1993. The structure of the Norwegian Central Trouh (Central Graben area). *In:* PARKER, J. R. (ed.) *Petroleum Geology of Northwest Europe: Procedings of the 4th Conference*. Geological Society, London, 1245–1254.

INESON, J., BOJESEN-KOEFOD, J., DYBKJÆR, K., & NIELSEN, L. H. in press. Volgian–Ryazanian 'hot shales' of the Farsund Formation in the Danish Central Graben, North Sea: stratigraphy, facies, and geochemistry. *In:* SURLYK, F. & INESON, J. R. (eds) *The Jurassic of Denmark and Greenland*, Geological Survey of Denmark and Greenland, Copenhagen.

JOHANNESSEN, P. N., DYBKJÆR, K. & RASMUSSEN, E. S. 1996. Sequence stratigraphy of Upper Jurassic reservoir sandstones in the northern part of the Danish Central Trough, North Sea. *Marine and Petetroleum Geology*, **13**, 755–770.

MAVER, K. G. & RASMUSSEN, K. B. 1995. Seismic inversion for reservoir delineation and description. *Society of Petroleum Engineers Technical Conference and Exhibition*, Bahrain, March 11–14, 267–276.

MØLLER, J. J. 1986. *Seismic structural mapping of the Middle and Upper Jurassic in the Danish Central Trough*. Geological Survey of Denmark, Series A, **13**, 37.

—— & RASMUSSEN, E. S. in press. Middle Jurassic–Early Cretaceous rifting of the Danish Central graben. *In*: SURLYK, F. & INESON, J. R. (eds) *The Jurassic of Denmark and Greenland* Geological Survey of Denmark and Greenland, Copenhagen.

RASMUSSEN, E. S. 1995. The structural evolution of the Gert–Mjølner area. *Marine Petroleum Geology*, **12**, 377–385.

SØDERSTRØM, B., FORSBERG, A., HOLTAR, E. & RASMUSSEN, B. A. 1991. The Mjølner Field, a deep Upper Jurassic oil field in the Central North Sea. *First Break*, **9**, 156–171.

VEJBÆK, O. V. & ANDERSEN, C. 1986. Cretaceous–Early Tertiary inversion tectonism in the Danish Central Trough. *Tectonophysics*, **137**, 221–228.

VOLLESET, J. & DORÉ, A. G. 1984. A revised Triassic and Jurassic lithostratigraphic nomenclature for the Norwegian North Sea. *Norwegian Petroleum Directorate Bulletin*, **3**, 53.

Chalk renaissance

Chalk renaissance

Introduction and review

S. A. R. BOLDY

Amerada Hess Norge A/S, Langkaien 1, 0150 Oslo, Norway

The chalk remains the miracle reservoir of the North Sea. It is hard to improve upon the comment by Campbell & Ormaasen (1987), when writing about the chalk in the context of reviewing the history of oil and gas exploration in Norway, that: 'it was regarded as a singularly unpromising reservoir for hydrocarbons, being deficient in porosity and permeability . . .'.

As noted by **Mackertich & Goulding**, the first oil discovery in the North Sea was the A1 well drilled in the Danish sector, and this found oil in a Danian chalk reservoir. Careful reservoir management has resulted in much greater recovery of the oil and gas contained in the chalk traps than was envisaged at the time of development. **Bramwell *et al.*** noted that the Greater Ekofisk area alone has produced more than 2×10^9 BBL of oil and 8.9×10^{12} SCF of gas.

The last few years have seen renewed exploration for chalk targets and this has been driven by:

(i) continued success in production;
(ii) improved seismic imaging from greater use of 3D seismic;
(iii) greater use of advanced seismic techniques – seismic attributes, seismic inversion, amplitude versus offset and rock physics;
(iv) more detailed stratigraphical analysis using sequence stratigraphy and improved biostratigraphy;
(v) extending the chalk play fairway into new areas.

The first two papers in the section detail the search for stratigraphic traps in the chalk in the Ekofisk area. **Bramwell *et al.*** document how the use of 3D seismic data combined with a major well based sequence stratigraphic study led to the identification of a number of potential stratigraphic traps in the chalk. The following paper by **Anderson** details the geophysical techniques used to attempt to predict porosity and fluid fill in such a stratigraphic trap, that was later drilled. This case history demonstrates that high porosity zones can be identified with a good degreee of confidence, but that differentiating between brine filled and oil filled chalk remains a problem.

The following paper by **Farmer & Barkved** on the Valhall and Hod fields, again documents how the combination of sequence stratigraphy, 3D seismic data and advanced geophysical techniques has been used to construct a revised geological model that identifies significant syn-depositional faulting, with associated resedimentation of chalk on the down-flank areas of the growing structures. This in turn has led to the identification of potential stratigraphic traps on the flanks of the field.

The paper by **Mackertich & Goulding**, on the South Arne Field in the Danish sector, highlights the difficulty in imaging caused by gas escape. This field, although discovered in 1969, was only shown to be commercial in 1995 following the drilling of an appraisal well into the gas cloud, proving thick pay in a crestal position.

The final paper by **Evans *et al.***, discusses the Banff Field, an accumulation that lies toward the western edge of the Central Graben in the UK sector, some 100 km to the west of the main chalk province. This field, discovered in 1991, again demonstrates the remarkable ability of the chalk to form surprising traps. A detached chalk raft sitting on the flank of a salt dome, dipping at more than 45°, displays an oil column of more than 1000 m (3300 ft).

Looking forward, we can expect more wells to test stratigraphic traps in the chalk and a reappraisal of the chalk potential throughout the Central Graben rather than just in the immediate area of the prolific Norwegian and Danish fields. Advances can also be expected in seismic imaging, particularly from increased use of ocean bottom cables in areas where gas clouds exist as a result of hydrocarbon leakage from chalk reservoirs. In the absence of gas clouds, porosity in chalk is relatively easy to detect from seismic data, but what is not easy to determine is whether the porosity is filled with hydrocarbons or water. It can also be anticipated that production technology will continue to advance, with greater use of complex well paths to drain lower permeability rservoirs,. The success in production will continue to act as a stimulus for further exploration activity.

Reference

CAMPBELL, C. J. & ORMAASEN, E. 1987. The discovery of oil and gas in Norway: an historical synopsis. *In*: SPENCER, A. M. *et al.* (eds) *Geology of the Norwegian Oil and Gas Fields*. Graham & Trotman, London, 1–37.

BOLDY, S. A. R. 1999. Chalk renaissance, introduction and review. *In*: FLEET, A. J. & BOLDY, S. A. R. (eds) *Petroleum Geology of Northwest Europe: Proceedings of the 5th Conference*, 909.

Chalk exploration, the search for a subtle trap

N. P. BRAMWELL,[1] G. CAILLET,[2] L. MECIANI,[3] N. JUDGE,[4] M. GREEN,[5] and P. ADAM[6]

[1] *Phillips Petroleum Company Norway, PO Box 220, Tananger, Norway (e-mail: npbramw@ppco.com)*
Present address: Phillips Petroleum Company, POB 1967, Houston, TX 77251-1967, USA
[2] *Elf Petroleum Norge as, POB 168, N-4001, Stavanger, Norway*
Present address: Elf Exploration Production, Avenue Larribau, 64018 Pau, Cedex, France
[3] *ENI s.p.a., Agip division, via Fabiani 1, 20097 S. Donato Milanese, Milan, Italy*
[4] *Phillips Petroleum Company Norway, POB 220, N-4056 Tananger, Norway*
Present address: Hunt Oil Company, 1445 Ross Street, Dallas, Texas
[5] *Fina Exploration Norway inc. POB 4055 Tasta, N-4004 Stavanger, Norway*
Present Address: Fina Exploration (UK) Ltd, Fina House, Epsom KT18 5AD, UK
[6] *Fina Exploration Norway inc. POB 4055 Tasta, N-4004 Stavanger, Norway*
Present Address: Fina Exploration, Minh Hai B.V., Phu Nhuan District, Ho Chi Minh City, Vietnam

Abstract: Over 2×10^9 STB of oil and 8.9×10^{12} SCF of gas have been produced from the chalk fields of the Greater Ekofisk area, more than 50% of that being produced from the giant Ekofisk Field. Phillips Petroleum Company Norway and the PL018 licence co-venturers have undertaken a comprehensive and integrated re-evaluation of the chalk exploration potential in Blocks 2/4 and 2/7 of the Norwegian Continental Shelf. Recent exploration models indicated the potential for significant untested reserves to exist in the chalk of Blocks 2/4 and 2/7. The Chalk Exploration Project (CEP) team was given the objective 'to define the risked value of the remaining chalk exploration potential in licence PL018'. All major structures and significant amplitude anomalies at chalk level had been drilled by 1986, leaving only the subtle field flank and stratigraphic plays for evaluation. Although many studies had been completed in the chalk over the years since discovery of Ekofisk Field in 1969, most of these studies had been focused on a single field and no regionally consistent stratigraphic framework or depositional model had been developed. As part of this project, a robust regional model for chalk prospectivity was developed covering the whole chalk basin, based on a sequence stratigraphic analysis of regional seismic and well databases, together with petrophysical, hydrodynamic, geochemical and other key technical studies. Acquisition of 3D seismic data over the chalk fields since the mid 1980s demonstrated the power of 3D seismic analysis to define stratigraphic detail within the chalk, and by 1993 the entire licensed area of Blocks 2/4 and 2/7 was covered by 3D data, giving the opportunity to undertake a semi-regional, sequence stratigraphic 3D analysis of the chalk reservoir in PL018, and determine the remaining exploration potential.

This paper describes the results of the 'Chalk Exploration Project' (CEP) a study performed by Phillips Petroleum Company Norway together with their Norwegian PL018 co-venturers and concludes by defining the seven key risk factors for evaluating subtle chalk stratigraphic prospects and leads.

In order to leverage the extensive chalk expertise available within the licence group, a team of geoscientists was assembled from PL018 co-venturer companies in early 1995. The study area was centred on the Ekofisk Field and included the whole of PL018 (Fig. 1). The project had three main phases; database compilation, development of a regional exploration model and lead/prospect analysis and risking. The development of a regionally standardized well and seismic database was a significant challenge, but this provided the foundation for the project and where possible all well data were captured in digital format. The well database was extensive, comprising exploration and development data from over 500 wells. The main components of the database were: (a) a regional, phase-corrected, 2D seismic grid and a semi-regional 3000 km^2 merged 3D seismic survey; (b) a regional velocity database; (c) a regional biostratigraphic rationalization, performed to develop a sequence stratigraphic framework (Fig. 2); (d) a quality controlled petrophysical database, including a standardized petrophysical interpretation and electrofacies analysis; and (e) a standardized core facies description of over 3900 m of core from 40 wells. A fast and effective computing environment was custom built to provide access to well and seismic databases through a full suite of geoscience computer applications. Identification of the key risks associated with trap, seal, reservoir and hydrocarbon system was of primary importance and the focus of the interpretation was to determine the significance of each of these parameters. Regional structural and stratigraphic interpretation of each major sequence was used to produce sequence, structure and thickness maps. These maps were integrated with semi-regional 3D seismic attributes, core description, electrofacies data and CPI derived parameters (phi and corrected shale volume) to produce regional palaeoenvironmental maps for each sequence. An understanding of the structural evolution of the chalk basin, migration pathways and timing of oil maturation and migration was developed from structural and 2D basin modelling studies. Statistical analysis of chalk reservoir parameters was performed in order to understand the factors affecting their distribution, including principal component and multi-variant statistical analysis. Depth of burial, water saturation, facies type, shale content, porosity, structural location, silica content, permeability and fracture type and intensity were among the variables studied. A regional hydrodynamic analysis was undertaken to develop a model for the overpressured hydrodynamic regime within the chalk, a critical factor in understanding and predicting chalk prospectivity.

Bramwell, N. P., Caillet, G., Meciani, L., Judge, N., Green, M. & Adam, P. 1999. Chalk exploration, the search for a subtle trap. *In*: Fleet, A. J. & Boldy, S. A. R. (eds) *Petroleum Geology of Northwest Europe: Proceedings of the 5th Conference*, 911–937. Published by the Geological Society, London.

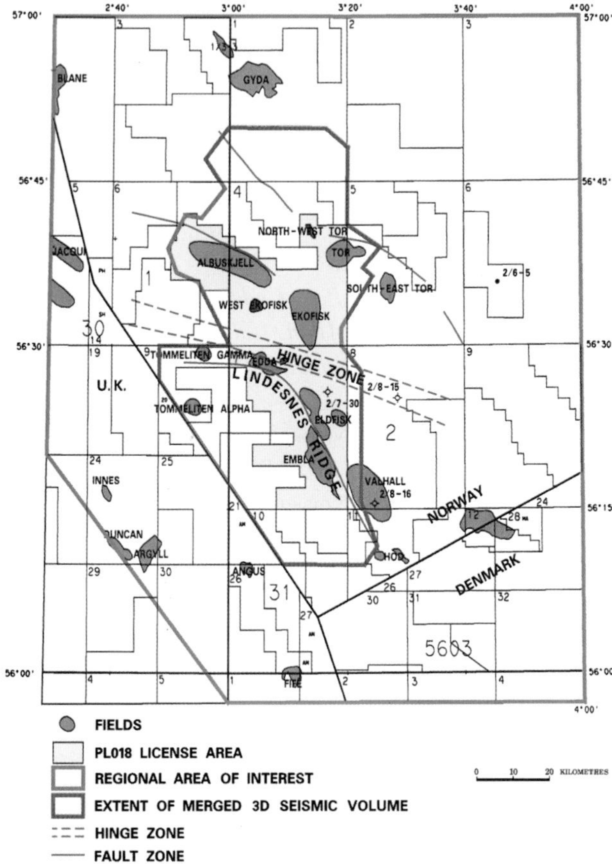

Fig. 1. Location map and structural domains.

An integrated reservoir engineering and geosciencetific evaluation of all existing well tests and undeveloped chalk discoveries, such as N2/7-2 and N2/4-10, was also performed to determine potential commercial viability of these discoveries in light of modern development technology. More than 40 leads were identified and evaluated using a petrophysical based seismic inversion technique to estimate porosity and net pay. Finally, prospect risking was performed using an understanding of exploration risk derived from the regional chalk exploration model.

A brief history of chalk exploration and development in the Greater Ekofisk area

The history of chalk exploration and production in the North Sea is as long as the exploration history of the North Sea. In 1966 the first oil discovery in the North Sea was made when the Danish A-1X well encountered hydrocarbons in Danian Chalk (Joergensen & Andersen 1991). This well led to the discovery of the Kraka Field which came on stream in 1991. Chalk exploration continued through the late 1960s and early 1970s with mixed success and three years after the Danish A-1X discovery, the Valhall and Ekofisk fields were discovered in the Norwegian sector. Chalk exploration reached an all time peak in 1973 (Fig. 3), with eight exploration wells completed in one year. The successful discovery of the Eldfisk, West Ekofisk and Tor fields in 1970 by the Phillips Group, Albuskjell Field by the Shell Group and Edda Field by the Phillips Group in 1972, Hod Field in 1974 by the Amoco group and Tommeliten, Alpha and Gamma fields in 1976 by the Statoil group, led to total combined inplace reserves of over $1761 \times 10^6\,m^3$ oil, $107 \times 10^6\,m^3$ condensate and $1015 \times 10^9\,m^3$ gas ($17\,431 \times 10^6$ BBL oil equivalent (BOE)) in the chalk play of the Greater Ekofisk area (Cornford 1994). By 1980 nearly all of the chalk four-way dip closures had been drilled in the Greater Ekofisk area and exploration for the classic structural play tailed off to a single well drilled each year until 1985. Production from the fields reached a plateau in the early 1990s and attention became focused on ways of extending the life of the chalk fields, including reservoir stimulation, water injection and field flank exploration. With the advent of a new chalk exploration concept, the chalk stratigraphic trap (Fig. 4), chalk exploration received renewed interest and in 1994 a combined structural/stratigraphic prospect called the 'Hod Pod' was drilled in Block 2/10 by the Amoco Group (Fig. 1), (Campbell & Gravdal 1995). This well was closely followed by the first true test of the chalk stratigraphic play, the Phillips group N2/7-30 Egdar well drilled in 1995, on an amplitude anomaly within the Tor and Ekofisk formations (Anderson 1999) and the N2/8-15 Noekkon well, drilled by the Amoco Group in 1996, on an Upper Tor seismic amplitude anomaly. Both wells were water wet. In 1997 the Saga led group drilled the N2/6-5 well, a classic structural chalk test on the flanks of the Norwegian Central Graben, and the Amoco Group (PL008) drilled the extended reach 2/8-16s well to test an amplitude anomaly on the flanks of Valhall Field. In late 1997 the Agip Group plan to drill a chalk stratigraphic trap in Block 2/5, and the Conoco and the Amoco Groups, in Blocks 1/5 and 2/8, respectively, plan diapir flank wells in search of a fractured chalk reservoir. Figure 5 shows the variety of chalk play types targeted in recent years in the Greater Ekofisk area.

The chalk stratigraphic play

The concept of the chalk stratigraphic play is summarized in Fig. 4 and relies upon the juxtaposition of chalk reservoir and seal pairs, i.e. porous hydrocarbon-bearing chalk encased and sealed within pelagic or tight chalks. Chalk is unique, in that it can act as both a seal and a reservoir rock. However, for the chalk reservoir to be most effective, fractures are essential. This poses a potential paradox for the chalk stratigraphic play, as fractures affecting the reservoir will undoubtedly affect and potentially breach the seal. It is demonstrated below that V_{shale} increases at sequence boundaries and an increase in V_{shale} will significantly reduce the fracture susceptibility of the chalk; therefore trapping potential is greatest when two sequence boundaries are juxtaposed.

Evidence for chalk stratigraphic trapping exists throughout the database, RFT pressure measurements plotted for the Norwegian 2/5-7 well (Fig. 6) show that a thin shale interval at 3366 m has the ability to seal and withstand 100 PSI pressure differential, effectively sealing one porous chalk facies from another. Conversely, this pressure difference noted in the N2/5-7 well, could demonstrate semi-regional pressure drawdown as a result of present-day production from Tor Field, 12 km to the southwest, although this is considered unlikely. The seismic database also contains examples of channel-like forms and pinch-out geometries, where potential stratigraphic traps may exist. Figure 7, a flattened seismic time slice on the Top Tor sequence boundary, displays a channel form trending NW–SE, penetrated by the N2/4-12 well. The corresponding flattened seismic line in Fig. 8 trends N–S through the same feature at the N2/4-12 well location. The N2/4-12 well encountered a 20% water wet Tor Formation at 3299 m subsea; an increase in V_{shale} at the base of the Ekofisk Formation provided a top seal, however no lateral or base seal was demonstrated by the well. Additionally, most of the producing fields appear to have a stratigraphic component (Caillet *et al.* 1997; D'Angelo & Brandel 1997), supporting evidence for a chalk stratigraphic play.

The key risk parameters associated with the chalk stratigraphic trap are discussed later, following summaries of the structural, stratigraphic, palaeoenvironmental and sedimentological evolution of the chalk within the Greater Ekofisk area.

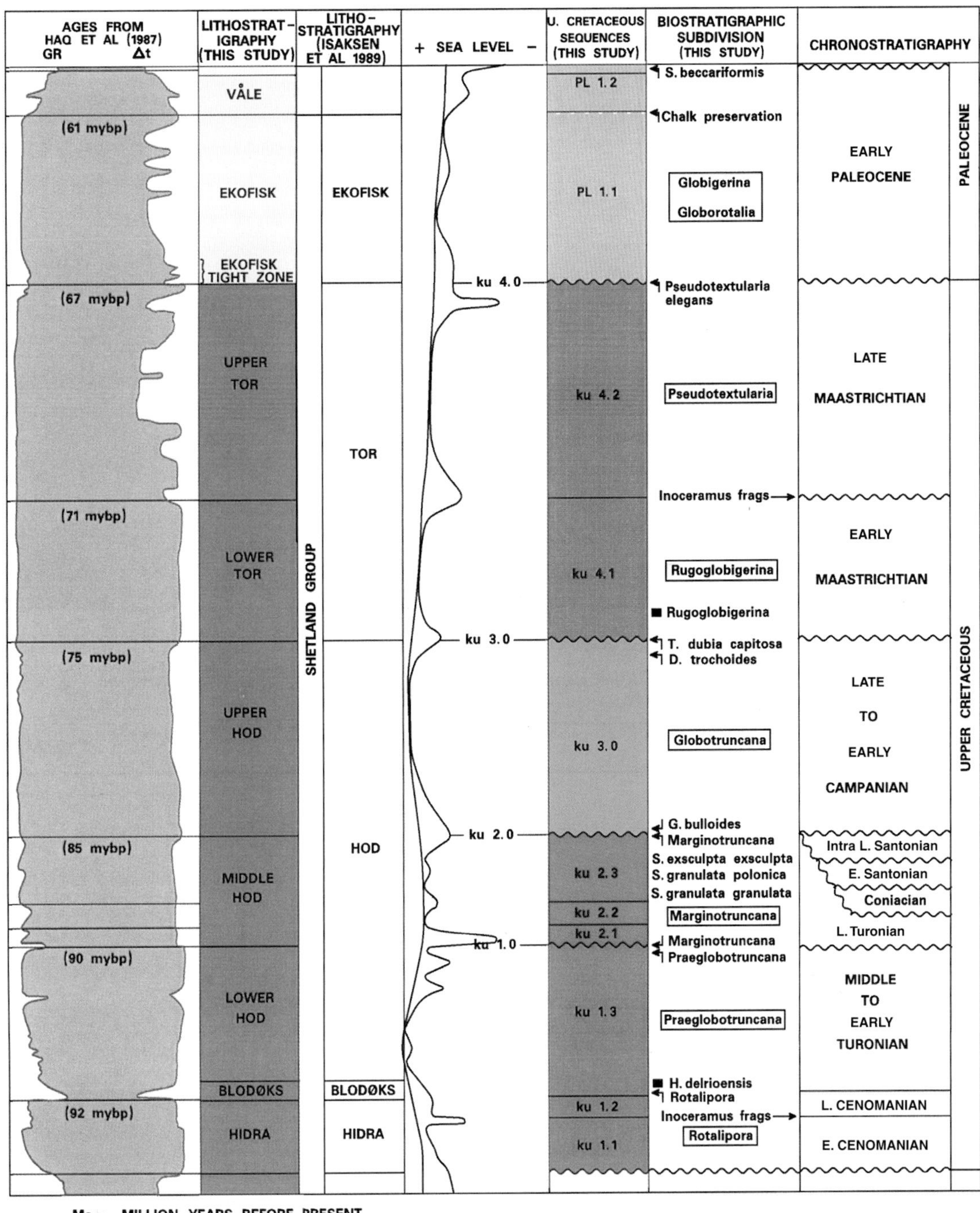

Fig. 2. Lithostratigraphic and sequence stratigraphic nomenclature used in this study for the subdivision of the Cretaceous and Lower Paleocene.

Structural history

The North Sea is an intracratonic basin with a complex structural configuration derived from a multiphase tectonic evolution and the presence of active kinematic Permian salt (Gowers *et al.* 1993; Caillet *et al.* 1997). The main tectonic events for the Central Graben as summarized by Knott *et al.* (1993) are: Permian extension (E–W); a Triassic extension (WNW–ESE); a Middle Jurassic extension (SW–NE); late Jurassic extension (SW–NE); an early Cretaceous inversion phase (Cimmerian inversion) and a minor E–W compression which caused cessation of North Sea rifting; and finally a Late Cretaceous to Oligo-Miocene compressional phase (SE–NW). The structure of the study area can be subdivided into three distinct domains characterized by different structural and faulting styles as shown in Fig. 1 (modified after Caillet *et al.* 1996). The southern domain (south of the hinge zone) is dominated by the Lindesnes Ridge (Valhall, Eldfisk, Edda and Hod fields), the northern domain (north of the hinge zone) by large tectonic and salt induced structures trending NW–SE (Ekofisk, West Ekofisk, Tor and Albuskjell fields) and a central domain dominated by salt induced structures along a WNW–ESE trending shear band/hinge zone (Tommeliten Gamma and N2/7-13 diapir structure). Figure 9 summarizes the structural evolution and deposition of the Chalk Group of the Greater Ekofisk area. Deposition commenced during a structurally quiescent period in a restricted basin. An initial compressional tectonic phase occurred in the mid-Turonian and continued intermittently through to the Danian. During this period the morphology of the basin was largely controlled

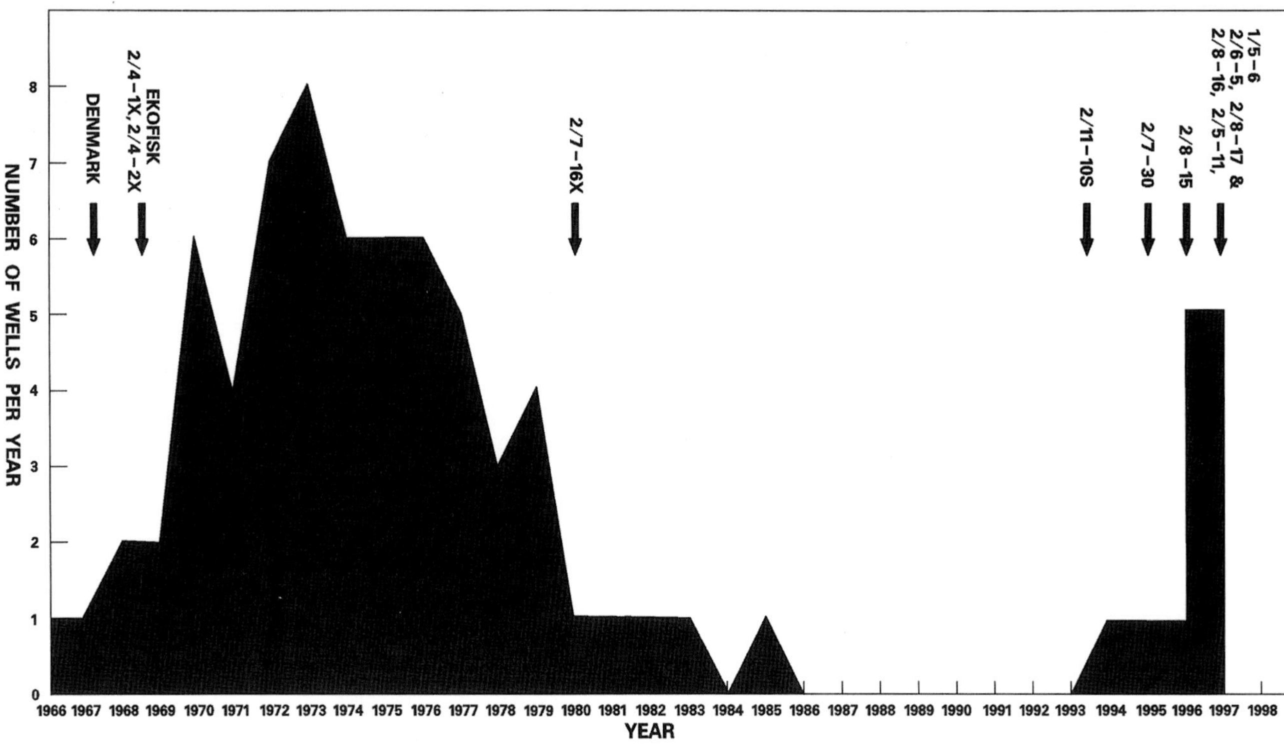

Fig. 3. Historical review of chalk exploration in the Greater Ekofisk area.

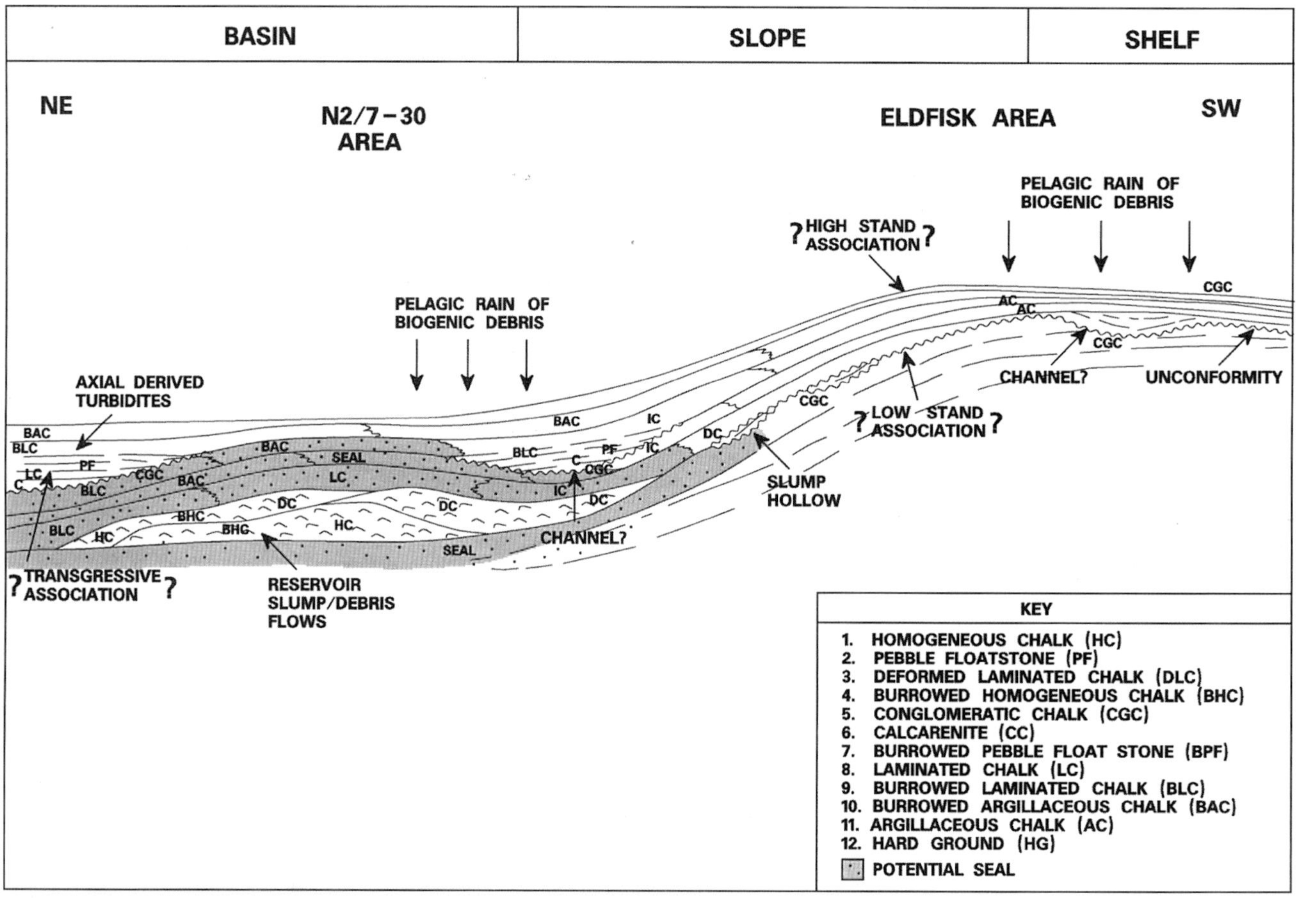

Fig. 4. Hypothetical chalk stratigraphic trapping model and play concept.

by the formation of major structures, such as the Lindesnes Ridge and salt cored inversion features (Albuskjell anticline) associated with deep-seated fault trends. Syn-depositional halokinetic and tectonic movements had a direct influence on facies distribution through this time interval and syn-sedimentary faults have been identified over the Valhall Field during the Maastrichtian (Farmer & Barkved 1999). A clear distinction is made between the structural grain during the Turonian

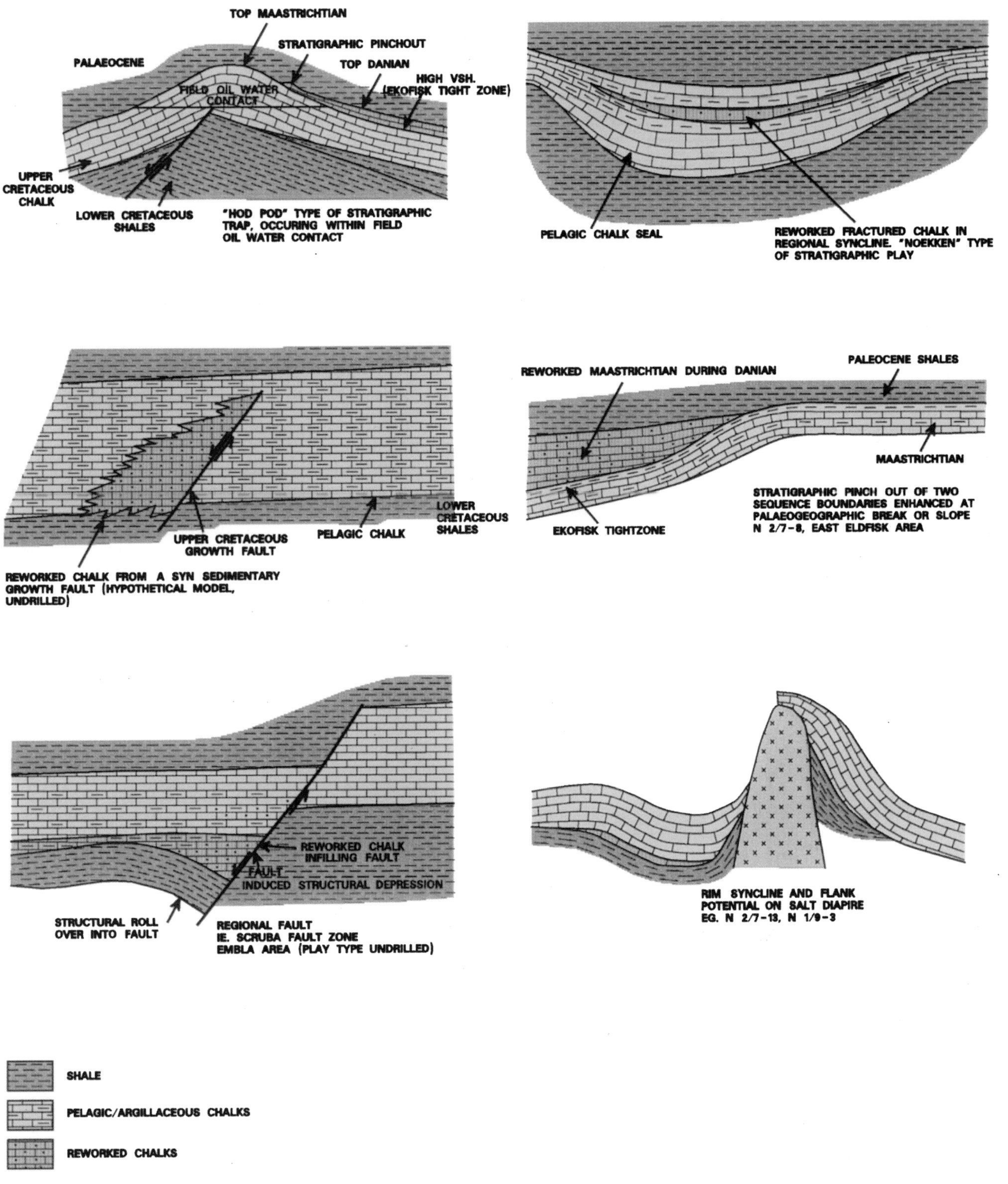

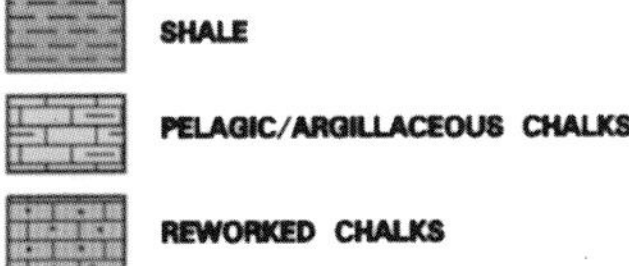

Fig. 5. Chalk play types found in the Greater Ekofisk area.

to Campanian (NNE–SSW compression, with right lateral strike slip along the Skrubbe Fault Zone) and the structural grain during the Maastrichtian and Danian (regional NW–SE subsidence forming the Ekofisk trough in Blocks 2/4 and 2/8, north of the hinge zone shown in Fig. 1). The Valhall area remained a prominent high from the mid-Turonian onwards and is characterized by condensed sections of chalk. A second major compressional tectonic phase occurred during the Eocene period (Alpine Phase) and is partly responsible for the emergence of the area around the Ekofisk Field. Other structures were also reactivated during this time with tectonic pulses continuing throughout the Oligocene and Miocene (Pyrenean phase) affecting chalk structures locally, i.e. diaprism and fracturing.

Stratigraphy

Traditionally the Shetland Group is divided into five lithostratigraphic intervals (Fig. 2), Ekofisk, Tor, Hod, Blodøks (= Plenus Marl) and Hidra formations (Deegan & Scull 1977; Isaksen & Tonstad 1989), although the application of these lithostratigraphic subdivisions is often difficult (Munns 1985).

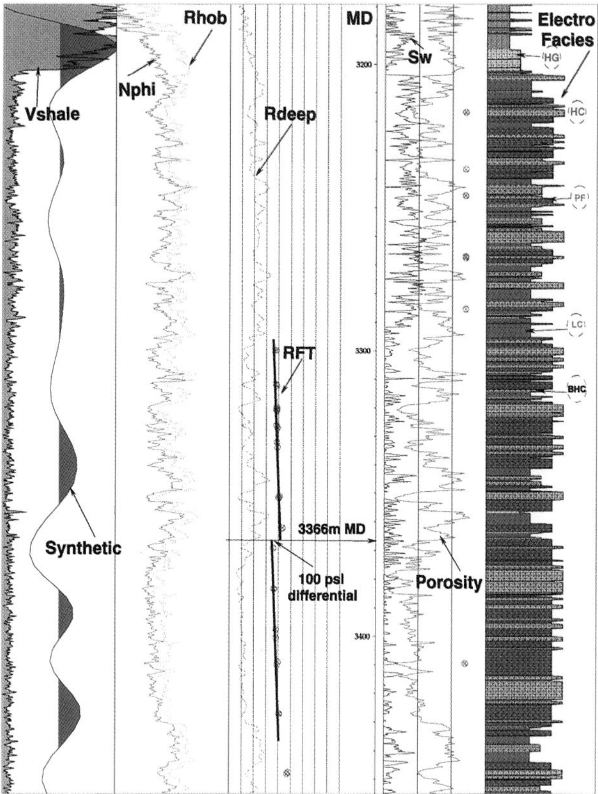

Fig. 6. Norwegian Well 2/5-7. RFT pressure data suggest that a pressure differential of 100 psi exists at 3366 m across a thin shale rich interval. For electrofacies coding, see Fig. 16.

These lithostratigraphic schemes do not recognize the intra Tor and Hod formation unconformities as interpreted from the seismic and biostratigraphic datasets from the Greater Ekofisk area (Figs 2 and 10) and where picked are generally inconsistent and rarely based on biostratigraphic evidence. In order to subdivide the Shetland Group into a meaningful sequence stratigraphic and seismically resolvable dataset, a re-evaluation, rationalization and standardization of the biostratigraphy from over 170 exploration and development wells in the Greater Ekofisk area was performed; the methodology used to define this scheme is described below. The iterative re-picking of the sequence boundaries from well data and tying these to seismic data, defined five second order and several third order sequences (Fig. 2). Although the main intention of this study was to develop a sequence stratigraphic scheme for the chalk sensu Vail & Todd (1981), it was soon realized this was not practical, because of the uncertainty in identifying depositional facies and their respective upward and downward shifts at unconformities, thus an allostratigraphic scheme was developed. Braum & Vail (1988) define allostratigraphy as the grouping of any genetically related sediments within the same depositional sytem between disconformable surfaces, (i.e. between maximum flooding surfaces and unconformities). The core database allowed the direct observation of an unconformity and therefore the associated subtle change in wireline log character. However, the core database is restricted to the commercially significant intervals and cannot be applied to the whole database; thus the un-cored intervals remained interpretive. Additionally, bias of the well database to structural highs resulted in the identification of many correlatable unconformities, but identification of their correlative conformities in basinal setting remains imprecise. Grain size variation as used in interpreting clastic lithology system tracts is not a factor applicable to chalk facies recognition. However, clean/dirty variations in gamma ray log-derived shale volume (V_{sh}) content are observed within the chalk and confirmed by XRD analysis. These variations were used to interpret the gamma ray into transgressive–regressive sequence cycles (Embury 1993) and where possible the biostratigraphic data provided clues to the system tract position in the cycle (Fig. 11). The basal parts of most transgressive system tracts commonly contain abundant fragments of the bivalve

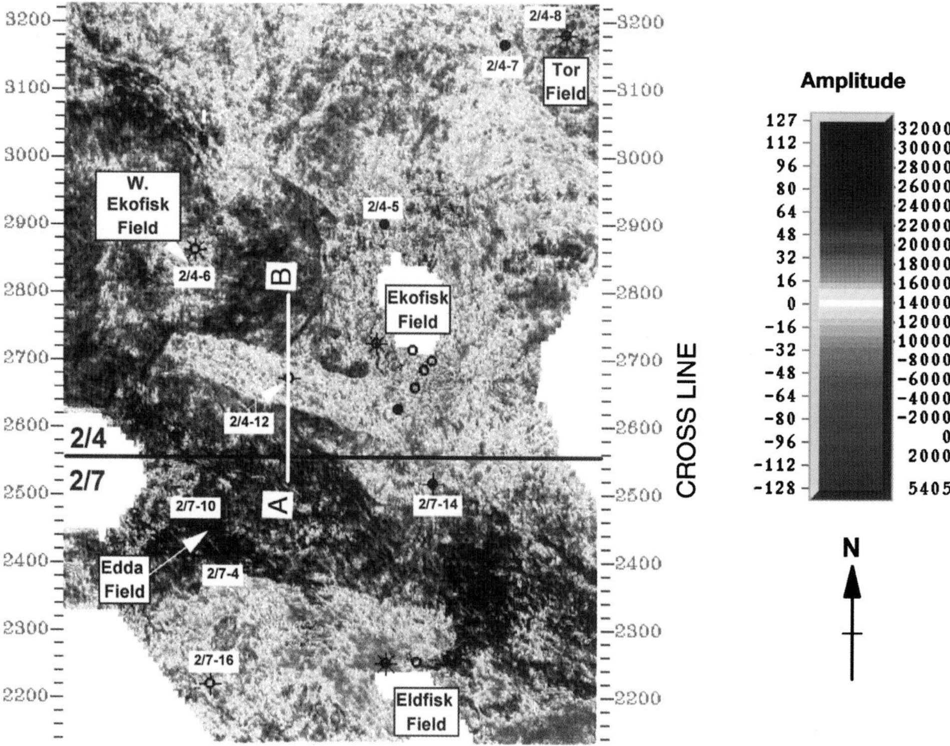

Fig. 7. Flattened 3D seismic time slice, 20 ms below Top Tor Formation. A channel trending NW–SE within the Tor Formation is clearly visible on this amplitude display. Figure 8 shows the N–S seismic section cutting this channel at the N2/4-12 well location.

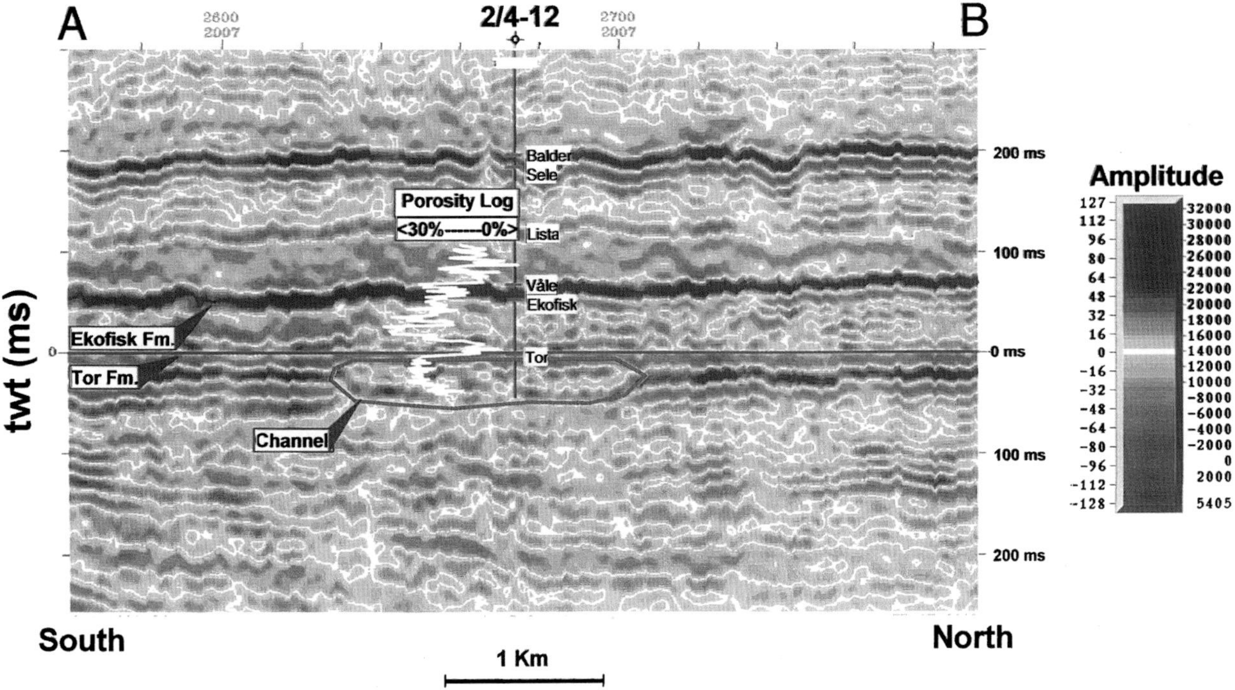

Fig. 8. 3D seismic in-line flattened on the top Tor horizon passing N–S through the Norwegian 2/4-12 well. Internal channel geometries are clearly visible. Note that the porosity log values show a marked decrease at the base of the Ekofisk (Ekofisk tight zone) which potentially seals the higher porosity chalks within the channel. The N2/4-12 well was water wet.

Inoceramus, derived from newly transgressed shelf areas, with planktonic foraminifera becoming more dominant up sequence. In high stand to late high stand sediments, an increase in benthonic foraminifera is observed. This leads eventually to the abundance of agglutinated foraminifera which are associated with the end of the eustatic cycle and environmentally harsher conditions. No lowstand systems tract was identified in well data from the Greater Ekofisk area. Figure 2 shows the three broad gamma ray patterns representative of the chalk interval: a basal stacking of cleaning-upward cycles between 96 and 90 Ma (Base Hidra to Top Lower Hod Formation); a middle interval of dirtying-upward cycles between 89 and 75 Ma (Middle Hod to Upper Hod formations) and an uppermost mixed pattern with an inter-bedded interval of re-sedimented and *in situ* chalk, dated between 74 and 61 Ma (Tor and Ekofisk formations). Each of these intervals has a characteristic seismic facies (Fig. 10): the lower package has low frequency/high amplitude parallel reflections, the middle package has terminating reflectors against a large number of onlap and downlap surfaces within tectonically active small basins and the upper package is typified by high frequency parallel reflectors with variable amplitude alternating with seismically quiet zones. Each package also has onlap terminations onto the Base Shetland Group transgressive surface, toward their respective basin margin.

Palaeoenvironment and lithofacies

That North Sea chalks were deposited under normal marine salinities is indicated by carbon isotope data ($\delta^{13}C$ ratios fall within the range 0 to +2.5). Additionally, chalks are associated with a widespread of fossil groups which could not flourish in lower salinities (Scholle 1974; Hancock 1975). Hardgrounds within chalks have carbon isotope ratios which are only slightly less positive than white chalks and therefore (where they have been encountered and tested) they formed in subaqueous marine environments. However, evidence as outlined later may suggest possible subaerial exposure or deposition in environments close to wave base. Assuming Cretaceous seawater had an oxygen isotope ratio of −12‰ (Shackleton & Kennett 1975) a palaeotemperature of 14.5°C can be extrapolated (Taylor & Lapre 1987). It is generally believed that during the Late Cretaceous the hinterland available for erosion in northwest Europe was small because of the high eustatic sea-level (Zeigler 1982). Additionally, an arid Cretaceous climate probably resulted in little erosion of that hinterland, hence the purity of the white chalk. Hancock (1975) suggested chalk was deposited in water depths of between 100 and 600 m. Distefano *et al.* (1980) agree and affirm that much of the chalk in the Norwegian Central Graben was deposited in outer shelf or shelf slope environments in water depths of 150 to 600 m. The biostratigraphic rationalization study and palaeoenvironmental mapping performed as part of this project suggest that chalk deposition occurred in water depths between near wavebase and 300 m, with potential for later subaerial exposure of the deposited chalks. Distefano *et al.* (1980) conclude from their study that terrigenous input was effectively constant during the sedimentation of the chalk, but that calcareous nannoplankton productivity and carbonate dissolution rates were subject to changes. They consider that the prime governing controls on sedimentation were of a global nature, e.g. sea-level fluctuations, variations in the position of the carbonate compensation depth, ocean currents and upwelling. The Ekofisk tight zone (Fig. 2), records a high proportion of terrigenous material and therefore is not merely a facies change, but represents a fairly major change in sedimentation and/or oceanographic global conditions. This is further supported by a major shift in carbon isotope ratios reflecting organic productivity.

Figures 12 and 13 show the wide range of palaeoenvironments in which individual chalk facies may occur, the combination of syn-depositional tectonic movements, eustacy, stratigraphy, climate and sedimentology are responsible for the wide variety of depositional lithofacies found within the Shetland Group. Caution is therefore advised when interpreting palaeoenvironment from chalk facies, as it is apparent that

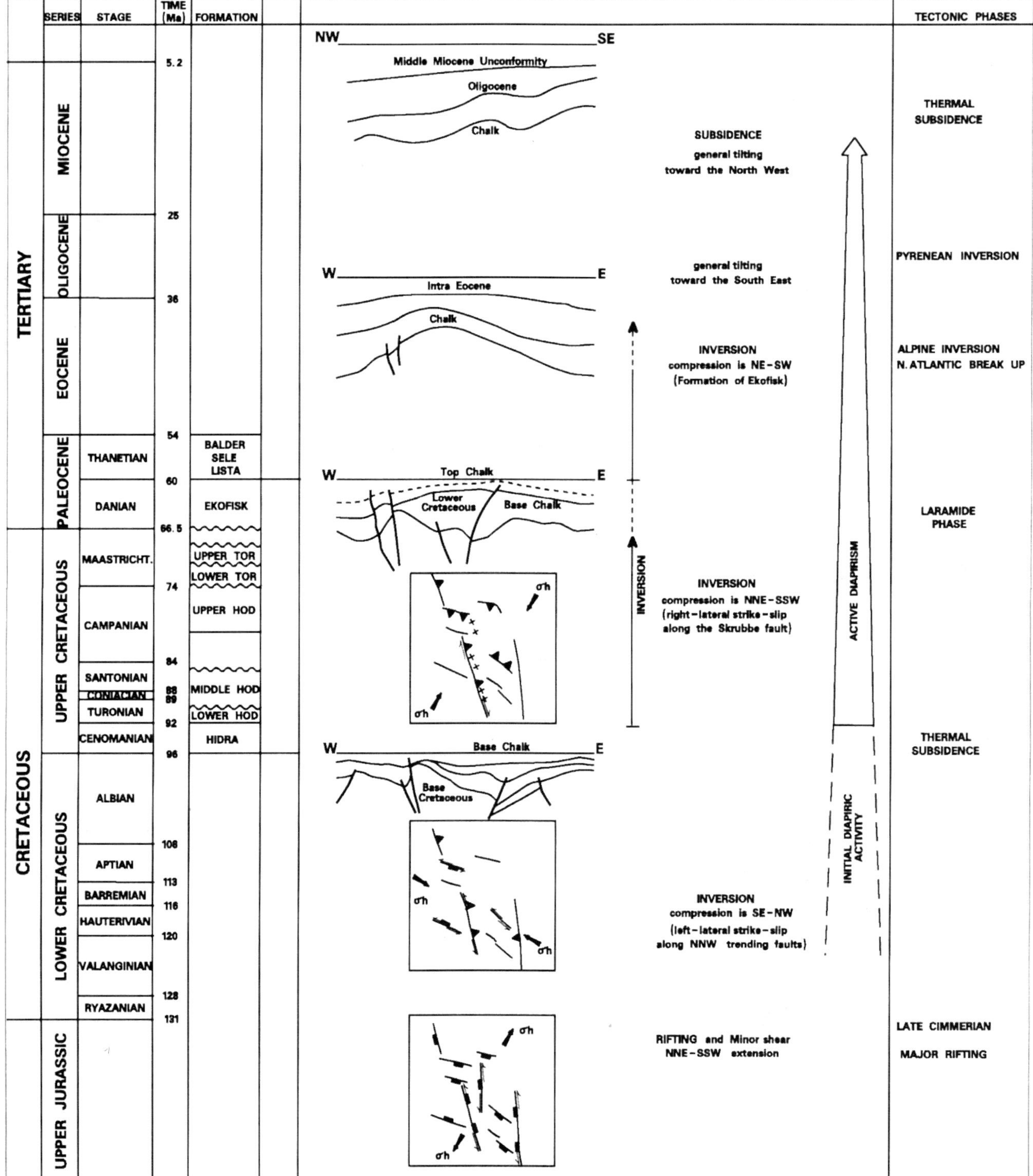

Fig. 9. Tectonostratigraphic chart summarizing the main structural elements in the Greater Ekofisk area from the Late Jurassic to Recent (modified from Caillet 1996).

no single facies is representative of a unique environment; rather a complex stacking and spatial distribution of facies types defines the environment of deposition. The model is further complicated in that each individual lithofacies may have more than one derivation, i.e. homogeneous chalks are derived by many processes including: (a) homogenization by re-working (slump or debris flow); (b) high sedimentation rates, restricting the time available for organisms to burrow or layer the sediment; (c) high water content obliterating primary textures upon sediment compaction; (d) dewatering of the sediment and subsequent texture destruction; (e) complete burrowing and homogenization of the sediment leaving no trace of the earlier fabric, etc.

Palaeoenvironmental maps for each sequence (as defined in Fig. 2) were assimilated from the integration of: core analysis data, 3D seismic attribute maps, 2D regional isopach maps, seismic character, lithofacies, electrofacies and CPI parameter maps (corrected shale volume V_{sh} and porosity). The palaeoenvironmental maps for the Upper Cenomanian (Hidra), Upper Hod, Upper Tor, and Upper Ekofisk are shown in Fig. 14a–d and provide risk domain maps for facies distribution within these key sequences.

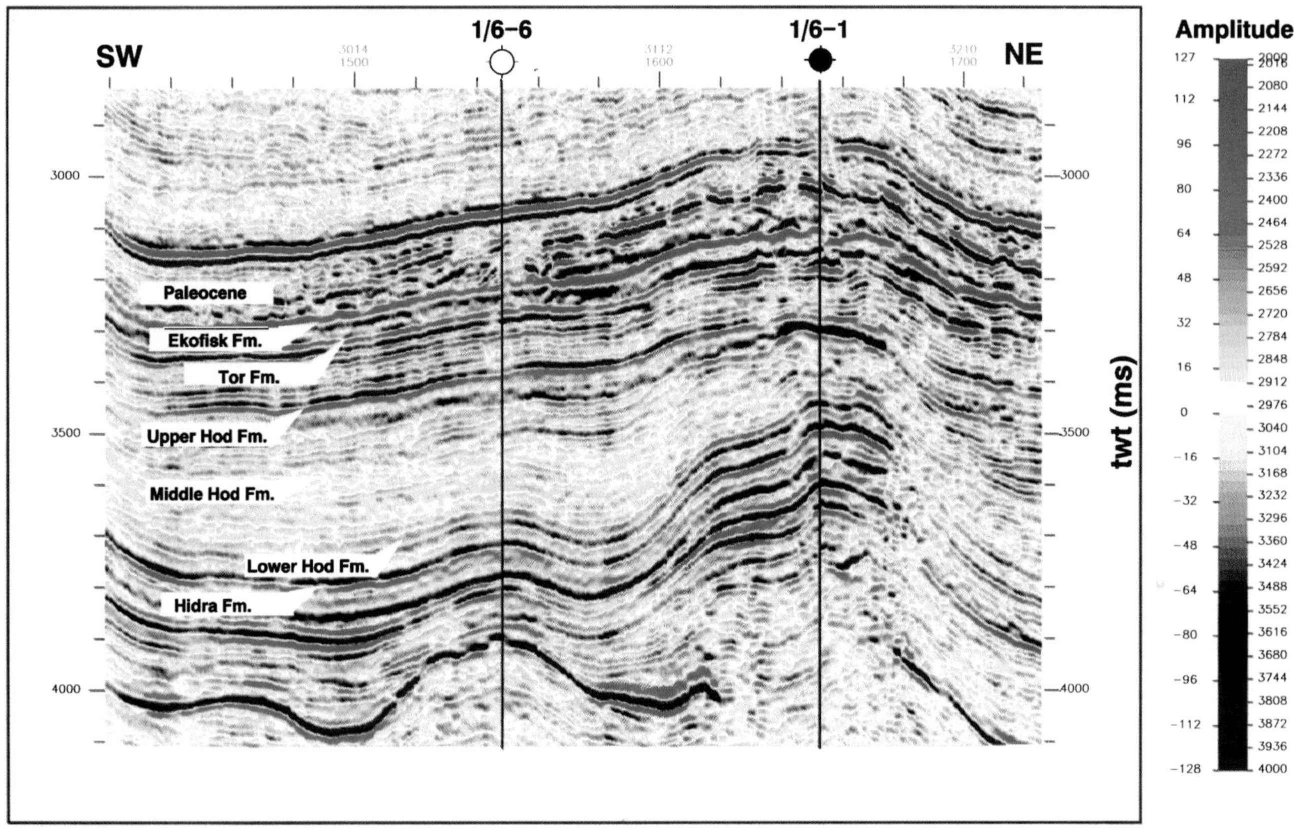

Fig. 10. ESE–WNW seismic section showing sequence subdivision, structural style and seismic character of the Shetland Group in the Greater Ekofisk area.

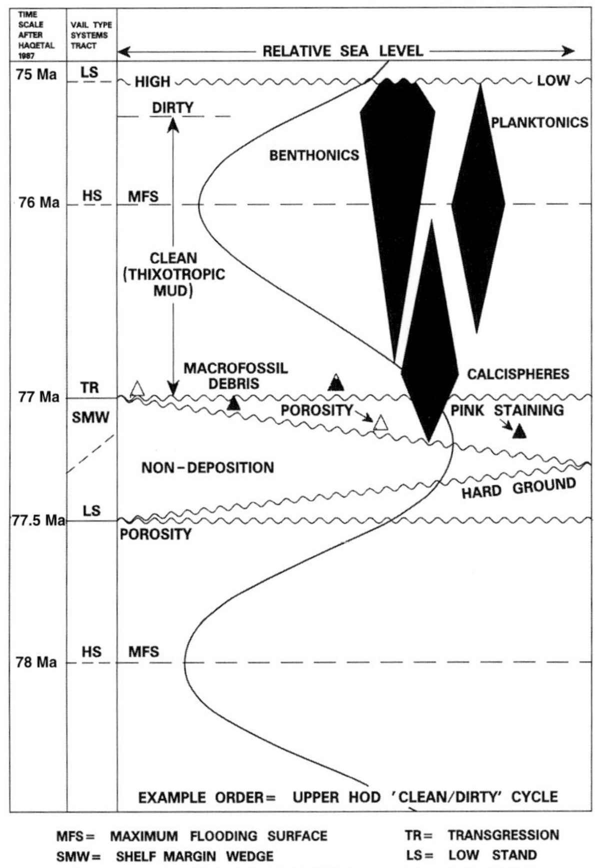

Fig. 11. Relationship of biostratigraphy and eustatic cycles in Upper Cretaceous chalks of the Greater Ekofisk area.

Hidra palaeoenvironment

Chalk deposition was initially confined to a small elongate basin trending NW–SE during the late Cenomanian (Upper Hidra) opening out into a basin toward the NW from a confined 'channel' in the SE (Fig. 14a). Argillaceous chalks and thin fine-grained winnowed siliciclastics, appear to fringe the palaeoshoreline and growing salt diapirs. Cleaner chalks dominate the centre of the basin together with calcarenites and siliciclastic turbidites. Note that mapping suggests an exposed hinterland or shelf area at or near wave-base toward the east and west. A cleaner carbonate restricted to the central portions of the basin characterized the final stages of deposition of the Hidra Formation. From a prospectivity point of view, fracturing these clean carbonates (eg. N1/9-1) and maintaining seal integrity of the Blodøks Formation may provide a viable exploration target. However, the timing of fracture formation and hydrocarbon migration into the chalk fracture network is critical for prospectivity as discussed later.

Upper Hod palaeoenvironment

The palaeoenvironment of the Upper Hod Formation (Fig. 14b) was dominated by a stable high trending NW–SE across the centre of the study area following the inversion axis of the Lindesnes Ridge. Reworked material from this high was directed toward the N, NE and SW of the Lindesnes Ridge, increasing the potential prospectivity of these areas. Argillaceous chalks, at the Upper Hod sequence boundary, appear to be concentrated toward the northern portion of the study area, which has implications for stratigraphic seals and prospectivity at this level. Mapping and core data for the Hod Formation also suggests an exposed hinterland or shelf area at or near wave base. Core from the N2/7-B11 well at the

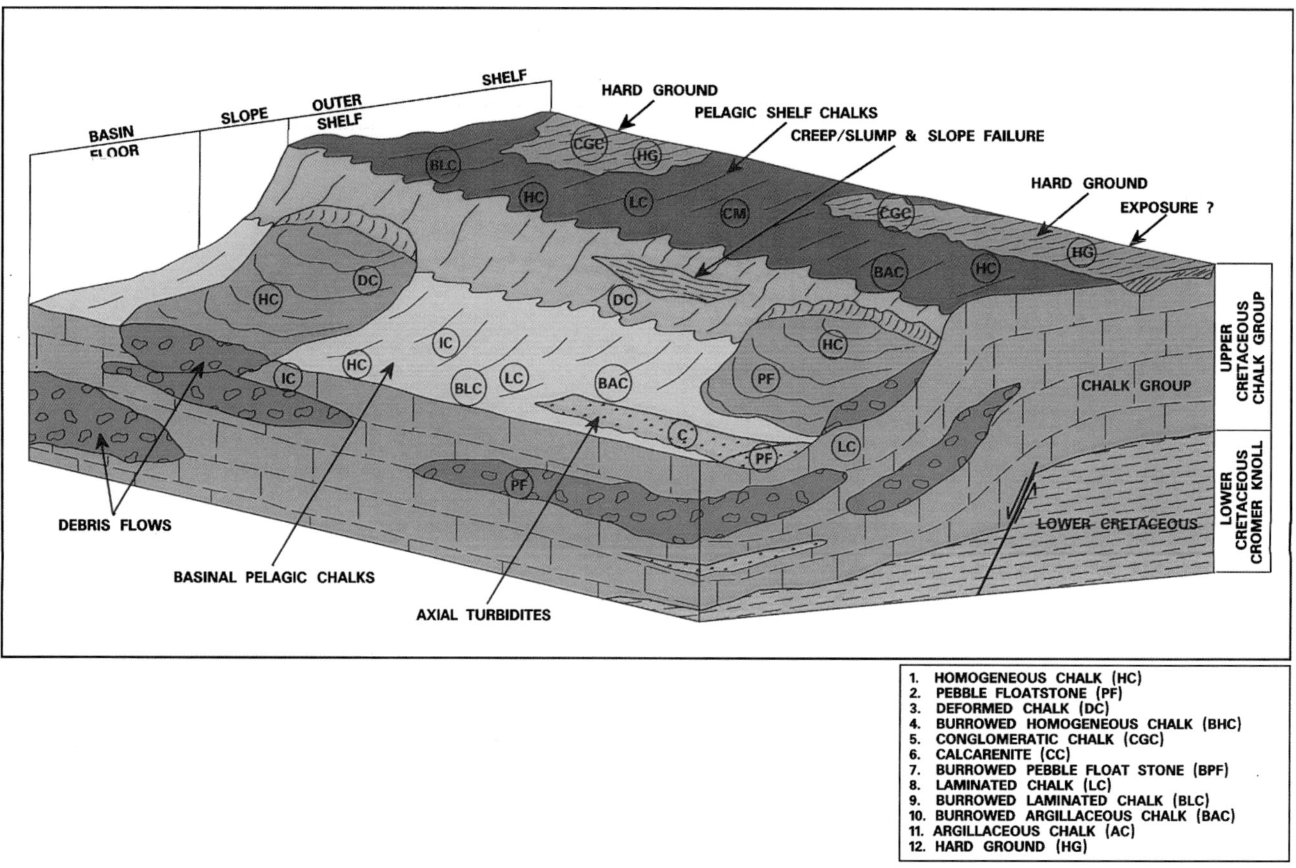

Fig. 12. Chalk sedimentological processes, products and depositional model.

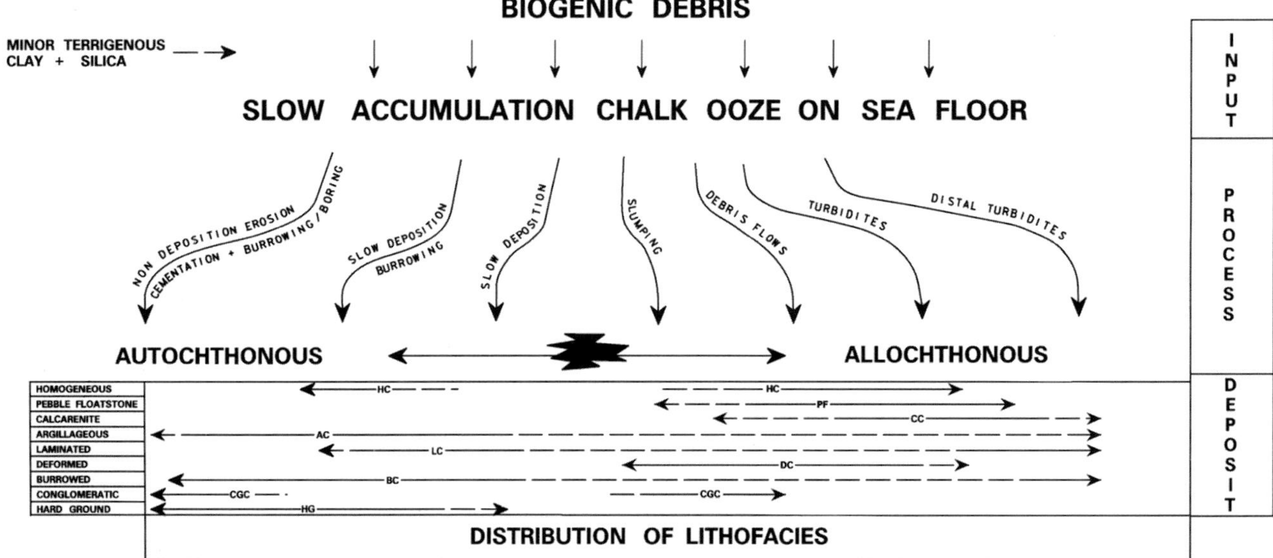

Fig. 13. Diagram illustrating the wide range of depositional environments associated with individual chalk lithofacies.

boundary between the Upper Hod and Tor sequences may show desiccation and subaerial exposure of the sediment. Further work is required to confirm this hypothesis as the sediment 'cracks' may have formed by the process of syneresis or clay flocculation.

Upper Tor palaeoevnvironment

The Upper Tor palaeoenvironmental map (Fig. 14c) indicates large-scale reworking over the entire chalk basin with the exception of the Valhall area where a generally thinner Tor section is encountered with local reworking filling in syn-sedimentary faults, (Farmer & Barkved 1999).

Ekofisk palaeoenvironment

The palaeoenvironment interpreted for Ekofisk chalk deposition appears to be more complicated (Fig. 14d). The Valhall High north of the Lindesnes Ridge was still prominent during the Danian and provided a source for allochthonous material. The NW–SE elongate 'Ekofisk Trough' appears to have confined and focused the deposition of stacked debris flows and reworked material from the Lindesnes Ridge and areas to the SE and NE of the study area. Southwest of the Lindesnes Ridge there appears to be a limit to the presence of stacked debris flows, which has implications for prospectivity.

Sedimentology

Key aspects of chalk sedimentology including: (a) chalk petrology; (b) processes; (c) diagenesis; and (d) facies, are summarized.

Chalk petrology

Chalk is deposited as a calcareous pelagic ooze with initial porosity as high as 80% (Scholle 1974, 1977; Distefano *et al.* 1980; Hatton 1986; Maliver & Dickson 1992). The principal biogenic constituents of chalk include micro-organisms such as planktonic and benthonic foraminiferal algae of the phylum Haprophyta, which are deposited after consumption and excretion by copepods into faecal pellets and subsequent settling through the water column (Hancock 1975), and macro fossils such as the bivalve *Inoceramus*, echinoderm fragments, bryozoa, radiolarians and corals. The European chalks are composed of 96–99% low magnesian calcite, with minor proportion of clay minerals and silica (Hancock 1975). North Sea chalk is predominantly bi-modal with particle sizes between 0.5–4 μm and 10–100 μm, the proportion of the two groups varies spatially, but in most white chalks the finer fraction makes up 75–90% of the total rock (Hancock 1975).

Processes

Chalk is mechanically very unusual. Although the bulk of the sediment is clay sized, very little is composed of clay minerals. Thus, the mechanical integrity of chalk is markedly different from similarly sized siliciclastic sediments. Hjulstrom (1939) showed that sediments with an average grain size of less than fine sand (0.25 mm) require greater flow velocity to move the sediment, i.e. mud size particles are harder to mobilize than sand particles owing to the presence of clay minerals with an imbalanced electrical charge and platy morphology, resulting in sediment cohesion. Clean chalk does not contain appreciable amounts of clay: it is composed almost entirely of calcite in the form of subequant scutiform coccoliths and rare rounded whole coccospheres. No imbalanced inter-particle electric charges of Ca^{2+} and CO_3^{2-} exist and no platy grains interlock, thus little or no sediment cohesion occurs. Therefore, as clean chalk oozes form on the seabed (autochthonous chalks) in layers 1–10 m thick overlying a more stable substrate, i.e. hard ground or argillaceous layers, any mild or exaggerated agitation of the thixotropic chalk ooze will result in down-slope movement as a viscous grain turbid gravity flow (allochthonous chalk). The trigger mechanisms for such agitation may be tectonic instability, earthquakes, storms, or possibly biogenic methane gas seepage. It has been suggested by Lewis (1971) that a slope with an inclination of 1–2° is sufficient for gravity flows to occur. Hatton (1986), Kennedy (1987), Nygaard *et al.* (1983) and Watts *et al.* (1980) provide a good summary of the types of post-depositional sedimentological processes occurring within the chalk, comprising sliding, slumping, and debris and turbidity flows.

Diagenesis

No new or additional work was performed on chalk diagenesis as part of this study. However, as this is a critical aspect controlling chalk prospectivity, a summary of the key aspects affecting chalk diagenesis are reviewed. Chalk diagenesis is well documented by Herrington *et al.* (1991), Maliver & Dickson (1992), Taylor & Lapre (1987) and Brasher & Vagle (1996). Diagenetically the chalk is very stable owing to the high proportion of low-magnesium carbonate. Maliver & Dickson (1992) note that 0.2 to 1.0 μm crystal size fraction is at the lower size limit for which excess solubility resulting from interfacial free energy is negligible. It is therefore possible that a smaller-size fraction has been dissolved owing to excess solubility making available the Ca/Mg ions for later cementation. However, in North Sea chalks extensive cementation between grains has not occurred. Mapstone (1975) noted from SEM photos that individual chalk grains are often spot welded at a number of point contacts resulting in a meniscus effect between adjacent grains. This very thin meniscus possibly results from the early pressure solution at sharp point contacts (Neugebauer 1973). However, Sorensen *et al.* (1986) consider the presence of clay minerals within the coccolith framework to weaken the chalk by preventing the formation of spot welding. Mechanical compaction and the relationship of porosity to effective stress remains one of the key controlling parameters on porosity preservation. However, it is noted that early cementation has little effect on the reduction or preservation of porosity. Brasher & Vagle (1996) conclude that the diagenetic history of chalk is controlled by five primary factors: burial depth, chalk type, overpressuring, presence of hydrocarbons and original grain size. Watts *et al.* (1980) also note that stylolitization and fractures play a major role in chalk diagenesis and fluid migration. Taylor & Lapre (1987) chart the diagenetic history of North Sea chalks (Fig. 15) and document the complicated evolution of the diagenetic history of the chalk. It is worthy of note, that the work performed on diagenesis to date does not discount the concept of a diagenetic stratigraphic trap. Hypothetically, if oil emplacement pre-dated flank cementation or porosity occlusion, an isolated 'pod' of oil might exist within a diagenetic trap.

Facies

Numerous facies classification schemes have been applied to chalk, e.g. Kennedy (1987), and Crabtree *et al.* (1996). However, the Chalk Exploration Project used the internal Phillips Petroleum chalk lithofacies scheme (Fig. 16) devised by Caldwell *et al.* (1994). This scheme is purely descriptive, subdividing chalk lithofacies into petrophysical reservoir units. Primary facies are identified (i.e. pebble floatstone) and modifiers added to determine post depositional modification (i.e. deformed burrowed pebble floatstone). Over 40 wells and 3900 m of chalk core were described using this lithofacies scheme, together with capillary pressure measurements, XRD, SEM, fracture information, ichnofacies, biofacies, and porosity/permeability data were collected for each lithofacies. This standardized dataset provided the basis for the statistical analysis of the chalk lithofacies and reservoir/seal characterization as described later.

Exploration model and risk: chalk reservoir

The following section summarizes the exploration model and key risks associated with the search for a subtle chalk stratigraphic trap.

The prediction of the presence and range of individual chalk reservoir parameters is the key to understanding the chalk play. Two tools were integrated in order to predict and constrain the distribution of chalk reservoir parameters: (1) statistical analysis of an elaborate database comprising over one million data points containing measurable reservoir parameters including: core facies, porosity, permeability, mineralogy, capillary pressure, log CPI porosity, shale volume, hydrocarbon saturation, depth, structural position, fracture

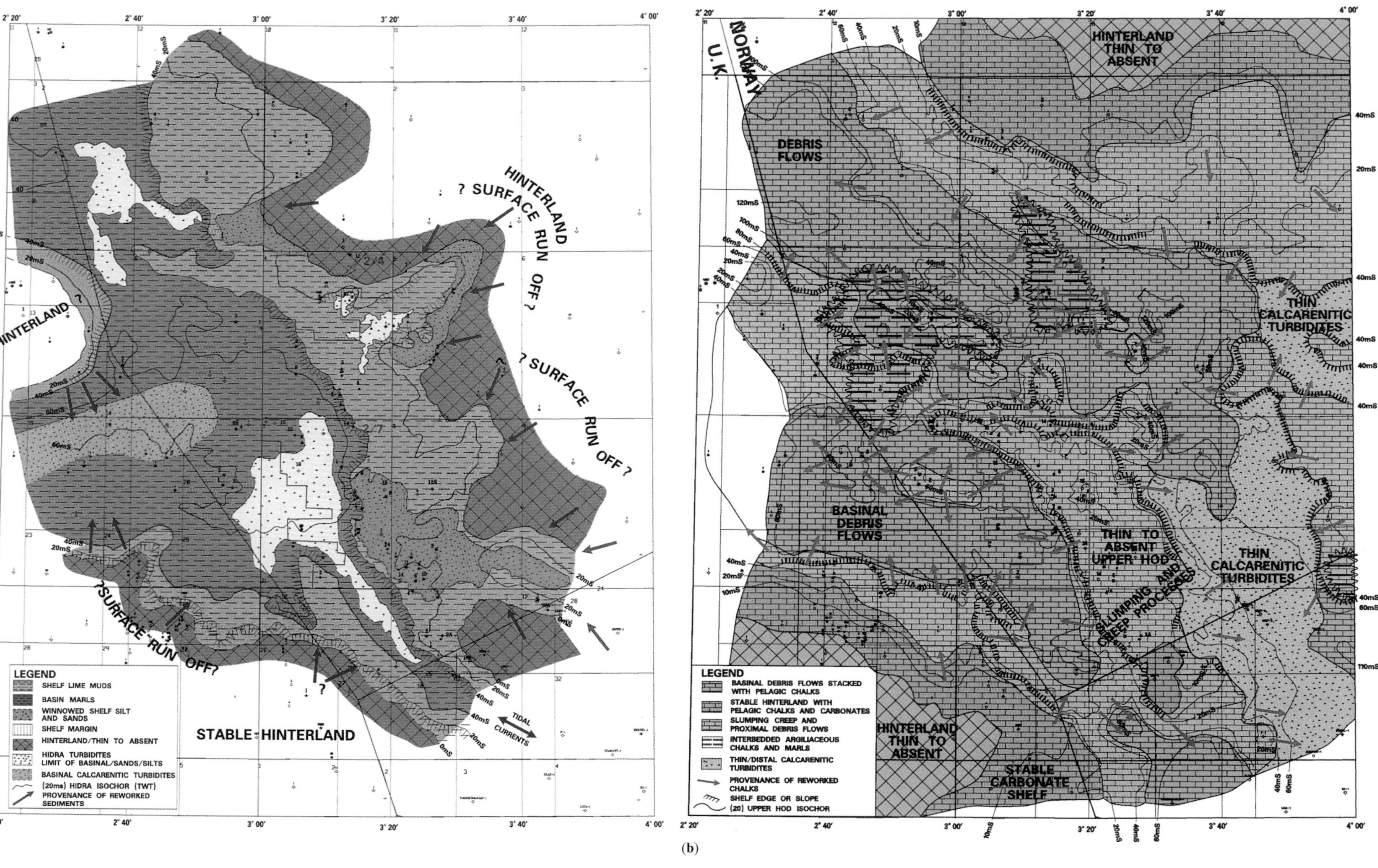

Fig. 14. Palaeoenvironmental map for: (**a**) the Upper Hidra Formation in the Greater Ekofisk Area; (**b**) the Upper Hod Formation in the Greater Ekofisk area; (**c**) the Upper Tor Formation in the Greater Ekofisk area; (**d**) the Ekofisk Formation in the Greater Ekofisk area.

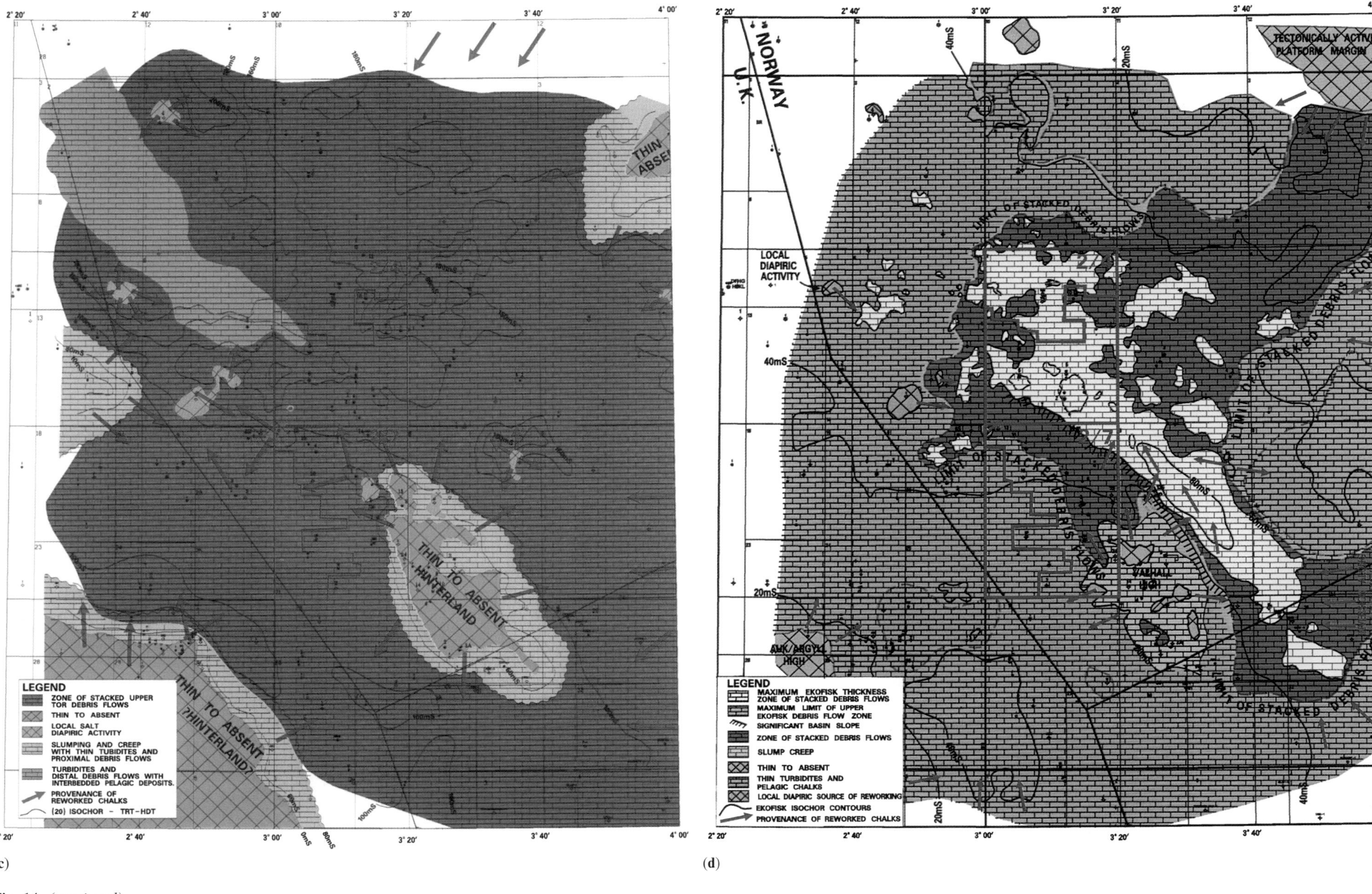

Fig. 14. (*continued*).

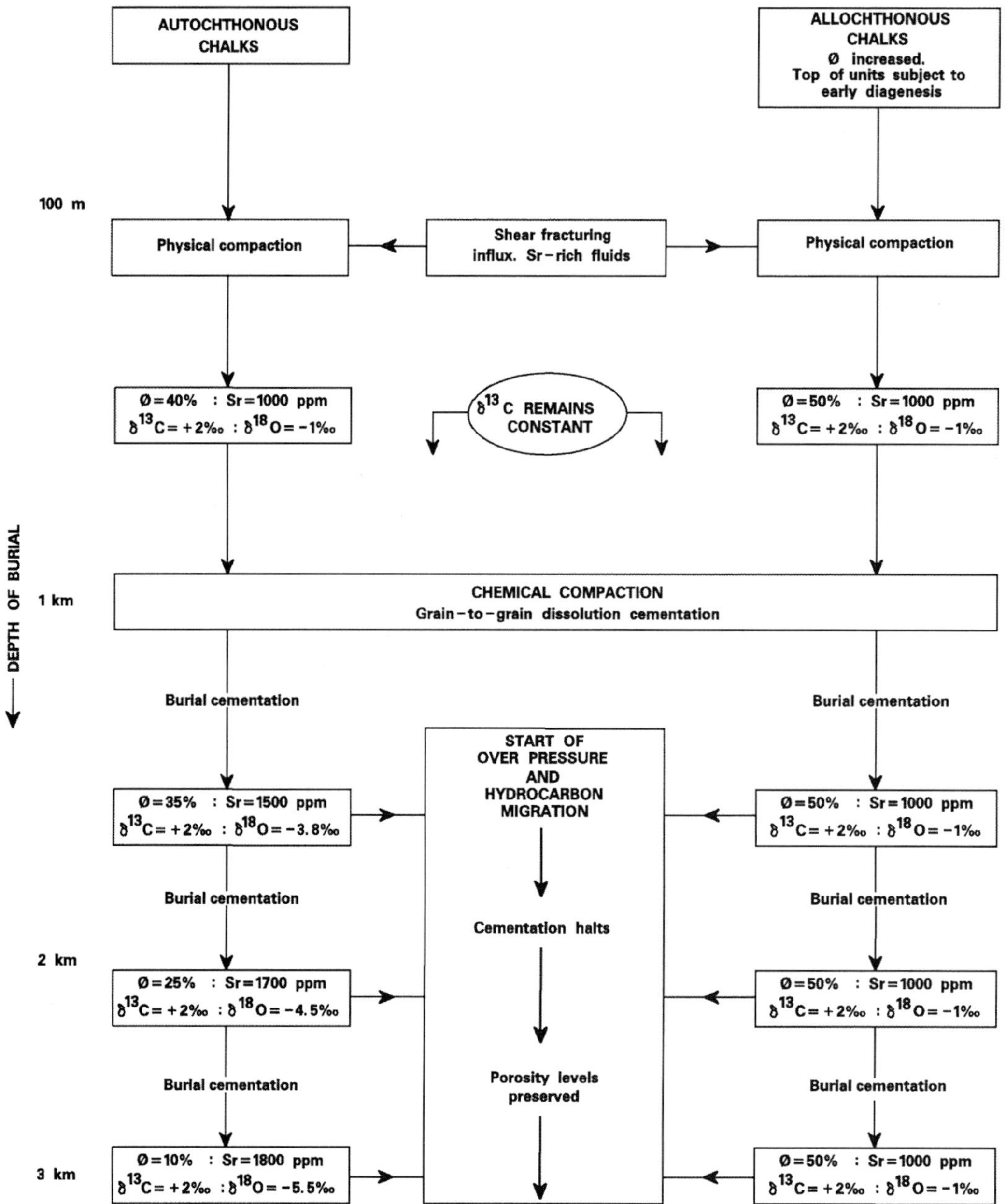

Fig. 15. Flow chart of North Sea chalk diagenesis, highlighting diagenetic modifying processes. Modified after Taylor & Lapre (1987).

DEP PROC. / POST. DEP PROCESS		PELAGIC: ARGILLACEOUS CHALK (A)	PELAGIC: LAMINATED CHALK (L)	RESEDIMENTED: HOMOGENEOUS CHALK Md (H)	RESEDIMENTED: PEBBLE FLOATSTONE Md/Wk (PF)	RESEDIMENTED: CALCARENITE Pk/Gm (C)	MISC.		
NONDEFORMED	NON BURROWED	CALC SH 35---65 AC	LC	HC	PF	CC	CONGLOMERATIC CHALK (CGC)	HARDGROUNDS (HG)	INTERBEDDED CHALK (IC)
	BURROWED (B)	BAC	BLC	BHC	BPF	BCC			
DEFORMED (D)	NON BURROWED	DAC	DLC	DHC	DPF	DCC			
	BURROWED (B)	DBAC	DBLC	DBHC	DBPF	DBCC			

COMMON RARE NOT OBSERVED

---- INEXACT BOUNDARY

Fig. 16. Phillips Petroleum Company, Greater Ekofisk area chalk lithofacies classification scheme. Modified after Caldwell *et al.* (1994).

intensity and type (healed, mineralized, stylotite, tectonic, slump, total etc.); and (2) multi-attribute 3D seismic analysis and 3D seismic inversion.

(1) Statistical analysis of the chalk database determined relationships between different parameters using principal component and multivariate statistical analysis. The results were used to define acceptable ranges for individual reservoir parameters within the study area. In addition, these results provided quality control of the reservoir parameters predicted from seismic inversion. Three key conclusions concerning: (a) porosity; (b) permeability; and (c) fractures are drawn from this statistical analysis.

(a) Porosity

The main factors affecting porosity preservation in chalk are: (i) depth of burial; (ii) hydrocarbon saturation; (iii) original depositional facies; and (iv) mineralogy and chalk overpressure which is discussed in a later section. Brasher & Vagler (1996) considered grain size to be an additional factor affecting porosity preservation. The statistical analysis performed as part of this study does not support or discount this observation, however, the relationship between original depositional facies and grain size within chalk is noted. The combination of these factors above, produces a very large porosity range (from 0 to 52%) for any given chalk in the Greater Ekofisk Area.

(i) Depth of burial. There is no clear relationship between depth of burial and porosity at a regional scale. For any given depth a large range in porosity may exist e.g. at 2900 m (9500 ft) 10–50 pu and at 3450 metres (11 300 ft) 0–31 pu (Fig. 17). The range is slightly reduced if the parameters are analysed on a sequence-by-sequence basis. However, the same data show that the maximum possible porosity preservation for any given depth can be estimated with reasonable accuracy. This maximum porosity prediction with depth was used in combination with minimum porosity production cut-offs for each sequence, to draw reservoir potential maps representing the maximum porosity expected for a given sequence at a given depth (e.g. Fig. 18). These maps can be used to define general porosity fairways for each sequence, to risk prospect porosity estimates, and to constrain and validate the porosity ranges from seismic modelling and inversion. Figure 17 also shows a significant break of slope at approximately 3450 m (11 300 ft). Below this depth, porous, reservoir-quality chalk is statistically unlikely to occur; however, this does not negate the potential prospectivity associated with deeply buried, low porosity, fractured chalk layers.

(ii) Hydrocarbon saturation. Inhibition of diagenesis owing to the presence of hydrocarbons is a phenomenon which is widely described in the literature and commonly invoked to explain unusually high porosities encountered in North Sea chalk. The effect of hydrocarbon presence on porosity preservation in chalk averages between 12 and 14 pu (Fig. 19). It is also possible to demonstrate that porosities as high as 35 pu can be found in water wet chalks and therefore, in chalk, the presence of high porosity is no guarantee of hydrocarbon presence and a combination of some other mechanism such as overpressure or the inhibition of porosity occlusion by diagenesis may be important. Brasher & Vagler (1996) show that the N2/7-30 well, located NE of the Eldfisk Field (Fig. 1), penetrated Tor Formation chalks with porosities near 35% at 3200 m. No indications of hydrocarbons (moveable or residual) were encountered.

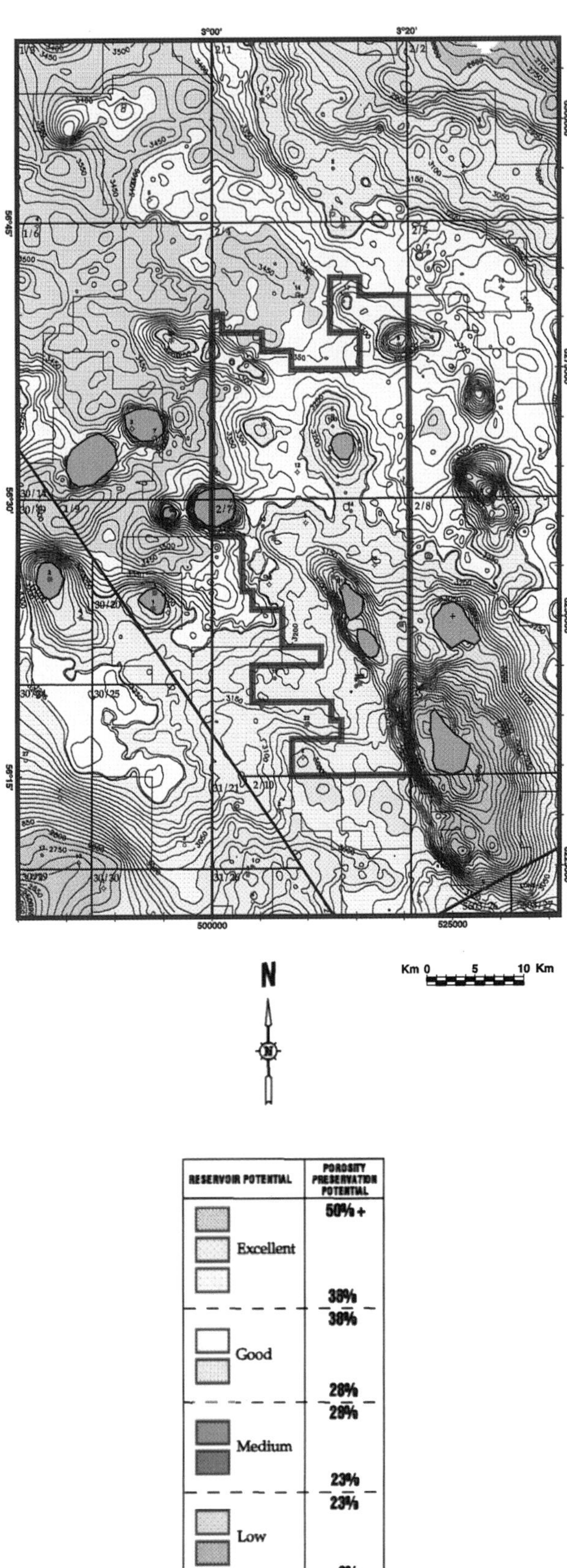

Fig. 18. Maximum porosity preservation potential map for the Tor Formation.

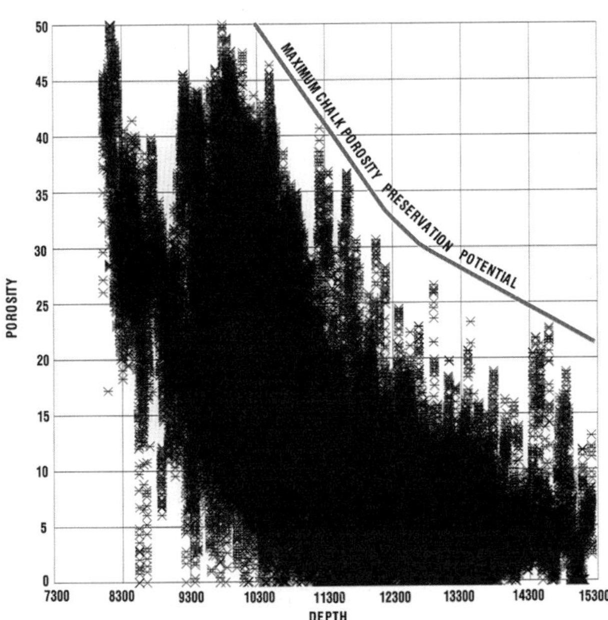

Fig. 17. Regional chalk porosity depth relationship for 72 wells in the Greater Ekofisk area. Database comprises 30 exploration and 42 development wells. See text for details.

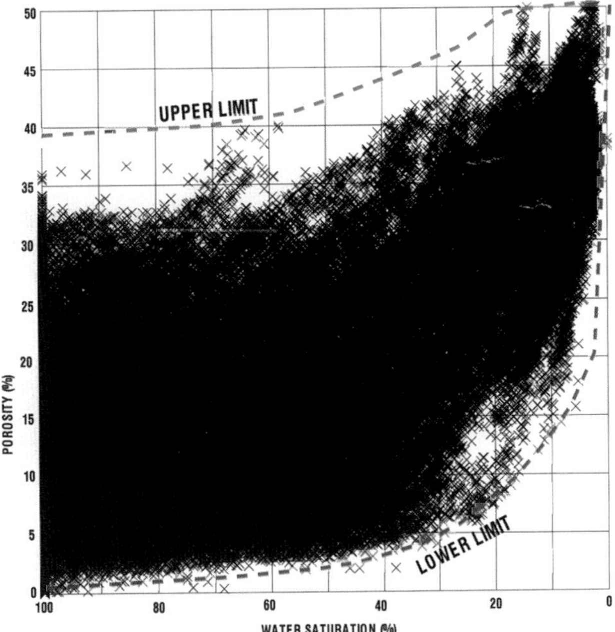

Fig. 19. Porosity vs water saturation for 72 wells in the Greater Ekofisk area. Porosity increases by 10–12 pu with hydrocarbon saturation. High porosities (35–40%) are recognized in water-bearing chalks.

(iii) Original depositional facies. Kennedy (1987) noted that allochthonous or reworked chalks constitute the best reservoirs while autochthonous or pelagic chalks generally have reduced reservoir properties. Analysis of the database demonstrated that facies variations can account for a 12 to 15 pu range in porosity and the occurrence of redeposited chalk facies alone is not an indicator of good reservoir quality (Fig. 20). Additionally each facies has a wide range of petrophysical properties (Fig. 21) and therefore mapping or predicting facies distribution by sequence stratigraphy is not a reliable tool for reservoir quality prediction. However, under the same conditions of burial, diagenesis and fluid fill a redeposited chalk should always have a higher porosity than a chalk which has not undergone a redepositional process.

(iv) Mineralogy. The presence of shale and quartz reduces preserved chalk porosities. The presence of diffused quartz in controlling porosity and permeability is shown in Fig. 22. This relationship shows that porosities greater than 40% only occur when less than 10% quartz is present. Quartz appears to have little effect on porosity values below 40%. This has regional implications, as quartz content within the chalk varies both spatially and stratigraphically, reducing the prospectivity of some areas especially toward the south of the Greater Ekofisk area.

(b) Permeability

The relationship between porosity and permeability for the entire database is shown in Figs 23 and 24. Two clearly defined trends are observed which are principally controlled by shale content: (a) clean chalk where corrected shale volume (V_{sh}) is between 0 and 2%; and (b) a lower trend characterized by dirty chalks where V_{sh} is greater than 3%. This differentiation is also seen stratigraphically (Fig. 24) with the Tor Formation having a higher porosity/permeability relationship than the Ekofisk, Hod and Middle Hod formations, reflecting a greater density of allochthonous flows in the Tor Formation than in the other sequences.

(c) Fracturing

Fracturing is extremely important for hydrocarbon production from chalk reservoirs. However, for the chalk stratigraphic

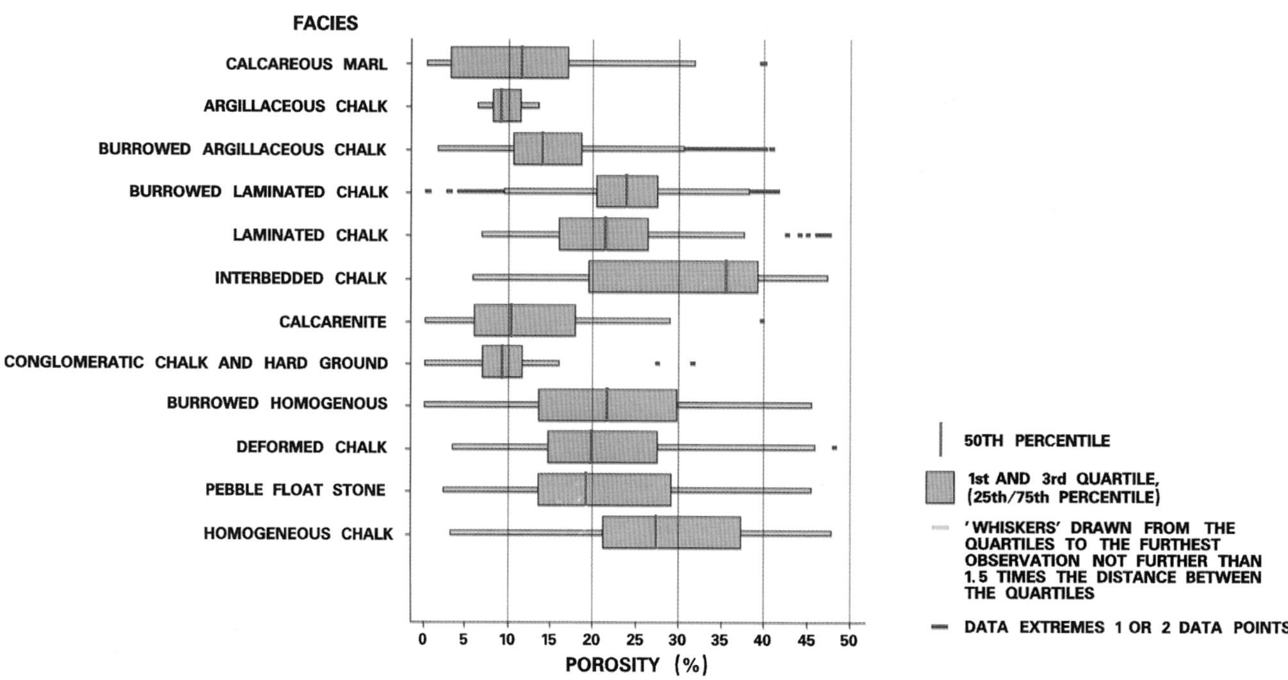

Fig. 20. Lithofacies and porosity distribution from over 40 wells and 3900 m of chalk core in the Greater Ekofisk area. Reworked chalk facies alone is not necessarily an indicator of good reservoir quality, however a 12–1 pu increase in porosity is noted for allochthonous vs autochthonous chalks.

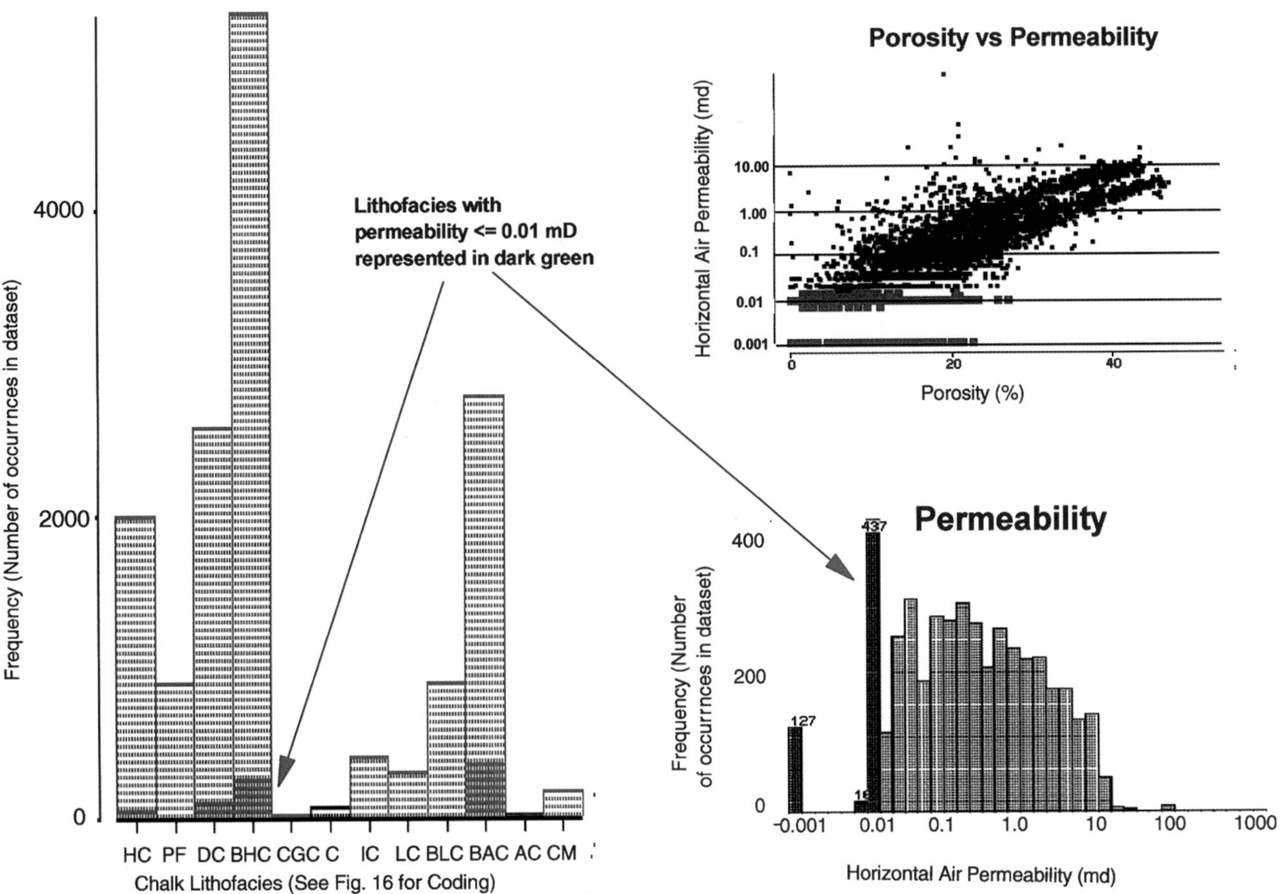

Fig. 21. Porosity/permeability distribution in low permeability lithofacies. Histograms show the proportion of the core lithofacies database represented in the porosity/permeability cross plots. For lithofacies coding see Fig. 12.

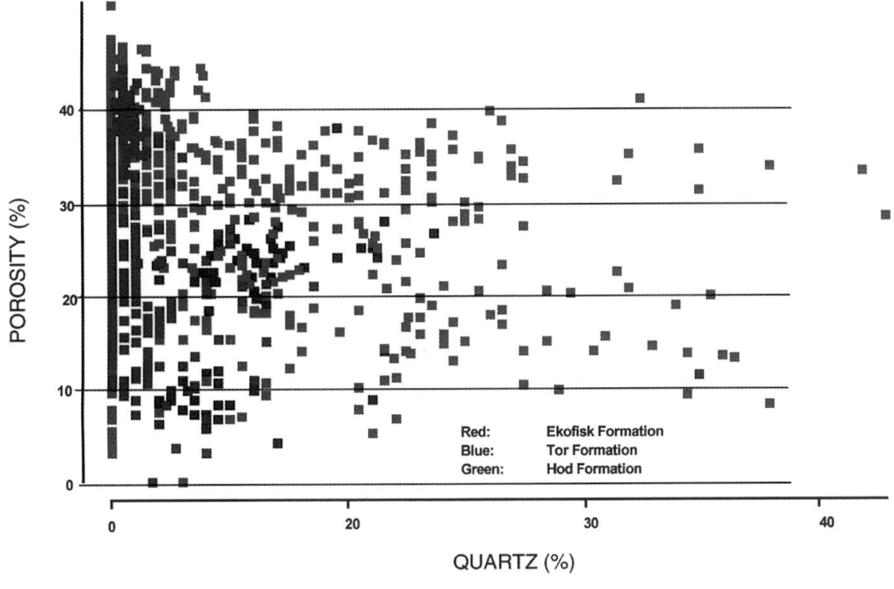

Fig. 22. Quartz presence vs porosity for 25 cored wells in the Greater Ekofisk area.

play, it is also necessary to maintain seal integrity. It is demonstrated that chalks with a high V_{sh} (>5%) are statistically less likely to be fractured than clean or low V_{sh} chalks. It is therefore possible that a fractured clean chalk reservoir can be sealed by an unfractured relatively high shale content cap rock, as shown in Fig. 25. It is also shown that redeposited chalks are more likely to be fractured than pelagic chalks. It is therefore theoretically possible for a chalk stratigraphic trap to work.

(2) Multi-attribute seismic analysis and inversion is a powerful tool for the explorationist to predict and map chalk reservoir parameters. A wide range of geophysical tools are

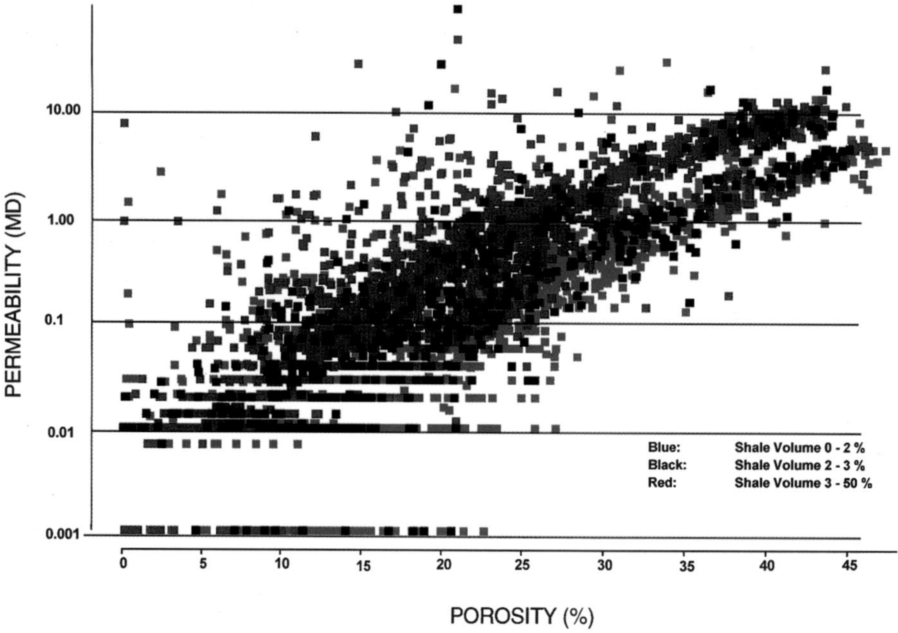

Fig. 23. Shetland Group permeability vs porosity, from 40 wells in the Greater Ekofisk area. The Ekofisk Formation (red) and the Tor Formation (blue) are clearly defined.

available from which to analyse the 3D seismic dataset. These are summarized here and in more detail in Anderson (1999).

(a) Structure mapping

Internal chalk sequence structure and isopach mapping enabled the prediction of internal structures within the chalk which may not be expressed at top chalk level. Because the stratigraphic play relies upon an intra-chalk seal, the prediction of pinch-out geometries on the flanks of the structures and intra-formational pinch out geometries are important to map. Figure 26 shows the structure map of the top Ekofisk Formation generated using ERmapper software to highlight the structural elements and potential fracture zones at this level.

(b) Amplitude mapping

The magnitude of an amplitude seismic reflection at a sequence boundary, or internally within a sequence, can generally be used to predict porosity distribution within chalk. Figure 27 shows the maximum negative amplitude map at the top of the Tor sequence boundary. This is perhaps the single most important map representing chalk prospectivity in the Greater Ekofisk Area, as most of the bright amplitudes undoubtedly reflect porosity at this level, e.g. the northern Point A on Fig. 27 shows the high amplitude associated with the N2/7-30 prospect and the interpreted high porosity (>35%) developed at this locality (Anderson 1999). A final caution with chalk amplitude mapping is that an increase of V_{sh} or seismic tuning may also result in a bright amplitude, potentially leading to a misinterpretation of porosity development; the B locations on Fig. 27 represent a hard ground developed on the flanks of the Lindesnes Ridge, at the top of the Tor Formation.

(c) Edge detection

This attribute, available on the Landmark workstation, is useful in predicting flexure at a mapped sequence boundary and therefore to model the fracture potential of the reservoir, the potential integrity breach of the top and bottom seal, regional lineaments, which may act as regional seals or pressure barriers, and potential hydrocarbon migration conduits. Figure 26 shows a merged overlay of the edge and structure maps for the Top Shetland Group and clearly shows regional fracture trends which are related to post-depositional or younger structural events.

(d) AVO analysis

AVO (amplitude vs. offset) analysis has been successfully used to predict reservoir presence within the chalk. D'Angelo & Brandel (1997) demonstrated the ability to predict the presence of high porosity chalks on the flank of the Hod Field. The analysis of the AVO method as part of the CEP project concludes that the AVO technique is not a reliable tool for distinguishing between brine, oil or gas pore fluids in the chalk; however, porosity prediction in chalk is possible. The AVO gradient shows a distinct trend when porosity increases in chalk, i.e. as the porosity increases so the *P*-wave impedance decreases. For the top of the chalk (Top Ekofisk) this results in an increasing AVO gradient while for the base chalk, the AVO gradient is reverse. The intensity of the AVO response is dependent upon the physical parameters of the chalk above and below the modelled layer. There are small detectable differences in AVO curve gradient when modelling the chalk response, but these small differences are negligible when performing AVO analysis upon real seismic data. The reflection coefficient (RCo) can be used as a predictor of pore fluid type if the porosity is known. Thus, with reasonable log data this type of AVO modelling/inversion can be performed. *P*-wave impedance decreases if oil replaces brine and *P*-wave impedance decreases if gas replaces oil in chalk. This will cause a relative decrease or increase in RCo, depending on the *P*-wave impedance contrast over the reflector being modelled (i.e. top and base).

(e) Seismic inversion

The inversion of a 3D seismic volume enables the spatial prediction of reservoir properties for reservoir mapping. The

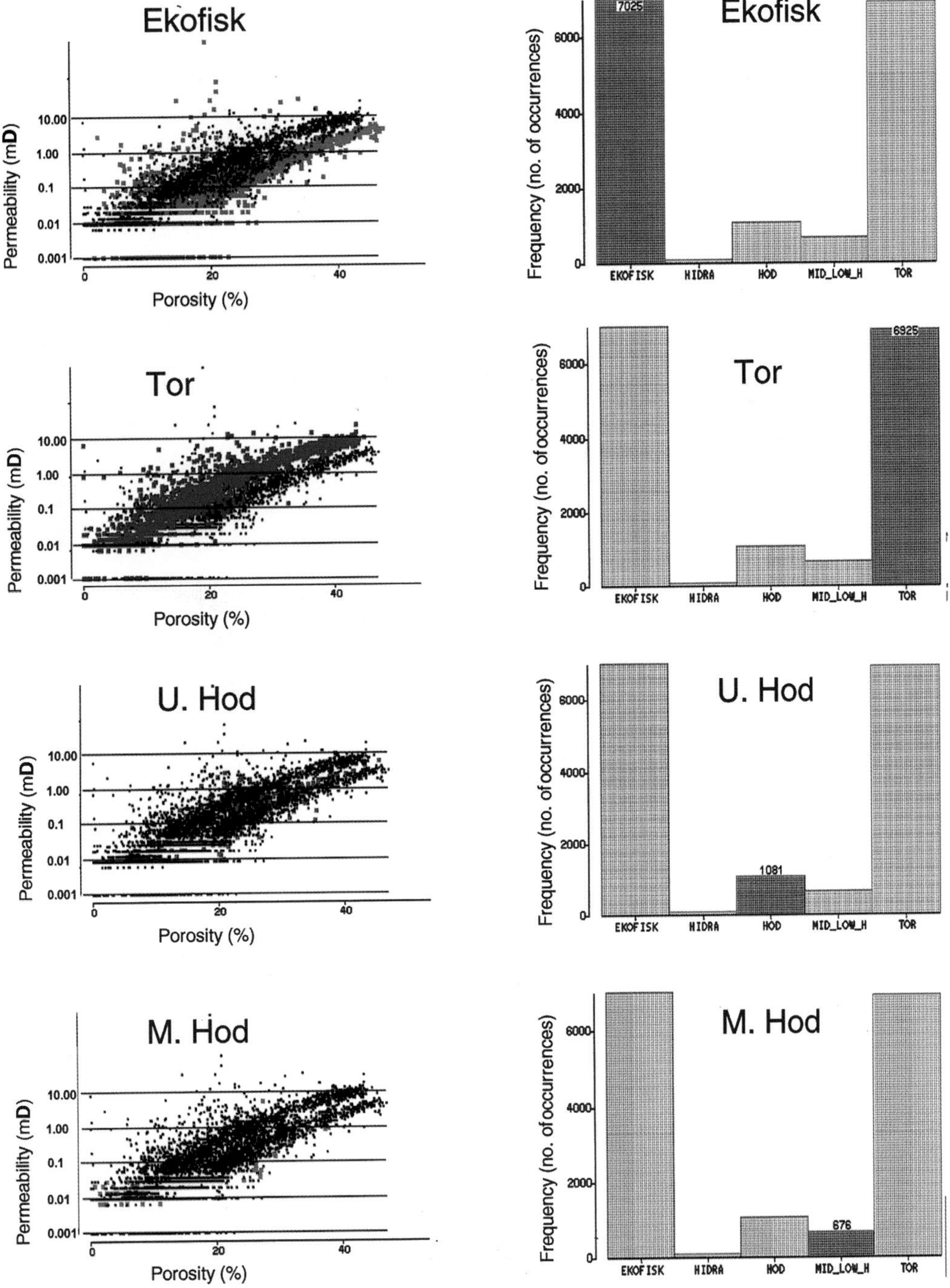

Fig. 24. Permeability vs porosity relationship for the principal chalk sequences. Histograms represent the proportion of the core database representing the sample distribution.

technique utilized within the CEP assigns reservoir or rock parameters to seismic attributes, such as wavelet shape, amplitude etc. and builds a catalogue of seismic responses associated with variations of the reservoir parameters calibrated to known well values. This catalogue is then tested against the real seismic volume and a map of the reservoir parameters is produced. The technique is non-unique, therefore mis-defining the parameters is always a possibility without good well control. This technique was used to predict the reservoir parameters for over 15 prospects in the CEP project. Anderson (1999) describes the full use of this technique with application to chalk reservoir parameter prediction for an exploration prospect. The prediction of fluid type within the chalk reservoir is not possible with this method.

In summary, the integration of the methods is useful in predicting both the quality of the reservoir present and its distribution; however, pore fluid type remains uncertain.

Exploration model and risk: chalk stratigraphic trap and seal

The highest risked parameter in the search for a chalk stratigraphic trap, is the efficiency of the top, bottom and lateral seals. The lateral seal may comprise a fault zone or a facies variation, juxtaposed against a chalk reservoir facies. Figures 4 and 5 show the many types of stratigraphic traps which have been drilled and tested in the Greater Ekofisk area,

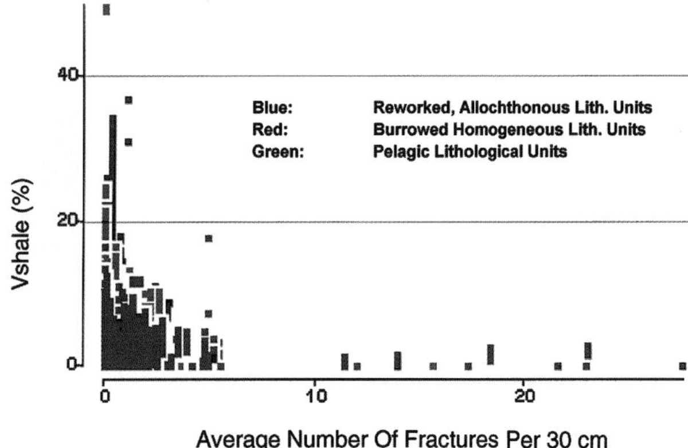

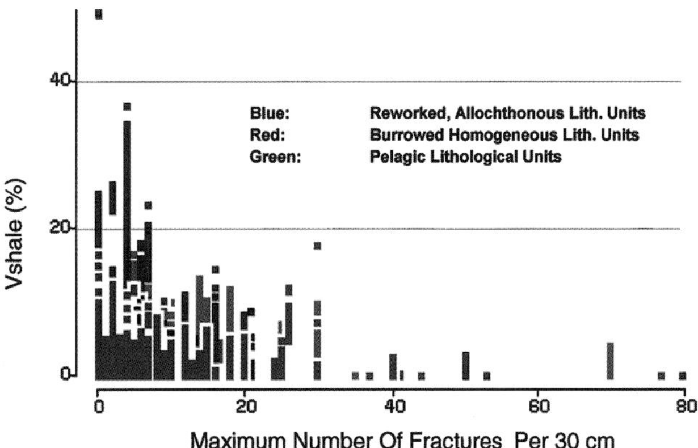

Fig. 25. Average and maximum number of fractures per 30 cm vs V_{sh} with lithofacies highlighted. Database comprises information from 39 cored wells in different structural stratigraphic settings in the Greater Ekofisk area.

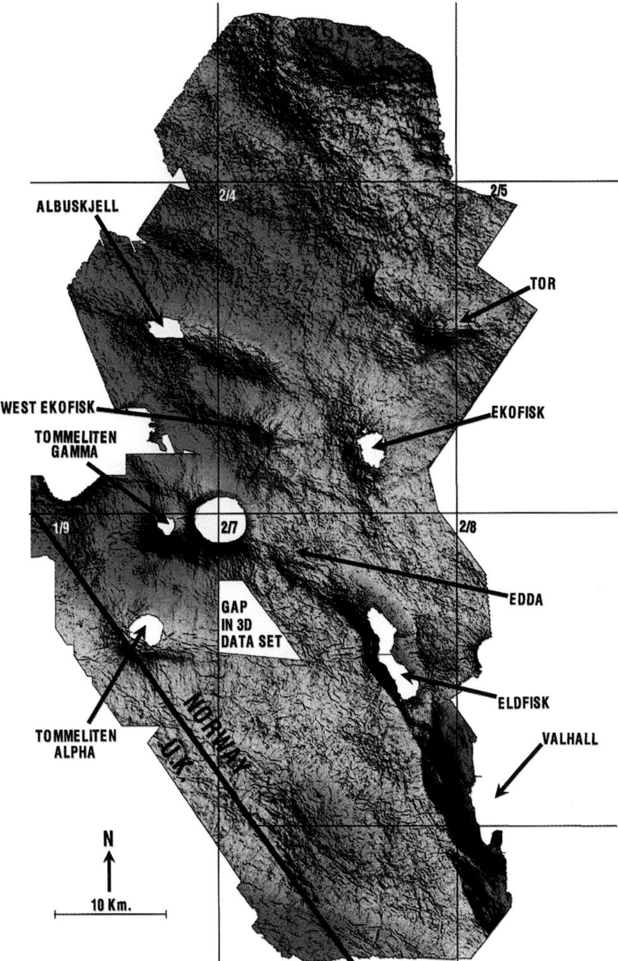

Fig. 26. Illuminated Top Chalk structure map with edge attribute overlay. Lineations and fractures are post-chalk deposition and therefore represent those which have had the most profound effect upon the reservoir and sealing properties of the Shetland Group in the Greater Ekofisk area.

together with hypothetical models for potential chalk stratigraphic plays. Of these possibilities, the search for the stratigraphically trapped, field flank plays is perhaps the lowest risk, as porosity lobes are known to exist within field closures above the oil–water contact (as demonstrated by the 'Hod Pod' play, D'Angelo & Brandel 1997) but remain isolated from the main producing reservoir by minor intra-formational seal. The detailed analysis of 3D seismic data and the mapping of the various seismic attributes and characteristics (edge, azimuth, amplitude) related to each of the principal sequence boundaries is by far the most powerful tool to identify the juxtaposition of the seal and reservoir pairs. Intra-chalk seals fall into two categories, those associated with facies and those associated with faults.

Facies

For a stratigraphic trap to be effective, top, bottom and lateral seal must be demonstrated. Such traps may be stratigraphic, diagenetic or mixed stratigraphic–structural plays. The sealing potential of the chalk is primarily a function of facies in terms of its permeability and capillary entry pressure; secondly, it is a function of the hydrodynamic regime; and thirdly, a function of fracture occurrence. In general, top seal for the chalk in the study area is a Paleocene shale. Where these shales become diluted with silt and sand the seal is less effective (Ziegler 1977). This is one of the principal reasons why the classic chalk play is restricted to a small area of the southern UK, Norwegian and Danish Central Graben. The Paleocene shales started to seal at about 25 Ma (Fig. 28) and caused the chalk to become overpressured with respect to the regional hydrostatic gradient. Intra-chalk seals are more difficult to quantify. As a rule of thumb, V_{sh} tends to be facies related and increases at sequence boundaries. Therefore, the pinch-out of two major sequence boundaries may provide the necessary geometry for a stratigraphic trap. However, as demonstrated in Fig. 21, chalk facies with a permeability of less than 0.001 mD are not only confined to the argillaceous chalks but also occur in the allochthonous type facies such as pebble float stones, homogeneous chalks and deformed chalks. Figure 25 shows that increased V_{sh} content reduces the susceptibility of the chalk to fracturing. An intra-Tor Formation chalk seal is demonstrated by RFT pressure measurements in the N2/5-7 well (Fig. 6) and by DST/RFT pressure measurements at an intra-Coniacian sequence boundary in the Danish Adda Field (Megson 1992). Potential intra-chalk seals include the Ekofisk tight zone located at the boundary between the Ekofisk and Tor formations, the Top Hod, the Top Middle Hod and the Blodøks formations (Fig. 2). Minor intra-formational seals are also noted within the Upper, Middle and Lower Hod, however, their regional extent is limited and requires detailed attribute and geological analysis to define their spatial limits.

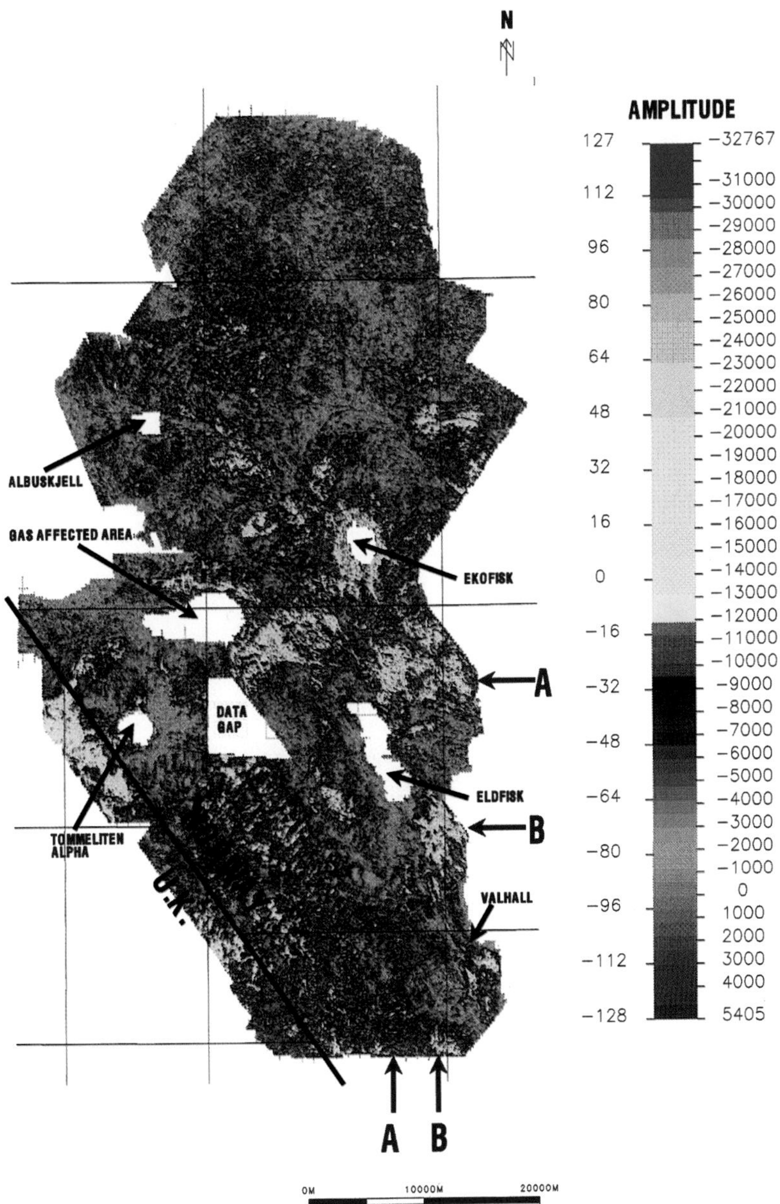

Fig. 27. Maximum negative amplitude map of the Top Tor Formation. Bright amplitudes (orange) indicate possible porosity at this level. Location A–A indicates the position of the N2/7-30 Egdar prospect and area B–B a hard ground.

Faults

Fault seals are more difficult to quantify than facies seals. Field studies have demonstrated that faults may in some circumstances act as lateral permeability barriers. Caillet *et al.* (1997), demonstrated that the regional aquifer or hydrodynamic regime for the chalk may be subdivided into individual pressure cells, with the cell boundaries comprising faults or the synclinal axis of regional structures (Fig. 29). However, late fractures resulting from post-chalk deformation may remain open and enhance the permeability of the reservoirs (Watts 1983), but these may also breach the intra-chalk seals and have significant impact upon stratigraphic trapping potential. Some intra-chalk fault zones can be characterized by cemented, microbrecciated zones providing effective permeability barriers. Thus, the most likely lateral permeability barriers are faults or fault zones, where significant shearing and cataclasis may have formed fine-grained seals. Up to 12 bars (180 psi) pressure differential has been noted across cell boundaries of the catchment area map (Fig. 29), which could potentially seal a hydrocarbon column in excess of 120 m. As discussed earlier, the use of the edge attribute provides a useful tool for defining regional and local faults, their presence through geological time, and therefore an indication of their seal potential.

Exploration model and risk: basin evolution and chalk hydrocarbon system

The principal source rock in the Central Graben is the Upper Jurassic Mandal Formation (Cornford 1994), which is present over the whole study area. In the Greater Ekofisk area the Mandal Formation consists of black shales and silty shales varying in thickness from several metres on the platform to thousands of metres in parts of the Central Graben, reaching a maximum depth of burial of 6800 m in the basin centre. Average total organic carbon contents are between 5% and 10%. The oils in the chalk fields of the Greater Ekofisk area range from early to late stage maturity, with medium to high

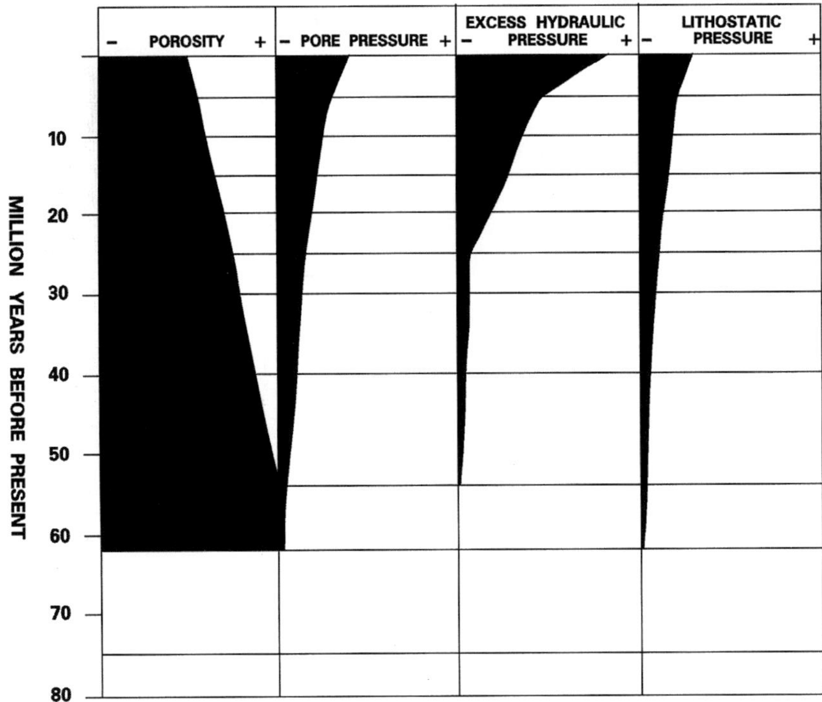

Fig. 28. Evolution of porosity and pressure within the Shetland Group through time, derived from basin modelling simulations. Note that the timing of overpressure within the chalk is concurrent with sealing of the Paleocene shales and the peak generation of hydrocarbons at about 15 Ma.

API gravity and a low sulphur and nitrogen content. The petroleum system has been active since the end of the Eocene (approximately 38 Ma) and oil migration started in the deepest parts of the basin when structural development was still occurring (approximately 70–75 Ma). The combined effects of structure and sedimentation upon the evolution of the study area have had a profound effect on the chalk play. The Shetland Group varies in thickness from 200 to 2000 m in the centre of the basin and the top of the group reaches a maximum depth of burial of 5000 m in the basin centre. Thickness maps at various intervals through the Palaeogene indicate that the basin underwent significant variations of morphology during this time. These post-chalk depositional structural events have fractured or modified the chalk morphology, impacted burial history, affected maturation of the source, and controlled trapping of migrated hydrocarbons and the chalk porosity/permeability relationships. Some of the major structures underwent tilting between the Oligocene and the present-day, which resulted in modified traps, e.g. Edda, Ekofisk and Eldfisk fields, with the associated consequences on charging, porosity preservation and diagenesis. Therefore, back-stripping on various Palaeogene sequences (e.g. Middle Miocene, approximately 15 Ma), which correspond approximately to the timing of peak migration and overpressure build up within the chalk, will help with the reconstruction of palaeostructures for potential entrapment at the time of migration. These palaeostructures may be absent or significantly modified on the present-day Top Chalk structure map. Edda Field is a good example of a structurally tilted closure post oil emplacement. A similar phenomenon is documented by Megson (1992) for chalk fields in the Danish sector of the North Sea. The Ekofisk structure, the largest chalk field in the area, formed later than the other fields as a result of salt doming and structural inversion during the Late Palaeogene. This may emphasize the role of early oil emplacement in the preservation of high porosity (i.e. the concurrent timing of hydrocarbon migration, entrapment, compaction and structural formation are critical for the classic chalk play). Faults cutting the base of the chalk are the most obvious and natural pathways for hydrocarbon migration to occur from source rock to the chalk reservoir. These fault conduits are summarized on the Base Chalk catchment area map (Fig. 29), which can be directly applied to the evaluation of the petroleum potential of the Shetland Group in the Greater Ekofisk area (Caillet *et al.* 1997). Basin modelling simulations show significant oil saturation almost everywhere in the topmost chalk layers, even within the Hod Formation at Eldfisk. This probably indicates that migration into chalk structures is not a key risk for exploration within the Central Graben portion study area. Caillet *et al.* (1997) reviewed all the available pressure data in the Greater Ekofisk area in order to understand the hydrodynamic system of the chalk and concluded that the potential for subtle oil traps within the chalk is probably more dependent on the pressure regime than on any other parameter. The main conclusions of their paper with respect to the stratigraphic play are summarized here.

The Chalk Group is highly overpressured and the porosity contained within the chalk is partly supported by pore pressure. The Shetland Group can be considered as a closed system with regard to regional fluid flow, and pressure cells can be defined (Fig. 29). Each cell is characterized by its own pressure regime and trapping potential, depending on depth, faulting and structure. The aquifer can be considered as near static, with hydrocarbon migration occurring vertically along major faults, often bounding each pressure compartment. Lateral migration is limited to the internal area within a pressure compartment and mainly depends upon permeability, capillary pressure and thermal convection. The total pore pressure induced by buoyant forces at the top of the main fields reaches fracture pressure (least horizontal stress) in the Valhall and Hod areas and the effective horizontal stress decreases towards the north with increasing depth. Caillet *et al.* (1997) demonstrate that the gas cloud observed on the seismic data above the Valhall Field is the result of present-day leakage, while the gas clouds above

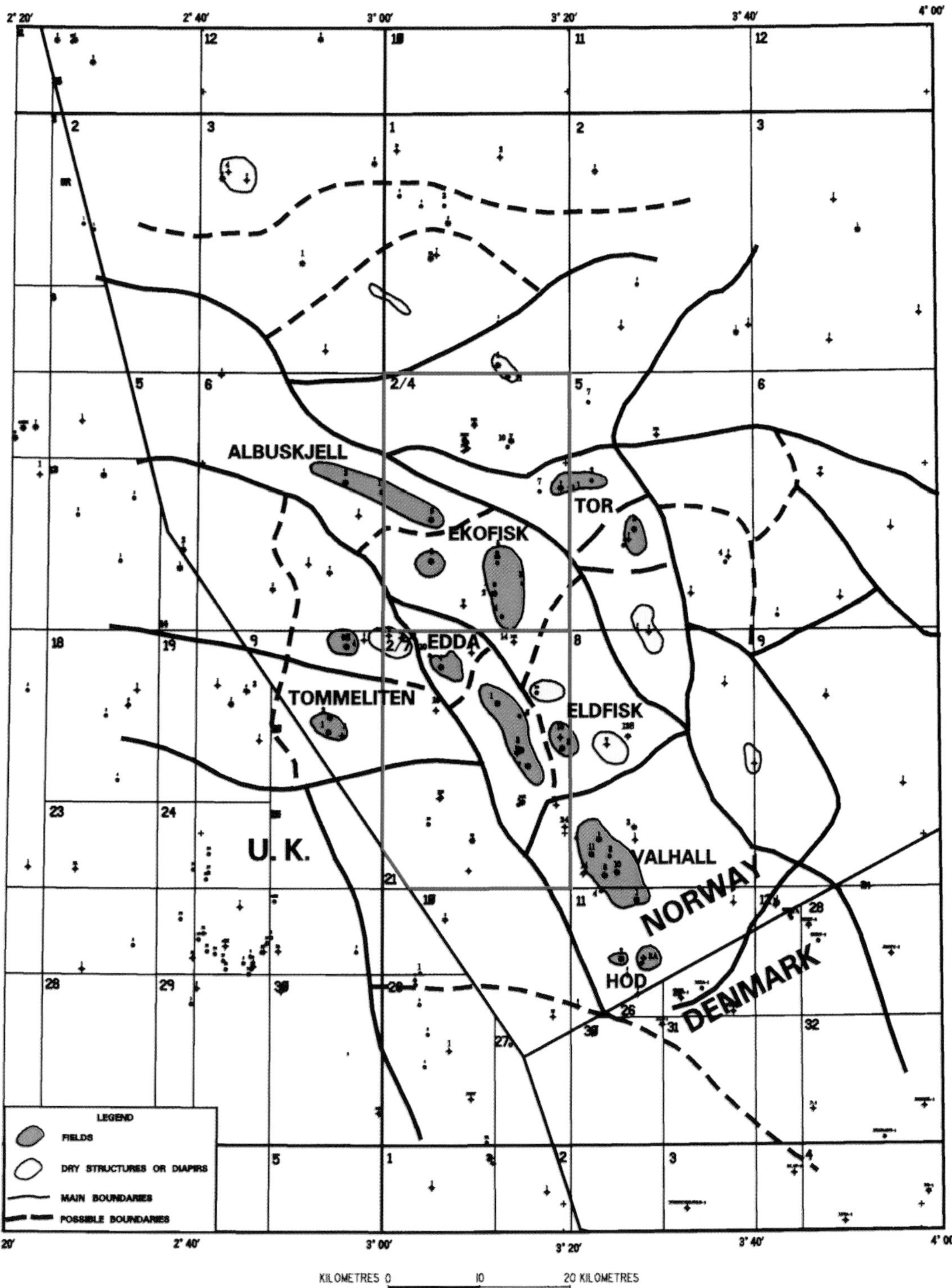

Fig. 29. Catchment area map and pressure cell boundaries at Base Cretaceous level for the Shetland Group of the Greater Ekofisk area (modified from Caillet 1997).

Eldfisk and Ekofisk fields are related to an older phenomenon, which occurred when the horizontal stress was as high as that observed today over Valhall Field.

Overpressuring within the Chalk Group started about 25 Ma when the effect of rapid burial and compaction created an efficient top seal in the Paleocene shales, effectively closing off the Shetland Group hydrodynamically from the Palaeogene above. Oil started to be generated and expelled around 70 Ma in the deepest parts of the basin and very recently on the crestal parts, with gas starting to be generated and expelled about 15 Ma in the basin. Vertical hydrocarbon migration was possible in the early stages of generation and expulsion between the source rock and the chalk, even without major faults, because of high pore pressures and the preserved porosity/permeability system. Hydrocarbon trapping probably occurred in the deepest structures as early as Late Oligocene with the recent influx of gas adding overpressure to the system. This perhaps explains most of the local variations in pressure between the different hydrodynamic pressure cells shown in Fig. 29. Oil migration therefore predates overpressuring, but oil entrapment probably started with overpressuring. When oil emplacement and early hydrocarbon migration occurred, stratigraphic traps were unlikely because of a relatively high porosity and permeability within the chalk layers, irrespective of their facies. Late geological evolution of the chalk however, (i.e. structural growth, compaction and diagenesis) produced significant porosity layering which has enabled secondary traps associated with palaeostructures, diagenetic or stratigraphic seals to form. Most producing fields appear to have a stratigraphic component, with either a tilt in the free water level or fault compartmentalization (Megson 1992; Caillet *et al.* 1997), the best example of this being the Edda Field in the Norwegian sector. Capillary pressure of the chalk facies is more relevant than the porous network, and secondary oil migration in chalk is probably dominated by capillary pressures rather than buoyancy pressure. The role of fractures at the present time is important for oil migration. Fractures provide the permeability pathways for production and it is likely, therefore, that in most cases larger fractures will degrade seal integrity. After more than 26 years of chalk production, reservoirs have been highly pressure depleted and it is likely that some of the permeability barriers both laterally and vertically may have been breached, as indicated above for the N2/5-7 well. Hydrodynamics can provide regional rules for understanding the petroleum system of the area, but it is clear that in the search for subtle stratigraphic traps, the detailed analysis of migration routes, seals and sealing faults is essential. Where structures are formed or where a stratigraphic trap is possible, oil saturation will be a direct function of porosity, permeability and capillary pressure. Lateral migration, therefore, has a significant role in the hydrocarbon distribution within the chalk of the area. However, lateral migration is not significant within the chalk at a regional scale, but is restricted to individual pressure compartments on a scale of 10 to 20 km (Fig. 29).

Test of the exploration model

A chalk stratigraphic prospect is shown in Fig. 30.

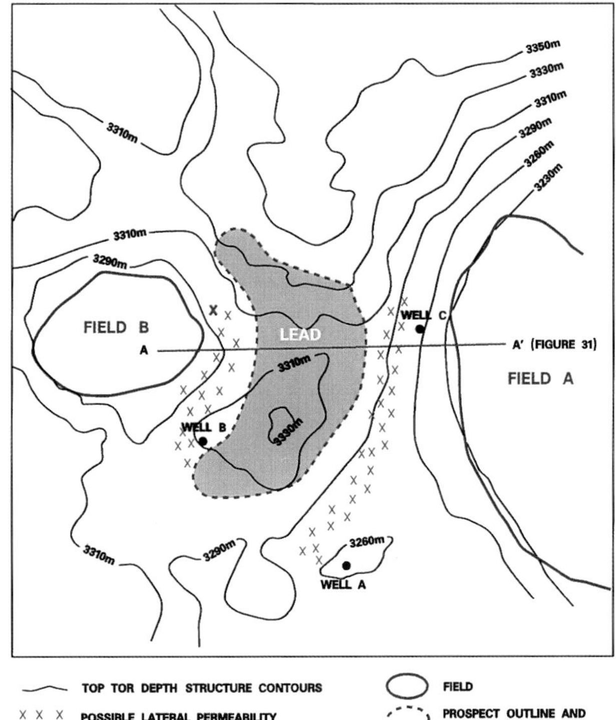

Fig. 30. Chalk prospect location map.

Prospect trap

The prospect occupies part of a broad saddle approximately 5 km^2 between Field A and Field B. The outline is defined by the extension of a seismic amplitude anomaly at Upper Tor level, and is divided from Field A by a SSW–NNE lineament that may form a lateral seal. The prospect can be considered either as an eastern extension of Field B gas/condensate accumulation, or as an isolated chalk stratigraphic trap with pressure and hydrocarbon characteristics similar to Field B.

Prospect seal

A lateral seal comprising a structural lineament is invoked to separate the prospect from Well A, which is dry and Field A which has an OWC above the lead depth (Fig. 31). Evidence for such a lateral barrier is as follows. A poorly defined SSW–NNE fault lineament is present between the lead, Well A and Field A. Well B tested hydrocarbons from the Tor Formation, below the structural level of a similar stratigraphic horizon in Well A (Fig. 32). This corroborates that the SSW–NNE lineament may be acting as a lateral seal between Well A and the lead. Pressure data, hydrocarbon characteristics and OWC values suggest that a separation exists between Field A and Field B (Fig. 32). This displacement in free water level could coincide with the SSW–NNE lineament and therefore, a possible narrow zone of tight fault brecciated chalk. The Ekofisk tight zone forms the vertical seal and a tighter intra Tor Formation chalk is invoked to act as a base seal.

Prospect reservoir

The main target is the Tor Formation. Seismic amplitude anomalies in the Tor Formation are noted indicating possible high porosity. Palaeoenvironmental mapping suggests that the lead is favourably located for reworked chalk. The depth of the lead lies within the good porosity preservation potential range (28–38%) as defined for the Tor Formation (Fig. 18). Seismic modelling and inversion studies predict a medium quality reservoir with an average porosity of 25%, ranging between 23 and 28%. Modelling suggests minor fracturing is expected within the prospect, therefore limiting the reservoir enhancement for production.

Prospect charge and migration

Well B tested condensate. A similar hydrocarbon type is expected in the lead. Back-stripping the Top Tor Horizon to an intra Miocene event, suggests that the prospect shared a common palaeostructural closure with Field A and B at this time.

Conclusions

The prospect has several positive factors, principally the prediction of a valid reservoir. However, negative elements in developing the prospect further include the poor definition of a lateral intra chalk seal and trap. This stratigraphic lead therefore has a high exploration risk.

Conclusion

Methods for identifying and predicting parameters affecting the exploration for chalk stratigraphic traps have been reviewed and a regional model for chalk prospectivity in the Greater Ekofisk area demonstrated. Seven principal factors control the chalk stratigraphic play, including depth of burial,

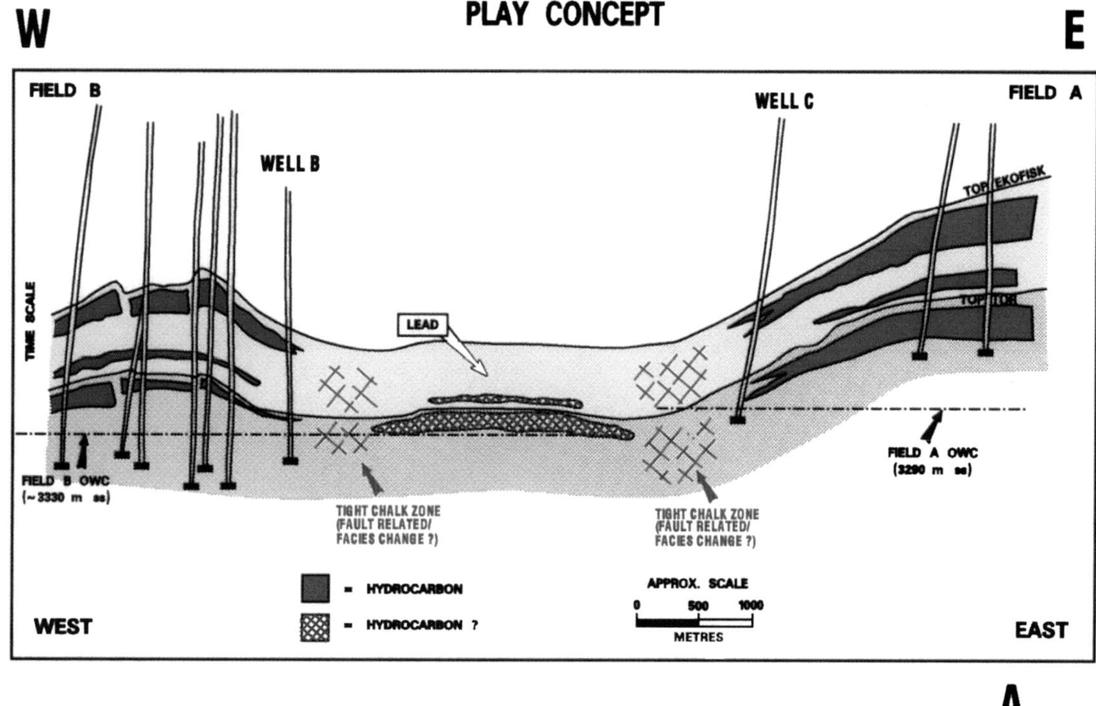

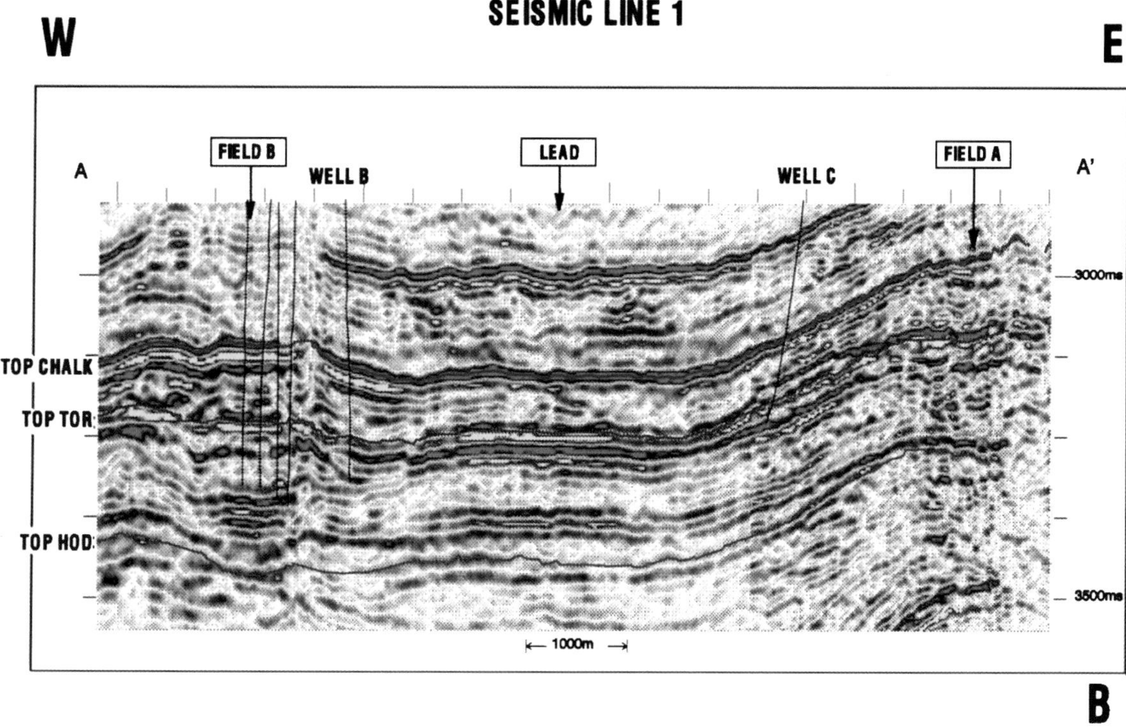

Fig. 31. Play concept and geological model for a 'real' stratigraphic trap, with corresponding 3D seismic section.

original depositional facies, early hydrocarbon migration, structural development concurrent with hydrocarbon migration, fracture definition, timing of chalk overpressure, and the effectiveness of the top, bottom and lateral seal. Although no structural or major amplitude anomaly prospects remain undrilled in the Greater Ekofisk area, many leads have been identified including subtle stratigraphic traps. However, the risks associated with these stratigraphic prospects are considered high.

The work presented in this paper is the result of the combined effort of all co-authors. Many additional personnel at Phillips Petroleum Company Norway, Elf Norge, Norsk Agip, Fina Exploration Norway and other chalk specialists, provided significant contributions to this work including R. Titterton, P. Marshall, C. O. Hauge, L. Van Zee, B. Crabtree, M. Reppart, K. Schjerverud, B. Farnan, C. Caldwell, T. Seimers, T. Harland, T. Moore and A. Foss. We would also like to thank the Norwegian Petroleum Directorate for their enthusiasm throughout the project, with special thanks to both Ase Moe and Astri

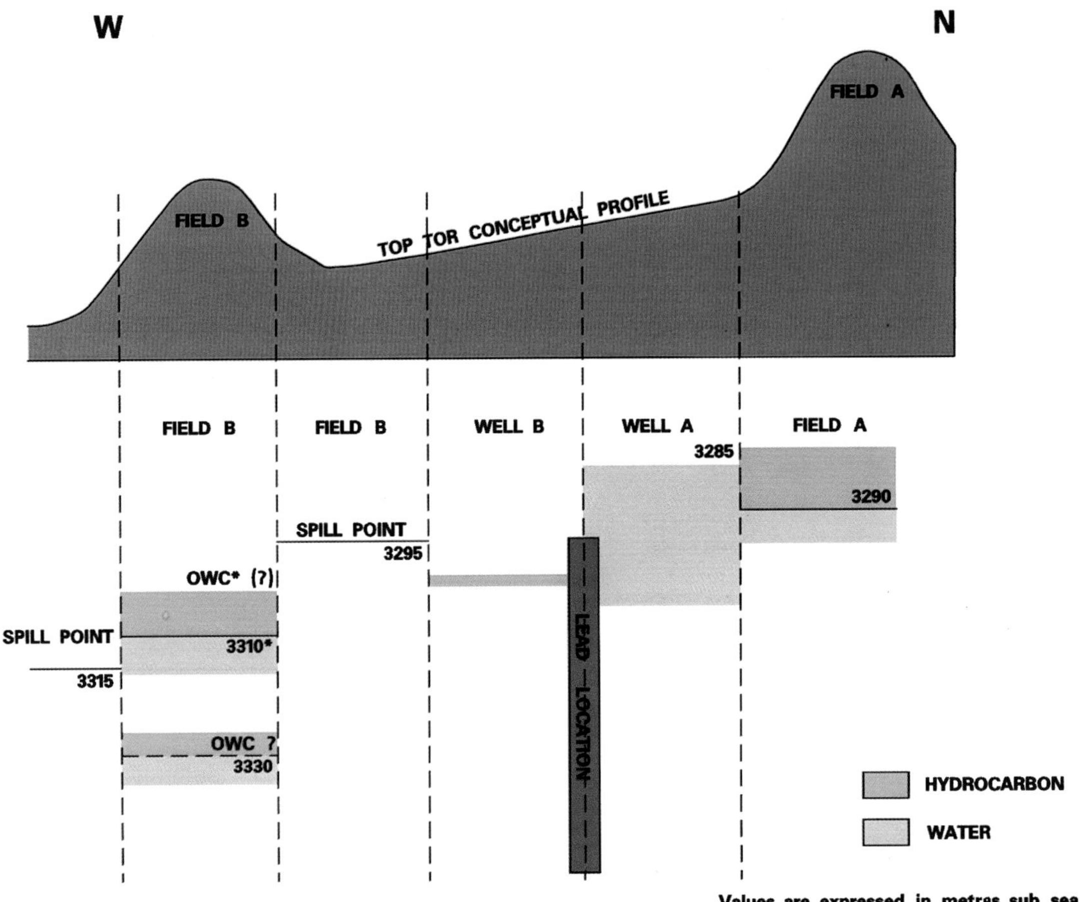

Fig. 32. Complex free water level demonstrating hydrocarbon–water contacts and spill points within the area of the lead shown in Fig. 30.

Fritsen for their encouragement and promotion of inter-company cooperation and exchange of chalk information and ideas. The accuracy and opinions contained within this manuscript remain the responsibility of the authors and do not necessarily represent the view of Phillips Petroleum Company Norway or the PL018 licence coventurers. Finally, the authors would like to thank the PL018 licence coventurers for permission to publish this work.

References

ANDERSON, J. 1999. The capabilities and the challenges of the seismic method in chalk exploration. *In*: FLEET, A. J. & BOLDY, S. A. R. (eds) *Petroleum Geology of Northwest Europe: Proceedings of the 5th Conference*. Geological Society, London, 939–947.

BRASHER, J. E. & VAGLE, K. R. 1996. Influence of lithofacies and diagenesis on Norwegian North Sea Chalk reservoirs. *American Association of Petroleum Geologists, Bulletin*, **80**(5), 746–769.

BRAUM, G. R. & VAIL, P. R. 1988. Sequence stratigraphic concepts applied to Paleogene outcrops, Gulf and Atlantic basins. *In*: WILGUS, C. K., POSAMENTIER, H., ROSS, C. A. & KENDALL, C. G. ST. C. (eds) *Sea Level Changes: An Integrated Approach*. SEPM Special Publications, **42**, 309–328.

CAILLET, G. JUDGE, N. C., BRAMWELL, N. P., MECIANI, L., GREEN, M. & ADAM, P. 1996. Structural history of the chalk fields in the Norwegian Central Graben. *In*: *Fifth North Sea Chalk symposium, Joint Chalk Research, Reims France* 1996.

——, ——, ——, ——, —— & ——1997. Overpressure and hydrocarbon trapping in the chalk of the Norwegian Central Graben. *Petroleum Geoscience*, **3**, 33–42.

CALDWELL, C. D., SIEMERS, W. T. & FARRELL, H. E. 1994. *Lithofacies and fracture types defined from the late Cretaceous and Early Palaeocene Shetland Group (Chalk Group Equivallent), Greater Ekofisk Area, Norwegian Sector, North Sea.* Phillips Petroleum Company In house report number 15050.

CAMPBELL, S. J. D & GRAVDAL, N. 1995, The prediction of high porosity chalks in the East Hod Field. *Petroleum Geoscience*, **1**, 57–69

CORNFORD, C. 1994. Mandal–Ekofisk(!) petroleum system in the Central Graben of the North Sea. *In*: MAGOON, L. B & DOW, W. G. (eds) *The Petroleum System – from Source to Trap*. American Association of Petroleum Geologists Memoir **60**, 537–571.

CRABTREE, B., FRITSEN, A., MANDZUICH, K., MOE, A., RASMUSSEN, F., SIEMERS, T., SOEILAND, G. & TIRSGAARD, H. 1996. A standard nomenclature for description and classification of chalks, North Sea Central Graben. *Norwegian Petroleum Directorate Special Publication.*

D'ANGELO, R. M. & BRANDEL, M. K. 1997. Porosity detection and mapping in a basinal carbonate setting, offshore Norway. *In*: PALAZ, I. & MARFURT, K. J. (eds) *Carbonate Seismology*. Geophysical Developments, No. 6, Society of Exploration Geophysicists, 321–336.

DEEGAN, C. E. & SCULL, B. J. 1977. *A standard lithostratigraphic nomenclature for the Central and Northern North Sea.* Institute of Geological Science Report **77/25**; NPD-Bulletin No. 1.

DISTEFANO, M., FEAZEL, C. T., PARK, R. K., PETERSON, R. M. & WILSON, K. M. 1980. *Geological Ekofisk task force, Volume IIa, lithostratigraphy, sedimentology and diagenesis.* Internal Phillips Petroleum Company Report.

EMBURY, A. F. 1993. Transgressive–regressive (T–R) sequence analysis of the Jurassic succession of the Sverdrup Basin, Canadian Arctic Archipelago. *Canadian Journal of Earth Sciences*, **30**, 301–320.

FARMER, C. L. & BARKVED, O. I. 1999. Influence of syndepositional faulting on thickness variations in chalk reservoirs – Valhall and Hod fields. *In*: FLEET, A. J. & BOLDY, S. A. R. (eds) *Petroleum Geology of Northwest Europe: Proceedings of the 5th Conference.* Geological Society, London, 949–957.

GOWERS, M. B., HOLTAR, E., SWENSSON, E. 1993. The structure of the Norwegian Central Trough (Central Graben Area). *In*: PARKER, J. R. (ed.) *Petroleum Geology of Northwest Europe: Proceedings of the 4th Conference.* Geological Society, London, 1245–1254.

HANCOCK, J. M. 1975. The petrology of chalk. *Proceedings of the Geological Association*, **86**(4), 499–535.

HATTON, I. R. 1986. Geometry of allochthonous chalk group members, Central Trough, North Sea. *Marine and Petroleum Geology*, **3**, 79–80.

HAQ, B. U., HARDENBOL, J. & VAIL, P. R. 1987. The chronology of fluctuating sea level since the Triassic. *Science*, **235**, 1156–1167.

HERRINGTON, P. M., PEDERSTAD, K. & DICKSON, J. A. D. 1991. Sedimentology and diagenesis of resedimented and rhythmically bedded chalks from the Eldfisk Field, North Sea Central Graben. *American Association of Petroleum Geologists, Bulletin*, **75**(11), 1661–1674.

HJULSTROM, F. 1939. Transportation of detritus by moving water. *In*: TRASK, P. D. (ed.) *Recent Marine Sediments*. American Association of Petroleum Geologists, 5–31.

ISAKSEN, D & TONSTAD, K. 1989. A revised Cretaceous–Tertiary Lithostratigraphic nomenclature for the Norwegian North Sea. *NPD-Bulletin*, **5**.

JOERGENSEN, L. N. & ANDERSEN, P. M. 1991. Integrated study of the Kraka Field. *Society of Petroleum Engineers, Paper no. 23082.*

KENNEDY, W. J. 1980. Aspects of chalk sedimentation in the southern Norwegian offshore. *Proceedings of 'The sedimentation of the north Sea reservoir rocks', Norwegian Petroleum Society*. Geilo 1980.

——1987. Sedimentology of Late Cretaceous–Palaeocene chalk reservoirs, in the North Sea Central Graben. *In*: BROOKS, J. & GLENNIE, K. W. (eds) *Petroleum Geology of North West Europe*. Graham & Trotman, London, 469–481.

KNOTT, S. D., BURCHELL, M. T., JOLLEY, E. J. & FRASER, A. J. 1993. Mesozoic to Cenozoic plate reconstruction of the North Atlantic and hydrocarbon plays of the Atlantic margins. *In*: PARKER, J. R. (ed.) *Petroleum Geology of Northwest Europe: Proceedings of the 4th Conference*. Geological Society, London, 953–974.

LEWIS, K. B. 1971. Slumping on a continental slope inclined at 1–4 degrees. *Sedimentology*, **16**, 98–110.

MALIVA, R. G. & DICKSON, J. A. D. 1992. Microfacies and diagenetic controls of porosity in Cretaceous/Tertiary chalks, Eldfisk Field, Norwegian North Sea. *American Association of Petroleum Geologists, Bulletin*, **76**(11), 1825–1838.

MAPSTONE, N. B. 1975. Diagenetic history of a North Sea Chalk. *Sedimentology*, **128**, 43–49.

MEGSON, J. B. 1992. The North Sea Chalk Play: examples from the Danish Central Graben. *In*: HARDMAN, R. F. P. (ed.) *Exploration Britain: Geological Insights for the Next Decade*. Geological Society, London, Special Publications, **67**, 247–282.

MUNNS, J. W. 1985. The Valhall Field: a geological overview. *Marine and Petroleum Geology*, **2**, 23–43.

NEUGEBAUER, J. 1973. The diagenetic problem of chalk – the role of pressure solution and pore fluid. *Neues Jahrbuch fur Geologie und Palaontologie. Abhandlungen*, **143**, 223–245.

NYGAARD, E., LIEBERKIND, K. & FRYKMAN, P. 1983. Sedimentology and reservoir parameters of the Chalk Group in the Danish Central Graben. *In*: KAASSCHIETER, J. P. H. & REIJERS, T. J. A. (eds) *Petroleum Geology of the Southeastern North Sea and the Adjacent Onshore Areas (The Hague, 1982)*. Geologie en Mijnbouw, **62**, 177–190.

SCHOLLE, P. A. 1974. Diagenesis of Upper Cretaceous Chalks from England, Northern Ireland, and the North Sea. *In*: HSU, K. J. & JENKYNS, H. C. (eds) *Pelagic Sediments: on Land and Under the Sea*. Special Publication of International Association of Sedimentology, **1**, 177–210.

——1977. Chalk diagenesis and its relation to petroleum exploration: oil from chalks, a modern miracle? *American Association of Petroleum Geologists, Bulletin*, **61**(7), 982–1009.

SHACKLETON, N. J. & KENNET, J. P. 1975. Palaeotemperature history of the Cenozoic and the initiation of Antarctic glaciation: Oxygen and Carbon isotopic analysis in DSDP sites 227, 279, 281. *In*: KENNEDY, J. P. & HOUTZ, R. E. (eds) *Initial Reports of the Deep Sea Drilling Project*, **29**, 743–755.

SORENSEN, S., JONES, M., HARDMAN, R. F. P., LEUTZ, W. K. & SCHWARZ, P. H. 1986. Reservoir characteristics of high and low-productivity chalks from the Central North Sea. *In*: *Habitat of Hydrocarbons on the Norwegian Continental Shelf*. Norwegian Petroleum Society, Graham & Trotman, London, 91–110.

TAYLOR, S. R. & LAPRE, J. F. 1987. North Sea chalk diagenesis: its effect on reservoir location and properties. *In*: BROOKS, J. & GLENNIE, K. (eds) *Petroleum Geology of North West Europe*. Graham & Trotman, London, 483–495.

VAIL, P. R. & TODD, R. G. 1981, Northern North Sea Jurassic unconformities, Chronostratigraphy and sea-level changes from seismic stratigraphy. *In*: ILLING, L. V. & HOBSON, G. D. (eds) *Petroleum Geology of the Continental Shelf of North-West Europe*. Heyden, London, 216–235.

WATTS, N. L. 1983. Microfractures in chalks of Albuskjell Field, Norwegian Sector, North Sea. Possible origin and distribution. *American Association of Petroleum Geologists, Bulletin*, **67**, 217–234.

——, LAPRE, J. F., VAN SCHIJNDEL-GOESTER, F. S. & FORD, A. 1980. Upper Cretaceous and Lower Tertiary chalks of the Albuskjell area, North Sea: deposition in a slope and base of slope environment. *Geology*, **8**, 217–221.

ZIEGLER, P. A. 1977. Geology and hydrocarbon provinces of the North Sea. *Geojournal*, **1**, 7–32.

——1982. *Geological Atlas of Western and Central Europe*. Shell International Petroleum Maatschappij, Elsevier Applied Science, Amsterdam.

The capabilities and challenges of the seismic method in chalk exploration

J. K. ANDERSON

Phillips Petroleum Company Norway, Postboks 220, 4056 Tananger, Norway (e-mail: jkander@ ppco.com)

Abstract: The success of seismic methods to detect and predict porosity within the chalk fields of the Norwegian North Sea, coupled with the awareness that chalk can behave as both reservoir and seal, has led to the deliberate search for stratigraphically trapped hydrocarbons within the chalk. This effort has relied on seismic methods, such as post-stack inversion and amplitude versus offset (AVO) techniques, to identify porous reworked chalk zones isolated within low porosity pelagic chalk. The excellent conditions for seismic acquisition and processing, slowly varying regional geology, and high correlation between porosity and seismic velocities and density produce reliable porosity predictions far from well control for all inversion techniques. However, the high exploration failure rate for stratigraphic tests demonstrates that migration and seal risk is higher in chalk stratigraphic prospects, and some method of predicting hydrocarbon presence is beneficial. Analysis of available velocity measurements demonstrates that porosity and fluid variations in chalk can be modelled best with the upper bound of Hashin and Shtrikmann (1963), modified with the critical porosity of Nur (1992). This model leads to the conclusion that chalk velocities are sensitive to pore fluid and that hydrocarbon effects may be observable on seismic data. Unfortunately, hydrocarbon effects overprint the larger porosity effects, making resolution of the hydrocarbons signal extremely difficult in practice. An exploration case study demonstrates that the current inability to distinguish the effect of hydrocarbons from that of porosity, in the presence of noise and other complicating factors, seriously limits the ability of seismic methods to directly detect hydrocarbons under normal exploration conditions.

The resurgence in hydrocarbon exploration targeting North Sea Cretaceous and Danian Chalks has been driven both by the success of reservoir management, making chalk reservoirs commercially more attractive, and by a shift from viewing chalk not only as reservoir but also as a potential intra-formational seal. Production from chalk is highly dependent on porosity, and effective field development requires that porosity variations within the reservoir be adequately characterized, a task in which 3D seismic and inversion methods are successful because porosity is the dominant control of seismic response. In addition, the observation that many of the presently producing fields show a component of stratigraphic trapping between highly porous reworked chalk and surrounding less porous pelagic units, has indicated the possibility that significant hydrocarbon accumulations may be stratigraphically trapped off the flanks of the presently producing fields. This combination of improved economics, an exploration target virtually beneath infrastructure, and the means of confidently detecting potential prospects has touched off the current 'chalk renaissance' in exploration and particularly development drilling activity.

Seismic techniques, specifically post-stack inversion and AVO (amplitude versus offset), have been instrumental in identifying untested porous units and mapping the trapping geometry, but most recent chalk tests have been water bearing, demonstrating that reservoir presence is not the dominant risk. In a simplistic sense, the migration and seal risks of chalk stratigraphic traps are inversely proportional – forces that tend to fracture the surrounding pelagic units and allow migration will also tend to destroy the seal. Because of the great uncertainties in migration and seal, a means of addressing these risks, specifically the direct detection of hydrocarbons through seismic methods, would be beneficial. However, despite the obvious utility of such a method, only one successful prediction of gas in chalk has been reported (Megson 1992), and most work has concentrated on porosity prediction. In addition, most predictions are based on empirical relationships between porosity and a seismically measured variable, such as velocity or density, and are of limited value in providing physical insight into the behaviour of chalk, particularly when attempting to predict the effects of pore fluid replacement. The main purpose of the work reported here is to investigate the applicability of seismic methods, specifically post-stack inversion and AVO analysis, to porosity and hydrocarbon prediction in chalk, examining the rock physics attributes these techniques exploit, and their capabilities and practical limitations. The use of post-stack inversion and pre-stack AVO analysis for chalk porosity prediction is reviewed, and the high correlation between porosity and measurements of acoustic impedance and seismic velocity. Second, rock physics theory is used to place the measurements in the context of a physical model that describes the velocity behaviour of chalk when porosity and pore fluid vary, which is then used to predict the expected seismic responses. Finally, an exploration case study demonstrates that while chalk units can exhibit a potentially measurable hydrocarbon response, this signature significantly overlaps that of changes in porosity, resulting in considerable ambiguity under normal exploration conditions. These investigations use seismic and well data examples from the Greater Ekofisk area of the Norwegian North Sea (Fig. 1), and concentrate on chalks of the highly productive Upper Cretaceous Tor Formation (Fig. 2). A brief discussion of the relevant aspects of chalk geology and porosity preservation is given as a necessary starting point, but for a more complete discussion the reader is referred to Bramwell *et al.* (1999).

Chalk geology

Porosity is the major variable controlling hydrocarbon production from chalk, and an understanding of its preservation and distribution is critical for both exploration and field

ANDERSON, J. K. 1999. The capabilities and challenges of the seismic method in chalk exploration. *In*: FLEET, A. J. & BOLDY, S. A. R. (eds) *Petroleum Geology of Northwest Europe: Proceedings of the 5th Conference*, 939–947. © Petroleum Geology '86 Ltd. Published by the Geological Society, London.

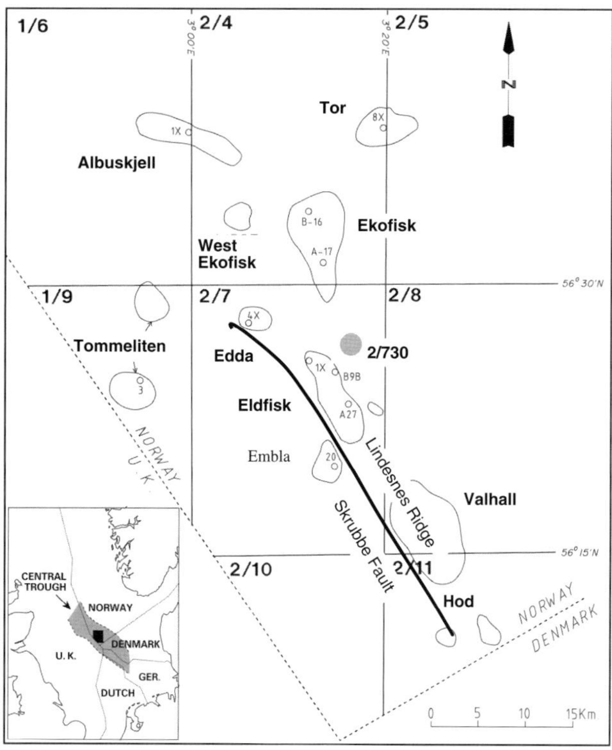

Fig. 1. Map of the Greater Ekofisk area showing fields and major structures.

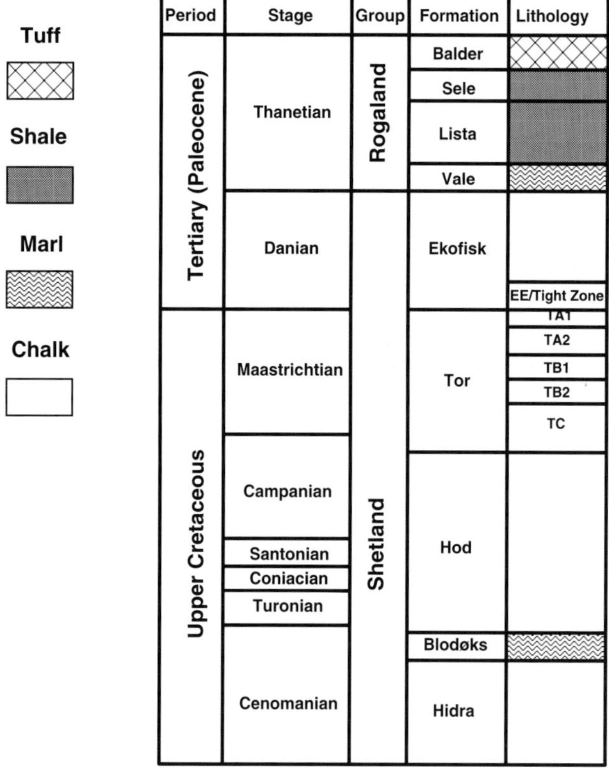

Fig. 2. Stratigraphic column with formations and local field zonations.

development. The diagenetic history of the chalk from deposition to present-day is controlled by five factors (Fig. 3):

(1) chalk type, broadly classified into end members of pelagic and redeposited chalks;
(2) burial depth;
(3) overpressure;
(4) original grain size; and
(5) hydrocarbon presence (Brasher & Vagle 1996).

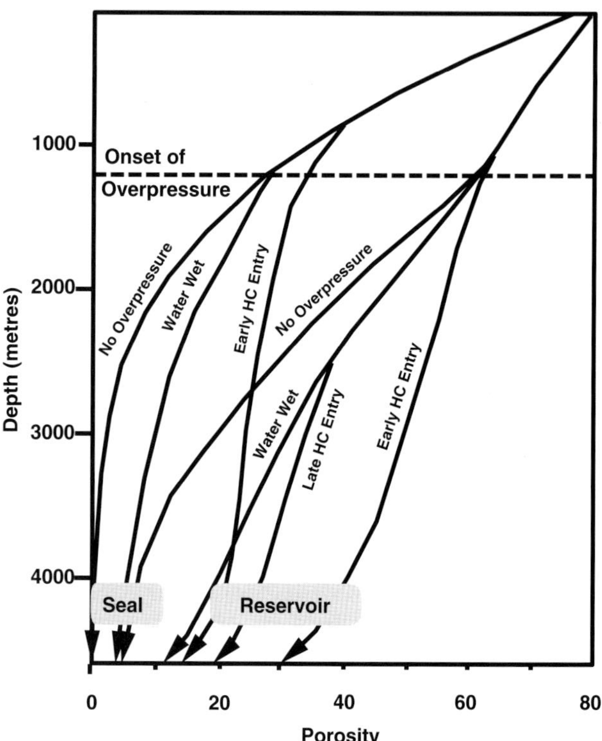

Fig. 3. Plot of porosity reduction with depth, showing the influence of reworking, overpressure, and hydrocarbon emplacement on diagenetic path. Adapted from Brasher & Vagle (1996).

Chalk grains, largely composed of the calcite skeletal debris (coccoliths) of unicellular algae, settle out of the water column individually as a slow pelagic 'rain' or in faecal pellets (Honjo 1975) and are deposited as ooze on the seafloor with an initial porosity of about 70%. This porosity is reduced by dewatering, chemical cementation by circulating sea-water, and closer grain packing, all of which are accelerated by burrowing and bioturbation (Taylor & Lapre 1987).

Remobilization of the chalk by gravity flow mechanisms, such as slumps, mud and debris flows, breaks up the initial cementation, destroys the packing of the grains, and restarts the diagenetic process. If sufficiently thick, portions of the redeposited unit deep enough to avoid bioturbation and circulating seawater will retain a higher porosity than more exposed pelagic or thin redeposited chalks. High porosity reworked units produce the majority of hydrocarbons from the North Sea chalk fields (Brasher & Vagle 1996), and include large regionally correlatable units caused by regional instability at the basin margins (D'Heur 1986) and local units created by halokinesis and tectonic movements (Brasher 1995). Intervening pelagic units, which record periods of quiet deposition, have lower matrix permeability and are less susceptible to fracturing, providing local seals (Bramwell *et al.* 1999). Both exploration and field development require the identification of reworked and pelagic units to identify potential prospects and determine the productive limits of the fields.

Porosity detection and estimation

Seismic attributes

The dominant variable affecting both velocity and density of chalk is porosity, and the differences in acoustic impedance between pelagic and redeposited chalk units are very obvious on seismic data. For example, the Edda Field (Fig. 4), a domal

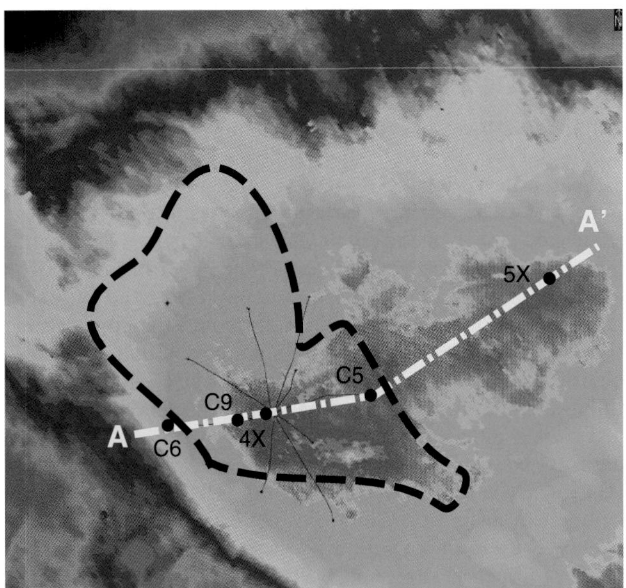

Fig. 4. Time structure map of the top Ekofisk Formation over the Edda Field. Production is confined to the western portion of the domal structure. (A–A′ is the seismic section shown in Fig. 5. The dashed line delineates the area of high seismic amplitude – see Fig. 6).

closure on the Lindesnes Ridge on trend with the Eldfisk and Valhall fields, produces largely from a single reworked unit of the Tor Formation, in field terminology the TA2 unit, which has an average porosity of approximately 26% and is encased in tighter pelagic chalks (Fig. 5). This difference in porosity creates an acoustic impedance contrast at the reservoir top and base, allowing mapping of the reworked Tor unit. Edda also exhibits a strong component of stratigraphic trapping, with the productive TA2 zone sealed by less reworked low porosity chalks to the north and east, pinching out to the south, and exhibiting a hydrocarbon contact below the structural spill point (Brasher & Vagle 1996). In addition, the underlying reworked TB2 unit, which is also visible on seismic data, is water wet suggesting a bottom seal in the intervening pelagic unit. The less reworked chalks of the TA2 to the north and east are lower in porosity and have a smaller acoustic impedance contrast with the overlying pelagic Ekofisk Tight Zone and TA1 chalks, allowing the productive limits of the field to be approximately delineated by the limits of the seismic amplitude anomaly (Fig. 6). Although analyses of seismic attributes such as amplitude and isochron were used in the early development of the chalk fields (Van den Bark & Thomas 1981), these techniques suffer from the effects of wavelet interference, limiting the resolution of complex stratigraphic changes and quantitative predictions of porosity and thickness.

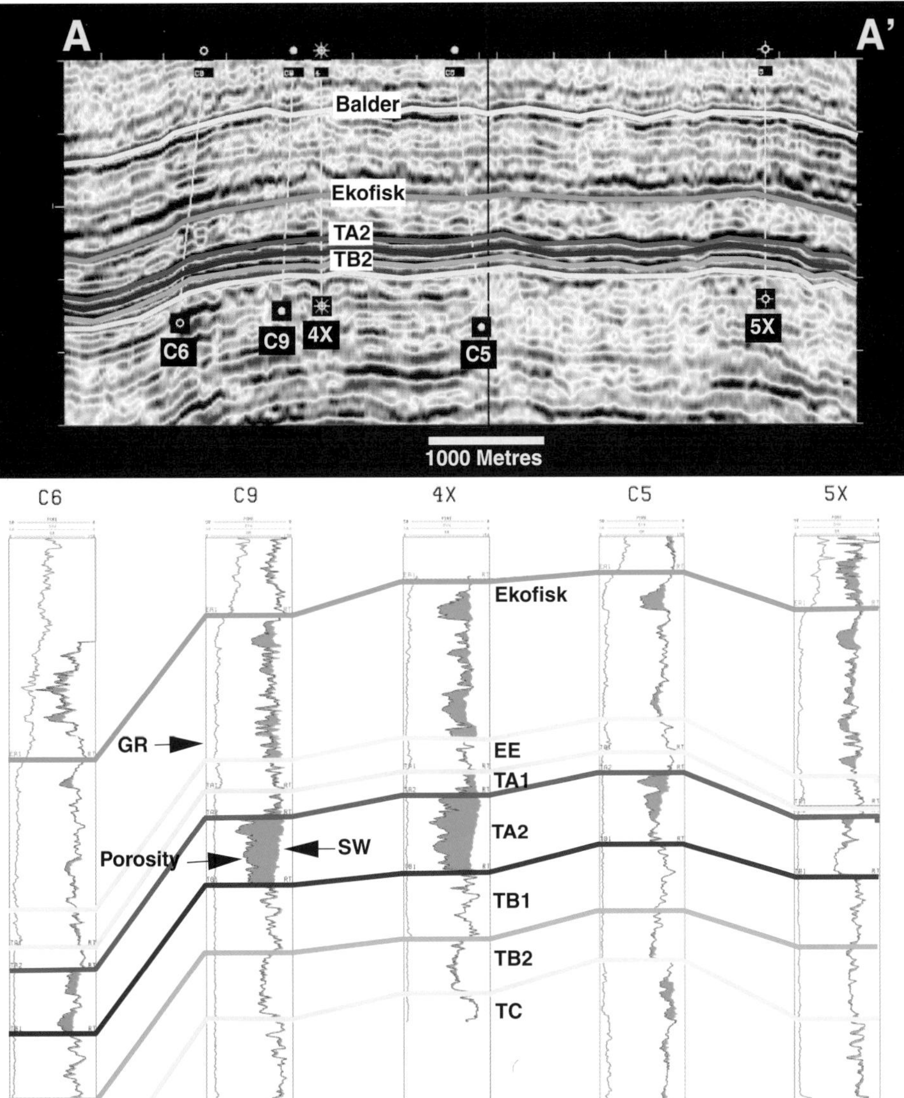

Fig. 5. Example of seismic correlation between porosity and seismic data. The top of the porous Tor TA2 reservoir unit is correlated to a drop in acoustic impedance (represented here as a black peak).

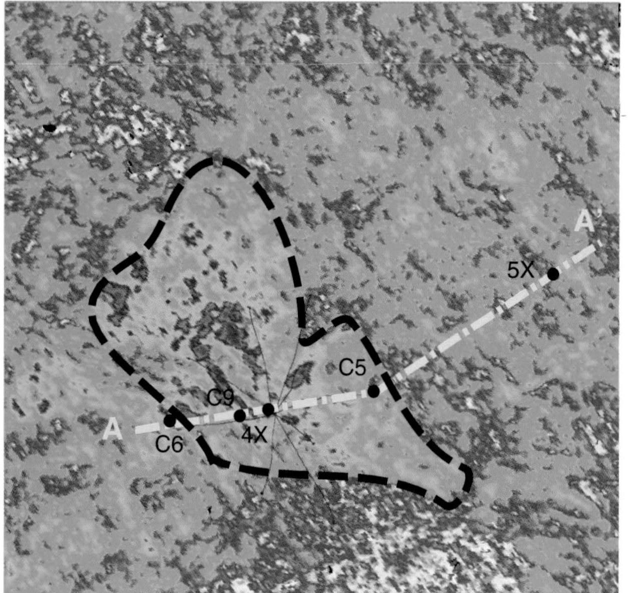

Fig. 6. Seismic amplitude map of the upper Tor TA2 unit on Edda Field. Wells encountering productive porous chalk are within the area of high seismic amplitude, while wells that encountered tighter unproductive chalks fall outside the amplitude anomaly.

Post-stack seismic inversion

Seismic inversion removes the effects of wavelet convolution and allows the closer integration of *a priori* information to produce more robust predictions of porosity and thickness than seismic attributes alone, within the limits of noise and signal bandwidth. Most inversions use either recursive or model-based algorithms on migrated seismic data to construct an acoustic impedance trace, which is then interpreted directly or combined with available geological information and a rock physics model to produce a prediction of lithology and porosity. Both types of algorithms must approximately honour the same assumptions about the input data. First, the signal wavelet embedded in the data must be known and stable with regard to frequency and phase over the time and area of interest. Second, seismic amplitudes must be scaled properly, i.e. the measured seismic amplitudes must be linearly related to the underlying reflectivity in the absence of complicating convolutional effects. Third, the data must be migrated properly.

Recursive inversion techniques attempt to reverse the convolutional process that produced the migrated seismic trace to estimate the 'original' reflectivity and underlying acoustic impedance. These algorithms require the restoration of the low frequency signal of the earth that is absent from the band-limited seismic trace, which can often be problematic. The estimated impedance calculated is non-unique in the sense that it is not the only solution that could produce the input seismic trace, but only the most likely solution of that particular algorithm, and a different algorithm will give another, hopefully similar, result. However, the high speed of these algorithms allows a greater number of possible inversions, allowing comparison of multiple results. A second benefit is the absence of an *a priori* assumption of the high frequency component of geology, allowing the inversion to give valid results away from well control where stratigraphy and lithological properties are not well known, which allows the detection of porosity anomalies not identified through routine seismic interpretation.

Model-based inversions match the synthetic responses of possible geological models, picking the one with the best 'fit' to the real seismic data. An example of this technique is Phillips' proprietary incremental pay thickness modelling and non-unique inversion (Neff 1996), which uses available petrophysical log information, such as porosity, shale volume, and water saturation, combined with a rock physics model, to predict sonic and density logs and the expected synthetic seismic response. A library of synthetic traces is constructed by changing lithology, pore fluid, and thickness, then comparing to each real seismic trace to find the best match. A benefit of this technique is that all possible answers above a quality-of-match threshold are in a sense equally valid, preserving the non-uniqueness of the input seismic data with respect to variations in impedance, velocity, thickness, lithology, and pore fluid effects, which can be helpful for risk assessment and stochastic modelling. This inversion technique can produce higher frequencies than recursive techniques, because the underlying geological model is preserved. Drawbacks include the need for a greater amount of *a priori* information in the form of well control and geological knowledge, computing limitations

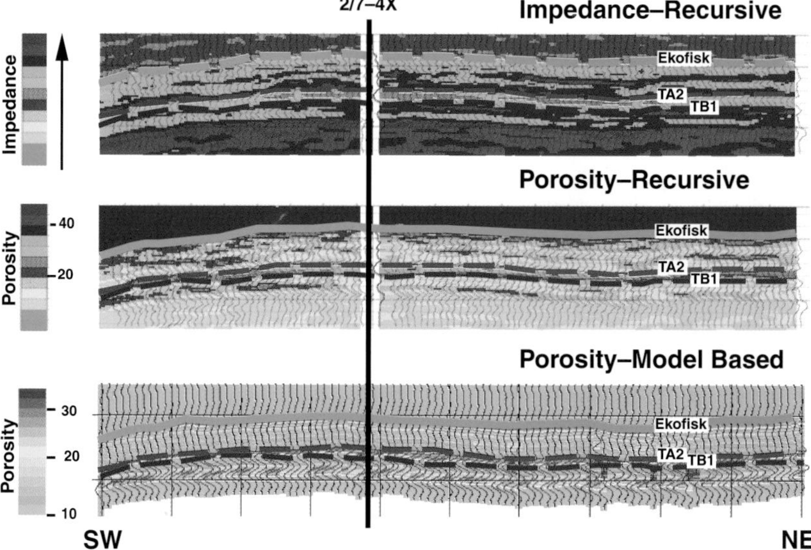

Fig. 7. Comparison between seismic trace data, recursive inversion, and model-based inversion over the Edda Field. Inversion removes the effects of convolution, producing an estimate of the underlying impedance or petrophysical parameters, such as porosity.

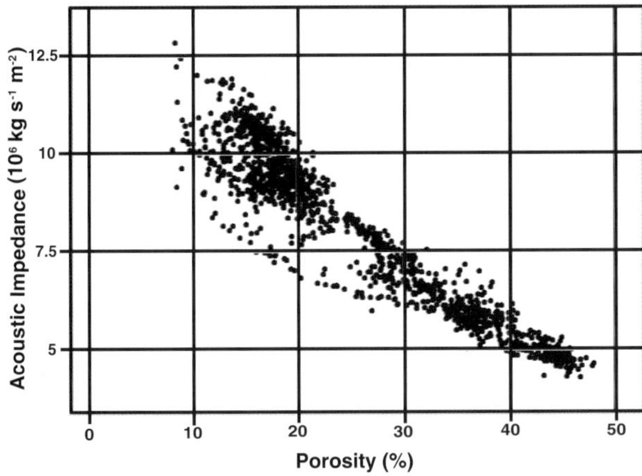

Fig. 8. Cross plot of porosity and acoustic impedance. The success of seismic inversion for porosity prediction is largely owing to the high correlation between porosity, and seismic velocities and density.

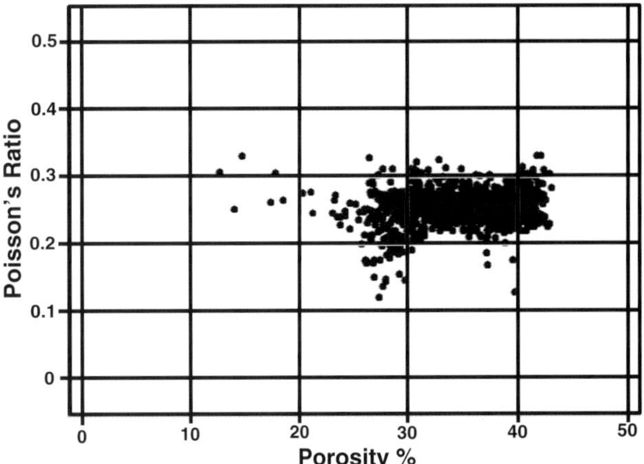

Fig. 9. Cross plot of porosity and Poisson's Ratio derived from full-waveform sonic data. Poisson's Ratio does not radically change over the range of porosity encountered in chalk exploration.

caused by each variable geometrically increasing the number of possible permutations to be tested, and the serious limitation that a trace can be inverted only if a forward model matching it exists.

Local regional geology and the specific characteristics of the chalk give these inversion techniques unique applicability to porosity detection and prediction (Fig. 7), and all produce robust results. Routine acquisition and 3D processing adequately meet the data assumptions of these algorithms (Anderson 1996; D'Angelo *et al.* 1997), resulting in a high degree of confidence in inversion predictions, even at considerable distances from well control. The relatively uniform nature of both the chalk and overlying Tertiary shale is a simplifying factor in the North Sea, allowing the missing low-frequency portion of the seismic trace required for recursive inversions to be extrapolated from the available well control using picked seismic events and stacking velocities. The general lack of background velocity changes allows synthetic model libraries calculated from specific wells to be applicable over a wide area, as only the high-frequency component is changing. The transformation of an estimated impedance to a lithological parameter, which is normally very non-unique because a single impedance value may describe rocks with wide variations in mineralogy, pore fluid, and pore geometry, is reduced in the chalk because of its mono-mineralic nature. Because the chalk is largely calcite, with only minor amounts of shale and silica impurities, robust empirical relationships can be constructed between porosity and impedance, or porosity and velocity (Fig. 8). The remaining variation in porosity, which will appear in the inversion as an additional noise component, reflects variations caused by small changes in mineralogy (shale content), pore geometry, and fractures, and typically does not introduce significant amounts of error into porosity estimates. This robust transformation from seismic measurement to petrophysical parameter is probably the key success factor in the application of these techniques to chalk.

Amplitude versus offset

Amplitude versus offset analysis (AVO) exploits the variation in reflectivity across a boundary as incidence angle changes, which is a function of the change in compressional and shear velocities, usually expressed in terms of Poisson's Ratio, and the bulk densities of the two layers juxtaposed. AVO has been highly successful in young siliciclastic rocks where the replacement of brine by gas causes a very dramatic change in Poisson's Ratio, but is seeing increasing use for lithology prediction using more subtle changes in Poisson's Ratio (see Isaacson & Neff 1999). The generally smaller variations in Poisson's Ratio in carbonates have limited its application, but successful use of AVO for fluid prediction in carbonates has been reported (Chiburis 1993), and in North Sea chalk for porosity detection and estimation (Landroe *et al.* 1995; D'Angelo *et al.* 1997).

AVO for porosity detection exploits the changes in compressional and shear wave velocities (and hence reflectivities) with porosity. In general, measurements of Poisson's Ratio either do not appreciably change (Fig. 9), because of a lack of underlying mineralogical change (present in sands and shale) or show a minor decrease as porosity increases, though the latter observation is difficult to reconcile with rock physics as Poisson's Ratio should *increase* with increasing porosity. In addition, there are few measurements of very low porosity pelagic

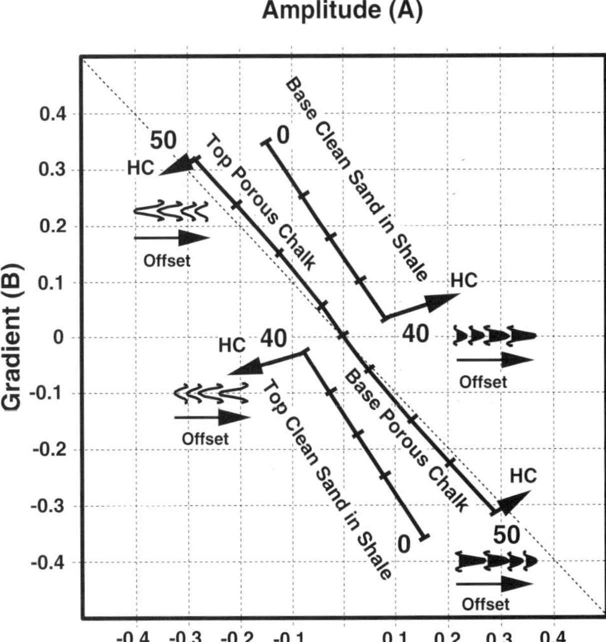

Fig. 10. AVO cross plot of expected chalk normal incidence amplitudes and amplitude gradients over a range of porosity, compared to a typical sand/shale response. The introduction of hydrocarbons will increase the absolute normal incidence amplitude, and create a slight decrease in amplitude gradient for both top and base. This effect is significantly smaller than that encountered in sand/shale sequences.

chalks, so the behaviour of these units, which tend to have a greater amount of shale, is difficult to predict. Cross plotting of the expected AVO response of porous chalks (Isaacson & Neff 1999) demonstrates that a change in chalk porosity is observable as changes in the normal incidence reflectivity resulting from change in impedance, and offset amplitude gradient caused by the change in shear velocity across the boundary (Fig. 10). Comparison with a typical sand/shale response shows the lack of a 'lithological' component to the response, although chalks juxtaposed against overlying Tertiary Shale may exhibit an AVO gradient where an impedance contrast may not be present, allowing resolution of shale and chalk units (D'Angelo *et al.* 1997). AVO techniques in chalk therefore exploit the same impedance change used by post-stack inversions, with the additional benefit of the shear wave response, which may make the measurement more robust. However, AVO for porosity suffers from the need to retain longer offsets in acquisition and processing, the need for greater care and time in processing, a general loss in resolution and signal quality caused by the absence of common midpoint stacking, and the need for greater well calibration caused by a less consistent response.

Rock physics, porosity, and hydrocarbon effects on seismic

Rock physics and fluid replacement

Replacing brine in the pore space of a rock with more compressible hydrocarbons, such as live oil and gas, reduces the bulk density and bulk modulus of the rock, and produces a potentially measurable effect on seismic data from the resulting velocity and impedance changes. This effect is most dramatic on compressional velocities, because, in theory, shear modulus is unaffected by pore fluid, although shear wave velocity will change when density varies. The magnitude of the change caused by fluid replacement is a function of pore space compressibility, rock mineralogy, and the difference in compressibility between fluids (Mavko & Mukerji 1995), and in general will be greater with increasing porosity and lighter hydrocarbons. Fluid replacement is typically modelled using Gassmann's relation (Gassmann 1951), which requires a knowledge of rock bulk modulus, available only from full waveform sonic logs or core measurement. Because of fluid invasion, sonic logs rarely measure the undisturbed zone surrounding the well bore, but rather the zone containing mud filtrate, making the question of what is being measured problematic. Core measurements of chalk are difficult because of high frequency dispersive effects and the disturbance of the core by compaction or chemical alteration during the introduction of brine. The difficulty of acquiring high quality velocity measurements from log and core force a reliance on rock physics theory to describe the velocity of chalk and the effects of fluid behaviour.

Effective medium theories attempt to predict the compressional and shear wave velocities of a rock based on mineral properties, fluid properties, porosity and pore shapes. Obviously a rock with little or no porosity will be relatively unaffected by changes in fluid compared to a rock with high porosity, and pore geometry is critical as some geometries are less 'rigid' than other geometries, making the whole rock more sensitive to changes in fluid. For carbonates this effect is illustrated in Fig. 11, where measured chalk sonic log velocities are compared to the models of Voigt (1928) and Ruess (1929), calculated using the density, bulk and shear moduli of calcite and water. The Voigt model, constructed of alternating slabs of fluid and calcite oriented parallel to the stress direction, is less sensitive to fluid than the Ruess model where the slabs are perpendicular to the stress direction. The relative sensitivity of chalk to fluid replacement can be judged by the distance of the measured points from these bounds, and although not descriptive, provides limits to expected chalk behaviour.

The match between chalk model and measurement is improved using the bounds of Hashin & Shtrikman (1963), which predict the highest and lowest possible moduli of a porous medium, in this case calculated for calcite and water

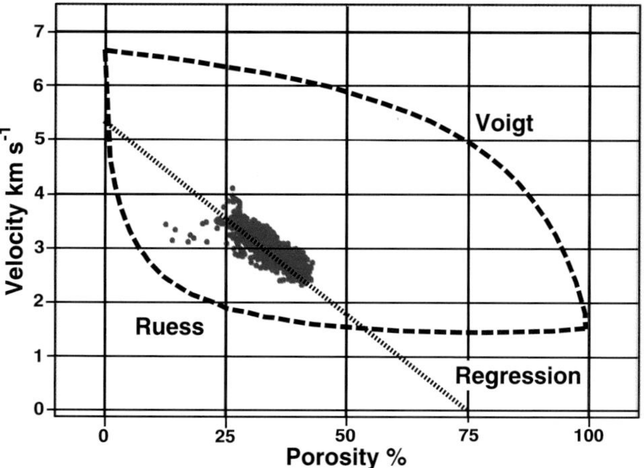

Fig. 11. Comparison of measured sonic log velocity (dots), with curves of the Voigt and Ruess bounds calculated for calcite and brine.

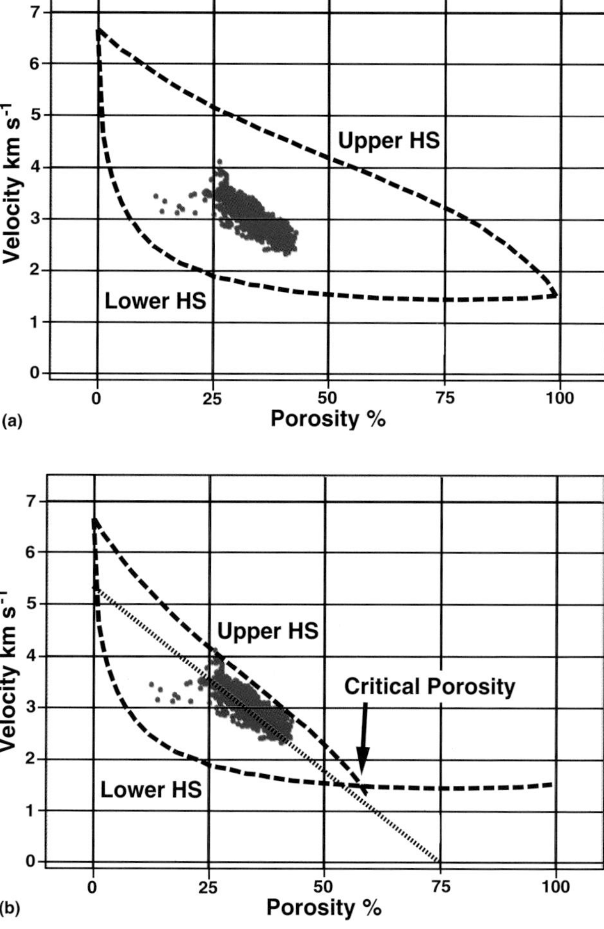

Fig. 12. (**a**) Comparison of measured sonic log velocities (dots), with the upper and lower Hashin–Shtrikman bounds calculated for calcite and brine. (**b**) Comparison of measured sonic log velocities (dots), with the upper Hashin–Shtrikman bound recalculated with a porosity normalized by the critical porosity of Nur (1992). The upper bound more closely describes the relationship between porosity and velocity when the chalk is load bearing (up to the critical porosity), while above this point the lower bound describes the chalk in suspension.

(Fig. 12a). Geometrically these bounds can be interpreted as either a distribution of hollow calcite spheres filled with brine (the 'stiffer' upper bound), or as hollow spheres of fluid filled with a solid sphere of calcite (the lower bound). These bounds are closer to the measured data and more closely match the porosity and pore geometry of chalk, which consists of both intra-grain porosity within the coccoliths and inter-grain porosity between them. The match between measurement and model can be further improved by recalculating the upper bounds using a porosity normalized by the critical porosity (Mavko & Nur 1996), which is the porosity at which the grains, or coccoliths in the case of chalk, are no longer load-bearing, i.e. in suspension (Nur 1992). For this exercise (Fig. 12b), critical porosity is taken to be 60%, and the upper bound describes the behaviour of the medium when it is load-bearing ('solid'), and the lower bound the behaviour when the coccoliths are in suspension.

There are a number of benefits to applying this model to chalk. Unlike an empirical relationship, this model predicts both compressional and shear wave velocities in a physically consistent and realistic manner over the entire possible range of porosity, avoiding the problem of incorrect predictions at the extremes of porosity and negative velocities. In the example shown, the critical porosity was chosen to describe the approximate porosity at which the chalk became 'solid,' and provides an upper bound to chalk velocities. Measured velocities below this bound represent effects not accounted for in the model, such as shale and fractures. and are an indication of the errors involved in prediction. By adjusting the value of the critical porosity, the upper bound can be adjusted to equalize these effects and predict porosity directly, useful when modelling wells where porosity is known (for example from density), but velocity is not. Lastly, the model is relatively simple, does not require *a priori* definition of porosity distribution or pore shapes, and most importantly, allows prediction of pore fluid changes consistent with Gassman's Relation.

Fluid effects on seismic

Fluid replacement effects can be modelled using this model directly, or with the bounding average method of Marion & Nur (1991). The latter re-maps measured data from an initial position between the upper and lower bounds to a position with the same proportional distance between the bounds recalculated with the replacement fluid (Fig. 13). Both methods are consistent with Gassmann's relation and applicable when compressional velocity is known but shear is not.

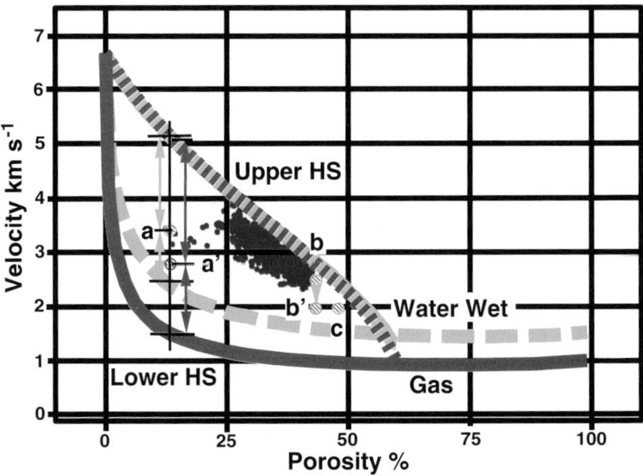

Fig. 13. Calculation of fluid replacment using the Bounding Average Method of Marion and Nur (1991). The brine filled data point 'a', is shifted to 'a' by measuring its distance between the calculated brine bounds, and placing it a proportional distance from the bounds calculated with hydrocarbon (in this case gas). While this demonstrates that hydrocarbons will effect the velocity of chalk, this effect is non-unique, as a brine saturated point 'b', remapped to 'b', has a similar velocity to a brine saturated point 'c' with greater porosity.

This model can be used to show that gas and oil can affect the velocity of chalk, but not at a magnitude to produce an unambiguous fluid response. In fact, a hydrocarbon saturated chalk will typically have a compressional velocity and density that is similar to that of a water saturated slightly more porous chalk (Fig. 13). In addition, this model indicates that Poisson's Ratio will vary slightly with fluid changes, although this effect is smaller in magnitude than those measured in siliciclastics (Fig. 10). Because the velocity change created by fluids mimics changes created by porosity, the difficulty lies in isolating the hydrocarbon effect from the larger porosity effects under exploration conditions.

An exploration example

The problem of direct detection is demonstrated using an example from Norwegian Block 2/7, where a large seismic amplitude anomaly was detected within the Maastrichtian Tor Formation, on a structural nose down-dip from the producing Eldfisk Bravo Structure (Fig. 14). This anomaly was correlated to the same Tor TA2 zone that produces the majority of the oil from the Edda Field, and is productive on the Ekofisk and Eldfisk fields.

Post-stack inversions were performed to predict porosity and thickness for the target, named the 2/7-30 'Egdar' Prospect. Seismic inversion predicted an average porosity over the prospect of 31% or greater in the Tor Formation (Fig. 15), with porosity diminishing to the east and north, and a stratigraphic pinch-out to the south. However, there appeared to be considerable seal risk to the southwest, where the unit diminished in porosity to approximately 23–25% along the flank of the Eldfisk Field, perhaps insufficient to seal. From a geological standpoint it seemed reasonable that hydrocarbons were present. The higher than average predicted porosity at 3300 m may be indicative of greater preservation of porosity owing to the presence of hydrocarbons. The prospect was structurally above the hydrocarbon contact on the nearby Ekofisk Field and hydrocarbons could spill into the higher structural position. Because the expected hydrocarbon response, in this case a live oil, was dominated by the larger

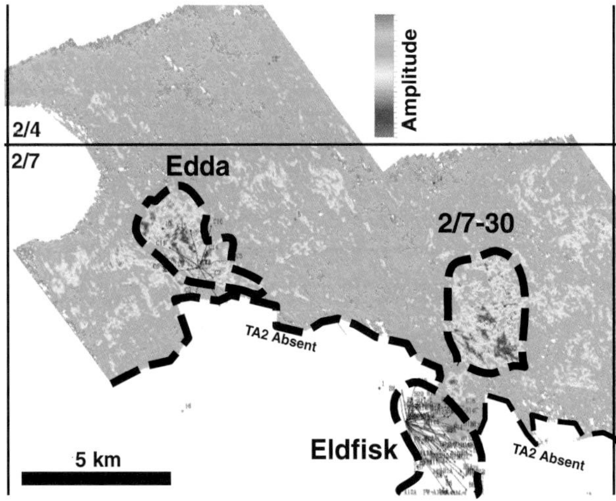

Fig. 14. Seismic amplitude map of upper Tor TA2 zone, with 2/7-30 'Egdar' amplitude anomaly.

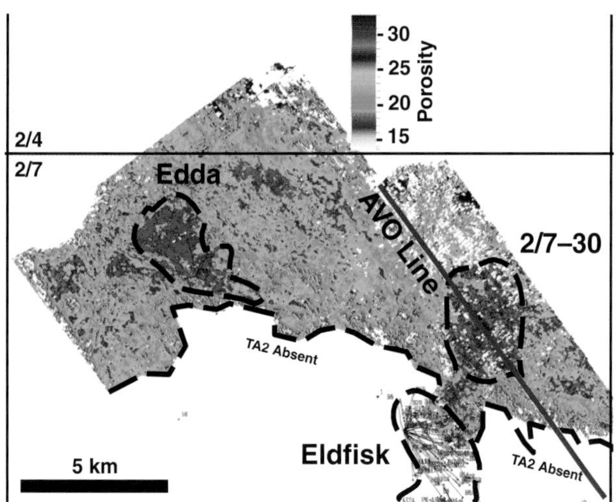

Fig. 15. Seismic inversion of 2/7-30 'Egdar' prospect anomaly. The anomaly is an isolated zone of high porosity situated on a structural nose down-dip of the producing Eldfisk Bravo structure.

effects of porosity, post-stack inversions could not prove the existence of hydrocarbons. Could AVO methods demonstrate the presence of hydrocarbons?

An AVO study was initiated to assess the likelihood of hydrocarbon presence. The AVO analysis technique of Chiburis (1993) was used to analyse the boundary between the overlying pelagic unit and the porous Tor zone, on a line running across the prospect to the producing East Eldfisk structure. The Chiburis technique normalizes the target amplitudes to those of a reference horizon, reducing the complications in amplitude analysis caused by unknown factors in processing and acquisition, yielding a relative measure of AVO response, or AVO difference. The results of modelling indicated that the highly porous zone should exhibit a positive AVO difference in comparison with an underlying non-porous reference horizon, which was in fact observed on the seismic data (Fig. 16). In addition, East Eldfisk, which lies to the southeast of the target anomaly, exhibited a strongly negative AVO Indicator for the top Tor, consistent with the very low porosity observed at this location. These two observations demonstrated the general utility of the technique, and confirmed the results of the post-stack inversions. Forward modelling indicated that hydrocarbons should decrease the magnitude of the AVO difference, although comparison of the target anomaly and down-dip areas exhibited no change in AVO difference not attributable to porosity. This highlights an acute problem in hydrocarbon detection in chalk, where the transition zone between water and hydrocarbon saturated chalks is typically large, preventing formation of a seismically observable hydrocarbon contact or 'flat spot.' In addition, the long transition zone is typically overprinted by changes in porosity, resulting in wide variations in observed hydrocarbon contact.

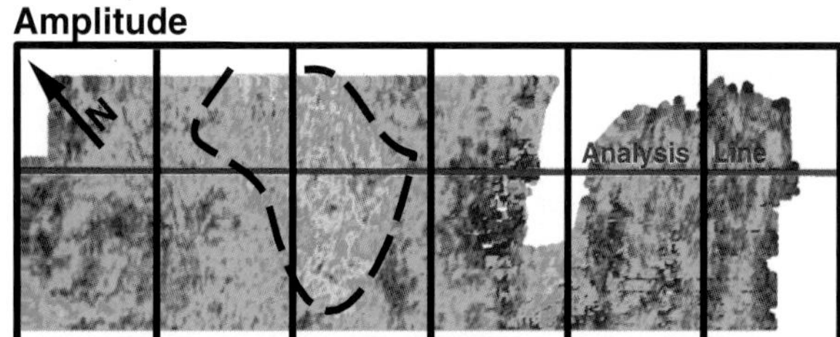

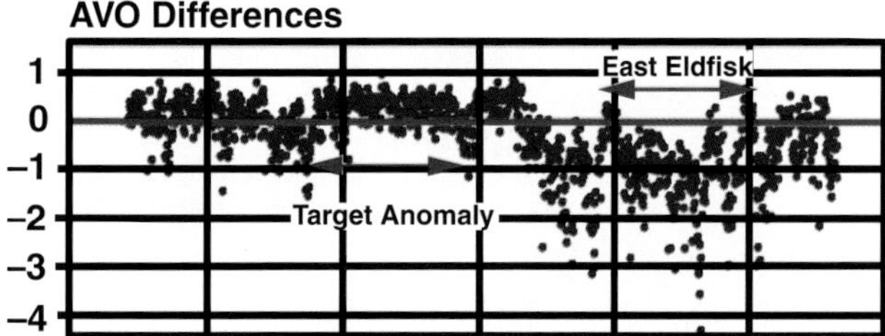

Fig. 16. AVO analysis of the Tor TA2 zone using the method of Chiburis (1993), with data extracted from the 3D seismic volume over the amplitude anomaly of Fig. 14. High porosity creates a positive AVO difference over the target anomaly, while the much lower porosity in East Eldfisk creates a negative difference. The presence of hydrocarbons should decrease the AVO difference of the anomaly, but comparison with down-dip areas to the northwest (left), assumed to be water wet, demonstrates that the effect of porosity obscures any fluid effect.

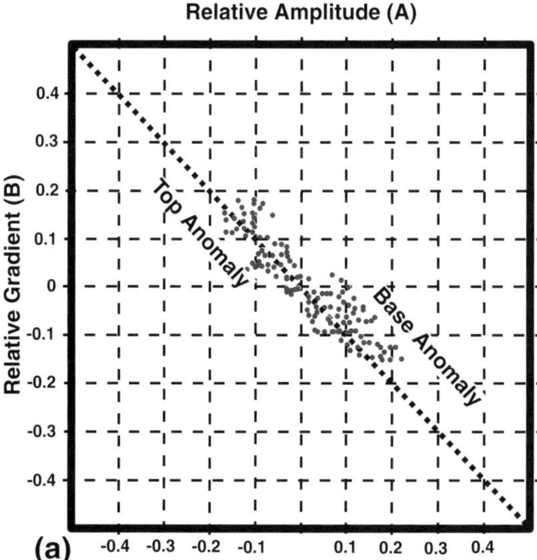

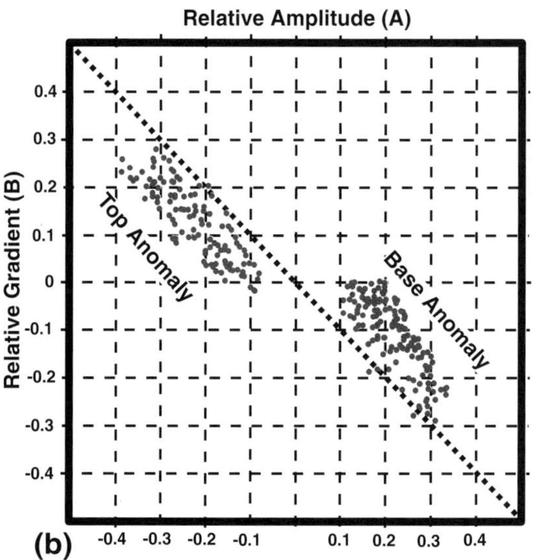

Fig. 17. Comparison of relative amplitude AVO cross plots from the low porosity TA2 zone down-dip of the 2/7-30 anomaly (**a**), and the high porosity anomaly itself (**b**). Clockwise rotation of data points is consistent with hydrocarbon fill (as in Fig. 10), and identical to the response over the Edda Field. However, the lack of calibration to a high porosity water filled chalk makes the observed effect untrustworthy. In fact the 2/7-30 anomaly was water filled, indicating that the observed AVO anomaly was an effect of porosity.

Comparison of AVO cross plots of relative normal incidence amplitude and relative amplitude gradient demonstrate a similar ambiguity (Fig. 17). In this case, cross plots constructed from data over the anomaly (17a) can be compared with a cross plot constructed down-dip in a low porosity, presumably water wet area (17b). The cross plotted anomaly data points have a slight rotation (counter-clockwise) compared to the non-porous zone data, identical with cross plots constructed from data over the Edda Field, and consistent with the modelled AVO response (Fig. 10). However, in the absence of calibration to a water wet zone of similar seismic amplitude (which in this case did not exist), it is impossible to determine if this is a true lithological signal or a processing artefact, and therefore untrustworthy as a direct indicator of hydrocarbons.

The problem of ambiguity is demonstrated by the results of the 2/7-30 exploration well, which did find high porosity in the Tor Formation, unfortunately water-wet. The prospect failed because of a lack of migration into the porous Tor zone, but did demonstrate significant porosity preservation at depth. Post-well comparison of the AVO data leads to the conclusion that, at least in the case of an Edda type oil, there was no seismically detectable difference in measured impedance or AVO response between the brine filled and hydrocarbon filled chalks.

Conclusions

Seismic methods have been beneficial in delineating high-porosity units within the chalk fields for well placement and reservoir characterization. With the advent of workstations these methods have become fast, robust, and routine. These same techniques can also detect and delineate potential stratigraphic traps within the chalk, mapping high-porosity reservoir and lower-porosity seal. Through an integration with structural interpretations of faults and fractures and the geological evolution of a trap through time, they can indicate which potential prospects may be on the end of a migration path, but cannot yet indicate with certainty the presence of hydrocarbons.

Resolving the difference between the seismic signatures of hydrocarbon saturation and porosity is the major challenge in managing the risk of chalk stratigraphic plays. These plays require adequate top, lateral, and base seals, all of which may be compromised by faults too minor to detect at seismic resolution. Rock physics modelling indicates that post-stack and AVO inversions are influenced by the presence of hydrocarbon, although this effect overlaps the changes caused by variations in porosity, making unambiguous detection unlikely. The detection of this signal is further complicated by rapid lateral changes in porosity and unit thickness and the general absence of discrete hydrocarbon–water contacts in the chalk. Only under the rare circumstances of very high porosity and gas saturation, such as observed in the Danish Tyra Field by Megson (1992), or constant porosity and thickness, will a very distinctive hydrocarbon signature exist. Unfortunately, this is a situation thus far rarely encountered in the present area of exploration interest, and with this limitation, the search for subtle traps within the chalk will remain high risk for the foreseeable future.

The author wishes to acknowledge Phillips Petroleum Norway and PL018 Coventurers, comprising Fina Exploration Norway u.a.s., Norsk Agip A/S, Elf Petroleum Norge AS, Norsk Hydro a.s., Den norsk stats oljeselskap a.s., TOTAL Norge A.S., Elf Rex Norge A/S and Saga a.s., for permission to publish this paper. The interpretations presented herein are those of the author, and do not necessarily reflect the opinions of Phillips Petroleum Norway and its coventurers. Special thanks to Hampson-Russell Software Services Ltd and John Coffin for use and permission to publish results from the Strata and AVO software packages.

References

Anderson, J. K. 1996. Limitations of seismic inversion for porosity and pore fluid: lessons from chalk reservoir characterization and exploration. *66th Annual International Meeting Expanded Abstracts, Society of Exploration Geophysicists*, **96**, 309–312.

Bramwell, N. P., Caillet, G., Meciani, L., Judge, N., Green, M., & Adam, P. 1997. Chalk exploration, the search for the subtle trap *In*: Fleet, A. J. & Boldy, S. A. R. (eds) *Petroleum Geology of Northwest Europe: Proceedings of the 5th Conference*. Geological Society, London, 911–938.

Brasher, J. E. 1995. Local tectonics and effects on sediment distribution within the Eldfisk Field. *In*: Hanslien, S. (ed.) *Petroleum Exploration and Exploitation in Norway*. NPF Special Publications, **4**, Elsevier, 67–84.

—— & Vagle, K. R. 1996. Influence of lithofacies and diagenesis on Norwegian North Sea chalk reservoirs. *American Association of Petroleum Geologists Bulletin*, **80**, 746–769.

Chiburis, E. F. 1993. AVO Applications in Saudi Arabia. *In*: Castagna, J. P. & Backus, M. M. (eds) *Offset-Dependent Reflectivity – Theory and Practice of AVO Analysis*. Society of Exploration Geophysicists, 211–229.

D'Angelo, R. M., Brandal, M. K. & Rorvik, K. O. 1997. Porosity detection and mapping in a basinal carbonate setting, offshore Norway. *In*: Palaz, I. & Marfurt, K. J. (eds) *Carbonate Seismology*. Geophysical Developments, No. **6**, Society of Exploration Geophysicists, 321–336.

D'Heur, M. 1986. The Norwegian chalk fields. *In*: Spencer, A. M. (ed.) *Habitat of Hydrocarbons on the Norwegian Continental shelf*. Graham & Trotman, London, 77–89.

Gassmann, F. 1951. Uber die elastizitat poroser medien. *Vierteljahrsschrift fur der Naturforschenden Gesellschaft in Zurich*, **96**, 1–23.

Hashin, Z. & Shtrikman, S. 1963. A variational approach to the theory of the elastic behaviour of multiphase materials. *Journal of Mechanics and Physics of Solids*, **11**, 127–140.

Honjo, S. 1975. Dissolution of suspended coccoliths in the deep-sea water column and sedimentation of coccolith ooze. *In*: Sliter, W. V., Be, A. W. H. & Berger, W. H. (eds) *Dissolution of Deep-Sea Carbonates*. Cushman Foundation for Foraminiferal Research Special Publications, **13**, 115–128.

Isaacson, E. S. & Neff, D. B. 1999. A, B AVO Cross plotting and its application in Greenland and the Barents Sea *In*: Fleet, A. J. & Boldy, S. A. R. (eds) *Petroleum Geology of Northwest Europe: Proceedings of the 5th Conference*. Geological Society, London, 1289–1298.

Landroe M., Buland, A. & D'Angelo, R. 1995. Target-oriented inversion of data from Valhall and Hod fields. *First Break*, **14**, 847–861.

Marion, D. & Nur, A. 1991. Pore-filling material and its effect on velocity in rocks. *Geophysics*, **56**, 225–230.

Mavko, G. & Mukerji, T. 1995. Seismic pore space compressibility and Gassman's relation. *Geophysics*, **60**, 1743–1749.

—— & Nur, A. 1996. Rock physics – the link between rock properties and seismic interpretation. *Geophysics for Lithology Prediction*, Norwegian Petroleum Society, **1A–D**.

Megson, J. B. 1992. The North Sea Chalk Play: examples from the Danish Central Graben. *In*: Hardman, R. F. P. (ed) *Exploration Britain: Geological Insights for the Next Decade*. Geological Society, London, Special Publications, **67**, 247–282.

Neff, D. B. 1996. 3D Seismic in field development. *Extended Abstracts, Contreso Venesolano de Geofisica*, 193–197.

Nur, A. 1992. Critical porosity and the Seismic Velocities in Rocks. *EOS, Transactions of the American Geophysical Union*, **73**(44), 76.

Ruess, A. 1929. Berechnung der Fleissgrenze von Mischkristallen auf Grund der Plastizitats bedingung fur Einkrisalle, *Zeitschrift für Angewandte Mathematics aus Mechanik*, **9**, 49–58.

Taylor, S. R. & Lapre, J. F. 1987. North Sea chalk diagenesis: its effect on reservoir location and properties. *In*: Brooks, J. & Glennie, K. (eds) *Petroleum Geology of North West Europe*. Graham & Trotman, London, 483–495.

Van den Bark, E. & Thomas, O. D. 1981. Ekofisk: first of the giant oil fields in Western Europe. *American Association of Petroleum Geologists Bulletin*, **65**, 2341–2363.

Voigt, W. 1928. *Lehrbuch der Kristallphysik*, B.G. Terebner, Leipzig.

Influence of syn-depositional faulting on thickness variations in chalk reservoirs – Valhall and Hod fields

C. L. FARMER and O. I. BARKVED

Amoco Norway Oil Company, Verven 4, 4003 Stavanger, Norway

Abstract: The depositional model for the Tor Formation at the Valhall and Hod fields has been revised to reflect the influence of syn-depositional faulting and reworking on reservoir thickness variations. New ideas for the structural and depositional model were based on detailed reservoir interval correlations in the Valhall–Hod area using biostratigraphy and graphic correlation techniques. Three-dimensional seismic data was also integrated and applied to develop the model. The Tor Formation was deposited during a tectonically active time in the Late Cretaceous and the Early Tertiary. During this time Valhall and Hod anticlines were forming as a result of inversion along the Lindesnes Ridge. Regionally the Tor and Hod formations thicken away from the Ridge. This indicates that the area was a structural high which is interpreted to be a large shoal. A major unconformity is present at the Hod/Tor Formation boundary. During continued uplift, crestal areas collapsed forming a series of horsts and grabens. The Tor Formation (Campanian and Maastrichtian, with documented Danian reworking) filled in the lows formed by these graben. Seismic data and well control demonstrate that the Tor Formation is thicker in graben and thinner over horsts. Removal of the Hod and Tor formations from local structural highs can be best explained by wave action and winnowing across a large shoal. The graben areas, sheltered from waves and protected from scouring and erosion, became local depositional centres for thicker slumped and reworked Tor Formation chalk. In the Tor Formation there is strong evidence for local erosion, formation of hard-grounds, grain size sorting, and down-slope movement through slumping and debris flows. Thickness and facies variations in the Tor Formation of Valhall and Hod fields can be linked to syn-depositional faults. Recognition of a fault controlled depositional model along with detailed mapping of thick reworked chalk in local graben led to the definition of additional reserves in the Valhall–Hod area.

The Valhall and Hod fields (Fig. 1) are located in the southern part of the Norwegian Central Graben just north of the Danish border in Blocks 2/8 and 2/11. Both fields are operated by Amoco Norway Oil Company. Valhall Field was discovered in 1975 and put on production in October 1982. Valhall has produced 280×10^6 BBL oil, 22×10^6 B NGL (natural gas liquids), and 282×10^9 SCF gas. Hod Field was put on production in November 1990, and has produced 33×10^6 BBL oil, 2×10^6 B NGL, and 30×10^9 SCF gas. Current booked reserves for both fields are about 650×10^6 BBL oil. New downflank discoveries, successful horizontal drilling and completion techniques, recent installation of a new wellhead platform, and possible water flood plans have increased potential reserves for the overall Valhall–Hod area to more than 1×10^9 BBL oil.

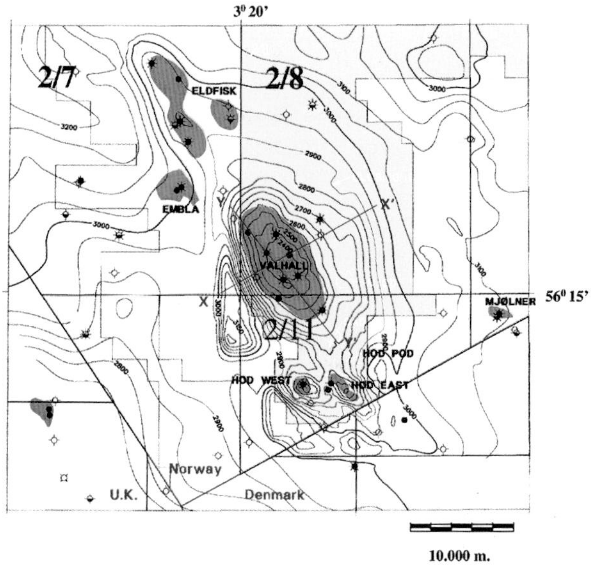

Fig. 1. Location map for Valhall–Hod area.

All production is from chalk. The primary reservoir is the Tor Formation with secondary production from the Hod Formation. The thickness of the Tor Formation reservoir varies rapidly, ranging from 0 to 80 m. The reservoir quality varies considerably with some of the best porosities (36% to 45%) and permeabilities (2 mD to 15 mD) developed in the thickest areas. The thin areas (0.5 m to 10 m) generally have a thin layer of high porosity chalk overlying a dense hard-ground. The lateral changes from thick to thin reservoir can occur abruptly – making for challenging horizontal drilling.

Stratigraphy and regional trends

A lithostratigraphic nomenclature chart for the Upper Cretaceous and Paleocene in the Valhall/Hod area has been included as Fig. 2. The chart shows the extent of the Tor and Hod formations and the extent of unconformities. The reservoir zonation is also shown on the chart. The West Hod Field exhibits the deepest erosion with Paleocene resting unconformably on Hod-4. Over the crest of the Valhall Field the Tor Formation is relatively thin and thickens down-flank into the Hod Saddle/Hod Pod area. Campanian age Tor Formation is present at East Hod and Hod Saddle, but is absent in the crestal area of the Valhall Field. The Ekofisk Formation is also absent over the crest of Valhall. The reservoir zonation scheme depicted on the chart has been based on biostratigraphy.

FARMER, C. L. & BARKVED, O. I. 1999. Influence of syn-depositional faulting on thickness variations in chalk reservoirs – Valhall and Hod fields. *In*: FLEET, A. J. & BOLDY, S. A. R. (eds) *Petroleum Geology of Northwest Europe: Proceedings of the 5th Conference*, 949–957. © Petroleum Geology '86 Ltd. Published by the Geological Society, London.

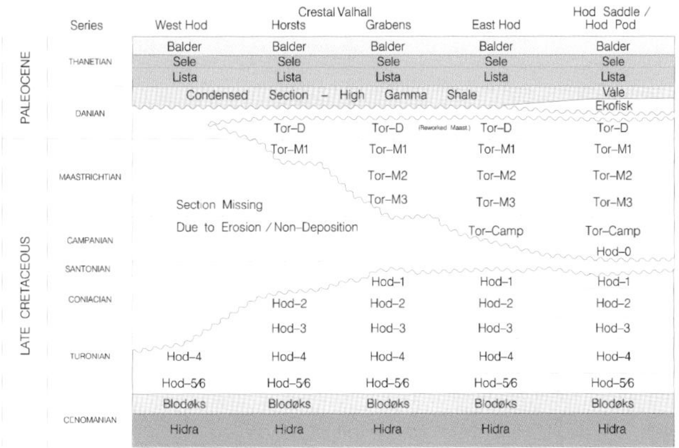

Fig. 2. Late Cretaceous and Paleocene Nomenclature for Valhall–Hod area.

The graphic correlation technique (Mann & Lane 1995) was used for detailed biostratigraphic analysis of the chalk and overlying shales. Application of graphic correlation makes accurate log correlations possible using high resolution sequence stratigraphy methodology. A local composite standard was built for the Valhall area and calibrated to Amoco's worldwide composite standard (Bergen *et al.* 1995). Wells with good core through the chalk and overlying Paleocene section were reanalysed and used as the foundation for the local standard.

Using graphic correlation and sequence stratigraphic techniques two major questions have been addressed that are relevant to understanding the distribution of the Tor Formation sequence in the Valhall–Hod area: (1) what is the age and nature of the contact between the Tor and Hod Formations? and (2) what is the age and nature of the contact between the top of the Tor Formation and overlying shales? These contacts are sequence boundaries that can be tied to seismic data and mapped regionally.

The contact between the Tor Formation and the underlying Hod Formation is a major unconformity . In the crestal area of the Valhall Field, the Maastrichtian Tor Formation rests directly on Coniacian Hod-2 (Leonard & Munns 1987). On the highest structure at the West Hod Anticline, late Coniacian (Hod-1), Santonian, Campanian, and Maastrichtian sediments are missing as a result of erosion or non-deposition at the unconformity surface. In down-flank areas that were structurally lower (East Hod/Hod Saddle), Coniacian Hod-1 is present beneath the unconformity and Campanian age Tor Formation onlaps the unconformity surface. Based on this evidence, the Tor/Hod Unconformity must have first formed in the Santonian and extended through the Maastrichtian over the highest structures. The regional Hod Formation isopach (Fig. 3) shows thinning of the total Hod Formation (Turonian–Coniacian) onto the broad uplifted area along the Lindesnes Ridge. Presently, the Valhall Field is at the highest structural position along the Lindesnes Ridge in both the strike and dip directions (Fig. 1). The Hod Formation isopach map (Fig. 3) indicates that the West Hod, Valhall and East Hod fields were also structural highs on the ridge during deposition of the Hod Formation.

The boundary between the chalk and overlying shales in the crestal Valhall area is an unconformity overlain by a condensed section (Fig. 2). A condensed section is defined here as a thin marine stratigraphic interval characterized by very slow deposition rates. No sea level 'high stand' is required in this definition as compared to previous definitions (Vail *et al.* 1988). In all Valhall wells this high gamma ray shale is present just above the chalk. Detailed biostratigraphic analysis of the interval gives an Early to Late Danian age. The 1–5 m shale, which is highly correlatable across the entire structure, represents the complete condensed equivalent of the Vale Formation and some of the Ekofisk Formation. In the saddle area between Valhall and Hod, this condensed section expands and contains normal (but thin) Vale Formation and Ekofisk Formation. The Ekofisk and Vale formations expand dramatically to the north in the Ekofisk Field area – which was structurally lower than Valhall Anticline during deposition.

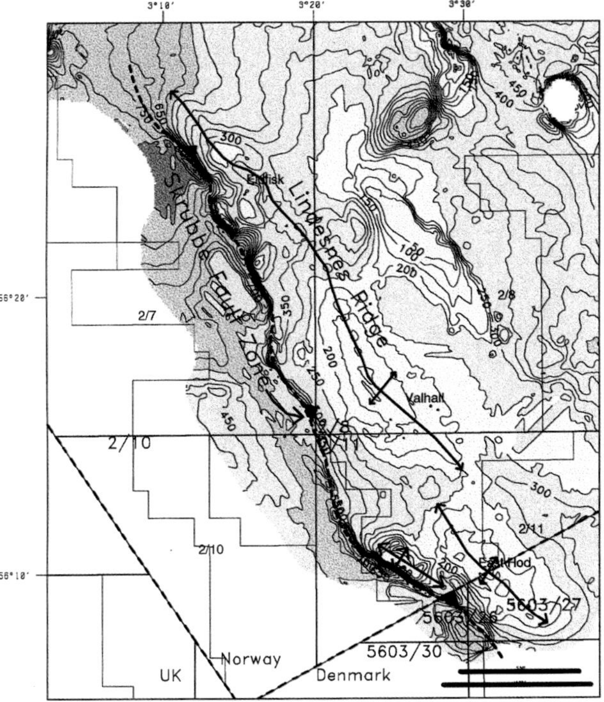

Fig. 3. Regional Hod isopach.

The Tor Formation has been divided into five reservoir zones based on detailed biostratigraphy (Fig. 2): Tor-D, Tor-M1, Tor-M2, Tor-M3, and Tor-Camp. The Tor Formation is bounded by unconformities at the top and base. The newly identified Tor-D occurs just below the condensed high gamma shale present in the Valhall area. It consists of a thin (0.5–14 m) early Danian chalk that is composed of 98–99% reworked Maastrichtian microfossils. The reworked interval commonly exhibits grain size sorting of microfossils and *Inoceramus* fragments and is interpreted to be a winnowed lag deposit beneath an unconformity surface. The Danian reworked interval (Tor-D) has reservoir properties comparable to the Maastrichtian Tor Formation and is therefore included as part of the Tor Formation sequence for mapping and reservoir modeling purposes. This is the rationale behind not assigning this sequence to the Ekofisk Formation, which strictly speaking would be more appropriate, according to the official nomenclature. A very thin dense streak is sometimes present beneath the reworked interval. The dense streak probably represents a thin hardground developed at a minor unconformity surface. A Danian age for part of the uppermost chalk at Valhall was originally suggested by Moe & Riis (1995), and has been confirmed by detailed biostratigraphic analysis.

The Maastrichtian Tor Formation reservoir zones (Tor-M1, Tor-M2 and Tor-M3) are present over the crest of Valhall Anticline as well as on the flanks in the East Hod and Hod Saddle areas. The Tor-M2 and Tor-M3 zones are confined to the deepest crestal grabens and down-flank areas. The uppermost Tor-M1 zone is more extensive and is present over many of the horsts. The West Hod Anticline was higher than the Valhall during the Maastrichtian, with non-deposition or erosion over the crest (Fig. 2). At Valhall Field, a 1 to 3 m thick basal Maastrichtian dense zone has been identified in core and on logs at the Tor/Hod Unconformity. This non-productive interval is interpreted as a hardground localized at the Tor/Hod Unconformity surface. A thin (5–10 cm) grey–green shale has also been observed in several locations on the Tor/Hod Unconformity surface. All the Tor reservoir zones are productive excluding the hardgrounds and dense zones.

On the flanks of Valhall Field, at East Hod Field, and in the Hod Saddle area, an older Campanian age zone is present beneath the Maastrichtian age Tor Formation and above the Tor/Hod Unconformity. This Campanian age chalk is thickest at East Hod Field, and is absent in the crestal area of Valhall Field. The Campanian section appears to onlap the Tor/Hod Unconformity (Fig. 2) and is present only in areas that were structurally low during deposition. Campanian age chalk containing reworked Turonian and Coniacian (Hod age) microfossils has also been identified in downflank areas – East Hod and Hod Pod. This chalk occurs beneath the Tor Formation and rests directly on the Tor/Hod Unconformity. The zone has been informally referred to as Hod-0 by Amoco (Fig. 2) because it is composed predominately of Hod Formation sediments that have been slumped and reworked in the Campanian. The Campanian Hod-0 only occurs in structurally low areas where a more complete stratigraphic section was deposited and preserved. The Campanian age chalk above the Hod Formation and below the Tor Formation is now being informally referred to as 'Magne Formation' rather than Hod-0.

The regional Tor Formation isopach map (Fig. 4) shows thinning of the total Tor Formation across the Lindesnes Ridge and Valhall-Hod anticlines indicating that the area was a broad structural and bathymmetric high (probably with shoaling) throughout Maastrichtian and Danian time. The shoaling or shallowing of the water during Tor Formation deposition to within the effective wave base (20–70 m) is also suggested by relative proportions of microfossil assemblages (Sikora *et al.* 1996). Tectonic influence on bathymetry with an unconformity in Santonian–Campanian and shoaling in the Maastrichtian is also recognized in the Eldfisk area (Brasher 1995).

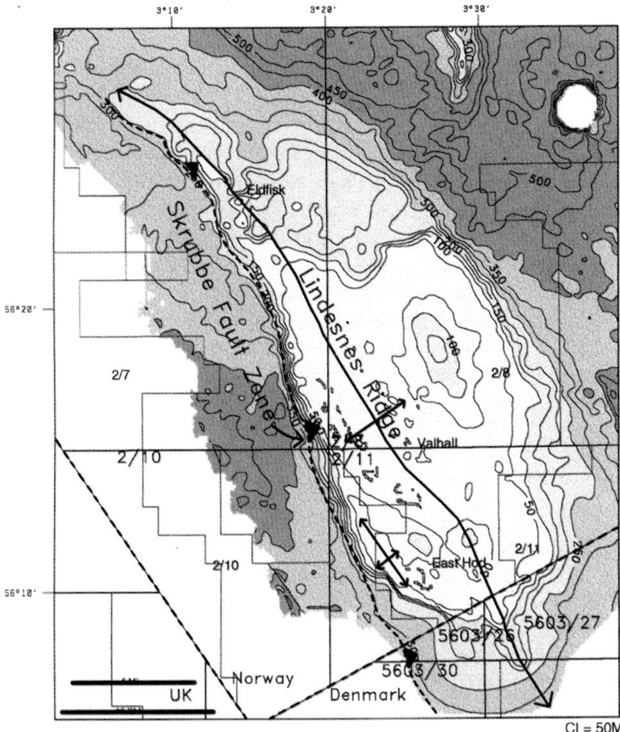

Fig. 4. Regional Tor isopach.

There probably were several mechanisms that contributed to the regional thinning of both the Hod and Tor formations across the broad positive shoal formed by uplift of the Lindesnes Ridge. The most obvious reason is that some chalk intervals have been eroded in the crestal area by wave action (Hod-1). Other intervals are present in their entirety, but are dramatically thinner over the broad shallow area. Onlapping relationships can also be seen in some intervals (Campanian Tor Formation) which indicates non-deposition on the structural highs. Thickening in the structural lows also resulted from down-slope movement of poorly consolidated chalk through slumping, sliding and sediment gravity flows (Andersen 1995). Thinning over bathymetric highs (and thickening in lows) during chalk deposition is well documented and demonstrates that structural inversion of the Lindesnes Ridge was ongoing from the Late Cretaceous into the Paleocene (Turonian through Danian).

Structural evolution

The structural evolution of the Valhall and Hod anticlines is directly linked to inversion of the Lindesnes Ridge along the Skrubbe Fault Zone (Wride 1995; Farmer & Humphreys 1996). Two major events led to the formation of the inversion structure:

(1) Regional oblique extension (transtension) occurred in the Late Jurassic and Early Cretaceous. A deep tilted half graben formed on the east side of the Skrubbe Fault Zone. The graben filled with very thick (800–1200 m) Upper Jurassic and Lower Cretaceous shales, siltstones, and marls. The thick Lower Cretaceous package beneath Valhall Anticline is illustrated on dip cross-section X–X′ (Fig. 5). The location for the structural cross-sections is shown on the Valhall structural map (Fig. 1).

(2) Regional oblique right lateral compression (or transpression) began in the Turonian and continued into the Miocene. The older graben was inverted and formed the Lindesnes Ridge along the east side of the Skrubbe Fault zone. The highest part of the ridge, at Valhall Field, generally corresponds to the area of thickest Lower Cretaceous graben fill (Fig. 5). In fact, the present-day shape and extent of the entire Lindesnes Ridge corresponds directly to the distribution and extent of the underlying Lower Cretaceous and Upper Jurassic thick sediment wedge. There is no direct evidence for involvement of halokinesis at Valhall Field. Local halokinesis at Eldfisk Field (Brasher 1995) may have been triggered by the compressional event that caused inversion along the entire Lindesnes Ridge.

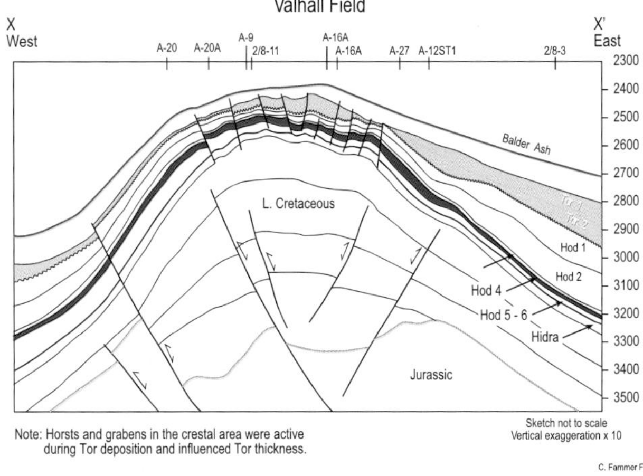

Fig. 5. Geological cross-section in dip direction X–X′. See Fig. 1 for location.

The Hod and Tor formations were being deposited over a growing anticline, and chalk thickness variations tell the story of that growth. As the anticline grew, stages of development can be identified. At first there was no evidence for bathymetric expression of the anticline as indicated by the consistent thickness and distribution of the Hidra and Blodøks formations. Broad arching began in the Early Turonian and extended through the end of the Turonian as evidenced by slight thinning of the lower Hod Formation (Hod-5/6, Hod-4, and Hod-3) across the structure. The rate of uplift increased in the Coniacian resulting in dramatic thinning of the Hod-2 over the structure. In the Santonian water became so shallow on the crest of the anticline that wave action eroded the Hod-1, and a major unconformity developed. Off the crest of the structure less erosion occurred. As a result, a thicker section is present in down-flank areas.

Pulses of uplift occurred from the Campanian through the Maastrichtian causing continued erosion over the highest parts of the Lindesnes Ridge (West Hod Anticline). The continued uplift resulted in crestal collapse of the Valhall and East Hod anticlines. At Valhall Field, horsts and graben formed in the Campanian as a result of extension across the top of the growing structure. Many of the faults that bound the horsts and graben are not deep seated and formed only in the upper part of the fold (Fig. 5). Other faults, particularly on the west side of Valhall Field, can be traced to deeper fault zones that form the boundaries of the inversion structure. In the Maastrichtian, chalk sediments of the Tor Formation filled the crestal graben. Only the deepest graben contain older Tor Formation zones (Tor-M3 and Tor-M2) and appear to have filled first. The uppermost Tor-D and Tor-M1 zones were deposited over the shallower horsts also, where hardgrounds also developed.

By the end of the Maastrichtian, most of the crestal graben were filled, and Valhall anticline remained structurally high. Winnowing, wave action and erosion caused reworking of the Maastrichtian chalk in the crestal area during the early Danian. Down the flank of the structure, pelagic and turbiditic Danian Ekofisk Chalk was deposited and covered by the overlying Vale Siltstone. A thin condensed section (high gamma shale) equivalent to the Ekofisk and Våle formations blankets the crest of the structure. Younger Thanetian sediments of the Lista, Sele and Balder formations also blanket the anticline and thicken regionally off the flank. Regional thinning of the Paleocene, Eocene, Oligocene, and Miocene intervals across the Lindesnes Ridge indicate that a structural high was present (possibly with active growth) until the early Miocene. There is also evidence (on seismic) for several later pulses of uplift (Paleocene–Miocene) when some of the crestal graben faults were reactivated with reverse throw.

Depositional model

Fallout of pelagic skeletal debris in a submarine setting forming chalk ooze can be likened to ice crystals falling through the atmosphere and forming snow. With chalk sedimentation, as with snow, the final result is very seldom a smooth, even, featureless blanket. The underlying bathymetry or topography strongly influences the thickness and distribution of chalk or snow. Processes such as storm-waves or current action (for chalk) and wind (for snow) redistribute the sediment unevenly across a pre-existing terrane.

To carry this analogy further, the broad Valhall submarine ridge could be likened to a wide mountain. Wind sweeping across the mountain would remove snow from the highest exposed areas where icy rocky patches would form. Blowing snow would then be redeposited in local, sheltered, low areas as thick drifts. Similarly, storm waves and currents sweeping over the crest of Valhall would winnow and remove chalk from high horsts, producing hardgrounds. Resuspended chalk particles would then be redeposited in local low graben areas as thick porous chalk (main Tor Formation reservoir at Valhall). In the sheltered deep valleys, snow accumulation would be much thicker and more continuous, similar to chalk deposited in the deep bathymetric lows surrounding Valhall. The deep valleys would also be the site of thick snow accumulating from avalanches, just as the bathymetric lows are the site of thick stacked gravity flows in the chalk. Table 1 summarizes the analogy between chalk and snow.

Table 1. Properties of chalk compared to snow

	Chalk	Snow
Composition	$CaCO_3$	H_2O
Grain origin	Biogenic, precipitated from seawater	Grown in atmosphere
Depositional processes	Pelagic rain resuspension by waves and currents gravity flows (slides, slumps, debris flows, turbidity currents)	Snowfall redistribution by wind into drifts local slumps and slides, avalanches
Erosion	Currents and waves	Wind
Hiatuses	Winnowed surfaces, hardgrounds from early cementation at the sediment–water interface	Deflation surfaces, hard layers ('skare') from freeze/thaw cycles on the upper surface of snow
Initial porosity	70–80%	90%
Burial processes (diagenesis)	Compaction, recrystallization, cementation	Compaction, recrystallization, cementation
Burial realms	Ooze, chalk, limestone	Fresh snow, granular snow, firm, ice

Applying this model to chalk illustrates the importance of continuity in the depositional process. In areas steadily receiving sediments (and where subsidence accommodates for the accumulating sediments) we expect homogeneous packages of porous chalk to be deposited. This is what we observe in local graben on the crestal of Valhall. On structural highs near storm wave base or on current swept areas sediments are resuspended. Net sediment accumulation is low, and 'dense zones' or hard grounds form as a result of early cementation at the seabed. Thin packages of porous chalk will be separated by layers of non-porous chalk, and the total package is highly heterogeneous. These features can be observed in chalk core from Valhall and Hod fields. On structural highs, sediment packages are thinner, hardground development is more pronounced and gaps in depositional record are more extensive than in deeper parts of the basin.

Examples of fault control on Tor Formation thickness variations

The Tor Formation is a graben fill sequence composed mostly of Maastrichtian and Danian age chalk. The Tor Formation is thickest in local graben and thinner across adjacent horsts. The faults that control Tor Formation thickness variations first formed in the Early Campanian (Fig. 6) as a result of crestal collapse of anticlines along the Lindesnes Ridge during a pulse of uplift. The top and base of the Tor Formation are unconformable. In the Valhall–Hod area the Tor Formation is overlain by a high gamma shale that represents a Danian condensed section stratigraphically equivalent to the Vale

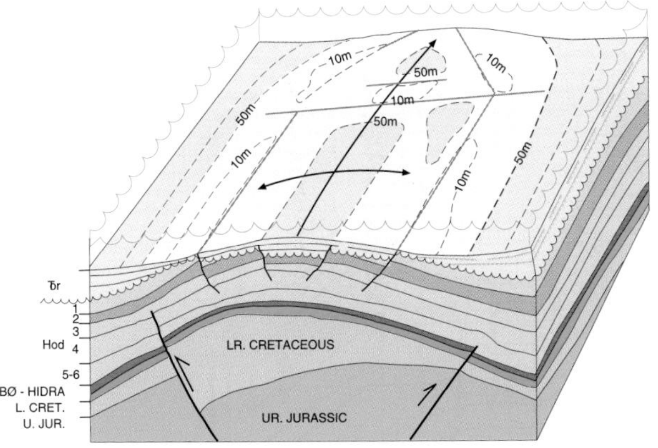

Fig. 6. Schematic illustrating the fault control and the presence of a crestal collapse which was first formed in the Early Campanian.

Formation. Examples of fault control on thickness variations can be seen on the crest of Valhall Field, at East Hod Field, and in the Mjød area.

Two isopach maps have been constructed to help demonstrate the crestal collapse of Valhall anticline and to explain the Tor Formation thickness variations in the crestal area. The first map (Fig. 7) is an isopach of the Upper Coniacian Hod-1. This isopach reflects the shape of the structure prior to the crestal collapse. At the top of West Hod Anticline the entire upper Hod Formation was removed (Hod-1 through Hod-3) by an unconformity that extends from the Santonian through the Maastrichtian. At Valhall Field the Hod-1 was removed from the highest part of the structure by erosion on the Tor/Hod unconformity. The Hod-1 thickens down the flank of the structure away from the eroded area. Across East Hod Anticline the Hod-1 is thinner but it was never eroded.

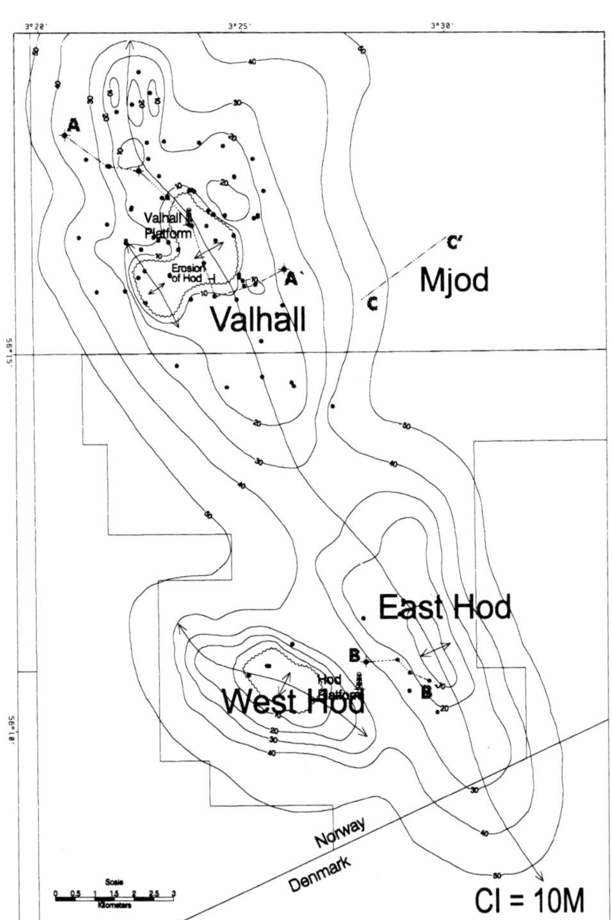

Fig. 7. Isopach of the Upper Coniacian Hod 1.

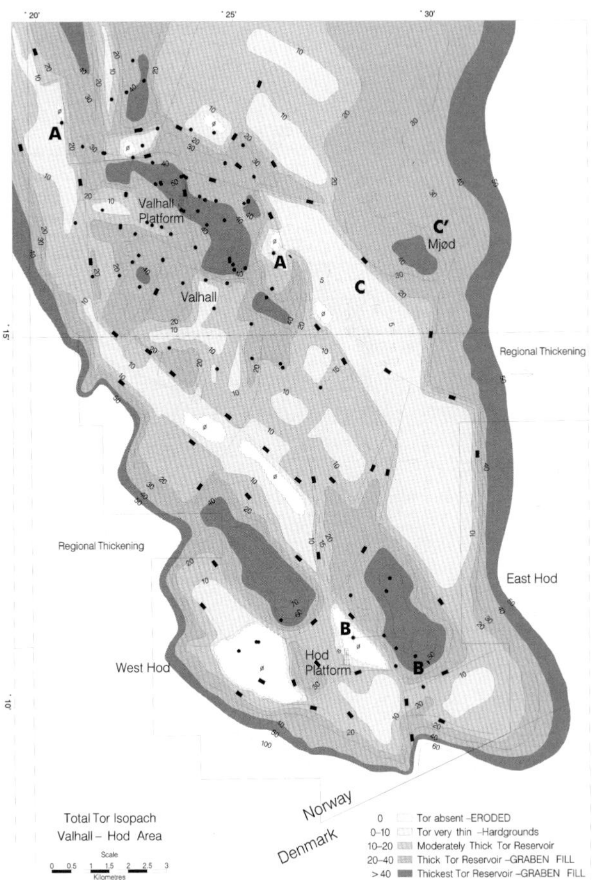

Fig. 8. Tor Isopach reflecting the shape of the fault bounded graben and horsts that controlled deposition.

The second map (Fig. 8) is a total Tor Formation isopach that shows the shape of the fault bounded grabens and horsts that formed as a result of crestal collapse of the structure in the Campanian and Maastrichtian. The Tor Formation Isopach includes all Tor Formation reservoir zones and is based on well control (120+ wells) and seismic mapping from a 3D seismic survey. The faults shown were based on the seismic mapping and horizontal well cuts. A number of smaller faults have been mapped, and can be inferred from linear trends in the contours. An effort has been made to simplify the map by including only major faults which control Tor Formation thickness changes.

Three example areas will be discussed to illustrate syndepositional fault control on the distribution of the Tor Formation reservoir: Crestal Valhall (Section A–A′), East Hod (section B–B′), and Mjød (Section C–C′). The location of these areas and lines of section are shown on the Hod-1 Isopach (Fig.7) and Tor Formation Isopach (Fig. 8).

Crestal Valhall

The first line of section A–A′ cuts across the crestal area of Valhall Field from the northwest side of the structure to the southeast side. A log cross-section hung on −2400 m (Fig. 9) shows the relative present-day structural position of the wells. To correct for deviation and to display true thickness the log curves have been plotted in true vertical depth. The broad structure can be seen with the fairly even thickness of Hidra Formation, Blodøks Formation, and the slight thinning of the

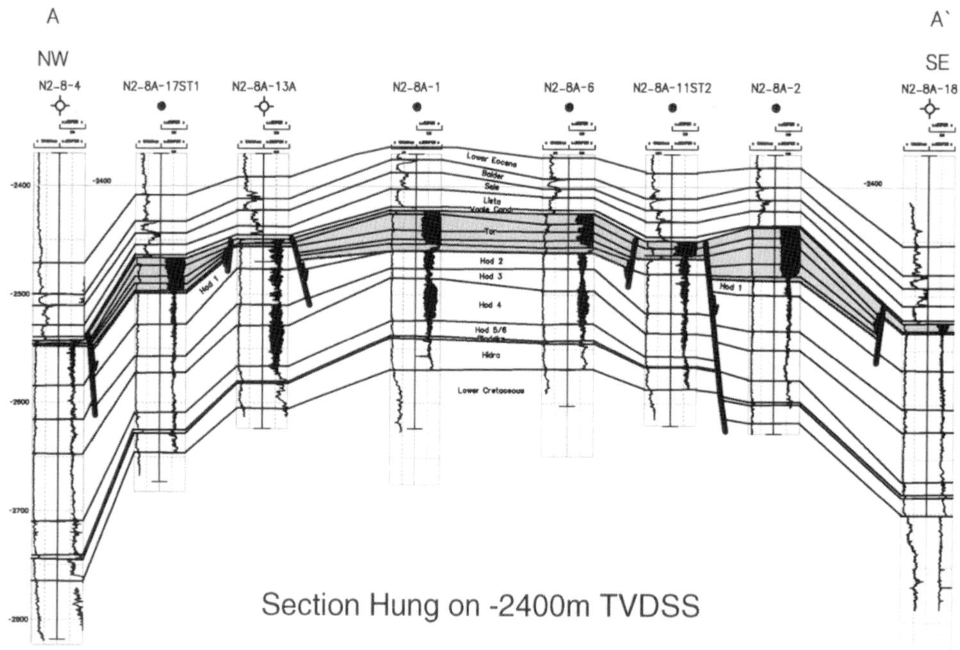

Fig. 9. Log cross-section A–A′ across the crestal Valhall area.

Hod Formation (Hod-5/6, Hod-4, and Hod-3). The Hod-2 exhibits even more thinning, and the Hod-1 is removed in the crestal area by the Tor/Hod Unconformity.

A stratigraphic cross-section flattened on the top of the Hod Formation has been constructed through the same line of section (Fig. 10). This cross-section graphically illustrates the thinning of the Hod Formation across the anticline and erosion of the Hod-1 in the crestal area. Hod Formation thickness variations are gradual and do not (in most cases) appear to have been influenced by faulting.

The next stratigraphic section along line A–A′ is flattened on the Danian condensed section (Vale equivalent) just above

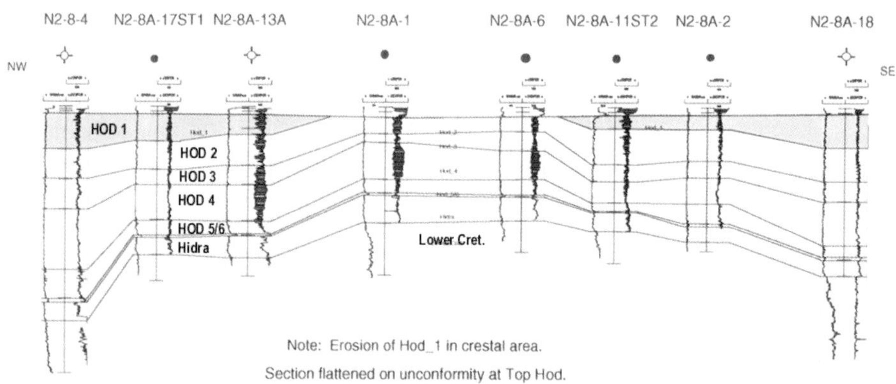

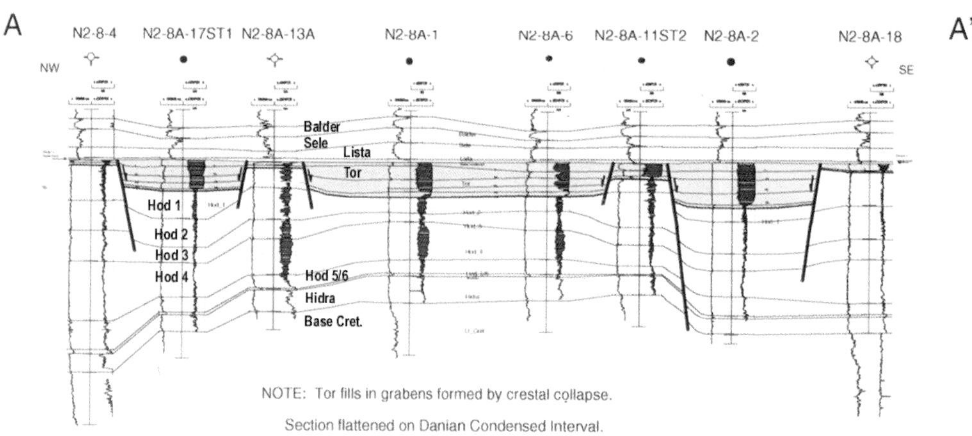

Fig. 10. Flattened log cross-section A–A′ across the crestal Valhall area.

the Tor Formation (Fig. 10). This cross-section illustrates the abrupt thickness variations in the Tor Formation which occur due to filling of the fault bounded graben.

The local graben were filled by slumping and debris flows. Cores from the Tor Formation in the Valhall/Hod area commonly exhibit small-scale syn-depositional slump folding and angular rip up clasts of partially lithified chalk. This evidence adds support for a slump/debris flow model. A dipmeter study of several wells in the crestal graben also indicated slump directions – down from local horsts and into local graben. Chalk particles were also resuspended and winnowed by wave action over high horsts and redeposited in graben. Local unconformities and hardgrounds (dense zones) developed on the horsts.

On high areas where the Tor Formation is thinnest (Wells 2/8-4, 2/8A-13A, and 2/8A-18) the thin layer of Danian age reworked Tor (Tor-D) rests directly on a Maastrichtian hardground just above the Tor/Hod Unconformity. Wells located in these thin areas are either 'dry holes' or have very low flow rates from the Tor Formation. In the deeper parts of the graben all three Maastrichtian zones (Tor-M1, Tor-M2, and Tor-M3) are present (wells 2/8A-17ST1, 2/8A-1, 2/8A-6, and 2/8A-2). The most productive wells, located in these thick areas, can produce 5000–18000 BOPD. Across an intermediate horst within the main crestal graben (Wells 2/8A-11ST) Tor-D and Tor-M1 are present but Tor-M2 and Tor-M3 are missing. The 2/8A-11ST2 had an initial rate of 4019 BOPD. It is evident that placement with respect to local horsts, graben, and fault zones is an important factor in determining initial flow rates and long term success for production wells. Problems with seismic imaging in the gas cloud make the fault controlled depositional model even more important in predicting reservoir distribution.

East Hod

Cross-section B–B′ (Fig. 11) is located south of Valhall in the East Hod area. The section extends from west to east across East Hod Field. The stratigraphic section was first flattened on the Top Hod Formation (Tor/Hod Unconformity) to illustrate

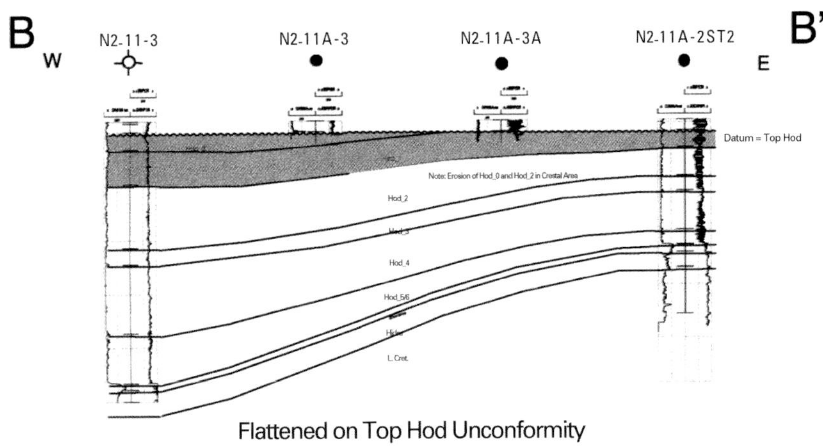

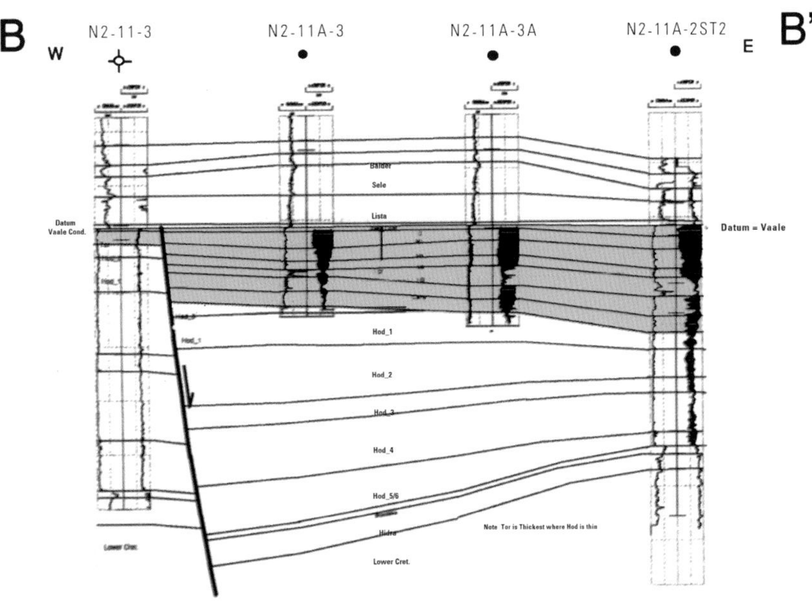

Fig. 11. Log cross-section B–B′ across the East Hod Field. See Fig. 8 for location.

thinning and erosion of uppermost Hod Formation across the crest of the anticline. The total Hod Formation is very thin (123 m) in Well 2/11A-2ST2; but 233 m in Well 2/11-3. This indicates that the East Hod Field was a structural high during Hod deposition (Fig. 7) with erosion in the Santonian followed by crestal collapse in the early Campanian and Maastrichtian.

When the crestal part of the anticline collapsed, a graben formed. The Tor Formation filled that graben. The second cross-section (Fig. 11) is flattened on the Danian condensed interval just above the Tor Formation to illustrate the thickening of the Tor Formation across the East Hod Fault. Well 2/11-3, located west of the fault, is a dry hole with very thin Tor Formation. Across the fault to the east, the entire Tor Formation is present and thick (Tor-D,Tor-M1, M2, M3). In addition, a Campanian reservoir zone is present. The abrupt thickness change in the Tor Formation across the East Hod Fault indicates that the fault was active and controlled sediment thickness in the Campanian and Maastrichtian.

The thickest productive Tor Formation in the entire area is present in Well 2/11A-2ST2 (83 m thick) which had an initial flow rate of 29 608 BOPD. Seismic data also show the thickening across the East Hod Fault which corresponds to thickening on the log cross-section B–B′. Continued inversion in the late Paleocene is indicated by the apparent reversal of throw on the normal fault that established the graben. For a discussion of seismic mapping in the East Hod area see Pearse & Ozdemir (1994).

Mjød

The Mjød area, located on the east of the Valhall Anticline, is outside of the area of crestal collapse. Distinct thickening of the Tor Formation is observed within an inverted graben on the eastern flank of the present-day Valhall structure. The thickening, fault locations, and structural configuration are illustrated by structural cross-section C–C′ (Fig. 12). The details of the cross-section, including faults and thickness changes, are based on 3D seismic data. The internal geometry observed in the thick lens of Tor Formation indicates that slumping may have played an important role in filling of the graben. A chalk reservoir with 20 m of slumped Maastrichtian Tor Formation overlain by 10–12 m of Danian reworked Tor Formation is predicted. Porosities are expected to range from 35–40%.

The high horst area east of the Mjød prospect (Fig. 12) was penetrated in Well 2/8A-18. The Tor Formation in this well is very thin but pay is present. No definite oil–water contact has been defined for the Valhall Field. The Mjød prospect is down-dip from Valhall Field and structurally up-dip from the deepest known production. In the Valhall–Hod area this production occurs at −2800 m in the saddle between the Valhall and East Hod fields. (Fig. 1). The −2900 m contour (shown on Fig. 13) is the overall closing contour for the Valhall–Hod structural complex. A discovery at Mjød would open up possibilities for future flank wells.

Valhall porosity–depth cube

The relationship between faulting and thickness variations in the Tor Formation reservoir is illustrated dramatically on the Valhall porosity–depth cube display (Fig. 13) – a porosity sub-volume from the northern Valhall area. The cube has been cut at the top Tor Formation level. The representative coherency slices were derived at Top Tor Formation to reflect seismic lineameant indicating fault cuts. The 'porosity–depth–volume' is based on inverting the seismic amplitude for acoustic impedance from a sub-volume in time (across 2200 ms to 3800 ms). The impedance volume is then converted to a velocity and porosity representation using linear relations derived from well data.

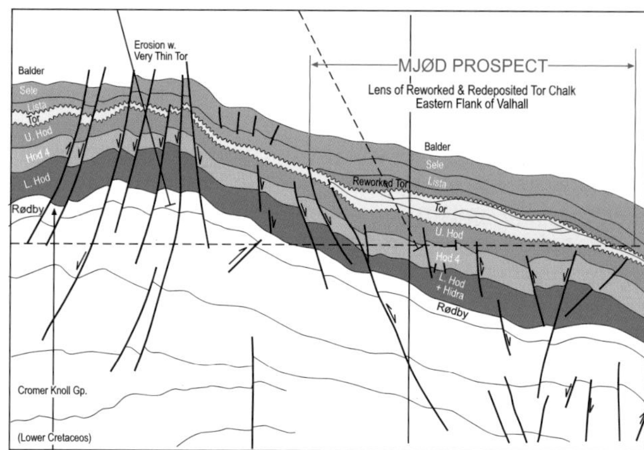

Fig. 12. Structural cross-section C–C′, down-dip to the east of Valhall, across the Mjoed prospect. See Fig. 8 for location.

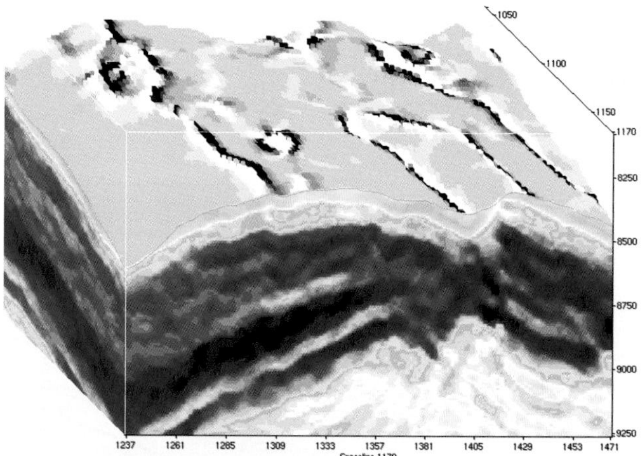

Fig. 13. Multirendering of seismic derived attributes cube. The vertical sections are extracted from a seismic derived porosity cube. This cube has been cut at Top Reservoir level and the horizontal face has been replaced by the a coherency map extracted from the coherency volume at Top Reservoir level. The black colours indicate low coherence values, which could reflect faults. The yellow to dark blue colours represent porosity, with the dark blue indicating tight chalk and the yellow reflecting the porous reservoir zones.

Since interval velocity is known in each cell, the thickness of each cell can be estimated, and the representative inferred seismic porosity can be mapped in a cube which is sampled as a function of relative depth. The cube has been converted from relative depth to 'true-depth' using a reference surface derived from velocity surveys mapped as a smooth surface at top chalk level. Next, the corrected volume was converted back to a representation suitable for applying Amoco's coherency algorithm. Using this technique a snapshot can be extracted at any structural level to illustrate the degree of coherence. In this case low coherence lineaments are interpreted to represent faults. Unlike instantaneous attributes (i.e. dip/azimuth maps), the coherency surface is less influenced by subjective interpolation.

Conclusions

The depositional model for the Tor Formation at the Valhall and Hod fields has been revised to reflect the influence of syn-depositional faulting on thickness variations. Detailed biostratigraphic analysis, graphic correlation techniques, analysis of well log data, concepts of sequence stratigraphy, and seismic mapping were used to develop the model. Valhall and East

Hod anticlines formed as a result of inversion along the Lindesnes Ridge. The growth history of the Valhall anticline can be interpreted based on thickness variations of chalk sediments that were deposited as the anticline grew. The faults that control Tor Formation thickness changes first formed in the Early Campanian as a result of crestal collapse along the Lindesnes Ridge during a pulse of uplift. The Tor Formation consists of Maastrichtian and Danian age chalk. The Tor Formation is thickest in local graben and thinner across adjacent horsts. The top and base of the Tor Formation are unconformable. In the Valhall–Hod area the Tor Formation is overlain by a high gamma shale that represents a Danian condensed section. Examples of fault control on thickness variations can be seen on the crest of Valhall Field, at East Hod Field, and in the Mjød area. The fault controlled model for reservoir distribution is being used to explore on the flanks of the Valhall structure, to plan the location of production wells, and to design a water flood plan for the field.

We would like to acknowledge colleagues from the Amoco Norway Chalk Team who have provided continuous input, helpful suggestions, and a sounding board for discussion of ideas. We would like to thank colleagues of the Valhall Partner group (Amerada Hess, Elf, and Enterprise) for their continued suggestions. In addition, we would like to commend colleagues at the NPD for their valuable insight and sound technical advice.

References

Andersen, M. A. 1995. Petroleum research in North Sea Chalk. *Joint Chalk Research Monograph Phase*, **IV**, pp. 13–16.

Bergen, J. A. *et al.* 1995. High resolution biostratigraphy of chalk sequences. *Abstract from Norwegian Petroleum Society Conference on Predictive High Resolution Sequence Stratigraphy*, Stavanger, Norway.

Brasher, J. E. 1995. Local tectonics and effects on sediment distribution within the Eldfisk Field. *NPF Special Publications*, **4**, 67–84.

Farmer, C. L. & Humphreys, R. J. 1996. Structural evolution of Valhall anticline – a 3D geometric modelling approach. *Extended abstract from Norwegian Petroleum Directorate Chalk Geoscience Workshop*, 2–3 December, Stavanger, Norway.

Leonard, R. C. & Munns, J. W. 1987. Valhall Field. *In*: *Geology of Norwegian Oil and Gas Fields*, Graham & Trotman, 153–163.

Mann, K. O. & Lane, R. 1995. Graphic Correlation, *SEPM Special Publications*, **53**.

Moe, Å. & Riis, F. 1995. A Re-evaluation of the main Chalk Reservoir of the Valhall Field. Southern North Sea. *Abstract from Norwegian Petroleum Society Conference on Predictive High Resolution Sequence Stratigraphy*. Stavanger, Norway.

Pearse, C. H. J. & Ozdemir, H. 1994. The Hod Field: chalk reservoir delineation from 3D seismic data using amplitude mapping and seismic inversion. *Norwegian Petroleum Society Geophysical Seminar*, 7–9 March, Kristiansand, Norway.

Sikora, P. J., Bergen, J. A, Stein, J. A. & Farmer, C. L. 1996. Chronostratigraphy and depositional environments of the Turonian to Danian Chalks – Valhall and Hod Fields. *Extended abstract from Norwegian Petroleum Directorate Chalk Geoscience Workshop*, 2–3 December, Stavanger, Norway.

Vail, P. R. *et al.* 1988. Sea level changes: an integrated approach. *SEPM Special Publications*, **42**, 110 and 186.

Wride, V. C. 1995. Structural features and structural styles from the five countries area of the North Sea Central Graben. *First Break*, **13**(10), 395–407.

Exploration and appraisal of the South Arne Field, Danish North Sea

D. S. MACKERTICH[1] and D. R. G. GOULDING[2]

Amerada Hess A/S, Østergade 26B DK-1100 Copenhagen K, Denmark
[1] *Present address: Amerada Hess (Malaysia) Ltd, Suite 9.02, Level 9, Menara Tan e Tan, 207 Jalen Tun Razak, 50400 Kuala Lumpar, Malaysia (e-mail: David.Mackertich@Hess.com)*
[2] *Present address: Amerada Hess Corporation, One Allen Centre, 500 Dallas Street, Houston, Texas 77002, USA (e-mail: DGoulding@Hess.com)*

Abstract: The South Arne Field lies in the Danish sector of the North Sea Basin 250 km WNW of Esbjerg on the Danish mainland. It is a chalk field 12 km by 3 km. The field was initially discovered in 1969 by the I-1 well which found a thin Maastrichtian Tor Formation producing up to 4040 BOPD upon test. The second well on the field (Baron-2) was drilled over 20 years later on the southwestern flank. The aim of this well, in addition to targeting deeper Jurassic prospectivity, was to test the concept that the chalk reservoir thickened off-structure. This well encountered no productive chalk reservoir and the prognosed Jurassic reservoir was not reached. Following a change of operator in 1994, the Rigs-1 well was drilled in the northern part of the field where the interpreted structure was most complex. The well was located on 2D seismic data towards the middle of what was interpreted to be a gas cloud. This well encountered a much thicker chalk reservoir sequence than had previously been drilled on the field. Following the acquisition of 3D seismic data and an intensive, integrated geological and geophysical work programme, an appraisal well (Rigs-2) and a down-dip sidetrack were planned in an area outside the gas cloud where the reservoir was predicted to be of high quality. These appraisal wells were very successful in their objectives and proved a stratigraphic element to the hydrocarbon trapping mechanism. The field development plan envisages the extensive use of horizontal wells and first oil is currently scheduled for mid 1999. Reserves are presently estimated to be 89×10^6 BBL oil, and 200×10^9 SCF of associated gas.

The South Arne Field lies in the Danish sector of the North Sea Basin 250 km WNW of Esbjerg on the Danish mainland (Fig. 1). It is an elongate northwesterly plunging anticline 12 km by 3 km and is one of the most northerly chalk fields in the Danish North Sea. Over the crest of the field, the volatile oil column is restricted to the thickness of the reservoir (35–85 m). The oil water contact (OWC) has not been penetrated in any wells drilled to date and stratigraphic trapping is considered to play an important role in the hydrocarbon distribution. The field lies at a depth of between 2700 m and 2940 m sub-sea. The primary reservoirs are the Tor and Ekofisk formations of Late Cretaceous/Early Paleocene age (Fig. 2). Individual reservoir units are not seismically resolvable over the crest of the structure. In addition, there is a gas cloud in the overburden which makes interpretation of seismic data in this area impossible (Fig. 3).

This paper, the first on the field, will summarize the exploration of the South Arne Field from its initial discovery in 1969 to its confirmation as a potentially commercial field in 1994.

Exploration phase

Early history

In 1962 the Danish shipowner, A. P. Møller, was awarded the sole concession (for 50 years) to explore the entire Danish area. The first offshore well, drilled in 1966, was located on a pronounced salt induced feature in the southern part of the Danish Central Graben. This well (A-1) drilled what is now known as the Kraka field, encountering oil and gas in Danian chalk and was the first oil discovery in the North Sea (Jørgensen & Andersen 1991). Given the success of this first well, subsequent exploration wells were targeted at similar features. By 1969 ten wells had been drilled in the Danish Offshore (A-1 to H-1). Of these, two were located on the Kraka Field, two on the Tyra Field and one on the Roar Field (Fig. 1).

The first well – discovery of South Arne

The South Arne structure was first identified on 1966–68 vintage 2D seismic data with five lines covering the field area (Fig. 4). Interpretation of these data and the recognition of an elongate closure at Top Chalk level prompted the drilling of the I-1 well (in 1969) by Gulf Oil Company on behalf of the Danish Underground Consortium, at that time a joint venture between A. P. Møller and Gulf Oil. This well was located at the crest and in the centre of the mapped closure. The well encountered a 28 m thick Ekofisk Formation at a depth of 2727 m sub-sea, overlying a 7 m thick Maastrichtian Tor Formation. Both intervals were interpreted to be hydrocarbon bearing and the Tor Formation was subsequently tested (Fig. 5). An initial stimulation with 120 BBL of acid achieved a maximum flow rate of 4040 BOPD on a 48/64″ choke. Although no core was recovered from this section it is interpreted to be highly fractured thus explaining the high flow rate.

Although the I-1 well tested at what is now regarded as a good flow rate for a thin chalk reservoir in a vertical well, the size of the accumulation was deemed to be uneconomic as the reservoir was thin in comparison to chalk sequences which had been encountered further to the south. In this light, no further appraisal drilling was undertaken on thc South Arne structure prior to the relinquishment of this part of the sole concession area in 1987.

The second well – field uneconomic

In 1989 a group led by Norsk Hydro applied for and were awarded the South Arne area as part of Licence 7/89 in the Third Danish licensing round. At this time the partnership consisted of Norsk Hydro (Operator), Danop, Dupont, British Gas, Dopas, Denerco and Danoil. The licence application was based on the interpretation of 1985/86 2D seismic data and the perception that the thin Tor Formation encountered in the I-1

MACKERTICH, D. S. & GOULDING, D. R. G. 1999. Exploration and appraisal of the South Arne Field, Danish North Sea. *In*: FLEET, A. J. & BOLDY, S. A. R. (eds) *Petroleum Geology of Northwest Europe: Proceedings of the 5th Conference*, 959–974. © Petroleum Geology '86 Ltd. Published by the Geological Society, London.

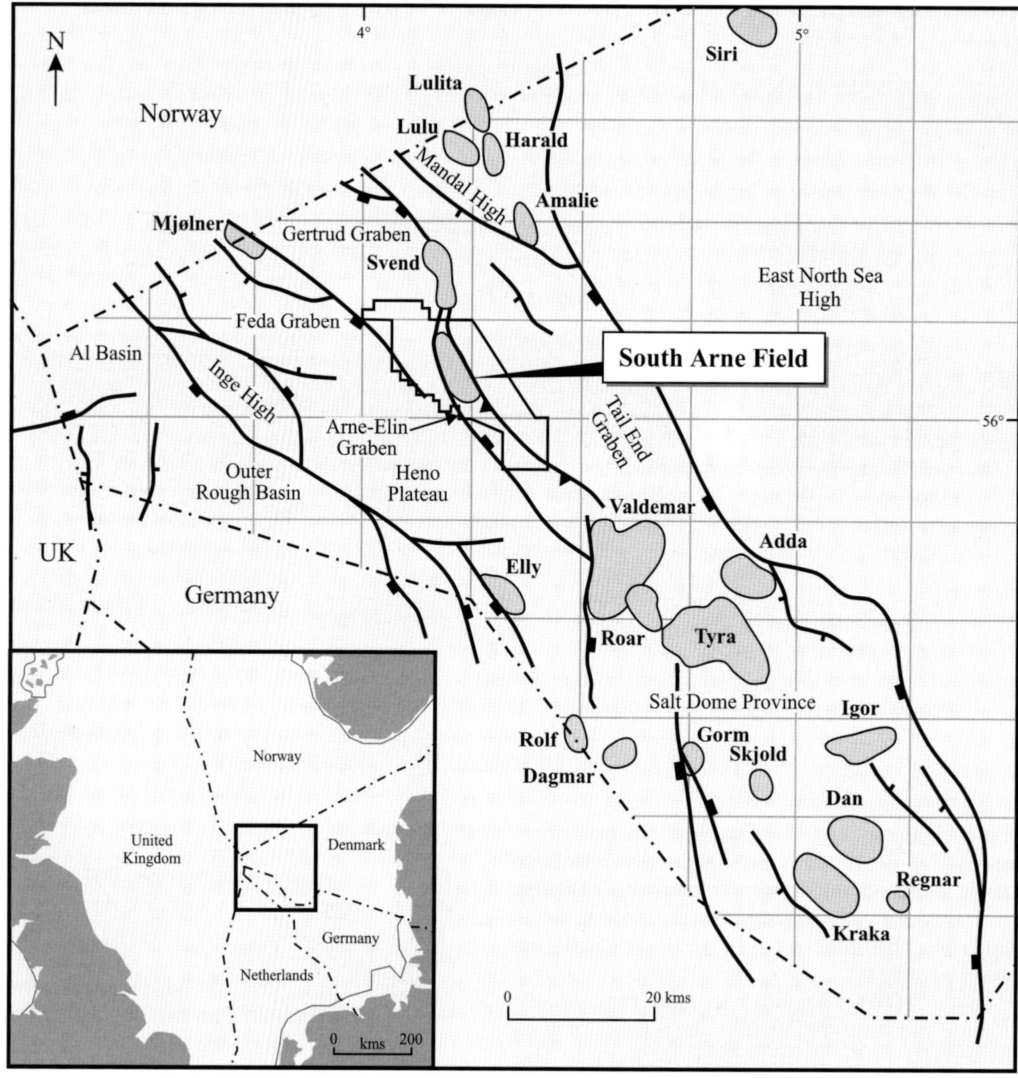

Fig. 1. Structural outline of the Danish Central Graben including location of commercial discoveries (modified from Damtoft *et al.* 1992).

well might thicken down-flank (Fig. 6) along with the recognition of potential Jurassic prospectivity. At Chalk Group level the structure was mapped as a simple anticline plunging to the northwest and closing to the southeast (Fig. 7). An additional target was identified within the Jurassic where hydrocarbons had been encountered in nearby wells. Proprietary 2D seismic data were acquired in 1990 and a well location was planned to test an area to the southwest of the I-1 well. The Baron-2 well was drilled in late 1991 to a total depth of 5209 m sub-sea and although the Chalk Group did thicken, the productive Tor Formation encountered in the I-1 well was absent (Fig. 8) and the prognosed Jurassic reservoirs were not reached.

In the 2 years following the completion of the Baron-2 well limited work was undertaken in the South Arne area. Inversion of selected 2D seismic lines indicated that neither the I-1 nor Baron-2 wells were located optimally and that some potential might exist to the north of the field, although the validity of these data were questioned. The absence of productive Tor Formation in a downflank location was thought to render the field uneconomic and various members of the partnership were keen to seek an alternative to the drilling of a second expensive commitment well on the 7/89 licence.

In 1994 Norsk Hydro presented data from South Arne to Amerada Hess as a farm-out proposal. At this time the northern part of the field was interpreted as a complex, heavily faulted area with little in the way of reserve potential (Fig. 9). Amerada Hess recognized that this area was likely to be affected by a gas cloud (Fig. 10) and was analogous to various fields in Norway such as Valhall (Ali & Alcock 1994) in which the company holds an interest. This interpretation prompted Amerada Hess to acquire Norsk Hydro's interest in, and Operatorship of, the field. Soon after Amerada Hess also acquired the interests of Dupont and British Gas.

The third well – 'rediscovery'

By late 1994 Amerada Hess was operator of the 7/89 licence with a partnership of Denerco, Dopas and Danoil. Technical evaluation strongly suggested that the northern part of the field was affected by a shallow gas cloud which had the effect of 'seismic push down' at Chalk level (Fig. 10). Simple modelling using a range of 3%, 6% and 9% reduction in average velocity to Top Chalk to simulate the gas effect in the centre of the gas cloud had the effect of pulling the depth structure up to such an extent that a large part of the field in the north came into structural closure (Fig. 11), thereby increasing the predicted oil in place. As the northern part of the field was affected by gas charged Neogene/Palaeogene layers, it was possible that this was in fact the crest of the field where reservoir characteristics of the chalk could also be enhanced. In addition, it was possible that major faulting in this area had not only caused the gas escape but also influenced the thickness of the reservoir during deposition.

Lithology	Lithostratigraphy		Chronostratigraphy	
		Forth Fmn.	Late Pleistocene to Holocene	Quaternary to Pleistocene
	Nordland Group		Pleistocene	Neogene
			Pliocene	
			Miocene	
	Hordland Group	Lark Fmn.	Oligocene	Palaeogene
		Horda Fmn.	Eocene	
	Rogaland Group	Balder Fmn.	Late Paleocene	
		Sele Fmn.		
	Montrose Group	Lista Fmn.		
		Vale Fmn.		
	Chalk Group	Ekofisk Fmn.	Early Paleocene	
		Ekofisk Tight Zone		
		Tor Fmn.	Maastrichtian	Late Cretaceous
		Hod Fmn.	Campanian	
			Santonian	
		Plenus Marl	Coniacian	
		Hidra Fmn.	Turonian	
			Cenomanian	
	Cromer Knoll Group	Rodby Fmn.	Albian	Early Cretaceous
		Sola Fmn.	Aptian	
		Tuxen Fmn.	Barremian	
		Valhall Fmn.	Hauterivian	
			Valanginian	
	Tyne Group	Farsund Fmn.	Ryazanian	Late Jurassic
			Volgian	
		Heno Fmn.	Kimmeridgian	
		Lola Fmn.	Oxfordian	
		Bryne Fmn.	Callovian	Middle Jurassic
			Bathonian	
			Bajocian	
				Triassic

Vertical sequence not to scale : Middle Jurassic/Triassic not penetrated in the field

Fig. 2. Generalized stratigraphy of the South Arne Field.

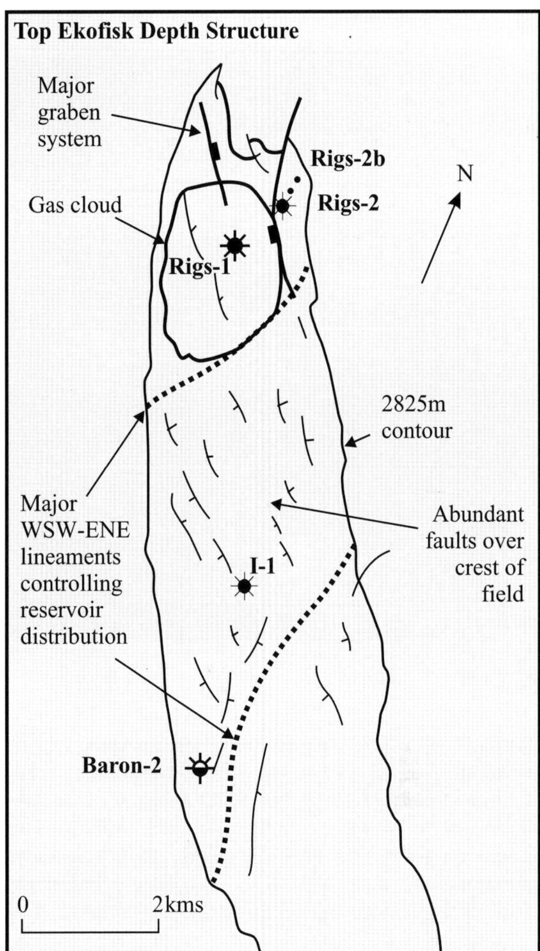

Fig. 3. South Arne Field – well locations and basic structural elements.

The Rigs-1 well was spudded in December 1994 with the primary objective of testing the productivity of the Danian Ekofisk and Maastrichtian Tor formations at a location that was considered to be close to the crest of the structure beneath the overburden gas. A secondary objective was to test Upper Jurassic sands which were thought to have been rafted by postulated halokinesis under the northern part of the field. The well registered high background gas readings throughout the Miocene and Oligocene sections (1240 m to 2100 m sub-sea). The gas was present within silts and claystones and, although of low concentration, was sufficient to affect the sonic log and the observed seismic velocities in this area (Fig. 12). The top of the Ekofisk Formation was encountered at a depth of 2741 m sub-sea just 14 m deeper than the equivalent stratigraphic level in the I-1 well. The velocity reduction associated with gas in the Tertiary is equivalent to 3.6 % at this location. Where the gas effect is greatest the velocity effect is estimated to be a 4.0% reduction in average velocity to Top Chalk. On the 1992 mapping of the field following the Baron-2 well, Top Chalk at the Rigs-1 well location plots some 160 m below actual depths at *c.* 2900 m (Fig. 9). This mapping did not take into account any gas effect and as a result the Rigs-1 area was predicted to have no associated oil in place or reserves.

At Chalk Group level the Rigs-1 well encountered a stratigraphic succession that was markedly different from the other two wells on the field. Not only were both the Ekofisk and Tor reservoirs of far superior quality to those encountered in either the I-1 or Baron-2 wells, but both were fully oil bearing (Fig. 13). In addition, the Hod, Plenus Marl and Hidra Formations which have a combined thickness of 46 m in I-1 and 67 m in Baron-1 were all absent in the Rigs-1 well. The Ekofisk and Tor formations in the Rigs-1 well were tested flowing at a surface constrained rate of 1700 BOPD of 34.2° API oil with a GOR of 1300 SCF/BBL on a 20/64″ choke.

Appraisal phase

Summary

After the success of the Rigs-1 well a 3D seismic survey was acquired over the field in mid 1995. A thorough technical evaluation of the field including seismic re-interpretation ensued during the following year and an appraisal well (Rigs-2) was planned and spudded in May 1996. A straight hole and high angle sidetrack were designed with the objective of testing the geological and geophysical model in which oil was believed to be stratigraphically trapped below the field wide structural closure. These wells were planned and drilled outside the gas cloud permitting more accurate calibration to seismic data. Both wells were successful in their objectives and a second sidetrack/sub-horizontal well was planned with the aim of evaluating the fluid content of the excellent reservoir quality rock down the flank of the structure.

The Rigs-2 well and associated sidetracks proved hydrocarbons throughout the reservoir section and in mid 1996 the South Arne Field was declared commercial. The field

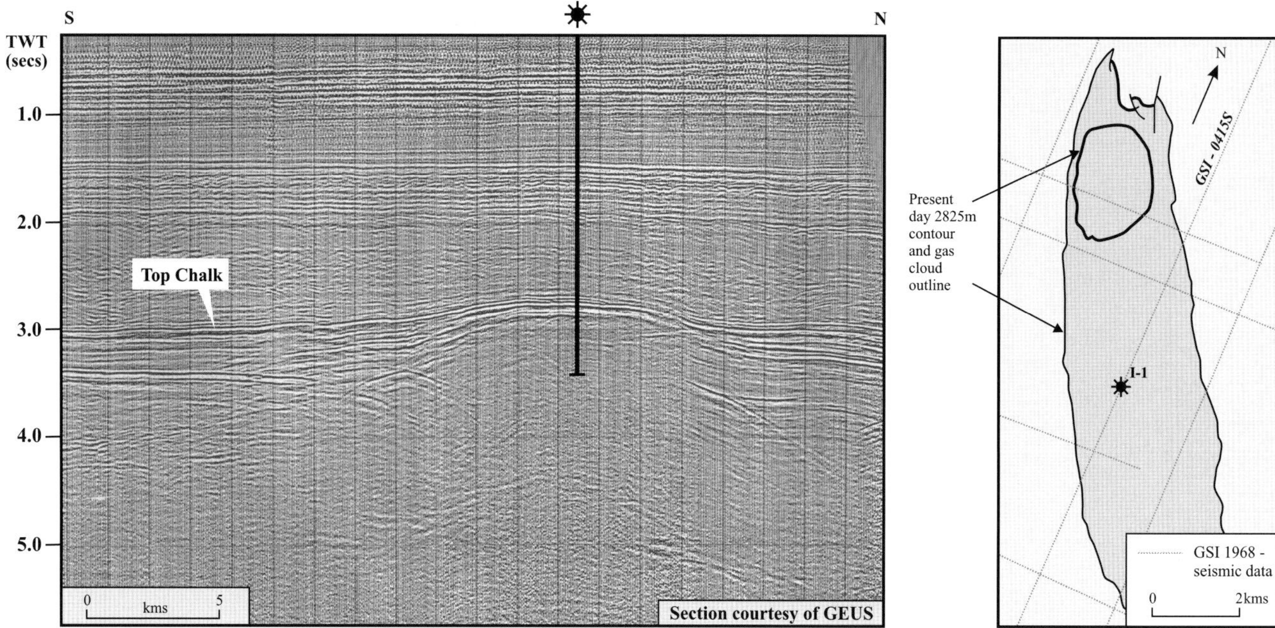

Fig. 4. South Arne pre-I-1 well.

development plan (PDO) was submitted in March 1997 and approved in August 1997. The first development well was spudded in December 1997. The PDO envisages extensive use of horizontal wells with completion and stimulation design dependent on formation and well productivity requirements. The field will be developed from a concrete based gravity structure with offshore oil loading and gas export via a pipeline to shore. The PDO has been based on an initial export rate of 50 000 BOPD from six wells. Most likely reserves are currently estimated at 89×10^6 BBL oil and 200×10^9 SCF of associated gas. First oil is scheduled for mid 1999.

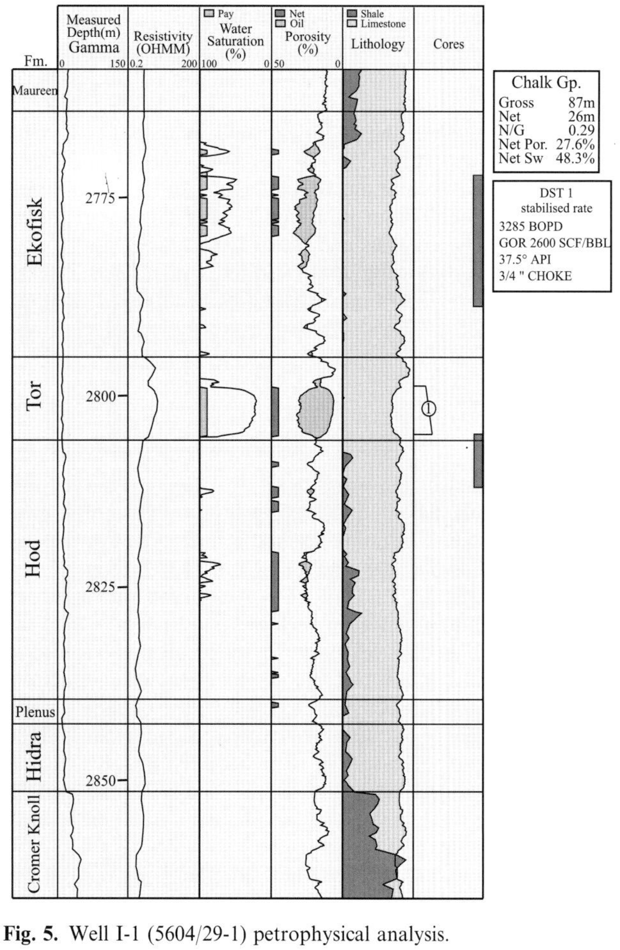

Fig. 5. Well I-1 (5604/29-1) petrophysical analysis.

3D seismic dataset

Following the successful testing of Rigs-1 in February 1995 the appraisal of the South Arne Field commenced with the acquisition of 182 km^2 of 3D seismic data. The data were acquired between May and July 1995 in a dual-source quadruple 4500 m streamer configuration providing a nominal 45-fold dataset. Processing was undertaken on board the seismic vessel to stack stage in order to reduce the turn-around time.

The primary objectives of the 3D survey were to improve understanding of reservoir distribution via dense spatial

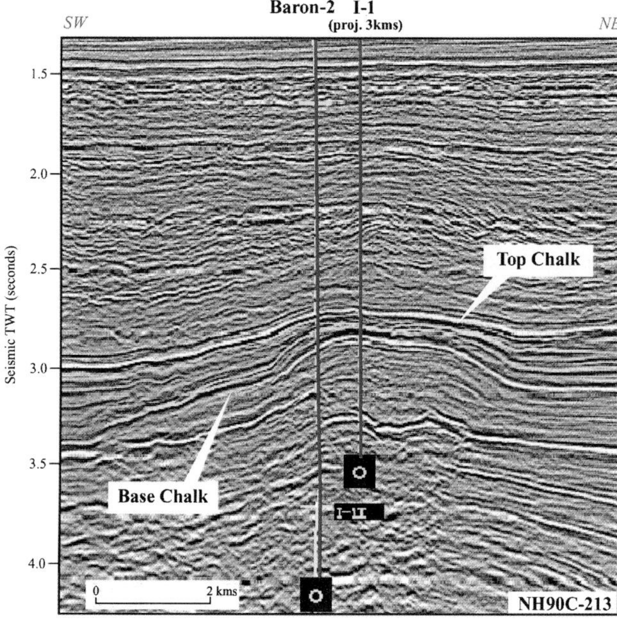

Fig. 6. Seismic section showing Baron-2 well location. Location of line shown on Fig. 11.

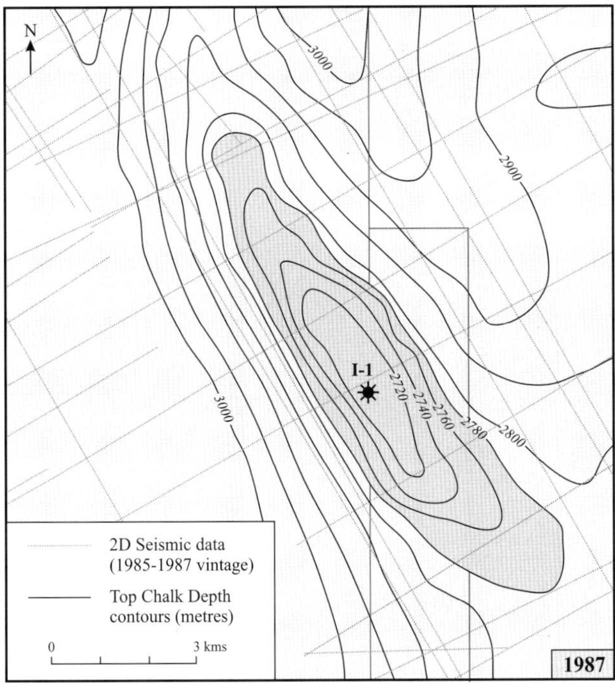

Fig. 7. South Arne structure – pre Baron-2 well.

sampling, provide good structural definition of the steep flanks of the structure along with 3D information on intra-reservoir fault orientation and distribution. The additional problem of imaging beneath the gas saturated overburden section encountered in Rigs-1 (Fig. 12) was also considered in the

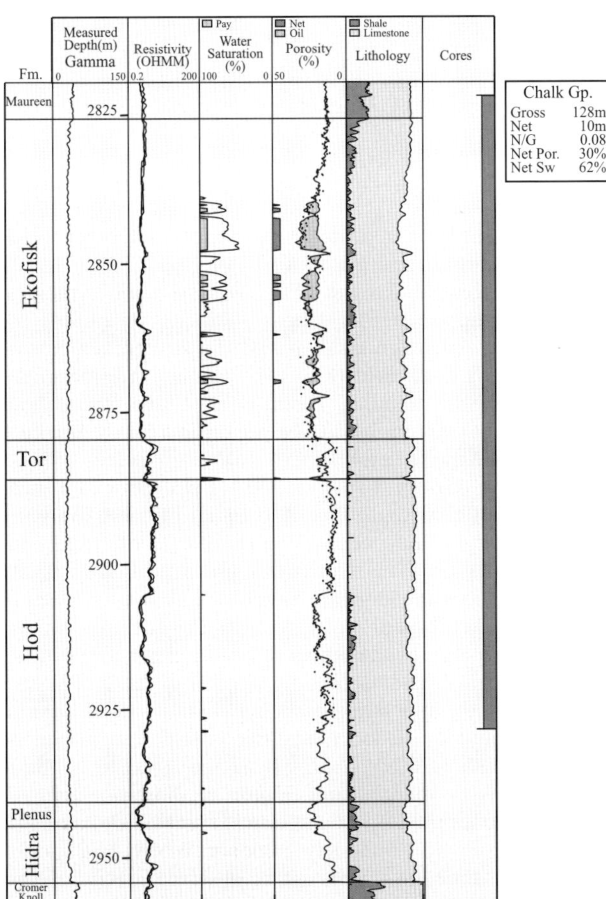

Fig. 8. Well Baron-2 (5604/30-3) petrophysical analysis.

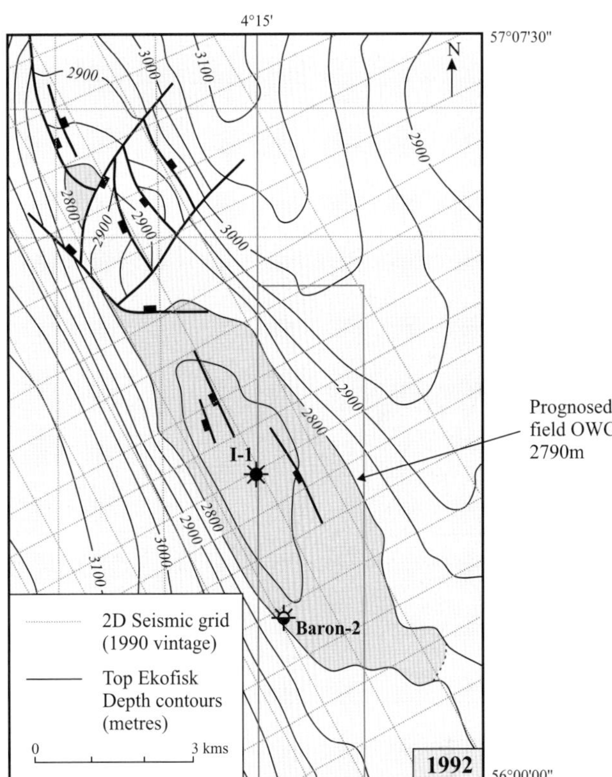

Fig. 9. South Arne structure – post Baron-2 well.

survey design and the 4500 m offset was included in order to record any possible undershooting of the gas anomaly. Pre-survey calculations indicated that critical angle for refraction at top reservoir would occur at offsets of around 4000 m, the 4500 m cable length ensuring some data redundancy. However, post survey analysis of pre-stack gathers and partial offset stacks indicate that the gas anomaly was not successfully undershot and that significant signal attenuation is present at all offsets across the anomaly.

Seismic ties were obtained to Wells I-1, Baron-2, Rigs-1, Q-1 and Iris-1 (Fig. 14) in order to gain good seismic stratigraphic control on the Chalk Group both on and off structure. Spectral analysis of the seismic data shows a dominant seismic frequency of around 40–45 Hz at reservoir level, equating to a quarter wavelength resolution of approximately 15 to

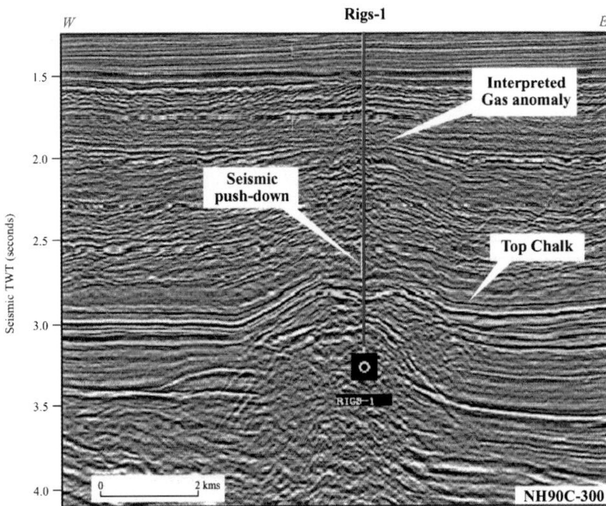

Fig. 10. Seismic section through the northern part of the South Arne Field. Location of line shown on Fig. 11.

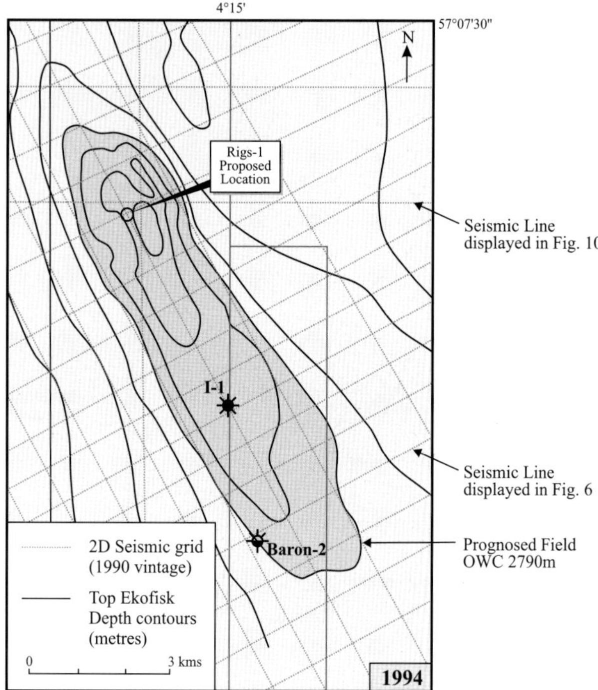

Fig. 11. South Arne structure with 6% velocity reduction in the north.

25 m, dependent upon chalk velocity. In order to improve the resolution of the data set and aid the understanding of reservoir distribution the raw migration of the 3D seismic dataset was inverted to acoustic impedance.

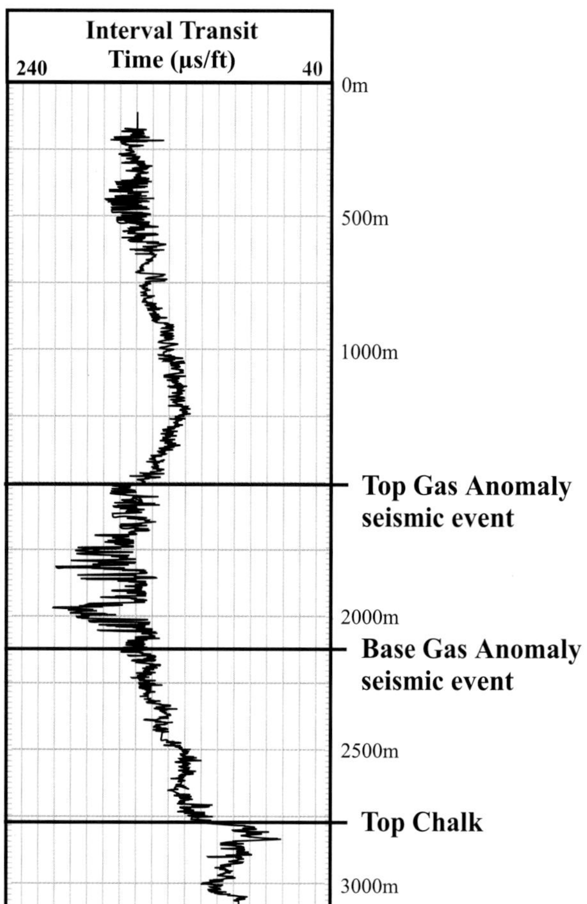

Fig. 12. Overburden gas in Rigs-1 sonic log.

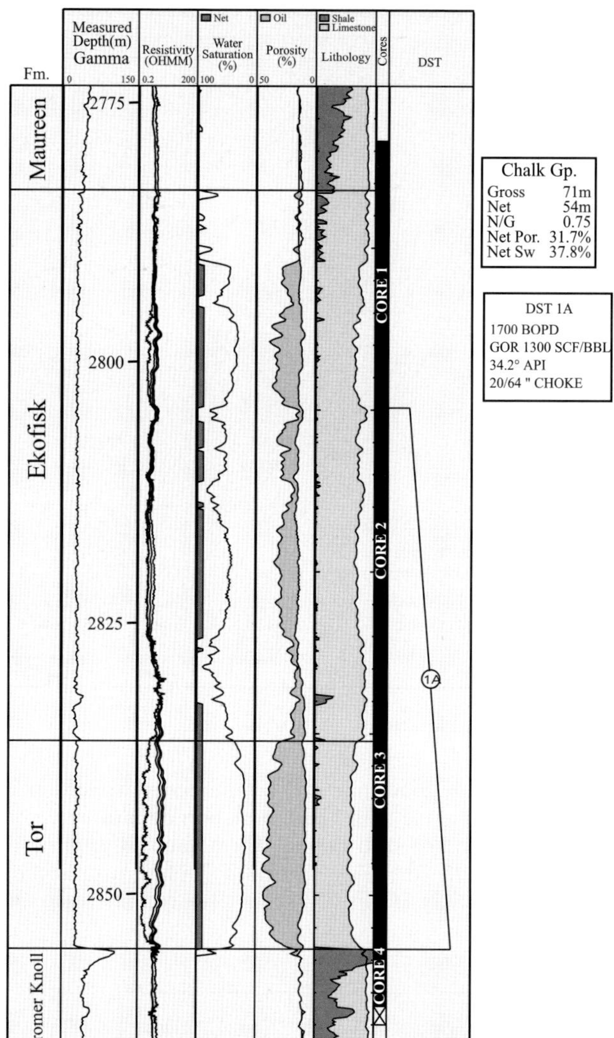

Fig. 13. Well Rigs-1 (5604/29-4) petrophysical analysis.

Structural definition

The South Arne Field is located in the Arne–Elin Graben which lies on the western margin of the Tail End Graben within the Danish Central Trough (Fig. 1). The main structural lineaments mapped at base Upper Jurassic level outline the extent of the Arne-Elin Graben and the structural elements underlying this chalk field (Fig. 14). Oblique inversion of the main NNW–SSE trending basin margin fault throughout the Cretaceous is interpreted to be responsible for the presence of the South Arne structure.

The Chalk Group two-way-time (TWT) isochore map illustrates that the Chalk Group is at its thinnest overlying the basin margin fault, supporting the theory of Cretaceous inversion (Fig. 15). The depth structure map at Top Chalk (Fig. 16) outlines the elongate anticlinal nature of the South Arne Field which broadly coincides with the isochore minima. The depth map displays a number of large faults in the northern part of the field, trending broadly parallel to the NNW–SSE orientation of the underlying basin margin fault. In addition to this major fault set, a secondary minor fault system can be observed trending WNW–ESE across the structure, oblique to the deep basin margin fault. Figure 17 shows the azimuth attribute map for the Top Chalk seismic event which highlights more effectively the obliquely trending WNW–ESE faults. In addition, subtle lineaments can be observed striking almost N–S in both the north and south of the field. All three fault trends are indicated on Fig. 17. Seismic illustrations of each

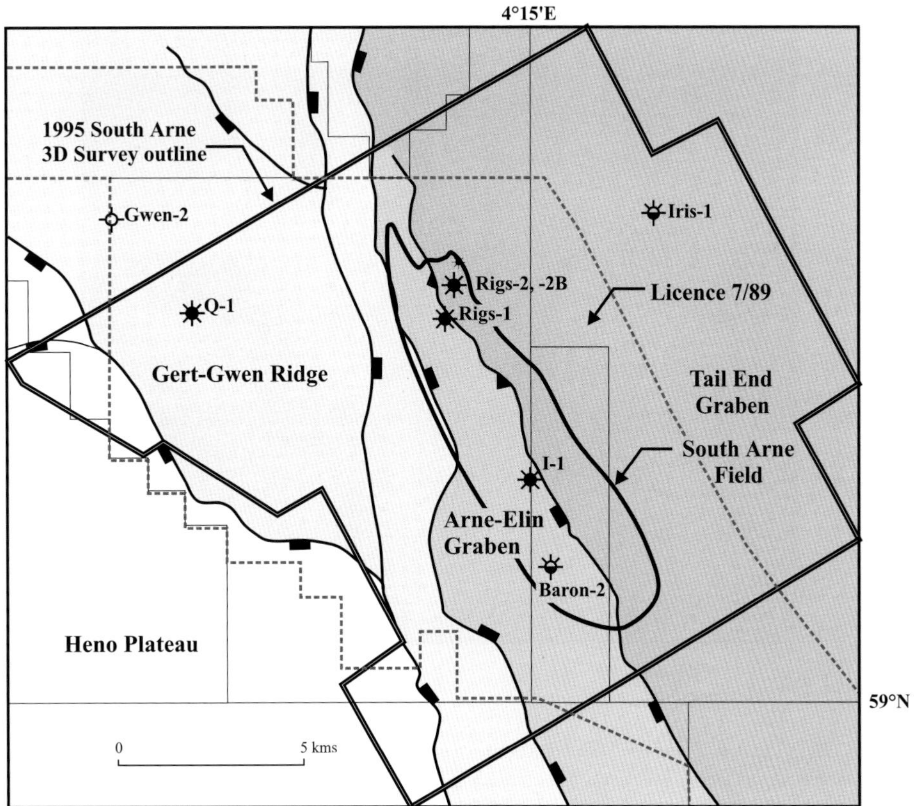

Fig. 14. 3D seismic dataset and principal structural elements.

fault trend are given in Figs 18a, b and c from which clear differences in structural style are apparent.

Figure 18a is a seismic in-line through the northern part of the field, to the north of the gas anomaly, illustrating the NNW–SSE striking fault set. This fault trend offsets the whole of the Chalk Group and is quite clearly post-Chalk Group in age. In addition, well correlations from Rigs-1 to Rigs-2 indicate little to no evidence for movement along these faults during chalk deposition.

The observed crestal collapse graben system is interpreted to be associated with local Zechstein salt withdrawal in Paleocene times, with re-activation of the trend in the late Miocene resulting in gas leakage from the South Arne accumulation into the overburden. Although Zechstein salt has not been

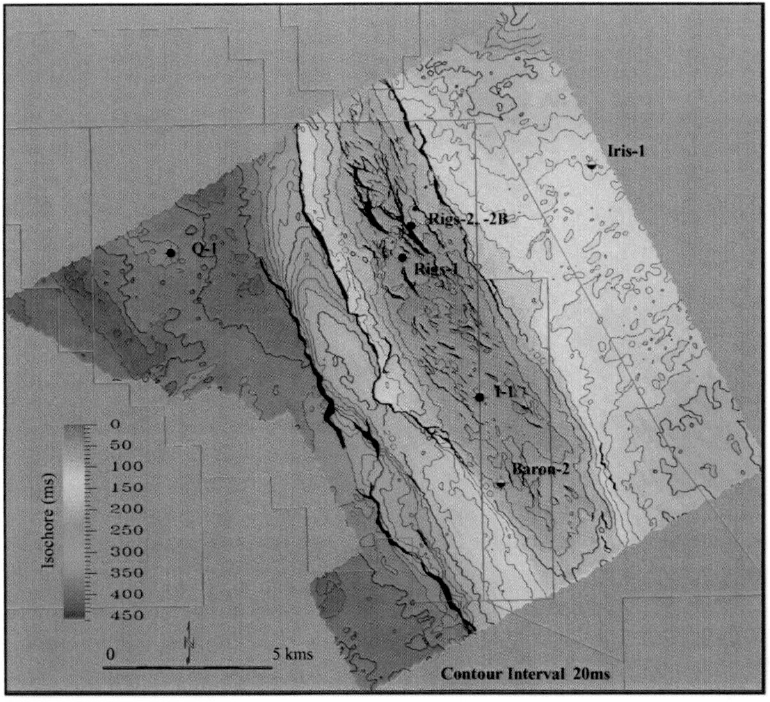

Fig. 15. Chalk Group TWT isochore.

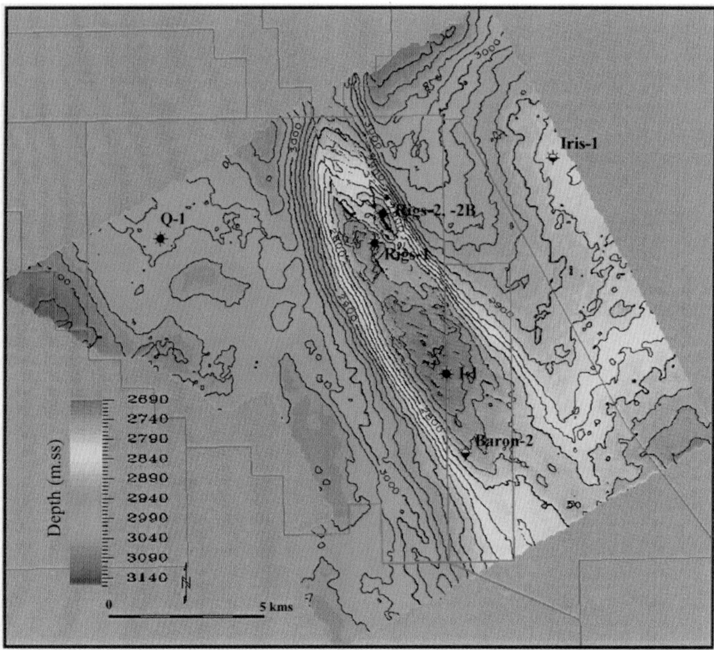

Fig. 16. Top Chalk depth structure map.

encountered in the field wells and 3D gravity data indicate little residual salt beneath the structure, it has been penetrated in the Svend Field to the north of South Arne (Fig. 1). This salt is postulated to have migrated locally westwards from the Tail End Graben.

Figure 18b illustrates the WNW–ESE trending fault set on a seismic in-line across the centre of the field. The fault offset is very clear at the top of the reservoir interval but seems to die out within the Chalk Group. The faults appear to be listric in nature and predominantly post-Chalk Group in age although some are associated with a degree of syn-tectonic chalk deposition.

Core from the Ekofisk Tight Zone indicates that many of the small-scale fractures and faults in this interval are listric in nature because of the lithologic heterogeneity within this unit. This interval may have acted as a décollement zone within the Chalk Group. The WNW–ESE fault trends are interpreted to have formed in reaction to oblique compression along the underlying basement fault, forming sinistral Riedel shears within the reservoir interval (similar to those described by Eggink *et al.* 1996). Inversion-induced anticlinal tightening is thought to have produced a null displacement surface within the Chalk Group, hence the difference in displacement between Top and Base Chalk.

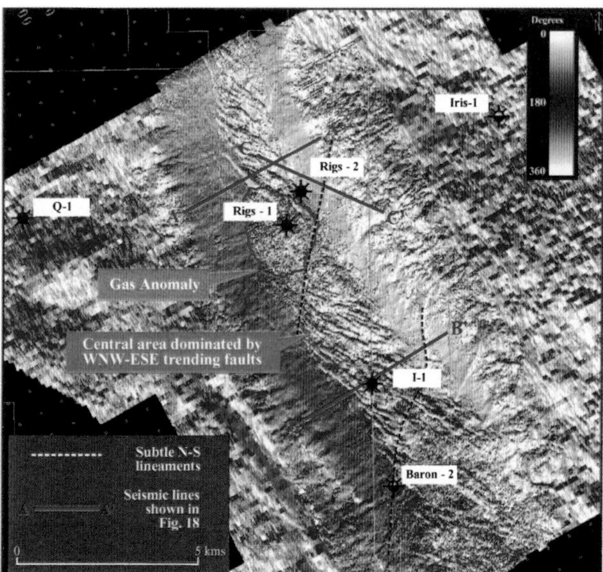

Fig. 17. Top Chalk azimuth map.

Figure 18c is a random seismic line flattened at Top Chalk through the northernmost N–S trending lineament. Although there is no clear offset at Top or Base Chalk, significant changes in Chalk Group stratigraphy are considered to occur at this boundary. In the central and southern parts of the field, the Chalk Group is represented by the Ekofisk, Tor, Hod and Hidra formations. In the north, the Hod and Hidra formations are absent and the Tor Formation rests directly on Lower Cretaceous claystones. This implies that the N–S trend was active throughout Chalk Group deposition. Lineaments along this trend are postulated to be associated with basinal halokinesis, but are not fully understood at this time. All of the observed faults and structural lineaments observed at top reservoir are summarized in strike histogram form (Fig. 19)

Reservoir sedimentology and poroperm characteristics

The primary reservoir in the South Arne Field is the Chalk Group of Late Cretaceous to early Paleocene age. The Chalk is less than 60 m in thickness over the crest, thickening to over 150 m on the flanks of the structure. Although hydrocarbons have been encountered in the Hod Formation and in the Lower Cretaceous Tuxen Limestone Formation (Fig. 2), these reservoirs are of poor quality in comparison to the two principal reservoir units, the Tor and Ekofisk formations, which have high matrix porosities but low matrix permeabilities (Fig. 20).

Cores from the Tor Formation in the South Arne Field are generally massive in appearance with few distinct bed boundaries and an abundance of healed hairline fractures (Fig. 21). Although true sedimentary structures are not common, rare parallel laminations are evident and often associated with *Planolites* and *Chondrites*, burrows thought to be indicative of distal turbidite deposition (Nygaard *et al.* 1983). Occasional chalk clasts are present as 'floating grains' and more rarely as

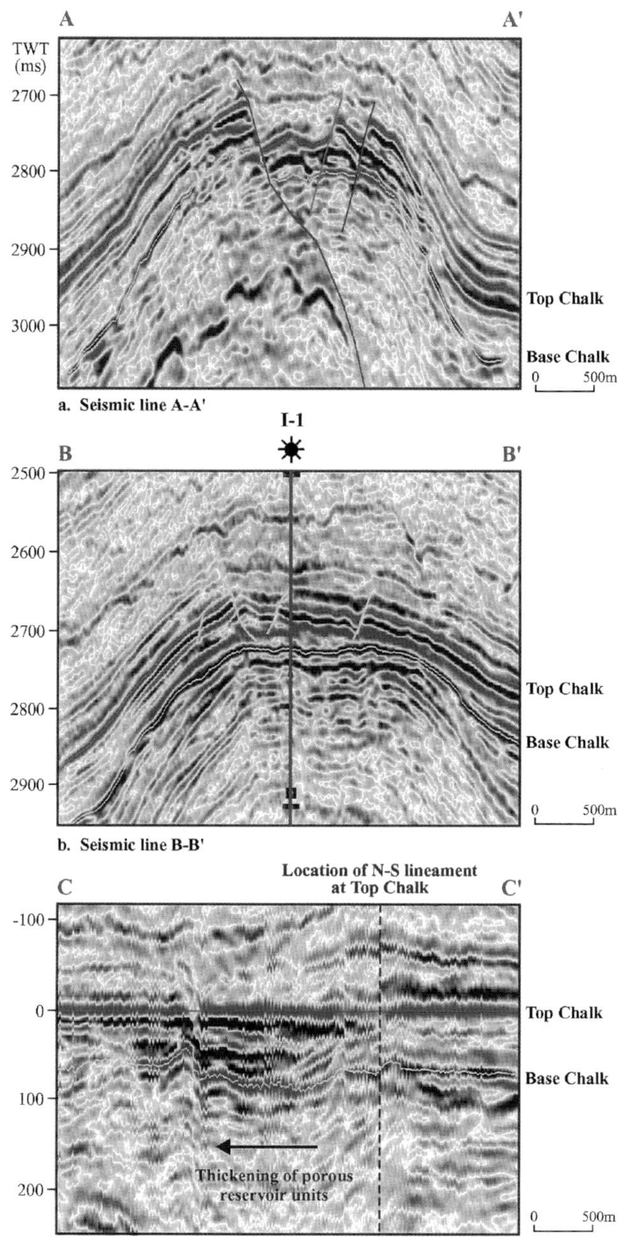

Fig. 18. (**a**) Seismic line A–A′, (**b**) Seismic line B-B′, (**c**) Seismic line C-C′' illustrating key structural trends. Location of lines shown on Fig. 17.

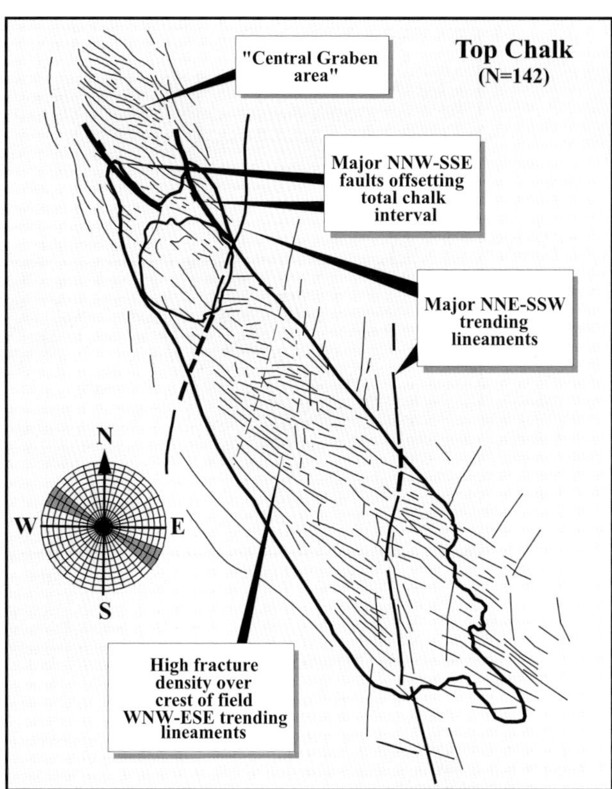

Fig. 19. Top reservoir structural lineaments summary.

discrete 'lag deposits' (Fig. 21). No bioturbation is seen within these intervals which are interpreted to represent either more proximal or higher energy debris flow deposits which were laid down during a period of active tectonism and are therefore prone to lateral variations in thickness. Dating of clasts from within these debris flow units reveals a Maastrichtian age indicative of intra-formational reworking. These allochthonous intervals often have little internal structure and image logs [Full-bore MicroImager/Formation MicroScanner^{TM} (FMI/FMS)] characteristically display chaotic bedding with high dips and a low correlation confidence from one pad image to the next (Fig. 22).

In common with many other chalk fields, the poroperm characteristics of the Tor Formation in the South Arne Field are thought to be dependent on three main factors; primary reservoir quality at the time of sediment deposition, over-pressuring of the sediments, and entry of hydrocarbons (Brasher & Vagle 1996). The Tor Formation has porosities in the range 25–46% with a field average of around 37%. The matrix permeabilities (gas permeabilities from core analysis) range from less than 1 mD to 10 mD with an average of around 6 mD. These poroperm characteristics are high for a chalk reservoir at a depth averaging 2810 m sub-sea but can be partially attributed to the high reservoir pressure, which is around 6300 PSI at this depth. As there are no true autochthonous deposits interpreted in the Tor Formation of South Arne a clear distinction between reservoir properties of different facies is not possible.

The boundary between the Ekofisk and the Tor Formation is marked by a 2 cm thick claystone layer which is considered to be the lateral equivalent to the Fish Clay (Birkelund & Bromley 1979). Overlying this layer there is a marked change in lithology from fairly homogeneous Tor Formation sediments to a nodular chalk unit, some 8 m in thickness, which possesses a 'horsetail' lamination (Fig. 23). This interval is capped by a 2–5 cm thick claystone unit which possesses a faunal assemblage indicative of accumulation in relatively deep water. Immediately overlying this argillaceous interval are chalk clasts which have been dated as Maastrichtian in age indicating re-working of the Tor Formation at this time. A semi-regional hardground is present 1 m above this claystone unit. The sedimentary succession at the Tor–Ekofisk boundary in the South Arne Field is thought to represent a period of subsidence followed by local tectonism and then a hiatus in deposition.

The majority of the Ekofisk Formation comprises interbedded biomottled chalk, marly chalk and massive chalk with intraclasts. Bioturbation is common to abundant with *Zoophycus*, *Chondrites* and *Planolites*, all being recognized. These sediments are interpreted as consisting of a sequence of slumped chalks, debris flow units and periodite/autochthonous chalk sediments. Deposition is considered to have occurred under both tectonically active and passive conditions. Stylolites and solution seams are common in the interpreted autochthonous units where they may serve to reduce the vertical permeability of the reservoir.

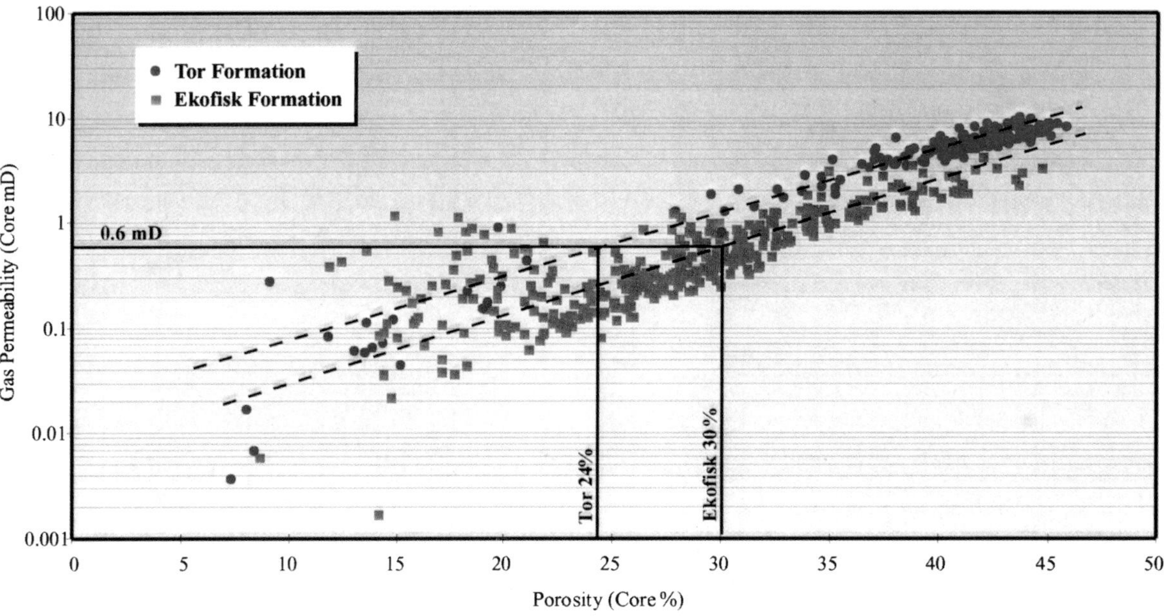

Fig. 20. South Arne Field: porosity vs permeability: Tor and Ekofisk formations (log scale).

A plot of porosity versus permeability for the Ekofisk Formation in South Arne shows the wide distribution of porosity values ranging from 15–45% (Fig. 20). Matrix permeability values for the Ekofisk Formation are generally lower than for the Tor Formation, with maximum values of around 4 mD and an average of 1–2 mD. This is because the Ekofisk sediments have smaller constituent grain and pore throat sizes than the Tor Formation (Andersen 1995). It should be noted that this relationship results in a different function relating porosity to permeability for the Ekofisk Formation to that derived for the Tor Formation (Fig. 24).

The poroperm characteristics of the Ekofisk Formation in the South Arne Field are strongly dependent on primary reservoir quality imparted at the time of deposition. The allochthonous deposits consistently have better properties than the interpreted autochthonous deposits. For this reason an understanding of the origin and distribution of these transported intervals is particularly important. This has been aided by core goniometry, image log analysis and high resolution dating of reworked clasts from debris flow units. The results of this work suggest that the Tor Formation sediments have been sourced from outside the field area and may have originated from the Coffee Soil Fault to the east. The deposition of the Ekofisk Formation appears to have been influenced much more by local tectonism, within the field area itself.

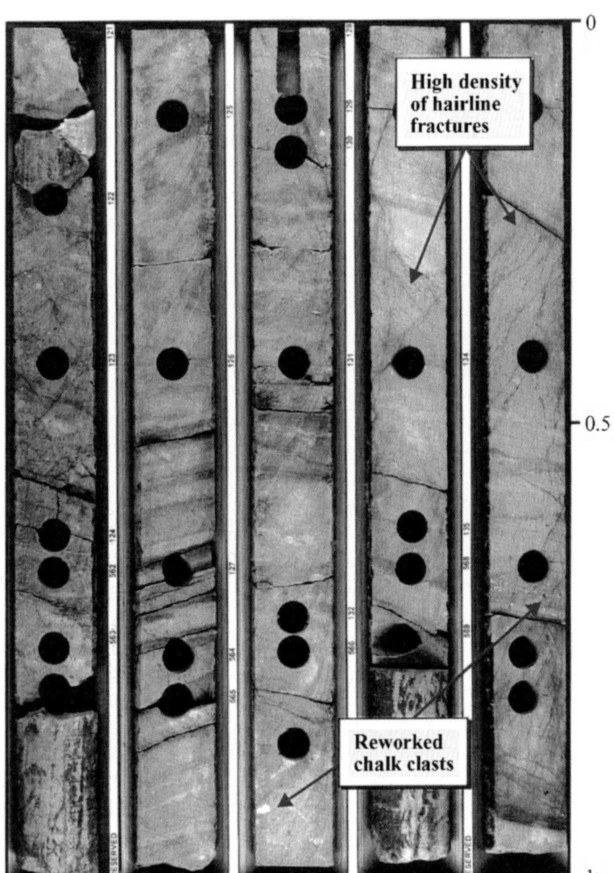

Fig. 21. Tor Formation: white light core photo.

Reservoir fracturing

The presence of natural fractures in the South Arne reservoir enables higher production rates to be achieved than would otherwise be obtainable from such low matrix permeability sediments. In order to fully exploit the benefit and avoid the potential negative effects of such fractures it is important to ascertain their distribution, size, orientation and effective contribution to flow (i.e. whether open or closed). Various techniques including 3D seismic, image log, core and well test data have been used to better understand fracturing in the field. A fuller description of fracture types in chalk reservoirs may be found in Fritsen (1996).

The resolution of the 3D seismic dataset across South Arne is such that displacements in the order of 15–20 m may be imaged at Top Chalk (Fig. 17). Image logs and core provide a higher resolution dataset which can detect faults and displacements down to a few centimetres. Image log analysis reveals that the WNW–ESE fault trends mapped on 3D seismic data in South Arne are also the dominant trends seen in the well bore (Fig. 19). However, image analysis shows a much wider azimuth of fracture strike than the seismic data. This is an important observation for subsequent planning of horizontal wells, as trajectories do not necessarily need to be perpendicular to principal fracture trends observed on seismic data.

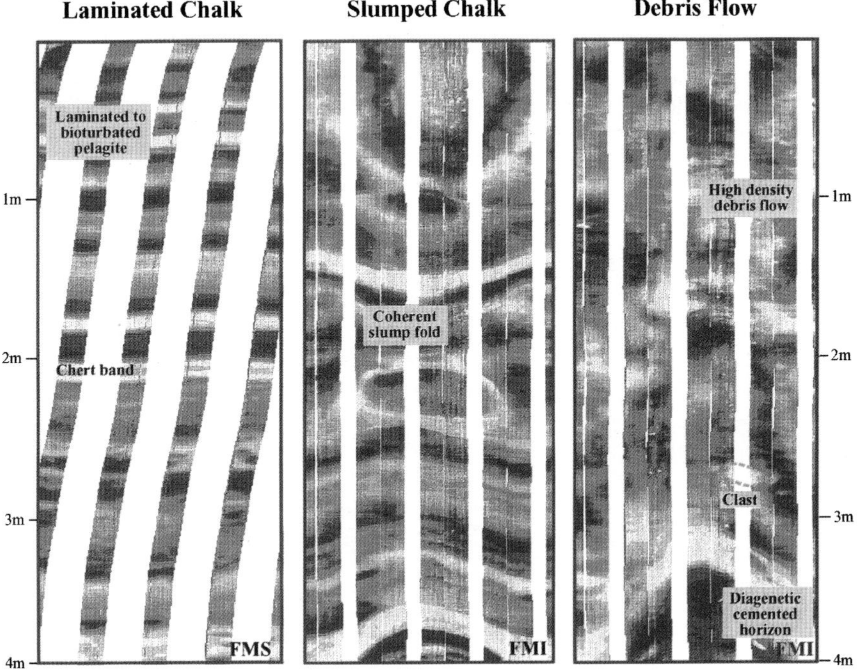

Fig. 22. Chalk lithofacies from image logs.

Tectonic fractures are considered to be the most important type of fracture in South Arne by virtue of the fact that, when open, they can contribute to increased permeability of the reservoir and hence increased production rates. In core and on image logs the tectonic fractures commonly appear as high angle (60–80°) planar features. Core recovery may be poor and represented by rubble. Calcite mineralization is sometimes present and slickensides indicating movement along the fault may also be seen.

Hairline fractures, which are common throughout the Tor Formation, are difficult to detect on image logs because of the lack of resistivity contrast. In core, these fractures appear as

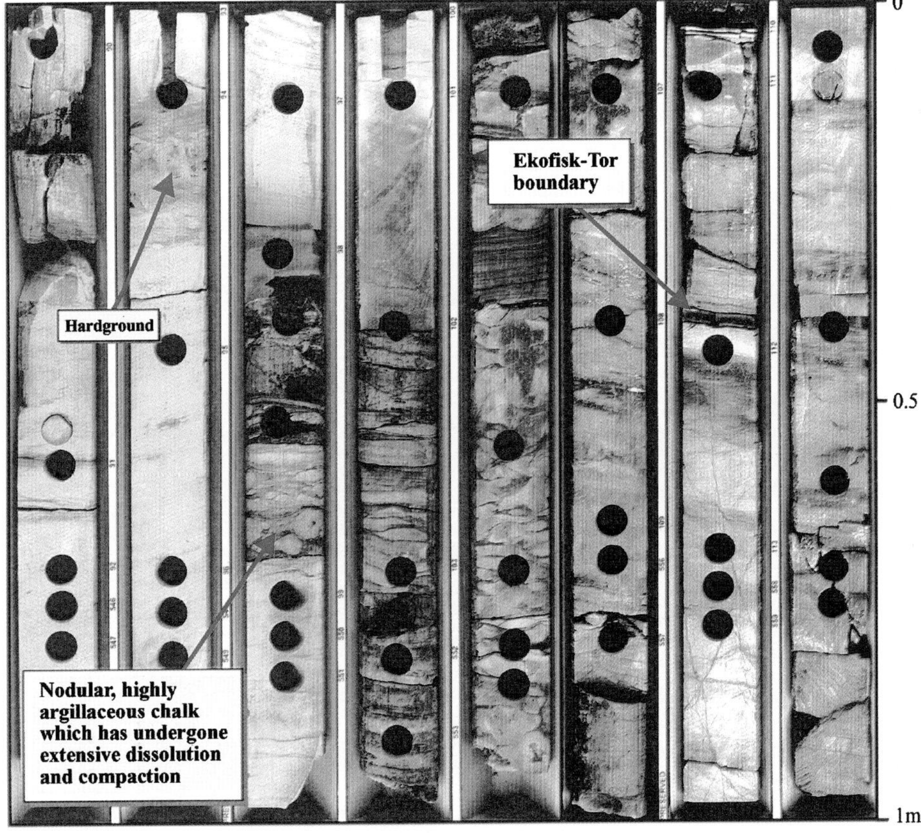

Fig. 23. Ekofisk–Tor boundary: white light core photo.

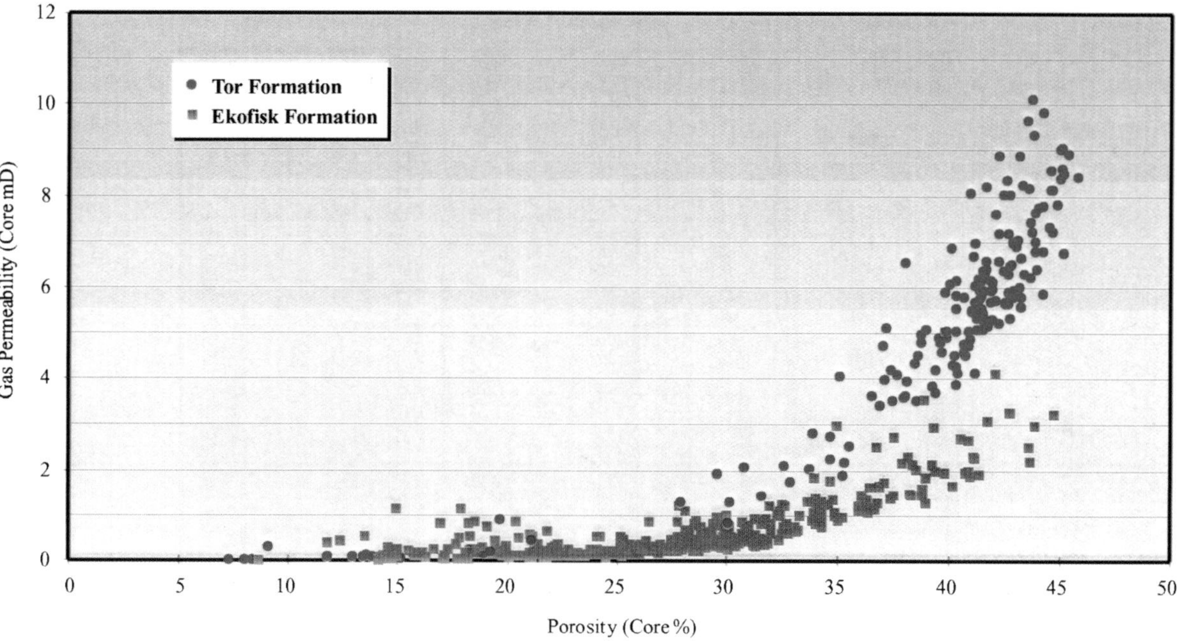

Fig. 24. South Arne Field: porosity vs permeability: Tor and Ekofisk formations (linear scale).

healed networks of fine dark brown features that are generally less porous and permeable than the adjacent chalk matrix, although tectonic fracturing may exploit these existing trends. They are often sub-vertical and appear to be developed in conjugate sets (Fig. 21). Having an average length of between 5 and 20 cm, they frequently terminate at stylolites and solution seam horizons. Healed hairline fractures, so characteristic of the Tor Formation, are almost totally absent from the Ekofisk Formation.

Well tests performed across the Ekofisk Formation in both the Rigs-1 and Rigs-2A wells indicate that the best production rates come from reworked and transported units which not only possess the best poroperm characteristics but also the highest density of fracturing. Detailed fracture studies also reveal different types of fractures developing in different lithofacies. In the Ekofisk Tight Zone where cleaner chalk intervals are interbedded with more argillaceous and solution seam rich horizons, the fractures tend to be of low angle and listric in nature, soling out into the more argillaceous intervals. This parallels what is observed on seismic data across the field but at a smaller scale. The clay content of the chalk is significant as it is considered to influence the frequency and type of fractures that are able to form and also impacts on later diagenesis (Hardman 1982).

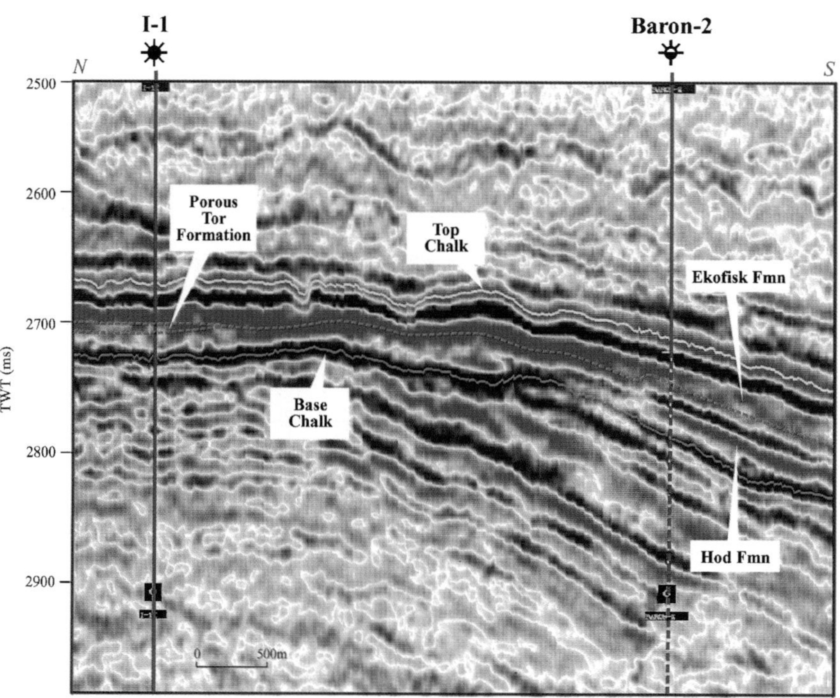

Fig. 25. Arbitrary 3D seismic line tying Wells I-1 and Baron-2.

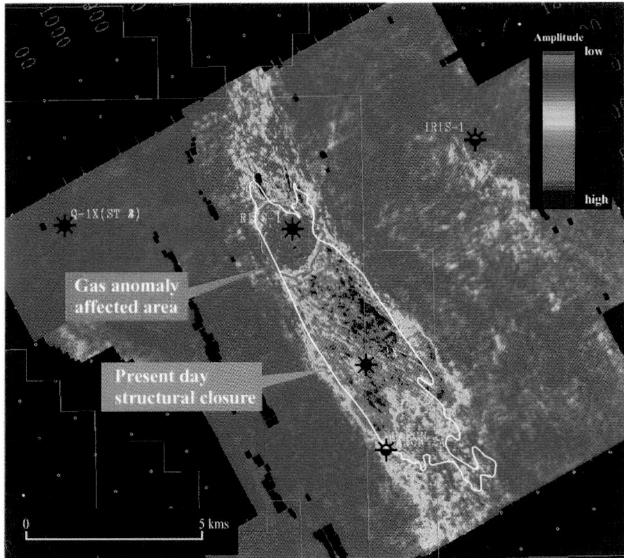

Fig. 26. Chalk Group average absolute amplitude map.

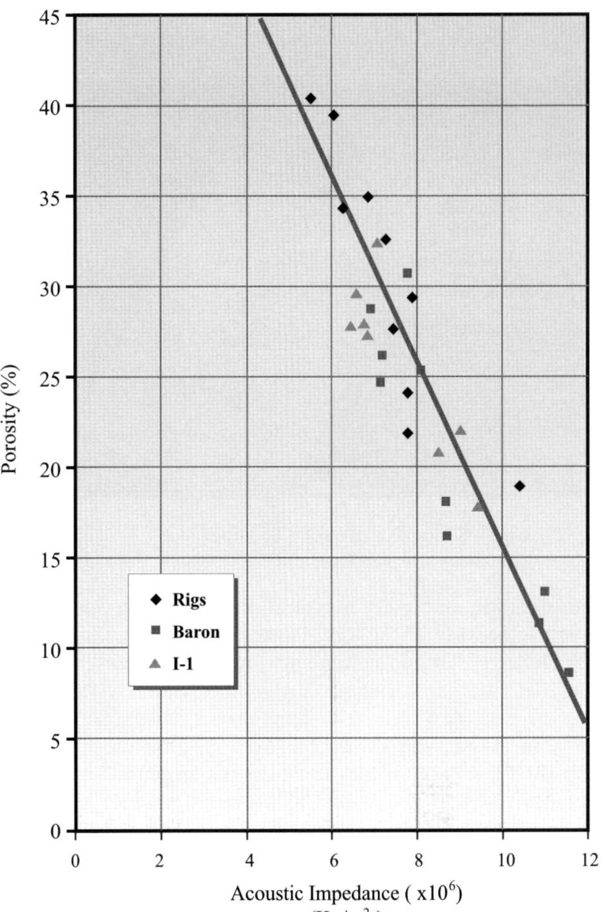

Fig. 27. Core porosity vs acoustic impedance from logs.

Reservoir prediction away from wells

3D seismic and well data. The basic structural analysis of the 3D seismic dataset incorporates seismic picks at Top and Base Chalk. The relatively thin nature of the Chalk Group over the South Arne structure generally precludes confident correlation of intra-Chalk picks. The random 3D seismic line presented in Fig. 25 tying Wells I-1 and Baron-2 illustrates the problem of intra-Chalk interpretation and offers some explanation as to why the Baron-2 well was drilled. Well I-1 encountered a 7 m allochthonous Maastrichtian Tor interval that produced up to 4040 BOPD upon test. The seismic line shows the chalk isopach thickening downflank from I-1 to Baron-2. A reasonable interpretation based on this section would be that the productive Tor Formation encountered in I-1 would thicken towards the Baron-2 location. However, although a thin Tor Formation interval was encountered in the Baron-2 well, the sequence was in non-reservoir facies. The thickening of the chalk interval as seen on seismic was restricted to the Ekofisk and Hod formations. The well is subsequently interpreted to have been drilled proximal to a long lived N–S fault trend where the reservoir facies were not deposited. This trend is thought to have been instrumental in preserving the thicker Tor Formation in the northern part of the field. Such seismic

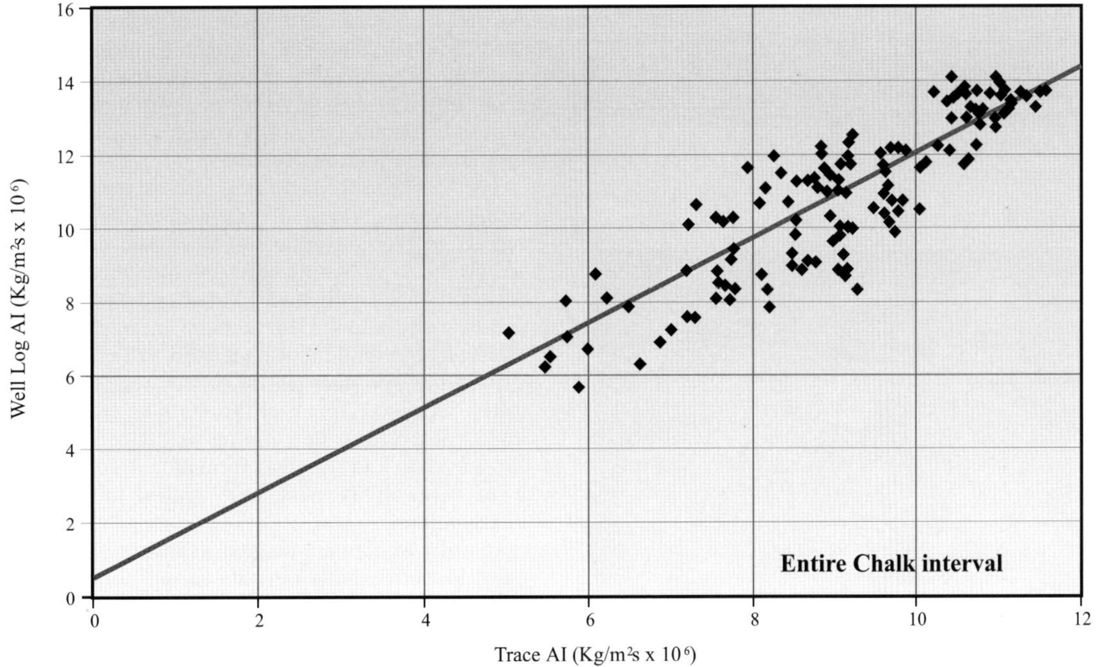

Fig. 28. Well log acoustic impedance vs trace inverted acoustic impedance.

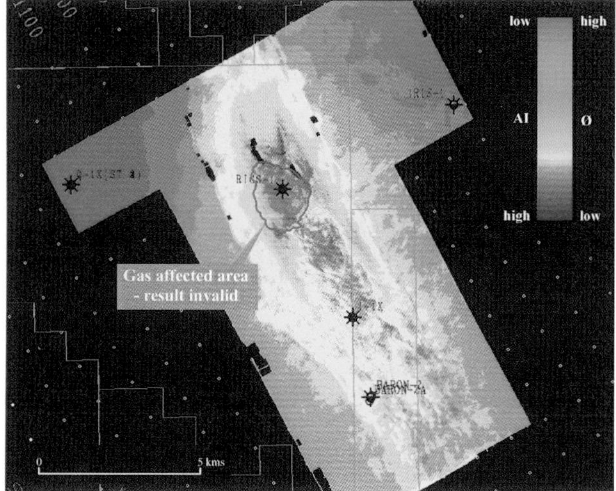

Fig. 29. Chalk Group average acoustic impedance.

interpretation ambiguity is typical of most of the South Arne structure because of the thin nature of the Chalk Group.

Analysis of seismic volume attributes does, however, indicate that internal variations within the relatively thin chalk interval over the South Arne structure are detectable from the 3D data. Figure 26 shows the average absolute amplitude map for the Chalk Group, in which the amplitude extraction excludes the Top and Base Chalk events in order to restrict the result to intra-chalk reflectivity only. The distribution of high average absolute amplitudes broadly mirrors structural closure at Top Chalk with exceptions on the northeastern and southeastern flanks of the field where the high amplitudes appear to extend beyond structural closure. The area affected by the overburden gas anomaly is visible around the Rigs-1 well where average amplitudes are very low because of signal attenuation (Fig. 26).

The presence of high average absolute amplitudes within the chalk can be interpreted in a number of ways. Reflectivity generated at interfaces of porous and non-porous reservoir intervals will give rise to a high average absolute amplitude. However, the presence of extensive hardgrounds, soft intra-chalk shale intervals (as observed in the Hod Formation of the Iris-1 well) or seismic tuning of thin, weakly contrasting interbeds may all also give rise to a high average absolute amplitude. The non-unique nature of the interpretation of the average absolute amplitude attribute coupled with the difficulties of conventional stratigraphic interpretation of thin

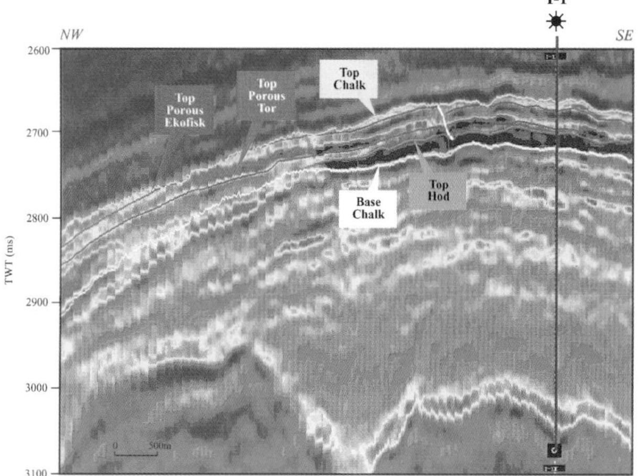

Fig. 30. Intra-chalk interpretation of acoustic impedance data.

seismic intervals required that an alternative method be employed to determine reservoir distribution over the South Arne Field.

3D acoustic impedance data. The process of acoustic impedance inversion removes the effect of the wavelet from the seismic data, providing a relative acoustic impedance earth model. This is subsequently converted to absolute acoustic impedance via the addition of a well-based low frequency model (Maver & Rasmussen 1995). The relationship of acoustic impedance to petrophysical parameters such as porosity allows the distribution of these parameters to be directly assessed from the 3D seismic data. Assuming the wavelet removal is perfectly successful, the resolution of the acoustic impedance data will be limited to the sampling interval of the seismic data, in this case 4 ms. This provides an ultimate thickness resolution at reservoir level of 6 to 10 m dependent upon chalk velocity.

Figure 27 shows the relationship between well log acoustic impedance and Chalk Group porosity based on core and log measurements taken in the I-1, Baron-2 and Rigs-1 wells. The generally monomineralic nature of chalk results in a very robust inverse relationship between porosity and acoustic impedance as demonstrated. Figure 28 shows the linear correction that is required to calibrate the inverted acoustic impedance values to the well-log derived values and thus directly derive porosity from the 3D volume. The average acoustic impedance map for the Chalk Group given in Fig. 29 is therefore inversely proportional to the average porosity over the field. The lowest average acoustic impedance values derived from the inversion appear to be concentrated in the north of the structure, providing a markedly different impression of reservoir distribution than that derived from volume seismic amplitude attributes.

As the acoustic impedance inversion result is derived from the 3D seismic data the values obtained in the gas affected data area are invalid. In addition to problems with the gas anomaly, there are other limitations associated with relying upon a volume average acoustic impedance and hence a volume average porosity value to determine reservoir distribution. Firstly, the measurement of average acoustic impedance in an interval will be dependent on its overall thickness i.e. the same net thickness of reservoir in two different thicknesses of gross reservoir will provide different average acoustic impedance values. Secondly, the intra-chalk formations display different poroperm characteristics because of grain size differences such that 25% porosity Tor Formation may be considered net reservoir, whereas 25% porosity Ekofisk Formation may not (Fig. 20). Hence the average acoustic impedance or average porosity attribute will not provide a unique solution to the net reservoir distribution problem.

The theoretically increased vertical resolution and greater visual dynamic range of the acoustic impedance data with respect to the conventional 3D seismic data were exploited to produce an intra-chalk interpretation (Fig. 30). The isolation of the individual Ekofisk and Tor reservoir intervals subsequently allowed for a more meaningful assessment of reservoir distribution. Rather than extracting average porosity values for each interval, net reservoir cut-off values were calculated for each formation, based upon permeability observed to flow during well test. The porosity values for the Tor and Ekofisk formations corresponding to the given permeability value were applied to the acoustic impedance volume.

In order to obtain a range of estimates of oil in place within the field, permeability/porosity cut-offs were used to constrain the volume of net reservoir. These cut-offs have been based on short duration (6–18 hr) well test information and therefore do not necessarily reflect what might be considered as being effective porosity/permeability cut-offs through field life.

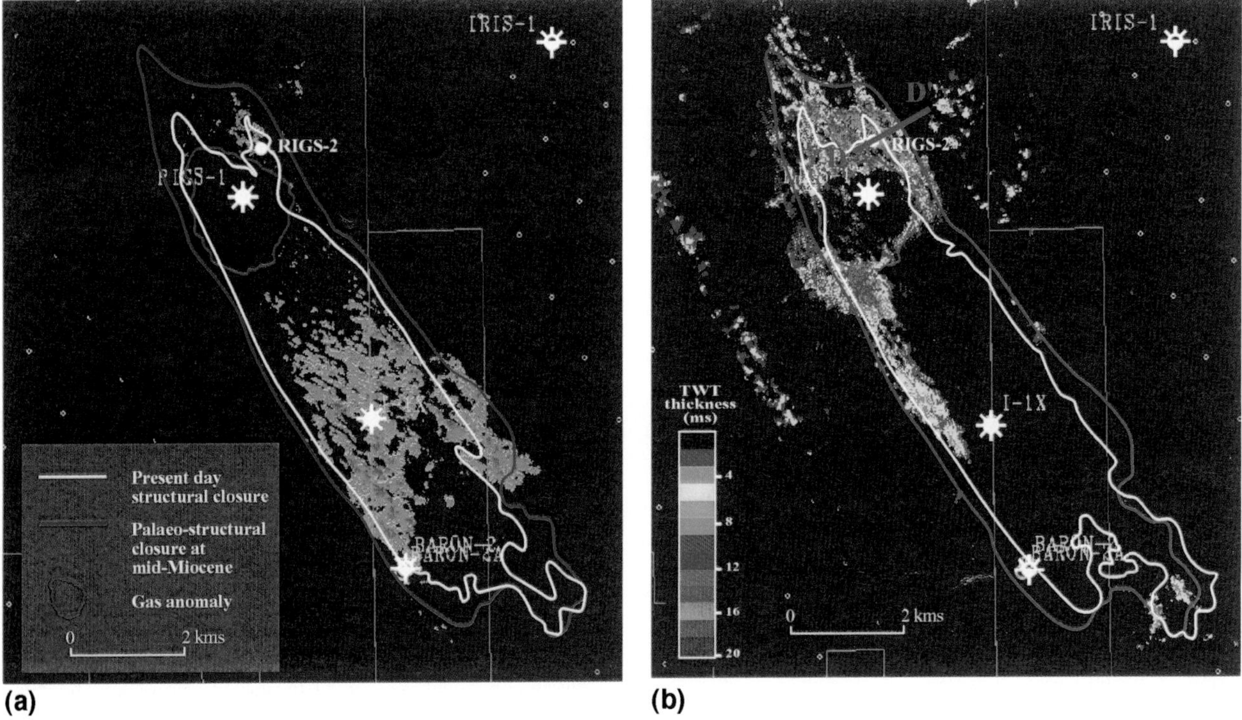

Fig. 31. (**a**) Ekofisk Formation net reservoir TWT isochore, porosity >30%. (**b**) Tor Formation net reservoir TWT isochore, porosity >24%.

In the base case, a 0.6 mD permeability cut-off was selected which equates to a 24% porosity cut-off in the Tor Formation and a 30% porosity cut-off in the Ekofisk Formation (Fig. 20). The porosity–acoustic impedance relationship is utilized to derive the two-way time isochore maps of net reservoir given in Fig. 31 by applying acoustic impedance cut-offs to the acoustic impedance volume. The distribution of net reservoir derived in this fashion is markedly different for the Ekofisk and Tor formations. The maps indicate the majority of net Tor reservoir lying in the north of the field with the majority of the net Ekofisk reservoir lying in the south. In order to gain a fuller understanding of reservoir distribution in the northern part of the field the data from Rigs-1 have been utilized to extrapolate the seismically-derived reservoir distribution maps into the gas affected area.

Rigs-2 Appraisal well

The net reservoir maps derived from acoustic impedance data (Fig. 31) indicated an area to the north of the field where a large volume of Tor Formation with good reservoir properties was predicted to lie below mapped structural closure. This

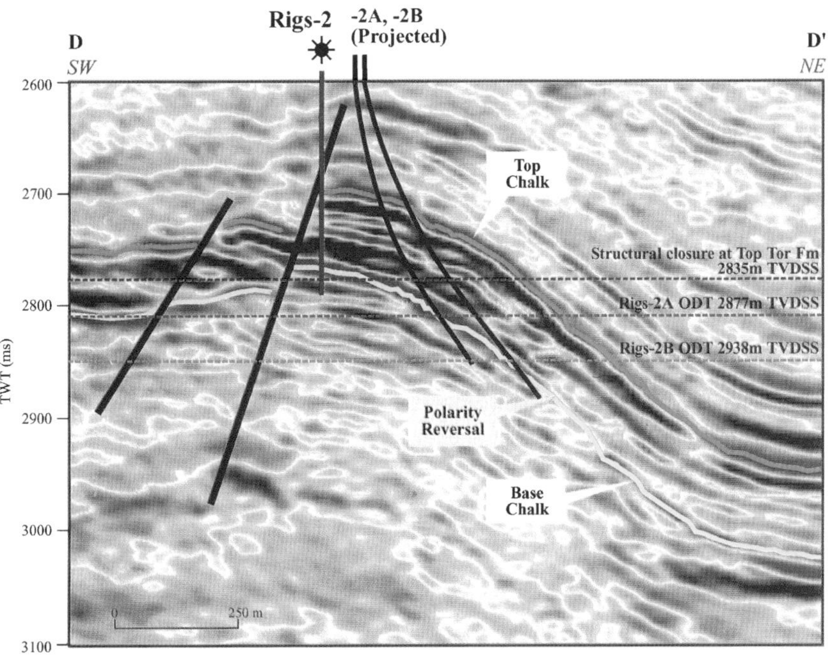

Fig. 32. Well to seismic tie, Rigs-2, -2A and -2B.

coincided with an area where a polarity reversal was interpreted at the base of the Chalk Group caused by the presence of porous allochthonous Tor Formation directly overlying Lower Cretaceous claystones, as had been observed in the Rigs-1 well. The Rigs-2 appraisal well (Fig. 32) was designed to calibrate and validate the seismic and acoustic impedance interpretations in this area on which the geological model was based. A subsequent down-dip side-track was also planned to test the section below structural closure in the event of an oil-down-to (ODT) the base of the reservoir being encountered in the vertical hole. The well was spudded in May 1996 and the vertical hole was successful in its objectives. The presence of an ODT at the base of the Tor Formation led to the drilling of sidetrack Rigs-2A. This well proved hydrocarbons 42 m below structural closure and again encountered an ODT at the base of the Tor Formation. Rigs-2A tested at a stabilized rate of 5263 BOPD on a 52/64″ choke. Encouraged by the Rigs-2A result, a second side-track, Rigs-2B, was planned and drilled to follow the hydrocarbon bearing section further down-dip. Rigs-2B proved hydrocarbons to a depth of 2938 m, 103 m below structural closure and again encountered an ODT at the base of the reservoir. The well and two sidetracks improved calibration to the geological and geophysical field model and supported the view that there was a stratigraphic trapping element to the accumulation (Fig. 32).

Hydrocarbon trapping mechanism

The stratigraphic element of the trap is believed to be partially facies-related and partly diagenetic in origin. The highest preserved porosities are recorded in hydrocarbon bearing, allochthonous units as observed in many Norwegian chalk fields to the north (Brasher & Vagle 1996); therefore, primary depositional facies are clearly important in relation to present-day hydrocarbon distribution. Early onset of overpressuring is also considered to have been important in preserving poroperm properties prior to hydrocarbon entry. Additionally, structural configuration at the time of hydrocarbon entry is also believed to have played a part in defining the present-day stratigraphic trap. At mid Miocene times, believed to be the time of peak hydrocarbon generation from the Tail End Graben (Damtoft *et al.* 1992), much of the present-day observed porous reservoir lay within structural closure (Fig. 31) and was likely to have been filled with hydrocarbons. Between 100 and 200 m of structural readjustment is thought to have taken place after oil emplacement. Subsequent water leg diagenesis may have provided enough of a permeability barrier to prevent hydrocarbon escape during subsequent tectonic subsidence. Evaluation of the 'aquifer' will therefore form an important aspect of understanding the stratigraphic trapping element of the South Arne Field during development drilling.

Conclusions

(1) The I-1 well tested oil at a high flow rate from a 7 m thick Tor Formation reservoir interval at a time when far thicker chalk reservoirs were being discovered. At the time of relinquishment of the acreage in 1987, the potential towards the north of the field was unrecognized.

(2) In 1991 the first appraisal well (Baron-2) was drilled with the philosophy of targeting thicker chalk deposits off structure, but was drilled on a major lineament which is considered to have influenced deposition of the allochthonous Tor Formation. The structural complexity of the area to the north of the field was recognized, but at this time the potential upside was not, because of poor quality seismic data below the gas cloud. The Top Chalk structure was depressed in time as a result of low velocities caused by gas escape to Palaeogene/Neogene sediments overlying the reservoir.

(3) The potential of the field was initially recognized (and subsequently rediscovered) owing to its similarity to fields in neighbouring Norway (especially Valhall), where excellent quality chalk reservoir sequences were encountered beneath gas clouds after initial avoidance of the area because of poor imaging and apparent structural depression.

(4) Following the drilling of two wells and two sidetracks, a previously unrecognized stratigraphic element is recognized in the field, further increasing potential reserves.

(5) 3D seismic and acoustic impedance data have allowed detailed structural mapping of the field and enabled reservoir distribution to be understood better, and integrated with well data. Trace inverted seismic acoustic impedance data have been calibrated to well data and used to provide an estimate of net reservoir distribution in the field.

(6) First oil is scheduled for mid 1999, some 30 years after the field's initial discovery. The field will be developed almost exclusively with horizontal wells, utilizing an advanced completion design.

The authors would like to thank the management of Amerada Hess for encouragement and permission to publish this paper. Personal thanks are also extended to the co-venturers in the 7/89 licence group: Denerco, Dopas, Danoil and Danop for their stimulating input to technical meetings throughout the appraisal phase of the field. Members of the partnership, Amerada Hess A/S and Amerada Hess Limited are also thanked for constructive input to the manuscript. The opinions and interpretations expressed in this paper are acknowledged to be solely those of the authors.

References

ALI, N. & ALCOCK, T. 1994. Valhall Field, Norway – the first ten years. *In*: *North Sea Oil and Gas Reservoirs – III*. Norwegian Institute of Technology, Kluwer Academic Publishers, 25–40.

ANDERSEN, M. A. 1995. *Petroleum Research in North Sea Chalk*. Joint Chalk Research Phase IV.

BRASHER, J. E. & VAGLE, K. R. 1996. Influence of lithofacies and diagenesis on Norwegian North Sea chalk reservoirs. *American Association of Petroleum Geologists Bulletin*, **80**, 746–769.

BIRKELUND, T. & BROMLEY, R. G. (eds) 1979. *Cretaceous–Tertiary Boundary Events Symposium* University of Copenhagen, Vol 1.

DAMTOFT, K., NIELSEN, L. H., JOHANSEN, P. N., THOMSEN, E. & ANDERSEN, P. R. 1992. Hydrocarbon plays of the Danish Central Trough. *In*: SPENCER, A. M. (ed.) *Generation, Accumulation and Production of Europe's Hydrocarbons II*. Special Publication of the European Association of Petroleum Geologists, **2**, Springer-Verlag, Berlin, 35–58.

EGGINK, J. W., RIEGSTRA, D. E. & SUZANNE, P. 1996. Using 3D seismic to understand the structural evolution of the UK Central North Sea. *Petroleum Geoscience*, **2**, 83–96.

FRITSEN, A. (ed.) 1996. *Description and Classification of Chalks – North Sea Central Graben*. Joint Chalk Research Phase IV. Norwegian Petroleum Directorate.

HARDMAN, R. F. P. 1982. Chalk reservoirs of the North Sea. *Bulletin of the Geological Society of Denmark*, **30**, 119–137.

JØRGENSEN, L. N. & ANDERSEN, P. M. 1991. Integrated study of the Kraka Field. *Society of Petroleum Engineers*, **SPE 23082**, 461–474.

MAVER, K. G. & RASMUSSEN, K. B. 1995. Seismic inversion for reservoir delineation and description. *Society of Petroleum Engineers*, **SPE 29798**, 267–276.

NYGAARD, E., LIEBERKIND, K. & FRYKMAN, P. 1983. Sedimentology and reservoir parameters of the Chalk Group in the Danish Central Graben. *Geologie en Mijnbouw*, **62**, 177–190.

Banff Field, UK Central Graben – evaluation of a steeply dipping, fractured chalk reservoir

N. EVANS, P. RORISON and G. SYKES

Conoco UK Ltd, Rubislaw House, Aberdeen AB15 6FZ, UK (e-mail : nigel.evans@gbr.conoco.com)

Abstract: The Banff Field is a steeply dipping raft of fractured Late Cretaceous and Danian chalk on the flank of a salt diapir structure on the western margin of the Central Graben in the UK North Sea. Paleocene sands draped over the raft and a carbonate cap rock provide additional reservoir potential.

The unusual geometry of the reservoir is a result of a complex structural history. Generally positive relief and minor pulsed growth through the Cretaceous and Lower Tertiary resulted in a condensed sequence of Cretaceous and Tertiary sediments over the structure. Contractional rejuvenation and active diapirism in the mid-Miocene deformed and fractured the thinned overburden to produce a tilted raft with reservoir dips generally over 45°. A vertical oil column of over 950 m (3000 ft) is present. Hydrocarbon migration began during the Oligocene, preserving good porosity in the chalk matrix during subsequent Late Miocene burial.

Seismic imaging difficulties caused by the steep dips and uncertainties over reservoir performance and connectivity led to a phased development plan. Phase 1 involved a six month early production system (EPS) via two imaginatively designed production wells, during which time 5×10^6 BBL oil were produced. The two wells were drilled from the crest of the raft down to the oil–water contact. Each well encountered over 1000 m (3300 ft) of oil-bearing chalk reservoir and provided important geological and reservoir performance data. Seismic data have been reprocessed using 3D pre-stack depth migration to improve image quality and lateral positioning. Geophysical, geological and biostratigraphical data have been integrated with the dynamic performance from the EPS to assess the controls on reservoir quality.

The bulk of the reserves, and highest productivity occur in the Late Cretaceous Tor Formation. Chalk porosity ranges from 15–35% but matrix permeabilities are low, generally less than 5 mD. High productivities (up to 40 000 BOPD) achieved during the EPS are attributed to specific zones within the Tor chalks which have a favourable combination of chalk lithofacies (including local reworking to produce chalk debris flows), open fractures, depth of burial, diagenetic history and stratigraphy. Sand units within the Ekofisk chalk may have a significant impact on fluid flow. *In situ* stress is expected to exert a major (favourable) influence on waterflood performance.

An effective phased development programme has resulted in an improved understanding of the complex controls on chalk reservoir performance in preparation for Phase 2 development. First oil is planned for mid-1998 and ultimate reserves are expected to be in excess of 60×10^6 BBL oil.

The Banff Field is a steeply dipping raft of fractured Late Cretaceous (Tor Formation) and Danian (Ekofisk Formation) chalk on the flank of a NW–SE elongate salt diapir structure on the western margin of the UK Central Graben. The field is located in Blocks 29/2a and 22/27a (Fig. 1) and is operated by Conoco (UK) Ltd on behalf of a partnership which includes Enterprise, Ranger, Hardy and Santos. The field is currently undergoing a phased development, with first oil from Phase 2 planned for 1998. Banff field is one of several salt diapir-related chalk discoveries in the UK sector of the North Sea currently under appraisal or early development. The BP operated Machar field (Foster & Rattey 1993) is considered to be the closest analogue.

The field was discovered in 1991 by the 29/2a-6 well and subsequently appraised by a further three wells (Fig. 2). The crestal Well 22/27a-3 and NE flank side-track 22/27a-3Z found the Cretaceous and Paleocene sections to be thin or absent. The three wells on the SW flank of the diapir have tested oil from each of the reservoir units: Lista sands, Maureen sands, Ekofisk and Tor chalks and a carbonate caprock of the salt diapir (Fig. 3), and proved a vertical oil column of over 900 m (3000 ft). Oil gravity ranges from 38° API at the base of the raft to 40° API at the crest, resulting from a variation in pressure and temperature. A small gas cap is present (Fig 4).

At the end of the appraisal stage, uncertainties regarding connected oil-in-place, the optimum recovery method and long-term productivity led to a phased development approach. The key uncertainties are detailed later in the description of Phase 1. Evaluation of the results of the Phase 1 development wells and subsequent six-month early production system forms the core of this paper. The bulk of the reserves and highest productivities occur in the Tor Formation chalk reservoir. High production rates have been established from the crest of the structure, despite low matrix permeabilities. Understanding the geological controls on chalk reservoir performance and in particular the influence of fractures and *in situ* stress are critical to the success of the field development. Other important reservoir factors such as chalk wettability and chalk compressibility are also being evaluated, but are considered to be outside the scope of this paper. The current understanding is that the chalks are likely to be neutral to water-wet. This paper will focus on the geological controls on reservoir performance and the impact on development strategy.

Plans for full-field development were optimized in parallel with the six month early production system (EPS) of Phase 1 as data became available. Phase 1 was successfully completed in March 1997. Phase 2 will begin in 1998 with two producers at the crest of the field and two horizontal injectors close to the oil–water contact. Oil production will be via a floating production system. Current reserves are estimated to be in excess of 60×10^6 BBL oil.

Evans, N., Rorison, P. & Sykes, G. 1999. Banff Field, UK Central Graben – evaluation of a steeply dipping, fractured chalk reservoir. *In*: Fleet, A. J. & Boldy, S. A. R. (eds) *Petroleum Geology of Northwest Europe: Proceedings of the 5th Conference*, 975–988. © Petroleum Geology '86 Ltd. Published by the Geological Society, London.

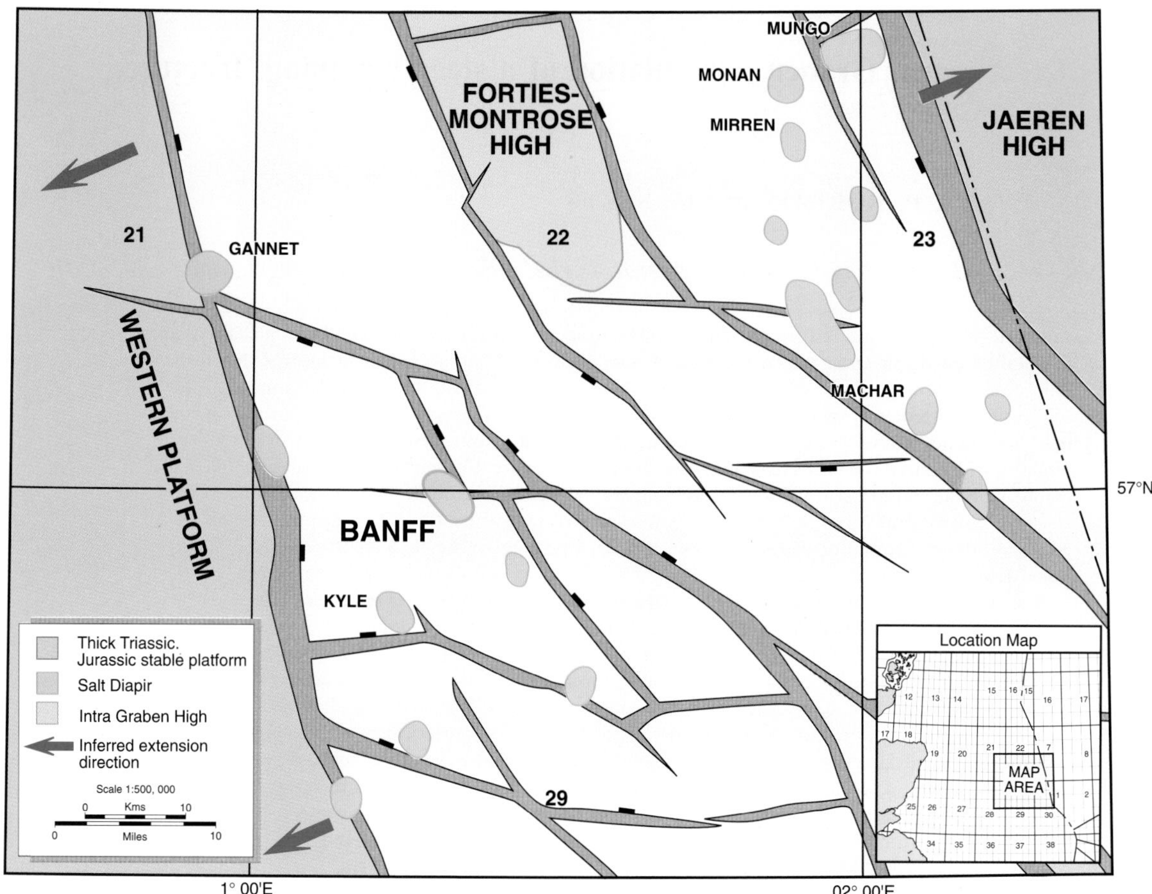

Fig. 1. Banff Field: location map with main structural features.

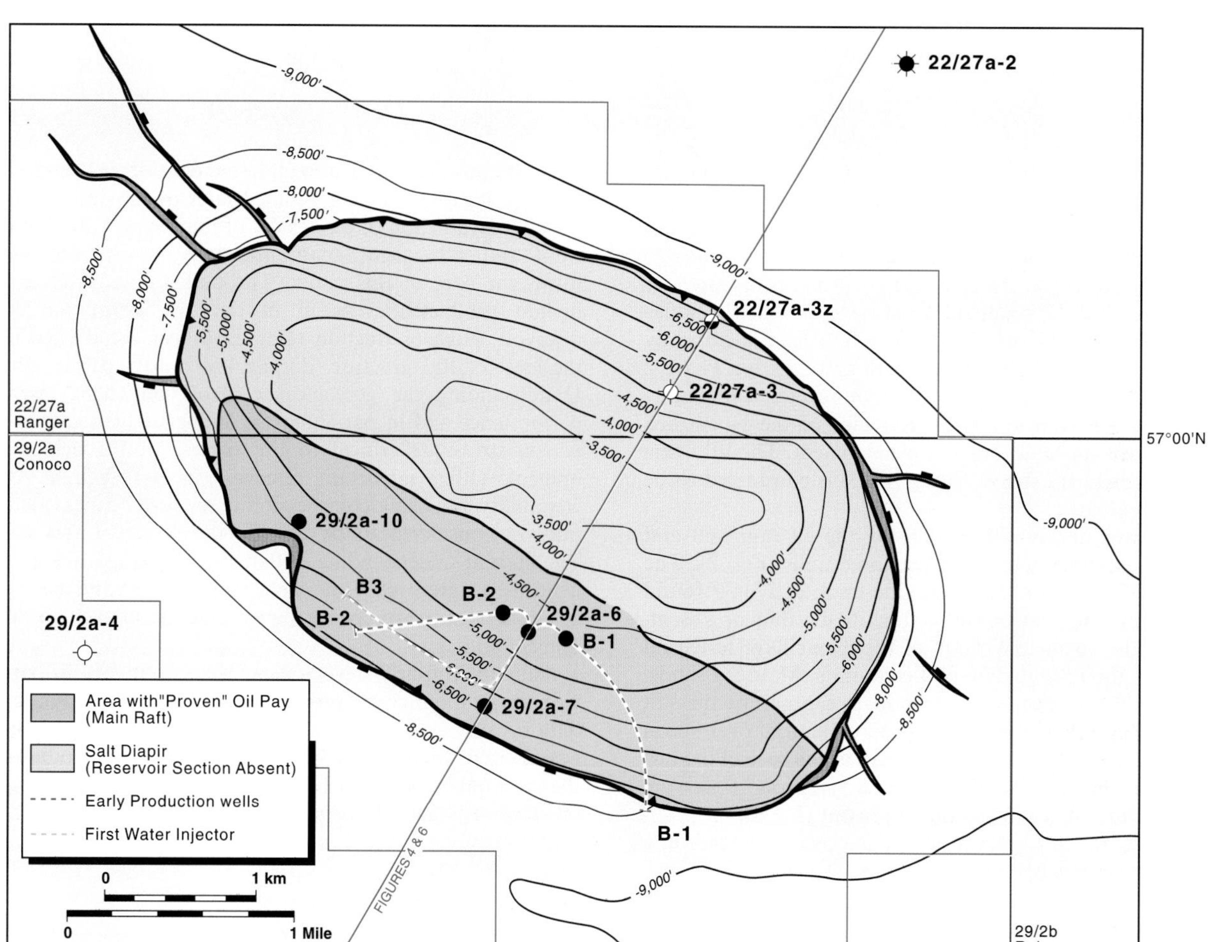

Fig. 2. Top Balder structure map with well locations and raft outline. Line of section for Figs 4 and 6 is indicated.

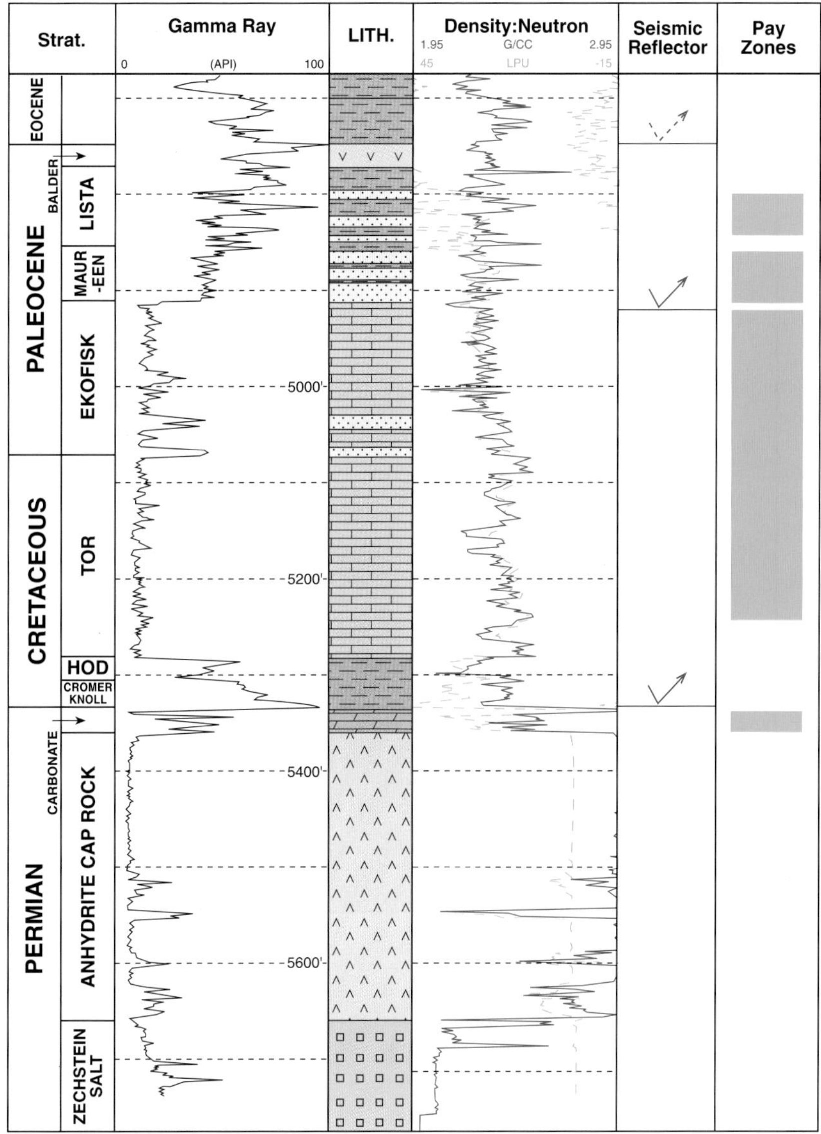

Fig. 3. Type well log with generalized stratigraphy of the reservoir section.

Structural history

The unusual geometry of the reservoir is a result of a complex structural history. The Zechstein salt has clearly had a strong influence on the structure, but growth of the salt dome was mainly passive or reactive, in response to extension and off-structure sediment loading (Vendeville & Jackson 1992). Evidence for active diapirism is confined to the Late Tertiary.

Triassic–Jurassic

The Zechstein salt began moving shortly after deposition, locally forming salt swells and walls in response to Early Triassic extension. A NW–SE oriented salt wall developed in the Banff area, controlled by basement lineaments (Bartholomew *et al.* 1993). A thick (over 2000 m) Jurassic section was deposited to the west of the Banff salt wall, reflecting continued extension. Growth on the graben-bounding fault on the western margin created the accommodation space. Sediment loading and tilting of the fault block to the west of Banff fed the gravity-driven passive growth of the salt wall. The salt maintained a position close to the sea bed throughout the Jurassic (Fig. 5a).

Cretaceous–Paleocene

The relatively thin Cretaceous and Paleocene sequences on the Banff raft are condensed equivalents of thick sections outside the diapir. Thinning of sequences onto the structure indicates that passive growth of the salt swell was continuing, but at a slower rate than sedimentation. Regional thermal subsidence during the Cretaceous led to high rates of sedimentation in the area. Although buried, the salt structure continued to generate positive relief on the seabed, sufficient during periods of pulsed growth to cause slumping and sliding of the semi-lithified chalk. The seabed topography also had a major effect on the distribution of sands during the Paleocene, with some channel sands by-passing the structure.

By mid-Cretaceous an elongate proto-diapir structure had begun to develop at the intersection of NW–SE and E–W fault lineaments (Figs 1 & 5b). Short periods of active, upward diapir growth may have accompanied fault-block tilting and mild inversion in the area (Sears *et al.* 1993). Asymmetry in the

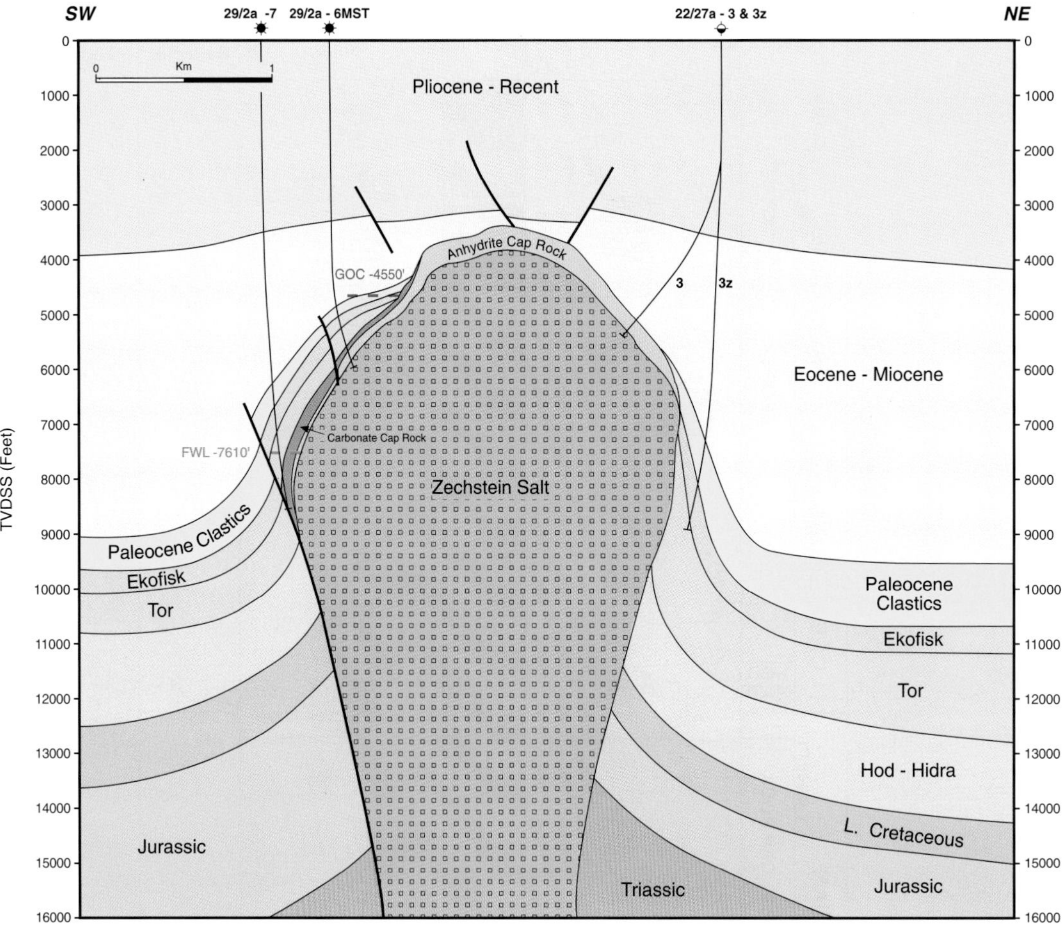

Fig. 4. Structural cross-section of the Banff diapir.

chalk thickness surrounding the diapir confirms a major switch in the locus of deposition from the west to the east side of the structure during the Late Cretaceous (Figs 5b & 6).

Early extensional faulting of the chalk raft probably began at this time during periods of diapir growth. Early faults would have been parallel to the axis of the elongate salt wall/diapir (Fig. 5b).

Eocene–Recent

There are at least two recognizable periods of active diapirism on the Banff structure, probably caused by regional compressive episodes. Tectonic squeezing of the diapir stem led to upward growth of the diapir, and deformation of the thinned cover. The earliest growth period occurred in the Late Eocene, resulting in faulting, stretching and thinning of the Cretaceous and Paleocene section over the diapir (Fig. 5c). Rupturing of the cover along the NE edge of the diapir probably occurred at this time, allowing a crestal salt high to develop. A period of inactivity and passive subsidence followed, and the structure was overlain by Oligocene and Miocene sediments.

A more spectacular period of active diapirism occurred at the end of the mid-Miocene, recorded by an angular unconformity above the structure. The raft on the SW flank tilted in the manner of a trap door, allowing the salt piercement to exploit the thin cover at the location of the earlier NE crestal salt high. The tilting and sliding of the raft was accompanied by further extensional faulting and fracturing (Fig. 5d). The original normal faults are now overturned in places to give the appearance of reverse faults. It was at this late stage that the chalk raft was partially disconnected from the surrounding chalks along a major fault zone at the SW edge of the structure.

Onlap of Upper Miocene sediments over the structure marks the end of active diapirism. Subsidence has continued since the Miocene so that the chalk is now at its maximum depth of burial. A low relief structure at the seabed reflects a combination of continued downbuilding and natural buoyancy.

Seismic imaging/reprocessing

Many of the uncertainties regarding reservoir geometry and oil-in-place can be attributed to poor seismic imaging and positioning problems around the diapir. The problems occur as a result of a combination of steep dips, rapid thickening away from the salt and large vertical and lateral velocity gradient changes. The 3D seismic dataset shot and processed in 1993 employed then state-of-the-art 3D pre-stack time migration processing to image the salt flanks (Fig. 6). However, interpretation of the chalk raft geometry is hampered by poor imaging and over scaling (Fig. 7a). Reprocessing of the data using 3D pre-stack depth migration (PSDM) over a 100 km^3 cube to a depth of 3.5 km has improved the image of the raft itself and interpretation of the structural geometry of the Banff Diapir in general (Fig. 7b). The amplitude character of the chalk raft, the imaging of the fault zone at the foot of the raft and the intra-raft faulting are particularly improved on the PSDM data.

The critical success factors for the PSDM technique are its ability to correctly handle the sharp increase in interval velocity between Tertiary overburden and Cretaceous/Danian chalk of 3000 m s^{-1} and the quality of the interpretation after each of the three velocity model building depth migration iterations. The improvement in seismic data quality enables more precise mapping of the extent of the chalk raft and therefore reduces uncertainty in oil-in-place estimation. The improved seismic data quality after PSDM reprocessing has also assisted in the successful positioning of the first of the horizontal water injectors in the steeply dipping lower raft.

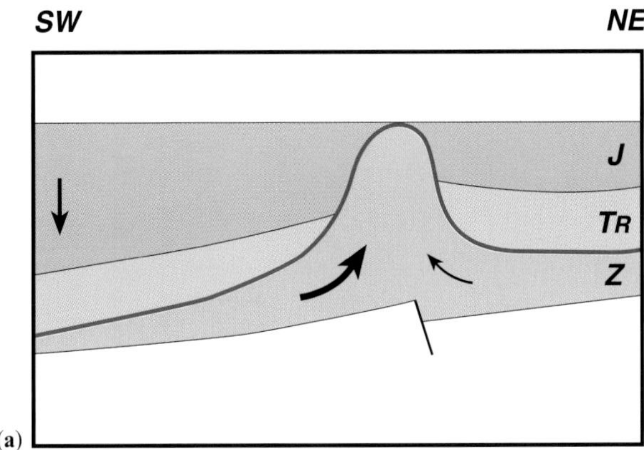

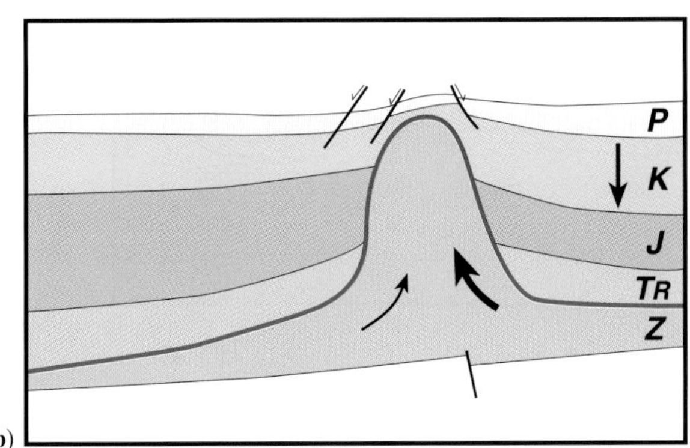

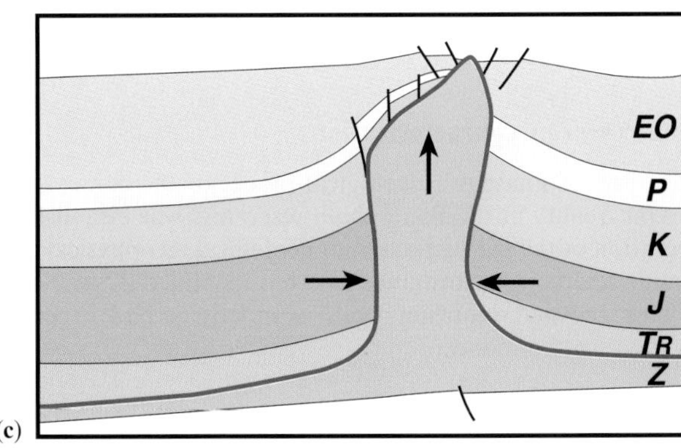

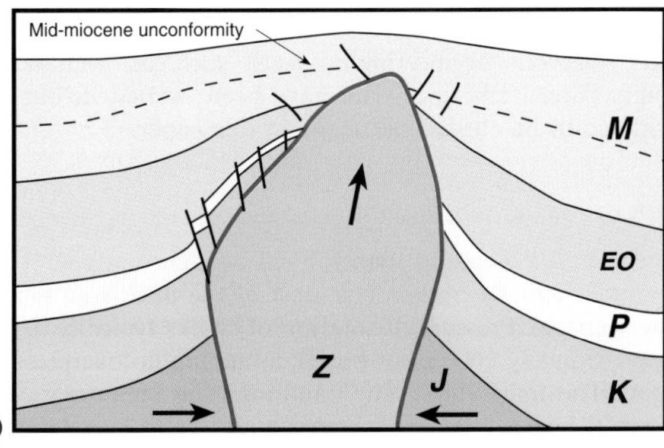

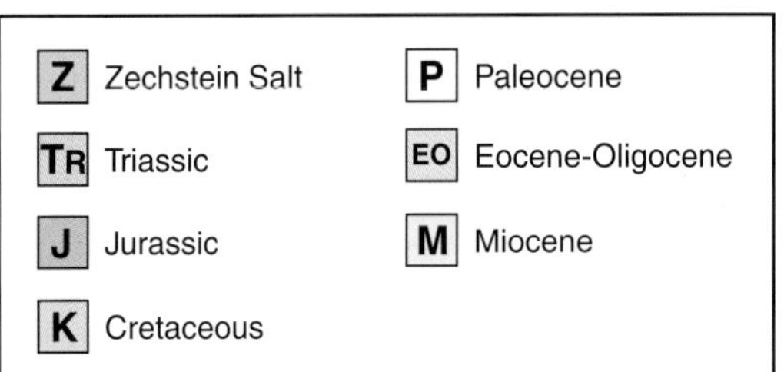

Fig. 5. Structural history of the Banff diapir (**a**) Triassic–Jurassic: reactive/passive phase. Sediment loading during extension allows the salt wall to keep pace with deposition. (**b**) Cretaceous–Paleocene: extension of thinned cover over the developing diapir. (**c**) Eocene–Oligocene: reactivation of the diapir during contraction. The thinned cover is breached to form a crestal salt high. Raft develops on SW flank. (**d**) Miocene: rapid diapir growth in reaction to regional compression. Extensional faults on the Banff raft are overturned as the structural dip increases.

Phase 1 development

A phased development approach was taken to address some major reservoir uncertainties in parallel with the planning for full-field development. At the end of the appraisal stage the key uncertainties with implications for the field development strategy were:

(i) reservoir geometry (i.e. seismic imaging difficulty caused by the steep dips);
(ii) the volume of oil-in-place;
(iii) a real and vertical connectivity;
(iv) long term productivity in the fractured, low permeability chalks;
(v) optimum recovery mechanism.

Specific geological information and dynamic reservoir performance data were required to fully evaluate the expected reservoir performance. A six month early production system (EPS) via two newly drilled wells was determined to be the optimum strategy. Phase 1 began in 1996 with the drilling of two purposefully designed production wells. The two wells, B-1 and B-2 (Fig. 8) were drilled 'stratigraphically horizontal' from the crest to the base of the dipping raft. The primary objective of each of the wells was to establish a long reservoir section within the Tor chalks. The well locations were designed to provide adequate separation to allow interference testing to assess the vertical and lateral connectivity of the chalk raft. Secondary 'appraisal' objectives were added to the well plans to improve understanding of the reservoir geometry at the down-dip edge of the structure where seismic imaging is poor.

Geosteering (including well site biostratigraphy) was a major factor in the success of the B1 and B2 wells. Each of the wells encountered over 1000 m (3300 ft) of reservoir section and provided valuable geological information for reservoir characterization. An extensive open hole data acquisition programme was carried out to complement and build on the existing database, specifically targetting the key reservoir uncertainties. Wireline logs included borehole image logs, nuclear magnetic resonance logs and full waveform sonic data to identify and characterize fracture zones. Oriented core was taken to calibrate the logs. Careful monitoring of mud-pit levels during drilling was used to identify open fracture zones. Structural information from image logs and dipmeter was integrated with detailed biostratigraphy and vertical seismic profiles to reconstruct the complex structural picture in each wellbore (Fig. 9). Dynamic reservoir performance was analysed during the six month production period, via a regular well intervention programme. Downhole pressure gauges, PLT

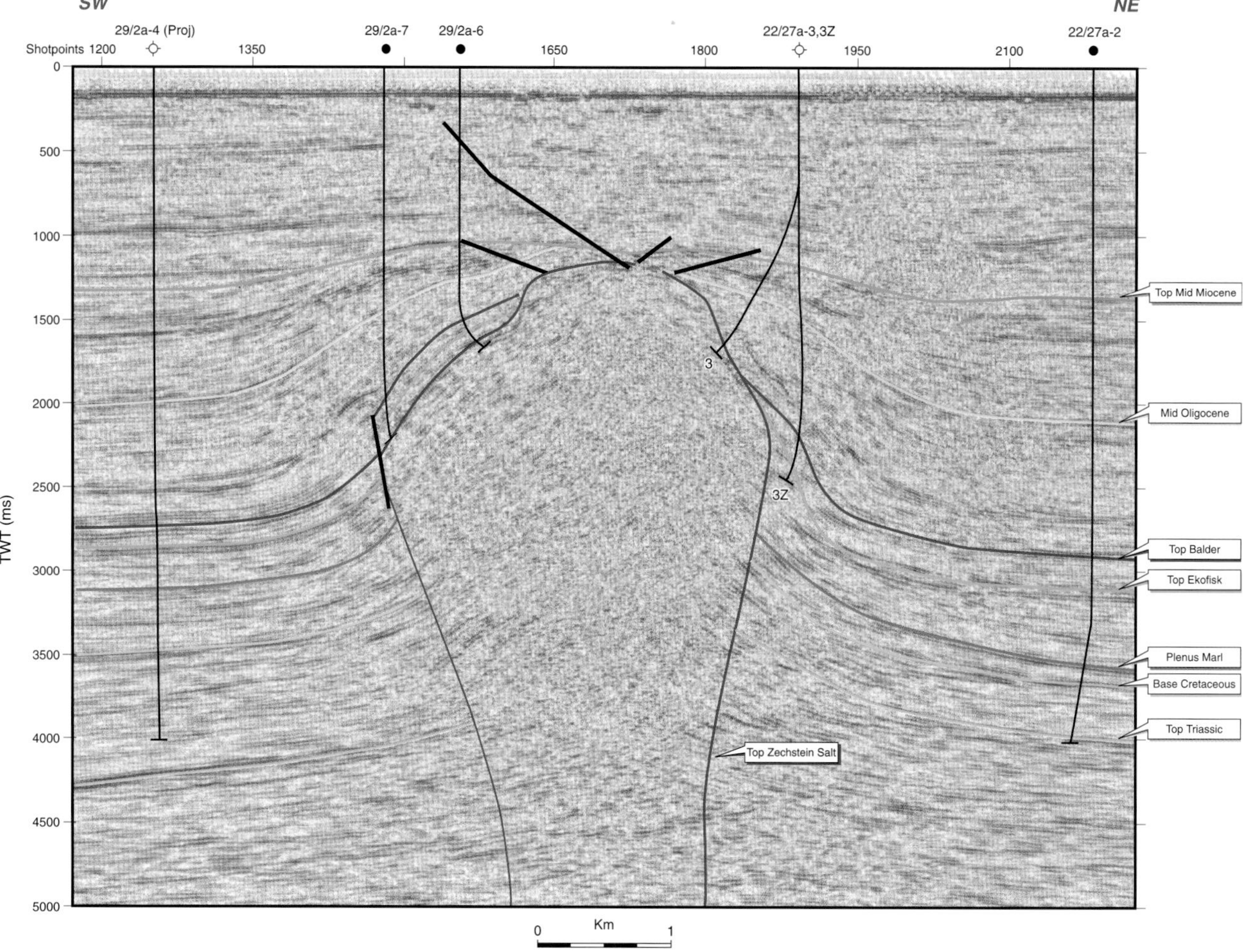

Fig. 6. Seismic section from 3D time migration (inline 1240).

and TDT logs were used to establish connectivity, and monitor well performance and phase saturations.

The Phase 2 development strategy has been designed on the basis of the geological and reservoir performance data gathered during Phase 1. Development will involve water injection into the Tor chalk at the base of the Banff raft to maintain pressure support during production from wells located in the Upper Tor Formation near the crest. Development of the secondary reservoirs (Paleocene sands, carbonate caprock) will be addressed during Phase 2.

Reservoir performance

The two EPS wells were selectively acid stimulated (using the ball sealer diversion technique) and established initial productivity indices (PI) of between 200 and 300 STB d^{-1} psi^{-1}. Production logs indicate that the bulk of the production in each well was coming from intervals near the crest of the structure. Highest production rates in B1 correspond to open fracture zones associated with debris flows within the Tor chalk.

Effective test permeabilities of hundreds of millidarcies were established. During the six month EPS almost 5×10^6 BBL oil were produced at rates of up to 40 000 BOPD. Such high test permeabilities and sustained high rates are not consistent with the low matrix permeability of the chalk. A composite flow model is required, where low permeability matrix blocks feed the high permeability fracture system to connect to the wellbore. Core logging and image log analysis indicate that the effective 'matrix blocks' in the upper part of the raft are unlikely to exceed 10 cm dimensions.

Down-hole pressure gauge data gathered during the six month early production period indicate excellent vertical and lateral communication between the two wells.

Chalk reservoir characterization

At the end of Phase 1 a geological model of the controls on reservoir quality in the Banff chalk reservoirs was established. Integration of the varying scales of geological, geophysical and dynamic reservoir performance data has identified a number of key controls that influence both productivity and expected waterflood performance:

(i) depth of burial/diagenesis;
(ii) stratigraphy;
(iii) lithofacies;
(iv) fracture density and type;
(v) *in situ* stress;

Other reservoir engineering aspects such as wettability, mobility, sweep efficiency, etc. have been evaluated, but are considered to be outside the scope of this paper.

Depth of burial/diagenesis

The chalk reservoirs of Banff Field are currently at their maximum depth of burial. The crest of the field is at 1350 m below sea-level. Pressure dissolution of chalks typically begins at approximately 1000 m of burial, assuming no overpressure support (Hardman 1982). The Banff reservoir pressure is close to normal hydrostatic and overpressure is not considered to

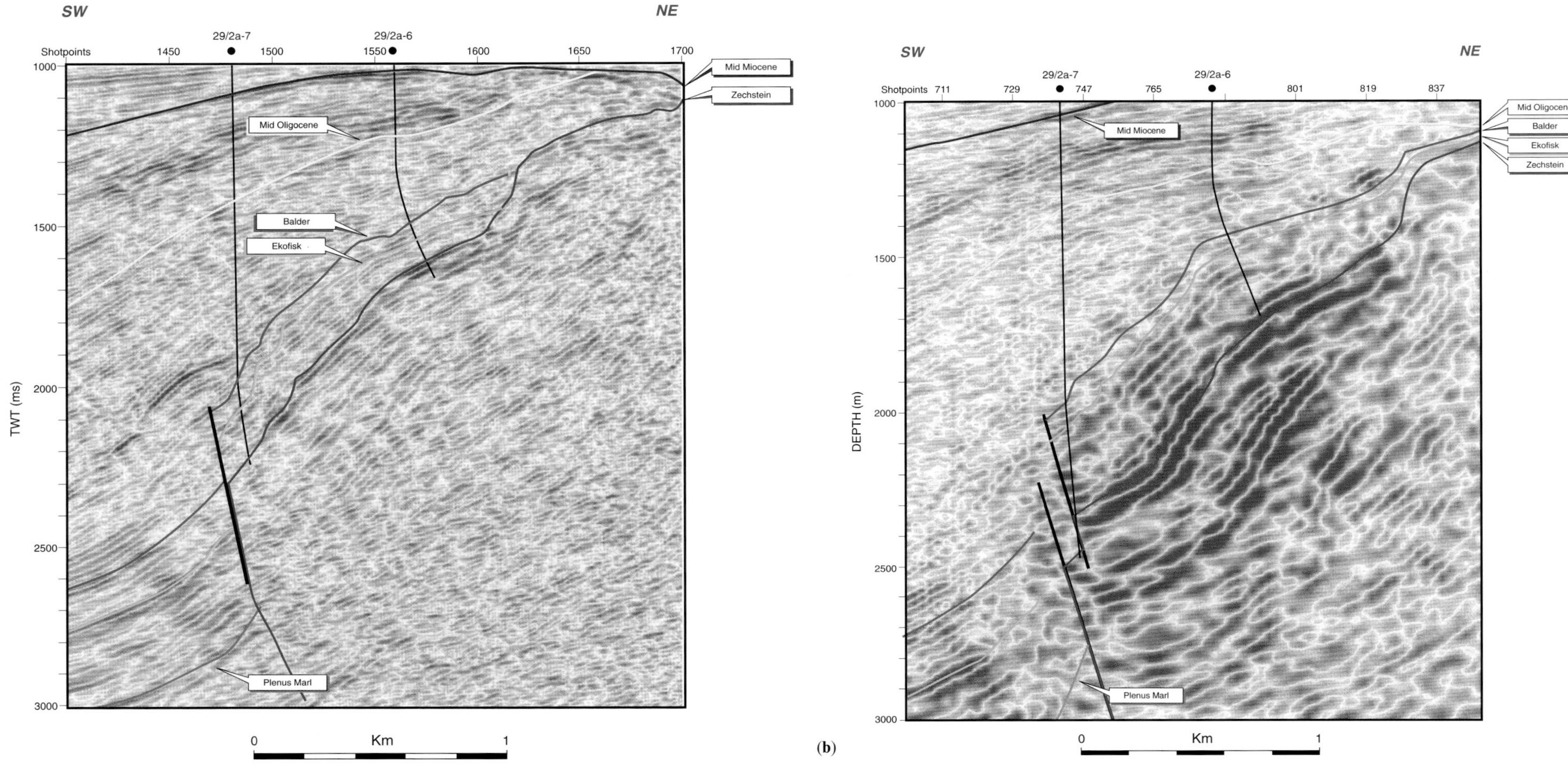

Fig. 7. Comparison of time migration and depth migration, Banff raft (**a**) 3D time migration; (**b**) 3D pre-stack depth migration.

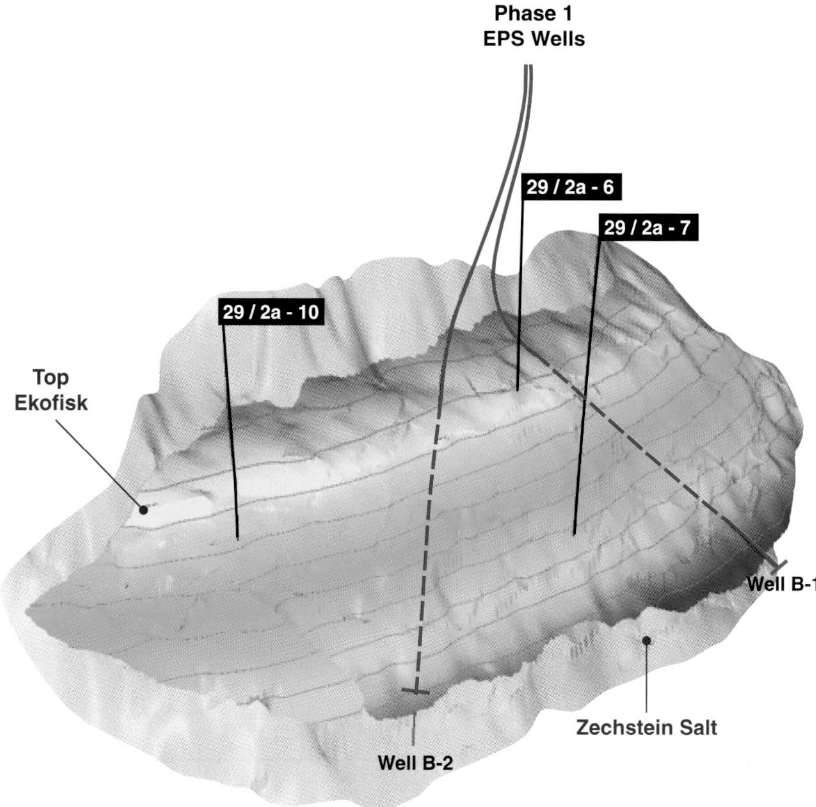

Fig. 8. 3D image of the Banff raft, showing the B1 and B2 (Phase 1 development) well paths.

have been a major factor in retaining porosity during burial. A seismically imaged gas cloud above the structure suggests that the structure is leaking at the present day. Gradual filling of the Banff raft with hydrocarbons during Oligo–Miocene burial effectively halted the porosity destroying process and can be related to depth in the high relief Banff raft. Similar relationships between reservoir quality, burial depth and timing of oil migration have been documented by other authors (e.g. Taylor & Lapre 1987; Foster & Rattey 1993).

A depth range of over 900 m from the top to the base of the Banff reservoir is accompanied by a marked decrease in reservoir quality. Porosity data are available from each of the wells and can be used as an approximation of reservoir quality (Fig. 10a). Chalk porosity decreases from over 30% at the crest to generally less than 15% at the base of the raft. This observation is consistent with drill stem test (DST) results from wells at various positions on the raft. A reasonable correspondence between log derived porosity and permeability/productivity is indicated. However, Fig. 10a also shows that major variations in porosity occur at any given depth, clearly indicating that other factors can over-ride the specific depth-related controls on reservoir quality.

Stratigraphy

The Danian Ekofisk and Maastrichtian Tor formations of the Banff Field can be subdivided by nannoplankton zones (Robertson Research pers. comm. 1995). The N1 to N4 zones comprise the Ekofisk Formation with basal occurrence of *Zygodiscus sigmoides* marking the Base of the Ekofisk. The Tor Formation is broken down into zones N5 to N8. A complete but condensed stratigraphic section from N7 to N1 is present in the crestal 29/2a-6 well, suggesting gentle positive structural relief over the Banff diapir during deposition of the chalk.

The clean Tor chalks have demonstrably better reservoir quality than the more argillaceous Ekofisk Formation. With excellent biostratigraphy data available from the five wells studied (particularly the long reach B1 and B2 wells), stratigraphic control within the Tor chalks has also become apparent. The Upper Tor, as defined by biostratigraphy, appears to have consistently better reservoir quality than the Lower Tor. Figure 10b illustrates that there is little difference above 6000 ft TVDSS (true vertical depth, subsea), suggesting that some other factor(s) are the dominant control on the crest of the structure. The Upper and Lower Tor populations diverge below 6000 ft TVDSS, where the Upper Tor has on average 7% greater mean porosity than the Lower Tor.

Intervals of sandstone occur within the Ekofisk Formation in each of the Banff wells, representing between 5 and 20% of the total section. The sands are easily identified from core or wireline logs (Fig. 3). The sands are immature, medium to coarse-grained and petrographically similar to the overlying Maureen sands.

Contemporaneous sands have rarely been recognized in Ekofisk chalks of the Central Graben and are not present in any of the wells surrounding the Banff structure. The stratigraphic relationship of the sand units within the chalk is therefore in question. Core descriptions vary from sand injection features and fissure fills to bedding features consistent with high density turbidites. Bedding relationships between sand and chalk range from discordant to apparently conformable.

The internal geometry of these sand units may have a significant impact on fluid flow and sweep efficiency within the Banff raft. The sands themselves have a higher intrinsic permeability than the chalks, but rarely exceed 20 mD. More significantly, the sand–chalk interfaces appear to have a relatively low mechanical strength and may provide natural conduits for water injection. The high initial rates recorded by the first water injector can be correlated with sand rich sections in the wellbore. Bedding-perpendicular sand filled fissures could have a markedly different effect on waterflood than a series of discrete beds.

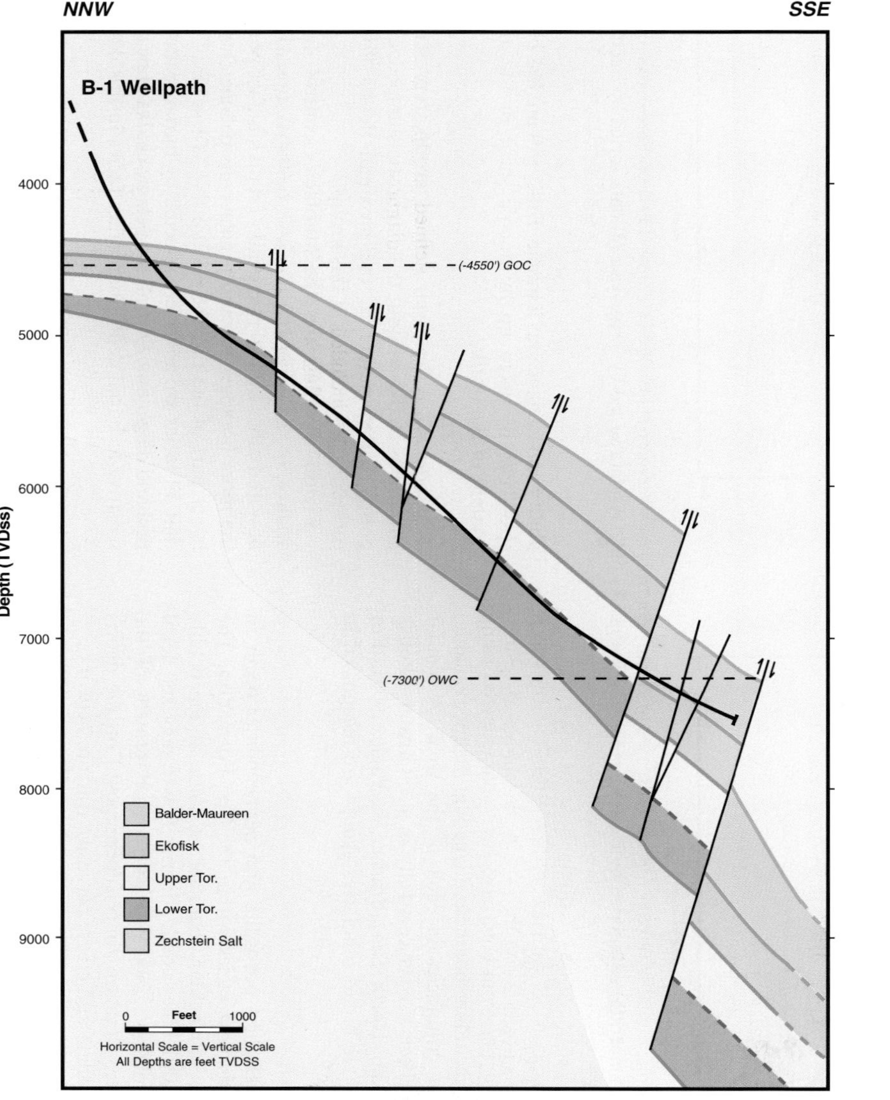

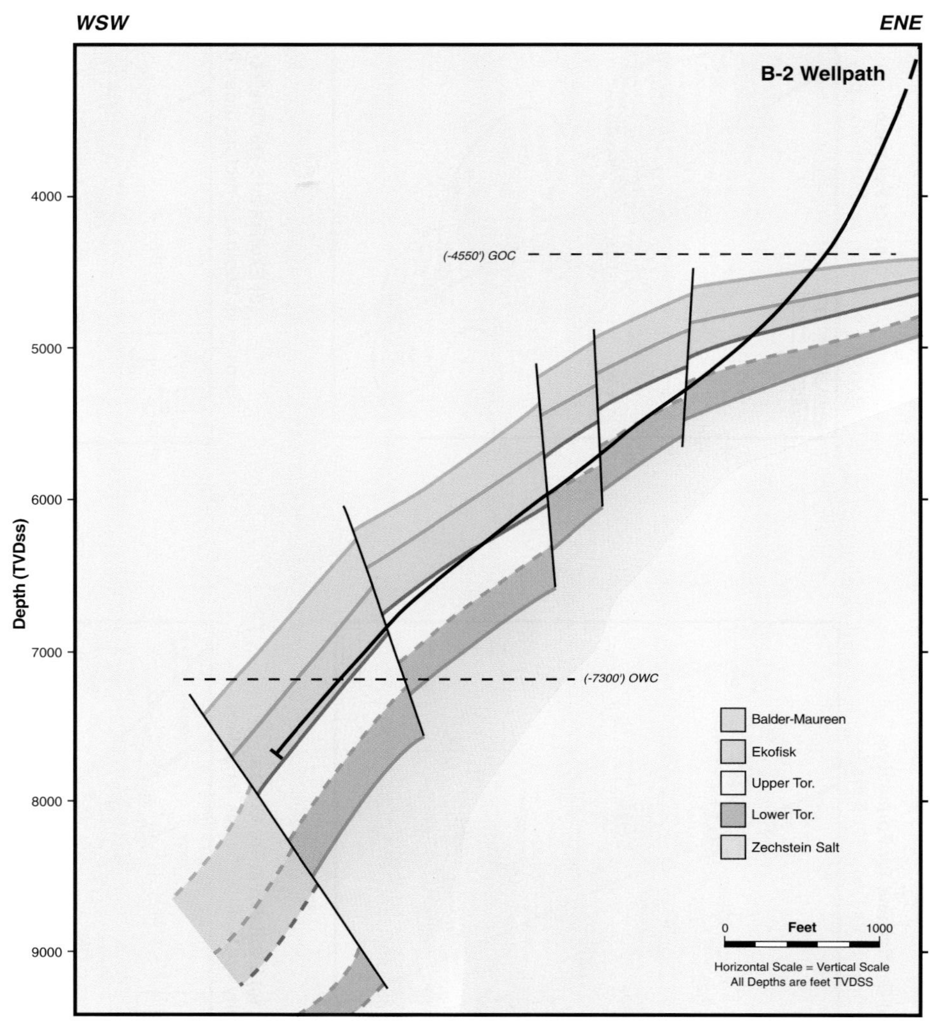

Fig. 9. Structural interpretation of the B1 and B2 wellpaths. Based on biostratigraphy, image logs and seismic data.

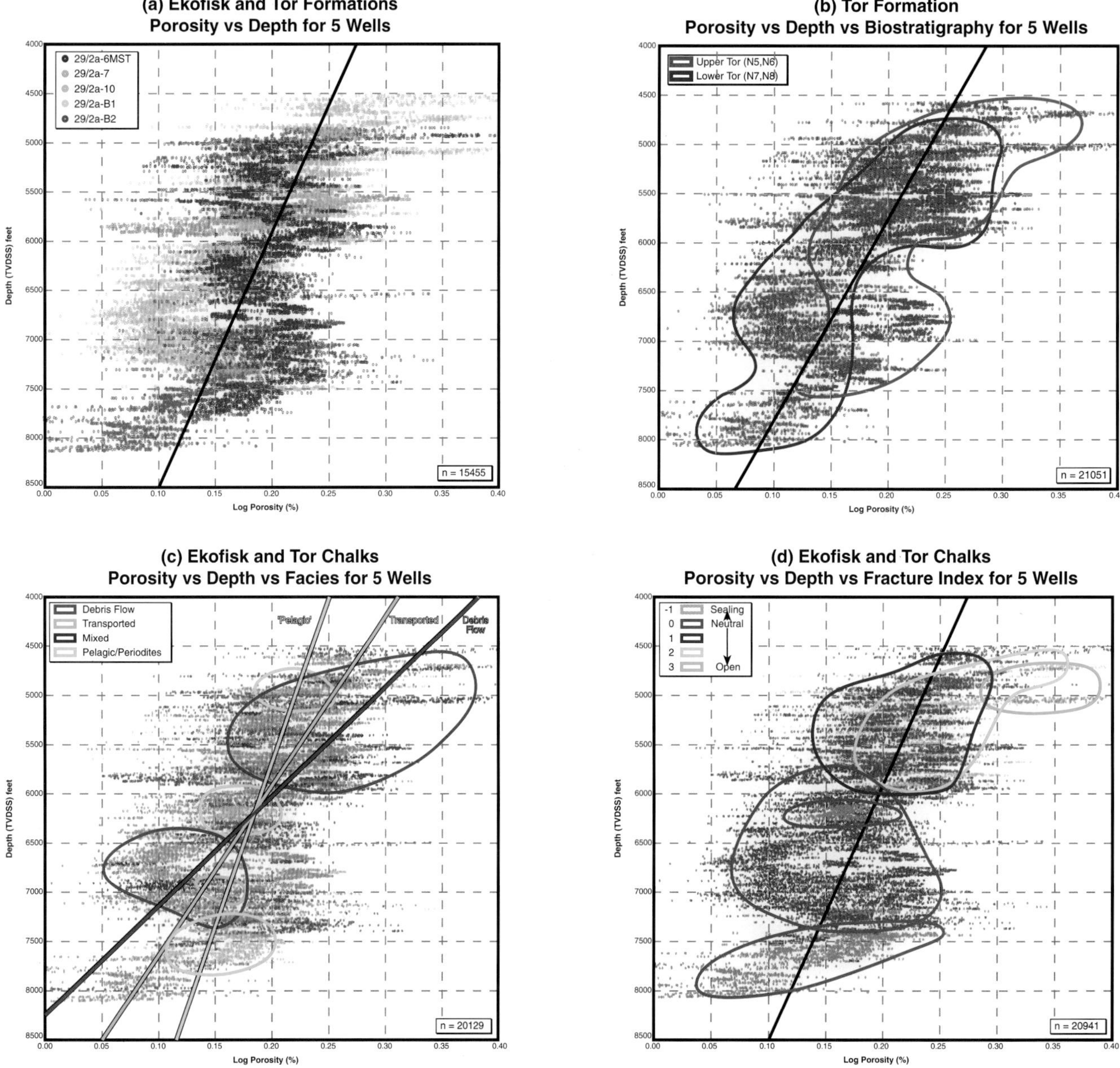

Fig. 10. Multi-dimensional cross plots for five wells, used to identify controls on reservoir quality (Z&S Geology 1997) (**a**) Porosity vs. depth – data sorted by well number; (**b**) data sorted by biostratigraphy, for Tor chalks only; (**c**) data sorted by facies type; (**d**) data sorted by fracture index.

Chalk lithofacies

Observed lithotypes from core have been characterized using wireline logs (including borehole image logs where available) to discriminate lithofacies in each of the wells. A similar approach has been used successfully in the Greater Ekofisk area, Norwegian North Sea (Brasher & Vagle 1996). For this analysis three broad lithofacies groups are recognized in the chalk:

Debris flow. Highest porosities and permeabilities occur in proximal debris flow facies within the Tor Formation. The poorly sorted, subangular character of some of the pebbly intraclasts within the chalk debris flows suggests local reworking, probably associated with pulsed growth of the diapir structure. Fracture zones superimposed on the debris flows tend to dilate and create pervasive fracture networks.

Pelagic. By contrast the more homogenous pelagic chalks have limited reservoir potential, characterized by low permeability and argillaceous laminae. Fractures are less pervasive as stress can be taken up by ductile shear in the argillaceous content of the chalk.

Transported. A less well defined group, representing allochthonous chalks without the diagnostic slumped, chaotic and poorly sorted nature of the proximal debris flows. Distal turbidites are included in this group.

Figure 10c illustrates the lithofacies control on reservoir quality. In the upper raft (i.e. above 6000 ft subsea) the debris flow and other transported chalks retain a higher porosity than the more homogenous and argillaceous pelagic chalks. In the lower part of the raft the relationship is less clear, indicating that all facies are adversely affected by burial related compaction and diagenesis. Overall the pelagic chalks appear to be less sensitive to burial depth than other facies in this dataset.

Fracture density and type

Fractures are the key to reservoir performance in low permeability chalks. The fracture system is critical to effective drainage of the tight matrix and facilitating the spontaneous imbibition process under waterflood. Analysis of the pressure data from the B1 and B2 wells during the EPS indicates that the upper and lower raft are in excellent pressure communication through the fracture network.

Fracture characterization using core observations to calibrate image logs (Western Atlas STAR2 and CBIL) and other wireline log data have been integral to the Banff reservoir modelling. Fracture associations range from sub-vertical faults and planar large-scale tectonic fractures to vuggy/brecciated zones with pervasive open fracture frameworks. A complex interaction of fracture and fault sets has been described (Z&S Geology pers. comm. 1996, 1997), with successive phases of rotation and reactivation of earlier systems. The key observations are:

(i) A consistent NW–SE tectonic fracture and fault strike is recognized in each of the Banff wells;
(ii) tectonic fractures appear to be extensional with respect to bedding and form well-developed parallel sets;
(iii) vuggy, pervasive open fracture zones are common in the upper raft. These high permeability zones are related to debris flow facies within the Tor chalk. Production logging data indicate a close relationship between high flow rates and the presence of these zones;
(iv) Healed fractures are common in the lower raft, described as narrow zones of comminuted chalk matrix healed by diagenesis.

For reservoir modelling purposes the fracture system has been simplified and coded using core and wireline data. Fractures are classified as open (codes 1–3 reflect increased flow enhancing capability), neutral (code = 0), or cemented and healed fractures which may be detrimental to reservoir performance (code = −1). A strong relationship with depth can be established. The multi-dimensional cross plot technique (Fig. 10d) shows that open, flow-enhancing fractures almost exclusively occur above the depth of −6000 ft TVDSS. Neutral and sealing fractures dominate below this depth. *In situ* stresses and present-day structural curvature of the raft are inferred to have exerted a strong influence on the fracture type. In summary, a tensional open fracture system exists at the top of the raft and a compressive, closed fracture system at the base.

In situ *stress*

The *in situ* stress regime in the Banff chalks exerts a strong control on the orientation of existing open fractures and is expected to have a major influence on the waterflood performance. Hydraulic fractures created during water injection should direct flow normal to the least principal stress.

The far-field (regional) stresses in the Mesozoic section of the Central Graben are believed to have low anisotropy, possibly decoupled from the deeper NW–SE trend in the Permo-Triassic (Cowgill *et al.* 1993). This means that local structures (e.g. salt diapirs, major faults) have a strong influence on local *in situ* stress. An elongate dome such as the Banff structure is expected to produce a radial maximum horizontal stress field (Ask 1997; Withjack & Scheiner 1982) and this is reflected in the radial fault pattern in the overburden (Fig. 11). However, within the Banff chalk raft itself the vast majority of observed fractures (from core or borehole image logs) are aligned NW–SE, consistent with the mapped fault pattern (Fig. 12). Very few 'radial' faults or fractures are observed. The

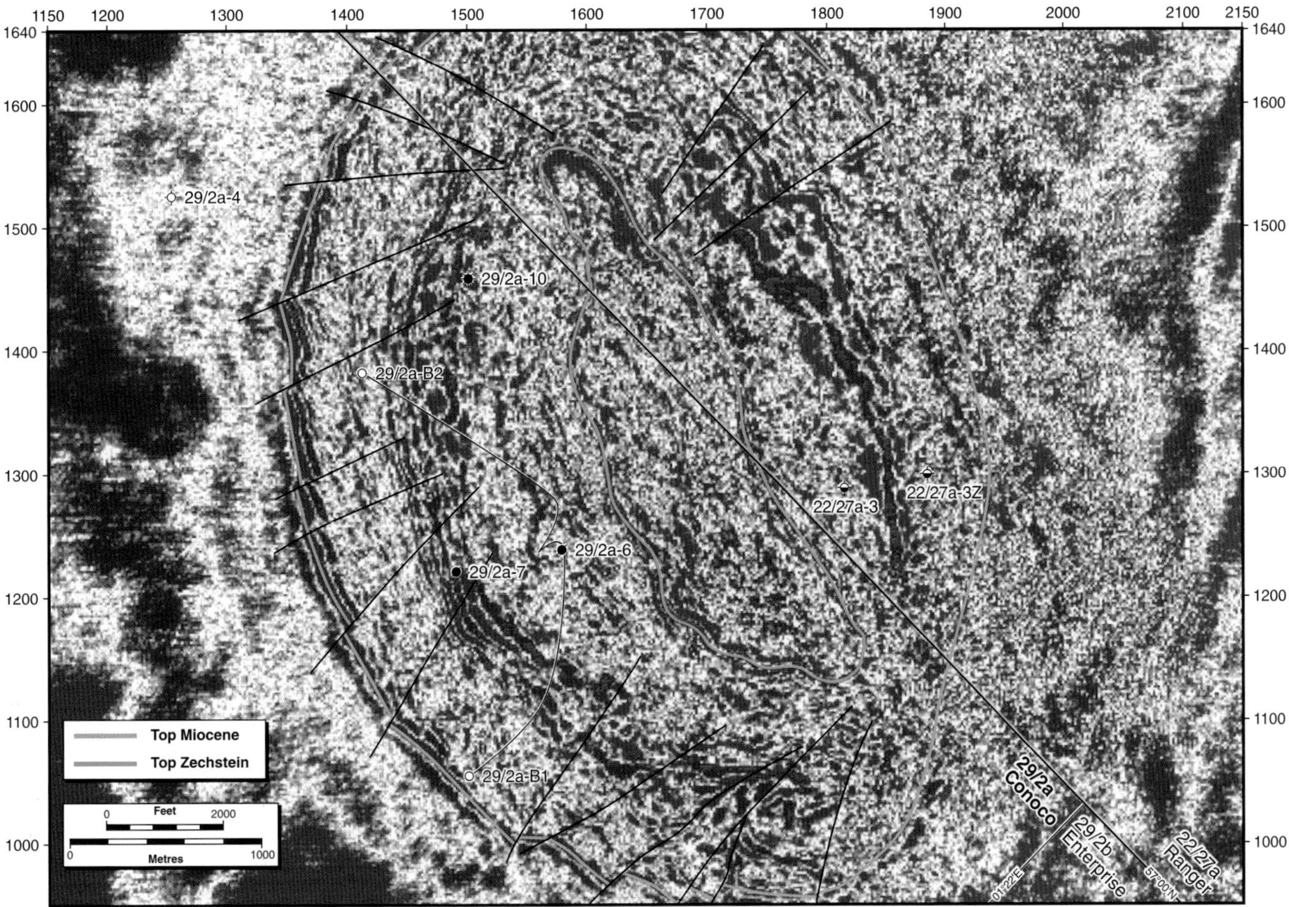

Fig. 11. Seismic timeslice (1248 ms) showing radial faults in overburden.

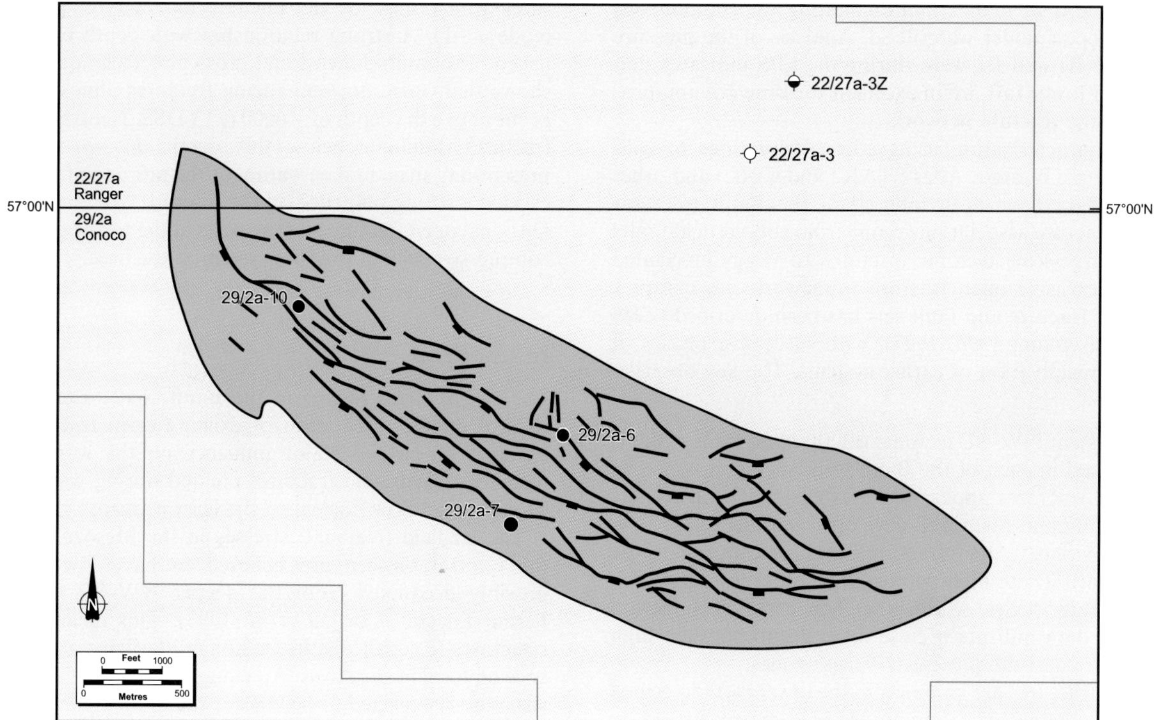

Fig. 12. Fault pattern in chalk reservoir, main raft.

influence of existing fault patterns on *in situ* stress has been noted in other fields. Yale *et al.* (1994) reported that maximum horizontal stress is rotated parallel to faults to influence water flood in the Scott Field.

Borehole break-out data and drilling induced fractures can be used to determine the orientation of contemporary horizontal stresses (Hillis & Williams 1992). Logs from the vertical Well 29/2a-7 have been interpreted to show a directional rotation of maximum horizontal stress (Sh_{max}) from the overburden to the chalk raft (Fig. 13). The break-out orientations in the Eocene section are consistent with a radial stress pattern, whereas the Sh_{max} orientation in the chalk raft is along strike of the structure. It is considered likely that the alignment of the *in situ* stress in the Banff raft is controlled by the extensional fault pattern being 'hard wired' into the chalks. The trend is parallel to the long axis of the structure and the deeper Palaeozoic fault pattern. Later reactivation of the structure has created a radial stress field in the overburden, but the stress field in the chalks remains linear.

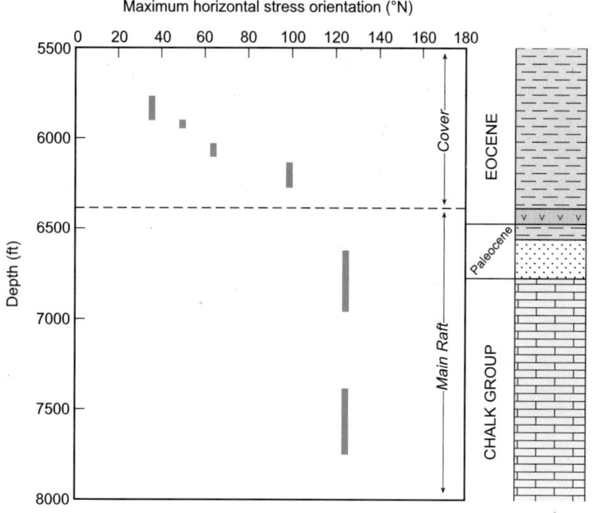

Fig. 13. Variation of inferred maximum horizontal stress orientation with depth, 29/2a-7 (Hillis pers. comm. 1997).

The key, favourable implication of *in situ* stress for Banff Field development is that fractures hydraulically induced during waterflood will tend to be near vertical and strike approximately 125°N. Injectors located at the base of the raft and drilled horizontally along strike will produce a 'line injector' system parallel to the edge of the raft. Induced fractures should be axial to the wellbore, increasing injection efficiency and reducing fracture twisting in propagation away from the wellbore. Sweep efficiency will be enhanced by directing water along strike of the raft rather than towards the up-dip producers. (Hillis pers. comm. 1997). This model appears to be confirmed by initial injectivity tests on the first injection well, B3 (see later section).

Geological model for the chalk reservoir

Integration of data from core, wireline logs, biostratigraphy and seismic interpretation with dynamic reservoir engineering data has allowed a geological interpretation of the controls on reservoir performance. The end result is a predictive model for reservoir development.

Figure 14 is a schematic cross-section through the Tor chalk, illustrating the main controls on reservoir quality described earlier. These external and internal controls provide the 'building blocks' of a 3D geological model for the Banff raft. Each of the controls can be modelled separately, but in reality most are intimately linked. Although the model is reasonably well constrained by an excellent dataset, the geological interpretations described earlier can also be accommodated.

Implications for reservoir development

The knowledge gained from the appraisal and early production phase has been used to design the Phase 2 development plan. Analysis of the EPS well performance confirms that excellent production rates are sustainable at the crest of the reservoir. Any future chalk production wells will be targetted at the Upper Tor Formation, above 1800 m (6000 ft) TVDSS. Conversely, healed fractures and low matrix permeability are expected in the lower raft regardless of facies or stratigraphy.

Pressure data from the EPS indicate that pressure maintenance (via voidage replacement) will be necessary to prevent early gas break-out. Water injection wells have been designed to exploit the favourable *in situ* stress and fracture orientation at the base of the raft. Water will be injected, at pressures most likely above the fracture gradient, using horizontal wells located just above the oil–water contact. The wells will be aligned with Sh_{max} to aid injectivity and create a 'line injector' system along strike of the raft. It is anticipated that gravity, stress orientation and the overturned nature of the extensional faults and fractures will work together to retard water breakthrough. The injection wells will be targetted at the Upper Tor Formation, but will also aim to access some of the Ekofisk sand units where weaker mechanical properties may create natural conduits. Initial information from the first injector (B3, Fig. 15) indicates that voidage replacement rates are readily achievable from wells drilled below 2100 m (7000 ft) TVDSS in the chalk reservoir. It appears that injection pressures are sufficient to re-open the closed and healed fracture and fault systems observed at the base of the raft.

Secondary reservoirs in the Paleocene sands and carbonate cap rock identified in the appraisal stage will be evaluated as potential development targets during Phase 2.

Conclusions

Integration of geological, geophysical and reservoir engineering data has resulted in an improved understanding of the complex controls on chalk reservoir quality. A valid 3D geological model for the chalk reservoirs is the result. The model is supported by an excellent dataset and can be used for well planning, volumetrics and future reservoir performance models.

A phased development strategy has been adopted for Banff Field and has proved very successful to date. Many of the reservoir uncertainties identified at the pre-development stage have been significantly reduced. Understanding of reservoir geometry has been greatly improved through structural reconstruction of the long-reach B1 and B2 wells and improved seismic imaging from 3D PSDM. Oil-in-place ranges have been narrowed. Excellent areal and vertical connectivity within the raft has been established from pressure data during the EPS. Long-term productivity at rates of up to 40 000 BOPD has been achieved from the two wells at the crest of the

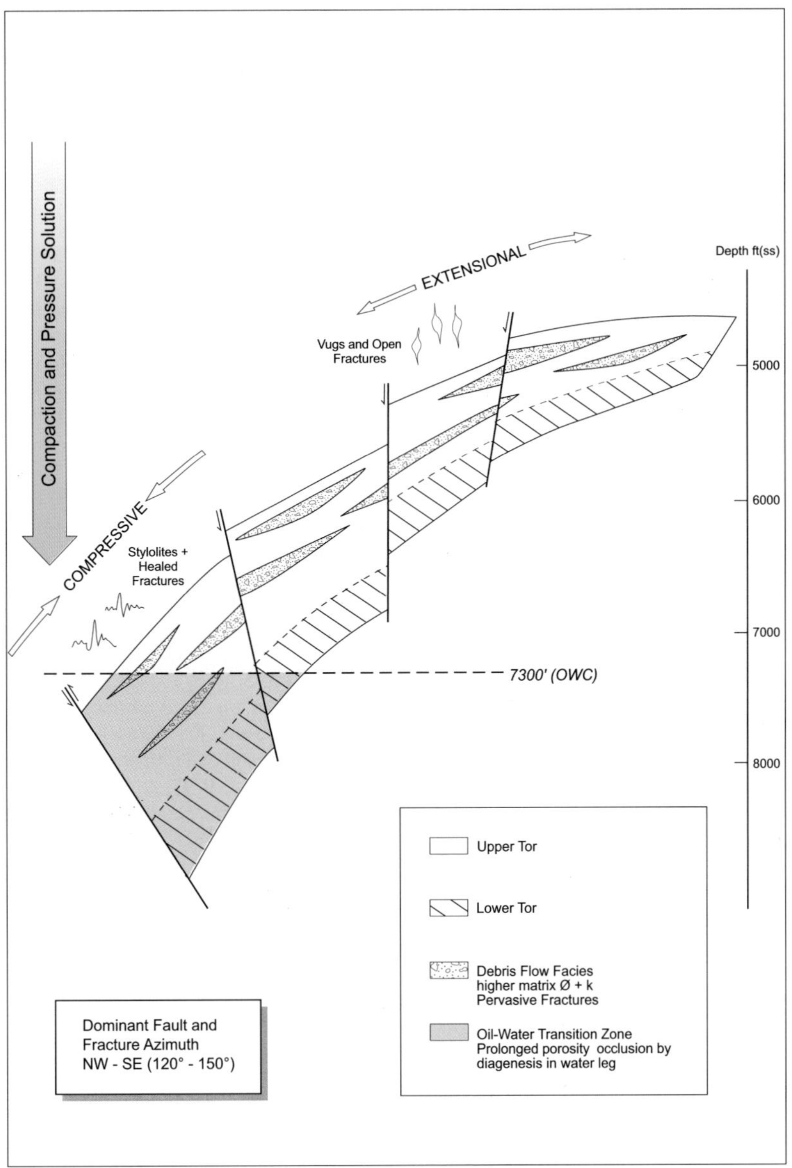

Fig. 14. Schematic summary of controls on reservoir quality in the Tor chalk of the Banff raft.

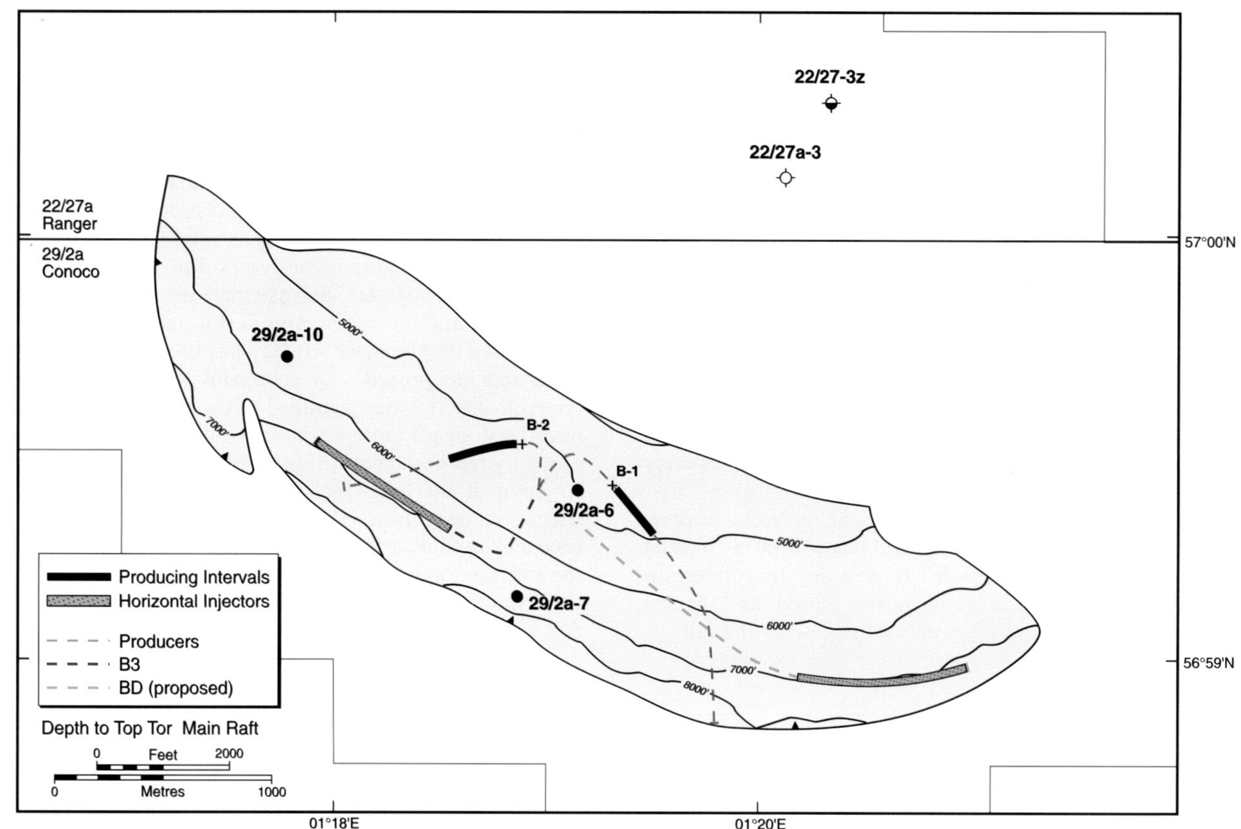

Fig. 15. Banff Phase 2 development wells (existing and planned). Tor chalk depth map.

structure. The Phase 2 development plan and production facilities have been designed to manage the remaining reservoir uncertainties.

The authors wish to thank the Banff Unit partners: Conoco, Enterprise, Ranger, Hardy and Santos for permission to publish this paper. In addition, special thanks to R. Hillis for his assistance with in-situ stress evaluation, Z&S Geology for fracture logging and interpretation, BP Machar staff for helpful discussions, the Salt Tectonics group at Royal Holloway University, led by I. Davison, and P. G. S. Tensor for their work on the 3D PSDM. We must also acknowledge the contributions of numerous previous workers on Banff Field at Conoco and within the partnership.

References

Ask, M. V. S. 1997. *In situ* stress from breakouts in the Danish sector of the North Sea. *Marine and Petroleum Geology*, **14**, 231–245.

Bartholomew, I. D., Peters, J. M. & Powell, C. M. 1993. Regional structural evolution of the North Sea; oblique slip and the reactivation of basement lineaments. *In*: Parker, J. R. (ed.) *Petroleum Geology of Northwest Europe: Proceedings of the 4th Conference*. Geological Society, London, 1109–1122.

Brasher, J. E. & Vagle, K. R. 1996. Influence of lithofacies and diagenesis on Norwegian North Sea Chalk Reservoirs. *American Association of Petroleum Geologists Bulletin*, **80**, 746–769.

Cowgill, S. M., Meredith, P. G., Murrel, S. A. F. & Brereton, N. R. 1993. Crustal stresses in the North Sea from breakouts and other borehole data. *International Journal of Rock Mechanics*, **30**, 1111–1114.

Foster, P. & Rattey, P. 1993. The evolution of a fractured chalk reservoir: Machar Oilfield, UK North Sea. *In*: Parker, J. R. (ed.) *Petroleum Geology of Northwest Europe: Proceedings of the 4th Conference*. Geological Society, London, 1445–1452.

Hardman, R. F. P. 1982. Chalk reservoirs of the North Sea. *Bulletin of the Geological Society of Denmark*, **30**, 119–137.

Hillis, R. R. & Williams, A. F. 1992. Borehole breakouts and stress analysis in the Timor sea. *In*: Hurst, A., Griffiths, C. M. & Worthington, P. F. (eds) *Geological Applications of Wireline Logs II*. Geological Society, London, Special Publications, **66**, 157–168.

Sears, R. A., Harbury, A. R., Protoy, A. J. G. & Stewart, D. J. 1993. Structural Styles from the Central Graben in the UK and Norway. *In*: Parker, J. R. (ed.) *Petroleum Geology of NW Europe: Proceedings of the 4th Conference*, Geological Society, London, 1231–1243.

Taylor, S. R. & Lapre, J. F. 1987. North Sea Chalk diagenesis : its effect on reservoir location and properties. *In*: Brooks, J. & Glennie, K. W. (eds) *Petroleum Geology of North West Europe*. Graham & Trotman, London, 483–495.

Vendeville, B. C. & Jackson, M. P. A. 1992. The rise of diapirs during thin-skinned extension. *Marine and Petroleum Geology*, **9**, 331–353.

Withjack, M. O. & Scheiner, C. 1982. Fault patterns associated with domes – an experimental and analytical study. *American Association of Petroleum Geologists Bulletin*, **66**, 302–316.

Yale, D. P. Rodriguez, J. M., Mercer, T. B. & Blaisdell, D. W. 1994. *In situ* stress orientation and the effects of local structure – Scott Field, North Sea. *In*: *Eurock '94. Proceedings of the 1994 Conference, Delft*, 945–951.

High pressure/high temperature plays

High pressure/high temperature plays

Introduction and review

B. LEVELL

Petroleum Development Oman, PO Box 81, Muscat 113, Sultanate of Oman

A substantial amount of costly high pressure/high temperature (HP/HT) exploration and appraisal drilling in the Central Graben was represented by four papers in this theme. HP/HT conditions are defined as greater than 10 000 psi and/or more than 300°F. For the exploration geologist, the HP/HT play represents an involved geological challenge:

(1) prediction of trap integrity, based on understanding of structural geology, seal strength, formation pressure evolution and hydrocarbon type;
(2) prediction of reservoir quality based on sequence stratigraphy, and diagenetic evolution (linked back to trap integrity); and
(3) interpretation of deep seismic data with frequently difficult multiple problems due to velocity inversion below the Chalk, and complex salt related structures.

For the development geologist further challenges include:

(1) the need to guarantee very high flow rates to sustain the high drilling costs;
(2) the difficulty in planning and drilling wells due to the small margins between formation pressures and shoe strengths, particularly at the crest of the fields; and
(3) production technological problems with the highly saline brines and condensates, as well as the hostile environment for tools and tubulars.

A theme of all the papers is the absolute necessity for a multi-disciplinary approach to such problems with early identification of critical risks. The competitor in the HP/HT play is mostly Mother Earth!

This is most clearly brought out in the paper by **Pooler & Amory** on the ETAP development, which although it includes just two fields which are strictly HP/HT (the Shell/ Esso Heron and Skua fields), highlights the variety of critical risks found in the Central Graben and how they had to be cooperatively attacked to enable the development of the smaller fields. The project would appear to indicate the way forward in the North Sea, with pooling of resources both technical and financial for the benefit of all partners in the ETAP group. Somewhat more straight-forward developments at Elgin, Franklin and Shearwater are described by **Lasocki *et al.*** and **Blehaut *et al.*** respectively. Both papers deal with the projects as a whole rather than solely the sub-surface aspects. The sub-surface is however highlighted by **Helgesen** who presents an interesting and appealing structural model for the post salt sequence based on the interaction of grounded post-salt (Triassic and Jurassic) blocks with the pre-salt structures. The precise structure depending on the fulcrum where grounding first occurred. This model explicitly disconnects faults in the Mesozoic section from the basement faults, and thus helps explain why lineament-type analyses of the fault patterns of the Central Graben tend to be unconvincing, or at least very involved.

It is clear from these four papers that while great strides have been made in the last 5 years, particularly with the planning of the first developments, the challenges presented by this play are still very great.

LEVELL, B. 1999. High pressure/high temperature plays. *In*: FLEET, A. J. & BOLDY, S. A. R. (eds) *Petroleum Geology of Northwest Europe: Proceedings of the 5th Conference*, 991.

A subsurface perspective on ETAP – an integrated development of seven Central North Sea fields

J. POOLER[1] and M. AMORY[2]

[1] *BP Exploration Operating Compamy Limited, Farburn Industrial Estate, Dyce, Aberdeen, AB21 7PB, UK (e-mail: poolermj@bp.com)*
Present address: BP Amoco Exploration, Uxbridge One, Uxbridge, Middlesex UB8 1PH, UK
[2] *Shell UK Exploration and Production, 1 Altens Farm Road, Nigg, Aberdeen AB12 3FY, UK (e-mail: a.h.m.paardekam@openmail2.uedc743.sukepabe.simis.com)*

Abstract: In December 1995 the UK Government gave approval to develop the Eastern Trough Area Project (ETAP) – a major new project consisting of the integrated development of seven Central North Sea fields. During the development phase BP will operate four fields (Marnock, Machar, Mungo and Monan) and Shell will operate three fields (Heron, Egret and Skua). On commencement of production in 1998 BP will act as operator of the overall facilities on behalf of the seven co-venturers (BP, Shell, Esso, Agip, MOC Exploration, Murphy and Total).

The reservoir architecture, conditions and fluids pose some unique challenges for the project which represents the single largest North Sea development for ten years. The challenges include:

(i) downhole sand control in high pressure/high temperature (HP/HT) horizontal wells;
(ii) management of uncertainty in forecasting target depths in diapir wells;
(iii) management of uncertainty in long term performance of fractured chalk under waterflood;
(iv) downhole salt/scale management under HP/HT conditions;
(v) management of uncertainty in long term productivity from Skagerrak reservoirs; and
(vi) well engineering in HP/HT conditions.

This paper gives a brief overview of the challenges that ETAP is facing during development of these reservoirs and outlines how these will be addressed during the early field development stage.

The Eastern Trough Area Project (ETAP) integrates the development of seven Central North Sea fields, which individually are considered economically marginal. The fields lie in the Eastern Trough (eastern arm of the Central Graben in the UK sector of the North Sea) some 250 km east of Aberdeen in water depths of 85–90 m (Fig. 1). During the development phase, BP will operate four fields (Marnock, Machar, Mungo and Monan) and Shell will operate three fields (Heron, Egret and Skua). On commencement of production operations in 1998 BP will act as operator of the overall ETAP facilities.

The reservoirs are contained in three different geological settings: turbidite sandstones of Paleocene age (Mungo, Monan and Machar), pelagic and turbidite chalks of late Cretaceous to early Paleocene age (Machar), and fluviatile sandstones of Triassic age (Marnock, Heron, Egret and Skua).

The reservoirs occur in two distinct types of structural setting. Triassic reservoirs are found in fault bounded structures related either to early rifting or salt withdrawal during Triassic and Jurassic times. Paleocene sandstones and chalk reservoirs are found in high relief structures occurring above and around the flanks of salt diapirs. Vertical closures exceed 1000 m, with reservoir beds dipping at up to 50°.

The hydrocarbons in ETAP reservoirs show a wide variation in reservoir pressure and temperature (see Table 1) from normally pressured reservoirs up to high pressure/high temperature (HP/HT) conditions (12 000 psi and 340°F). The Triassic reservoirs are typically overpressured by some 4000–7000 psi, whereas the Paleocene and chalk reservoirs are essentially normally pressured although the very high hydrocarbon column heights and presence of free gas result in some overpressuring at the crests. The wide range in reservoir pressures and temperatures combined with compositional differences give rise to a wide variety of fluid types – gas condensate in Marnock, saturated oils with free gas caps in Mungo, Monan and Machar, and under-saturated or volatile oils in Heron, Egret and Skua.

After a description of the overall ETAP development concept, the specific challenges of each individual field and the outline development plans in place for their exploitation are described.

Outline of the development concept

The seven ETAP fields will share common facilities for processing and export of the hydrocarbons – the Central Processing Facilities (CPF) comprising two linked platforms located over the Marnock Field (Fig. 2) with oil export from the CPF via a spur line to Forties Pipeline System and gas export from the CPF via a spur line to the Central Area Transmission System (CATS). The CPF will be the only permanently manned installation in ETAP – there will be a normally unmanned installation (NUI) located over the Mungo Field and tied back to the CPF – all other field facilities will be located subsea and tied back to the CPF. The CPF will manage a peak oil capacity of some 215×10^3 BOPD and a peak gas handling capacity of some 553×10^6 SCF(D) – in addition, services for 120×10^3 BOPD water injection and 113×10^6 SCF(D) gas injection will be provided at the CPF. There will be no permanent drilling facilities on the ETAP installations and a significant number of ETAP development wells will be predrilled with mobile drilling units. In 1997, development drilling was undertaken on the Marnock, Mungo and Monan fields, with operations on the Machar and Heron fields planned for later in the year. Future wells drilled after jacket installations on Marnock and Mungo will be carried out as cantilever operations from a heavy duty jack up unit (HDJU).

POOLER, J. & AMORY, M. 1999. A subsurface perspective on ETAP – an integrated development of seven Central North Sea fields. *In*: FLEET, A. J. & BOLDY, S. A. R. (eds) *Petroleum Geology of Northwest Europe: Proceedings of the 5th Conference*, 993–1006. Published by the Geological Society, London.

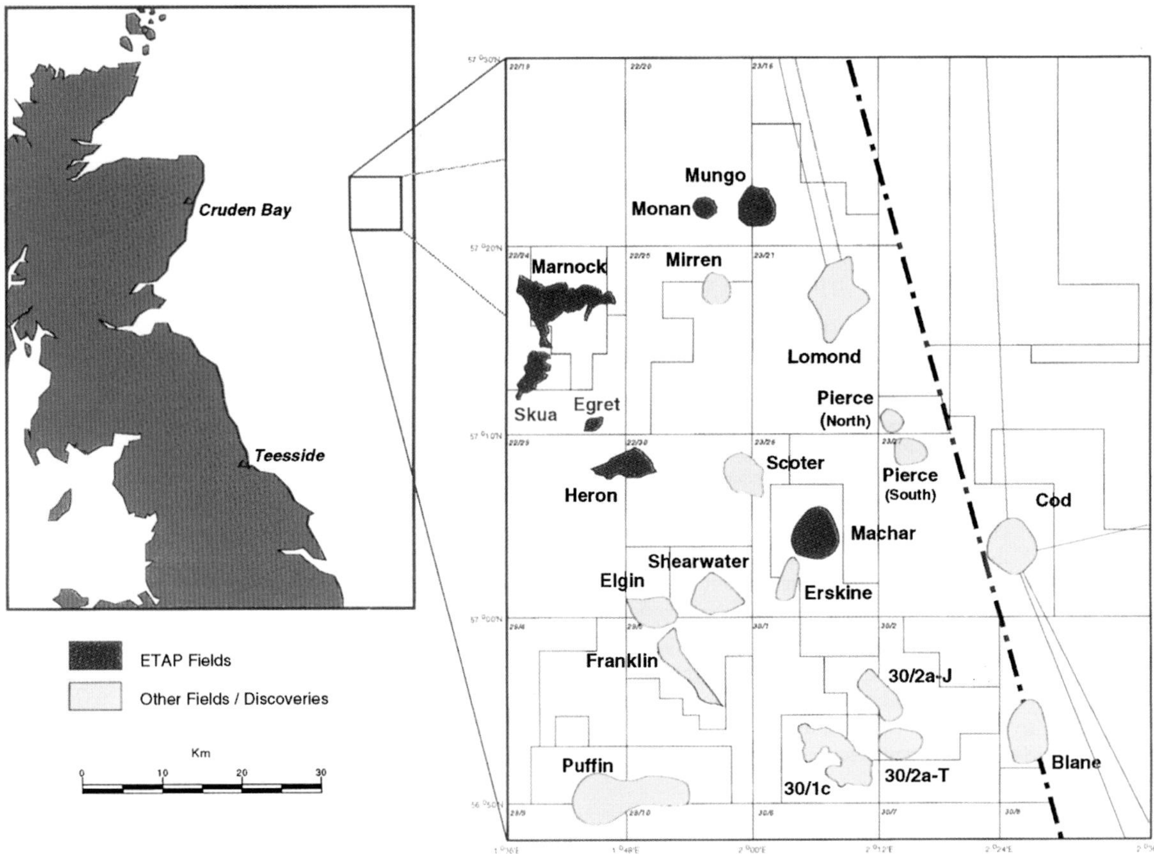

Fig. 1. ETAP location map.

Table 1. Summary of ETAP reservoir characteristics

Field	Fluid type	Reservoir age	Oil reserves ($\times 10^6$ STB)	Gas reserves ($\times 10^9$ SCF)	Pressure (psi)	Temperature (degrees F)	Datum depth (mss)
Marnock	gas condensate	Triassic	50	595	9125	300	3579
Mungo	saturated oil	Paleocene	155	79	4160	253	2645
Monan	oil and gas	Paleocene	9	89	4211	238	2700
Machar	saturated oil	Pal.–late Cret.	123	120	3800	225	2000
Heron	volatile oil	Triassic	86	140	12882	350	4660
Egret	volatile oil	Triassic	17	27	12568	340	4505
Skua	volatile oil	Triassic	27	17	9394	307	3700

The seven fields lie within four different licence groupings each with different company ownership. The ETAP development is not unitized and therefore companies retain their interests in the production from the fields according to the four licence groupings. The history of the project and commercial outlines are the subject of a separate publication (Rattey & Suller 1997).

Reservoir description of the fields

The Marnock Field

The Marnock Field was discovered by BP in 1982 and appraised by drilling an additional four wells on the field during 1983–1986. The Marnock partners are:

BP	62.05%
Agip	10.95%
Shell	13.50%
Esso	13.50%

The Marnock Field is a structural and stratigraphic trap – the overall structure is a tilted fault block dipping south with closure along strike to the west provided by juxtaposition against older Triassic mudstones, probably in an up-thrown fault block (Figs 3 and 4). The internal reservoir structure shows a southeast plunging synclinal geometry interpreted to be related to a localized Triassic depocentre or 'pod' located between bounding salt ridges (Smith *et al.* 1993).

The Triassic reservoir comprises very fine- to medium-grained sandstones with high net : gross (over 80%) and an overall gross thickness of 500 m (Fig. 5). The sandstones are believed to be deposited in a sand-rich alluvial braidplain axial to the Central Graben (Fig. 6). The sandstones exhibit chlorite cement deposited as pore-rimming platelets. Sandstone porosities are in the range 18–21%. The chlorite and other clay minerals trap connate water and so petrophysical logs show high initial water saturations of over 45%, even though the zones produce dry gas on test. The water saturations used for calculation of gas-in-place are based upon capillary pressure data. The chlorite is a mechanically weak cement and

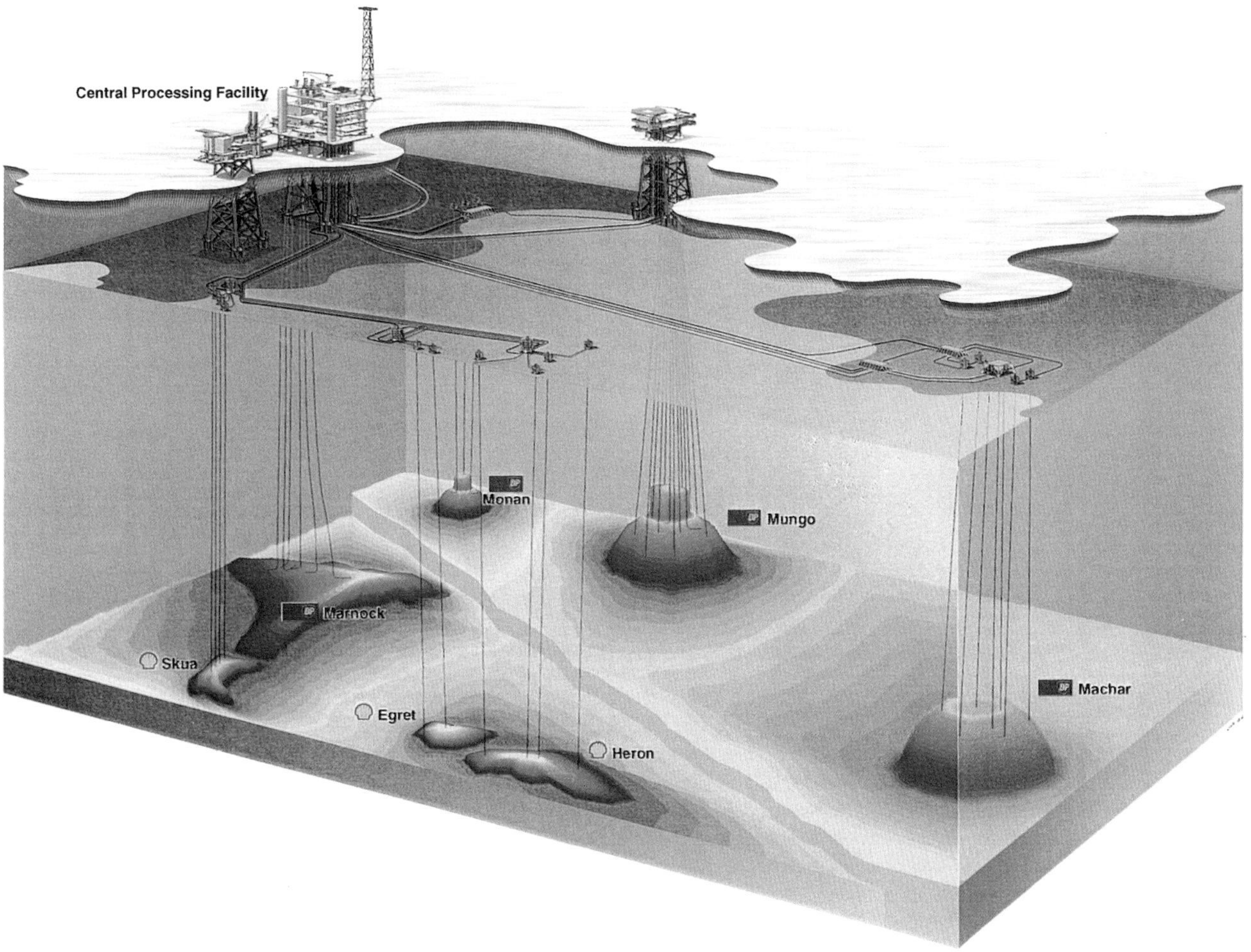

Fig. 2. ETAP development concept.

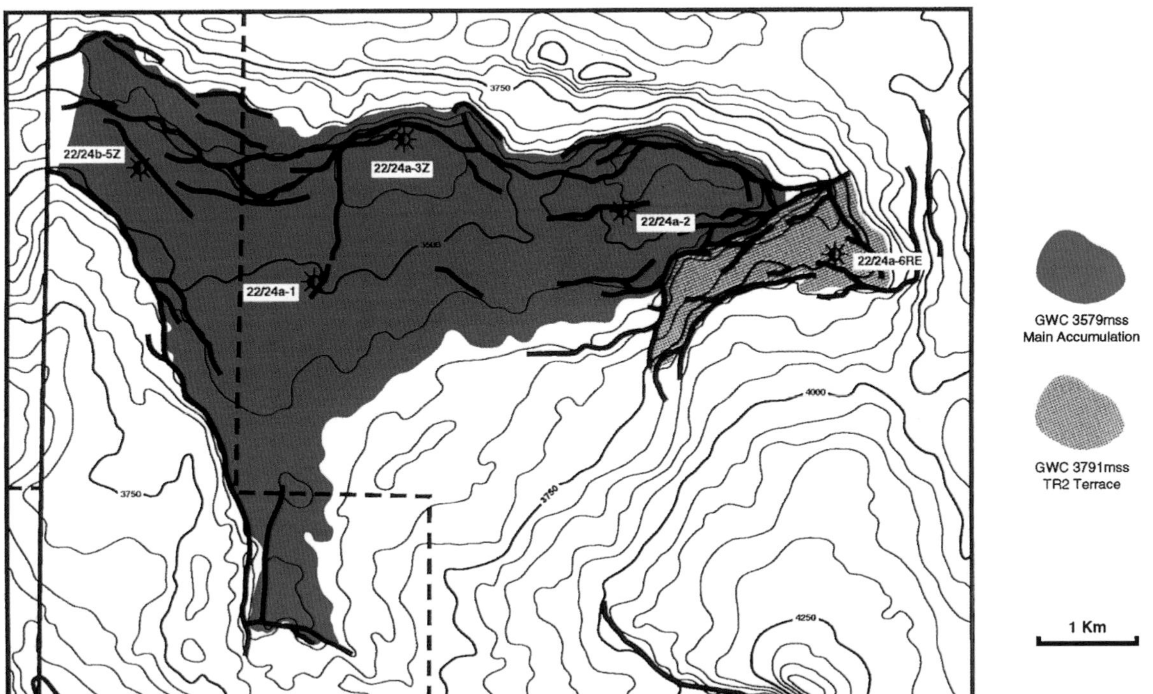

Fig. 3. Marnock Field: top reservoir depth map.

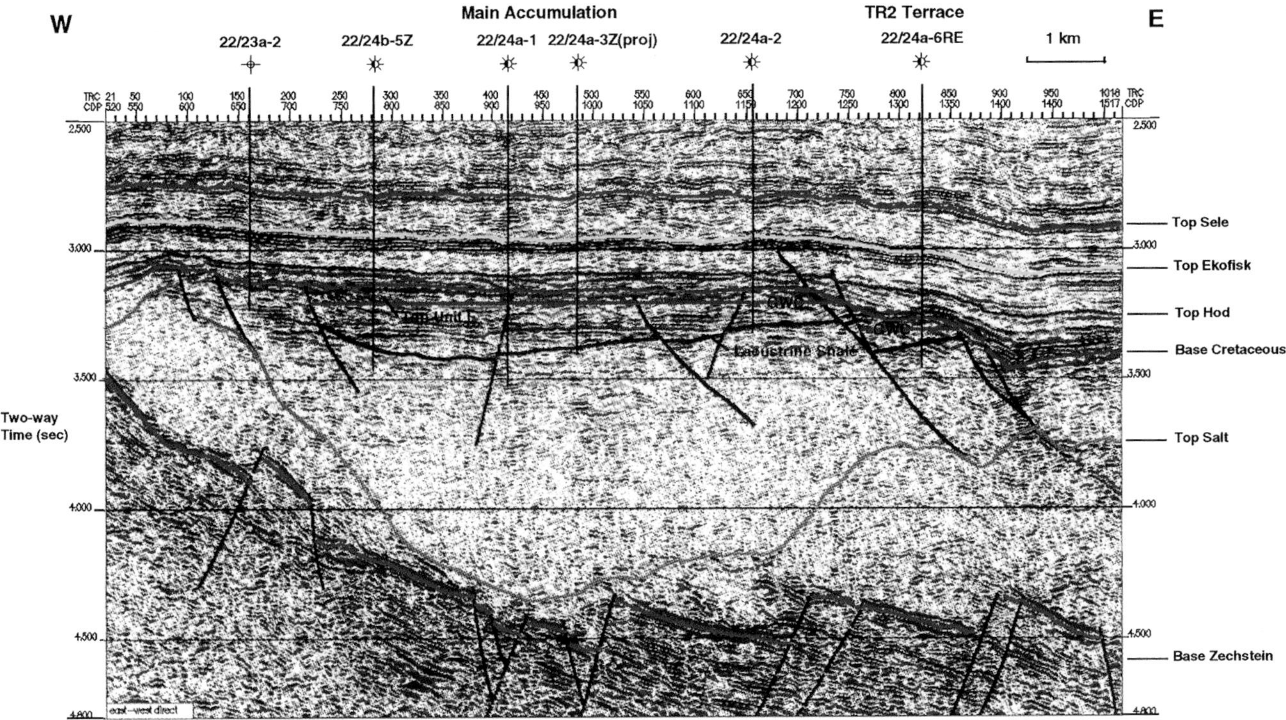

Fig. 4. Marnock Field: east–west 3D seismic traverse.

down-hole sand control is required. The horizontal reservoir sections of the development wells will be completed with wire wrap screens to prevent sand production. The reservoir fluid properties vary across the field – condensate: gas ratios (CGR) for example increase from 33 BBL/10^6 SCF in the east to 173 BBL/10^6 SCF in the west. The P50 gas-in-place is estimated at 990×10^9 SCF and associated condensate-in-place is estimated at 113×10^6 STB.

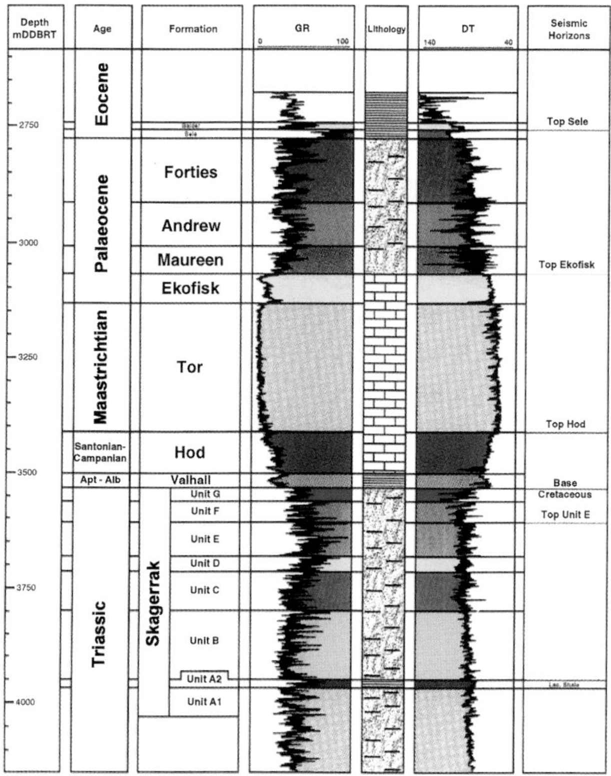

Fig. 5. Marnock Field: typical well log (22/24a-1).

Core and test permeabilities show a wide range related to the channelized nature of the braidplain. Permeabilities for simulation purposes were determined by stochastic techniques which allow for estimates intermediate between the extremes of geometric and arithmetic averages of core data. The permeabilities used in the reservoir model varied between 1 and 27 mD for different layers. Full field 3D compositional reservoir simulation was carried out with sensitivity studies. The results support recovery factors of 62% for gas and 42% for condensate based on a natural depletion development by six horizontal wells each with reservoir section lengths of between 500 and 1000 m. Base case reserves are 595×10^9 SCF sales gas and 50×10^6 STB condensate.

The principal challenge to development of the Marnock reservoir is the implementation and management of down-hole sand control in horizontal well sections of up to 1000 m length under reservoir conditions of some 4000 psi overpressure and 300°F temperature.

The Mungo Field

The Mungo Field was discovered in 1989 and the field appraised by an additional five wells during 1990–1993 (Fig. 7). The partners in both Mungo and Monan are:

BP	69.92%
Murphy	12.65%
Total	12.43%
MOC Exploration	5.00%

The final appraisal well drilled was a high angle well which was put on an extended well test (EWT) in 1993. The Mungo structure is a pierced four-way dip closure around a salt diapir with up-dip seal against the central salt stock (Fig. 8). The vertical relief is 1500 m from the crest at 1330 mss (metres sub-sea) and reservoir units are tilted to dips of up to 50° (Fig. 9). During the deposition of the reservoir sandstones in Paleocene times, the Mungo salt diapir is believed to have been in a state of buoyant equilibrium probably not far below the seabed. The Paleocene sandstones were deposited as deepwater turbidites in submarine fans with the seabed topography likely to have

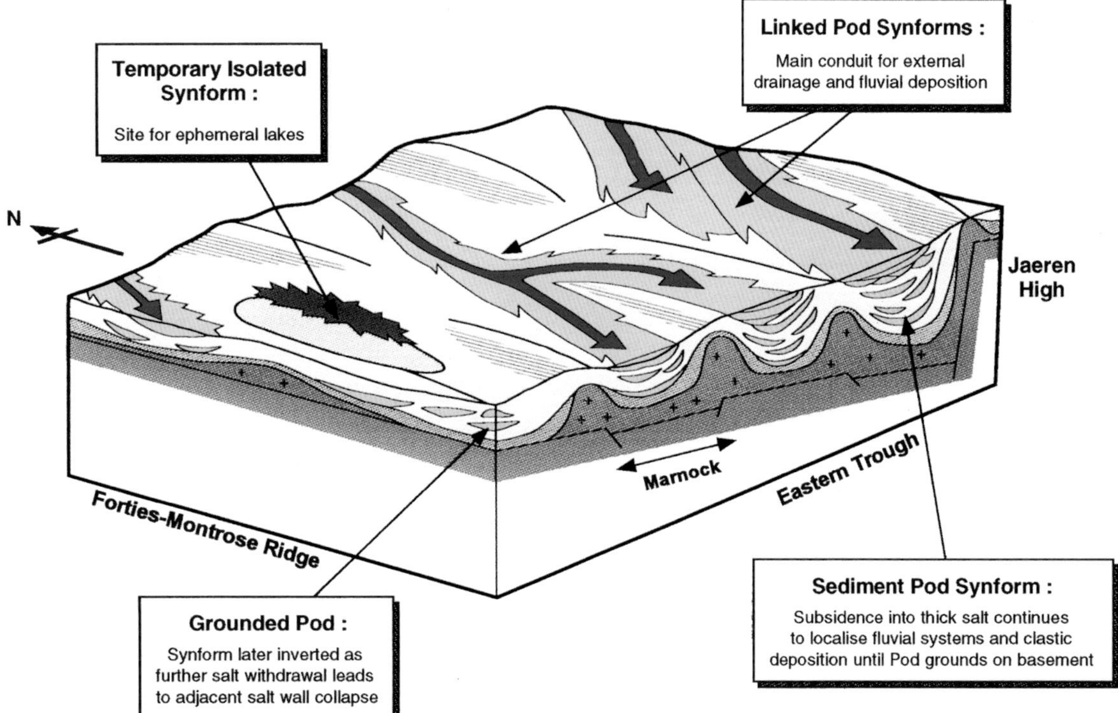

Fig. 6. Schematic late Triassic depositional environment.

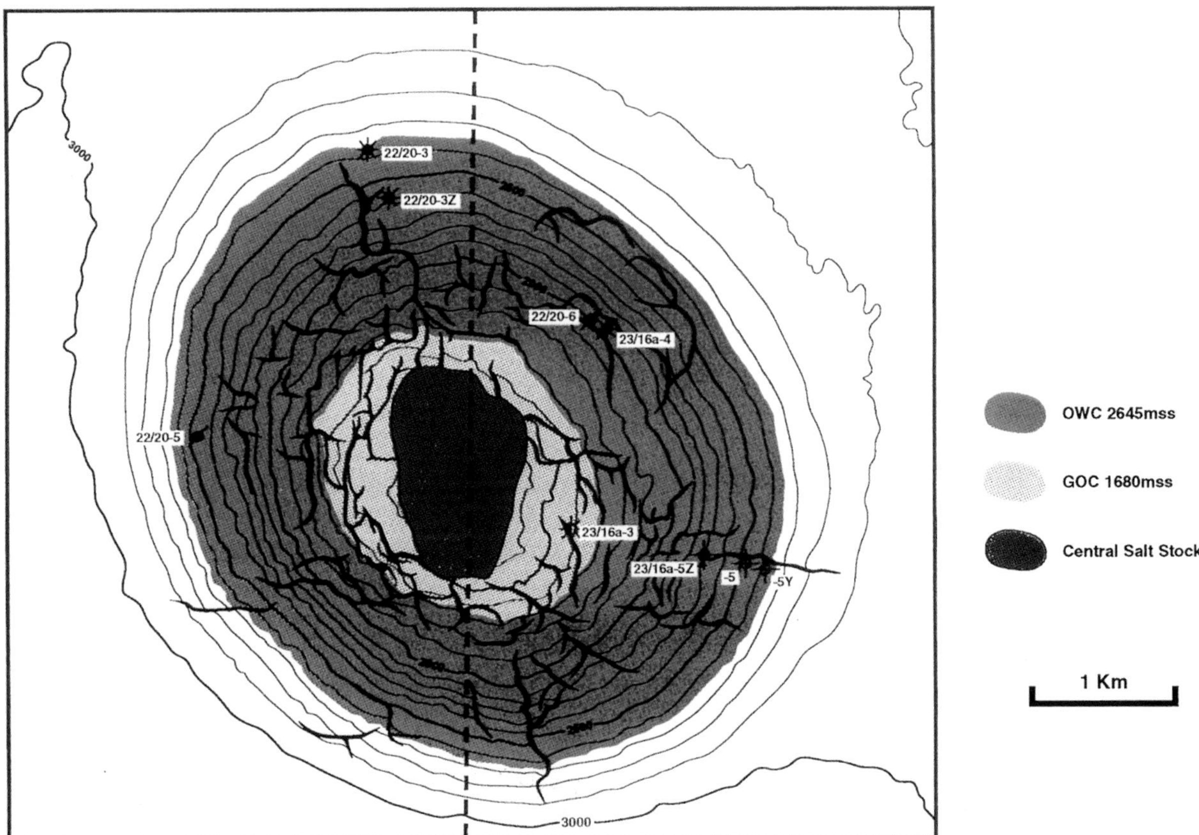

Fig. 7. Mungo Field: top reservoir depth map.

been influenced by the underlying salt stock. The internal structure of the Paleocene deposits suggests widespread syn-depositional slumping and sliding of sediment packages along low angle slopes on the seabed above the salt stocks. The resultant deformations produce stratigraphic inversions and numerous soft sediment deformation stuctures (Fig. 10). Some time after the deposition of the Paleocene sandstones, the salt stock was reactivated in a major phase of diapirism – this phase produced the extreme vertical relief of the structure and tilted the reservoir units to the present-day dips of up to 50°.

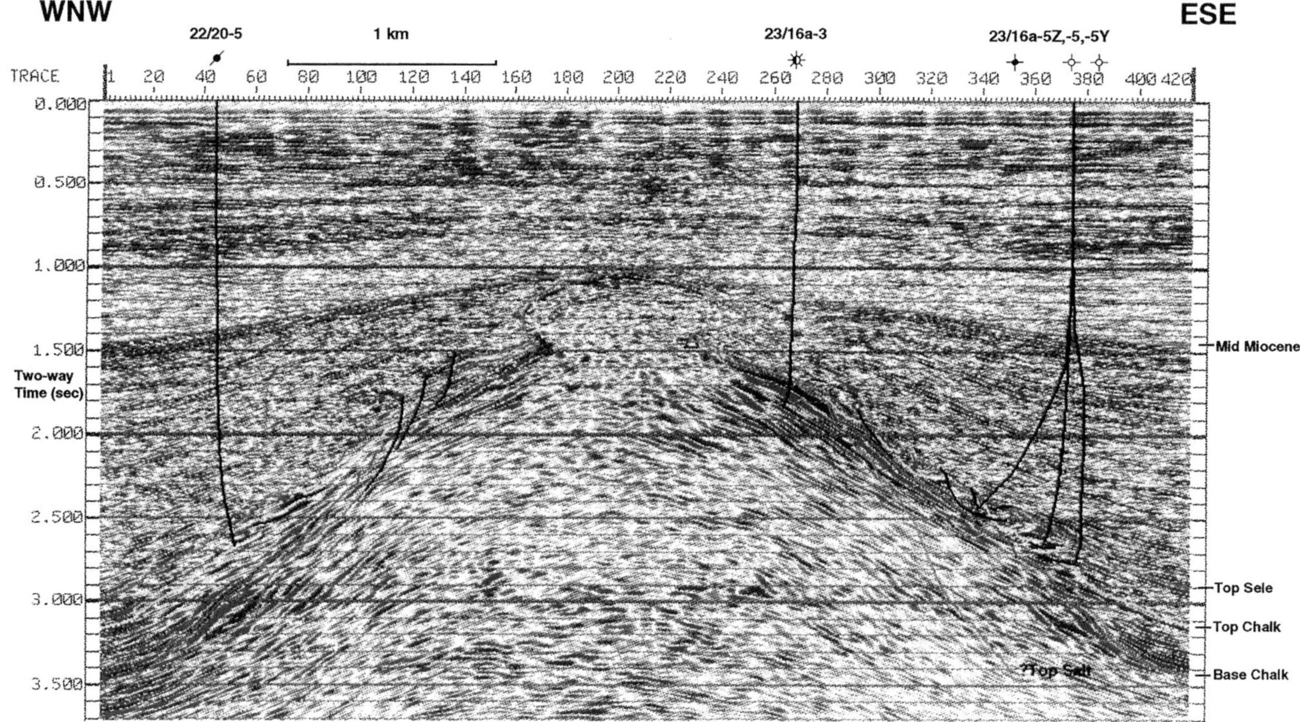

Fig. 8. Mungo Field: west-northwest–east-southeast 3D seismic traverse.

The gross thickness of the reservoir units varies between 100 and 400 m in the oil leg (Fig. 11). The sandstones are interbedded with non-reservoir siltstones and mudstones and the complex early deformation history results in rapid lateral facies changes and highly variable net-to-gross ratios of 0.43–0.63 in oil leg wells, down to 0.25 in the aquifer. Where the net : gross is over 0.4 the sandstones are expected to be well connected but where the net : gross is below 0.3 they will tend to be isolated. Repeat formaties test (RFT) data from the appraisal wells show that nearly all the pressures in the oil leg lie close to a single pressure gradient. Average porosities for the wells lie in the range 19–24%. Water saturations are based on capillary pressure data because of the poor reliability of saturations derived from logs in thin beds with steep dips. The reservoir fluid in Mungo is a saturated black oil with a small crestal free gas cap. The P50 STOIIP for Paleocene sandstones is estimated at 414×10^6 STB.

Core and test permeabilities show reasonable agreement, with typically 10–50 mD average permeability for net tested intervals. Stochastic techniques were used to describe the field-wide variation in permeability – although the major uncertainty in reservoir description is the highly variable net : gross which has

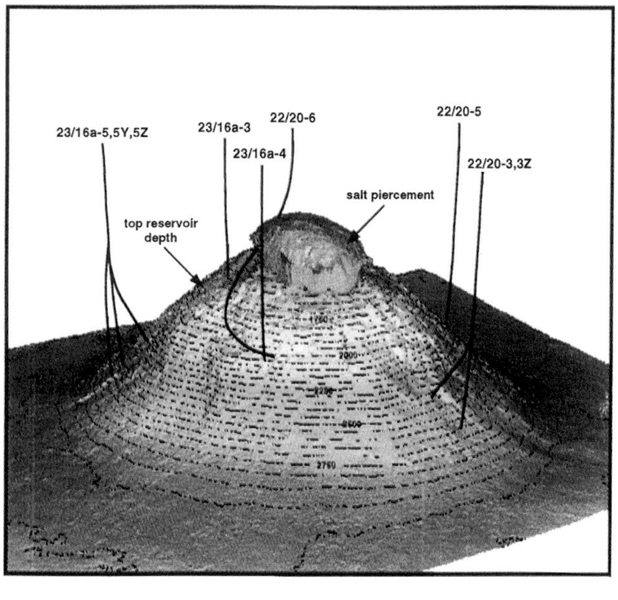

Fig. 9. Mungo Field: top reservoir depth 3D image.

Fig. 10. Mungo Field: core photographs from Well 22/20-5.

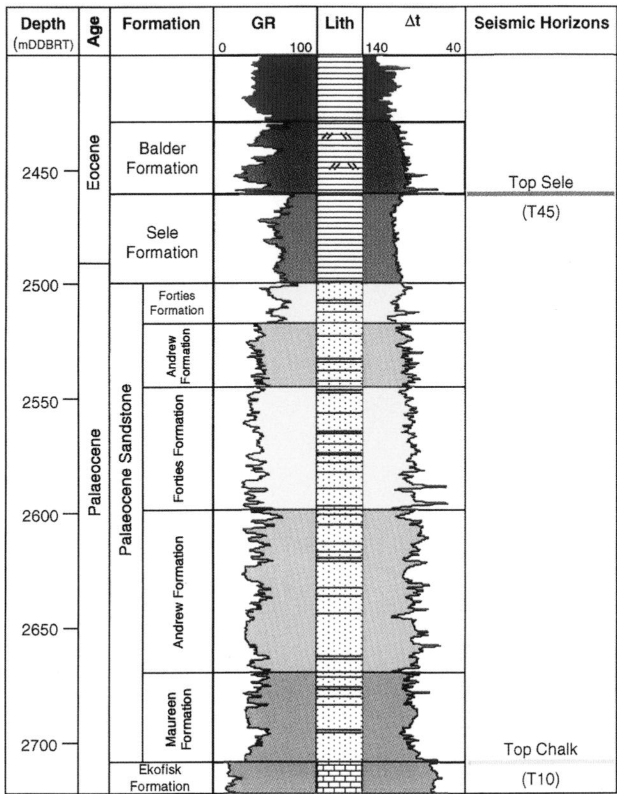

Fig. 11. Mungo Field: typical well log (22/20-5).

been sampled only at the well points. The uncertainty in net : gross not only affects the oil-in-place but also determines the connectivity and hence has a strong influence on recovery. Three-dimensional reservoir simulation on a sector of the field was carried out to investigate the variation in recoveries with different net : gross assumptions and under different depletion schemes. History matching the EWT performance with the simulations from the sector model under different reservoir assumptions provided valuable conditioning data for the reservoir model.

The results show that a combined gas and water injection scheme yields the most favourable recoveries and offers the greatest flexibility in terms of pressure support. Recoveries vary between 25 and 40%, according to the reservoir assumptions, with a field average of some 35%. Base reserves are 155×10^6 STB oil with 79×10^9 SCF gas, assuming eight producers, four water injection and one gas injection well. The preferred design for seven producers will allow for 'proppant frac' stimulation in near-vertical wells. The requirement for frac stimulation will depend upon the quality of the reservoirs encountered in the well bores. The eighth producer will be the 1993 high angle well recompleted.

The Monan Field

The Monan Field is a smaller diapir structure than the Mungo Field, and the salt piercement forms a pronounced canopy over part of the field. The reservoir consists of Paleocene turbidite sandstones which are disturbed by syndepositional slumping and sliding in a similar style to Mungo. Salt stock reactivation has produced great vertical relief on the structure and has tilted the reservoir units to present-day dips of up to 50°. Hydrocarbon in-place volumes are estimated at 50×10^6 STB oil and 46×10^9 SCF associated plus 82×10^9 SCF free gas within the gas cap. The field will be developed under natural depletion with two or three high angle wells recovering some 9×10^6 STB oil and 89×10^9 SCF sales gas. Development of Monan would normally be uneconomic on a stand alone basis but becomes viable as a low cost sub-sea tie back to the CPF, sharing part of the flow-line costs with Mungo.

The principal challenge to development of both the Mungo and Monan reservoirs is to ensure sufficient flexibility in the development well planning and operations to accommodate the uncertainty in reservoir depth, thickness and quality.

The Machar Field

The Machar Field was discovered by BP in 1976. The field is owned 100% by BP and has been extensively appraised by data from 11 wells plus data gathered from 20 months 'early' production both under natural depletion and a pilot waterflood.

The Machar structure is a four-way dip closure around a salt diapir which pierces the crest of the structure (Foster & Rattey 1993). The structure has great vertical relief from the crest at 1300 mss with closure extending down to some 3000 mss. The crest is divided by faults down-throwing to the east and north. The reservoir units are tilted to dips of up to 50° on the flanks of the diapir (Figs 12 and13).

Because of reservoir quality deterioration with depth, an unambiguous OWC has not been established – for the purposes of calculating oil-in-place, a free water level of 2497 mss in the chalk and 2617 mss in the Paleocene sandstone have been assumed on the basis that they are consistent with observed core and log data. The reservoir fluid in Machar is a saturated black oil with a small incipient free gas cap at the crest. The reservoir comprises productive intervals in sandstones of Paleocene age, in fractured chalks of late Cretaceous–Paleocene age and in the celestite unit believed to be a diagenetic product formed by local alteration of the anhydrite from the salt diapir (Fig. 14). The Paleocene sandstones were deposited as deep-water turbidites in a series of submarine

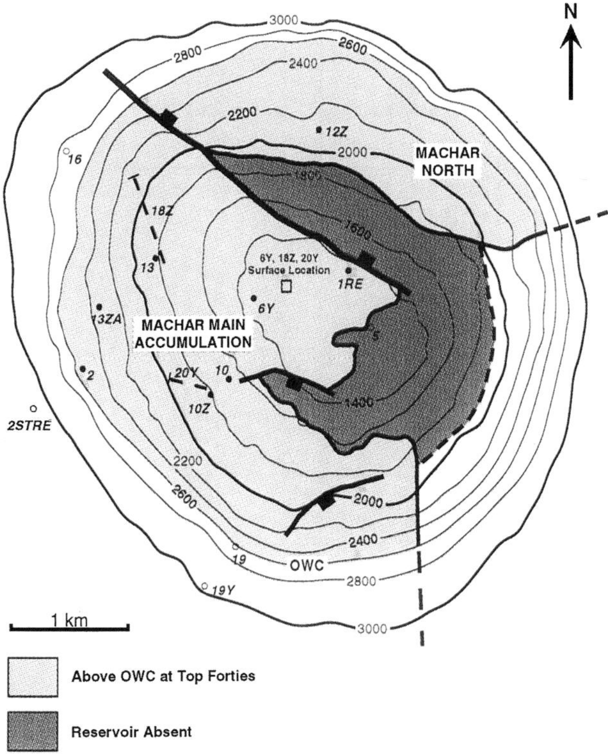

Fig. 12. Machar Field: top reservoir depth map.

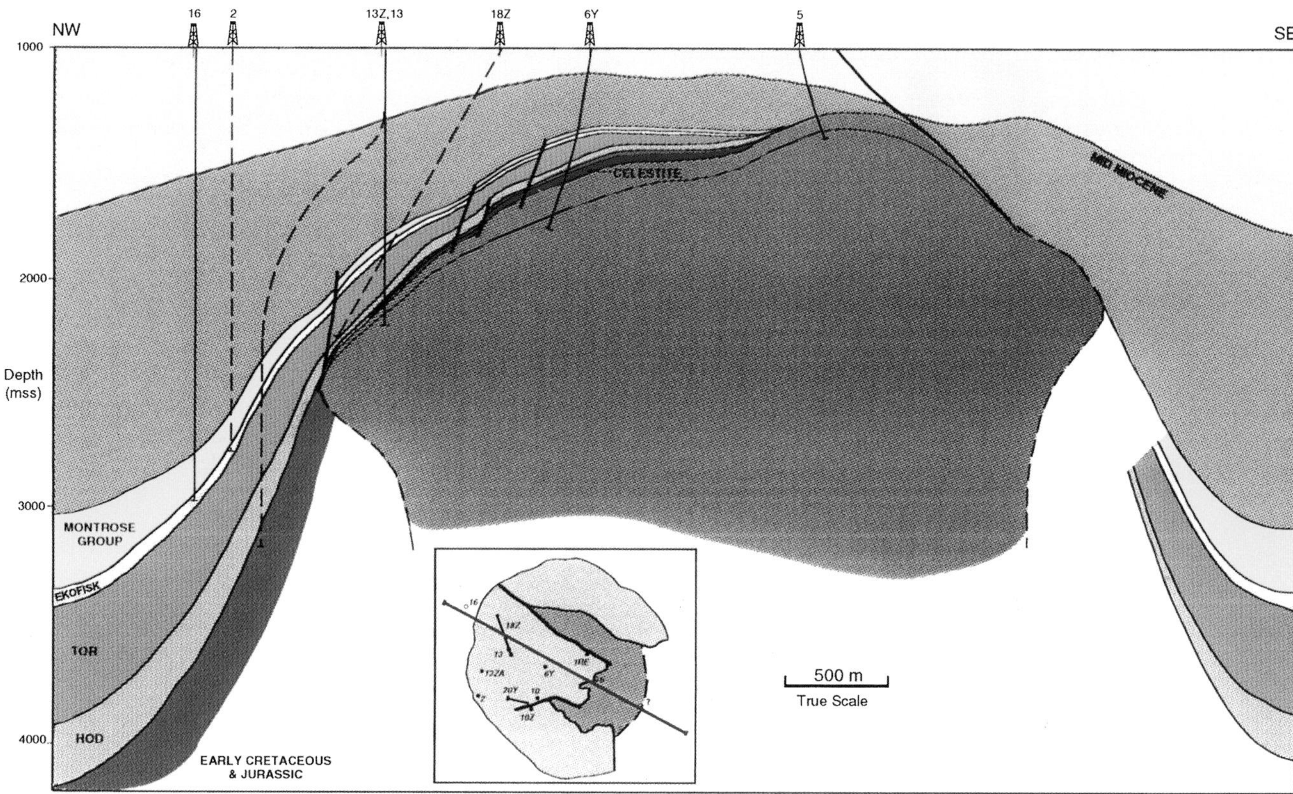

Fig. 13. Machar Field: geological cross-section.

fans. The seabed topography is likely to reflect the presence of an underlying salt stock and the topography will have influenced the deposition of the Paleocene submarine fans. Porosities for the sandstones average 21% and the permeability is variable with averages of between 5 and 50 mD. The chalk reservoir units comprise coccolith fragments deposited as pelagic sediments or as turbidites and the chalk is believed to have been extensively reworked with slumping and redeposition, influenced by the local sea bed topography. Porosities in the chalk matrix of the Tor Formation vary between 10 and 35% across the field and permeabilities are typically less than 1 mD. Production is dependent upon the presence of fractures which can increase test permeabilities to 1500 mD but contribute little to the porosity. The productivity index of Machar wells is increased significantly through stimulation by massive diverted acid fracturing treatment (Gilchrist *et al.* 1994). The celestite unit is developed in one well only and consists of laminae of coarsely crystalline celestite with large inter crystal pores separated by finer siderite. The oil-in-place in Machar is estimated at 439×10^6 STB using deterministic volumes, and this compares well with the range suggested by history matching to production data.

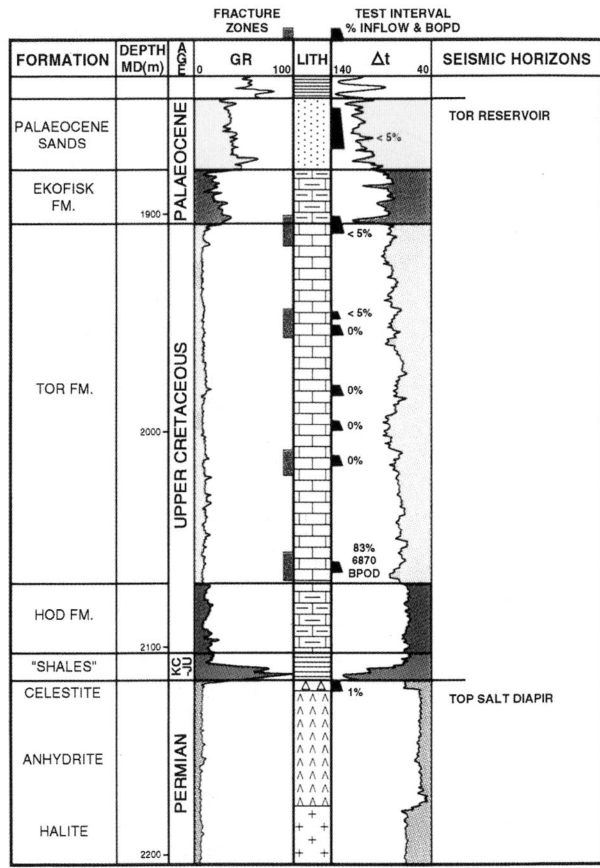

Fig. 14. Machar Field: typical well log (23/26a-13).

The principal uncertainty in Machar concerns the difficulty in prediction of the long-term production performance from the fractured chalk reservoir and in particular the response in the reservoir to pressure support by waterflood. In order to reduce these uncertainties to a level upon which both commitment to full field development could be made, and the appropriate depletion scheme selected, BP sought DTI approval to a phased development plan. The plan comprised an early production phase under natural depletion, followed by a second phase incorporating a pilot waterflood. The first phase took place between June 1994 and May 1995 and a total of 7.7×10^6 STB were produced from 2 wells under natural depletion. The two objectives were to establish viable long term productivity from the fractured chalk intervals and to test natural depletion as a recovery mechanism. Both objectives were satisfactorily achieved. The second phase between August 1995 and June 1996 tested the reservoir response under water injection by producing 6.8×10^6 STB from two wells and injecting water into a third well. Productivity and the GOR (gas : oil ratios) remained stable and no water was produced.

The Machar Field performance is modelled by combining a single and a dual porosity system, respectively, for the Paleocene sandstones and fractured chalk plus celestite. Recovery predictions in a dual porosity system are very dependent upon variables which are not easily observed and so history matching of the model with the two production periods provides valuable conditioning data. The reservoir simulation studies show that an additional 15% recovery is achievable under waterflood relative to the natural depletion base case of 18%. The remaining reserves recoverable under waterflood are estimated at 123×10^6 STB, with 120×10^9 SCF associated gas based on 5 high angle producer wells supported by 2 water injection wells.

The full field development plan is therefore based on a sub-sea waterflood scheme tied back to the CPF over a distance of some 35 km. Power supply, water injection and chemical injection will be provided from the CPF. The scheme incorporates a sub-sea production booster system (SMUBS) which increases the flowing pressure of the produced fluids using energy from the injected water pressure.

The principal challenges to development of the Machar reservoir are firstly to ensure sufficient flexibility in well planning and operations to accomodate the uncertainty in reservoir depth and the presence of fractures in the chalk. A major challenge will be to ensure a flexible reservoir management strategy to allow interventions later in field life to address potential surprises in oil, gas or water production from the fractures.

The Heron, Egret and Skua fields

The Heron, Egret and Skua fields were discovered by Shell/Esso between 1985 and 1988. The main reservoir for all three fields is the fluviatile Triassic Skagerrak formation. In the past this formation was considered a poor candidate for development mainly because of uncertainty over the long term production potential. The confidence required to develop the Skagerrak play was gained by conducting integrated petroleum engineering studies within a multi-disciplinary team. The Pentland Formation generally shows very poor reservoir quality and has not been incorporated in the development plans.

Heron, Egret and Skua will be developed from separate sub-sea drilling centres but will share the same flowlines which will be routed to the Marnock CPF via the Skua Field (Fig. 2). The Shell/Esso Cluster will produce almost 30% of the total ETAP oil and 23% of ETAP gas reserves. The development of these fields represents a unique technical challenge created by the combination of:

- complex reservoir characteristics;
- high reservoir pressure and temperature (HP/HT); and
- challenging reservoir fluids.

The Heron Field

The Heron Field was discovered in 1988 by well 22/30a-2 and is located some 17 km southeast of Marnock (Fig. 15).

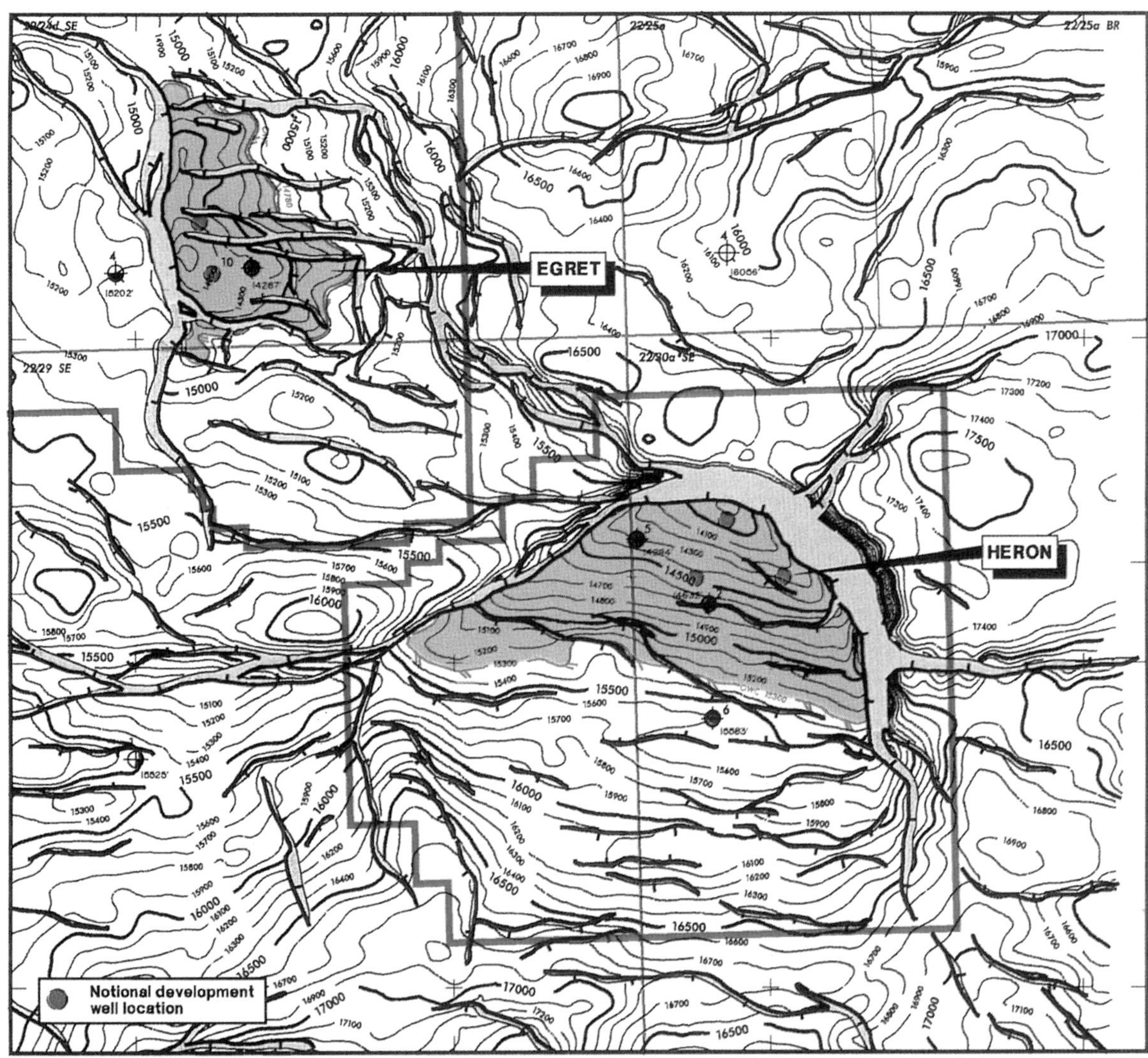

Fig. 15. Heron and Egret fields: top reservoir depth map.

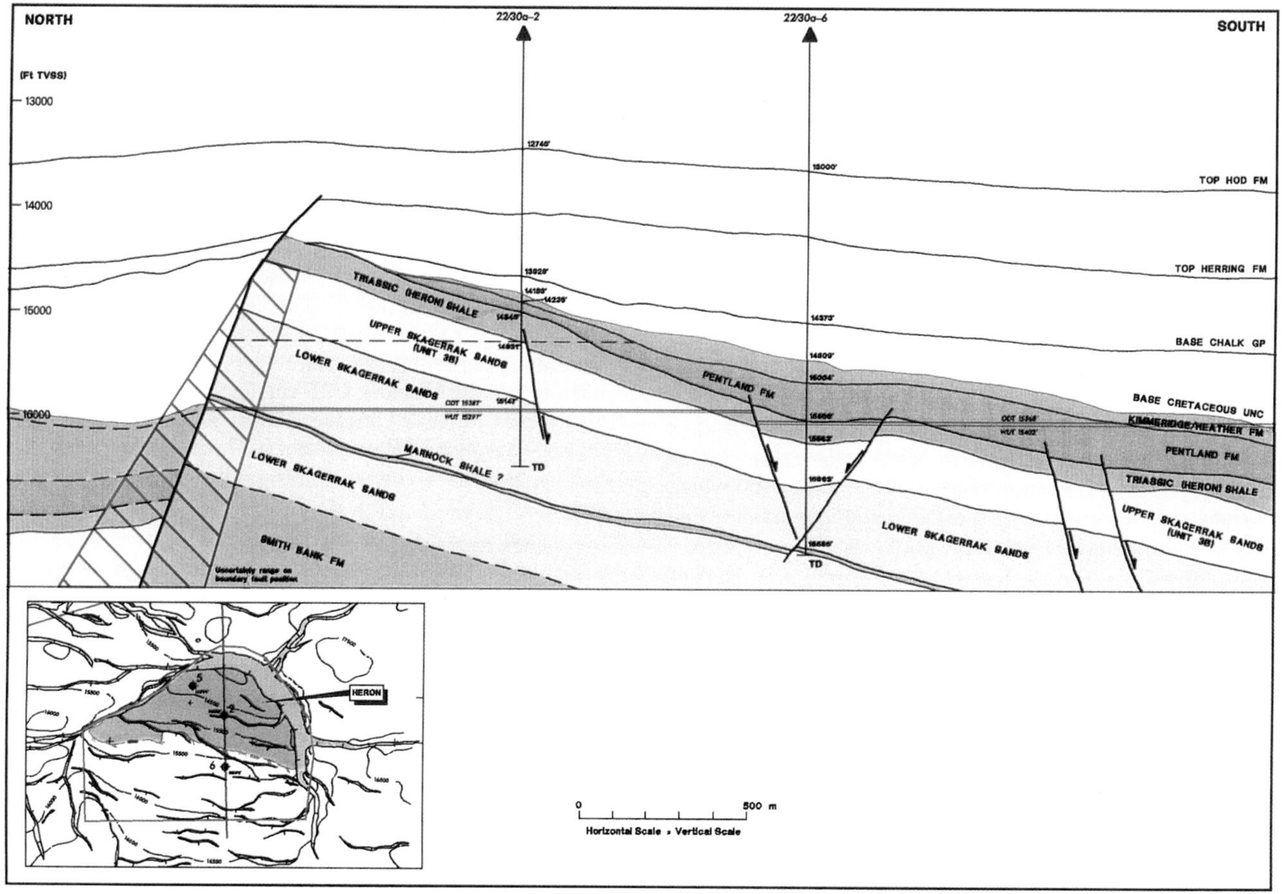

Fig. 16. Heron Field: geological cross-section.

The discovery well found both the Pentland and the Skagerrak formations to be oil bearing (Fig. 16). The Skagerrak tested at a maximum oil rate of 14 000 BOPD. Appraisal Well 22/30a-6 tested the Pentland at a stable rate of 580 BOPD. The Skagerrak was water bearing and was production tested to acquire formation water samples. In 1994 the field was further appraised by the Well 22/29-5, and showed better than expected reservoir quality, producing at rates in excess of 10 000 BOPD from a limited reservoir interval.

The Egret Field

The Egret Field (Fig. 15), located about 3 km northwest of Heron, was discovered in 1985 by Well 22/24b-4, which tested oil at a rate of 50 BOPD from low quality Pentland reservoirs. Well 22/24d-10, drilled in 1991, penetrated the structure up-dip and found the better quality Skaggerak sandstones, oil bearing, which tested at a rate of up to 4700 BOPD.

The Heron and Egret fields are classified as HP/HT reservoirs with pressures and temperatures in excess of 12 000 psi and 340°F, respectively.

The Skua Field

The Skua Field (Fig. 17), located south of Marnock, was discovered in 1986 by Well 22/24b-7 which tested the Skagerrak at a rate of 7500 BOPD. The reservoir conditions are less severe than in the Heron and Egret Fields.

Skagerrak reservoir fluids

The Shell/Esso fields contain light (*c.* 42°API), highly undersaturated oil with high GOR (800–1900 SCF/BBL) and low CO_2 and H_2S contents. The highly volatile character of the crude promotes relatively high recovery factors under natural depletion. However, the crude is also susceptible to wax deposition and asphaltene flocculation, two important considerations for field development planning.

An extremely high formation water salinity was detected in the Heron discovery well and a dedicated aquifer test was carried out in a subsequent appraisal well in order to acquire representative water samples. It was established that the formation water for the Heron, Egret and Skua fields are salt saturated at reservoir conditions and have a high calcium, barium and strontium content. This characteristic, unique for the North Sea area, has been found in a number of fields around the world. This challenging water chemistry in conjunction with the high pressures and temperature gradients experienced in the production system leads to a severe scaling potential. Recent experience with HP/HT wells has shown scaling may be so severe that it is a major factor determining the overall profitability or even viability of this type of development.

Skagerrak reservoir modelling

The Skagerrak Formation (Fig. 18) consists of fluvial sandstones that were deposited in a north–south trending braidplain extending across the Greater Marnock area (Fig. 19). During the Triassic, basin extension resulted in the development of salt ridges over Permian age faults. Associated salt withdrawal in the intervening basins resulted in the development of a series of north–south trending ridges and salt pods. The subsiding pods became the locus for the deposition of the main fluvial channel belts, which are characterized by the deposition and preservation of thick Skagerrak sequences. The main reservoir facies in

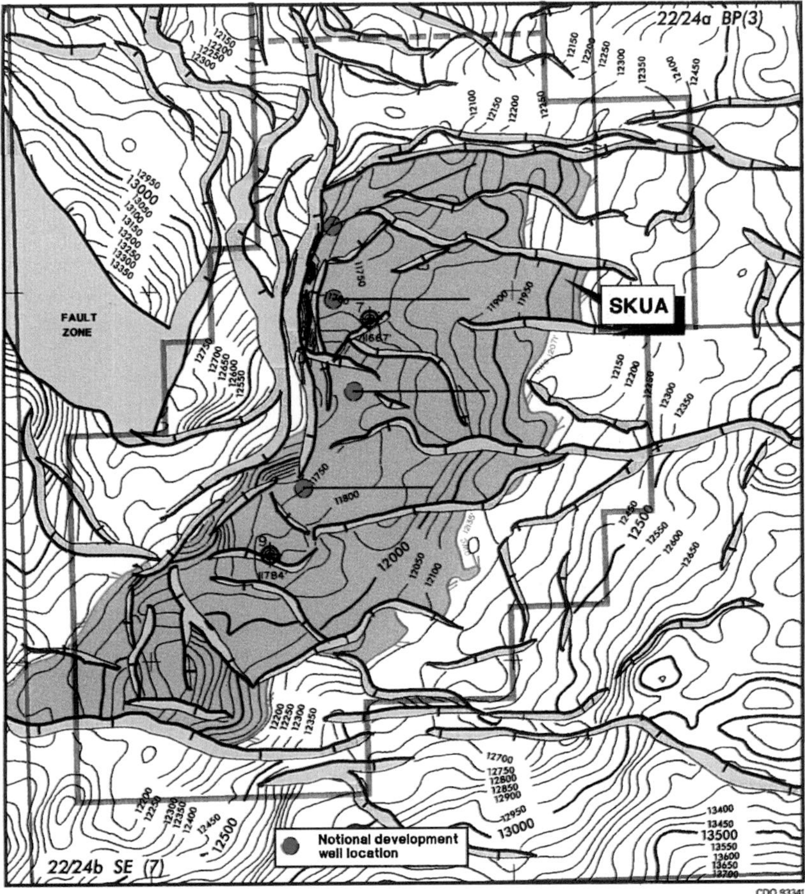

Fig. 17. Skua Field: top reservoir depth map.

the Skagerrak Formation are related to specific deposition processes in the fluvial braid plain:

(1) Channel sandbodies which comprise vertically and laterally amalgamated, fine- to medium-grained sandstones. They range from 3 m to 50 m in thickness and consist of several individual channel storeys that are typically up to 3 m thick. They represent the stacked and partially reworked deposits of relatively large migrating sand-bed streams that were most likely perennial but subject to large variable flow fluctuations.

(2) Sheetflood sands which typically comprise very fine- to fine-grained sandstones. Individual beds are generally thin and are often separated by thin mud or siltstone partings.

Appraisal drilling results had suggested that the key controls on reservoir connectivity were the lateral extent of good quality channel sands versus the detrimental effects of faulting. In order to evaluate and assess sensitivities to reservoir architecture, detailed geological studies were undertaken to develop a depositional model for the formation. This involved lithofacies determination from cores and logs and comparisons with analogues from outcrop studies and literature, to determine ranges for sandbody dimensions and internal connectivity. The results of these studies were used to develop probabilistic geological models. The depositional model of reservoir sand distribution for the Greater Marnock area greatly reduced the uncertainty on the dimensions of the better reservoir quality channel sandbodies. The study indicated that the better reservoir quality occurred in multi-storey channels sands which were laterally extensive, and that the effects of faults and fractures are the main limiting factors on reservoir performance. Detailed core studies were undertaken to quantify the type, extent and causes of fracturing. The results were used to assist in well test interpretations and to provide a comprehensive dataset of fracture density, spacing and distribution for input into reservoir simulations model. A petrophysical review of the Skagerrak was undertaken to improve reservoir definition. Saturation calculations were complicated by high temperatures, heavy muds and thinly laminated sand/shale sequences which adversely affect resistivity tool response. The resolution of resistivity curves was enhanced by application of proprietary deconvolution algorithms. An appraisal well drilled into the largest field, Heron, was completed and tested at the end of 1994. The well results supported the existing geological and petrophysical models and therefore increased the confidence in the decision to develop the fields.

Reservoir simulation models were created directly based on the geological models and petrophysical evaluations. The direct incorporation of the geological and petrophysical studies has resulted in much better estimates of recoverable reserves. The effects of a full range of geological parameters, such as lithofacies and reservoir quality distribution, were assessed by full field simulation models. In addition it has significantly assisted in development well planning by enabling the optimization of development well locations, away from faults and fault zones, and more realistic estimates of porosities, hydrocarbon column and permeability height for any given well trajectory.

Field specific models were used to define the range of uncertainty on production performance and to estimate potential recovery for various depletion schemes.

Scale prediction and control

Scale control in the most general sense is a key production engineering challenge for the Shell/Esso fields. The extreme water salinity combined with the HP/HT reservoir conditions

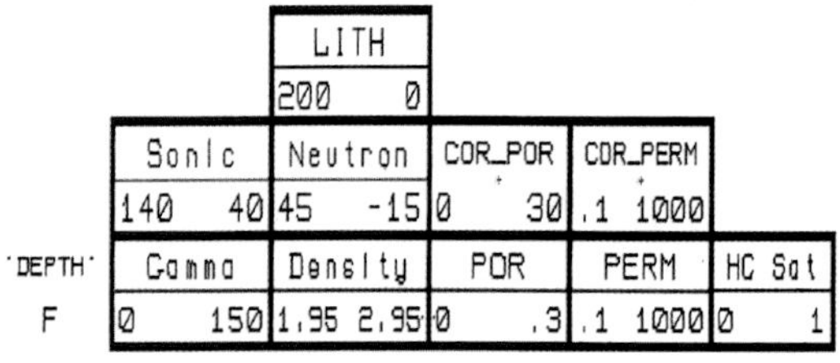

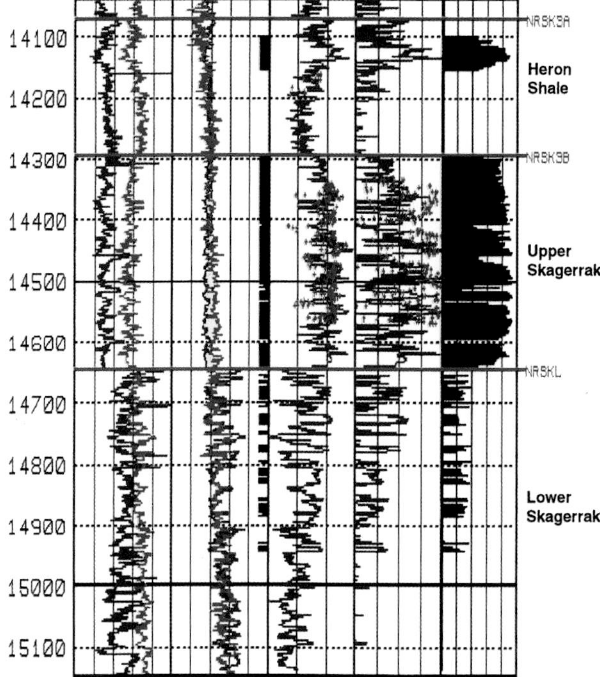

Fig. 18. Skagerrak type log.

leads to a unique scaling environment which warrants scale control measures unprecedented in the North Sea.

An extremely high formation water salinity was detected in the Heron discovery well based on RFT samples and log resistivity data. A dedicated aquifer test was carried out during appraisal in order to acquire representative water samples which were found to be supersaturated in halite under laboratory conditions. Compositional modelling based on this information together with geological evidence and estimates of down-hole water density from RFT data concluded that the formation water was saturated with halite in the reservoir. The water also has a high calcium, barium and strontium content.

A number of scaling studies were carried out in order to predict the occurrence of both inorganic and organic scales throughout the production system over the anticipated life cycle.

Salt deposition is perceived as the main threat to production. The main drivers for this scaling process are the decrease in halite solubility with decreasing temperature, exacerbated by the evaporation of water vapour from the formation water phase as pressure falls within the production system. The process is further complicated by the exchange of water vapour with the associated gas liberated in a multiphase stream. Carbonate scales are also expected to occur in the production system mainly as a result of CO_2 release resulting from depressurization of the produced fluids.

Salt deposition will be prevented by dilution of the produced water with low salinity water both down-hole and in the evacuation system. This will be the first application of down-hole water dilution in HP/HT wells for Shell Expro in the North Sea. The sub-sea wells have been designed for concurrent injection and production (Fig. 20).

Treated seawater will be used for salt dilution purposes. The seawater requires to be desulphated to prevent severe sulphate scaling when mixing with formation water. A scale inhibitor will be mixed with the wash water to prevent carbonate scales.

The Heron, Egret and Skua fields require the use of chemical inhibitors at temperatures beyond the proven limits of current technology. Screening studies have indicated that this technology gap could be bridged in the required time-frame. A comprehensive chemicals development programme is ongoing with the objective of screening, developing and qualifying chemical inhibitors for the challenging operating conditions at hand.

The crudes encountered in these reservoirs are light and highly under-saturated and are susceptible to asphaltene precipitation. Although the potential severity of this problem is largely unknown, remedial measures (i.e. solvent washes) have been incorporated in the development plans. There is currently no proven asphaltene inhibitor for the Shell/Esso field crudes but facilities provisions have been made to enable the use of inhibitors should they become available.

Remedial scale removal measures rely mostly on spotting fluids in the wellbore and also, possibly, squeeze of acid or wash water in the formation to remove impairment. All scale removal treatments are assumed to be carried out by coiled tubing intervention.

Skagerrak sand control

Reservoir sands present a wide range of reservoir properties and some channel sands have a permeability in excess of 1 D. Detailed sand prediction studies using proprietary models were carried out based on special core analysis. The main factors controlling sand stability are the rock strength and the increase in effective in-situ stress during depletion. Although the Skagerrak Formation is generally competent enough to support sand free production even for the highest depletion scenarios, a selective perforation policy which excludes the more permeable i.e. weaker sands, will be required in order to exclude the risk of sand production.

The main uncertainty in formation integrity studies is the assumption of the transmission of overburden stress to the reservoir rock as a result of depletion. It has been established that natural arching effects will occur with deep, compact structures with steep flanks such as the Heron and Egret fields and thus significantly limit the increase in effective stress on the reservoir rock.

Field development plans

Development of the Shell/Esso fields is based on natural depletion aided by some degree of aquifer support. In view of the high overpressures and high degree of undersaturation, simple expansion of the volatile reservoir fluid will result in higher than usual depletion recovery factors, particularly when supported by the expected aquifer expansion. Initial production will be from the Heron and Egret fields with the Skua Field as ullage filler from the end of year 2002. Phasing of Skua offers flexibility in field start-up date and risk management. Some uncertainty remains with regards to the long term production performance of the Skagerrak as all production tests were of short duration. It was therefore considered prudent to allow flexibility in the development plan. The Shell/Esso fields processing capacity at the CPF is 55×10^3 BOPD gross liquids and 100×10^6 SCF(D) wet gas. This level was found to be optimum after considering the uncertainties in reservoir performance and the costs/benefits of various development scenarios. Secondary recovery schemes like water injection and WAG (water–alternating-gas) were investigated

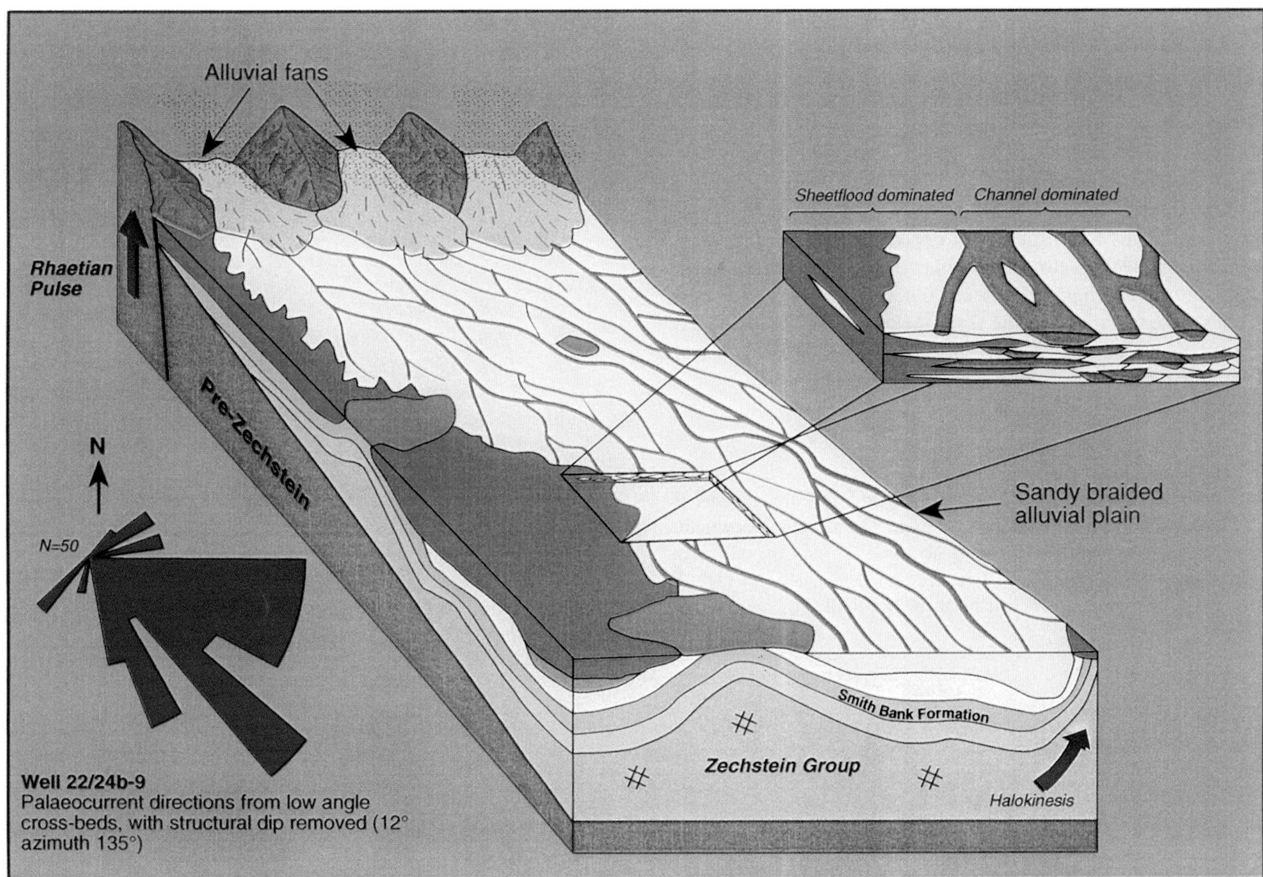

Fig. 19. Schematic of Skagerrak depositional environment.

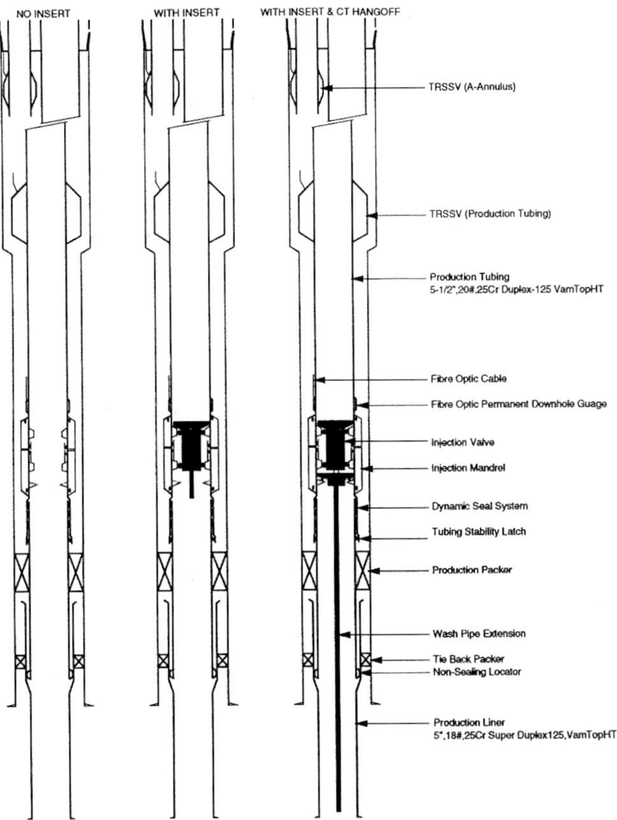

Fig. 20. Completion schematic showing down-hole wash-water system.

but were shown to be uneconomic. The Heron Field will be developed with three sub-vertical wells. Once on stream, production performance of the three wells will be monitored in order to assess connected STOIIP and aquifer influx and contingent provisions have been made for a potential fourth well. Similarly, the Egret development plan envisages two sub-vertical production wells. The first well will be drilled prior to production start-up and the second well some two years later targeting a separate fault block. The Skua Field will be brought on stream when Heron and Egret production has started to decline *c.* the year 2002. The development plan envisages four near-horizontal production wells in order to optimize drainage of the stratigraphic sequence above the OWC. The first two wells will be drilled prior to production start-up, the third and fourth well some two years later.

Conclusions and current status

New developments in the mature North Sea tend to exploit increasingly complex and challenging prospects. In ETAP the drive to secure future production has led to the development of new types of reservoir which in the past would have been marginal candidates for conventional development. The subsurface confidence required to develop ETAP has been achieved through integrated reservoir and well engineering studies within multi-disciplinary teams to address and manage the following key subsurface uncertainties and development challenges:

(i) Marnock Field: down-hole sand control in high pressure/high temperature horizontal wells;
(ii) Mungo, Machar and Monan fields: management of uncertainty in forecasting target depths in development wells;

(iii) Machar Field: management of uncertainty in long term performance of fracture chalk under waterflood;
(iv) Heron, Egret and Skua fields: long-term Skagerrak productivity, salt and scale management and high pressure/high temperature well engineering.

During 1997 development drilling activities were undertaken on Marnock, Mungo, Monan, Machar and Heron fields. Pipelaying operations for in-field and export flow lines were completed and the jackets for the two platforms at the CPF and the jacket for the Mungo NUI were installed in 1997. In 1998 topsides were installed for the three jackets and the production and processing facilities were commissioned for delivery of first oil on July 18 1998 and first gas on 27 October 1998.

We are grateful to BP Exploration, Shell, Esso, Agip, Murphy, MOEX and Total for permission to publish this paper. Most of the information about the fields in the paper is based upon in-house documents, in particular the field development programmes. The in-house documents represent the collective understanding achieved through the efforts of all the individuals in the ETAP Team present and past, and include important contributions from our partners and the DTI.

The authors are especially indebted to P. Allan, A. Brown and A. Marshall from BP and also to generations of Shell petroleum engineers who have contributed to the success of the ETAP project.

References

Foster, P. T. & Rattey, R. P. 1993. The evolution of a fractured chalk reservoir: Machar Field, UK North Sea. *In*: Parker, J. R. (ed.) *Petroleum Geology of Northwest Europe: Proceedings of the 4th Conference*. Geological Society, London, 1445–1452.

Gilchrist, J. M., Stephen, A. D. & Lietard, O. M. N. 1994. Use of high angle acid fractured wells on the Machar Field development. *SPE Paper 28917 prepared for presentation to the European Petroleum Conference, London UK on October 25–27th 1994.*

Rattey, R. P. & Suller, J. N. 1997. Development of marginal fields through technical and commercial innovation – a case history from the UK North Sea. *SPE Paper 37954 prepared for presentation to the SPE Hydrocarbon Economics and Evaluation Symposium in Dallas, TX on March 15–18th 1997.*

Smith, R. I., Hodgson, N. & Fulton, M. 1993. Salt control on Triassic reservoir distribution, UKCS Central North Sea. *In*: Parker, J. R. (ed.) *Petroleum Geology of Northwest Europe: Proceedings of the 4th Conference*. Geological Society, London, 547–557.

The Elgin and Franklin fields: UK Blocks 22/30c, 22/30b and 29/5b

J. LASOCKI,[1,2] J. M. GUEMENE,[3] A. HEDAYATI,[1] C. LEGORJUS[1] and W. M. PAGE[2]

[1] *Elf Exploration UK PLC, 1 Claymore Drive, Bridge of Don, Aberdeen AB23 8GB, UK*
[2] *Present address: Kerr-McGee North Sea (UK) Ltd, Ninian House, Crawpeel Rd, Aberdeen AB1 4LG, UK*
[3] *Elf Exploration and Production, 64018, Pau Cedec, France*

Abstract: The Elgin and Franklin fields are high pressure/high temperature (HP/HT) (1100 bars, 190°C) gas condensate accumulations lying in the southern Central Graben in UK Blocks 22/30c, 22/30b and 29/5b. The Elgin Field comprises a complex faulted anticlinal structure and the Franklin Field, a tilted fault block. The principal reservoir comprises highly bioturbated, very fine-grained, shallow marine sandstones of the Upper Jurassic Fulmar Formation. A significant amount of secondary porosity (up to half the observed porosity) developed in these deep fields (>5 km subsea) which together with the extreme overpressure (500 bars excess) and stable grain mineralogy resulted in preservation of high quality reservoirs. The hydrocarbons have been sourced from the Upper and Middle Jurassic shales and coals and are sealed by the Upper Jurassic shales and Lower Cretaceous marls. The gas condensates are liquid rich with condensate yields of up to 1345 g Sm^{-3} in Elgin and 695 g Sm^{-3} in Franklin.

The fields, discovered in 1985 (Franklin) and 1991 (Elgin), are currently being developed with production start-up scheduled for 2000. Recoverable reserves are estimated to be around 25×10^9 m^3 (890×10^9 SCF) gas and 29×10^6 tonnes (245×10^6 BBL) condensate for Elgin and 23×10^9 m^3 (820×10^9 SCF) gas and 15×10^6 tonnes (120×10^6 BBL) for Franklin.

The aim of this paper is to provide a basic description of the petroleum geology of the Elgin and Franklin fields which are currently under development. The fields are located in the UK southern Central Graben in Blocks 22/30c, 22/30b and 29/5b, approximately 240 km east of Aberdeen (Fig. 1). Due to their high pressure/high temperature (HP/HT) conditions, 1100 bars formation pressure (2.02 sg EMW), and 190°C reservoir temperature, the fields pose a considerable development challenge.

The fields are structural traps with the Elgin Field comprising a complex faulted anticline divided into three main panels, Western, Central and Eastern, to the north of the Franklin Field which is a tilted fault block with a distinctive horst shape in the north. The fields are separated by a 1 km wide complex collapse zone. The main reservoir is formed by the Upper Jurassic Fulmar Formation sandstone. These very fine-grained sandstones are characterized by their highly bioturbated nature and were deposited in a shallow marine shoreface setting. The sandstones shale out and inter-finger with co-eval Heather Formation shales towards the southeast of the Franklin Field. The best reservoir quality is found in those reservoir sections that have significant amounts of secondary porosity developed. The Elgin and Franklin hydrocarbons were generated from a combination of Upper and Middle Jurassic source rocks. The gas condensates are surprisingly liquid rich and have condensate yields of up to 1345 g Sm^{-3} in the Elgin Field. The fields will be produced by natural depletion with wells drilled from two wellheads platforms and with a central processing facility located on Block 22/30c (Fig. 2).

The Elgin Field is named after the Scottish town on the Moray Firth coast and the Franklin Field after Rear Admiral Sir John Franklin, the famous eighteenth century British explorer and discoverer of the Northwest Passage, Canada.

History

The Elgin and Franklin fields lie on three UK Offshore Licences P362, P666 and P188 (Fig. 3). The Franklin Field was discovered by Ranger in 1985 with the farm-in Well 29/5b-4. It was appraised by Ultramar with Well 29/5b-6 in 1989 to confirm the northwestern extent of the field and appraise the underlying Pentland Formation. Well 29/5b-8 was drilled (Ultramar/Lasmo) in 1991 in the southeast to determine the gas–water contact. Elf Exploration UK PLC took over operatorship in 1992. The Elgin Field was discovered in 1991 by Elf UK with Well 22/30c-8 located in the Central Panel. Wells 22/30c-10 (1993) and 22/30c-13 (1995) successfully appraised the Western and Eastern panels, respectively.

All three wells were drilled from the same surface location as they were intended to be retained as possible future production wells as a result of the high well costs (two will in fact be re-entered). The Elgin and Franklin fields are being developed as part of a joint agreement with the P666, P362 and P188 (south) licencees. A single unit area encompassing the Elgin and Franklin fields has been defined and each of the owners has agreed its fixed equity in this unit area (Fig. 3). The agreed Unit Area is different from Field Determination Area as granted by the DTI. The development programme for the two fields was approved by the DTI in April 1997 and production start-up is anticipated in the second quarter of 2000. There are potential problems of drilling a heterogeneously depleting HP/HT reservoir; consequently it is planned to drill all the development wells before a 100 bar differential depletion limit (either within the reservoir or between the depleting reservoir and the over/under burden) is reached, approximately one year after start-up on Franklin and within four months on Elgin. Five new development wells are planned on Elgin, giving a total of seven producing wells (subject to the successful recovery of Wells 22/30c-8 and -13). Five development wells are planned on Franklin. In order to optimize the number and location of these wells a joint 3D seismic survey was acquired over the Elgin, Franklin and Shearwater (Shell operated) fields during 1996.

Geological history

The Elgin and Franklin fields lie in a structurally complex area in the southern part of the Central Graben (Fig. 1). This area has been affected by two major phases of extension, one during

LASOCKI, J., GUEMENE, J. M., HEDAYATI, A., LEGORJUS, C. & PAGE, W. M. The Elgin and Franklin fields: UK Blocks 22/30c, 22/30b and 29/5b. *In*: FLEET, A. J. & BOLDY, S. A. R. (eds) *Petroleum Geology of Northwest Europe: Proceedings of the 5th Conference*, 1007–1020.

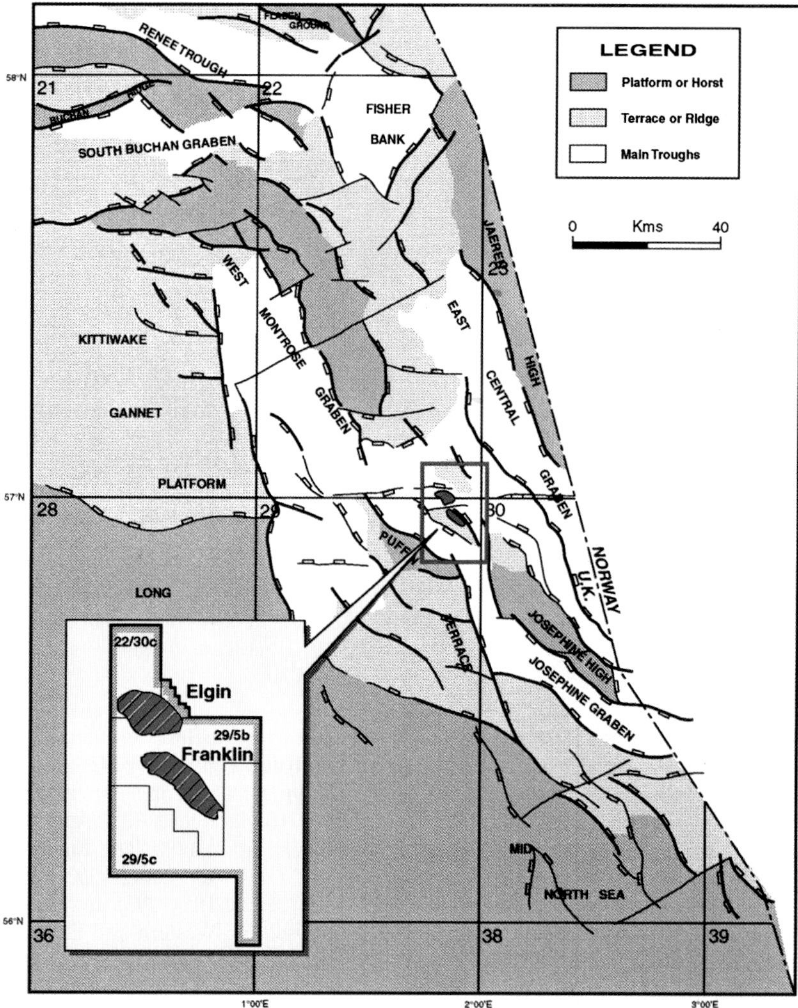

Fig. 1. Location map for the Elgin and Franklin fields.

the Triassic and a second during the late Jurassic/early Cretaceous followed immediately by a minor compressive phase lasting until the late Tertiary (Eggink *et al.* 1996).

The generalized stratigraphic succession for the Elgin and Franklin fields is shown in Fig. 4. The deepest observable seismic event is the Permian Top Rotliegend, unfortunately due to the great depth, approximately 7 km (over 5 s TWT), and the structural complexity of the overlying succession this horizon is poorly imaged. The predominant basement faults appear to trend N–S to NNW–SSE with a secondary fault direction of E–W to ENE–WSW. In addition, the Base Triassic (Top Zechstein Salt) cannot be confidently picked in this area and so reconstructing the Permo-Triassic history is difficult. What is clear is that there is a marked detachment between the pre- and post-salt. The ductile salt layer has significantly influenced the nature of the transfer of the extension in the basement to the overlying 'pod' complex.

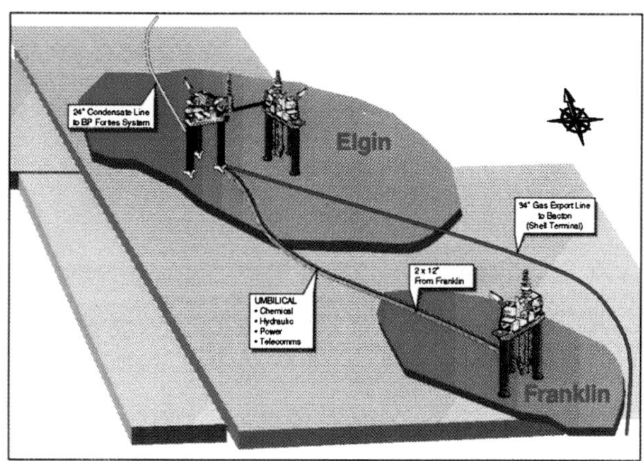

Fig. 2. Elgin and Franklin fields development architecture.

The Triassic has not yet been penetrated in this very deep part of the graben but the Smith Bank Formation non-marine red-brown shales and silty sandstone succession is predicted to be overlain by continental Skagerrak sandstones deposited by southerly flowing ephemeral fluvial systems (Goldsmith *et al.* 1995; Dickinson 1996).

A series of Triassic pods and interpods has been defined which reflects a complex interplay between sediment loading (down building) and extension (salt thinning). The present-day salt thickness, which is generally thin with localized grounding of the Triassic 'pods' onto the Rotliegend, suggests that significant amounts of withdrawal have occurred. The salt appears to have withdrawn both eastwards up onto the Block 30/1 high (this high separates the West from the East Central Graben) and possibly west-southwestwards towards the Puffin Horst. In contrast to the pod–interpod model proposed by Dickinson (1996) for the Puffin Field, the Elgin and Franklin fields lie in what was to become, during the Jurassic, the major basin of the West Central Graben (Buchanan *et al.* 1996). Here the pattern of salt swelling and withdrawal was more regular, resulting in a more constant Triassic sediment thickness. The salt swells/interpods have subsequently variably deflated

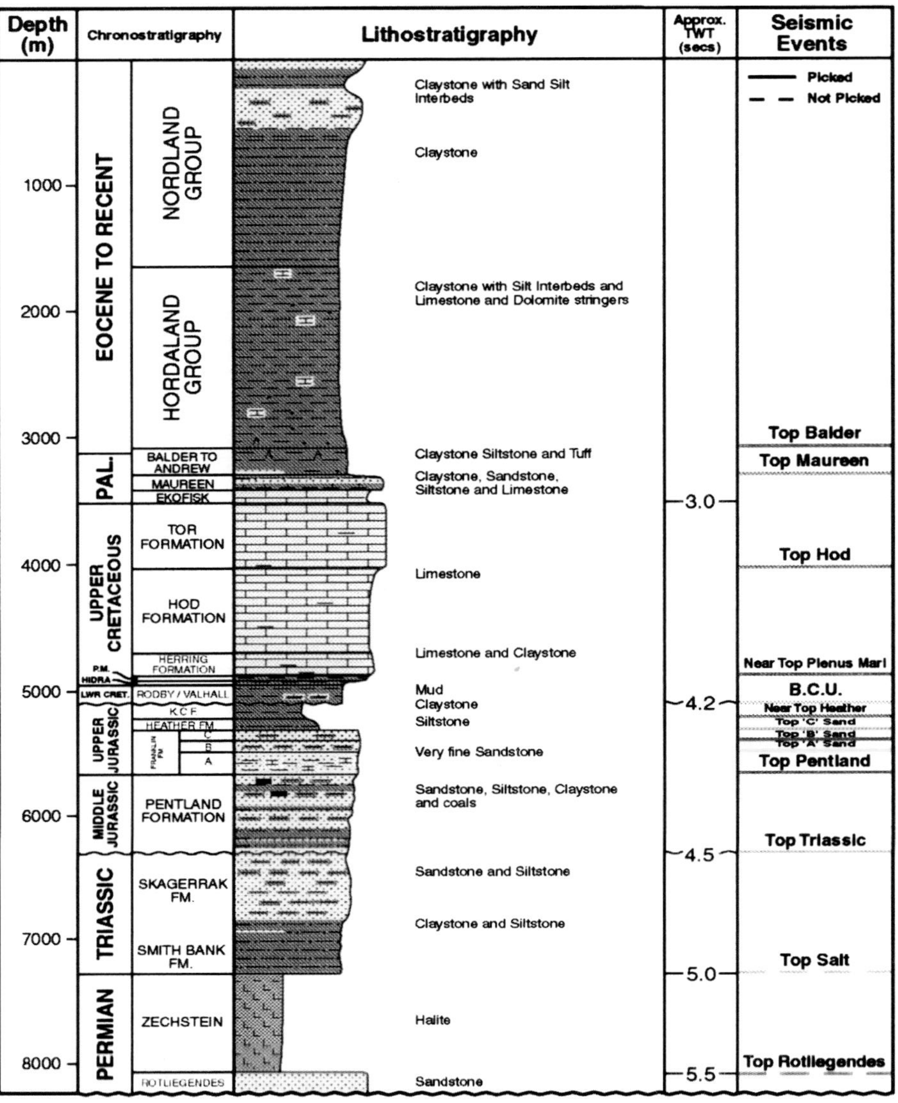

Fig. 3. Structure map of the Elgin and Franklin fields with unit area equities.

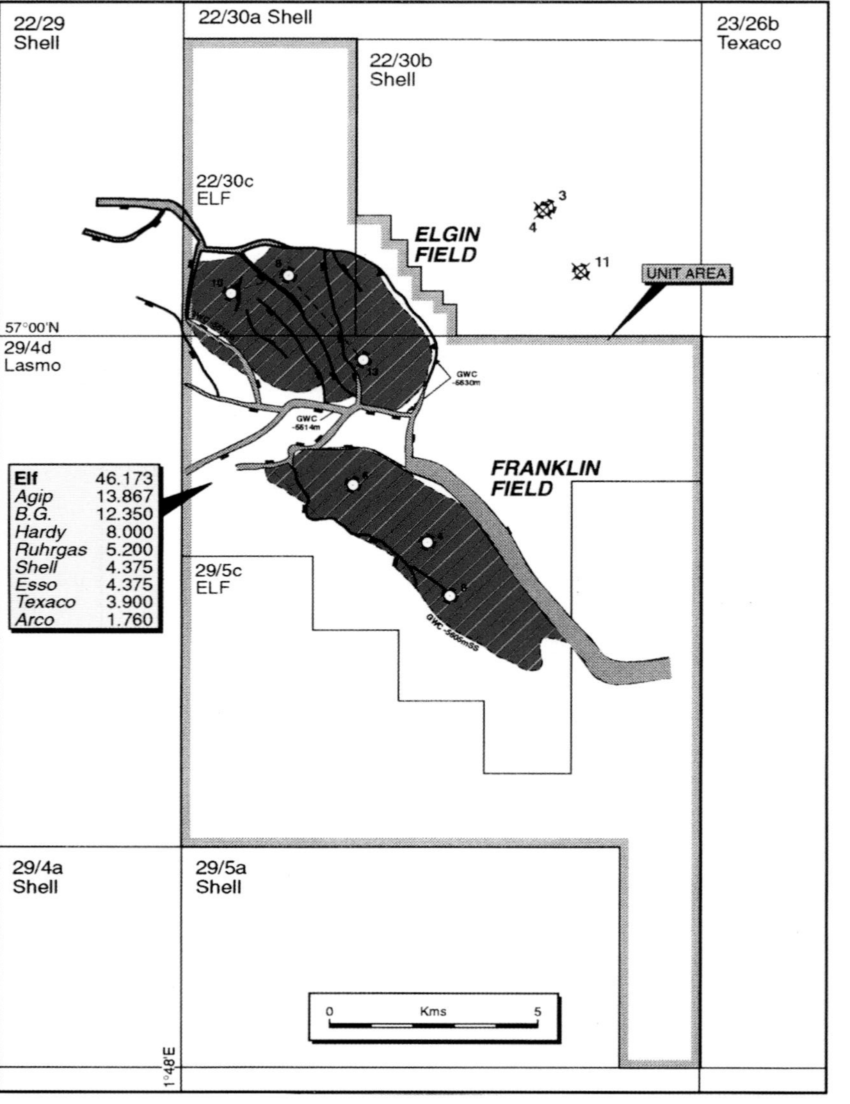

Fig. 4. Generalized stratigraphic succession.

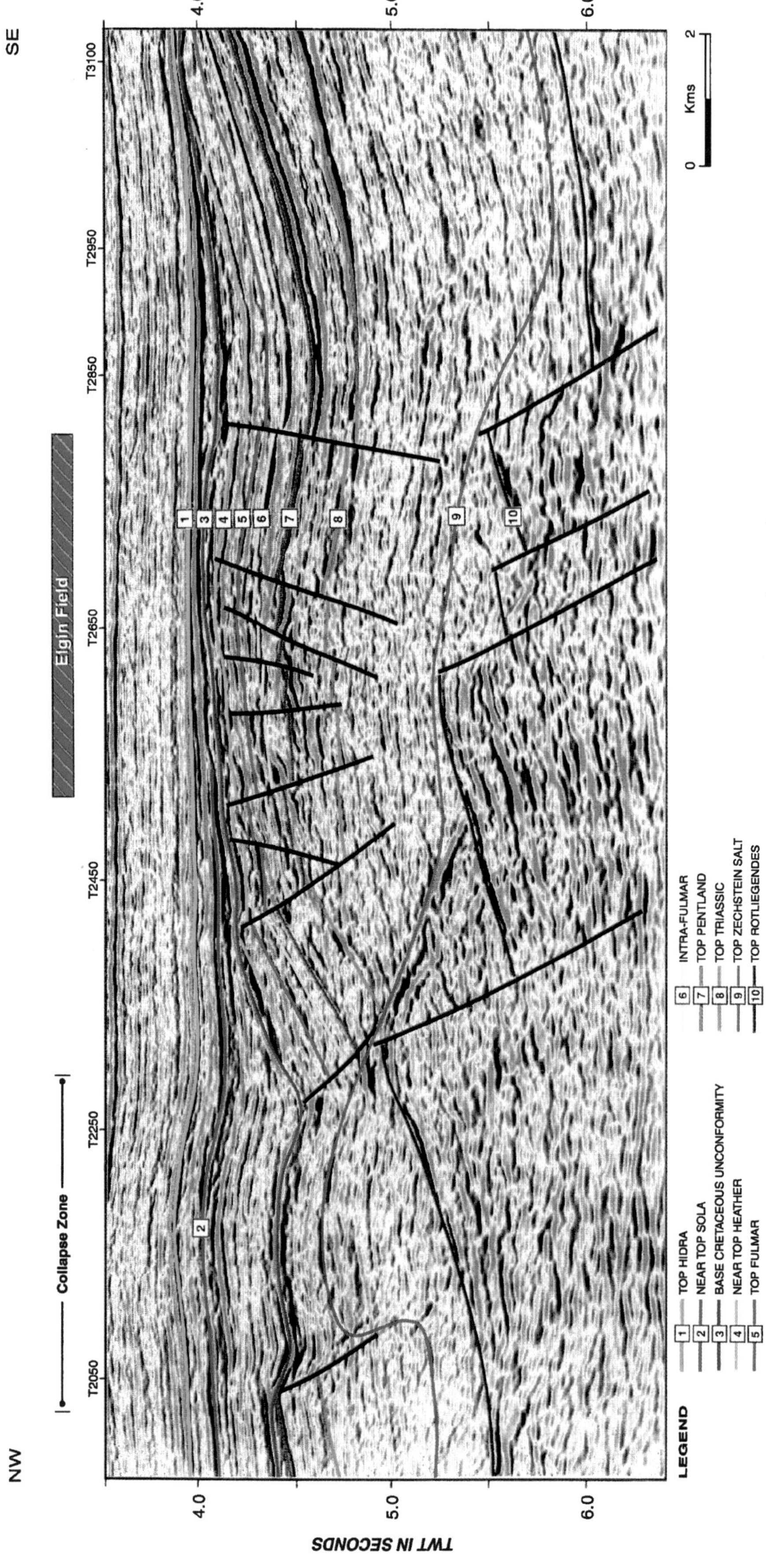

Fig. 5. Elgin Field: NW–SE random seismic line (1996 3D).

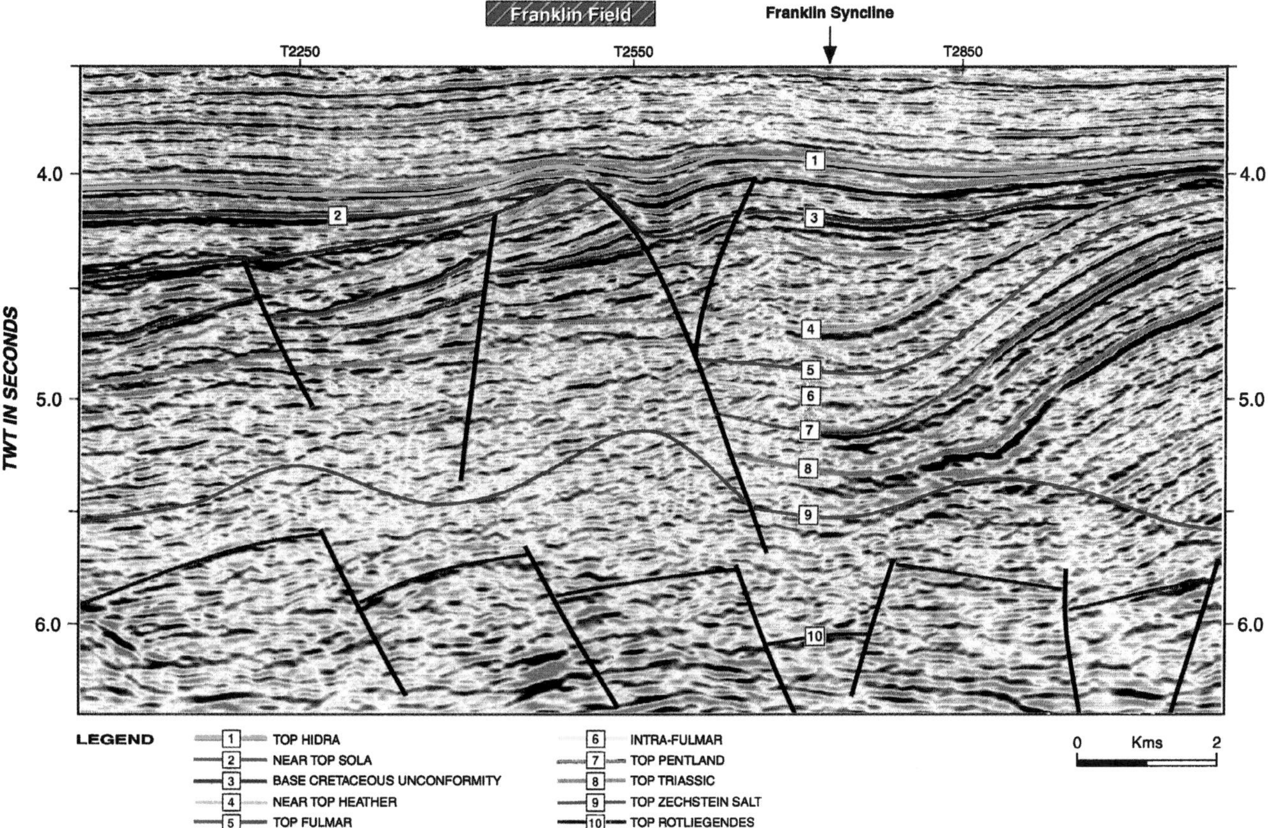

Fig. 6. Franklin Field: SW–NE random seismic line (1996 3D).

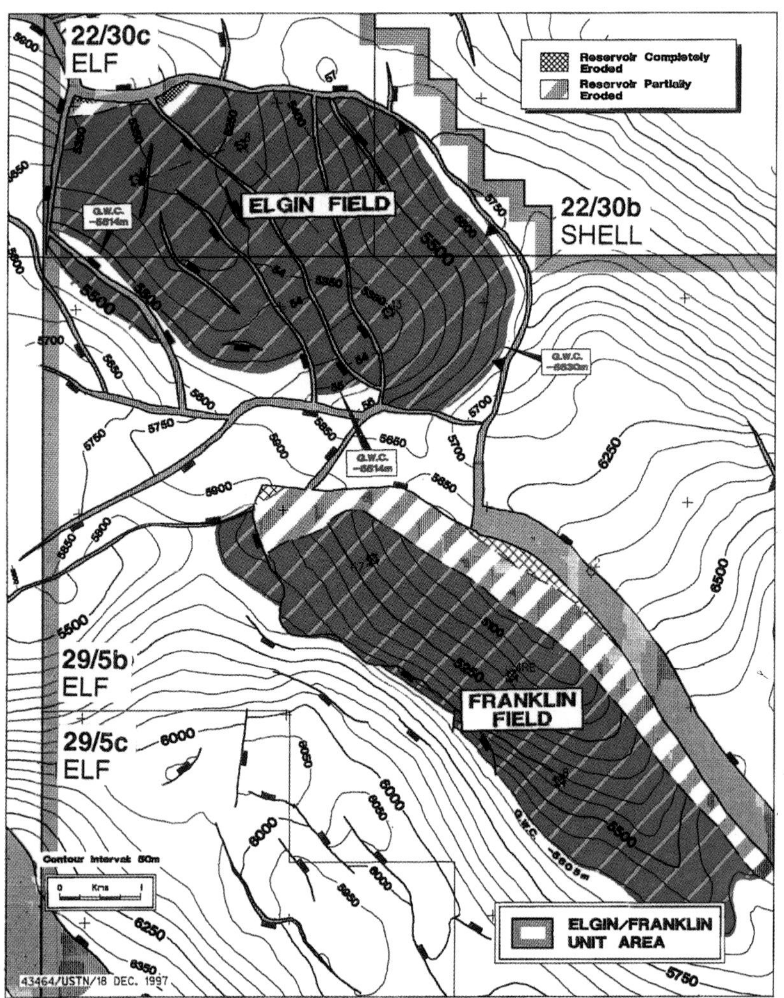

Fig. 7. Top Fulmer depth structure map.

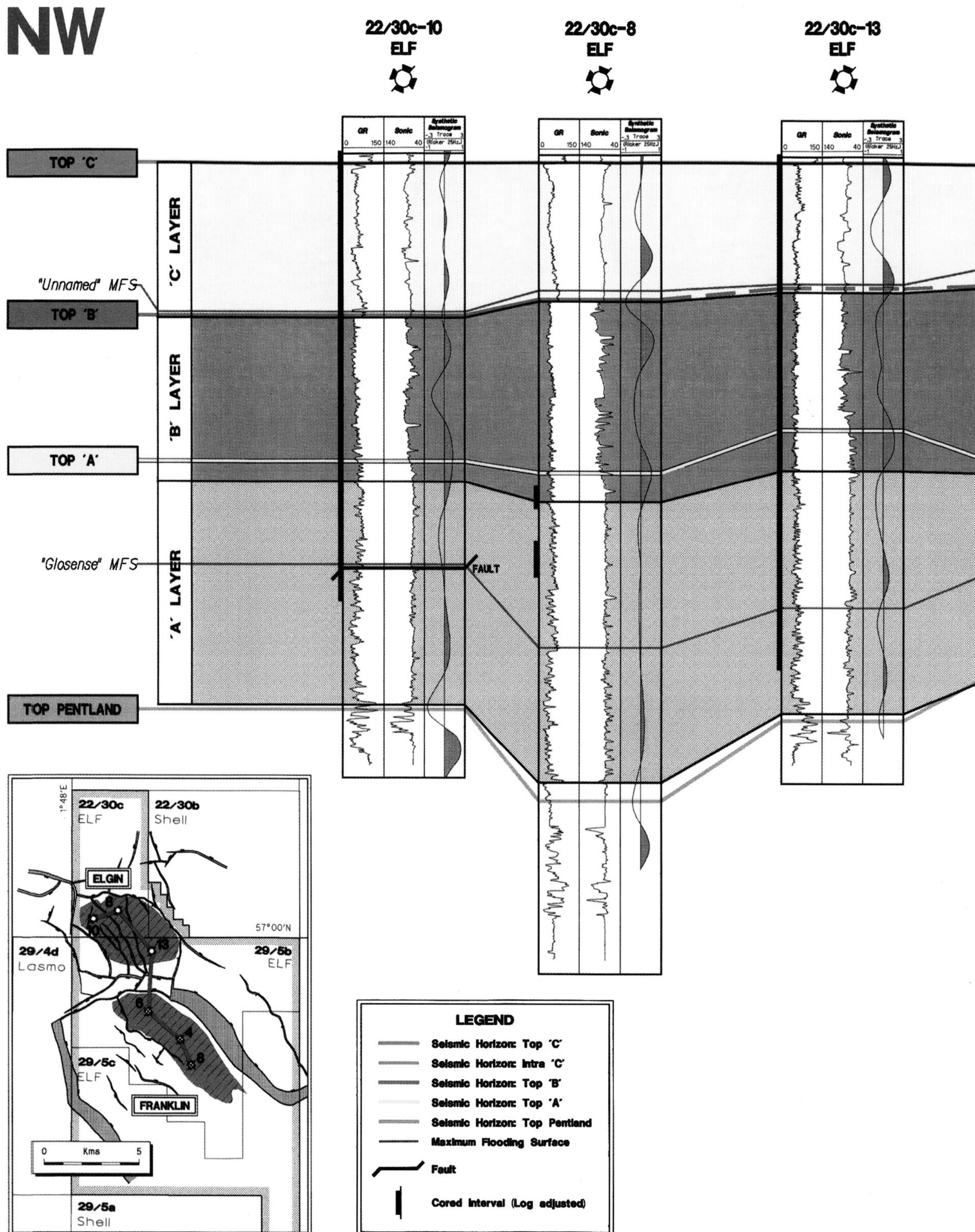

Fig. 8. Elgin and Franklin fields: Fulmar Formation well correlation.

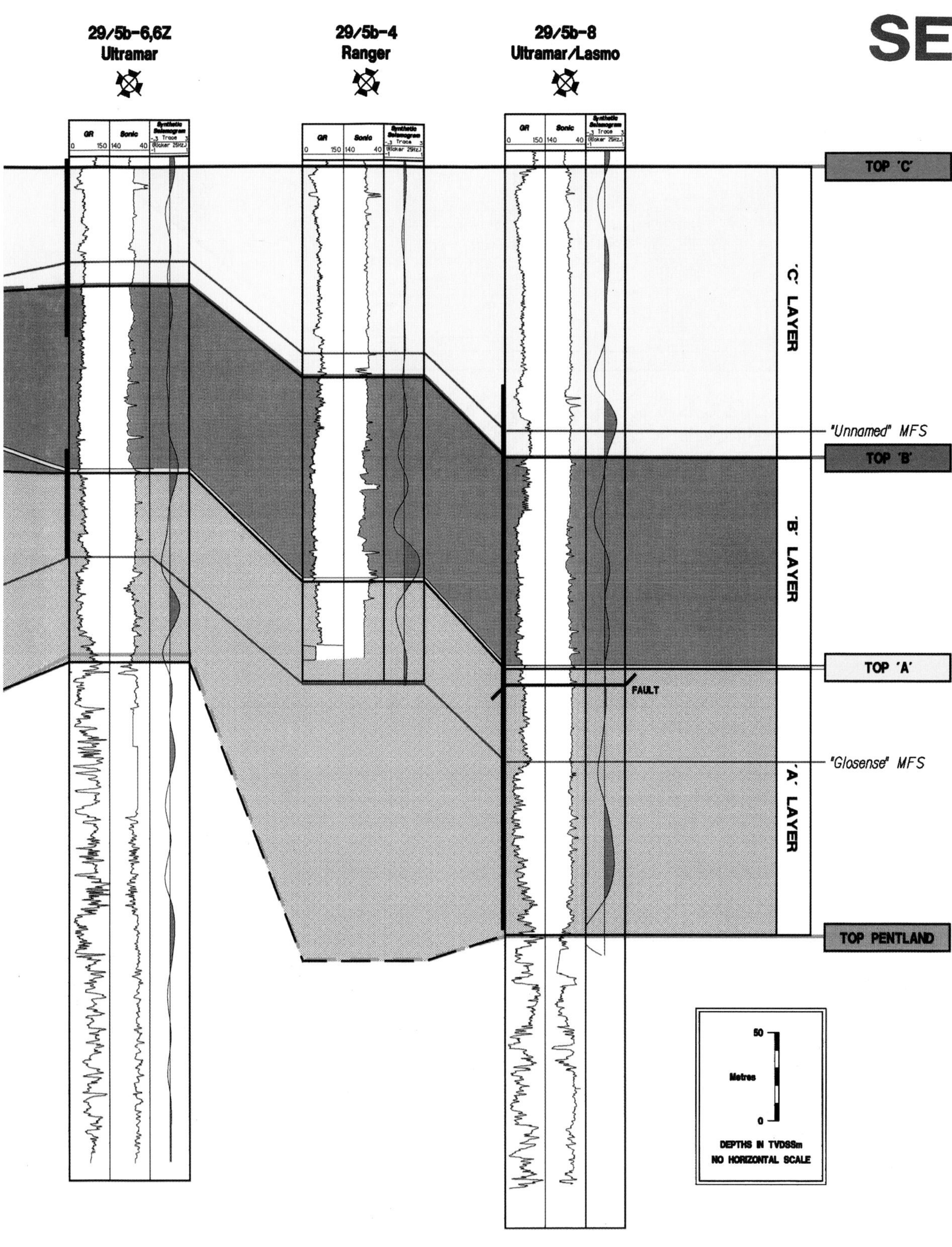
SE
29/5b-6,6Z
Ultramar
29/5b-4
Ranger
29/5b-8
Ultramar/Lasmo
GR
Sonic
TOP 'C'
'C' LAYER
"Unnamed" MFS
TOP 'B'
'B' LAYER
TOP 'A'
FAULT
"Glosense" MFS
'A' LAYER
TOP PENTLAND
Metres
DEPTHS IN TVDSSm
NO HORIZONTAL SCALE

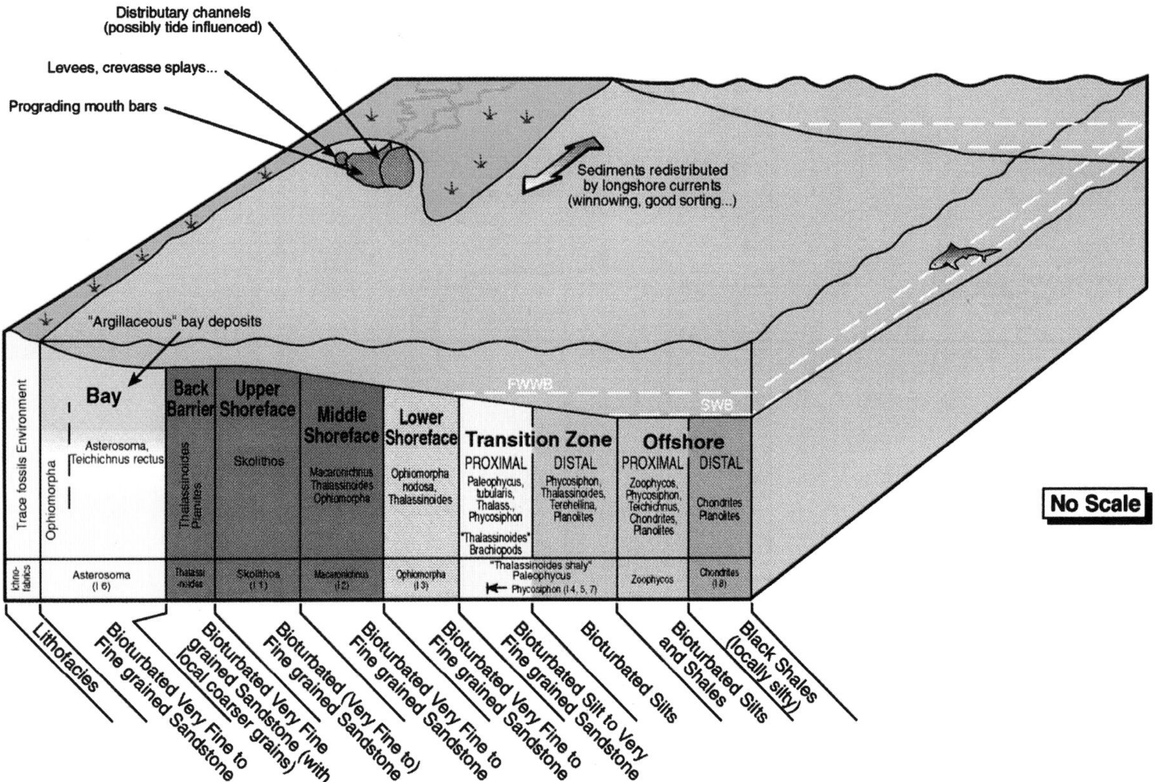

Fig. 9. Fulmar Formation depositional profile.

during the Jurassic–Early Cretaceous in a manner similar to that proposed by Vendeville & Jackson (1992*a*, *b*).

It has not been possible to seismically differentiate any Lower Jurassic sediments in the Elgin/Franklin area. They are reported to be absent in the area of the Puffin Field immediately to the southwest (Dickinson 1996). It is probable that they were eroded (if deposited) by the development of the mid Cimmerian unconformity. The Middle Jurassic Fladen Group, Pentland Formation fluvial (alluvial plain) sandstones, siltstones and mudstones with minor coals overlies the Triassic succession. Hydrocarbons (gas condensates) have been encountered within the Pentland Formation in the Franklin Field (separate hydrocarbon column). The Pentland Formation yields relatively long-ranging non-marine miospores and pollen. The effects of high thermal maturity on these robust palynomorphs are less of a problem than for the more fragile marine dinocysts of the overlying Humber Group. Precise age dating of the unit is difficult, however, because of the long ranges of most of the taxa and the scarcity of the more precisely age-diagnostic species. Much of the unit is Bathonian or older although the upper part is possibly Callovian and may even be as young as earliest Early Oxfordian. The Lower to Middle Oxfordian marine transgressive sediments at the base of the overlying Humber Group may be virtually conformable with the Pentland Formation in axial parts of the Central Graben.

The different thickness trends of the Middle Jurassic and Triassic intervals reflect how the 'pods' were differentially tilting in response to complex salt swelling and withdrawal patterns. The major Upper Jurassic depocentre appears to lie to the east of the Franklin Field where a major synclinal axis trends southeastwards. Locally, there is evidence of salt withdrawal leading to partial collapse of the flanks of the salt swells/walls. It must be stressed that at the present-day depths, it is very difficult to seismically image the structurally complex pod boundaries where the salt swelling and withdrawal has occurred. The ongoing interpretation of the new 3D seismic data over the two fields is attempting to resolve this complexity.

The older late Jurassic sediments are overlain by the shallow marine Fulmar Formation (Oxfordian) sandstones, which have a similar depocentre to the Pentland. The Fulmar succession can be seen to thin towards the west, southwest and northwest with evidence of onlap towards the southwest. Over 300 m of sand were deposited in the area of the Elgin and Franklin fields, resulting in a more or less 'layer-cake' reservoir stratigraphy. This contrasts with the Fulmar Field (Stockbridge & Gray 1991) and the Puffin Field (Howell & Flint 1996) where respectively shifting depocentres and periods of emergence have been identified.

The cessation of Fulmar sandstone deposition was accompanied by a general westerly back-stepping of the sands during a retrogradational phase leading eventually to the deposition of the Heather Formation. Major rift-related structural movements occurred during Late Kimmeridgian–Volgian times. The Kimmeridgian Clay Formation was deposited during this period and exhibits marked thickness variations. It was indeed at this time that the Elgin and Franklin structures were formed. The Late Jurassic faulting effectively overprints the Triassic faults (i.e. the main pod boundaries were reactivated). There was localized collapse of the salt walls/swells in the pod boundary areas, for example, the complex zone between the two fields and to the west and northwest of Elgin, and of the interpod underlying the Franklin syncline (Fig. 6).

The Base Cretaceous unconformity (BCU) erodes down to the Fulmar level in the northwest of Elgin and in the north-northeast of Franklin. The overlying Lower Cretaceous succession varies greatly in thickness over the Elgin and Franklin

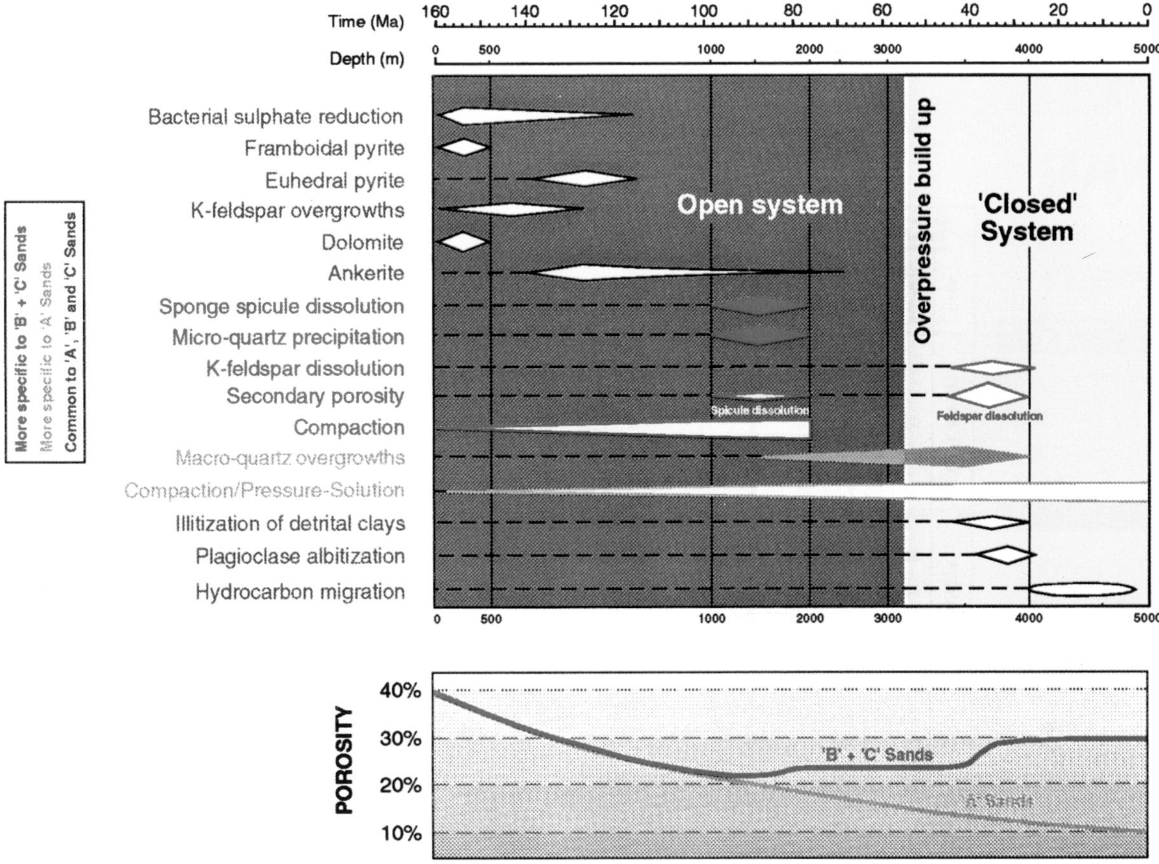

Fig. 10. Generalized paragenetic sequence Fulmar formation.

structures, being very thin on the crestal areas Locally, further collapse occurred as a result of salt withdrawal. Mild inversion is recognized within the Cretaceous and up to the Paleocene Balder Horizon (Well 29/5b-2 was drilled to evaluate a Tertiary structural closure). The pattern of sedimentation of the Chalk Group and the Tertiary is essentially regional. During the Tertiary, the rate of burial has been quite rapid particularly during the Quaternary. This has given rise to the extreme overpressure in the Jurassic/Early Cretaceous which has been generated mainly by disequilibrium compaction together with a component from oil cracking and late gas generation from source rocks (Osborne & Swarbrick 1997).

Geophysics

The Franklin Field was originally identified using 760 km of pre-1985 conventional 2D seismic data. After the 29/5b-4 discovery well was drilled, some 3D seismic data were acquired in 1987 with a 50 m spacing (120 km^2 coverage). The Elgin Field was defined with 3D seismic data acquired in 1989 with a 50 m line spacing (248 km^2 coverage). In 1993–4 the Franklin and Elgin 3D datasets were reprocessed and merged in order to improve the data quality and continuity at the reservoir level. Multiples generated by the Cretaceous Plenus Marl and BCU horizons were partially removed by further seismic processing.

In 1996, new 3D seismic data were acquired jointly with Shell, operator of the adjacent Shearwater Field, over the Elgin and Franklin fields, to provide a homogeneous seismic dataset with a higher resolution. The new 3D is expected to help refine the seismic interpretation over the two fields and to optimize the final locations of the development wells. This has a bin spacing of 12.5 m inline by 18.75 m crossline and was acquired with 6 streamers of 4.6 km cable length and single, source 4017 in^3, Bolt airgun. Anti-multiple processing has been performed on the post stack time migrated data. A post stack depth imaging is planned to be performed during 1997.

Trap

The Elgin Field is a complex faulted anticlinal trap subdivided into three main compartments; the Western, Central and Eastern panels (Figs 5 & 7). The field-bounding faults are sub-vertical in nature with the eastern bounding fault slightly reverse. Throws are variable and can be as large as 500 m. Intra-field faults which compartmentalize the reservoir have been seismically identified. These faults seal and have given rise to different hydrocarbon fluid types and contacts across the field. These are normal faults with variable throws of up to 100 m. The Western Panel is structurally more complex with a series of predominantly NW–SE trending minor faults present. This panel is also vertically compartmentalized, a result of the *glosense* maximum flooding surface (mfs; J54A after Partington *et al.* 1993*a*, *b*) acting as a barrier and separating a lower gas condensate (more gas rich, no pressure data) accumulation from the main upper gas condensate bearing section.

The Franklin Field comprises a large tilted fault block, with a major NW–SE trending fault with up to 1200 m of throw separating the field from a deep synclinal area to the east (Figs 6 and 7). The northern limit is defined by a complex WSW-ENE trending collapse (salt withdrawal) fault zone.

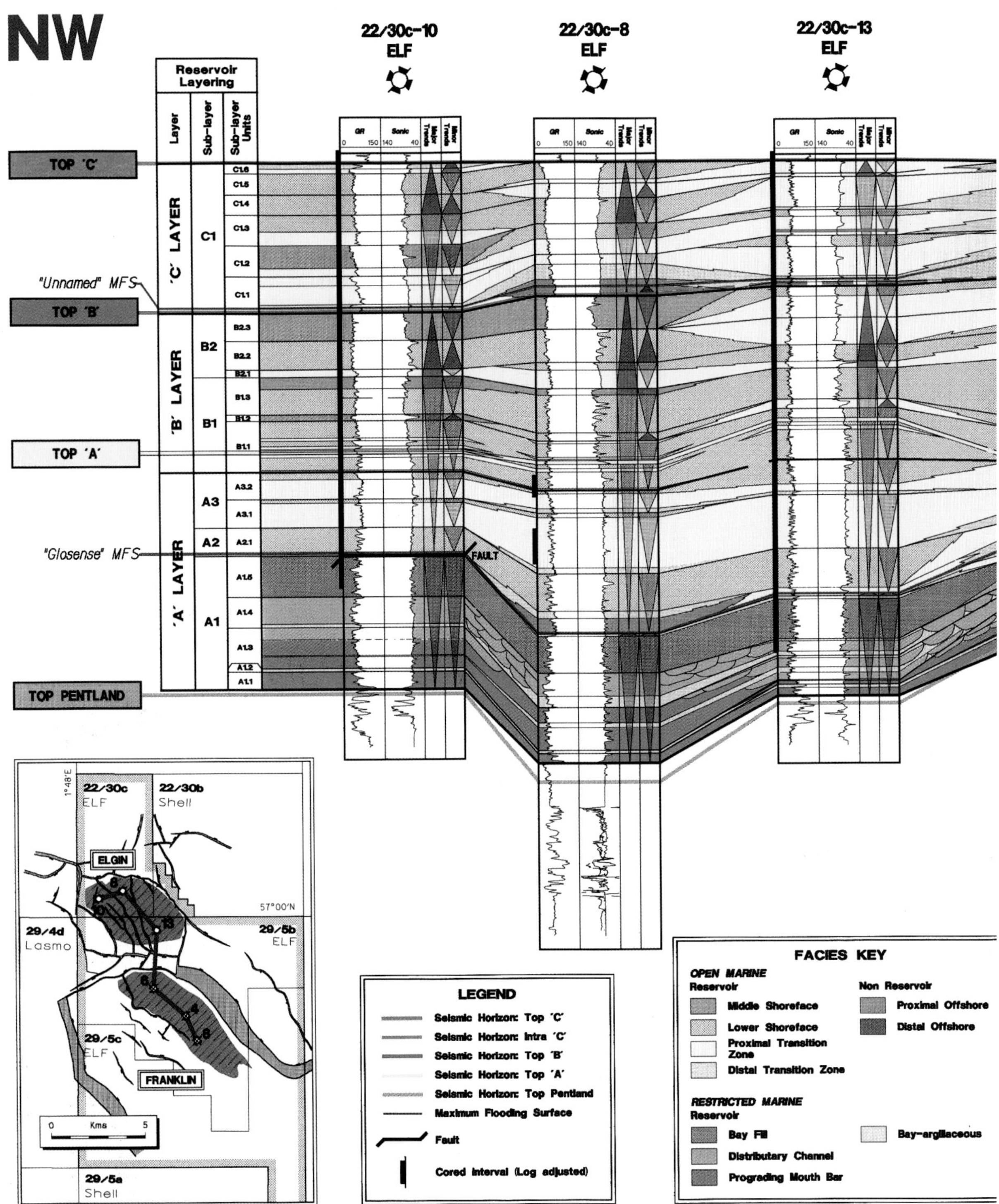

Fig. 11. Elgin and Franklin fields: Fulmar Formation reservoir layering.

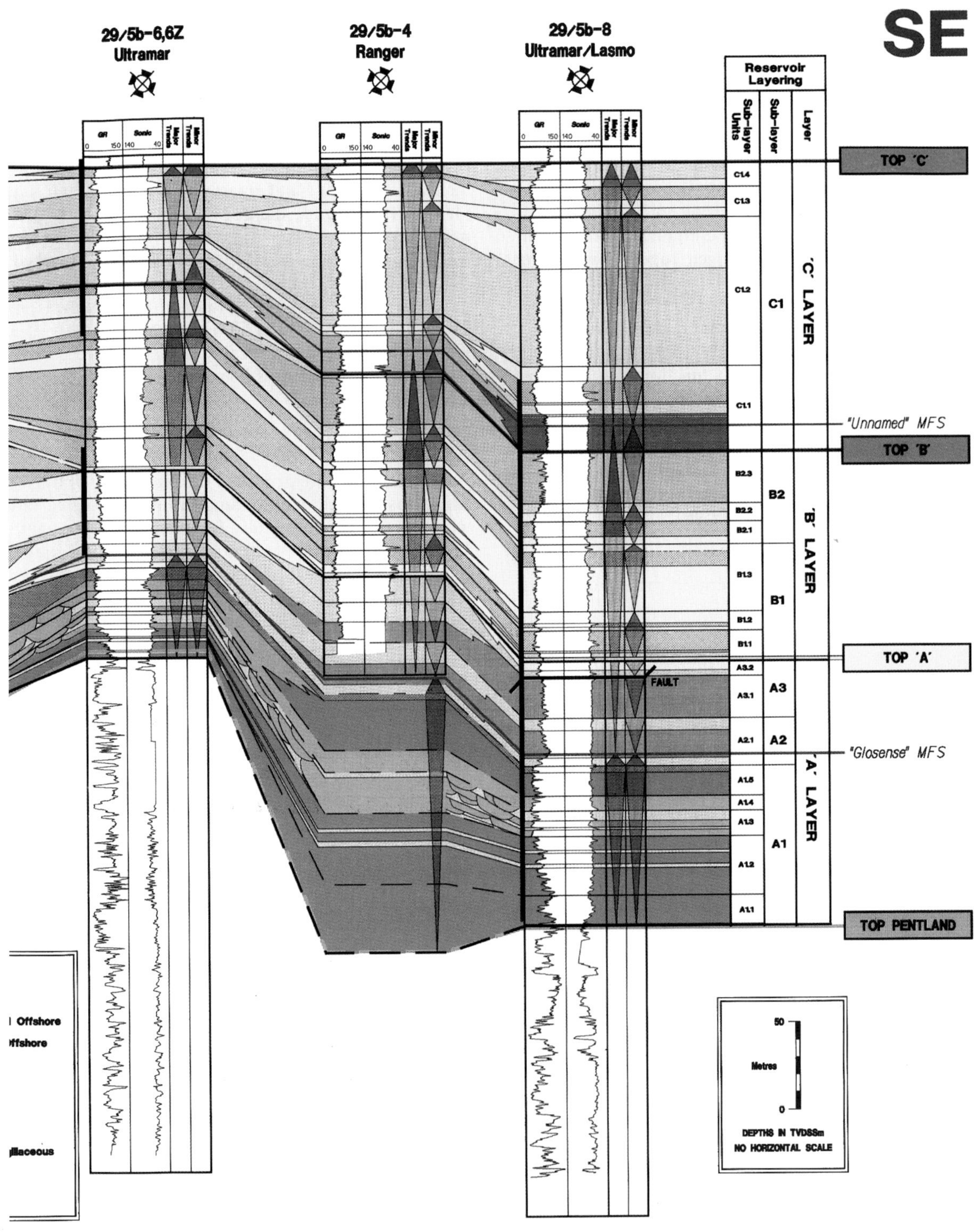

SE
29/5b-6,6Z
Ultramar
29/5b-4
Ranger
29/5b-8
Ultramar/Lasmo
Reservoir Layering
Sub-layer Units
Sub-layer
Layer
TOP 'C'
C1.4
C1.3
C1.2
C1.1
C1
'C' LAYER
"Unnamed" MFS
TOP 'B'
B2.3
B2.2
B2.1
B1.3
B1.2
B1.1
B2
B1
'B' LAYER
TOP 'A'
A3.2
A3.1
A2.1
A1.5
A1.4
A1.3
A1.2
A1.1
A3
A2
A1
'A' LAYER
FAULT
"Glosense" MFS
TOP PENTLAND
Offshore
Offshore
llaceous
50
Metres
0
DEPTHS IN TVDSSm
NO HORIZONTAL SCALE

In the north, the Franklin Field has distinctive horst shape. Closure to the south-southeast is defined by moderate dip.

Reservoir

The Fulmar Formation reservoir has been extensively cored (Fig. 8) and this has resulted in a nearly complete coverage of the reservoir in both fields. The reservoir has an average thickness of 300 m. Lithologies identified in the core comprise highly bioturbated and virtually unstructured sandstones forming the majority of the reservoir. Sedimentary structured sandstones with horizontal lamination, planar bedding through to medium-scale cross stratification constitute a minor component of the reservoir. Because of the lack of sedimentary structures, detailed ichnofabric analysis techniques have been used (Taylor & Gawthorpe 1993). The lithologies have been grouped into different lithofacies which together with the ichnofabrics (Fig. 9) help define a shoreface to offshore depositional profile (after Elliot 1986). In both the Elgin and Franklin fields, upper shoreface to offshore transition zone deposits predominate. No higher energy deposits, foreshore and backshore, have been recognized, a function of either non-deposition (in this part of the depositional basin) or possible cannibalization during the transgressive phases. The spatial and temporal distribution of the different sandbodies has resulted in a patchwork of facies reflecting the complex interplay between sediment flux, accommodation space development, minor syn-sedimentary fault activity and relative sealevel changes. Overall, towards the southeast of Franklin the shoreface succession inter fingers with the true offshore environment where a major, salt withdrawal-related, depocentre has been identified.

Diagenesis

The development/preservation of sandstones with up to 30% porosity and over 2 Darcy permeability at depths of over 5 km reflects a complex diagenetic history (Fig. 10). Average porosities are 16% and 17% with permeabilities of 10 mD and 25 mD, respectively for the Franklin and Elgin fields. Although there is a broad facies control on the poroperm characteristics of the reservoir, there is a strong, yet variable, diagenetic overprint. This overprint reflects varying scales of original reservoir heterogeneity linked to the primary facies architecture, with fluid flow concentrated within the better-connected reservoir layers and further focused when good reservoir sections are overlain by laterally extensive barriers and baffles. Detailed petrographic analysis of the core indicates that the reservoir sandstones are very fine-grained subarkoses with clay contents occasionally as high as 37%. Early compactional effects have been lessened as a result of the growth of early authigenic minerals, in particular microquartz and carbonate (dolomite), which helped provide a rigid framework (and may have inhibited later pore filling cements). During subsequent burial, further dolomite, ankerite and quartz cements developed; these did not significantly occlude the pore networks, other than where they form concretions.

The most significant diagenetic event in the burial history of the sandstones was the development of secondary porosity resulting from feldspar, sponge spicule and carbonate (mainly shell debris) dissolution. This accounts for up to half of the point-counted porosity in some sections of the reservoir. Even more critically this does not appear to have resulted in the precipitation of significant amounts of illite (from the feldspar dissolution) which would otherwise have led to a serious deterioration in reservoir quality. All of the clays within the reservoir are, however, illitized; this makes it impossible to differentiate authigenic from detrital clays. It is not clear whether there has been a net export of the by-products of feldspar dissolution from the reservoir or whether they have been concentrated in the more argillaceous intra-reservoir sandstone layers. This process may be related to the ingress of organic acid-rich pore waters expelled from the surrounding compacting mudrocks and/or the initial generation/migration of hydrocarbons. The precise timing of this significant phase of secondary porosity development is not well constrained. It certainly began before the development of the high overpressures but may have continued after the establishment of the 'closed' system (Fig. 10). The development of increasingly high overpressure within the reservoir has helped to minimize further compactional effects, as evidenced by the general lack of significant pressure solution (chemical compaction). Fluid inclusions are rare and apart from minor albite and some mesoquartz cements, diagenesis appears to have been minimal prior to the influx of hydrocarbons into the reservoir. Most recently (last 5 Ma), when temperatures reached 175°C (current reservoir temperature is 190°C), thermal cracking may have resulted in the precipitation of pyrobitumen (less than 2% of total rock volume), although the possibility of a subtle interaction between chemical and thermal processes (permanent exchange concept) is being researched.

Reservoir layering

The sandstones were deposited during an overall transgression which has resulted in a flooding surface dominated succession where minor sea-level falls have tended to be suppressed. Individual sequences tend to be coarsening/cleaning-upward punctuated by occasional fining/dirtying-upward transgressive pulses.

The gross reservoir section has been subdivided into three main reservoir layers utilizing the available limited biostratigraphic data, core and wireline log correlations, calibrated with the seismic horizons and integrated into a sequence stratigraphic interpretation (Fig. 11). Only one unequivocal biostratigraphic event has been recognized in both the Elgin and Franklin fields and is comparable to the *glosense* mfs of Partington *et al.* (1993*a*, *b*). It is defined as the mfs occurring immediately above the acme occurrences of *Epistomina parastelligera* and *Rhaxella perforata* (opaline) in wells from the Elgin, Shearwater and Erskine fields. A second equivocal mfs event has been identified in the upper reservoir section. These two mfs events subdivide the reservoir into three broad regressive/ transgressive sequences.

Source and hydrocarbons

The gas condensate in the Elgin and Franklin fields has been generated by a combination of source rocks. Both the Heather Formation claystones, which interdigitate with the Fulmar Formation reservoir, and the Kimmeridge Clay Formation claystones drape over the two fields. These are considered to be the principal contributing source rocks (unpublished). Only in a small part of the northwestern area of the two fields does the BCU cut down and erode into the reservoir. The Middle Jurassic Pentland Formation coals and carbonaceous shales have provided an additional charge (unpublished). Modelling suggests that oil generation began during the late Cretaceous to Early Tertiary, but that the main oil generation phase occurred during the Early Miocene (Cornford 1994; Elf unpublished). The initial hydrocarbons trapped were oils. Gas generation began during the Early Pliocene, with a significant gas charge linked to the very rapid Plio-Quaternary burial phase.

A number of factors have helped to preserve the high condensate yield (up to 1345 g Sm^{-3} in the Elgin Field) of the hydrocarbons occurring within the fields. Firstly, the initial

Table 1. Elgin and Franklin fields data summary

	Elgin	Franklin	
Type	Structural – complex faulted anticline	Structural – tilted fault block	
Formation	Fulmar Formation	Fulmar Formation	Pentland Formation
Age	Upper Jurassic (E.–L. Oxfordian)	Upper Jurassic (E.–L. Oxfordian)	Middle Jurassic (Bathonian Callovian)
Gas column (m)	290–305	525	395
Gross thickness (m)	250–350	250–350	500
Net : gross ratio	0.83	0.50	0.15
Average porosity	0.17	0.16	0.13
Hydrocarbon saturation	0.62	0.60	0.70
Average permeability (mD)	25	10	5
Gas gravity (air = 1)	0.68	0.67	–
Condensate yield ($g\,Sm^{-3}$)	1200–1440	740	850
Gas-oil ratio ($Sm^3\,Sm^{-3}$)	520–620	1020	870
Gas expansion factor ($Sm^3\,Rm^{-3}$)	225–247	268	309
Formation water salinity (mg/l TDS)	292 000	89 000	–
Formation water resistivity (ohm m)	0.014	0.022	–
Reservoir temperature (°C)	189 @ 5364 mss	189 @ 5364 mss	200c @ 6000 mss
Reservoir pressure (bar)	1106	1093	1117 @ 5488 mss
Reservoir pressure gradient ($bar\,m^{-1}$)	0.051	0.042	0.052
Drive mechanism	Pressure depletion	Pressure depletion	Pressure depletion
Number/type of wells	3 exploration/appraisal	3 exploration/appraisal	–
Planned production wells	7 (2 are re-entries)	5	–
First gas (planned)	2000	2001	

hydrocarbons were trapped under monophasic conditions because of the high overpressures that existed in the Miocene (over 450 bars). Overpressure continued to build to the present level of 1100 bars (1D and 3D unpublished modelling results). Therefore, all the trapped hydrocarbons have always existed under monophasic conditions. The initial 'oil' fill gradually becoming richer in gas until the system 'flipped' to gas condensate. This contrasts with the fill and spill model of Gussow (1954) where the originally trapped oil is progressively displaced by later gas charging. The present-day variations in condensate yield between Elgin and Franklin (Table 1) reflect the relative quantity of gas that has entered each structure, which is in turn a reflection of the differences in source rock drainage volumes and level of maturity versus actual trap volume. At the present-day, and as modelled in the recent past, the formation pressures in both fields have never exceeded the 96% of the minimum lateral stress (unpublished results) and consequently seal fracture of the type described by Holm (1996) has not occurred. There has also been minimal thermal cracking of the hydrocarbons. Pyrobitumens have been encountered in both the Elgin and Franklin fields (<2% by volume, <10% of the pore volume) and reflect very recent cracking when reservoir temperatures exceeded 175°C (Pepper & Dodd 1995). It has not proven possible to differentiate pyrobitumens formed by thermal cracking from any which may have formed as a result of de-asphaltening (Lomando 1992); both processes are considered to have occurred in the two fields.

Reserves

The gas condensate from the Elgin and Franklin fields will be recovered by pressure depletion. Detailed simulation modelling results give rise to the currently estimated reserves of $25 \times 10^9\,m^3$ (890×10^9 SCF) gas and 29×10^6 tonnes (245×10^6 BBL) condensate for Elgin and $23 \times 10^9\,m^3$ (820×10^9 SCF) gas and 15×10^6 tonnes (120×10^6 BBL) for Franklin. Hydrocarbon production from the fields will result in a massive blow-down of the formation pressures by up to 1000 bars. Based upon extensive rock mechanical studies it is currently estimated that the reservoir will experience 1.5 m of compaction with an accompanying 0.20 m of surface subsidence. It is planned that despite the hostile HP/HT operating conditions this depletion will be closely monitored at the surface and in the sub-surface.

The authors would like to thank Elf Exploration UK PLC, the operator of the Elgin and Franklin fields and the present joint-venture partners for their permission to publish this paper: Agip (UK) Ltd, ARCO British Ltd, BG Exploration and Production Ltd, Esso Exploration and Production UK Ltd, Hardy Exploration and Production Ltd, Ruhrgas UK, Shell UK Exploration and Production and Texaco Britain Ltd.

References

BUCHANAN, P, G., BISHOP, D. J. & HOOD, D. N. 1996. Development of salt-related structures in the Central North Sea: results from section balancing. *In*: ALSOP *et al.* (eds) *Salt Tectonics*. Geological Society, London, Special Publications, **100**, 111–128.

CORNFORD, C. 1994 Mandal–Ekofisk Petroleum System in the Central Graben of the North Sea. *In*: MAGOON, L. B. & DOW, W. G. (eds) *The Petroleum System – From Source to Trap. American Association of Petroleum Geologists* Memoirs, **60**, 537–571.

DICKINSON, B. 1996. The Puffin Field: the appraisal of a complex HP–HT gas–condensate accumulation. *In*: HURST *et al.* (eds) *Geology of the Humber Group: Central Graben and Moray Firth, UKCS*. Geological Society, London, Special Publications, **114**, 299–327.

EGGINK, J. W. *et al.* 1996. Using 3D seismic to understand the structural evolution of the UK Central North Sea. *Petroleum Geoscience*, **2**, 83–96.

ELLIOT, T. 1986. Siliciclastic Shorelines. *In*: READING, H. G. (ed.) *Sedimentary Environments and Facies*. Blackwell Scientific Publications, 155–189.

GUSSOW, W. C. 1954. Differential entrapment of oil and gas: a fundamental principle. *American Association of Petroleum Geologists Bulletin*, **38**, 816–853.

HOLM, G. M. 1996. Central Graben: a dynamic overpressure system. *In*: GLENNIE, K. W. & HURST, A. (eds) *AD1995: NW Europe's Hydrocarbon Industry*. Geological Society, London, 107–122.

HOWELL, J. A., & FLINT, S. S. 1996. A model for high resolution sequence stratigraphy within extensional basins. *In*: HOWELL, J. A. & AITKEN, J. F. (eds) *High Resolution Sequence Stratigraphy: Innovations and Applications*. Geological Society, London, Special Publications, **104**, 129–137.

GOLDSMITH, P. J., RICH, B. & STANDRING, J. 1995. Triassic correlation and stratigraphy in the South Central Graben, UK North Sea. *In*: BOLDY, S. A. R. (ed.) *Permian and Triassic Rifting in Northwest Europe*. Geological Society, London, Special Publications, **91**, 123–143.

LOMANDO, A. J. 1992. The influence of Solid Reservoir Bitumen on Reservoir Quality. *American Association of Petroleum Geologists Bulletin*, **76**, 1137–1152.

OSBOURNE, M. J. & SWARBRICK, R. E. 1997. Mechanisms for generating overpressure in sedimentary basins: a reevaluation. *In*: *American Association of Petroleum Geologists Bulletin*, **81**, 1023–1044.

PARTINGTON, M. A., MITCHENER, B. C., MILTON, N. J. & FRASER, A. J. 1993*a*. A genetic sequence stratigraphy for the North Sea Late Jurassic and Early Cretaceous: stratigraphic distribution and prediction of Kimmeridgian – Late Ryazanian reservoirs in the Viking Graben and adjacent basins. *In*: PARKER, J. R. (ed.) *Petroleum Geology of Northwest Europe: Proceedings of the 4th Conference*. Geological Society, London, 347–370.

——, COPESTAKE, P., MITCHENER, B. C. & UNDERHILL, J. R 1993*b*. Biostratigraphic calibration of genetic stratigraphic sequences in the Jurassic – lowermost Cretaceous (Hettangian–Ryazanian) of the North Sea and surrounding areas. *In*: PARKER, J. R. (ed.) *Petroleum Geology of Northwest Europe: Proceedings of the 4th Conference*. Geological Society, London, 371–386.

PEPPER, A. S & DODD, T. A 1995. Simple kinetic models of petroleum formation Part II: Oil–gas cracking. *Marine and Petroleum Geology*, **12**, 321–340.

STOCKBRIDGE, C. P. & GRAY, D. I. 1991. The Fulmar Field, Blocks 30/16 & 30/11b, UK North Sea. *In*: ABBOTTS, I. L. (ed.) *United Kingdom Oil and Gas Fields,* 25 *Years Commemorative Volume*. Geological Society, London Memoirs, **14**, 309–316.

TAYLOR, A. M. & GAWTHORPE, R. L. 1993. Application of sequence stratigraphy and trace fossil analysis to reservoir description: examples from the Jurassic of the North Sea. *In*: PARKER, J. R. (ed.) *Petroleum Geology of Northwest Europe: Proceedings of the 4th Conference*. Geological Society, London, 317–336.

VENDEVILLE, B. C. & JACKSON, M. P. A. 1992*a*. The rise of diapirs during thin-skinned extension. *Marine and Petroleum Geology*, **9**, 331–353.

—— & ——1992*b*. Fall of diapirs during thin-skinned extension. *Marine and Petroleum Geology*, **9**, 354–371.

Shearwater prospect development: a high pressure/high temperature challenge

J. F. BLEHAUT, F. VAN BEEK, C. BILLEAU, J. K. GAUSE, S. KIMMINAU, A. PAARDEKAM, N. RADCLIFFE, R. RADEMAKER, L. STORMS, B. J. WELSH and A. WITTEMANN

Shell UK Exploration and Production, Shell-Mex House, Strand, London WC2R 0DX, UK

Abstract: The Shearwater development involves exploitation of a high pressure/high temperature (HP/HT) (15 000 psi, 185°C) prospect in the Central Graben of the North Sea which contains sour gas/condensate reserves equivalent to 406 × 10^6 BBL oil. The prospect is divisible into four blocks with reservoir intervals in the Upper Jurassic Fulmar Sands and the Middle Jurassic Pentland Formation at depths *c.* 4700–5000 m. Progress of the Shearwater project, from feasibility to detailed engineering design, was achieved by breaking down traditional project boundaries on both management and technical sides and by integrating exploration and engineering tools in order to investigate and quantify wide numbers of options and scenarios to assist in reducing subsurface uncertainties.

The 15 000 psi, 380°F (185°C) Shearwater high pressure/high temperature (HP/HT) project in the UK Central North Sea is poised to develop sour gas/condensate reserves of 406 × 10^6 BBL oil equivalent at depths of between 15 500 ft and 17 000 ft (*c.* 4700–5000 m), with drilling commencing in 1997 and first gas expected in the year 2000. The field is operated by Shell, in a joint venture with Esso, ARCO and Mobil.

This paper reviews the definition phase of the Shearwater project, from the completion of the feasibility study to that of the field development programme as issued in 1996. It covers the main petroleum engineering challenges that were adressed during this process, most of which are expected to be relevant to projects of a similar type. One of these challenges, which is of wide interest and in line with new business approaches generally taken by the petroleum industry, was the introduction of methodologies aimed at minimizing the economic impact of subsurface uncertainties while accelerating the time to project commerciality.

Regional setting

The Shearwater prospect is located in one of the deepest parts of the North Sea Central Graben. The structural history of the area is dominated by movements along deeply rooted NNW–SSE orientated fault trends and by movements of the Permian Salt. The oldest penetrated sediments, the continental deposits of the Middle Jurassic Pentland Formation, were deposited in a period of relatively low tectonic activity. In the Late Jurassic and Early Cretaceous, the onset of rifting resulted in NE–SW extension and the creation of rotational fault blocks orientated along the earlier mentioned fault trends. The shallow marine Fulmar Sands were deposited during that time. The Shearwater Main Block and Northwest Block are both located in the footwall of a rotated fault block, bounded to the NE by a normal fault (Fig. 1). The Shearwater Northern Block is a salt-induced structure located on the downthrown side (NE side) of the same fault. Failure of the rift system resulted in rapid burial of the structure during Late Cretaceous and Tertiary times. The overburden consists of largely unfaulted Cretaceous marls, chalks and limestones and Tertiary marls, shales and sandstones.

Appraisal history

The prospect was discovered in 1991 by Well 22/30b-4RE, which penetrated 605 ft of gas/condensate-bearing Fulmar Sands and 889 ft of Pentland Formation with gas shows. At the time of drilling, only limited coverage 2D seismic data were available.

In 1993, the first appraisal well, 22/30b-11, was drilled. The well found 763 ft of Fulmar reservoir of which 500 ft contained gas/condensate. A 186 ft spot core was acquired in the Upper Fulmar. Total depth (TD) was 660 ft into the Pentland Formation where low hydrocarbon saturations were interpreted. Hydrocarbons were also interpreted in low porosity stringers in the overlying chalk, and in a 42 ft thick sand interval at the top of the Upper Heather Formation above the reservoir. The well was tested over three zones within the Fulmar. First pass processing of a subset of Shell-operated 3D seismic data became available during the drilling of this well, leading to the first full field 3D interpretation and volumetric assessment in the second half of 1993. In 1994, a newly processed version of the survey, covering the entire area, became available.

The second appraisal/development well, 22/30b-15S1, was drilled in 1995 and confirmed the areal extent of the Fulmar, where 553 ft of gas/condensate-bearing interval and 236 ft of water-bearing sands were encountered, with a free-water level at 16 900 ft TVDSS. The well also penetrated 440 ft of water-bearing Pentland Formation to reach TD at 19 760 ft AHBDF (17 600 ft TVDSS). A 517 ft core was cut in the Upper and Lower Fulmar and a 51 ft spot core in the Pentland.

Seismic data

At the start of the project definition phase (end 1994), Block 22/30b was covered by a 1992 exploration 3D seismic survey, shot in a north–south direction with a 25 m line and 12.5 m trace spacing, using a 1 boat (2 sources of 1716 cu in)/3 streamers (cable length of 3000 m) configuration. This dataset provided the basis for the interpretation and volumetrics presented in the 1996 field development plan.

Processing was carried out using pre-stack time migration and post-stack depth migration. Multiples generated by Base

BLEHAUT, J. F., VAN BEEK, F., BILLEAU, C., GAUSE, J. K., KIMMINAU, S., PAARDEKAM, A., RADCLIFFE, N., RADEMAKER, R., STORMS, L., WELSH, B. J. & WITTEMANN, A. 1999. Shearwater prospect development: a high pressure/high temperature challenge *In*: FLEET, A. J. & BOLDY, S. A. R. (eds) *Petroleum Geology of Northwest Europe: Proceedings of the 5th Conference*, 1021–1027. © Petroleum Geology '86 Ltd. Published by the Geological Society, London.

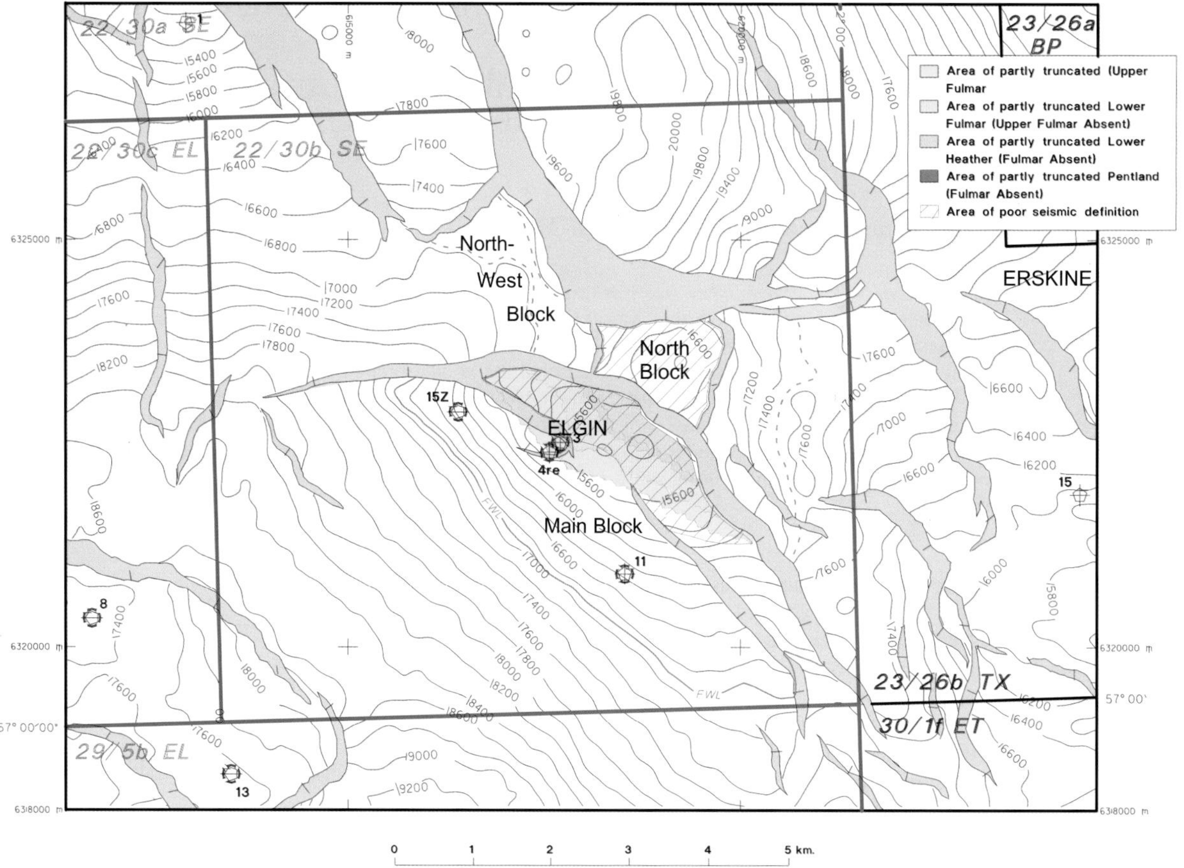

Fig. 1. Shearwater prospect, present-day (field development plan) interpretation.

Chalk and Base Cretaceous unconformity were suppressed by the Western Atlas image processing tool, TMA. In general, data quality is reasonable with the exception of the Northern Block and crestal region of the Main Block, where seismic imaging is poor.

Feasibility stage: uncertainties and constraints

The feasibility study was completed at the end of 1994. This was primarily based on limited data from the discovery well, data from the first appraisal well, 22/30b-11, and the 1992 seismic survey discussed above. In that study, the field was interpreted as consisting of 4 blocks (Fig. 2). Gas in place (GIIP) expectation volumes were estimated at 3.1×10^{12} SCF, and condensate in place volumes (CIIP) at 540×10^6 BBL. Two-thirds of these volumes were attributed to the larger South Block, split between 1.6×10^{12} SCF in the Fulmar and 0.4×10^{12} SCF in the Pentland. Volume ranges showed a substantial spread, with an 85% probability level (P_{85}) of 1.6×10^{12} SCF of gas and a 15% probability level (P_{15}) of 4.6×10^{12} SCF, i.e. 48% lower and 51% higher than the expectation value. These ranges of potential hydrocarbon volumes and the resultant uncertainty in project design had justified the decision, in 1994, to plan a second appraisal well in the Main Block, to the northwest of 22/30b-11. The seismic definition of the prospect was considered then sufficient for that purpose and, depending on appraisal success, also adequate for the planning of most of the remaining appraisal and development locations.

Uncertainties

Following the feasibility study, it was recognized that a number of subsurface uncertainties required further assessment prior to the major financial commitments involved. These uncertainties were ranked as a function of their potential impact on project value, in order to develop a work programme aimed at settling all major issues within a year, a challenging task considering that the second appraisal well had not yet been drilled. The above uncertainties were seen to relate to the following (in ranked order).

- The geological model for the Southern and Central blocks, which could significantly impact on gross rock volumes and HCIIP, number of wells, platform size and drilling times. The Central Block, with its poor seismic resolution, was, at this stage, very much an unknown while in the Southern Block the correlation between Wells 22/30b-4 and -11 was ambiguous.
- The size and distribution of the aquifer, impacting the amount of condensate recovery, the timing of water breakthrough in producers and the degree of communication with the nearby Elgin prospect.
- The tubing lift performance, with resulting uncertainties on production plateau length, ultimate recoveries and well numbers. No correlations were available at the time between tubing size and performance for the type of fluid and high well rates expected in Shearwater (up to 120×10^6 SCF(D)well).
- Inelastic reservoir compaction. Laboratory experiments carried out by Shell's research centre at very high depletion

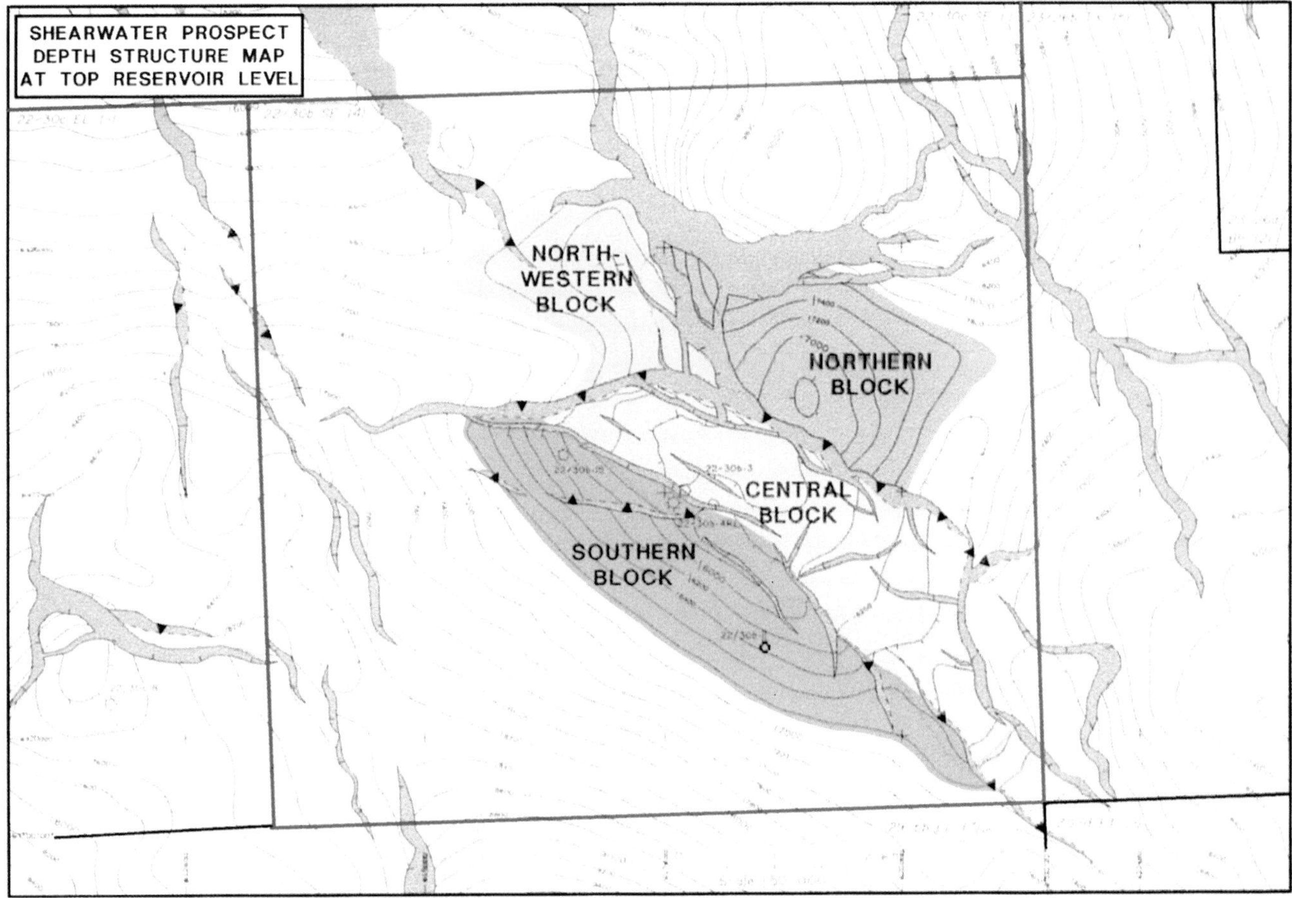

Fig. 2. Shearwater prospect, 1995 (feasibility study) interpretation.

levels (*c.* 10 000 psi), and of the same order as those expected in Shearwater, had shown that irreversible reservoir compaction could occur, which might affect not only permeability but also platform and well design, through subsidence of the sea-bed or compaction at reservoir level.

- Connectivity and log interpretation within the fluviatile Pentland reservoir, where only one penetration was available, would largely determine the importance and viability of an incremental development (which could be up to 4 wells) of that reservoir.
- Gas/condensate relative permeabilities. These were seen as potentially having a strong impact on well impairment due to the phenomenon of condensate drop out upon depletion. Moreover, the condensate dew point pressure coincided with the pressure at which the onset of inelastic compaction had been observed.
- Reservoir facies properties and associated heterogeneities, which could be expected to determine, to a large degree, water production profiles. These would in turn affect water disposal solutions and number of wells, as water production was likely to result in wells dying out quickly.
- Production chemistry issues, which required accurate resolution because of the high ion concentration in the formation water and the large change in PVT conditions between reservoir and surface (possibility of salt and scale deposition). This had a potentially large impact on wells and facilities (downhole washing equipment, platform weight and space, operating expenditure).
- Sand production, for which the probability of occurrence and associated rates had to be determined with some accuracy, in order to avoid expensive overdesign of the production platform and to assist in completion design and planning.

Initial constraints

The above uncertainties had to be addressed within the following project planning framework and considerations.

- A first gas date of early 2000, seen then as commercially strategic, and a perceived advantage in synchronicity with the development of the Elgin and Franklin prospects. This requirement on first gas also met the objective of reducing as much as possible the first part of the project life cycle (exploration to commerciality). It allowed no more than 12–16 months to bring the project from feasibility to field development plan (FDP) stage, including the drilling and evaluation of an appraisal well.
- The Shearwater project had been shown to be sensitive to capital expenditure, with a total investment then estimated at around £1.5 billion. Drilling expenditure accounted for some 25% of that amount, with future development wells estimated at £26 million each (average figure) and drilling times between 7 and 11 months per well. Drilling, rather than engineering, was on the project's critical path, with total drilling times estimated at 9.5 years for 15 wells.
- The size of Shearwater and its potential regional impact on gas development implied that the project could not be looked at in isolation, and that a large number of engineering scenarios involving different timings and infrastructures

had to be evaluated. In particular, the position of the undeveloped but substantial Puffin Field had to be taken into account, as well as that of other HP/HT prospects close to Shearwater.

- The economics of the project were modest and any delays would further erode profitability, which meant that a delicate balance had to be struck between data gathering, uncertainty/cost reduction and time.
- Critical safety/drilling aspects implied that opportunities arising from the application of new technologies had to be balanced against the reliability of proven techniques.
- A high degree of interaction within the joint venture, with the Elgin/Franklin operators and with the Government was required, in addition to the interaction within the large Shell organization.

Later constraints

As the subsurface work gathered pace, additional constraints became apparent.

- The difficulty in drilling into depleted reservoirs after first gas was recognized as a major problem. This meant that, shortly after the beginning of gas production, no additional development could take place, i.e. full development had to be planned from the start, without the benefit of dynamic reservoir data. This also prevented balancing the timing of drilling expenditure against ullage availability, putting an additional constraint on the economics.
- Moreover, the ability to drill the crestal part of the prospect was questionable in view of the very high reservoir fluid pressures, which were predicted to be close to the formation leak point, resulting in very narrow drilling margins.
- An expected tightening of the rig market before Shearwater drilling was due to start necessitated an early rig commitment. The type of rig, which also had an impact on the development, consequently had to be chosen early on.

From feasibility to FDP: managing and reducing uncertainties

The following section reviews some of the key uncertainties above and how these were addressed during preparation of the FDP.

Identification of project building blocks. An important step in the subsurface study process was to identify, within the total field development, a number of sub-projects related to different reservoir/blocks, each with various levels of appraisal and carrying different risks. The Fulmar South Block, the largest reservoir and the only one with proven reserves, was recognized as the core project; the other blocks and the Pentland South Block, which could not be developed by the same wells as the Fulmar, were considered incremental projects. The South Block Fulmar on its own was to carry the bulk of the surface facilities. This was an important driver towards cost reduction and a key element of the management process.

Field definition. At the end of the feasibility study, the existing 3D survey was being reprocessed using pre-stack time migration and post-stack depth migration. This, the fourth reprocessing of that particular dataset, had been justified on the basis that it would support the drilling of a Central Block appraisal well in an area of poor seismic quality. Before the results were available, a new survey with improved parameters was proposed as a means to optimize all development locations and to further extend the drillable area over the Central Block. This was a marked departure from common practice and required a step-change in culture. Optimization of the acquisition parameters for the future survey was done in parallel with reprocessing of the existing data.

The added value potential of the new survey, the cost of which was estimated at £5 million, (only 20% of the cost of one of the 15 wells to be drilled), was backed up by an economic study which showed a strong value (on the assumption that the Shearwater development would proceed as planned) for a 1995/1996 acquisition. Although the 1995 acquisition could not be achieved, a swathe with the new acquisition parameters was shot in that year over the surface location of the second appraisal well, so that later undershooting would be avoided, as the full shooting and the appraisal drilling were to coincide. The swathe results provided extremely valuable input to the final field model by locally defining the relationship between the Main and Central blocks. The entire survey acquisition was completed in 1996, and, despite moderate success from pre-swathe tests and modelling studies, it is now considered that the results have more than justified the initial investment.

Avoidance of port calls by offshore bunkering allowed advantage to be taken of short weather windows and contributed to the operation ending ahead of schedule and below budget. Accelerated transmission of survey subsets to shore by helicopter data drop and real time quality control from shore using satellite transmission took place in order to achieve the processed data target of end 1996, intended to allow the first of the development wells to benefit from the new survey.

The other element in reducing the uncertainties in field definition was the drilling of the second appraisal well. The main challenge there was the need to integrate the appraisal well results within the limited time frame available. Implications on volumes and on the static reservoir model are discussed below.

Volumes. The high impact of volume uncertainties compared with other subsurface parameters led to several reviews after (i) mapping the re-processed dataset, (ii) receiving the swathe results, (iii) drilling the second appraisal well and (iv) following seismic studies results. Final volumes were calculated from a combination of deterministic and probabilistic approaches (Figs 3 and 4). In the former, maps for high and low scenarios were constructed with the aim of representing end point probability levels. In the probabilistic approach, an expectation curve was generated via a proprietary software by investigating three different and equiprobable geological scenarios and merging their three expectation curves. The good agreement between results based on both methods is felt to reflect a good level of confidence on the entire distribution, while the narrow GIIP ranges in the Main Block (*c.* 15% either side of the expectation) are explained by the position of the two appraisal wells, which provide a very tight control. The reduction in ranges when compared to the 1994 feasibility study largely reflects the success of the 22/30b-15 appraisal well.

The volumes derived from average property mapping were compared with those obtained through the MONARCH geological modelling software and found to be closely matching, providing additional confidence on the ranges in reservoir parameters.

Aquifer size. A better understanding of the aquifer was achieved through an integrated study involving structural mapping, reservoir quality predictions based on porosity vs depth trends, and the regional comparison of reservoir pressure data. This led to a reduction in the range of aquifer size estimates to between 3 and 9 times the hydrocarbon pore

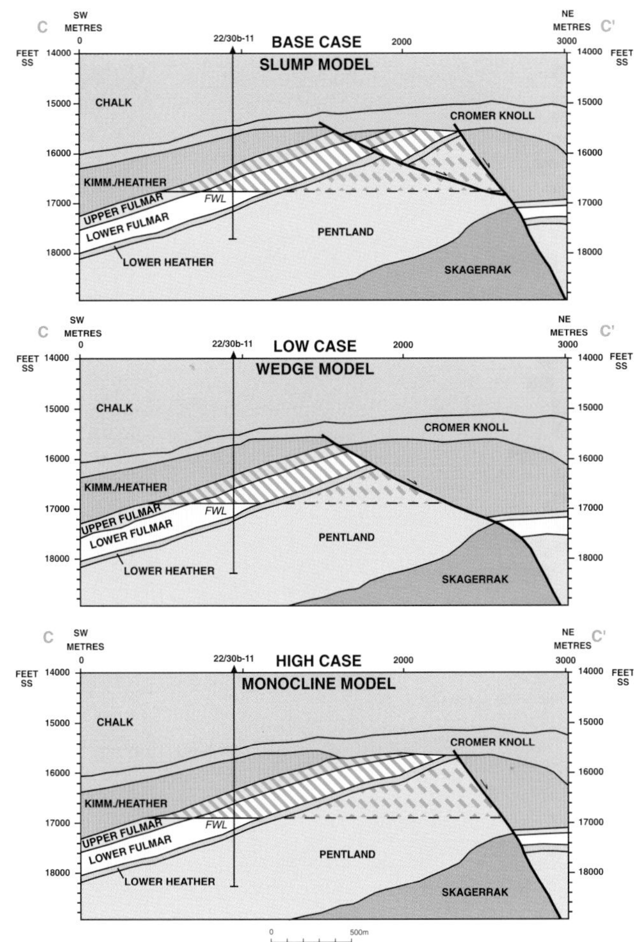

Fig. 3. Shearwater geological scenarios.

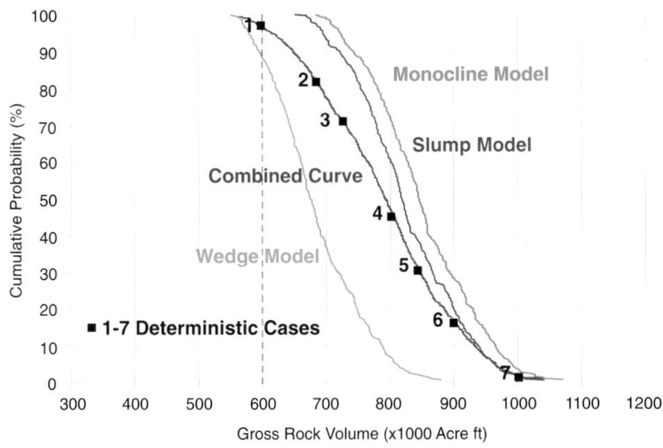

Fig. 4. Shearwater prospect: expectation curves and deterministic cases.

volume. The early recognition of the value of aquifer studies is fundamental, as it allows a combined reservoir/aquifer structural interpretation, trend prediction and explicit 3D modelling without substantial impact on lead times.

Reservoir compaction. The quantification of reservoir compaction and subsidence at an early stage was a particularly important requirement in Shearwater, since the water depth over the field (300 ft/90 m) is close to the operational limit of heavy jack-up rigs, and access to the drilling platform needs to be maintained until the end of field life.

Following the early experiments which had demonstrated the occurrence of inelastic compaction at high effective uniaxial stresses, a broad estimate of sea bottom subsidence was made, taking into account expected reservoir depletion levels from early reservoir engineering sector models. These were used by facilities well engineers in the initial steps of their designs. Meanwhile, additional compressibility measurements, some of which were performed under different sets of conditions (higher temperatures, slower loading rates) were undertaken at Shell research facilitities. Data from these were combined with depletion models resulting from both full 3D dynamic runs and predictions for the nearby Elgin and Franklin fields. Subsidence values from simple subsidence models were later checked and confirmed against those from more detailed models. It was also possible to characterize the compaction behaviour as a function of porosity, so that total compaction estimates were realistically related to reservoir thickness. Equations relating the permeability decrease as a function of both pressure depletion and porosity were introduced in the dynamic reservoir models.

Facies model. Full 3D static and dynamic models were developed for the Main Block Fulmar reservoir before the results of the new appraisal well became available. The assumption was made that the sand distribution would be broadly as predicted. Uncertainties that had been shown from earlier sector models to have limited impact were not included. The static model was then set up in such a way as to retain maximum flexibility for later modifications. The approach involved the definition of flow facies (as opposed to geological facies) based on poroperm relationships only. The original MONARCH model enabled the preparation and checking of the dynamic simulation deck, and the running of a number of sensitivities. When the updated static model incorporating the appraisal results of the 22/30b-15 well was delivered to the reservoir engineers, the first run results were available within an hour. This enhanced model was used as a basis for well number optimization in the Main Block, which saw a reduction from 9 to 6 drainage locations, amounting to savings of some £75 million.

Production profiles. The subsurface information used in project economics is largely condensed in the production profiles. These profiles, therefore, encapsulate most of the subsurface uncertainties considered during appraisal. In view of the modest economics of the Shearwater project, it was felt that the realistic definition of a 'low' economic case was particularly critical. Conventional methodologies for reserves calculations tend to elaborately define ranges of HCIIP while the step to ranges of ultimate recovery is usually cruder, more subjective, and fails to capture dependencies between main variables. This is because the probabilistic representation of dynamic uncertainties requires the actual simulation of a large number of scenarios, an unrealistically tedious task using conventional methods.

The application of a 'scenario management' software to the MONARCH-MoRes tool, however, enabled the generation of a large number of input decks corresponding to different scenarios and the simulation of these in a continuous fashion and in a minimum amount of time. The definition of the various scenarios involved the identification, from sensitivity runs, of the four most important variables (structural model, aquifer size, residual gas saturation and Upper Fulmar permeabilities, Fig. 5). Low, medium and high values with corresponding probabilities were then assigned to each of these four variables and all 81 combinations (scenarios) were run (Fig. 6), resulting in 81 production profiles. Out of these, truly probabilistic low expectation and high gas production profiles

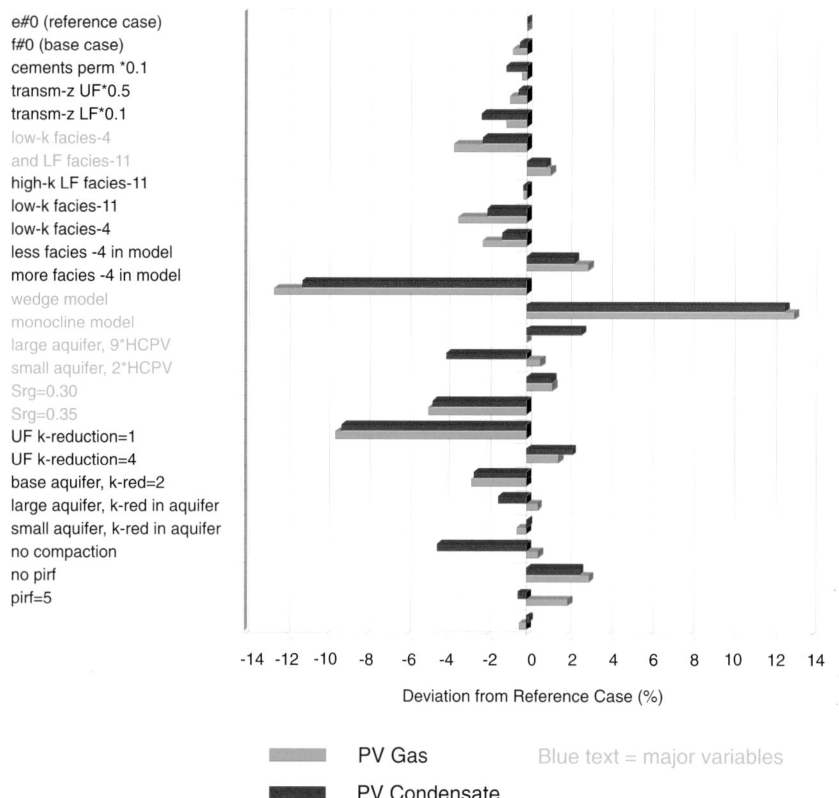

Fig. 5. Shearwater prospect: MoRes sensitivities vs PV production (deviations from reference case).

were obtained (Fig. 7). As was the case for volume estimates, the results were compared with deterministic 'low' and 'high' cases and found to be in good agreement.

Another important characteristic of the model set up was to allow quick simulation of sensitivities requested by third parties, instead of debating the need for such further sensitivity work. These two facts allowed a quick build up of the required confidence levels for the next project steps to proceed.

Conclusions

The Shearwater project, in spite of a number of new subsurface challenges and the drilling of an appraisal well, was moved from feasibility to detailed engineering design in just over a year. This was achieved through an effort to break traditional project boundaries on both management and technical sides. At the same time, a cost reduction was achieved by decreasing well

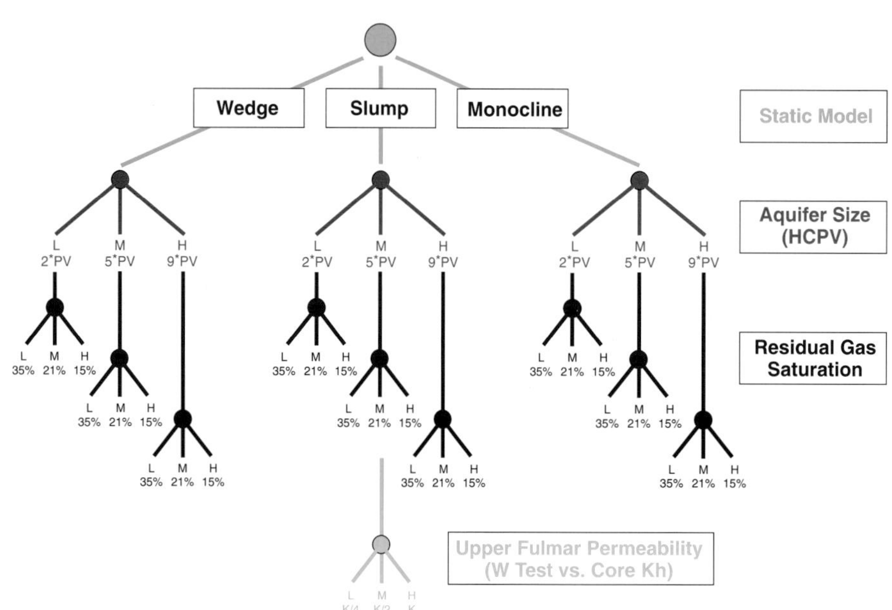

Fig. 6. The scenario tree: a simulation is performed for each combination of main reservoir parameters (structural model, aquifer size, residual gas saturation and core-to-test permeability reduction factor), resulting in 81 scenarios.

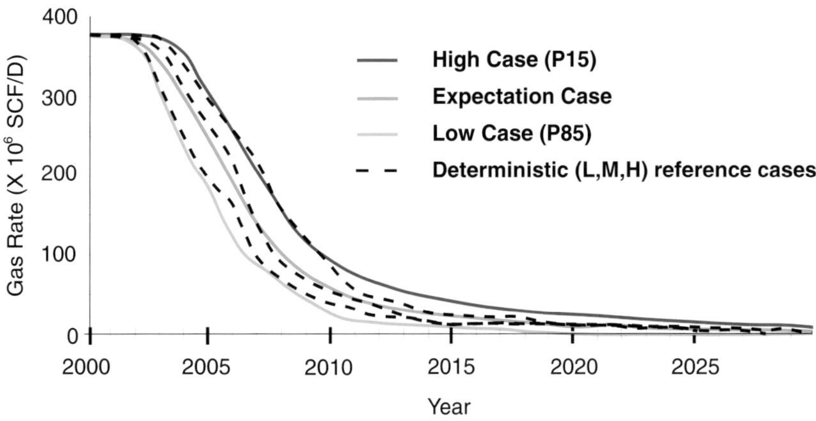

Fig. 7. Comparison of probabilistic production curves shows similar (though slightly lower) estimates when applying the new approach.

numbers from 9 to 6, while the uncertainty on HCIIP estimates in the Main Block Fulmar decreased from ±45% to ±15%.

The systematization of the parallel process at every level represents possibly the single greatest opportunity to reduce life cyle times in the early stages of a project. Shell Exploration and Production's new organization, in which activities from exploration to pre-design have been placed under a single directorate is a major step forward in this respect.

Finally, Shell's newest integrated technology applied to exploration and petroleum engineering tools, is shown to affect the bottom line in a significant way, both as a means to reduce lead times to project commerciality and to investigate and quantify wide numbers of options or scenarios. The latter assists in reducing subsurface uncertainty ranges, as well as increasing confidence by allowing comparison of different approaches. The integration of the MONARCH and MoRes softwares and the advent of probabilistic mapping packages combined with increasingly flexible interpretation and mapping applications have largely contributed to this process.

Structural development and trap formation in the Central North Sea HP/HT play

D. E. HELGESON

Esso Exploration and Production UK, Ltd, Esso House, Ermyn Way, Leatherhead, Surrey, KT22 8UY, UK
Present address: Exxon Exploration Company, 222 Benmar, Houston, Texas 77381, USA (e-mail: dan.helgeson@exxon.sprint.com)

Abstract: This paper describes a new family of structures and class of tectonism; it is not wholly detached nor basement linked but falls between the two. The 3D interplay between basement extension and salt movement is used to describe the formation of a continuum of genetically linked trap styles in the Central North Sea HP/HT province. This style of deformation is progressive and manifests itself from simple low relief tilted fault blocks to large diapiric structures common to the UK eastern Central Graben. The proposed kinematic model attempts to unite basement structure, behaviour of salt, and observed map patterns into a simple continuous process. The model is composed of a succession of 6 time-ordered elements:

(1) an initial basement (Permian/Triassic) framework of north–south and east–west normal faults;
(2) Zechstein salt infill;
(3) deposition of Triassic and Jurassic strata;
(4) Late Jurassic basement extension, initiation of salt movement;
(5) grounding and rotation of Triassic/Jurassic strata about the edges of basement fault blocks; and
(6) upward movement of salt localized at the apex of the Triassic/Jurassic fault pattern.

The relative amount of salt involved varies, and produces structures of similar architecture, but of varying scale. The Triassic/Jurassic fault pattern and block orientation reflect this structural process in an apparently random nature (i.e. with no dominant trend in either fault or bedding strike). The orientation of each block and the resultant faulted boundaries are mainly an indirect reflection of the underlying 3D-basement configuration. Rotation occurs about a fulcrum between the Triassic/Jurassic section and the point of first contact with a basement fault block, with subsequent rotation into an adjacent graben. This allows for a range of possible fault and bedding orientations inherited from the initial and evolving basement structure, combined with interaction between the rotating Triassic/Jurassic blocks. Although the overall process is simple, the observed map patterns may be complex.

This model inherently decouples faults in the basement from the faults in the Triassic/Jurassic section. The Upper Jurassic and basement faults are different ages, and formed in response to different regional tectonics. Thus, common appeals to wrench tectonics, based on opposing offset along a single fault, seem to be unwarranted. This model is additionally supported by experimental analogues, where the seismic based observations can be reproduced in a qualitative manner.

The structural style of the Central North Sea (CNS) has been a subject of great interest to workers for many years (Cayley 1987; Bartholemew *et al.* 1993; Erratt 1993; Erratt *et al.* 1999; Glennie 1986; Roberts *et al.* 1990; Sears *et al.* 1993; Ziegler 1981, 1990). Structural models to describe the observations have continually evolved, in part because of the continuing infill of 3D seismic surveys. Presently, complete 3D seismic coverage of the high pressure/high temperature (HP/HT) province (Fig. 1) is available, as well as very nearly all of the remaining CNS graben. Thus, we are now in a position to integrate these data, without gaps, and develop a model that applies continuously across the CNS.

Structures in the CNS have attracted attention, mainly because they yield prolific reserves, but also because there is no immediate text book solution for their mapping or interpretation. The structures are bounded by faults with many thousands of feet of normal offset. Salt also plays a significant role, forming some of the most spectacular examples of diapirs. To date, published structural models for this region range from pervasive wrench faulting (Bartholomew *et al.* 1993; Sears *et al.* 1993) to floating blocks above very thick salt (Penge *et al.* 1993).

The intention of this paper is to describe a new qualitative structural model based on interpretation of 3D seismic data, focused on the HP/HT province. It is thought that the model applies equally well across the CNS graben, as there are many observations consistent with this province. The model enables all structural levels to be considered, from the basement faults, the significant salt movements, to the present day. It is not the intention of this paper to address regional tectonics or timing, as others consider this complex topic (Davies *et al.* 1999; Erratt *et al.* 1999; Ziegler 1990). Regional tectonic events are important for the necessary elements of this structural model, but detailed discussion of regional tectonics and timing of these events would be distracting to the description of this process-based model.

This paper specifically addresses structures within the CNS graben, and for simplicity, excludes the large-offset graben-margin faults (e.g. Western Graben margin fault and Jaeren High bounding fault). These graben-bounding faults are larger-scale features that greatly offset the entire section, including the basement, salt, and the Mesozoic section. The structures discussed here are smaller scale, at the field and prospect size, and occur within and above the graben. These faults generally do not pass from the basement to the overlying section.

This paper describes the detailed observations in map view and then in cross-section. A kinematic model that accounts for

HELGESON, D. E. 1999. Structural development and trap formation in the Central North Sea HP/HT play. *In*: FLEET, A. J. & BOLDY, S. A. R. (eds) *Petroleum Geology of Northwest Europe: Proceedings of the 5th Conference*, 1029–1034.

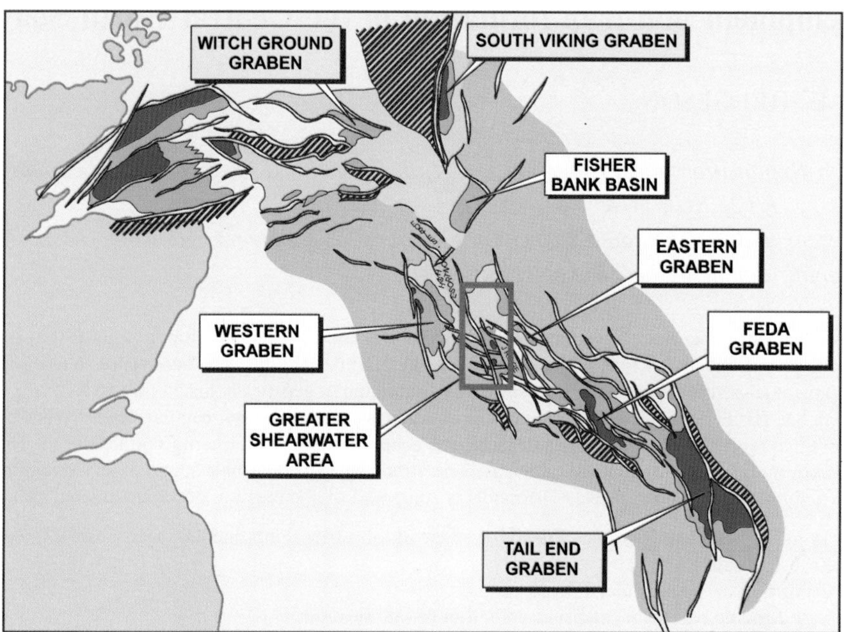

Fig. 1. Location map of the Central North Sea. HP/HT province shown in box around the greater Shearwater area. Faults shown are major graben bounding faults and blue shading represents (after Erratt *et al.* 1999) Upper Jurassic isopach (thickest strata darkest).

these observations is then developed, centred on the HP/HT province (Greater Shearwater area, Fig. 1). Experimental analogues and a display of a continuum of structures from across the basin add support to the characteristics of the model.

Map pattern

Figure 2a shows the map pattern of the structural blocks of the HP/HT province. The map is of Base Upper Jurassic (BUJ), which in this area is the Top Pentland Formation, an unambiguous reflection. Thus, there is very high confidence in the fault pattern and block orientation. The main features of the map pattern shown in Fig 2a are:

(1) each rotated fault block has a different orientation;
(2) blocks are bounded by arcuate faults, with the downthrown block on the convex side;
(3) an apparently overall random fault pattern; and
(4) salt resides at the apex of the arcuate faults.

This map pattern differs markedly from the map pattern (Fig. 2b) of the basement (Top Rotliegendes), which shows very distinct sets of fault trends, reflecting the sum total of all regional extensional events imposed on the CNS. The dominant fault trend, in terms of frequency of faults, is N–S and E–W, with a subsidiary NW–SE trend. Thus, the basement is a configuration of many horst and graben, whose edges will become the important connection to the overlying structural blocks and their resultant map pattern.

Note the position of the BUJ crests (Fig. 2a) in relation to the Rotliegendes map, where the BUJ crests overly basement edges, with opposing offset. The Zechstein salt separates the overlying section from the basement, and serves to partially decouple the two levels. Regardless, the highly faulted nature of the basement (Fig. 2b) influences the location and trend of cover rock structuration (i.e. the strike of the overlying block is parallel to the basement fault, and the location of the overlying crest is above a basement edge).

Seismic cross-section

Figure 3 is a seismic line from a recent 3D survey across several of the structures on the map in Fig. 2a. Given the apparent randomness of the map pattern at BUJ level, the cross-sectional seismic view shows a remarkably consistent pattern among the individual structures. The main features of the seismic cross section are:

(1) opposing dip and offset between basement and overlying faults;
(2) rotation of overlying blocks into basement graben; and
(3) salt positioned on lowside of overlying faults.

One of the most intriguing observations is that fault offset of the basement is opposite to that of the overlying section (Fig 3). The crests of the overlying structure always overly a basement fault with the opposite sense of normal offset. While this consistency does suggest a common process of deformation, these observations were also the basis for previous interpretations in this area, where wrench faulting was thought to be the main structural style (Sears *et al.* 1993), as variation in offset along a single fault is characteristic of such style. The important difference here is that what was previously interpreted as a single fault is now regarded as two separate faults, each of which have responded to different mechanisms at different times, and are separated by salt.

Rotation of the overlying block is nearly always away from the basement. Each block appears to have grounded on the edge of the underlying basement horst and rotated as salt withdrawal continued in the adjacent basement graben. This similarity further points to a common genetic mechanism. The timing of significant rotation of each block is similar, and can be constrained to the Late Jurassic, Kimmerdgian time, as evidenced by the Upper Jurassic growth stratigraphy down the flank of the rotating fault block. Additionally, there is no apparent thickness variation in the Triassic or Middle Jurassic section across individual blocks, suggesting that deposition at that time was not affected by block rotation or salt movement.

Salt also seems to have a consistent placement around each structural block (Fig. 3). It is nearly always on the low side of the rotating block, with a diameter much less than the width of the structural block. Its map pattern is distinctively circular, and almost always located at the apex of the arcuate block-bounding fault. The salt rises to varying structural levels from block to block, from relatively subtle salt swells, to the large piercing diapirs. This salt–fault association is quite consistent,

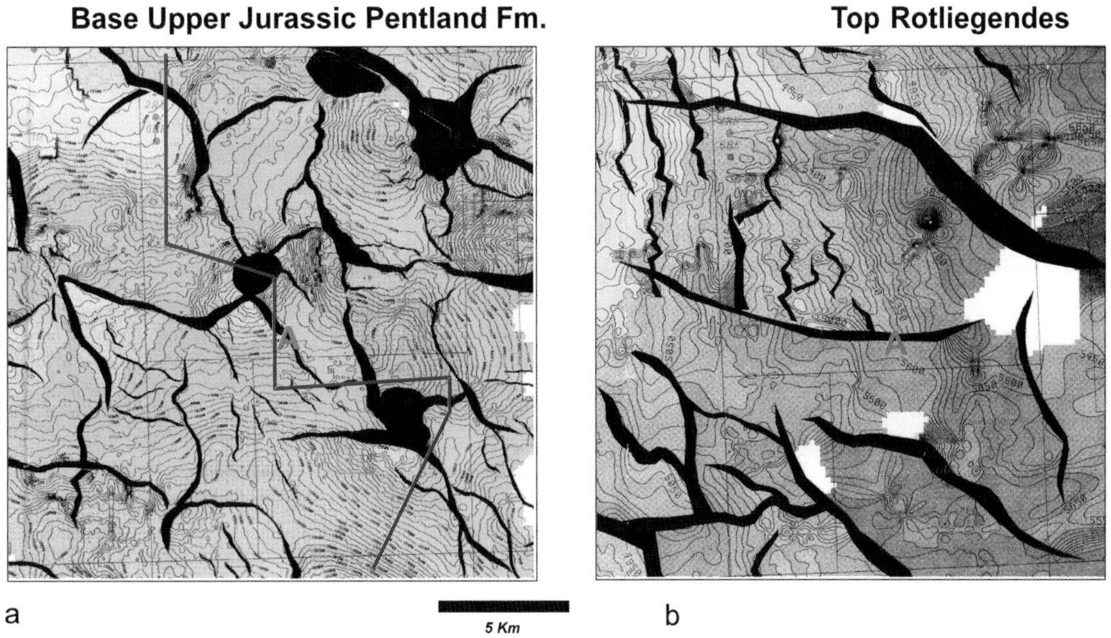

Base Upper Jurassic Pentland Fm.

Top Rotliegendes

a

5 Km

b

Fig. 2. Structure maps of (**a**) Base Upper Jurassic (BUJ) (in depth); and (**b**) Top Rotliegendes. Areal coverage of the maps is the same. Yellows are structural highs and blues are progressively deeper. Fault polygons are shaded black, and salt is shown by the more circular dark shadings. The position of the BUJ crests overly edges in the Rotliegendes basement surface, best typified by the centrally located BUJ structure A. (Red line on Fig. 2a shows position of seismic line shown in Fig. 3.)

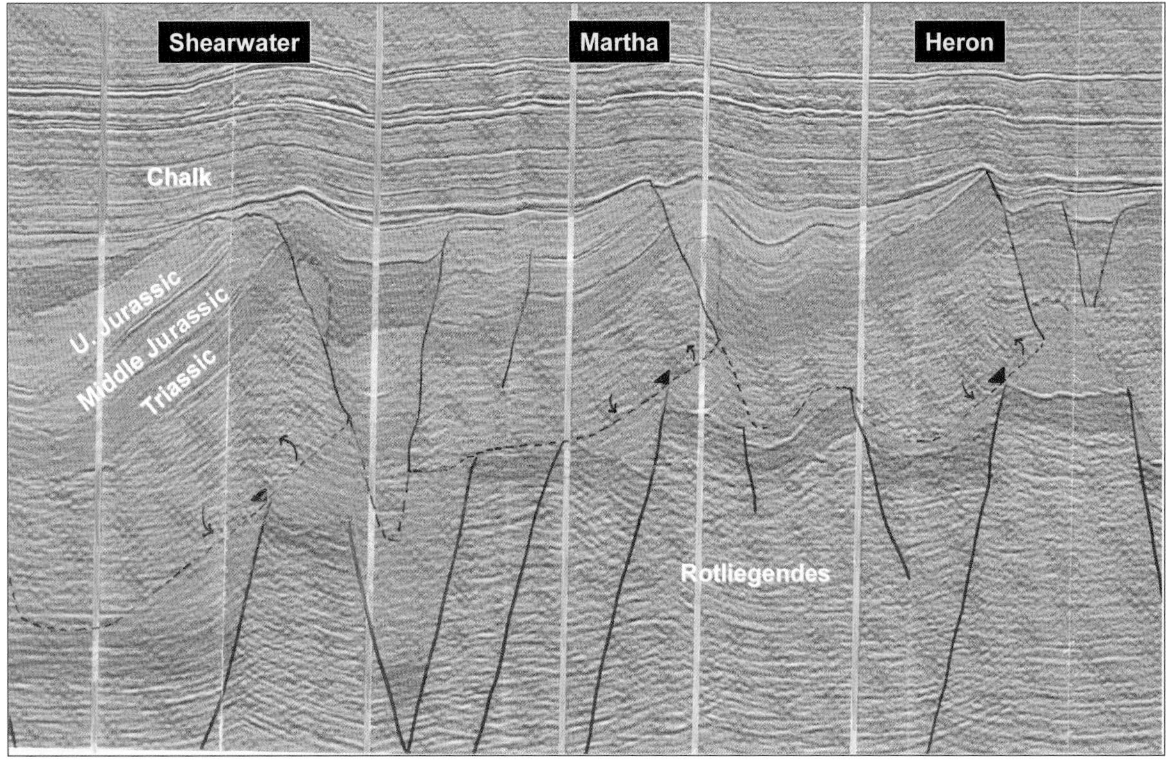

Fig. 3. 3D seismic line through structures of Fig. 2a (see Fig. 2a for location). Time-equivalent packages are shaded in each block, and salt is pink. Each structural block overlies a basement fault of opposing offset, rotating about a pivot point (shown with arrow) into adjacent Rotiegendes lows. Salt rises on the low side of each block, to varying heights.

and again suggests a common mechanism of formation of these structures.

Structural model

A structural model can be developed that attempts to explain the observations outlined earlier. It unifies the basement structure, the behaviour of salt, and the configuration of the Triassic/Jurassic blocks. In a time ordered sense, the process involves six basic steps:

(1) initial basement horst and graben structure;
(2) Zechstein salt deposition, infilling topography;
(3) deposition of the Triassic and Jurassic section;

(4) Upper Jurassic basement extension, initiating salt movement;
(5) grounding and subsequent rotation of Triassic/Jurassic blocks about basement horst edges; and
(6) upward movement of salt, localized at the apex of the main block-bounding faults.

Figure 4 schematically illustrates the critical stages of this kinematic model, along with a more detailed map view and seismic cross-section of a representative structure. These six elements are discussed in detail in the following section.

Initial basement structure

As shown in Fig. 2b, there are three dominant fault orientations in the basement: N–S, E–W, and a less frequent NW–SE orientation. These orientations record the various regional tectonic events that have affected the basement topography since the Permian/Triassic. It is not the intent of this paper to discuss the relative timing and orientation of each event, which is the subject of other papers (Coward 1993; Davies *et al.* 1999; Erratt *et al.* 1999). It is important, for this model to establish that a basement topography existed prior to the deposition of salt, and that at least one regional extensional event affected the region in the Late Jurassic (Cayley 1987).

Zechstein salt infill

Zechstein salt infilled a pre-established Permian/Triassic horst and graben system. Thus, a planar depositional surface was restored at the onset of Triassic clastic deposition.

Deposition of Triassic and Jurassic sections

Post-salt deposition continued, accumulating a thick sequence (>2000 m) of roughly parallel stratigraphy. Variations in stratigraphic thickness exist regionally, such as thinning onto large basement highs (e.g. Forties Montrose High, Puffin Horst), and thickening into deep graben. At the scale of the individual structures, however, the sedimentary package does not show thickness variation until Kimmeridgian time, marking the onset of Late Jurassic rifting.

Late Jurassic basement extension

Rotation of all the blocks occurred during this time, as recorded in the growth stratigraphy around each structure (Kimmeridgian through Lower Cretaceous). These sediments infill the space created by the rotation of the underlying block into the adjacent basement graben. Erosional truncation of block crests occurred as a result of footwall uplift during rotation about the underlying pivot point.

The general parallelism of the Triassic through Callovian interval suggests that density instability was not a dominant control on overburden structure at that time. Therefore, an external mechanism must be appealed to in order to initiate salt movement. The most common mechanism invoked to initiate salt movement is regional extension (Jackson & Vendeville 1994) or compression. Therefore, the identified Late Jurassic extensional event most likely initiated significant salt movement. Indeed, salt withdrawal is what allows such dramatic block rotation of the overlying Triassic/Jurassic section. This extensional event can also reactivate pre-existing normal faults with favourable orientation, while also generating new fault trends that overprint older structures.

Grounding and rotation

With increased extension, salt withdraws continuously and the overlying section eventually grounds on the up-thrown edges of rigid basement blocks, thereby prohibiting further downward movement. Rotation about these pivot points occurs in

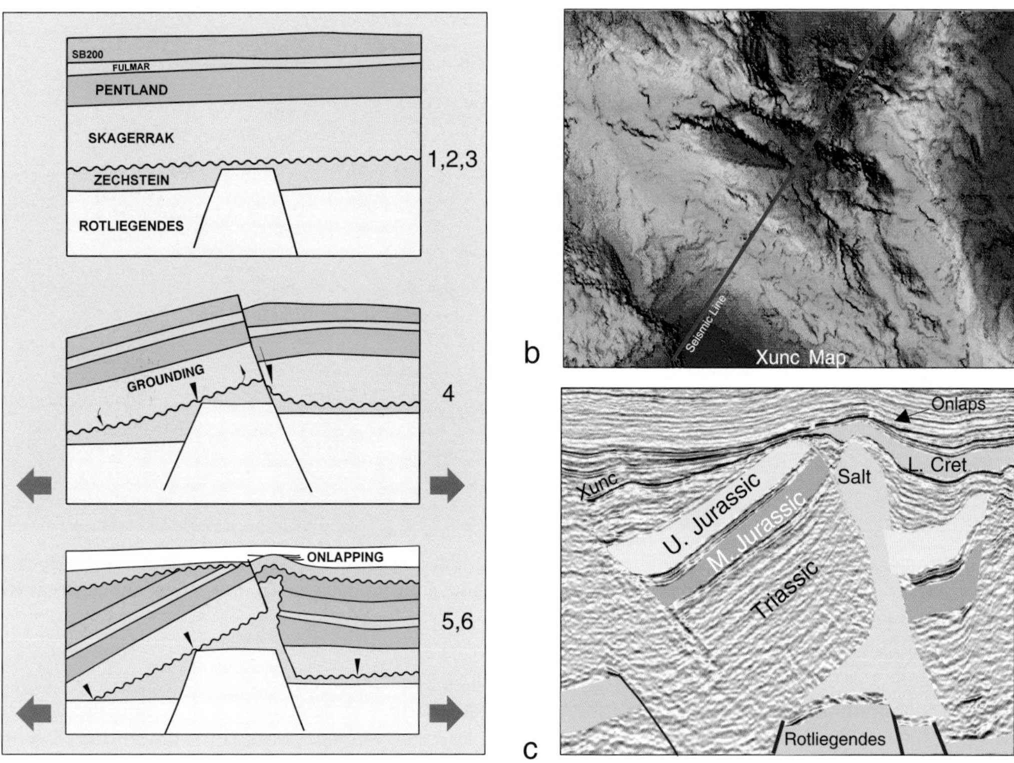

Fig. 4. Structural model. (**a**) Simple kinematic model consisting of 6 steps. (1) Initial basement horst and graben structure. (2) Zechstein salt infill. (3) Deposition of Triassic and Jurassic sediments. (4) Late Jurassic basement extension. (5) Grounding and rotation of Triassic/Jurassic block about basement horst edge. (6) Upward movement of salt from under rotating block. (**b**) Map view pattern of X unconformity (see 'c') showing position of salt feature at apex of overall structural block. (**c**) Seismic line indicated in 'b' showing structural and stratigraphic detail.

response to further salt withdrawal until the overlying block fully settles, 'marooned' into the adjacent graben (Fig. 4). This vertical process of deformation is fundamental to the overall model, and it is this aspect that deviates the most significantly from previous models. Recognizing that there is consistent placement of block crests over an underlying basement edge is the key observation that lends support to this aspect of the model. Variations of this grounding and rotation theme can be envisioned, as the basement configuration and 3D-block interaction can be complex in detail. Interaction between rotating blocks can produce secondary structures such as small faults and folds that are internal to the blocks themselves. However, the fundamental process of vertical grounding and subsequent rotation appears to be common to all structures in the Central North Sea.

Upward movement of salt

As Figure 2a shows, salt resides consistently on the low side of the arcuate block bounding faults, and at the apex. The salt-cored high locally uplifts thick Lower Cretaceous stratigraphy (Fig. 4), thus dating its movement to this time. This upward movement of salt must be after the Late Jurassic block rotation and faulting, which can be identified by the Upper Jurassic growth stratigraphy. Careful observation of the Lower Cretaceous onlapping geometries (Fig. 4) around the salt feature can pinpoint the actual timing quite accurately. In all cases, the significant upward movement of salt occurs after block rotation. The levels to which salt rises are variable, from very little to those of the impressive large diapiric features of the eastern CNS, where salt has risen some 6000 m from its source level. The variation in salt height is a function of the local availability of salt, and the dynamics of the overlying block, which rotates, captures, and directs salt into the developing diapir.

Experimental analogues

In an independent study conducted by the Applied Geodynamics Laboratory at the University of Texas, sandbox experiments were used to model salt movement during basement extension. These experiments reproduce the observed geometry of the structures in the CNS quite well. Figure 5 is an example where grounding and rotation of a sedimentary package takes place about the edge of a rigid basement normal fault undergoing extension. The salt can be seen to flow from under the rotating block towards the low side of the fault, with eventual piercement separating the high and low side of the main bounding fault. The process is very similar to that proposed in the structural model described earlier, and the general geometry of the resultant structure in cross-section agrees with the structures of the CNS (Fig. 3). The experimental reproduction of observed CNS structures provides further evidence that the forward kinematic structural model described earlier is viable.

Extrapolation

The examples shown in Figs 3 and 4 involve relatively little salt, which rose only to near the level of the Base Cretaceous unconformity. Alternatively, Fig. 6 exhibits a continuum of structures from across the CNS, wherein progressively greater amounts of salt are involved. The same structural process appears to have operated under the large diapirs, although here much more salt was available to continuously feed the developing diapir. Therefore, the process is common to a range of structures, from those with only a minor degree of tilt, with little or no salt, to those where major diapirs have developed over more steeply tilted fault blocks. It is thought that nearly every structure in the CNS will follow the basic characteristics of this structural model.

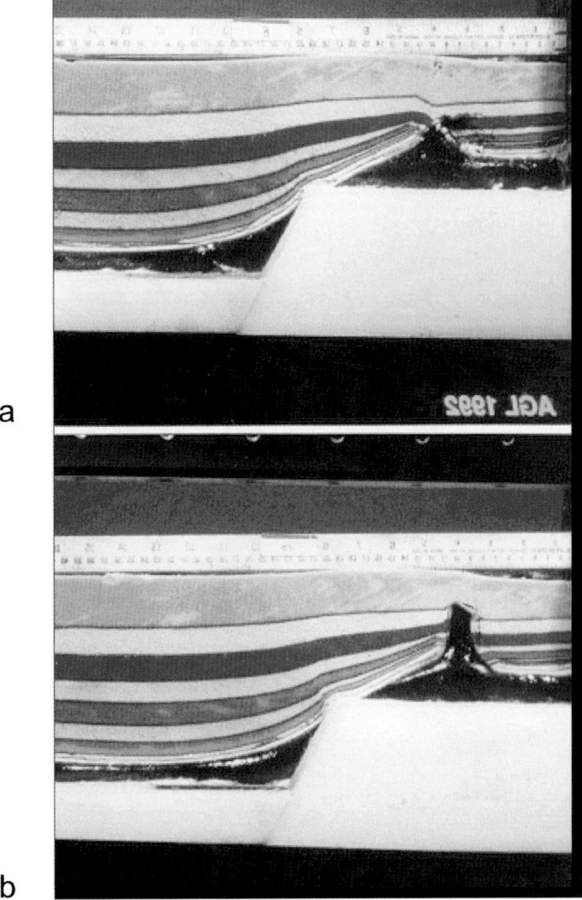

Fig. 5. Experimental analogues. Layered package pivoting about rigid underlying block during extension. Note the salt position and height with increasing (**a** to **b**) basement extension. Compare to structural model detailed in Fig. 4. (Printed with permission of Applied Geodynamics Laboratory at the Universtiy of Texas, Bureau of Economic Geology.)

Conclusions

A new kinematic structural model is offered to account for the observed map pattern and cross-sectional characteristics of the structural blocks in the HP/HT province of the CNS graben. This unified model is thought to be applicable across the CNS graben, wherever mobile salt is present. Downward settling of the Triassic/Jurassic blocks onto a pre-existing horst and graben network in the basement produced a wide range of structures, from gently tilted fault blocks to more steeply rotated fault blocks with large diapirs, such as those common to the eastern CNS. A common set of physical elements and sequence of events links a continuum of fault block geometries and related degrees of halokinesis. It is this commonality of process which permits the unravelling of an apparently complex structural pattern, and provides a simple solution to an apparently difficult and complex problem.

I would like to thank G. Cayley, D. Erratt, L. Magennis, and numerous other colleagues from Esso UK and Shell UK for their help and encouragement in developing and preparing the ideas within this paper. Esso Expolration and Production UK, Shell Expro UK, Arco UK, and Mobil UK are thanked for permission to publish this paper and to reproduce the seismic examples. Thanks also to the Applied Geodynamics Laboratory at The University of Texas, Austin, for permission to reprint Fig. 5. All conceptual ideas and conclusions, of course, remain my responsibility.

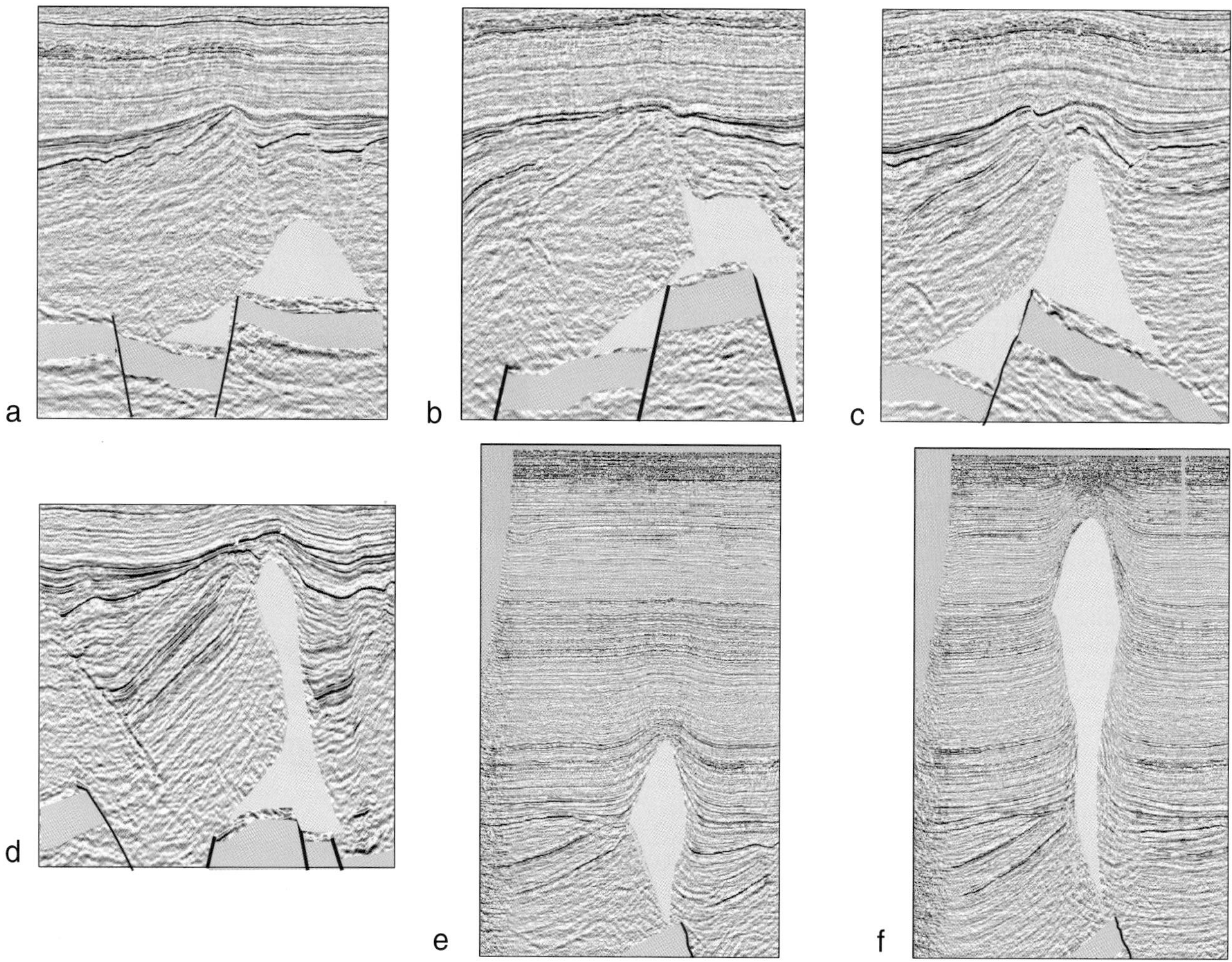

Fig. 6. Applicability of structural model across CNS basin; **a–d** are at same scale and show salt rising to varying levels on the lowside of block fault, while **e–f** logically progresses from a–d, but at a different scale (sea-level at top of seismic section).

References

BARTHOLOMEW, I. D., PETERS, J. M. & POWELL, C. M. 1993. Regional structural evolution of the North Sea: oblique slip and the reactivation of basement lineaments. *In*: PARKER, J. R. (ed.) *Petroleum Geology of Northwest Europe: Proceedings of the 4th Conference*. Geological Society, London, 1109–1122

CAYLEY, G. T. 1987. Hydrocarbon migration in the Central North Sea. *In*: BROOKS, J. & GLENNIE, K. W. (eds) *Petroleum Geology of North West Europe*. Graham & Trotman, London, 549–555.

COWARD, M. P. 1993. The effect of Late Caledonian and Variscan continental escape tectonics on basement structure, Palaeozoic basin kinematics and subsequent Mesozoic basin development in NW Europe. *In*: PARKER, J. R. (ed.) *Petroleum Geology of Northwest Europe: Proceedings of the 4th Conference*. Geological Society, London, 1095–1108.

DAVIES, R. J., O'DONNELL, D., BENTHAM, P. N., GIBSON, J. P. C., CURRY, M. R. & MAYNARD, J. R. 1998. The stratigraphic result of multiphase Jurassic extension within the North Sea triple junction. *In*: FLEET, A. J. & BOLDY, S. A. R. (eds) *Petroleum Geology of Northwest Europe: Proceedings of the 5th Conference*. Geological Society, London, 000–000.

ERRATT, D. 1993. Relationships between basement faulting, salt withdrawal and Late Jurassic rifting, UK Central North Sea. *In*: PARKER, J. R. (ed.) *Petroleum Geology of Northwest Europe: Proceedings of the 4th Conference*. Geological Society, London, 1211–1220.

——, THOMAS, G. M., WALL, G. R. 1998. The evolution of the Central North Sea Rift. *In*: FLEET, A. J. & BOLDY, S. A. R. (eds) *Petroleum Geology of Northwest Europe: Proceedings of the 5th Conference*. Geological Society, London, 000–000.

GLENNIE, K. W. 1986. The structural framework and the pre-Permian history of the North Sea area. *In*: GLENNIE, K. W. (ed.) *Introduction to the Petroleum Geology of the North Sea, 2nd edn*. Blackwell Scientific Publications, Oxford, 25–62.

JACKSON, M. P. A. & VENDEVILLE, B. C. 1994. Regional extension as a trigger for diapirism. *Geological Society of America Bulletin*, **106**, 57–73.

PENGE, J., TAYLOR, B., HUCKERBY, J. A. & MUNNS, J. W. 1993. Extension and salt tectonics in East Central Graben. *In*: PARKER, J. R. (ed.) *Petroleum Geology of Northwest Europe: Proceedings of the 4th Conference*. Geological Society, London, 1197–1210.

ROBERTS, A. M., PRICE, J. & OLSEN, T. S. 1990. Late Jurassic half graben control on the siting and structure of hydrocarbon accumulations: UK/Norwegian Central Graben. *In*: HARDMAN, R. F. P. & BROOKS, J. (eds) *Tectonic Events Responsible for Britain's Oil and Gas Reserves*. Geological Society, London, Special Publications, **55**, 229–257.

SEARS, R. A., HARBURY, A. R., PROTOY, A. J. G. & STEWART, D. J. 1993. Structural styles from the Central Graben in the UK and Norway. *In*: PARKER, J. R. (ed.) *Petroleum Geology of Northwest Europe: Proceedings of the 4th Conference*. Geological Society, London, 1231–1244

ZIEGLER, P. A. 1981. Evolution of sedimentary basins in North-West Europe. *In*: ILLING, L. V. & HOBSON, G. D. (eds) *Petroleum Geology of the Continental Shelf of North-West Europe*. Heyden, London, 3–39.

——1990. Tectonic and palaeogeographic development of the North Sea rift system. *In*: BLUNDELL, D. J. & GIBBS, A. D. (eds) *Tectonic Evolution of the North Sea Rifts*. Clarendon Press, Oxford, 1–36.

Integrated field development and reservoir management

Integrated field development and reservoir management

Introduction and review

S. S. FLINT[1] and H. D. JOHNSON[2]

[1] *Stratigraphy Group, Department of Earth Sciences, University of Liverpool, Liverpool LGP 3BX, UK*
[2] *T. H. Huxley School of Environment, Earth Science and Engineering, Imperial College, London SW7 2BP, UK*

The papers presented in this section cover a wide range of field examples and reservoir types, mainly from the North Sea, which collectively demonstrate the value of modern integrated studies in geology, geophysics and reservoir engineering for enhanced reservoir characterization and modelling. The fields under discussion fall into three main categories: (1) large, mature accumulations in advanced stages of reservoir management (Brent, Tern, Fulmar, Ekofisk and Wytch Farm), (2) new developments of medium-sized oil fields (Nevis and Captain) and the UK's largest undeveloped gas field (Britannia) and (3) smaller, economically-marginal fields in the early stages of development (Arkwright, Telford and Fife). A common feature of all these examples is the application of new and developing technologies, which are having a major impact on all types of field development, including extending the life of mature fields and providing opportunities for the economic development of marginal fields. The main technology applications discussed include high resolution 3D seismic, imaging VSP, 3D visualization and modelling, and a range of new drilling technologies (e.g. horizontal, extended reach and multilateral wells). The economic drivers for the integrated approach include (1) 'more seismic, less wells', (2) shorter time required to 'first oil', (3) improved marginal economics of smaller discoveries, including satellite accumulations near to existing facilities (near field potential), and (4) maximizing ultimate recovery through extending late field life.

The above themes and objectives have been met by eleven papers that cover mainly clastic reservoirs, and one carbonate (chalk) reservoir, which range in age from Triassic to Tertiary. They represent depositional environments which range from fluvial channel/overbank systems, through coastal/deltaic to shallow shelf deposits, into deep marine chalk and clastic submarine fan systems.

One important theme is the use of 3D visualization and modelling, which provides the common link between the three main subsurface reservoir description and modelling disciplines (geology, geophysics and reservoir engineering). This technology is now important throughout the whole lifetime of a field, enabling (1) optimum early development decisions on the type, number and location of development wells (e.g. Arkwright, Captain, Britannia and Telford), (2) guiding the placement of complex well trajectories (e.g. Nevis, Wytch Farm and Tern), and (3) helping locate and recover remaining oil in complex, depleted reservoirs (e.g. Brent, Ekofisk and Fulmar). One priority is to get 3D models into place as early as possible in field development and for these models to be rapidly updated as new static well data and dynamic reservoir performance information are acquired. In some cases such models are needed to site minimal numbers of development wells in small discoveries, as demonstrated in Arkwright (**Kantorowicz *et al.***) and in Telford (**Syms *et al.***). This early development of 3D models places increasing emphasis on seismic data, particularly 3D data, for reservoir characterization purposes, which presents a challenge to modelling packages and their developers in being able to better integrate differing proportions of well and seismic data over field life.

The use of 3D visualization is increasingly important in the planning of complex well trajectories and improving recovering in complex reservoirs. This is particularly well illustrated in the multidisciplinary team approach to horizontal well planning in the Nevis Field (**Dickson *et al.***). Here a high-resolution VSP, supplementing the existing 3D seismic data, was acquired to maximize imaging of the planned horizontal well trajectory and to minimize the risks associated with reservoir uncertainties and tight target tolerances. The visualization allowed all members of the multidisciplinary well planning team to fully and concurrently appreciate all the risks associated with the trajectory of the well. In the Tern Field (**Black *et al.***) horizontal and multilateral wells have opened-up enhanced recovery opportunities in three different situations: (1) economically-marginal and low quality Triassic fluvial reservoirs, (2) targeting bypassed oil in the more difficult parts of the Brent reservoir (e.g. the Rannoch shoreface and Upper Ness coastal plain reservoirs), and (3) developing small Brent reservoir satellite accumulations. While these successful activities have been achieved through the application of new drilling technology, this has been supplemented by improved reservoir definition methodologies, including seismic inversion modelling, seismic body mapping and improved integration between static and dynamic reservoir modelling.

The successful integration of modern drilling technology with improved reservoir description is clearly demonstrated in several, large fields in the late stages of development. In the Wytch Farm oil field (**Hogg *et al.***) the well-known extended reach drilling programme continues to break world records (currently >8 km). Furthermore, when combined with carefully planned integration of static and dynamic well data and modern 3D seismic data, this can lead to exceptional improvements in both production rates and ultimate recovery. Hogg *et al.* demonstrate that these data have provided a much better understanding of structural uncertainties and have improved the prediction of the 3D distribution of flow barriers, baffles and high permeability flow-units. Integration of all aspects of the reservoir management process at Wytch Farm also ensures a better framework for economic evaluation and a clearer appreciation of the uncertainties across the disciplines. A similar theme is demonstrated in two mature, giant oil fields in the North Sea, Brent and Fulmar, where the recovery of relatively simple, early oil is now being replaced by the late stage development of much more complex and strongly depleted reservoirs. In the case of the Brent Field (**James *et al.***) locating the remaining oil has been a major activity, which

FLINT, S. S. & JOHNSON, H. D. 1999. Integrated field development and reservoir management. *In*: FLEET, A. J. & BOLDY, S. A. R. (eds) *Petroleum Geology of Northwest Europe: Proceedings of the 5th Conference*, 1037–1038. © Petroleum Geology '86 Ltd. Published by the Geological Society, London.

has been achieved through the acquisition of a new 3D seismic dataset (in 1995) and continuous updating of the field's stratigraphically- and, in places structurally-, complex reservoir model. The latter has benefited from parallel developments in geological and reservoir simulation computing, which together have significantly improved the quality of both the static and dynamic reservoir models. These activities have been dovetailed into key late field life management decisions, most notably the timing of depressurization (in 1997) when the UK's largest oil field will be converted to its largest gas field. Similar technologies and approaches have been applied in the Fulmar Field (**Spaak *et al.***), as well as sequence stratigraphic and basin modelling studies, which have resulted in an improved understanding of the reservoir architecture within the broadly retrogradational shallow marine Fulmar Formation.

The importance of multidisciplinary, high-resolution reservoir characterization and modelling studies is further emphasized in the context of chalk reservoirs in the Ekofisk Field (**Key *et al.***). This has involved the development a detailed 3D history matched flow model, in which it can be shown that three major fault/fracture systems control dynamic reservoir behaviour. The new model contains around 25 million grid cells, each defined by some 30 attributes, which is considerably more heterogeneous than previous versions; the upscaled fluid flow model represents the highest resolution model that is computationally manageable. The complete process loop allows rapid feedback of data from new wells to ensure that the model has maximum impact on reservoir management decisions. Seismic simulations are also underway to evaluate the potential of implementing time-lapse (4D) seismic monitoring of a very mature field, but one that still contains very significant reserves.

Finally, one common link between all the papers is the importance of having models based on a sound understanding of the sedimentology and stratigraphy of the reservoir, which provide a vital backstop to the modelling technologies. A case in point is the complex depositional processes in turbidites of the Britannia gas and condensate field and the associated uncertainty in modelling reservoir geometry, architecture and rock quality variations in a low-moderate permeability (<100 mD) reservoir (**Jones *et al.***). The facies-based reservoir model highlights unusual deep water slurry flow deposits as well as more conventional high density turbidites. Integrated correlation studies incorporating petrography, ash bands, facies types and well log character have resulted in a high resolution, 2.2 million grid cell static 3D reservoir model, which provides the basis for (1) sensitivity analysis of variations in facies, rock quality and heterogeneities, (2) optimizing well locations and completion strategy, and (3) sensitivity of long-term field performance to large-scale structural and stratigraphical reservoir compartmentalization. Complex and variable reservoir geometries in Lower Cretaceous turbidites in the Captain Field (**Rose**) reflect deposition within different parts of structurally controlled submarine fans, which directly influences reservoir architecture, connectivity and thickness patterns. Variability in Volgian shallow marine sandstones in the Fife Field (**Currie and Woodward**) resulted in a mismatch between static reservoir descriptions and initial field performance, most notably the unexpected early water breakthrough. Integration of sedimentology, trace fossil characteristics and all well log, test and production data, resulted in a higher resolution stratigraphic model, comprising 6 genetic units and 19 flow units. The occurrence and distribution of anomalously coarse grained, 1–4 ft thick layers, with 2–3 Darcy permeabilities is the major control on early water breakthrough. Detailed sequence stratigraphic studies in similar shallow marine sandstones in the Telford Field (**Syms *et al.***), focusing on the nature and extent of key stratal surfaces, provides the framework for reconstructing reservoir heterogeneities and sand body architecture.

Together, the papers in this section demonstrate the economic and technical value of various geoscience specialists, operating within the multidisciplinary reservoir development team environment, and supplemented by modern technological tools both in their own specialist and related disciplines.

The Brent Field: improving subsurface characterization for late field life management

S. JAMES,[1] D. PRONK,[2] F. ABBOTS,[3] V. WARD,[3] A. VAN DIERENDONCK[3] and D. STEVENS[3]

[1] *Shell International Exploration and Production, PO Box 60, 2280 AB, Rijswijk, The Netherlands*
[2] *Shell UK Exploration and Production, 1 Altens Farm Road, Nigg, Aberdeen AB9 2HY, UK*
[3] *Shell UK Exploration and Production, Seafield House, Hill of Rubislaw, Aberdeen AB9 2BL, UK*

Abstract: The Brent Field was discovered in 1971 and is now a mature asset. In order to increase oil and gas ultimate recovery, the field commenced depressurization in 1997. The re-development of the field has been underpinned by extensive static and dynamic modelling studies. Developments in geological computing and the numerical processing power of reservoir simulation platforms have significantly improved the quality of the Brent Field static and dynamic models. These models have been used for a range of studies including gas cap volumetrics, by-passed oil investigations and to select the appropriate reservoir access well technology. The constant optimization of hydrocarbon recovery from the structurally and stratigraphically complex reservoir sequence of the field requires, however, that the static reservoir models are continually revised as new data become available and existing data is re-interpreted. A new 3D seismic survey was acquired in 1995. Interpretation commenced in mid-1996 and immediately showed that significantly improved subsurface resolution had been obtained. This initiated the next major iteration of static reservoir modelling which will ultimately result in the next generation of static and dynamic reservoir models. As the first results of this work have become available, the reservoir modelling effort has focused on some of the most complex areas of the field.

The Brent Field, located 160 km (100 miles) northeast of Lerwick, Shetland Islands (Fig. 1) was discovered by Well 211/29-1 in July 1971. With total hydrocarbons initially in place of some 3.8×10^9 BBL oil and 7.5×10^{12} SCF gas, the Brent Field ranked as one of the largest fields in the Northern North Sea. It was brought on production just over 5 years later, on the 11th November 1976. Following almost 21 years of production, remaining reserves are estimated to be some 200×10^6 BBL oil and 2.6×10^{12} SCF gas and in these terms the Brent Field continues to rank as the largest field in the UK sector of the North Sea.

The Brent Field is a mature asset. Facilities comprise four platforms providing a total of 154 well slots. Oil export is via the Brent systems pipeline to Sullom Voe and gas export via the FLAGS line to St Fergus. Production from the extensive West Flank area commenced in 1976 and reached a peak average annual oil production rate of 410 000 BOPD in 1984. By January 1997 cumulative production amounted to 1.6×10^9 BBL oil, some 80% of anticipated waterflood ultimate recovery, and 3.2×10^{12} SCF gas. Although oil production has been declining since the mid-1980s, the high solution GOR (ranging from 250 to 980 v/v) has resulted in substantial remaining gas reserves dissolved in the residual and by-passed oil. In order to exploit these gas reserves and significantly increase ultimate recovery through field depressurization, an extensive brown-field redevelopment project costing £1.3×10^9 was initiated in 1994 (Braithwaite *et al.* 1992; Schulte *et al.* 1994). This is now reaching completion with depressurization commencing this year and low pressure operation by the year 2000.

The re-development planning of the Brent Field involved extensive static and dynamic reservoir modelling studies (Schulte *et al.* 1994) which will guide reservoir management during depressurization. However, the constant optimization of hydrocarbon recovery from the field's structurally and stratigraphically complex reservoir sequence requires that the static reservoir models are continually revised as new data become available and existing data are re-interpreted. The static reservoir models currently in use were the result of an integrated 3D seismic and reservoir geological study carried out between 1990 and 1994. With the acquisition of a new 3D seismic survey in 1995 the next iteration of static reservoir modelling was initiated in mid-1996. This paper reviews the development of the current generation of static reservoir models and discusses the improvements that are being made as a result of the on-going Brent Field re-interpretation.

Geological summary

The Brent Field is a north–south orientated, westerly-dipping fault block about 17×5 km (10.6×3.1 miles) in size, located within the central part of a fault terrace on the western margin of the Viking Graben (Fig. 1). The terrace can be traced over some 65 km (40 miles) from the North Alwyn Field in the south to the Statfjord Field in the north. It is some 20 km (12 miles) wide from the western boundary, the Hutton–Dunlin–Murchison fault zone, to the eastern boundary which is defined by a series of faults just to the east of the crestal slump area of the field.

The field comprises two crestally eroded reservoirs, the Upper Triassic/Lower Jurassic Statfjord Formation and the Middle Jurassic Brent Group which are separated by the non-reservoir shales of the Lower to Middle Jurassic Dunlin Group (Fig. 2). Two different structural styles are super-imposed on this reservoir. The gently dipping West Flank area forms the up-dip eastern margin of the fault terrace. A series of steeply dipping west–east faults segment the West Flank and define the Main, Graben and Horst Block elements of the Brent field and partially delimit the Brent North area, Brent South and Strathspey fields (Fig. 1). The development of the eastern terrace margin fault system was associated with the collapse of gravitationally unstable fault scarps and the formation of the crestal slope degradation complexes, referred to as slumps in field terminology (Underhill *et al.* 1997). Separate slump

James, S., Pronk, D., Abbots, F., Ward, V., Van Dierendonck, A. & Stevens, D. The Brent Field: improving subsurface characterization for late field life management. *In*: Fleet, A. J. & Boldy, S. A. R. (eds) *Petroleum Geology of Northwest Europe: Proceedings of the 5th Conference*, 1039–1049.

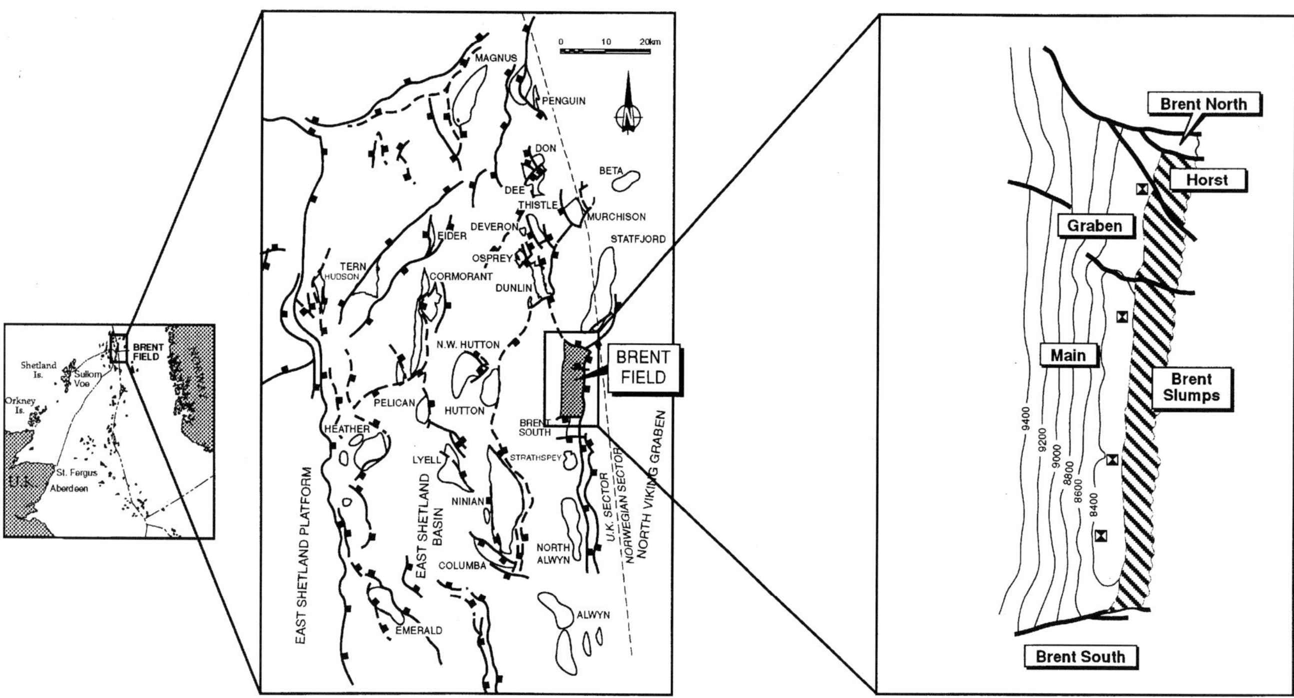

Fig. 1. Brent Field location and structural elements.

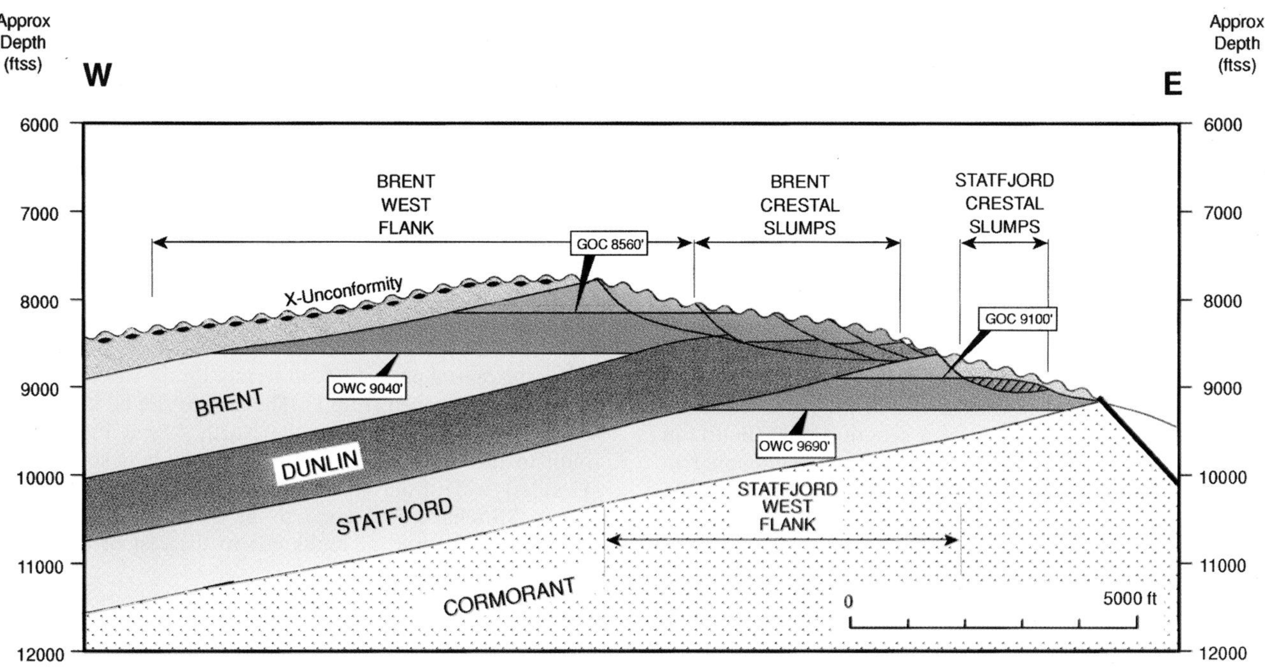

Fig. 2. Brent Field W–E cross-section.

systems formed within the Brent Group where the master listric faults sole out in the Dunlin Group and in the Statfjord Formation where they sole out in the shaly lower part of the formation (Fig. 2).

This combination of reservoir sequence and structural style has resulted in the four different reservoir entities that comprise the main Brent Field: the West Flank Statfjord; the West Flank Brent; the Statfjord Slumps; and the Brent Slumps. The West Flank Brent and Brent Slumps and the West Flank Statfjord and Statfjord Slumps combinations each had common original fluid contacts (Fig. 2). Since production from the Brent Slumps commenced, variable West Flank Brent aquifer pressure support has been experienced because of the nature of the juxtaposition of these entities across the main slump fault.

Field development summary

Development of the Statfjord and Brent West Flank reservoirs commenced in 1976, both being developed with north–south rows of producers. The wells dedicated to the Statfjord reservoir were crestally positioned and those dedicated to the Brent reservoir were targeted in mid-oil column positions at the top of each of the major reservoir units (Schulte *et al.* 1994).

Pressure support for both reservoirs was provided by down-dip water injection wells. Gas produced in excess to export requirements was reinjected into the reservoirs. This development strategy combined with the highly stratified nature of both reservoirs led to the evolution of numerous thin oil rims which, with continuing production, have become thinner and moved upwards into the originally gas-bearing crest of the West Flank. The future development of the West Flank reservoirs is focused on the depressurization and low pressure operation (Braithwaite *et al.* 1992; Schulte *et al.* 1994).

The development of the crestal Brent Slumps area was initiated in 1994 (Coutts *et al.* 1996). The overall structural configuration of thin, north–south orientated slump fault blocks dictated a requirement for west–east orientated horizontal oil producers. Pressure support is partly obtained from limited communication with the West Flank aquifer and also provided by several parallel horizontal water injection wells. A phased approach to this development has been instituted so that initial reservoir behaviour could be used to modify later drilling and completion policy.

A comprehensive development plan for the Statfjord Slumps has not yet been implemented, because of uncertainty in communication both internally and with the West Flank. Future development will be contingent upon encouraging production results from existing Statfjord Slump well completions.

Development of the current reservoir models

Following the decision, in 1991, to re-develop the Brent Field, it was recognized that a full field simulation model (FFSM) incorporating realistic crestal faulting would be required to manage the depressurization. This was constructed between 1992 and 1994 and relied heavily on the experience gained in building an earlier model version that had been in use since 1988 (James 1997).

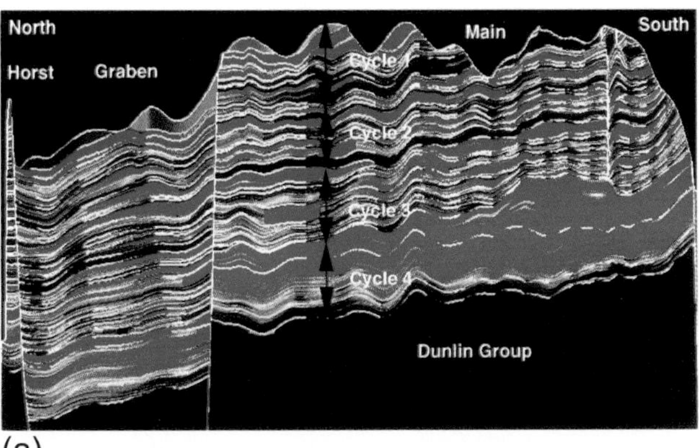

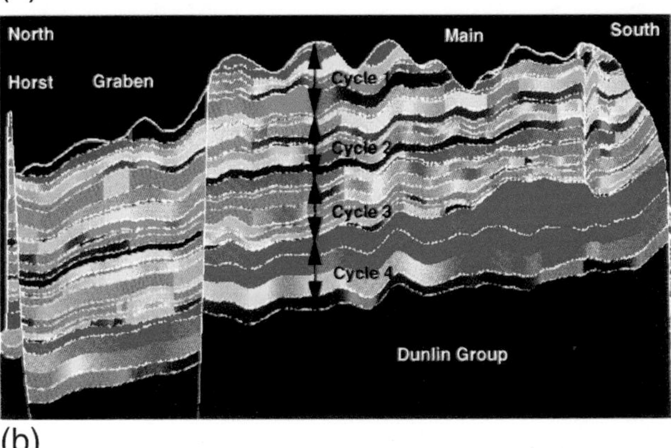

Fig. 3. (**a**) Brent reservoir SGM high resolution model (net : gross attribute, blue = 0.0, red = 1.0); (**b**) Brent reservoir SGM low resolution model (net : gross attribute, blue = 0.0, red = 1.0).

Static models for each of the West Flank and Slumps areas were constructed with the Stratamodel SGM (Stratigraphic Geocellular Modelling) package which enabled interactive manipulation of grids and reservoir attributes (James 1997). It also allowed rapid real-time modifications to be made to the model without time-consuming re-mapping and digitization. This functionality was fully exploited: separate high and low resolution static models were constructed (Fig. 3) as a basis for pseudo-capillary pressure and relative permeability curve generation and to facilitate up-scaling to the FFSM.

Input to these models comprised depth surfaces, well models, facies templates and petrophysical data (net : gross, porosity, horizontal permeability, hydrocarbon saturation). The depth surfaces defined the stratigraphic framework of the model, de-limiting the boundaries of each reservoir subdivision. The well models and petrophysical data were imported into this framework which was then populated with data by the creation of an attribute model. This involved the deterministic interpolation of petrophysical data between wells, using a distance weighted method. It was controlled by facies templates generated for each reservoir layer to ensure that geological variation in the reservoir layers was honoured (Fig. 4). The SGM calculation functionality allowed additional attributes to be generated from petrophysical and other attributes introduced to the models in this way.

Input data

The static models were the end product of an extensive seismic, geological and petrophysical review of the West Flank and Slumps areas and represented the first integrated reservoir characterization study of the Brent and Statfjord reservoirs. The extensive amount of work that had been undertaken since the field was discovered in 1971 was built on and unified. The experience gained from building and using the previous FFSM was also extremely valuable in focusing on critical areas, particularly capturing geological detail and improving the modelling of the crestal West Flank and Slumps areas.

Structural mapping. The 3D seismic survey that had been acquired over the field in 1986 was reprocessed in 1989 and re-interpreted as the starting point for the re-mapping of the field. Depth surfaces for each of the West Flank reservoir sub-divisions were created using seismic maps for the Base Brent and Top Statfjord horizons and reservoir subdivision isochore maps. Additional depth surfaces for crestal unconformities, West Flank faults and the Main Slump faults were also created. SGM functionality enabled 3D visualization of these depth surfaces, both individually and collectively, and was critical in establishing a rigorous error identification and correction process.

Development of a representative model of the Brent Slumps was critical since the inadequate history match for this area in earlier simulation models had been attributed mainly to over-simplification of the structure. Although the reprocessed seismic provided improved imaging of the crestal slump faults, sparse well control prevented a truly realistic model from being constructed. Depth surfaces copied from the main slump fault and pseudo-wells, defining reservoir subdivision depth surfaces, were used to create a schematic model that honoured the observed 120 m (400 ft) spacing of the east-hading slump faults, the north–south slump block extent of about 1830 m (6000 ft), and the progressive increase in slump fault block dip from west to east (Fig. 5). This approach was validated with balanced cross-section work (Coutts *et al.* 1996).

Reservoir subdivision and geology. This part of the review resulted in a series of well models and facies templates for each reservoir subdivision.

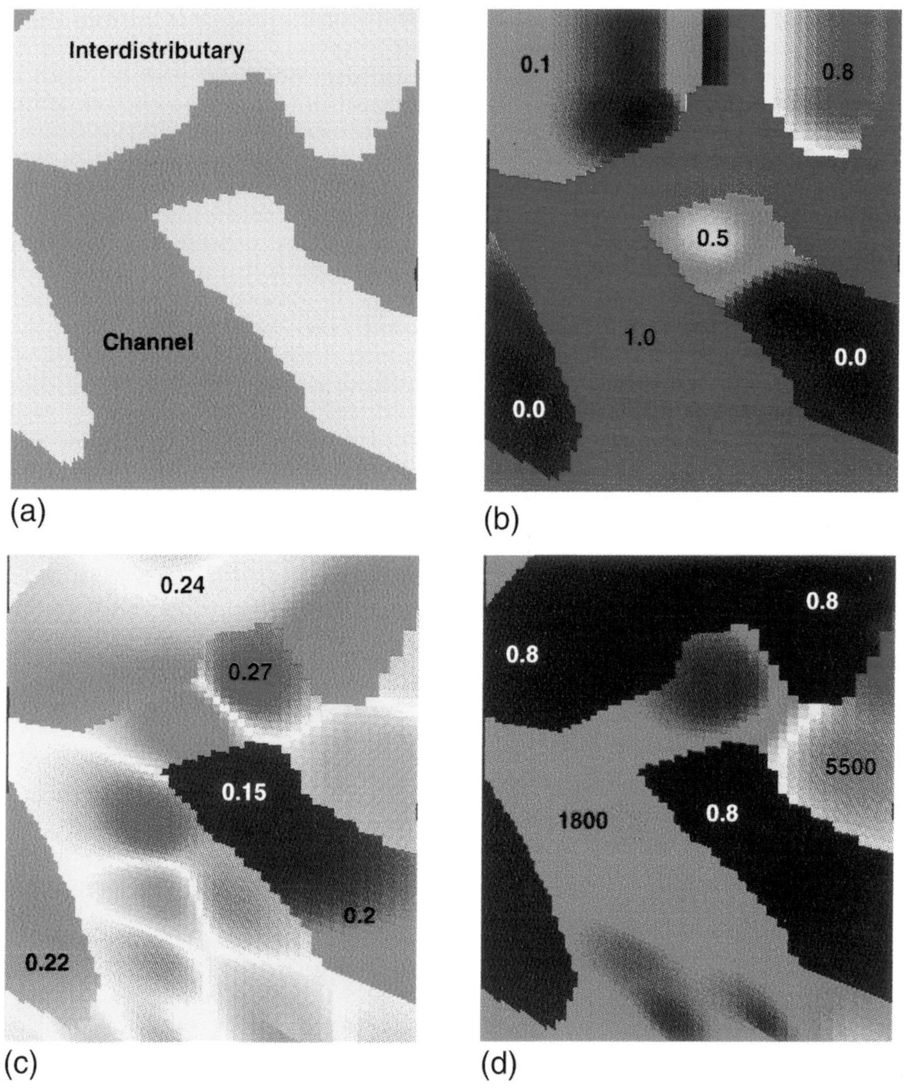

Fig. 4. (**a**) Facies template; (**b**) net : gross; (**c**) porosity; (**d**) horizontal permeability.

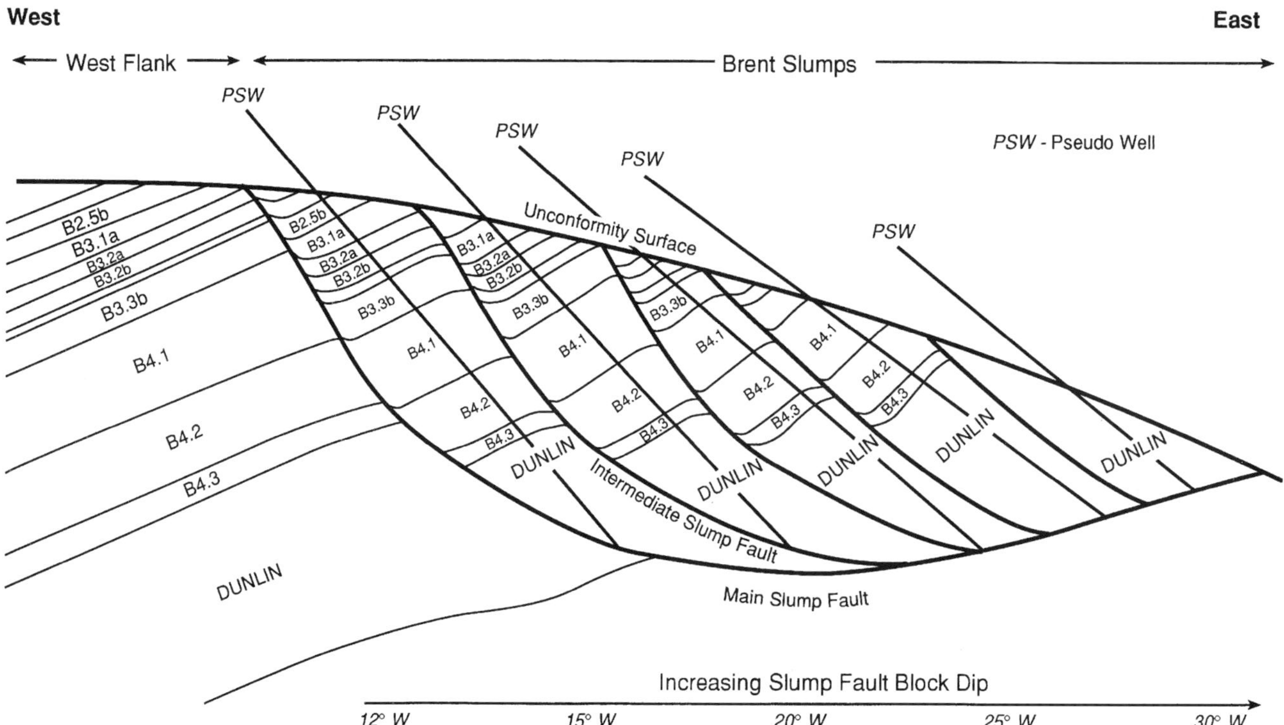

Fig. 5. Schematic Brent slumps SGM model, W–E cross-section.

The Statfjord reservoir, ranging in thickness from 245 m (800 ft) to 305 m (1000 ft), is composed of a lower fluvial interval (the Eiriksson and Raude Members) and an upper shoreface sand interval (the Nansen Member) (Fig. 6). The reservoir was initially divided into 8 layers, the boundaries being defined by shale beds forming vertical permeability barriers. Reliable correlation is difficult in such sequences but field performance data indicated two of the shale beds to be of field-wide extent and later heavy mineral studies (Morton *et al.* 1995) have provided further validation. The Raude Member subdivision was extended during the geological review, additional layers being added to refine this lower net : gross interval, increasing the total number of layers to 14.

The Brent reservoir, ranging in thickness from 238 m (780 ft) to 260 m (850 ft), comprises the Tarbert, Ness, Etive, Rannoch and Broom formations of which the Ness Formation is mainly a fluvial to shoreface delta plain reservoir and the others are shallow marine (Fig. 7). Early in field life the five fold regional correlation subdivision of the Brent reservoir was found to be inadequate for field management purposes, partly because of the very thick Ness Formation interval. Instead, the reservoir was subdivided into four genetic units based on geological core description and wireline log correlation (Budding & Inglin 1981). These were further subdivided, using pressure data and common laterally continuous coal beds to define barriers to vertical pressure communication, creating 16 separate layers. In constructing the SGM models considerable further refinement of this subdivision was necessary for facies mapping purposes and the total number of layers was increased to 27.

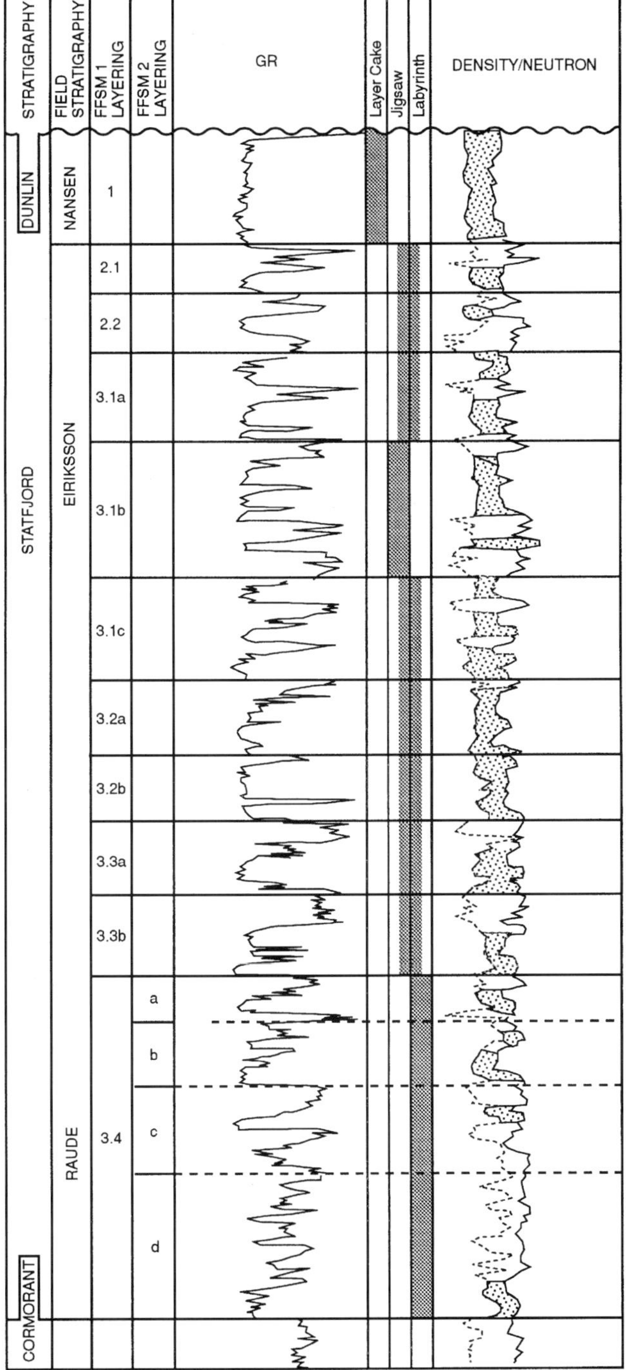

Fig. 6. Statfjord type log.

The subdivision of the Brent and Statfjord reservoirs defined a series of intervals that were correlateable throughout the field. The distribution of jigsaw and labyrinth reservoir types (Weber *et al.* 1990) in both the Brent and Statfjord reservoirs (Figs 6 and 7) required that further reservoir geological work was undertaken to develop a representative facies architecture for each subdivision. This involved an extensive study of cored wells in the Brent Field (Statfjord 10, Brent 13). A similar approach was taken for both reservoirs. Lithofacies types were identified and lithofacies assemblages used to define genetic reservoir units such as single channels, composite channels, crevasse splay and flood plain units in the Eiriksson and Raude members, for example. These were then used to discriminate genetic reservoir units in uncored wells based on their wireline log response. Using this data the distribution of such genetic reservoir units within each reservoir subdivision was mapped manually, thereby introducing a significant interpretative element based on sedimentological knowledge. These maps were used to create digital facies templates from which reservoir property models were ultimately derived (Fig. 4).

The business need for model improvements

Both the SGM static reservoir models and the resultant FFSM have been used extensively, fulfilling the objectives set out for them. The FFSM is currently the only tool available for full field simulation studies of the Brent field whilst the high resolution SGM models have provided a continuing resource for a variety of independent reservoir and volumetric studies (James 1997). These include:

(i) an annual gas cap volumetrics study which is used as an independent check of the FFSM predictions and as input to gas nomination decisions;
(ii) by-passed oil prospect identification and evaluation; and
(iii) target sizing to guide the selection of the most appropriate subsurface access technique e.g. conventional well, coiled tubing sidetrack, through tubing sidetrack with slim pipe or through-tubing workover.

As these models and their input data have continued to be used to great advantage, their limitations have also been explored. With this information, plans have been put in place which will lead to an overall upgraded static reservoir model. A total of 200×10^6 BBL oil are estimated to remain in the Brent Field, some 65% of which is estimated to come from the West Flank reservoirs and 35% from the Slumps areas. Construction of models which are valid with respect to both reservoir architecture and structure for simulation and well planning purposes is thus extremely important for safeguarding these reserves.

Seismic

The 1986 3D seismic survey, although a significant improvement over the earlier seismic data, was found to be progressively less useful in meeting the demands for more

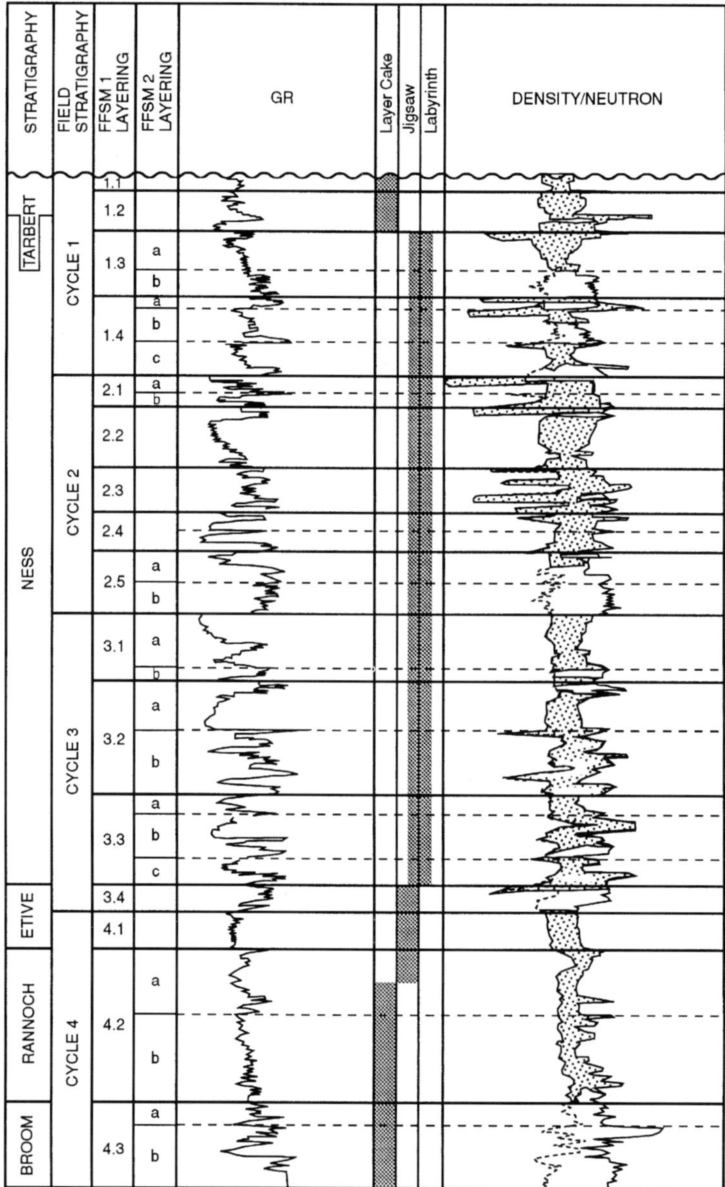

Fig. 7. Brent type log.

detailed input to the static models and drilling operations. Re-processing of this survey, carried out in 1989 and again in 1993, resulted in only marginal improvements in the quality of the original dataset. After promising results from a Walkaway 3D VSP shot in 1993 (Van der Pal *et al.* 1996) a new high resolution survey was acquired in 1995.

Facies architecture

Whilst SGM provided a significant step forward in static model construction, reservoir subdivision facies data was compressed into a 2D template. This was applied equally to each of the subdivision gridblock layers consequently losing most of the vertical component of the facies distribution. The Shell proprietary reservoir modelling package GEOCAP (Taylor 1996) overcomes this problem, enabling modelling of realistic 3D reservoir bodies at the intra-subdivision scale using interactive wireline log correlation and geometric modelling functionality. The individual facies bodies of the resultant model are used to control the modelling of facies-specific petrophysical properties. An additional advantage of this package is that using a sector approach, alternative reservoir architecture scenarios can be quickly modelled and evaluated prior to finalizing a full field model.

Realistic fault modelling

It has always been recognized that realistic modelling of the crestal West Flank and Slumps area in the FFSM would be crucial to achieving a high quality history match with reservoir behaviour. Whilst the SGM static models captured the listric fault geometrys in a schematic sense, ultrasonic borehole imaging logs (UBI) acquired in horizontal wells from the Brent Slumps and the 1995 3D seismic survey indicate a significantly more complex slump fault block geometry. An improved methodology for modelling this area of the field is now being sought through integration of the seismic, UBI and reservoir geology data with the EarthVision and GEOCAP packages.

Upscaling

Updates to the SGM static models have remained difficult to implement in the dynamic model owing to the complex and time-consuming nature of the up-scaling process. The release, in 1995, of the Shell proprietary integrated static/up-scaling/dynamic modelling system, GEOCAP/REDUCE/MoReS, enabled efficient cycling from the static to dynamic model in response to either primary (new data) or secondary (dynamic model feedback) updates in the static model. This approach has recently been successfully applied in building the FFSM of the Brent South Field. Although the current FFSM will continue to be used for some time the GEOCAP/REDUCE/MoReS system is seen as leading to the next generation of Brent Field FFSM. This may not entail a complete model rebuild but a replacement of critical areas of the existing FFSM by segments constructed with GEOCAP/REDUCE.

The 1995 3D seismic survey

The 1995 survey was acquired over a 3 month period in the summer of 1995 with an eight streamer/one source acquisition configuration. The total survey area covered some 320 km^2, acquired with subsurface sampling four times more dense than the previous survey, shot in 1986.

The seismic resolution of the new dataset has clearly improved with respect to that of the 1986 survey (van Dierendonk *et al.* 1997). Although the improved acquisition techniques have contributed substantially to this good result, a large part of the improvement is a result of the energy and time expended on data processing. Concurrently with the main processing sequence, fast track processing was applied to the dataset in order to produce an interpretable 3D dataset within 7 months of acquisition. This fast track survey highlighted problem areas, which were subsequently addressed in great detail during the main 3D processing. Detailed interactive velocity picking by the seismic interpreter, carried out on a 250 m grid, has improved the data quality at reservoir level, and contributed substantially to multiple elimination. The considerable effort spent on velocity analysis also paid off in the interpretation stage, as the resulting high quality of the stacking velocities has facilitated the depth conversion of the time horizons. Further resolution improvements were obtained by pre-stack time migration of the data. Total processing time for the 1995 Brent survey was 10 months.

Impact of the seismic survey

In order to better understand the current areal distribution of hydrocarbon volumes in the field as part of the LTRO (locate the remaining oil) project (Wetzelaer *et al.* 1996), seismic interpretation work to date has focused on the generation of detailed field-wide structural maps. Small faults have an

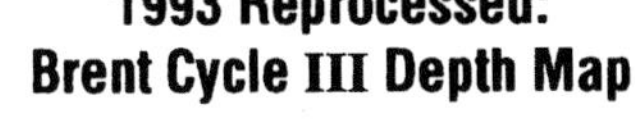

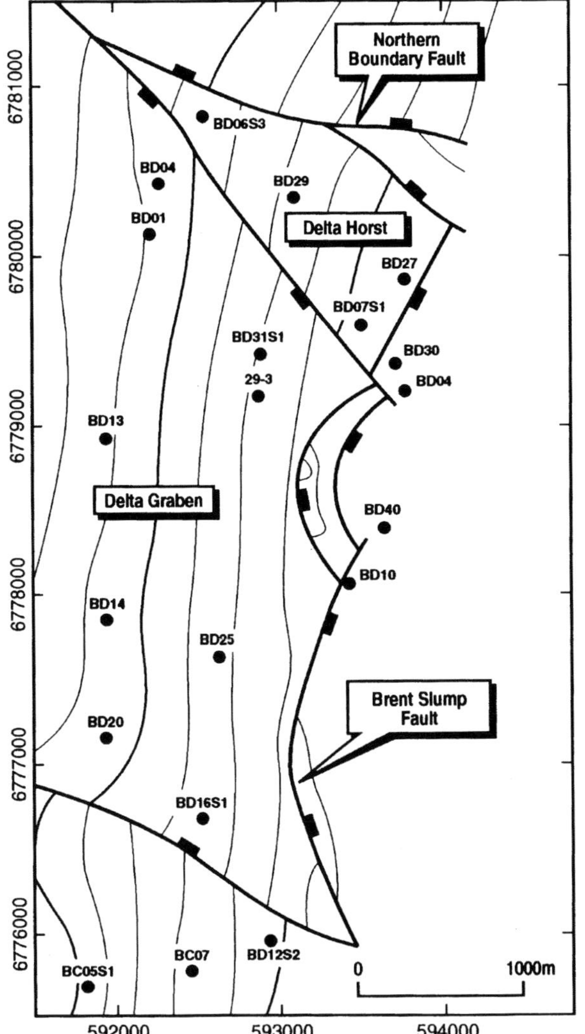

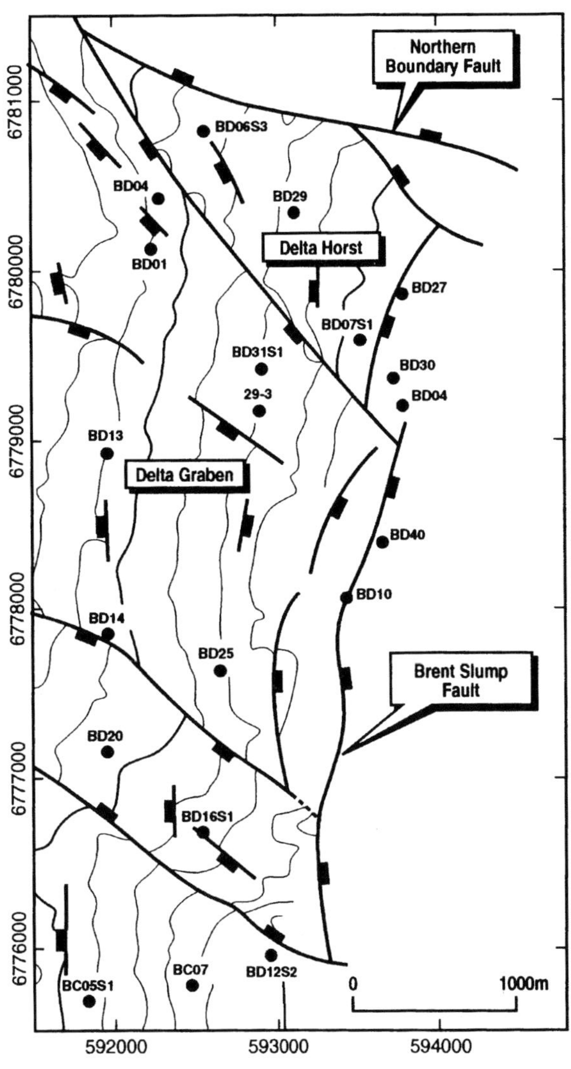

Fig. 8. 1993/1995 Cycle III depth map comparison.

increasingly important effect on hydrocarbon drainage patterns in the late stages of field life and the improved horizontal and vertical seismic resolution of the new 3D survey has greatly aided the definition of these faults throughout the field (Fig. 8). With the finalization of these structural maps, the emphasis of the geophysical work currently being carried out is gradually moving towards quantitative interpretation studies.

Improved fault definition. Improved fault definition can clearly be demonstrated in the Brent North appraisal area (Fig. 9). Faults in the order of 250 ft throw which could previously not be resolved on the old dataset are clearly visible on the 1995 dataset. The result is an increase in confidence regarding the areal extent and degree of internal faulting at both Brent and Statfjord levels, which in turn impacts the development options.

In addition the new seismic survey has also enhanced the resolution of the faults in the Brent and Statfjord Slumps. In these crestal areas, complex rotational slides offset the thin reservoir sub cycles. Accurate fault definitions combined with a thorough understanding of the sub-zone reservoir juxtaposition across these faults is therefore essential for optimization of the sweep efficiency and recovery factors of the slump area (Coutts *et al.* 1997). The definition of these slumped fault blocks is critical to the successful positioning of horizontal water injector and oil producer pairs. The uncertainty in the horizontal resolution of the main Brent and Statfjord slump faults is very much reduced on the new seismic dataset.

The improved positioning of faults on the new seismic dataset is borne out by the results of a number of recent wells in which UBI logs have confirmed the seismic interpretation. In addition, the results of crestal wells, such as BD36S1 (van Dierendonk *et al.* 1997), which were drilled prior to the acquisition of the new survey and often sub-optimally positioned as a result of the poorer fault imaging, can now be unambiguously resolved. The clarity of the 1995 seismic in these geologically complex areas, combined with the encouraging UBI to seismic ties, has increased confidence in well track optimization based on the new dataset.

Quantitative studies

As the conventional horizon and fault mapping on reflectivity data is being finalized, the emphasis of the geophysical work is gradually shifting toward quantitative interpretation. State of the art geophysical techniques are being applied in an attempt

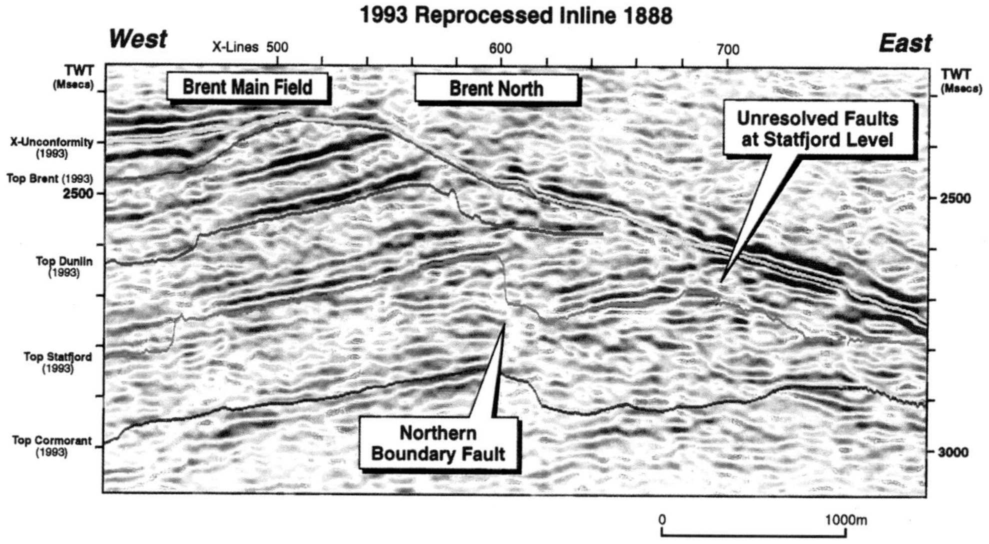

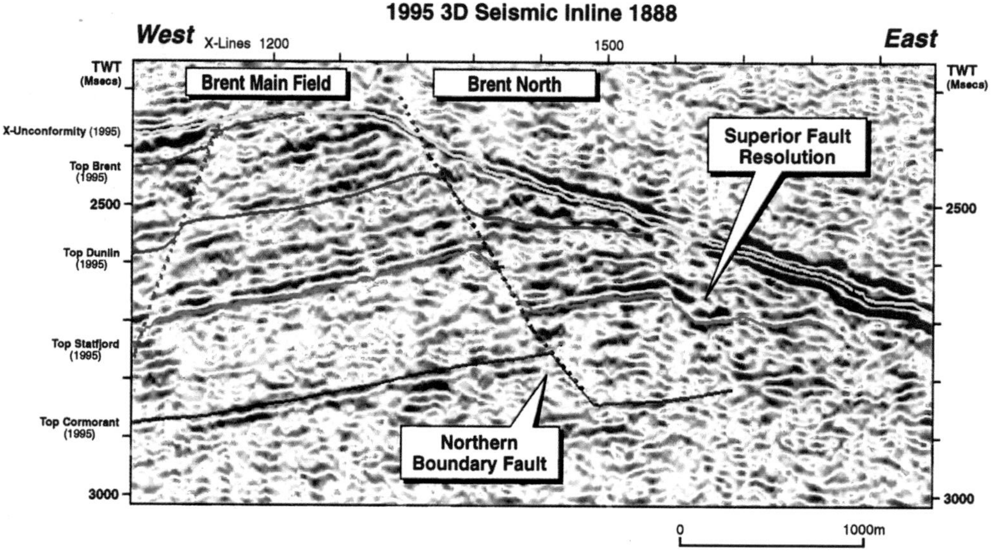

Fig. 9. Comparison of fault resolution using 1993 reprocessed seismic data and 1995 3D seismic data.

to locate producing hydrocarbon contacts, predict reservoir properties and to further enhance the resolution of the dataset. These techniques include amplitude studies, 4D time lapse studies, AVO and seismic inversion. Some preliminary results are discussed here.

Amplitude Studies. Acoustic impedance modelling studies carried out in the Brent field have shown that given good data quality, hydrocarbon production effects should be weakly visible on seismic in both the Brent and Statfjord reservoirs. However, gas effects in the Statfjord reservoir would be difficult to observe because of the compressibility of the gas. Preliminary amplitude studies, which compare the 1993 reprocessed (shot in 1986) and 1995 datasets confirm that production effects at both Statfjord and Brent reservoir levels are visible. Figure 10 shows the RMS (root mean square) amplitude of the Rannoch (Brent Cycle IV) event as extracted from the 1993 re-processed dataset. Higher amplitudes are seen on the crest of the structure above the original field-wide oil–water contact. The same measurement carried out on the 1995 survey shows a reduction in amplitudes in the crestal area with respect to the 1986 survey. Patches of high amplitude remaining on the 1995 survey are dominantly in the Brent Slumps, the most crestal areas of the field. Preliminary work indicates a good correlation between reducing amplitude and increasing watercut. However, as a result of continued production offtake from all reservoir subzones over the 2 years since the survey was shot, any predictions of fluid content or remaining oil from amplitude studies on the 1995 dataset will reduce in value with elapsed time.

Time lapse seismic. With the encouraging results from single trace modelling work the possibility of acquiring 4D datasets to monitor production contact movement has been investigated. A number of 3D synthetic seismic datasets are being generated from the FFSM for various critical times in field life. These times will coincide with the dates of acquisition of the 1986 and 1995 seismic surveys, as well as with key times in the future with a view to assessing the viability of acquiring time-lapse seismic surveys as a means of monitoring producing contacts.

Amplitude verses offset (AVO). Near/far trace cubes have been generated and are being analysed in order to aid the identification of undrained and attic oil within the field and of remaining hydrocarbon potential in the area outside of the field. AVO effects can be demonstrated at Top Statfjord reservoir level, where clear amplitude effects can be seen on the far offset data (Fig. 11). Modelling to establish whether these amplitude effects are related to hydrocarbons or lithology is currently in progress.

Seismic inversion. An acoustic impedance (AI) dataset was generated using sparse spike inversion. The AI dataset will be used with a view to guiding the generation of reservoir property maps. These maps will support the lateral variation of reservoir properties which will be incorporated in the new static geological model and hence ultimately in the up-graded FFSM. Although this study is still ongoing, structural mapping of complex areas such as the Brent and Statfjord Slumps

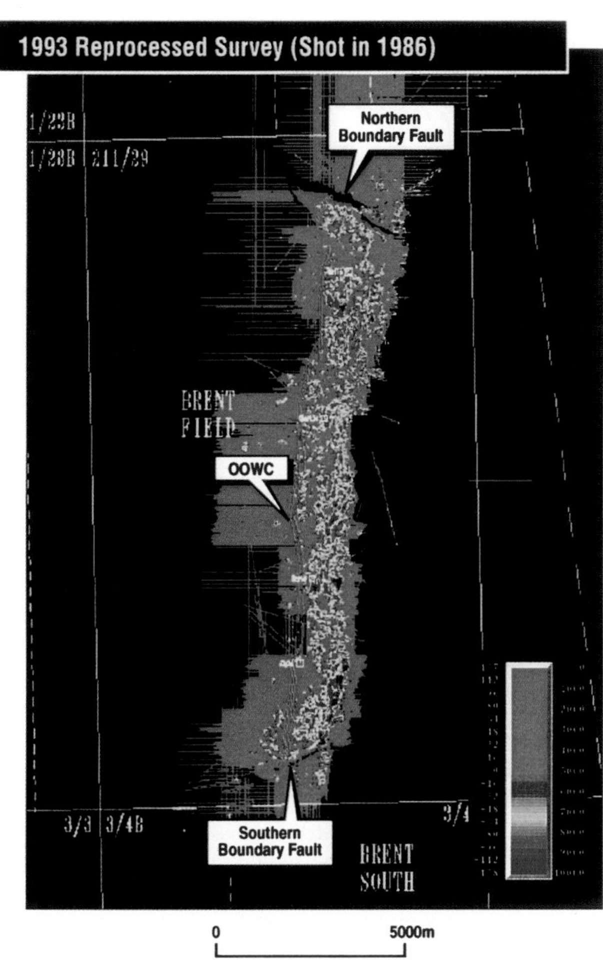

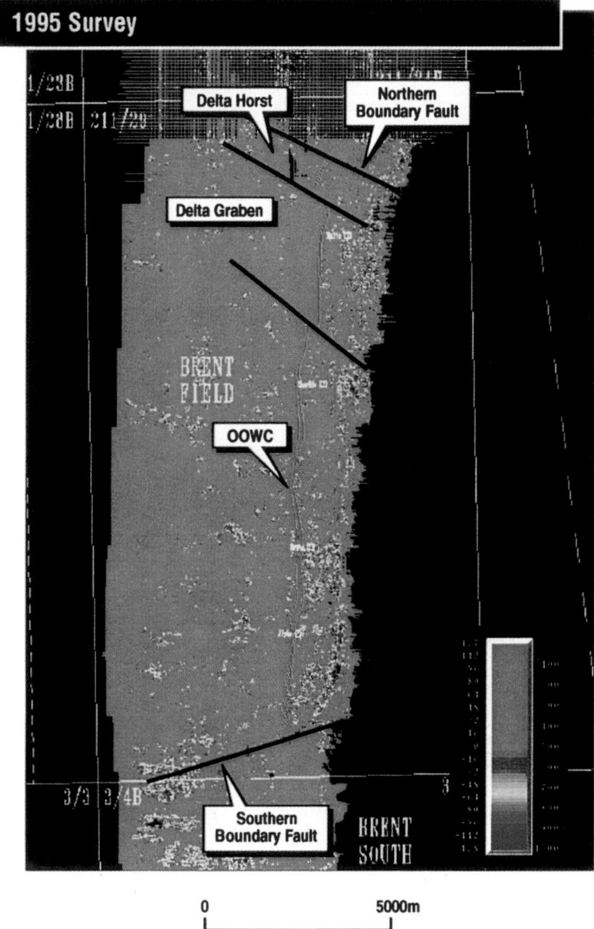

Fig. 10. Comparison of Rannoch interval amplitude anomalies from 1993 and 1995 surveys.

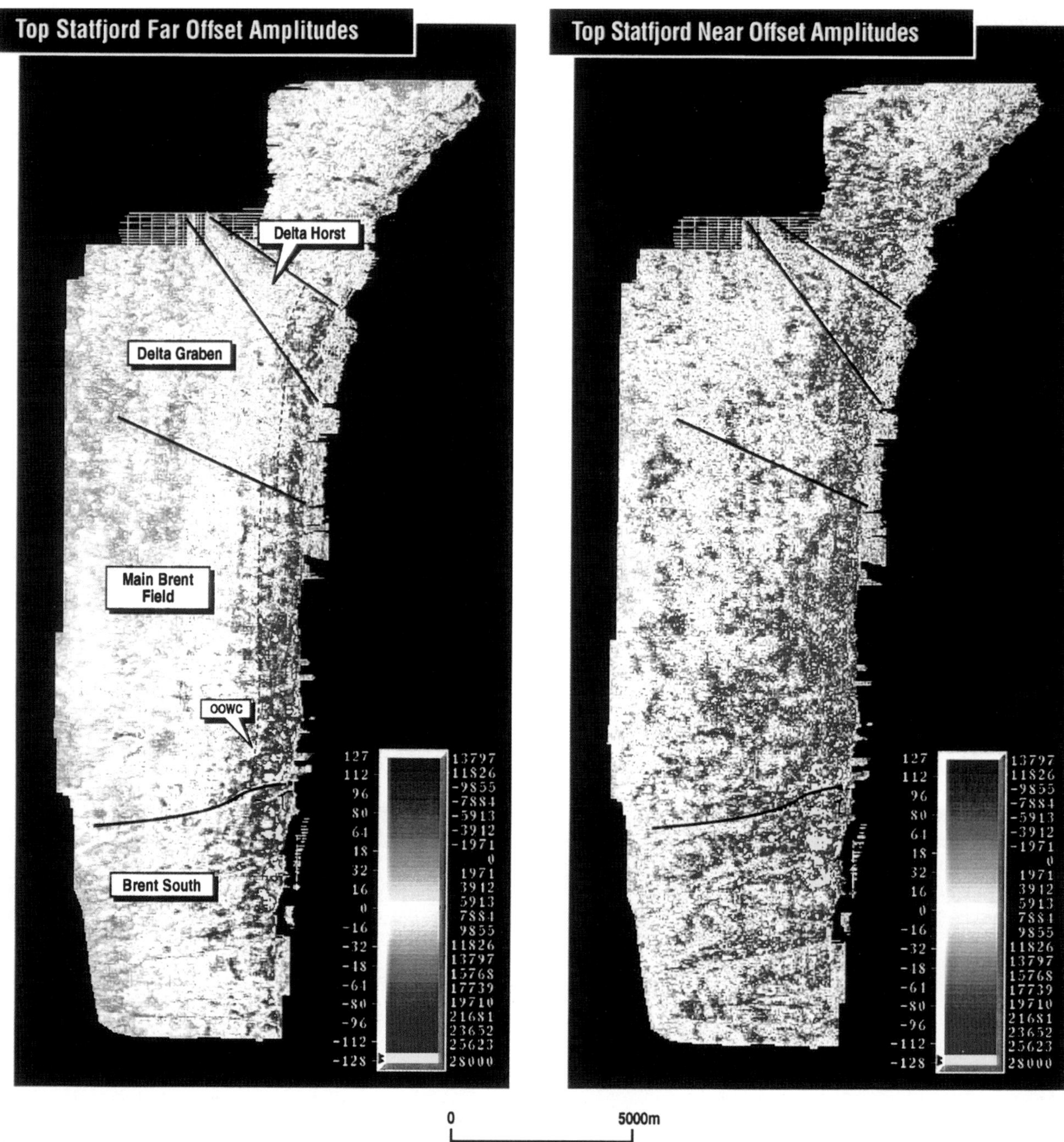

Fig. 11. Amplitude vs offset (AVO) effects at top Statfjord.

have been greatly aided by the increase in resolution resulting from the inversion dataset. In particular, the delineation of the Brent Slumps can be more clearly defined and elsewhere areas of reservoir can be differentiated from non-reservoir where the reflectivity dataset is ambiguous, thus helping to reduce gross rock volume uncertainties (van Dierendonk *et al.* 1997).

Additional projects. Parallel to these initiatives, data processing refinements are continuously being tested. Pre-stack depth migration is being carried out as a pilot project to further improve the positioning of the seismic reflectors and, as a result, improve fault resolution.

In addition, the generation of a seismic cube in depth is being undertaken. This is made possible by the significant number of wells (more than 200) available in the survey area with which to calibrate the depth cube. The benefits of having the seismic dataset imaged directly as a volume in the depth domain will be great. The main impact will be during the design and drilling of new wells and in the generation of structurally consistent depth models i.e. consistent with palinspastic restoration principles. The laborious and time-consuming process of depth-converting horizons and faults will be removed. Having the seismic dataset in the depth domain may also facilitate the detection of potential hydrocarbon indicators (flat spots).

The next phase of reservoir characterization

Following the acquisition of the 1995 3D seismic survey, the next iteration of static modelling was initiated in mid-1996 with the start of the seismic re-interpretation phase. As the extent of improvement over the earlier seismic datasets became evident, the scope of the overall Brent Field re-interpretation could be defined. This was also a convenient time to incorporate fundamental modifications to the models arrived at as a result of revised reservoir geological interpretation.

The scope of the Brent Field re-interpretation

The overall plan is similar to that employed before but will also utilize geological modelling packages that have been upgraded or developed since the current static reservoir models were first built. A series of depth surfaces for reservoir subdivisions, crestal unconformities and faults are being created using depth-converted seismic horizons and reservoir subdivision isochore maps, prior to completely re-building the SGM static models. Although the initial products of this process are being created with the CPS-3 mapping package, the EarthVision 3D mapping package will ultimately be used for a rigorous QC procedure and to provide direct input to SGM and into the realistic fault modelling module of GEOCAP. As the GEOCAP models become more mature the full proprietary integrated static/up-scaling/dynamic modelling system, GEOCAP/REDUCE/MoReS, will be used in an iterative manner. This package enables efficient cycling from the static to dynamic model, in response to either primary (new data) or secondary (dynamic model feed-back) updates in the static model. This approach has been successfully applied in building a new FFSM of the Brent South Field.

Initial feed-back from the 1995 3D seismic survey

Correlation of the uppermost interval of the Brent reservoir in crestally-located wells has generally proved to be very problematic. Prior to the interpretation of the 1995 3D seismic survey these intervals were thought to represent reworking of the Brent Group sediments during and immediately following slump development. As a result they were modelled as a separate stratigraphic unit. An iterative interpretation process combining both detailed wireline log correlation and the improved fault imaging of the new seismic has shown that these intervals can be assigned to established reservoir units lying in discrete fault blocks. This interpretation provides valuable additional control on facies distributions, particularly in the crestal areas of the field, and has given additional insight into the overall geometry of the slump fault complex. At present, facies distributions are being modelled in the Delta West Flank area using the new faults and correlation in anticipation of producing an improved and refined static model for this complex area of the field.

Brent reservoir facies distribution; new insights

In 1996 construction of a GEOCAP model of the West Flank Brent reservoir commenced, at first using the same facies data as that employed in the SGM models. As a result of the initial GEOCAP modelling work it became apparent that some facies distributions were not consistent with their interpreted depositional environments. A sedimentological, ichnofacies (trace-fossil) and sequence stratigraphic review of all the Brent reservoir core was undertaken to support this modelling study. The results formed the basis of a new facies and wireline log classification, and showed amongst others, that the Ness Formation contained several shoreface sand sequences that had previously been interpreted as mouthbars and lagoonal shoals. Subsequent correlation in the Lower Ness also led to the mapping out of an incised channel system. Construction of the GEOCAP model continued, using these new facies descriptions, and was used as the basis for modelling porosity and permeability and subsequently the identification of potential remaining oil targets (Abbots & van Kuijk 1997).

Conclusions

Brent Field depressurization, commencing in 1997, will increase ultimate oil and gas recovery from the West Flank Statfjord and Brent reservoirs. Field life will be extended, increasing the ultimate recovery from the Slumps areas and the Brent South Field. The current generation of static reservoir models have provided the basis for the full field simulation model that is currently in use. The impact of the 1995 3D seismic survey and concurrent developments in reservoir modelling technology have provided the impetus to upgrade the existing static reservoir models in the drive to continually optimize hydrocarbon recovery. The currently available combination of static/dynamic reservoir modelling and subsurface access technology comes at a critical time in the overall development of the Brent Field and faces petroleum and well engineers with a vast challenge to use it to realize the remaining reserves of the field.

Shell UK Exploration and Production and Esso Exploration and Production UK are thanked for their permission to publish this paper. The SGM modelling work was undertaken over several years by J. Whitworth, A. Hildebrandt, A. Wetzelaer, C. Berge, T. Kuud, Ap van der Graaf and C. Bruce.

References

ABBOTS, F. V. & VAN KUIJK, A. 1997. Using 3D geological modelling and connectivity analysis to locate remaining oil targets in the Brent reservoir of the mature Brent field. *Paper SPE 38473, presented at Offshore Europe 97 Conference, Aberdeen.*

BRAITHWAITE, C. I. M. & SCHULTE, W. M. 1992. Transforming the future of the Brent field: Depressurisation – the next development phase. *Paper SPE 25026 presented at the European Petroleum Conference, Cannes.*

BUDDING, M. C. & INGLIN, H. F. 1981. A reservoir geological model of the Brent sands in southern Cormorant. *In*: ILLING, L. V. & HOBSON, G. D. (eds) *Petroleum Geology of the Continental Shelf of North-West Europe.* Heyden, London, 326–334.

COUTTS, S. D. LARRSON, S. Y. & ROSMAN, R. 1996. Development of the slumped crestal area of the Brent reservoir, Brent field: an integrated approach. *Petroleum Geoscience*, **2**, 219–230.

——, JURGENS, T., VAN KESSEL, O., PRONK, D. & WARD, V. C. 1997. Phase 2 development of the slumped crestal area of the Brent reservoir, Brent Field. *Paper SPE 38476 presented at Offshore Europe 97 Conference, Aberdeen.*

JAMES, S. J. 1997. Brent field reservoir modelling: Laying the foundations of a brown-field redevelopment. *Paper SPE 38472 presented at Offshore Europe 97 Conference, Aberdeen.*

MORTON, A. C. & BERGE, C. 1995. Heavy mineral suites in the Statfjord and Nansen Formations of the Brent field, North Sea: A new tool for reservoir subdivision and correlation. *Petroleum Geoscience*, **1**, 355–364.

SCHULTE, W. M., VAN ROSSEM, P. A. H. & VAN DE WIJVER, W. 1994. Current challenges in the Brent Field. *Journal of Petroleum Technology*, **46**, 1426–1433.

TAYLOR, S. R. 1996. 3D modelling to optimise production at the successive stages of field life. *SPE Formation Evaluation*, **11**, 205–210.

UNDERHILL, J. R., SAWYER, M. J., HODGSON, P., SHALLCROSS, M. D. & GAWTHORPE, R. L. 1997. Implications of fault scarp degradation for Brent Group prospectivity, Ninian field, northern North Sea. *American Association of Petroleum Geologists Bulletin*, **81**, 999–1022.

VAN DER PAL, R., BACON, M. & PRONK, D. 1996. 3D walkaway VSP, enhancing seismic resolution for development optimisation of the Brent field. *First Break*, **14**, 463–469.

VAN DIERENDONCK, A. I., PRONK, D. W. & WARD, V. C. 1997. New Seismic on an old field: The impact of the 1995 Brent 3D Seismic. *Paper SPE 38471, presented at Offshore Europe 97 Conference, Aberdeen.*

WEBER, K. J. & VAN GEUNS, L. C. 1990. Framework for Constructing Clastic Reservoir Simulation Models. *Journal of Petroleum Technology*, **42**, 1248–1253.

WETZELAER, A., HILDEBRANDT, A., COUTTS, S. D. & VEEMAN, S. 1996. Locating The Remaining Oil in the Brent field prior to depressurisation. *Paper presented at Europec Milan.*

Application of 3D visualization and VSP for horizontal well positioning – 9/13a-N1 case history, Nevis Field, UKCS

A. J. DICKSON, G. C. BINGHAM, G. C. STYLIANIDES, H. W. A. THOMPSON and N. A. WAY

Mobil North Sea Limited, Caledonian House, Union Row, Aberdeen, AB10 1SA, UK

Abstract: The Nevis Field, operated by Mobil North Sea Limited, came on stream in September 1996. This was achieved by completion of an existing vertical well in the Triassic and the drilling and completion of a horizontal well in the Middle Jurassic Beryl Formation. Horizontal wells are necessary for the economic development of the field. However, these wells are high risk because of the relatively thin and faulted reservoir interval. A multi-disciplinary team was formed to manage the risk of the crucial first horizontal well.

3D visualization was used to allow all disciplines the opportunity to understand the structure and difficulties associated with the well. A pilot well was planned to maximize the chance of penetrating the oil–water contact. A wide range of possible horizontal well trajectories, dependent on the results of the pilot, were constructed interactively in 3D. Using an iterative process, a well path was engineered that catered for the range of outcomes.

An imaging vertical seismic profile (VSP) was acquired in the pilot well to help optimize the location of the final horizontal section. Thorough planning resulted in faults not apparent in the 3D dataset being identified on the VSP. Detailed structure maps were created based on the faults and bed dips interpreted from the VSP and fault trends observed from the 3D seismic data. The well design work in 3D meant that the required horizontal well trajectory could be drilled. The final horizontal section proved 610 m (2000 ft) of oil bearing section. The successful drilling of the well is considered to be largely as a result of extensive multi-disciplinary contingency planning.

The Nevis Field is located 290 km (180 miles) northeast of the Scottish Mainland within UK Blocks 9/13a and 9/12, in the Northern North Sea. It lies to the west of the Beryl and Ness fields which lie wholly within Block 9/13. The average water depth is 122 m (400 ft).

The Nevis Field comprises a number of accumulations trapped in the footwall of a major fault system, known as the Nevis–Ness Fault (Fig.1). Nevis South is the major accumulation located 6.5 km (4.1 miles) southwest of the Beryl Alpha platform. Nevis South was discovered by well 9/13-4 in 1974. After the early appraisal phase a further two appraisal wells were drilled in 1987/8. In all, six appraisal wells have been drilled.

Two primary reservoirs have been identified in Nevis South: the Middle Jurassic Beryl Formation which is a 47 m (155 ft) oil rim overlain by a gas cap, and the Triassic Lewis Units 3 and 4 which is an undersaturated black oil reservoir. Three secondary reservoirs have also been identified, Cretaceous gas, Upper Jurassic Heather oil and gas and Triassic Lewis Unit 1 oil. A subsea development plan to waterflood both the Beryl and Lewis Units 3 and 4 reservoirs went as far as detailed engineering in 1990 but the project was marginal with commercial hurdles, and was suspended in 1991. In 1992 reservoir simulation indicated that increased recovery and reduced drilling costs could be achieved from the Beryl Formation oil rim without water injection, using horizontal production wells. Horizontal wells can achieve very low drawdown reducing the potential of gas and water coning, and improving areal sweep compared to conventional wells. In 1993/4 Nevis South was remapped using 3D seismic, and reservoir simulation was used to optimize horizontal well locations in the Beryl Formation. Equity interests and commercial issues were resolved by the end of 1994. The Development Programme Document (DPD) was approved in September 1995. Based on this new work Nevis South reserves are estimated at 50×10^6 STB oil and 174.5×10^9 SCF gas. The current equity position in Nevis South is Mobil (Operator), with 41.3425%, Amerada Hess, 35.9075%, Enterprise 13%, British Gas 6.5% and OMV 3.25%.

Nevis South is the first part of a staged development of the Nevis accumulations. Nevis South is itself a phased development. The Beryl Formation will be developed using a total of 3 horizontal production wells using gas cap expansion and aquifer drive. The Lewis reservoir will be developed by waterflood using 5 wells: 3 producers and 2 water injectors. Phase 1 was completed in 1996 and involved the drilling and completion of the first Beryl horizontal producer, N1y, and re-entry of suspended Well 9/13a-36 which was completed as N2. Three flowlines were laid in mid 1996, one for each well, with one for future water injection. First oil was achieved on 17 September 1996.

This paper describes the planning, drilling and results of the first horizontal well. 3D visualization was used by a multi-disciplinary team to plan the pilot and horizontal wells, and was a focal point for discussion on risk management and contingency planning. A methodology for planning horizontal wells was developed. A vertical seismic profile (VSP) was acquired in the pilot well to manage the risk of drilling the horizontal section. Detailed maps were created which incorporated the VSP interpretation and fault trend information from 3D seismic data. These maps were used to finalize the position of the horizontal well. A detailed small scale [1:1, 4 cm = 30 m (100 ft)] working cross-section along the prognosed horizontal well trajectory was used to plot the course of the well. This served as a focal point for multi-disciplinary decision making. A subsequent VSP in the horizontal section was used to identify faults and aid perforation strategy.

Structure and stratigraphy

The Nevis Field is situated at the western edge of the Beryl Embayment in the South Viking Graben (Fig. 1). The

Dickson, A. J., Bingham, G. C., Stylianides, G. C., Thompson, H. W. A. & Way, N. A. 1999. Application of 3D visualization and VSP for horizontal well positioning – 9/13a-N1 case history, Nevis Field, UKCS. *In*: Fleet, A. J. & Boldy, S. A. R. (eds) *Petroleum Geology of Northwest Europe: Proceedings of the 5th Conference*, 1051–1061.

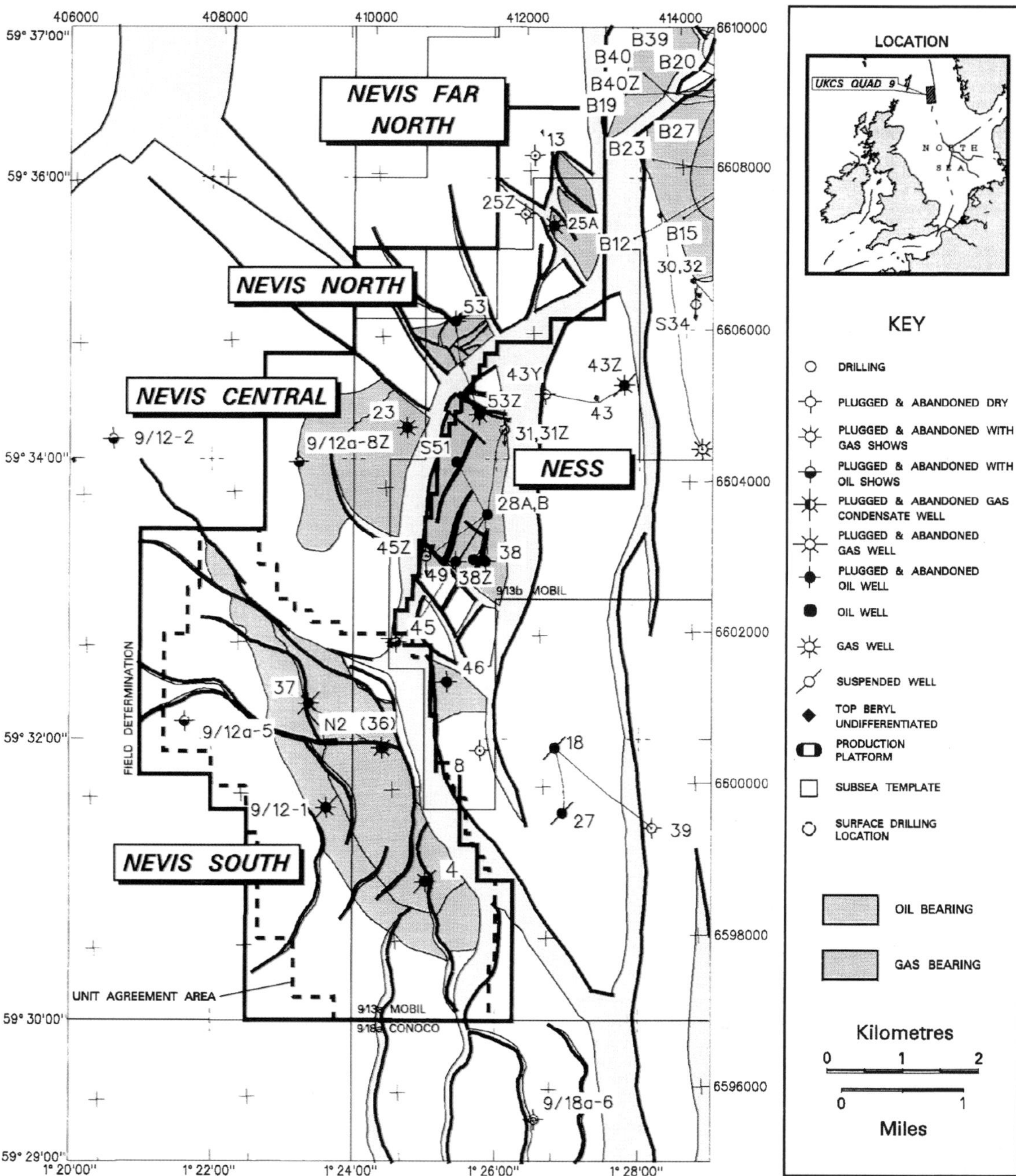

Fig. 1. Nevis Field location. Distribution of Beryl Formation hydrocarbons (Beryl or Deeper).

Embayment is a large relay ramp system, which results from the interaction of fault systems along the western edge of the graben. In the Nevis Field hydrocarbons are trapped in a tilted fault block formed during Jurassic extension. The eastern bounding fault trends north to south, separating the Nevis Field on the footwall from the Ness Field on the hanging wall and is referred to as the Nevis–Ness Fault. A northwest to southeast extensional fault which intersects the Nevis–Ness Fault and throws down to the north, defines the northern limit of Nevis South. Faults within Nevis South are generally sub-parallel to the field bounding faults and have throws of up to 46 m (150 ft). Figure 2 shows a west to east seismic line, through Well 9/13a-N2, from Nevis South to the Beryl Field.

A stratigraphic column, which compares the Upper Triassic to Upper Jurassic section in the Nevis Field and nearby Beryl Field, is displayed in Fig. 3. Overall the sequence represents increasing water depth from lacustrine to marine conditions. The lithostratigraphic nomenclature used by Mobil for the Beryl and Nevis Fields is based on Deegan & Scull (1977) with informal modifications (Knutson & Munro 1991). Stratigraphic subdivisions, depositional interpretations and reservoir parameters for the Beryl Field are described in Robertson (1993).

Early rifting of the Viking Graben is interpreted to have commenced during the Triassic (Robertson 1993). The oldest rocks penetrated in the Nevis Field are the fluvio–lacustrine sands and mudstones of the Triassic, Cormorant Group. The Cormorant Group is split into a lower undifferentiated section of Anisian–Ladinian age and the overlying Lewis Formation of Ladinian–Norian age. In the Nevis South area, sub-parallel dipping reflectors, suggesting little or no syn-rift thickening towards the East Shetland Bounding Fault, define this sequence.

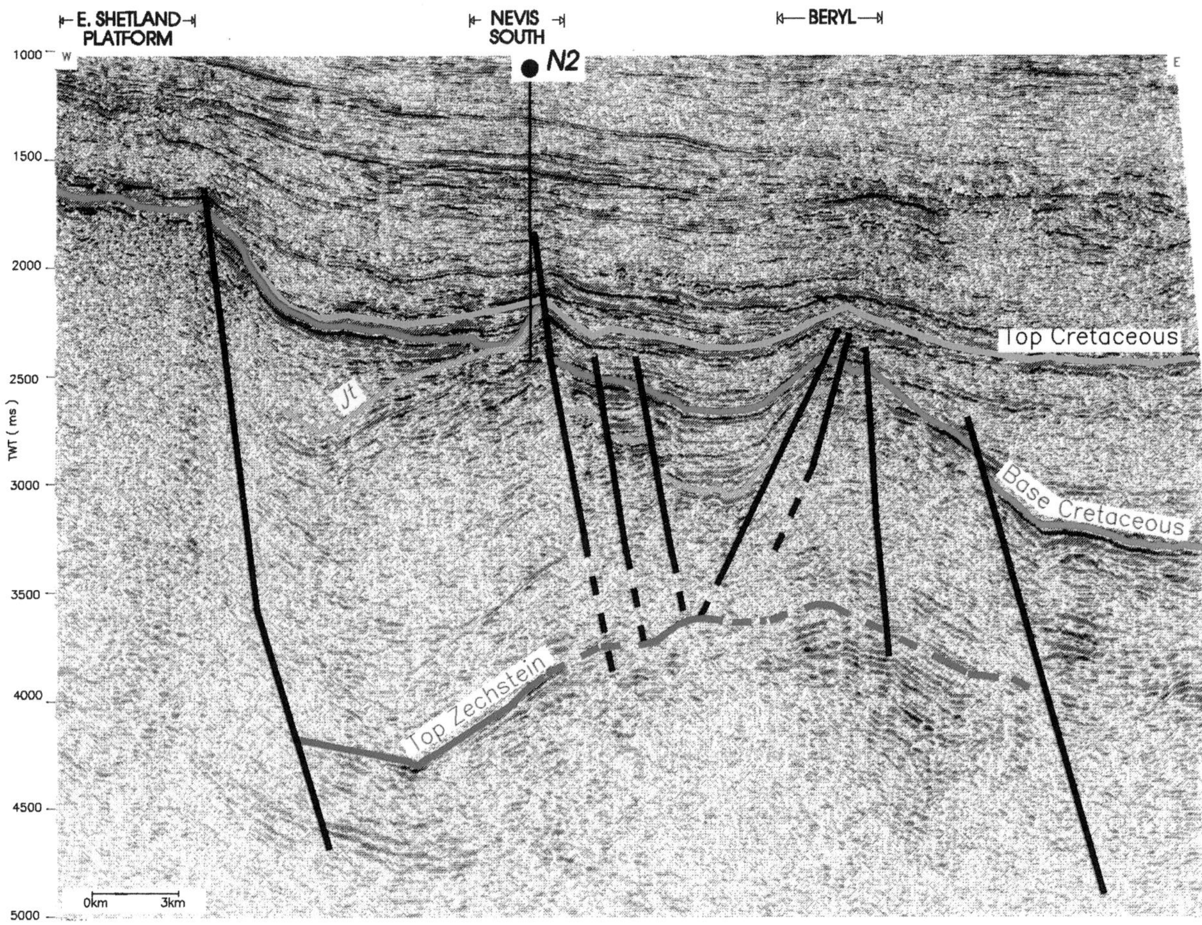

Fig. 2. West to east seismic inline through Nevis South Well N2.

Period	Age	Group	Fm/Member	Unit Beryl	Unit Nevis
JURASSIC	Volgian	J	Kimmeridge Clay Fm. (Brae Mbr.)		W E
	Kimmeridgian	Humber Group			
	Oxfordian		Heather Fm. (Katrine Mbr.)	II	
	Callovian			I	
	Bathonian	Beryl Embayment Group	Beryl Fm.	V, IV, III, II, I	D, C, B, A
	Bajocian		Linnhe Fm.	II, I	
	Toarcian				
	Pliensbachian	Jt / Dunlin Group	Undiff.	II	
	Sinemurian	Statfjord Group	Nansen Fm.	I	
	Hettangian		Eiriksson Fm.		
TRIASSIC	Rhaetian		Raude Fm.		II, I
	Norian	Cormorant Group	Lewis Fm.	IV	IV
	Carnian			III, II	III, II
	Ladinian			I	I
	Anisian		Undiff.		

Fig. 3. Nevis Field stratigraphic column.

The Cormorant Group is conformably overlain and sealed by the Rhaetian to Hettangian age red mudstones of the Raude and Eiriksson formations. These are separated from the overlying Middle Jurassic, Bathonian age sediments of the Beryl Formation, by a significant unconformity referred to informally as the 'Jt'. More section has been removed at this unconformity in the Nevis Field than the Beryl Field. The missing section is likely to be present down-dip. The Jt may indicate the onset of more active rifting and fault block rotation.

The Beryl Formation is a fluvio–tidal, sand dominated sequence, which varies in thickness from 34 m (110 ft) in Well 9/13a-36 at the crest of the structure, to 126 m (412 ft) down-dip in Well 9/12a-5. Associated with the down-dip, westerly thickening of the Beryl Formation is an increased development of coal and shale. Syn-rift deposition and Jurassic and Cretaceous erosion are responsible for the crestal thinning. Evidence for active rifting in the Beryl Embayment during Beryl Formation deposition is supported by thickness variations recorded in the Beryl (Robertson 1993) and Bruce Fields (Beckly *et al.* 1993).

The Beryl Formation reservoir is both gas and oil bearing. In Nevis South the formation has been sub-divided into four units (A–D) based on lithostratigraphic correlation using facies types interpreted from core and wireline log response. Four main facies types have been identified. These are fluvial channel, tidal channel, lagoonal and marine shoreface. There is an increase in marine influence towards the top of the formation. Unit C is dominantly mudstone, probably deposited in a hypersaline, lagoonal environment, whereas the other units are dominantly fluvio–tidal sandstone. Unit C mudstone is a barrier to vertical permeability. Both Units A and B comprise very clean, homogeneous high porosity sandstone. Unit B contains the highest quality sandstone reservoir, with permeabilities averaging 2–3 D and occasionally considerably higher. Interbedded shales are locally developed in Unit A and permeability is typically about 1 D. Unit D is a clean sand of poorer permeability in the range 200–400 mD.

Conformably overlying the Beryl Formation is the Upper Jurassic Humber Group. This is a mudstone dominated sequence, with locally developed shallow marine sands and deeper marine debris flows. The Humber Group is of Callovian to Volgian age in the Nevis Fault Block as a whole, and is penetrated by four wells. It varies in thickness from 52 m (171 ft) in Well 9/12-1 to more than 549 m (1800 ft) in Well 9/12a-10. The thickness variation is as a result of continued active rifting and erosion/non deposition at the crest of the fault block during the Jurassic and Cretaceous. Oil and gas have been encountered in Callovian and Oxfordian age sands.

The Base Cretaceous unconformity ('J' event Fig. 3) is a major unconformity across Nevis South. Upper Cretaceous marls with limestone interbeds unconformably overlie and seal the Beryl Formation at the crest of the field.

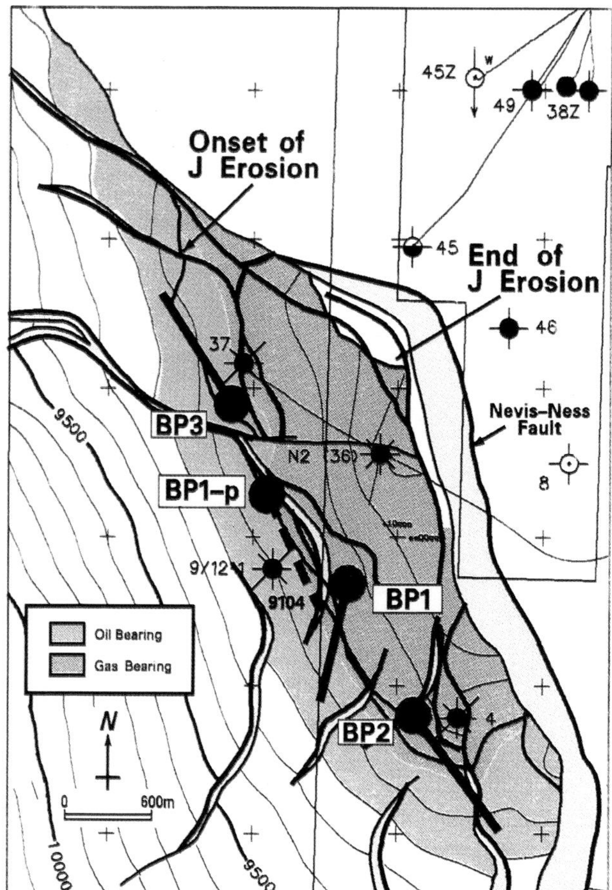

Fig. 4. Nevis South Beryl reservoir simulation well locations. Top Beryl Formation depth map. Note extensional fault at BP1-p location. Well path re-orientated to BP1 location to avoid possible fault zone and orientated at a high angle to anticipated trend of faults.

9/13a-N1 horizontal well planning

Reservoir simulation derived location

In 1993/94 a new reservoir simulation model was built for the Nevis South Beryl Formation to assist in the determination of the optimal development plan for the reservoir. The model was constructed using top and base reservoir surfaces and faults interpreted on 1991 3D seismic data. The model indicated that the accumulation would be most effectively developed by three horizontal producing wells. Figure 4 displays the top Beryl reservoir surface used in the model and three horizontal well paths (BP1-p, BP2, BP3) derived from the simulation. These well paths were almost parallel to strike, 15 m (50 ft) above the oil–water contact (OWC) (2800 m (9190 ft) TVDSS) and represent the optimal well locations for draining the reservoir from the reservoir simulation model.

BP1-p was proposed as the first well, as it was in the area of highest permeability, close to Well 9/12-1 and therefore of lower geological uncertainty. A well path from the top hole location at the 9/13a-36 well was engineered to achieve a 853 m (2800 ft) horizontal section. When viewed on seismic, the proximity of the horizontal section to a mapped fault was clear. The extensional fault, as indicated on Fig. 4, trends from NW–SE, throws down to the west and is located within ±45 m (±150) ft of the horizontal well path. Although the geological model assumes that faults are not sealing, the proposed horizontal trajectory was altered to avoid degraded reservoir associated with the fault damage zone, and premature gas or water breakthrough if the fault acted as a conduit. The new location, BP1, was further south with the horizontal section trending NNE–SSW (Fig. 4). The modified horizontal well was closer to dip direction and designed to penetrate all reservoir units, a significant improvement on the original design. Reservoir simulation indicated a minor reduction in ultimate recovery from BP1 compared to the original BP1-p location.

Well planning methodology and risk management

A well trajectory was engineered for the BP1 location. Viewing the well path on 3D seismic data, indicated that the part of the well where the angle of deviation is increased to horizontal (build section) penetrated the Raude mudstones below the Beryl Formation. Drilling experience in the Beryl area had shown that there is a high risk of borehole collapse in the Raude mudstones. Increasing the angle to horizontal through the Raude Formation would compound the drilling hazards.

It was clear that at this stage in the well planning it was important to include all disciplines (geophysics, geology, reservoir engineering, drilling and operations engineering) in the decision making process required to finalize the well path. Mobil had adopted a team-based organization where these disciplines were represented in the same team. In order to facilitate useful debate and discussion, reservoir surfaces, faults and well paths were loaded into a 3D visualization package. The manipulation of the reservoir model and well trajectory in 3D allowed all disciplines to interact and contribute effectively to the well design at an early stage. For instance, because the operations engineer was involved, completion related issues associated with running the liner and perforating could be addressed, and incorporated into the well design.

The objective of using the 3D visualization software was to design a well path that would achieve the desired horizontal section and minimize the chance of penetrating the Raude Formation beneath the reservoir. The original well path, that penetrated the Raude, was loaded into the 3D visualization software. Figure 5 displays the base reservoir with the original well path along the fault and the revised well path with the heel penetrating base reservoir. The well path was altered interactively to achieve the horizontal section but to avoid the Raude Formation. Several iterations were required to engineer this well path.

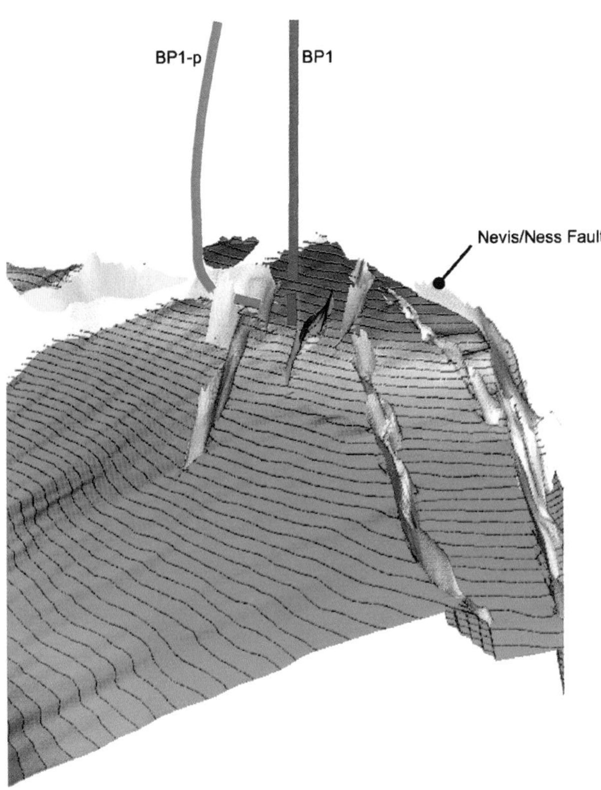

Fig. 5. 3D visualization plot of top Raude Formation and reservoir simulation well paths. BP1-p cuts fault. BP1 penetrates Raude Formation mudstone beneath reservoir.

The errors assigned to top and base reservoir were ±30 m (100 ft). This error was assigned because of uncertainty in the seismic interpretation and depth conversion as well as from experience of drilling wells in the Beryl area. The well path fitted the model but took no account of these error margins in depth of target. A pilot well was planned to identify the OWC. Defining the OWC was critical to the success of the horizontal well as the optimum field development placed the horizontal section 15 m (50 ft) above the OWC. There was uncertainty in the OWC because although it had been encountered during appraisal, pressure depletion had also been observed. Further depletion in the intervening 10 years may have led to movement of the contact. Confirmation of formation tops was the other prime objective of the pilot well. Possible errors in reservoir depth were considered at the well planning stage to ensure that the well design allowed for a range of possible reservoir depths.

To achieve this, error surfaces were constructed using 3D visualization software assuming base reservoir ±30 m (100 ft) and top reservoir ±30 m (100 ft). The horizontal well 'fairway' was constructed by intersection of top and base reservoir with the target depth (Fig. 6a) and represents the area in which horizontal sections could be drilled (Fig. 6b). The intersection with the error surfaces indicates the range of error of the fairway. Demonstration of this work on the screen to all members of the technical team ensured an awareness of error margins and potential range of horizontal well trajectories that may result after confirmation of contacts/tops by the pilot well. This was critical at the well planning stage as it ensured that the basic well design allowed for a wide range of horizontal trajectories. As a consequence, initial well design was changed with the pilot well drilled from the 20″ casing shoe rather than the 13 3/8″. Kicking off the horizontal well at this shallower point was necessary to ensure that the range of possible horizontal well trajectories visualized could be achieved.

Using 3D visualization and the same methodology the team optimized the location of the pilot well to maximize the probability of penetrating the OWC. Top reservoir +30 m (100 ft) and base reservoir −30 m (100 ft) surfaces were intersected with a surface at the expected OWC (2801 m (9190 ft) TV(D)SS). Figure 6c illustrates this and Fig. 6d displays the resulting pilot well fairway. The optimum pilot well location was simply located by selecting the centre of the fairway along the planned horizontal well path

The 3D visualization software acted as a focal point for discussion of operational scenarios at the planning stage. It allowed the entire team to work concurrently such that the impact of ideas or concerns raised by one discipline could be immediately considered by others. Key discussion points associated with possible outcomes from the well planning exercise were captured on decision trees which had the dual purpose of managing risk at the planning stage, planning for contingencies and providing clear guidelines to facilitate rapid and effective decision making during operations.

Application of VSP

Figure 7 shows a cross-section of the planned pilot and horizontal well paths. Although the pilot well was optimally located to penetrate the OWC it was not ideally placed to manage the risk of penetrating base reservoir at the heel of the well. In order to address this issue VSP modeling was performed to test whether or not an imaging VSP in the pilot well could aid the prediction of top and base reservoir surfaces up-dip from the pilot to the heel of the horizontal section.

Modeling confirmed that a vertical incidence VSP using a boat source would adequately image the reservoir events up-dip from the pilot hole location, where the horizontal section was planned (Fig. 8). A concern was that highly reflective events above the reservoir (top Heimdal, Maureen and Cretaceous) would reduce transmission of seismic energy and lead to deterioration of the reservoir reflections. These events lie between the pilot well and the reservoir towards the heel of the horizontal well. There was therefore concern that the transmission problems would be greatest where imaging of base reservoir in particular was most critical.

Modelling of a rig source VSP indicated that energy from further up-dip would be received by the geophones. This enabled recording of stronger reflected energy further up-dip than would be possible with the boat source VSP alone. Consequently a rig source VSP was acquired simultaneously. In addition a much larger boat source than normal was employed (3 × 250 cubic inch plus 3 × 150 cubic inch compared to 3 × 150 cubic inch) to attempt to increase the energy transmitted to the reservoir horizons. The rig source was restricted to 3 × 150 cubic inch as the boat source array was too large to be close to the rig.

Pilot well results and final horizontal well planning

Drilling of pilot well

Well 9/13a-N1 spudded on 22 February 1996 and deviated from vertical at the 20″ casing shoe, 823 m (2700 ft) subsea in the Tertiary. The well penetrated the reservoir section at approximately 45°. Core was cut in the Heather and Beryl formations. Unfortunately the well was lost at total depth because of the bottom hole assembly packing off and becoming stuck while pulling out of the hole. The well objectives of core collection and formation top identification had been met but OWC, saturation, lithology and VSP data had not been acquired as wireline logs had not been run. Instead a minor sidetrack

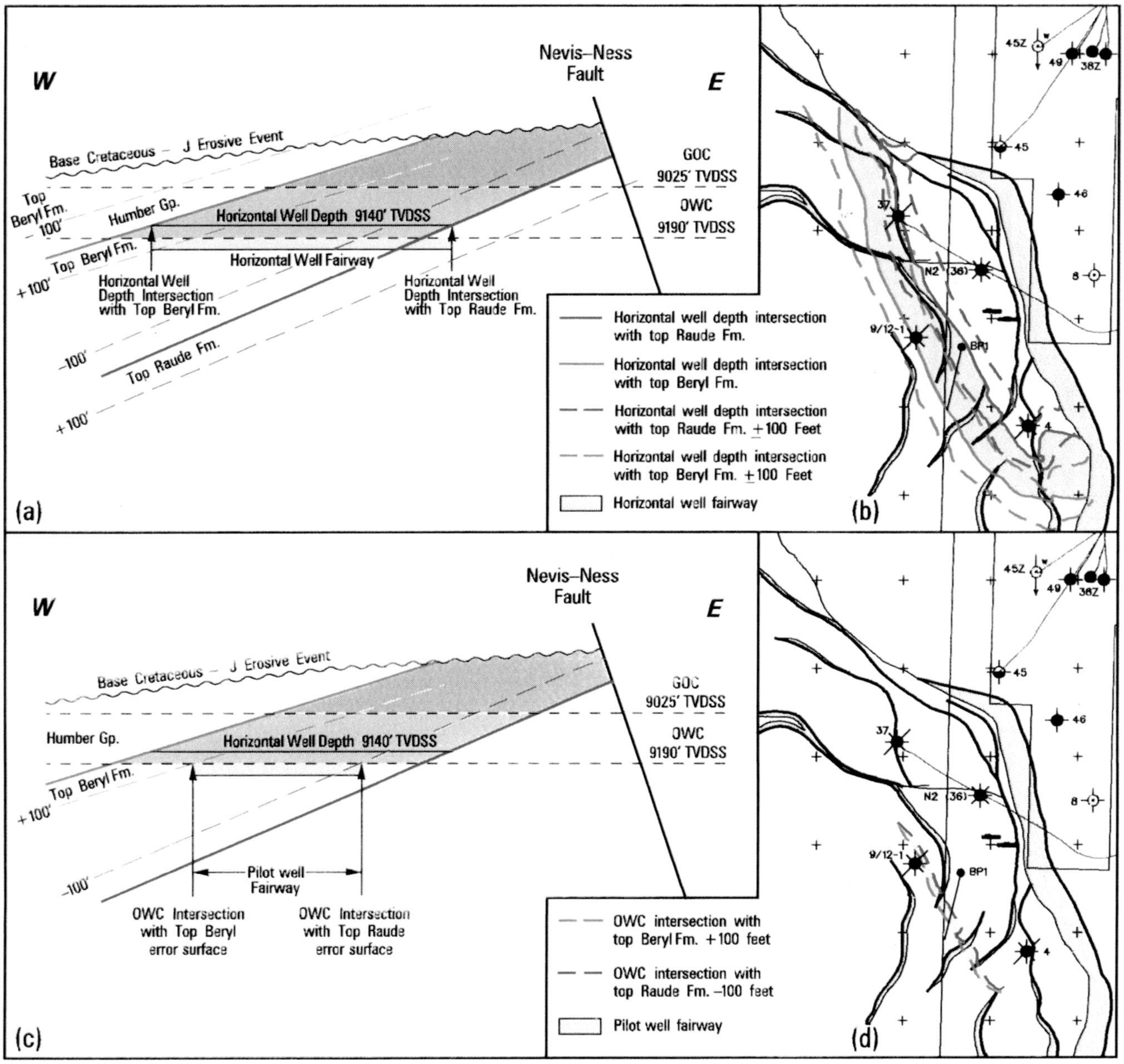

Fig. 6. (**a**) Well planning method for horizontal well. Horizontal well fairway is constructed by intersection of top and base reservoir with target depth. The intersection with the error surfaces indicates the range of error of the fairway. (**b**) Map view of horizontal well fairway. In 2D, the horizontal well fairway represents the area in which horizontal sections could be drilled. (**c**) Well planning method for pilot well. The pilot well fairway was constructed to maximize the chance of penetrating the OWC. Top reservoir +30 m (100 ft) and base reservoir −30 m (100 ft) surfaces were intersected with a surface at the expected OWC (2801 m (9190 ft) TVDSS). (**d**) Map view of pilot well fairway.

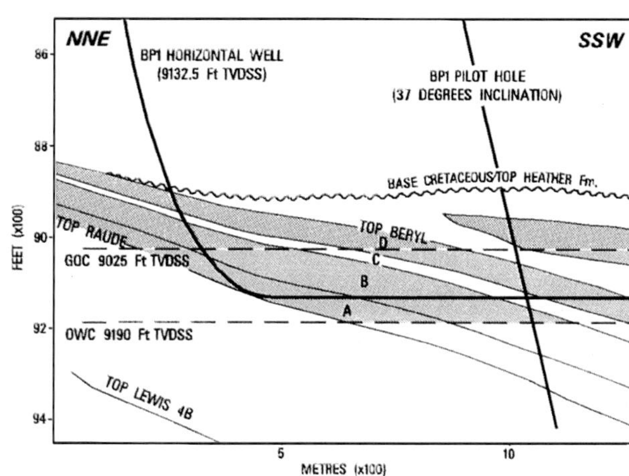

Fig. 7. Cross-section along planned well path.

(9/13a-N1z) was drilled to obtain the data. In order to reduce the risk of getting stuck a second time, the drill string was minimized (e.g. no logging while drilling gamma ray and hole cleaning was improved).

Well 9/13a-NIz drilled through a near identical section to Well 9/13a-N1. The hole was deviated at 46°. The VSP was acquired before the main logging suite to maximize time for processing and interpretation of results.

Pilot well results

The results of the pilot well are compared to the well prognosis and offset wells in Fig. 9. Wireline logs confirmed that all formation and unit tops were encountered within 9 m (30 ft) of prognosis. The OWC was encountered 30 cm (1 ft) low to prognosis at 2801 m (9191 ft) TVDSS. Repeat formation test (RFT) data confirmed no further depletion of the Beryl reservoir since 1988.

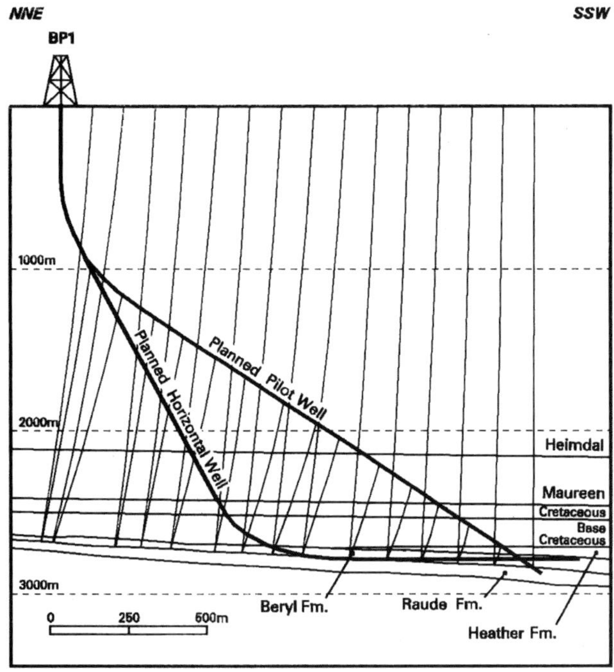

Fig. 8. Pilot well VSP planning. Note highly reflective Heimdal, Maureen and Cretaceous events between the pilot well and the reservoir, towards the heel of the horizontal well.

The vertical incidence boat source VSP was processed within 2 days of acquisition to produce a depth converted time migrated section. The data quality was excellent and there was no requirement to process the rig source VSP to enhance the image up-dip from the pilot well. Thorough planning was the key to the success of the VSP. Detailed planning included VSP modelling which resulted in the use of a larger source. Test processing of the model was performed before the well was drilled to help determine appropriate processing parameters. The optimum migration was tested to ensure that processing time was minimized. The time migrated depth section is displayed in Fig. 10.

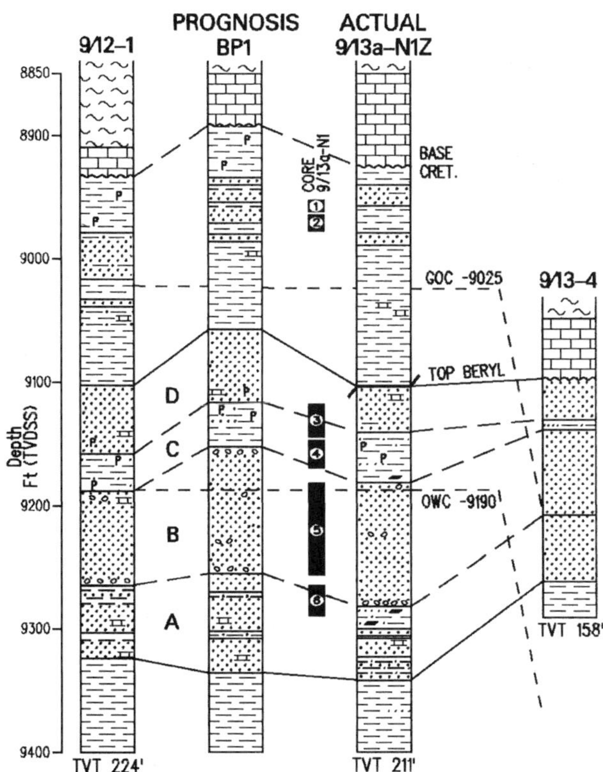

Fig. 9. Pilot well prognosis compared with actual and offset wells.

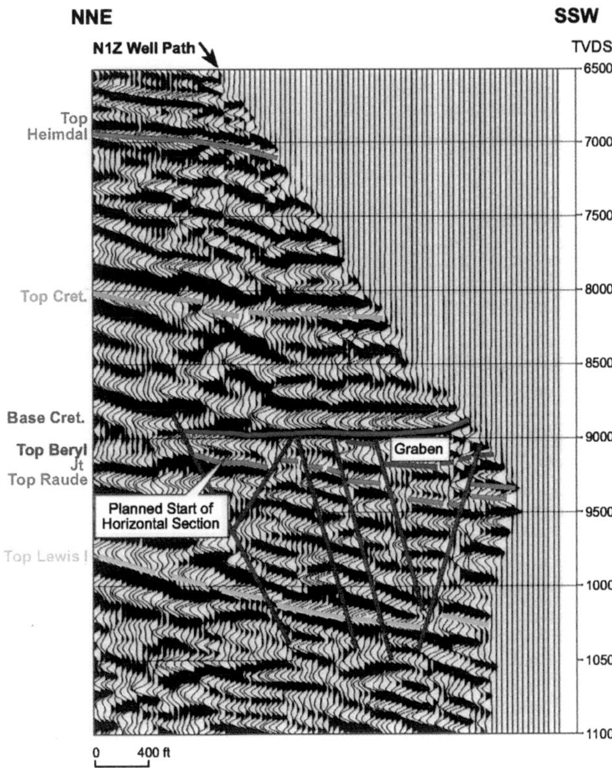

Fig. 10. Time migrated pilot well VSP in depth. The graben throws top Beryl Formation deeper than the planned horizontal well depth such that the well would encounter the Heather Formation before the desired well length was attained.

The VSP provided significantly higher resolution data than the 3D seismic dataset. Figure 11 is a comparison of the pilot well unmigrated VSP in time, and colocated time migrated section from the 3D dataset. Reflectors and faults are more clearly defined on the VSP. A finer resolution fault pattern was interpreted which was not apparent on the 3D dataset. The planned start of the horizontal section is indicated on Fig. 10. This is located just above the base of the Beryl Formation. On the VSP data a graben was interpreted along the planned well path at approximately 366 m (1200 ft) from the start of the horizontal section. The graben throws the top Beryl Formation deeper than the planned horizontal well depth such that the well would encounter the Heather Formation before the desired well length was attained. The well trajectory was therefore changed to maximize horizontal section length.

Final horizontal well planning

The VSP provided higher resolution data than the 3D surface seismic data. The value of this interpretation was limited by the fact that it was 2D and because it was not possible to interpret the same level of detail on the 3D dataset away from the line. Consequently, moving the horizontal well away from the original planned location had associated risks. Firstly, the VSP interpretation could have been wrong if, for example there existed out-of-plane interference. Secondly, moving away from the planned location meant moving away from the pilot well.

To manage the risks of drilling the horizontal well, it was important to incorporate the new data and to attempt to

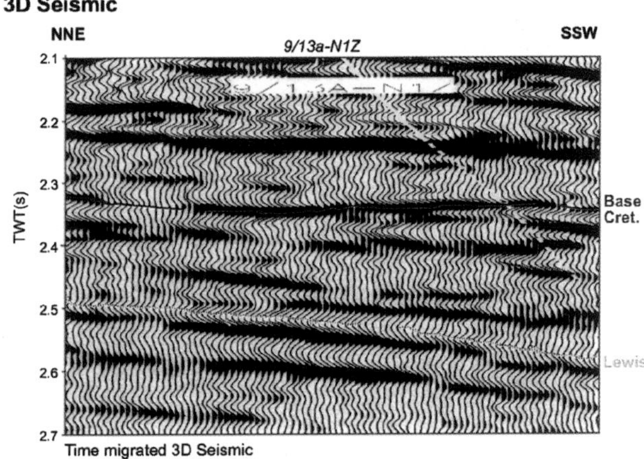

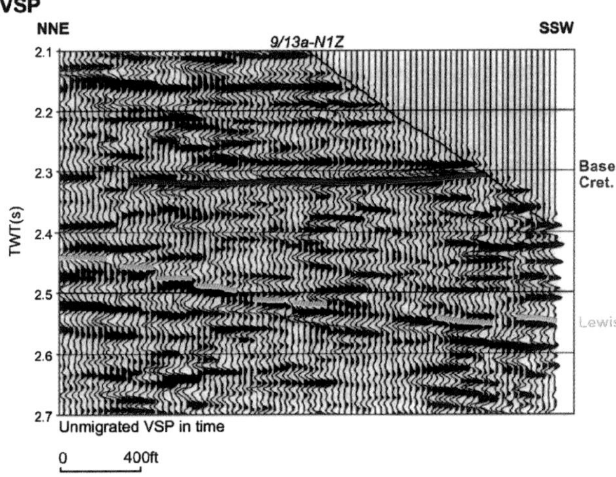

Fig. 11. Comparison of pilot well VSP and 3D seismic data. The VSP provides significantly higher resolution data (bandwidth approximately 80 Hz) than the 3D seismic dataset (bandwidth approximately 50 Hz).

extrapolate the interpretation in 3D. Detailed structure maps were created based on the VSP and on the fault trends observed from the 3D seismic data. An edge map was generated to help identify the trend of minor faults. The resulting base reservoir map is indicated in Fig. 12a. In addition, a map at the horizontal well depth was constructed using the base reservoir structure map and unit isopachs (Fig. 12b). This map was used to determine a well path that lay within the horizontal well fairway and would maximize the exposure to Beryl Formation sand.

Horizontal well drilling and results

$12\frac{1}{4}''$ build section

The pilot hole was plugged and abandoned and the horizontal well kicked off from vertical at the 20″ shoe. The target elevation for drilling the horizontal section was set at 2783 m (9132 ft) TVDSS, ± minus 2.4 m (8 ft) so that the minimum offset from the OWC would be 15 m (50 ft). The well path was designed to enter the Beryl Formation with $12\frac{1}{4}''$ hole at an angle of 68° and build to horizontal at 2783 m (9132 ft) TVDSS close to the base of the reservoir. It was planned to case the $12\frac{1}{4}''$ hole and then drill up to 853 m (2800 ft) of $8\frac{1}{2}''$ horizontal hole.

Top Beryl sand was encountered 8 m (26 ft) lower than prognosed and the expected full section of Beryl Formation was not present. A thick, clean, high quality sand section was drilled and the first shale horizon encountered was deeper than expected. Hot shot biostratigraphy on the cuttings suggested that it was Unit A shale. The Unit C shale and consequently the poorer quality Unit D sand were missing and Unit B had been encountered directly below Base Cretaceous.

The top Unit A shale was encountered 12 m (40 ft) higher than prognosed. It was therefore likely that base reservoir would also be shallow and the planned well path would penetrate the Raude Formation shales. Because of low formation dip along the orientation of the well path, several hundred feet of horizontal drilling would be required to re-enter the Beryl Unit A sands. The decision was made to drill ahead but to continue to build angle faster than planned so that the TD point of the $12\frac{1}{4}''$ hole would land higher and reduce the risk of entering the Raude. The $8\frac{1}{2}''$ hole would then be drilled some 152 m (500 ft) at the higher elevation before dropping to the target elevation once the danger of penetrating base reservoir had receded. The possibility that base reservoir would be encountered high had been considered as part of the contingency planning and the action to be taken, identified in a decision tree. The impact on well performance of producing from a ‘stepped horizontal’ as was now proposed had also been quantified in the contingency planning process. Although gas breakthrough was predicted earlier, the effect on overall recovery was minimal.

In spite of the more aggressive build the well penetrated the Raude Formation at 86° inclination, 10 m (34 ft) TVD shallower than prognosed. In order to allow time to evaluate the situation the decision was taken to stop drilling and log the $12\frac{1}{4}''$ section. It was estimated that 3 m (10 ft) TVD of shale had been penetrated and, with a 2–3° relative bed dip in the plane of the well, a further 61 m (200 ft) of shale would be drilled before the base Beryl sand was re-entered. This was considered an acceptable drilling risk and the decision was made to drill ahead rather than make a short sidetrack. The Beryl sand was re-entered as prognosed and the shale was cased off. The errors in prognosis were within the anticipated range. However, because the heel of the well was positioned at the edge of the horizontal well fairway, no provision was made for the base reservoir being shallow. This was a risk considered worth taking in order to achieve a horizontal section that would avoid the graben identified on the VSP.

Horizontal hole

Before drilling the $8\frac{1}{2}''$ horizontal hole section a detailed small scale (1:1, 4 cm = 30 m (100 ft)) working cross-section was constructed which combined the data from the build section with the faults interpreted from the VSP and extrapolated using the trend data interpreted from edge maps. This was used to plot the course of the well, compare with prognosis and determine corrective action to achieve the horizontal target elevation. It served as a focal point for team discussion and later to assist in determination of perforation strategy. The post-drill version of this cross-section is shown in Fig. 13.

The $8\frac{1}{2}''$ hole section was started at an elevation of 2779 m (9117 ft) TVDSS, 4.6 m (15 ft) higher than the mid-target of 2783 m (9132 ft) TVDSS. The well was drilled at a high rate of penetration, often in excess of 30 m hr^{-1} (100 ft hr^{-1}). A variable gauge stabilizer was used as part of the drill string to attempt to control bit elevation without having to trip. This tool failed and the hole did not descend to the required elevation. With 610 m (2000 ft) of excellent quality Units A and B reservoir drilled, and the well elevation at 2777 m (9112 ft) TVDSS, the hole again built beyond 90°. The decision was taken to change the bottom hole assembly to attempt to reduce (drop) angle. While tripping out of hole the bottom hole assembly became differentially stuck within the Beryl

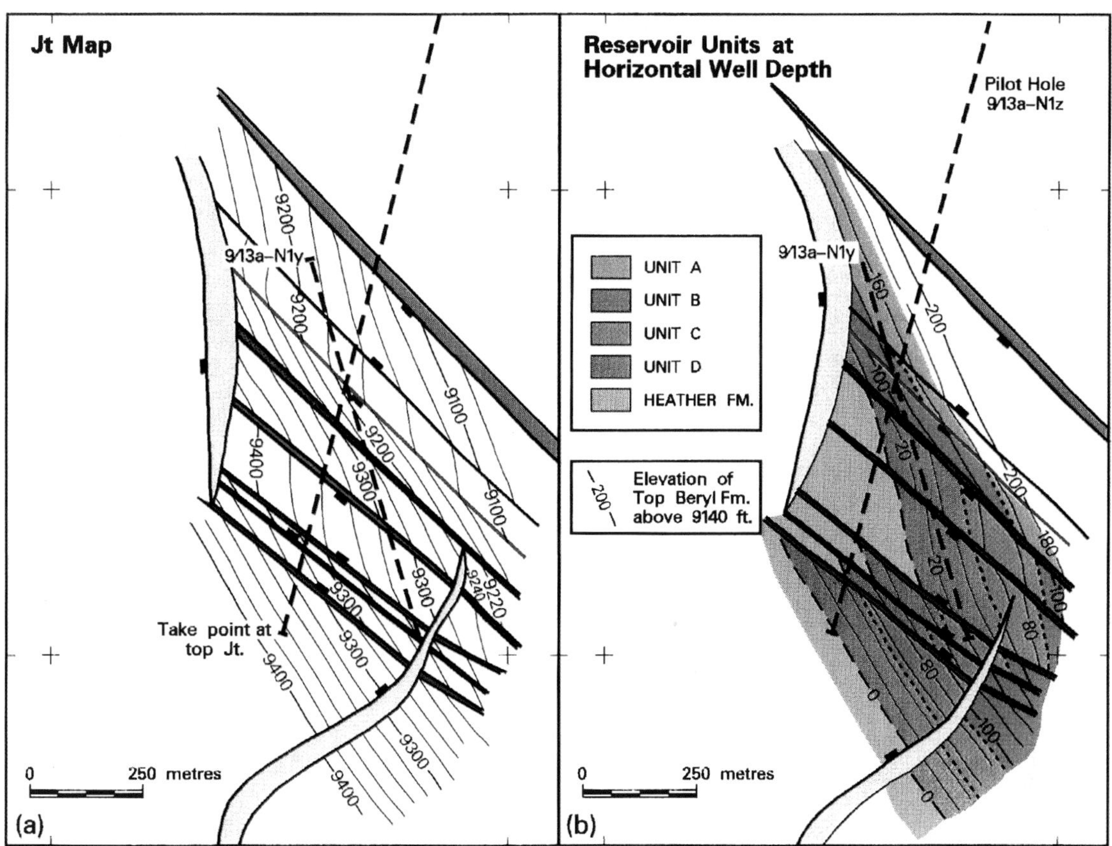

Fig. 12. (**a**) Post pilot well Jt map. Fault pattern constructed using fault trend from 3D seismic edge maps and faults identified on VSP. (**b**) Post pilot well map of reservoir units at horizontal well depth. Indicates units the well would penetrate at the horizontal well depth.

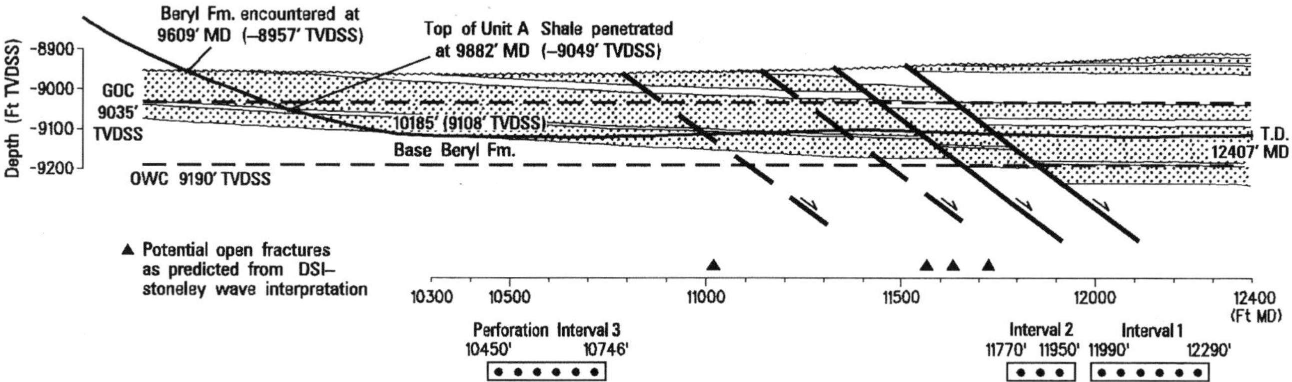

Fig. 13. Post drill cross-section along N1y well path. In three out of four cases, the VSP fault position coincided with potential open fractures/faults predicted from the DSI Stoneley Wave interpretation.

Formation. The mud weight was reduced and the drill string jarred free with considerable overpull.

Sufficient Unit A and B sand had been drilled to achieve the desired well productivity albeit at what was regarded at the time to be a sub-optimal elevation. Moreover, it was unlikely that the elevation could be dropped to the target elevation within Unit B. There were indications that the well was nearing the base of Unit C and there was the prospect of having to drill 91 m (300 ft) of shale before reaching the Unit D sand. The Unit C shale required a high mud weight for control, increasing the risk of differential sticking. The loss in recovery from not penetrating the Unit D sand had already been estimated at less than 10% of the overall recovery. The $8\frac{1}{2}''$ hole was successfully logged and cased with $5\frac{1}{2}''$ liner. A composite log summarizing the well results is shown in Fig. 14.

Perforating

The perforating philosophy was to perforate selectively using coiled tubing in order to avoid contribution from parts of the horizontal section that were either too high or too low in elevation or close to fault zones, and which would risk early gas or water production. Coiled tubing perforating was selected to avoid having to kill the well which would risk formation damage and reduce well productivity.

The strategy was to perforate 238 m (780 ft) of sand in three perforating runs, run a production logging tool, and if the measured well PI was unacceptably low perforate up to two additional intervals. In practice, 165 m (540 ft) of sand was opened up before guns left down-hole precluded more perforating runs. Unit B was perforated at the toe and Unit A at the

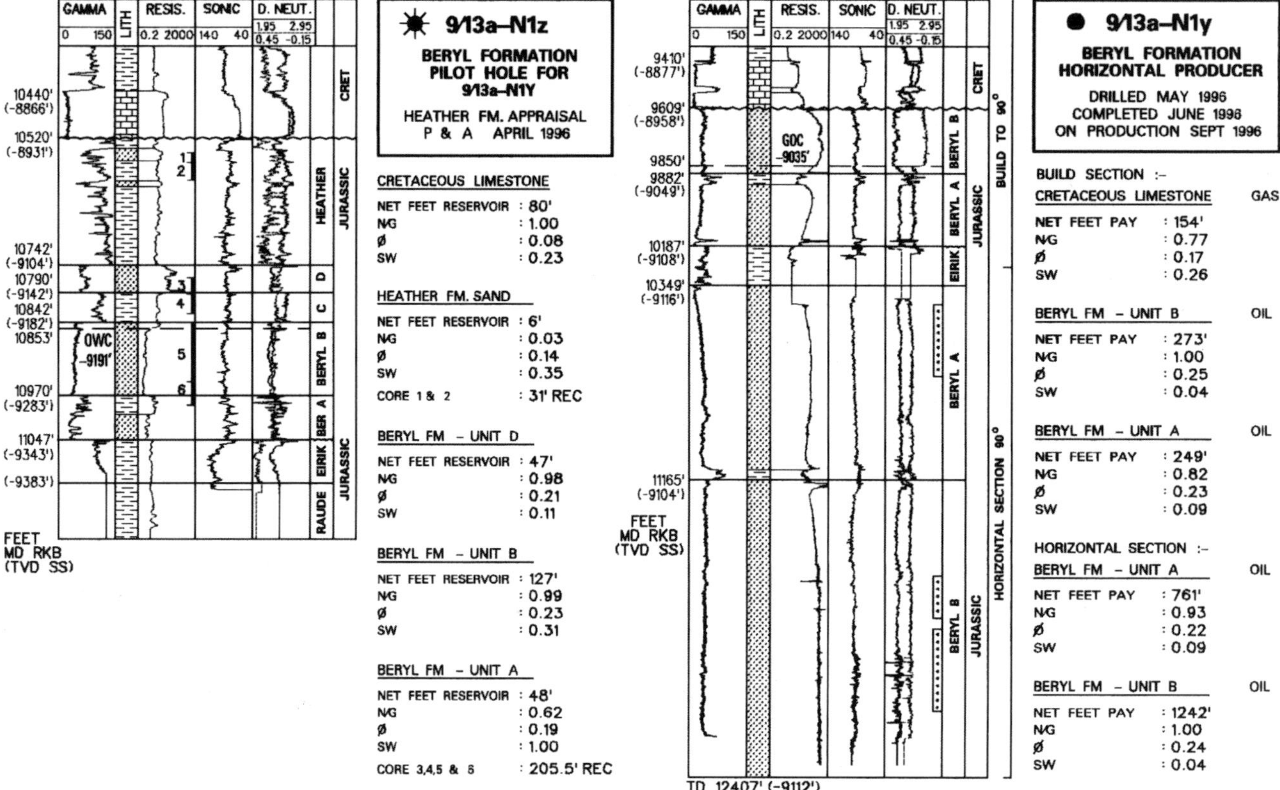

Fig. 14. 9/13a-N1z and N1y petrophysical evaluation.

heel of the well where the elevation was closest to target and where shales provided vertical barriers to the gas–oil contact (GOC.)

The horizontal well VSP in conjunction with Stoneley Wave analysis of the Schlumberger DSI log was used to avoid perforating potential fault zones. The interpretation of the horizontal well VSP was complex and produced less reliable results than the pilot hole VSP. However, in three out of four cases the VSP fault position coincided with potential open fractures/faults predicted from the DSI Stoneley wave interpretation (Fig. 15).

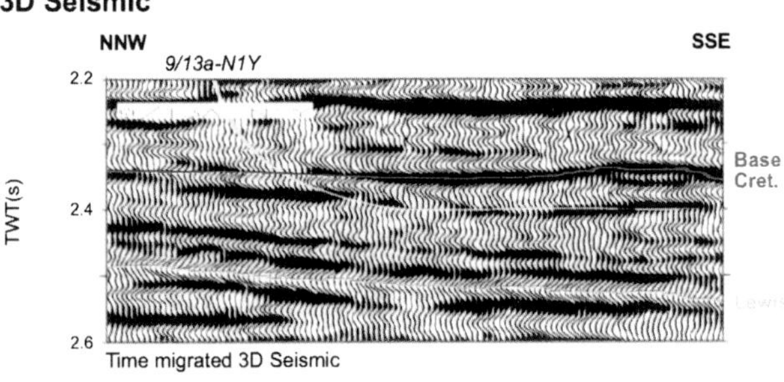

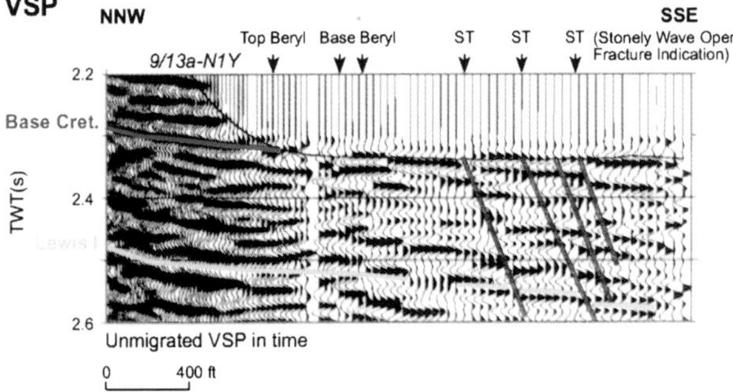

Fig. 15. Comparison of horizontal well VSP and 3D seismic data. The processing and interpretation of the horizontal well VSP close to the borehole was complex and produced less reliable results than the pilot hole VSP. Interpretation of deeper events was more reliable and faults were extrapolated up to the borehole.

Well performance

Upon completion, the well tested at 3174 BOPD, with a gas:oil ratio (GOR) of 1036 SCF STB^{-1} and zero water production. At this rate the drawdown measured above top perforations was 4 psi, indicating a PI of 774 STB D^{-1} psi^{-1}, higher than anticipated.

N1y was completed in June 1996 and tied back to the Beryl Alpha as one of two Phase 1 producing wells. First oil was achieved in September 1996 at a target oil rate of 7000 STB D^{-1}. At this rate the effective PI of the well was in the order of 400–500 STB D^{-1} psi^{-1} as a result of the frictional pressure drop associated with the perforating guns left in the hole.

The reservoir simulation model was used to match the observed well performance through to April 1997 and to establish the optimum production rate. The recorded wellhead pressure at the subsea tree and the riser pressure upstream of the choke on the Beryl Alpha riser access tower indicated a decline in reservoir pressure of the order of 30 psi in 8 months of continuous production compared to the predicted decline of 100 psi. This difference was significant, indicating a much larger aquifer than had previously been assumed. As a result, N1y production was increased to 10 000 STB D^{-1} in May 1997, and the horizontal placement of the well, although high to original target, is now considered to be optimal. Cumulative production as of end July 1997 was 2.4×10^6 STB oil, 2.8×10^9 SCF gas and no water.

Future plans

The performance of N1y has exceeded expectations. Two more horizontal producers are still planned as originally outlined in the Phase 1 DPD. The planning of the second horizontal producer (BP2) is now complete and the well is scheduled to spud at the end of 1997. BP2 is even more ambitious than N1y. It will be a longer step out to the south of N1y. The horizontal section is planned to be in excess of 914 m (3000 ft) penetrating a number of fault terraces.

Conclusions

The 9/13a-N1y well is a very successful horizontal production well. 3D visualization was used for detailed well design and provided an excellent tool for risk management and contingency planning. A well planning methodology was developed which defined 'fairways' for the pilot and horizontal wells and ensured that the basic well design allowed for a wide range of horizontal well trajectories. A VSP was run in the pilot hole to image top and base reservoir along the planned horizontal well path. The VSP provided higher resolution data than the 3D seismic data and enabled detailed reservoir mapping to optimize the horizontal well location.

The successful drilling of the well is considered to be largely as a result of the extensive multi-disciplinary contingency planning that resulted from the well planning stage. Possible scenarios were identified, built into decision trees, and the impact of deviations from the base design quantified. This process helped to manage risk and provided clear guidelines to facilitate the rapid and effective decision making that was necessary during drilling operations.

The authors would like to thank the following for their contribution to the well planning: S. Hayes and L. Smith (Reservoir Management Ltd); K. Dodds and S. Jackson (Schlumberger) and P. Oakes (Halliburton). We would also like to thank the DTI and Nevis partners, Amerada Hess Ltd, Enterprise Oil Ltd, British Gas North Sea Holdings and OMV UK Ltd, for their contribution and continued support to the Nevis South project. Thanks also to Derek Horne and Mary Cruikshank who drafted the figures and to our colleagues at Mobil for their input to this paper.

References

BECKLY, A., DODD, C. & LOS, A. 1993. The Bruce Field. *In*: PARKER, J. R. (ed.) *Petroleum Geology of Northwest Europe: Proceedings of the 4th Conference*. Geological Society, London, 1453–1463.

DEEGAN, C. E. & SCULL, B. J. 1977. *A standard lithostratigraphic nomenclature for the Central and Northern North Sea*. Institute of Geological Sciences Report **77/25**.

KNUTSON, C. A. & MUNRO, I. C. 1991. The Beryl Field, Block 9/13, UK North Sea. *In*: ABBOTTS, I. L. (ed.) *United Kingdom Oil and Gas Fields, 25 Years Commerative Volume*. Geological Society, London, Memoirs, **14**, 33–42.

ROBERTSON, G. 1993. The Beryl Field: geological evolution and reservoir behaviour. *In*: PARKER, J. R. (ed.) *Petroleum Geology of Northwest Europe: Proceedings of the 4th Conference*. Geological Society, London, 1491–1502.

Tern Field development: a marriage of new technologies for business benefit

R. C. BLACK, H. J. POELEN, M. J. ROBERTS and S. E. RODDY

Tern/Hudson Development Team, Northern Business Unit, Shell UK Exploration and Production, Seafield House, Aberdeen, UK

Abstract: The Tern Field, in the Northern North Sea, started production in 1989 and until 1995 was subject to conventional development, surface facilities improvements matching subsurface development priorities, and production. The principal Lower Ness/Etive reservoir was the focus of early development; production from the poorer quality Rannoch and Upper Ness reservoirs increasingly lagged behind. Development of sub-economic Triassic oil sands below, and small Brent satellite accumulations around the field, were not addressed. Since 1995 an 'asset management' approach to the Tern area, focused on maximizing full-field life value of the combined surface and subsurface assets has been adopted. Appropriate development of all potential hydrocarbon streams available to the Tern platform has been prioritized, and technology drivers to improve profitability of all streams have been aggressively pursued. In anticipation of rapid watering-out of Lower Ness/Etive reservoir, this wider development strategy incorporates the integration new technology in reservoir definition and exploitation to ensure continuing profitability in the Tern Field while maximizing reserves appreciation and development.

The strategy encompasses the poorer Brent and Triassic reservoir formations, several 'near facilities potential' accumulations, third-party development volumes. Reservoir definition methodologies comprise seismic inversion, bodymapping and time-lapse work, while modelling integrates seismic, geological and dynamic reservoir simulation technologies.

Exploitation methods comprise horizontal development within 15 ft thick sands, and more recently multilateral wells across Brent and Triassic objectives. These methods will lead to fundamentally improved opportunities to enhance profitability. Further plans to integrate extended-reach drilling and concurrent platform activities will enhance efficiency/effectiveness of the Tern area development. This paper illustrates the successful marriage of several technologies to the continuing benefit of a most successful field development.

The Tern Field was discovered in 1975 by Well 210/25a-1 (Fig. 1). Productive reservoir-quality sandstones were found in the Middle Jurassic Brent Group; unproductive, less abundant oil-bearing sandstones were also established in the underlying Triassic Cormorant formation (Van Panhuys-Sigler *et al.* 1971). The Tern–Eider horst is an elongate NE–SW (Caledonide) trending structure, delimited by arcuate NNW–SSE trending scissor-type faults into a number of lozenge-shaped pressure/accumulation cells, of which the Tern Field is the most southerly. The Field is bounded by a major NE–SW trending fault (>500 m throw) on its northern boundary, by an arcuate fault of variable throw to the east, and is dip closed to the southwest (Fig. 2).

First production from Tern Field was in 1989. Development is effected by down-dip water injection and crestal evacuation. The field contains an estimated 631×10^6 STB in the Brent Group; ultimate recovery is estimated as 277×10^6 STB from this undersaturated reservoir. Table 1 indicates the split of reserves and estimated recovery factor per reservoir member.

Early well and production data indicated that the permeability–thickness contrast between the better quality Lower

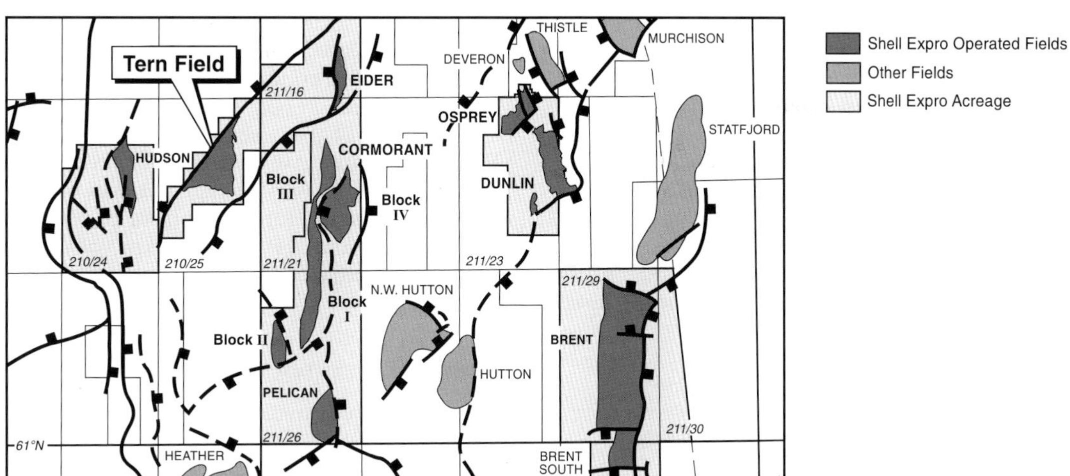

Fig. 1. The Tern Field in the Northern North Sea.

BLACK, R. C., POELEN, H. J., ROBERTS, M. J. & RODDY, S. E. 1999. Tern field development: a marriage of new technologies for business benefit. *In*: FLEET, A. J. & BOLDY, S. A. R. (eds) *Petroleum Geology of Northwest Europe: Proceedings of the 5th Conference*, 1063–1073. © Petroleum Geology '86 Ltd. Published by the Geological Society, London.

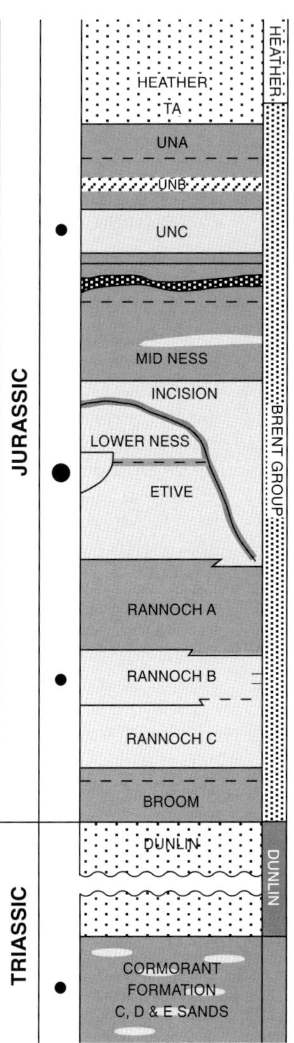

Fig. 2. Tern Field – Structure Map at Top Brent.

Ness/Etive principal reservoir and the over- and underlying Upper Ness and Rannoch formations was much greater than had been previously interpreted. As a result, development efforts between 1990 and 1994 were concentrated on the better-than-anticipated Etive/Lower Ness formations, resulting in acceleration of the oil production profile and an enhanced economic performance from the field in a period of relatively low oil price. As full development of the Lower Ness/Etive reservoir was approaching in early 1995, it became apparent that cost effective and efficient strategies were going to be required to develop the poorer quality reservoirs of the Tern Field, the development of which lagged behind (Fig. 3).

In tandem with this challenge, the fundamental relationship between surface and subsurface assets was addressed. Historically, surface facilities were constructed to effect the anticipated production profile from a defined subsurface asset (the field). The existence of such surface facilities on this historic basis poses a major business challenge with regard to continuing to optimize the hydrocarbon return. The existing facility can be utilized to develop, profitably oil accumulations previously perceived as uneconomic. Such accumulations constitute a 'near facilities potential' (NFP) around any mature facility with ullage in oil, gas, water, gross or drilling capacity capabilities. The period 1995–98 has seen several NFP opportunities being progressed.

The success of the 'asset development' strategy in the Tern Field area is principally ascribed to three factors: (1) understanding detailed reservoir characteristics of both in-field and NFP opportunities; (2) development of reservoir description technologies; and (3) development of appropriate well engineering technologies.

Table 1. Reservoir split of ultimate recovery reserves, Tern Field

Formation	STOIIP ($\times 10^6$ STB)	Recovery Factor (%)	UR reserves $\times 10^6$ STBOE
Tarbert	11	15	1.6
Upper Ness	76	20	15
Etive/Lower Ness	387	55	213
Rannoch	139	21	29
Broom	18	21	4

Developed Brent reservoir formations

In the Tern Field area, the Broom Formation at the base of the Brent Group is predominantly calcite cemented. Due to the patchy and unpredictable nature of this cementation, the member is usually not recognized as reservoir rock, other than on an opportunity basis. The Tarbert Formation at the top of the Brent Group is similarly rarely present on the Tern structure, and is developed only on an opportunity basis. Developed reservoirs are the Lower Ness/Etive, the Upper Ness and the Rannoch.

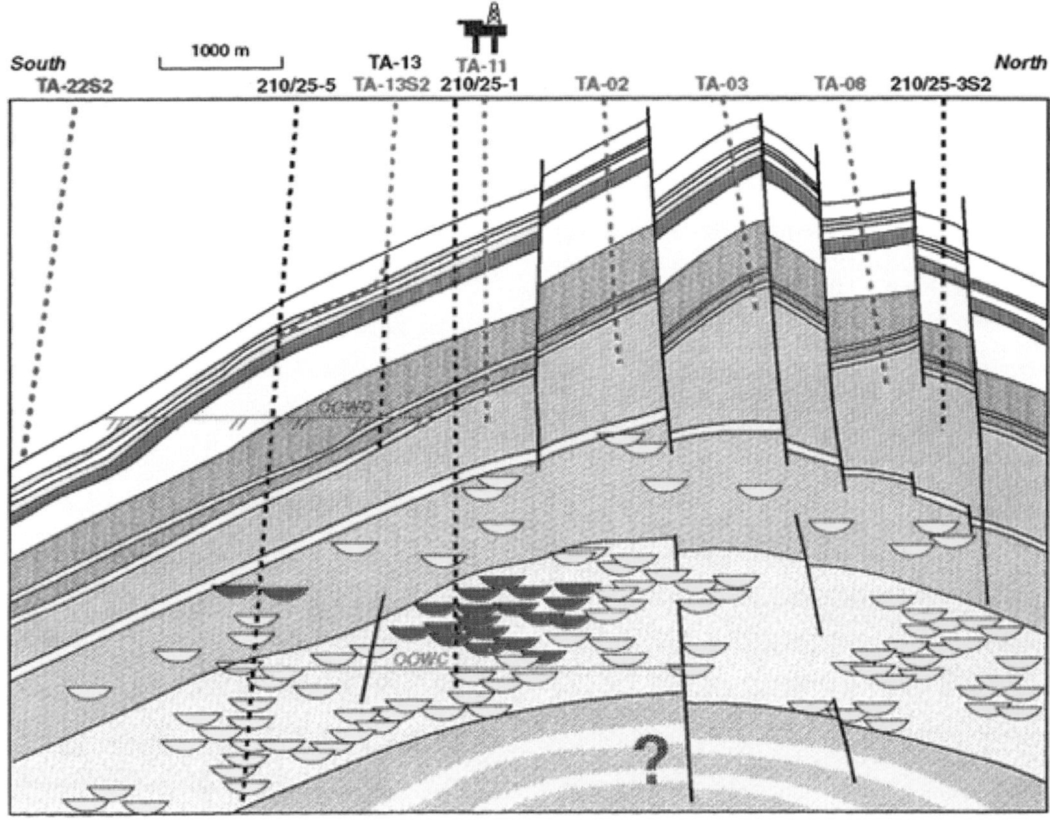

Fig. 3. Cross-section A–A′ of Tern Field (see Fig. 2 for location).

Etive/Lower Ness formations

As in many Northern North Sea fields the principal productive reservoir members are the thick high net/gross multi-Darcy upper shoreface/foreshore aggradational sands of the Etive Formation. In Tern, Etive reservoir thickness averages 80 m, thins to the east and south and is crestally eroded to the north. Recent well results have demonstrated very low residual oil saturations in the Etive, opening up further development opportunities in areas by-passed by either structural closure (e.g. attic locations) or as a result of fault geometries and juxtaposition. The challenge for further Etive development (where primary development is essentially complete), is to define and develop such by-passed opportunities. It has recently been demonstrated that a major structural closure element to the Etive in the Tern Field is realized by a Lower

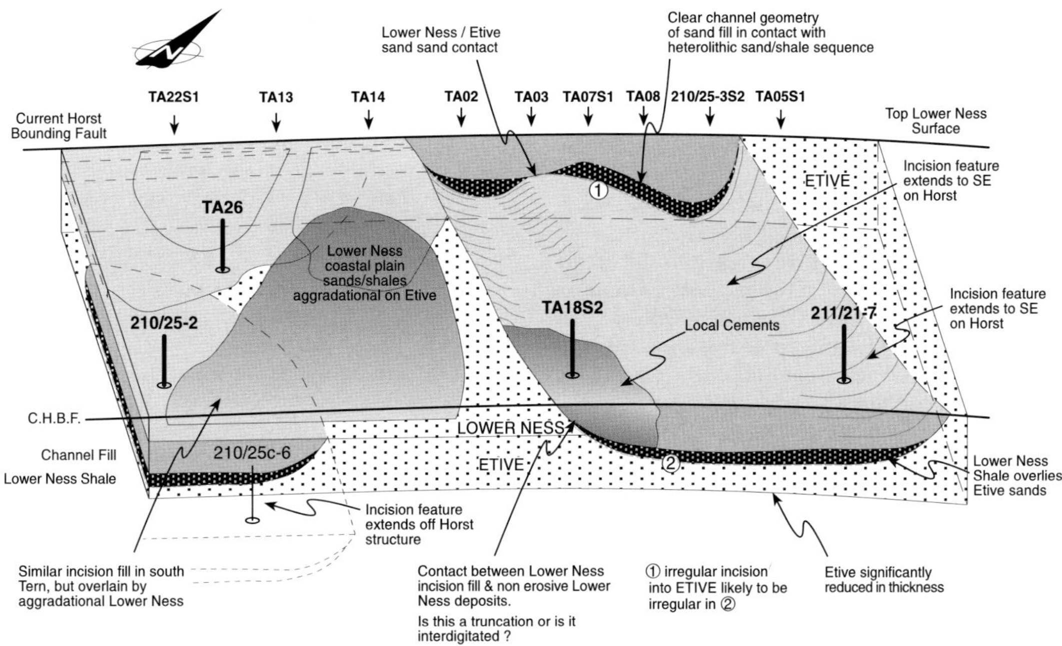

Fig. 4. Lower Ness incised valley fill in Etive Formation substrate.

Ness Formation incised channel-fill deposit in the northeast of the field, with a NNW–SSE channel complex axis orientation.

The Lower Ness has been the least understood of the reservoir formations in Tern, and the recent identification of the scale and impact of a Lower Ness incised channel-fill facies on both Lower Ness development and indirectly, Etive and Rannoch reservoir development, has been significant (Fig. 4). Traditionally the detailed definition of the base of the Lower Ness Formation has been ambiguous due to the lithologically constrained nature of the boundary definition (Cannon *et al.* 1992). Where the base contact lithology is a coal or related shale this ambiguity is minimal; where sand juxtaposition pertains there is greater ambiguity.

The Lower Ness consists principally of metre-scale interbedded sands and shales interpreted to be deposited in a flood plain environment in the lee of the Etive foreshore–shoreface system (Livera & Calive 1990). The reservoir varies in thickness from some 20 m thick in the south of Tern Field through a thinned central area of the field, to *c.* 20 m thick in the core of the channel facies.

The succession is aggradational, and its down-cutting relationship into the underlying Etive substrate gives rise to issues of vertical permeability restriction in Lower Ness (and underlying Etive) development, lateral permeability connection between Etive and adjacent Lower Ness channel sands, and small-scale lateral stratigraphic trapping of remnant oil within Lower Ness channel complexes. Development opportunities identified within the Lower Ness are based upon these new relationships, identified through detailed 3D geological modelling, supplemented by a review of well performance data in the field.

Rannoch Formation

Below the principal Lower Ness/Etive reservoirs are the poorer quality sands of the Rannoch Formation. Some 25–35 m thick, the Rannoch in Tern has three subdivisions. The lowermost Rannoch C Member comprises a lower shoreface/distal lower shoreface facies, shaley in the north of the field and slowly improving in quality southwards, but does not greatly contribute to development. The Rannoch B reservoir is the principal target for Rannoch development. Although inferior in quality to Etive sands, those of the Rannoch B are homogeneous with little K_v/K_h contrast and negligible cement. Stratigraphically the Rannoch B is anomalous, disrupting the uniform transition from the Rannoch C lower to Rannoch A upper shoreface facies. Recent work interprets this member as a shoreface sequence associated with a local regression (Scott 1992). This excellent quality facies thins from 20 m in the southwest of the field, to 10 m in the north, and represents a challenging development target.

The relationship between Rannoch B and A members is significant for development of the Rannoch Formation. Gravity drainage of oil from the underlying Rannoch into the highly developed Etive reservoir is a potentially significant mechanism for effecting Rannoch drainage via Etive completions. This process is controlled by the effectiveness of the Rannoch A to seal in the vertical direction. Factors contributing to seal are the location, extent and frequency of occurrence of calcareous cements and micaceous lenses in proximity to the Rannoch/Etive interface. Modelling both cement and micaceous lens distribution is key to understanding where adequate drainage of the Rannoch is being effected via Etive perforations, and where alternative means of Rannoch development are required. Conversely there is significant risk to development in the Rannoch B, in areas where sealing potential is low, since downward water coning from the more developed and swept overlying Lower Ness/Etive may result in premature water cutting of Rannoch B producers.

Upper Ness Formation

The Upper Ness Formation is subdivided into a continuous sandy facies the Upper Ness C, an overlying shaley Upper Ness B, and a poorly characterized stringer sand member, the Upper Ness A. Only the Upper Ness C is currently considered economically developable. It is interpreted as an originally fluviatile deposit reworked in a mouthbar/shoreface environment. Several variable thickness but laterally extensive sands are separated by 5–8 m thick shale layers, and more importantly by an extensive cement horizon, which subdivides the Upper Ness C2 and C3 sands. The Upper Ness C sands are themselves only some 3–8 m thick, providing challenging development drilling targets.

A constraint to effective development of the Upper Ness reservoir is the potential for compartmentalization caused by small scale faulting in the field. In the down-flank areas of Tern, horizontal well developments in 1994/95 (Wells TA 13 and TA 15) illustrated a directionally variable impact of this effect on production, albeit with generally adequate aquifer support (Fig. 2). Further north in Tern, towards the more faulted crest and upper flanks of the field, faulting is more intense and the likelihood of standalone economic development of these reservoirs is at substantially more risk because of increased compartmentalization.

Undeveloped potential reservoir formations

Triassic Cormorant Formation

The Triassic Cormorant Formation underlying the Brent reservoirs of the Tern Field have been known to contain oil since the first exploration well was drilled in 1985. Well tests were carried out in five Triassic exploration/appraisal wells between 1985 and 1989, without producing Triassic oil to surface.

The Triassic sandstones in the Tern area were deposited in an arid fluviatile environment, interpreted as very early syn-Viking Graben continental rift fill deposits. The succession consists of some 500 m of ephemeral fluvial and flood plain sediments; a mix of channel and sheet flood sandstones within flood-plain siltstones and mudstones. The nature of their deposition does not facilitate detailed correlation, and indicates that the degree of connectivity between reservoir entities is likely to be low. Previous attempts to define economic development options have foundered on the necessarily high risking applied to the geostatistical methodologies employed to target development wells.

As the economic margin on Brent reservoir development reduced with time, and as low cost Triassic deepening opportunities matured, Triassic reservoir potential needed to be re-addressed in the context of new reservoir definition and exploitation technologies, and in the context of mature Tern Field development economic parameters.

Tern east, north & south Brent Group accumulations

As the Tern and adjacent Eider fields were developed on the Tern–Eider horst, several small Brent Group accumulations were identified between the fields and had, between 1985 and 1990 been periodically addressed by drilling. This activity showed oil presence, limited oil columns, and a stair-step pressure regime compartmentalized between the two fields. (Fig. 5)

The potential for hydrocarbon charge was identified as a risk in the area. A focused effort in new 3D seismic acquisition and interpretation, in geochemical modelling and in appraisal drilling into the near-Tern western area between the fields has indicated that there is potential commensurate with other projects in the Tern and Eider fields. Exploration drilling of

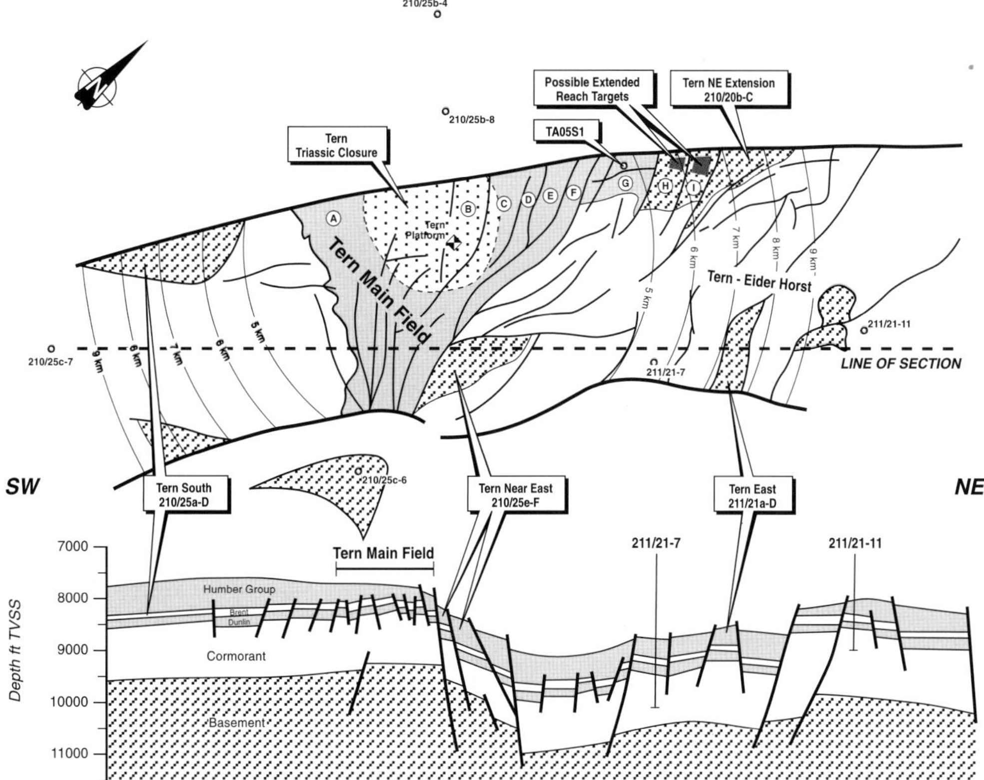

Fig. 5. Tern Field near facilities potential.

these prospects will (in 1997) clarify the stratigraphy of the Brent and Triassic Groups in these prospects. Although initial penetration of these prospects will be by remote wells, it is likely that development will be an integrated activity by extended-reach drilling from the Tern and Eider platforms.

Reservoir definition technologies

Seismic

To assist in ranking of all the development opportunities available to the Tern Asset team, a completely new 3D seismic survey over the entire Tern–Eider horst was planned and shot in 1995. It replaced the previous survey shot in 1980, upon which most of the development drilling was based. The new survey was shot in an E–W direction to allow a general coverage of the NFP prospects in the general area. The grid spacing of 18.75×18.75 m was significantly more dense than the previous 75×25 m. Navigation accuracy and frequency content in the new survey are therefore superior to that of 15 a before. With new, better focused and detailed seismic data to hand, the distribution of reservoir parameters within the traditionally-derived but updated structural framework was a major priority. Three approaches proved to add significant value to both intra-Brent and intra-Triassic definition, clarifying targets for development and better identifying, ranking and managing development risks.

Pseudo-acoustic impedance mapping. The use of reflectivity seismic allows a detailed structural interpretation. However, the reservoir architecture is better revealed by use of pseudo-acoustic impedance seismic data. At no additional time or cost the reflectivity seismic can be transformed to pseudo-acoustic impedance seismic by a 90° phase rotation in the workstation. In Tern Field, the low impedance reservoirs of the Lower Ness–Etive stand out as a well developed, consistent soft impedance loop wedged between the high impedance loops of the Mid Ness shales and the Rannoch. Below that, the expression of the Rannoch–Broom sequence varies from south to north. In the south the Rannoch–Broom has developed a secondary soft loop which disappears northwards. This supports the observation in wells where there is a degradation in reservoir quality towards the north. After calibration, these seismic observations can be used to refine the reservoir architecture of the Rannoch–Broom. The same holds true to a lesser extent in mapping the Tarbert–Upper Ness development (Fig. 6).

Seismic inversion. A further refinement of the quantitative use of seismic data is seismic inversion. In this process the seismic data volume is used in combination with well information and the structural interpretation to generate an impedance (inversion) dataset. These data are directly related to the porosity and hydrocarbon fill of the reservoir. Once the hydrocarbon saturation is established, the porosity can be deduced. This is only possible for seismic data which was recorded prior to production of the field. It contributes to further refinement of the reservoir architecture.

Once porosity distribution has been estimated prior to field production, its impact on impedance variations can be backed out of the seismic data. This allows us to estimate fluctuations in follow-up seismic surveys which are caused by variation of hydrocarbon saturations. Theoretically these effects can be calculated by combination of estimates from dynamic reservoir modelling and petrophysical programmes. A wide variety of techniques is being developed to allow measurement of production effects from seismic (4D seismic). Since the acquisition of a second 3D seismic survey in 1995, a 4D (time lapse) seismic programme has been initiated over Tern to monitor production effects by use of seismic.

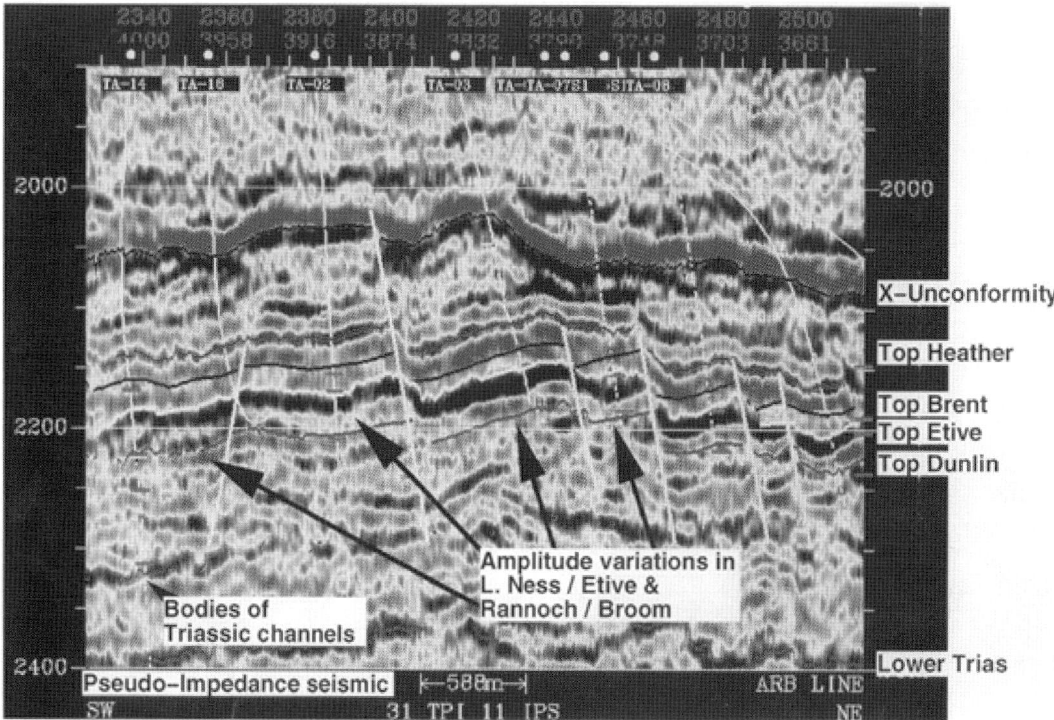

Fig. 6. Pseudo-acoustic impedance.

Seismic bodychecking. The general purpose of 'bodychecking' is to extract 'bodies' (or groups of voxels), which correspond to connected volumes of a specified seismic attribute range. These should in turn correspond to a reservoir volume of a specific parameter range, which can then be used as a basis for volumetric calculations. Moreover, the shape of bodies may reflect depositional features (e.g. channels) and bodies with a flat base can be regarded as direct hydrocarbon indicators (DHI).

'BodyChecking' has been applied to the seismic pseudo-impedance data covering the Tern Field at two potential reservoir levels (The major impact was when the 'bodychecking' technique was applied to the Triassic sub-volume):

- The sub-volume representative of the Brent reservoirs: in the Brent reservoir sequence it has defined connected bodies in the Etive sequence, in this way adding to the refinement of the intra-Brent reservoir architecture.
- The sub-volume containing Triassic channels (Fig. 7): irregularly shaped bodies of low impedance were characterized. These bodies could be correlated with well penetrations of the high porosity channel facies complexes in the potential Triassic reservoir. This resulted in a more deterministic description of the channel complex which now forms the target for appraisal and development.

The latter point is critical for the realization of value to the Tern Asset. Previously the probabilistic approach to the Triassic reservoir development had indicated risk factors which prejudiced economic development. By removing the high-level (formation scale) probabilistic approach and replacing it with a deterministic approach, risking could be reduced to a lower level probability envelope (i.e. probability of productive sand within defined channel complexes), and appraisal/development activity could be justified, enabling reserves to be accrued and developed.

Static reservoir description

All static reservoir descriptions of fields operated by Shell in the Northern North Sea are now based on the Shell proprietary 3D static reservoir modelling system 'GEOCAP' (**GEO**logical **C**omputer **A**pplications **P**ortfolio). The modelling system utilizes sequence stratigraphic principles and correlations to set facies distributions within a hierarchical correlation and 3D spatial framework (Taylor 1996). Rapid correlation and spatial distribution updating is an essential feature of such a system, to allow iterative testing of alternative geological realizations and development scenarios against dynamic model history matching and predictions. (Fig. 8)

The facility which enables GEOCAP to combine regional, wireline log, and core scale data into a probabilistically constrained but defined set of interpretations is highly effective iterations towards 'most likely' geological realizations in the interwell and extrapolation-from-well data domains. Calibration of GEOCAP derived facies groups using detailed seismic amplitude analysis is a further useful constraint to the range of feasible realizations.

The consequent reduction of risk by quantitative assessment of previously marginal economic development opportunities, affords real potential to enhance both full-field life ultimate recovery and economic reward from fields such as Tern.

Dynamic reservoir description and simulation

In parallel with developments in seismic and static modelling technology, a new dynamic reservoir modelling system 'MORES' (**MO**dular **RE**servoir **S**imulation) is being used in Shell Northern North Sea fields. This new and more powerful simulator has close interactive links with the GEOCAP modelling system and, of equal importance, can be interactively conditioned at similar scale levels of resolution against the 3D seismic data content for a field.

The degree of integration between the production geosciences and reservoir engineering effected by the use of these reservoir development tools has been greatly enhanced over the past two years in Shell. This has led to better definition of detailed development opportunities, with a greater degree of challenge and risk/reward definition in targeting activities.

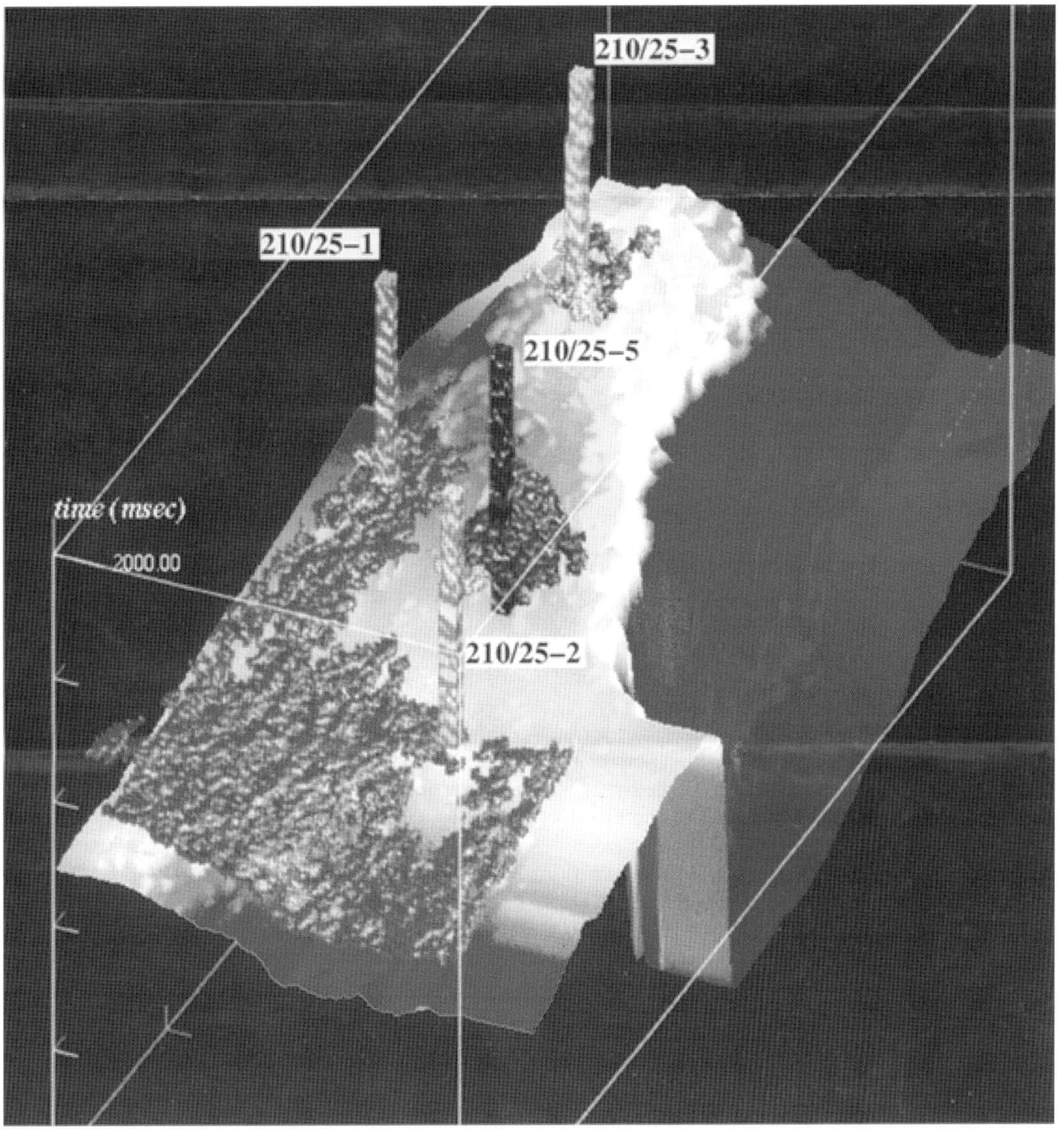

Fig. 7. Seismic bodychecking applied to Triassic 3D volumes, Tern Field.

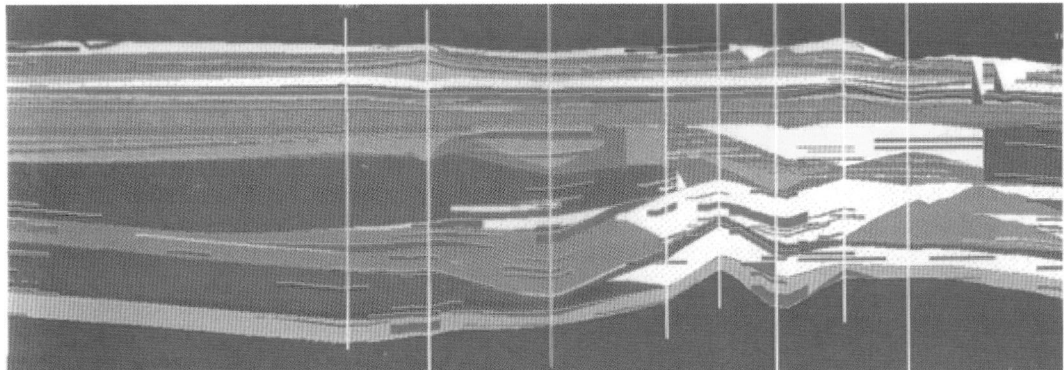

Fig. 8. Example cross-section 2D slice of a GEOCAP realisation of Tern Field.

Well engineering technologies

Better definition and risk reduction of previously marginal development opportunities has been addressed by better seismic, lithofacies and fluid-distribution description and prediction.

In parallel, improvements in both the effectiveness and efficiency of well engineering methods have been complementary in effecting economic reward and mature field development.

Well engineering

There are four main areas where improvements in well engineering technology both benefit from better reservoir definition, and provide challenges for better reservoir definition. These are multilateral drilling and sidetracking, extended-reach drilling, concurrent-to-rig activities, and coiled-tubing sidetracking.

The prime technology employed to date has been multilateral drilling (Roberts & Tolstyko 1997), the role and interdependence of the other three developing technologies are summarized below, prior to describing the success of the multilateral approach in Tern.

Extended-reach drilling, rig concurrency and coiled-tubing sidetracking. The future development of Brent reservoir satellites in the Tern asset area was addressed by comparing two approaches: satellite developments connected to the platform by subsea pipelines, and drilling of extended reach wells from the Tern platform. Because of the economic conditions prevailing in 1996/97, the volumes of oil, and the locations of the Tern North and East prospects, extended reach drilling is the preferred option. This decision is under continued review as it is primarily an economic one.

However, two factors in this evaluation are of interest. Currently prospects up to 8 km laterally away from the Tern platform are technically feasible to drill with essentially existing equipment at acceptable risk levels. This has extended the previously estimated drilling radius of 5 km, and may indicate that prospects 10 km from existing facilities can be developed extended reach drilling in the future. An apparent weakness of extended-reach drilling, extensive time utilization of the drilling rig, has been overcome by the introduction of concurrent activities on platforms. With judicious choice of drilling slots for extended-reach wells, it is generally possible to continue workovers, in-well surveillance and remedial activities concurrent with drilling long upper sections of extended-reach wells. The opportunity is also created for use of self-contained coiled-tubing units to carry out concurrent capital activities.

The development of drilling capabilities using coiled tubing (CT) was pioneered in the early 1990s in the US and Canada in land drilling. In Shell, the pioneering application was in the North Cormorant Field in 1996, where a through-tubing, coiled-tubing drilled sidetrack allowed a small volume of otherwise uneconomic oil to be exploited.

In applications to 'mop-up' small attic or bypassed oil volumes, CT sidetracking from abandoned wells through existing production tubing comes into its own. The activity can be carried out concurrently with platform rig activity (the CT rig has a small footprint). There is no need to pull existing tubing before sidetracking, and existing reach limitations of such sidetracks are already being addressed. Shell has already carried out five CT sidetracks. In the Tern Field applications are planned from 1998, initially addressing Lower Ness/Etive attic oil; future applications in the poorer Upper Ness and Rannoch formations are also envisaged.

Multilateral drilling. Over the past 2–4 years the ability to drill and complete two or more wellbores concurrently in the same well has been successfully developed and applied. Early applications were in shallow US land fields, and the procedure was taken up by several North Sea contractors in 1994/95.

Upper Ness/Rannoch multilateral wells

In Tern Field the development issue was how to develop economically, the two lesser reservoirs on either side of the well-developed Lower Ness/Etive reservoir, while preferably maintaining the field production profile and hence asset value (Roberts & Tolstyko 1997).

The Upper Ness reservoir is thin and liable to compartmentalization by small-scale faulting but is of good quality over the field area. In the primary development (sub-vertical) wells, perforation of the Upper Ness had proven ineffective because of the volumetric contrast with the highly productive Lower Ness/Etive. In 1994/95 two horizontal wells were drilled down-flank in the Upper Reservoir in an early test of geosteering capabilities in such thin sands, and to validate productivity levels from the Upper Ness. These wells demonstrated that in the open flank area the Upper Ness could be successfully developed by geosteered horizontal wells and produce at economic rates. In one well, parallel to the dominant fault trend (NE–SW) no minor faulting was found and over 300 m of oil sands were developed (average 4 m thick). In the second well two minor subseismic offsets were unexpectedly encountered and subsequent geosteering corrections reduced completion length to some 100 m. In the more faulted crestal area of the field, subseismic faulting and lateral drainage areas restricted by faulted compartments were issues of concern.

To address optimized UR reserves, a scheme of pattern-flooding using horizontal wells, with injector and producer pairs per reservoir compartment was envisaged in the early 90s. However, given the well economics and the platform's drilling slot constraints, this approach was clearly impractical and uneconomic.

It was decided to address the economics of drilling for the Upper Ness by combining an Upper Ness horizontal well with another reservoir horizon by multilateral drilling. It was estimated that the cost of developing the Upper Ness as a component of a multilateral well could be reduced to some 60% of the cost of a dedicated well. Water injection was envisaged as being managed by conversion of watered out Lower Ness/Etive subvertical producer wells. A trial of this concept was carried out in 1996 in Well TA 11 (simply by running a plug and converting the well function at surface) and this has proved highly successful.

The Rannoch was addressed as a complementary target reservoir for horizontal drilling, since it was also a marginal standalone reservoir development. The Rannoch reservoir is thick, but of variable quality over the field and has a marked K_v/K_h contrast, impacting effective drainage, particularly when allied to the propensity for vertical gravity influx of water from the (partially) flooded Lower Ness/Etive reservoir above. The prime risk to subvertical Rannoch completions was early water breakthrough via this mechanism.

It was apparent that areas of the Rannoch B sands, overlain by poor quality Rannoch A micaceous/cemented sands and hence protected by a Rannoch A vertical permeability barrier from gravity drainage of overlying Lower Ness/Etive water, could be a prime horizontal well target for development. Low pressure draw-down effected by horizontal drilling, combined with vertical permeability waterflood protection facilitates maximum horizontal drainage radius from Rannoch B oil reserves.

A screening exercise was carried out using existing reservoir models, new seismic and GEOCAP correlation, to find locations which combined likely Rannoch and Upper Ness development targets with the required characteristics in close aerial juxtaposition. Three targets were identified, of which two have been drilled to date and are successfully producing Upper Ness and Rannoch oil at highly economic comingled rates.

The first of these wells supports the integration of new well technology, reservoir definition technologies, and an asset management approach into a strategy for optimal development (Fig. 9). The TA 14 well, drilled in late 1995, was planned to develop both Upper Ness and Rannoch reservoirs by multilateral technology, but overlay an area identified by seismic bodychecking as being fruitful for Triassic oil appraisal and development. In addition it was crestally located with respect to the underlying basement topography below the field. Hence, prior to multilateral Brent reservoir development the well was drilled through the defined seismic 'body' in the Upper Triassic, and to basement via the Lower Triassic. A thin oil column was established in the lowermost Triassic, indicating exploration success. The Upper Triassic 'body' proved

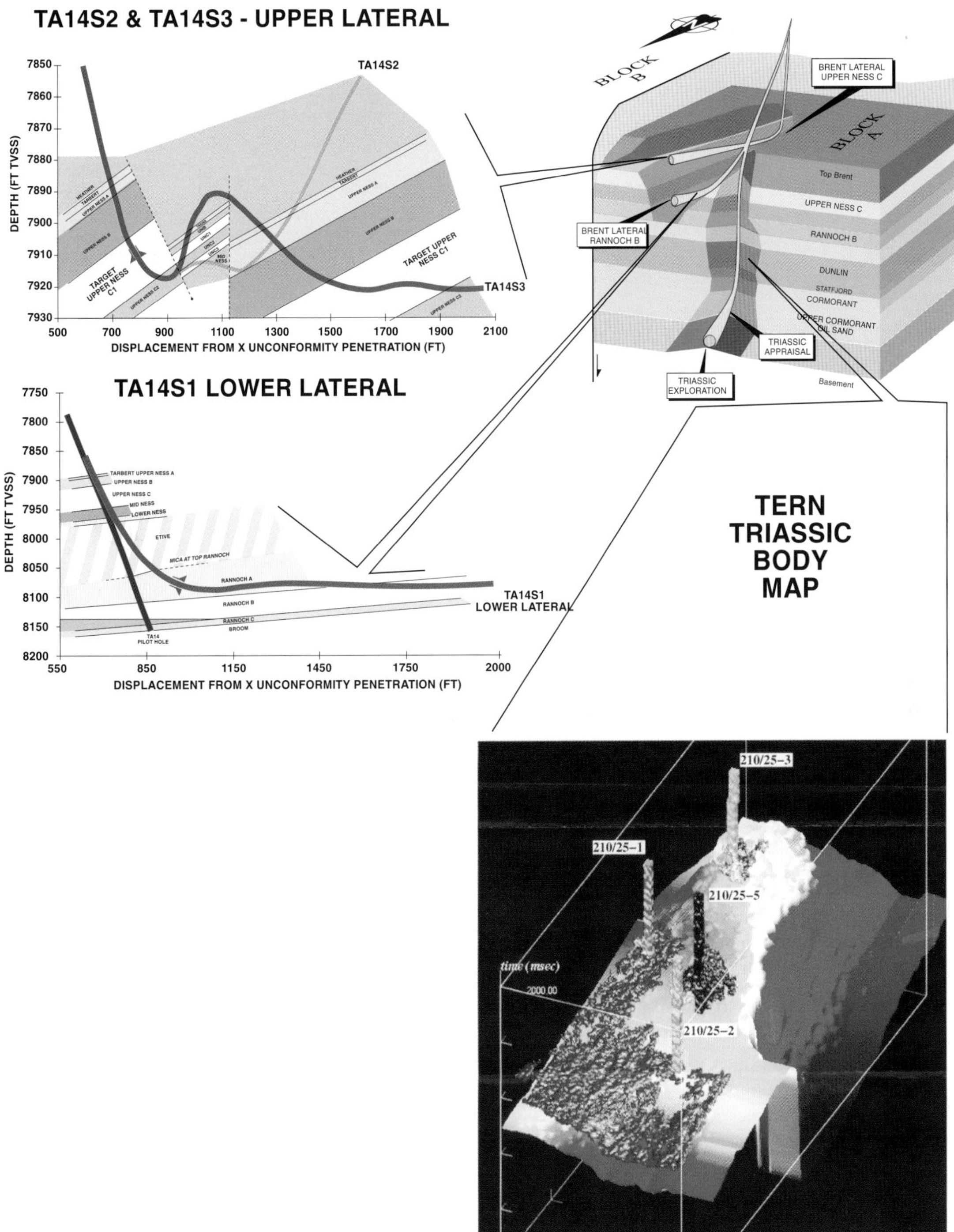

Fig. 9. Tern 14 multipurpose Triassic exploration and appraisal, and Brent Group multilateral well.

to be a complex of interconnected sand units, which was production tested. The production test volume, produced into platform facilities, generated income which paid for all Triassic activities in the well. Some 10×10^6 BBL reserves and 10×10^6 BBL scope for oil recovery in the Upper Triassic were established prior to plugback. Following this success, TA 14 was successfully drilled and completed as a multilateral well.

Development/appraisal multilateral wells

On the basis of the TA 14 Triassic appraisal success, a dedicated Triassic multilateral development/appraisal well is being drilled mid–late 1997 (Fig. 10). Well TA 17 will drill a lower development leg in the seismic sand-complex body, proven to exist between exploration Well 210/25-1 and the TA 14 appraisal location. A second leg will be drilled into an adjoining westerly fault block, through a second seismic body to test reservoir development and oil fill. This well will be geosteered to drill down through the appraisal accumulation down-flank, and then to drill up through the accumulation near the crest. In the event of success, both Triassic legs of the well will be produced together.

Accelerated sidetracking multilateral wells

In addition to candidates for Upper Ness/Rannoch multilateral development, other opportunities for multilateral drilling in Tern Field became apparent; these opportunities may have a more widespread and fundamental impact on North Sea field developments in general.

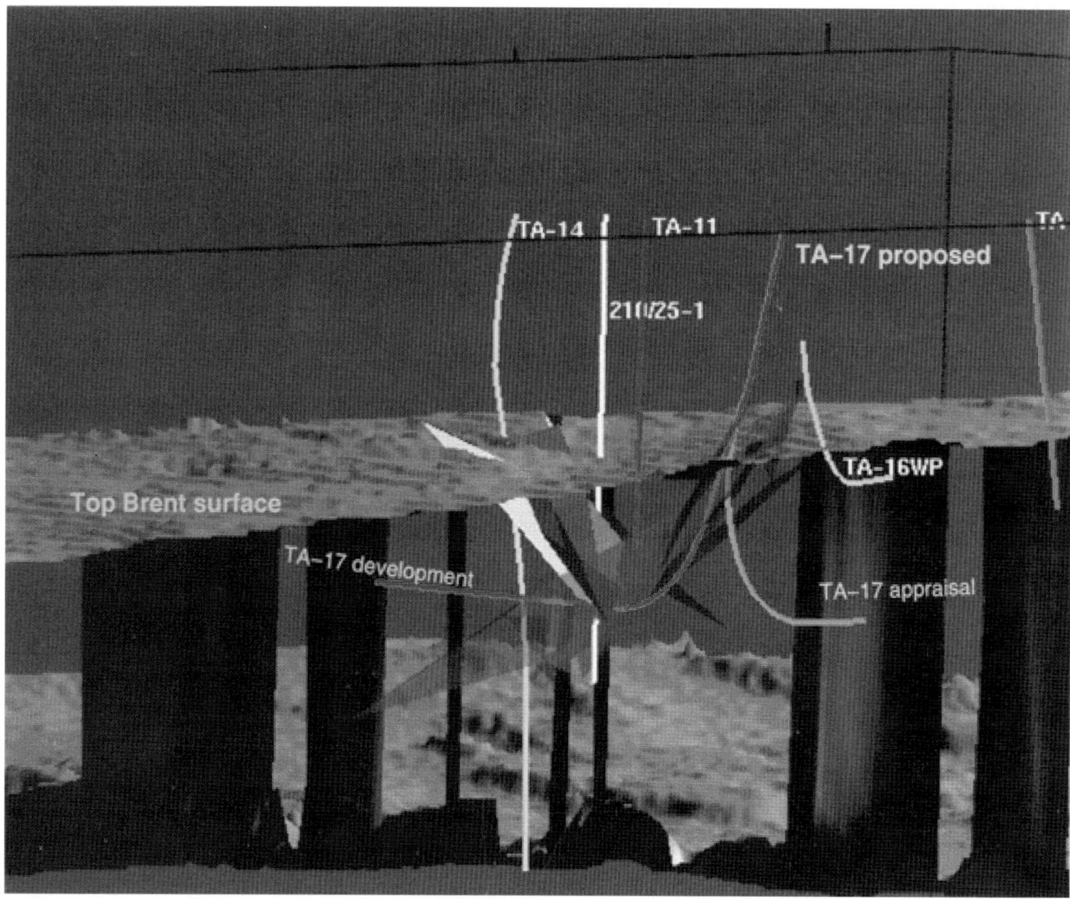

Fig. 10. Tern 17 Triassic multilateral development and appraisal.

In Tern Well TA 19 (Fig. 11), the Lower Ness/Etive reservoir was producing at a steady 40% water-cut. During GEOCAP correlation however, it was noted that the uppermost perforated zone in the Lower Ness was marginal to the incised valley channel fill which trends NNW–SSE in the northern part of the field. This correlation implied that volumes of Lower Ness oil within the body of the channel might be isolated by intra-channel shale baffles from the TA 19 wellbore.

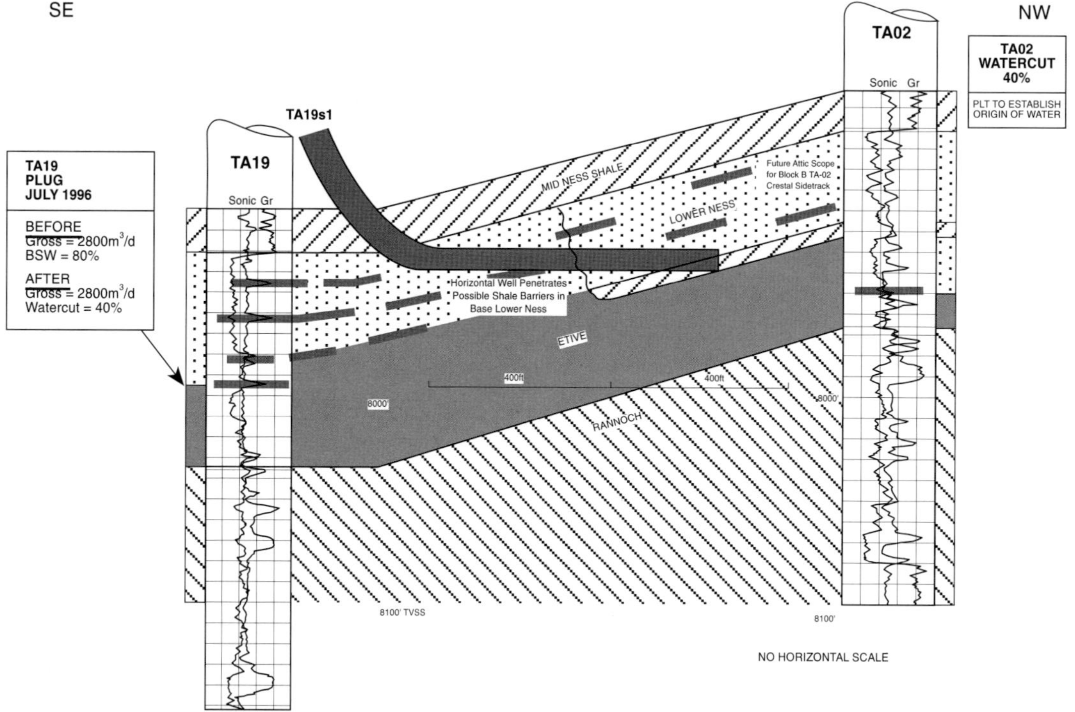

Fig. 11. TA 19 multilateral Lower Ness sidetrack on pre-existing Lower Ness/Etive well.

It was realized that multilateral technology afforded the possibility to sidetrack from the existing TA 19 well into the Lower Ness channel sands, cross-cutting shale barriers and communicating with channel sands, while at the same time not necessitating abandonment of the current wellbore, which would become the lower leg of a multilateral well.

The sidetrack was successfully carried out, the Lower Ness perforations were flowed for several months until water-cut rose in the upper leg of the multilateral, when the lower leg (the original Lower Ness/Etive completion) was additionally opened, and the well then flowed at a significantly higher gross rate, still at 40% watercut. This multilateral sidetracking opportunity has applications over a wide range of field development situations.

Traditionally, in order to conserve UR reserves, it has been necessary to await the onset of very high water-cut levels before a well is abandoned and sidetracked. Thus a trade-off is necessitated between original well UR volumes and deferral of high oil-cut production from a sidetrack location (e.g. in developing attic oil volumes, or where platform drilling slot opportunities are constrained).

With the advent of multilateral sidetracking, it is possible to sidetrack to new locations at much lower original well water-cuts, accelerating new oil volumes. Appropriate management of production volumes after sidetracking in multilateral wells ensures a highly profitable outcome from this technique.

In the future, it would be desirable to be able to drill multilateral coiled-tubing sidetracks from both new and existing wells, without pulling tubing, as a means of optimizing both oil recovery and economic reward from the Tern Field. This is being aggressively addressed (Fig. 12). In the interim each of the reservoir units contributing to the Tern asset development strategy (the Lower Ness/Etive, the Upper Ness, the Rannoch, the Triassic and the NFP accumulations) is being described and defined using a combination of advanced reservoir characterization techniques, and is subsequently being profitably developed to maximum extent using advanced and appropriate well engineering technologies. This approach is designed to accrue the maximum value over the economic lifetime of the Tern asset, and to extend such economic lifetime.

The authors wish to acknowledge the contributions of former Tern asset development team members E. Follows, P. Boerrigter and A. van Schaik to the work detailed above. Graphics were co-ordinated by I. Riley. Permission of Shell (UK) Exploration and Production (Shell Expro) and Esso UK Exploration and Production Ltd to publish this paper is gratefully acknowledged. Shell Expro operates in the UK sector of the North Sea on behalf of Shell and Esso.

References

CANNON, S. J. C., GILES, M. R., WHITIKER, M. F., PLEASE, P. M. & MARTIN, S. V. 1992. A regional reassessment of the Brent Group, UK Sector, North Sea. MORTON, A. C., HAZELDINE, R. S., GILES, M. R. & BROWN, S. (eds) *Geology of the Brent Group*. Geological Society, London, Special Publications, **61**, 81–107.

LIVERA, S. E. & CALIVE, B. P. R. 1990. The sedimentology of the Brent Group – the Cormorant Block IV oilfield. *Journal of Petroleum Geology*, **3**, 367–396.

ROBERTS, M. J. & TOLSTYKO, M. F. 1997. *Multi lateral rewards in Tern Field*. SPE 38496, Offshore Europe Aberdeen, United Kingdom.

SCOTT, E. S. 1992. The palaeoenvironments and dynamics of the Rannoch of the Ranoch Etive nearshore and coastal successions. Brent Group, North North Sea. *In*: MORTON, A. C., HAZELDINE, R. S., GILES, M. R. & BROWN, S. (eds) *Geology of the Brent Group*. Geological Society, London, Special Publications, **61**, 129–148.

TAYLOR, S. R. 1996. *3D Modelling to optimise production at successive stages of field life*. SPE 35501.

VAN PANHUYS-SIGLER, M., BAUMANN, A. & HOLLAND, T. C. 1991. The Tern Field, Block 210/25a, UK North Sea. *In*: ABBOTS, I. L. (ed.) *United Kingdom Oil and Gas Fields, 25 Year Commemorative Volume*. Geological Society, London, Memoir, **14**.

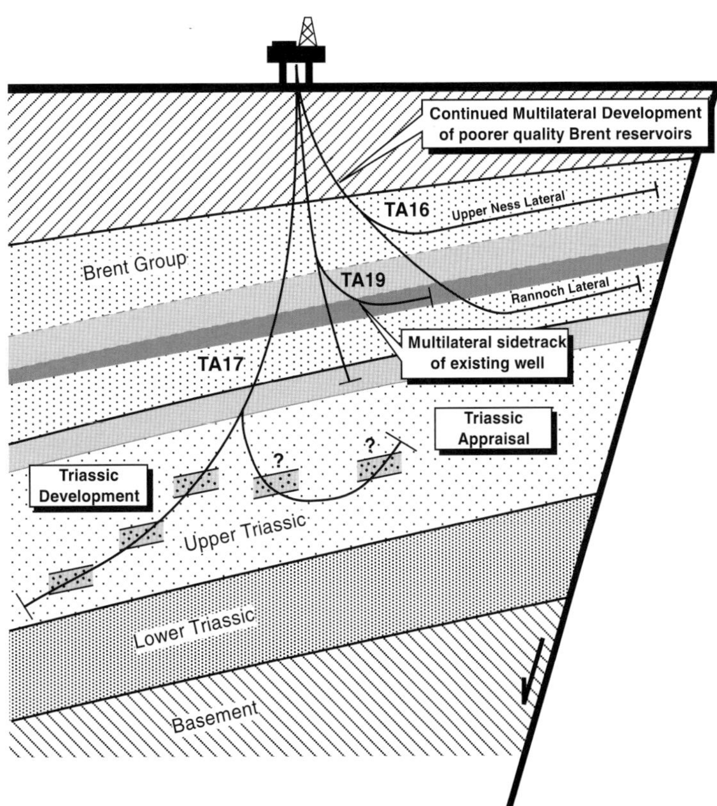

Fig. 12. Cartoon illustrating the well technology applications facilitated by reservoir definition technologies currently being employed in the Tern area.

Integrating sequence stratigraphy in field development and reservoir management – the Telford Field

R. M. SYMS,[1,2] D. F. SAVORY,[3] C. J. WARD,[1,4] C. C. EBDON[5] and A. GRIFFIN[6]

[1] *AMOCO (UK) Exploration & Production Company, Amoco House, West Gate, London W5 1XL, UK*
[2] *Present address: BP Amoco, Dyce, Aberdeen AB21 7PB, UK (e-mail: symsrm@bp.com)*
[3] *Present address: Robertson-Blackwatch Limited, 8 Buckingham Street, London WC2N 6BU, UK*
[4] *Present address: Veba Oil & Gas UK Ltd, Bowater House, 114 Knightsbridge, London SW1X 7LD, UK*
[5] *Present address: AMOCO Production Company, 501 Westlake Park Boulevard, Post Office Box 3092, Houston, Texas 77253–3092, USA*
[6] *Present address: Enterprise Oil plc, Griffin House, 5 Strand, London WC2N 5HU, UK*

Abstract: The Telford Field is located in Quad 15 of the UK North Sea and is reservoired in Late Jurassic shallow marine sandstones of the Piper Formation. The field has been developed with three producer–injector pairs and came on stream at the end of 1996 following a twelve month development programme.

In terms of sequence stratigraphy, the Upper Jurassic Piper Formation reservoir occurs within sequences LJ2 and LJ3 of the Amoco regional framework. In the Telford Field these sequences include a wide variety of facies representing delta-front to delta-margin settings. As a result the reservoir section displays distinct vertical and lateral heterogeneities.

Prior to development a high resolution sequence framework was established comprising seven genetic sequences bounded by maximum flooding surfaces. This framework formed the basis of the reservoir zonation and was integral to the success of the development wells.

The sequence based reservoir zonation was refined following the development drilling into 17 zones which were further enhanced with the aid of k/ϕ plots to form a total of 22 flow units. When applied in the reservoir simulation the sequence stratigraphic model allowed predictions of lateral continuity and extent of transmissibility barriers and baffles. Consequently, waterflood performance could be assessed and a perforation strategy adopted which would delay early water breakthrough whilst optimizing production and ultimate recovery.

By attempting to understand the bounding surfaces of the zones and their internal flow characteristics, we can go some way to predicting reservoir architecture and connectivity and, in theory, reservoir performance.

The Telford Field is located within the Outer Moray Firth in Blocks 15/21a and 15/22 of the United Kingdom Continental Shelf, approximately 170 km northeast of Aberdeen and 9 km south of the Scott Field (Fig. 1). The field comprises four structurally compartmentalized, normally pressured oil and gas accumulations within Upper Jurassic reservoirs of the Piper Formation (*sensu* Richards *et al.* 1993) trapped within an east–west trending tilted fault block (Figs 2 and 3). These accumulations are termed East Telford, West Telford, Central Telford and Marmion (Fig. 2).

Exploitation of the field is by phased development through a sub-sea tie back system to the nearby Scott platform (Jewell & Ward 1997). Phase I of the development, which involves production from the Central Telford and Marmion accumulations, came on stream in October 1996. Phase II will involve the further appraisal and development of the West and East Telford areas and is expected to begin in 1998. Hydrocarbons in place have been determined at between 107 and 126 $\times$ 10^6 STB with associated GIIP of 181 to 211 $\times$ 10^9 SCF, to be recovered over a field life of approximately 9 years at a peak rate of 35 000 BOPD.

The reservoir interval in the area corresponds to the Piper Formation which is locally divided by Richards *et al.* (1993) into two members: a lower member called Pibroch and an upper member called Chanter (Fig. 4). This nomenclature will be used throughout this paper unless stated otherwise.

In the Telford Field, the Piper Formation comprises a complex series of high energy, shallow marine clastic deposits that manifest rapid lateral and vertical variations resulting in significant lithostratigraphic variation (Fig. 5). In Marmion and West Telford three distinct sand units with clear shale breaks are seen, in Central Telford a single, almost entirely sand-prone unit occurs, whilst in the east, two sand-prone units with thin shale breaks are observed. A sequence stratigraphic framework was constructed in order to understand the relationships between these individual lithostratigraphic units, resulting in the identification of seven genetic stratigraphic sequences.

The sequence stratigraphy was based on a regional framework relying on the identification of genetic stratigraphic sequences (Galloway 1989) bound by maximum flooding events and tied to biostratigraphy using graphic correlation techniques (Shaw 1964; Miller 1977). A high resolution sequence framework was constructed prior to development drilling using a limited dataset to identify higher order surfaces, including Exxon style unconformities (Jervey 1988; Posamentier & Vail 1988) and their subsequent modifications (e.g. Posamentier *et al.* 1992; Posamentier & Allen 1993*a*, *b*; Koll *et al.* 1995). A number of authors have highlighted the benefits of using high resolution sequence stratigraphy over conventional lithostratigraphy in reservoir description (e.g. Pulham 1994; Jennete & Riley 1996; Wehr & Brasher 1996).

The sequence stratigraphic model was also used to generate a base reservoir pick, because of poor seismic resolution (Fig. 3). In addition, stacking of the sequence isochore maps allowed prediction of the amount of reservoir erosion that could be expected at the crest of the structure. Ultimately,

SYMS, R.M., SAVORY, D. F., WARD, C. J., EBDON, C. C. & GRIFFIN, A. 1999. Integrating sequence stratigraphy in field development and reservoir management – the Telford Field. *In*: FLEET, A. J. & BOLDY, S. A. R. (eds) *Petroleum Geology of Northwest Europe: Proceedings of the 5th Conference*, 1075–1087. © Petroleum Geology '86 Ltd. Published by the Geological Society, London.

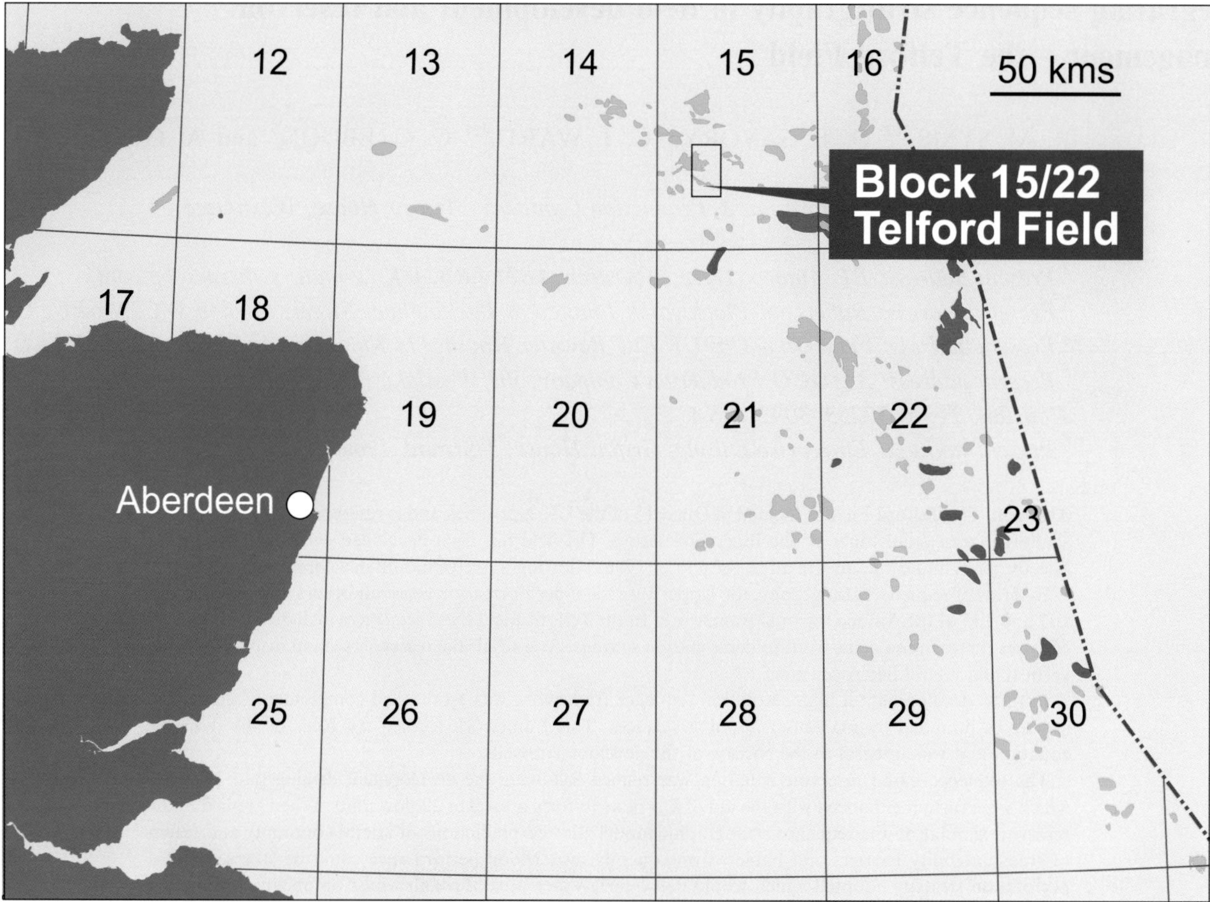

Fig. 1. Location of the Telford Field in the UKCS.

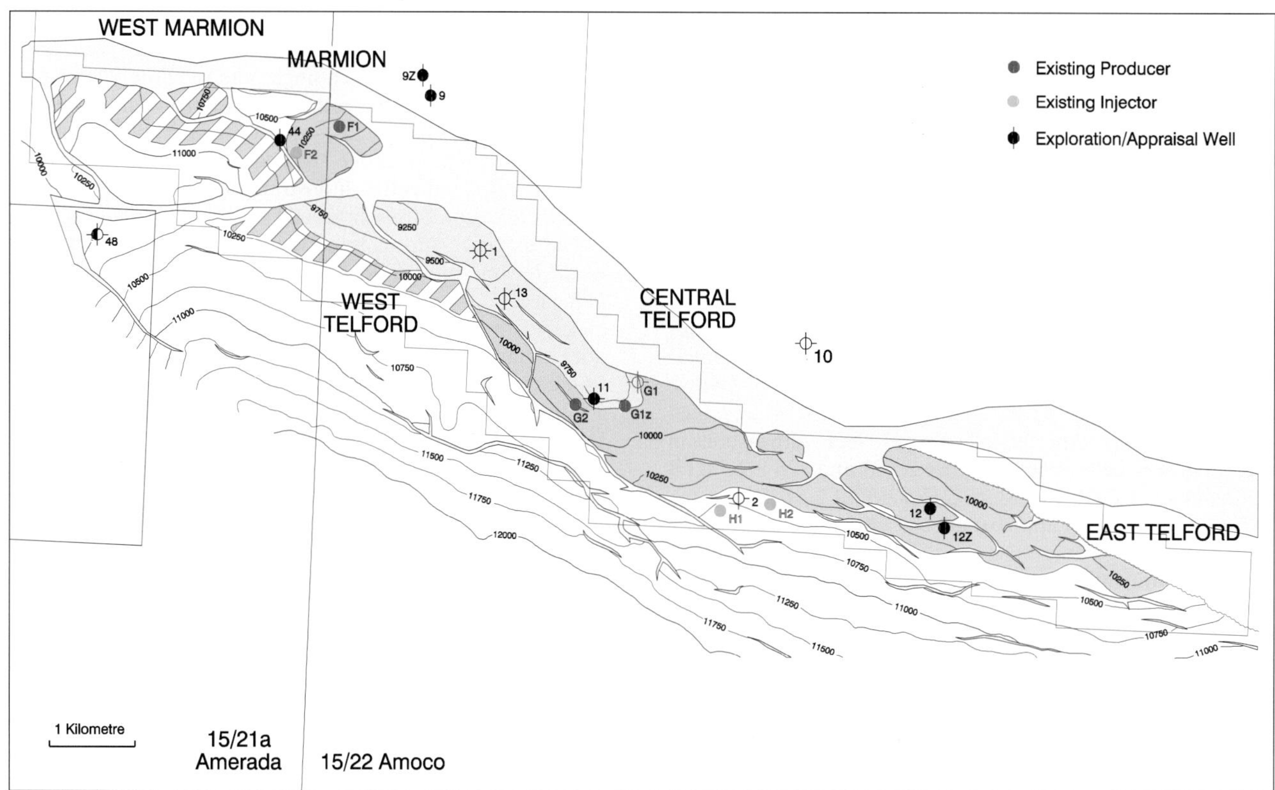

Fig. 2. The Telford Field development comprising Marmion and Central Telford (Phase I) and East Telford and West Telford (Phase II). The gas cap is shaded pink and the oil accumulation green.

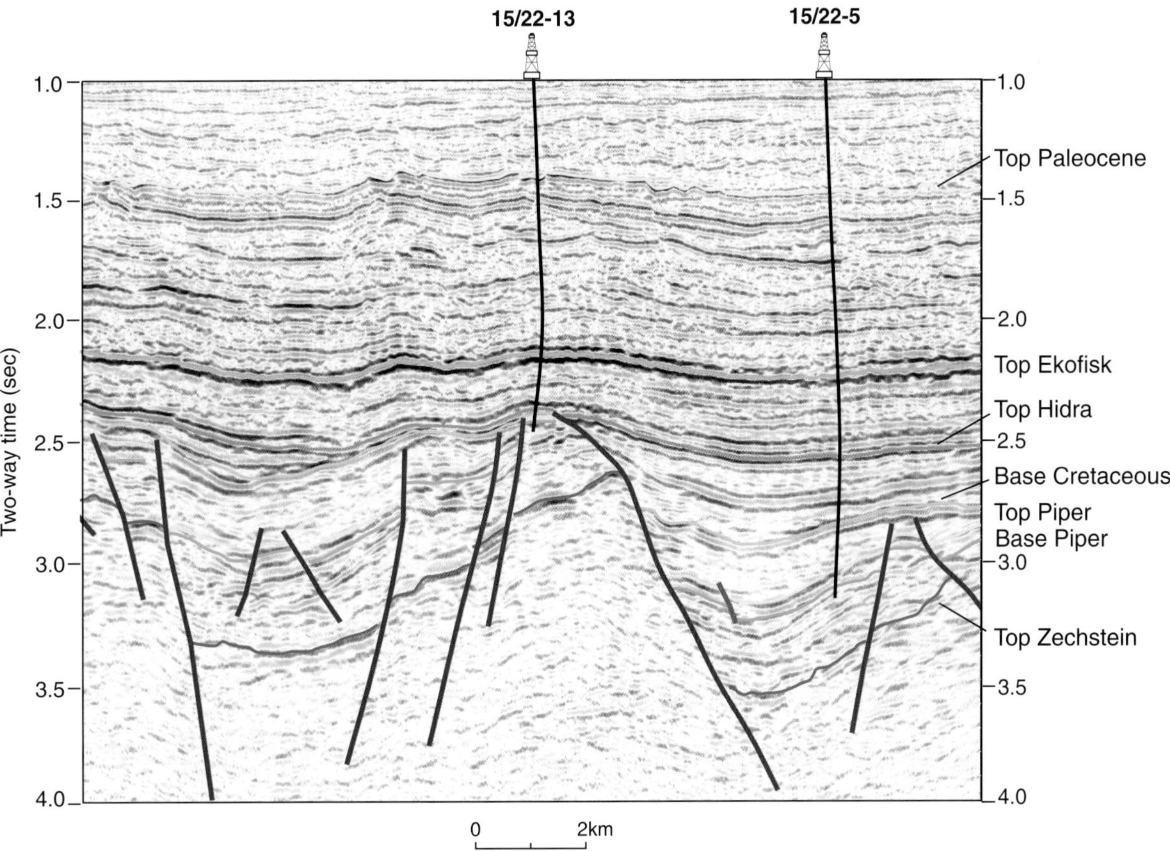

Fig. 3. Northeast–southwest seismic section through the Central Telford area (Well 15/22-13). The reservoir in the crestal areas and along the leading edge of the tilted fault block has been eroded during rifting.

the pre-development reservoir model employed the sequence framework and erosion modelling to optimize well positioning, resulting in the successful completion of six development wells.

Development wells provided more data with which to enhance the sequence model and, ultimately, better define the reservoir zonation. The final zonation provides a useful framework for reservoir characterization and reserve distribution and has been used to model the influence of various stratigraphic surfaces on transmissibility, sweep efficiency and injection support for reservoir management purposes.

Discovery, appraisal and development

The drilling history in UKCS Blocks 15/21 and 15/22 is chiefly concerned with the discovery and appraisal of the Scott Field which was discovered in 1986 and came on stream in 1993. The installation of the Scott Platform and its associated transportation facilities opened up surrounding areas for the development of smaller, previously uneconomic satellite fields such as Telford.

The first well in the field area was 15/22-1 (Fig. 2), drilled in 1973 at the crest of a tilted fault block, which encountered a 31 ft gas bearing Piper Formation sandstone and was interpreted to represent a thinned stratigraphic section resulting from crestal erosion (Fig. 5). This was followed by the down dip Well 15/22-2, which encountered 250 ft of water-bearing reservoir indicating that the hydrocarbon accumulation was of limited extent (Fig. 2).

The discovery of the large Scott Field to the north by both Amerada Hess and Amoco during the 1980s reignited interest in the area. In 1991 Amerada Hess drilled Well 15/21a-44 in Marmion to the west of the main Telford fault block, across a down-thrown NE–SW trending fault (Fig. 2). This well encountered approximately 400 ft of Piper Formation with a limited column of low GOR oil restricted to the Pibroch Member sandstone (Fig. 5).

In 1992, Amoco drilled Well 15/22-11, between the 15/22-1 gas discovery and Well 15/22-2 which was water-wet (Fig. 2). This discovered 190 ft of Piper Formation reservoir containing high GOR oil in an accumulation which was later termed Central Telford (Fig. 5). A follow-up well, 15/22-12, was drilled in 1993 to the east of Central Telford and encountered a thin, possibly eroded, oil-bearing section in what is now termed East Telford (Figs 2 and 5). The 15/22-13 appraisal well, drilled towards the crest of Central Telford to determine the extent of the oil accumulation, found an eroded gas-bearing reservoir similar to that in 15/22-1 (Fig. 5). Although further prospectivity was identified in West Telford and West Marmion, processing restrictions at the Scott facilities caused appraisal activity to cease following the Well 15/22-13.

Development of the field was based around the Central Telford and Marmion accumulations, which are hydraulically separated and contain very different fluids. In Marmion the producer–injector pair (F1–F2) were drilled to support a 10 000 BOPD off-take. In addition to the oil leg in the Pibroch Member proved up by Well 15/21a-44, oil was also discovered in the Chanter Member of the Piper Formation by the producer–injector pair.

In Central Telford, two producer–injector pairs (G1z–H2 and G2–H1) were drilled with an off-take target of 20 000 BOPD. A vital aspect of the development scheme was the effectiveness of the injection support in maintaining pressure to avoid excessive gas production, and in providing efficient sweep.

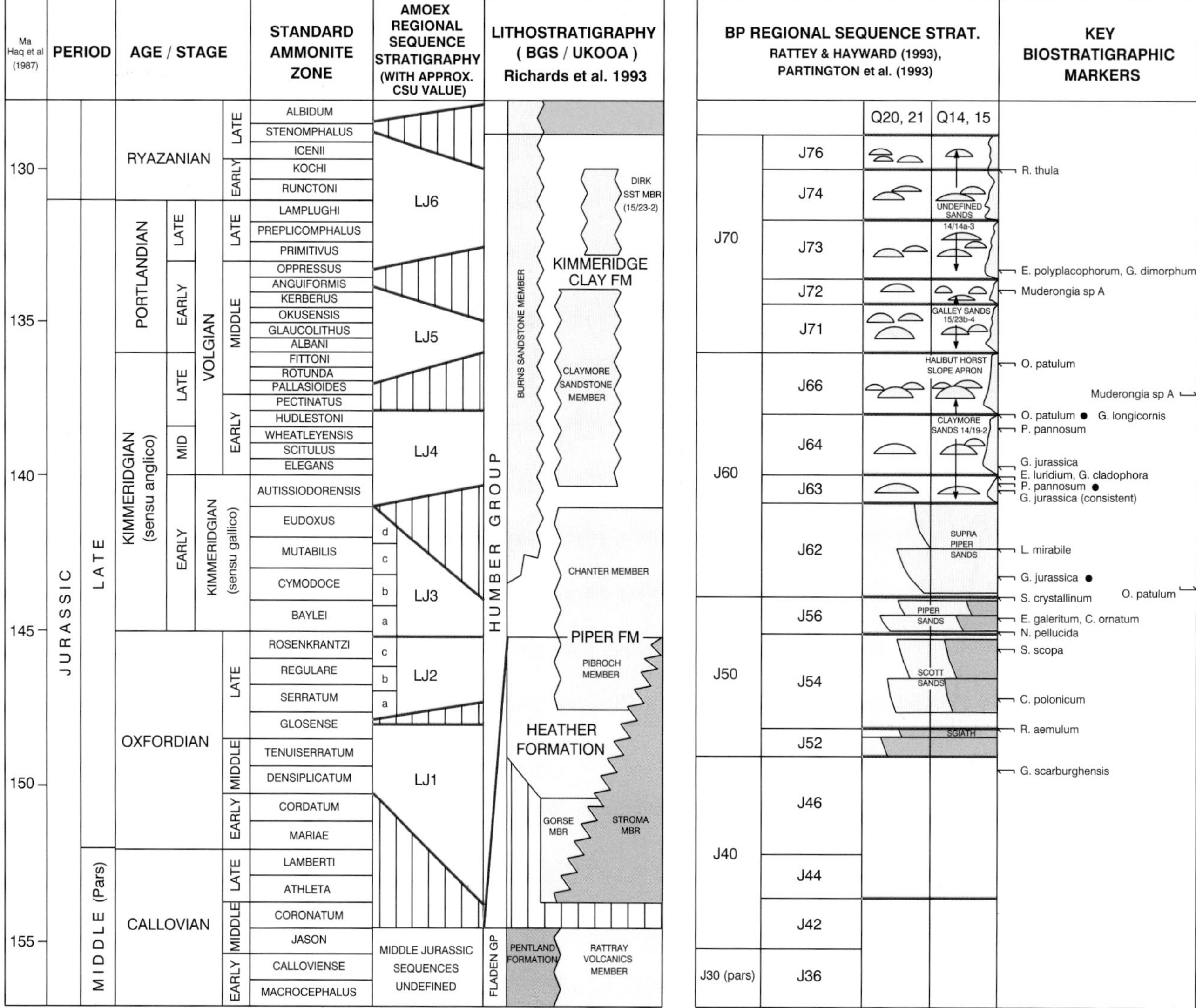

Fig. 4. Late Jurassic stratigraphic nomenclature of the Scott/Telford area illustrating the Amoco sequence stratigraphic scheme and a comparison with that of BP and conventional lithostratigraphy. The Amoco framework identifies six regional Late Jurassic (LJ) sequences bound by periods of basinwide condensation. Note that the duration of the condensation can be variable. The base of Sequence LJ1 is difficult to date because of the dominance of paralic facies. Sequences LJ2 and LJ3 are the main reservoir bearing sequences and are further subdivided into seven higher order sequences within Blocks 15/21 and 15/22 (LJ2a–c and LJ3a–d).

Regional sequence stratigraphy and geological evolution

Partington *et al.* (1993*a*, *b*) indicate that the North Sea Jurassic can be subdivided into a number of genetic stratigraphic sequences (*sensu* Galloway 1989) based on the identification of regionally extensive maximum flooding surfaces (Fig. 4). These maximum flooding surfaces, which can be calibrated and correlated on the basis of their biostratigraphy, define periods of basin-wide sediment starvation and bound periods of shelf outbuilding. The use of graphic correlation techniques (Shaw 1964; Miller 1977), calibrated to gamma–sonic maxima, complements this methodology and builds on it by allowing the relative significance of these maximum flooding surfaces to be defined. The most significant periods of condensation, in terms of duration, are likely to be the most regionally extensive flooding surfaces. These major periods of condensation define Amoco's regional Late Jurassic (LJ) sequence stratigraphic nomenclature (Fig. 4) and provide a framework within which the depositional evolution can be described (Fig. 6).

Sequence LJ1

Sequence LJ1 essentially corresponds to the Stroma Member of the Pentland Formation. The upper maximum flooding event is tentatively correlated with the *glosense* Ammonite Zone (Fig. 4).

The sequence comprises coal overlain by a dominantly mudstone succession of paralic and marine origin which onlaps a pre-existing irregular volcanic topography, comprising Rattray Volcanics Member of the Fladen Group. In Central and East Telford this volcanic topography remained largely exposed and influenced the distribution of pre-rift facies. The bottom seal for the field is provided by this sequence where it is present and by the Rattray Volcanic Member where it is absent.

Sequence LJ2

Sequence LJ2 includes the Pibroch Member of the Piper Formation and represents the first of the Late Jurassic sand-prone shelf systems in the area (Fig. 6).

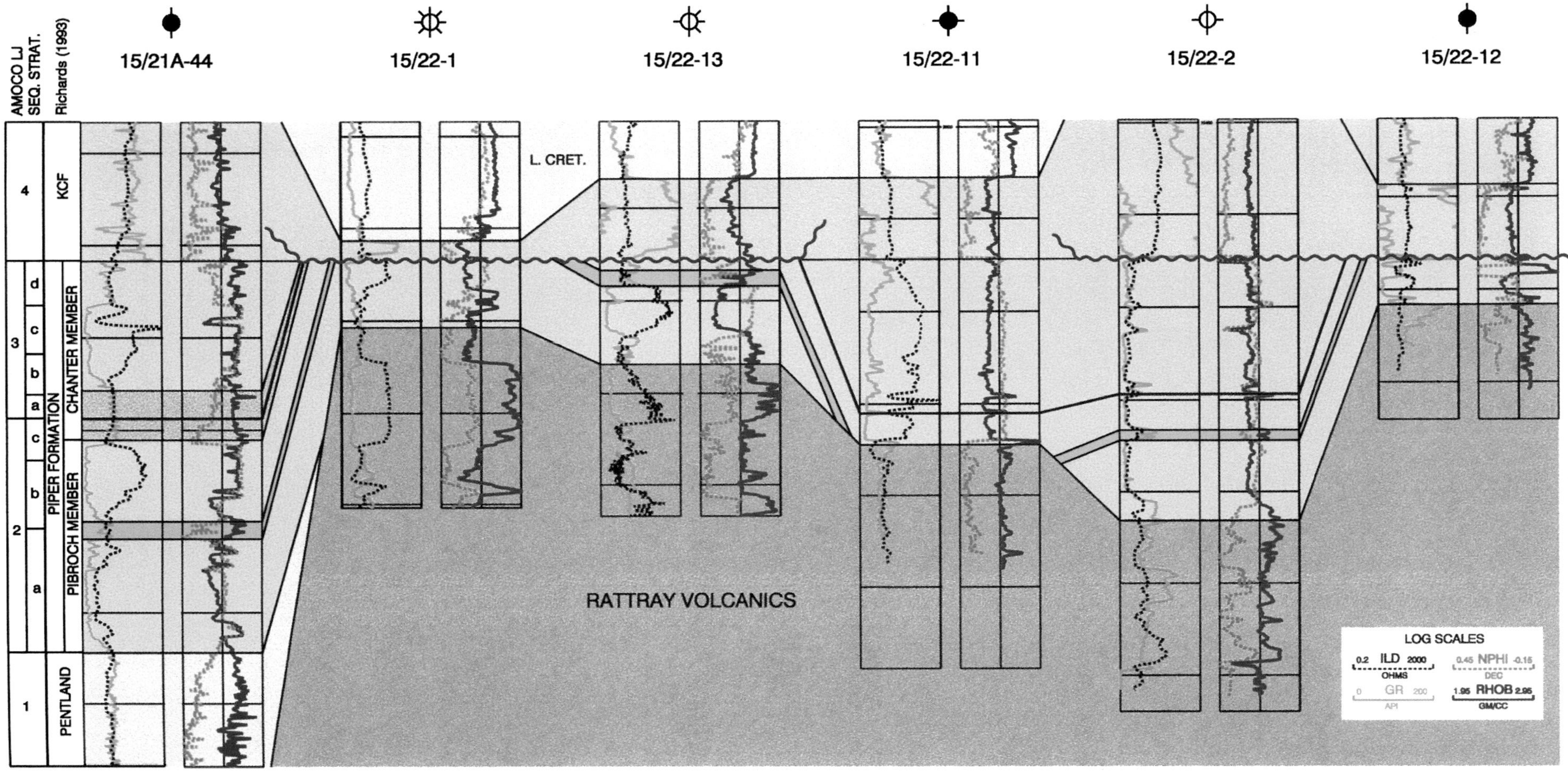

Fig. 5. Pre-development wireline correlation from west to east through the Telford Field illustrating the significant thickness variation and differing wireline response from well to well (hung on top Piper Formation). The Piper Formation is depicted in yellow and can only be readily subdivided into the Pibroch and Chanter Members (Richards *et al.* 1993) in Well 15/21a-44. Two key surfaces were recognized and correlated in order to understand sandbody continuity. The green surface represents the semi-regional LJ2a maximum flooding surface whilst the purple depicts the regional LJ2 *rosenkrantzi* flooding event. Note the progressive onlap of the irregular Rattray volcanic topography and the top reservoir erosion (Late Cimmerian) towards the crest of the structure.

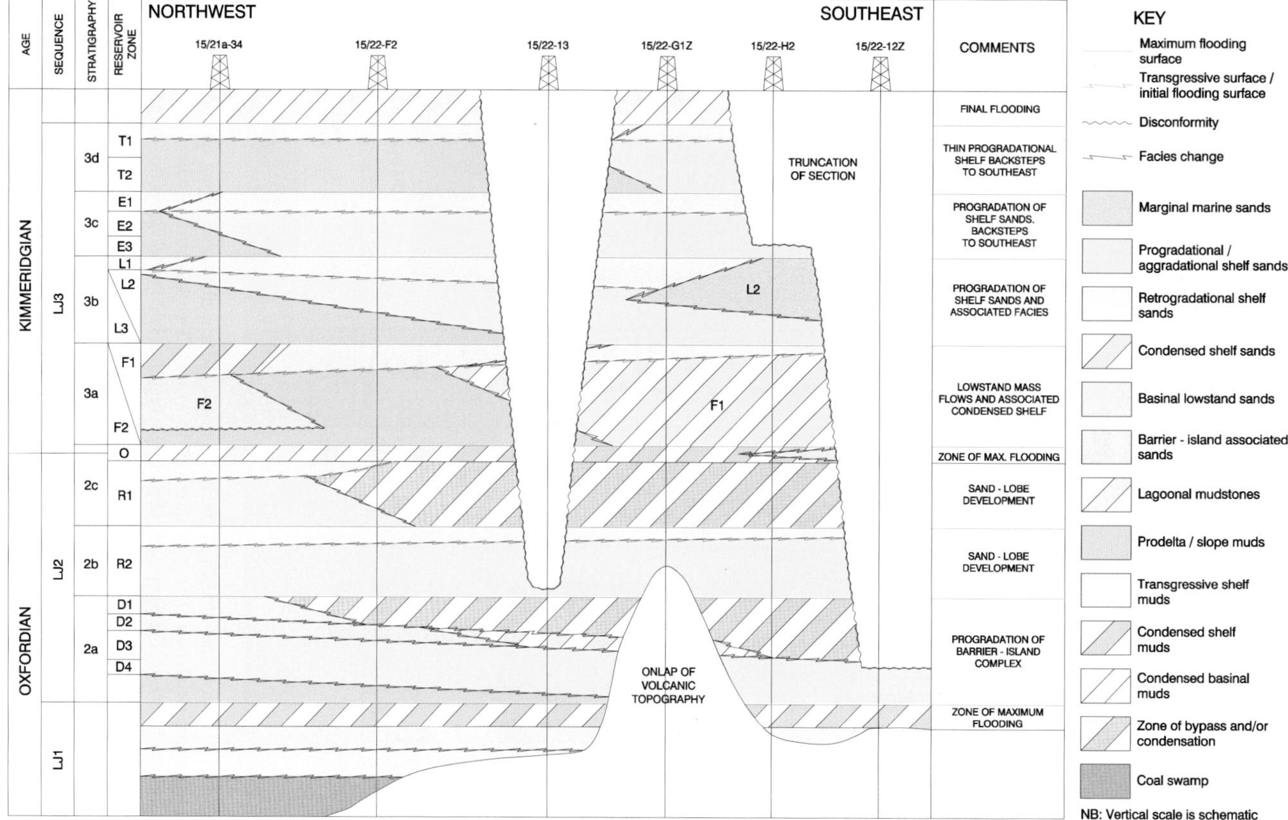

Fig. 6. Schematic chronostratigraphic correlation illustrating the stratigraphic evolution of the Telford Field and the component depositional systems.

Locally, LJ2 is further subdivided into sequences LJ2a, b and c on the basis of higher order correlative flooding events. Sequence LJ2a records the westerly outbuilding, upbuilding and final abandonment of a tidally influenced barrier–island system whilst sequences LJ2b and LJ2c record the successive development of two sand-prone deltaic lobes (Fig. 6).

In the Telford Field this sequence is host to a well-developed reservoir in the Marmion and West Telford areas but has limited reservoir thickness in Central and East Telford because of the effect of the volcanic topography which remained exposed until LJ2b/c times.

Sequence LJ2 is terminated by the flooding event corresponding to the *rosenkrantzi* Ammonite Zone which resulted in the deposition of a semi-regional shale unit known as the I-Shale (Harker *et al.* 1993) or the Mid-Shale (Boldy & Brealey 1990) as illustrated in Fig. 4.

Sequence LJ3

Sequence LJ3 includes the Chanter Member of the Piper Formation and represents another period of widespread sand-prone deposition. It is further subdivided locally into LJ3a–d on the basis of higher order flooding surfaces.

Sedimentation is dominated by high energy, fluvially dominated deltaic systems which prograded in a westerly direction over the entire Telford area. A significant lowstand event is recorded semi-regionally during the development of LJ3a resulting in the deposition of thick mass flow facies towards the northwest (Fig. 6). During this period, the Central and East Telford areas were largely zones of sediment by-pass. Indeed, compared to surrounding areas, much of sequence LJ3 would appear to be relatively condensed, with the recognition and correlation of key surfaces relying heavily on core and well ties within less condensed sections elsewhere.

Sequences LJ3b–d record the westerly progradation of successive deltaic systems over the Telford area, making up the bulk of the reservoir encountered in Central Telford (Fig. 6).

The upper bounding surface to this sequence equates to a significant period of basinal condensation, initiated during the *baylei* Ammonite Zone and culminating in the *eudoxus* Ammonite Zone (Fig. 4).

Sequences LJ4–6

The overlying sequences of LJ4–6 record a significant change in the depositional style of the basin with the development of thick mudstone successions, lithostratigraphically attributed to the Kimmeridge Clay Formation. These mudstones form the top seal in the Telford Field area and, regionally, are the hydrocarbon source.

Erosion of the reservoir, mainly in sequence LJ3 at the crest of the field, is attributed to events of the Late Cimmerian unconformity.

Reservoir zonation of the Telford Field

The reservoir zonation was the most critical aspect of field description in that it divided the reservoir into effective flow units, describing their spatial distribution and providing the basis for predicting and understanding the movement of fluids within the reservoir. In particular it determines the efficiency of pressure support and how the injected water will advance both areally and in the vertical plane, allowing decisions to be made on offtake and perforating strategies .

Prior to development, correlations were based predominantly on wireline log data (Fig. 5). However, the log character is extremely variable from well to well because of significant lateral and vertical changes in facies. Correlations are further complicated as a result of facies onlapping an irregular volcanic topography and Late Cimmerian erosion.

A much improved dataset was available after development drilling, allowing a more refined definition of the higher order sequences. In particular, the increased core coverage permitted detailed sedimentological interpretations and stratal surface recognition. The resultant seven sequences (LJ2a–c and LJ3a–d) are the fundamental stratigraphic building blocks of the reservoir and were assigned a single character from top to base; T, E, L, F, O, R and D to define reservoir units (Fig. 7).

A further stratigraphic breakdown, essentially into sequence system 'tracts', was performed to achieve a flow unit framework. For example, LJ3c (zone E) could be subdivided into progradational (zone E3), aggradational (zone E2) and retrogradational (zone E1) components (Figs 7 and 8). This seventeen layer zonation was analysed utilizing k/ϕ plots, which divide the reservoir into flow units on the basis of the diffusivity profile. The hydraulic diffusivity equation describes the fluid advance through the rock, which is a function of both flow rate and storage capacity of the formation. The diffusivity constant η is given by:

$$\eta = k/\phi\mu c_t$$

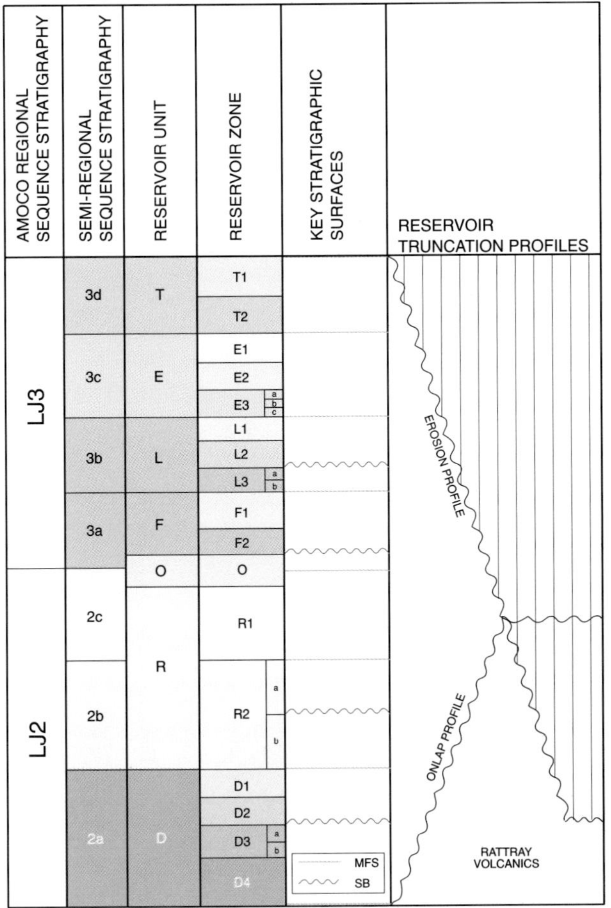

Fig. 7. Tabulation of the sequence and reservoir zonation nomenclature for the Telford Field. The reservoir units are taken directly from the sequence framework and are, as such, bound by stratal surfaces allowing a geological prediction of lateral continuity. Note that the combination of topographic onlap and crestal erosion significantly reduces the chance of reservoir presence in areas particularly towards the crest of the structure. In addition to onlap and crestal erosion, areas of non-deposition result in the preservation of a maximum of 15 of the 22 zones in any one well.

where: k = permeability, ϕ = porosity, μ = fluid viscosity, and c_t = total system compressibility.

For most oil systems the two latter quantities vary little with pressure, and diffusivity is a function of the ratio k/ϕ only. Plotting this ratio versus depth enables the identification of vertical changes in diffusivity which were integrated with the sequence framework, to identify laterally correlative units (Fig. 8).

Most vertical changes in diffusivity coincided with the identified stratigraphic breaks, confirming that the reservoir zonation conformed to a breakdown of flow units. In addition to providing a validity check for the zonation scheme, the k/ϕ ratios also enhanced subtle variations in reservoir characteristics allowing the identification of localized flow units. Consequently, a further subdivision of zones E3, L3, R2 and D3 was possible within the Central Telford area (Figs 7 and 8).

The final scheme defines a total of 22 reservoir zones or flow units. However, owing to non-deposition, erosion, pinch-out or facies change, no well in the field area encounters all the reservoir zones, the maximum in any one well being 15.

Reservoir geology

Generally, reservoir quality is good to excellent throughout the field, with clean, moderate to well sorted, shallow marine sandstones containing little or no authigenic cements or clays. Where minor quartz overgrowths do occur, they often enhance reservoir quality through a reduction in tortuosity. However, localized fault related diagenesis has been encountered in the Marmion injector well (15/22-F2) which significantly reduced reservoir quality in sequences LJ2b/c and much of sequence LJ3. Similar reductions in reservoir quality were also encountered in the earlier exploration well (15/21a-44) (Fig. 5). Net : gross values are in excess of 0.85 in the Central Telford area where proximal shallow marine facies are encountered and decrease towards the west as the distal expression of the shallow marine facies is seen, and to the east where delta-top facies occur.

In general, permeabilities are in excess of 1 Darcy whilst porosities typically fall in the range 17–19%. Neither permeability nor porosity display a relationship with depth and are predominantly related to facies type. Marked variations in reservoir quality do however occur, through variations in grain size and detrital clay content, which are essentially functions of facies type. Figure 6 summarizes the main facies associations in the field, which are dominated by the occurrences of fluvially influenced deltaic sandstone lobes of sequence LJ3.

Facies variations result from lobe switching and changes in the dynamics of the depositional systems across the volcanic topography. Where accommodation space was limited, such as on the main volcanic high, progradational cycles were dominated by sand-prone systems, some of which may be relatively condensed (Fig. 8). In this instance, permeability barriers may occur in the form of coals, lagoonal mudstones and zones of early cementation. However, as the influence of the volcanic topography diminished, the reservoir sections became more aggradational and included higher proportions of mudstone facies associated with periods of maximum flooding (Fig. 8). Potential permeability barriers in this instance are shale interbeds.

The effect of the volcanic topography is accentuated by compaction of the underlying coals and mudstones within sequence LJ1. In the Telford area, LJ1 is variable in thickness, occurring in the volcanic lows, attaining a penetrated thickness of 238 ft in Well 15/22-44 but is known to be absent in the Central Telford wells (Figs 5 and 8). Compaction, under the weight of the water column and sediments deposited during sequences LJ2 and LJ3 has resulted in this variable reservoir thickness over relatively small distances.

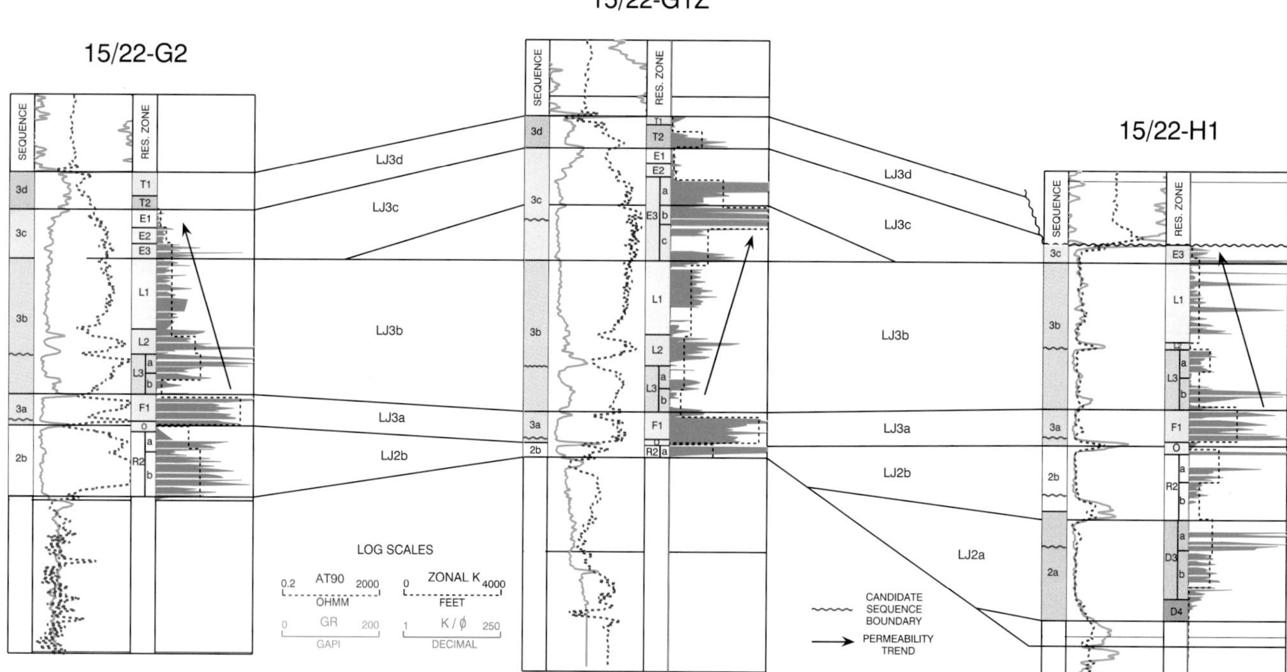

Fig. 8. Combined sequence and reservoir zonation correlation through the two Central Telford producers (15/22-G2 and G1z) and one of the injectors (15/22-H1), hung on top LJ3b. The diffusivity is essentially a function of k/ϕ whilst the zonal permeability (zonal K) is the geometric average per zone. High diffusivity (green) indicates high flow rate whilst low diffusivity is indicative of high storage capacity. Note the upward increase in zonal permeability and diffusivity above zone F1 in well G1z compared to a decrease in G2 and H1. This is primarily the result of the occurrence of a localized, high energy delta lobe in G1z which was not encountered in other surrounding wells (zones E3b and E3c).

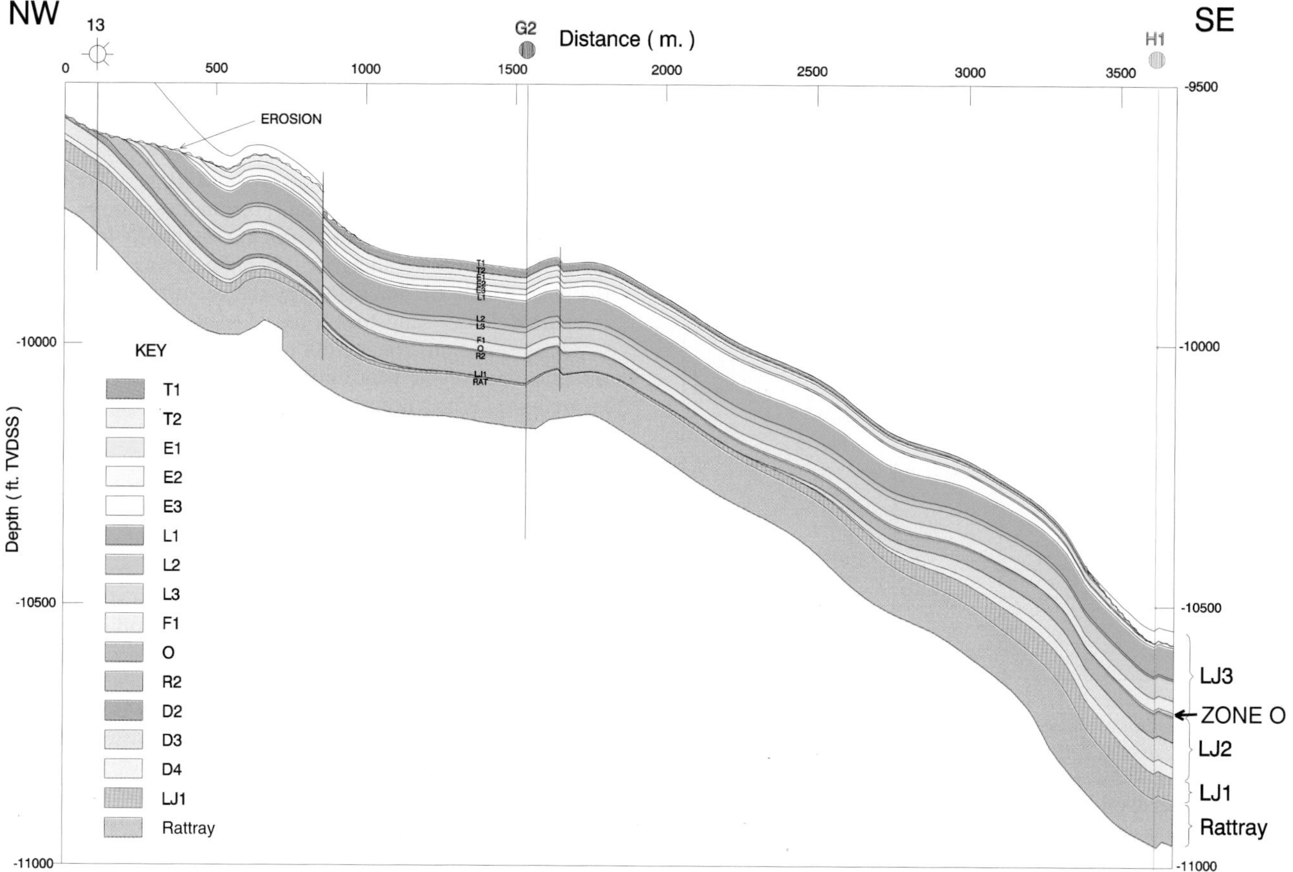

Fig. 9. Reservoir zonation cross-section through the producer–injector pairing G2–H1 in Central Telford. Note the progressive onlap of the volcanic topography and the potential isolation of LJ2 from LJ3 by zone O.

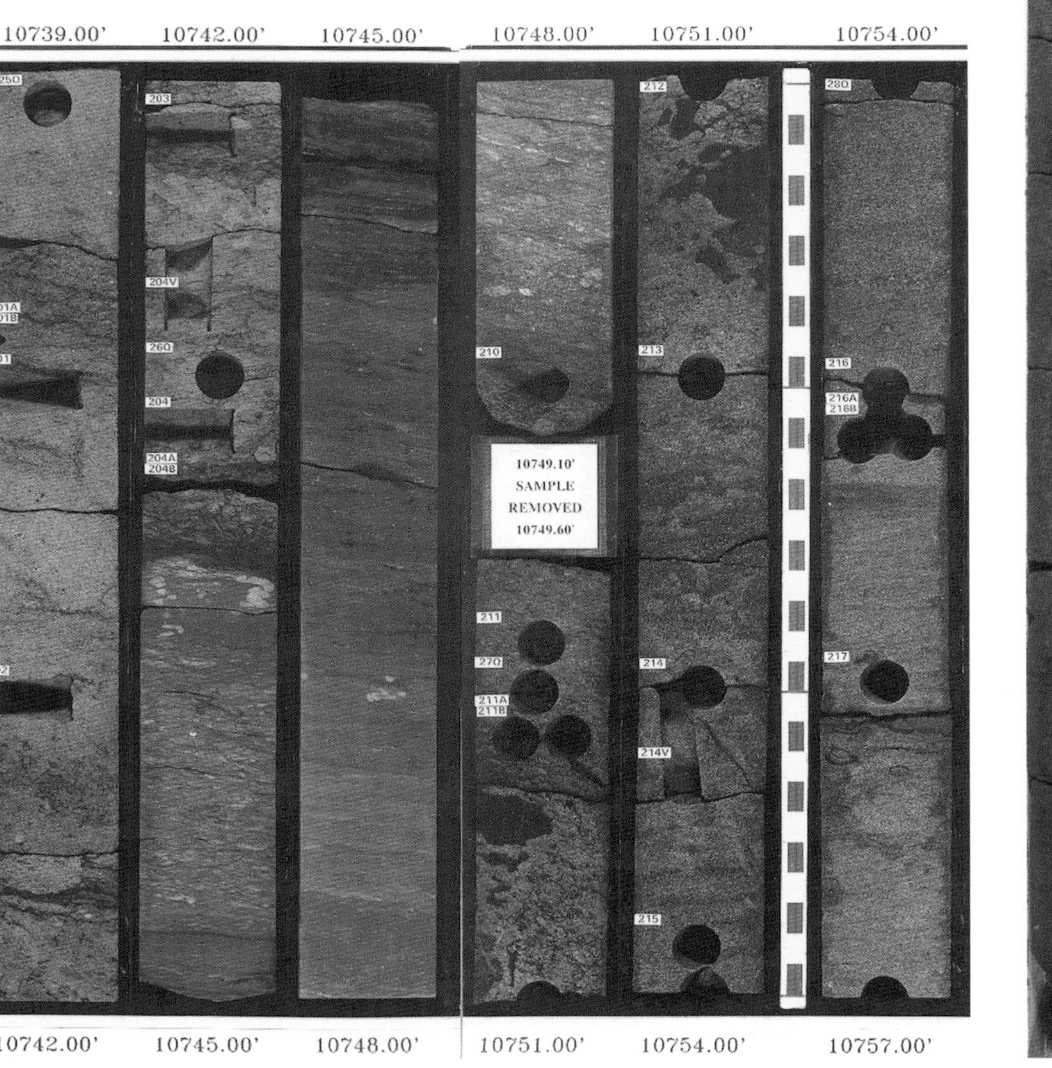

Fig. 10. Core photographs from Well 15/22-H1 (10 739–10 760 ft) illustrating the basinal mudstone attributed to zone O (10 743.5–10 749 ft). This correlates with the LJ2 *rosenkrantzi* flooding event and separates zone R2a below (upper shoreface facies of LJ2b) from zone F1 above (*ophiomorpha* bioturbated lower shoreface facies to offshore transition of LJ3a). The onset of flooding is marked by accumulations of articulated and disarticulated bivalves. Sandstones below and above zone O have average permeabilities in excess of 1 D and average porosities of 19%. The sharp based sandstone of F1 is a candidate forced regression and is recognized semi-regionally as the LJ3a Exxon-style sequence boundary.

Fig. 11. Core photographs from Well 15/22-G1z (10 617–10 630 ft). The basal portion of the core displays Rattray volcanics overlain by good quality, shallow marine sandstone of zone R2a containing scattered quartz grains aligned along weakly defining bedding (sequence LJ2b). Permeabilities in this zone average over 4 D with porosities in the region of 16–17% for this particular well. The thin shale below 10 620 ft corresponds to zone O (LJ2 maximum flooding event) and is overlain by a sharp based, bioturbated shallow marine sandstone attributed to zone F1 (sequence LJ3a), once again displaying excellent reservoir properties (average permeability over 3 D, porosities 18–19%).

Key stratal surfaces and their impact on fluid flow

The impact of stratigraphic surfaces on fluid flow and reservoir modelling has been considered in recent years by a number of authors, using outcrop studies to determine their lateral importance (e.g. Cross *et al.* 1993; O'Byrne & Flint 1993, 1995, 1996). By interpreting the significance of stratal surfaces it is possible to understand and model vertical transmissibility and lateral fluid flow.

Because of the high net sand content in Central Telford, most zonal interfaces are sand-on-sand and vertical transmissibility is expected to be very good. However, the reservoir in Central Telford is host to coals, shale breaks and cemented horizons, many of which are beyond wireline log resolution, relying on core for identification. Cross-sectional simulation models were used to determine the impact of such surfaces on reservoir performance. Figure 9 illustrates the vertical cross-sectional model used to evaluate Central Telford. Many of the surfaces have a relatively subtle impact on reservoir modelling, and provide a useful technique of subdividing the reservoir for detailed characterization. However, some surfaces have had a significant impact on engineering decisions – these are the focus of the remainder of this paper.

Maximum flooding surface (MFS)

A MFS marks the maximum landward extent of a transgression and is commonly present within a fine-grained condensed section with potential to form a barrier to fluid flow. In more proximal settings, such as those encountered in Central and East Telford, the MFS will be marked by the deepest water deposits recorded in a sand-on-sand boundary and can be identified in core by the occurrence of local cementation and/or the trace fossil assemblage (Taylor & Gawthorpe 1993). Recent publications have highlighted the importance of recognizing cemented horizons in sand dominated successions owing to their possible lateral continuity and effect on fluid flow (Gibbons *et al.* 1993; Taylor & Lovell 1995; Taylor *et al.* 1997).

LJ2a MFS. Sequence LJ2a is bound above by a shale unit which in Central Telford divides zone D3 below from zone R2 above (Figs 8 and 9). However, correlations suggest that this surface is present only within the area around the injectors, lapping out against the Rattray Volcanics up-dip towards the producers, thus reducing potential sweep efficiency in the lowermost reservoir zones.

LJ2c (LJ2) MFS. The semi-regional *rosenkrantzi* event defines the upper bounding surface to sequence LJ2c, coinciding with the top of sequence LJ2. This event resulted in the widespread deposition of a basinal shale known as the I-Shale or the Mid-Shale which forms zone O (Figs 8, 10 and 11). In Marmion, this shale clearly separates LJ2 from LJ3 resulting in different pressure regimes and different oil–water contacts in the reservoirs above and below the MFS. The effect in Central Telford, however, is more ambiguous.

Zone O in Central Telford separates zone R2a below from zone F1 above (F2 is absent), both zones displaying average permeabilities greater than 2 Darcy. However, these zones are thin and potentially laterally discontinuous (zone F1 is discussed in more detail in the following section). In particular, the distribution of zone R2a is controlled by the amount of accommodation space during an overall transgressive period – the flooding event associated with zone O may well lap out on the Rattray Volcanics topography (Fig. 9).

Between the injector and producer locations in Central Telford, zone O is interpreted to occur over the entire area, thinning dramatically over the volcanic topographic high (Fig. 8). Initial pressures showed that the reservoirs in this area, above and below the zone, were in mutual hydraulic equilibrium, and this probably reflects a breach somewhere in zone O. This may be a result of fault offset, or erosion either by overlying successions or by the linking of sequence LJ2 and sequence LJ3 through the occurrence of sands within the zone, as observed in Well 15/22-H2 (Fig. 6).

Sequence boundary

The term sequence boundary is used here to describe an unconformity separating younger strata from older strata along which there is evidence of subaerial exposure, erosional truncation or correlative submarine erosion with hiatus recorded (Van Wagoner *et al.* 1988). A forced regression is a related term referring to an abrupt basinward shift of the shoreline and associated facies in response to relative lowering of sea-level (Posamentier *et al.* 1992).

Semi-regional correlations have identified a number of candidate sequence boundaries within both LJ2 and LJ3. In most instances, the facies immediately above the sequence boundary display significantly better reservoir quality than those below because of the basinward shift. Identification of these surfaces was enhanced using k/ϕ plots, particularly those that were more subtle in core (Fig. 8).

LJ3a sequence boundary. The most significant sequence boundary in a semi-regional context occurs within sequence LJ3a which correlates to the base of the F1 reservoir zone in Wells 15/22-G1z and 15/22-H1 (Fig. 6). Elsewhere, this boundary coincides with a significant influx of sediment into the basinal areas resulting in the accumulation of thick mass-flow sandstones to the northwest of the Telford Field.

The facies of zone F1 in Central Telford occur as a sharp-based single bed of 20–25 ft thickness, comprising medium-grained lower shoreface deposits, with scarce *Ophiomorpha*, and dispersed pebbles, fragmented carbonaceous material and decalcified bivalves (Figs 10 and 11). Since this overlies the marine shale of zone O, this unit may represent a forced regression. If this is the case, it is possible that there may be areas where this facies is absent as a result of sediment by-pass.

Reservoir zone F1 provides a significant flow unit (Fig. 8), with an average permeability in the order of 2–3 D and porosities of 18–19%. Its down-cutting nature may be more prominent locally, resulting in the breaching of the underlying mudstone of zone O (corresponding to the LJ2 MFS described earlier) and allowing cross-flow between zones R2a and F1.

Reservoir engineering

The detailed zonation described earlier has been incorporated into a number of reservoir simulation models: cross-sectional models were used to determine perforation strategies, and a full 3D model was used both to verify those strategies and predict full-field recovery. This latter model will be history-matched to actual field performance as an ongoing reservoir management tool.

Because of the high intervention cost for sub-sea wells, an underlying objective of the technical analysis was to limit the need for subsequent well re-entry, such as to shut off watered out zones. In Well 15/22-G2, further down-dip of the Central Telford producers, the perforation strategy was designed to maximize water breakthrough time without jeopardizing well productivity or field recovery. Conversely, in Well 15/22-G1z, which is closer to the gas cap, perforation depths had to be carefully selected to avoid any tendency to cone gas.

In Marmion, the two accumulations have different oil–water contacts and water leg pressures. Here the aim was to determine whether there was any advantage in a staggered development, with the need for two separate completion operations, as opposed to co-mingling the accumulations from the outset.

To accomplish these objectives it was necessary to clearly understand the fluid flow through the reservoir by way of a description of the distribution, continuity and interconnection of the reservoir zones. Detailed vertical cross-sectional models honouring the stratigraphy and spatial heterogeneity were used to investigate vertical sweep and optimize perforation strategies for the three producers. Cross-sectional models do however involve some compromise in that they cannot account for fluid movement normal to the plane, so the full-field 3D model was also used to check the benefits of the various perforating options identified and their impact on rate and recovery.

Well 15/22-G2 perforation strategy

To illustrate some of the aspects of this process, the following describes the cross-sectional model study to determine the 15/22-G2 well perforations.

In a reservoir containing light oil and with good vertical transmissibility, upwardly increasing permeability is more conducive to a vertical flood front, as the tendency for water in the upper zones to over-run those below is offset by gravitational forces. A vertical front is economically more favourable as the majority of the reserves are then produced during a dry oil plateau. Below zone O, zonal permeability values in Central Telford rise from an average 46 mD at the base (zone D4) up to 2.6 D in zone R2a, a distribution which in isolation would provide optimal sweep.

By contrast, above zone O the average permeability decreases steadily from 2.6 D in zone F1 to 80 mD in zone T1, a distribution that will promote a more horizontal water surface. In this region the producer will therefore start cutting water before the upper zones are fully swept.

However, the flood profile over the entire section also depends on the persistence of any barriers and on the perforation strategies adopted. Adequately modelling the flood profile development in these circumstances requires numerical simulation, although to achieve sufficient definition a much finer horizontal resolution has to be employed than is practical in a full-field model. Such resolution can however be achieved by using a vertical cross-section which, provided it is oriented parallel to the principal fluid flow direction, will be a reasonable representation of the whole area.

The two-dimensional grid used lies along a section between 15/22-H1 and -G2, with some 50 cells between injector and producer and a layering corresponding to the reservoir zonation. Following the assessment of the stratigraphic surfaces only two were considered to be barriers to vertical flow in this part of the field, i.e. zone O and the mfs at the top of sequence LJ2a. These were assigned zero vertical transmissibility in the model.

As discussed earlier, zone O thins over Central Telford and is probably breached in one or more ways. However, there remains a possibility that this is not so, and the waterflood development will then be different. For this reason both scenarios were evaluated, corresponding to the zone being continuous or breached, and a perforation strategy was determined that allowed for either. In all cases the injector was perforated throughout, as it is demonstrable that no benefits derive from restricting perforations.

Base cases: producer fully perforated

Figure 12 illustrates the development of the flood for each scenario with Well 15/22-G2 perforated throughout the entire interval. All of the cross-sectional models show the situation after 2 a production and represent equal volumes of oil withdrawn and water injected.

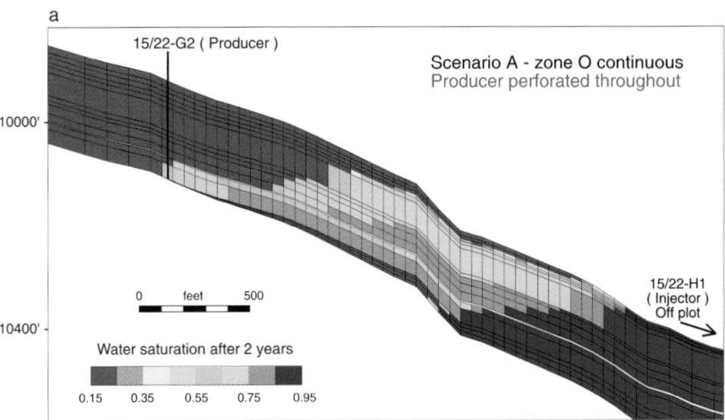

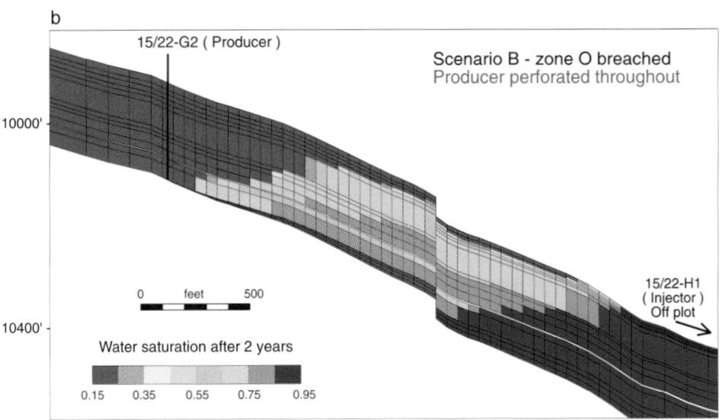

Fig. 12. Cross-sectional simulation model through G2–H1 illustrating the development of the waterflood when Well G2 is perforated throughout for the cases where (**a**) zone O forms a continuous barrier and (**b**) zone O is breached.

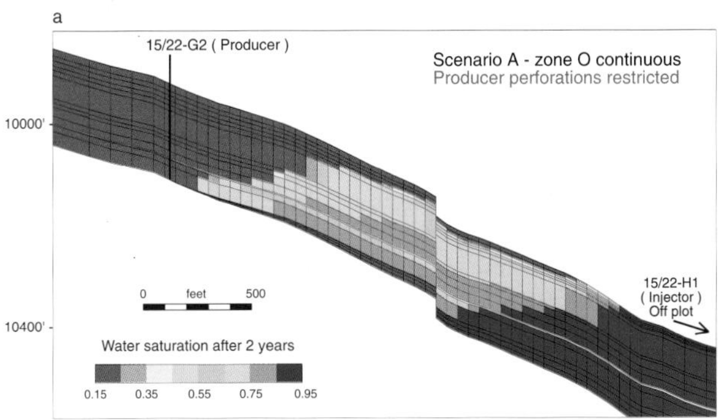

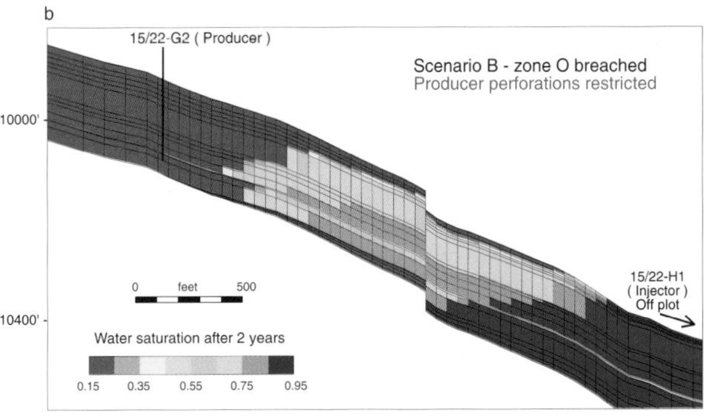

Fig. 13. Cross-sectional simulation model through G2–H1 illustrating the improved waterflood when G2 is optimally perforated for the cases where (**a**) zone O forms a continuous barrier and (**b**) zone O is breached.

In Fig. 12a water has just entered the base of Well 15/22-G2, below zone O, while in Fig. 12b the cross-flow allowed by the breach of zone O gives a more even flood. Water breakthrough is four months later in the latter case. The very lowermost and uppermost zones, which pinch out between injector and producer, remain unswept in both scenarios.

Optimized cases: restricted producer perforations

The high permeability–thickness of the Central Telford producers meant that sufficient productivity could still be maintained even with reduced perforation intervals. Attempts were made to improve the flood and delay water breakthrough by leaving various zones unperforated in the producer.

Leaving all the zones below zone O unperforated was not a viable option. Even though the G1z well will access them, they will remain relatively unswept around G2 regardless of whether zone O is breached or not. The zone immediately below zone O was therefore kept open and options were investigated for the layers above zone O.

The modelling suggested that the optimal solution would be to fully perforate Well 15/22-G2 down as far as zone R2a, which immediately underlies zone O. In all cases where restrictions were imposed on the upper interval, the model displayed a performance inferior to this optimum case. This is because improving the flood profile above zone O also retards it, which in turn promotes that below zone O, causing water breakthrough to be accelerated overall.

The results in the optimized case are illustrated in Figs 13a and b. They show an improvement in the flood profile under both scenarios, and water breakthrough times are four to five months later relative to the base cases. This optimized strategy furthermore leads to increases both in the plateau duration and ultimate recovery.

Conclusions

High resolution sequence stratigraphy provided a means not only of stratigraphically balancing the interpretation, but also a framework for detailed reservoir description. Sedimentary environments tend to be partitioned by surfaces which define a change in reservoir characteristics. Correlation of these surfaces provides a representation of the architectural arrangement of potential flow units.

Cross-sectional reservoir models suggested that the optimal perforation strategy would be to fully perforate Well 15/22-G2 down as far as zone R2a. The results in this case lengthen the period to water breakthrough by four to five months relative to the base cases and increases both plateau duration and ultimate recovery.

Overall field performance to date has met or exceeded expectations. First oil was achieved 90 days ahead of schedule on 23rd October 1996 with production from the Marmion Well 15/22-F1. Completion activities continued until all three producers and three water injectors were on-line by the end of January 1997.

A plateau production rate of around 30–35 000 BOPD has been sustained since it was first achieved early in 1997. To date no production problems have been encountered in Central Telford, although Marmion has recently shown water production and total liquid rate decline, which has been in part restored by a squeeze intervention. The Central Telford wells proved readily capable of making up for the Marmion shortfall. Water injection has also met its target of 60 000 BWPD, the injection well capacity greatly exceeding the minimum required.

This paper is published with the kind permission of Amoco (UK) Exploration Company and the Telford Field Unit owners: Amerada Hess Limited; Deminex UK Oil & Gas Limited, Enterprise Oil plc, Kerr-McGee Oil (UK) plc, Mobil North Sea Limited and Pict Petroleum plc. The authors would also like to thank Amoex's drafting and graphics offices, in particular G. Ball, for preparing the figures.

References

BOLDY, S. A. R. & BREALEY, S. 1990. Timing, nature and sedimentary result of Jurassic tectonism in the Outer Moray Firth. *In*: HARDMAN, R. F. P. & BROOKS, J. (eds) *In*: *Tectonic Events Responsible for Britain's Oil and Gas Reserves*. Geological Society, London, Special Publications, **55**, 254–279.

CROSS, T. A., BAKER, M. R., CHAPIN, M. A., CLARK, M. S., GARDNER, M. H. *et al.* 1993. Applications of high-resolution sequence stratigraphy to reservoir analysis. *In*: ESCHARD, R. & DOLIGEZ, B. (eds) *Subsurface Reservoir Characterisation from Outcrop Observations*. Editions Technip, Paris, 11–34.

GALLOWAY, W. E. 1989. Genetic stratigraphic sequences in basin analysis 1: architecture and genesis of flooding – surface bounded depositional units. *American Association of Petroleum Geologists Bulletin*, **73**, 125–142.

GIBBONS, K., HELLEM, T., KJEMPERUD, A., NIO, S. D. & VEBENSTAD, K. 1993. Sequence architecture, facies development and carbonate-cemented horizons in the Troll Field reservoir, offshore Norway. *In*: ASHTON, M. (ed.) *Advances in Reservoir Geology*. Geological Society, London, Special Publications, **69**, 1–31.

HAQ, B. U., HARDENBOL, J. & VAIL, R. R. 1987. Chronology of fluctuating sea levels since the Triassic. *Science*, **235**, 1156–1167.

HARKER, S. D., MANTEL, K. A., MORTEN, D. J. & RILEY, L. A. 1993. The stratigraphy of Oxfordian–Kimmeridgian (Late Jurassic) reservoir sandstones in the Witch Ground Graben, United Kingdom North Sea. *American Association of Petroleum Geologists Bulletin*, **77**, 1693–1709.

JENNETTE, D. C. & RILEY, C. O. 1996. Influence of relative sea-level on facies and reservoir geometry of the Middle Jurassic lower Brent Group, UK North Viking Graben. *In*: HOWELL, J. A. & AITKEN, J. F. (eds) *High Resolution Sequence Stratigraphy: Innovations and Applications*. Geological Society, London, Special Publications, **104**, 87–113.

JERVEY, M. T. 1988. Quantitative geological modeling of siliciclastic rock sequences and their seismic expression. *In*: WILGUS, C. K., HASTINGS, B. S., KENDALL, C. G. ST. C., POSAMENTIER, H. W., ROSS, C. A. & VAN WAGONER, J. C. (eds) *Sea-level Changes: an Integrated Approach*. Society of Economists, Paleontologists and Mineralogists Special Publications, **42**, 47–70.

JEWELL, S. J. & WARD, C. J. 1997. The Telford Field Development. *In*: *Proceedings of the Fifth Latin American and Caribbean Petroleum Engineering Conference and Exhibition*. Society of Petroleum Engineers Special Publications.

KOLL, V., POSAMENTIER, H. W. & EICHENSEER, H. 1995. Stranded parasequences and the forced regressive wedge systems tract: deposition during base level fall – discussion. *Sedimentary Geology*, **95**, 139–145.

MILLER, F. X. 1977. The graphic correlation method in biostratigraphy. *In*: KAUFMAN, E. G. & HAZEL, J. E. (eds) *Concepts and Methods of Biostratigraphy*. Dowden, Hutchinson and Ross, Stroudsberg Pa., 165–186.

O'BYRNE, C. J. & FLINT, S. 1993. High-resolution sequence stratigraphy of Cretaceous shallow marine sandstones, Book Cliffs outcrops, Utah, USA – application to reservoir modeling. *First Break*, **11**, 45–459.

—— & ——1995. Sequence, parasequence and intra-parasequence architecture of the Grassy Member, Blackhawk Formation, Book Cliffs, USA *In*: VAN WAGONER, J. C. & BERTRAM, G. T. (eds) *Sequence Stratigraphy of Foreland Basin Deposits: Outcrop and sub-*surface Examples from the Cretaceous of North America. American Association of Petroleum Geologists Memoirs, **64**, 225–255.

—— & ——1996. Interfluve sequence boundaries in the Grassy Member, Book Cliffs, Utah: criteria for recognition and implications for subsurface correlation. *In*: HOWELL, J. A. & AITKEN, J. F. (eds) *High Resolution Sequence Stratigraphy: Innovations and Applications*. Geological Society, London, Special Publications, **104**, 115–128.

PARTINGTON, M. A., MITCHENER, B. C., MILTON, N. J. & FRASER, A. J. 1993*a*. Genetic Sequence Stratigraphy for the North Sea Late Jurassic and Early Cretaceous: distribution and prediction of Kimmeridgian–Late Ryzanian reservoirs in the North Sea and adjacent areas. *In*: PARKER, J. R. (ed.) *Petroleum Geology of Northwest Europe, Proceedings of the 4th Conference*. Geological Society, London, 347–370.

——, COPESTAKE, P., MITCHENER, B. C. & UNDERHILL, J. R. 1993*b*. Biostratigraphic calibration of genetic stratigraphic sequences in the Jurassic–lowermost Cretaceous (Hettangian to Ryazanian) of the North Sea and adjacent areas. *In*: PARKER, J. R. (ed.) *Petroleum Geology of Northwest Europe, Proceedings of the 4th Conference*. Geological Society, London, 371–386.

POSAMENTIER, H. W. & VAIL, P. R. 1988. Eustatic controls on clastic deposition II: sequence and system tracts models. *In*: WILGUS, C. K., HASTINGS, B. S., KENDALL, C. G. ST. C., POSAMENTIER, H. W., ROSS, C. A. & VAN WAGONER, J. C. (eds) *Sea-level Changes: an Integrated Approach*. Society of Economists, Paleontologists and Mineralogists Special Publications, **42,** 125–154.

—— & ALLEN, G. P. 1993*a*. Variability of the sequence stratigraphic model: effects of local basin factors. *Sedimentary Geology*, **86**, 91–109.

—— & ——1993*b*. Siliciclastic sequence stratigraphic patterns in foreland ramp-type basins. *Geology*, **20**, 455–458.

——, ——, JAMES, D. P. & TESSON, M. 1992. Forced regressions in a sequence stratigraphic framework: concepts, examples and exploration significance. *American Association of Petroleum Geologists Bulletin*, **76**, 1687–1709.

PULHAM, A. J. 1994. The Cuisiana Field, Llanos Basin, eastern Colombia: high resolution sequence stratigraphy applied to Late Palaeocene–Early Oligocene estuarine, coastal plain and alluvial clastic reservoirs. *In*: JOHNSON, S. J. (ed.) *High Resolution Sequence Stratigraphy: Innovations and Applications, Abstract Volume*. Department of Earth Sciences, University of Liverpool, 63–68.

RATTEY, R. P. & HAYWARD, A. B. 1993. Sequence stratigraphy of a failed rift system: the Middle Jurassic to Early Cretaceous evolution of the Central and Northern North Sea. *In*: PARKER, J. R. (ed.) *Petroleum Geology of Northwest Europe: Proceedings of the 4th Conference*. Geological Society, London, 215–250.

RICHARDS, P. C., LOTT, G. K., JOHNSON, H., KNOX, R. W. O. B. & RIDING, J. B. 1993. Jurassic of the Central and Northern North Sea. *In*: KNOX, R. W. O. B. & CORDEY, W. G. (eds) *Lithostratigraphic Nomenclature of the UK North Sea*. British Geological Survey, Nottingham.

SHAW, A. B. 1964. *Time in Stratigraphy*. McGraw-Hill, New York.

TAYLOR, A. M. & GAWTHORPE, R. L. 1993. Application of sequence stratigraphy and trace fossil analysis to reservoir description: examples from the Jurassic of the North Sea. *In*: PARKER, J. R. (ed.) *Petroleum Geology of Northwest Europe: Proceedings of the 4th Conference*. Geological Society, London, 317–335.

TAYLOR, D. R. & LOVELL, R. W. 1995. High-frequency sequence stratigraphy and paleogeography of the Kenilworth Member, Blackhawk Formation, Book Cliffs, Utah, USA *In*: VAN WAGONER, J. C. & BERTRAM, G. T. (eds) *Sequence Stratigraphy of Foreland Basin Deposits: Outcrop and Subsurface Examples from the Cretaceous of North America*. American Association of Petroleum Geologists Memoirs, **64**, 257–275.

TAYLOR, K. G., GAWTHORPE, R. L. & VAN WAGONER, J. C. 1995. Stratigraphic control on laterally persistent cementation, Book Cliffs, Utah. *Journal of the Geological Society, London*, **152**, 225–228.

VAN WAGONER, J. C., POSAMENTIER, H. W., MITCHUM, R. M., VAIL, P. R., SARG, J. F., LOUTIT, T. S. & HARDENBOL, J. 1988. An overview of sequence stratigraphy and key definitions. *In*: WILGUS, C. K., HASTINGS, B. S., KENDALL, C. G. ST. C., POSAMENTIER, H. W., ROSS, C. A. & VAN WAGONER, J. C. (eds) *Sea-level Changes: an Integrated Approach*. Society of Economists, Paleontologists and Mineralogists Special Publications, **42,** 39–45.

WEHR, F. L. & BRASHER, L. D. 1996. Impact of sequence-based correlation style on reservoir behaviour, lower Brent Group, North Cormorant Field, UK North Sea. *In*: HOWELL, J. A. & AITKEN, J. F. (eds) *High Resolution Sequence Stratigraphy: Innovations and Applications*. Geological Society, London, Special Publications, **104**, 115–128.

Fulmar: a mature field revisited

P. SPAAK,[1] J. ALMOND, S. SALAHUDIN, Z. MOHD SALLEH[2] and O. TOSUN[3]

Shell UK Exploration and Production, 1 Altens Farm Road, Nigg, Aberdeen AB12 3FY, UK (e-mail: p.spaak@openmail2.uesc8.sukepabe.simis.com)
Present addresses: [1] Petroleum Development Oman, PO Box 81, Muscat, Sultanate of Oman
[2] Sarawak Shell Berhad, Locked Bag No. 1, 98009 Miri, Sarawak, Malaysia
[3] Shell Philippines, Exploration B.V., Shell House, 156 Valero St, Salcedo Village, Makati City, Phillipines

Abstract: The original STOIIP of the Fulmar Field is currently estimated as 853×10^6 STB and it is considered that approximately 540×10^6 STB of oil has so far been produced, representing 63.4% of the original reserves. This high recovery factor coupled with an increasingly high water-cut (currently averaging 90%) suggests that the end of field life is drawing close. Prior to making an abandonment decision however it was considered prudent to review and update both the geological and dynamic reservoir models in order to ensure that the full field potential has been realized before making provisions for abandonment. In this context, the depositional model and stratigraphic architecture of the Upper Jurassic Fulmar Sands have been reviewed. Two geological models have been considered: (1) the pre-existing model; and (2) an alternative model, which reflects continuing uncertainties in the field's stratigraphic architecture.

The main part of the Fulmar reservoir consists of a stacked sequence of shoreface sediments that were deposited within an extensional, back-stepping shallow marine setting. This sequence is punctuated by several minor flooding events, which are characterized by distal, poorer quality shoreface sediments. The latter deposits locally form small, but distinct, pressure and flow discontinuities in the reservoir. These heterogeneities were captured in detail, in a 3D geological model and input into the full field reservoir simulation using the Shell proprietary GEOCAP/MoReS software. The history match of the dynamic reservoir model predicted that by-passed oil could be locally trapped below these flooding events. This concept was confirmed in mid 1997 by two wells drilled on the crest of the field. The simulation model also indicates that a significant volume of potentially unswept oil may be present on the NE flank of Fulmar within the poorer reservoir quality, lower shoreface 'Clyde sands'. This concept will be tested by drilling a horizontal well into these sands in the mid part of 1998. As the architecture of the alternative geological model showed some differences to the pre-existing field geological model, particularly in the down flank areas, this model was also input into the GEOCAP simulation in order to compare and test the reliability of the simulation predictions. Only minimal differences were observed between the two simulation models, which reflects the dominantly high net : gross (N : G) in the main producing western part of the field and the similarity of the correlations in the crestal and eastern parts of the field.

Both similation models show a significant improvement in the history match, which highlights the potential benefits to be gained by constructing detailed 3D reservoir models that better describe the architecture of the flow units and barriers in the reservoir than more 'traditional' layer-based (CPS-3) models. These studies are helping to maximize recovery from this high-quality, strongly depleted reservoir.

This paper primarily presents a review of the stratigraphic architecture models proposed for the Fulmar Formation in the field. The study integrates new biostratigraphic and ichnofacies data from cores with log and pressure data in order to establish an updated genetic (sequence stratigraphic) framework. The main differences to the pre-existing field geological model (Van der Helm *et al.* 1990; Stockbridge & Gray 1991) are described, and the implications of the simulation results for further infill drilling are discussed.

Field history and production performance

Field history

The Fulmar Field was discovered in 1975 by Well 30/16-6 in the Upper Jurassic Fulmar Formation and is located approximately 170 miles southeast of Aberdeen (Fig. 1) in Blocks 30/16 (Shell/Esso) and 30/11b (Shell/Esso/Amoco/Amerada Hess). The field has been on production since 1982 and was unitized in 1989. It is operated by Shell UK Ltd on behalf of the Fulmar Unit.

The hydrocarbons (40° API undersaturated oil) were encountered in a thick, high N : G package of Upper Jurassic, shallow marine sandstones of the Fulmar Formation and within a thin overlying interval of deeper marine turbidite sands encased within the Kimmeridge Clay Formation known as the 'Ribble' (Fig.2). The combined STOIIP of the two reservoir intervals is currently estimated at 853×10^6 STB, of which 90% is contained within the Fulmar Formation.

The initial field development focused on the Fulmar Formation and in 1978 the pre-drilling of 4 production wells commenced from a template. The 36 slot Fulmar Alpha Platform was installed in 1980 and oil production started in 1982. The development plan was a peripheral water injection scheme designed to maintain reservoir pressures sufficiently high to allow the wells to flow naturally even at high watercuts. The initial development comprised 12 production wells supported by 10 down-dip water-injectors and one crestal gas injector (Fig. 3). The producing wells were completed bottom up and as these intervals watered out, shallower intervals were perforated. Because of the lack of gas export facilities, gas was

SPAAK, P., ALMOND, J., SALAHUDIN, S., MOHD SALLEH, Z. & TOSUN, O. 1999. Fulmar: a mature field revisited. *In*: FLEET, A. J. & BOLDY, S. A. R. (eds) *Petroleum Geology of Northwest Europe: Proceedings of the 5th Conference*, 1089–1100. © Petroleum Geology '86 Ltd. Published by the Geological Society, London.

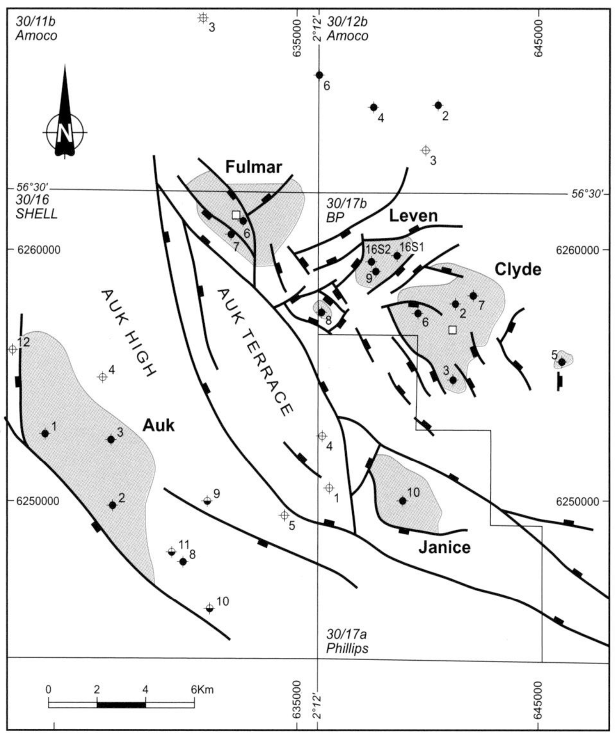

Fig. 1. Location of the Fulmar Field in the Central North Sea area.

re-injected into the field until 1986, forming a secondary gas cap. The field reached a plateau of *c.* 160×10^3 STB(D) in 1985 (Fig. 4), which was maintained until 1991 by the drilling of five more crestal Fulmar sands producers and additional perforations of the Ribble sandstones. Production has subsequently declined and, by the end of 1997, the field was producing at 12×10^3 STB(D) of oil with a 90% water-cut.

Production performance

The Ribble sandstones are generally of excellent reservoir quality with average porosities of 25 to 35% and permeabilities of 1 to 5 D. However, the occurrence of different oil–water contacts (OWCs), coupled with pressure and production performance data has indicated that these sands have a complicated fault/stratigraphic trapping mechanism, particularly on the crest of the field (Fig. 5). This is evident from: (1) the production history of Well FA-33ST1, located in the south, which required the drilling of a dedicated water injector (FA-29); and (2) the intermittent production behaviour of Wells FA-16 and FA-06, located on the crest of the field.

In general, the Fulmar Formation (Fig. 6) comprises very fine to medium-grained, moderate to well sorted, heavily bioturbated sandstones. The sands are generally of excellent reservoir quality, with porosities typically averaging 23% and permeabilities of 100 to 4000 mD. A reduction in reservoir quality is seen on the eastern flank of the field (average por-

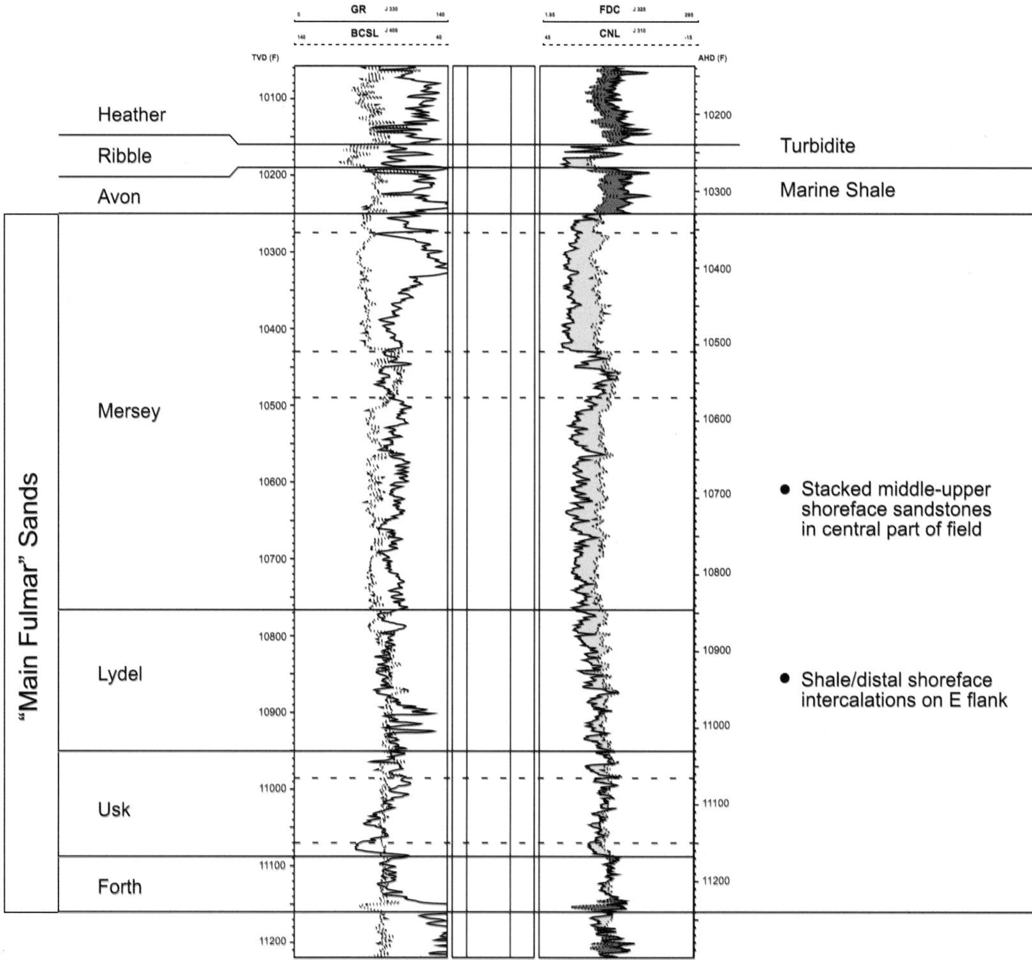

Fig. 2. Fulmar Field discovery well (30/16–6), showing lithostratigraphic subdivision and main environments of deposition.

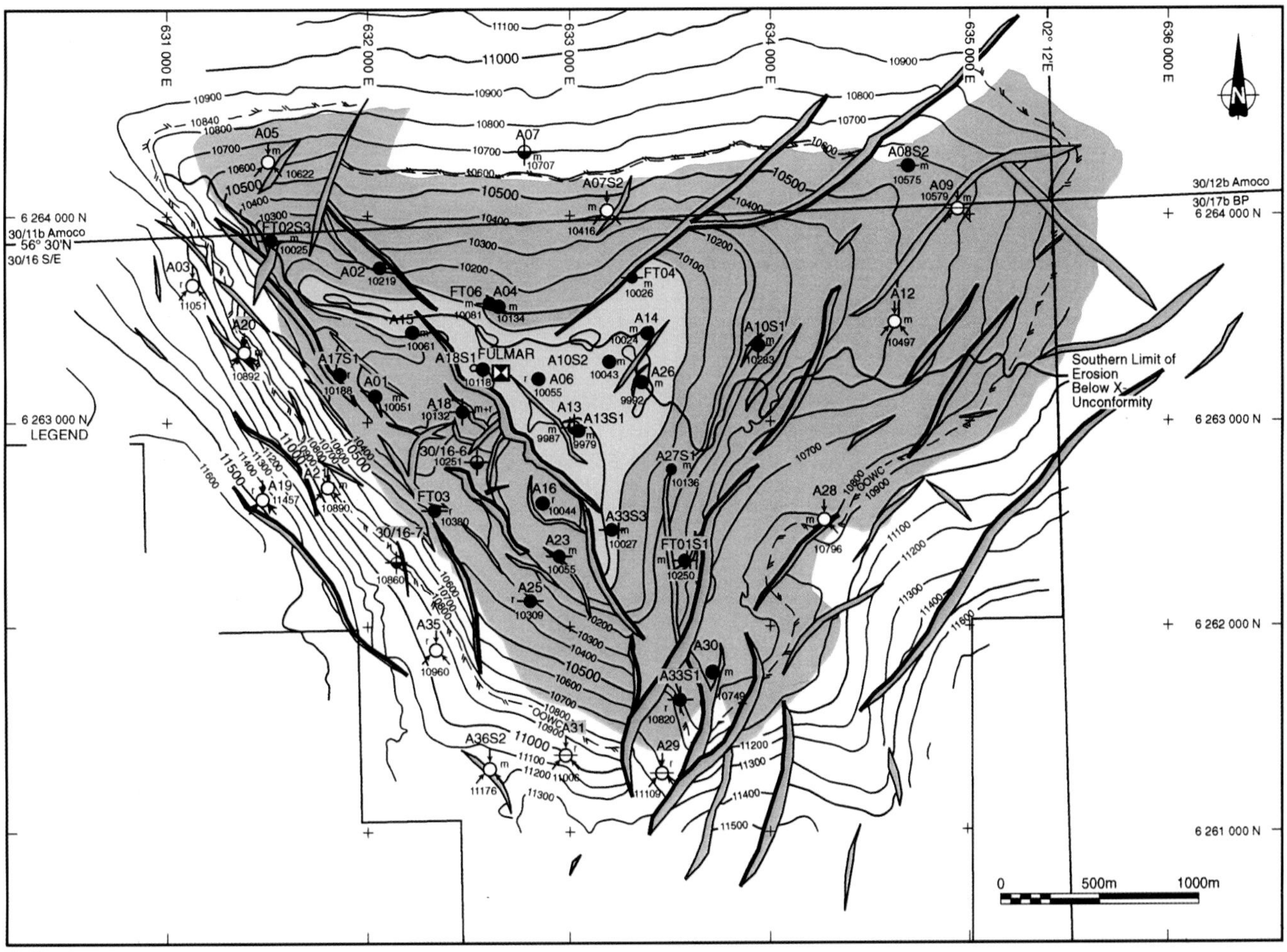

Fig. 3. Top Fulmar Formation depth map.

osity 20%, permeability 10 to 500 mD), which reflects the more distal depositional setting of these sands and more extensive diagenesis.

Historically the Fulmar Formation has been considered to comprise a relatively simple domal closure (Fig. 3) and, because of the overall high N:G and generally uniform pressure history, the sands were assumed to be in good vertical and lateral communication (Fig. 5). A shallower OWC, seen in

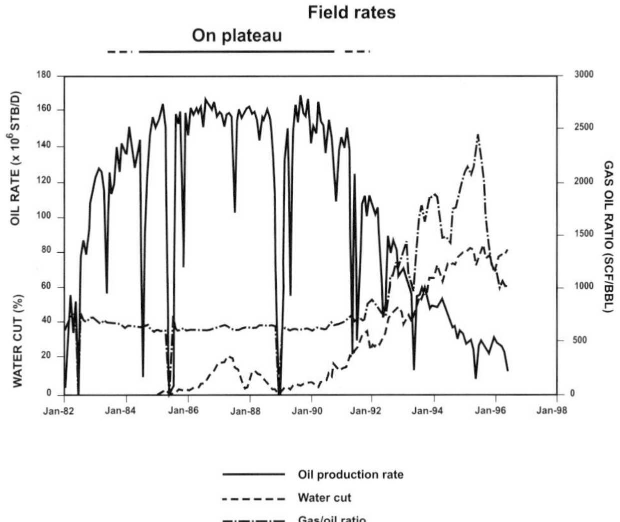

Fig. 4. Production rates. High rates of oil production were maintained until 1991, when the water-cut increased significantly.

the northern part of the field, was interpreted as a perched contact resulting from a combination of fault juxtaposition of reservoir sands (northern area) against non-reservoir (main field area) and the restricted extent of the reservoir sands to the north (Johnson *et al.* 1986). The reservoir level faults were not considered to be sealing and this has been largely borne out by the field performance history, which has shown communication between the northern and main field areas, and the relatively uniform sweep that has been seen on the highly faulted western flank of the field.

Previous model

The pre-existing geological model for the field was developed in the mid 1980s (Johnson *et al.* 1986) and this model was adopted and expanded during the middle part of field life (Van der Helm *et al.* 1990; Stockbridge & Gray 1991). Based on log response and N:G variations (seen mainly in the crest and eastern parts of the field), the Fulmar Formation was subdivided into five reservoir units: Forth,Usk, Lydell, Mersey and Ribble (Figs 2 & 6). This framework formed the basis for the further lithostratigraphical subdivision of the reservoir into 14 layers which were input into a simple layer-cake dynamic reservoir simulation that utilized averaged reservoir properties per layer. During the early years of development, when production came mainly from the stacked high N:G sand interval in the western part of the field, this model adequately matched the field performance. However, with an increasing water-cut and diminishing oil column, this coarse full field model was considered to require updating in order to improve the match with historical data.

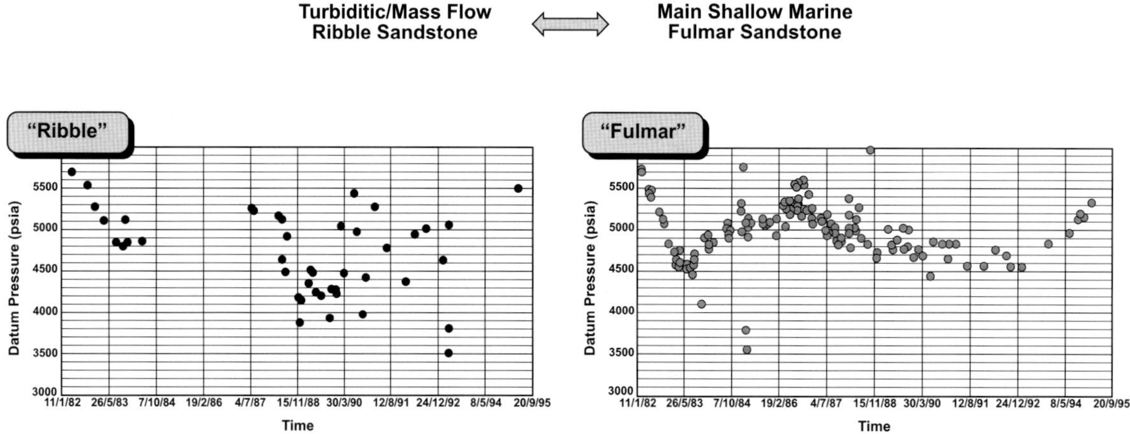

Fig. 5. Pressure data. Uniform pressure history of stacked, shallow marine 'Fulmar' sandstones contrast sharply with the 'scattered' pressure data from the thin turbiditic 'Ribble' sands.

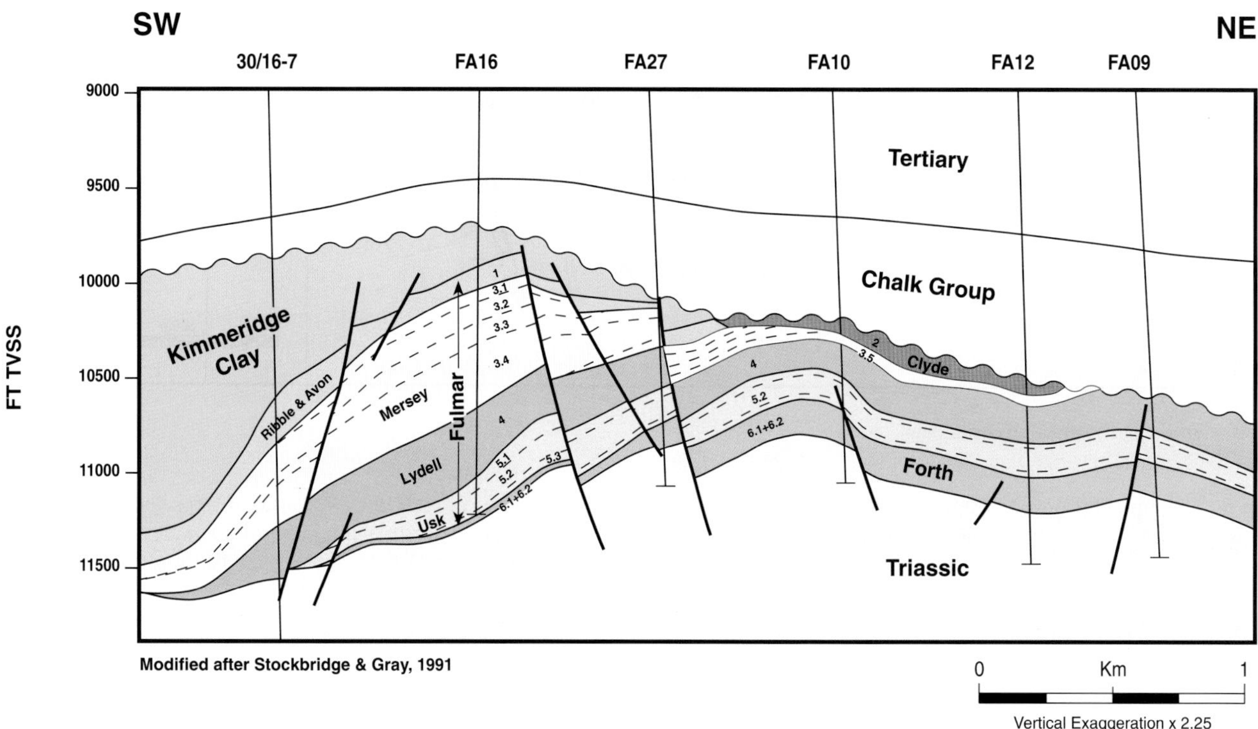

Fig. 6. Fulmar Field cross-section, showing the pre-existing reservoir subdivision based on variations in N : G and illustrating deep truncation by the Base Cretaceous unconformity on the NE flank. The Clyde sands are considered to unconformably overlie the Fulmar sands.

Regional setting and structural history

Regional setting

The structural history of the North Sea Basin, including the Greater Fulmar area, was significantly influenced by Late Triassic to Early Jurassic regional thermal doming. This led to multi-directional (N–S and E–W) extension which initiated large-scale basement faulting, salt halokinesis and the formation of NW–SE trending rift structures. A complicated basin topography was created during the late Middle to Late Jurassic of ramp-like transfer zones alternating with more pronounced topographic breaks related to footwall highs and hanging wall troughs (Fig. 7). This complex topography had a significant impact on the local depositional and accommodation space history (Gawthorpe *et al.* 1994; Howell *et al.* 1996). However, ongoing crustal thinning and subsequent post-rift thermal cooling created a dominantly transgressive depositional regime during the Oxfordian to Kimmeridgian, which resulted in the development of an overall back-stepping trend within the basin (Partington *et al.* 1993). This transgressive trend was further enhanced by a reduction in sediment supply, as hinterlands were drowned (Milton 1993). Basin formation in the Greater Fulmar area started in the northeast, during the Oxfordian, and progressed in a southwesterly direction affecting the Fulmar Field during the latest Oxfordian to early Kimmeridgian.

Structural history

The Fulmar Field is situated on the western edge of the Central Graben, adjacent to the Auk Horst (Fig. 8). Syn-depositional movement along the NW–SE trending Auk Horst boundary fault zone and related salt withdrawal were responsible for the trapping and stacking of a significant interval (*c.* 1200 ft) of

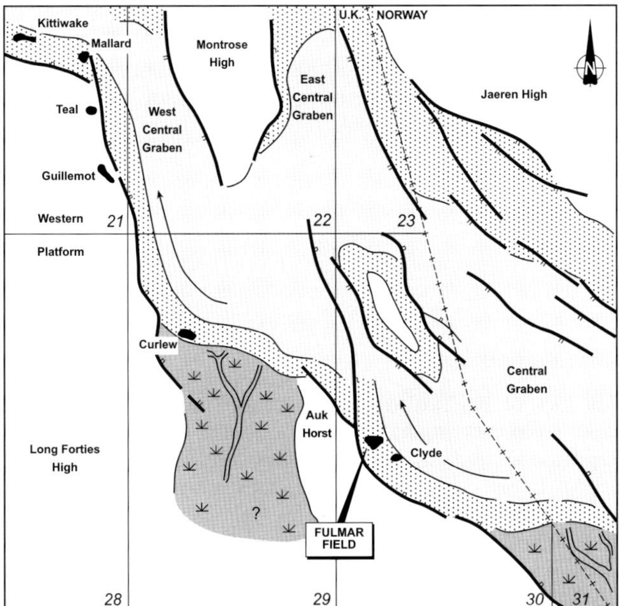

Fig. 7. Schematic basin architecture and facies distribution in the Central North Sea area during the Kimmeridgian. Sediments are assumed to be supplied to the basins via major relay ramps and subsequently redistributed by wave-generated longshore currents. In hanging wall settings, such as the Fulmar area, shallow marine shorefaces accumulate without an attached coastal plain. Dark shading with grass symbol is coastal plain; pale shading is deepwater facies; larger stipple is shallow marine shoreface.

Fulmar sands in the hanging wall trough. This is further reflected in the dominant NW–SE orientation of thickness trends and facies belts across the field.

Fault/salt movements continued during the late Jurassic after the major Kimmeridgian transgression, which terminated sand deposition in the Fulmar area and resulted in a considerable interval of Kimmeridge Clay deposited in the hanging wall trough. The rotation of the Fulmar 'sediment wedge' associated with these movements caused relief for erosion at the Base Cretaceous unconformity on the crest and northern flank of the field (Johnson *et al.* 1986). As a result, the Kimmeridge Clay Formation comprises the reservoir seal in the west and south of the field whilst in the north and northeast, the deeper levels of the Fulmar Formation are sealed by the Chalk (Figs 6 & 8).

Reservoir facies and depositional setting

Reservoir facies

As in previous studies the Ribble sands are interpreted as deeper water turbidite and mass flow deposits. The sandstones are generally massive, although locally graded beds with partly developed Bouma sequences are preserved. Although bioturbated, diagnostic ichnofacies have not been recognized. The sands are generally thin (10 to 30 ft) and separated by thin shales.

A review of the litho- and ichnofacies present in the cored Fulmar wells resulted in the identification of six facies associations indicative of deposition within a relatively low energy shoreface setting. The Fulmar facies interpretation follows the scheme of Gowland (1996) and this interpretation is in keeping with other published models for the Fulmar Formation in the Central Graben (Martin & Pollard 1996). The six lithofacies associations are summarized below.

(1) Offshore: laminated mudstones locally containing very fine sand laminae and *Chondrites* burrows, deposited below storm wave base.
(2) Offshore transition: heterolithic facies of interbedded mudstones, siltsones and very fine to fine-grained, argillaceous sandstones, characterized by *Anchonichus* and *Teichichnus* ichnofacies, deposited between fair weather and storm wave base (Fig. 9).
(3) Lower shoreface: comprising very fine to fine-grained sandstones. *Ophiomorpha* burrows (*Ophiomorpha irregulaire* dominant) are common, bivalve tubes, shell fragments and remnants of wave-generated structures, deposited above or close to fairweather wave base (Fig. 10).
(4) Middle shoreface: fine to medium-grained sandstones, abundant *Ophiomorpha* (mixed *Ophiomorpha irregulaire* and *Ophiomorpha nodosa*) ichnofacies and relict horizontal and low angle stratification. A transitional facies to the upper shoreface (Figs 9 & 10).
(5) Upper shoreface: fine to medium-grained sandstones with parallel bedding and low to high angle cross-bedding

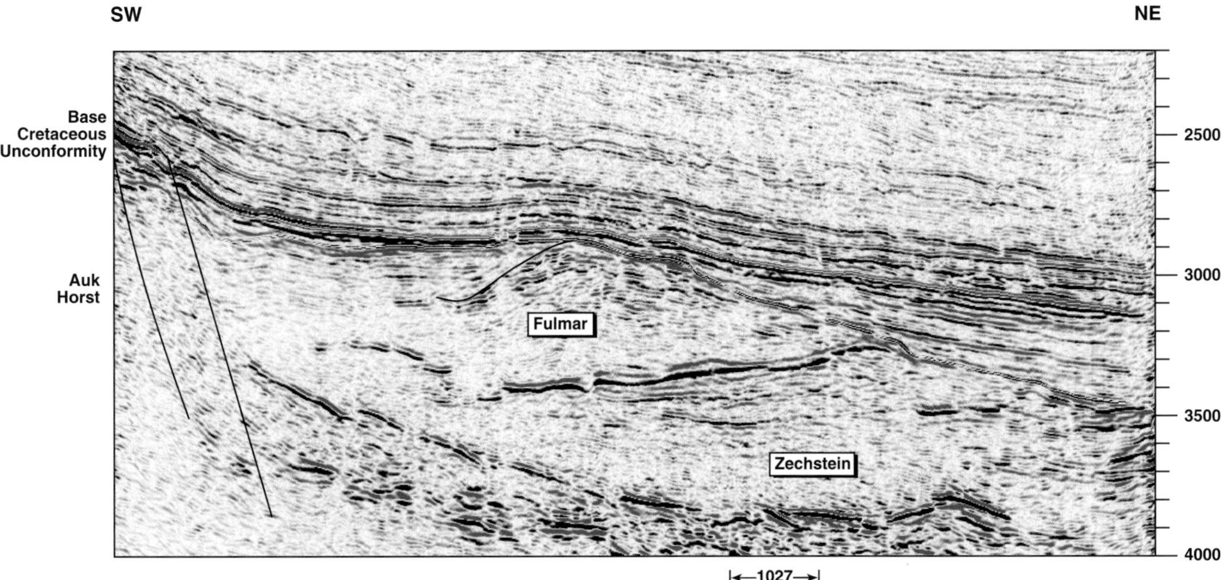

Fig. 8. 3-D seismic line: Fulmar Field (centre) adjacent to the Auk Horst (left), showing a simple domal structure created by extensional faulting and salt withdrawal.

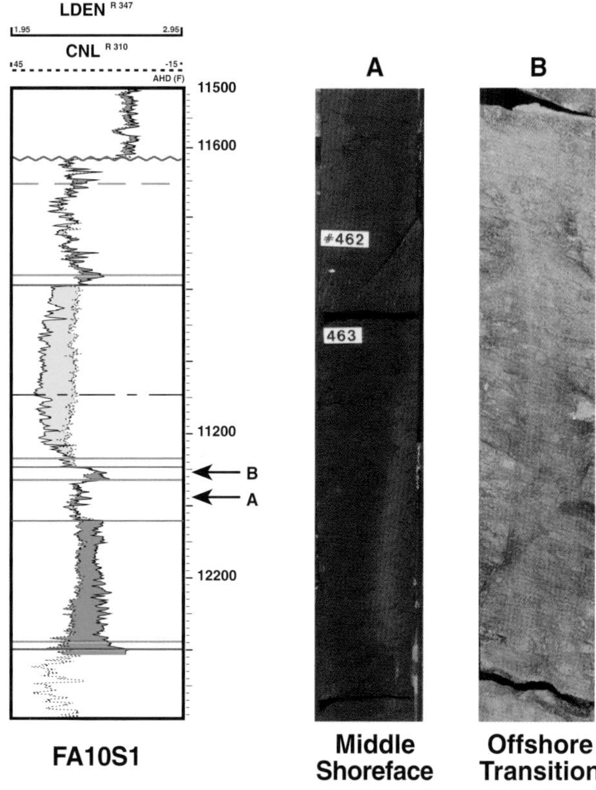

Fig. 9. Log and ichnofacies expression of a flooding event on the east flank of the Fulmar Field (well FA-10S1). Offshore transition facies with diverse ichnofacies (including *Anconichnus* and *Teichichnus*) are found on top of middle shoreface sandstones with scattered *Ophiomorpha*.

containing abundant *Ophiomorpha* ichnofacies (*Ophiomorpha nodosa* dominant), which represent the highest energy sediments found in the field (Fig. 10).

(6) Disrupted, slumped sediments: this facies (previously known as the 'Clyde Sands') is present on the NE flank of the field and dominantly comprises offshore transition and lower shoreface sediments in which the bedding has been highly disrupted. This more distal facies is rich in siliceous sponge spicule debris which has been largely redistributed within the pore space, resulting in a much reduced permeability (Stockbridge & Gray 1991). This redistribution process may also be responsible for the disruptive nature of some of the bedding as evident from the local interbedding of this facies within normal Fulmar sands. Zones of more intense deformation, however, are thought to be the result of slumping in response to syn-sedimentary faulting and/or (flooding induced) instability on an over-steepened depositional slope that developed during the final drowning stage of the Fulmar sands. The occurrence of slumped intervals within these sediments could have implications for the connectivity of this facies to the Fulmar sands in the rest of the field.

Depositional setting

The lack of any features of emergence and associated coastal plain sediments originally threw doubt on whether the Fulmar sands comprised shoreface or shelf sediments (Johnson *et al.* 1986). In the mid 1980s the shelf setting was preferred and the large-scale coarsening upwards sequences that are clearly depicted on the logs (Figs 2 & 11) were interpreted as regressive cycles representing the stacking of a complex series of offshore sand ridges separated by thin transgressive intervals of poorer reservoir quality sands (Van der Helm *et al.* 1990; Stockbridge & Gray 1991).

However, the upper shoreface facies (equivalent to 'facies association A' of Gowland 1996) is taken to indicate deposition under intermediate wave energy conditions which are more likely to occur in an attached shoreface setting. The absence of associated coastal plain deposits may possibly be explained by the position of the Fulmar field directly adjacent to a footwall high. Sediment input to the area is assumed to be via a relay ramp located to the southeast (Fig. 7). In these transfer zones the occurrence of attached coastal plain facies is considered to be more likely. These sediments were then redistributed by longshore currents and accumulated in the hanging wall trough. This model is comparable to those proposed by other workers for similar Jurassic settings (Gawthorpe *et al.* 1994; Howell *et al.* 1996; Ravnås & Steel 1998).

Stacking patterns and discontinuities

The core facies data were calibrated with the well logs in order to interpret the large-scale upwards coarsening sequences present within the Fulmar sands and to establish a correlation framework across the field. To assist in this study, stratigraphic modelling was undertaken using the Shell proprietary

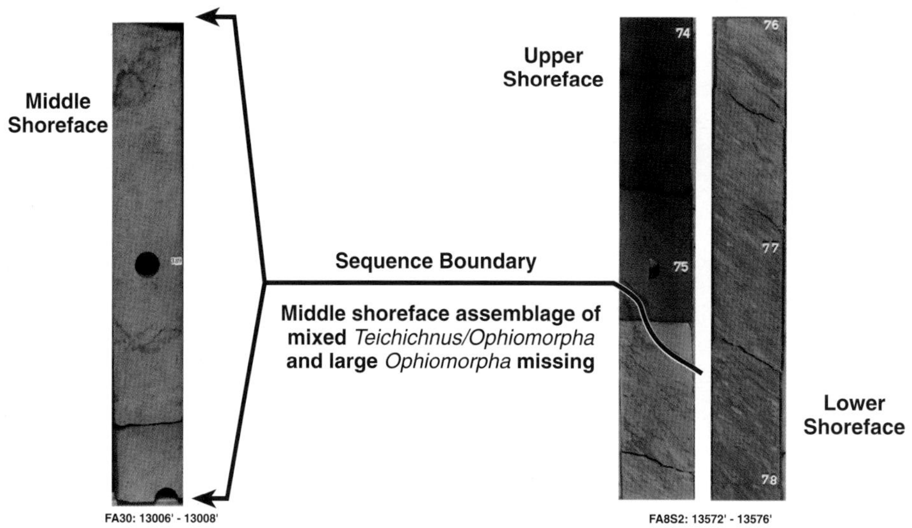

Fig. 10. Ichnofacies supporting a downward shift in the environment of deposition; Well FA-8S2.

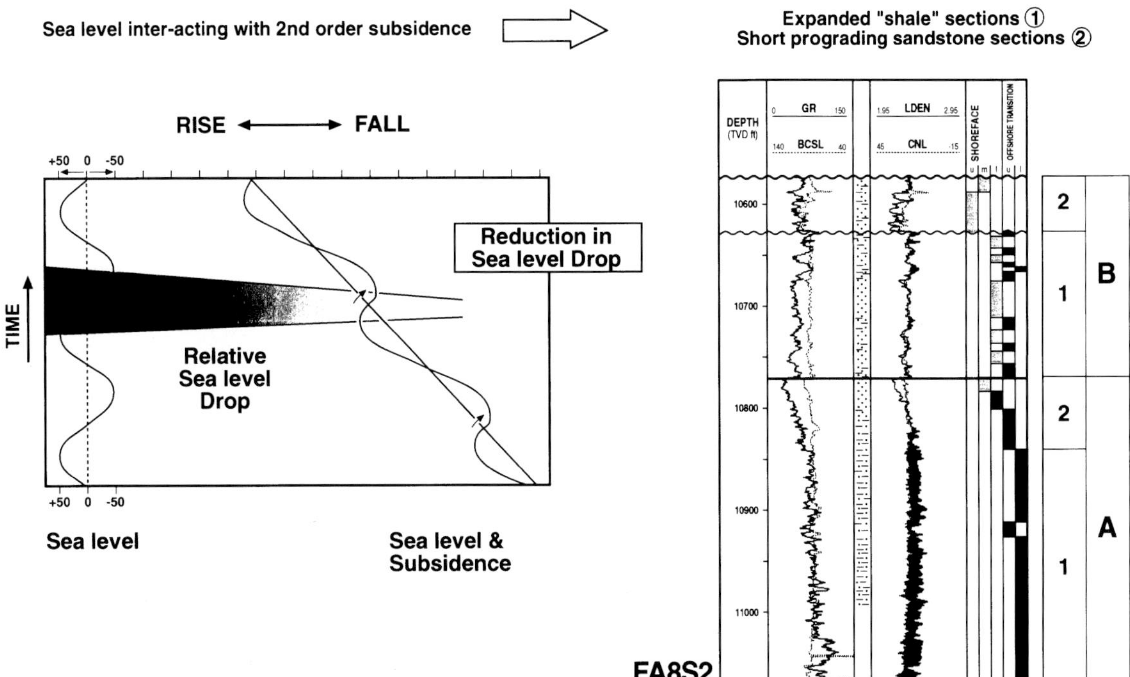

Fig. 11. Stratal stacking patterns in Well FA-8S2. Depositional sequences show expanded shaly transgressive systems tracts in response to strong tectonic subsidence. The upper prograding sandstone package is sharp based and has a distinct basinward shift in the environment of deposition (see also Fig. 10).

STRATAGEM software, which is a stratigraphic forward-modelling program (Levell & Leu 1993). This enabled the generation of stacking patterns using different rates of subsidence and sea-level rise within an extensional transgressive regime, which could be compared with the stacking patterns seen in Fulmar.

The large-scale upward coarsening sequences are interpreted as stacked prograding shorefaces. The lowermost parts of these cycles comprise offshore transition or lower shoreface facies that are usually gradationally overlain by middle to upper shoreface deposits. On the eastern flank of the field, expanded offshore transition/lower shoreface intervals are prominent, representing the occurrence of long transgressive intervals and short periods of relative sea-level fall (Fig. 11). These stacking patterns, which are also reported from other Upper Jurassic North Sea sequences (Carruthers *et al.* 1996; Veldkamp *et al.* 1996), are indicative of deposition within an extensional transgressive regime.

In the central and eastern parts of the Fulmar Field, the tops of prograding sequences are generally overlain by finer-grained, lower shoreface/offshore transition facies (Fig. 9). These minor deepening events are often associated with small, but distinct pressure breaks (Fig. 12) and are easily correlated across the field. In the western part of the field, syn-sedimentary faulting resulted in trapping of a thick aggradational succession of fine to medium-grained, middle and upper shoreface sands. Distal, poorer reservoir quality facies were not deposited in the main reservoir interval and therefore the reservoir sands are in good vertical communication.

On the eastern flank, some variations in stacking patterns are observed that point to the occurrence of more prominent erosion within the prograding sequences. In Well FA-08ST2 for example, sequence A (Fig. 11) shows an extended aggradational phase followed by a rapid progradation into middle shoreface sands. Sequence B however has a lower aggradational interval that is sharply overlain by upper shoreface facies (Figs 10 & 11). This rapid progradation points to shoreface erosion or even the occurrence of a 'forced regression' (Plint 1988; Posamentier *et al.* 1992). Such sequences may remain attached to the preceeding highstand shoreface succession but,

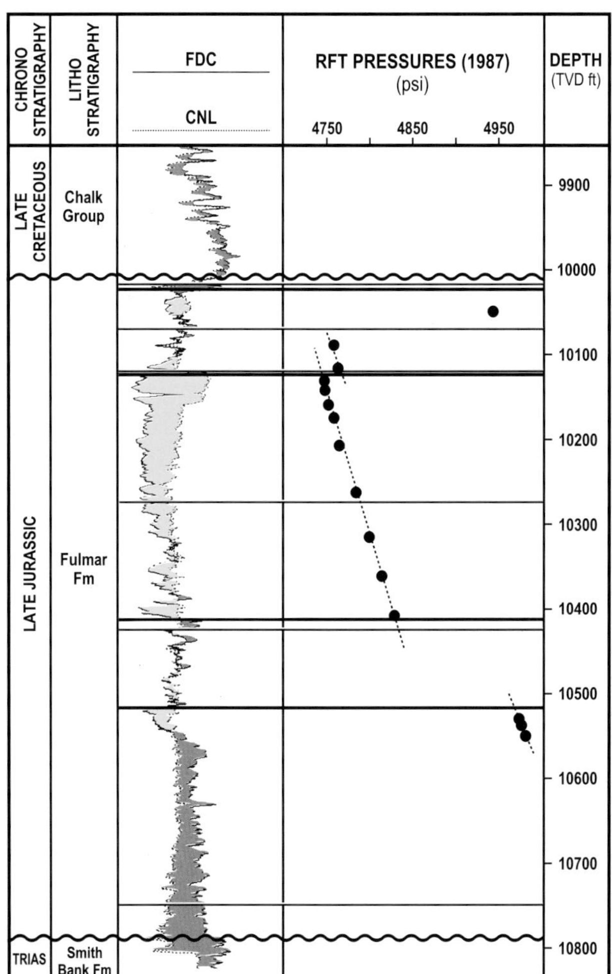

Fig. 12. Pressure data from Well FA-14; flooding events on the eastern flank of the field are clearly associated with breaks in the RFT pressure trends.

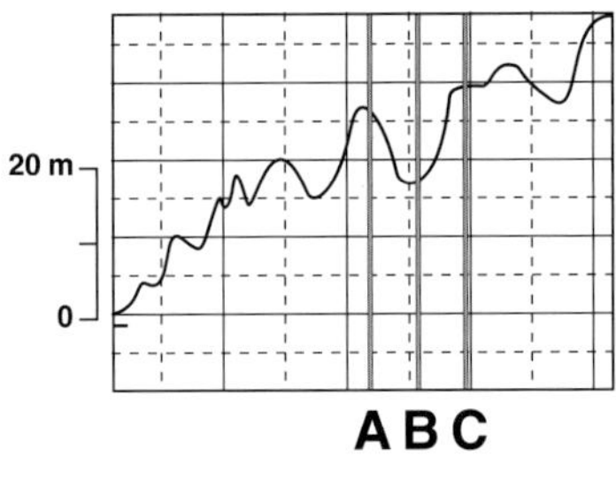

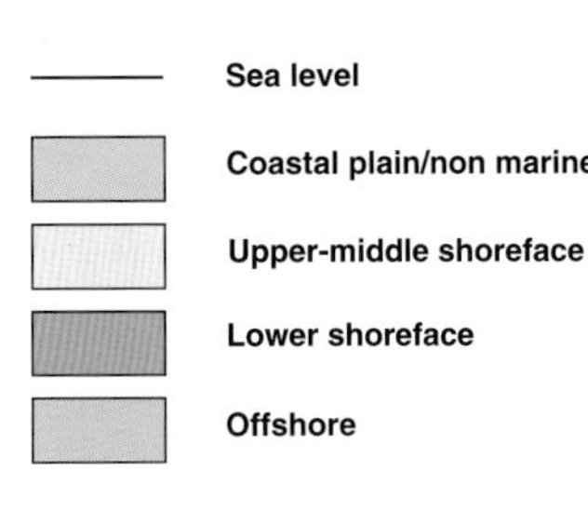

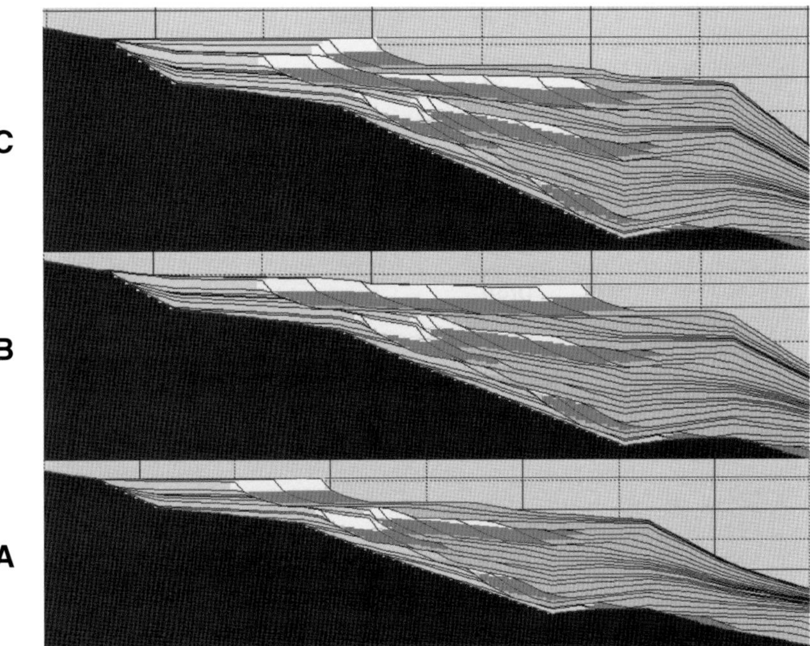

Fig. 13. Three successive stages of a stratigraphic modelling run, simulating a second order back-stepping system, punctuated by several small higher frequency cycles. Sediment input and subsidence were kept constant (the latter increasing slightly down-dip). During the initial part of the run, relative sea-level fluctuations were not big enough for good quality prograding systems to be formed/preserved and consequently the shoreface system was effectively held back. (**A**) Onset of relative drop in sea-level (accommodation) and shoreface prograding. (**B**) A drop in relative sea-level of approximately 10 m results in a rapidly prograding shoreface sequence but although downward shifts are present, the system does not become detached. To create stratigraphic/reservoir discontinuities by base-level fall, the rate or magnitude had to be significantly increased. (**C**) During a base-level rise (section C) using approximately the same magnitude and rate as the preceding base-level drop, the prograding shoreface unit is seriously modified by the back-stepping shoreface erosion, and stratigraphic (reservoir) discontinuities can occur.

if the rate of relative sea-level fall increases, they can become detached, creating discontinuities in the reservoir.

In order to get an appreciation of the likelihood of such discontinuities occurring in the Fulmar reservoir, this process was modelled in STRATAGEM. Three different stages of a sea-level cycle were modelled within a transgressive regime (Fig. 13): (1) highstand/onset of a relative seal-level fall; (2) relative sea-level fall (*c.* 10 m); and (3) relative sea-level rise. The results suggest that in order to get detached shorefaces, the rate and magnitude of drop in relative sea-level has to be considerable and therefore the presence of such detached shorefaces in the Fulmar reservoir is considered unlikely. Prograding shorefaces can also become detached, however, as a result of transgressive erosion even during a moderate sea-level rise (Fig. 13), but no evidence for the occurrence of such sequences has been observed.

Correlation framework

The pre-existing and alternative geological models of the Fulmar Field are both based on a genetic (sequence stratigraphic) framework and therefore in many areas are similar. However, new biostratigraphic data suggest that a different architecture is possible on the flanks of the field.

As in other parts of the Central Graben, the sequence stratigraphic framework for the shallow marine Upper Jurassic sediments is best established from the recognition of flooding surfaces within the shoreface sequences. These events are much easier to identify and correlate than other genetic horizons and are usually prominently developed with aggrading to slightly prograding shoreface successions in between (cf. Partington *et al.* 1993). One such shoreface succession occurs between the 'Balyei' and 'Eudoxus' maximum flooding events, which bound the main part of the reservoir in the Fulmar Field (Fig. 14). Within this major cycle, several higher frequency cycles are recognized in the crestal and eastern parts of the field that are correlated with minor flooding events in the basin. These minor higher frequency events have formed the basis for the reservoir correlation in the field.

In the alternative geological model three main stages in the deposition of the Fulmar Formation in the Fulmar Field are identified (Fig. 14).

1. Initial onlap stage. Biostratigraphic age data (Fig. 15) point to the occurrence of an older ('pre-Baylei') Fulmar sequence in the northern part of the field which represents the initial onlap of the Fulmar sands onto the Triassic. This interpretation is radically different to the pre-existing geological model which, based on well log correlation, considers these sands to be of equivalent age to the rest of the Fulmar in the main part of the field (Fig. 15). The evidence for this older sequence is based on fairly robust biostratigraphical data, derived from core samples from three of the northern wells. It also fits with regional age relations seen in the Fulmar Formation to the north of the field in Block 30/12. The presence of this older sequence, however, requires rapid lateral facies and thickness changes over short distances in the field, which contrasts with the wider and more gradational changes seen elsewhere in the Fulmar succession.

2. Main progradation stage. The lower boundary of this stage coincides with the basin-wide 'Baylei' maximum flooding event. In the eastern part of the field, the basal part of this succession comprises an offshore shaley interval and the biostratigraphic data suggest that it is laterally equivalent to stacked shoreface sandstones deposited in the western part of the field (Fig. 15).

In the crestal and eastern flank areas the reservoir correlation is based on the occurrence of minor flooding events. The correlation of these deepening events into the western, sand-dominated part of the field is difficult, however,

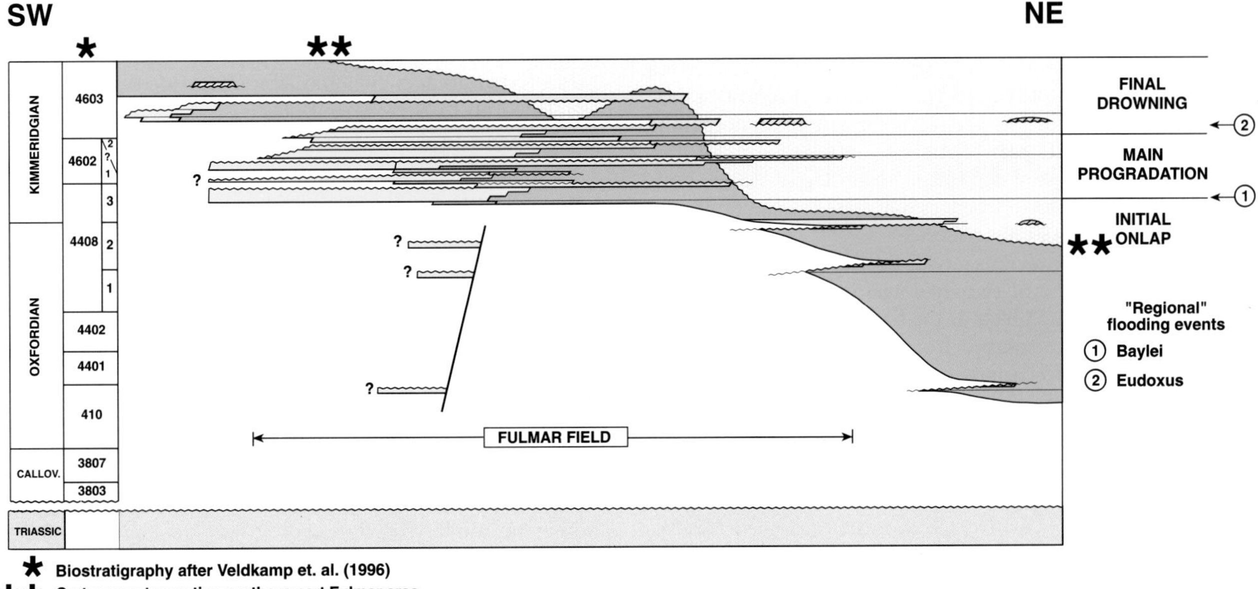

Fig. 14. High-resolution chronostratigraphic chart of the Fulmar Field. The main part of the reservoir is formed by stacked aggrading to slightly prograding shorefaces between the 'Baylei' and 'Eudoxus' flooding events (Partington *et al.* 1993). In this package several high frequency cycles can be recognized.

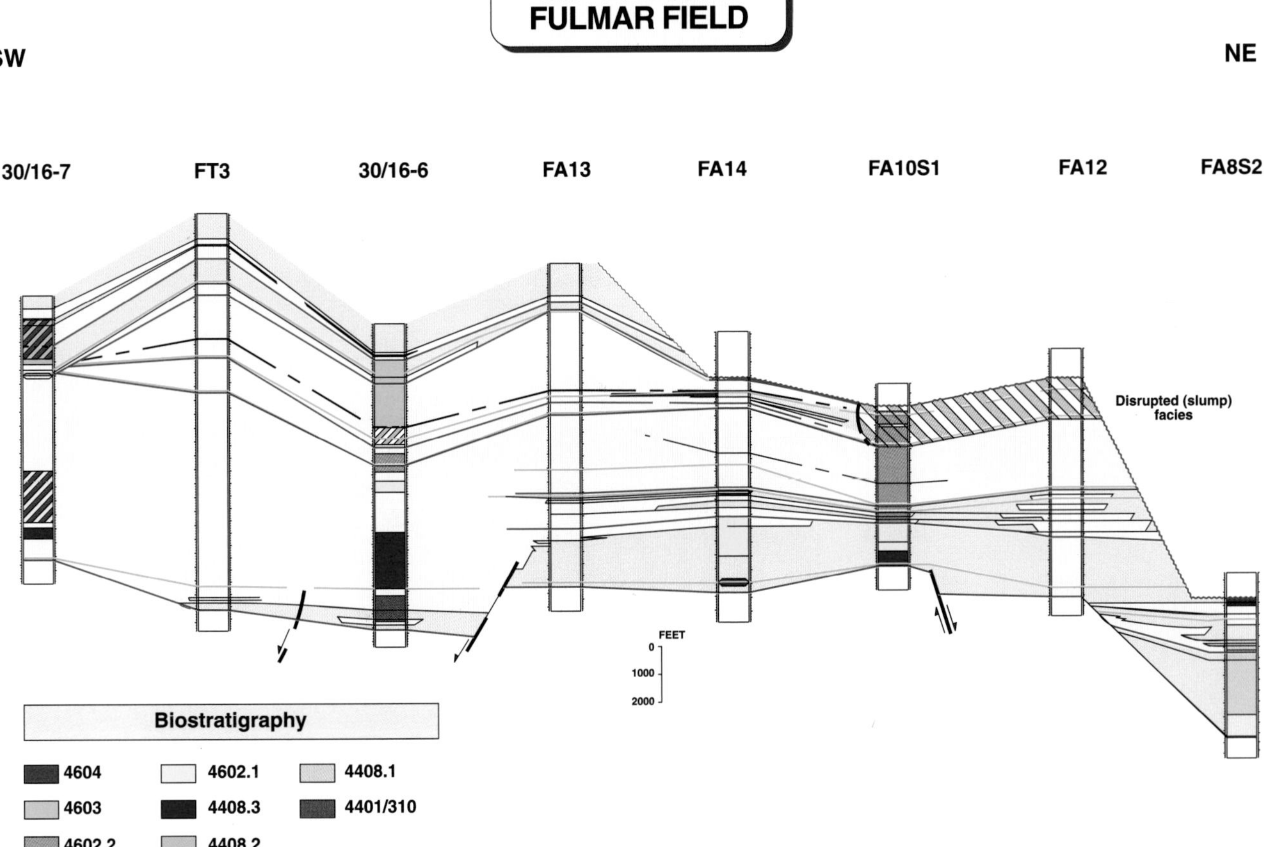

Fig. 15. Schematic dip cross-section showing facies distribution and biostratigraphic constraints. The biostratigraphy suggests the presence of an older section on the northern area of the field. Shale sections in the northeastern area are time equivalent with stacked shoreface sandstones in the west.

because of the limited biostratigraphic control (low preservation potential) and is often tentative. Some differences to the pre-existing correlation are therefore seen in the western part of the field but their impact on the field dynamics is expected to be minimal due to the overall high N : G of the interval.

3. Final drowning stage. The new biostratigraphic data suggest that the deepening in the Fulmar area which culminated with the basin wide 'Eudoxus event' occurred in several stages. The correlation points to the development of a deepening embayment in the SE part of the field into which mass flow and turbidite sands were deposited. These deeper water sands are interpreted as lowstand wedges that were formed down-dip of the youngest Fulmar shorefaces.

This differs to the previous model, in which the Ribble sands were considered to be of the same age and deposited after a single major drowning phase at the end of Fulmar Formation time. The sands were sourced from the Auk Horst area and deposited as thin sheet sands across the western and crestal parts of the field.

3D reservoir models

The Shell proprietary GEOCAP software was used to construct 3D reservoir models of both the pre-existing and the alternative geological models for both the Fulmar and Ribble reservoir intervals. The GEOCAP software (MONARCH) uses a hierarchical approach to construct the 3D models and this enables lateral facies transitions within the reservoir units/cycles to be modelled in detail (Fig. 16). The architecture of the non and poor reservoir quality facies intervals can be clearly visualized (Fig. 17).

Reservoir property models were constructed by interpolating between wells following the hierarchical correlation framework and honouring facies dependent trends in porosity and permeability. Calculated porosity logs and facies dependent porosity/permeability transforms were used to construct the permeability logs. By interpolating these properties between close spaced wells, a detailed 3D description of the internal heterogeneity of the reservoir was achieved, which provides a clear description of flow units and barriers within the reservoir.

The static models were up-scaled to twenty-two layers and transferred to the dynamic simulator (MoReS) and history matched up to September 1997.

By-passed hydrocarbons – observations from the dynamic models

No major differences were observed between the history matches of both the pre-existing and the alternative geological models. This is taken to reflect the dominant contribution of the western part of the field on the historical production performance. In the western area, the main part of the Fulmar reservoir comprises a high N : G interval of stacked shorefaces and the poorer reservoir quality flooding/deepening events present in the crestal and eastern flanks are not developed. The absence of vertical permeability baffles in this area means that differences in the correlation of the two geological models have little impact on the production performance. This is evident from the TDT logs run in the western flank wells and is reflected in both simulation models by the uniformity of the sweep seen in this part of the field.

The main differences in the geological models occur in the down flank areas of the field, which also appear to have little impact on the field production performance. A possible exception however is in the southwest, where the alternative geological model points to the occurrence of stratigraphically isolated Ribble sands. As no obvious differences in the history match were seen in the simulation of both geological models in

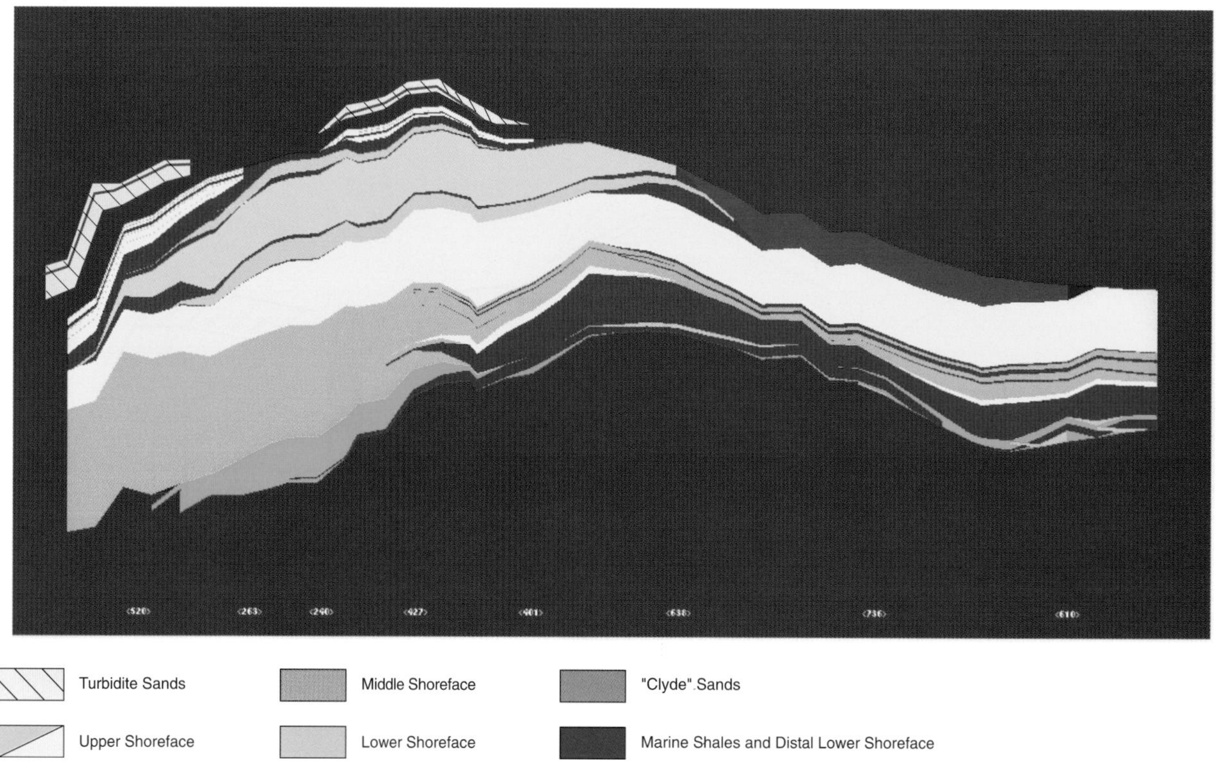

Fig. 16. Cross-section through the 3D static reservoir model, showing the modelling of facies distribution. Non-reservoir distal shorefaces and marine shales are indicated in brown.

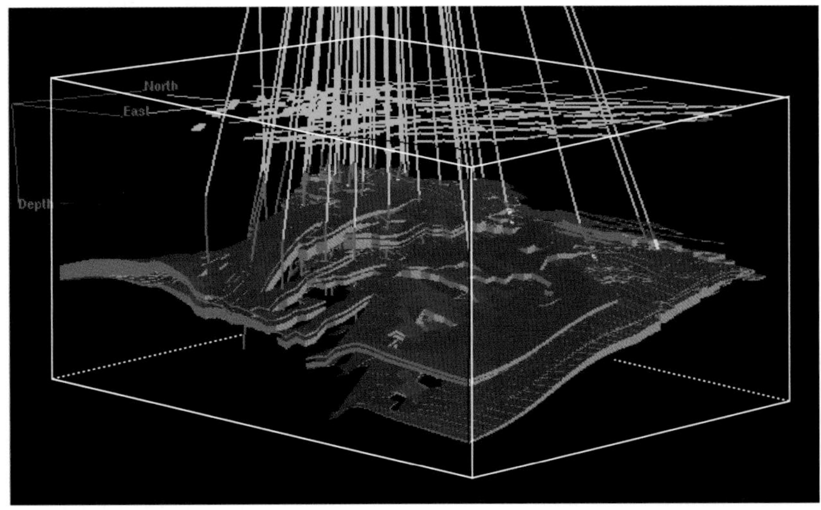

Fig. 17. Static 3D reservoir model, showing distribution of non-reservoir distal shorefaces and marine shales (view from SE).

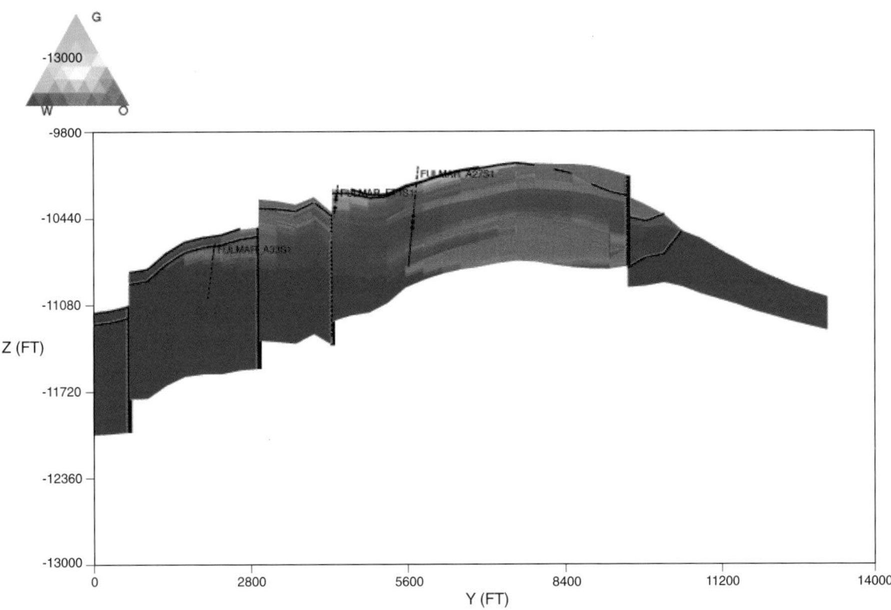

Fig. 18. Cross-section through the full field dynamic model, showing the occurrence of by-passed oil below discrete flooding events and in the poorer quality 'Clyde sands' interval.

this area it is considered that faulting has the greater influence on reservoir performance.

Both simulation models indicate the potential for trapping by-passed oil below finer-grained more distal facies associated with minor flooding events in the reservoir. This is particularly evident in the crestal and eastern parts of the field where, in the deeper stratigraphic levels of the Fulmar reservoir (Usk), the models predict the presence of by-passed oil (Fig. 18). This concept was tested during mid 1997 by the drilling of two crestal Wells FA-10ST2 (Fig. 19) and FA-18ST1. The prime objective of both these wells was to recover undrained attic oil and benefit from accelerated production from the remaining thin oil zone in the crest of the field. Both wells were deepened into the flushed reservoir intervals and each encountered a significant column of by-passed oil below the watered-out sands. The wells have been brought onto production but the initial results are disappointing, pointing to limited connected volumes. The seismic dataset for the field is currently being re-processed and a re-interpretation of the faulting at this reservoir level will be undertaken.

In addition, both simulation models have also indicated the potential for unswept oil being present in the more distal and poorer reservoir quality facies (Clyde sands) located on the NE flank of the field. These poor quality sands are vertically separated from underlying flushed sands by a minor (non-reservoir quality) flooding event and the sweep pattern in both simulation models indicates that this area has been by-passed. This concept will be tested by drilling a near horizontal well into these sands in the mid part of 1998.

A significant improvement in the history match of both models has highlighted the potential benefits to be gained by constructing detailed 3D reservoir property models that better describe the architecture of the flow units and barriers in the reservoir.

We would like to acknowledge C. Berge and M. G. Gaillard for their technical contribution and H. Johnson for his comments on the manuscript. We thank Shell UK Exploration and Production, Esso Exploration and Production, Amoco and Amerada Hess for permission to publish this paper.

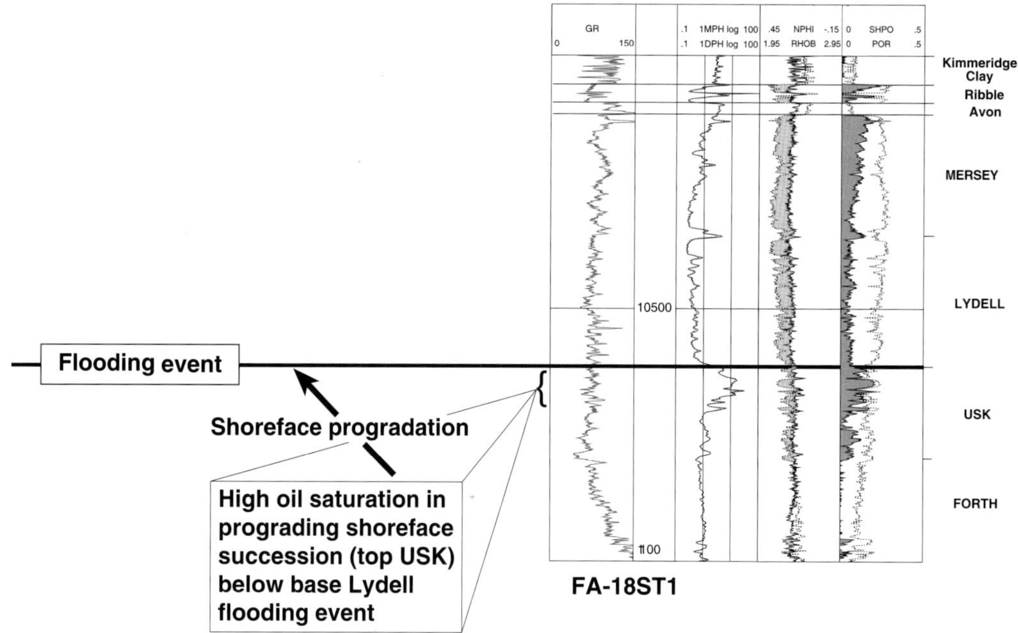

Fig. 19. Well FA-18ST1 confirmed the presence of by-passed oil, locally trapped below a minor flooding event.

References

CARRUTHERS, A., MCKIE, T., PRICE, J., DYER, R., WILLIAMS, G. & WATSON, P. 1996. The application of sequence stratigraphy to the understanding of Late Jurassic turbidite plays in the Central North Sea, UKCS. *In*: HURST, A., JOHNSON, H. D., BURLEY, S. D., CANHAM, A. C. & MACKERTICH, D. S. (eds) *Geology of the Humber Group: Central Graben and Moray Firth, UKCS*. Geological Society, London, Special Publications, **114**, 29–46.

GAWTHORPE, R. L., FRASER, A. J. & COLLIER, R. E. L. 1994. Sequence stratigraphy in active extensional basins: implications for interpretation of ancient basin fills. *Marine and Petroleum Geology*, **11/6**, 642–658

GOWLAND, S. 1996. Facies characteristics and depositional models of highly bioturbated shallow marine siliciclastic strata: an example from the Fulmar Formation (Late Jurassic), UK Central Graben. *In*: HURST, A., JOHNSON, H. D., BURLEY, S. D., CANHAM, A. C. & MACKERTICH, D. S. (eds) *Geology of the Humber Group: Central Graben and Moray Firth, UKCS*. Geological Society, London, Special Publications, **114**, 185–214.

HOWELL, J. A., FLINT, S. S. & HUNT, C. 1996. Sedimentological aspects of the Humber Group (Upper Jurassic) of the South Central Graben, UK North Sea. *Sedimentology*, **43**, 89–114.

JOHNSON, H. D., MACKAY, T. A. & STEWART, D. J. 1986. The Fulmar Oil-field (Central North Sea): geological aspects of its discovery, appraisal and development. *Marine and Petroleum Geology*, **3**, 99–125.

LEVELL, B. K. & LEU, W. 1993. Stratigraphic basin modelling – recent advances. *In*: DORÉ, A. G. *et al.* (eds) NPF Special Publications, **3**, Elsevier, Amsterdam, 71–83.

MARTIN, M. A. & POLLARD, J. E. 1996. The role of trace fossils (ichnofabric) analysis in the development of depositional models for the Upper Jurassic Fulmar Formation of the Kittiwake field (Quadrant 21, UKCS). *In*: HURST, A., JOHNSON, H. D., BURLEY, S. D., CANHAM, A. C. & MACKERTICH, D. S. (eds) *Geology of the Humber Group: Central Graben and Moray Firth, UKCS*. Geological Society, London, Special Publications, **114**, 163–184.

MILTON, N. J. 1993. Evolving depositional geometries in the North Sea Jurassic rift. *In*: PARKER, J. R. (ed.) *Petroleum Geology of Northwest Europe: Proceedings of the 4th Conference*. Geological Society, London, 425–442.

PARTINGTON, M. A., COPESTAKE, P., MITCHENER, B. C. & UNDERHILL, J. C. 1993. Biostratigraphic calibration of genetic stratigraphic sequences in the Jurassic of the North Sea and adjacent areas. *In*: PARKER, J. R. (ed.) *Petroleum Geology of Northwest Europe: Proceedings of the 4th Conference*. Geological Society, London, 371–386

PLINT, A. J. 1988. Sharp-based shoreface sequences and 'offshore bars' in the Cardium Formation of Alberta: their relationship to relative changes in sea-level. *In*: WILGUS, C. K., HASTINGS, B. S., KENDALL, C. G. ST. C., POSAMENTIER, H. W., ROSS, C. A. & VAN WAGONER, J. C. (eds) *Sea Level Changes: An Integrated Approach*. Society of Economic Paleontologists and Mineralogists Special Publications, **42**, 357–370.

POSAMENTIER, H. W., ALLEN, G. P., JAMES, D. P. & TESSON, M. 1992. Forced regressions in a sequence stratigraphic framework: Concepts, examples, and exploration significance. *American Association of Petroleum Geologists Bulletin*, **76/11**, 1687–1709.

RAVNÅS, R. & STEEL, R. J. 1998. Architecture of marine rift-basin successions. *American Association of Petroleum Geologists Bulletin*, **82/1**, 110–146.

STOCKBRIDGE, C. P. & GRAY, D. I. 1991. The Fulmar field, blocks 30/16 & 30/11b, UK North Sea. *In*: ABBOTTS, I. L. (ed.) 1991. *United Kingdom Oil and Gas Fields, 25 Years Commemorative Volume*. Geological Society, London, Memoirs, **14**, 309–316.

VAN DER HELM, A. A., GRAY, D. I. & SCHULTE, M. A. 1990. Fulmar: the development of a large North Sea field. *North Sea Oil and Gas Reservoirs – II*. Norwegian Institute of Technology. Graham & Trotman, 25–45.

VELDKAMP, J. J., GAILLARD, M. G., JONKERS, H. A. & LEVELL, B. K. 1996. A Kimmeridgian time-slice through the Humber Group of the central North Sea: a test of sequence stratigraphic methods. *In*: HURST, A., JOHNSON, H. D., BURLEY, S. D., CANHAM, A. C. & MACKERTICH, D. S. (eds) *Geology of the Humber Group: Central Graben and Moray Firth, UKCS*. Geological Society, London, Special Publications, **114**, 1–28.

Reservoir characterization in the Captain Field: integration of horizontal and vertical well data

P. T. S. ROSE

Texaco Ltd, Langlands House, Huntly St, Aberdeen, UK (e-mail: rosept@texaco.com)

Abstract: The Captain Field lies in UKCS Block 13/22. It is a large viscous oil field with an excellent quality Lower Cretaceous sandstone reservoir. Development of this high viscosity crude (88 cp at the *in situ* temperature, 87°F) in the offshore environment was possible only after the development of reliable horizontal drilling technology, combined with high volume down-hole electric pumps, and the ability to run long pre-packed sand control screens. As the first development of this type within Texaco, the development decision was helped by the extremely favourable reservoir conditions present in the Captain Field.

The Captain reservoir is encountered directly beneath the chalk and consists of Late Aptian aged turbidite sandstones, with high porosity (av. 31%) and permeability (av. 7 D). The sandstones were deposited on the feather edge of a large turbidite fan system derived from the East Shetland Platform to the north and which thins onto the Captain Ridge. The reservoir sequence consists of two principal sand bodies, the Upper and Lower Captain Sandstones with contrasting reservoir geometry. The Upper Captain Sandstone is developed in a continuous sheet that systematically thins and pinches out to the southeast whereas the Lower Captain Sandstone is concentrated in a sand fairway, interpreted to be a back-filled submarine canyon cutting across the Captain ridge. Core description show the sandstones to be predominantly massive suspension fall out sediments (S3 deposits, Lowe 1982) with rare intra-reservoir claystones.

In this paper the reservoir geometry and sedimentology of the Captain Sandstone Member is described with particular attention being drawn to how horizontal drilling has tested and enhanced the geological model. Key reservoir parameters (e.g. connectivity, claystone distribution, grain size distribution, porosity, horizontal and vertical permeability) are discussed and their contribution to the success of the project evaluated.

The Captain Field is a large viscous oil field located in UK Block 13/22a in the Western Moray Firth; equity in the field is divided between Texaco UK North Sea Company (85%, operator) and Korea Captain Company Ltd (15%). The Field was discovered in 1977 by the 13/22a-1 well which encountered oil in over 200 ft of massive unconsolidated Lower Cretaceous sandstones with over 30% porosity at 2791 ft TVDSS (True vertical depth subsea). However, the oil is a heavy (19–21° API) biodegraded crude with *in situ* viscosity of 88 cP; the well did not flow to surface on test. A potential STOOIP of 2×10^9 BBL was recognized at that time but the field was not judged to be an economic development because of the large number of drilling centres (up to 7) that would have been required for a vertical well development. Advances in horizontal drilling, sand control and down-hole pump technology in the late 1980s prompted a detailed re-evaluation of the field and an extensive appraisal programme in the early 1990s (see Pinnock & Clitheroe 1997, for field history). The field is now being developed exclusively with horizontal wells. These are completed with wire-wrapped pre-packed screens for sand production control and large-volume down-hole pumps. First oil was achieved in March 1997 and the field is now producing at up to 65 000 BBL day^{-1}. The oil is produced from well-heads on a platform (WPPA) directly to a floating production storage and offloading vessel (FPSO); export is via shuttle tankers. The engineering aspects of the Captain Field development are discussed by Etebar (1997), Lach (1997), Tavendale (1997), Cohen (1997), Cohen & Dallas (1997) and Sutton (1997).

Reservoir challenges in the Captain development

The principal challenges in the development of the Captain Field result from the high viscosity of the crude, the poor consolidation of the reservoir sandstones and the existence of a free gas cap: close well-bore spacing is required to achieve economic oil recovery from the reservoir (Lach 1997); down-hole pumps are required to flow the oil but the efficiency of the pumps is greatly impaired by gas production (Cohen 1997); sand control screens are essential to prevent damaging sand production; and separation of the oil and water is only efficient at water cuts greater than 50% (Sutton 1997).

Well bore contact with the reservoir has been achieved by drilling long closely-spaced horizontal wells (up to 6000 ft long with a lateral spacing down to 350 ft), each of which is capable of delivering up to 15 000 BOPD with down-hole electric pumps. With this well design only two drilling centres are required by the current development plan in contrast to six or seven required by a vertical well development. The western drilling centre, WPPA, is now under development and producing to the FPSO; the eastern drilling centre is still at the planning stage.

Gas production control is best achieved by keeping the reservoir at close to virgin pressure by water injection from production start-up; this prevents gas coming out of solution (the virgin pressure, average 1340 psi, is close to the bubble point pressure, 1186 psi) and inhibits migration of the free gas cap. Horizontal injection wells are drilled parallel to the production wells and are completed with selectively spaced slotted liners to ensure an even injection profile. Produced water is injected to prevent scaling and crude souring problems which are a common consequence of seawater injection. In order to provide injection water from production start-up and to allow full voidage replacement later in field life an aquifer production well, 13/22a-C4, has been drilled in the Lower Wick Sands, a large water bearing reservoir below the Captain accumulation. This Lower Wick Sand water is also required

ROSE, P. T. S. 1999. Reservoir characterization in the Captain Field: integration of horizontal and vertical well data. *In*: FLEET, A. J. & BOLDY, S. A. R. (eds) *Petroleum Geology of Northwest Europe: Proceedings of the 5th Conference*, 1101–1113. © Petroleum Geology '86 Ltd. Published by the Geological Society, London.

for the separation process, boosting the total water cut in the production line above 50% to allow efficient separation.

Critical reservoir parameters in a horizontal well development such as Captain are:

(1) a predictable reservoir to ensure cost-effective drilling;
(2) high horizontal and vertical permeability so that horizontal wells have sufficient well deliverability;
(3) good connectivity and continuity of the reservoir to ensure that the production wells are supported by water injectors; and
(4) a coarse enough reservoir to allow effective sand control design.

In this paper the sedimentology, reservoir architecture and internal character of the reservoir are described to illustrate how the Captain Sandstone Member amply fulfills these requirements. Uncertainty in the geological model derived from the vertical well control is then discussed and the methods by which this uncertainty has been accommodated during horizontal drilling are described. Finally an illustration is given of possible refinements to the geological model using the horizontal well data.

Structural and stratigraphic context of the Captain Field

Structure and stratigraphic context

The Captain Field lies above the Captain Ridge, a major east–west Mesozoic tilted fault block that forms a west-plunging extension of the Halibut Horst (Fig. 1) and defines the northern boundary to the West Halibut Basin. The trap for the Captain Field is a combined dip–stratigraphic closure (Fig. 2). The dip closure at Base Chalk to the north, west and south is caused by drape over the west-plunging stratigraphically deeper fault block; closure to the east is defined by stratigraphic pinch-out of the reservoir against the Halibut Horst. The structure is defined along three important fault trends, northeast–southwest, northwest–southeast and east–west. Only very minor faulting is observed at Base Chalk within the Captain Field but all three trends appear to have influenced deposition during the lower Cretaceous.

The Mesozoic stratigraphic development of this area was controlled by Permian and Jurassic rifting events (Roberts *et al.* 1990, Underhill 1991). The Carboniferous, Permian and Triassic are absent from the Captain Ridge and a condensed Jurassic sequence directly overlies Devonian sediments (Fig. 3). The lack of Permo-Triassic sediments and the condensed Jurassic succession indicates that the Captain Ridge defined a fault block high during both basin forming events. The Jurassic consists of a pre-rift Oxfordian shore-face sandstone, the Heather Sandstone Member (Pinnock & Clitheroe 1997), overlain by a syn-tectonic wedge of Kimmeridgian–Volgian age that thickens to the northwest. The Jurassic sequence is greatly expanded to the south in the West Halibut Basin.

Seismic stratigraphic relationships show that the Lower Cretaceous sediments generally on-lap the Captain Ridge implying post rift basin infill (Fig. 3). The on-lap relationship is confirmed by well control. A thick Hauterivian to Albian sequence of interbedded turbidite sandstone and claystone overlies the Jurassic to the north of the Captain Field, whereas in 13/22a-3, which lies on the crest of the Captain Ridge, the Lower Cretaceous is only represented by a thin sequence of Late Aptian claystones (Fig. 4). The Albian was a time of sediment starvation over the Captain Ridge with only a thin (0–20 ft) veneer of claystone being deposited.

Differential compaction and the infilling of residual basin topography resulted in a relatively condensed Cenomanian to Turonian chalk succession being deposited over the Captain Ridge in contrast to the Santonian to Maastrichtian chalk which has a more uniform thickness distribution over the Captain area. During the early Tertiary, a sequence of sandstones and claystones accumulated with the addition of locally

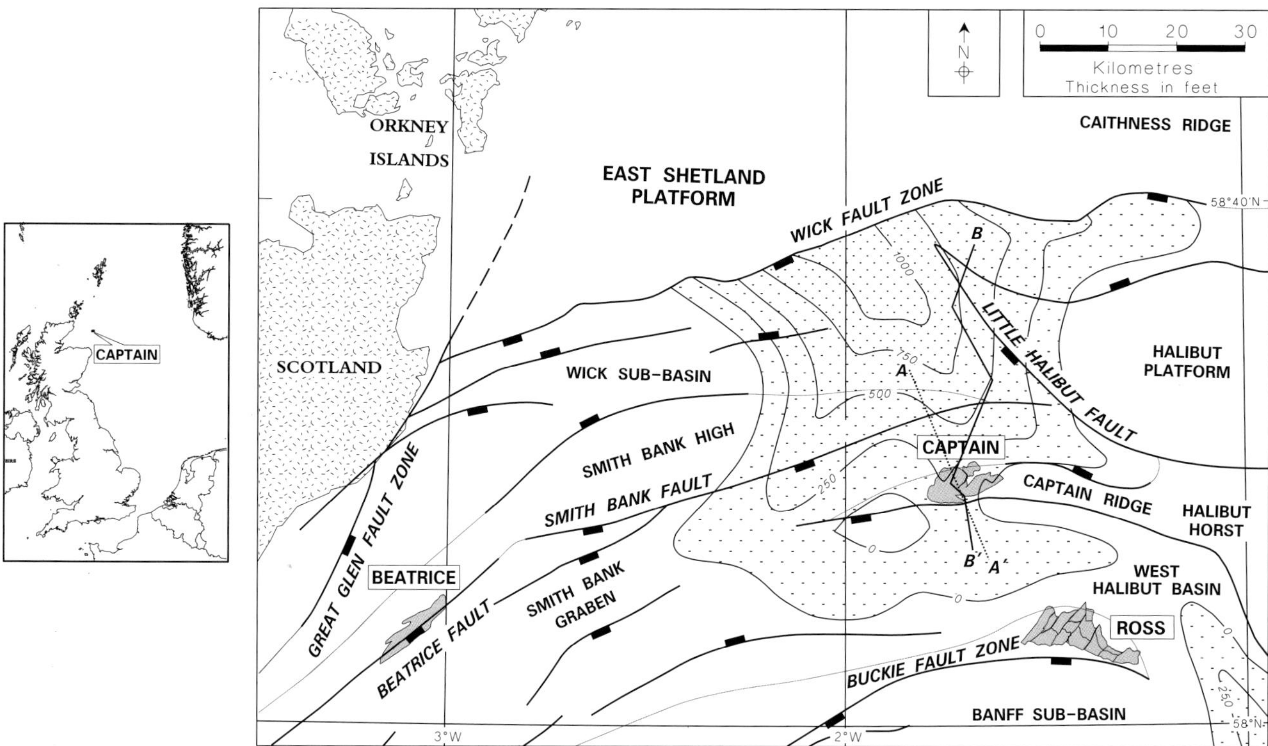

Fig. 1. Captain Field location and geological context (structural elements after Roberts *et al.* 1990). The isochore contours indicate the thickness distribution of the Captain Sandstone member derived from regional well correlations. Line A–A′ shows the line of cross-section drawn in Fig. 3 and line B–B′ the well correlation displayed in Fig. 4.

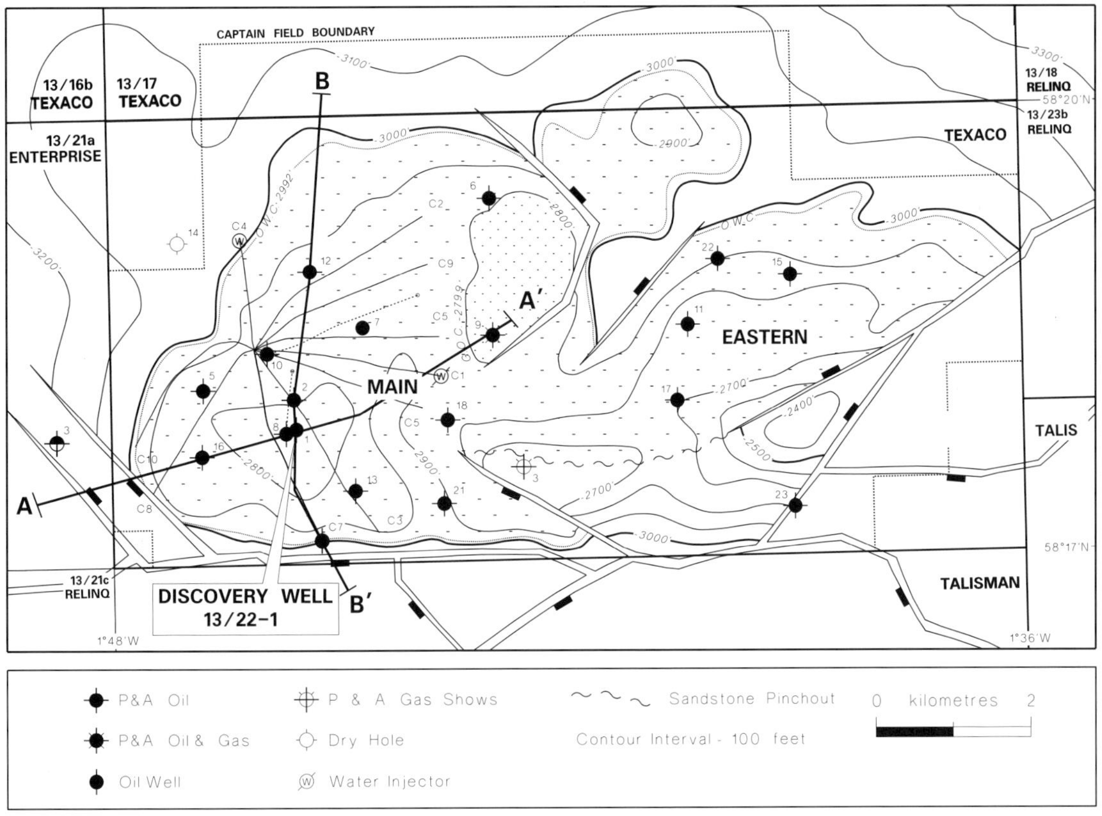

Fig. 2. Captain Field outline. Line A–A′ indicates the seismic and geological section line drawn in Fig. 9. Line B–B′ the geological section in Fig. 10.

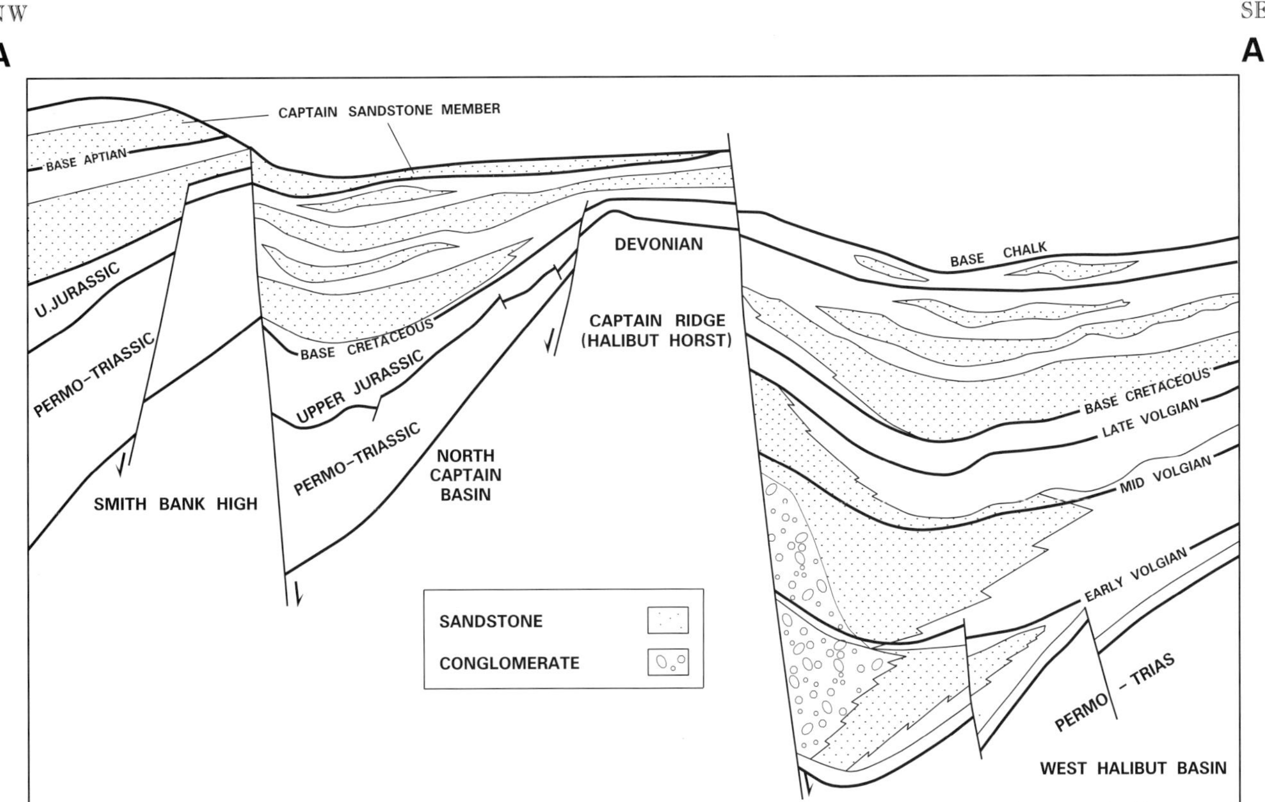

Fig. 3. Seismic stratigraphic cross-section illustrating the pre-Upper Cretaceous stratigraphy of the Captain area. Drawn along line A–A′ shown in Fig. 1.

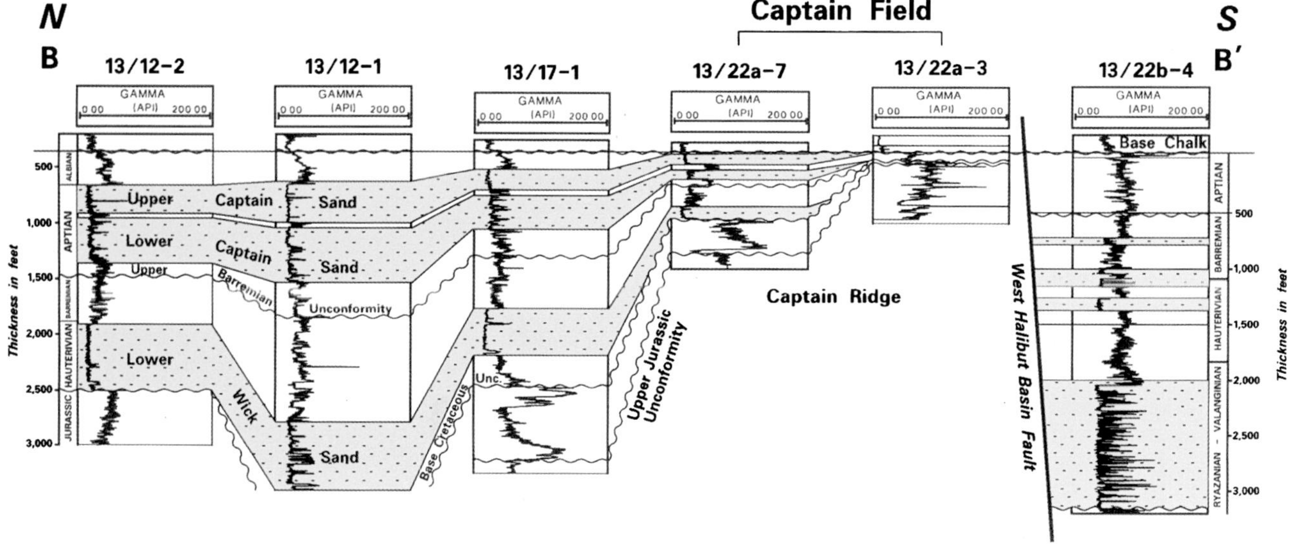

Fig. 4. Regional well correlation illustrating the distribution of the Captain and Wick sandstones. Drawn along line B–B′ from Fig. 1.

developed redeposited chalk in the Lower Maureen Formation at the base of this sequence. The Paleocene commonly subcrops a thin veneer of Quaternary sediments at the seabed over much of the field but an east–west orientated Quaternary filled channel is cut into the Paleocene above the crest of the Captain Ridge. Reflector truncation relationships imply that significant uplift and erosion has truncated the Tertiary succession above the Captain Field. This is a local expression of the post Paleocene uplift and erosion event that resulted in the removal of the entire Tertiary and Chalk Group succession in the Inner Moray Firth to the west of the Smith Bank Graben.

Reservoir stratigraphy

The type reservoir section is provided by Well 13/22a-7 (Fig. 5). The Valanginian and Ryazanian are absent from the Captain Ridge but the Hauterivian to Aptian succession is represented by a northwest-thickening sequence of turbidite sandstones and claystone. This sequence contains two important sandstone sequences. The oldest is Hauterivian in age and is informally referred to as the Lower Wick Sandstone (equivalent to the Coracle Member of the Valhall Formation as defined by Johnson & Lott 1993). It provides an important aquifer from which water is produced for injection and to support the separation process on the Captain FPSO which is most efficient at high water cut (see earlier). The younger sandstone body is the Lower to Upper Aptian Captain Sandstone Member (Pinnock & Clitheroe 1997) which forms the hydrocarbon reservoir for the Captain Field. Between these major sandstone bodies the Barremian to Lower Aptian contains hemi-pelagic claystones, distal low density turbidites interbedded with occasional thin (10 to 30 ft thick) massive sandstones. These are not economically significant.

The Captain Sandstone Member is itself divided into two reservoirs, the Lower and Upper Captain Sandstones, which are separated by a distinctive claystone interval, the Mid Captain Shale. Both the Upper and Lower Captain Sandstones are clean and massive with a blocky wire-line log signature. The Lower Captain Sandstone is less laterally homogeneous and on average has a slightly higher gamma reading than the Upper Captain Sandstone. Petrographical studies indicate that the Lower Captain Sandstone is slightly more arkosic, has a lower lithic clast content and is slightly finer grained.

The Mid Captain Shale is correlated on both lithological and biostratigraphic grounds. Gamma logs and neutron density logs typically indicate a fining-up signature through the Mid Captain Shale, with siltstone and sandstone horizons less common at the top than the bottom. The top half of the interval contains a number of prominent green glauconite rich horizons, thought to be tuffaceous in origin (Jeans *et al.* 1982). These horizons are extremely reactive to water and, where well developed, are picked out on the spectral gamma log as local thorium peaks. The Mid Captain Shale was deposited at a time when the bottom waters became progressively more anoxic. This is indicated by a loss of calcareous benthonic foraminifera resulting in micro-faunas dominated by agglutinating foraminifera. The timing of the Mid Captain Shale deposition is consistent with the *Nutfieldiensis* Zone transgression proposed by Rawson & Riley (1982) which would imply that clastic input into the Wick Sub-basin was temporarily terminated by rising sea-level.

Reservoir provenance

The Aptian Captain Sandstone Member has been identified and mapped in the exploration wells to the north and south of the Captain Field. The sands are very well developed to the north of the Captain Ridge and consist of predominantly medium-grained sand with very little interbedded claystone and a clean blocky gamma log signature as seen in the Captain Field. To the south of the ridge, Aptian sandstones are poorly developed: the interval consists predominantly of silty claystones and argillaceous sandstones (Fig. 4).

The regional Captain Sandstone Member isopach (Fig. 1) shows that the maximum sandstone thickness is developed just to the south of the Wick Fault zone and that the sandstone package thins onto the Captain Ridge. The shape of the isochore suggests a major submarine fan system with the main point of input to the basin being due north of the Captain Field. The consistent grain size population and low clay content of the system suggests that it has been derived from well-sorted shallow marine sands stored on the East Shetland platform to the north of the Wick Fault zone.

Captain Field geological model

Geophysics

The top of the Captain Field reservoir is well imaged on seismic data by a strong reflector at the base of the chalk; the

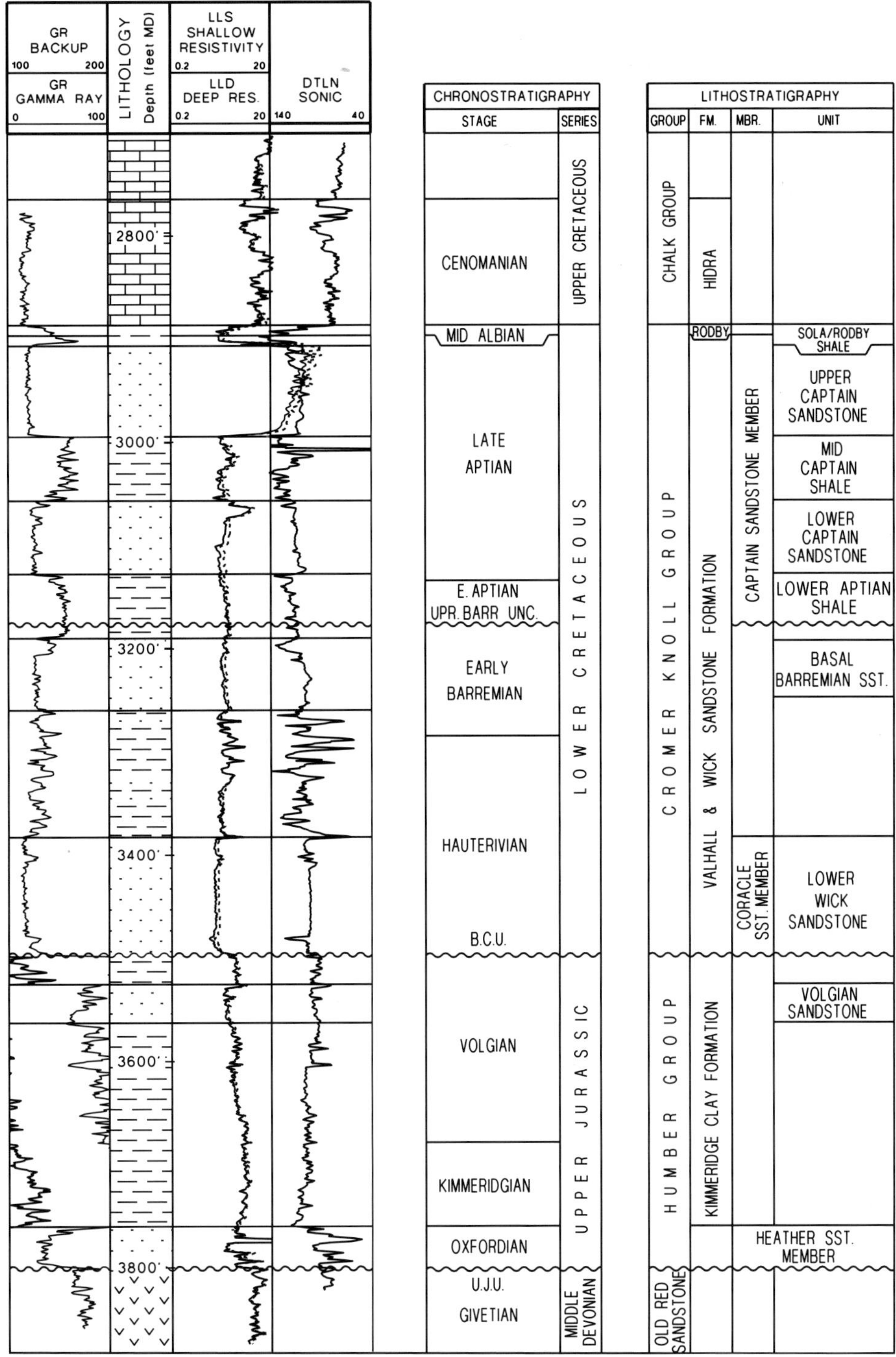

Fig. 5. Captain reservoir type well log (Well 13/22a-7).

geometry of this reflector is well constrained by a 3D seismic dataset acquired in 1990. Depth conversion is problematic over the Captain Field because of variable velocities encountered in the Chalk Group and significant lateral velocity variations in the Tertiary to Recent section, which result from the laterally heterogeneous Lower Maureen interval (see earlier) and a Quaternary channel developed over the southern portion of the field. Prior to drilling the first horizontal development wells, depth uncertainty was as high as 2% or plus or minus 60 ft in areas away from the vertical well control.

Internally the Captain Sandstone Member is poorly imaged on seismic data. The seismic energy spectrum is greatly reduced by the strong reflectors at the top and base of the Chalk Group and the reservoir interval tends to be masked by water bottom and other multiples. As a result of this the geological model for the distribution of the reservoir beneath the base of the Chalk Group has been driven by interpretation of the vertical well control.

Captain Sandstone member facies

Facies analysis of the Captain Sandstone member is based on the description of 600 ft of conventional core recovered from the Upper and Lower Captain Sandstones together with wireline log interpretations. The cores have been principally cut in the reservoir (345 ft in the Upper Captain Sandstone and 184 ft

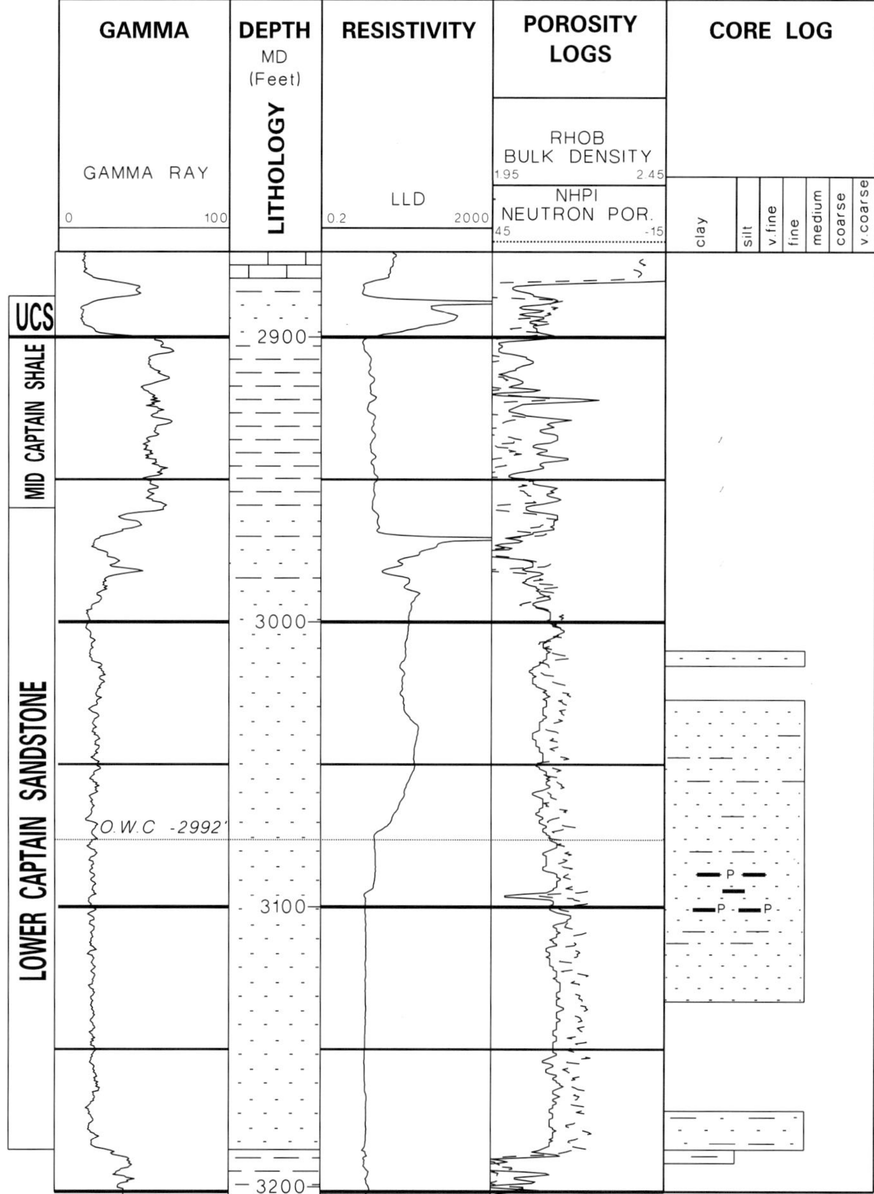

Fig. 6. Example of Lower Captain Sandstone core and wireline logs from the channel axis fairway (Well 13/22a-2).

from the Lower Captain Sandstone) but the Mid Captain Shale (50 ft) and Lower Aptian Shale (21 ft) have also been sampled.

Upper and Lower Captain Sandstone facies. The Upper and Lower Captain Sandstones are clean low-gamma high-porosity sandstones (Figs 6 and 7). Even if a net porosity cut-off as high as 20% is used, the net to gross ratio is close to 1 where the sandstones are well developed with an average porosity of 31%. Core plug permeabilities range from 1 to 12 D with a field average of 7 D; petrographical analysis shows that the sandstones are only slightly compacted and diagenetic alteration is minimal.

The sandstones occur in thick amalgamated sequences that can be over 100 ft thick with only rare bed boundaries recognized by a slight increase in granular material. Few bedding structures are observed in core, even using CAT-scan images, but rare bedding parallel laminations and de-watering structures, including vertical pipes, vague concave-up laminations (interpreted to be incipient dish structures) and occasional horizons with better developed cup shaped dish structures are observed. Evidence for traction current deposition is rare, but occasionally clay clasts are concentrated into imbricated horizons and there are a few occurrences of parallel laminated horizons overlain by cross-bedded units in more obviously graded beds.

The predominantly massive non-graded character of the reservoir, lack of evidence for significant traction current deposition and de-watering structures imply that the sands were rapidly deposited by mass-gravity flow processes. The massive sandstones are closely comparable to the S_3 unit defined by Lowe (1982), deposited from the suspension collapse of high density turbidite currents. In general the beds are amalgamated but rare more obviously graded beds represent the deposits of discrete turbidity flows.

Thin interbedded non-reservoir intervals have been locally cored. A 2.5 ft intra-reservoir claystone was cored in the Upper Captain Sandstone of 13/22a-6 (Fig. 7). Evidence for isoclinal folding combined with a sharp top but injected and loaded base imply that the shale was introduced as a slump sheet. Wells 13/22a-9A and 13/22a-11 contain beds of heterolithic argil-laceous sandstones, a facies restricted in core to the Lower Captain Sandstone in the east of the field. In this facies

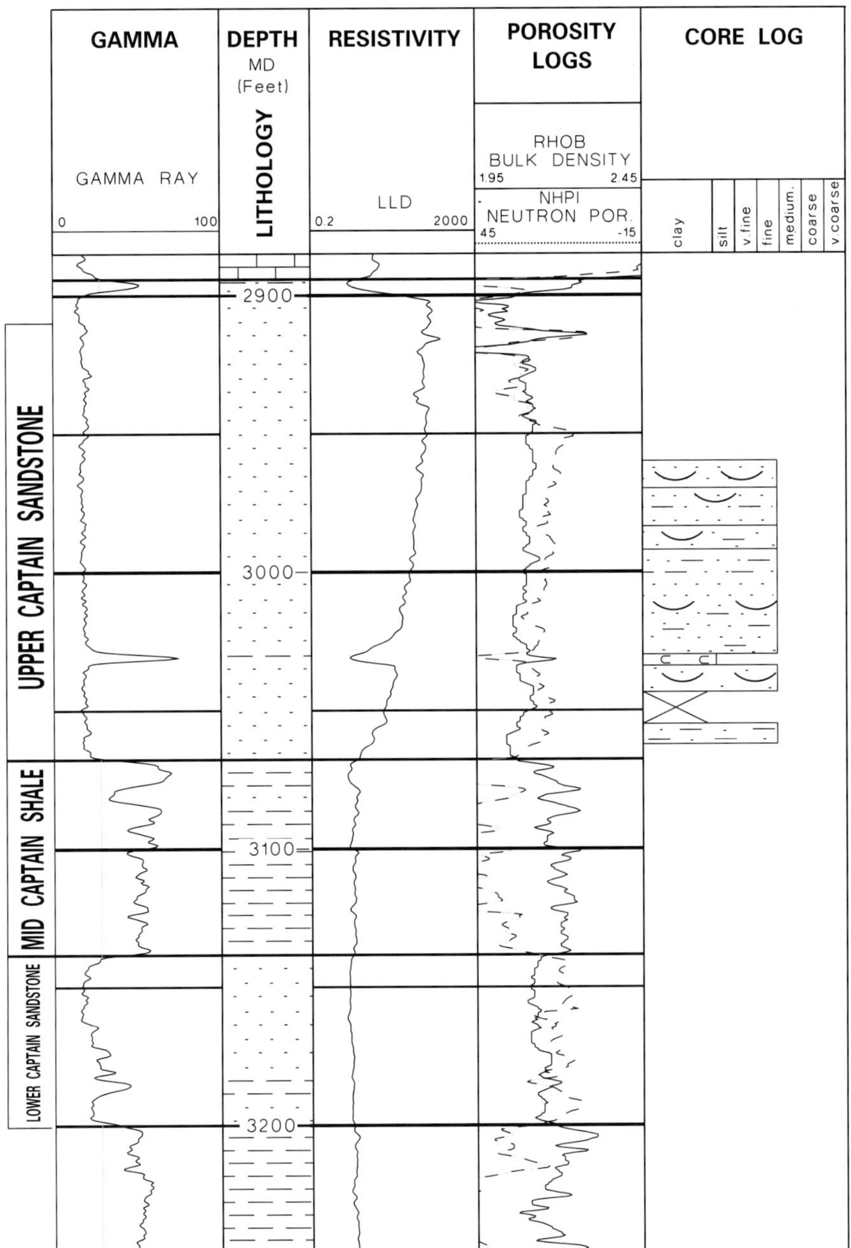

Fig. 7. Example of Upper Captain Sandstone core and wireline logs (Well 13/22a-6).

the porosity and permeability of the sandstone is occluded by matrix clay and the sandstones contain a wide mixture of large angular claystone and siltstone clasts in a variety of orientations. These are interpreted as debris flow deposits.

Reservoir grain size distribution and detrital composition. The sandstones are sub-arkoses and contain a varied lithic clast content (5–8%) including volcanic fragments, polycrystalline quartz and claystone intra-clasts up to 1 in. across. Detrital clay also forms a patchy inter-granular cement and thin variably orientated clay laminae which are thought to have developed during de-watering processes.

The reservoir sandstones are moderately well sorted: individual sample grain size varies from very fine to coarse with a mean grain size from sieve analyses in the range 290–250 microns. Seive analyses show the grain size distribution to be relatively tight, typically only 10% of the sample is less than 100 microns in diameter and less than 30% of the sample has grain sizes greater than 500 microns. The low percentage of reservoir fines and moderate sorting provide favourable conditions for sand production control with wire-wrapped pre-packed screens.

Mid Captain Shale and Lower Aptian Shale sedimentary facies. The Mid Captain Shale and Lower Aptian Shale consist of laminated claystones, with thin siltstones, some of which are tuffaceous, locally interbedded with sandstone. These are interpreted to be hemi-pelagic claystones interbedded with distal turbidites and redeposited tuffs. Deformation structures are common in the laminated claystones of the Mid Captain Shale and the Lower Aptian Shale. These include the common recognition of slide planes, slump folds and angular claystone breccias. Slumping and sliding down an unstable slope was clearly an important process during the Aptian.

Reservoir architecture and facies relationships

Lower Captain Sandstone. The Lower Captain Sandstone is best developed along a northwest to southeast fairway that crosses the western half of the field (Fig. 8a). In this fairway

(a)

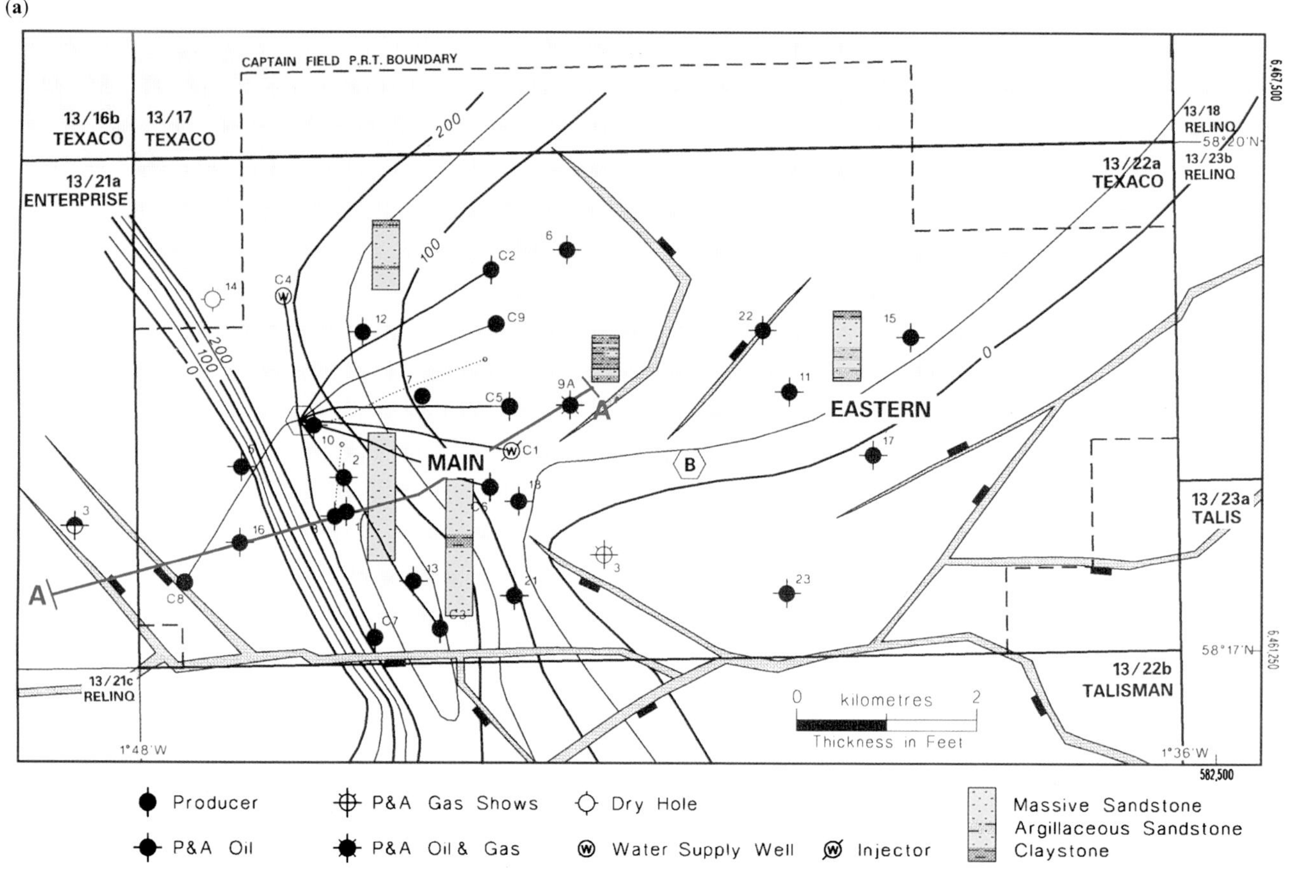

(b)

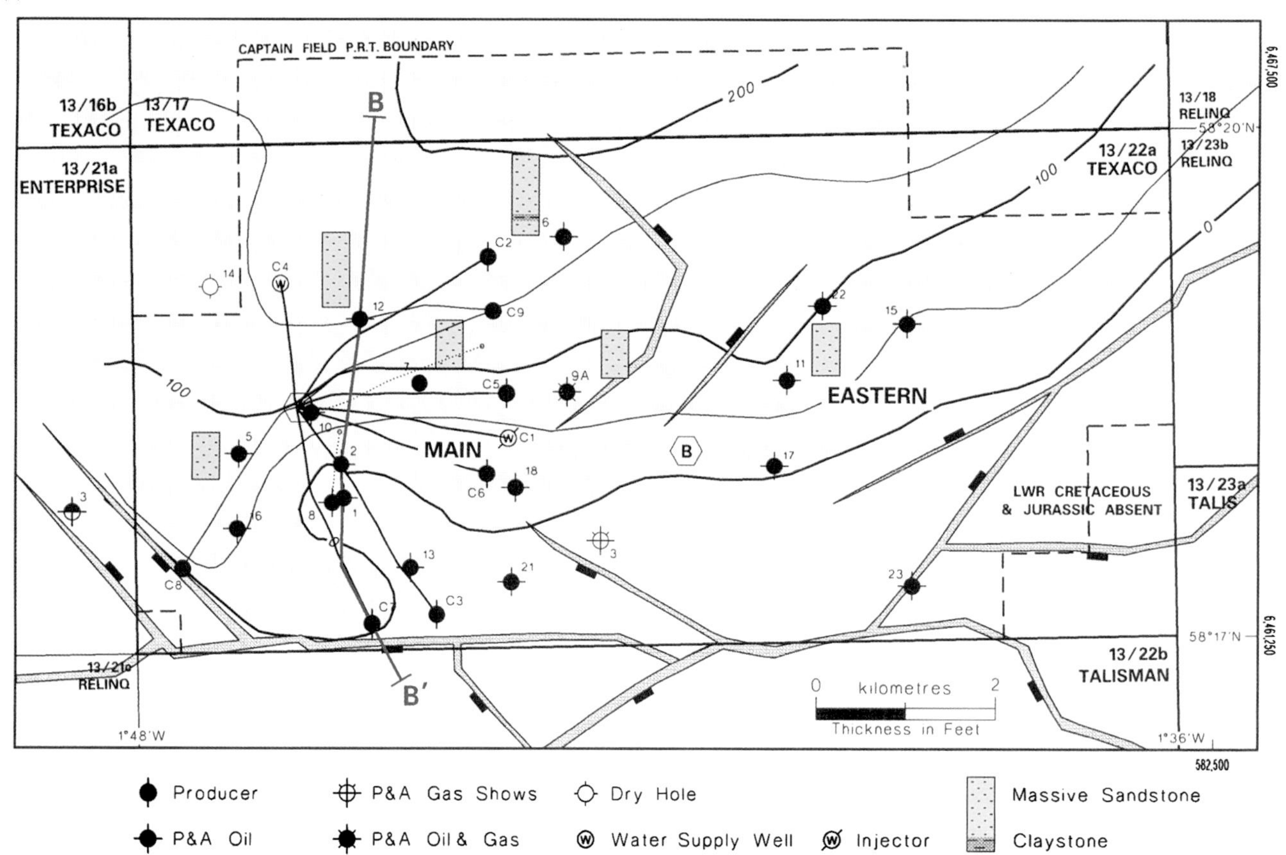

Fig. 8. Isochore and lithology distribution from the Captain Field: (**a**) Lower Captain Sandstone; (**b**) Upper Captain Sandstone.

(a)

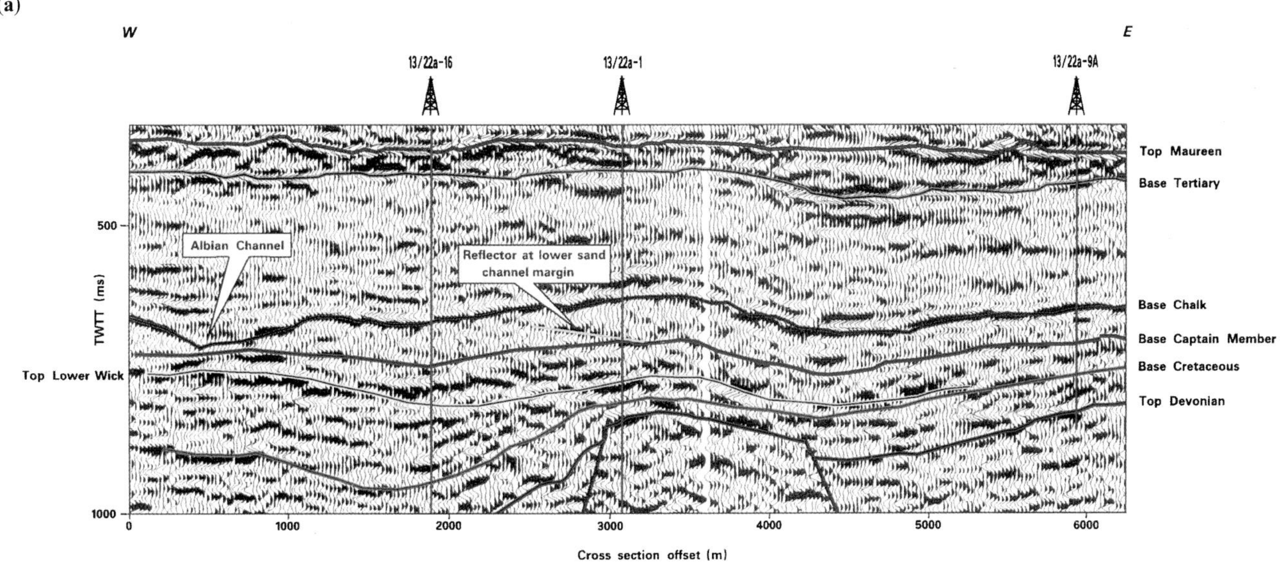

(b)

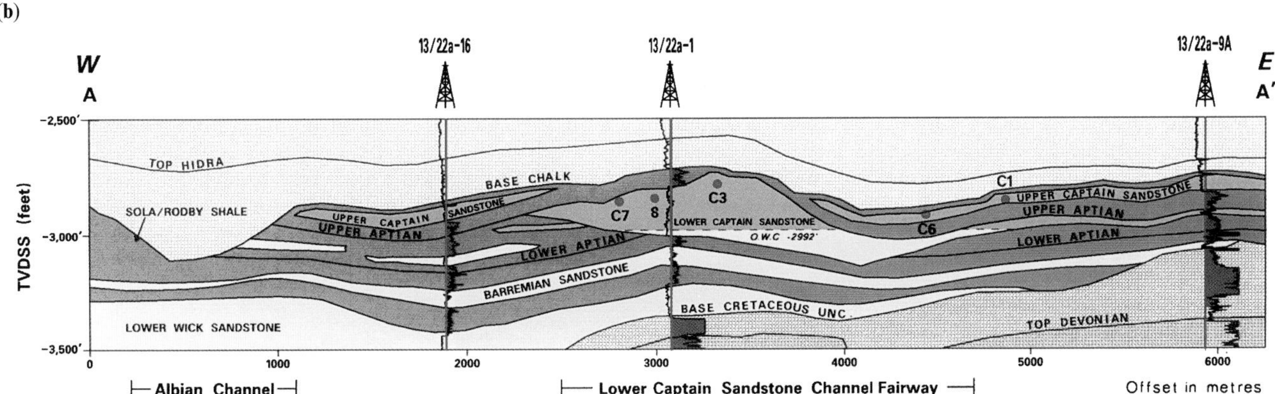

Fig. 9. East–west 3D arbitrary well-tie seismic and geological interpretation (2 × vertical exaggeration).

the sandstones are dominated by stacked high density turbidites of the massive sandstone facies with intra reservoir claystones developed only at the top of the interval and in a 10 to 30 ft zone in the middle of the sandbody, layer LCS3 in the reservoir model. To the east of the fairway, the Lower Captain Sandstone isochore is never more than 100 ft thick and it thins to the southeast onto the Captain Ridge. In this area the Lower Captain Sandstone contains a significant percentage of non-reservoir debris flow deposits and intra-reservoir claystones. The Lower Captain Sandstone isochore is sharply truncated to the west (Fig. 8a).

The abrupt western margin of the Lower Captain Sandstone was defined after careful examination of the correlation between Wells 13/22a-1, 2 and 13, and 13/22a-5 and 16. In Well 13/22a-5 and 16, the base of the Mid Captain Shale coincides with the base of the Upper Aptian. This is underlain by a Lower Aptian claystone-prone sequence, 100–140 ft thick, with interbedded sandstones. In Wells 13/22a-1, 2 and 13, the Lower Captain Sandstone forms a sequence of stacked high density turbidite deposits greater than 200 ft thick, divided in two by the thin, locally claystone-prone layer, LCS3. In this area the Lower Captain Sandstone is dated as Upper Aptian, at least above the base of LCS3, and the Lower Aptian Shale is absent in 13/22a-1 and 2 and only 13 ft thick in 13/22a-13. The age relationships imply that the Lower Captain Sandstone fairway was deposited in a channel fill which cut across the Captain Ridge into a pre-existing Lower Aptian shale-prone sequence (Fig. 9b). Supporting evidence for this model is provided by an east-dipping seismic reflector to the west of 13/22a-1 and 2, within the Lower Captain Sandstone interval (Fig. 9a). This reflector may represent the interface at the channel margin where high net : gross massive sandstones within the channel juxtapose against the claystone-prone Lower Aptian sequence of Wells 13/22a-5 and 16.

Upper Captain Sandstone. The Upper Captain Sandstone is more consistently developed across the Captain Field than the Lower Captain Sandstone. The reservoir remains of the highest quality in both the eastern and western closures of the field and the isochore defines a wedge that thins systematically to the southeast onto the Captain Ridge (Figs 8b and 10). The Upper Captain Sandstone pinch-out edge is deflected to the north over the axis of the Lower Captain Sandstone fairway in the western closure of the Captain Field and the sandstone body is truncated by erosion at the western margin of Block 13/22a (Fig. 9b). The rarity of intra-reservoir shales seen in vertical wells implied high vertical permeability and excellent reservoir connectivity in the Upper Captain Sandstone. This has been confirmed by horizontal drilling and early production performance; production Wells 13/22a-C5 and C6 respond very rapidly to changes in the injection rate in Well 13/22a-C1. Using the extended well test appraisal data a reservoir scale, a horizontal : vertical permeability ratio of 0.2 was calculated (Pallant *et al.* 1995).

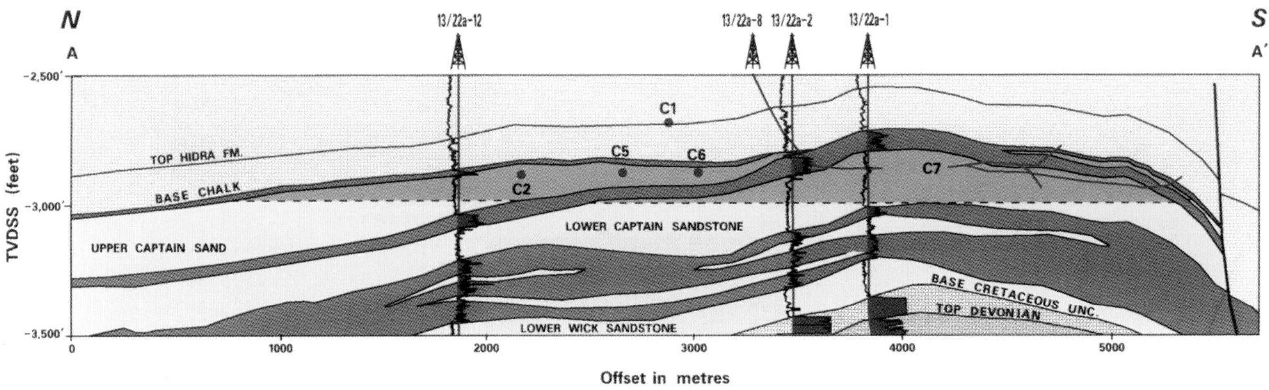

Fig. 10. North–south geological cross section (2 × vertical exaggeration).

Depositional model

The sandstone distribution described above implies that the Captain Ridge remained a positive feature throughout the deposition of the Captain Reservoir sequence. In the following section a simple depositional model is described in an attempt to relate the contrasting sandbody geometry of the Lower and Upper Captain Sandstones to interactions of turbidite flows with the evolving topography of the Captain Ridge.

From the evidence described earlier, the Lower Captain Sandstone depositional fairway is thought to have been formed by a back-filled channel cut through the Captain Ridge. This implies that prior to the deposition of the Lower Captain Sandstone, turbidite flows that were energetic enough to bypass the Captain Field area eroded a channel through the Captain Ridge as they passed from the restricted Wick Sub-Basin to the West Halibut Basin. The channel was back-filled with the massive sandstone facies of the Lower Captain Sandstone as either the accommodation space in the West Halibut Basin was reduced or the turbidite flows became less energetic (Fig. 11).

Further circumstantial evidence for the channel fill origin of the Lower Captain Sandstone fairway is provided by the seismic image of a channel cutting across the Captain Ridge at the base of the Chalk Group to the west of the Captain Field. In this area a northwest to southeast fault-bounded low defines the western margin of the field (Fig. 2). Reflector truncations demonstrate that the Captain reservoir sequence has been removed by erosion from the centre of this low which is now infilled by the Hidra Formation of the Chalk Group (Fig. 9a). It is likely that this channel developed in the latest Aptian, exploiting a pre-existing tectonic fracture orientation. Sediment starvation after the formation of the channel, the result of sea-level rise in the Albian (Rawson & Riley 1982; Crittenden *et al.* 1997), has resulted in a lack of coarse clastic infill. Thus the channel remained a topographic low until it was passively infilled by chalk deposition in the Cenomanian. It is possible that channels were cut through the Captain Ridge during times of relative sea-level lowstand to enable fluvial input from the East Shetland Platform to exit the restricted West Halibut Basin.

In the eastern closure of the field, the Lower Captain Sandstone is heterolithic; massive sandstones are interbedded with slump deposits, debris flows and hemipelagic claystones. This area had a less consistent coarse clastic supply and was possibly fed from turbidite flows that spilled over the edge of the main channel during the deposition of particularly high volume turbidite flows. The interbedded debris flows and slump sheets resulted from re-deposition of unconsolidated sediment from the flanks of the Captain Ridge during episodes of seismic fault activity effecting the structure.

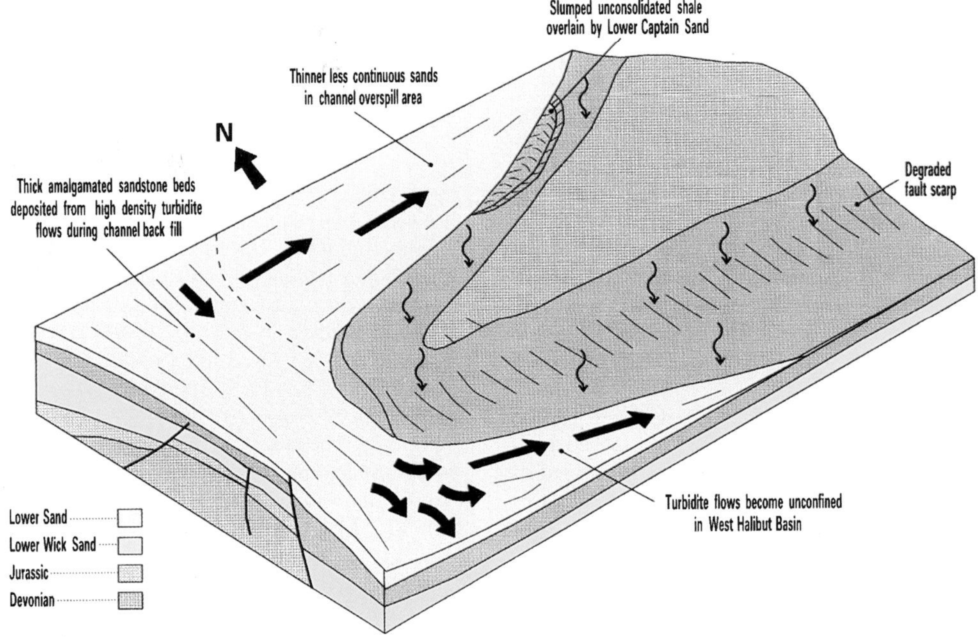

Fig. 11. Lower Captain Sandstone depositional model. The Captain Ridge is breached by the Lower Captain Sandstone channel.

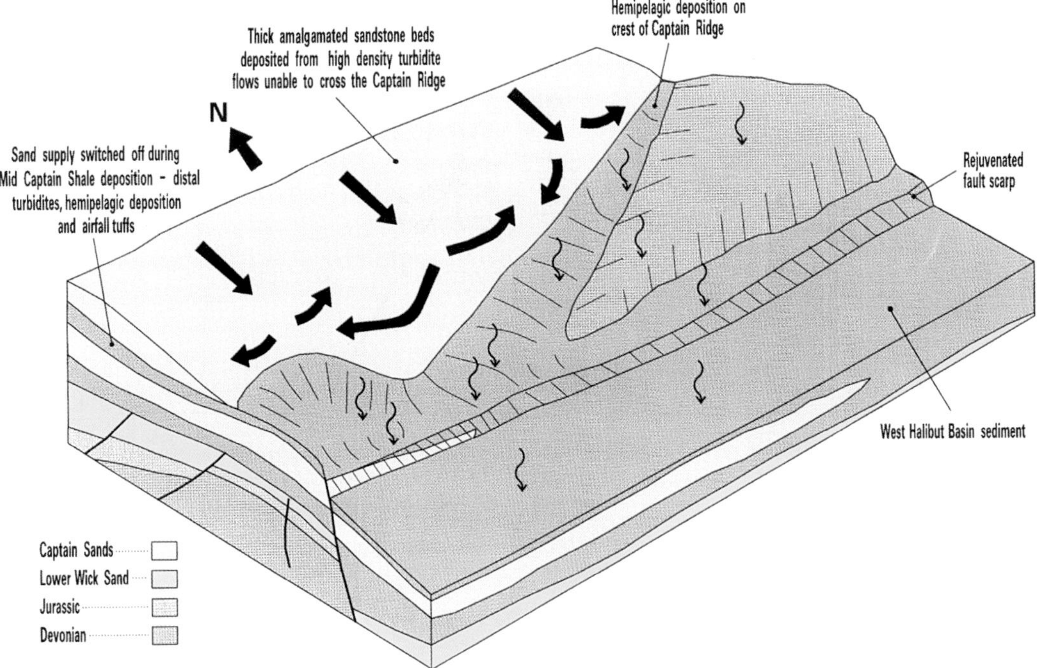

Fig. 12. Upper Captain Sandstone depositional model. The Captain Ridge prevents sand bearing turbidity flows crossing into the West Halibut Basin.

The laterally extensive pinch-out wedge defined by the Upper Captain Sandstone isochore implies that the Captain Ridge was not breached at this time. It is suggested that the West Halibut Basin bounding fault, to the south side of the Captain Ridge, had been rejuvenated, increasing the topography across the ridge. As a result, turbidite flows ponded to the north of the ridge resulting in a more broadly distributed high quality sandstone sheet (Fig. 12).

Reservoir uncertainty and horizontal drilling

The geological model for the Captain Field derived from the vertical well control contains a number of key uncertainties: error on depth to top reservoir, irregularities in the sandstone isopach distribution between vertical well control, and the distribution and dimensions of intra-reservoir shales. The first two parameters need to be accommodated to allow horizontal development wells to be drilled cost effectively. Data from horizontal wells can be used to help constrain the intra-reservoir shale distribution in the reservoir model which will influence predictions of long-term reservoir performance.

Geosteering and open-hole sidetracks

To drill successful horizontal development wells, a geosteering programme is required. This must enable $12\frac{1}{4}''$ hole section to reach TD in a horizontal orientation at the appropriate level in the reservoir and ensure that the $8\frac{3}{4}''$ completion hole section remains within the targeted horizon; close to the roof of the reservoir for production wells and close to the floor or beneath the oil–water contact for injector wells.

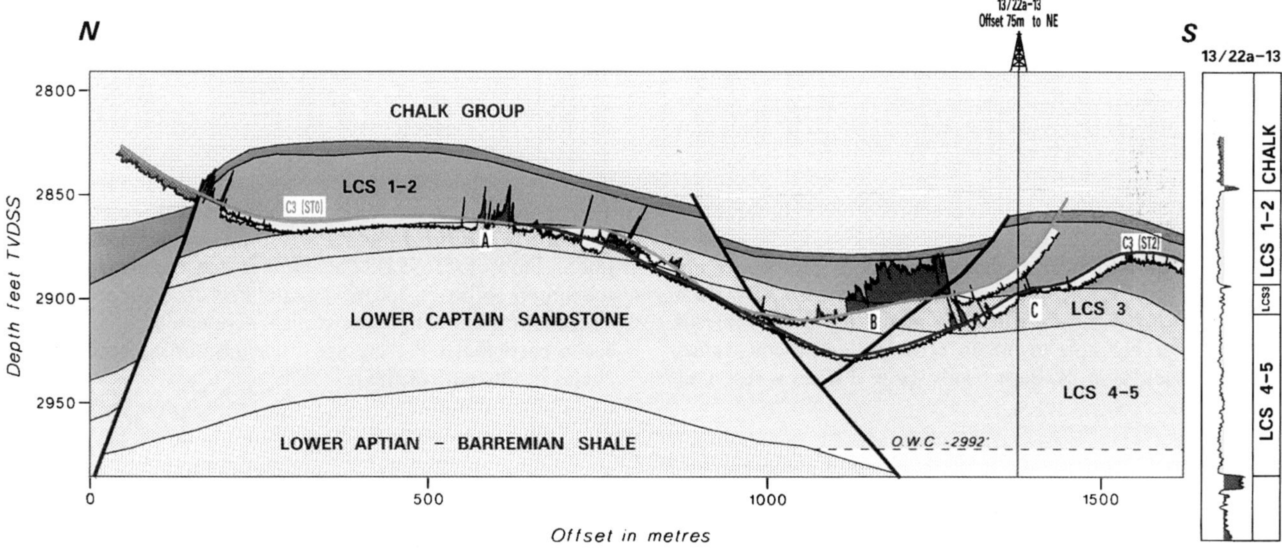

Fig. 13. 13/22a-C3 well interpretation cross-section. Note the contrasting sand clay ratios seen in layer LCS3 at locations A, B and C. C3(ST0) is the first hole to be drilled, it was sidetracked after encountering shale section at B. C3(ST2) is the second sidetrack to be drilled, C3(ST1) is very similar but was abandoned because it was not possible to turn the well down beyond C.

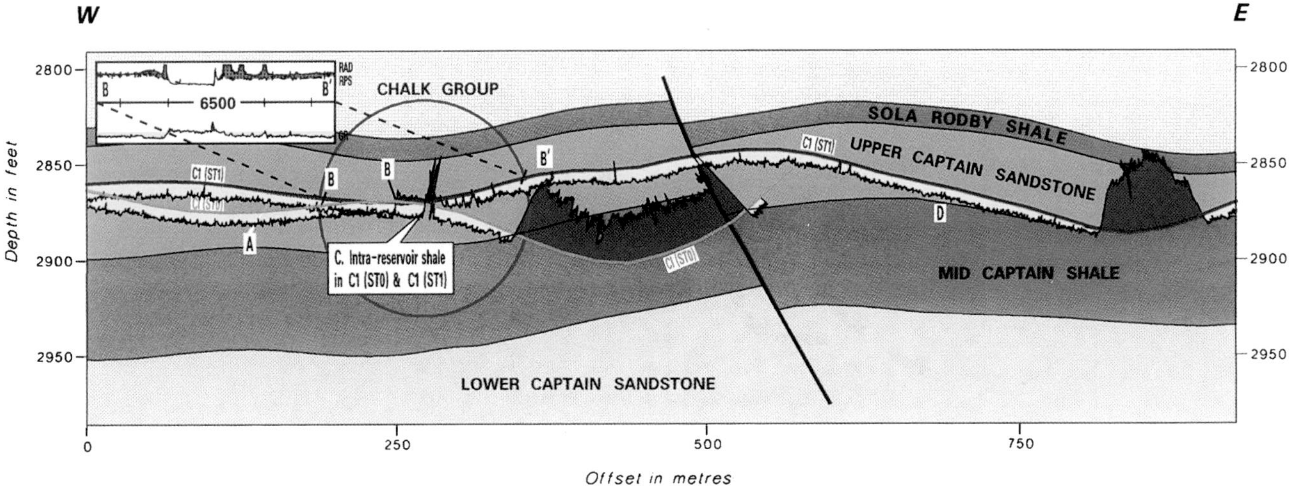

Fig. 14. 13/22a-C1 well interpretation cross section. Note asymmetric proximity effects on resistivity logs on log insert B–B′. The claystone horizon penetrated at location C is absent at locations A and D. Well C1(ST0), the original hole, was sidetracked to C1(ST1) after penetrating 600 ft mD of Mid-Captain Shale.

The first critical target for the production wells is to land the heel of the well, the TD (total depth) of the $12\frac{1}{4}''$ hole section, in a horizontal orientation near the top of the reservoir. Well-site micropalaeo and log correlations from real-time gamma and resistivity data, recorded by Anadrill's compensated dual resistivity (CDR) tool, provide a good fix on the stratigraphic position within the Flounder and Hidra Formations while drilling the lower portion of the Chalk Group. Early accurate forward predictions of the depth to Base Chalk are possible because thickness trends within the Flounder and Hidra Formations are well constrained by seismic and vertical well control. If the top reservoir is then anticipated, high or low forecast adjustments to the well trajectory can be made without causing severe dog-legs or significantly over-shooting the heel target location.

In the horizontal completion section, it is important to maximize the net sand penetrated by the well bore in order to achieve the required production or injectivity index; long shale sections are also expected to be a potential cause of sticking and screen damage when running completions. Geosteering data are obtained from Anadrill's geosteering tool (GST) motor which provides real-time inclination, gamma and resistivity at the bit combined with the CDR tool and directional package located behind the motor. In many of the wells drilled to date, early indications of the approach of the roof of the reservoir from the GST data were sufficient to adjust the well trajectory so that less than 100 ft of shale was penetrated and the well continued. In instances where more than 200 ft of shale was penetrated sidetracks were commonly drilled (e.g. Figs 13 and 14). These have proved to be quick and cost effective to undertake in the soft Captain Sandstone because open-hole low-side sidetracks are possible in which the abandoned hole is left uncemented. In many instances, once the decision to sidetrack had been made, it was possible to extend the junked hole to obtain extra geological constraints such as penetration of Base Chalk (Fig. 13) or a reservoir isopach thickness.

Intra-reservoir shale distribution

The horizontal well data provide an improved understanding of the distribution and nature of intra-reservoir claystone horizons in the Upper and Lower Captain Sandstones. Where a well porpoises through the reservoir sequence it is possible to have multiple penetrations of the same stratigraphic horizon. This has allowed the lateral dimensions and variability of some intra-reservoir claystone horizons to be constrained as documented in the two following examples.

Data from 13/22a-C3, a Lower Captain Sandstone production well, indicates that the LCS3 horizon in the Lower Captain Sandstone is very heterogeneous. A rafted claystone block is penetrated by C3(ST0), the original hole, at location B on Fig. 13. At the other two penetrations, at A and C on Fig. 13, LCS3 consists of argillaceous sand, indicated by low gamma combined with depressed resistivities, interbedded with clean sands and thin claystone horizons; this is similar to the section penetrated by vertical Well 13/22a-13, 75 m to the NE of point C. This horizon is now interpreted as a slump/debris flow horizon. The C3 data indicate that LCS 3 has the potential to provide a barrier to vertical flow in a zone at least 800 m broad.

In Well 13/22a-C1, an Upper Captain Sandstone water injector, a thin claystone horizon can be demonstrated to be of limited lateral extent and unlikely to provide a significant barrier to vertical flow (Fig. 14). The claystone was first penetrated at point C on Fig. 14 in C1(ST0), the original hole. The well was sidetracked as C1(ST0) penetrated a significant length of Mid-Captain Shale (the reservoir was thinner here than anticipated), and C1(ST1), the sidetrack, skimmed the top of the intra-reservoir claystone also at point C. The asymmetric proximity effect on the CDR resistivity log between B and B′ on Fig. 14, together with the fact that no claystone was encountered on the rising limb of C1(ST0) at A, suggests that the claystone lamination is truncated to the west, close to point C. The claystone lamination must also be truncated to the west of point D on Fig. 14 as no claystone was penetrated on the falling limb of C1(ST1). This implies that the claystone has a maximum width of 350 m; it is unlikely to compartmentalize the reservoir but will reduce vertical permeability on a reservoir scale, particularly if there are other unsampled discontinuous shales in this part of the reservoir.

Summary

The Captain Sandstone Member provides an excellent reservoir with few barriers to fluid flow. The continuity of the reservoir and excellent porosity and permeability has made the drilling of long horizontal wells with a high percentage of net sandstone relatively low risk, resulting in a high productivity index (PI) for production wells (design basis PI is

150 BOPD psi^{-1}). Geological model uncertainty has been accommodated by using geosteering techniques. Biosteering is used to land the $12\frac{1}{4}''$ hole and at-the-bit inclination, gamma and resistivity allow rapid reactions to claystones encountered in the $8\frac{3}{4}''$ completion hole. Where it was not possible to make well-trajectory corrections rapidly enough to minimize shale encountered in the $8\frac{3}{4}''$ hole, open-hole low-side sidetracks have proved a cost-effective strategy. Production history to date confirms the excellent pressure communication between injectors and producers. The consistent grain size population and lack of reservoir fines provide a favourable environment for sand control design. All of these factors have made the Captain Field a viable horizontal well development of a viscous oil accumulation in the offshore environment.

This paper has been based on work carried out within Texaco and by outside contractors over the last seven years. Key contributors to the current geological understanding are S. Pinnock, A. Clitheroe, J. Foreman, A. Manighetti and K. Regan within Texaco and outside contractors Paleo Services and Reservoir Associates. R. Chambers is thanked for her hard work drafting the figures. Texaco Inc. and Korea Captain Company Ltd are thanked for their permission to publish the paper. The paper was much improved by incorporation of the comments of L. Jones and an anonymous reviewer.

References

COHEN, D. J. 1997. Captain Field electric submersible pump, condition monitoring and completion systems. *Paper SPE* 8510.

—— & DALLAS, J. 1997. Development of a gas handling hydraulic submersible pump and planning a field trial, Captain Field. *Paper SPE* 8511.

CRITTENDEN, S., COLE, J. M. & KIRK, M. J. 1997. The distribution of Aptian sandstones in the Central and Northern North Sea (UK Sectors): a low-stand systems tract "play". Part 1: Stratigraphy, biostratigraphic age determination and genesis of the sandstones. *Journal of Petroleum Geology*, **20**, 3–25.

ETEBAR, S. 1997. Captain Field development project overview. *Paper SPE* 8507.

JEANS, C. V., MERRIMAN, R. J., MITCHELL, J. G. & BLAND, D. J. 1982. Volcanic clays in the Cretaceous of Southern England and Northern Ireland. *Clay Minerals*, **17**, 105–156.

JOHNSON, H. & LOTT, G. K. 1993. Cretaceous of the Central and Northern North Sea. *In*: KNOX, R. W. O'B. & CORDEY, W. G. (eds) *Lithostratigraphic Nomenclature of the UK North Sea*. British Geological Survey, Nottingham.

LACH, J. R. 1997 Captain Field reservoir development planning and horizontal well performance. *Paper SPE* 8508.

LOWE, D. R. 1982. Sediment gravity flows: II. Depositional models with special reference to the deposits of high density turbidity currents. *Journal of Sedimentary Petrology*, **44**, 484–501.

PALLENT, M. A., COHEN, D. J. & LACH, J. R. 1995. Reservoir engineering aspects of the Captain expended well test appraisal program. *Paper SPE* 30437.

PINNOCK, S. P. & CLITHEROE, A. R. J. 1997. The Captain Field, UK North Sea: appraisal and development of a viscous oil accumulation. *Petroleum Geoscience*, **3**, 305–312

RAWSON, P. F. & RILEY, L. A. 1982 Latest Jurassic–Early Cretaceous Events and the "Late Cimmerian Unconformity" in North Sea Area. *American Association of Petroleum Geologists*, **66**, 2628–2648.

ROBERTS, A. M., BADLEY, M. E., PRICE, J. D. & HUCK, I. W. 1990. The structural history of a transtensional basin: Inner Moray Firth, NE Scotland. *Journal of the Geological Society*, **147**, 87–103.

SUTTON, J. E. 1997. Process equipment for offshore viscous crude handling: Captain Field. *Paper SPE* 8512.

TAVENDALE, F. M. 1997. Captain horizontal development wells: a review of key design and operational issues. *Paper SPE* 8509.

UNDERHILL, J. R. 1991. Implications of Mesozoic to Recent basin development in the western Inner Moray Firth, UK. *Marine and Petroleum Geology*, **8**, 359–369.

Britannia Field, UK Central North Sea: modelling heterogeneity in unusual deep-water deposits

L. S. JONES, S. W. GARRETT, M. MACLEOD, M. GUY, P. J. CONDON and L. NOTMAN[1]

Chevron UK Ltd and Britannia Operator Ltd, Royfold House, Hill of Rubislaw, Aberdeen AB15 6GZ, UK

[1] *Present address: Reservoir Development Services Ltd, Peregrine Road, Westhill Business Park, Aberdeen AB32 6JL, UK*

Abstract: Britannia Field is currently the UK's largest undeveloped gas field, containing 4.3×10^{12} SCF gas in place and condensate reserves of 150×10^6 BBL. Lower Cretaceous reservoir sands of low-moderate permeability (average 50 mD) form a combination structural–stratigraphical trap. Understanding the stratigraphy is a critical factor in reservoir description, geostatistical modelling and deliverability prediction.

The Britannia Formation is unique amongst known deep-water deposits in being dominated by slurry flow deposits which present challenges in reservoir interpretation and modelling. Slurry flow deposits contain most of the gas in the upper reservoir zones of UK Blocks 16/26, 16/27a and 16/27b. Many of these slurry flow sand events may be correlated over several kilometres using petrological, sedimentological and lithostratigraphical data. In contrast, clean high density turbidite (HDT) sandstones are well developed in the lower reservoir in UK Blocks 15/29a and 15/30. These sands are less extensive, and their interpretation is constrained by high resolution biostratigraphic and lithostratigraphic data.

An integrated 3D modelling environment links surface modelling, reservoir characterization, and fluid flow simulation at three different scales. Firstly, the sensitivity of production to geological heterogeneity from pre-drilled wells is tested on single-zone models. Secondly, optimization of well types and completions to maximize deliverability uses sector models containing all zones. Thirdly, the sensitivity of long-term field performance predictions to large-scale structural and stratigraphical reservoir compartmentalization is tested using full-field models. The use of different scales of reservoir model for different business purposes will contribute significantly to the optimization of drilling and production strategies as the Britannia Field moves into operation during 1998.

Field summary

Field history and development status

Britannia is the largest undeveloped gas/condensate field on the UK Continental Shelf, lying 200 km northeast of Aberdeen. The field was discovered in 1975 by Well 15/30-1 which tested 19.6×10^6 SCF(D) of gas and 3065 BOPD (barrels of oil per day) of 47° API condensate. The extension of the play to the east was proven in 1977 by Well 16/26-2. Interest in the pay was rekindled in the late 1980s by a string of successful appraisal wells on Blocks 16/26 and 15/30, when it was thought there were two separate accumulations named Lapworth (15/30) and Kilda (16/26). Well 16/26-21z, drilled in 1990 at the block boundary between 15/30 and 16/26, confirmed that the two accumulations were linked. The limits of the field were demonstrated in 1991 by Texaco Well 15/29a-5 and Phillips water-wet Well 16/27a-7. Appraisal drilling was completed in 1993 following a 21 well delineation programme including two extended well tests. A field-wide 3D survey was acquired during 1991–1993 which was then the largest 3D survey in the North Sea. Government sanction for field development was granted in 1994. A 17 well pre-drilling programme was completed in 1996, running £23 million under the original development plan budget and more than 250 days ahead of the original schedule.

The field will be exploited via a 28 600 tonne steel platform (drilling, accommodation and production) in Block 16/26, tied via a 15 km heated pipeline to a 750 tonne 14 slot subsea manifold in Block 15/30. Up to 740×10^6 SCF(D) of wet gas will be transported by a dedicated 27″ pipeline to St Fergus, to be processed at SAGE to give dry gas and NGL (natural gas liquids) products. Over 50 000 BOPD of condensate will be separated offshore and exported via a 14″ pipeline to Forties Unity. First commercial gas is scheduled for the second half of 1998.

Britannia is unique in that the operatorship is shared between two companies (Chevron and Conoco) through a new company, Britannia Operator Limited. During field development, Chevron was responsible for subsurface and drilling activities, while Conoco took responsibility for construction and operational management. Superior performance during the project reflected exceptional collaboration across boundaries which traditionally divided contractors from clients. This spirit of co-operation will be enhanced during operations by an integrated team of staff from Chevron, Conoco and contractors (Hemmens 1997).

The Britannia Reservoir

Britannia Field (Fig. 1) forms a combination structural/stratigraphical trap on the northern flank of the Witch Ground Graben. The gross reservoir interval (Fig. 2) is 350–650 ft thick, and pinches out to the north on the Fladen Ground Spur. The shallowest mapped gas sand is at around 12 000 ft TVDSS. A continuous normal gas pressure gradient exists across the field, with an initial pressure of around 5990 psia at the gas–liquid contact. Condensate–gas ratios reported from DSTs (drill stem tests) range from 70–100 STB per 10^6 SCF. Porosity is constant at around 15%, and permeabilities are

Jones, L. S., Garrett, S. W., Macleod, M., Guy, M., Condon, P. J. & Notman, L. 1999. Britannia Field, UK Central North Sea: modelling heterogeneity in unusual deep-water deposits. *In*: Fleet, A. J. & Boldy, S. A. R. (eds) *Petroleum Geology of Northwest Europe: Proceedings of the 5th Conference*, 1115–1124.

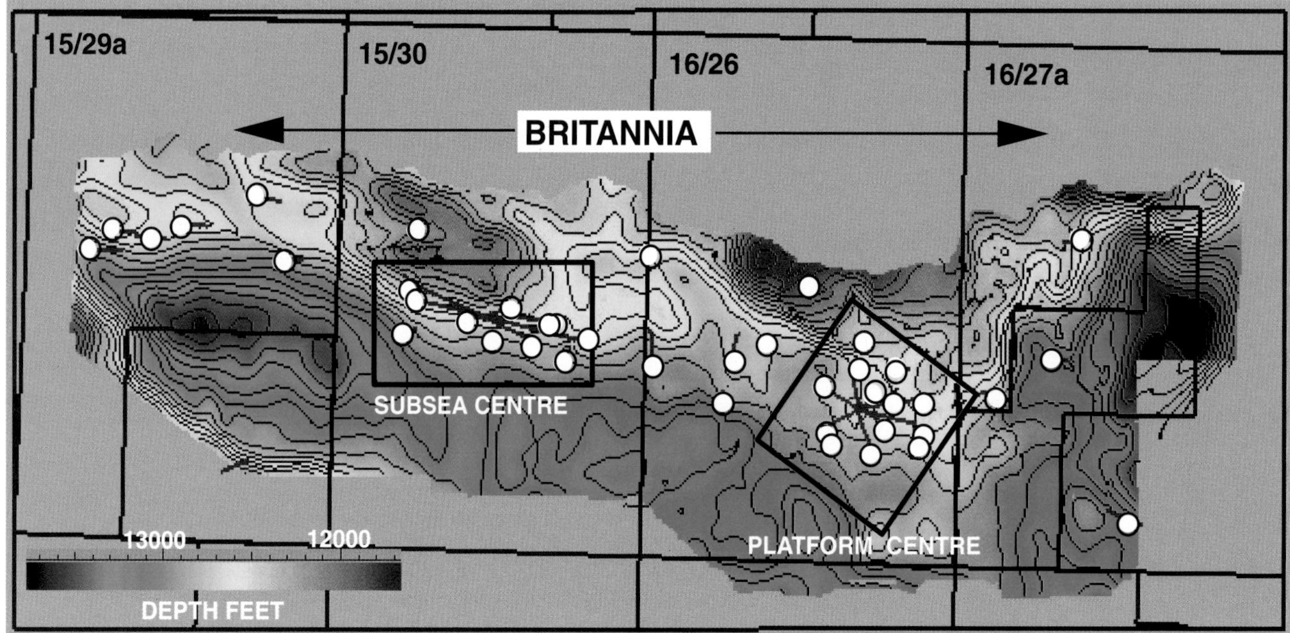

Fig. 1. Britannia Top structure map. Model areas to assess the impact of facies heterogeneity on single phase fluid flow are shown at the platform location and the subsea centre outlined in blue.

0.1–400 mD in the east (average 30 mD) to 0.1–800 mD in the west (average 60 mD). The gas field is underlain by a thin (40 ft) oil leg (Table 1) which appears to be compartmentalized and occurs mostly within poor-quality upper reservoir sands. Asphaltene is precipitated when Britannia oil rim samples are mixed with gas/condensate. The potential for economic production of the oil rim is under review.

Analysis of data from pre-drilled production wells

Seventeen production wells were pre-drilled to allow the facilities to come on-stream at full capacity and ensure sufficient deliverability to satisfy commercial requirements through the first winter of gas production. The wells were not tested immediately, to allow an aggressive drilling schedule, and to minimize the risk of formation damage during killing of wells. Near-wellbore permeability has been assessed through interpretation of core analysis data in conjunction with wire-line log data including nuclear magnetic resonance (NMR) and formation pressure tests (RFT/MDT).

Core totalling 7900 ft was acquired from 13 of the 17 pre-drilled wells as part of a conscious data acquisition strategy to provide a firm foundation for reservoir management. In order to ensure that the data were available in a timely fashion, an alliance of sedimentological, biostratigraphical, structural and rock property measurement consultants was established. A target was set, and incentives created, to complete all analyses and for reports to be delivered within 28 days of core arriving at the lead contractors warehouse. This scheme allowed the Britannia subsurface team to focus immediately on reservoir description and modelling following the cessation of pre-drilling.

Britannia facies

High density turbidite (HDT) facies

In the western part of the field (UK Blocks 15/29a and 15/30), the main reservoir facies are clean, blocky sands which may be assigned to the HDT facies (Figs 3 and 5) of Lowe (1982). These sands have a restricted grain size range and fall exclusively within the S3 division, and are either structureless or show dish structures. Near-vertical water-escape pipes and sandstone dykes are common towards the top of beds. Coarser S1 (traction) and S2 (traction carpets) divisions are not seen in Britannia Field wells drilled to date.

Slurry flow facies

Britannia contains an unique association of deep-water facies (Figs 3 and 4) first described by Guy (1992). Largely restricted to the upper reservoir zones (Fig. 5), the sandstones exhibit unusual sedimentological structures and divisions attributed to high mud contents, and cannot be fitted into any existing classification scheme. Lowe *et al.* (1995) and Lowe & Guy (in press) suggest that these muddy sandstones, termed slurry flows, were deposited by flows rheologically transitional between turbidity currents and debris flows. The Britannia Formation is unique amongst deep-water deposits in being dominated by slurry flows, which in turn presents challenges in reservoir interpretation and modelling.

Our current (1997) view of an idealized Britannia slurry flow sequence (Fig. 3) shows M1–M3 divisions analogous to the S1–S3 divisions of HDT deposits. This is a variation on the divisions presented in Lowe & Guy (in press). The idealized sequence is upward-cleaning and marginally upward-fining, and may be expressed as either complete sequences (Fig. 4), or individual sedimentation units:

(i) M1–Current (traction) structured division exhibiting large-scale cross-stratification, sweeping low angle stratification or flat lamination. M1 divisions are often the coarsest parts of individual sedimentation units.

(ii) M2–Layered light and dark sand couplets or bands at scales that grade from decimetre to millimetre thick wispy laminations. The light bands commonly show flat laminae disrupted by sets of vertical to steeply inclined (sheared) water escape structures. The dark bands characteristically exhibit sheared and twisted water escape pillars and foundered clean sands. These are the most distinctive components of slurry flows.

(iii) M3–Fine grained sandstone that is structureless or dish structured, grading upward from or interbedded with M2 units. Common cross-cutting homogeneous sandstone dykes represent vertical water escape conduits.

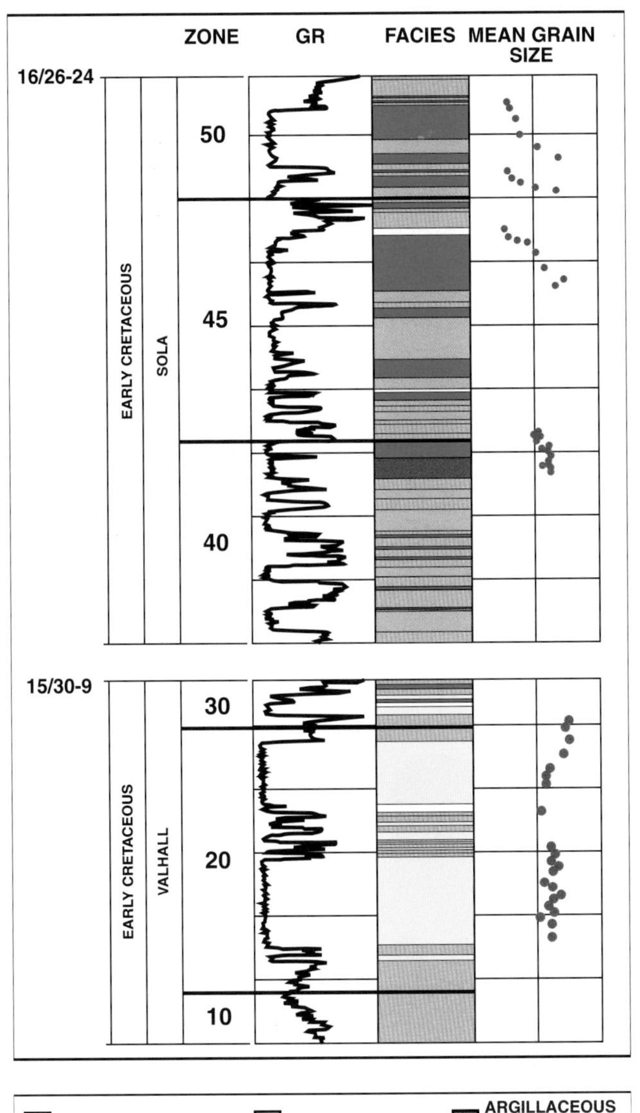

Fig. 2. Type well logs from the upper reservoir (Sola) of 16/26-24 and the lower reservoir (Valhall) of 15/30-9.

Table 1. Britannia Field, UK Central North Sea: reservoir parameters

Facilities	West	East
	Subsea manifold	Platform
Blocks	15/29a, 15/30	16/26, 16/27a
Area	112 square kilometres	
Shallowest mapped gas sand	12 100 ft TVDSS	11 800 ft TVDSS
Gas contact	13 155 ft TVDSS	13 060 ft TVDSS
Gas column	≈1000 ft	≈1260 ft
Average reservoir thickness	350–550 ft	200–650 ft
Net pore volume	131 360 acre feet	461 546 acre feet
Net : gross	12–30%	28–58%
Average gas saturation	68%	
Porosity	15%	
Formation temperature	129°C	145°C
Formation pressure at gas contact	5990 psia	
Formation volume factor	245–262	
Gas in place (10%, 50%, 90% probability)	3.7×10^{12} SCF, 4.4×10^{12} SCF, 5.2×10^{12} SCF	
Dominant gas-bearing zone	Zone 20	Zone 45
Average permeability (core, air horizontal)	60 mD	30 mD
Net gas sand (1 mD cut-off)	50–120 ft	100–240 ft
Permeability–thickness	1800–9000 mD ft	500–2000 mD ft
Condensate–gas ratio from DSTs	100 STB per $\times 10^6$ SCF	70 STB per $\times 10^6$ SCF
Dew point	5600 psi	
Oil column	40–85 ft	0–70 ft
Formation water resisitivity	0.05–0.11 ohm m	0.04–0.06 ohm m
Formation water ions	low Ca^{2+}, high SO_4^{2-}	high Na^+, Ba^+, Cl^-

Formation of Slurry Flow deposits

Being unique, the origin of M2 divisions provide the key to understanding the dynamics of slurry flow evolution and deposition. A lack of direct experimental or outcrop data makes interpretation problematic. It appears that the distinctive structuring of slurry flows results from the abundance and behaviour of mud within the flow resulting in flow types transitional between turbidity currents and debris flows. The following model for deposition of M2 divisions is in accordance with our current understanding and Lowe & Guy (in press).

Flows carrying mud contents from 15 to 30% were turbulent and non-cohesive throughout most of their existence. Clay moved and was deposited as sand-sized grains, chips or floccules; these particles showed little inter-particle cohesion and were able to move in turbulent suspension. During sedimentation, high shear rates and particle interactions in the lower parts of the flow split the clay particles, resulting in an increase in effective clay surface area, increased viscosity and cohesion, and the formation of a cohesion-dominated laminar sub-layer or cohesive traction carpet. The shear rate dropped below the yield strength of the mud–sand–water slurry, and the laminar sub-layer began to freeze. Sediment continued to settle from the turbulent flow above, initiating formation of a light band. This layer increased the load on the cohesive traction carpet below, causing gradual compaction, water loss and increasing strength, leading to freezing of the laminar sublayer and formation of a dark band. The bed surface shifted to the top of the light sand layer, and the process was repeated to form multiple dark–light sand couplets of the M2 division.

M1 divisions form from traction sedimentation from steady flows in which turbulence reaches to or near the bed. Direct suspension sedimentation of sand to form M3 dish structured to massive divisions occurs mainly during the waning stages of individual flows or flow sequences.

Stratigraphical zonation and correlation

The Britannia reservoir straddles the boundary between the Sola Formation and the Valhall Formation, and is subdivided into seven zones (Figs 2 and 5). Upper reservoir zones (Sola Formation) are defined and correlated using sand lithostratigraphy, based on facies type, texture, log signature, and volcanic ash band markers. Upper reservoir shales are mostly turbiditic in origin and do not lend themselves to biostratigraphic correlation. In contrast, in the lower reservoir (Valhall Formation) a robust biostratigraphical scheme has been established using palynology, micropalaeontology and calcareous nannoplankton from hemipelagic Valhall shales.

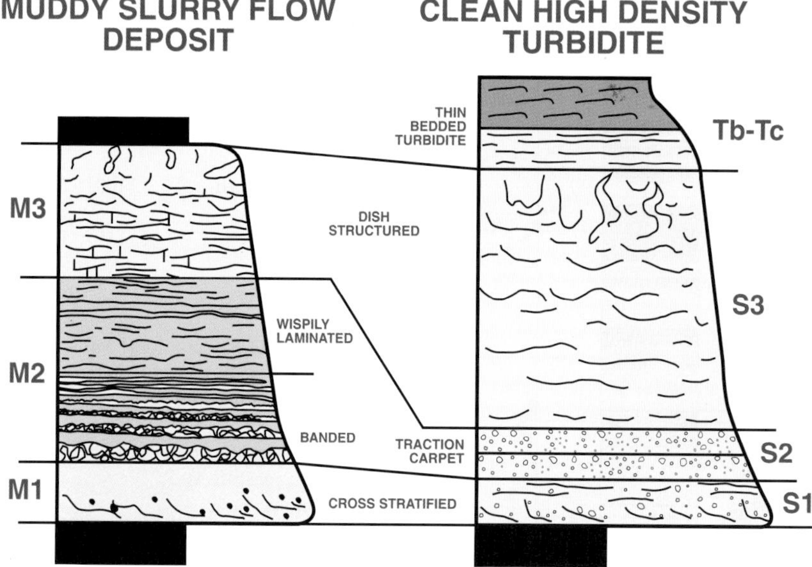

Fig. 3. Sedimentary structure divisions of an ideal slurry flow bed, M1–M3, compared to those of an ideal sedimentation unit deposited by a sandy, high density turbidity current S1–S3.

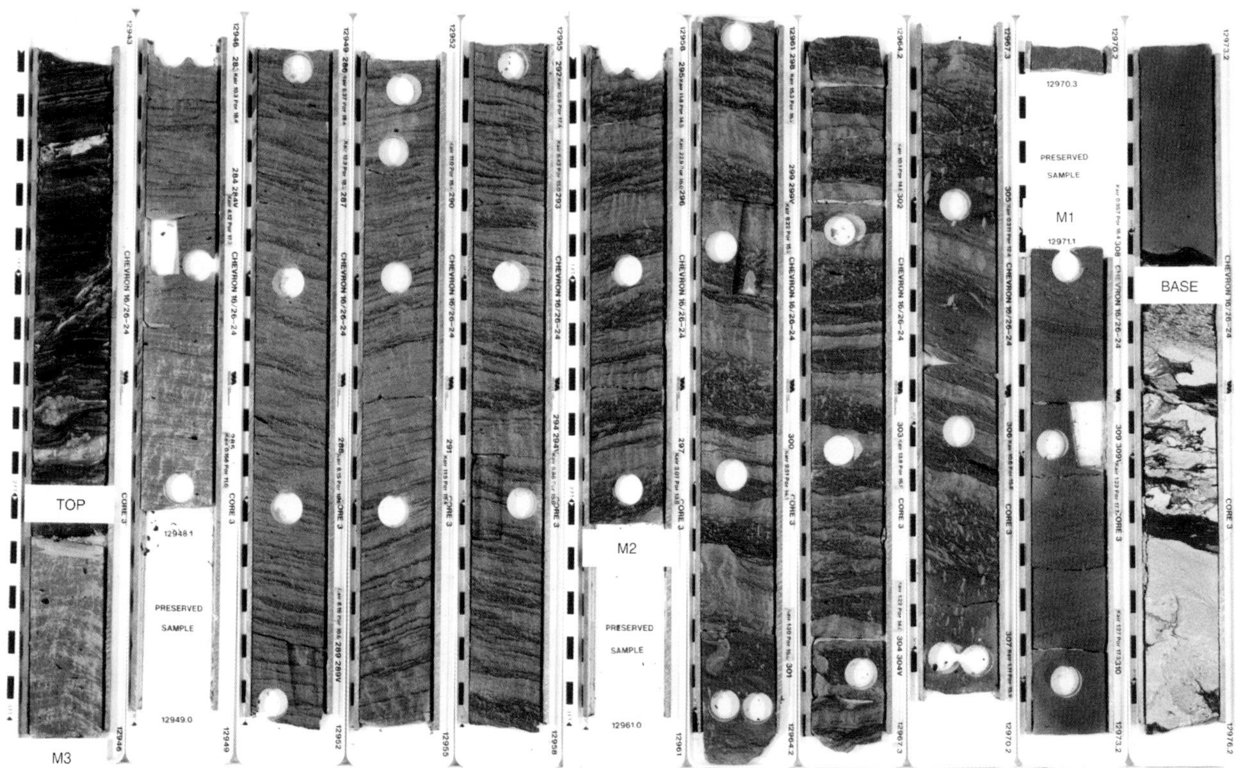

Fig. 4. A complete slurry flow bed, M1–M3 from Britannia Well 16/26-24.

Biostratigraphy and lithostratigraphy together are used to define and correlate zones in the lower reservoir. The boundary separating zone 20 (Valhall Formation) from zones 30 and 40 (Sola Formation) represents a significant change in depositional style. In the lower reservoir clean HDT (S3) sands are set in open marine shales, whereas dysaerobic shales occur along with dirty slurry flow sands in the upper reservoir. Less dramatic changes are recognized at other zonal boundaries based on facies character, sand architecture and textural patterns. Although most zones can be extended across the whole field as single chronostratigraphic events, zone 30 is not defined in the east, and zone 40 is not defined in the west (Fig. 5). The stratigraphic framework forms the foundation for reservoir interpretation, modelling and performance prediction.

Zone 10

This zone represents the first major influx of sand into the basin. Unusually, these sands are both non-erosive and fine-grained, conspicuously lacking a coarse component. The facies suite is dominated by sand and mud-rich slurries set within hemipelagic shale. Both facies types are related in a proximal

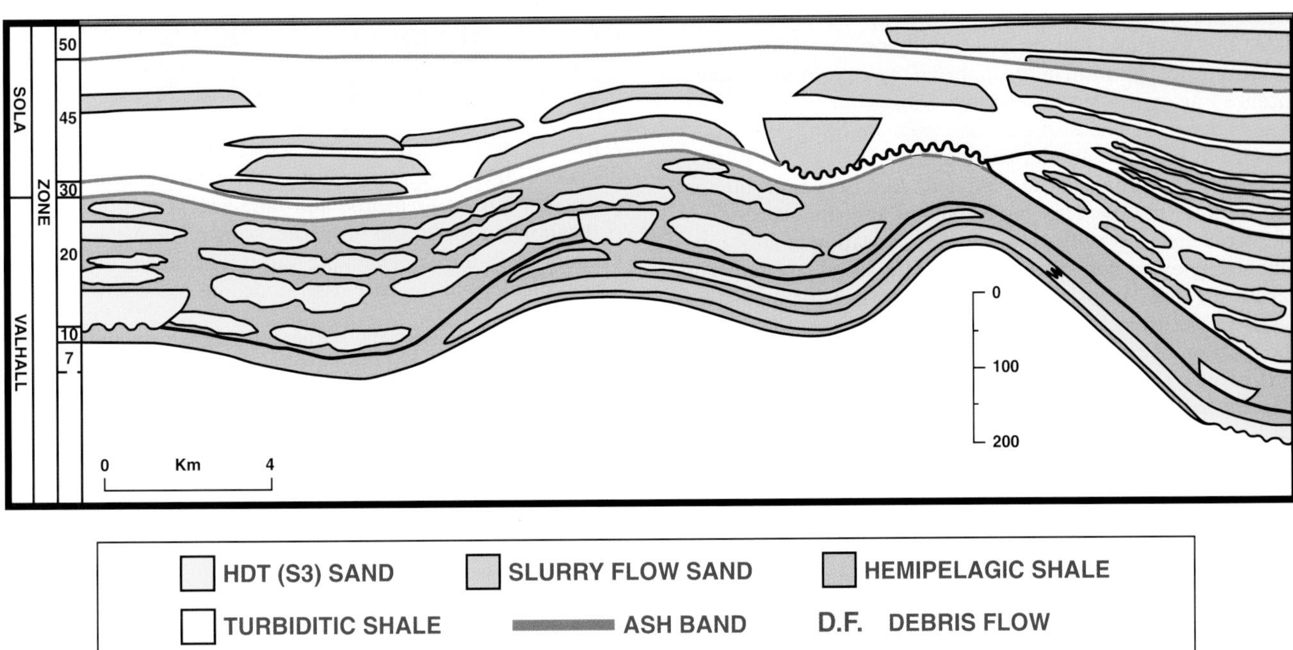

Fig. 5. Schematic depth cross-section showing reservoir zonation and architecture.

to distal sense, and are well correlated across the length of the field, sitting on a large unconformity in the east, associated with their source area.

Zone 20

The facies suite within this zone is dominated by clean HDT (S3) set within hemipelagic shale. These form the best quality reservoirs of the field, and are particularly important in Block 15/30. Typically they have a blocky gamma ray log profile, are inversely graded, and show little or no evidence of erosion. Because of the conspicuous lack of levee deposits and characteristics normally associated with channel development, these sands are interpreted to represent deposition as lobes developed within localized depressions created by differential subsidence. In the west, zone 20 sands occur at distinct stratigraphic intervals and may be separated by laterally extensive shales.

Zone 30

Zone 30 is defined only in the west and probably represents a quiescent period of low energy conditions. It is characterized by hemipelagic shales with volcanic ashes, thin bedded turbidites, and locally developed debris flows. It is insignificant in terms of reservoir volume.

Zone 40

Zone 40, defined in the east only, is characterized by slurry flow sandbodies which are ungraded, show a blocky GR log profile and a lack of correlation. The uppermost bed in this zone is, however, distinct in that it is widely correlated, and is characteristically banded yet shows rapid local facies variations. Interpretation of the morphological element that these sandbodies represent is problematic.

Zone 45

Zone 45 contains 50% of the gas in place and is the main reservoir in the eastern part of the field (Table 1). Sands are normally graded, and individual units may develop very coarse bases which are useful in sandbody correlation. Zone 45 sands are present across the whole field, but were deposited independently in eastern (16/26 & 16/27) and western (15/29 & 15/30) provinces.

In the eastern province, net : gross is high. Facies within blocky sands are banded to laminated M2 divisions. Upward-fining units grade from a clean S3 base into a banded M2 division which in turn grades into a thin-bedded turbidite cap. In the eastern province, Zone 45 is informally subdivided into upper and lower, the upper zone showing greater lateral correlation. Some sands which may be correlated over several kilometres represent sheet-like deposits created by the lateral amalgamation of individual flows bringing sand into the basin simultaneously from multiple sources. We believe that correlated sands were initiated by the same event or trigger, such as a seismic tremor.

The western province contains less sand which was deposited only during the early part of zone 45 times. Hence, the net : gross is much lower and blocky sands are restricted to the base of the zone. These sands are also slurry flow beds, but are harder to correlate than in the eastern province.

Zone 50

Zone 50 sands are confined to Blocks 16/26 and 16/27, and pinch-out close to the boundary with block 15/30. The sands are generally banded to wispy laminated M2 slurry flow deposits. They show normal grading and are finer grained than other zones. As with zone 45, these sands are interpreted to represent the amalgamation of individual depositional units formed in response to discrete basin-wide events. Because of the restricted grain size range of the sands and the occurrence of high concentrations of glauconite, they are interpreted to be sourced from a mature shelf system.

Modelling of geological heterogeneity

Selection of the number and approximate placement of pre-drill wells relied on reservoir models made from hand drawn and digitized zonal average maps of facies proportions and properties. However, significant fine-scale lateral variations in facies and properties were highlighted by the pre-drill well data. For example, five 'twinned' wells drilled within 200 m of existing exploration and appraisal wells proved extreme localized heterogeneity in terms of both geometry and facies type. The recent phase of detailed reservoir correlation, constructed at bed scale and based on a hierarchy of architectural elements has provided an updated reconstruction of the depositional model. This model allows for characterization of internal heterogeneity as well as the delineation of flow units and stratigraphic compartments to address drainage patterns across the field. It also provides a framework for predicting reservoir occurrence and quality away from well control for the location of post production wells.

Britannia reservoir modelling is based on the 3D Gocad (Geological Object Computer Aided Design) environment facilitated by application links built within Chevron. This allows the use of Gocad as a common or shared Earth model (Gawith & Gutteridge 1996; Garrett *et al.* 1997) for velocity modelling, seismic interpretation, data analysis, framework modelling, reservoir characterizarion and scale-up, and visualization. In addition, the recent implementation of geostatistical techniques within Gocad allows its use for rapid facies and rock property modelling.

Impact of facies heterogeneity on single-phase fluid flow

Motivation for study

Moving into the reservoir management phase of field life, the Britannia subsurface team wanted to assess:

(i) the impact of geological reservoir heterogeneity on fluid flow to production wells; and
(ii) possible stratigraphical controls on reservoir compartmentalization.

The generation of, and insight into, the new depositional model allowed selection of facies and property variograms for input into geostatistical modelling.

Modelling approach

Stratigraphical grids were built for each of the two main reservoir zones in the two pre-drilled areas (Fig. 1), that is zone 45 in the platform area and zone 20 at the subsea centre. The model cells were 100 m × 100 m in area and approximately 1 m thick, giving models of approximately 290 000 cells and 130 000 cells, respectively. The input data were a five-fold division of facies (Fig. 6), core mini-permeameter and wire-line permeability measurements, and wire-line porosity. Multiple realizations of facies and properties were made using different random seeds and by changing variogram ranges and trends. The main steps in the base case modelling work flow were:

(1) interpolate facies using sequential indicator simulation;
(2) interpolate permeability within each facies region using sequential Gaussian simulation; and
(3) interpolate porosity guided by the prior estimate of permeability within facies regions using sequential Gaussian simulation with collocated co-Kriging.

Different modelling methodologies were also used:

(a) one vertical cell per zone and hand-contoured average porosity and permeability (tank model); this was done to simulate the method used for selecting pre-drill well locations;
(b) geostatistical interpolation of porosity followed by permeability (no facies constraints); and
(c) hybrid deterministic/geostatistical modelling of facies, followed by geostastical modelling of permeability and porosity.

The impact on production predictions of different geological scenarios was assessed by passing the models to the ECLIPSE reservoir simulation package. Typical simulation models had approximately 100 000 active grid cells. Once work flows were established and streamlined, the team were able to generate and simulate about six of these models in a working day. The measure used to assess the effect of different facies and property models on fluid flow is the area under the curve of a plot

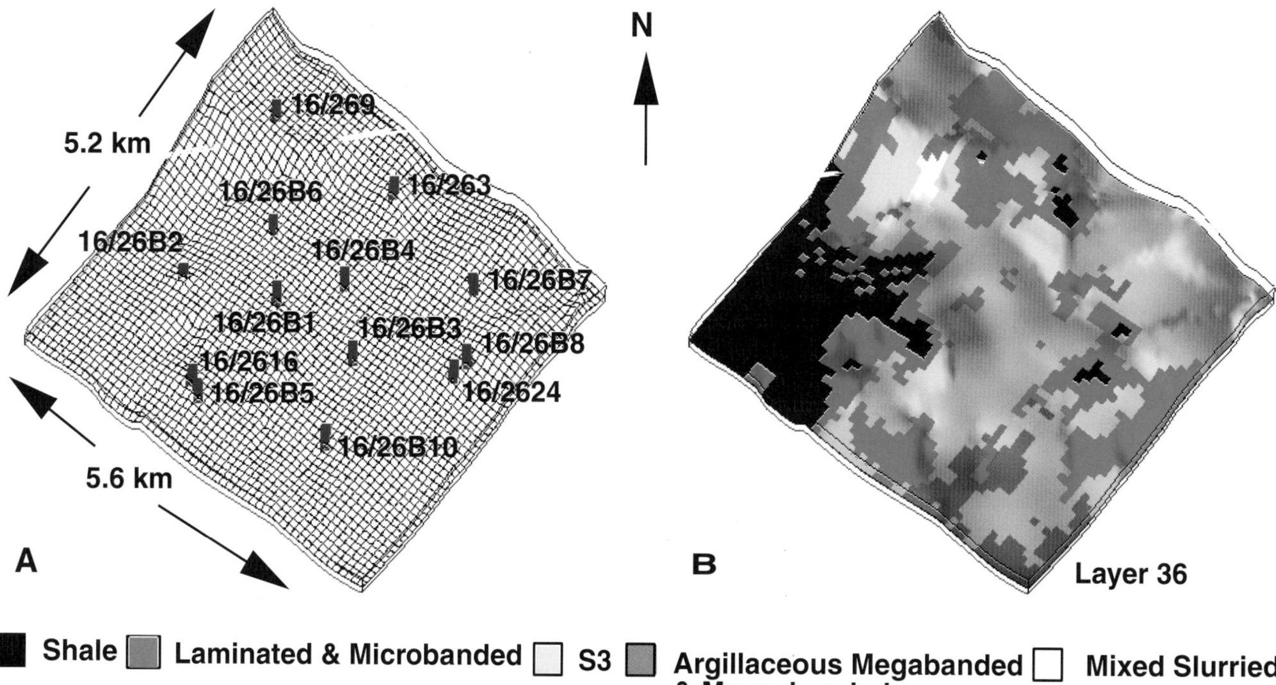

Fig. 6. (**A**) Plan view of the grid and wells used for modelling platform area Zone 45. Grid cells are 100 m × 100 m × ≈2 ft, giving a total of 285 376 cells. (**B**) The basecase realization of facies. See Table 2 for variogram parameters.

Table 2. Facies and fluid flow scoping study: variogram parameters. Lateral ranges are in kilometres and vertical ranges are in feet

	East			West		
	'Short'	'Base'	'Long'	'Short'	'Base'	'Long'
Shale	$0.75 \times 0.75 \times 5$	$6.0 \times 6.0 \times 15$	–	$4.0 \times 4.0 \times 60$	$4.0 \times 4.0 \times 60$	$4.0 \times 4.0 \times 60$
Laminated/Microbanded	$1.0 \times 1.0 \times 10$	$4.0 \times 4.0 \times 25$	$6.0 \times 6.0 \times 40$	–	–	–
S3	$0.5 \times 0.25 \times 5$	$2.0 \times 1.0 \times 20$	$4.0 \times 2.0 \times 14$	$2.0 \times 0.15 \times 40$	$4.0 \times 0.25 \times 40$	$5.0 \times 1.5 \times 60$
Argillaceous/Megabanded	$0.5 \times 0.25 \times 5$	$2.0 \times 1.0 \times 15$	$4.0 \times 2.0 \times 40$	–	–	–
Mixed Slurried	$25 \times 0.125 \times 3$	$1.5 \times 0.75 \times 15$	$3.0 \times 1.5 \times 30$	–	–	–
Azimuth	N–S, E–W	NE–SW	NW–SE	NW–SE, NE–SW	N–S	E–W
Permeability variogram lengths		$0.25 \times$ facies		$0.1 \times$ facies	$0.25 \times$ facies	$1.0 \times$ facies
Porosity variogram lengths		$0.75 \times$ permeability				

of the model cumulative production ($\times 10^9$ SCF) against deliverability ($\times 10^6$ SCF(D)), illustrated in Fig. 7 and Fig. 9. This is a measure of compartmentalization, since if all models had the same level of connectivity all curves would be expected to overlie each other.

The models did not take account of faults and fractures, multi-phase fluid effects (e.g. condensate banking), and existing well test data. In addition, all models had the same well data and were normalized to the same pore volume allowing any variations in flow predictions to be attributed to reservoir heterogeneity alone.

Platform area Zone 45

This set of models was generated using 13 wells, of which 9 were pre-drilled production wells (Fig. 6). In this area Zone 45 has a high net : gross and sands are sheet-like in character. The predictions of platform area zone 45 production varied only by $\pm 5\%$ from a 'base case' model generated using P50 estimates of correlation ranges. This is not surprising since for Britannia, production is controlled by near-wellbore permeability which is similar for all models with fixed well locations. However, the predictions of individual well performance varied between different models by as much as 15% and is attributed to local changes in connected pore volume. We were able to show that facies correlation ranges must change by an order of magnitude before they begin to effect production. All models gave lower predicted flow rates than tank-like models of this zone.

A set of simulation runs was generated with producing wells in random locations. This was similar to drilling in-fill production wells in areas where near-wellbore permeability would be uncertain. This set of runs demonstrated that performance predictions are most effected by facies depositional trend (Fig. 7). For example, imposing an E–W correlation trend 'dragged' shale bodies and poor reservoir properties from the western part of the model across the central platform area, significantly reducing the predicted performance.

Sub-sea area Zone 20

This suite of models was based on 9 wells of which 4 were pre-drilled producing wells (Fig. 8). These were two component facies models with 55% S3 sand and 45% shale derived from well control. It had been interpreted that the sandbodies were linear but with uncertainty as to the level of connection of sandbodies between wells. The suite of models, produced with a very wide range of variogram lengths, resulted in performance predictions which varied by $\pm 15\%$. Because of the relatively high net : gross ratio of the well data, which is honoured in the construction of geostatistical models, the result was excellent sand connectivity in 3D, demonstrated by analysis of connected volumes ('geobodies').

An extreme model was generated with facies proportions of 35% S3 sand and 65% shale (Fig. 8C), which although it violated the facies proportions indicated by well data, was considered a downside case for net : gross ratio in parts of the field which had not yet been penetrated by producing wells. With an interpreted source area to the north, a variogram with a long N–S range of correlation and a very short E–W range was used to extend shalebodies perpendicular to the main trend of the producing wells. This was the only model in which significant compartments could be generated, reducing the overall performance prediction (Fig. 9).

Impact of different well types on deliverability for different geological scenarios

Motivation for study

The platform area pre-drilled wells were conservative in their lateral reach and were, with the exception of high-angle Well 16/26-B9Z, conventional wells. Given the low permeability of the main reservoir in the platform area and an initial reservoir pressure slightly above dew point, it was recognized that multiphase fluid flow effects such as condensate banking and velocity stripping will occur shortly after production start-up. Condensate banking has a detrimental effect on deliverability by reducing the relative permeability to gas. It was anticipated that a variety of different well geometry (e.g. high-angle, multilateral) and completion (e.g. fracturing) options could be exploited to increase the deliverability from conventional platform wells. A cross-disciplinary study was set up to examine the cost, feasibility, risks, and predicted deliverability of a variety of well geometries and completion types. These findings would be integrated through decision-risk analysis to allow selection of optimum strategies for Britannia. The foundation of this work was a suite of geological models for the reservoir in five different regions of the field (Fig. 10) to be drained by platform wells yet to be drilled.

Modelling approach

A significant challenge was provided by limited well data control in each of the model areas, there being a maximum of 2 wells in each model. This was considered insufficient data to allow a purely stochastic modelling approach, such as that outlined above. Facies maps were used as soft data to bridge the gap between deterministic and stochastic modelling. Property interpolation required particular attention as limited well statistics in each model were not representative of the full geological volume.

A typical modelling workflow for each zone in each model was:

(1) draw deterministic facies map based on sand input and pinchout lines;

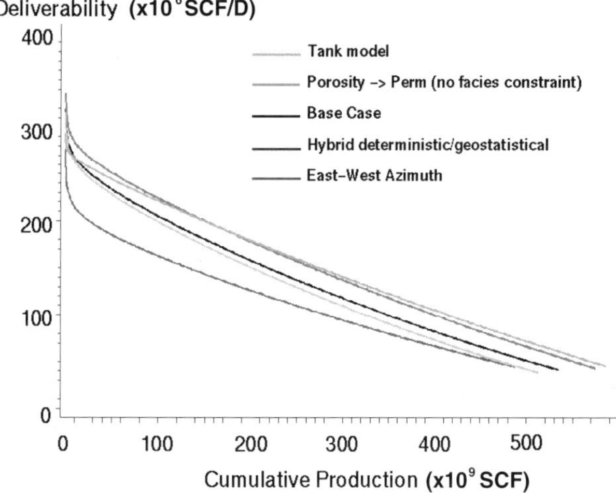

Fig. 7. Platform area zone 45 simulation results generated with producing wells in random locations. The measure used to assess the effect of different facies and property models on fluid flow is the area under the curves for the above plot. This is a measure of compartmentalization, since if all models had the same level of connectivity all the curves would be expected to over-lie.

(2) decimate facies map and 'sprinkle' remaining values into model to be used as soft data;
(3) interpolate facies using sequential indicator simulation guided by sub-sampled version of facies map;
(4) enter deterministic shale layers to form vertical permeability barriers if necessary according to the geological description;
(5) distribute permeability within facies using un-conditional sequential Gaussian simulation of well data, or histograms of permeability distribution derived from near-by wells where there is insufficient control within the model;
(6) interpolate porosity by sequential Gaussian co-simulation of well data, or histograms of porosity distribution derived from near-by wells where there is insufficient control within the model, using permeability as a soft constraint; and
(7) combine zonal models to form a single grid of the entire reservoir.

Each model was 3000 m × 4000 m in area to give approximately 2000 acres drainage for a single well. Grid cells were 50 × 50 m areally and approximately 1.5 m thick, a size which simulation modelling had established as an appropriate scale for capturing multi-phase effects such as condensate banking and velocity stripping. Model sizes ranged between 86 000–370 000 cells.

Model 1

To the south of the platform location this model contains zones 50 and 45 only above the gas–liquid contact and two control wells (Fig. 11A & B). Facies modelling was made simpler by the fact that the geology here is considered near layer-cake, and discrete shales were incorporated that isolated individual sands vertically. Net : gross is high.

Model 2

This model is to the northwest of the platform and contains zones 50, 45, 40 and 20. It contained two control wells in the far southeast, which were insufficient to model sand pinch-out to the northwest (Fig. 11C) in an area interpreted as a sediment source fairway. The use of facies maps to restrict sand distribution proved crucial here. Net : gross is moderate to the southeast and low to the northwest.

A. Basecase

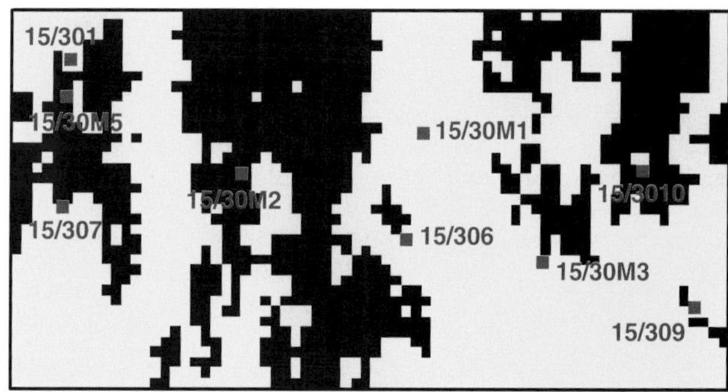

B. East–West trend sensitivity

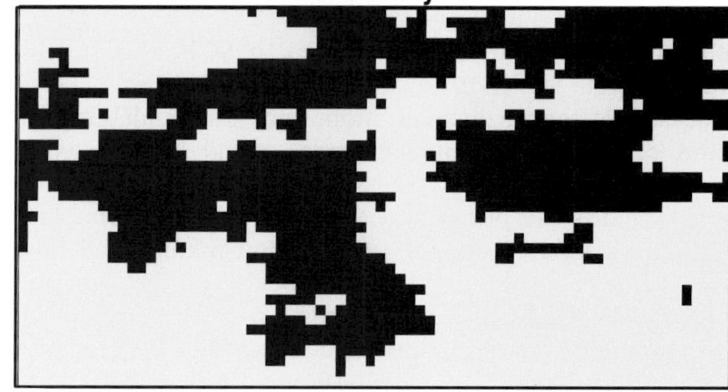

C. Low Net:Gross sensitivity

Fig. 8. Plan view examples of subsea area zone 20 facies models. A and B have a net : gross of 55% derived from well control. C has a reduced net : gross of 35%. See Table 2 for variogram parameters.

Model 3

Directly north of the platform this model is in an up-dip structural location where the reservoir thins and sands pinch-out northwards (Fig. 11D). Facies maps were necessary, along with two control wells, to model the pinchout line and to restrict the distribution of S3 sands in the lower reservoir that dominate the permeability-thickness. Net : gross is generally high south of the pinchout line.

Model 4

This model is to the northeast of the platform and contains two wells that penetrate zones 50, 45, 40 and 20. Facies maps were used in what is overall a high net : gross area with sands developed laterally over large areas.

Model 5

Model 5 is in an undrilled area to the northeast of the platform where only zones 45 and 50 are mapped. Without well control it was essential to create pseudo wells of the interpreted facies

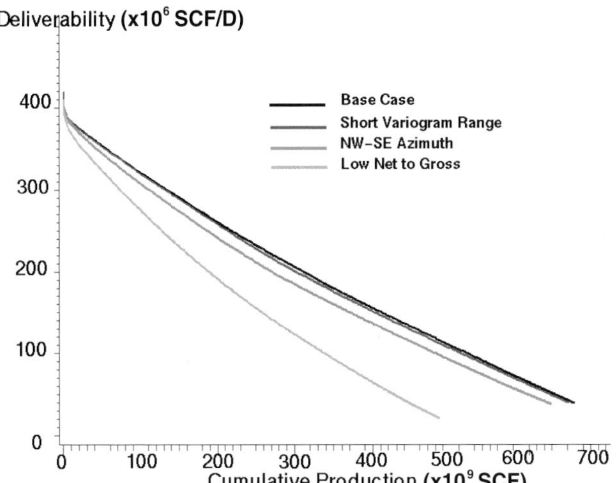

Fig. 9. Subsea area Zone 20 simulation results generated with producing wells in pre-drilled locations.

and facies maps to control lateral sand distribution. This model has a high net : gross with laterally continuous, sheet-like shales vertically distributed.

Fluid flow simulation

The results of the flow simulation in each model using different well geometries and completions is on-going. A problem in interpreting the results is that different well geometries access different connected pore volume within the same model. This is reduced where the geology is layered such as in Models 1 and 5. However, early results indicate that significant performance enhancements are predicted for high-angle, multi-lateral and fractured wells. High-angle wells do not show a significant deliverability improvement over conventional wells where laterally continuous shales restrict flow to bedding-parallel. Because Britannia reservoir permeabilities are very low and condensate banking occurs for conventional wells with high draw-down, fractured wells significantly enhance production by improving access of the reservoir to the well-bore, reducing draw-down and therefore suppressing formation of a condensate bank.

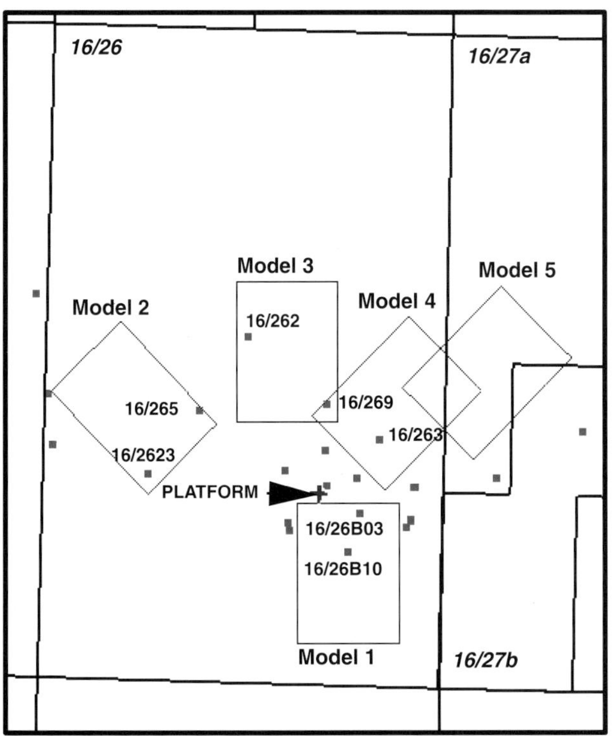

Fig. 10. Location of model areas to assess the impact of different well geometry in different geological settings on deliverability in the platform area.

Full-field stratigraphical and simulation modelling

A full-field reservoir simulation model for Britannia is required to give long-term production profiles to satisfy gas marketing contractual obligations. The full-field model will also give an idea of the requirement for additional wells, the gross well locations and spacing, and an indication of the impact of gross geological uncertainties such as structural and stratigraphical compartmentalization. The model scoping studies described above show that the full-field model with large grid cells is not appropriate for the selection of detailed well locations, for capturing fine-scale heterogeneity or for geological prediction.

The subsurface team are currently building a full-field model which is designed to be constrained by DST data and have less than 100 000 cells for 10 year predictions. The underlying full-field fine-scale geological models are critical, as these allow the rapid update of the model with new well information, make the fine-scale model independent of scale-up techniques required to get to a coarse-scale model, and provide the level of detail required to plan well locations and the geometry or completion required.

From the lessons learned during the facies and fluid flow scoping study, the subsurface team are comfortable with simulation modelling of zones 50 and 45, with few cells vertically per layer, as these zones exhibit tank-like behaviour. More grid cells vertically will be assigned to zone 20 to allow modelling of stratigraphical compartments in low net : gross parts of the section. Other sensitivities to be tested will include compartmentalization by sealing faults based on seismic interpretation and fault sealing studies currently underway.

Conclusions

Britannia Field is unique in being dominated by slurry flow deposits which present challenges in reservoir interpretation and modelling. A large set of core and log data has allowed the identification of seven main reservoir zones which describe the broad layering of the reservoir. The lower reservoir (zones 10 and 20) is dominated by clean high density turbidite sands within hemi-pelagic open marine shales. The upper reservoir (zones 40, 45 and 50) is dominated by slurry flow deposits and contains most of the gas in place. Pre-drilled wells demonstrated considerable heterogeneity within zones.

Production performance from pre-drilled wells was based on geostatistical facies models of zone 20 in the west (subsea manifold) and zone 45 in the East (platform). Predictions are more pessimistic than tank models as small compartments of gas are created. Despite the uncertainties associated with facies interpretation, it is difficult to model significant compartments in modelled areas with high net to gross ratios. Correlation azimuth has the greatest effect on production, and facies correlation lengths must change by an order of magnitude before they effect production.

New well locations in areas of lower net : gross should be determined using simulation models that honour the geological model and capture the appropriate scale of heterogeneity. This allows the planning of complex 3D high-angle and multi-lateral well paths through heterogeneous 3D geological models. The model scoping studies described here show that the full-field model with large grid cells is not appropriate for the selection of detailed well locations, for capturing fine-scale heterogeneity or for geological prediction.

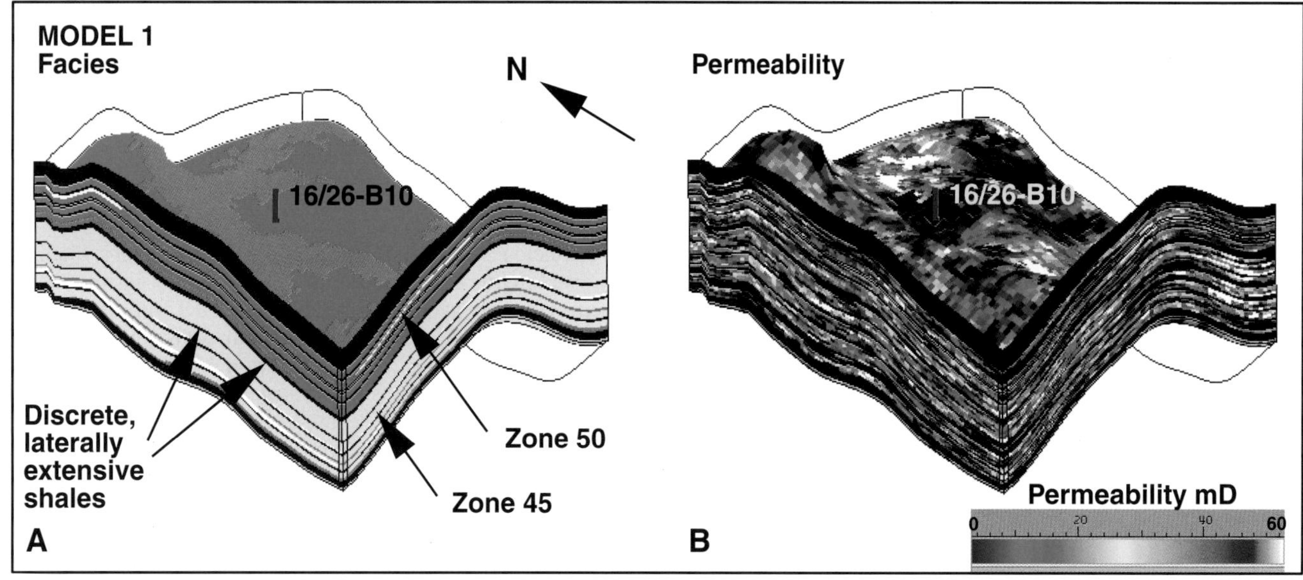

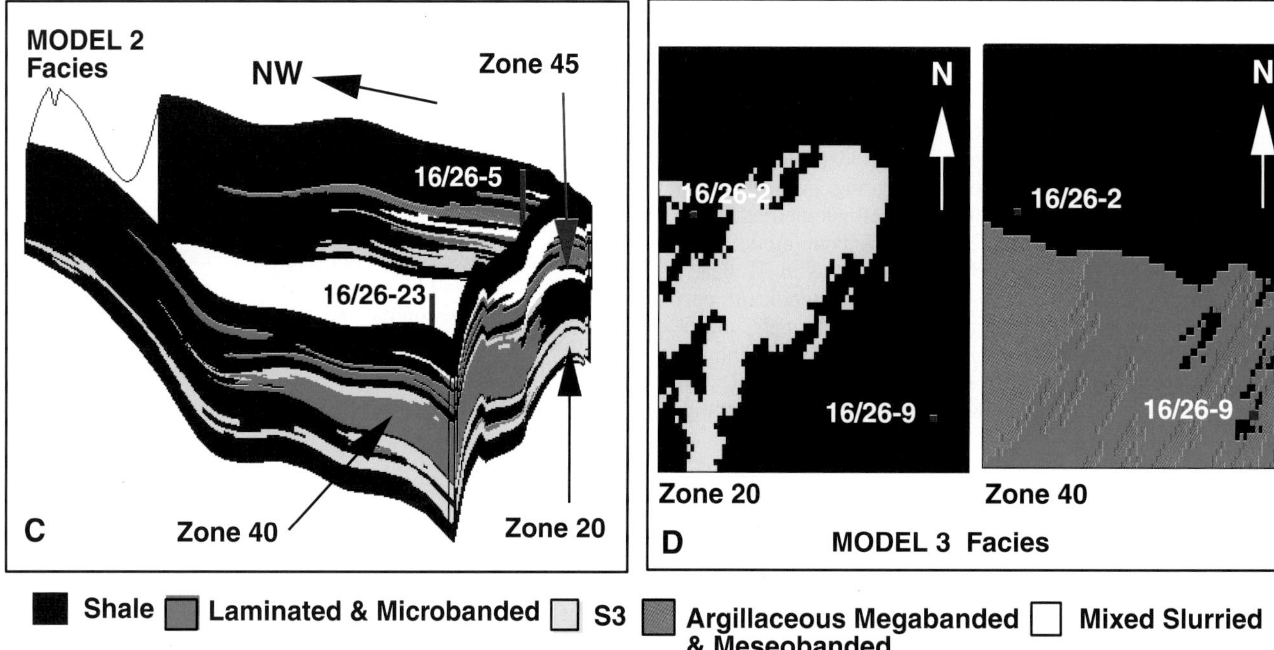

Figure 11 Examples of facies and property models generated to assess the impact of different well geometries on deliverability for different geological settings.

This paper summarizes material discussed during 1997 reservoir modelling workshops with Britannia co-venturers (Chevron, Conoco, Union Texas, Saga, Phillips and Texaco); we thank them for their participation and for permission to publish. Our work was enabled by the success of the Britannia data analysis alliance (Core Laboratories, Blackbourn Geoconsulting, Network Stratigraphic Consulting, Leeds University Rock Deformation Research) in providing large volumes of timely quality data from pre-drilled wells.

References

GARRETT, S. W., GRIESBACH, S. L., JOHNSON, D. P, JONES, R. C., LO, M. W., ORR, W. P. & SWORD, C. H. 1997. Earth model synthesis. *First Break*, **15.1**, 13–20.

GAWITH, D. E. & GUTTERIDGE, P. A. 1996. Seismic validation of reservoir simulation using a shared earth model. *Petroleum Geoscience*, **2**, 97–104.

GUY, M. 1992. Facies analysis of the Kopervik sand interval, Kilda Field, Block 16/26, UK North Sea. *In*: HARDMAN, R. F. P. (ed.) *Exploration Britain: Geological Insights for the Next Decade*. Geological Society, London, Special Publications, **67**, 187–220.

HEMMENS, P. D. 1997. Britannia: preparing for superior operational performance. *Society of Petroleum Engineers* 38527.

LOWE, D. R. 1982. Sediment gravity flows II. Depositional models with special reference to the deposits of high-density turbidite currents. *Journal of Sedimentary Petrology*, **52**, 279–297.

——, HICKSON, T. & GUY, M. (1995). Slurry flows: an important class of sediment gravity flows with examples of slurry-flow deposits from the Lower Cretaceous of the North Sea. *Geological Society of America Abstracts with Programs*, **27**, A128–A129.

—— & GUY, M. In press. Slurry flow deposits in the Britannia Formation (Lower Cretaceous), North Sea: a new perspective on the turbidity current and debris flow problem. *Sedimentology*, **47**.

Innovation and risk management in a small subsea-tieback: Arkwright Field, Central North Sea, UK

J. D. KANTOROWICZ,[1,3] I. J. ANDREWS,[1,4] S. DHANANI,[1,5] M. GILLIS,[1,4] C. JENNINGS,[1,5] P. J. LUMSDEN,[1,4] G. ORR,[1,4] R. W. SIMM[2] and J. WILLIAMS[1,3]

[1] *Amoco (UK) Exploration Company, Amoco House, West Gate, Ealing, London W5 1XL, UK*
[2] *Enterprise Oil Plc (on secondment to Amoco (UK) Exploration Company)*
[3] *Present address: BP Amoco, Chertsey Road, Sunbury-on-Thames, Middlesex TW16 7LN, UK (e-mail: kantorj@bp.com)*
[4] *Present address: BP Amoco Farburn Industrial Estate, Dyce, Aberdeen AB2 0PB, UK*
[5] *BP Amoco, 501 Westlake Park Blvd, Houston, Texas 77079, USA*

Abstract: Arkwright is a 50×10^6 BBL oil field located within a single Forties Sandstone Member turbidite 'channel' system. Arkwright was discovered in 1990 and developed in 1996. Earlier start-up was precluded by reservoir risk and lack of export pipeline capacity. Reservoir definition improved after acquiring a 3D survey and applying imaging and attribute studies. This, combined with subsurface analogue, core, and carbon, oxygen and strontium isotopic studies, improved understanding of reservoir architecture and connectivity. Geostatistical techniques were used to quantify the STOIIP. The main risks identified were the absence of aquifer support, and possible vertical and lateral baffling. As these could not be tested by appraisal drilling it was decided to commence development.

Low-cost, two-well development options were considered and rejected because of the subsurface risk. Without guaranteed aquifer support, the productivity from early sub-bubble point flow would be lost waiting for injection support to be added. Risk-weighting highlighted the advantage of initial expenditure to safeguard the project, and so a third initial production well was planned, in a location suitable for conversion to injection.

Predicted rates were increased and the impact of lateral baffling minimized by drilling deviated producers on opposite sides of the structure, and not reusing the discovery well. Costs were reduced by using a drilling centre outside the field. The perforation strategy ensures drainage above and below potentially sealing abandonment shales, and facilitates future zonal isolation. Communication within the reservoir was tested at start-up with an interference test.

The Arkwright Field is located in Block 22/23a. The Block was originally awarded to the Amoco Group in the 1st Round in 1964 as part of Licence P.019, and was reassigned to Licence P.291 in 1978 when the P.019/P.020 Licences were restricted to the area of the Montrose Field. The current partnership consists of:

Amoco (UK) Exploration Company	30.77%
Amerada Hess Ltd	28.20%
Enterprise Oil plc	41.03%

The initial focus of activity in the area was the Arbroath Field, discovered in 1969 and the Montrose Field shortly thereafter in 1971. Montrose was developed first, in 1976, and Arbroath came on stream in 1990, after Montrose production declined. Montrose crude was initially exported by tanker, but since 1984 has been exported by pipeline via the Forties Pipeline System. Both fields are developed from platforms, with Arbroath tied back to Montrose (Fig. 1, Crawford *et al.* 1990)

Arkwright was one of several smaller Paleocene prospects in the area identified for potential drilling and tieback to the existing facilities. The prospect was mapped in part from 3D seismic shot over Marnock in 1986, and from 2D seismic acquired previously. The prospect was mapped as a 4-way dip closure, in an area where all previously drilled 4-way dip closures had been found to be hydrocarbon-bearing. The main perceived risk was of the impact of depth conversion on the volume of the closure and consequently STOIIP, and the economic viability of the field.

The 22/23a-3 discovery well was drilled in 1990 using a semi-submersible drilling rig, cored, logged, tested and suspended. The results were interpreted during late 1990 and early 1991. At the time, depth conversion and internal reservoir parameter uncertainty lead to a range of possible field sizes from 30 to 70×10^6 BBL oil. With the technology available, a tie back to Montrose was not viable, whilst the nearer Arbroath Field had only just come on stream and so there was insufficient pipeline ullage to justify developing Arkwright. Appraisal drilling was considered, but it was felt more appropriate to explore the remaining prospects in the hope that development cost savings could be achieved from a combined programme in the future. This analysis lead to a recommendation to acquire 3D seismic over the entire licence area, and base future development decisions upon a consistent seismic database. The 3D survey was shot by PGS in 1993, processed and received in house in 1994.

This paper outlines the initial well results, characterizing reservoir description uncertainty in terms of its impact on field performance, reviews the appraisal and development options that were considered during 1994 and 1995, focusing on the impact of subsurface uncertainty, and discusses how the data gathering plan was intended to reduce uncertainty and so improve performance predictions. The field Development Plan

Kantorowicz, J. D., Andrews, I. J., Dhanani, S., Gillis, M., Jennings, C., Lumsden, P. J., Orr, G., Simm, R. W. & Williams, J. 1999. Innovation and risk management in a small subsea-tieback: Arkwright Field, Central North Sea, UK. *In*: Fleet, A. J. & Boldy, S. A. R. (eds) *Petroleum Geology of Northwest Europe: Proceedings of the 5th Conference*, 1125–1134.

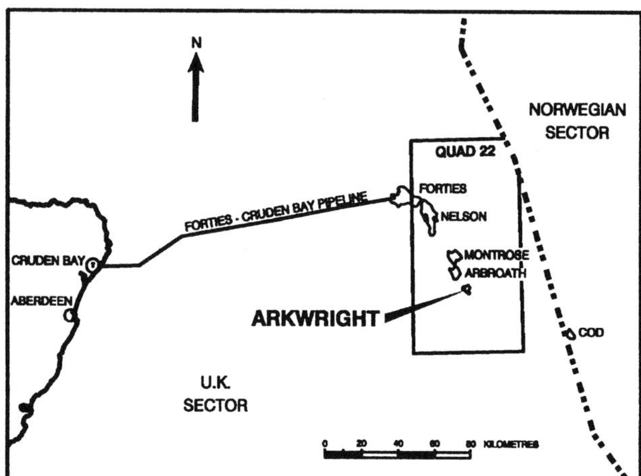

Fig. 1. Location map of Arkwright Field in the UK Central North Sea.

was approved by the Department of Trade and Industry in December 1995 and the field came on stream in November 1996.

Well 22/23a-3 results and initial reservoir model

Stratigraphy and sedimentology

The discovery well penetrated a 46 m (150 ft) oil column within the 153 m thick Forties Sandstone Member (after Knox & Holloway 1992). The well was cored throughout most of the oil column and utilizing a scheme modified after Mutti & Ricci Lucchi (1972), interpreted in terms of a turbidite depositional system comprising channelized and channel margin facies (Fig. 2). Broadly, the reservoir comprises two thick-bedded or channelized sandstone intervals separated by a shalier interval of more marginal and hemipelagic deposits that may be of regional significance. The lowermost interval, Layers E2&3, is partially cored and contains thick-bedded probable submarine channel sandstones and prograding sand-lobes with minor abandonment sandstones and siltstones. Layer E1 comprises thinner bedded sand lobe deposits and abandonment shales and is highly slumped and distorted. The remainder of the sequence comprises submarine channel sandstones, thick-bedded submarine sand lobe deposits and occasional slumped and abandonment facies. Layers D and C are more heterolithic. Layer B is a well developed channel sandstone. Layer A is a channel margin to abandonment facies. A free water level (FWL) was interpreted from formation pressure data, to be at 2623.3 m (8607 ft) TVDSS (true vertical depth subsea), close to the base of Layer D.

Geophysical mapping and depth conversion

In the Arkwright area the Top Forties Sandstone Member seismic pick is relatively clear, given the impedance contrast between the sandstones and the Sele Formation shales above. Also, the top is rarely broken by faults, although one obvious offset occurs within the middle of the field, close to the original discovery well (Fig. 3).

Depth conversion uncertainty and the gross rock volume (GRV) of the closure had been identified as uncertainties prior to drilling. At the time this was considered to be the largest uncertainty and so had the clearest bearing on whether or not the project would be viable. The discovery well came in off the original depth prognosis but within the estimated range of uncertainty at the time. Following the processing of the full field 3D seismic in 1994, several approaches to depth conversion were attempted. These included VoK (velocity increasing with depth) combining seismic and well data, and using only seismic data, variable average velocities and conditional simulation. The first three traditional approaches gave larger GRVs within closure, but did not offer an automated way of quantifying the range of possible outcomes. Conditional simulation (Journel & Huijbregts 1978), therefore, was employed to provide a base case map (Fig. 4). Confidence in, and support for the depth conversion came from the use of direct hydrocarbon indicators. The shape of the field was constrained using amplitude versus offset (Barrett *et al.* 1995) and seismic approximate impedance logs (Waters 1978; Simm *et al.* 1996).

Combined with seismic mapping of the Forties interval, intensity and pseudo colour drape imaging of the Top Forties was used to elucidate the depositional history. Isochore mapping reveals an elongate thick depositional unit running through the field from the northwest. Pseudo-colour imaging of the Top Forties time structure map reveals a prominent high on the same trend (Fig. 5), and from local well control it is known that the Top Forties topography is a function of sandstone content, with shalier areas being compacted and topographically lower. The Forties, Nelson, Montrose and Arbroath Fields all are known to contain channelized sandstones (Wills & Peattie 1990; Crawford *et al.* 1991; Whyatt *et al.* 1991). Colour drape imaging enables channelized depositional patterns to be mapped over the entire area of Blocks 22/17 and 22/18, and specifically from Arbroath into the northwest of the Arkwright Field. By contrast, there is no obvious thick entering the northeast of the field. This work presents a model for the Forties that is consistent with Den Hartog Jager *et al.* (1993) in that the more ‘distal’ portions of the depositional system exhibit marked lateral facies variations with channelized sandstones rather than the thin-bedded and laterally extensive patterns expected from more traditional fan models (Fig. 6).

Petrophysical results

The petrophysical interpretation of the well logs is summarized in Table 1.

Well test

The well was tested in a two stage drill stem test (DST), initially with perforations in Layers C and D, and then with Layer B added. Total flow rates of 5662 BOPD and 3.7×10^6 SCF(D) were recorded from all three layers combined, with an apparent degradation in permeability 100 m away from the well interpreted from the analysis. This could represent a fault (Fig. 3), or the transition from channel axis to channel marginal facies. After testing, the well was suspended in case it could be used during future development.

Volumetrics

Volumetric analysis from the petrophysical parameters above combined with the layering scheme and depth map (Fig. 4) produced a base case STOIIP estimate of 43×10^6 BBL oil. However, it was recognized that further work would be required to quantify the range of possible STOIIP.

GRV uncertainty was quantified from the conditional simulation approach to depth conversion. The prediction was more pessimistic than from the traditional depth conversion methods, but provided a robust basis for planning, given the low oil price at the time (see below). In terms of the internal reservoir parameters, sixty wells penetrate the Forties, locally providing sufficient data to build distributions (histograms) of properties such as net : gross (NG) for stochastic modelling. In this case 22/23a-3 was found to represent one of the best wells in the area, guaranteeing that the use of an offset database would downgrade the field. Secondly, channelized sandbodies are usually elongate, with a width-to-thickness

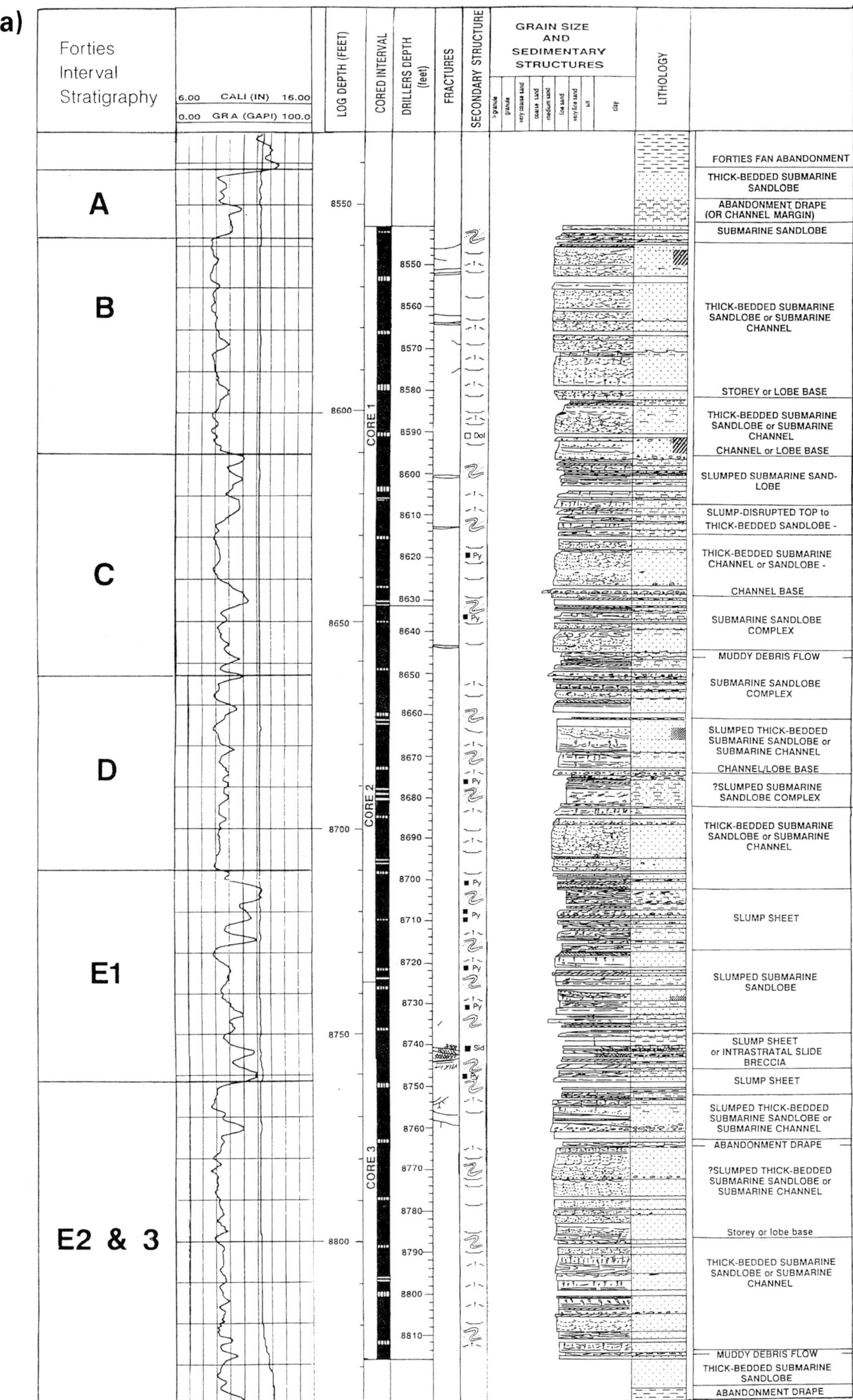

Fig. 2. Sedimentological interpretation of core from 22/23a-3. (**a**) A total of 83 m (283 ft) of core was cut from the base of Layer A through into Layer E2&3. The six-fold layering scheme was adapted from the Arbroath Field to subdivide the reservoir for modelling purposes. Layers E2&3, E1, B and A contain distinct lithofacies assemblages. Layers D and C define an interval that could have been divided further given the number of hemipelagic shales that could form field-wide barriers. Two layers were felt to be sufficient for modelling purposes. (**b**) Summary.

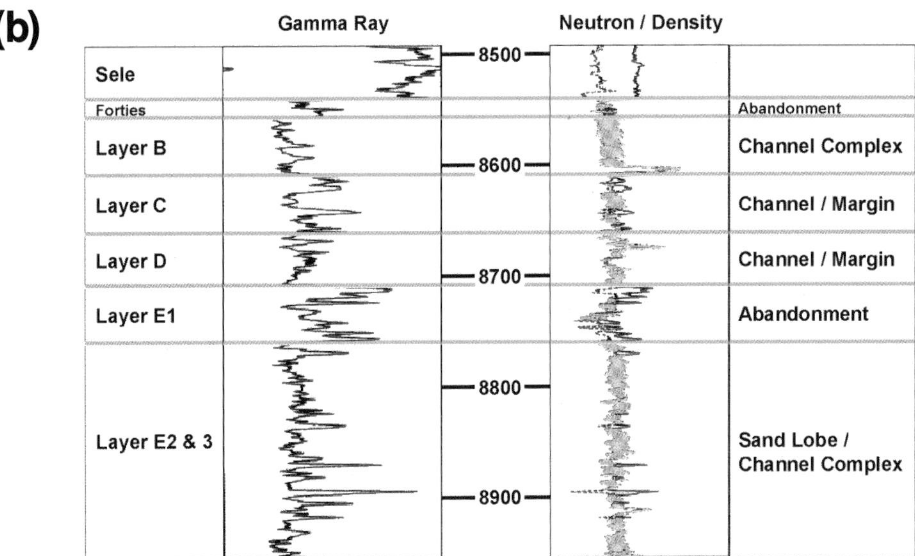

Fig. 2. (*continued*)

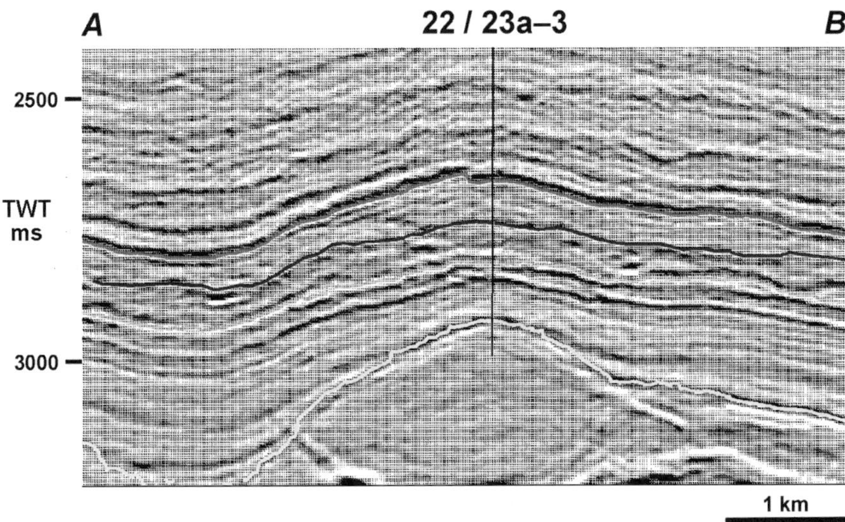

Fig. 3. SW–NE orientated reflection seismic line across Arkwright. The line of section is located on Fig. 4. The Top Forties pick is shown in green Top Lista in red, Top Chalk in orange and Base Cretaceous in yellow. Seismic mapping reveals that Arkwright sits above a Triassic basement high over which is draped the Cretaceous. Lower Paleocene sediments also drape over the high, with Mey Sandstones preferentially thickening into the lows on either side. The Forties thickens over the original high, as a result of large scale lobe switching back into a seafloor topographic low created between the Mey Sandstone thicks. Present-day closure results from continued differential compaction of the Cretaceous and Paleocene sediments over the basement high. Vertical Axis: two-way time in milliseconds.

ratio within some finite range (Schuppers 1993). Similarly, sand lobe deposits may be the lateral or the down-slope equivalents of channelized sandstones. Consequently, the reservoir properties at the well may be extrapolated for some distance, but exactly how far differs between depositional strike, and laterally. In the fields nearby, most wells drilled along the channel axes show little or no change in reservoir quality over a km or more.

Conversely, rapid changes in NG occur between channel axial and channel margin wells. Isochore mapping and visualization of the channel system (Fig. 5) provided a deterministic constraint on the area within which channel axial reservoir properties might be expected. For example, the northeastern corner of the field is not obviously part of the same channel system and therefore is an area in which reservoir quality might be poor. A Monte Carlo approach to stochastic modelling was employed, varying GRV, NG, porosity and water saturation, and using different distributions of internal reservoir parameters for different areas of the field. The formation volume factor was not varied. The distribution of STOIIPs shown in Fig. 7 was produced. In addition to the base case model, upside and downside cases were generated to assess the impact of volumetric uncertainty on the development plan, and its economics.

Development implications

From the preceding analysis, and knowledge of the production histories of the Montrose and Arbroath fields, four aspects of the reservoir description were identified for further analysis, in view of the impact they might have on a development.

Firstly, aquifer support varies around the Montrose and Arbroath fields. In Arbroath, aquifer support varies between 'edge' and a combination of 'edge' and 'bottom-water drive', and can be related to depositional sandbody architecture below the Forties Sandstone Member. In Montrose, aquifer

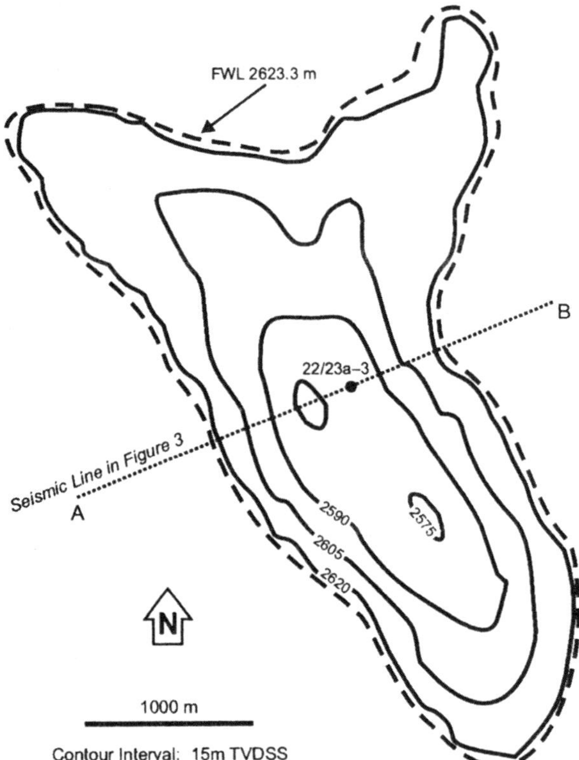

Fig. 4. Top Forties Sandstone Member depth structure map, Arkwright Field. Well 22/23a-3 penetrated the Top Forties at 2577.7 m (8457 ft) TVDSS, and established a 45.8 m oil column. The field is an elongate anticlinal feature, characterized by low relief areas to the northwest and northeast, and a central area around and south of the discovery well. The field is wholly within Block 22/23a.

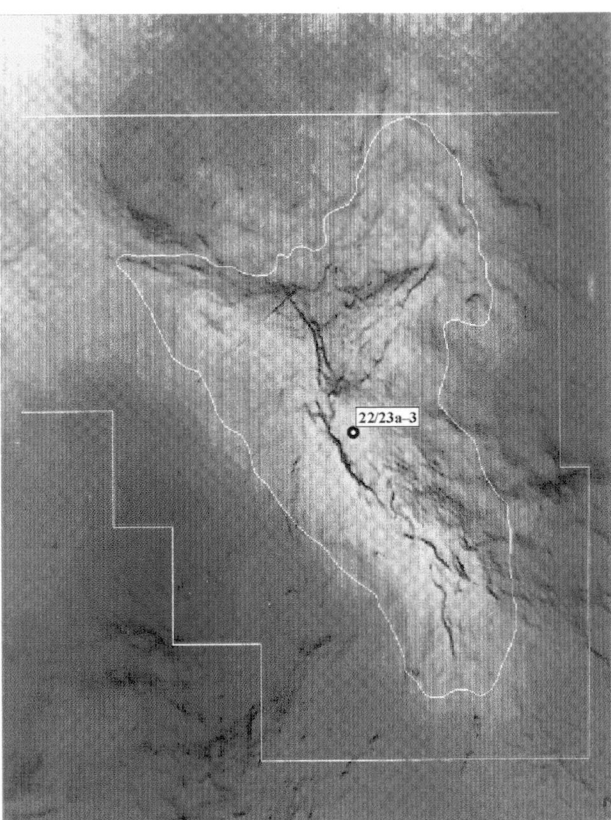

Fig. 5. Time structure visualization of the Top Forties Sandstone Member in the Arkwright Field area, Block 22/23a. Intensity and pseudo colour drape shows the Arkwright Field outline (within the field area) as an elongate northwest to south-southeast trending anticlinal structure. The 22/23a-3 location is shown on the eastern side of the centre of the field. The top of the reservoir is characterized by shaded areas that correspond to possible fault scars in a trend running along the length of the crest of the structure. The colour transition from yellow to green to blue corresponds to increasing time (depth). Sun angle 70° from the south.

support is strong on one side of the field, and poor on the other, necessitating water injection. Consequently, whilst extensive Forties Member Sandstones are mapped axially along the depositional fairway in Arkwright, indicating that at least edge aquifer support may be expected, it is not possible to calculate accurately when, and with what strength, any pressure support will arrive. The presence or absence of aquifer support was, therefore, modelled as a sensitivity.

Secondly, the shales in the field could form barriers to vertical flow at various scales. The major shaley interval, Layer E1 could act as a barrier between the water-bearing sandstones below, and the oil column above. This would delay any pressure support from below during development. Also, the minor shale breaks within the more heterolithic intervals, Layers C and D, that are hemipelagic in origin, could be laterally extensive and also act as barriers to vertical communication. The lateral extent and continuity of the shales is uncertain as some are obvioulsy slumped in the core, whilst away from the well, channel bases could erode down into the shales below. The potential for the shales to produce barriers was addressed through a strontium isotopic residual salt analysis study (Smalley *et al.* 1992). This technique addresses sealing over geological time, rather than in reaction to production. However, seals that are identified will certainly impact production, whilst failure to seal over geological time does not rule out local effects on fluid flow. This indicated that similar pore water compositions are trapped within the oil column, but that the water composition in the aquifer (below Layer E1) differs. The smaller shales might be local barriers but should not be field wide in extent. Layer E1 is probably at least field wide and may be of regional lateral extent, delaying the onset of any bottom water drive. Vertical permeability through these layers was varied accordingly during reservoir modelling.

Thirdly, faulting is seen at top reservoir on seismic (Figs 3 and 5) a small cemented fault was cored within Layer E1 (Fig. 2), and permeability degradation was interpreted from the DST, leading to the concern that a barrier to lateral communication might exist within the reservoir. Carbon, oxygen and strontium isotopic analysis revealed that the fault was locally cemented by a cone-in-cone concretion within the fault zone that had been partially dissolved and reprecipitated. Cement is unlikely to extend throughout the reservoir. However, Fig. 5 shows faulting running along the crest of the structure. By analogy to Arbroath where similar features appear to act as baffles as a result of lithological juxtaposition and deformation, it was thought that this might represent a slump feature that could cause compartmentalization between the two sides of the field.

The fourth uncertainty to consider was the possibility of a tilted oil–water contact. In the nearby Arbroath and Montrose fields the oil–water contacts vary from well to well, and define a tilt towards the northwest. The tilt is a hydrodynamic phenomenon caused by overpressured saline formation waters entering the Paleocene in the eastern Central Graben, and flowing northwestwards towards the lower pressure and less saline formation waters in the Forties Field area (Coleman 1992). Formation waters beneath Montrose and Arbroath have salinities of 110 000 to 130 000 ppm. In Arkwright this could cause a tilt of 12 m from one end of the field to the other, with a deepening to the northwest.

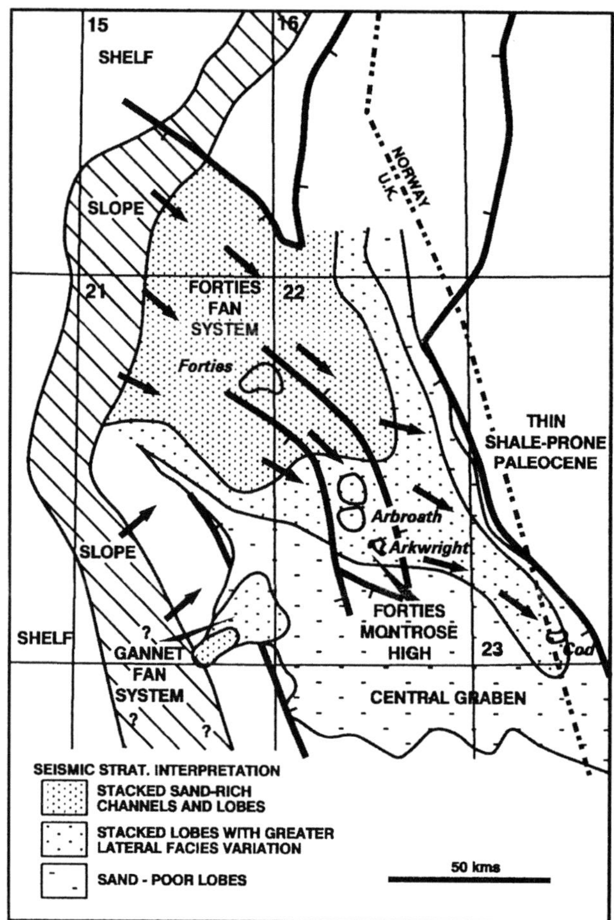

Fig. 6. Paleocene palaeogeography of the Central Graben area illustrating the Forties Sandstone Member depositional system (modified after Kulpez & van Geuns 1990). The Arkwright Field is located in a more distal area now known to be characterized by lateral facies variations between channelized sandstones that extend at least to Cod, and marginal non-reservoir facies.

Development planning

The reservoir model described earlier was completed during 1994 and early 1995 at a time when the oil price dropped to around $13 BBL^{-1}. Preliminary development scenarios were therefore developed bearing in mind the possibility that future oil prices might be equally low, or fall as dramatically as they had in the previous two or three years. There was a strong drive to identify an option with low initial capital expenditure.

Scoping studies

Initial scoping study work focused on several fundamentally different development schemes. These included using a floating production system (ruled out on the grounds that long term production rates were likely to be too low to justify the rental), building a new platform with a tieback to Montrose or Arbroath (ruled out on the basis of cost), or subsea tieback to either Montrose or Arbroath. Given that Arbroath is closer this was the favoured option.

Table 1. Arkwright Field: petrophysical log analysis summary

Layer	Net-to-Gross[1]	Porosity (%)	Perm (mD)	Sw(%)
A	0.84	20.9	–	0.43
B	0.91	21.0	78	0.32
C	0.76	19.6	28	0.58
D	0.93	19.8	24	0.70
E1	0.61	18.3	34	1.00
E2&3	0.64	15.9	28	1.00

[1] Net reservoir sandstone has a permeability of >1 mD (air), equivalent to >15% porosity.

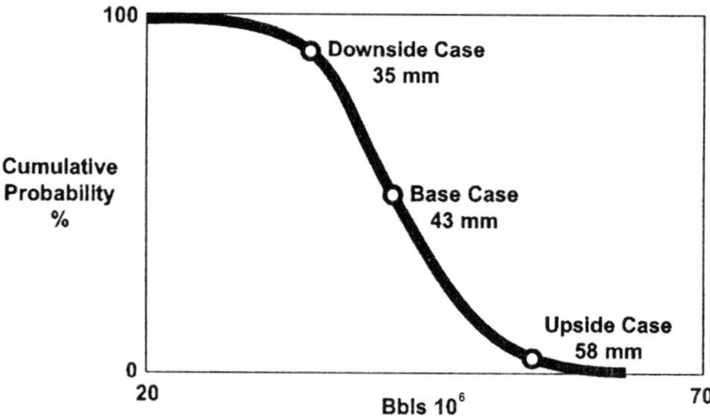

Fig. 7. Risked STOIIP distribution. The STOIIP was calculated using a proprietary Monte Carlo simulator, from GRVs generated by conditional simulation and histograms of other properties from regional data. The histograms were varied between channel axial and channel marginal data sets to apply to different areas taking account of height, and of the facies inferred from seismic mapping and imaging. Three maps were then selected for reservoir simulation modelling, a downside, base case and upside model.

Base development plan

Having identified an Arbroath subsea tieback as the base case, work began to assess how to maximize the value of the field. This involved balancing the benefits of revenues gained from a greater number of production wells at the start of field life, against the risk of failure arising from the uncertainties described earlier. A summary of the range of development options is outlined in Fig. 8. It was realized that the ability to flow the wells below the bubble point from start up would be beneficial (Batten 1995) and so cases were run with and without sub-bubble point flow at the wells. This process involves flowing the wells below the bubble point whilst maintaining the field average pressures above the bubble point.

The simplest plan was to tie back the existing suspended development well. This minimized the initial drilling costs but given the cost of pipelay barges, required almost the full development pipeline costs even if only the oil pipeline was laid, as well as modifications to the host platform. Little value was perceived in what was essentially a very expensive extended well test. Incremental developments considered included further production and then injection pipelines and wells at varying times into the future (Fig. 8a). In each case, significant additional mobilization costs were involved, always assuming that appropriate vessels and rigs would be available. Perhaps more fundamentally, plans with one well initially suffer from only obtaining a limited amount of additional data with which to update the static reservoir model and help locate future wells.

Re-using the suspended exploration well and drilling a second producer in the south of the field at the start of field life enhanced the economic value, particularly as a higher production rate could be obtained by deviating the second producer through the reservoir at 55° (see later, Fig. 8b). If a sufficiently strong aquifer existed in the area, then average reservoir pressures would not fall below the bubble point, and injection support (from a third well) would not be necessary. However, as noted earlier, aquifer performance in the area varied. Also, it was possible to seismically map the volume of

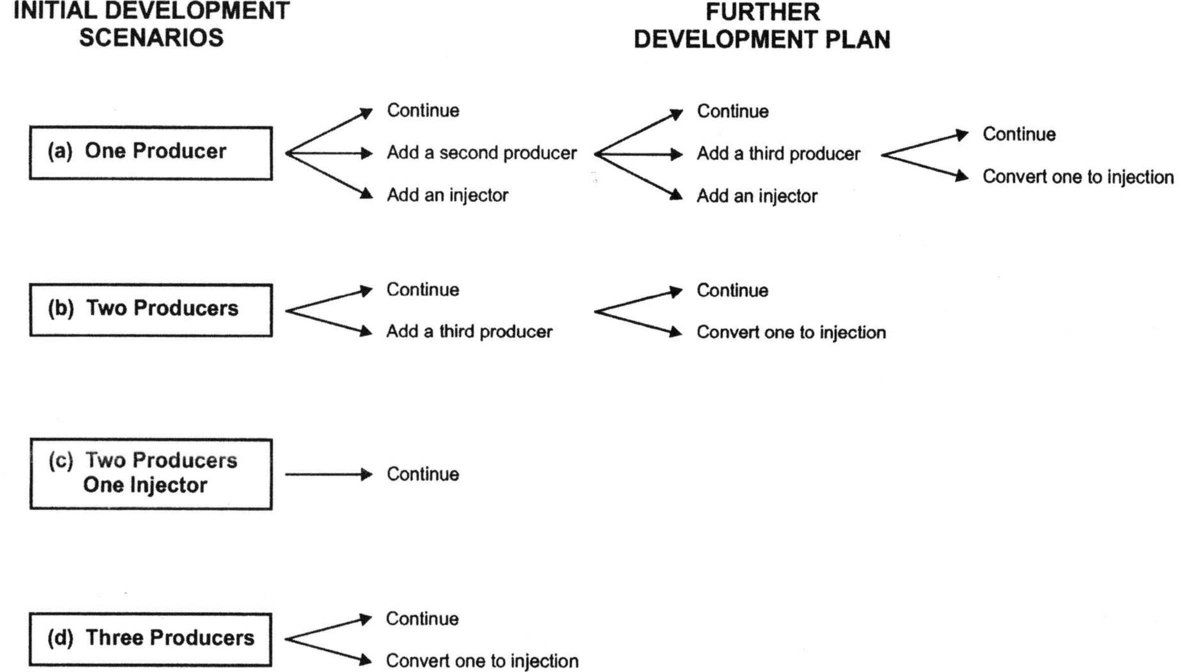

Fig. 8. Development option decision trees. Options starting development with (**a**) one, (**b**) two and (**c**) and (**d**), three wells are shown, together with the range of subsequent modifications to the plan that might occur. Economic evaluation of all options took place assuming sub-bubble point flow, with a series of cases compared to more conventional depletion, as well as a number of upside and downside cases.

connected Forties Sandstone Member and so estimate the size of the potential aquifer. However, it was recognized that if pressure support from the aquifer did not occur, then injection might be needed within a year of start-up in order to retain the benefits of sub-bubble point flow. The key to deciding if this option was feasible was determining whether it would be possible to react sufficiently quickly to falling pressures and mobilize a rig to drill an injection well. The rig market at the time was tight, and price escalation was predicted.

In the analysis of a two-well development, a variety of well types were considered for the second well, ranging from 30° penetrations, to horizontal. Generally speaking, increasing angle should lead to increased productivity. However, a variety of factors combined to recommend limiting the angle to below 60° through the reservoir. Firstly, increasing angle increases the risk of drilling problems. Secondly, at angles over 60° wireline logging may not be possible, requiring drill pipe or coiled tubing conveyed logging and additional costs. Thirdly, future well intervention would require more than a simple workover boat, and potentially a drilling rig. Finally, and most fundamentally, the analysis of the shales in the reservoir had shown that they had the potential to be laterally extensive. It was not possible to predict where to place a horizontal well without, for example, the risk of leaving significant by-passed oil in Layers C and D, after the higher permeability Layer B had watered out. A pilot hole might confirm where shales are within the sequence, but without dynamic information, as might be obtained from an infill well within a producing field, would not confirm which were significant barriers to flow.

A comparison was made between a two-well development with a third (injection) well added later, or three-well development from the start of field life (one of which might be converted later, Fig. 8c, d). Several conclusions came from this analysis. Firstly, although designed as a well to convert to injection, the third producer to the north would aid early production. Secondly, in the event that there was a tilt within the field then the additional column to the north would be drained by the third well. Thirdly, even with aquifer support assumed, the aquifer volume available would not necessarily provide pressure support sufficiently quickly. Cases with injection had higher value than those without. Finally, the highest value option involved three production wells at start-up, with one converted to injection later. This option, with the water injection pipelines laid and a well drilled for conversion possibly a year before it would be needed provided the flexibility to react to aquifer pressure performance at the appropriate time. This was felt to be preferable to taking the risk that re-mobilization of pipelay barges and drilling rigs would be needed within a year, at short notice, but at a time when they might not be available or when the price might have increased. However, this option involved the highest capital expenditure prior to production, with £22 million of drilling costs out of a total budget of £55 million. Further consideration was given to finding ways to reduce the impact of reservoir uncertainty.

Appraisal

Consideration was given to reducing risk by drilling an appraisal well. The objective of the well would be to target an area of uncertainty that had a significant impact on the viability of the project. In this case the key uncertainties were GRV and internal parameters such as water saturation, and dynamic properties such as the strength of vertical and lateral flow barriers, and the power of the aquifer. Three factors influenced the decision not to appraise the field. Firstly, none of the dynamic uncertainties could be tested by a well. Secondly, GRV and parameter uncertainty was greatest on the flanks of the structure. However, at the time, the project value was sufficiently small that it was felt any appraisal well should be suspended for use in the development. The best place to appraise would, in the case of confirming the downside, not be the best place in which to locate a suspended development well. The casing design required for the over-burden precluded a quick reservoir test and sidetrack of anything over 100 m.

Thirdly, appraisal would delay the project by a year and given the methodology of net present value calculations, lead to a loss in value. Consequently it was decided to proceed with the development planning for 1996 production.

Drilling centre

After concluding that the base development plan should involve re-use of the suspended discovery well plus two new producers at the northern and southern ends of the field, detailed analysis of the drilling programme began. This quickly highlighted two problems. Firstly, the suspended well had been drilled with a semi-submersible drilling rig through over 30 m of soft sediment (mud) on the seabed. Re-entering this well would be easiest with a similar rig, but no suitably priced rigs were available for a short contract in mid-1996. The most likely rig was a giant jack-up. However, given the thickness of superficial mud, several days were likely to be spent both positioning and then retrieving the rig. Secondly, a drilling centre in the middle of the field necessitated drilling virtually straight holes to 2000 m then building angle through overpressured and faulted shales in order to enter the reservoir at 55°, increasing the risk of drilling problems (see Hughes *et al.* 1999).

Another factor to take into account when assessing the significance of the difficulties associated with the drilling centre was the location of the planned wells (Fig. 9). The southern well was to be located on a high on the same side of the field as the suspended well. Hence, if the slump scar/fault zone along the structural crest was likely to cause compartmentalization, then both the main production wells would be located on the same side, whilst the well intended for conversion in the north would be in a separate compartment.

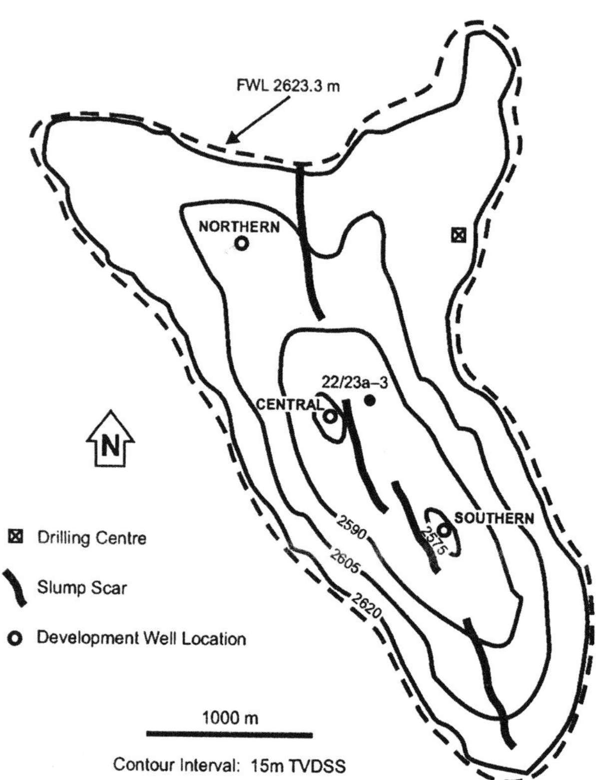

Fig. 9. Schematic development options, Arkwright Field. The central and southern wells are designed as long term production wells. The northern well is located in a position where it could be converted to injection after a year or so if needed, or where it would encounter a deeper contact if the contact tilted to the north. The central well location was picked instead of re-using 22/23a-3 in order to drain both sides of the slump zone. A new drilling centre was chosen off the crest of the structure for the three new wells.

These problems could all be easily avoided by using a different drilling centre, but as this would require drilling three new wells at the start of field life, the additional cost had to be justified, or savings found. Three factors supported using a new drilling centre. Firstly, batch drilling operations could be conducted saving several days from the overall 120 day drilling programme. This involves drilling all three wells to 1000 m, all three to TD (total depth), and then testing all three, rather than drilling and testing sequentially. Secondly, it was possible to build the drilling angle to 55° in the shallow overburden and drill to the reservoir at a constant angle through the overpressured zones. Thirdly, the new central well could be drilled at a high angle, yielding additional early production. Consequently, it was recommended to place the drilling centre off the crest of the structure, in an area with a sandy seabed, and drill three new wells in batch mode to the northern, central and southern locations. The suspended discovery well was left for possible future use in case severe compartmentalization was confirmed, requiring an additional injection well to provide pressure support to the western side of the field.

Development drilling

The overall development plan involved a new drilling centre, and well paths designed to minimize potential drilling problems, reservoir penetrations designed to maximize flow rates, wells located to drain all areas of the field, and included a well for conversion to injection when it might be needed. In addition, aspects of the casing plan, completion and field start-up plan were designed to accommodate reservoir uncertainty and gather futher data.

Sidetracks

Even with the confidence that existed, of finding reservoir quality sandstones within the core of the field, issues such as the variability of the contacts in Arbroath combined with the suggestion of fault compartmentalization opened up the possibility that the western side of the field might not contain sufficient oil to support a production well. Given this possibility, sidetrack contingencies were made for all the wells, although the central well was of most concern prior to drilling. In this area casing is generally set above the top of overpressured overburden shales at 1000 m, and between the overpressured shales and above the Eocene Balder Formation, around 30 m above the reservoir. Consequently, there is little room to sidetrack below the last casing shoe, with a sidetrack of no more than 100 m being possible. Also the well path for the central well was oriented in the wrong direction for the fallback location (at the original discovery well). The wells, therefore, were designed with a 700 m gap in the cement behind the last casing string so that it could be cut and pulled at around 1200 m TVDSS and the sidetrack started from there. The need to sidetrack was based upon a minimum productivity index calculation that would ensure the required oil rates at the end of a year's production, with permeability to be predicted from a measurement while drilling gamma ray. The permeability calculation was based on a core-to-log comparison from 22/23a-3. With real time surface read out of the gamma ray it was possible to calculate the well productivity index shortly after drilling past the oil–water contact and several hours before reaching TD.

Target tolerance

The crestal target areas for the central and southern wells were relatively small. Therefore, a number of measures were taken to ensure that they could be hit during drilling without increasing cost, or endangering future productivity. The primary reason to hit the crestal areas was to avoid leaving attic oil. The small size also arose because both wells had the potential to penetrate the suspected slump zone if they missed the target. To ensure that the targets were met, high-specification surveys were run at intermediate stations within the overburden. These enabled changes to the well trajectories to be made, ensuring success. They also removed the need for high-specification surveys at TD, because extrapolating the small error bars of the intermediate surveys to TD did not significantly increase the depth uncertainty of the final measurements. Running intermediate surveys also facilitated early decision making on the shooting of velocity surveys, avoiding any unnecessary mobilization and consequent costs.

Perforation policy

The issue of where to perforate the wells revisits the question of the lateral continuity of the intra-reservoir shales and their relative strength as barriers to vertical flow. In this case, the choice in perforation policy would be to perforate only Layer B, or perforate deeper sandbodies also. The argument in favour of restricting perforation to Layer B only is that this would delay the onset of any water breakthrough from the aquifer below. The perceived risk of deeper perforations is that early water breakthrough would substitute water for oil during plateau production, reducing revenues. The argument in favour of deeper perforations is two-fold. Firstly, if early pressure draw-down drops average pressures too quickly towards the bubble point in Layer B it would be necessary to choke the wells back, reducing production (and revenues). Secondly, if the shales below are strong barriers, Layer B might be swept by 'edge' water running along the shale from the aquifer at either end of the structure before oil could permeate from below. Hence, oil within Layers C and D might be by-passed. If the shales were weak barriers the oil might be drained more quickly, but again pressure support to Layer B would be slow and the chance of water over-running in the higher permeability Layer B would remain (Wills & Peattie 1990). The wells, therefore, were perforated to at least 15 m above the free water level, with 3 m gaps left across the shales to facilitate setting cement plugs and shutting off lower layers that were swept in the future.

Pressure measurement

Fundamental to the development plan was the ability to monitor reservoir pressures (to ensure that average pressures stayed above the bubble point) and to record the onset of water breakthrough in any of the producers. This was to be accomplished using permanent downhole pressure gauges and flow meters. One objective was to preclude the need for differential testing and so maximize well-up time in the early life of the field. The pressure gauges were used in the interference test (see below) and were intended to record pressures for at least a year in order to be able to monitor aquifer pressure response and determine the appropriate time for any conversion to water injection. Unfortunately, most of the gauges failed immediately prior to first oil and all within eight months of start-up. Consequently, it became necessary to revert to testing by differencing between flowing and shut in wells.

Interference testing

After successfully drilling all three wells it was recognized that there was an ideal opportunity to utilize the static nature of the reservoir and test the strength of any potential fault-related compartmentalization. This would be achieved by starting field production from one of the wells and monitoring pressure decline in the others. This required assuming varying *in situ* permeabilities between the wells and calculating, for given flow rates, the length of time before a significant pressure drop could be expected to occur in the observation wells. In the event that a barrier or barriers had been confirmed, the northern well might have provided injection pressure support to the central well but might not support the southern producer. It would have been possible to adjust production forecasts accordingly and consider drilling a fourth well as and where appropriate. The failure of the pressure gauges prevented testing to the north. Testing to the south was successful and confirmed communication from the central well.

Development well results

In almost every respect, the results of the three wells met or exceeded expectations. The wells were drilled within the original budget estimate. The central well came in on depth prognosis but encountered a higher oil saturation in better quality reservoir sandstones than expected. The net hydrocarbon column encountered was 60% greater than in the original discovery well. The southern well came in 6 m high to prognosis with, again, 60% more oil than expected. Finally, the northern well came in 4 m high to prognosis. (All three wells matched the original VoK depth conversion). The interference test demonstrated high permeability communication between the central and southern producers. Interpretation of the field STOIIP is hampered by encountering a pressure gradient across the area created by 6 years of Arbroath production, resulting in widely varying apparent free water levels. Current estimates are that the field contains at least 50 and probably 60×10^6 BBL oil.

Summary

The Arkwright Field is a small four-way dip-closure containing a channelized turbidite sandstone reservoir. The field development plan was prepared at a time of considerable uncertainty in the oil industry with the oil price dropping to $13 per barrel during the evaluation. This lead to a desire to reduce the initial capital expenditure as much as possible. However, a number of areas of uncertainty were identified in the reservoir description and, after careful consideration, it was felt that a robust development with three wells at the start of production provided the most flexibility in the event that adverse reservoir properties were confirmed.

The main areas of uncertainty were: the presence or absence of a strong aquifer, a tilted oil–water contact, potential fault sealing along the crest of the structure, and the sealing capacity of intra-reservoir shales. The development involved sub-bubble point flow around the wells whilst the field average pressures were maintained above the bubble point. The plan required the ability to monitor pressure depletion caused by production and add water injection in the event that aquifer support did not materialize. As it was found that water injection was beneficial under most circumstances, even in the presence of an aquifer, a third production well was added to the two main producers to be converted at a later date. This well catered for the second issue, namely the possibility that the oil–water contact tilted towards the north. Thirdly, compared to the original plan of re-completing the suspended discovery well, new wells were planned to either side of the slump scar that runs along the crest of the field. This ensured that both sides of any potential barrier would be drained. An interference test was run at start-up to test this theory. The cost of drilling an additional well, rather than recompleting 22/23a-3, was saved by batch drilling, undertaking build work in the shallow normally pressured overburden, and increasing the angle of penetration and hence productivity of the central well. The final area of concern, that the sealing capacity of the intra-reservoir shales was unknown, was overcome by drilling at 55° rather than horizontal, and perforating throughout the oil column.

The authors wish to thank: Amoco (UK) Exploration Company, Amerada Hess Ltd, and Enterprise Oil plc for permission to publish this paper, PGS for permission to reproduce the seismic line in Fig. 3, B. Cullen of Reservoir Associates for describing the core, J. Marshall of Liverpool University for carbon and oxygen isotopic analysis, Isotopic Analytical Services for the RSA data, R. Chambers of Amoco Technology Centre for the conditional simulation, and A. Challis, M. Gauer and Amoco Graphics for drafting the figures and slides. A. Dickson kindly reviewed the manuscript.

References

Barrett, R. F., Margesson, R. W. & D'Angelo, R. M. 1995. Use of rock properties and AVO in the Everest Field development, UKCS. *Petroleum Geoscience*, **1**, 311–317.

Batten, A. 1995. Arbroath Field – production below the bubble point. DTI–SPE *Best Practise IOR Conference. SPE Paper 35283.*

Coleman, M. L. 1992. Water composition within one formation. *In*: Kharaka, Y. K. & Maest, A. S. (eds) *Proceedings Water–Rock Interaction Symposium, Balkema, Rotterdam*, 1109–1112.

Crawford, R., Littlefair, R. W. & Affleck, L. G. 1991. The Arbroath and Montrose Fields, Blocks 22/17, 18, UK North Sea. *In*: Abbots, I. L. (ed.) *United Kingdom Oil and Gas Fields, 25 Years Commemorative Volume*. Geological Society Memoirs, **14**, 211–217.

den Hartog Jager, D., Giles, M. R. & Griffiths, G. R. 1993. Evolution of Paleogene submarine fans of the North Sea in space and time. *In*: Parker, J. R. (ed.) *Petroleum Geology of Northwest Europe: Proceedings of the 4th Conference*. Geological Society, London, 59–72.

Hughes, M. J., Dhanani, S., Frimpong, R. K., Gainski, M., Haskell, N. L., Heath, R. P., Kantorowicz, J. D., Maguire, P. M. & Nissen S. E. 1999. Applications of the Coherency Cube in the UKCS. *In*: Fleet, A. J. & Boldy, S. A. R. (eds) *Petroleum Geology of Northwest Europe: Proceedings of the 5th Conference*. Geological Society, London, 1299–1305.

Journel, A. G. & Huijbregts, C. 1978. *Mining Geostatistics*. Academic Press, London.

Knox, R. W. O'B. & Holloway, S. 1992. 1. Paleogene of the Central and Northern North Sea. *In*: Knox, R. W. O'B. & Cordey, W. G. (eds) *Lithostratigraphic Nomenclature of the UK North Sea*, British Geological Survey, Nottingham.

Kulpecz, A. A. & van Geuns, L. C. 1990. Geological modelling of a turbidite reservoir, Forties Field, North Sea. *In*: Barwis, J. H., McPherson, J. G. & Studlick, J. R. J. (eds) *Sandstone Petroleum Reservoirs*. Springer Verlag, 489–507.

Mutti, E. & Ricci Lucchi, F. 1972. Le torbidit dell'Apennino settentrionale: introduzione all'analisi di facies. *Memoirs of the Geological Society of Italy*, **11**, 161–199. (English translation by Nilsen, T. H. 1978. *International Geological Review*, **20**, 125–166.)

Schuppers, J. D. 1993. Quantification of turbidite facies in a reservoir analogous submarine-fan channel sandbody, southern Central Pyrenees, Spain. *International Association of Sedimentologists, Special Publications*, **15**, 99–112.

Simm, R. W., Batten, A. H., Dhanani, S. & Kantorowicz, J. D. 1996. Fluid effects on seismic: Forties Sandstone Member – Arbroath, Arkwright and Montrose Fields, Central North Sea. Extended Abstract. *Norwegian Petroleum Society, Biennial Geophysical Seminar: "Geophysics for Lithology Prediction", Kristiansand, Norway, 11–13 March 1996*, 14a–d.

Smalley, P. C., Lonoy, A. & Raheim, A. 1992. Spatial $^{87}Sr/^{86}Sr$ variations in formation water and calcite from the Ekofisk chalk oilfield: implications for reservoir connectivity and fluid composition. *Applied Geochemistry*, **7**, 341–350.

Waters, K. 1978. *Reflection Seismology*. J. Wiley & Sons, 218–233.

Whyatt, M., Bowen, J. M. & Rhodes, D. N. 1991. Nelson – Successful application of a geo-seismic model in North Sea Exploration. *First Break*, **9**, 265–280.

Wills, J. M. & Peattie, D. K. 1990. The Forties Field and the evolution of a reservoir management strategy. *In*: Buller, A. T., Berg, E., Hjelmeland, O., Kleppe, J., Torsaeter, O. & Aasen, J. O. (eds) *North Sea Oil and Gas Reservoirs II*. Graham & Trotman, 1–23.

The reservoir development of the Fife Field

S. CURRIE,[1] S. GOWLAND,[2] A. TAYLOR[2] and M. WOODWARD[3]

[1] *Amerada Hess Ltd, Scott House, Hareness Road, Altens, Aberdeen, AB12 3LE, UK*
[2] *Ichron Limited, 5 Dalby Court, Gadbrook Business Centre, Rudheath, Northwich, CW9 7TN, UK*
[3] *Present address: Shell International, c/o Shell Centre, London, UK*

Abstract: The Fife Field, located in the southern part of the Central North Sea, produced first oil in August 1995 after a fast-track appraisal and development programme. At that time it was predicted to contain 120×10^6 BBL STOIIP in a predominantly fine-grained sandstone of Volgian age of which an estimated 50×10^6 BBL was recoverable over a 4 year field life. Rapid water breakthrough and a fast water-cut rise in the first three production wells, all located crestally on the field, led to significant reappraisal and remodelling of the field. This paper describes the initial field development, gives an account of the work which followed the start-up of the field, and accounts for the early water breakthrough.

The Fife Field is situated in Block 31/26a in the Central North Sea (Fig. 1). To date, the Fife/Fergus fields form the southern-most oil field development in the UKCS. The Fife Field was discovered in 1991 by Well 31/26a-9A (Fig. 2) which is 6 km from the Danish/UKCS median line. This well encountered nearly 500 ft of Upper Jurassic sandstones of which 159 ft were oil bearing. The well tested over 11 500 BOPD of 36° API oil from the Volgian age Fife sandstones and shortly afterwards a 3D seismic survey was obtained for the area. Two appraisal wells were drilled in 1993. Well 31/26a-10 (Fig. 2) was drilled near the crest and encountered 430 ft of Fife sandstones of which about 250 ft were oil bearing. The other appraisal well, 39/1-2, was drilled to the south to delineate the reservoir and characterize the acquifer. At that location the Fife sandstone was of poor quality and the well was subsequently abandoned. Further appraisal and pre-development drilling followed in 1994 and 1995.

The initial field development plan required six wells to be available at the start of production, four producers and two injectors. A series of mechanical drilling and cementing problems meant that only two producers were available at start-up. Problems included difficulties with cementing casing in wells and one injection well (A4, see Fig. 2) was completed only to be abandoned before start-up when it was found that there was water flow behind the casing. These difficulties later compounded the problems of the post start-up interpretation of production well behaviour. The field came on-stream in August 1995 with two production wells, P1 and P4. Water injection was available from one well (I3) by late 1995. A summary wireline log plot of the reservoir is shown in Fig. 3.

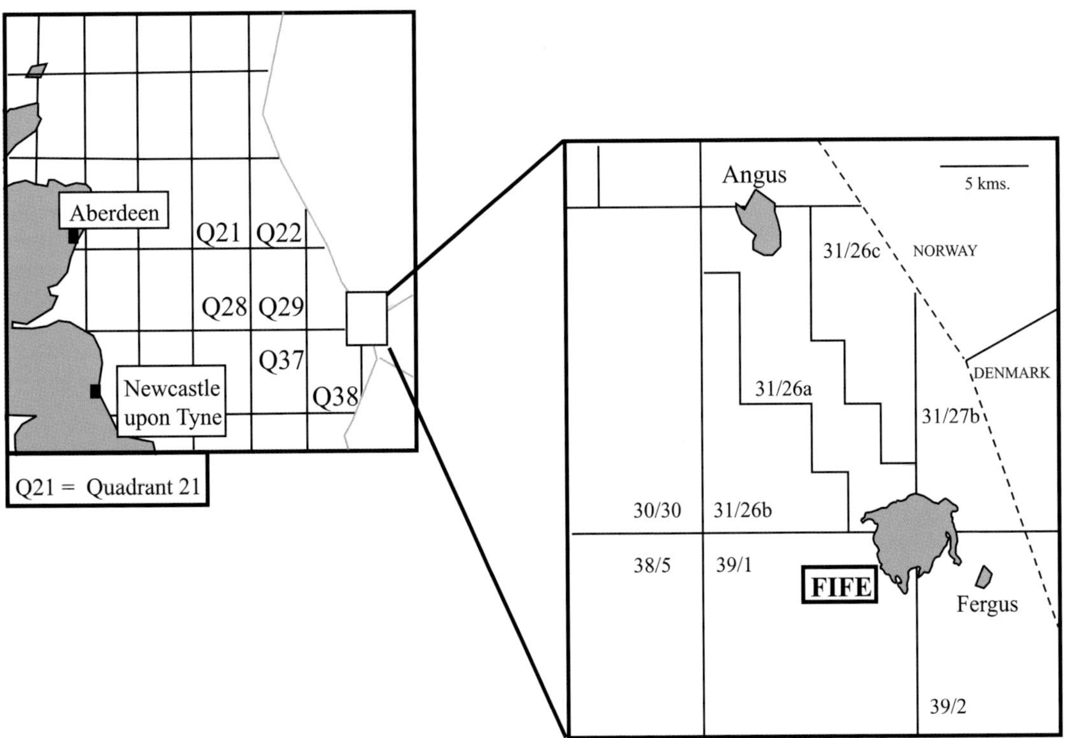

Fig. 1. Location map of the Fife area. The Fife Field is situated across four quadrant boundaries close to the UKCS/Danish Sector median line.

CURRIE, S., GOWLAND, S., TAYLOR, A. & WOODWARD M. 1999. The reservoir development of the Fife Field. *In*: FLEET, A. J. & BOLDY, S. A. R. (eds) *Petroleum Geology of Northwest Europe: Proceedings of the 5th Conference*, 1135–1145.

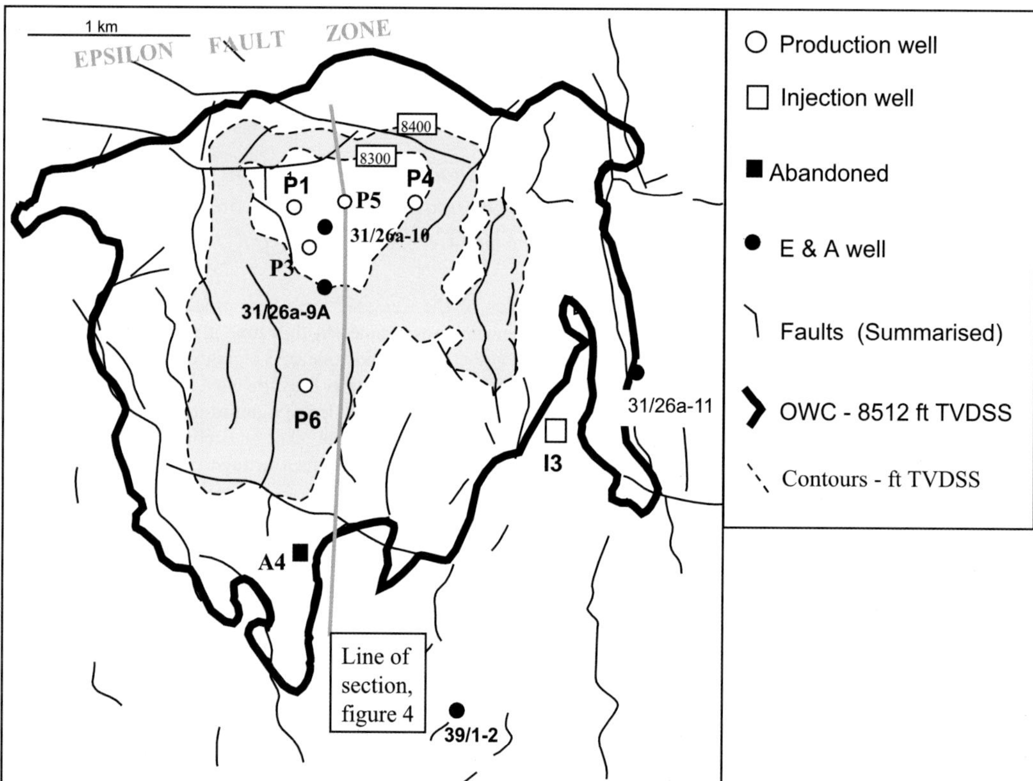

Fig. 2. Location map of the Fife Field to show well locations referred to in text. The crestal area of the field is shown around Wells P1, P4 and P5 together with a line of section which forms Fig. 4.

Well P1 was prognosed to produce dry oil for about 4 months with water-cut rising slowly to 30%. Water broke through in the well six weeks after start-up and rose rapidly to 50%. Similarly in P4, the pre-production prognosis of dry oil for 2 months with a slow rise to 40% water-cut was not realized. In this well, water broke through after 6 weeks and the water-cut stabilized at 22%. Considering the pre-development drilling problems, it was possible that the water seen in the wells was caused by flow behind casing. Hence, a logging intervention programme was set up as quickly as possible and was carried out during early January 1996.

During November/December 1995, a third producer, P5 (Fig. 2), was drilled. On the basis of a revised simulation model, the prognosis for this well was dry oil for 4 months and a slow rise to a temporary plateau of 10% water-cut. The well was tested for 17 h before it was completed for production and only dry oil was recorded during the test. Once production started, water broke through in the well within 24 h and rose to 40% within a month. Core taken from P5 revealed the presence of three significant coarse sand to pebble grade intervals in the well of which two were in the lower, water-bearing reservoir and one in the upper, oil-bearing reservoir (Fig. 3). The two lower coarse-grained horizons were prognosed prior to drilling and had been encountered in all other wells. The upper coarse-grained horizon was unexpected and had not been seen in any other well location.

In the pre-production phase, Well P1 had had one core taken in the lower reservoir section and no core was obtained in P4. Cores taken from each of the other 6 exploration and appraisal wells had not revealed any coarse-grained sandstone in the upper reservoir section. During examination of the core from P5, the logging intervention on P1 confirmed that there was no flow behind casing. The most likely explanation for early water-breakthrough in the three producers was that the coarse-grained sandstone seen in P5 in the oil-bearing reservoir section was also present in P1 and P4 and was initiating early water-breakthrough (acting as a thief zone). The porosity log did not indicate unusually high porosity in the interval but subsequent conventional core analysis indicated permeability to be in the 2000–5000 mD range. The thief zone had been identified. Unluckily, this zone was not present in any of the exploration and appraisal wells which were cored so it had not been possible to identify it before production start-up.

A 'recovery plan' for the Fife Field was devised and initiated in early 1996. This involved a thorough re-appraisal of all the core, log and test data from all wells, a full sedimentological study of the Fife sandstones, including an ichnofabric analysis, and a subsequent rebuilding of the geological and reservoir simulation models. While this work was on-going two wells were planned for 1996. The objective of these wells was to drill and complete sections which did not contain the coarse-grained sandstone in the upper reservoir. The wells were prognosed to produce dry oil at lower rates and, importantly, would provide invaluable production and pressure information to better constrain modelling of production away from the crestal area of the field.

All wireline log data were reviewed in the light of the new data, and a new reservoir zonation for the reservoir was constructed based primarily on wireline logs, but conditioned to core and test data. A detailed sedimentological and ichnological study was also performed, culminating in the construction of a pragmatic sequence stratigraphic model for reservoir prediction purposes. Meanwhile, a petrophysical review revealed significant short-comings in core analysis sample coverage and a new petrophysical interpretation of the log data was performed. This led to a new appreciation of reservoir heterogeneity and its effect on oil production rates.

Database

At production start-up in August 1995 geoscience data were available from a good quality 3D seismic survey across the

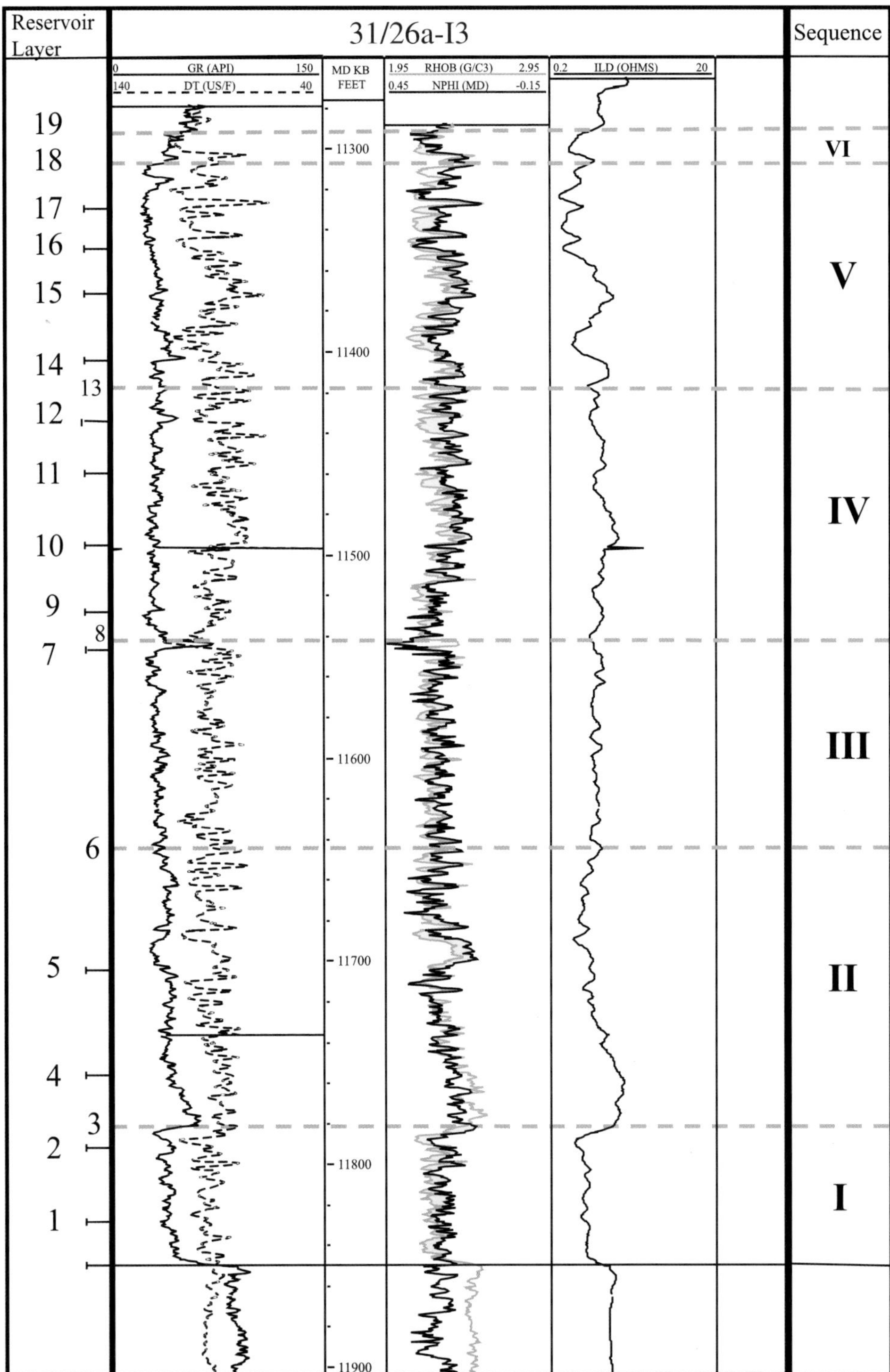

Fig. 3. A wireline log summary plot for Well 31/26a-I3. Sequence Sets I to VI and reservoir flow-unit layers 1–19, all referred to in text, are illustrated together with typical wireline log signatures.

field. The survey, acquired in 1991, comprises 4110 line km within a survey area of 88 km^2. The Top Chalk Group is a good reflector across the entire area. In the crestal area the Base Chalk/Top Jurassic is a clear reflector but off-crest, where the Kimmeridge Clay Formation (KCF) lies between the Chalk and the reservoir sandstones, there is a reduction in the impedance contrast and interpretation of the Base Chalk and Top Reservoir horizons is more difficult. The seismic reflector corresponding to the Base Reservoir/Top Triassic is weak and, off-crest, it is adversely affected by interference with the first sea-bottom multiple of the Base Cretaceous event.

At production start-up, data were available from eight wells in or adjacent to the field (Fig. 2): 31/26a-9A, -10, -11, A4 (subsequently abandoned due to mechanical problems in the well), I3 (the only injection well), -P1 (now abandoned), -P4 and 39/1-2. Most of the wells were partially cored, but there was no core in the oil leg of well P1, one of the pre-drilled production wells, and no core in the other pre-drilled production well, P4. In late 1995 and during 1996 information became available from three further oil production wells P5, P6 and P3, which were all extensively cored. The total core available amounts to over 2700 ft. Probe-permeameter data on core are available from three exploration wells in addition to the conventional core analysis data.

All wells have been extensively logged with conventional wireline tools. Image log data (UBI) are available from four wells, and extensive RFT (repeat formation test) suites are available from wells drilled in pre- and post-production phases. Production logs were run in exploration and appraisal wells and test information is available from two exploration and five appraisal/development wells.

Overall, the database is of a high quality and there is a large amount of core, log and test data. Much of the well data are grouped together on the crest of the field and the unevenness of the data distribution leads to increased uncertainty in mapping and simulation in the western and southern parts of the field.

Reservoir structure

The Fife Field lies some 10 km south of the abandoned Angus Field (Fig. 1) at the northern end of the Fife embayment (Mackertich 1996). Structurally, it is in an area transitional between the Mid North Sea High and the Central Graben proper. To the north end of the field lies the Epsilon Fault zone (Mackertich 1996), a major ENE–WSW trending lineament.

The field is a low-relief, domal structure (Fig. 4) formed by inversion during the late Cretaceous/early Tertiary (Mackertich 1996). The Volgian reservoir is capped by either Kimmeridge Clay Formation mudstones or Chalk Group limestones and it is underlain by Triassic mudstones. The Kimmeridge Clay Formation (KCF) is generally encountered in flank wells, while the Chalk overlies the reservoir on the crest of the field. The KCF ranges from late Volgian to Ryazanian in age. The oil-bearing reservoir is partly fault-bounded (Fig. 4). The reservoir is extensively faulted but the seismic resolution is insufficient to enable faults with throws of less than about 40 ft to be mapped.

The low relief domal structure means that the gross rock volume of the reservoir above the oil–water contact is sensitive to depth conversion uncertainties on the seismic data. There are known to be velocity variations in the overlying Chalk Group so that depth conversion of the seismic, especially in the western part of the field where there are few wells to condition the conversion algorithms, carries a significant degree of uncertainty.

Stratigraphy

The oldest rocks penetrated in the field area are interbedded shales and volcanics assigned to the Lower Permian Rotliegendes Group. The Rotliegendes is overlain by Zechstein Group evaporites which comprise anhydrites and interbedded dolomites. These in turn are succeeded by Triassic Smith Bank Formation sediments. The Smith Bank Formation comprises red–brown shales and siltstones which are thought to have accumulated in an arid, continental environment. The Smith Bank Formation is unconformably overlain by Jurassic sandstones belonging to the informally named Fife sandstones.

The Fife sandstones have not been assigned to any formal stratigraphic nomenclature. There is poor palynomorph recovery from the base of the Fife sandstones so the recorded basal age varies from Middle Kimmeridgian (Robertson Research International: palynozone PUJ10) to ?Upper Kimmeridgian (Millennia: palynozone JP8). The top of the Fife sandstones is dated as Middle Volgian (Robertson Research International: palynozone PUJ5) and Upper Volgian (Millennia: palynozone JP1). The bulk of the sandstone deposition is thus interpreted as early to middle Volgian in age.

In crestal areas, Fife sandstones are unconformably overlain by Upper Cretaceous chalks. Off-crest Kimmeridge Clay Formation mudstones of late Volgian to late Ryazanian age overlie the sandstones which are in turn overlain by Upper Cretaceous Chalks (Fig. 4). Examination, in cores, of the boundary between the Fife sandstones and the overlying KCF suggests that it is unconformable. The thinning of the KCF towards the crest of the field is believed to record the start of the Fife inversion phase (Mackertich 1996).

Post-Cretaceous sediments overlying the Chalk Group comprise interbedded Tertiary claystones, siltstones and occasional limestones. While intervals within the Chalk Group limestones are oil bearing, no reservoir potential is recognized in the Tertiary sediments.

Reservoir sedimentology

This section is in three parts. The first deals with the basic lithology of the Fife sandstones and describes the two main aspects of diagenesis which affect reservoir quality: silica and carbonate cements. The second part is a summary of the facies associations recognized through integrated sedimentological analysis, while a third section describes the sequence stratigraphic model adopted for the Fife field.

Principal lithologies

The Fife reservoir mainly comprises two elements: (i) carbonate- and/or quartz-cemented very fine to lower medium-

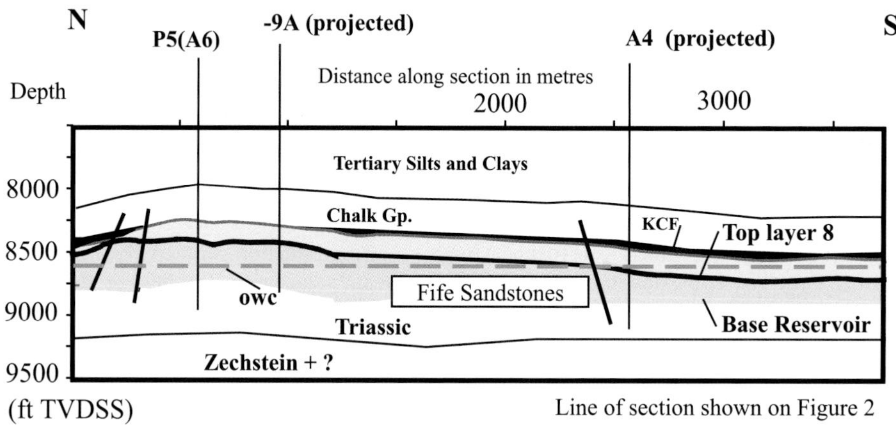

Fig. 4. North–south schematic ('geoseismic') cross-section through the Fife field. The shallow relief domal structure of the reservoir is partly fault-bounded to the north. The top reservoir surface dips gently below the OWC (oil–water contact) to the south.

grained sandstones; and (ii) subordinate beds of coarse sand to pebble grade material (Fig. 5). These two forms of deposit are believed to reflect a two-component depositional system.

Fine-grained deposits. The Fife reservoir, some 300–500 ft thick, consists mainly of highly bioturbated, 'clean' to slightly silty, fine-grained sandstones, although upper very fine and fine–medium-grained sandstones are developed locally. The sandstones are mainly quartzose, moderately to well sorted and may be quite micaceous, particularly very fine-grained examples. As a result of high levels of bioturbation, primary bedding is rarely preserved, although subtle changes in grain size, detrital silt content and tiering within ichnofabrics suggest deposition in cm- to lower dm-scale beds. Close examination of cores and logs reveals that these sandstones may be developed in m-scale 'cleaning'/coarsening-upward and 'dirtying'/fining-upward cycles, although strongly aggradational units are also present (Fig. 3). The sandstones are interpreted as being deposited in a low/moderate energy shallow marine shelf setting, devoid of major storm influence. Mackertich (1996) describes the possible structural controls on the sediment thicknesses developed in this setting.

Two major diagenetic phases are recognized which significantly influence reservoir quality in these fine-grained sandstones: nodular carbonate (mainly calcite) and irregular, patchy silica. Both phases are ubiquitous throughout the reservoir.

Carbonate cementation in the sandstones generally occurs in the form of regularly shaped zones which in core range in thickness from <3–30 cm (Fig. 5). Forty to fifty percent of the carbonates display rounded edges, indicating that they are nodular in form and not laterally persistent layers. With low porosity and negligible permeability (<0.1 mD) the carbonate nodules ('doggers') significantly reduce the volume of net sandstone in the reservoir.

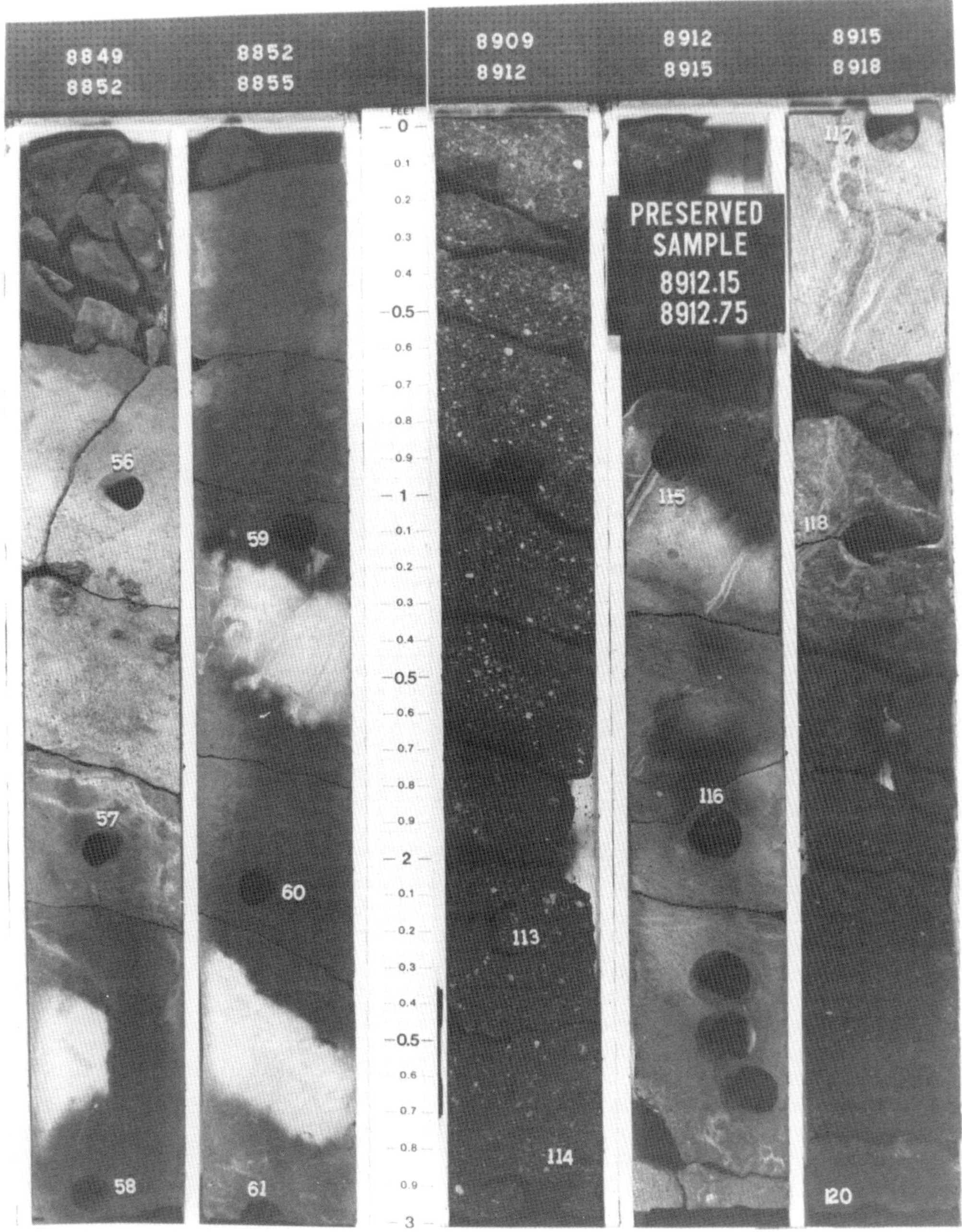

Fig. 5. Cored sections of Well 31/26a-P5. The two columns on the left of the scale bar (in feet) show typical fine-grained reservoir sandstones with prominent carbonate nodules. The three columns to the right show two coarse-grained sandstone layers, containing prominent granules and pebbles, interlayered with fine-grained sandstone. Both lithologies are discussed in the text.

The original source of the carbonate forming the nodules is interpreted to be shelly debris, which is prominent throughout the succession. Indeed, many intervals are characterized by clay films that represent the dissolution of what were probably aragonitic bivalves. Similar nodular carbonates occur in the Bridport Sands in Dorset (Bryant *et al.* 1988), although there the nodules tend to amalgamate into more continuous layers.

Ubiquitous patchy silica cement (Fig. 5) is largely chert associated with the presence of abundant siliceous sponge spicules. Patches of silica cement occur at least every 1 to 2 m in core, are often irregular in shape, and range in diameter from ≈1.0 cm–0.50 m. They enclose spicules and/or spicule dissolution voids and, in some cases, preferentially cement spicules passively infiltrated into Thalassinoides burrow systems. In other cases the burrow-fills are actually highly friable, while the surrounding sediment is well cemented.

Chert cements reflect the early diagenetic dissolution of unstable biogenic silica incorporated within siliceous sponge spicules, and the subsequent reprecipitation of a more stable, yet highly microporous phase of silica. This process, allied with the sheer abundance of sponge spicules in the sediment, has led to a severe degradation in permeability, although only a minor reduction in porosity.

Unfortunately, the degree and extent of chert cementation in the reservoir cannot be estimated outwith cored intervals. Although a range of logs has been run in the Fife Field, for example sonic, density and neutron logs, a range of resistivity logs, nuclear magnetic resonance, and ultra-sonic imaging logs they fail to differentiate and quantify the chert. To date, chert cementation remains undetectable using open-hole or cased-hole logging techniques, because of the small scale of the heterogeneity involved and the fact that it does not generally produce significant changes in measured porosity.

In addition to sandstones, siltstone horizons are present in the lower part of the reservoir, with the thickest example (m-scale) reflecting maximum flooding surface development and a field-wide vertical permeability barrier (e.g. layer 4, Fig. 3).

Coarse-grained deposits. Three reservoir units in the Fife Field display significant horizons of coarse sand to pebble grade material developed against a background of highly bioturbated fine-grained sandstones (Fig. 5). Two of these horizons are in the water-bearing lower reservoir (layers 3 and 6, Fig. 3) and one in the oil-bearing upper reservoir (layer 13, Fig. 3). The latter is the thief zone not detected before production start-up.

Discrete coarse-grained units range in thickness from cm- to m-scale, with the thicker deposits (>≈1.0 m) clearly the product of multiple depositional events. The units are 'clean' and generally poorly to moderately sorted. They are also generally massive and display sharp tops and bases. Clast types are dominated by an exotic range of quartzose types, including pink, yellow, grey, grey-green and red varieties, along with grey siltstone and claystone clasts. Also present are belemnite guards, bivalve and brachiopod fragments, sponge spicules and serpulid remains. Bioturbation appears to have been minimal compared with the finer-grained background deposits.

For several reasons these coarse-grained units are tentatively interpreted as gravity flow deposits derived from a different source to that of the finer-grained background shelf. Deposition from storm-generated currents can be ruled out on the basis that many of the deposits are too thick, show no evidence for waning storm activity (e.g. fining-upward wave rippled tops) and occur interbedded with finer-grained deposits which themselves display no significant storm influence. Additionally, derivation from a more proximal, up-dip component of the finer-grained shelf system (i.e. the sediment-supplying shoreface), is unlikely given that mapping reveals major areas of coarse sediment accumulation which actually cross-cut the shelfal facies belts. The fact that the coarse-grained intervals contain a shelly fauna indicative of normal marine salinities (e.g. belemnites, sponge spicules and serpulids) and occur interbedded with highly bioturbated finer-grained sands, precludes deposition in distributary channels during periods of lowstand.

The precise source for the coarse-grained deposits is unknown at present. However, one of the more likely source areas is to the north of the field, where tectonic activity associated with a fault zone (Mackertich 1996) may have triggered the failure of accumulated coarse-grained sediment packages, resulting in the southward dispersal across the shelf of coarse sand to pebble grade material.

Facies associations

As part of the reservoir modelling work carried out in 1996, an integrated sedimentological and ichnological study was carried out, with special emphasis on ichnofabric (trace fossil) development (Taylor & Gawthorpe 1993). Trace fossils, while requiring significant interpretation, provide an *in situ* record of the depositional environment and can be used to calibrate depositional facies and facies shifts, record salinity change and contribute towards the recognition of key surfaces and condensed sections for use in stratigraphic correlation.

In the Fife Field review twenty-eight discrete ichnofabrics were defined, based on sixteen different taxa (Fig. 6). These ichnofabrics were subsequently grouped into seven recurring facies-significant ichnofabric associations, namely *Planolites*, *Chondrites*, *Phycosiphon*, *Teichichnus*, *Palaeophycus*, *Ophiomorpha* and *Thalassinoides*. Combined with lithofacies data these ichnofabric associations underpin a two-component depositional model comprising a fine-grained shelf system and an adjacent coarse-grained gravity flow system. The shelf system is defined as a time-averaged palaeoenvironmental energy gradient comprising four main facies associations (inner proximal sandy shelf, outer proximal sandy shelf, transition zone and distal muddy shelf; Fig. 7; cf. Gowland 1996), whilst a single facies association categorizes the gravity flow deposits. Also developed in the Fife sandstones is a probable volcanic ash layer, while an assemblage of sandy turbidites occurs at the base of the overlying KCF. Details of the subenvironments recognized are presented in the next section.

Inner proximal sandy shelf. This, the most proximal facies belt, comprises 'clean' to slightly silty, moderately to well sorted, very fine-to fine-(occasionally medium-)grained sandstones which are locally glauconitic. Bioturbation levels are moderate to high and any silt present is usually in the form of ductile faecal pellets rather than primary suspension fall-out. A wispy, generally horizontal ichnofabric is prevalent that arises from the abundance of *Palaeophycus* (*Palaeophycus* ichnofabric association; Fig. 6a). Other common ichnotaxa include *Planolites*, *Thalassinoides* and *Skolithos*. Colonization styles are dominated by the shallow-tier, deposit feeding (?annelid) burrow systems of *Palaeophycus* and *Planolites* which are occasionally cross-cut by larger, mid- to deep-tier dwelling/suspension feeding burrows attributed to crustaceans (e.g. *Ophiomorpha* and *Thalassinoides*) and bivalves. Original bed thicknesses were of mainly lower cm-scale as evidenced by repeated shallow-tier bioturbation. The shelly component comprises the remains of belemnites, bivalves/brachiopods, serpulids and, of course, siliceous sponge spicules.

Outer proximal sandy shelf. This facies belt was developed adjacent to the inner proximal sandy shelf in a slightly lower energy setting. It is dominated by moderately to well sorted, silty, very fine- to fine-grained sandstones. The sandstones are commonly micaceous and highly to completely bioturbated.

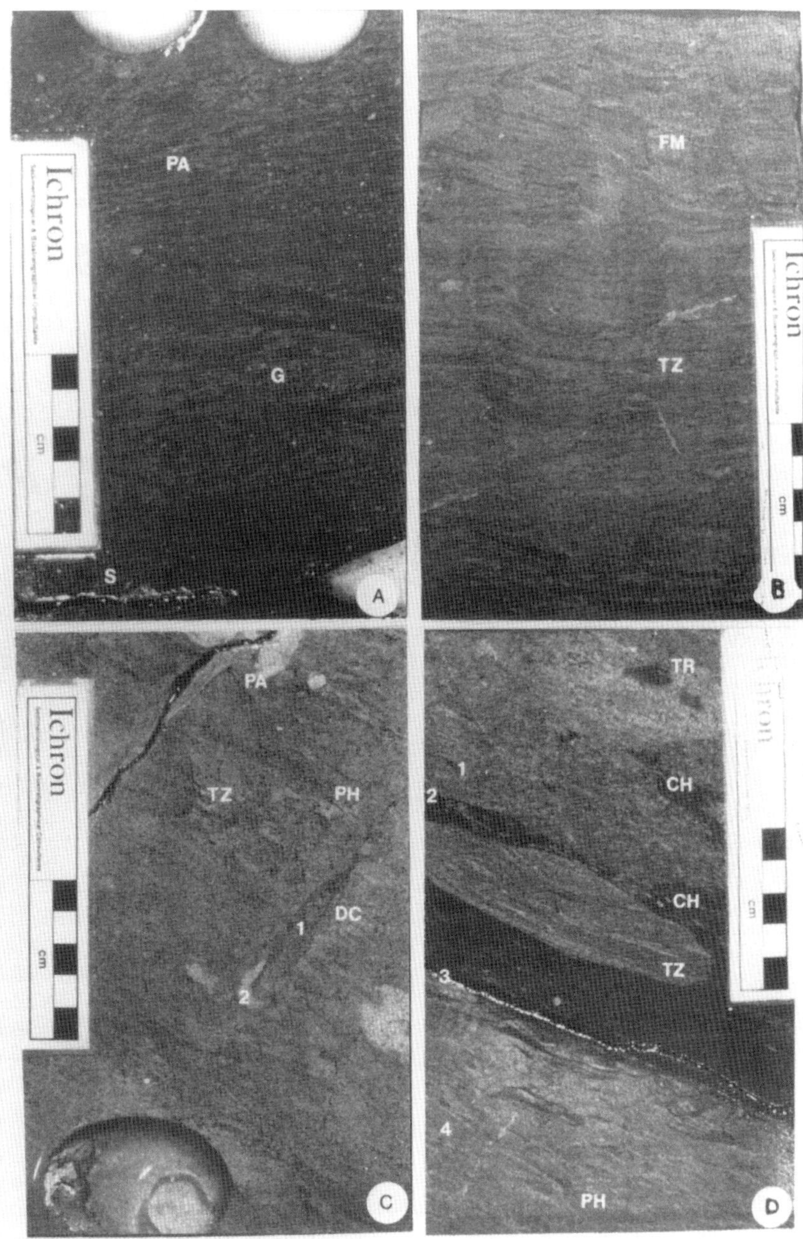

Fig. 6. Examples of ichnofabrics in Fife Field cores. All examples discussed in text. (**a**) Intensely bioturbated, silty, poorly sorted fine- to medium-grained sandstones with abundant *Palaeophycus* burrows (PA), and occasional scattered granules (G) and shell debris (S). Facies Association = Inner proximal sandy shelf. (**b**) Completely bioturbated, silty, very fine-grained sandstones colonized by *Teichichnus zigzag* (TZ) with faecal pellets (FM). Longitudinal and transverse sections of *Teichichnus* burrows are seen. Facies Association = Outer proximal sandy shelf. (**c**) Completely bioturbated, silty, very fine-grained sandstone with *Phycosiphon incertum* (PH), *Teichichnus zigzag* (TZ) and *Palaeophycus* (PA). These burrows are cross-cut by *Diplocraterion coloradoensis* (DC) where the U-shaped, sand- filled arm (2) and internal spreiten (1) can just be discerned. Facies Association = Transition Zone. (**d**) Intensely bioturbated, interbedded siltstones and silty claystones colonized by *Phycosiphon incertum* (PH), *Teichichnus zigzag* (TZ), *Chondrites* (CH) and *Teichichnus rectus* (TR). Bioturbated siltstones (1) overlie *Chondrites* burrowed silty claystones (2). The claystones have a burrowed contact (3) with the underlying siltstones. Facies Association = Distal muddy shelf.

A horizontal ichnofabric is often evident which is interpreted to result from the compaction of pervasive *Teichichnus zigzag* burrows (*Teichichnus* ichnofabric association; Fig. 6b). Hiatal colonization events are represented by bivalve burrows, *Thalassinoides*, *Skolithos*, *Cylindrichnus* and *Diplocraterion*. In the main, colonization is dominated by a deposit feeding community with shallow-tier *Palaeophycus* and *Planolites*, and mid-tier *Teichichnus* and *Chondrites*. In addition, shelly remains including sponge spicules, bivalves/brachipods, serpulids, crinoids, belemnites and occasional ammonites are recorded. Deposition is inferred to have taken place above storm wave base at a pace which was easily exceeded by the rate of infaunal reworking.

Transition zone. This facies belt represents the transition zone between the proximal sandy shelf and distal muddy shelf environments. It is stongly heterolithic in character, comprising sandy siltstones and silty sandstones in which the sand component is moderate to well sorted and very fine- to fine-grained. The sediment is commonly micaceous and invariably highly bioturbated. Deposition is inferred to have taken place below fair-weather wave base. *Phycosiphon incertum* and *Teichichnus zigzag* are the dominant ichnotaxa in an assemblage which is often diverse (*Phycosiphon* and *Teichichnus* ichnofabric associations; Fig. 6c). *Teichichnus rectus*, *Planolites*, *Skolithos*, *Cylindrichnus*, *Diplocraterion* and *Trichichnus* are all present.

Colonization was dominated by a deposit feeding community with shallow tier *Phycosiphon* and *Planolites* burrows. Also present are mid-tier *Teichichnus* and *Chondrites* burrows and mid-tier dwelling structures such as *Schaubcylindrichus* and *Skolithos*. Rates of deposition were easily exceeded by the rate of infaunal working. Siliceous sponge spicules are less common than in the adjacent sandy shelf, as are the remains of serpulids, crinoids and bivalves/brachiopods.

Distal muddy shelf. This low energy facies belt is present at only one level (layer 4, Fig. 3) but occurs in all wells in the Fife Field. Sediments are dominated by highly bioturbated siltstones and sandy siltstones. *Phycosiphon incertum* and *Chondrites* dominate the ichnotaxa (*Phycosiphon* and *Chondrites* ichnofabric associations; Fig. 6d). The colonization style, mainly that of a shallow-tier deposit feeding community dominated by annelids, is thought to reflect the muddy nature of the substrate. Shelly remains are largely confined to belemnites and bivalves/brachiopods.

These distal muddy shelf deposits contrast markedly with the sealing mudstones developed at the very top of the Fife reservoir. The latter are well laminated, with limited colonization evident, and were probably deposited under deeper water conditions.

Gravity flow deposits. As previously indicated, three horizons in the reservoir contain numerous coarse-grained gravity flow deposits interbedded with those of the finer-grained shelf. In the upper oil-bearing reservoir (layer 13, Fig. 3) gravity flow deposits sourced from north of the Fife Field clearly cross-cut the facies belts of the shelf (Fig. 7), thereby indicating that one is dealing with a two-component depositional system. Although the presence of coarse-grained gravity flow deposits in a shelfal setting (as opposed to a deep-water basin) may be regarded as somewhat problematic, no other obvious mechanism of emplacement is apparent. Irrespective of progradation directions after flooding of the shelf (see section on sequence stratigraphy and reservoir layering) gravity flow deposition was effectively tied to the north of the Fife Field, and individual flow events probably travelled no more than 2 km across the shelf prior to 'freezing' on the low gradients encountered. Certainly, in the more northern wells gravity flow deposits are much thicker and coarser-grained than those developed just to the south.

Repeated footwall uplift along the northern fault zone, followed by erosion by wave action and subaerial processes, may have concentrated a fringe of coarse-grained sediment around a local high. Episodic failure of these sediments, possibly triggered by fault movements, may have accounted for their southward dispersal.

The shelly component present within the gravity flow deposits includes the remains of belemnites, bivalves/brachiopods, serpulids and sponge spicules. Bioturbation is generally absent or sparse, although an ovate fabric in some examples is tentatively assigned to *Thalassinoides*. This ichnotaxon reflects colonization of the substrate between discrete gravity flow events and typically comprises a large dwelling burrow network which can extend up to 2 m from a colonization surface.

Ash-fall deposits. Evidence of a volcanic ash-fall event is present in all wells. This deposit is a 0.5 to 1.0 m thick horizon of olive green mudstone containing a strong swelling clay component. Comparison of clay-fraction XRD (x-ray diffraction) data with data derived from distal muddy shelf deposits reveals a significantly greater chlorite composition for the interpreted ash-fall deposit.

Trace fossil colonization of the ash-fall also contrasts markedly with that of the distal muddy shelf deposits. The latter display pervasive bioturbation related to slow deposition, with a diverse tiered community established. The former, however, simply displays a post-depositional colonization style, with sporadic burrows of *Chondrites* and *Diplocraterion coloradoensis* extending down from the top of the deposit. There is no evidence in any of the wells, for which core is available, of bioturbation during deposition of the bed. The ash-fall was therefore a rapidly deposited unit which became colonized by a pioneer community of organisms.

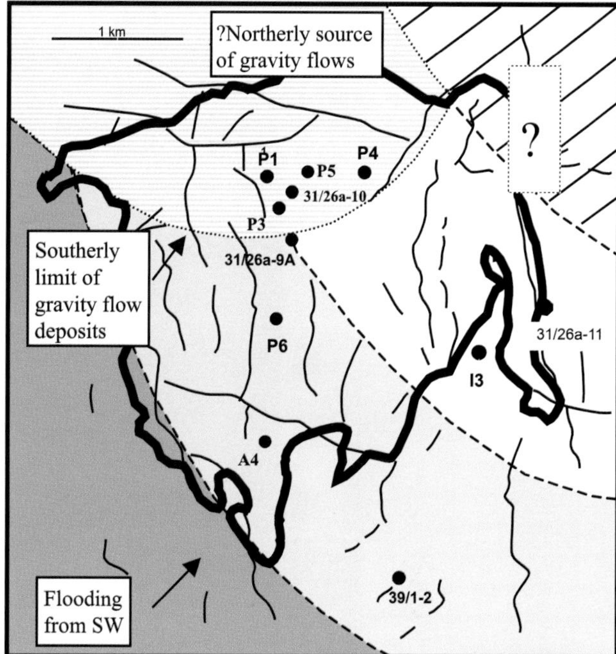

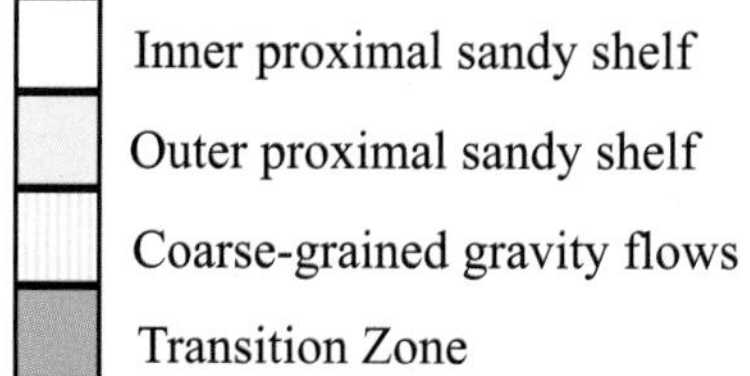

Fig. 7. Schematic representation of the interpreted palaeogeography of Sequence Set IV. Initial flooding from the southwest establishes transition zone facies across the area and a new phase of shelfal progradation southwestwards. Coarse-grained sediments, interpreted as gravity flow deposits, are concentrated in the north, with a pronounced pinchout north of Well 31/26a-9A. The most laterally extensive gravity flow deposit is also the most coarse-grained.

Sandy turbidites. This facies association is not part of the Fife sandstone, but occurs in the lower part of the overlying KCF. The basal contact with the Fife sandstone is unconformable (base of Sequence Set VI, Fig. 3). The sandy turbidites comprise cm- to lower dm-scale beds of very fine- to fine-grained sandstone deposited against a background of siltstone. They occur as distinct event beds which may be massive, stratified or deformed through liquefaction. Some beds contain layers of coarse sand grains and/or small mudstone clasts. These beds are interpreted as the deposits of relatively low density turbidity currents discharged basinwards from an as yet unknown source area.

Sequence stratigraphy and reservoir layering

Part of the remit of the sedimentological review of the Fife sandstones was to attempt to construct a sequence stratigraphic model which would be of sufficient resolution to assist with intra-reservoir flow-unit layering and correlation between wells. Developing a high-resolution sequence stratigraphy depends on the identification of a hierarchy of stratal units bounded by chrono-stratigraphically significant surfaces. Recognition of these surfaces may form the basis for interpretation of the subsurface data. The main stratal surfaces are usually either hiatal events associated with erosion or non-deposition, or are zones of stratigraphic condensation.

In the Fife Field, discrete depositional sequences are recognized which can be correlated with confidence. However, since it is often difficult to rank the marine flooding surfaces (thereby defining parasequences or true sequences), the main building blocks adopted are actually sequence sets, which are considered to provide the most effective means of sub-dividing the reservoir. Six sequence sets are recognized and collectively form the framework for the higher resolution, field-specific layering scheme.

Sequence Set I records the onset of Upper Jurassic deposition with marine transgression, possibly from the southeast, inundating a basin floored with Triassic fluvial/alluvial strata (Smith Bank Formation). Maximum flooding and sequence boundary development appear to have been co-incident. An overall 'cleaning'/coarsening-upward trend within highly bioturbated very fine- to fine-grained sandstones reflects progradation of the shallow marine shelf towards the southeast. Towards the top of the sequence set there is an interval containing coarse-grained gravity flow deposits derived from the north (layer 3, Fig. 3).

Overall, Sequence Set I is subdivided into three reservoir layers for modelling purposes. The uppermost layer, layer 3, is a coarse-grained sandstone which may extend field-wide. All three intra-reservoir layers (1, 2 & 3) in the sequence set correlate across the field. Each reservoir modelling layer has a different porosity and permeability character. Layer 1 is characterized by relatively low porosity and permeability and is generally non-net in the reservoir model. Layer 2 has variable porosity and permeability but is a net sandstone in the reservoir model. Layer 3 is very 'clean', has generally good porosity (20–25%), and can be highly heterogeneous in permeability character, with the coarse-grained units having a permeability of >2 D.

Sequence Set II commenced with a regional transgressive event, initiated in the east, which resulted in a thick succession of distal muddy shelf deposits (layer 4). Above the maximum flooding surface a 'cleaning'-upward/coarsening-upward trend reflects renewed progradation to the south and east (layer 5). In common with Sequence Set I, the upper part of Sequence Set II is prone to contain coarse-grained gravity flow deposits (layer 6). All three of the reservoir modelling layers in Sequence Set II have generally similar porosity and permeability characteristics to layers 1, 2, and 3, respectively, in Sequence Set I.

Sequence Set III records initial flooding from the southwest, with transition zone deposits developed at the base in all but the most crestal wells (e.g. P5 and 31/26a-10), which indicate outer proximal shelf deposition. As with Sequence Sets I and II, a broad 'cleaning'/coarsening-upward trend is observed, but this time reflecting progradation to the southwest. Inner proximal shelf deposits occur towards the top of the sequence set over the crest of the field, with lower energy, outer proximal shelf sediments, developed at the same stratigraphic level southwest of Well 31/26a-9A. The top of the sequence set comprises a field-wide, 0.5–1.0 m thick, volcanic ash-fall deposit. Previously (and erroneously) interpreted as a maximum flooding surface, this deposit has been named the Mid-Fife Silt.

The sequence set is divided into two layers for reservoir modelling purposes. Layers 6 and 7 have a similar character on logs and in cores and are often separated using subtle log responses. Layer 6 sometimes shows a 'cleaning'-upward trend. Part of the need to subdivide this section of the reservoir is to satisfy reservoir simulation requirements, where numerical dispersion problems arise in the modelling of layers which are relatively thick. Layer 8 is represented as part of sequence set III for convenience.

Sequence Set IV commenced with flooding above the Mid-Fife Silt (Fig. 3), resulting in the deposition of a transition zone and outer proximal shelf facies. It is more difficult to define a 'cleaning'/coarsening-upward trend in this sequence set than in the lower part of the reservoir, but an overall progradational signature is seen, with inner proximal sandy shelf facies established field-wide. Towards the top of the sequence set is another interval containing coarse-grained gravity flow deposits. This unit, unlike the two other coarse-grained units developed in the lower part of the reservoir, has a limited distribution in the field and seems to be restricted to the northern crestal area (Fig. 7).

Within Sequence Set IV five reservoir layers, 9–13, are defined on the basis of subtle wireline log signatures and core data. Each of these layers correlate across the field, although layer 13 changes character abruptly north of Well 31/26a-10 (Fig. 2). To the south of this well the layer comprises fine-grained sandstones with moderate porosity and permeability. However, to the north, coarse-grained gravity flow deposits occur with good porosity and, especially, permeability

Sequence Set V was initiated by flooding from the southwest which subsequently fixed the proximal shelf–transition zone boundary close to Well 31/26a-A4. Progradation from the northeast established NW–SE orientated facies belts, with the most proximal deposits ('clean', well sorted fine-grained sandstones) developed in the eastern part of the field. Gravity flow deposits encountered in the sequence set are tied to the northern part of the field and are thinner and finer-grained than those developed lower down in the reservoir. The final event in Sequence Set V was a transgressive pulse resulting in the widespread incursion of outer proximal shelf and transition zone facies, although inner proximal shelf deposits locally occur beneath the unconformity associated with the base of Sequence Set VI (e.g. in Well P3).

The sequence is subdivided in to five layers for reservoir modelling purposes. Again, this subdivision is based on often very subtle changes in log character. All five layers correlate across the field.

Sequence Set VI (Kimmeridge Clay Formation) is the youngest stratigraphic unit and is defined at the base by a distinctive transgressive surface colonized by *Diplocriterion parallelum* and *Thalassinoides* burrows. The unit comprises thinly bedded, glauconitic sandy turbidites developed against a siltstone background, which pass upwards into laminated Upper Volgian/Ryazanian basinal claystones. Preservation of the sequence set is constrained by the magnitude of the Base Chalk unconformity.

Reservoir modelling

Mapping

Once a stratigraphic framework had been established for the Fife sandstones, an intra-reservoir flow unit layering scheme, containing 19 layers, was devised for modelling purposes. This scheme was based on wireline logs, sedimentological and core analysis (mainly permeability) data. Although most of the reservoir layers extend over most of the field, layer 13 contains coarse-grained deposits in the crestal area, but elsewhere comprises predominantly fine-grained sandstones. It was mapped as two layers for reservoir simulation modelling, but is considered as one layer for geological modelling and oil-in-place calculations.

Using the 19-layer scheme, average petrophysical parameters in wells were calculated using a combination of conventional core analysis data, test and production logging data, and infill data points. Because of the difficulty in sampling coarse-grained gravity flow deposits to generate conventional core porosity and permeability data, these deposits were initially under-represented statistically in the calculation of layer average properties.

By using a combination of 'educated guesstimates' based on adjacent core plug or adjacent well data, test data and production logging data, a representative net : gross ratio and porosity and permeability layer average value was calculated on a 1/2 ft basis in all cored sections. This involved a lot of estimation of properties to 'infill' data points as most of the conventional core analysis had sampled at a 1 ft spacing. The geologist, reservoir engineer and petrophysicist assigned to the project worked closely in order to achieve the best data interpretation. Water saturation averages in the reservoir layers were calculated as a function of porosity and height above the oil–water contact.

The layer average data were gridded using a computer-aided mapping package and the reservoir oil volume of the revised model was calculated to be 132×10^6 STB. These data were used as the basis for the dynamic reservoir simulation.

Simulation

The simulation grid was constructed using corner-point geometry and comprises some 36 000 grid cells ranging in size down to 100 m. The simulation model splits the field into four volumes (Fig. 8a):

(1) the lower, predominantly water-bearing reservoir across the field;
(2) the upper, oil-bearing, coarse-grained reservoir in the crestal area of the field only;
(3) the upper, oil-bearing, fine-grained reservoir equivalent to (2) over the remainder of the field
(4) the uppermost, oil-bearing, reservoir units across the whole field.

Most of the faults interpreted from the seismic do not appear to significantly affect flow through the reservoir. This is interpreted from interference testing and on the basis of dynamic production data. Consequently, most of the faults interpreted from seismic (Fig. 2) are not represented as transmissibility baffles or barriers in the simulation model.

The fault to the west of the P6 well and the fault west of P1 are however, important, in the modelling (Fig. 8b). They are interpreted to affect flow largely as a result of well test data. In mid-1996 an RFT in Well P6, when the field had been producing oil for over 8 months, showed a greater reduction in reservoir pressure in the lower reservoir than in the upper, oil-bearing reservoir, relative to the pressures at field start-up (Fig. 8b). No well at that time was producing from the lower reservoir and three wells were producing from the upper oil-bearing reservoir.

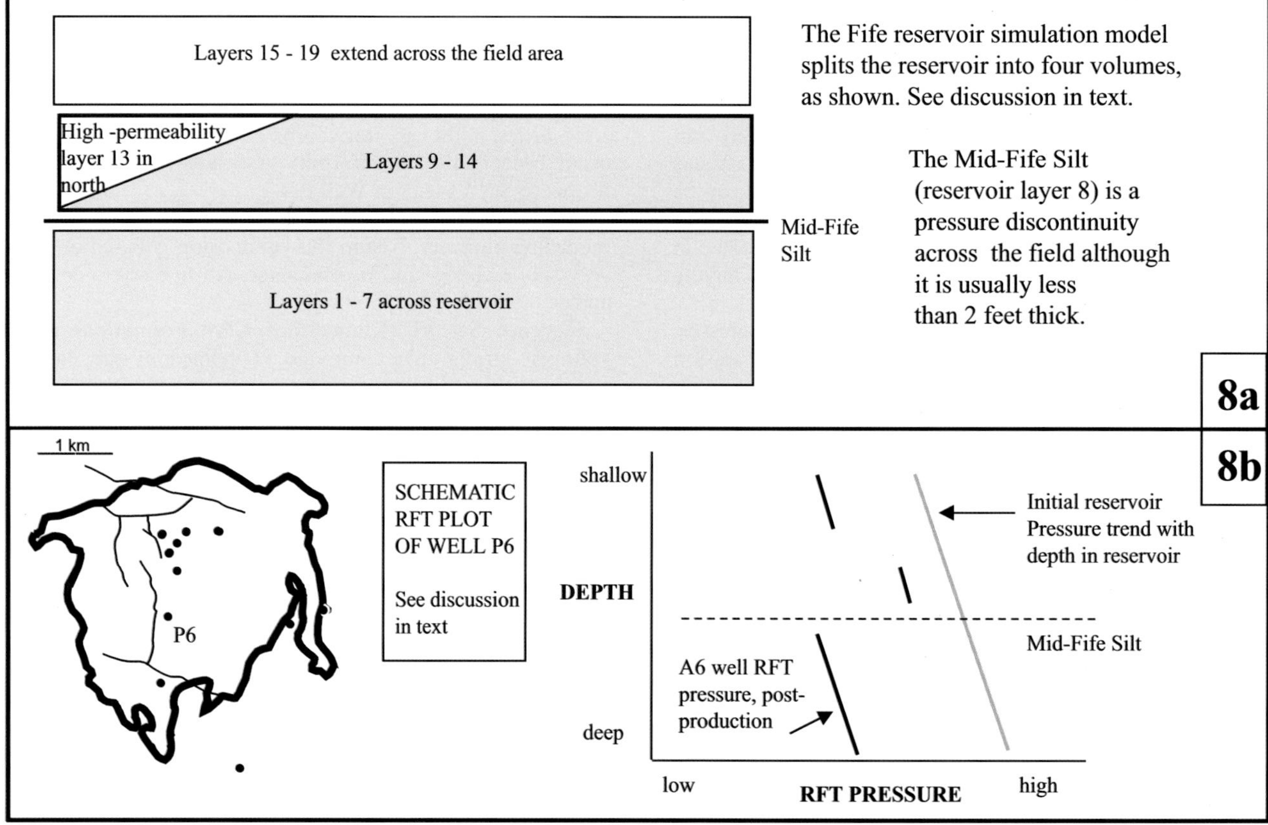

Fig. 8. Schematic representation of the simulation model and interpretation of the 31/26a-P6 well RFT result. (**a**) The upper and lower reservoirs are split vertically by the Mid-Fife Silt, interpreted here as an ash-fall deposit. Most layers extend laterally across the field but layer 13, discussed in text, changes character significantly and is modelled in the dynamic reservoir simulator as two separate units. (**b**) The diagram on the left shows the field outline and position of Well 31/26a-P6. The diagram on the right is a sketch of the post-production RFT result from the well compared to an RFT taken prior to field start-up. Increased depletion in pressure, relative to the upper reservoir, is shown in the lower reservoir below the Mid-Fife Silt. The lower reservoir was not completed in any well at the time the P6 RFT was taken. The RFT result is interpreted to be the result of pressure communication between highly permeable, water-bearing, units of the lower Fife sandstones in the south and highly permeable units in the oil-bearing zone to the north which have been juxtaposed across faults.

The most likely explanation for the RFT result was that there was fault juxtaposition of the coarse-grained, water-bearing layers in the lower reservoir off-crest with coarse-grained, oil-bearing layers of the upper reservoir in the crestal area. Rapid oil production at the crest from the coarse-grained deposits was lowering pressure in the coarse-grained (water-bearing) layers off-crest. The fault juxtaposition of reservoir layers is incorporated in to the simulation model.

On the basis of the sedimentological model, reservoir layering and petrophysical parameter data described here, a simulation model has been built which provides a satisfactory history-match of well pressures, production history, water-breakthrough and water-cut trends. The P5 well is less well-matched than the other wells owing principally to the difficulties in reproducing the very rapid water-breakthrough.

Discussion

The Fife Field reservoir is an unusual and challenging example of Central North Sea Upper Jurassic oil field developments. The level of depositional and diagenetic heterogeneity in the reservoir has proven difficult to model effectively. A combination of sedimentological and ichnological studies and examination of wireline log, dynamic flow data, and test data from wells across the field, has permitted the construction of a sequence stratigraphic model for the field. Within this correlation a 19 layer flow-unit correlation has been constructed which forms the basis for both the static and dynamic reservoir modelling.

From a depositional modelling point of view, the source area and precise mechanism of emplacement of the coarse-grained deposits remain equivocal. Although these deposits form a relatively small part of the reservoir, their primary importance in reservoir management dictates that they should be as fully understood as possible. The current understanding is that although the alternation of coarse-grained gravity flow deposits and highly bioturbated, fine-grained shallow marine sandstones is unusual, the character of each, supported by ichnological evidence, strongly suggests a two-component depositional system of the type described herein.

From a field development perspective, and with the benefit of hindsight, the fact that neither of the two pre-drilled production wells were cored in the oil-bearing section of the reservoir was unfortunate. The omission of any core being obtained over the upper reservoir in the crestal area of the field prior to production start-up led to a perforation strategy for the wells that proved to be less than optimal. It is almost certain that if the upper reservoir coarse-grained deposits had been identified in the pre-production phase, the development plan would have been modified.

The pre-drilled well cementing problems, which led to water flow behind casing, conditioned the interpretations of the early water-breakthrough and made the planning of remedial options to deal with the water, more complicated. It was not until core data from the P5 well demonstrated the presence of a highly permeable thief zone in the upper reservoir that a reasonable explanation for the water production history was established.

Once the thief zone in the upper reservoir had been identified, rapid and positive action was taken. The drilling of two off-crestal wells, with a prominent data-gathering element in their financial justification, was a modification to the development plan which paid off. Without the data from these two wells it is likely that the reservoir modelling would be subject to significantly greater uncertainty.

In November 1997, during preparation of this written contribution, a further oil production well, P8, was drilled in the western part of the Fife Field (Fig. 2). The well, a step out to the west in a previously undrilled area, was located as crestally as possible in the field in an area where there was estimated to be a low risk of intersecting the thief zone. The well provided a good test of the reservoir model and came in as prognosed. It has been completed as an oil production well.

The authors would like to thank Amerada Hess Ltd and Premier Oil (UK) Limited for permission to publish this data. Many helpful suggestions for revision of the original text were made by S. Burley, A. Hurst and an anonymous referee.

References

BOURKE, L. & MACKERTICH, D. 1994. Permeability imaging and petrographic analysis of burrow fabrics in the Fife field. *Dialog*, 4–5

BRYANT, I. D., KANTOROWICZ, J. D. & LOVE, C. F. 1988. The origin and recognition of laterally continuous carbonate cemented horizons in the Upper Lias Sands of Southern England. *Marine and Petroleum Geology*, **5**, 108–133.

GOWLAND, S. 1996. Facies characteristics and depositional models of highly bioturbated shallow marine siliciclastic strata: an example from the Fulmar Formation (Late Jurassic), UK Central North Graben. *In*: HURST, A. *et al.* (eds) *Geology of the Humber Group: Central Graben and Moray Firth, UKCS*. Geological Society, London, Special Publications **114**, 185–214.

MACKERTICH, D. 1996 The Fife field, UK Central North Sea. *Petroleum Geoscience*, **2**, 373–380.

TAYLOR, A. M. & GAWTHORPE, R. L. 1993. Application of sequence stratigraphy and trace fossil analysis to reservoir description from the Jurassic of the North Sea. *In*: PARKER, J. R. (ed.), *Petroleum Geology of Northwest Europe: Proceedings of the 4th Conference*. Geological Society, London, 317–335.

Ekofisk Field redevelopment: improved reservoir management through cross-discipline technology and integration of three dimensional models

S. C. KEY, B. AGARWAL, G. V. SØILAND and H. H. NIELSEN

Phillips Petroleum Company Norway, PO Box 220, 4056 Tananger, Norway

Abstract: The Ekofisk Field is currently undergoing a major field re-development in which 45 new wells will be drilled before the end of 1998. This requires that the most comprehensive and detailed reservoir description and geological and fluid flow models be used as the basis for the planning of such a re-development. This situation, as well as new developments in hardware and software and multidisciplinary database and applications integration, led to the decision in 1994 to completely re-evaluate the reservoir characterization of the field. A major multi-disciplinary effort involving geoscience, petrophysical and reservoir engineering work was initiated through the Ekofisk reservoir characterization (ERC) project. The objective of the reservoir characterization project was to improve the existing reservoir description using all available data through the application of new techniques and technology, and to construct and history match a new 3D reservoir fluid flow model using this updated, detailed reservoir description. Greater demands are being made on geoscientists and engineers to model and manage processes taking place within the reservoir. At the same time systems are evolving which allow large and complex models to be developed and modeled in simulators. The development of these models, and asset management based on these models, are becoming requirements for effective reservoir management. Our biggest challenge is to maintain, update and interchange data between the large 3D reservoir description models and fluid flow models through integration of new data. Up-scaling of the detailed description produced the highest resolution model that is computationally manageable. The resulting history-matched fluid flow model provides the primary reservoir management tool for the field re-development programme and for the evaluation of reservoir and geoscience monitoring technologies. Down-scaled reservoir parameters are currently being integrated with petrophysical data and laboratory core analysis to drive seismic forward modelling of present and future reservoir conditions. These seismic simulations are being used to evaluate the implementation of a time-lapse seismic (4D) monitoring programme for the field.

The Ekofisk Field, located in the Norwegian Sector of the North Sea was discovered in 1969. Production started from the Cretaceous Danian chalks in 1971. Current estimates indicate about 8×10^9 BBL oil equivalent originally in place. The field has produced over 1.2 billion barrels of oil to date from a total of 160 wells. Current production from about 67 deviated and horizontal wells is about 240 000 BBL oil per day (BOPD) and 600×10^6 SCF(D) of gas. A pilot water injection project was initiated in 1981 in the highly fractured Tor Formation (Thomas *et al.* 1987) and in the Lower Ekofisk in 1986 (Sylte *et al.* 1988). Fieldwide water injection began in 1987 (Hallenbach *et al.* 1989). Current water injection rates are 840 000 BWPD into 37 active injection wells. A number of additional improved oil recovery techniques are being evaluated and currently ongoing is a water-alternating-gas (WAG) pilot in the southern area of the field. Figure 1 shows a structure map of the Ekofisk Field drawn on the top of the Ekofisk Formation.

As a result of large reserves remaining in Ekofisk and the potential for increased recovery, significant resources were allocated to the Ekofisk reservoir characterization (ERC) project. An integrated, multi-disciplinary team consisting of geologists, geophysicists, petrophysicists, engineers and technicians comprised the ERC team and twenty person years of work have been dedicated to the project to date. The reservoir description phase and construction of the 3D geological model were completed earlier in 1997, and the process of history matching the 3D reservoir flow model with 25 years of production data from over 160 wells is now underway.

Numerous strategies were employed during the course of the ERC project, including: (1) reprocessing of seismic and petrophysical data; (2) an integrated team and project plan incorporating the concept of front-end loading; (3) use of state-of-the-art technologies in both software and hardware; (4) a focus on permeability, heterogeneity, and anisotropy; (5) integration of data and tasks; (6) development of new structural/sedimentological models; (7) upgrades to the reservoir flow model software to allow refined grid definition and orientation; and (8) an improved link between the geological model and the reservoir flow model.

Reservoir characterization on Ekofisk was directed at gaining a detailed understanding of reservoir hydrocarbon volumes, the architecture of the reservoir and at fully describing the heterogeneity and anisotropy of reservoir parameters. Significant attention was also given to capturing as much heterogeneity as possible, both laterally and vertically, in the new geological model, and subsequently in the new flow model. This would enable better prediction of fluid movement within the reservoir, particularly water movement and possible breakthrough, resulting in improved field wide production forecasts, well placement analysis and special high definition EOR studies.

Reservoir description

The most important aspects in reservoir characterization are understanding the distribution and connectivity of pore volume, as this represents the total energy in the fluid flow system. Once pore volume and additional rock properties such as permeability have been defined at a high resolution, the reservoir description will be up-scaled to a coarser resolution 3D reservoir flow model. To describe the distribution of pore volume an architecture must first be built in three dimensions that constrains the rock–fluid system being described; within this architecture the heterogeneity and anisotropy present in

KEY, S. C., AGARWAL, B., SØILAND, G. V. & NIELSEN, H. H. 1999. Ekofisk Field redevelopment: improved reservoir management through cross-discipline technology and integration of three dimensional models. *In*: FLEET, A. J. & BOLDY, S. A. R. (eds) *Petroleum Geology of Northwest Europe: Proceedings of the 5th Conference*, 1147–1155. © Petroleum Geology '86 Ltd. Published by the Geological Society, London.

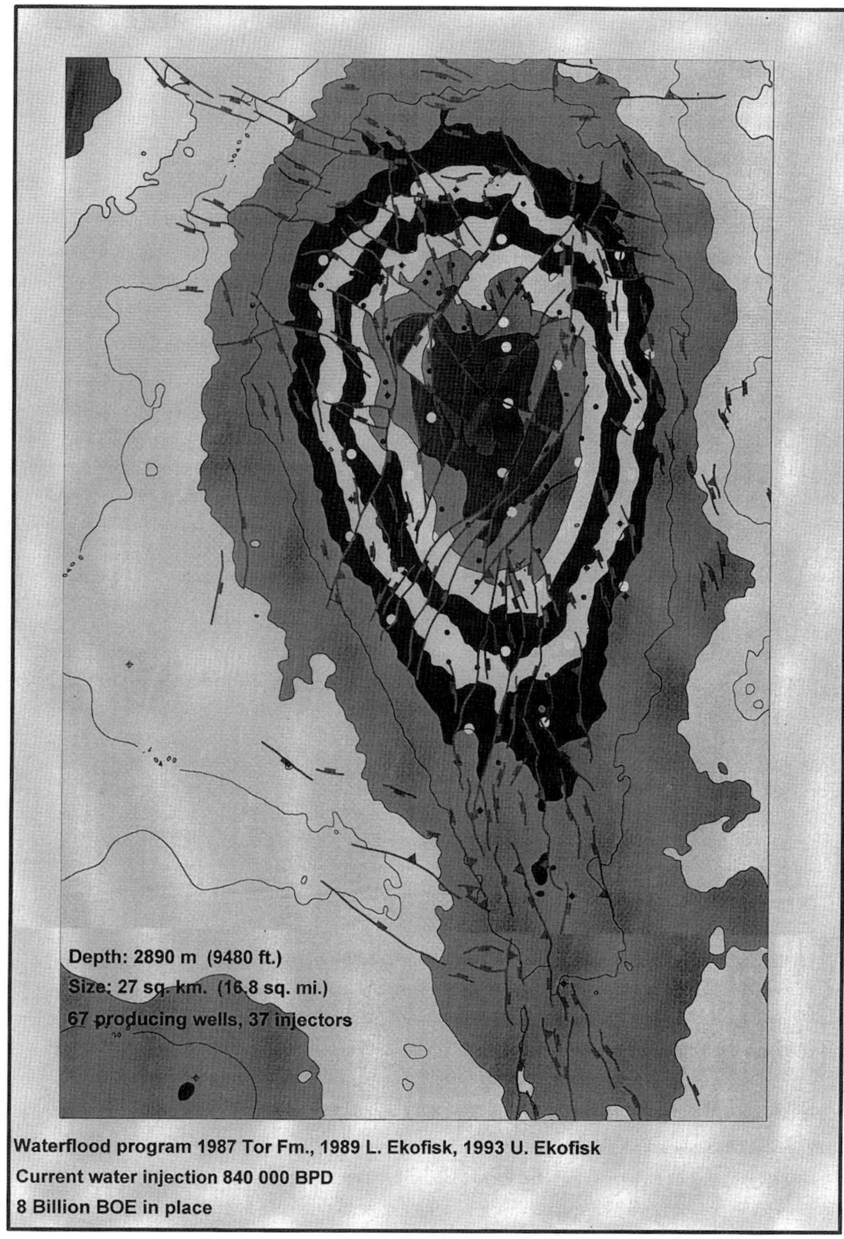

Fig. 1. Top structure map of the Ekofisk Formation of the Ekofisk Field.

rock properties must be captured; and the individual properties distributed. Figure 2 illustrates this process.

The reservoir descriptive phase of the ERC project consisted of detailed mapping and three-dimensional distribution of reservoir properties such as thickness, porosity, water saturation, permeability, petrofacies and quartz in a high resolution geological model. An up-scaling technique was used to translate the reservoir description to a lower resolution reservoir fluid flow model such that heterogeneity was preserved. In the following sections we describe highlights of the various tasks associated with this phase.

Data

The first characterization task was the careful editing, integration and analysis of data collected from Ekofisk over 25 years of drilling and production. This included over 160 wellbores with resistivity and porosity data, 125 with well test data, 40 with dipmeter data, 30 with core and 25 with full waveform sonic data. These data were integrated with 3D seismic data acquired in 1989 and recently reprocessed in 1994.

Figure 3 is an illustration of the work process flow chart for ERC showing the interaction and integration of software, data, and databases with the two main platforms, the 3D geological model and the 3D reservoir flow model. The figure illustrates the complexity of the ERC project and the numerous data sources that were employed during the project.

Architecture

A new structural and sedimentological framework for the field was generated based on an integration of seismic interpretation and wireline log correlation. All wells were carefully re-examined using mineralogy-constrained layer-correlations in the workstation environment. Linear modelling of log responses yielded volume curves for common minerals. Careful use of silica identifier algorithms made it possible to significantly improve previous layer definitions. Synthetic seismograms were generated for over 100 wells outside the gas obscured zone, which guided the seismic interpretation. This produced a consistent reservoir subdivision into 12 layers that honoured both well and seismic data.

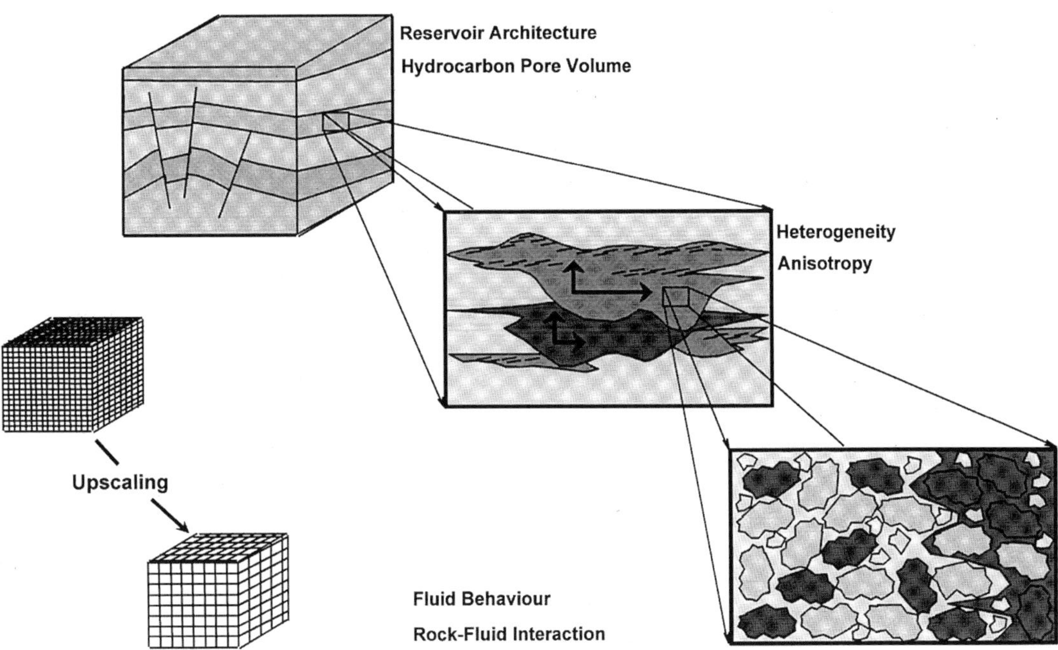

Fig. 2. Reservoir characterization process. To describe the distribution of pore volume, an architecture must first be built in three dimensions that constrains the rock–fluid system being described.

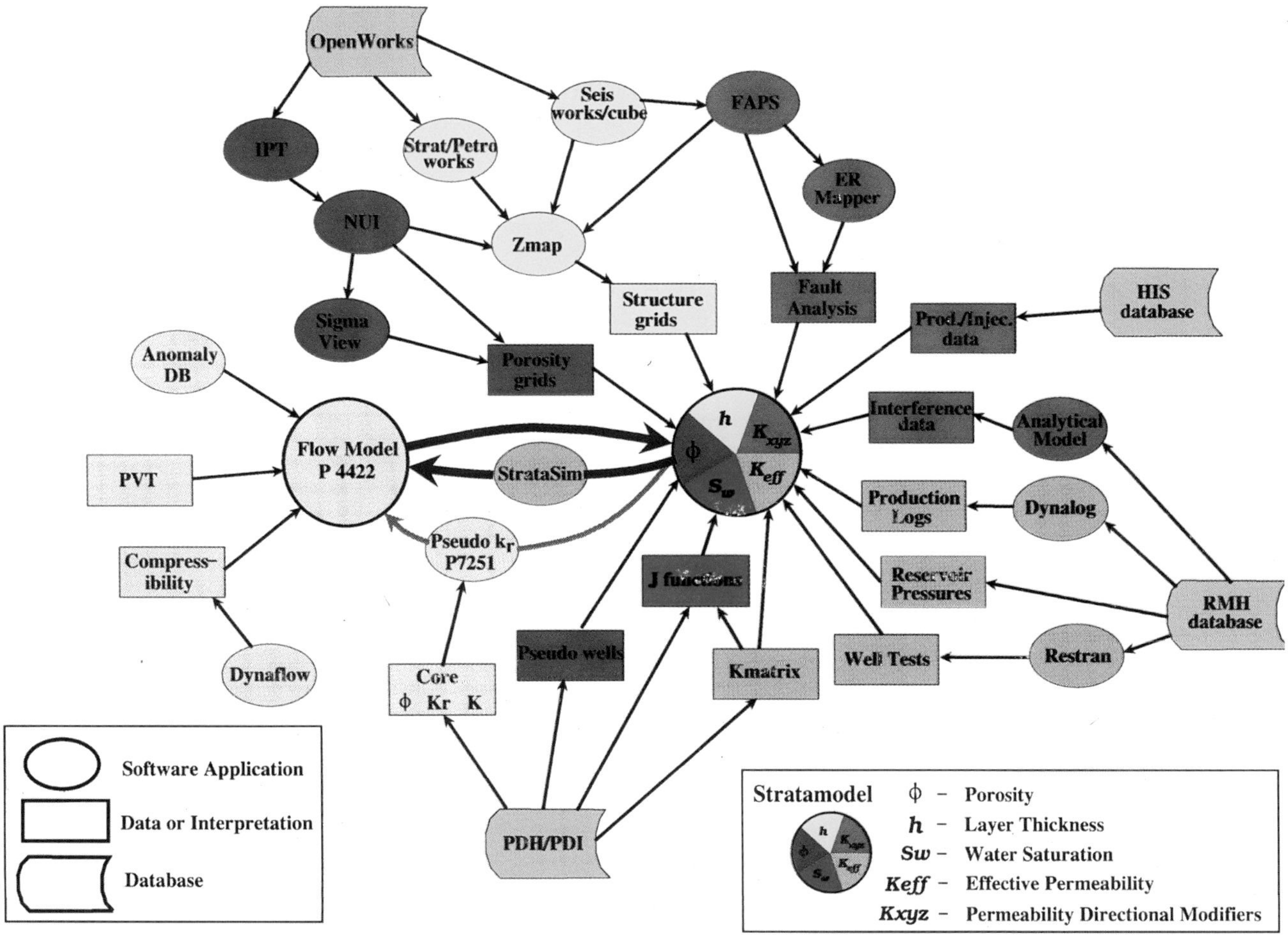

Fig. 3. Reservoir characterization work process flow chart. The interaction between all the data and databases used in the Ekofisk reservoir characterization project.

Heterogeneity

Fault interpretation

Spatial heterogeneity was preserved in the 3D geological model through detailed layer-based seismic modelling and interpretation of over 300 fault planes in three dimensions. The basis for the fault interpretation was analysis and integration of a number of seismic attributes generated at the major reservoir boundaries. This analysis was linked in three dimensions to provide fully correlated fault planes for each fault. Figure 4 compares a model generated in 1991 to the ERC interpretation.

Petrofacies

Production characteristics on Ekofisk are closely related to lithofacies. Chalk petrofacies with individual flow-characteristics were described and characterized from core analysis. These different petrofacies were then distributed in 3D using cluster analysis based on comparison between core and log data. Lithofacies were described in detail from core data available from 24 wells. The core description was correlated with cluster analysis of log data, combining activity, *V*-shale and porosity. This generated a distribution of likely facies types where the dominant or 'most likely' facies was determined. This process provided a 98% correlation coefficient when compared to foot by foot descriptions from core in target wells. Petrofacies derived for 80 wells were distributed in 3 dimensions generating a continuous 3D facies description. Petrofacies distribution is the basis for the algorithm developed to distribute effective permeability.

Porosity

A petrophysical re-evaluation resulted in more accurate porosity (and water saturation) estimation. The application of new technology allowed seismic inversion techniques to successfully map porosity and isopach values for reservoir units resolvable with seismic. A full waveform inversion was carried out for each formation using Phillips proprietary inversion software incorporating simultaneous layer and formation isochron constraints. Forward modeling was carried out with an empirical formula developed for Ekofisk chalks from core and log data with Biot–Gassman used for fluid substitution. Forward models were constructed at 40 wells, generating over 100 000 reservoir models representing the full range of possible petrophysical and geological parameter variation.

Geostatistical methods were used to simulate porosity distribution within thinner, unresolvable layers. A set of pseudo-wells placed across the non-drilled flanks of the field were given synthetic porosity logs, guided from the mapped thickness and porosity and nearby well logs. The synthetic logs ensured a heterogeneous porosity distribution throughout the model. Figure 5 is a map of one of the Ekofisk Formation layers, comparing the resulting porosity distribution with the previous characterization based on well control alone. A considerable amount of the intrinsic reservoir heterogeneity is captured as a result of the inversion effort in the well control area and the application of pseudo-wells in the flank areas. Although both datasets match the well data, the location and orientation of significant depositional and diagenetic controls are captured only by characterization of the inter-well space through seismic inversion.

Water saturation

Accurate distribution of initial water saturation in the geological and fluid flow models was of extreme importance because of the significant impact it has on hydrocarbon pore volume, hydrocarbon flow characteristics and ultimately on hydrocarbon recovery. The model employed to distribute water saturation was based on a combination of the Bentsen and Anlie (1975) correlation, the Leverett J-function (Leverett 1941) and the relationship between capillary pressure and height above the free water level. The physical model governing the correlations was a single free water level and water saturation as a function of porosity and height above free water level. All well log data were normalized before standard petrophysical parameters were calculated. A single free water level was established by analysing pressure data from the first 4 wells drilled on Ekofisk; the intersection of the oil and water gradients defined the free water level. Twenty-four non-linear correlations were

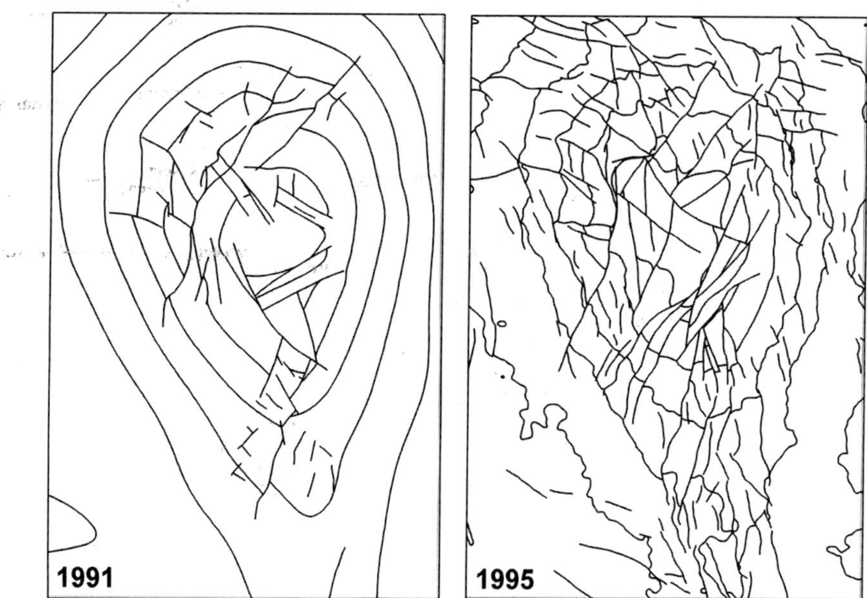

Fig. 4. Comparison of the fault model developed through the Ekofisk reservoir characterization project to a fault model developed through a previous effort in 1991.

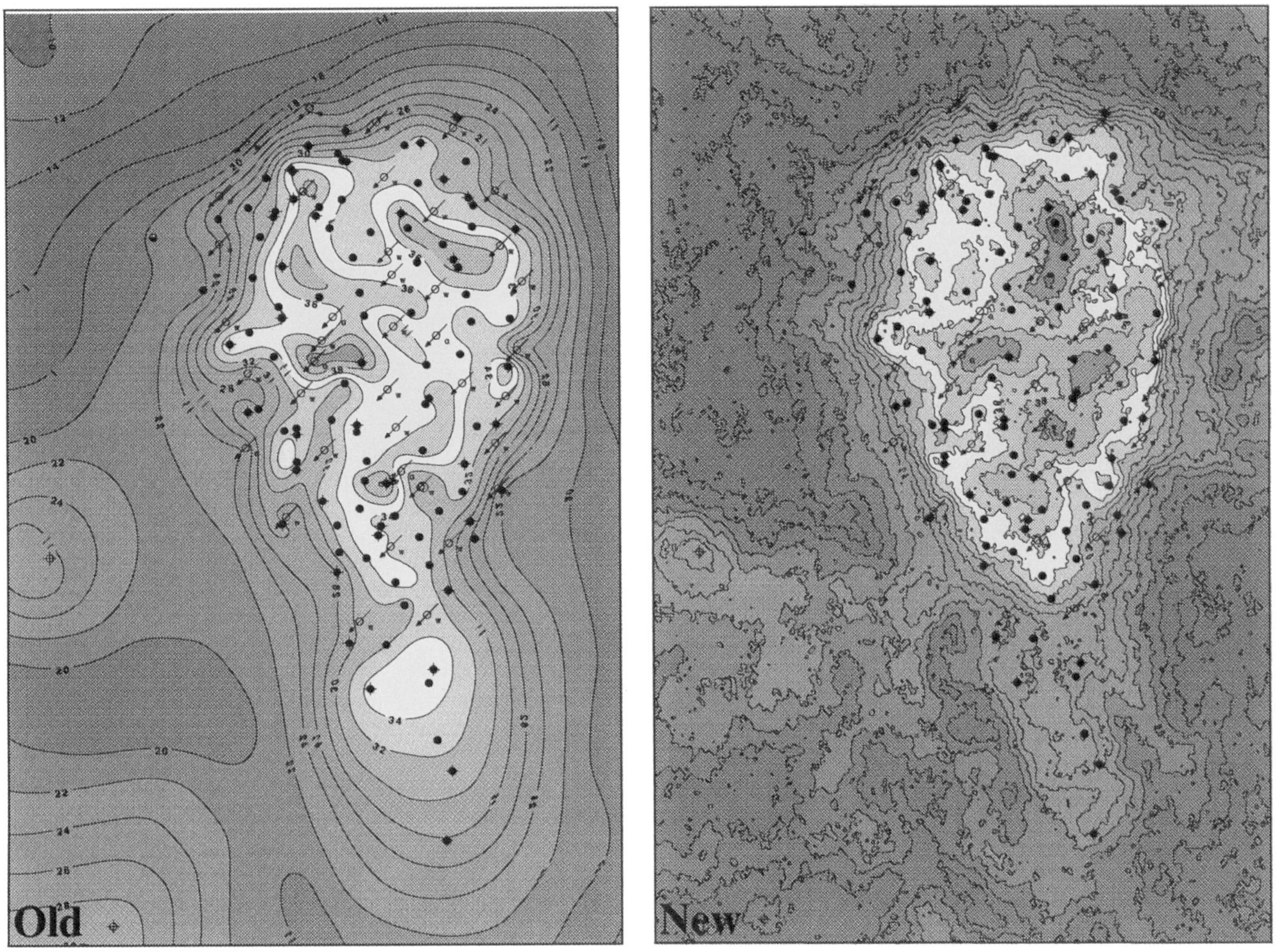

Old

New

Fig. 5. Map of one of the Ekofisk Formation layers comparing the ERC porosity distribution with a previous characterization effort.

generated, representing different geological layers and areal zones, based on fit to actual log data. Comparisons to actual log data suggested the correlations were well behaved.

Permeability

Developing a good understanding of the fracture distribution in the chalk is fundamental in predicting the absolute permeability distribution, the hydrocarbon recovery mechanisms and efficiencies for various hydrocarbon recovery techniques. In the Ekofisk Field, fracture intensity can be related directly to petrofacies. Five types of fractures, mapped and classified from core data, were identified as healed, stylolite, tectonic, irregular and slump fractures. Each fracture type was then correlated to three distinct facies categories grouped based on general chalk type and analysed with respect to the fracture intensity (number of fractures per foot).

Permeability and its heterogeneity are critical parameters affecting reservoir fluid flow both in terms of volume and direction. Fluid flow characteristics of Ekofisk Field are largely governed by the distribution, orientation and interconnectivity of the natural fracture system. To honour this mechanism, and to capture the intrinsic heterogeneity and complex nature of the field, an algorithm was developed based on the log linear relationship between fracture intensity data from core and well test effective permeability (Agarwal *et al.* 1996). During development, the basic relationship was modified to incorporate variations associated with: (1) chalk

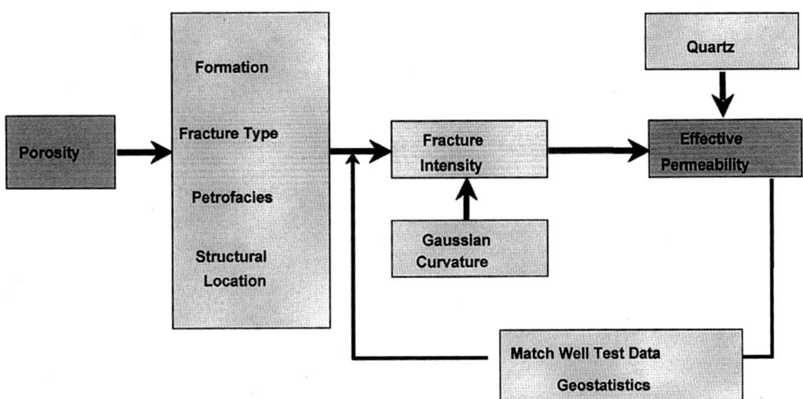

Fig. 6. Flow chart representing the process for calculating effective permeability within the 3D geological model.

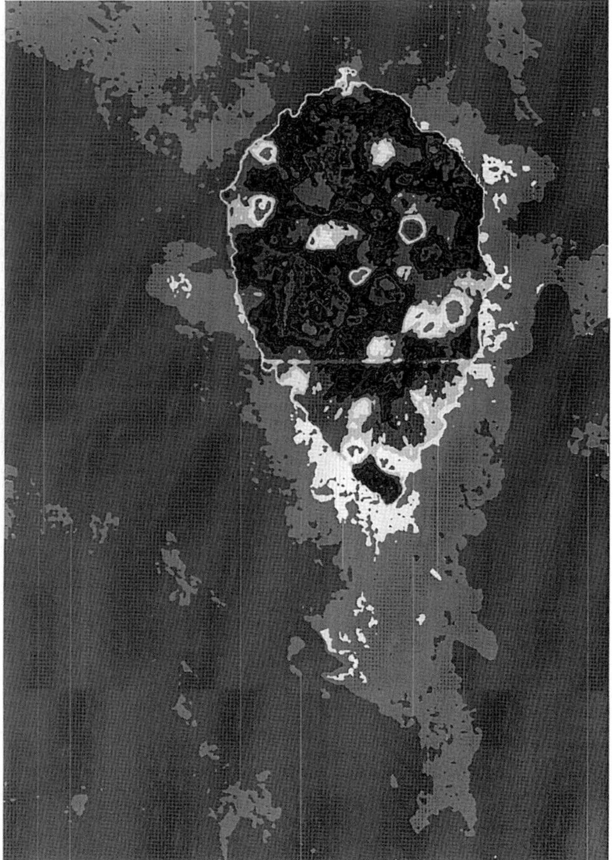

Fig. 7. Areal view of a stratigraphic slice of from the Ekofisk Formation extracted from the 3D geological model. Lighter areas represent higher permeability, darker areas tend towards matrix permeability.

petrofacies; (2) fracture type; (3) porosity; (4) structural location; (5) structural curvature; and (6) silica content.

To calibrate the algorithm, permeability determined from distributing total well test flow capacity (k_h) based on production log contribution was used as a tuning parameter. As a final step, geostatistical techniques were applied to tune the algorithm to the well test data. Figure 6 represents a flow chart of the effective permeability algorithm. The algorithm is implemented within the geological model and, therefore, provides a three-dimensional distribution of permeability.

Figure 7 is an areal view of a stratigraphic slice of the Ekofisk Formation taken from the geological model. Immediately obvious from this figure is the heterogeneity, as depicted by the various degrees of shading, present between grid cells; the lighter areas represent higher permeability while the darker areas trend towards matrix permeability.

Relative permeability

Mechanistic studies were performed to generate pseudo-relative permeability curves for the 3D reservoir flow model. Pseudo-relative permeability is employed to account for fine-scale variations in effective permeability, to reduce the dimension of the model and to control numerical dispersion, when up-scaling from the fine-scale geological model to the coarser resolution of the flow model. The pseudo curves were developed from 2D fine-scale cross-sectional models, extracted directly from the 3D geological model to capture vertical heterogeneity. The number of pseudo relative permeability curves were limited by identifying areas having similar maximum to average flow capacity ratio and vertical heterogeneity. A total of 30 areas were identified with sufficiently diverse characteristics. Figure 8 illustrates the process in detail for calculating the pseudo-relative permeability curves.

Anisotropy

Detailed seismic mapping of fault planes in 3D resulted in the mapping of more than 300 faults. The basis for the fault interpretation was analysis and integration of a number of seismic attributes generated at the major reservoir boundaries. This analysis was linked in three dimensions to provide fully correlated fault planes for each fault. The faults were resolved into three distinct systems, seen in the fault orientation analysis in Figure 9. Here the interpreted Ekofisk faults systems are compared with theoretical data. The excellent agreement between regional data, field data and theoretical models allows the direction of compressional and extensional forces to be

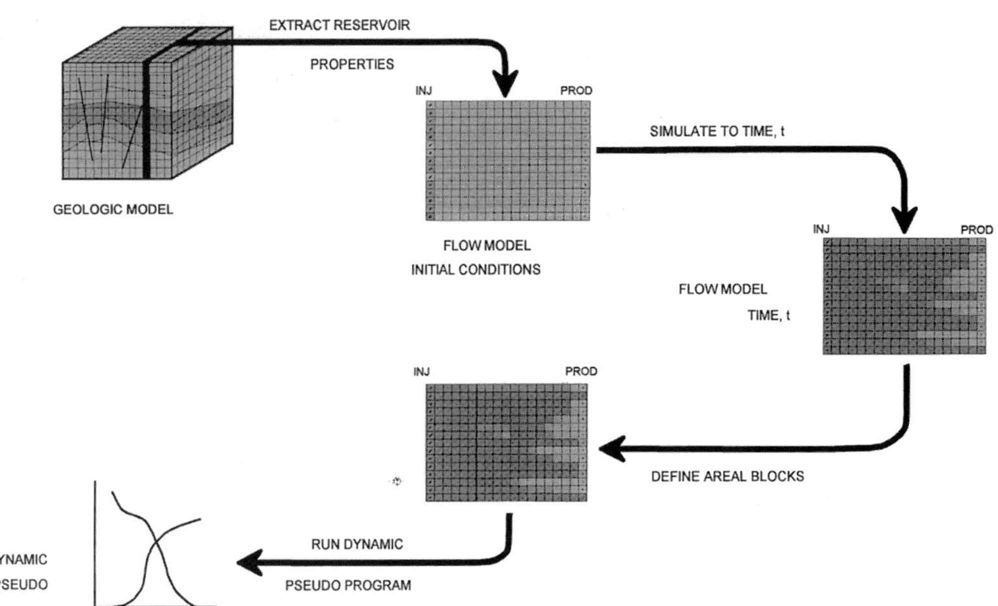

Fig. 8. Process for calculating pseudo-relative permeability curves based on a 2D fine-scale cross-sectional model extracted directly from the 3D geological model.

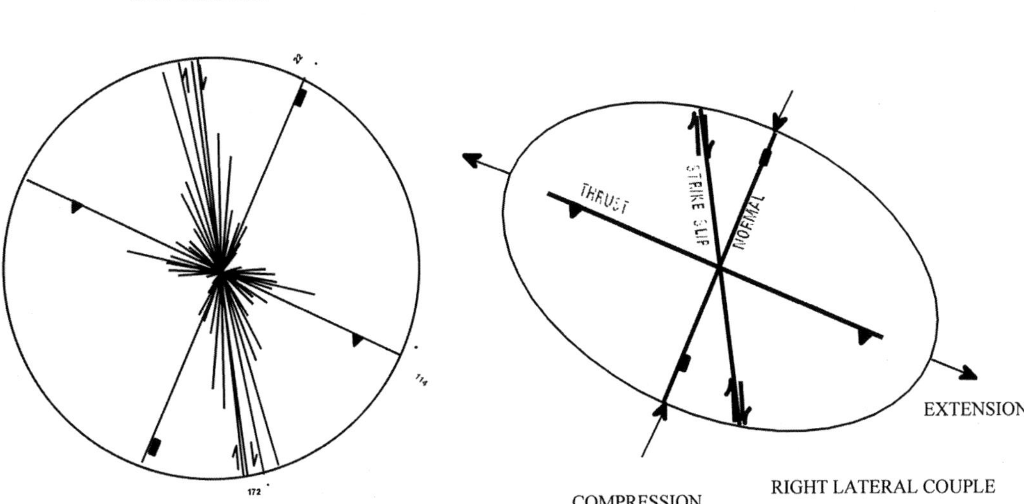

Fig. 9. Fault orientation analysis depicting the interpreted Ekofisk fault systems with theoretical assemblage data.

established and verifies the orientations of the three fault types; thrust, normal faults and strike-slip faults.

From the orientation of these fault systems and the interpreted stress field it is anticipated that the normal faults and strike-slip faults likely provide higher permeability conduits for fluid flow. The evaluation of well to well tracer tests, interference tests, production/injection well responses and initial history match results suggest these relationships are correct. These data suggest preferential flow NE–SW along open normal faults, secondary flow N–S along partially open strike slip faults and no clear preferential flow NW–SE along closed thrust faults.

The application of a structural curvature correction to permeability and X and Y directional permeability modifiers associated with mapped faults allowed: (1) areas with higher fault density to have higher permeability values; and (2) anisotropy to be captured through the high structural curvature values associated with large normal faults.

3D Model

Geological attributes

Reservoirs in Ekofisk are found in the Ekofisk and Tor formations. Each formation is characterized by a number of well defined depositional sequences. High quality Ekofisk reservoir units are composed primarily of eroded and reworked chalks deposited as debris flows. Pelagic deposition characterizes units with poorer reservoir quality. As a result of the structural and sedimentalogical history of the Ekofisk area, depositional sequences are characterized as being composed primarily of, high porosity, high reservoir quality reworked chalk facies or lower porosity/reservoir quality pelagic facies. These characteristics result in each of the 12 defined depositional sequences within the Ekofisk and Tor formations to be commonly defined with reservoir model flow units, as each have independent flow characteristics.

A brief overview of depositional characteristics and associated structural setting of each of the defined sequences follows, beginning at the base of the Tor Formation.

Tor C layer. The Tor C layer is poorly defined on seismic data and is also poorly represented by well data. This unit falls below any reservoir quality chalks and is defined to represent the aquifer in the flow model.

Tor B layer. The period of Tor B deposition represents a quiet period tectonically and is characterized by broad basinal subsidence. Pelagic deposition dominates and as a result the sequence has a uniform low porosity structure.

Tor A layer. The Tor A is divided into three recognizable sequences, Lower, Middle and Upper.

Tor A Lower: a compressive tectonic pulse is interpreted at the boundary of Tor B and Tor A Lower deposition. This pulse resulted in reactivation and reverse motion along preexisting NW–SE trending Jurassic basement rift faults. This compressive episode generated local topography and resulted in an influx of reworked chalks from the developing basin margins. The sequence was characterized by infill of local subbasins and the onlapping of reworked units onto local highs which resulted from the compression.

Tor A Middle: an extensional period is interpreted as commencing at the Tor A Middle/Tor A Lower boundary. This period resulted in the development of strong depositional controls defined by local fault bounded channels and broad fault-bounded highs. These controls were associated with movement along deep-seated N–S Permian faults and NW–SE oriented Jurassic faults. Continued regional basin subsidence drove the extension. Deposition during this period was characterized by infill of the developing local channels and broad lows by reworked chalks, derived from local highs and the basin margins. Deposition of reworked chalks reached its maximum during this period.

Tor A Upper: represents the onset of a tectonically quiet phase which continued through the end of Cretaceous period. This period is dominated by the infill of relict topography resulting from the previous extension, and is associated with declining rates of influx of redeposited chalks.

Ekofisk E layer. The beginning of Ekofisk Formation deposition is marked by a continuation of the tectonic stability that characterized the upper Tor. The Ekofisk E/Tor A Upper boundary is interpreted as representing a hiatus in chalk deposition associated with a possible collapse in the algal system. The lower Ekofisk E is characterized by purely pelagic deposition and high shale and silica levels which is interpreted to represent a significant shift in water conditions.

The Ekofisk E is a gradational as well as transitional unit. As deposition continued the influx of reworked deposits increased with an associated drop in silica and shale content.

Ekofisk D2 layer. The Ekofisk D2 represents a continuation of conditions associated with upper Ekofisk E deposits. The level of erosion and chalk re-working continues to increase and shale and silica levels continue to drop. This shift in depositional character is interpreted as being the result of renewed regional compression which began during late Ekofisk E deposition. Compression reached its apex within the Ekofisk D2 resulting in the development of a central up-lift zone on Ekofisk as well as the development of a number of local wrench-related highs. Reworked chalks were deposited into this system from the basin margins, primarily to the south of the present-day field. These deposits on-lapped the central highs and basin margins to the north, where sediments are thin or absent.

Ekofisk D1 layer. A relative relaxation of regional stresses took place during Ekofisk D1 deposition. This was associated with reversal of the wrench motion which characterized the Ekofisk D2. Left-lateral wrench motion along N–S orientated Permian basement faults and interaction with NW–SE Jurassic trend faults resulted in the development of pronounced extensional sub-basins. Deposition was dominated by debris flows of reworked material and re-sedimentation by local slumping. Intermediate pelagic deposition of thin low porosity/high silica Danian chalk punctuated these events. The basin axis continued to be south of the present-day structure resulting in thinning deposition to the north.

Ekofisk C layer. The onset of Ekofisk C deposition marked the beginning of a tectonically quiet period. This period was dominated by infill of relict topography and intermittent deposition of reworked sediments. A decrease in reworking is evident over time with a gradual increase in silica content. This was associated with greater pelagic deposition in the more silica-rich Danian water environment.

Ekofisk B layer. The Ekofisk B represented a continuation of trends developed during Ekofisk C deposition. During this period the direction of regional dip and the basin axis shifted from the southwest to the northeast.

Ekofisk A2 layer. The onset of Ekofisk A deposition was associated with rejuvenation of regional compressional stresses which resulted in further right-lateral wrenching. This was associated with strike-slip motion along controlling N–S orientated basement faults and inversion of NW–SE orientated faults. These forces resulted in the development of a number of local highs and lows which were further modified by redistribution of deep seated mobile salt. Deposition during this period was dominated by re-sedimentation of chalk though local slumping and debris flows.

Ekofisk A1 layer. Compression appears to have diminished during Ekofisk A1 deposition. Both reworked deposits and silica-rich pelagic deposits are characteristic of Ekofisk A1 deposition. These represent infill of the relict topography associated with the previous compressional pulse.

Model attributes

Field architecture and reservoir attributes were assembled within the 3D geological model. Grid cell size in the model is 36 metre square with a total of 365 rows and 251 columns for each horizon. The following criteria were considered in determining cell size: (1) single wellbore per cell; (2) optimize seismic horizon interpretation; (3) optimize utilization of seismic modeling results; and (4) model fault planes with sufficient detail. Seismic data were based on a 12.5 m sampling but because of software limitations it was not feasible to define a grid based on this spacing. The fourteen sequences defined in the model represent the geological layers, or flow units, present in the Ekofisk Field. The fourteen sequences were further subdivided into a total of 275 layers. These were designed to represent anticipated depositional relationships within each sequence and are defined by the structural and sedimentological model developed for the field. Optimum layer thickness within each sequence was determined by applying vertical variogram analysis to gamma ray, water saturation and porosity traces to determine the degree of variation in each of the attributes in the vertical direction.

The high resolution definition of the 3D geological model grid in vertical and lateral directions allows for a fairly fine resolution representation of the reservoir description and the ability to capture the intrinsic heterogeneity associated with the field. The final model contains over 20 million data cells. Each model cell is populated by 30 reservoir attributes which include porosity, petrofacies, water saturation, permeability and silica content. The geological model and the detailed 3D picture of the reservoir became the basis for up-scaling to a new full field 3D reservoir flow model.

Up-scaling

The geological model has captured the heterogeneity of the reservoir at a high degree of resolution. In the up-scaling process to the fluid flow model, preservation of heterogeneity is critical. Standard up-scaling techniques based on simple averages of permeability do not suffice; for this reason an alternative approach was employed, a technique based on fluid flow, or flux, within the geological model (Agarwal *et al.* 1997). This technique uses simplified flow simulations for calculating effective properties of complex, 3D reservoir models and addresses several of the drawbacks of standard methods. The method averages flow potential and does not require the user to choose a particular averaging technique. By emphasizing transmissibility over permeability it easily incorporates transmissibility multipliers for modelling flow barriers. In addition it ensures proper volumetric averaging of properties, such as porosity, across no-flow regions. The resulting fluid flow model of 40 thousand cells is defined using the same structural grids as the geological model such that geological units within the two models are identical. Comparisons have shown that the intrinsic heterogeneity of transmissibilities is preserved in the up-scaling process.

The direct link between the geological and reservoir models provides new opportunities for multi-disciplinary teams to work with consistent tools at all times and opportunities for multi-disciplinary resolution of well and reservoir performance issues. It also provides a feedback loop between geological and reservoir models using up-scaling and down-scaling technologies.

4D seismic monitoring

An ongoing evaluation of time-lapse 3D seismic for reservoir monitoring incorporates core studies, logging and 3D seismic/VSP data, coupled with seismic forward modeling linked to fluid flow simulations. Laboratory studies indicate that:

(1) changes in saturation have significant impacts on Ekofisk chalk seismic response; direct fluid substitution (oil to water) results in a 5–10% increase in seismic velocity associated with the change in fluid properties only. This 'fluid effect' is more pronounced in high porosity chalks (i.e. higher fluid volumes).

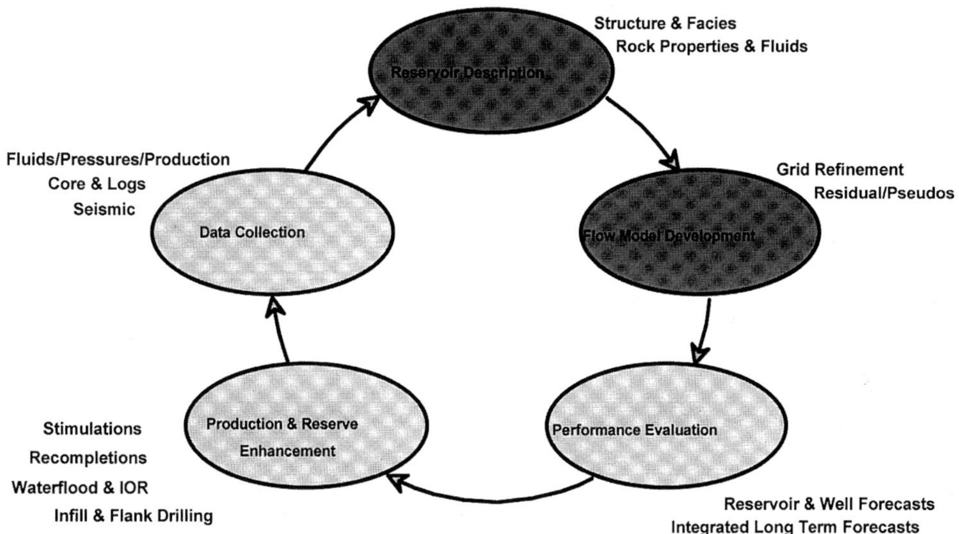

Fig. 10. Reserves optimization cycle as associated with the Ekofisk reservoir characterization project.

(2) Changes in reservoir pressure impact both the rock matrix and pore fluid as a result of the compressibilities of each. A decrease in reservoir pore pressure from initial pressures to present-day pressures results in a 10–15% increase in seismic velocity. This suggests a 'pressure effect' of 5–8% variation in seismic velocity at anticipated reservoir pressures.

(3) Changes in reservoir temperature affect both the rock matrix and pore fluid. The change in pore fluid temperature has the largest impact on seismic velocities. A decrease in temperature from average reservoir temperature to injected water temperatures results in a 5–10% increase in seismic velocity.

These effects act in concert to increase seismic velocity, going from a high pressure (6000 psi), high temperature (268°F), high-porosity oil-saturated state to a depleted water-swept state (low pressure, temperature, reduced porosity). The combined effect in reservoir intervals can be expected to result in a seismic velocity/impedance change as high as 50%. These laboratory results give encouragement to proceed with a time-lapse seismic acquisition program at Ekofisk.

Concluding remarks

An integrated high resolution geological model and a lower resolution reservoir flow model have been developed for the detailed planning of the redevelopment of the Ekofisk Field. A number of innovative techniques have been applied within the disciplines of geoscience, petrophysics and reservoir engineering resulting in integrated models which enable team-driven decisions to be made regarding reserves optimization (Fig. 10). The models have been developed using all data, information and knowledge available during the time span of the project and processes have been and are being put in place to ensure the continuous and rapid updating of the geologoical and fluid flow models as new data, information and knowledge becomes available.

The authors acknowledge permission to publish the above paper from Phillips Petroleum Company Norway and Co-venturers, including Fina Exploration Norway SCA, Norsk Agip A/S, Elf Petroleum Norge AS, Norsk Hydro A. S., Den norske stats oljeselskap a.s., TOTAL Norge A. S. and Saga Petroleum A. S. Special acknowledgement is given to the following individuals for their comments, suggestions and support throughout this work: B. J. Crabtree, L. R. Allen, D. J. Ellen, R. G. Harris, S. Tevik, S. Våge, G. Santellani, C. T. Feazel and G. H. Landa.

References

AGARWAL, B., ALLEN, L. R. & FARRELL, H. E. 1996. Ekofisk field reservoir characterisation: mapping permeability through facies and fracture intensity. SPE 35527 presented at the SPE European 3-D Reservoir Modelling Conference, Stavanger, Norway, 16–17 April 1996.

——, THOMAS, L. K., SYLTE, J. E. & O'MEARA, D. J. 1997. Reservoir characterisation of Ekofisk Field: a giant, fractured chalk reservoir in the norwegian North Sea – upscaling. Paper SPE 38875 presented at the 1997 SPE Annual Technical Conference, San Antonio, 5–8 October 1997.

BENTSEN, R. G. & ANLI, J. 1975. Using parameter estimation techniques to convert centrifuge data into a capillary–pressure curve. SPE 5036 1975.

HALLENBECK, L. D., SYLTE, J. E., EBBS, D. J. & THOMAS, L. K. 1989. Implementation of the Ekofisk full field waterflood. SPE 19838 presented at the 1989 SPE Annual Technical Conference, San Antonio, Texas, 8–11 October 1989.

LEVERETT, M. C. 1941. Capillary behavior in porous solids. *Transactions of the American Institute of Mining Engineers*, **142**, 152–169.

SYLTE, J. E., HALLENBECK, L. D. & THOMAS, L. K. 1988. Ekofisk Formation pilot waterflood. Paper SPE 18276 presented at the 1988 SPE Annual Technical Conference, Houston, Texas, 2–5 October 1988.

THOMAS, L. K., DIXON, T. N., EVANS, C. E. & VIENOT, M. E. 1987. Ekofisk Waterflood Pilot. *Journal of Petroleum Technology, February*, 221–232.

Reservoir management of the Wytch Farm Oil Field, Dorset, UK: providing options for growth into later field life

A. J. C. HOGG,[1] I. J. EVANS, P. F. HARRISON, T. MELING, G. S. SMITH, S. D. THOMPSON and G. F. T. WATTS

BP Exploration Operating Company Ltd, Blackhill Road, Holton Heath, Poole, Dorset, BH16 6LS, UK
[1] *Present address: BP Exploration Operating Co. Ltd, Farburn Industrial Estate, Dyce, Aberdeen AB21 7PB, UK (e-mail: hoggaj@bp.com)*

Abstract: The Wytch Farm Oil Field, currently on plateau, produces up to 110×10^3 BOPD, 17.6×10^6 SCF gas and 725 tonnes LPG per day. Original reserves are 450×10^6 BBL with a proven 230×10^6 BBL oil equivalent remaining. The Triassic fluvio–lacustrine Sherwood Sandstone, at 1535 mTVDSS (true vertical depth, subsea), is the largest and most prolific reservoir. Approximately half the reserves are in an offshore extension being developed by extended reach drilling (ERD) at step-outs of up to 10.1 km from onshore Poole Harbour. Projects to increase reserves, extend plateau and slow decline include: additional ERD wells; infill drilling; miscible gas injection; and pattern water flooding of the low nett : gross Upper Sherwood all whilst maintaining reservoir pressure.

Reservoir description is central to realizing these opportunities for growth. Structural uncertainty has been reduced through acquisition of the first transition-zone 3D seismic survey in the UK. An extensive RFT (repeat formation test) and production log database has been acquired in the onshore and ERD wells. These dynamic data, together with static data from core and outcrop studies, and >21 km of ERD formation evaluation logs, are used to develop a high-resolution, fluvio–lacustrine sequence architecture of the Sherwood. The deterministic model enhances predictability of flow barriers, baffles and high permeability intervals. This understanding of fluid flow and recovery provides the framework for economic evaluation, which, with clear communication of uncertainty across disciplines, is the key to successful management of the reservoir into later field life.

The Wytch Farm Field is located in Dorset, southern England, within onshore licence blocks PL089 and PL259, and extends offshore into P534 (Fig. 1). It contains an estimated 450×10^6 BBL oil-equivalent reserves expected to be recovered over 35 years. The principal reservoir is the fluvial Triassic Sherwood Sandstone Group which contains about 416×10^6 BBL reserves at 1585 m true vertical depth subsea (mTVDSS). There are two minor reservoirs; the Bridport Sandstone, a Lower Jurassic shallow marine sandstone holding some 31×10^6 BBL reserves at 900 mTVDSS; and the Frome Clay Limestone, a Middle Jurassic shelly limestone, with an estimated 4×10^6 BBL reserves at 810 mTVDSS.

The Sherwood Sandstone was deposited in an E–W Early Triassic rift system, which developed as a result of extension along a pre-existing Variscan thrust front. The sandstone rests unconformably on the playa mudrocks of the Permian Aylesbeare Group and is conformably overlain by the playa mudrock of Mercia Mudstone Group caprock. The field structure comprises a series of northerly dipping fault blocks formed during early Cretaceous extension (Fig. 2) (Hawkes *et al.* 1998). The source rocks are Middle and Lower Lias (Lower Jurassic) mudrocks which are mature in blocks downfaulted to the south of the Purbeck–Isle of Wight disturbance (Selley & Stonley 1987). Oil generation and accumulation began when thermal subsidence in the late Cretaceous gave rise to mature source kitchens in the hanging walls of the extensional faults. The reservoir description of the Sherwood Sandstone is discussed in Dranfield *et al.* (1987), Bowman *et al.* (1993), McClure *et al.* (1995) and Hogg *et al.* (1996). Reservoir parameters and fluid properties are given for the Sherwood Sandstone in Bowman *et al.* (1993).

The field was discovered in 1974 and since then development has taken place in three stages (Fig. 3). The discovery and early field history are outlined by Colter & Havard (1981). The development of the onshore field, appraisal and early planning for extended reach drilling (ERD) are discussed in McClure *et al.* (1995). During Stage I, oil was first produced from the Bridport Sandstone reservoir in 1979, reaching 6×10^3 BBL per day by 1984 (Fig. 4). Development of the onshore section of the Sherwood (Stage II) began in 1984 and when fully commissioned in 1990, the field production was some 60×10^3 BBL per day, 500 tonnes of LPG per day and 10×10^6 SCF of gas per day. Stage III, which began in 1993, saw the development of the offshore extension of the Sherwood Sandstone reservoir via a series of ERD wells drilled up to 10.1 km from drill-sites located onshore. The major pressure support mechanism for the Sherwood Reservoir is bottom-water drive, with water injection into the underlying aquifer. The field now has 10 well-sites with 69 production and 26 injection wells producing, at plateau, 110×10^3 BOPD, 725 tonnes of LPG and 17.6×10^6 SCF gas per day. Current recovery factors are estimated to be 50% in the Lower Sherwood Sandstone and 35% in the poorer quality Upper Sherwood Sandstone reservoir.

Since development of the offshore extension began in 1993, management of the Sherwood Sandstone reservoir has aimed at increasing reserves and extending field plateau. The purpose of this paper is to show how this has been achieved through continuous improvement of the reservoir description, and by improved access to reserves made possible by technological advances in ERD. By integrating the static with dynamic reservoir data acquired in ERD wells, horizontal well trajectory

Hogg, A. J. C., Evans, I. J., Harrison, P. F., Meling, T., Smith, G. S., Thompson, S. D. & Watts, G. F. T. 1999. Reservoir management of the Wytch Farm Oil Field, Dorset, UK: providing options for growth into later field life. *In*: Fleet, A. J. & Boldy, S. A. R. (eds) *Petroleum Geology of Northwest Europe: Proceedings of the 5th Conference*, 1157–1172. © Petroleum Geology '86 Ltd. Published by the Geological Society, London.

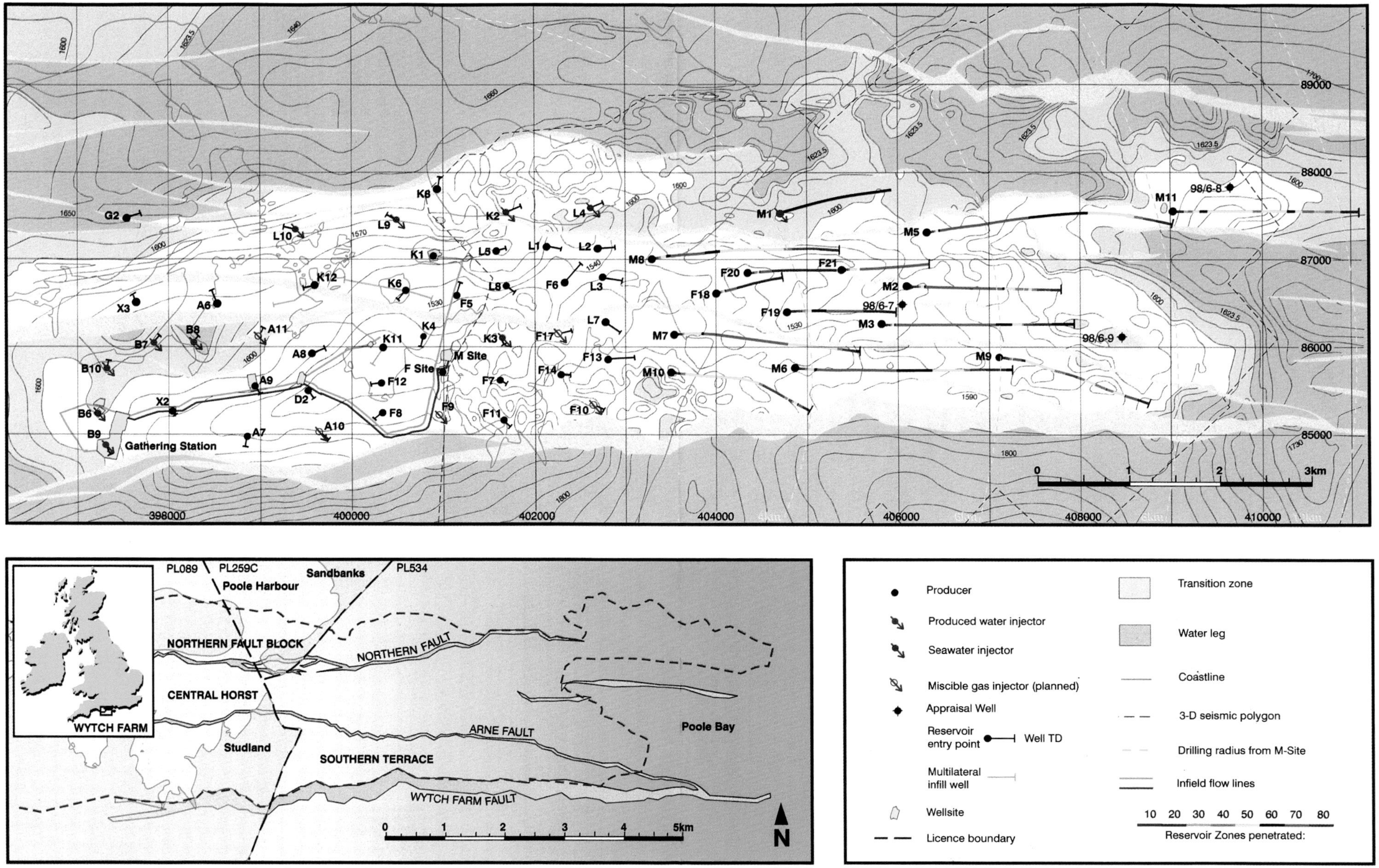

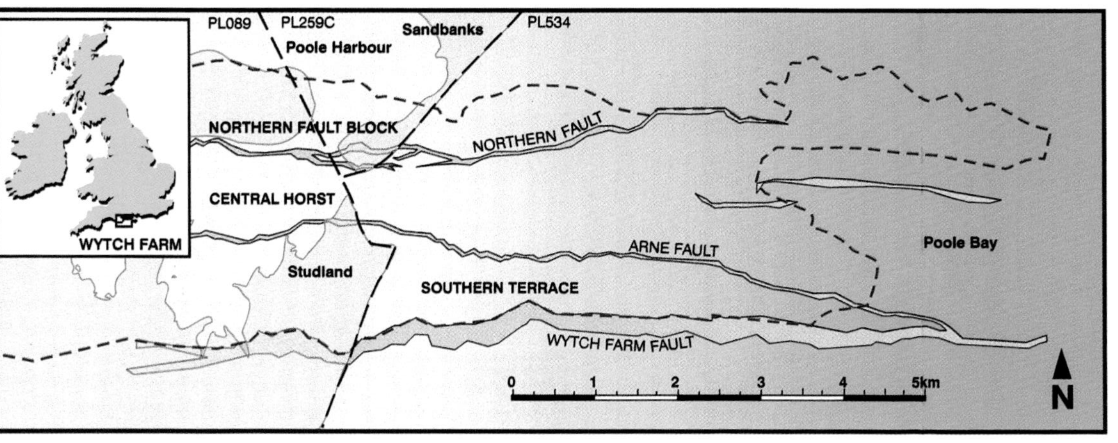

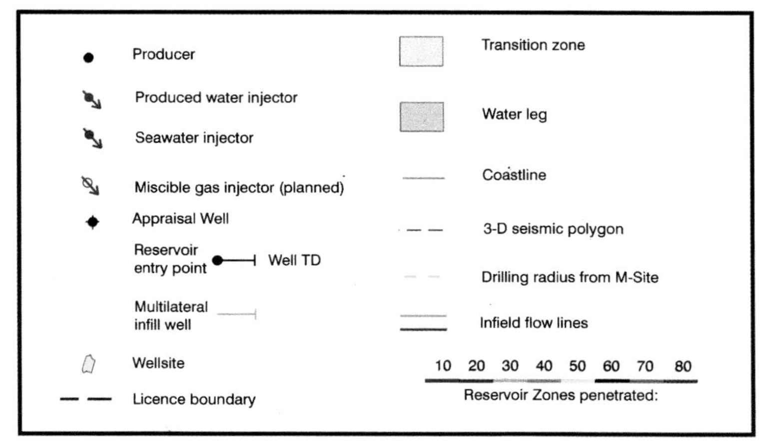

Fig. 1. Location map of the Wytch Farm Oilfield showing the reservoir structure at Top Sherwood Sandstone with well-sites, infield pipelines and the trajectories of appraisal and development wells within the reservoir. The area of the 1994 3D seismic survey is outlined in dashed red. The extended reach wells are colour coded to show the reservoir zones penetrated by each wellbore. The inset map shows the location of the Wytch Farm Field together with the main geographical and structural features.

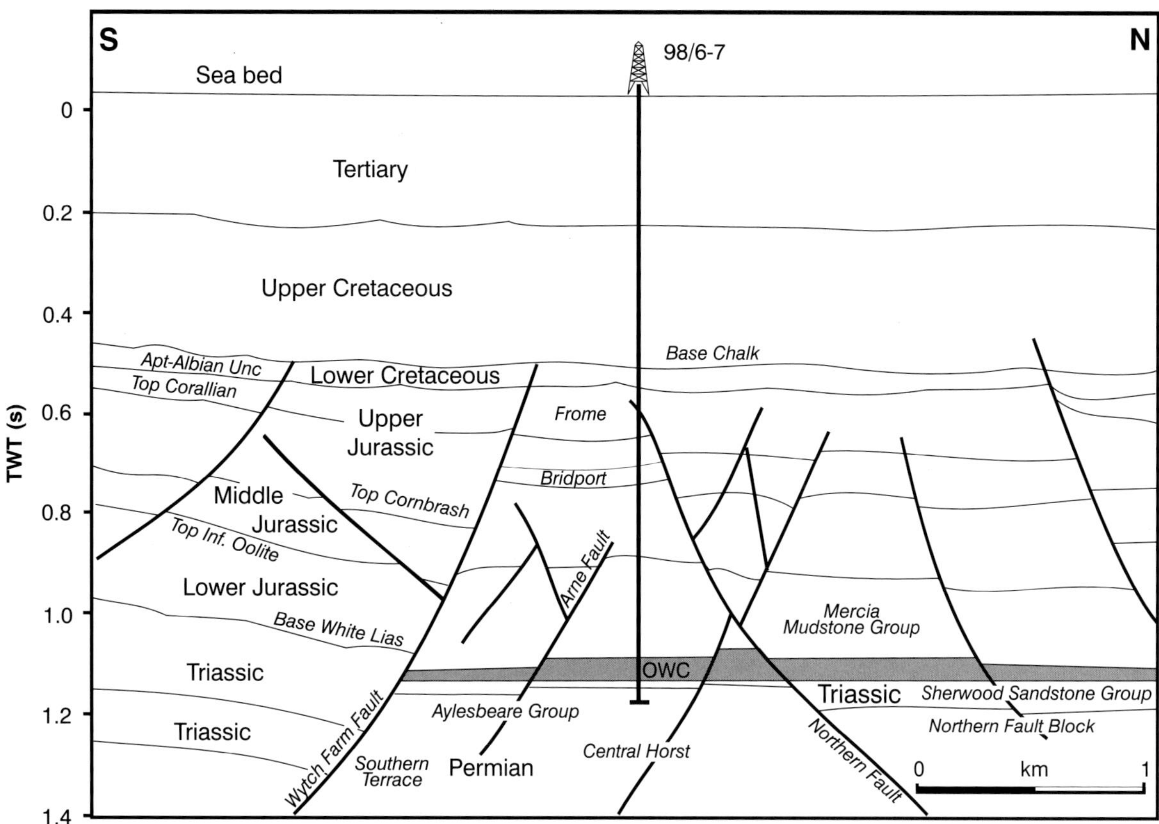

Fig. 2. Geoseismic section, N–S line BP86-196, though appraisal Well 98/6-7 illustrating the structure and stratigraphy of the Wytch Farm Oilfield.

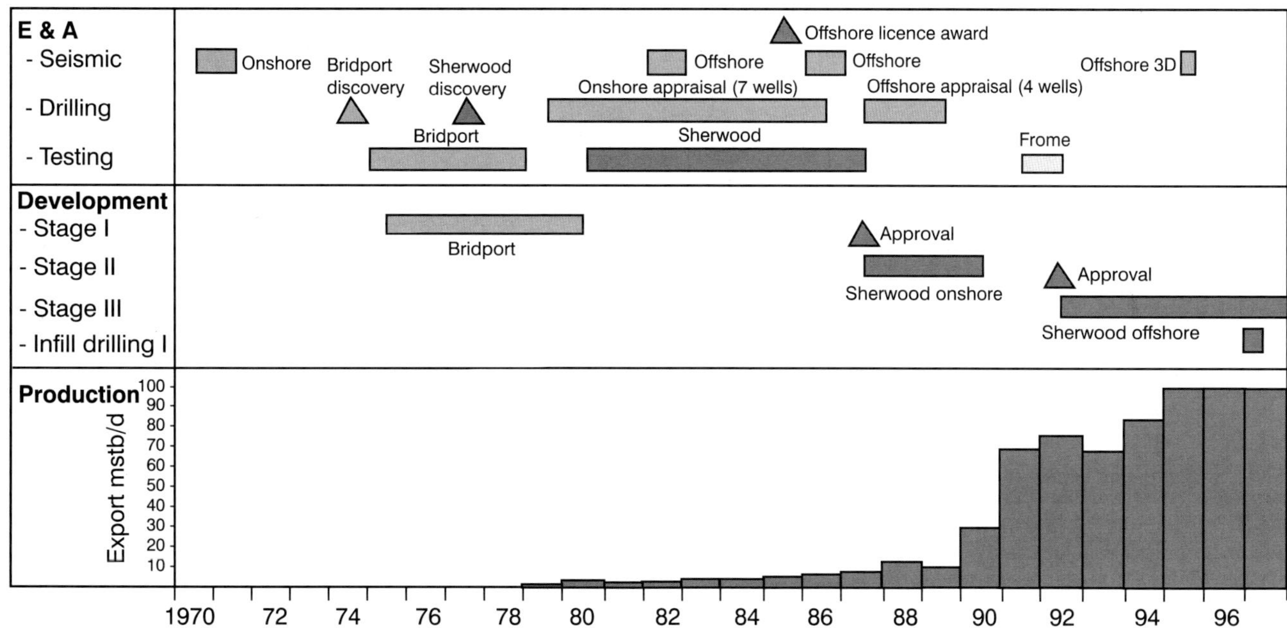

Fig. 3. Development history and production profile of the Wytch Farm Oilfield, Dorset, UK, shown against year since 1970.

design has evolved both to increase reserves recovery and prolong well life. In addition, increased resolution of the reservoir description and understanding of field performance have provided opportunities for growth into later field life. Improved oil recovery (IOR) schemes such as infill drilling, pattern flooding and water-alternating-gas (WAG) injection aim to bring ultimate field recovery to 60% and beyond. The paper also presents new information on calibration of LWD (logging while drilling) logs using core and wireline data and on fluid mapping from tracer breakthrough data.

Reservoir description

Reservoir description has concentrated firstly on reserves definition and, secondly, on providing a robust framework for field development projects. This has been achieved by improved

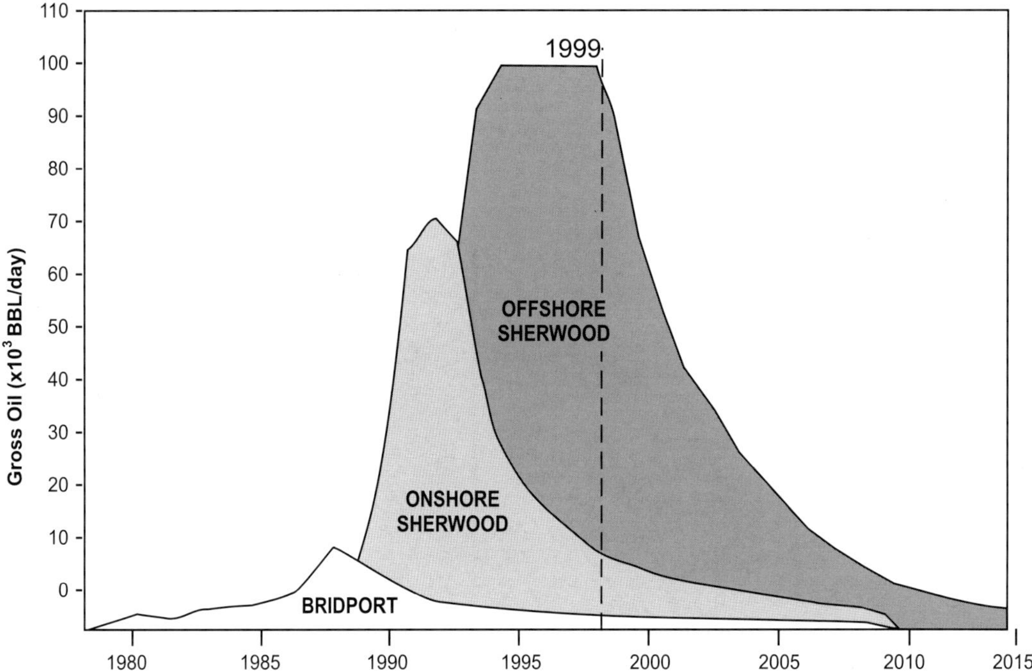

Fig. 4. Wytch Farm Field production profile showing the relative contribution of each development phase.

structural resolution from an offshore 3D seismic survey and development of a consistent sedimentological model across the on- and offshore sectors of the field. Sedimentological studies were focused on the Upper Sherwood Sandstone. These aimed to improve the stratigraphic understanding of the eastern part of the reservoir, thereby aiding positioning of ERD wells, and to model the permeability architecture of the western part of the reservoir prior to miscible gas flooding.

Field structure

The Sherwood Sandstone reservoir is contained within an elongate terrace bounded to the north and south by east–west striking normal faults (Figs 1 and 2) and to the east and west by gradual structural flexing giving a broad anticlinal feature. Faulting is all post-depositional and dominated by Early Cretaceous east–west striking faults. The reservoir may be considered as three panels: a Northern Fault Block, Central Horst and Southern Terrace (Figs 1 and 2). Dips in the offshore extension are generally not greater than 2°, and usually <1° to the east. The original oil–water contact is at a uniform depth of 1623.5 mTVDSS across the field. Oil column thickness is, therefore, controlled by structural height and is up to 120 m true vertical thickness (TVT) in the Central Horst but feathers-out through dip closure to the eastern and western rims of the reservoir.

The terrain around Wytch Farm is challenging for seismic acquisition and this is reflected in the diverse and rather patchy seismic database. Seismic quality is generally poor as a result of the variable land and transition zone conditions combined with stringent environmental and social constraints on acquisition which needed to be considered along with purely technical objectives. Over a third of the field is covered by 2D data with a spacing from 200 m to about 1 km. Seismic sections dating back to 1973 are still in use. Identification of the Top Sherwood reflector is not possible on any of the 2D data partly because of the transitional acoustic contrast and partly because of the low spatial resolution. Reservoir structural maps up to 1992 were generated by isopaching from the overlying Base White Lias event (Fig. 2) giving an accuracy of less than ±40 m. This represented considerable uncertainty when predicting oil column thicknesses of 120 m or less. In these circumstances effective development of the field using ERD technology would have carried high economic risk.

Consequently, the first transitional 3D in the UK was shot in 1994 covering about half the Wytch Farm Field (Fig. 1) (Thompson & Bligh 1995). Shallow water data (<12 m water depth) were acquired using a grid of hydrophone receivers on cables laid on the seabed and overshot with an airgun array. Each patch was laid, shot and removed in 3 h and gave 1 km^2 of 16-fold data. In transitional and land areas the patch was modified to include vibroseis and dynamite sources, with marsh phone and geophone receivers. This arrangement gave great operational flexibility and minimized disturbance to other users of the area. In total, 37 ‘patches’ were acquired giving 34 km^2 of full-fold coverage data.

Overall quality of the 3D data is superior to the 2D. Despite a slight decrease in temporal resolution (as a result, in part, of the cable ghost in deeper waters), the spatial resolution is much higher, multiple supression is more effective and the Top Sherwood reflector was clearly identified for the first time (Fig. 5). Depth conversion was achieved through a simple polynomial equation modified to reflect changes in the velocity and overburden thickness. Accuracy is ±5 m over the crest of the field and ±10 m elsewhere, except where the quality is adversly affected by low fold and residual multiples. Faults with throws as low as ±5 m can be detected and have a spatial uncertainty of about ±50 m (4 traces). In addition to the dominant east–west striking Early Cretaceous fault system, a fainter WNW–ESE trend is also revealed reflecting older underlying Hercynian strike-slip faults. Detailed analysis of the east–west striking faults shows multi-phase formation. Early formed segments are breached with relay ramps by the later phase of extension.

The interval resolution of the seismic data was determined through acoustic impedance inversion and comparison at the wells. Results show excellent correlation between the seismic and well traces (Fig. 5). However, seismic quality is very variable over the field, particularly under the transition and land areas in the West. In addition, the bottom cable acquisition technique used in the offshore areas causes variation in the

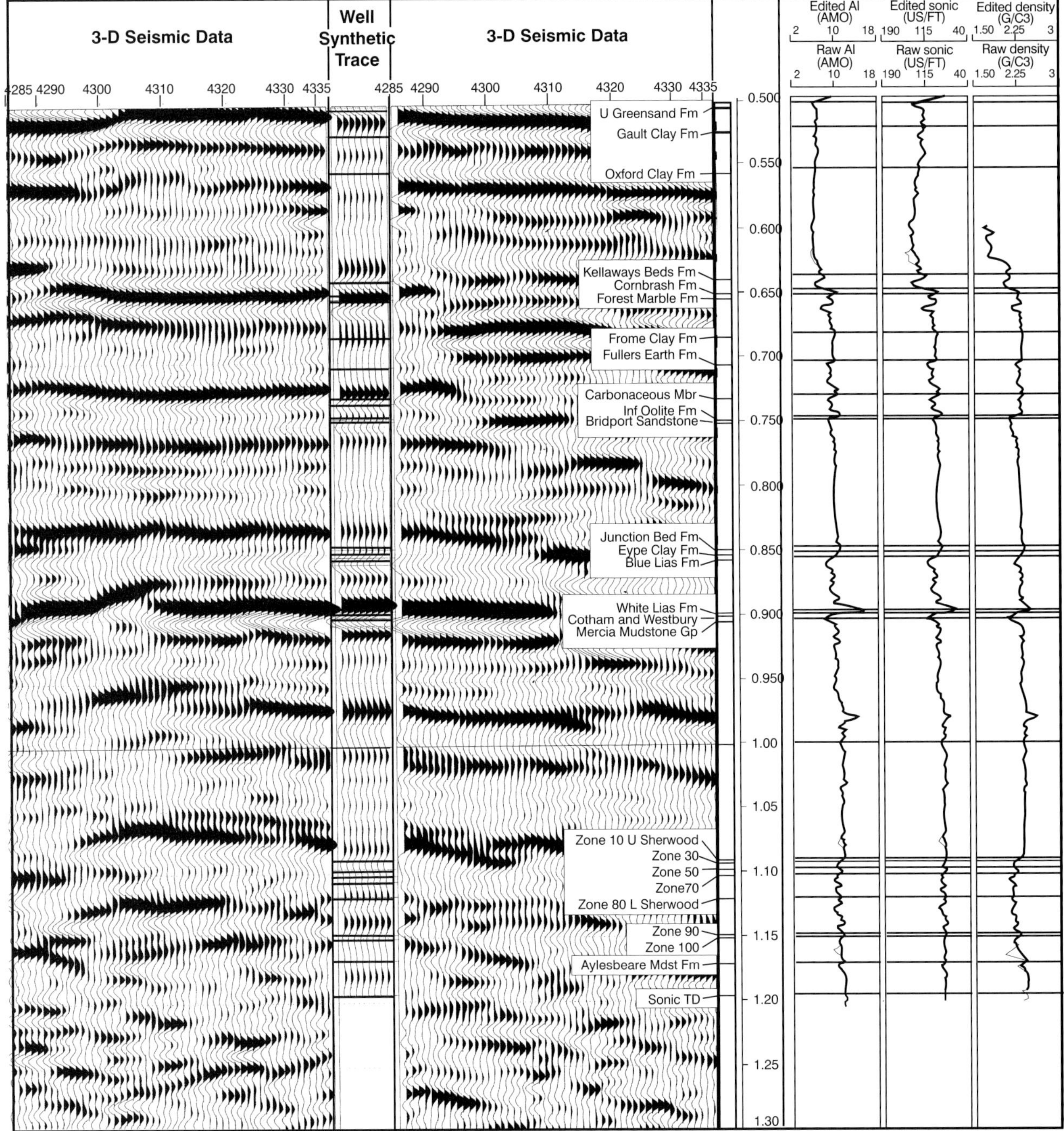

Fig. 5. Correlation between 3D seismic and well traces at appraisal Well 98/6-7. Formation tops relate to horizons marked on log and synthetic traces.

seismic phase with water depth which cannot be corrected. Individual channel bodies and packages of channels in reservoir zones are <10 m thick, so consistent stratigraphic resolution of reservoir properties using seismic data is not possible.

Significant primary structural changes were evident on the 3D data compared with the old 2D interpretation. The Arne Fault, which bisects the field (Fig. 1), extends much further into the offshore area giving 30 m thicker reservoir at the crest of the structure. This major change is largely associated with statics problems around the entrance to Poole Harbour where acquisition difficulties in the transition zone have clearly affected the 2D data. Further readjustments to the northern and southern terraces resulted in a total volumetric increase in the reservoir of more than 100×10^6 BBL oil. Operationally, an immediate result of the 3D data was to redirect an ERD well north of the Arne Fault (Fig. 1). This decision resulted in a well with an initial rate of 20×10^3 BBL which alone nearly paid for the entire 3D operation (Thompson & Bligh 1995).

Reservoir architecture

An extensive database of over 25 km of log data from 65 wells, 26 cored wells (including core from five ERD wells), and excellent outcrop of the stratigraphically equivalent succession in largely accessible sea cliff 100 km to the west has allowed a high-resolution sequence stratigraphic description of the reservoir to be constructed

The sedimentology of the Sherwood Sandstone reservoir is discussed by McKie *et al.* (1998). The interval comprises arkosic sandstones and mudrocks deposited in a variety of fluvial, aeolian, lacustrine and floodplain environments. Within this a number of facies 'cycles' can be identified:

(i) a 'first-order' trend over the entire Sherwood section evolving from perennial braidplain to sheet flood to ephemeral lacustrine conditions. This culminated in deposition of the Mercia Mudstone Group and reflects a long-term reduction in slope, or rise in base level.
(ii) 'second-order' cycles defined by five areally widespread floodplain deposits (up to 10 m thick) with minimal development of fluvial sandstones. These can be correlated into lacustrine heterolithics to the northwest, each becoming successively more mud-rich upwards through the stratigraphy. These floodplain deposits bracket more sand-rich fluvial intervals, which have successively finer and narrower grain size ranges, and show a greater proportion of lacustrine (and aeolian) facies and preservation of floodplain deposits. These second-order cycles form the basis of the reservoir zonation.
(iii) 'third-order' cycles characterized by thin (<2 m), areally widespread floodplain/lacustrine horizons. Within the fluvial deposits between the third-order floodplain horizons, incised multistorey channel-fill deposits occur. Locally, these rework earlier floodplain deposits and contain coarse-grained sandstones with abundant pebbles and rip-up clasts of calcrete and mudstone. They are the principal producing sandstones in the Upper Sherwood.

At outcrop, the stratigraphically equivalent Otter Sandstone Formation shows comparable evolutionary patterns with sandbody geometries that are sufficiently similar to form useful analogues for the subsurface. The second order cycles in the Wytch Farm reservoir may be correlated to this exposure via the widespread floodplain horizons. The overall stratigraphic evolution of the Sherwood can, therefore, be viewed as the product of three 'nested' cycles of climate/base-level change (McKie *et al.* 1998). The duration of these cycles is unknown as a result of the lack of biostratigraphic control.

The recognition of a hierarchy of climatically driven cycles within the reservoir permits high-resolution correlation and the recognition of subtle changes in sandbody geometry and connectivity within successive cycles. This has allowed a fine scale reservoir model to be derived in which the deterministic components are maximized and the type of analogue data used to model the stochastic elements is tightly constrained. The reservoir zonation is based on the second order floodplain deposits (Zones 20, 40, 60 and 90) which define 1–10 m thick vertical transmissibility barriers enclosing reservoir sandstone intervals (Zones 10, 30, 50, 70, 80 and 100) (Figs 6 and 7). Heterogeneities with the sand-prone zones are provided by discontinuous floodplain/lacustrine deposits, channel abandonment plugs and lag deposits of reworked calcrete which are variably cemented. The sand-prone sections are characterized by:

(i) Zone 10; a 10 m thick peri-lacustrine section of sandflat and lacustrine heterolithic deposits. Lacustrine deposits encroach successively southeastwards, but are locally eroded by the sandflat deposits resting sharply above.
(ii) Zone 30; a 7 m thick interval of sheet flood sandstones interbedded with mud-prone floodplain and lacustrine deposits. Two incised fluvial systems are found in this zone.
(iii) Zone 50; a 12 m thick section of channel-fills, sheet flood deposits and floodplain mudrocks, with locally developed patches of aeolian sand which can be mapped between wells. At least five incised fluvial systems dissect this interval, with well developed calcrete palaeosols on their interfluves.
(iv) Zone 60; a 5 m thick floodplain mudrock onshore but with increasing frequency of channel fills eastwards towards the offshore.
(v) Zone 70; a 20 m thick section of floodplain mudrocks and sand-prone channel-fills.
(vi) Zones 80 and 100; 60 and 30 m thick, respectively comprising high net : gross, vertically and laterally amalgamated, multistorey channel-fill sandstones capped by variably preserved floodplain deposits.

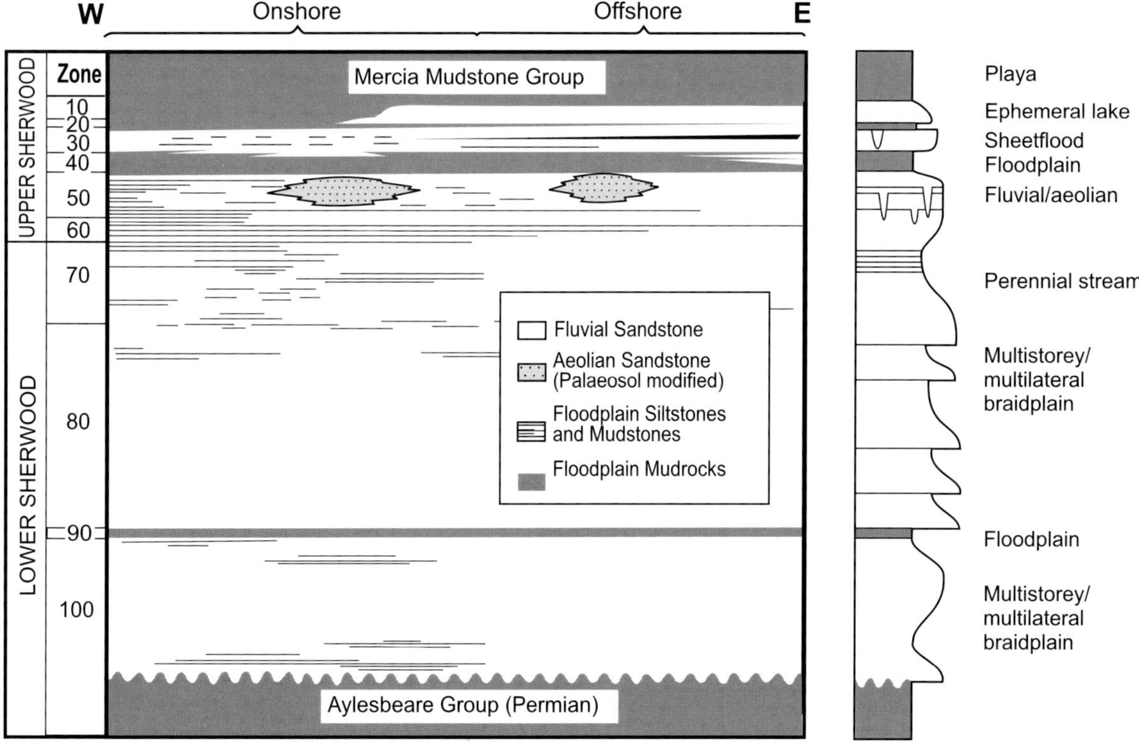

Fig. 6. Summary stratigraphy and zonation of the Sherwood Sandstone in the Wytch Farm area (reproduced from McKie *et al.* in press). At Wytch Farm the succession is informally divided into an Upper Sherwood comprising reservoir Zones 10 to 60 and a Lower Sherwood comprising Zones 70 to 100.

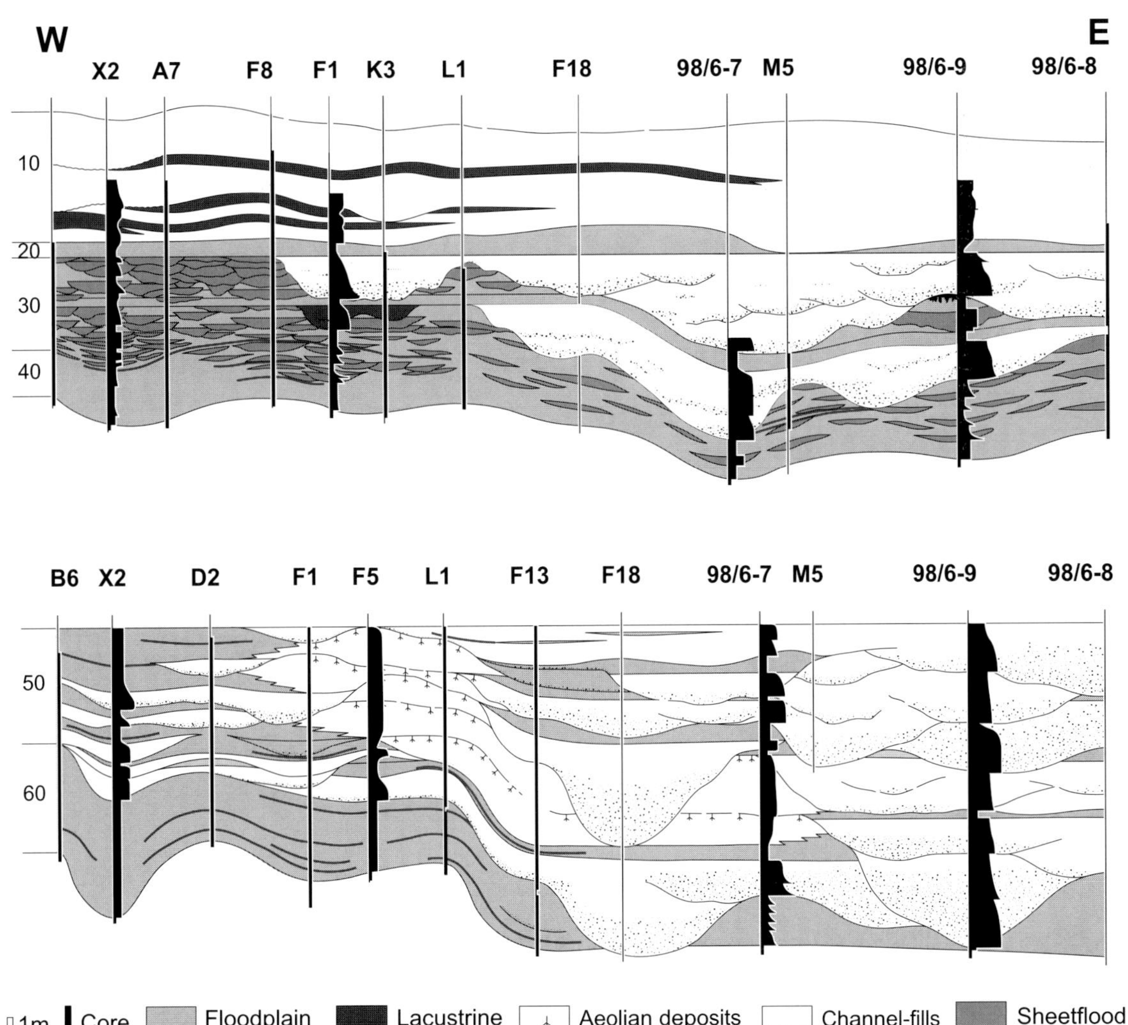

Fig. 7. West–east cross-sections with grain size profiles for selected wells, showing the facies architecture of the Sherwood Sandstone reservoir: (**a**) Zones 10 to 40 and (**b**) Zones 50 to 60 (adapted from McKie *et al.* 1998).

The succession is informally divided into the Upper Sherwood comprising reservoir Zones 10 to 60 and the Lower Sherwood Sandstone Zones 70 to 100.

Reservoir quality

The reservoir quality of the Sherwood Sandstone is primarily a function of grain size and detrital clay content with localized calcite and anhydrite cements. Overall, quality deteriorates up-reservoir because of a decrease in maximum grain size, sandbody thickness and poorer connectivity. The Lower Sherwood Sandstone has a mean porosity of 18% and permeability often >1.5 D. In contrast, average porosity in the Upper Sherwood Sandstone ranges from 10 and 15% with permeability about 150 mD. This results in a strongly layered reservoir with K_v/K_h (vertical/horizontal permeability) ratios of around 0.01 in the Lower Sherwood compared with 0.001 in the Upper Sherwood Sandstone (Bowman *et al.* 1993). More detail on the reservoir quality is given in Hogg *et al.* (1996).

Formation evaluation

The onshore part of the field was developed using conventional sub-vertical wells. These were logged using the full suite of open hole tools available at the time. Most wells were drilled using water-based muds. This, together with the high formation water salinities (120 000–130 000 mg l^{-1} chloride) made laterologs the resistivity tools of choice. Approximately half of the onshore development wells were cored leading to excellent core calibration of the log-derived rock properties. The offshore part of the field was appraised by 4 vertical wells in which conventional open hole logs were run and the full reservoir interval was cored. Development of the offshore reservoir has been exclusively by ERD wells which typically have inclinations of >80° through the reservoir section.

The ERD wells penetrate three main pay sands (Zones 30, 50 and 70) which are separated by mudstone barriers (Zones 20, 40 and 60). These sands have no unique log character or biostratigraphic signature which would allow unequivocal interpretation of the reservoir zones. Neither are they resolvable using seismic data. To 'geosteer' these wells to optimize the reservoir trajectory, a full suite of logging while drilling (LWD) tools is deployed. The objective is to determine the zonation by integrating all available data, to give a consistent interpretation during drilling. The reservoir zonation is determined by correlation of the LWD logs with adjacent wells, by 'counting down' through the stratigraphy and by using constraints from seismic data. When faults are encountered it is difficult to identify which sandstone or mudstone zones are juxtaposed; often several models are equally valid. After the well has been completed, an integrated interpretation is made using all available static (cuttings, LWD, core, seismic) and dynamic (repeat formation tester (RFT), mud losses and production log) data. Even at this stage several different interpretations are possible. The result of this approach has been a better understanding of reservoir architecture and flow behaviour which is essential to optimize location of wells, field management strategy and plan future development options.

In early wells, LWD density, neutron porosity, resistivity and gamma-ray data together with MWD downhole torque,

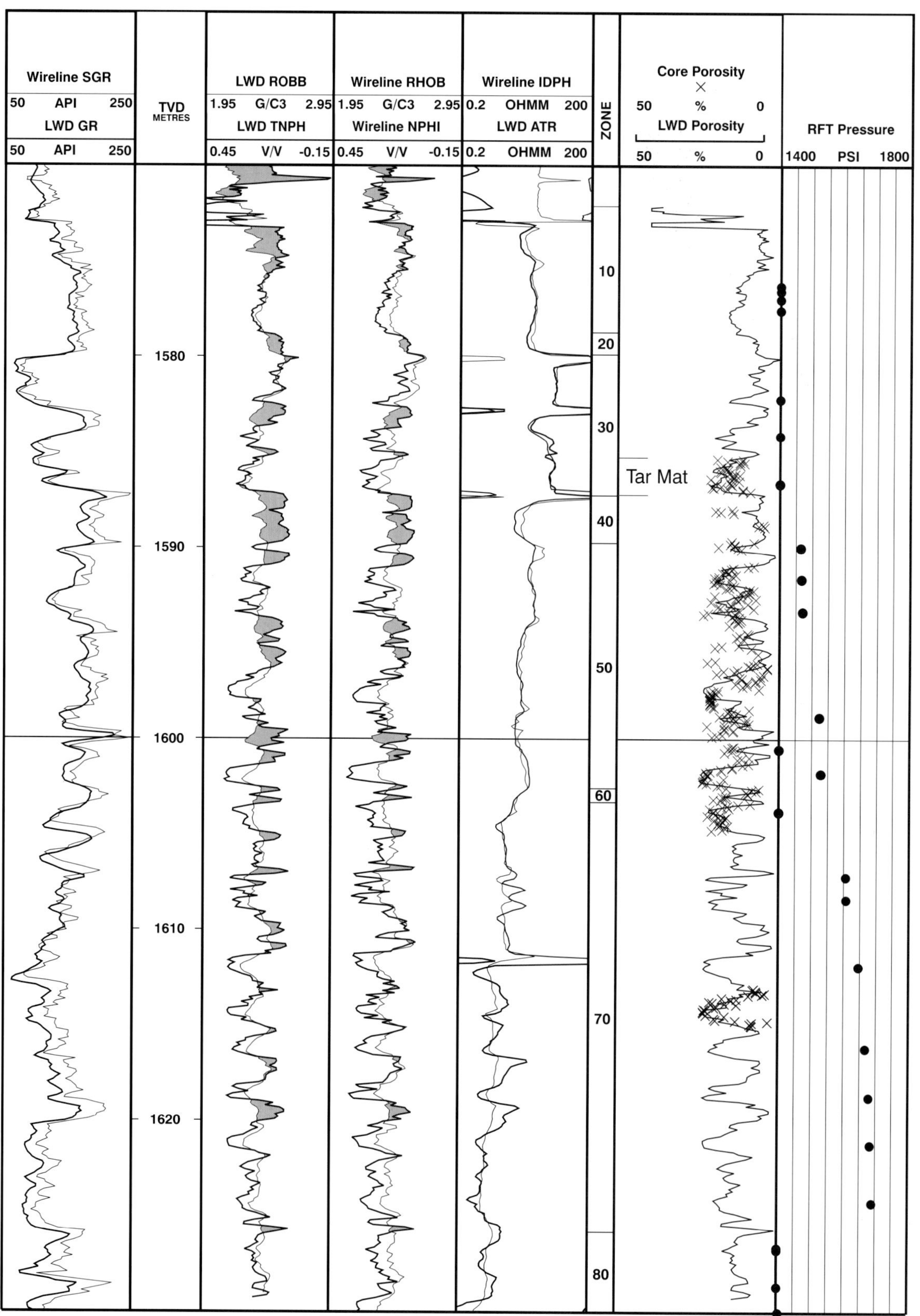

Fig 8. Reservoir zonation of the Sherwood Sandstone illustrated by log and core from pilot hole L98/6-M09. The core was taken at 77° inclination at a step-out of 6150 m, a record for the industry. The hole was subsequently logged using LWD and with drillpipe-conveyed wireline logs while running RFTs. Results, calibrated to the core, indicate excellent agreement between the two modes of data acquisition.

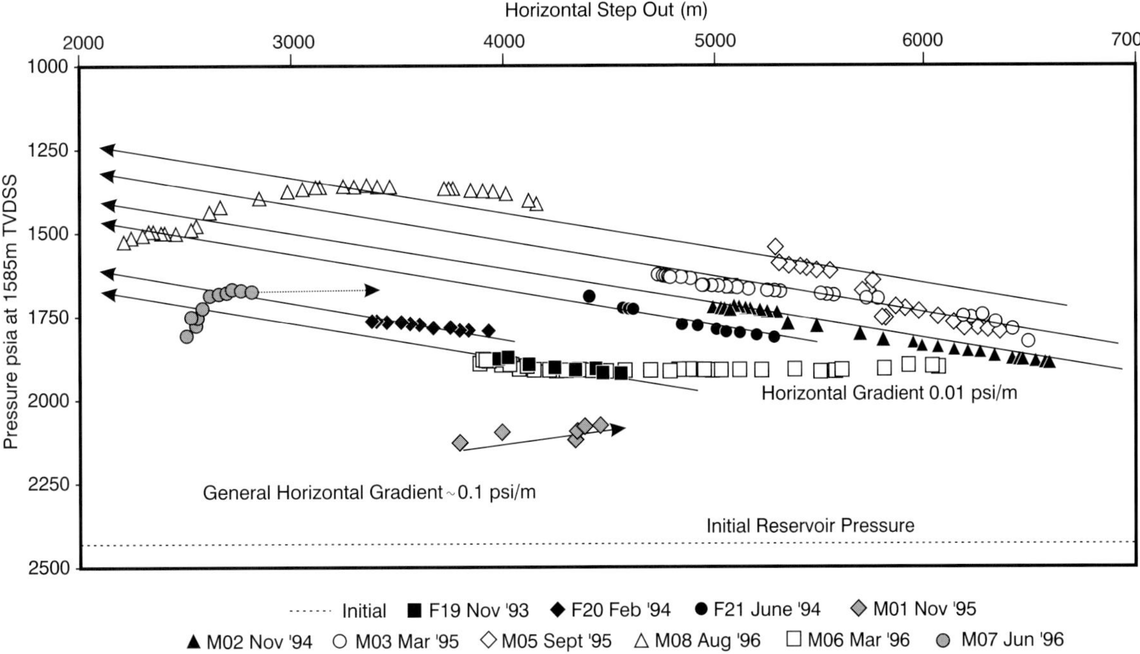

Fig. 9. Plot of RFT pressure data against easting for Wytch Farm ERD wells. For further discussion see Smith & Hogg (1997).

weight-on-bit, 3-axis shock and directional data were routinely recorded throughout the $8\frac{1}{2}$ in. reservoir section. In later wells, data acquisition has become more sophisticated as greater precision in well trajectory has been demanded. The LWD suite run currently comprises:

(i) Azimuthal Density–Neutron (ADN[1]) giving bulk density readings for 4 quadrants and average neutron porosity. The ADN[1] is also used to provide detailed bed-boundary information on which to steer the well.
(ii) Compensated Dual Resistivity (CDR[1]) giving phase shift and attenuation measurements of resistivity using an electromagnetic propagation technique.
(iii) Spectral Gamma Ray (SGR[1]) giving U, Th, K and total gamma-ray curves.
(iv) The Geosteering Tool (GST[1]) to measure azimuthal gamma-ray inclination and resistivity.
(v) Dynamic performance of the reservoir is monitored by RFT in each well and production logging where field operations permit.

Cores have been cut in five ERD wells (L98/6-F18, M1, M5, M6 and M9) (Fig. 1). These provide an independent check of the validity of the density log data obtained in the vertical and horizontal wells. To check the calibration of the other LWD logs, compared with the conventional open hole wireline logs, both sets of logs were acquired in the high angle pilot hole L98/6-M9 (M9). In addition, this well was cored and RFT measurements were obtained. A comparison of LWD and wireline logs from M9 is shown in Fig. 8. Within the oil zone, the conventional and LWD logs are practically identical. Both sets of logs give porosity estimates which match the core data closely. The data gathered during drilling have therefore proved to be of sufficient quality to allow petrophysical evaluation without the need to run drillpipe conveyed open hole logs after drilling.

Porosity is calculated from the density log using matrix densities interpolated from core measurements. This interpolation is guided by the depositional model for each zone. Water saturation is calculated from the shallowest resistivity measurement using an Archie clean sand equation. Using the shallow resistivity log minimizes the influence of adjacent beds within the horizontal wellbore. Since the logs are recorded during drilling, invasion effects on the logs are very limited. Formation water resistivity (R_w) is very low owing to the high salinity of the pore fluids. There is evidence for slight variation in R_w across the field which may be related to variations in the evaporite content of the upper part of the reservoir.

Reservoir pressure

RFT surveys have been central to integrating the static and dynamic reservoir descriptions. Production logs in very long reservoir sections (up to 2.7 km) at extreme step-out have proved expensive because of the cost of both deployment and deferred oil in these high-rate wells. Access for production logging has also been limited becaue of other site activities such as drilling and workovers. Consequently, RFT surveys have been included in all ERD wells except L98/6-F18 (F18). Pressure measurements have been made at 250 locations in 10 wells, and at departures up to 7.4 km (Fig. 9). Further detail regarding operational experience and acquisition can be found in Jariwala *et al.* (1996) and Lenn *et al.* (1996). The data are used to confirm the geological interpretations of the reservoir layering and faulting made from LWD log data in individual wells. Surveys run as wells are drilled have allowed the response of the offshore Sherwood reservoir to be monitored over the first three years of production (Smith & Hogg 1997).

Production logging

Production logs have been run in two ERD wells, F18 and L98/6-F21 (F21) (Fig. 10). Operational details are given in Jariwala *et al.* (1996) and Lenn *et al.* (1996). Both wells were drilled in the Central Horst with trajectories consisting of a single downwards penetration of the Upper reservoir, with the main high-angle section in Lower Sherwood Zones 70 and 80.

[1] Mark of Schlumberger Anadrill.

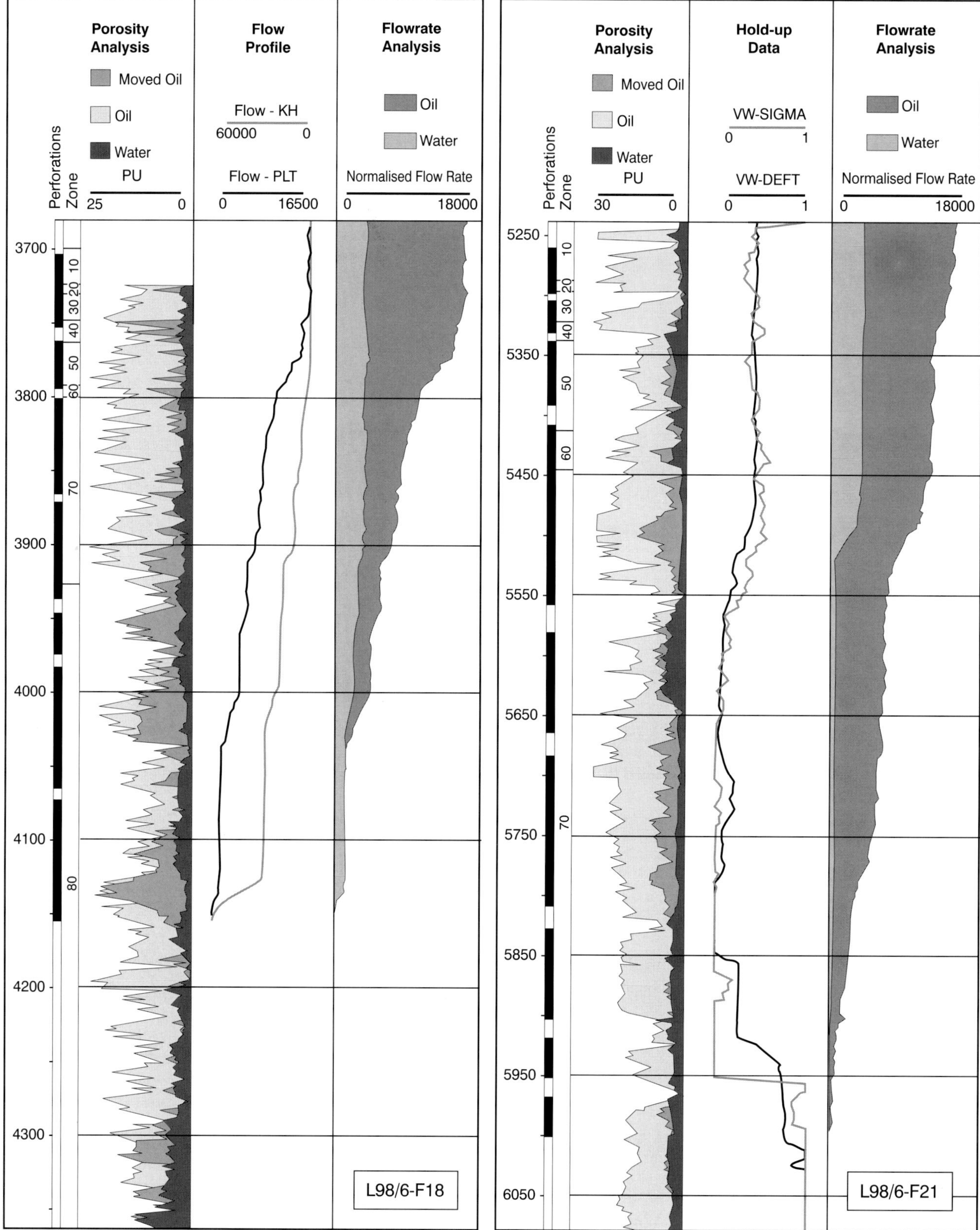

Fig. 10. Production logging data from Wytch Farm extended reach Wells L98/6-F18 and L98/6-F21. For further information on the logging suite and operational details see Jariwala *et al.* (1996) and Lenn *et al.* (1996).

F18, having the shortest step-out and tail section drilled below the oil–water contact, was logged first. Objectives were to establish inflow profile along the wellbore, nature of water entry, and degree of oil–water contact movement. F21 was logged with the specific objective of identifying intervals responsible for the early water cut development in this well.

Tracers

To help understand the connectivity of the Upper Sherwood reservoir in advance of pattern water flooding (see below) tritium tracers were injected into Well L97/10-A10 (A10) in September, 1994 and into Well L98/6-F17 (F17) in August,

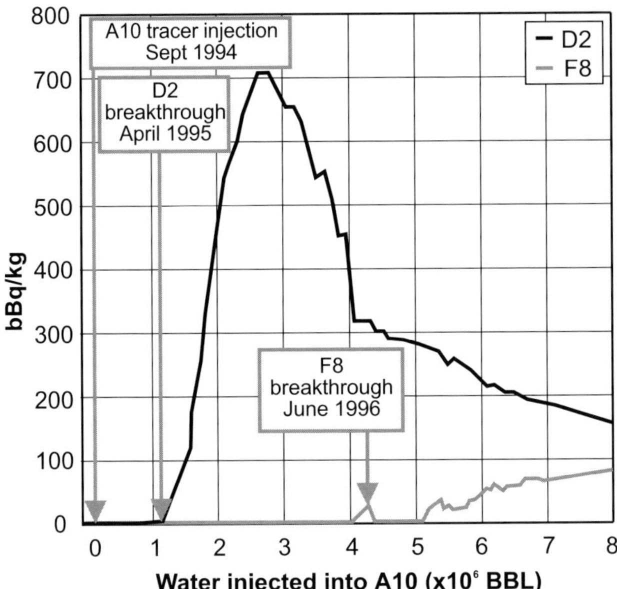

Fig. 11. Plot showing time taken for Tritium tracer to breakthrough from pattern flood injector well L97/10-A10 to offset producer L98/6-F8.

1996 (Fig. 1). Tracer returns from A10 were detected in Well L97/10-D2 (D2) to the north within 7 months, and in Well L98/6-F8 (F8) in June 1996 (Fig. 11). Tracer has not yet been detected in wells to the west. Sampling of fluids from wells offset from F17 revealed an instantaneous tracer response in Well L98/6-L3 (L3) but no tracer has been detected in the other offset wells to date. Tracer injection will continue in parallel with implementation of a pattern waterflood programme (see later).

Offshore reservoir development

The offshore Sherwood Sandstone reservoir contains an estimated 240×10^6 BBL oil-equivalent reserves. It was recognized that recovery of these reserves would be a major challenge because of the environmental and amenity importance of the area. Permission to develop the onshore section of the field was granted in 1987 but with a requirement to submit a development plan for the offshore section by the end of 1991. In 1990 the concept of building an artificial island in Poole Bay to access offshore reserves using conventional deviated wells was proposed. Meanwhile, research into the emerging ERD technology was embarked on. This concentrated firstly, on development of a drill string programme to simulate the torques and drags to which ERD wells might be subjected. Secondly, a drilling mud dynamics programme was developed to model the ability to clean long, almost horizontal extended reach wells (Payne *et al.* 1994; Payne & Abbassian 1996).

As a result of this research the decision was taken in 1991 to abandon the proposed artificial island in favour of drilling development wells from a concealed location onshore. This would involve drilling extended reach wells to an unprecedented distance of 6 km. At that time, the maximum horizontal departure at Wytch Farm was 2.1 km and the maximum distance achieved at similar depth was 4.5 km.

These original targets have since been dramatically exceeded. To date, fourteen ERD wells have been drilled at step-outs ranging from 3.8 to 10.1 km, a world record to date (Fig. 1). They include: twelve producers; an ERD injector L98/6-M1 (M1); and a dual completed well, L98/6-M10 (M10), which allows for simultaneous production and injection. The wells have been designed to optimize rate ($10–20 \times 10^3$ BBL/day on start-up), maximize oil recovery and delay water-cut development. The principal constraints on well design are: the ability to drill and complete the well, structure, oil column thickness and reservoir architecture. All Stage III wells have been drilled in $8\frac{1}{2}$ in. hole and lined with $5\frac{1}{2}$ in. liner. They are then cemented and perforated to allow for future intervention and water shut-off. The drilling and completion of Wytch Farm ERD wells has been documented extensively (Brodie *et al.* 1994; Payne *et al.* 1994; Summers *et al.* 1994; Wood *et al.* 1995; Bruce *et al.* 1996; Payne & Abbassian 1996; Cocking *et al.* 1997). ERD well trajectory design and perforation strategy is considered in more detail by Harrison & Mitchell (1995), McClure *et al.* (1995), Hogg *et al.* (1996) and Smith & Hogg (1997).

The first ERD wells (L98/6-F18 to F21) were drilled in the Central Horst Block. These were constrained by the drilling technology then available to relatively short step-outs of 4–5 km. Oil columns were of the order of 100 m and reservoir sections were drilled to penetrate the oil–water contact (OWC) with simple profiles at inclinations between 80–85° and productive intervals of 750–1000 m (Fig. 12). With increasing confidence, later ERD wells were drilled to recover reserves at the reservoir rim with step-outs of up to 8 km (Wells L98/6-M2, M3 and M5). Here, well geometry is constrained by the proximity of the OWC and poor reservoir connectivity. The wells were drilled horizontally at inclinations of 80–90° and reservoir sections of up to 2.5 km within narrow vertical corridors of ±10 mTVT (Fig. 12). They were placed above laterally extensive shales (Zones 20, 40 and 60), which reservoir modelling suggested may limit water coning. To provide adequate sweep in the poorly connected Upper Sherwood, these wells were inverted at the tail to >95° (Fig. 12).

RFT pressures showed that offtake from the onshore and early ERD wells field had created a significant east–west pressure gradient. Simulation modelling suggested that, in these circumstances, enough production to satisfy a 20×10^3 BBL per day pump could be achieved by perforating only the tail sections of these rim wells. Oil recovery from the edge of the field could thereby be increased by as much as 2×10^6 BBL (Harrison & Mitchell 1995). The head of the wells could then be perforated at a later date as well capacity demanded. This strategy was adopted for Wells L98/6-M3 and M5 which came on-stream at 20 and 10×10^3 BOPD from gross perforated intervals of 1103 and 1161 m, respectively (Fig. 12).

The Southern Terrace wells were planned to maximize reservoir sweep both vertically and areally. Thus, Wells M6, M7 and M10 were drilled with reservoir penetrations one reservoir zone higher (or conversely lower) than the adjacent well (Fig. 1). M9 was the first of the ERD wells to be drilled with a pilot hole for data acquisition purposes (see earlier). Like M1, the well was drilled with provision for later conversion to aquifer injection.

M01 was the only Stage III well to be drilled in the structurally low Northern Fault Block. It has a horizontal producing interval through Zones 10–30 and a 70 mTVT tail in Zones 70 and 80 to provide for later conversion to water-injection.

Initially, reservoir management strategy of the Stage III area was to allow pressure decline in the core area, thereby encouraging westward flux of oil from the eastern extremities, improving overall recovery. A significant pressure sink developed caused by high offtake from the Central Horst Block, and to arrest further decline, offshore injection is being increased. There are currently two offshore injectors; M1 and M10 (Fig. 1). Well M1, which had disappointing initial production rates, was converted to produced water injection duty. It is now injecting at 15×10^3 BBL per day seawater in the original producing perforations and over a 93 m interval beneath the original OWC. Well M10 was completed as a

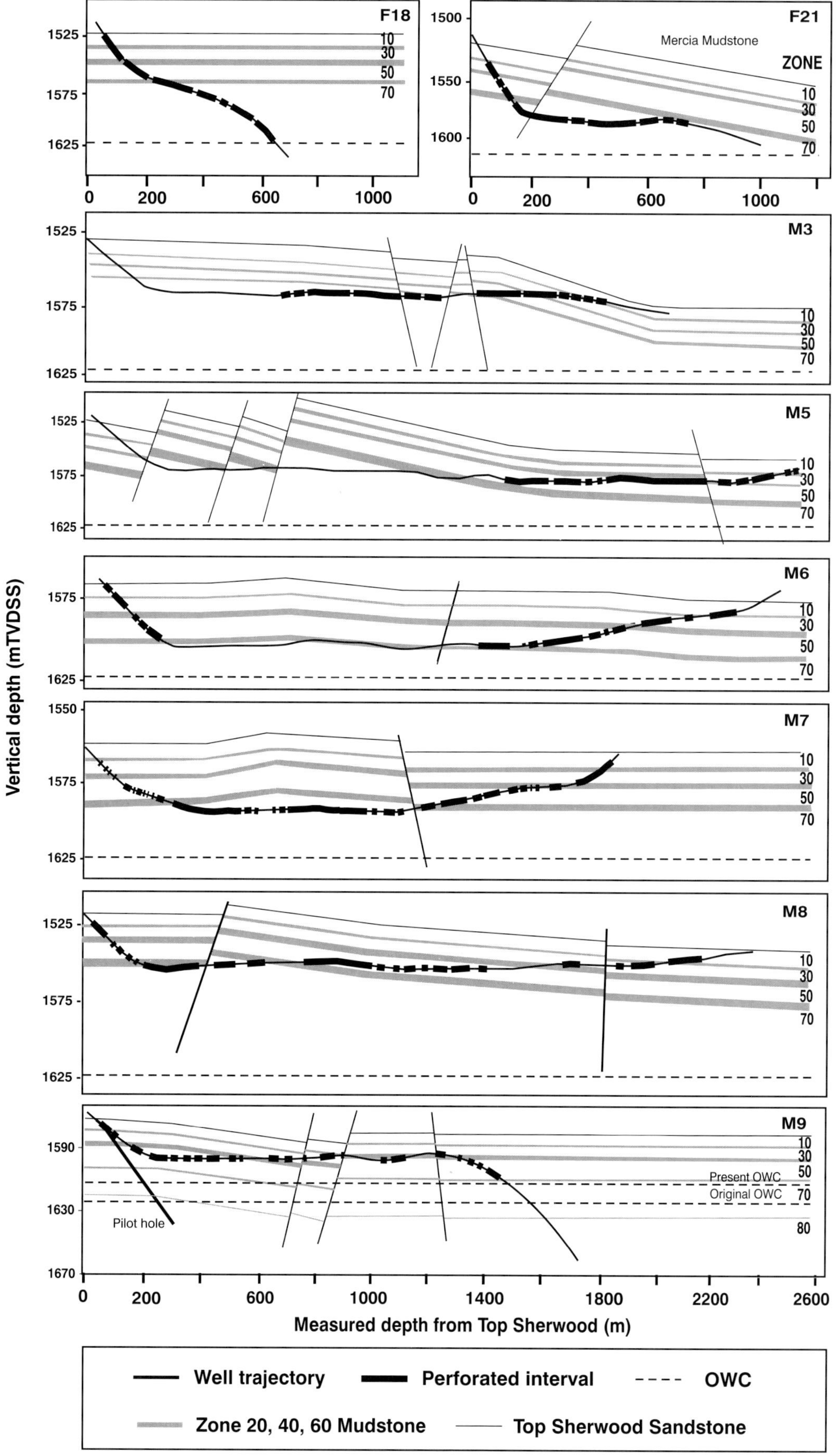

Fig. 12. Diagrams showing the trajectories in the Sherwood Sandstone reservoir of representative Wytch Farm extended reach wells.

simultaneous production/injection well, utilizing a novel cross-over packer installed beneath the ESP. The well currently injects 20×10^3 BBL of produced water while producing 3×10^3 BOPD.

Transmissibility between the Northern Fault Block, Central Horst and Southern Terrace is important when estimating recovery and planning adequate well density in each area of the reservoir. RFTs in the Northern Fault Block Well M1 and Southern Terrace Wells M6 and M7 revealed pressure differentials across intervening faults significantly greater than those observed vertically across mudstones. Approximately 650 psi differential was evident across the Northern Fault, with 300 psi across the Arne Fault (Fig. 9). The higher differential in the Northern Fault Block pressure may be a result of impaired transmissibility because of clay smearing during faulting across the lower net : gross Upper Sherwood in this area. Conversely, deeper in the section (and particularly where clean Zone 80 sands are juxtaposed) transmissibility is predicted to be higher. Thus, greater flux is expected between fault blocks at the Lower Sherwood level, as a result of both higher permeability of the sands and more transmissible fault planes.

West to east pressure trends were also different from the central area. In the Central Horst, formation pressure (corrected to datum depth) was generally seen to increase at about 0.1 psi m^{-1} step-out. This behaviour was repeated as consecutive wells pushed further east and average offshore pressure fell by around 20 psi per month (10 psi per 10^6 BBL produced). Discontinuities were evident, and these were often associated with small scale faults or lineaments.

In short, pressure in step-out Wells M7 and M8 and the Northern Fault Block Well M1, initially decreased with step-out (Fig. 9). Emphasis had been placed on increasing overall seawater injection volumes, balancing oil production from offshore development. The eastern-most injectors (L98/6-K3, L4 and F10) were about 1.5 km to the west (Fig. 1). These 'reverse' gradients indicated that a degree of support was being achieved, as the main pressure sink migrated eastwards. In M6 (and at greater step-out in M7 and M8), a relatively flat (<0.01 psi m^{-1}) horizontal gradient was observed. The majority of M6 was drilled in good quality Lower Sherwood sands, and similarity in pressure profile between M6 and M8 was interpreted as further evidence of south to north flux across the Arne Fault.

Production logs in F18 and F21 showed contribution to flow along the majority of the wellbore (Fig. 10). The inflow profile was in general agreement with that predicted by estimates of productivity determined from grain size analysis and logging whilst drilling (Hogg *et al.* 1996). Contrary to experience in many horizontal wells where wellbore friction can reduce drawdown at the extremities of long horizontal sections, flow was recognized from the tail of the well. Of the early ERD wells, F21 was completed with the largest stand-off to the original oil–water contact (40 m) (Fig. 12). It was also the first to develop significant water cut. 3D seismic data, acquired after the well had been drilled, suggested that a northwest–southeast trending splay from the Northern Fault had been intersected. It was concluded, from production logging data, that the fault was open and water was being drawn up from the underlying aquifer (Fig. 12).

Other than such localized ingress, water production was seen from deeper perforations to be a result of cresting. Well F18 was drilled to total depth beneath the original OWC, and an upwards movement of the latter by about 10 m was observed behind casing. A plot of moveable hydrocarbon volume against height above original OWC had predicted a rise of between 5 and 20 m, given the cumulative offshore oil production at the time. The range was driven primarily by uncertainty in drainage area that should be considered; a 5 m change was predicted if the OWC had risen uniformly across the whole offshore acreage, or 20 m if the Northern and Arne faults were completely sealing. The observed rise agreed with a model of partial communication across the major faults.

The performance of the producing area of the offshore Sherwood Sandstone was predicted to be sensitive to the fault and mudstone transmissibility employed in the model. Matching the extensive RFT dataset and PLT log interpretation provided constraints on these parameters. Uncertainty in reservoir connectivity was thus reduced, and evaluation of reserves for given well locations and development strategy enhanced. However, working at the limits of ERD technology, development planning also took into account the anticipated rate of development of drilling technology. To allow drilling studies to progress towards spudding L98/6-M11 (M11) which was planned to total depth at 10 km step-out (Gammage *et al.* 1997; Modi *et al.* 1997), Wells M8, M9, M10 were drilled alternately to short and long-reach departures (4.5, 8.5 and 4 km, respectively) (Fig. 1). In this way, learning from drilling the more ambitious M9 well could be consolidated and drilling practices improved while drilling the shorter step-out targets. Similarly, pilot multilateral drilling of the onshore field (see below) has been implemented before the main development phase has finished. This ensures that the technology is developed whilst still on plateau and in advance of a full infill well programme as the field approaches decline.

Improved oil recovery

Infill drilling

In the onshore part of the Sherwood Sandstone reservoir, there are currently 24 producing wells with an average spacing of around 700 m ($\approx$100 acre spacing). Many of these wells now have high water cuts and the best quality lower reservoir has essentially watered out. Significant reserves remain in the poorer quality, upper reservoir but this oil is unlikely to be produced through the existing sub-vertical wells. There is considerable geological uncertainty in the onshore part of the field since it is covered only by a sparse ($\approx$500 m line spacing) 2D grid of variable age and quality.

A programme of infill drilling has commenced which aims to improve oil recovery from the onshore part of the Sherwood reservoir. By drilling horizontal laterals from existing wells into un-drained areas of the reservoir, additional oil will be recovered at lower water cuts. The infill drilling programme will complement other IOR schemes (e.g. pattern waterflood and miscible gas injection) through improving the areal sweep efficiency.

Preliminary screening of locations and candidates for infill wells focused on underperforming wells and potential attic oil accumulations. The early wells have targeted reservoir sands in Zone 50. This is a compromise between the deeper sands in Zone 70, which although of better quality are more likely to be watered out, and the poorer quality sands of Zone 30, which although of higher oil saturation will produce at a significantly lower rate because of reduced K_h. Zone 50 is approximately 10 m thick; well within the steering capability of MWD.

The economics of drilling laterals from existing wells are much more favourable than drilling new wells. A 4 lateral pilot infill drilling programme was completed in early 1997 (Fig. 1). These wells were designed to allow progressive learning beginning with a single short (250 m) lateral with abandonment of the existing producing wellbore and culminating in a dual lateral, including a short-radius lateral, in a well where the existing perforations were retained for production. To minimize risk, the first four laterals were drilled from existing wells which were poor producers or which were in need of workover to replace pumps. Drilling was performed by an upgraded workover rig, the wells were completed barefoot to minimize costs. Prior to drilling the key geological risks were the presence of watered-out sands, conductive/sealing faults and sand stability in the barefoot completions planned. To mitigate against these, the laterals were targeted in structurally high locations away from known faults and the lateral entry points were kept >50 m away from the original wells within the target zone.

The wells all found high oil saturations suggesting that the shale zones (20, 40 and 60) are effective baffles to water cresting. Structural uncertainty remains the greatest geological risk. All of the laterals encountered unmapped faults with throws of <5 m. In the first lateral an unmapped fault lead to catastrophic mud losses and to high water production on start-up. In the second and subsequent laterals, unmapped faults threw the target zone out of the wellbore and led to shorter pay intervals than anticipated. Despite this, results from these wells gave encouragement for further infill work. Planning is now underway for the second phase of onshore infill drilling and for infill drilling from the offshore ERD wells.

Pattern waterflood

Pressure support to the Sherwood Sandstone is currently provided through water injection into the aquifer. This bottom waterflood efficiently sweeps oil from the relatively well-connected Lower Sherwood Sandstone. To enhance oil recovery in the more stratified Upper Sherwood reservoir, a pattern waterflood is being developed, with water injection directly into the oil leg (see Satter & Thakur (1994) for an introduction). To test the principle, a pilot pattern was established in the southwestern area of the field. Well A10, a low productivity (productivity index <1 STB day^{-1} psi^{-1}) was converted to oil-leg injection in September 1993 (Fig. 1). A tritium tracer was introduced into the well shortly after injection started.

Soon after injection began, increases in bottom hole pressures and gross fluid rates were observed in the offset wells F8, A7, D2. The response was most marked in Well D2 and was accompanied by the breakthrough of the tritium tracer (injected in A10) in that well first (Fig. 11). Hydraulic impedance testing indicated formation of thermal fractures in the Upper Sherwood. Fracture full-height is estimated to be 5.1–6.7 m and half-length 3.5 m at 812 psi well head injection pressure and 10×10^3 BBL per day rate, the typical operating rate for the injector. Thermal fracturing presumably formed in a north–south orientation, sub-parallel to the present-day principal stress direction. Logs in Well A7 showed that production from Zone 30 had increased significantly. However, simulation of the A10 pattern showed that a significant volume of the injected water must be flowing into the Lower Sherwood. Consequently, when Well F17 was converted to pattern flood injection duty in August 1996 commissioning was undertaken in two stages, with initial injection into Zones 10 and 30, followed by injection into Zones 10, 30, 50 and 70 combined. By this means injection into the poorer quality upper reservoir was maximized. An injection log showed 62% of the injection water was passing into Zones 10 and 30 despite their lower permeability. In the first phase of the project, five injection wells, selected for their compatability with gas injection, will be converted for pattern flooding (Fig. 1). An estimated additional 8×10^6 BBL reserves are predicted to recovered by this scheme.

Miscible gas injection

Commencing in mid-1999, a total of 23×10^6 SCF per day of miscible produced gas will be injected into five wells in a water alternating gas (WAG) cycle sweeping the Sherwood reservoir through inverted nine-spot patterns (Harrison *et al.* 1997) (see Satter & Thakur (1994) for an introduction and Stalkup (1992) for an advanced survey of miscible displacement techniques). The project will be extended to a further five patterns over a 10 year period to cover almost 50% of the reservoir (Fig. 1). Injection of 60×10^9 SCF of miscible gas is predicted to recover 12.6×10^6 BBL of incremental oil over a 15 year period.

The detailed description of the Upper Sherwood, laboratory corefloods, fluid analyses and simulation modelling were used to predict the performance of a miscible flood. As part of the project design the residual oil saturations to a waterflood and a miscible gas flood were measured on core samples. A calibrated equation of state determined the degree of enrichment required to ensure that the injection gas will be miscible with the reservoir oil.

To predict the performance of the project a fine-scale geological model of an inverted quarter nine-spot pattern was constructed. Using the Todd & Longstaff (1972) technique, simulations were undertaken on a number of different geological realizations, and the effects of reservoir parameters examined. Results were combined parametrically to obtain a range of incremental oil recoveries. Scale-up to a 10-pattern project was achieved by determining a number of scaling factors from the quarter nine-spot model. Patterns were then phased according to the volume of gas available for injection.

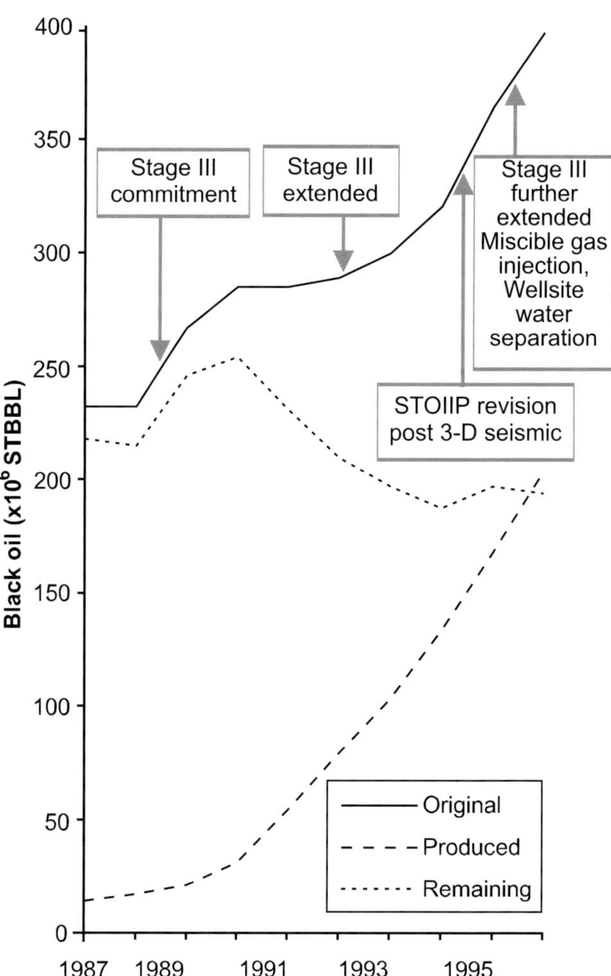

Fig. 13. Plot of Wytch Farm proven reserves, produced and remaining oil against time showing the principal contributions to reserves growth with time.

The design of the gas injection project has taken into account the existing production facilities and well completions. The electrical submersible pumps used will be upgraded to handle 40% free gas at the pump inlet. Phasing of the gas injection patterns will prevent returned gas bottlenecking the gas plant and, by pumping the liquified petroleum gas (LPG) to injection pressure, the size of the gas compressor is minimized.

Conclusions

Growth in Wytch Farm reserves is illustrated against time in Fig. 13. Unusually, the reserves yet to be produced for the field have been relatively constant over time. In 1997, remaining reserves were close to those perceived in 1987. This remarkable record of growth has been achieved both by improved definition of oil originally in place and technological advances, particularly in ERD drilling, which have allowed improved access to those reserves. Continuous improvement of the offshore Sherwood reservoir description has been brought about through maintainance of a strong emphasis on static (core and LWD logs) and dynamic (RFT and PLT logs) data acquisition throughout development drilling. Maximizing learning during the ERD drilling programme has, within four years pushed the limits of reservoir access from 3.8 to >10 km step-out. Success is attributable through closely co-ordinated integration, and mutual understanding, across all oilfield disciplines. This has allowed ideas to be promoted and implemented with confidence taking the teams to high standards of performance. The integrated approach to reservoir management will provide for further growth as IOR projects, infill drilling, pattern and miscible gas floods are implemented, driving ultimate Sherwood Reservoir oil recovery to 60% and beyond.

This paper owes much to the work of our predecessors and colleagues in the Reservoir Development Group, Wytch Farm. They include: A. Cowley, A. P. Drayton, A. Hardy, J. R. B. Harris, I. A. Mcleod, M. N. McClure, K. J. Mills, A. W. Mitchell, P. D. Parsons, C. Reynolds, A. Rodriquez, D. W. Sherrard, G. B. Taylor, C. Telford, A. P. Topham, M. D. Tothill, D. Wilkinson and C. Witt. The paper is published with the kind permission of the Wytch Farm partnership: BP Exploration Operating Company Ltd (Operator), ARCO British Ltd, Clyde Petroleum (Dorset) Ltd (a subsidiary of Gulf Canada Resources Ltd), Premier Oil plc, ONEPM Exploration Ltd, and Talisman (North Sea) Ltd.

References

BOWMAN, M. B. J., MCCLURE, N. M. & WILKINSON, D. W. 1993. Wytch Farm Oilfield: deterministic reservoir description of the Triassic Sherwood Sandstone. *In*: PARKER, J. R. (ed.) *Petroleum Geology of Northwest Europe: Proceedings of the 4th Conference*. Geological Society, London, 1513–1517.

BRODIE, A., ALLAN, J. & HILL, G. 1994. Operating experience with ESPs and permanent downhole flowmeters in Wytch Farm extended reach wells. *Paper SPE 28528 presented at the 69th Annual Technical Conference and Exhibition of the Society of Petroleum Engineers, New Orleans, LA*, 25–28 September.

BRUCE, S., BEZANT, P. & PINNOCK, S. 1996. A review of three year's work in Europe and Africa with an instrumented motor. *Paper IADC/SPE 35053 presented at the 1996 IADC/SPE Drilling Conference, New Orleans, LA*, 12–15 March.

COCKING, D. A., BEZANT, P. N. & TOOMS, P. J. 1997. Pushing the ERD envelope at Wytch Farm. *Paper SPE 37618 presented at 1997 SPE/IADC Drilling Conference, Amsterdam, The Netherlands*, 4–6 March.

COLTER, V. S. & HAVARD, D. J. 1981. The Wytch Farm Oilfield, Dorset. *In*: ILLING, L. V. & HOBSON, G. D. (eds) *Petroleum Geology of the Continental Shelf of North-West Europe*. Heyden, London, 494–503.

DRANFIELD, P., BEGG, S. H. & CARTER, R. R. 1987. Wytch Farm Oilfield: reservoir characterisation of the Triassic Sherwood Sandstone for input to reservoir simulation studies. *In*: BROOKS, J. & GLENNIE, K. W. (eds) *Petroleum Geology of North West Europe*. Graham & Trotman, London, 149–160.

GAMMAGE, J. H., MODI, S. & KLOP, G. W. 1997. Beyond 8 km departure wells: The necessary rig and equipment. *Paper SPE/IADC 37600 presented at 1997 SPE/IADC Drilling Conference, Amsterdam*, The Netherlands, 4–6 March.

HARRISON, P. F. & MITCHELL, A. W. 1995. Continuous improvement in well design optimizes development. *Paper SPE 30536 presented at 70th Annual Technical Conference and Exhibition of the Society of Petroleum Engineers, Dallas, TX*, 22–25 October.

——, COCKIN, A. P. & SKINNER, R. 1997. The design of a miscible gas flood for the Wytch Farm Sherwood Reservoir. *Presented at the 9th European Symposium on Improved Oil Recovery*, The Hague, 20–22 October.

HAWKES, P. W., FRASER, A. J. & EINCHCOMB, C. C. G. 1998. The Tectono-stratigraphic development and exploration history of the Weald and Wessex Basins, Southern England. *In*: UNDERHILL, J. (ed.) *The Development, Evolution and Petroleum Geology of the Wessex Basin*. Geological Society, London, Special Publications, **133**, 39–66.

HOGG, A. J. C., MITCHELL, A. W. & YOUNG, S. 1996. Predicting well productivity from grain size analysis and logging while drilling. *Petroleum Geoscience*, **2**, 1–15.

JARIWALA, H., DAVIES, J. & HEPBURN, Y. 1996. Advances in the completion of 8 km Extended Reach ESP Wells. *Paper SPE 36579 presented at the 1996 Annual Technical Conference and Exhibition of the Society of Petroleum Engineers, Denver, CO*, 22–25 October.

LENN, C. P., BAMFORTH, S. A. & JARIWALA, H. 1996. Production logging in an extended reach well at the Wytch Farm Oilfield using a new toolstring combination incorporating novel production logging technology for horizontal wells. *Paper SPE 36580, presented at the 1996 SPE Annual Technical Conference and Exhibition, Denver, CO*, 6–9 October.

MCCLURE, N. M, WILKINSON, D. W., FROST, D. P. & GEEHAN, G. W. 1995. Planning extended reach wells in Wytch Farm Field, UK. *Petroleum Geoscience*, **1**, 115–127.

MCKIE, T., AGGETT, J. & HOGG, A. J. C. 1998. Reservoir architecture of the Upper Sherwood Sandstone, Wytch Farm Field, southern England. *In*: UNDERHILL, J. (ed.) *The Development, Evolution and Petroleum Geology of the Wessex Basin*. Geological Society, London, Special Publications, **133**, 399–406.

MODI, S., MASON, C. J., TOOMS, P. J. & CONRAN, G. 1997. Meeting the 10 km Challenge. *Paper SPE 38583, presented at the 1997 SPE Annual Technical Conference and Exhibition, San Antonio, TX*, 5–8 October.

PAYNE, M. L. & ABBASSIAN, F. 1996. Advanced torque and drag considerations in extended reach wells. *Paper SPE 35102 presented at the 1996 IADC/SPE Drilling Conference held in New Orleans, LA*, 12–15 March.

——, COCKING, D. A. & HATCH, A. J. 1994. Critical technologies for success in extended reach drilling. *Paper SPE 28293 presented at 69th Annual Technical Conference and Exhibition of the Society of Petroleum Engineers, New Orleans, LA*, 25–28 September.

SATTER, A. & THAKUR, G. 1994. *Integrated Petroleum Reservoir Management: a Team Approach*. PennWell Publishing Company, Tulsa, OK.

SELLY, R. C. & STONLEY, R. 1987. Petroleum habitat in south Dorset. *In*: BROOKS, J. & GLENNIE, K. W. (eds) *Petroleum Geology of North West Europe*. Graham & Trotman, London, 139–148.

SMITH, G. S. & HOGG, A. J. C. 1997. Integrating static and dynamic data to enhance extended reach well design. *Paper SPE 38878 presented at 1997 Annual Technical Conference and Exhibition* of the Society of Petroleum Engineers, San Antonio, TX, 5–8 October.

STALKUP, F. I., JR 1992. *Miscible Displacement*. Henry L. Doherty Series. Monograph Volume 8. Society of Petroleum Engineers, Richardson, TX.

Summers, T. A., Larsen, H. A., Redway, M. & Hill, G. 1994. The use of coiled tubing during the Wytch Farm extended reach drilling project. *Paper SPE 28558 presented at 69th Annual Technical Conference and Exhibition of the Society of Petroleum Engineers, New Orleans, LA*, 25–28 September.

Thompson, S. D. & Bligh, R. P. 1995. Wytch Farm Oilfield, England: Reducing 3D cycle time and quantifying the benefit for a mature Field. *Paper SA 2.6 presented at 65th Annual Meeting of the Society of Exploration Geophysicists, Houston, TX*, 8–13 October, 973–975.

Todd, M. R. & Longstaffe, W. J. 1972. The development, testing and application of a numerical simulator for predicting miscible flood performance. *Journal of Petroleum Technology*, July, 874–82.

Wood, G. L., Hulbert, G. B. & Cocking, D. 1995. Drill cuttings disposal into a producing sandstone formation. *Paper SPE 30432 presented at 70th Annual Technical Conference and Exhibition of the Society of Petroleum Engineers, Dallas, TX*, 22–25 October.

Reservoir studies

Reservoir studies

Introduction and review

A. HURST

University of Aberdeen, Department of Geology & Petroleum Geology, King's College, Aberdeen AB24 3UE, UK

The need to appraise and develop smaller and technically challenging fields, and to maximize recovery from mature fields, requires a high level of geoscientific input and application of innovative methods. Optimal positioning and geosteering of wells, and drilling and completion of 'intelligent' wells, are only successful if the relevant reservoir data are available and implemented in reservoir models. Modern seismic data reveal ever more information about reservoir heterogeneity and fluid distribution, often allowing definition of intra-reservoir features. In mature fields, production data frequently identify reservoir compartmentalization and validate models of geological heterogeneity.

Recognizing that existing reservoir models may be inconsistent with current data is an important motivation for revisiting existing concepts and hypotheses. Recognition that all reservoir models are approximations of reality produced from incomplete data leads to the use of probabilistic methods to estimate uncertainty. As new data are acquired, new methods of processing and analysing data are developed, or new concepts are applied to interpretation of data, the need to change models becomes apparent. New concepts may come from reworking and re-examination of existing data or from acquisition of new data. Sometimes changes are enforced as predictions of reservoir behaviour prove erroneous and remedial action is required to secure profitability or to cut further losses. The stimulation to carry out reservoir studies may occur at any time during field appraisal and development. For example, a study may be carried out to assess uncertainty and reduce risk during planning of field development or, to extend the life of a super-mature field or, at any time between these. Equally, reservoir studies may feed back into exploration activities by providing new understanding and concepts for reservoir distribution and prediction of reservoir quality.

Papers by **Yielding *et al.***, **Maxwell *et al.*** and **Garland *et al.*** demonstrate different aspects of reservoir studies on mature fields. Using examples from the Brent Province Gullfaks Field **Yielding *et al.*** characterize the shale gouge ratio and its distribution on fault surfaces. The effects of specific faults on pressure compartmentalization is successfully demonstrated by correlation between estimates of fault zone permeability and dynamic pressure drops registered following production. Using a sedimentological approach **Maxwell *et al.*** revisit an earlier zonation of the Beryl Formation in the Beryl Field and, by applying a combination of sedimentology, ichnology and biostratigraphy with well-log and dynamic data, they generate an improved deterministic reservoir zonation that is validated by drilling and production data. The study demonstrates the importance of recognizing regionally extensive, low permeability units, in this case marine/brackish mudstones, that constitute pressure barriers during production. Individual units record the progradation and transgression of tidally dominated deltas. Using data from the sand-rich deep-water clastic reservoirs of the Upper Jurassic Miller Field, **Garland *et al.*** provide an example of how a sedimentologically-based stoichastic model of reservoir heterogeneity is used to constrain uncertainty in the mapping of reservoir parameters. The Miller Field has been in decline since mid-1997 and evaluation of the role of reservoir heterogeneity on optimising recovery is part of a general investigation of possible extension of field life. Stochastic models are demonstrated to give a better estimate of uncertainty than earlier deterministic models.

Olsen *et al.* present documentation from the Heidrun Field of integrated reservoir characterization of alluvial plain and low energy deltaic and mixed tidal and marginal marine facies. Geostatistically-based 3D modelling is used to assess reservoir heterogeneity and to provide a basis for uncertainty analysis. On a field-wide scale they conclude that uncertainty related to GRV is most significant, whereas facies-related parameters play a minor role. Facies-related parameters are, however, significant on an interwell-scale.

For reservoirs with such a long history of production in the context of the North Sea it is perhaps remarkable that many fundamental aspects of Chalk prospectivity are poorly understood. In an integrated approach to understanding the preservation of reservoir quality in a mature chalk play, **Øxnevad & Taylor** propose a new approach for the prediction of reservoir quality in undrilled areas. Quantitative basin modelling proves successful for the prediction of reservoir quality and should lower exploration risk in future prospecting.

A common theme in all papers is the need to re-examine existing data and interpretations in order to develop new concepts, explain current deficiencies in reservoir models or, to assess the uncertainty associated with models. All the papers demonstrate that 'unexpected' problems with existing models can be addressed by acquiring simple data or applying well-tried methods; new technology is not always a prerequisite for improving a reservoir model! Introducing new concepts and ideas that are grounded in solid basic science serve as valuable tools in reservoir studies.

HURST, A. 1999. Reservoir studies: Introduction and review. *In*: FLEET, A. J. & BOLDY, S. A. R. (eds) *Petroleum Geology of Northwest Europe: Proceedings of the 5th Conference*, 1175.

Characterization of fault zones in the Gullfaks Field for reservoir modelling

G. YIELDING,[1] J. A. ØVERLAND[2] and G. BYBERG[2,3]

[1] *Badley Earth Sciences Ltd, North Beck Lane, Hundleby, Spilsby, Lincs PE23 5NB (e-mail: graham@badleys.co.uk)*
[2] *Norwegian Petroleum Directorate, Prof. Olav Hanssensvei 10, N-4001 Stavanger, Norway*
[3] *Present address: Statoil, 4035 Stavanger, Norway*

Abstract: A fault-seal study has been performed for faults around the A platform of the Gullfaks Field, Northern North Sea. The operator's depth grids and isochore maps were used to build a FAPS database. Together with petrophysical logs, these data were used to compute the distribution of shale gouge ratio (SGR: fault-zone % shale) over each fault surface.

Pressure data from exploration and production wells have been projected onto the modelled fault surfaces. Where well data permit, across-fault pressure drops at particular time instants during production are displayed. These dynamic pressure drops provide a guide to the permeability of the fault zones once flow has started.

The calculated fault parameters (throw and SGR) can be converted to other parameters such as fault-zone thickness and permeability. These can be used to derive fault transmissibility modifiers for reservoir simulations. The calculated properties are compatible with the recorded pressure history and tracer movement between wells.

The objective of this study was to investigate the sealing potential of the internal faults in the Gullfaks Field (Norwegian Block 34/10), both with regard to a static model (differences in original fluid contacts) and with regard to a dynamic model (production history). The linkage between fault properties and differences in fluid contacts has been clearly demonstrated in several studies in recent years (e.g. Fristad *et al.* 1996; Yielding *et al.* 1997). It has been more difficult to find a quantitative expression for fault behaviour when exposed to the sudden changes in pressure caused by production (e.g. Jev *et al.* 1993). In this study we analyse the areas of probable leakage in the faults by comparing measured pressure differences over faults with the sealing properties (expressed as shale content in the fault zone) of those faults. An ultimate aim for the study is to be able to produce a quantitative expression, in grid format, of the fault-zone permeabilities. Based on the permeability values, fault transmissibility modifiers for simulation models can be calculated.

Gullfaks Field

Structural setting

Internally the Gullfaks fault block is highly faulted (Fig. 1). Fossen & Hesthammer (1997) divide the Gullfaks fault block into two structurally distinct subareas: a major domino system, and an eastern horst complex, separated by an accommodation zone. The two subareas show significant differences with respect to fault geometry, rotation and internal block deformation. The major internal faults on the Gullfaks block are E-dipping with strike approximately N–S. Kinematic studies show that these faults are dip-slip extensional structures (Fossen & Hesthammer 1997). E–W-striking minor faults, both N- and S-dipping, divide the major domino blocks into smaller fault compartments. The operator's names for the internal fault compartments (E1, E2 etc.) are used in this study.

Reservoir properties

Erichsen *et al.* (1987) and Petterson *et al.* (1990) describe the reservoir properties on the Gullfaks Field. (The operator's petrophysical interpretation has been used throughout this study.) The present study focuses on the Brent Group, although the Cook and Statfjord Formations are also important reservoir units.

The Brent Group reservoir consists of the sandstone units within the Tarbert, Ness, Etive and Rannoch formations (the Broom Formation is thin and considered non-reservoir). Tarbert consists of massive, homogeneous and highly permeable (3–10 D) sandstone units with a few shale, coal and carbonate layers. Ness/lower Tarbert consists of thin sandstone units interbedded with shale and coal layers, which act as vertical flow and pressure barriers. The massive sandstone of the Etive Formation has excellent reservoir properties (2–7 D). Reservoir properties degrade from top to bottom of the Rannoch Formation (2–0.050 D).

Need for better understanding and characterization of fault properties

Production from the Gullfaks Field commenced in December 1986. In the planning and early production phase, it was realized that the extent of faulting on the field would have a major impact on the strategy for reservoir management (Petterson *et al.* 1990). Pressure measurements, both with repeat formation tester (RFT) in new wells and with permanent downhole gauges, and the use of non-radioactive tracers, were considered important to measure the effects of the production and the injection across the faults. From these data it was realized already in 1988 that some degree of pressure communication existed between the separate fault compartments.

On the Gullfaks Field surplus gas, which has not been sold because of restrictions in transportation capacity, has been reinjected for storage. Attempts have been made to use some of the surplus gas for WAG (water alternating gas) injection to

YIELDING, G., ØVERLAND, J. A. & BYBERG, G. 1999. Characterization of fault zones in the Gullfaks Field for reservoir modelling. *In*: FLEET, A. J. & BOLDY, S. A. R. (eds) *Petroleum Geology of Northwest Europe: Proceedings of the 5th Conference*, 1177–1185. © Petroleum Geology '86 Ltd. Published by the Geological Society, London.

(a)

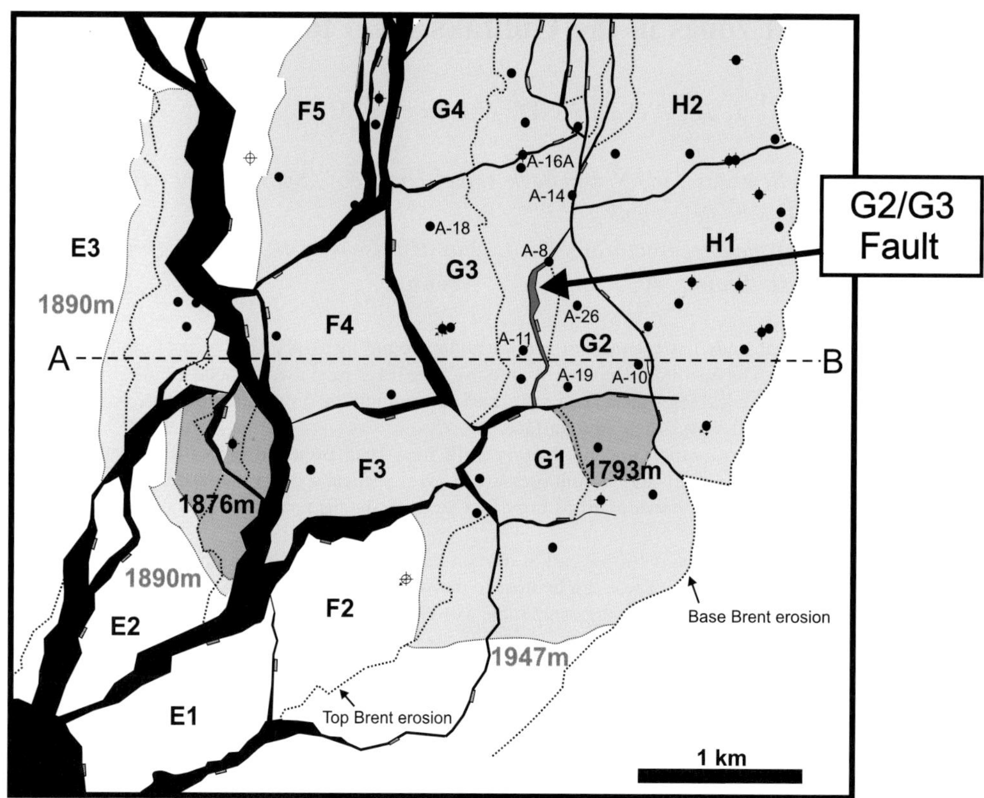

(b)

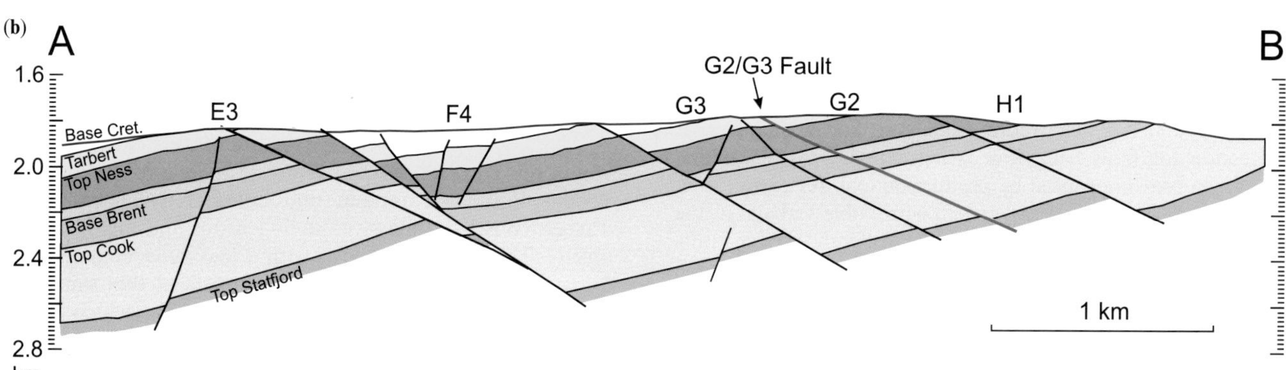

Fig. 1. (**a**) Top Brent structure map of the study area around the A-platform, showing fault compartments and well locations, redrawn from a map provided by Statoil (field operator). The fault highlighted in red is the example fault discussed in detail ('G2/G3 fault'). The dashed line labelled A–B shows the line of the section shown in (b). (**b**) Cross-section along the line marked A–B in (a). E3, F4, G3, G2 and H1 refer to the fault compartments identified in the map view. The G2/G3 fault is highlighted in red.

improve the displacement of attic oil. In both of these cases, the injected gas has been produced back from unexpected well locations, often within a relatively short time. This movement of injected gas has been documented by the application of tracers (Kleven *et al.* 1995). The Norwegian Petroleum Directorate was interested in evaluating the possibility of applying gas injection on a larger scale as an integrated part of the reservoir management on the Gullfaks Field. One obvious requirement to be able to achieve this goal is a better understanding of the flow and pressure patterns in the reservoir. During this study special attention was given to explaining the observed movements of gas.

Focus of study

The study was focused on the part of the Brent reservoir that is drilled and produced from the A-platform (Gullfaks A-area) (Fig. 1). The reason for this is three-fold:

(1) The Brent Group reservoir contains the major part of the oil resources on the Gullfaks Field. This has resulted in a large number of production wells penetrating this reservoir, giving a dense well database.
(2) Production on Gullfaks started in the A-area, so this area would contain the earliest, most undisturbed, and therefore probably most reliable, pressure measurements.
(3) The quality of the acquired 3D seismic data deteriorates over the eastern part of the field, because of gas leakage. Over the western part of the field, where the presence of Upper Jurassic shales has prevented gas leakage, clearer seismic data allow credible fault identification. The 3D-seismic line spacing is 12.5×12.5 m, and the effective resolution for fault offsets is believed to be about 20–30 m (Hesthammer & Fossen 1997). The detailed structural data collected in the production wells are incorporated into the operator's seismic interpretation, resulting in detailed and accurate fault mapping.

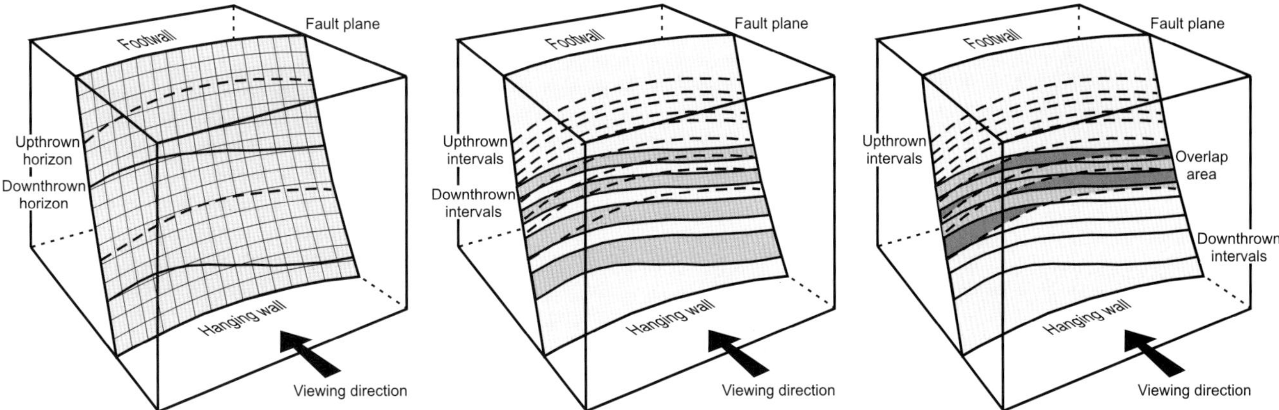

Fig. 2. Sequence of diagrams showing (**a**) modelled fault grid with seismically-mapped horizons; (**b**) interpolation of detailed reservoir zonation between the mapped horizons; and (**c**) reservoir–reservoir overlap area.

Although the study was focused on the Brent reservoir, parameters for the overlying Upper Jurassic Shale (Viking Group) and the underlying Dunlin Group were added to be able to calculate fault properties where these units juxtapose the Brent reservoir.

Most of the Brent Group reservoir in the Gullfaks Field has a common oil–water contact of 1947 m below msl. The exceptions are the westernmost fault blocks, E2 and E3 (Fig. 1), which have a shallower oil–water contact. In addition, a small gas cap is observed in fault block G1 (Fig. 1). For estimating the fault seal potential during production, high-quality pressure measurements (RFT) taken in open boreholes are used. Pressure measurements taken early in the production history, before the start of water injection, are expected to show a more unique relation to the fault properties, than the complex pressure situation experienced after years of production and injection. Particularly suitable calibration points are pressure measurements in 'undrained' fault blocks that showed pressure drops caused by the production in adjacent blocks.

Methodology

A more complete description of the general methodology used by FAPS software for fault analysis and fault-seal analysis is given by Needham *et al.* (1996), Freeman *et al.* (1997) and Yielding *et al.* (1997).

The principal steps by which the fault-seal analyses were constructed from the map and well database were as follows:

(i) Use the fault traces at all mapped horizons to define the positions of the fault surfaces in depth. Seven horizons had been mapped by the operator (Base Cretaceous, Top Brent, Top Ness, Top Rannoch, Base Brent, Top Cook, Top Statfjord).

(ii) Model each fault surface as a three-dimensional grid, with principal axes along-strike and down-dip, and grid-cell size 25 m × 25 m (see schematic illustration in Fig. 2).

(iii) Define the detailed reservoir zonation (from well data), by interpolating zone boundaries between the mapped horizons at the fault surface (also illustrated in Fig. 2). A total of 23 reservoir zones were used within the Brent Group.

(iv) Input relevant RFT (pressure) measurements to each reservoir, to display the pore-pressure field in the fault-block. Where pressure data have been collected on both sides of a fault, the pore-pressure field can be constructed for both fault-blocks (i.e. both walls of the fault). The difference between these distributions is the pressure difference across the fault zone (assuming that the pressure field within each compartment is relatively uniform, i.e. all pressure changes occur across the faults).

(v) Assign shale-volume ('V_{shale}') data to the reservoir zones, by deriving zonal averages from the V_{shale} logs. Shale content is a critical parameter in the calculation of fault seal capacity (Yielding *et al.* 1997; Gibson 1998). We use an attribute called the shale gouge ratio (SGR) which is simply the percentage of shale or clay in the rock interval that has slipped past any point on the fault (see Fig. 3). Core and outcrop data suggest that this parameter is a good guide to the proportion of phyllosilicates in the fault gouge (Gibson 1997; Foxford *et al.* 1998), which in turn is a major influence on the capillary and permeability properties of the fault zone. In the fault analyses, SGR is calculated over the fault surface on a refined grid of 5 m × 5 m (i.e. five times the resolution of the basic fault grid described earlier).

Permeability measurements on fault gouge samples (Gibson 1997; Ottesen Ellevset *et al.* 1998) permit a first-order correlation between phyllosilicate content (~SGR) and fault-zone permeability. For example, a phyllosilicate content of <15% in the fault zone is characteristic of cataclasites with permeability *c.* 0.5 mD, whereas archetypal clay smears have phyllosilicates >40% and permeability ≤0.003 mD. Fault-related diagenesis/cementation is not significant in the Gullfaks reservoir, and hence fault-gouge phyllosilicate content is expected to be the main control on across-fault permeability. The SGR distribution on the modelled fault surface can therefore be used as a prediction of fault-zone permeability.

In turn, the fault-zone permeability can be used to derive a transmissibility modifier for each grid node on the fault grid. The transmissibility modifier is simply the ratio between the transmissibilities across the fault with and without the effect of the fault-zone material. To calculate the cell-to-cell transmissibility in the absence of fault-zone material requires the permeabilities of the juxtaposed reservoir units, and the dimensions of the grid cells in the reservoir model. Calculating the transmissibility with fault-zone material between the cells additionally requires the fault-zone permeability and its thickness. Here the fault-zone permeability is derived from the SGR (as described earlier). The fault-zone thickness can be input as a constant (e.g. based on fault penetrations in well cores) or can be considered as a simple function of the local fault displacement (typically one hundredth, e.g. Evans 1990).

In this paper only the mapped faults in the field are described. However, the same methodology can in principle be extended to synthetic faults of small displacement, to investigate the possible effect of sub-seismic faulting (see Yielding *et al.* in press).

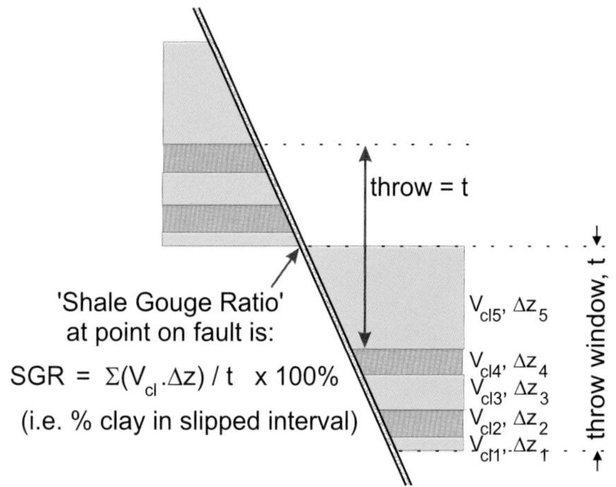

Fig. 3. Definition of shale gouge ratio (SGR). For a sequence of reservoir zones with specified V_{shale} (or V_{clay}) and thickness, SGR equals the net shale/clay content in the rock interval that has slipped past any point on the fault. SGR is considered to be a good estimate of the likely phyllosilicate content of the fault gouge on that part of the fault.

Results of fault analyses

A total of 23 fault segments were analysed by the methods outlined in the previous section. The analysed faults form an interconnected network that defines a number of separated fault compartments (Fig. 4). Fault throw in the Brent Group is typically in the range 0–200 m, which is less than the total Brent Group thickness. Only one of the faults analysed (in the southwest of the area) has sufficient displacement to offset the Brent Group completely (Fig. 4). Fault-zone thickness for these faults will typically be about one-hundredth of the local displacement (e.g. Evans 1990).

Figure 5 shows, in map view, the distribution of SGR on all 23 analysed fault segments in the Gullfaks A area. The colour-coded areas are those parts of the fault planes where there is Brent–Brent overlap (Fig. 2c). A wide overlap area on the map indicates a relatively small fault displacement, whereas a narrow (or zero) overlap area corresponds to larger displacement. The analysis of each fault uses zone thickness and V_{shale} data from the wells adjacent to that fault. The SGR scale can be considered as representing static seal capacity, or being inversely related to fault-zone permeability. It can be seen from Fig. 5 that faults with small displacements (wide areas on map) have a heterogeneous SGR distribution. Faults with large displacements (narrow areas) have a more uniform (and moderately high) SGR distribution.

The next section focuses on one of the analysed fault segments, to show in detail how the fault surfaces can be characterized geometrically and in terms of their fluid flow behaviour.

G2/G3 fault

This example fault lies between fault blocks G2 and G3, which originally had the same oil–water contact. Therefore, on a geological timescale it probably did not constitute a 'sealing' fault. However, the two fault-blocks underwent differential depletion once production had started, implying that the fault was a barrier to flow on the production timescale.

Figure 6 is a perspective view of the fault surface, colour-coded by the fault throw. The throw reaches about 50 m on the northern part of the fault but is much less in the south (*c.* 10–20 m). At both ends the fault links onto other faults (Fig. 1), i.e. there are no lateral tips. The fault was penetrated near its southern end by well A-19 (unfortunately the fault plane was not cored).

Figure 7 shows the calculated SGR in the reservoir–reservoir overlap areas using the lowest V_{shale} values from adjacent wells. Table 1 summarizes V_{shale} values from the wells, and the min. and max. values used in the calculations. A prominent feature of the plot is the area of lower SGR values in the Lower Brent,

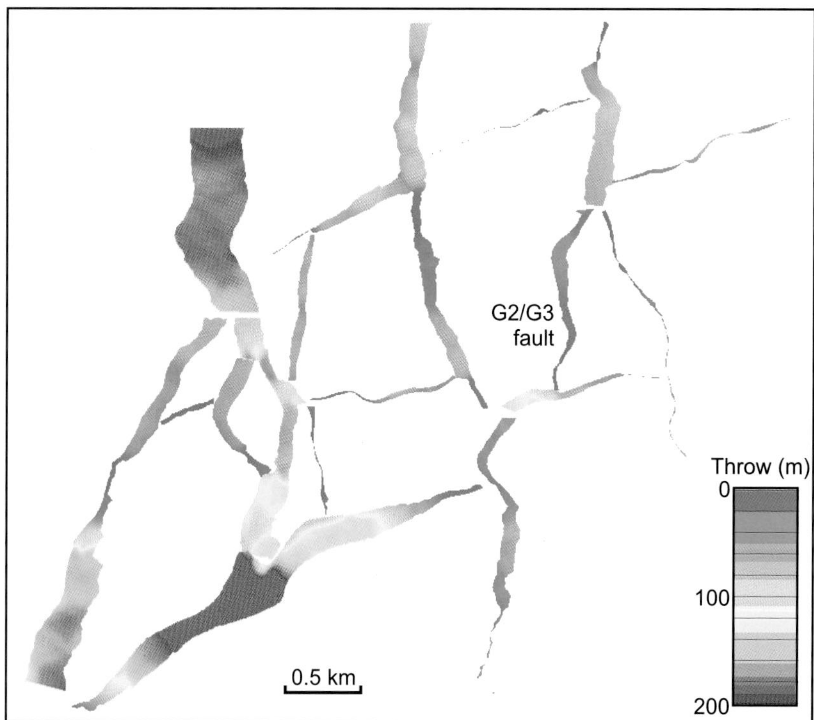

Fig. 4. Map view of the analysed faults showing the throw (vertical offset) distribution at the level of Top Ness. The large fault in the southwest has throws reaching 350 m; on all other faults the Top Ness throw is <200 m and does not completely offset the Brent Group. Fault-zone thicknesses are likely to be about 1/100 of the fault displacement (Evans 1990).

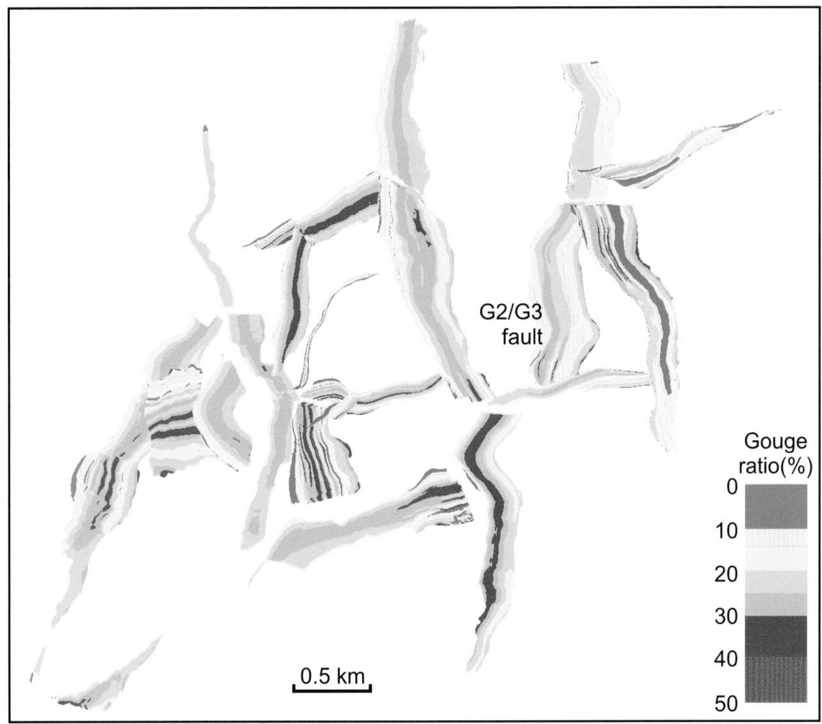

Fig. 5. Map view of the analysed faults showing SGR in the Brent–Brent overlap zones. The calculation for each fault uses the 'low-case' V_{shale} values from adjacent wells. The mapped width of each overlap zone depends upon the fault dip and amount of offset; for the largest fault in the southwest there is total Brent offset and therefore no overlap zone (cf. Fig. 4).

especially on the southern half of the fault. The small offset of the clean Etive Formation is the main cause of this.

In Fig. 8, the SGR distribution has been used to calculate a transmissibility modifier at all reservoir–reservoir overlaps. A transformation was used from gouge ratio to fault-zone permeability, and another transformation from fault throw to fault-zone thickness. In combination with the permeability values in the reservoir zones, these transformations allow a comparison of the transmissibility from footwall to hanging wall, with and without the fault-zone, at all points on the fault surface. Expressed as a ratio, this comparison is by definition the transmissibility modifier.

Because a number of variables affect the transmissibility modifier, it does not necessarily have a simple relationship with SGR. In general, for a given SGR, juxtapositions of highly permeable reservoirs have a lower transmissibility modifier, because the fault zone has a more significant effect on the transmissibility. Conversely, when poorly permeable reservoirs are juxtaposed the fault zone has relatively less effect and the transmissibility modifier is higher (i.e. nearer to 1).

The first well in block G3 was Well A-8 in mid-1987; RFT data showed only very minor depletion from earlier production to the northeast. A-8 production began in June 1987. Well A-10 was drilled into block G2 in July 1987 and found 7.5 bar

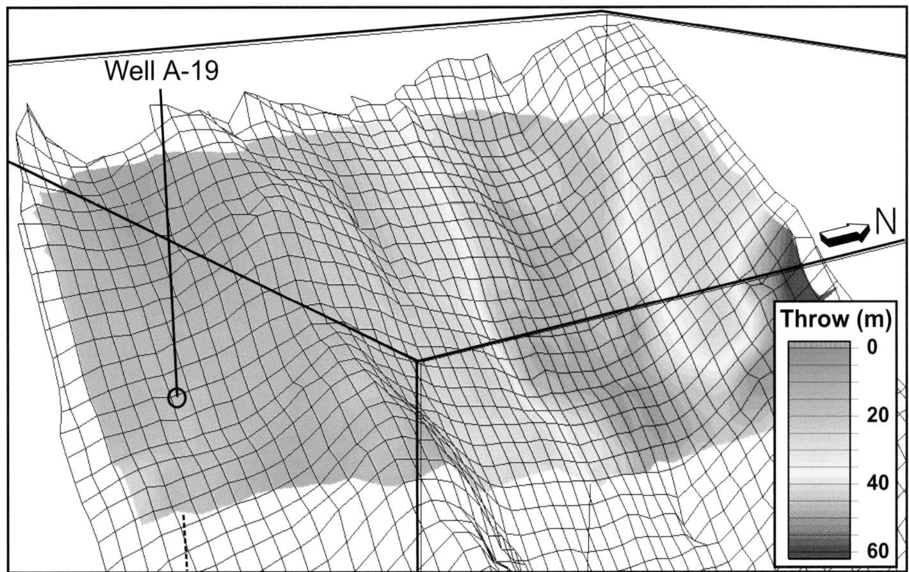

Fig. 6. G2/G3 fault, between fault-blocks G2 and G3 (see Figs 1, 4 & 5 for location). The fault surface is colour-coded by throw (vertical displacement). The total length of the fault is about 1.2 km and each grid cell is 25 m × 25 m.

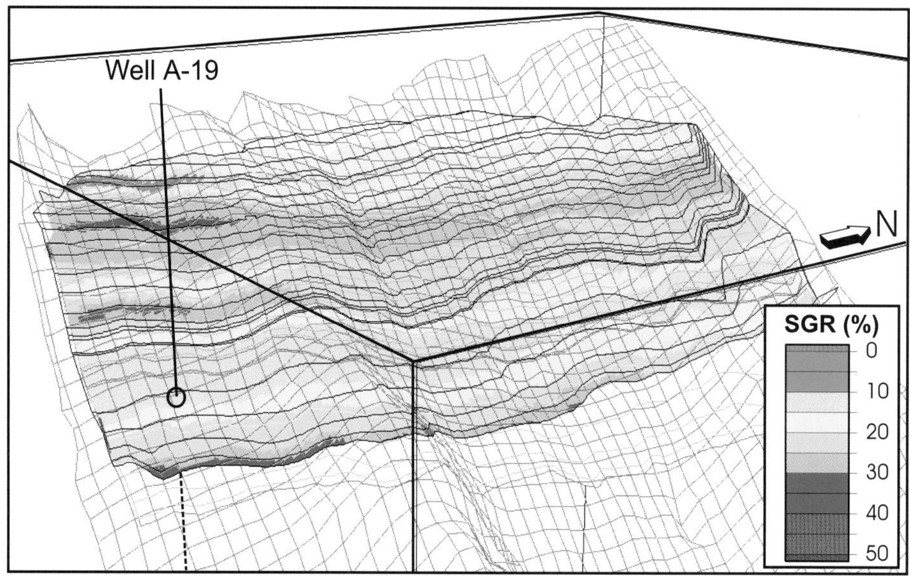

Fig. 7. G2/G3 fault, showing low-case distribution of SGR (or fault-zone %-shale) in reservoir overlap zones (using 'Min' values from Table 1). Note the area of low SGR on the deeper part of the Brent–Brent overlap (adjacent to the Etive Fm). The fault grid is shown in light grey. The thin black lines show reservoir zone boundaries in the upthrown (G3) side of the fault. The thin coloured (orange/yellow) lines show reservoir zones on the downthrown side (G2).

depletion in the Rannoch/Etive. This must have been caused either by A-8 production in G3, or by ongoing production to the east in block H1, or both. Well A-11 (RFT Sept. 1987) in G3 found that drawdown by A-8 production had now reached 24 bar.

In late 1988, RFT measurements were taken in rapid succession in Well A-18 (block G3) and Well A-19 (G2/G3). Well A-19 penetrated the G2/G3 fault, passing from Etive in the downthrown block G2 to Rannoch in upthrown block G3. Between these units, Well A-19 found a 6 bar pressure difference. In every other well, the Rannoch/Etive forms a continuous pressure compartment because of the lack of shaly breaks. Well A-19 is therefore directly sampling the pressure drop at one point on the fault surface.

Wells A-18 and A-19 together provide pressure profiles for both sides of the fault for late 1988. In the footwall (G3) depletion was greatest in the Rannoch/Etive (>15 bar) and in the upper Ness (produced in A-14). In the hanging wall (G2)

Table 1. V_{shale} data for G2/G3 fault

Mapped	Zone	Thickness (m)	V_{shale} values from wells				V_{shale} values used		
			A30	A19	A8	A26	Min.	Average	Max.
Top Brent	t3	21	0.193	eroded	eroded		0.193	0.19	0.193
	t2b2	15	0.168				0.168	0.17	0.168
	t2b1	15	0.190		0.327	0.189	0.189	0.24	0.327
	t2a	11	0.039	0.185	0.092	0.054	0.039	0.09	0.185
	t1c	5	0.511	0.319	0.459	0.371	0.319	0.42	0.511
	t1b	12	0.275	0.236	0.301	0.313	0.236	0.28	0.313
	t1a	10	0.360	0.410	0.311	0.328	0.311	0.35	0.410
Top Ness	n3d	11	0.298	0.314	0.335	0.301	0.298	0.31	0.335
	n3c	8	0.239	0.303	0.287	0.271	0.239	0.28	0.303
	n3b	8	0.280	0.309	0.324	0.339	0.280	0.31	0.339
	n3a	13	0.220	0.272	0.472	0.282	0.220	0.31	0.472
	n2c	14	0.321	0.348	0.195	0.152	0.152	0.25	0.348
	n2b2	14	0.428	0.366	0.405	0.336	0.336	0.38	0.428
	n2b1	10	0.166	0.235	0.318	0.217	0.166	0.23	0.318
	n2a	6	(F)	0.243	0.416	0.292	0.243	0.32	0.416
	n1c	2	0.060	0.468	0.171	0.040	0.040	0.18	0.468
	n1b	9	0.483	0.159	0.529	0.546	0.159	0.43	0.546
	n1a	2	0.148	0.015	(F)	0.021	0.015	0.06	0.148
	etive	34	0.154	0.113	0.144	0.119	0.113	0.13	0.154
Top Rannoch	r3	25	0.291	0.254	0.222	0.219	0.219	0.25	0.291
	r2	21	0.217	0.231	0.252	0.253	0.217	0.24	0.253
	r1	14	0.360	0.319	0.336	0.336	0.319	0.34	0.360
	broom	7	0.653	0.585	0.576	0.560	0.560	0.59	0.653
Base Brent	drake		0.535	0.523	0.558	0.533	0.523	0.54	0.558

V_{shale} data used in the analysis of the G2/G3 fault. Data from 4 wells were used to derive min., max. and average V_{shale} values for each reservoir zone. (F) = faulted out.

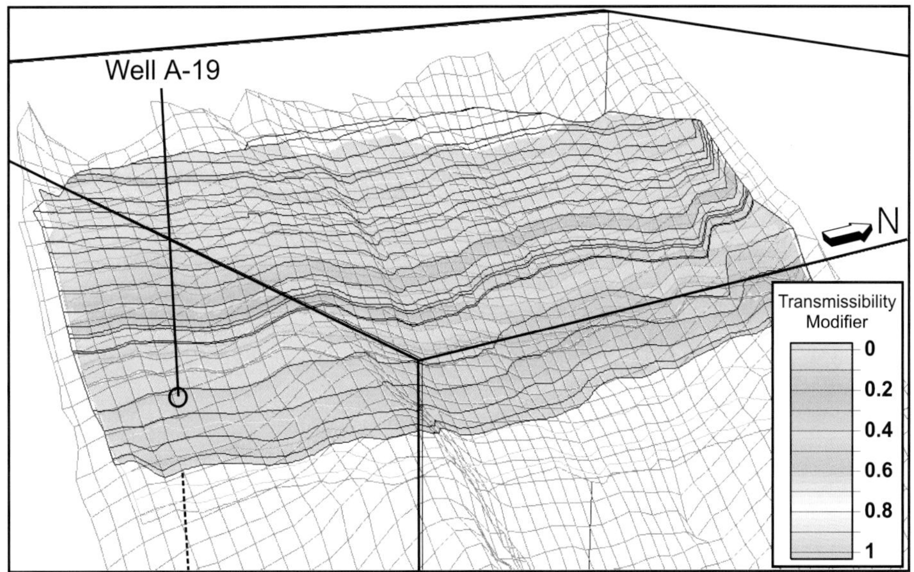

Fig. 8. G2/G3 fault, showing transmissibility modifier in overlap zone. Values are mainly <0.1, indicating that the fault will reduce transmissibility between juxtaposed grid cells in G2 and G3 by a factor of 10 or more.

depletion was more uniform (Rannoch and Ness production from A-10). The difference between these depletion patterns at the fault surface is illustrated in Fig. 9. In general block G3 is more depleted than block G2 (area shown as blue on figure) as there were more producing wells in G3. However, the central part of the Brent–Brent overlap zone shows G2 (hanging wall) depletion locally greater than G3 (red), depending on the precise juxtaposition of Ness zones. The complexity of this plot is illustrative of the complex nature of the fault response to production.

One year after Wells A-18 and A-19 were drilled, another pair of wells (A-16A, A-26) were drilled in blocks G2 and G3, allowing a second measurement of pressures in both blocks. By this time, the Ness and Tarbert pressures in G2 and G3 had dropped substantially because of production, but pressures in the Lower Brent had recovered to near-original as the rate of water injection in several wells exceeded the rate of production. Figure 10 shows the calculated pressure drop at the fault surface at this time. Juxtaposition of downthrown depleted Ness against upthrown recovered Lower Brent gives a very large pressure drop (>40 bar) in the central part of the overlap area. This contrasts with the lower part of the overlap area (Lower Brent against Lower Brent) where the pressure drop is only about 5 bar from footwall to hanging wall, and also with the upper part of the fault (downthrown Tarbert) where the footwall was slightly more depleted.

The pressure observations summarized in Figs 9 and 10 highlight a number of points. Firstly, the changing production/injection pattern can produce not only changes in the across-fault pressure drops, but complete reversals in the direction of the pressure drop. If these pressure drops are associated with fluid flow, then the direction of fluid flow across the fault will have reversed between late 1988 and late 1989. Secondly, the direction of pressure drop (and, therefore, fluid flow) can be in different directions on different parts of the same fault, at the same time.

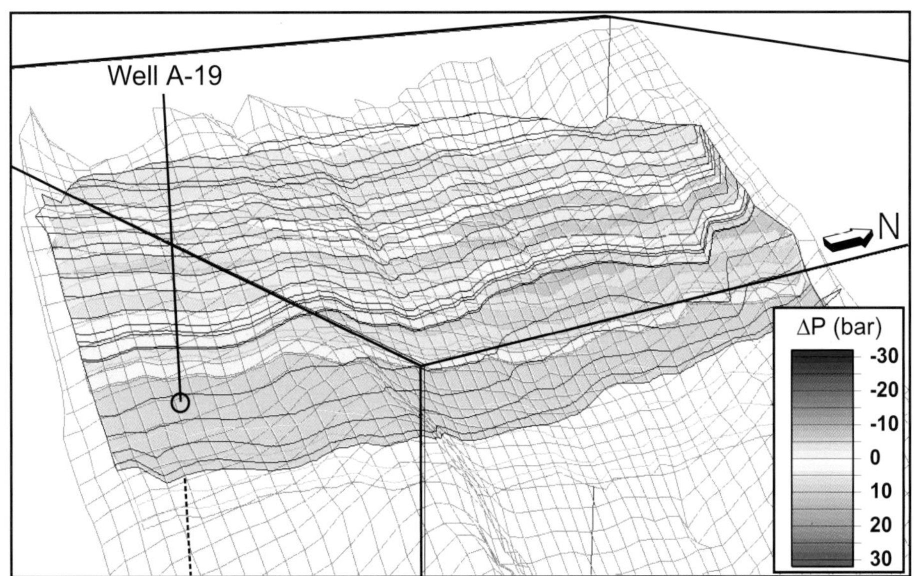

Fig. 9. G2/G3 fault, showing dynamic pressure drop between juxtaposed reservoirs in late 1988, based on RFT data from Wells A-18 and A-19. Blue areas have a higher pressure in the downthrown side and so fluid movement will be from the downthrown (G2) to upthrown (G3) side. Well A-19 measured a 6-bar pressure drop across the fault.

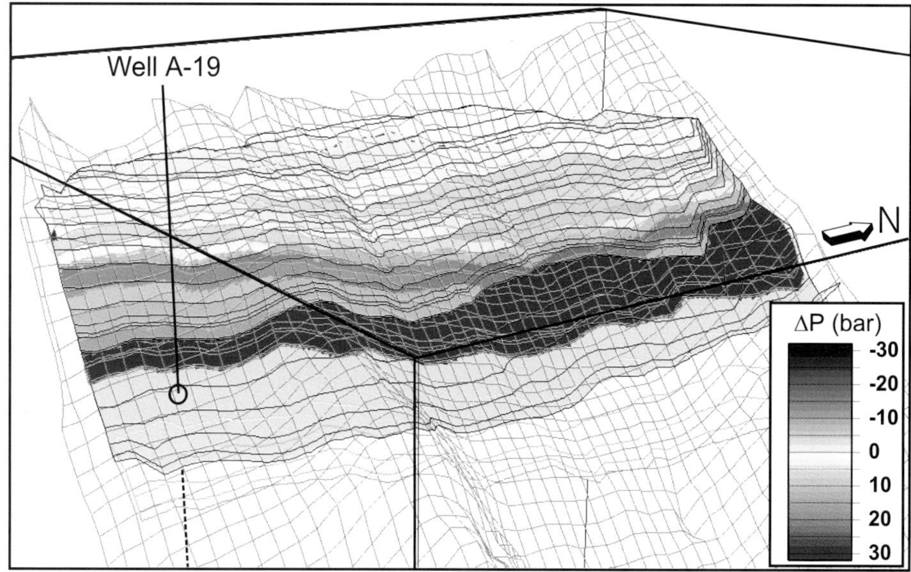

Fig. 10. G2/G3 fault, showing dynamic pressure drop between juxtaposed reservoirs in late 1989, based on RFT data from Wells A-16A and A-26. Note the complete change in across-fault pressure difference relative to that shown in Fig. 9. On the lower part of the fault the driving pressure is now from the upthrown to the downthrown side (red areas).

In March 1991, non-radioactive tracer was injected into Well A-11 in block G3 during a phase of gas injection (Kleven *et al.* 1995). Tracer injection was into the Rannoch (Lower Brent). There was very rapid detection of tracer across the fault in block G2 (lower Ness in Well A-19) after only 1–2 months. This contrasted with detection in other wells in injection block G3, where the tracer did not appear for more than three years. These observations imply that the dominant flow direction in the G3 Lower Brent at Well A-11 was across the fault into block G2. This flow route can be easily understood in terms of the juxtapositions and gouge ratio on the southern part of the fault, together with the prevailing pressure regime. The juxtaposition geometry is shown simplified in the cross-section in Fig. 11. Injection of tracer was into the Rannoch of Well A-11, and tracer would therefore have risen into the overlying Etive since the Rannoch/Etive behaves as a continuous sand (no shale barriers). The Etive is juxtaposed against lowermost Ness at the fault, and the SGR plot of Fig. 7 suggests that SGR is relatively low on this area of the fault (i.e. fault permeability relatively high). Flow across the fault into the lower Ness is therefore possible. Pressure measurements in early 1991 suggest that the pattern seen in Fig. 10 was continuing, i.e. strong pressure drive from footwall Etive into depleted hanging wall Ness.

Well A-10, the Rannoch producer closest to the A-11 Rannoch injector, did not detect tracer until a year after injection. Figure 11 shows that the route from A-11 Rannoch to A-10 Rannoch would be a difficult one, passing down at the fault offset at a region where the SGR is rising (fault permeability decreasing). Thus, most of the tracer moving into block G2 would have by-passed the A-10 Rannoch section and is likely to have been higher in the sequence.

Conclusions

(1) Fault-surface modelling of the faults in the Gullfaks A area has provided a framework in which to visualize the reservoir zone juxtapositions at faults.

(2) Pressure data from appraisal and development wells can be incorporated into the fault-surface modelling to provide displays of the across-fault pressure differences before and during production. The dynamic pressure drops across fault surfaces provide a general guide to the permeability of the fault zones once across-fault flow has started. However, an overriding control on dynamic pressure drop is the reservoir management strategy, i.e. the degree to which pressure drawdown is imposed in particular fault-blocks in this area of poor aquifer support. Flow direction across a fault can reverse direction as the production/injection pattern changes. Moreover, flow can be in opposite directions on different parts of the same fault at the same time.

(3) The fault-surface modelling also includes predictive algorithms (SGR) that can be used to derive fault-zone permeabilities and transmissibility modifiers for reservoir simulation studies. Areas of higher SGR on the fault surface correspond to lower fault-zone permeability. On the Gullfaks Field the areas of high and low SGR are compatible with the recorded pressure history and tracer movement between wells. The relationship between gouge ratio and transmissibility modifier is more complex,

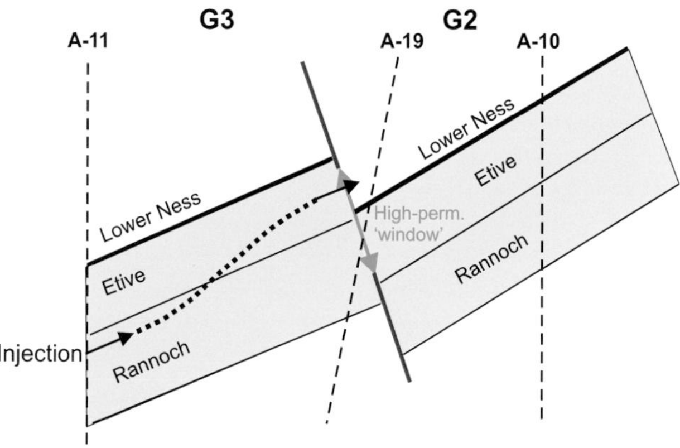

Fig. 11. Cross-section of the southern part of the G2/G3 fault between Wells A-11 and A-10. On the fault trace, red indicates high SGR, green indicates low SGR (taken from Fig. 7). Tracer injected into the Rannoch in Well A-11 travelled rapidly to the Lower Ness at producing Well A-19, across an area of fault plane with low SGR (relatively high permeability).

depending also on the permeabilities of the reservoir units separated by the fault, and the fault-zone thickness. The lowest transmissibility modifiers (i.e. largest degradation in across-fault transmissibility) occur where a thick fault-zone of high SGR separates highly permeable reservoirs.

We are grateful to members of the PL050/050B licence group, headed by Statoil as operator, for permission to publish this study, though the views expressed here are ours and not necessarily those of Statoil or the licence partners. We are also grateful to Eva Halland of Norwegian Petroleum Directorate for the impetus to publish this work. We thank W. de Boer, T. Reston and A. Hurst for their comments on the first version of this manuscript.

References

ERICHSEN, T., HELLE, M., HENDEN, J. & ROGNEBAKKE, A. 1987. Gullfaks. *In*: SPENCER, A. M. (ed.) *Geology of the Norwegian Oil and Gas Field*. Graham & Trotman, London, 273–286.

EVANS, J. P. 1990. Thickness–displacement relationships for fault zones. *Journal of Structural Geology*, **12**, 1061–1065.

FOSSEN, H. & HESTHAMMER, J. 1997. Structural geology of the Gullfaks Field, northern North Sea. *In*: COWARDS, M. P. *et al.* (eds) *Structural Geology in Reservoir Characterization*. Geological Society, London, **127**, 231–261.

FOXFORD, K. A., WALSH, J. J., WATTERSON, J., GARDEN, I. R., GUSCOTT, S. C. & BURLEY, S. D. 1998. Structure and content of the Moab fault zone, Utah, U.S.A. *In*: JONES, G., FISHER, Q. & KNIPE, R. (eds) *Faulting, Fault Sealing and Fluid Flow in Hydrocarbon Reservoirs*. Geological Society, London, Special Publications, **147**.

FREEMAN, B., YIELDING, G., NEEDHAM, D. T. & BADLEY, M. E. 1998. Fault seal prediction: the gouge ratio method. *In*: JOHNSON, H. D., & COWARD, M. P. (eds) *Structural Geology in Reservoir Characterization and Field Development*. Geological Society, London, Special Publications, **127**, 19–25.

FRISTAD, T., GROTH, A., YIELDING, G. & FREEMAN, B. 1996. Quantitative fault seal prediction – a case study from Oseberg Syd area. *In*: *Hydrocarbon Seals – Importance for Exploration and Production (conference abstracts)*. Norwegian Petroleum Society, Oslo.

GIBSON, R. G. 1998. Physical character and fluid-flow properties of sandstone-derived fault gouge. *In*: JOHNSON, H. D. & COWARD, M. P. (eds) *Structural Geology in Reservoir Characterization and Field Development*. Geological Society, London, Special Publications, **127**, 83–97.

HESTHAMMER, J. & FOSSEN, H. 1997. Seismic attribute analysis in structural interpretation of the Gullfaks Field, northern North Sea. *Petroleum Geoscience*, **3**, 13–26.

JEV, B. I., KAARS-SIJPERSTEIJN, C. H., PETERS, M. P. A. M., WATTS, N. L. & WILKIE, J. T. 1993. Akaso Field, Nigeria: use of integrated 3D seismic, fault-slicing, clay smearing and RFT pressure data on fault trapping and dynamic leakage. *American Association of Petroleum Geologists Bulletin*, **77**, 1389–1404.

KLEVEN, R., HØVRING, O., OPDAL, S. T., BJØRNSTAD, T., DUGSTAD, Ø. & HUNDERE, I. A. 1995. Non-radioactive tracing of injection gas in reservoirs. *Society of Petroleum Engineers, reprint 35651*.

NEEDHAM, D. T., YIELDING, G. & FREEMAN, B. 1996. Analysis of fault geometry and displacement patterns. *In*: BUCHANAN, P. G. & NIEUWLAND, D. A. (eds) *Modern Developments in Structural Interpretation, Validation and Modelling*. Geological Society, London, Special Publications, **99**, 189–199.

OTTESEN ELLEVSET, S., KNIPE, R. J., OLSEN, T. S., FISHER, Q. J. & JONES, G. 1998. Fault controlled communication in the Sleipner Vest Field, Norwegian Continental Shelf; detailed, quantitative input for reservoir simulation and well planning. *In*: JONES, G., FISHER, Q. J. & KNIPE, R. J. (eds) *Faulting, Fault Sealing and Fluid Flow in Hydrocarbon Reservoirs*. Geological Society, London, Special Publications, **147**, 283–297.

PETTERSON, O., STORLI, A., LJOSLAND, A. & MASSIE, I. 1990. The Gullfaks Field: geology and reservoir development. *In*: BULLER, A. T., BERG, E., HJELMELAND, O., KLEPPE, J., TORSÆTER, O. & AASEN, J. O. (eds) *North Sea Oil and Gas Reservoirs – II*. Graham & Trotman, London, 67–90.

YIELDING, G., FREEMAN, B. & NEEDHAM, D. T. 1997. Quantitative fault seal prediction. *American Association of Petroleum Geologists Bulletin*, **81**, 897–917.

——, OVERLAND, J. A. & BYBERG, G. in press. Characterisation of fault zones for reservoir modelling: an example from the Gullfaks Field, northern North Sea. *American Association of Petroleum Geologists Bulletin*.

High resolution zonation within a tide-dominated deltaic reservoir: the Middle Jurassic Beryl Formation, Beryl Field, UKCS

G. MAXWELL,[1,3] A. HARTLEY[1] and J. CRANE[2,4]

[1] *Department of Geology & Petroleum Geology, University of Aberdeen, Meston Building, King's College, Aberdeen, AB24 3UE, UK (e-mail: hartley@geol.abdn.ac.uk)*
[2] *Mobil North Sea Limited, Grampian House, Union Row, Aberdeen, AB1 1SA, UK*
[3] *Present address: Texaco North Sea UK Co, Langlands House, Huntly Street, Aberdeen, AB10 1SH, UK (e-mail: maxweg@texaco.com)*
[4] *Present address: Mobil Exploration & Producing Australia Pty Ltd Level 29, QV1 Building, 250 St Georges Terrace, Perth WA 6000, GPO Box L902, Perth WA6001, Australia (e-mail: john_w_crane@mepa.mobil.com)*

Abstract: The Middle Jurassic (Bajocian–Bathonian) Beryl Formation of the Beryl (Bravo) Field (Viking Graben), has been produced since 1979 and contains estimated remaining reserves of 180×10^6 BBL oil. Previous studies of this deltaic/shallow marine succession have defined five reservoir units. Production characteristics indicate that this lithostratigraphically-based zonation scheme does not adequately define reservoir flow units and constrain sweep efficiency. Here, a more refined reservoir zonation is used to form the basis for an upgraded reservoir simulation model.

High density well coverage (50 wells) in the Beryl Bravo area allows the construction of a high resolution reservoir zonation scheme within the main producing interval of the Beryl Formation: Unit 3. The scheme is based on integration of sedimentology, ichnology, biostratigraphy, dynamic data and well log character. Nine reservoir zones (consisting of nine genetic sequences) have been defined and confirmed and are supported by drilling and production data.

The complex reservoir zonation scheme is based upon the recognition of regionally extensive marine/brackish mudstones which, in many cases, form traceable pressure barriers across tilted fault blocks. This framework has allowed subdivision into 3 to 25 m thick correlatable units. Individual units record the progradation and transgression of tide-dominated deltaic deposits. Variations in the thickness and development of these units result from sedimentation in actively subsiding half-graben that were subject to regionally extensive base-level changes. The integrated approach taken here has substantially improved the understanding of the architecture and production characteristics of the Beryl Formation.

The Beryl Field is located 215 miles northeast of Aberdeen within UK Block 9/13 (Fig. 1). The field was discovered in 1972. Production commenced in 1976 and is centred on two platforms: Beryl Alpha in the south of the field and Beryl Bravo in the north (Knutson & Munro 1991). Initial reserves were estimated at 2633×10^6 BBL of oil and 3330×10^9 SCF gas in place of which the majority (65% and 70%, respectively) is reservoired within the Middle Jurassic Beryl Formation (Robertson 1993).

The outstanding reservoir quality of the Beryl Formation resulted in an initial production model which predicted that the reservoir would 'drain' like an homogenous tank (Knutson & Erga 1991); early production performance supported this model. The original lithostratigraphic subdivision of the Beryl Formation (Fig. 2), which defined five layer-cake reservoir units, was considered largely adequate for much of the field production life. However, in June 1985, the pressure testing of the Alpha platform A40 development well indicated that differential pressures had developed (Knutson & Erga 1991) in what had previously been considered an homogenous reservoir section. Knutson & Erga (1991) recognized that the differential pressures were generated by vertical pressure barriers of low permeability which, in turn, were related back to sedimentary facies. Consequently, the original, coarse, five-fold division of the Beryl Formation over-simplified the field stratigraphy. In particular, the original scheme did not adequately define reservoir heterogeneity, such that flow units and sweep efficiency were poorly constrained. In addition, the scale of heterogeneity variation (metres to tens of metres) was beyond the resolution of biostratigraphic techniques.

The purpose of this paper is to integrate sedimentological and reservoir engineering data from the main producing interval of the Beryl Formation (Unit 3) in the Beryl Bravo platform area, in order to develop a more refined reservoir zonation scheme complementing the existing scheme. This information will form the basis of an upgraded reservoir simulation model.

Geological setting

Detailed descriptions of the Beryl Field have been provided by Knutson & Munro (1991) and Robertson (1993), and a brief outline of pertinent information is given here. The Beryl Field lies in the centre of the Beryl Embayment, a complex area of tilted fault blocks located between the East Shetland Platform and the Viking Graben (Fig. 1). Fault block development took place in two discrete rift phases, initially during the Triassic, and subsequently in the Middle Jurassic to early Cretaceous. Each rift phase was followed by a period of thermal subsidence in the Early Jurassic, following the early rift phase, and in the Cretaceous to Tertiary, following the later rift phase (Robertson 1993). Strata penetrated within the embayment range from Carboniferous to Tertiary in age. A simplified lithostratigraphy for the Upper Triassic to Upper Jurassic interval is shown in Fig. 2.

MAXWELL, G., HARTLEY, A. & CRANE, J. 1999. High resolution zonation within a tide-dominated deltaic reservoir: the Middle Jurassic Beryl Formation, Beryl Field, UKCS. *In*: FLEET, A. J. & BOLDY, S. A. R. (eds) *Petroleum Geology of Northwest Europe: Proceedings of the 5th Conference*, 1187–1198.

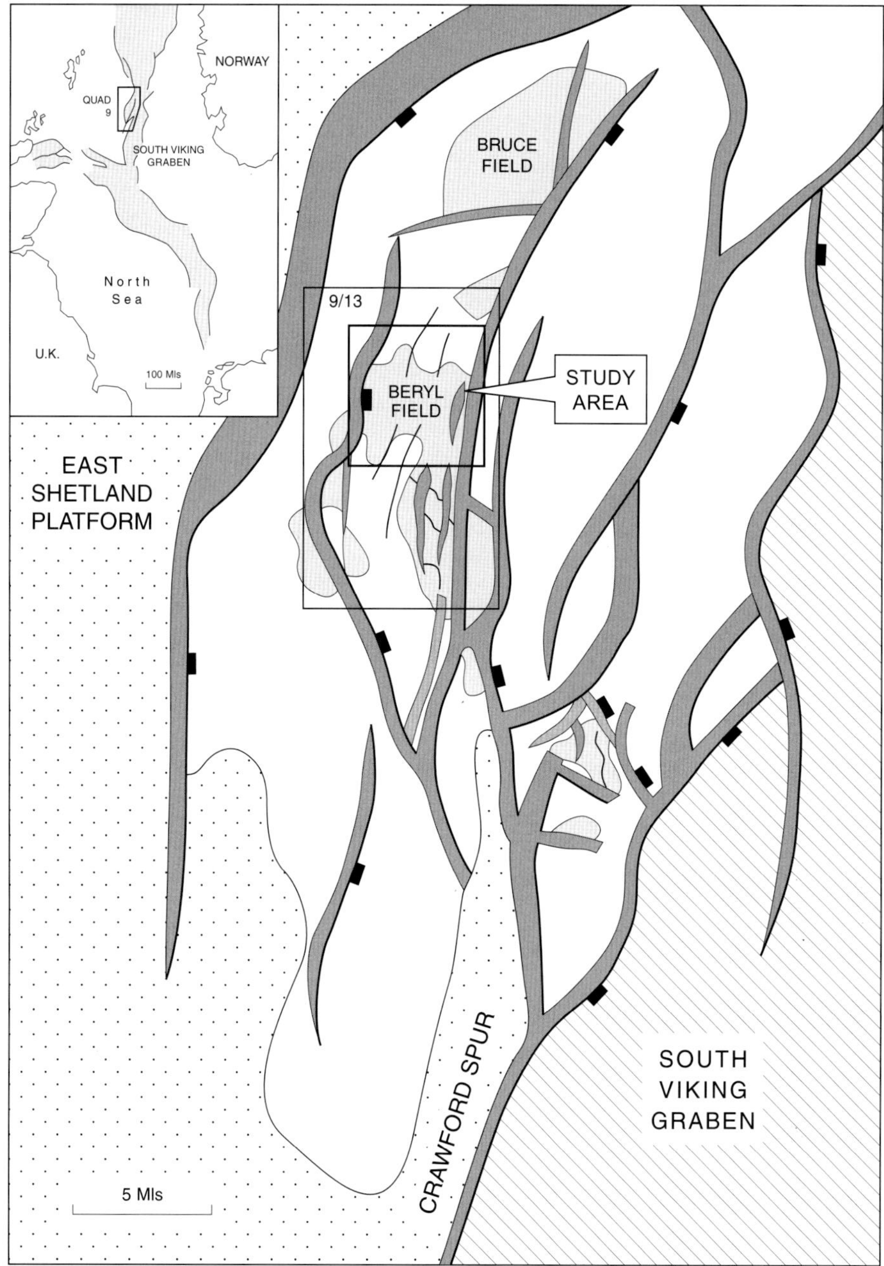

Fig. 1. Location map of the Beryl Embayment, Block 9/13 and the Beryl Bravo study area which forms the northern part of the Beryl Field.

Beryl Formation

The Beryl Formation ranges in age from Late Bajocian to Bathonian (Mitchener *et al.* 1992; Robertson 1993). It is equivalent to the Hugin Formation of the Fladen Group as defined by Richards *et al.* (1993). The formation consists predominantly of sandstones and siltstones with subordinate mudstones, coals and conglomerates. The base is placed at the first coal taken as the top of the underlying Linnhe Formation. The top is represented by either an abrupt upward change from clean sandstones into mudstones of the Heather Formation, or a gradual change from interbedded sandstones, siltstones and mudstones to Heather Formation mudstones.

The Beryl Formation is present throughout much of the Beryl Embayment but may be absent on structural highs. It varies in thickness from zero on the East Shetland Platform to over 400 m within the embayment proper. Some of this variation can be attributed to post Middle Jurassic footwall uplift and erosion but is considered to be mostly syn-depositional in origin. Seismic and well data indicate gross thickness changes with thickening towards, and thinning away from faults, supporting a structural control during sedimentation (Robertson 1993).

A general estuarine deltaic depositional model has been proposed for the Beryl Formation (Knutson & Munro 1991). The deltaic system prograded northeastwards and was supplied by a northerly flowing fluvial system. Sediments in the south of the field (Beryl Alpha) are sandstone-dominated and pass northwards (Beryl Bravo) into interbedded sandstones and finer-grained sediments deposited in a more marine setting, where wave and tidal processes affected sedimentation (Knutson & Munro 1991).

Beryl Bravo area

The Beryl Bravo area comprises a series of north–south trending, westerly-dipping tilted fault blocks (Fig. 3). The Beryl Formation in the Beryl Bravo area has been producing since 1979 and contains estimated remaining reserves of

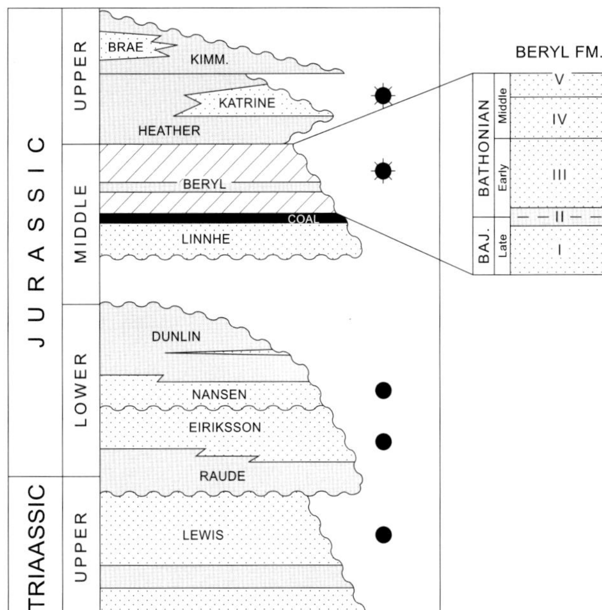

Fig. 2. Simplified stratigraphy of the Upper Triassic to Upper Jurassic interval of the Beryl Field. Note that the Linnhe and Beryl formations are equivalent to the Sleipner and Hugin formations of the Fladen Group as defined by Richards *et al.* (1993).

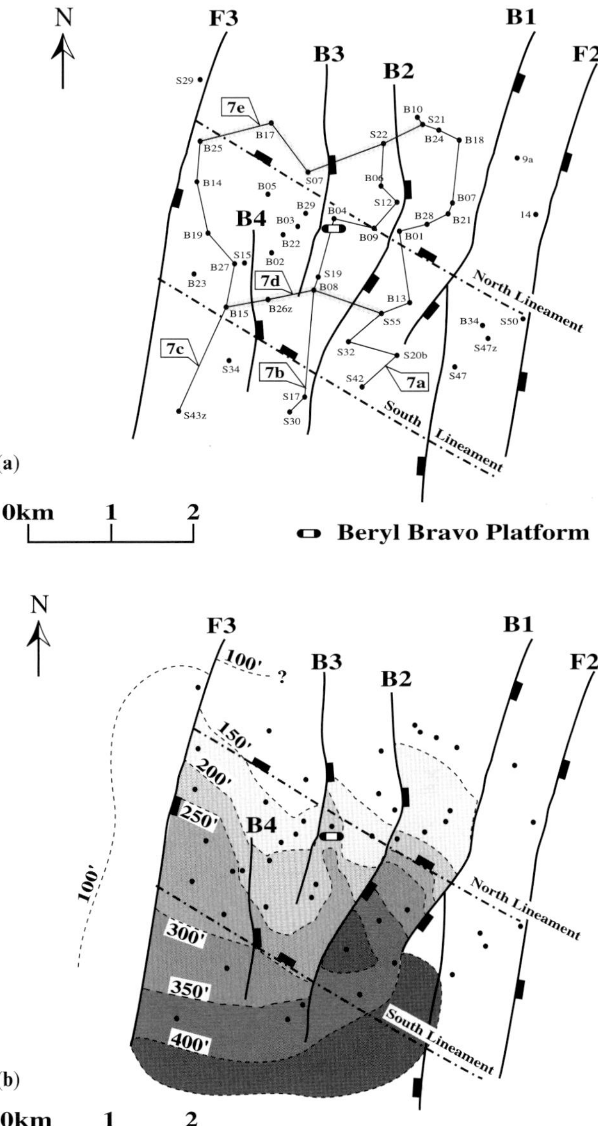

Fig. 3. (**a**) General top Beryl Formation structure map with well locations and lines of sections shown in Fig. 7. (**b**) Isopach map of Beryl Unit 3 (isopachs are in feet) in the Beryl Bravo area. All wells with a complete Unit 3 section have been used in construction of the isopach map.

180×10^6 BBL oil. The five reservoir zones of the Beryl Formation are recognizable throughout the Beryl Bravo area. The thickest and most productive interval (Unit 3) is considered here. In the Beryl Bravo area Unit 3 is bounded above and below by regionally extensive, biostratigraphically correlatable mudstones. The underlying mudstone interval is referred to as Unit 2 within the Beryl Field zonation scheme. The unit is up to 18 m thick, is present throughout the Beryl Bravo area, and is taken to correspond to the Bathonian/Bajocian boundary (Mitchener *et al.* 1992). The boundary between top Unit 3 and base Unit 4 is a regionally extensive marine mudstone within which lies the Early/Middle Bathonian boundary (Mitchener *et al.* 1992; Fig. 2). Complete sections of Unit 3 range in thickness from 30 to over 150 m (Fig. 4). The thickest sections are preserved in the hanging wall of faults and thinner successions on footwall crests.

Beryl Unit 3: thickness variation

Thickness variations within Beryl Unit 3 in the Beryl Bravo area are illustrated in Fig. 3. The principal variations observed are a regional increase in thickness from north to south and localized thickness increases in the hanging wall of the two main faults: F3 (the most westerly fault) and B2 (the fault immediately southeast of the Beryl Bravo platform), together with a minor amount of thickening in the hanging wall of the B3 fault. Thickness increases across F3 in the southern part of the Beryl Bravo area range from 100 to 200%. Thickness increases across B2 are variable along strike. There is no change in thickness across B2 in the northern part of the study area, but in the south, a localized increase from 80 m to over 140 m takes place, an approximate increase of 75% across the fault. An approximate thickness increase of 75% is also present across the B3 fault at the Beryl 'B' platform location. These observations indicate that at a regional scale subsidence was greatest in the southern half of the Beryl Bravo area, with local thickness increases associated with the F3, B2 and B3 faults indicative of synsedimentary fault activity.

Two northwest–southeast trending lineaments with minor vertical separations are also present in the Beryl Bravo area (Fig. 3). These lineaments are poorly understood but bound areas of thickened Beryl Formation (e.g. east of B2, Fig. 3) and may have played a role in controlling accommodation space during the deposition of Unit 3.

Sedimentology

Wireline log suites and 670 m of core have been studied from the Unit 3 interval within the 50 wells drilled in the Beryl Bravo area. Five facies associations are recognized within the cored sections and extrapolated into uncored intervals via characteristic wireline log patterns (Fig. 4):

(1) The offshore transition zone facies association consists of thinly bedded, parallel laminated, siltstones and mudstones with a silt/mud ratio of 0.15. Thicknesses vary from 30 cm to 5 m. The sediment is almost completely bioturbated and contains the trace fossils *Phycosiphon* and *Helminthopsis* with associated *Terebellina* or *Schaubcylindrichnus* in the finer-grained beds. *Schaubcylindrichnus* is only encountered within this facies. A marine macrofauna consisting of belemnites and ammonites is also present.

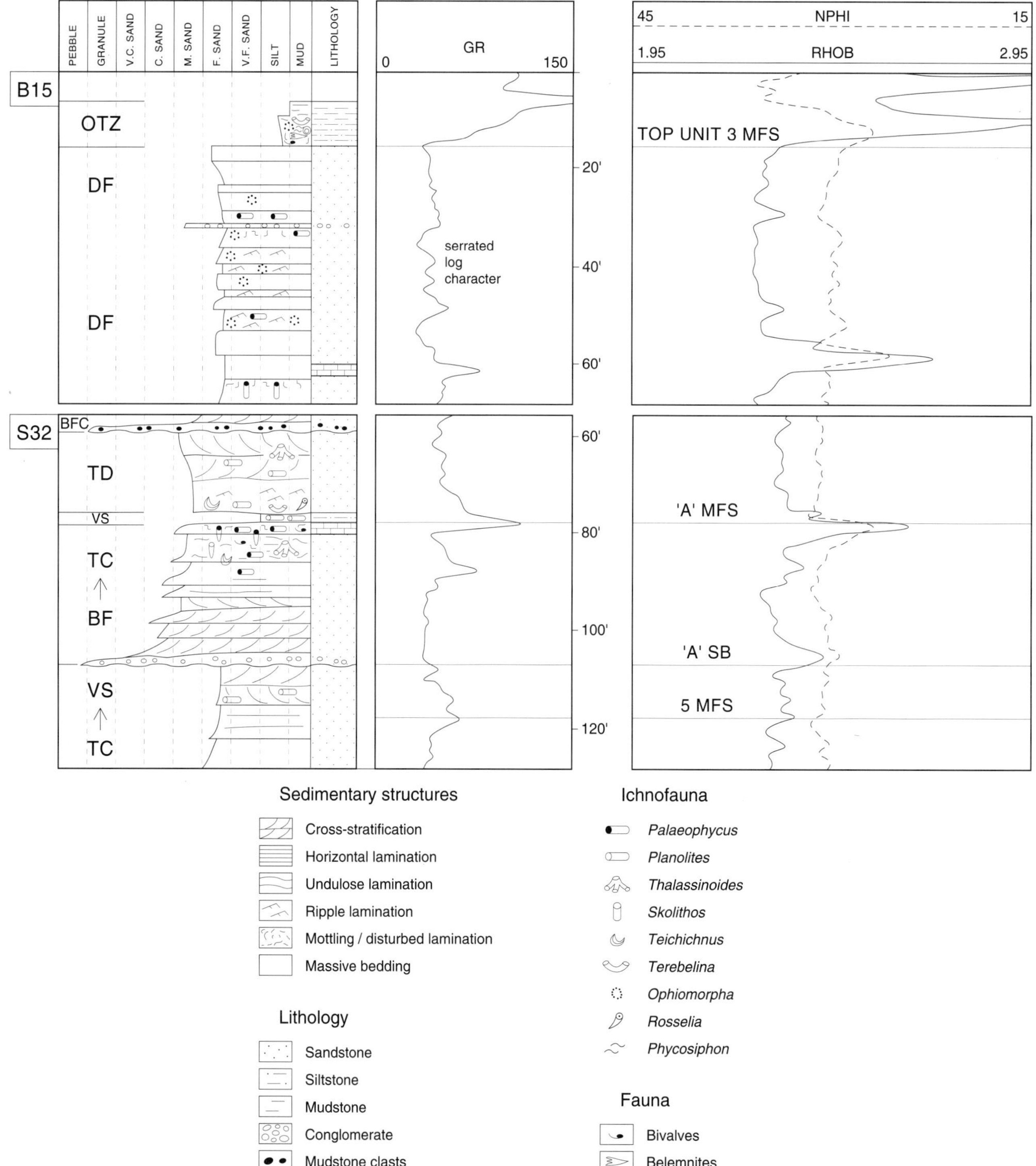

Fig. 4. Examples of core and wireline logs from Unit 3, Beryl B area, wells B15 and S32. OTZ = offshore transition zone; DF = delta front; BFC = braided fluvial channel; MFS = maximum flooding surface; SB = sequence boundary; TD = tidal dune; VS = variable salinity; TC = tidal channel.

The presence of bioturbation within mudstone beds suggests deposition above the anaerobic–aerobic boundary. The dominance of the horizontal grazing traces of *Phycosiphon* and *Helminthopsis* reflects deposition close to the photic zone (Pemberton *et al.* 1992), with the almost complete bioturbation of the substrate indicative of low sedimentation rates. The facies association is considered to represent deposition in a low energy marine environment possibly in the offshore transition zone between mean storm wave base and mean fair-weather wave base. However, evidence for storm deposition is not present because of the high levels of bioturbation, and so exact classification is not possible.

(2) The delta front facies association consists of very fine- to fine-grained sandstones with a sand/mud ratio up to 0.80 which form coarsening upward units 120 to 450 cm thick. It gradationally overlies the offshore transition zone facies association. Sandstones may be structureless, normally graded, current and wave rippled, or completely bioturbated. Structureless and graded beds are 2 to 45 cm thick and sharp to non-erosively based and may have current or wave-rippled tops. Sparse colonization bioturbation (bioturbation index (Taylor & Goldring 1993) = 2–3) is commonly present on bed tops consisting predominantly of downward penetrating *Ophiomorpha* burrows which also show a decrease in trace density

downwards. Millimetre-thick mudstone laminae commonly drape these beds. Graded beds form a series of fining-upward units within the overall coarsening-upward trend. The massive sandstones are interbedded with almost completely bioturbated beds (B.I. = 5–6). The trace fossil assemblage is diverse containing predominantly *Teichichnus* and *Ophiomorpha* with *Diplocraterion*, *Palaeophycus*, *Planolites*, *Siphonichnus*, *Helminthopsis*, *Skolithos*, *Thalassinoides*, *Asterosoma*, *Terebellina*, *Rhizocorallium*, *Phoebichnus* and *Rosselia*.

The increase in sand/mud ratio relative to the offshore transition zone facies association and the change from grazing traces to larger traces constructed by filter feeding organisms suggests a higher clastic input. The substrate is completely bioturbated with the exception of the structureless sandstone beds and thin rippled horizons. These beds record rapid, higher magnitude sedimentation events through which organisms were unable to colonize the substrate rapidly enough to keep pace with the accelerated rate of deposition. The largely structureless nature and fining upwards profile of these beds suggests an origin as gravity flows with sediment transported in turbulent suspension. A delta front depositional environment is suggested where rapidly deposited event beds were separated by periods of colonization and complete bioturbation of the substrate. The facies association is considered to be located within a bathymetric zone equivalent to the lower shoreface but with a higher clastic input, consequently a delta front environment is proposed.

(3) The tidal dune facies association consists of coarsening upward units 3 to 17 m thick with a sand/mud ratio of 0.85, and may grade upward from delta front deposits or variable salinity facies association. The base of the association contains lenticular, wavy and flaser bedded fine-grained sandstones with *Ophiomorpha* burrows within sand-rich units, and *Planolites* and *Palaeophycus* restricted to the muddy laminae. In places the trace fossil assemblage grades into a diverse *Ophiomorpha*-dominated assemblage with a wide variety of trace types such as *Teichichnus*, *Phycosiphon*, *Helminthopsis*, *Asterosoma*, *Diplocraterion*, *Rhizocorallium* and *Thalassinoides*. As the unit coarsens upward from fine- to medium-grained sandstones, the mudstone content (in the form of drapes) decreases and flaser bedding dominates together with sets of mud-draped trough cross-strata less than 25 cm thick. The bioturbation index decreases from 3–5 to 2–3 as the unit coarsens upward. The diversity also decreases upwards. The upper part of the facies association coarsens upward from medium- to coarse-grained sandstones dominated by trough and planar cross-strata (maximum observable preserved set thickness of 1 m) often displaying mud-draped foresets. The sandstones also show a decrease in mudstone content up the unit, with an upward decrease in mudstone drape frequency.

Flaser bedding together with mud-draped ripples and foresets reflect large fluctuations in energy conditions during deposition. The trace fossil assemblage is representative of brackish to normal marine salinity conditions and the common restriction of traces to mudstone laminae suggests opportunistic colonization bioturbation during low energy conditions. The above features, although not diagnostic, are indicative of a tide-influenced marginal marine setting. The upward increase in grain size, decrease in mudstone drape preservation and reduction in bioturbation, records increasing energy conditions within a shoaling upwards succession. The coarse-grained cross-stratified units are interpreted as subtidal dunes.

(4) The fluvio–tidal channel facies association comprises 8 to 25 m thick fining upwards units with a sand/mud ratio of 0.95. These units have erosive bases overlain by pebble lags composed of both intra- and extra-basinal material followed by horizontally and cross-stratified, granular to fine-grained, moderately to well sorted sandstones. Maximum preserved set thicknesses range from 7 to 100 cm. The sandstones display an upwards increase in bioturbation (B.I. = 1–2 to 4–5), and decrease in scale of sedimentary structure passing into fine- to medium-grained parallel to wavy laminated, massive and current rippled sandstones. Burrows are normally small and restricted to one or two types (*Planolites* and *Palaeophycus*), developed within organic-rich, silty laminae, whilst *Ophiomorpha irregulaire* with thin, incomplete wall linings is present within the sandstone intervals. Macrofauna include disarticulated and broken *Ostrea* and *Neomiodon*, commonly interpreted as euryhaline forms (e.g. MacLennan & Trewin 1989). Carbonaceous and mudstone drapes with a regular mm to cm interval spacing are common, particularly towards the top of the fining upward unit. Drape thickness increases upwards within the unit with increasing mudstone content. Reactivation surfaces are common. These features, together with the restricted ichnofaunal and macrofaunal characteristics, are the principal diagnostic criteria for recognizing tidal influence. In some cases, where the basal part of the facies is poorly sorted, coarse-grained, with no mudstone drapes, bioturbation or broken shell material, a braided fluvial interpretation is favoured.

(5) The variable salinity facies association comprises both fining upward and coarsening upward grain size profiles which vary in thickness from 100 to 500 cm and consist of fine- to very fine-grained sandstones. The association can either directly overlie fluvio–tidal channel deposits or lie beneath tidal dune deposits. The association commonly has a low sand/mud ratio of 0.3 to 0.5 and displays flaser, wavy and lenticular bedding. It is variably bioturbated by an impoverished *Ophiomorpha–Planolites–Palaeophycus* assemblage and occasional *Cylindrichnus* (B.I. = 3–6). The amount of bioturbation increases up the section. The sandstones also contain disarticulated and broken shell debris (*Ostrea*). Overlying these beds are completely bioturbated, very fine-grained sandstones and siltstones which fine upward into black, laminated mudstones. The sandstones (B.I. = 6) display either an *Ophiomorpha–Cylindrichnus* trace fossil assemblage or an indiscriminate mottling of the substrate. Mudstones are occasionally bioturbated with mm diameter *Planolites*/*Chondrites* burrow forms restricted to the upper part of the bed. This bioturbation suggests an oxygenated substrate prior to deposition of overlying sandstone beds. The mudstones at the top of these fining upward profiles also contain shell beds composed of largely *in situ* or slightly winnowed *Ostrea* and *Neomiodon*. This macrofaunal assemblage is taken to indicate a low salinity, brackish water environment, an interpretation supported by proprietary microfaunal studies carried out on similar facies in another area of the Beryl Embayment.

The mudstones are indicative of low energy deposition. The low diversity, impoverished micro- and macrofauna and trace fossil assemblages in the underlying sandstones suggest brackish salinities. However, this facies association is often laterally extensive, and can form traceable pressure barriers across the Beryl Bravo area (see later). Previous internal reports have interpreted the association as a lagoonal deposit. However, the considerable areal extent of the deposits (they can be traced across different fault blocks) indicates that they are the product of regional flooding events. A depositional environment with similar water depths to the offshore transition zone association is envisaged but with a lesser marine influence. Outcrop examples of this type of salinity variation developed in similar facies are found in the Middle Jurassic of Skye (e.g. Elgol, Cuillaidh and Garantiana Clay formations; Harris 1989; Hudson *et al.* 1995). The sandstones and siltstones are interpreted to represent sand sheets developed during transgressive reworking of tidal dune and channel deposits.

Wireline facies analysis

The Unit 3 cored sections have been used to generate a wireline-based facies scheme in order to correlate between uncored sections. This was done using the major wireline log suites (gamma-ray, sonic, neutron–density combination) to give a basic identification of lithology and guide correlation between cored sections. Only the gamma-ray trace and cored facies associations are shown in the correlation panels presented here.

The offshore transition zone and variable salinity facies associations have similar wireline responses with high gamma-ray and density values, the latter related to the common occurrence of siderite and calcite cemented zones at the base of these facies associations (Fig. 4). The delta front and tidal dune facies associations all display cleaning upward trends recognizable by an upward decrease in gamma-ray values and a characteristic increase in the separation between the neutron and density log suite (Fig. 4). The tidal dune facies association has a smooth cleaning upward trend representing a gradual decrease in clay content (Fig. 4). The delta front facies association is more difficult to define and may have either a serrated or smooth cleaning upward trend, depending on the frequency and thickness of the intercalated siltstone and massive sandstone beds. The tidal channel facies association has a bell shaped log signature (Fig. 4) with increasing gamma-ray values and an upward decrease in separation between the density and neutron log suites.

Reservoir engineering data

Knutson & Erga (1991), Knutson & Munro (1991) and Robertson (1993) noted that production performance and pressure histories within the Beryl Formation indicated the presence of facies-controlled vertical permeability barriers within the original reservoir zonation. In order to facilitate correlation between Unit 3 sections in the Beryl Bravo area, a detailed analysis of pressure data was undertaken. Examination of permeability barrier distribution initially required identification of boreholes largely unaffected by production from the nearby Beryl Alpha platform in order to establish initial reservoir pressures. In Beryl Bravo wells, the appearance of offset fluid gradients on a pressure–depth plot was considered sufficient evidence for the interpretation of a vertical permeability barrier at some point between the offset fluid gradients (Fig. 5). Care was taken to avoid pressure barriers caused by cemented horizons in sandstone sections and faulted sections.

The repeat formation tester (RFT) pressure data were primarily used to confirm the wireline-based identification of the two shale horizons that bound Unit 3, across both of which substantial pressure differentials are present. The Unit 2 shale separates the major producing zone, Unit 3, from the subordinate Unit 1 reservoir zone. Differential pressures of over 1564 psi have been observed (e.g. B18, drilled in 1988). A pressure differential also exists across the shale separating Unit 3 from Unit 4, but this rarely exceeds 230 psi (e.g. S55, drilled in 1992). Within the Unit 3 zone itself, there are smaller scale vertical permeability barriers present. These have considerably lower pressure differences across them (10–100 psi, Fig. 5), and represent a smaller scale of reservoir heterogeneity which is less consistent in distribution than that of the two major bounding shales.

An additional correlation method used when pressure or core data were not available was the analysis of permeability injection profiles (Fig. 6). The injection profiles reflect variations in stratal permeability which are often facies controlled. For example, high permeability streaks are commonly associated with coarse-grained fluvio–tidal channel deposits. Observations of this nature, together with a characteristic wireline log pattern, may help constrain specific facies associations over uncored intervals.

Beryl Unit 3: correlation

A series of north–south and east–west correlation panels have been constructed to illustrate the lateral and vertical variations in thickness and facies association distribution of Unit 3 in the

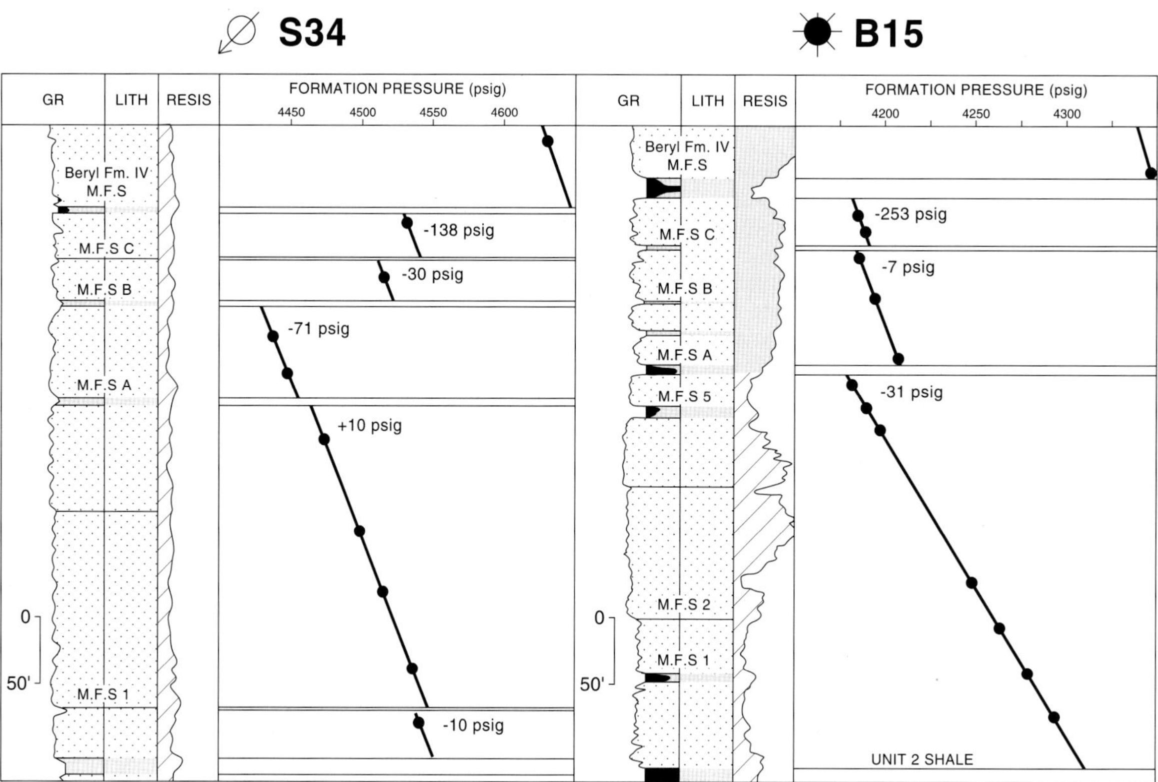

Fig. 5. Illustration of vertical permeability variations from pressure data. RFT profiles from a wells in the oil leg (B15) and water leg (S34) drilled at similar times. Fine stipple in resistivity column of B15 refers to the oil leg (note that the oil column occurs above a regional pressure barrier), diagonal lines refer to the water leg in this well and in S34. MFS = maximum flooding surface.

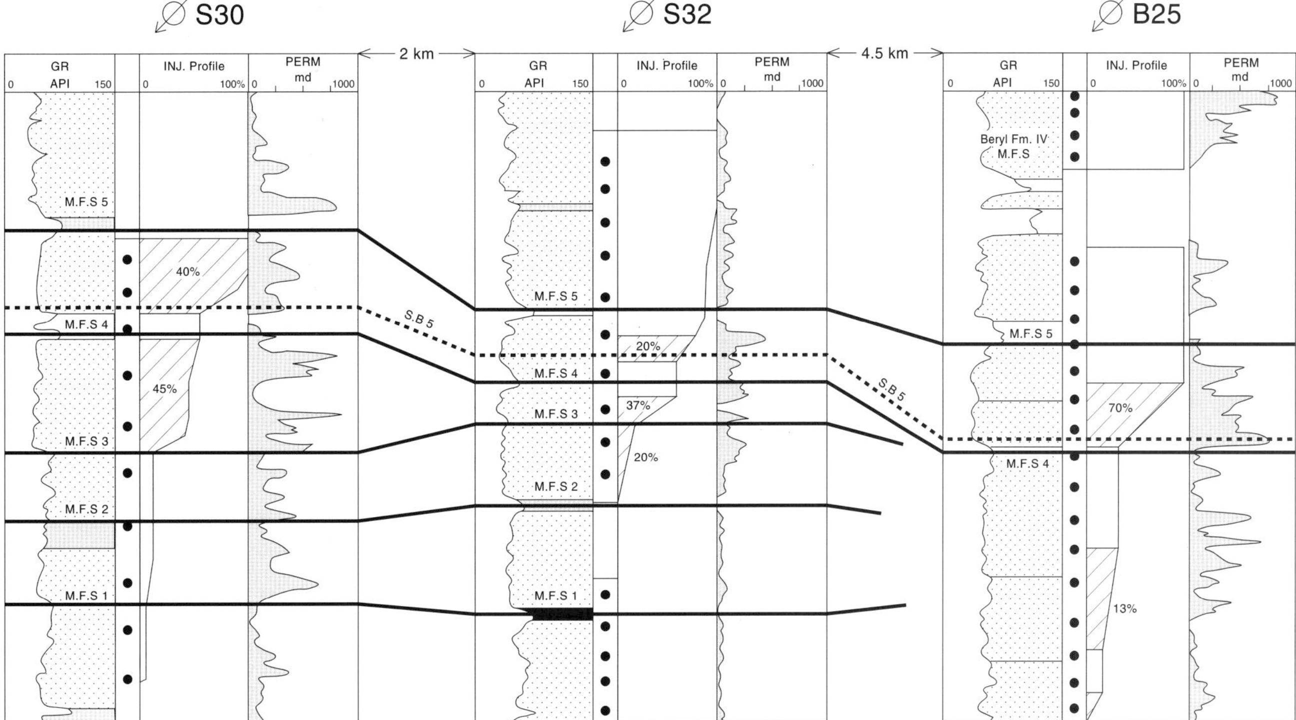

Fig. 6. Injection profiles from Beryl Unit 3. MFS = maximum flooding surface; SB = sequence boundary.

Beryl Bravo area (Fig. 7). Unit 3 can be divided into two sections which can be broadly located on all correlation panels. The upper section ranges from 0 to 100 m in thickness and consists of a maximum of four genetic sequences *sensu* Galloway (1989). The lower section ranges in thickness from 30 to 85 m and contains a maximum of five sequences. The approach of Galloway (1989) is used here as mudstone units recognizable in core and interpreted as maximum flooding surfaces (MFS) are often associated with pressure breaks and have an obvious wireline signature, facilitating correlation in uncored wells. In contrast, the identification of sequence boundaries (as defined by Van Wagoner *et al.* 1988) within sandstone-dominated units is more problematic in uncored wells. Sequence boundaries (SB) (*sensu* Van Wagoner *et al.* 1988) are identified where possible however, for a fuller reservoir description.

The lower section of Unit 3 consists of up to five sequences (*sensu* Galloway 1989), numbered from 1 to 5 from the base upwards. The base of the lower section is taken at the Unit 2 shale which is clearly defined on wireline logs. Unit 2 is interpreted to contain a major MFS which corresponds to the Bajocian–Bathonian boundary (Mitchener *et al.* 1992). The top of the lower section is taken at the 5 MFS. The 5 sequence boundary (SB; *sensu* Van Wagoner *et al.* 1988) which occurs within the 5 sequence is erosional and overlain by coarse-grained, extrabasinal material (Fig. 4) which form a highly permeable unit picked out by injection profiles (Fig. 6). The 5 sequence boundary marks the most northerly progradation of the tidal delta into the basin.

Sequences within the lower section of Unit 3 are 6–25 m in thickness. They consist of stacked, sharp-based fining upward log trends which in cored wells correspond to erosive-based, fluvio–tidal channel sandstones overlain by lower energy, variable salinity and delta front sediments (Fig. 8). The base of each fluvio–tidal sandstone package is interpreted as a depositional sequence boundary (*sensu* Van Wagoner *et al.* 1988) with the channel sandstones interpreted as lowstand to early transgressive systems tract deposits (Fig. 8). The finer grained variable salinity and delta front facies are interpreted as late transgressive systems tract sandstones and highstand deposits (Fig. 8). These stacked sequences are identified clearly within the southern Beryl Bravo area where Unit 3 thickness is greatest (Figs 3 & 7a–c). To the north of the Beryl Bravo area however, such sequences are less obvious, with the section consisting of 30–70 m of homogenous sandstones of the tidal dune and fluvio–tidal channel facies associations. Within these sections, sequence correlation is problematic, even within cored sections.

The four sequences identified within the upper section are designated A, B, C and D, with A being the lowest. The A sequence is present throughout the study area. The base of the sequence is taken at the underlying (sequence 5) MFS, which in cored sections is represented by either variable salinity facies (e.g. S30, Fig. 7b) or delta front facies (B04, Fig. 7b). The top of the A sequence is taken at the A MFS which is readily identified within cored sections as a variable salinity facies in the south of the area (Fig. 4b) or offshore transition zone mudstone facies further to the north (B04). Small-scale pressure breaks also occur across this unit within several wells (Fig. 5) in addition to changes in water injection profiles (Fig. 6).

Three other sequences (B, C and D) overlie the A sequence. These are best defined within the thicker sections of Unit 3 in the south of the study area (Fig. 7a & b) and may have pressure breaks corresponding to their maximum flooding surfaces. The development of Sequence B (Fig. 7a & c) is restricted to areas of the thickest Unit 3 deposition near wells S55 and B15 where it ranges from 0 to 20 m in thickness (Fig. 3). It is interpreted to record the local progradation and transgression of fluvio–tidal and tidal dune deposits. Sequence C extends further northwards than B and is up to 13 m thick, but shales out to the northeast (Fig. 7a & b). It is characterized by well-defined pressure breaks across the C MFS particularly in the west of the field (Fig. 7c & d). Facies associations within C are relatively more distal than those present in either the A or B sequences, being dominated by delta front deposits with

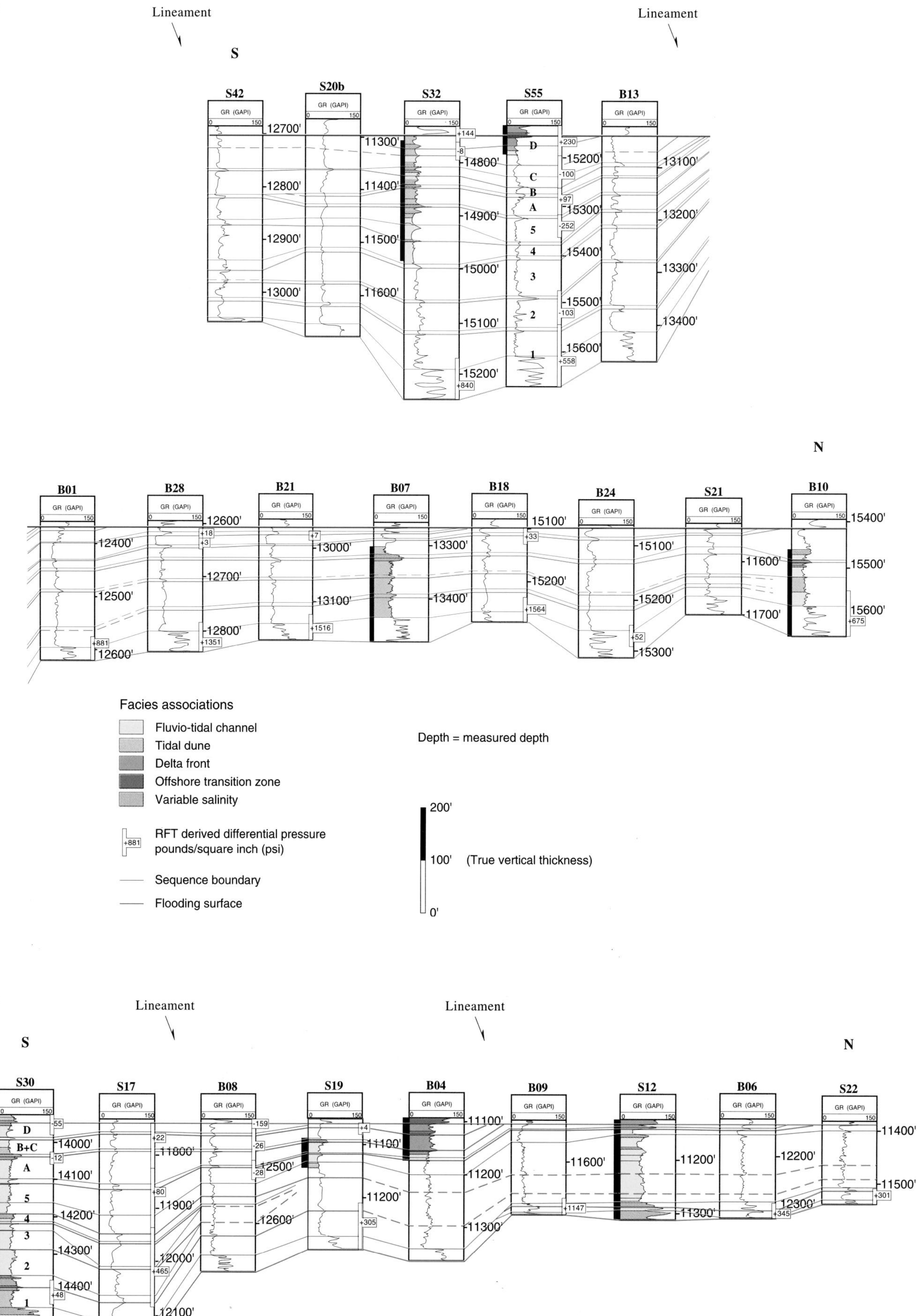

Fig. 7. Correlation panels for Beryl Bravo area (all logs used are true vertical thickness): (**a**) north–south section eastern flank; (**b**) north–south section east-central area; (**c**) north–south section west-central area; (**d**) north–south section western flank; (**e**) east-west section southern area. Location of sections shown in Fig. 3a.

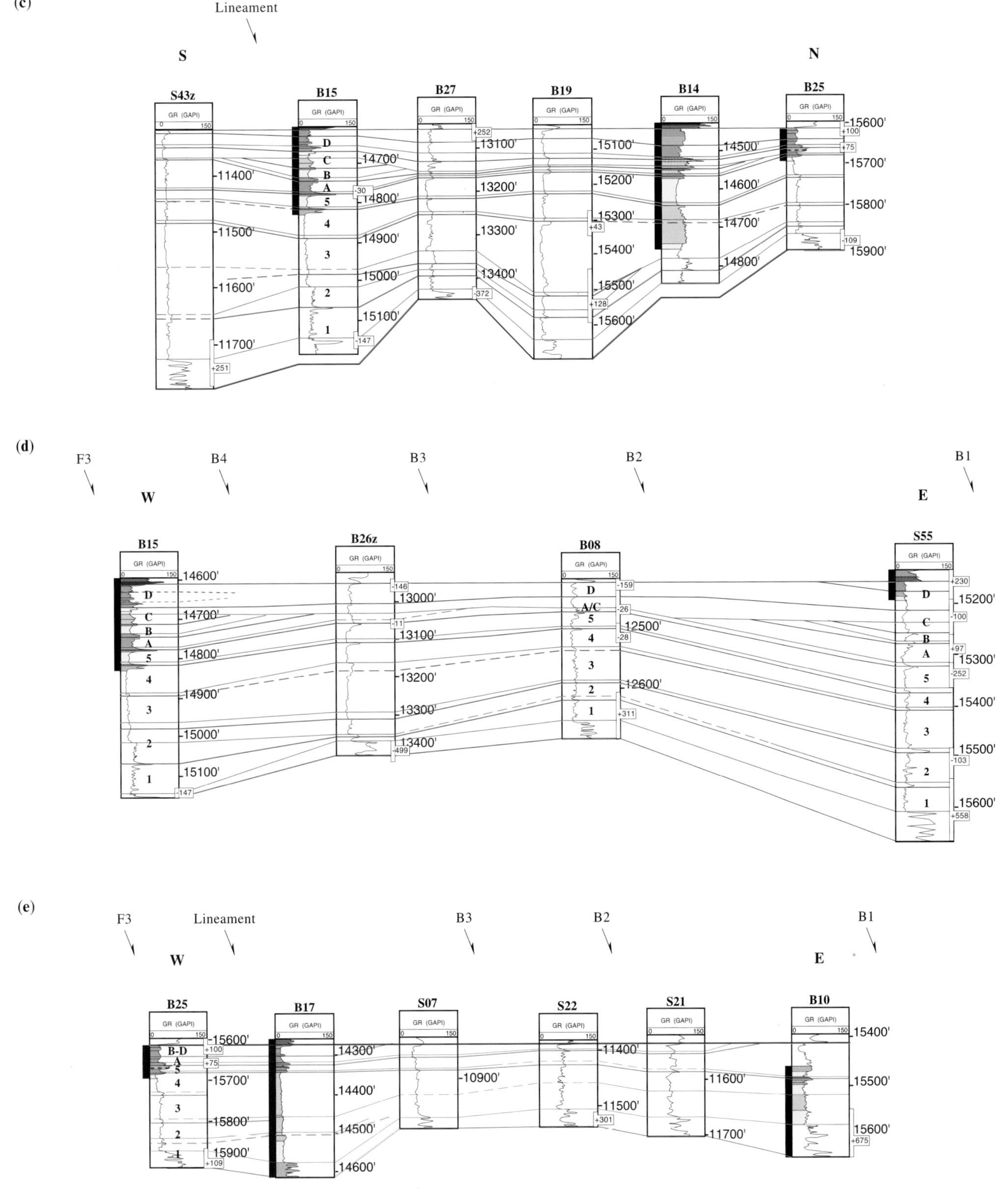

Fig. 7. *(continued)*.

fluvio–tidal facies only developed in the southern wells such as S30 (Fig. 7b). The D sequence is up to 10 m thick and has a similar distribution to the C sequence. The top of the D sequence is taken at the top Unit 3 MFS which has a pressure differential of up to 252 psi across it and corresponds to the Early–Middle Bathonian boundary (Mitchener *et al.* 1992). Facies associations within the D sequence consist solely of fine-grained delta front deposits with fluvio–tidal channel and tidal dune sediments restricted to the southern extremity of the study area.

Discussion

The Beryl Unit 3 is interpreted as a tide-dominated deltaic succession (Emery & Myers 1996). It contains ubiquitous tidal sedimentary structures such as mudstone couplets (Visser 1980) and reactivation surfaces (Allen 1980; Dalrymple 1984) throughout sections of the tidal dune and fluvio–tidal channel facies associations. The delta is considered to have been supplied from the south-southwest by a very high net : gross braided fluvial system penetrated in Well S43z (Fig. 7c) and by

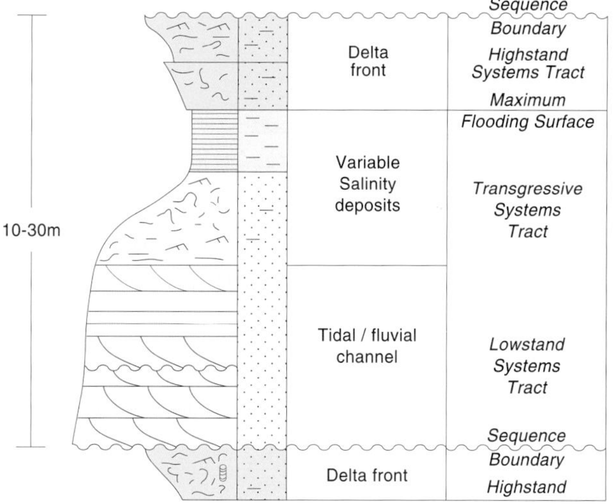

Fig. 8. Schematic diagram of large-scale fining upward trend interpreted as a depositional sequence, representative of the lower five sequences in Unit 3 within the Beryl Bravo area.

wells studied outside of the area under discussion here. Facies associations pass down depositional dip from fluvio–tidal channel to tidal dune, delta front into offshore transition zone deposits from south to north. The dip section (Fig. 7a) within sequence 4 through the delta facies illustrates this transition where fluvio–tidal channel facies (S32) pass into tidal dune facies (B07) down depositional dip. The variable salinity facies association which bounds the fluvio–tidal channel and tidal dune facies can be correlated with the marine delta front facies association using pressure data (Fig. 7c, A MFS from B15 to B25) and are thought to record low energy, distal tidal sedimentation associated with tidal sand sheet development on the landward fringe of the delta front (Emery & Myers 1996). Lower net : gross examples of this facies are thought to represent an equivalent to the low net : gross offshore transition zone facies association. The variability in salinity may be caused by either extensive fresh water input from the delta causing the creation of different faunal assemblages or stagnation of sections of the delta front caused by the strong tectonic control on the basin topography.

Similar facies and facies associations to those within Beryl Unit 3 have been have used to create predictive models for tide-dominated deltas (Coleman & Prior 1982; Emery & Myers 1996). These models are based upon the limited number of descriptions of tidal deltas (e.g. Coleman 1976; Wright *et al.* 1975) and composite models derived from estuarine sand bar complexes (Dalrymple *et al.* 1990), sub-tidal bars (Mutti *et al.* 1985; Nio & Yang 1991) and distal sand sheets (Levell 1980; Surlyk & Noe-Nygaard 1991). Tidal sedimentary structures have also been described from estuarine (Dalrymple *et al.* 1992), tidal inlet (Hubbard *et al.* 1979; Rhodes & Moslow 1993) and offshore sand ridge (McCave 1971; Stride 1982; Tye & Moslow 1993) depositional environments, and within these settings the facies associations are well documented. However, many of the facies associated with tidal deltas and estuarine successions such as supra/inter-tidal flats and shoreface and barrier bar successions have not been recognized within the Beryl Unit 3 section. The offshore tidal sand ridge is similar to the tidal dune facies association; however, the variable ichnofaunal assemblages within this association suggests a similar type of bedform, but one deposited in a variable salinity environment in close proximity to freshwater run-off.

The distal part of the Beryl Unit 3 delta system is marked by the occurrence of the variable salinity facies association which is interpreted as a tidal sand sheet. A further basinwards transition is seen with the change from sand sheet to delta front deposition recording a marked change in depositional process. The distal parts of the deltaic system predominantly found within sequences A to D have mudstone-dominated offshore transition zone sediments overlain by delta front facies (Fig. 7c). The gravity flows within the delta front may have been caused by either tidal drawdown (Smith *et al.* 1990), river flood or tectonic events which then shed material off the delta top toward the delta front and pro-delta. These finer grained lithologies are less common in the lower five sequences which may mean that either the location of the delta front for these sequences was outside of the study area, or that they are only present within the upper four sequences.

On a large-scale, Unit 3 in the Beryl Bravo area records the initial northeastwards progradation of a tidal delta over the Unit 2 MFS (Fig. 9a). The five sequences within the lower section are interpreted as a progradational sequence set, recorded by an increase in fluvial sedimentation, particularly within the top 2 sequences. These sequences are dominated by fluvio–tidal channel and tidal dune facies across the whole area. The four sequences in the upper section record a gradual southwardly directed transgression across the tidal delta culminating in deposition of the top Unit 3 MFS, and represent a retrogradational sequence set (Fig. 9a). The upper sequences are dominated by more distal facies of the delta front but also have fluvio–tidal channel and tidal dune facies preserved in the south of the area (Fig. 7a–c). The presence of all the facies within the upper sequences suggests a narrowing of facies belts at this time, possibly as a result of an increase in depositional slope with a possible tectonic cause during an overall long term relative sea-level rise. Changes in proportions of facies associations in different system tracts are not easy to establish because of the lack of well developed highstand systems tracts in the area. This is shown by the proximity of the MFS to the SB in the sequences (Fig. 7). This lack of preserved highstand deposits is not fully understood and may be a result of tectonic controls on accommodation space development.

In addition to the large-scale variation in deltaic sedimentation, deposition of Unit 3 was also strongly controlled by tectonic elements present within the Beryl Bravo area. Thickened sections are developed in hanging wall areas adjacent to the two main faults active during sedimentation (F2 and B3). Sections drilled in these areas contain full, heterogeneous sequences. In contrast, when correlated across faults onto footwall crests, the full sequences are equivalent to thinner sections of homogenous tidal sandstones (Fig. 7d). Active fault control has strongly influenced sequence development, with full sections developed in areas of greater accommodation space in the hanging wall, whereas equivalently aged sections in areas of low accommodation space on the footwall crest have been subject to extensive reworking and homogenization by tidal processes. The NW–SE lineaments which cross-cut the study area appear to control facies belts in some places, but also had an indirect affect on sequence development by controlling the subsidence on the larger N–S faults (Figs 3b & 7a–c).

A number of mechanisms are considered to have controlled facies development and associated reservoir architecture during deposition of Unit 3. The Unit 2 and top Unit 3 maximum flooding surfaces are coincident with two regionally correlative events as documented throughout the Viking Graben by Mitchener *et al.* (1992). Any causal mechanism for these events must have operated at a basinwide or larger scale, and consequently, they may well be eustatic in origin.

Fault activity strongly influenced sequence stacking patterns by locally controlling the available accommodation space, as shown by the development and preservation of full, thickened sequences in hanging wall areas (Fig. 7e) and thin, homogenized sequences of tidally reworked deposits on footwall crests. The exact control on small-scale sequence development

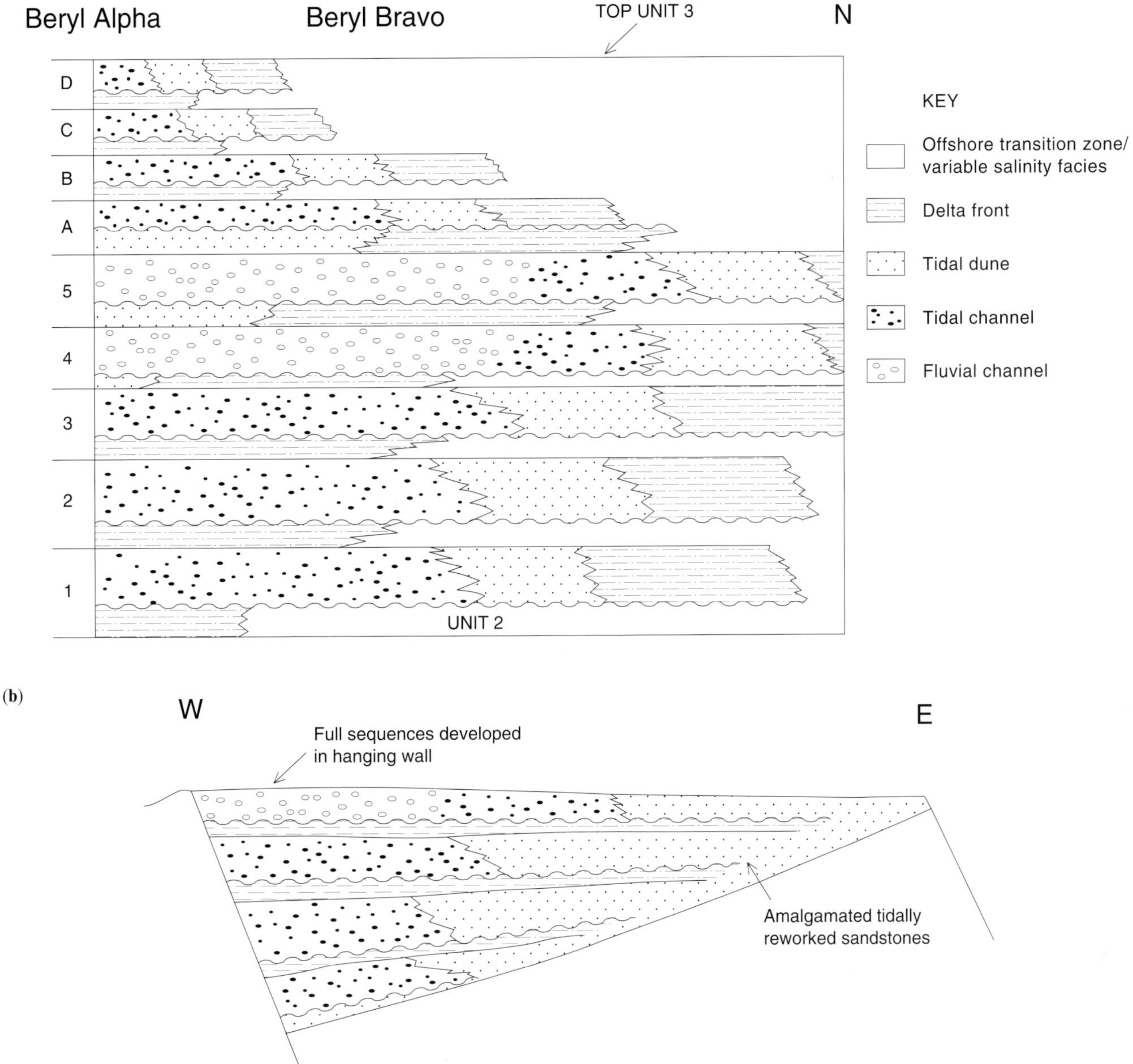

Fig. 9. Schematic representation of: (**a**) depositional dip section; and (**b**) cross-section across a half-graben, showing sequence development within Unit 3. The flooding surfaces correspond to either the variable salinity or offshore transition zone facies association.

is unclear and may be a function of local variations in sediment supply or high frequency changes in relative sea-level or a combination of both.

Implications for reservoir zonation

The combined static and dynamic description of Beryl Unit 3 in the Beryl Bravo area presented here is a substantial remodification of the previous reservoir zonation accounting for the heterogeneity and unpredictable reservoir performance described earlier (Knutson & Erga 1991). The revised scheme highlights the lateral variability and heterogeneity of individual reservoir zones, illustrating the importance of thin shales in forming laterally extensive pressure and fluid flow barriers. The scheme accounts for compartmentalization of the reservoir, and may allow for the identification of likely thief zones and areas of by-passed oil in the future, resulting in better completion strategies and targets for infill drilling.

Conclusions

The study of Beryl Formation Unit 3 in the Beryl Bravo area has highlighted the variability of reservoir geometry and architecture in a tidal deltaic setting. Nine genetic sequences were identified within this setting by detailed sedimentological correlation and integration with dynamic data. The latter constrain the lateral extent of the sequence bounding impermeable lithologies and therefore the importance of a refined reservoir zonation. These sequences are interpreted as an initial progradational and later transgressive sequence sets. Within this rigorous, dynamically constrained framework a predictive model has been developed which accounts for the tectonic development and the environmental response to changes in rates of accommodation space generation. This work further highlights some of the difficulties involved in correlation within a tide-dominated deltaic succession deposited within a series of active half-graben affected by high frequency changes in relative sea-level.

The authors would like to thank Mobil North Sea Ltd and the Beryl Field partners for access to the data and technical support. Financial support was provided by Mobil PhD studentship (GM) and by a Mobil lectureship (AJH).

References

ALLEN, J. R. L. 1980. Sand waves: a model of origin and internal structure. *Marine Geology*, **26**, 281–328.

COLEMAN, J. M. 1976. *Deltas: Processes of Deposition and Models for Exploration*. Continuing Education Publication Co. Champaign, Illinois.

—— & PRIOR, D. P. 1982. Deltaic environments of deposition. *In*: SCHOLLE, P. A. & SPEARING, D. (eds) *Sandstone Depositional Environments*. American Association of Petroleum Geologists Memoirs, **31**.

DALRYMPLE, R. W. 1984. Morphology and internal structures of sandwaves in the Bay of Fundy. *Sedimentology*, **31**, 365–382.

——, KNIGHT, R. J., ZAITLIN, B. A. & MIDDLETON, G. V. 1990. Dynamics and facies model of a macrotidal sandbar complex, Cobequoid Bay – Salmon River Estuary (Bay of Fundy). *Sedimentology*, **37**, 577–612.

——, ZAITLIN, B. A. & BOYD, R. 1992. Estuarine facies models: conceptual basis and stratigraphic implications. *Journal of Sedimentary Petrology*, **62**, 1130–1146.

EMERY, D. & MYERS, K. J. 1996. *Sequence Stratigraphy*. Blackwell, Oxford.

GALLOWAY, W. E. 1989. Genetic stratigraphic sequences in basin analysis I: architecture and genesis of flooding-surface bounded depositional units. *Bulletin of the American Association of Petroleum Geologists*, **73**, 125–142.

HARRIS, J. P. 1989. The sedimentology of a Middle Jurassic lagoonal delta system: Elgol Formation (Great Estuarine Group), NW Scotland. *In*: WHATELY, M. K. & PICKERING, K. (eds) *Deltas: Sites and Traps for Fossil Fuels*. Geological Society, London, Special Publications, **41**, 147–166.

HUBBARD, D. K., OERTAL, G. & NUMMEDAL, D. 1979. The role of waves and tidal currents in the development of tidal inlet sedimentary structures and sand body geometry: examples from North Carolina and Georgia. *Journal of Sedimentary Petrology*, **49**, 1073–1092.

HUDSON, J. D., CLEMENTS, R. G., RIDING, J. B., WAEFIELD, M. I. & WALTON, W. 1995. Jurassic paleosalinties and brackish-water communities – a case study. *Palaios*, **10**, 392–407.

KNUTSON, C. A. & ERGA, R. E. 1991. Effect of horizontal and vertical permeability restrictions in the Beryl reservoir. *Journal of Petroleum Technology*, **43**, 1502–1509. SPE Paper 19299.

—— & MUNRO, I. C. 1991. The Beryl Field, Block 9/13, UK North Sea. *In*: ABBOTTS, I. L. (ed.) *United Kingdom Oil and Gas Fields, 25 Years Commemorative Volume*. Geological Society Memoirs, **14**, 33–42.

LEVELL, B. K. 1980. A late Precambrian tidal shelf deposit, the Lower Sanjfjord Formation, Finnmark, North Norway. *Sedimentology*, **27**, 539–557.

MCCAVE, I. N. 1971. Sand waves in the North Sea off the coast of Holland. *Marine Geology*, **10**, 199–225.

MACLENNAN, A. M. & TREWIN, N. H. 1989. Palaeoenvironments of the late Bathonian–mid-Calovian in the Inner Moray Firth. *In*: BATTEN, D. J. & KEEN, M. C. (eds) *Studies in Northwest European Micropalaeontology and Palynology*. British Micropalaeontological Society, 92–117.

MITCHENER, B. C., LAWRENCE, D. A., PARTINGTON, M. B., BOWMAN, M. B. J. & GLUYAS, J. 1992. Brent Group: sequence stratigraphy and regional implications. *In*: MORTON, A. C., HASZELDINE, R. S., GILES, M. R. & BROWN, S. (eds) *Geology of the Brent Group*. Geological Society, London, Special Publications, **61**, 45–80.

MUTTI, E., ROSELL, J., ALLEN, J. P., FONNESU, F. & SGAVETTI, M. 1985. The Eocene Baronia tide dominated delta-shelf system in the Ager Basin. *In*: MILA, M. D. & ROSELL, J. (eds) *Excursion Guidebook: 6th European Regional Meeting*. International Association of Sedimentologists, Lerida, Spain, 579–600.

NIO, S.-D. & YANG, C.-S. 1991. Diagnostic attributes of clastic tidal deposits: a review. *In*: SMITH, D. G., REINSON, G. E., ZAITLIN, B. A. & RAHMANI, R. A. (eds) *Clastic Tidal Sedimentology*. Memoir of the Canadian Society of Petroleum Geologists, **16**, 3–28.

PEMBERTON, S. G., MACEACHERN, J. A. & FREY, R. W. 1992. Trace fossil facies models: environmental and allostratigraphic significance. *In*: WALKER, R. G. & JAMES, N. P. (eds) *Facies Models: Response to Sea Level Change*. Geological Association of Canada, 47–72.

RICHARDS, P. C., LOTT, G. K., JOHNSON, H., KNOX, R. W.O'B. & RIDING, J. B. 1993. Jurassic of the Central and Northern North Sea. *In*: KNOX, R. W.O'B. & CORDEY, W. G. (eds) *Lithostratigraphic Nomenclature of the UK North Sea*. British Geological Survey, Nottingham.

ROBERTSON, G. 1993. The Beryl Field: geological evolution and reservoir behaviour. *In*: PARKER, J. R. (ed.) *Petroleum Geology of Northwest Europe: Proceedings of the 4th Conference*. The Geological Society, London, 1491–1502.

SMITH, N. D., PHILLIPS, A. C. & POWELL, R. D. 1990. Tidal drawdown: a mechanism for producing cyclic sediment laminations in glaciomarine deltas. *Geology*, **18**, 10–13.

STRIDE, A. H. (ed.) 1982. *Offshore Tidal Sands: Processes and Deposits*. Chapman & Hall, London.

SURLYK, F. & NOE-NYGAARD, N. 1991. Sand bank and dune facies architecture of a wide intracratonic seaway: late Jurassic–early Cretaceous Raukelv Formation, Jameson Land, East Greenland. *In*: MIALL, A. D. & TYLER, N. (eds) *The Three-Dimensional Facies Architecture of Terrigenous Clastic Sediments, and its Implications for Hydrocarbon Discovery and Recovery*. Concepts in Sedimentology and Palaeontology 3, SEPM, Tulsa, 261–276.

TAYLOR, A. M. & GOLDRING, R. 1993. Description and analysis of bioturbation and ichnofabric. *Journal of the Geological Society*, London, **150**, 141–148.

TYE, R. S. & MOSLOW, T. F. 1993. Tidal inlet reservoirs: insights from modern examples. *In*: RHODES, E. G. & MOSLOW, T. F. (eds) *Marine Clastic Reservoirs. Examples and Analogues*. Frontiers in Sedimentary Geology.

VAN WAGGONER, J. C., POSAMENTIER, H. W., MITCHUM, R. M., VAIL, P. R., SARG, J. F., LOUTIT, T. S. & HARDENBOL, J. 1988. An overview of the fundamentals of sequence stratigraphy and key definitions. *In*: WILGUS, C. K., HASTINGS, B. S., KENDALL, C. G. ST. C., POSAMENTIER, H. W., ROSS, C. A. & VAN WAGGONER, J. C. (eds) *Sea-Level Changes: An Integrated Approach*. Society of Economic Paleontologists and Mineralogists, Special Publications, **42**, 39–45.

VISSER, M. J. 1980. Neap-spring cycles reflected in Holocene subtidal large-scale bedform deposits: a preliminary note. *Geology*, **8**, 543–546.

WRIGHT, L. D., COLEMAN, J. M. & THOM, B. G. 1975. Sediment transport and deposition in a macro-tidal river channel: Ord River, Western Australia. *Estuarine Research*, **II**, 309–322.

Capturing reservoir heterogeneity in a sand-rich submarine fan, Miller Field

C. R. GARLAND,[1] P. HAUGHTON,[2] R. F. KING[1] and T. P. MOULDS[1]

[1] *BP Exploration Operating Company, Dyce, Aberdeen, AB2 0PB, UK*
[2] *University of Dublin, Belfield, Dublin 4, Republic of Ireland (formerly of Badley-Ashton & Associates)*

Abstract: Miller production began its decline phase in July 1997. To investigate the challenges of the decline period and the options for extending field life a detailed reservoir heterogeneity model was set up based on analysis of 26 wells, of which 19 were cored. The Miller fan is a high net : gross sandy submarine fan system in which lobe abandonment facies and numerous thin shales form the important heterogeneities. Each reservoir zone was described in terms of eight depositional elements and fourteen lithotypes. These descriptions were incorporated into the model at a resolution which ensured capture of the most significant heterogeneities. A stochastic generator was used to build a detailed static description of the permeability of the reservoir. The important heterogeneities were captured in a cell size of 60 m × 60 m × *c.* 0.02 m. Volumetric rock properties such as zone isochore, net : gross and porosity were mapped using conventional methods. The static description was up-scaled into an area of local grid refinement of the Eclipse reservoir simulator with 33 dynamic subzones at a cell size of 100 m × 100 m × *c.* 2.5 m. The detailed reservoir model matched well and field performance in the decline period more closely than the previous deterministic model. Stochastic realizations of the model enabled a better estimate of uncertainty to be demonstrated. The success of the process indicated that greater benefit would be obtained by its extension over a larger area of the field.

The Miller Field is located near the western margin of the South Viking Graben in Blocks 16/7b & 16/8b (Fig. 1). It had been producing oil at plateau rates of 130 000 BOPD since shortly after production started in 1992, but in July 1997 these rates began to decline, as had been predicted by full-field reservoir simulation. The main challenges of the decline period were optimization of the gas injection project, the necessity for infill wells and the viability of field depressurization. To address these challenges a reservoir description programme was set up in 1995 in which a detailed static model was built to be used in conjunction with the full-field simulator. The structure of the project is shown on the flow chart (Fig. 2) depicting the categories of geological input (zone boundaries; floating heterogeneities; permeable lithotypes; volumetric rock properties) and the stages of the project (digital core description; interpretation; stochastic modelling; up-scaling; dynamic simulation; analysis of results and iterations).

The Miller reservoir is a very high net : gross turbidite succession and one of the key outcomes of the study has been the recognition that even the subdued heterogeneity and minor non-permeable elements within this reservoir have a significant impact on reservoir performance. This paper first addresses the

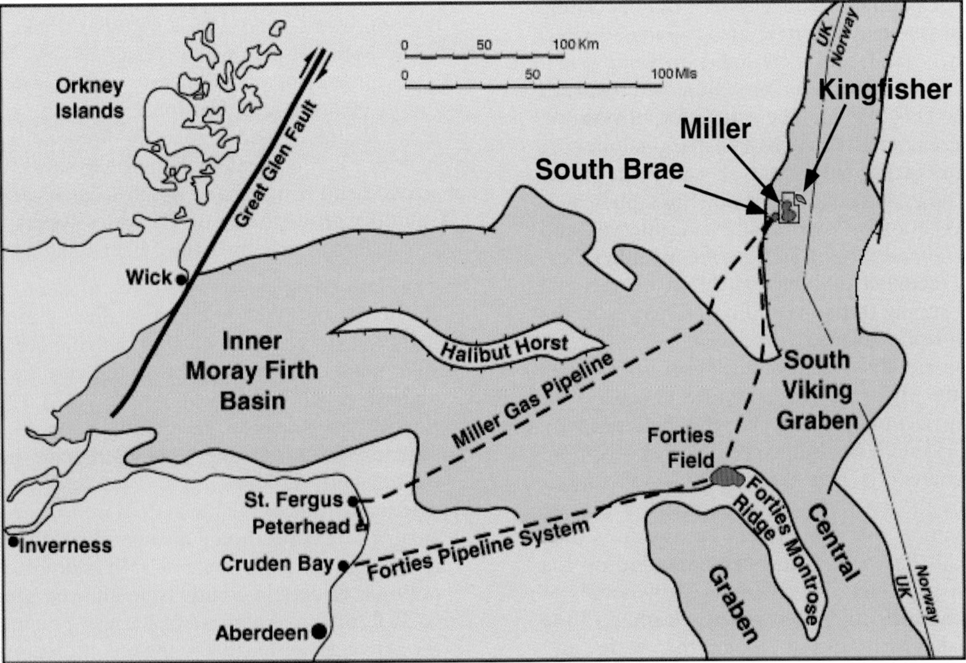

Fig. 1. Location map.

Garland, C. R., Haughton, P., King, R. F. & Moulds, T. P. 1999. Capturing reservoir heterogeneity in a sand-rich submarine fan, Miller Field. *In*: Fleet, A. J. & Boldy, S. A. R. (eds) *Petroleum Geology of Northwest Europe: Proceedings of the 5th Conference*, 1199–1208.

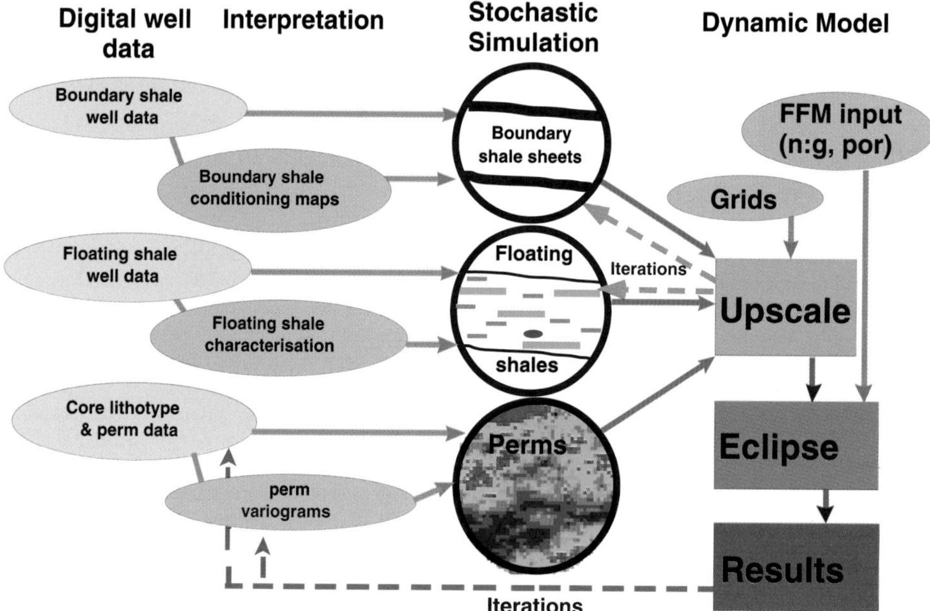

Fig. 2. Miller model elements and process flow.

geological rationale behind the new static description and then illustrates how key elements of the geology have been treated in the more detailed reservoir model. The performance of the new model against production data is then considered together with results and their relevance for the future life of the field.

Static geological model

At the outset, it is worth stressing that permeability heterogeneity in turbidite reservoirs can be treated at various scales. The behaviour of density currents depositing turbidites can impart textural variations and sedimentary structures which contribute to permeability heterogeneity at probe permeameter, core plug and bed scale. The frequency of sand-depositing density currents, and whether they were able to scour the bed before depositing their sand load, determines to what extent non-reservoir 'background' deposits are preserved between successive turbidites. This can often be a function of position within the system e.g. channel axis vs channel margin, lobe core vs lobe fringe. These 'background' intervals can form baffles and barriers to fluid flow, particularly at production timescales. At a larger scale, alternations between sand-prone intervals and more heterogeneous 'abandonment' sections record either local re-routing of flows (channel or lobe switching) or regional fluctuations in sand supply to the basin floor. Changes in the slope to basin floor profile can also introduce major intercalations of non-reservoir slope sediment on the basin floor.

Heterogeneity in the Miller reservoir is apparent at all these levels. The following sections outline how this heterogeneity has been incorporated into a new static geological description. The overall 'fan' context is first described, as this has a significant bearing on the heterogeneity structure. Correlation leading to layer definition within the reservoir interval is then briefly considered: this has been a key step in setting up the larger-scale reservoir geometry. This is followed by details of lithotype make-up and bed-scale heterogeneity, leading to the depositional template used to condition the scale and distribution of heterogeneities between wells.

The term 'lobe' is used below in a geometrical sense to refer to discrete lobate bundles (in planform) of turbidite beds deposited at the end of the main feeder channels. Lobes used in this sense are not synonymous with a sheet architecture, but embrace a spectrum of nested channel, amalgamated sheet to isolated sheet geometries. The ensuing discussion focuses on permeability heterogeneity of depositional origin. Note, however, that the Miller sandstones have undergone variable quartz cementation (Gluyas *et al.* 1998) which introduces a level of diagenetic heterogeneity.

System context

The Miller reservoir was assigned to Unit 2 of the Brae Formation of Kimmeridgian-Volgian (J66) age (Turner *et al.* 1987). It is part of a small sand-rich fan 'complex' which extended *c.*15 km from the western margin of the South Viking Graben (Garland 1993; Rooksby 1991). Elements of the same system are also present in the South Brae Field to the southwest, and the Kingfisher Field to the northeast. The South Brae area, traversed as it is by a number of elongate tongues of conglomerate and sandstone interpreted as the fill of large-scale erosional channels, appears to have straddled the main feeder zone for flows emerging on to the basin floor. The equivalent Kingfisher succession is a lower net : gross distal fringe made up of isolated sand sheets.

A number of attributes of the wider system are relevent to treating heterogeneity over the Miller Field area.

(1) The fan complex was fed by a clean and texturally restricted supply of fine and medium-grained sand which had been stored in coastal and shelf depocentres. The flows were consequently depleted in silt/clay fraction sediment and were poorly efficient (*sensu* Mutti 1985), collapsing rapidly on reaching the basin floor to deposit thick structureless sandstone beds. Bed scale heterogeneity is consequently subdued.
(2) The small-scale of the fan system led to marked across-field changes in depositional geometry as the flows radiated away from the feeder channels. In addition, the presence of multiple feeders in South Brae allowed sand to enter the basin floor across a broad front, with potential switching of the active feeder localizing the accumulation of sand on the basin floor.
(3) The northwestern edge of the basin was constrained by a co-eval slope system (Fig. 3), the position of which changed as the fan complex built up against it. This made for complex interfingering of slope and basin floor facies over the northwestern part of the field.

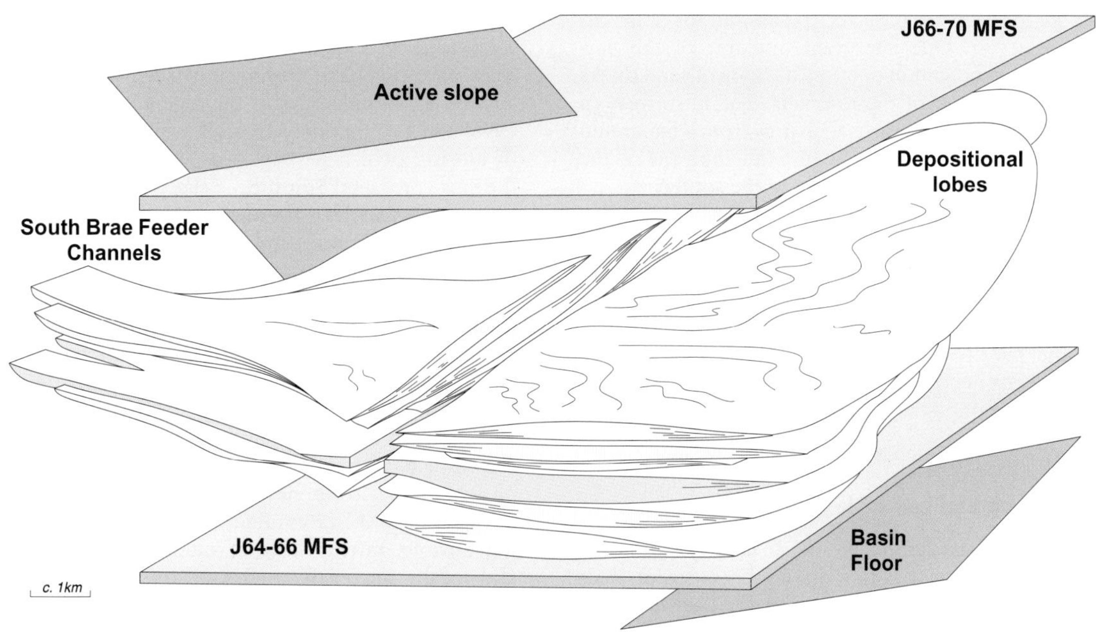

Fig. 3. Miller fan schematic architecture.

Reservoir subdivision

Reservoir subdivision is a critical step in capturing the larger-scale reservoir architecture. In a deep-water fan complex like Miller, the subdivision ideally needs to isolate coherent episodes of fan deposition within which there are systematic lateral and vertical trends in net : gross, geometry and degree of internal heterogeneity. Such trends can then be used to guide the spatial modelling of reservoir properties and barriers to flow. The Miller succession is amenable to subdivision in this way in that it has an aggradational architecture with step-like vertical changes in net : gross which correspond to local and field-wide abandonments and repeated lateral relocation of the fan axes (see later). The zonation therefore highlights surfaces across which a significant re-configuration of the fan system occurred as a consequence of either feeder channel switching, lobe offset, slope-basin floor profile changes, and/or a variable sediment flux. The tendency for more heterogeneous abandonment packages to lie directly beneath many of these has led to them forming significant vertical barriers to flow within the reservoir.

Subdivision of the Miller reservoir was constrained by RFT data and high resolution biostratigraphy tied to the step-changes in lithology and inferred geometry deduced from core and wireline logs. Poor resolution precluded seismic mapping of surfaces within the reservoir (McClure & Brown 1992), hence the importance of the biostratigraphical zonation and good core coverage. Ten zones were recognized (Fig. 4). Two of these (zones M6 and M8) incorporate thin (cm-scale) mud-prone packages which can be traced throughout the field representing significant periods during which the sand supply was inhibited. The remaining layers are sand-prone, variations in lithotype composition and overall net : gross giving a subtly different make-up for each layer (M4, for instance, is of particularly high overall net : gross). The section across the northwestern edge of the fan stack (Fig. 4) demonstrates

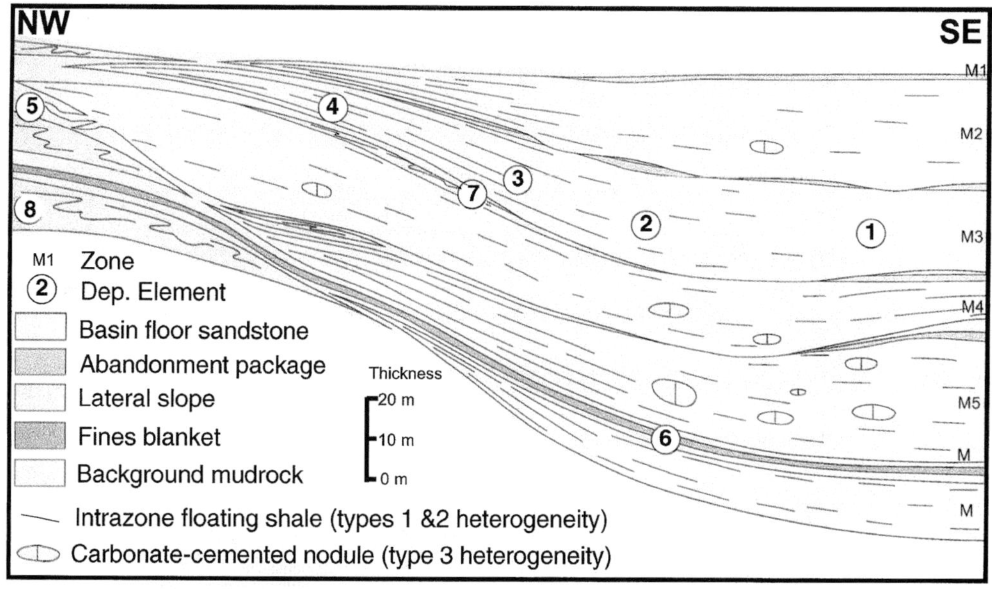

Fig. 4. Model section: reservoir zones and depositional elements.

the changes in location of the sand pinch-out for different levels in the reservoir. One important outcome of the new subdivision was the recognition of offset stacking of sand thicks and pinch-outs at the top of the reservoir. The northwestern lateral margin steps southeastwards with time from a maximum slope onlap during M4 to the youngest fan lobe (M1), the margin of which had stepped some 6 km to the southeast.

Mapping of the surfaces arising from the reservoir subdivision had previously been found to be an effective means of capturing the larger-scale heterogeneity. Significant heterogeneity is also apparent between these surfaces: here the depositional context is important in specifying the style, dimensions and distribution of heterogeneous elements. The rationale behind the depositional model is therefore discussed in the following sections, starting at a process/bed scale.

Lithotype make-up and bed scale heterogeneity

The Miller reservoir is dominated by structureless fine to medium-grained sandstones, often in thick (m-scale) beds showing varying degrees of amalgamation. The lithotype inventory (Fig. 5) demonstrates that some 85% of the succession comprises sandstones which are either structureless or faintly mottled, the latter with a distinctive fabric produced by scattered mm-scale carbonaceous and mudrock flecks. Less commonly, granule or pebble-rich, dewatered or stratified sandstones occur together with the structureless sandstones. Where bed tops are preserved, many of the thick beds have distinctive 'slurried' caps characterized by an argillaceous sandstone with common mudclasts and large carbonaceous fragments. The latter are seen as the tails to flows which emplaced the underlying sand, implying that the flows were turbulent enough to allow segregation of material with different densities and settling velocities. This suggests that the structureless sandstones were deposited by the rapid collapse of flows that were once turbulent (ruling out a debris flow origin for the structureless sandstones of the type advanced by Shanmugam 1996) and also that they are significantly down-range of the site of erosion (which perhaps was the channel incisions seen in the more proximal South Brae succession). The broad assemblage of structureless, mottled, pebbly, slurried, stratified and dewatered sandstones are grouped as high-density turbidite (HDT) deposits.

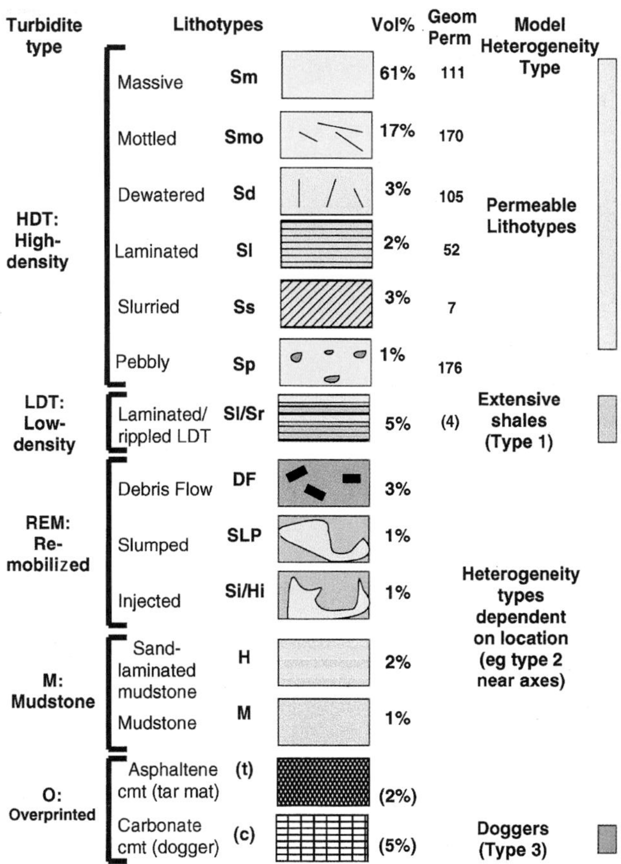

Fig. 5. Lithotype inventory.

Structured (parallel and ripple-laminated), graded and often more thinly-bedded sandstones are subordinate (5%) and attributed to the passage of less common low-density turbidity (LDT) currents. They tend to occur as discrete beds in their own right, rather than capping structureless sandstone beds, and they are typically found in more heterogeneous intervals recording back-stepping and abandonment of the sand system, or within the lower net : gross lateral fringes of some sand fairways (e.g. M2). Remobilized deposits include beds containing obvious rafted clasts of mudrock, carbonaceous matter and locally unconsolidated sandstone blocks set in a matrix which can be either sand- or mud-prone. These are interpreted as debris flows sourced from muddy slopes further up the system or, where sand-prone, to local remobilization of the fan surface as consequence of over-steepening following deposition. Rare breccias containing indurated footwall sandstone blocks occur in wells along the northwestern fringe of the field, indicating debris flows which tapped into and remobilized the coarse aprons of material associated with the basin margin faults. Additional remobilized lithologies include post-depositional injection complexes and slumped units in which original depositional features are contorted in a coherent fashion by gravity-driven deformation.

The above lithologies are interbedded with sand-laminated silty mudrocks or, less commonly, unstructured mudrock in packages of variable thickness. Over the high net : gross intervals, preserved mud-prone horizons are typically a few cm thick at most, although they reach several metres in thickness in the M6 and M8 'fines blankets' which can be traced across the field (Fig 4). Thicker mud-prone intervals occur along the northwestern fringe of the field where the sand-laminated mudrocks are cut by soft-sediment faults, and heavily slumped. These are interpreted as sections through the lateral confining slope which evidently was highly unstable.

Permeability measurements from core plugs show that there is an underlying relationship between permeability, lithology and original emplacement mechanism. Thus the best reservoir quality (ignoring local calcite-cemented nodules) is seen in the structureless, mottled, pebbly and dewatered sandstones attributed to deposition from high-density turbidity currents (geo. mean $K_h = 111$, 170, 176 and 105 mD, respectively). Quality deteriorates in the associated stratified sandstones (geo. mean $K_h = 52.4$ mD): the 'slurried' bed top divisions (geo. mean $K_h = 6.9$ mD) support only marginal permeability and act to baffle flow. The finer-grained parallel and ripple-laminated sandstones deposited by low-density turbidity currents are mostly of poor reservoir quality (geo. mean $K_h = 4.0$ mD) as are the various remobilized deposits and the background mud-prone intervals (Fig. 6). It follows that heterogeneity in the reservoir mainly lies in areas where: (1) slurried bed caps repeatedly intervene between individual sandstone beds; (2) interbedded LDT deposits and background mudrock packages separate otherwise amalgamated HDT sandstones; and (3) where significant remobilization has occurred. Guidance as to how to distribute such intervals within the reservoir relies on the depositional model. The depositional context is also important when it comes to assigning lateral dimensions to both the permeable and heterogeneous elements identified in core.

Depositional model and overall architecture

Although major conglomerate-plugged channels are developed up-dip in South Brae (Stow *et al.* 1982), channel filling is less easily demonstrated in the sand-prone Miller Field wells. Several features indicate that most of the field was an area associated with flows which were fundamentally depositional:

(1) inclined bed bases are rare, and, where seen, can generally be referred to post-depositional sliding and over-steepening rather than erosion;
(2) residual granule or pebble lags (Mutti & Normark 1991) lining erosional surfaces have not been recognized: where granules are present, these are dispersed through the structureless sandstones suggesting en-masse dumping from flows which rapidly lost their capacity to transport material in suspension (Hiscott 1995);
(3) mudclast-strewn surfaces at bed bases indicating local basal erosion do not occur: instead mudclasts are restricted to bed capping 'slurried' divisions discussed above;
(4) traction structures and evidence for bedform migration (features of some channel fills) are not seen;
(5) although upward-fining and/or upward muddying motifs (m to 10s m thick) which could be attributed to channel filling are developed, the lateral relationships deduced from relatively densely-spaced wells suggest that many of these are widespread signatures, seen over significant areas of the field. Such trends appear to characterize episodes of fan building (separated by interruptions in sand supply or re-location of the feeder conduit up-dip) rather than local channel filling and abandonment; and
(6) the integrity of thin (cm-scale) fines blankets (as revealed by associated pressure breaks and their fieldwide occurrence) suggests that at least the immediately overlying sandstones cannot be significantly channelized or the former would be more commonly punctured.

On the above evidence, and given the wider context outlined earlier (i.e. feeder channels up-dip, isolated sheets down-dip), the Miller sandstones are interpreted as having accumulated down-dip from the main feeder channels in an area where flow capacity dissipated rapidly as the overcharged flows spread radially to blanket the basin floor. Poorly-resolved, shallow (m-scale) distributive channels and/or scours are almost certainly present, particularly over higher net : gross sections of the reservoir immediately down-dip from the feeder conduits. These pass laterally and down-slope into amalgamated sheets and eventually into lower net : gross more layered successions where greater lithological heterogeneity will be preserved. Analogous trends have been described from 'depositional lobes' in outcrops (e.g. Mutti & Normark 1987, 1991; Chapin *et al.* 1994): areas of high bed amalgamation occupy the most frequently-swept axial parts of the lobe where the flows were commonly scouring, whilst increased preservation of interbedded fines characterizes the lateral or distal fringe of the system. Furthermore, the lateral extent of the interbedded background fines will increase as the succession becomes more layer-like. Chapin *et al.* (1994) report that although local scouring can still be anticipated in lower net : gross layered sheets, the frequency and depth of incision decreases, allowing greater lateral continuity of the interbedded 'background' deposits.

Switching between up-slope feeders traversing South Brae area would have meant that areas of preferred sand deposition would periodically relocate. As a result, the basin floor was probably irregular, caused by a combination of depositional mounding and differential compaction which would have influenced the planform of the deposited sands. Mounding may also have caused switching of lobe axes. Broadly lobate geometries are anticipated, issuing from the active feeder(s). Where more than one feeder was active at any one time, lobes may have coalesced to form a sand-prone apron (e.g. M4, Fig. 6). Flows which intersected the lateral slope to the northwest may have become confined by topography and hence more erosional again (cf. the 'headless channels' of Normark (1985), and the accelerative flows of Kneller (1995)). This might explain why net : gross locally increases close to pinch-out of the sand against the slope.

Depositional elements

In a dissipative system such as is envisaged for the Miller fan complex, trends in net : gross and geometry are likely to be continuous down and across the palaeoslope. In order to rationalize the patterns across the well database, four types of lobe

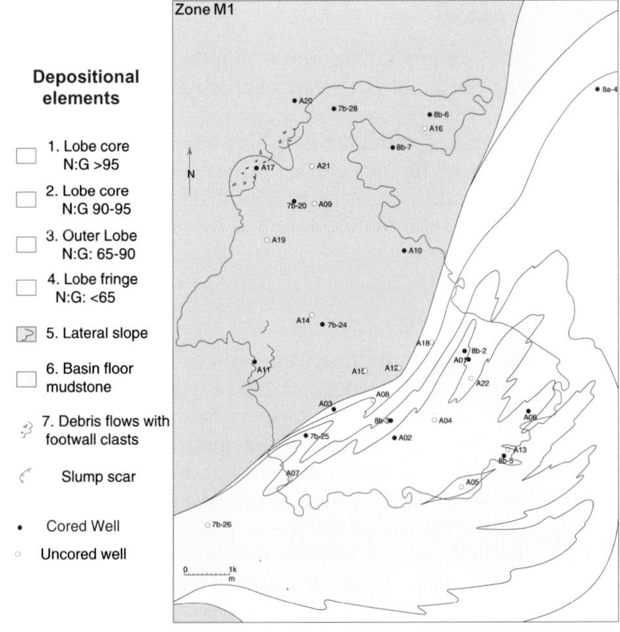

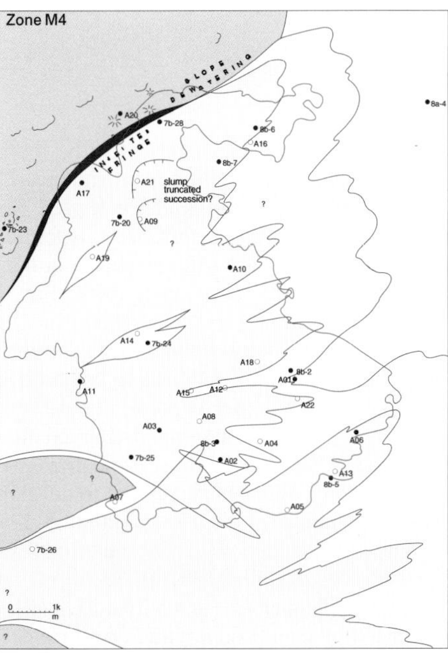

Fig. 6. Depositional elements and relocation of axes.

succession (depositional elements) have been arbitrarily defined (recognizable in both cores and on wireline logs), the character of which is related to their position with respect to the axis of the active lobe (Fig. 6). These capture the range of net : gross, from 0.95 at the lobe axis falling to <0.65 in the lobe fringe (where these are not influenced by topography). A fifth element acknowledges the possibility of topographically-confined lobe margins. Additional elements have also been introduced to account for interbedded non-lobe sections. These different elements (Fig. 4) are described by number in more detail here.

Element 1

Stacked, amalgamated HDT beds, with or without 'abandonment' successions forming a sand-prone, fan-lobe axial or slope-adjacent association, with only minor devlopment of non-permeable lithotypes mostly in the form of slurried caps to individual beds. The degree of amalgamation suggests extensive scouring; hence, the subdued internal low permeability horizons are likely to be diced up and of restricted lateral extent (10–100 m). More significant heterogeneity is associated with abandonment sections which record shut-down or relocation of the lobe core. These involve more thinly-bedded stacks of structureless sandstones, debris flow deposits and sand-laminated mudrocks arranged in crudely upward-muddying units up to a few metres thick. These more heterogeneous abandonments potentially have more extensive lateral dimensions (100 m) draping the underlying higher net : gross sections.

Element 2

Stacked HDT beds in which a significant number of thin (*c.* 1–5 cm) mud-prone interbeds are preserved, reflecting less active scouring or less frequent flows in an immediate off-axial site where sheet amalgamation was less intense. The sandstones are again thickly bedded (m-scale) and largely structureless: they commonly preserve slurried caps recording flow evolution towards a debris flow-like rheology. The inhibited scouring suggests that the associated heterogeneities will be more extensive than in the more amalgamated lobe core element (10 to 100 m in this case), although they are still thin and liable to be cut out where scouring does occur. The clay-prone abandonment packages draping many of these intervals are potentially more extensive than heterogeneities within the element itself.

Element 3

The above sand-prone sections pass laterally (both across strike and down depositional dip) into significantly more heterogeneous sand-prone sections characterized by thicker background deposits. Thick, sharp-based, structureless and dewatered HDT sandstones are still developed, either isolated or in amalgamated bundles a few beds thick, but these are separated by sections now several tens of cm thick made up of interbedded fine- to very fine-grained, laminated and rippled sandstones, sand-laminated mudrocks and debris flow deposits. Their overall character suggests deposition in areas less frequently swept by the main sand-charged flows, with subdued erosion at the base of those sandstones which do occur allowing a strongly layered succession to develop (cf. the layered sheets of Chapin *et al.* 1994; Mahaffie 1994). The interbedded fine-grained deposits will therefore extend for considerable distances laterally (100s m). Such areas occupied the lateral margin of higher net : gross lobe axes (where these were not influenced by lateral slopes) and down range from the more heavily amalgamated facies in areas accessed only by the more vigorous sandy flows. The greater heterogeneity of these deposits means that a discrete 'abandonment' section cannot be recognized.

Element 4

A heterogeneous outermost fringe of generally thin-bedded, structureless and commonly laminated sandstones interbedded with fine-grained background deposits characterizes the outermost fringe of the active sand system (where this is not modified by the influence of lateral slopes). The occurrence of well-laminated sandstones, suggesting lower flow densities and hindered collapse of the sand suspension, may not be characteristic of the fringe of all the fan units but it is particularly obvious in the lateral fringe of the M2 fan system. It is possible that variations in the calibre of material supplied to different systems may have meant that lower density flows were only achieved at certain times. At other times, the dominant structureless sandstones appear to have extended to the lateral and distal edge of the system as relatively thin beds interfingering with dominantly mud-prone lithologies.

Element 5

Along the northwestern margin of the field, the basin floor sands abutted against a contemporary slope: at certain times, the active sand lobe lay well to the south of the slope and the sandstones feathered northwards into lower net : gross packages of the type described earlier. At other times, very high net : gross sandstones were deposited right at the base of the slope: well control indicates that net : gross in these instances must fall rapidly along a narrow heterogeneous fringe characterized by sand injections or slump-modified sheets (Fig. 6).

The 3 non-lobe elements distinguished are:

Element 6

Distinctive mud-prone successions up to several metres thick comprising thinly bedded, very fine-grained sandstones, laminated mudrocks and rare debris flow deposits. Although thin, these intervals appear to be laterally extensive and are recognized over most of the field. They stand out on wireline logs as the most prominent high-gamma intervals within the reservoir section, and they record periods when the sand supply to the basin floor was interrupted for significant periods of time.

Element 7

Intra-fan remobilization (slumping and debris flows transporting blocks of fan sandstone) is recognized in cores at certain levels in the reservoir section. Such deposits are particularly associated with lobe-switching between units M3 and M2 when zones of the fan appear to have been over-steepened and to have failed. The failures impose new geometries on the original depositional architecture and are therefore flagged as a separate element.

Element 8

A complex interfingering between the basin floor sandstones and the co-eval slope section is recognized over the northern part of the field. The slope system was dominantly mud-prone, characterized by laminated mudrocks with many cm-scale, fine- and very fine-grained sandstone layers and lenses, in places displaced by syn-sedimentary faults or heavily contorted by slumping and sliding. Locally, clast- to matrix-supported breccias up to several metres thick are present. These represent debris flows which transported indurated sandstone blocks (Devonian?) downslope and may identify periods of tectonic activity on the basin-bounding faults. These slope elements are wholly composed of non-reservoir lithologies.

Palaeogeography

The spatial distribution of the depositional elements identified earlier was examined in each zone and it was found to be possible to map out areas of sand-prone lobe core facies (elements 1 and 2) surrounded by progressively more heterogeneous elements (Fig. 6). The lateral limit of each sand system could also be fixed. Well control was locally sufficiently dense to constrain lateral transitions between elements to within a kilometre tolerance or better, although there was greater uncertainty around the margins of the field. The style and dimensions of the non-permeable lithotypes were related both to zone and to depositional element.

Heterogeneity model

As channels could not be confidently recognized in Miller cores, it would have been impossible to condition an object-based model to the wells using software-defined objects such as channels, lobes or splays. The small scale of the depositional system also implied that object dimensions and types might not be stable across the field. For these reasons it was decided to concentrate on modelling shales and to distribute these within zones made up of permeable sandstone lithotypes. This was accomplished using BP's 'TORCH' stochastic simulator.

The model was built to represent three classes of heterogeneity (Fig. 2): boundary shales (the surfaces between reservoir zones), intrazone shales (the heterogeneities within the zones) and permeable lithotypes. The model comprised 490 layers of geological description varying between 1 and 20 cm in thickness. These fine layers, though not implying correlations at this scale, represented the smallest unit of heterogeneity created, in other words the resolution of the model. Fine layers were necessary because of the high net : gross nature of the reservoir and the importance to fluid flow of thin shales (1–10 cm scale). The stochastic simulator scattered elements of shale and permeability, layer by layer, over a 60 m square mesh according to conditioning parameters tailored to each of the ten reservoir zones. Following a quality control process, the model was up-scaled into an area of grid refinement of ECLIPSE reservoir simulation model in which conventional grids of depth structure, isochore and porosity were already in place. The up-scaled description for the dynamic simulator comprised 33 subzones, each derived from up to 20 geological layers, at a grid cell size of 100 m. Each zone, with thickness varying from 5 m to 30 m was bounded above and below by a zone boundary shale and contained four subzones. Each subzone, with thickness averaging 2.5 m ranging up to a maximum of 4m, was bounded above and below by the up scaled heterogeneities (or floating shales, Fig. 7). Thus, from a static reservoir description at a cell size of 60 m × 60 m × 0.01 m, analysis of field performance in dynamic mode was possible at the subzone level with cell size 100 m × 100 m × *c*. 2.5 m.

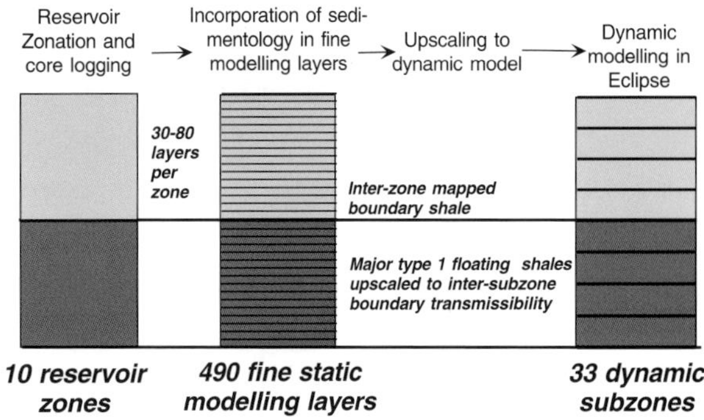

Fig. 7. Reservoir zones, subzones and modelling layers.

Boundary (interzone) shales

During production the zone boundaries described earlier had become increasingly well-marked by discontinuities in the RFT pressure gradient as each zone depleted at a slightly different rate. Quality control of the dynamic model included the matching of these pressures at wells which, even at the coarse scale, had been facilitated by the mapping of shale transmissibility. In earlier cross-sectional models incorporating three-phase flow the explicit mapping of shales had been found to be essential and so shale mapping was considered to be the first priority in the heterogeneity model.

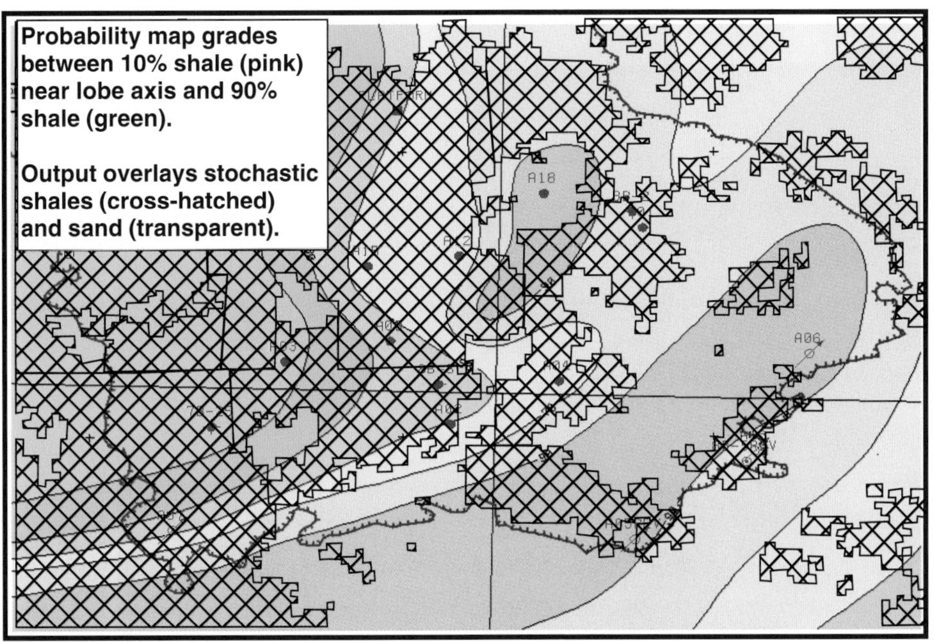

Fig. 8. Boundary shales: probability and stochastic maps.

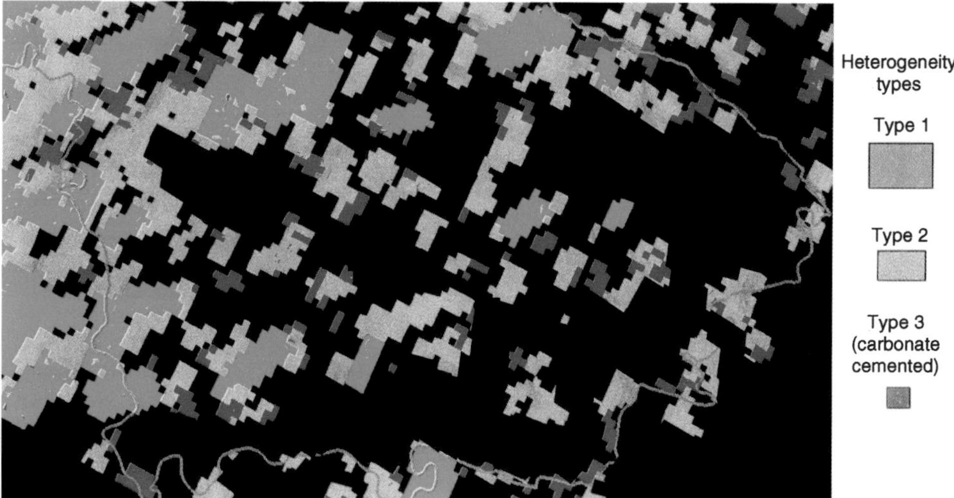

Fig. 9. Intrazone heterogeneities.

To condition the stochastic shale generator, maps of shale probability varying from 0 to 1 based on the zone palaeogeography maps (Fig. 6) were designed around the well data. Thick shales or strong pressure barriers were honoured as shale and as a very low probability of erosion in the surrounding map area: shales with no pressure difference across them were honoured at wells but were assigned a high probability of erosion nearby. These maps for each zone boundary were input as conditioning parameters together with overall values of shale percentage (based on the importance of the zone boundary as a baffle) and range (for shale continuity governing the resultant shape of the shale masses). The stochastic simulator placed barriers of various dimensions over the area (Fig. 8) representing the boundary shale and permeable holes through it. A variety of realizations with different distributions of shale could be produced by this method. Several iterations with different modified parameters were necessary to optimize both the geological sense of the shale distribution and the value of eventual up-scaled transmissibility.

Intrazone heterogeneities

The various intrazonal non-permeable lithotypes described in detail in each of the cores had been assigned to seven classes (Fig. 5). A coarser classification was required to extend the conditioning to uncored wells where the full range of clay-prone lithotypes could not be identified from wireline logs alone. This coarser classification was also more appropriate for inclusion in the static simulator. Three classes of heterogeneity were identified in each of the wells.

Type 1

Laterally-extensive (100s m–km scale) barriers with low aspect ratio planforms, potentially of interwell extent, and identified in abandonment sections resting on top of element 1 and 2 stacks, as the interbedded sand-laminated mudrocks and debris flows found in the layer-like elements 3 and 4 on the fringes of the system, and forming the key component in the element 5 ‘fines blankets’.

Type 2

Laterally restricted baffles and barriers which characterize the higher net : gross element 1 and 2 stacks where scouring is deemed to be more important. These slurried bed caps or thin sand-laminated mudrock partings are inferred to have short dimensions (20–100 m) and potentially higher aspect ratio planforms dictated by the local palaeoflow.

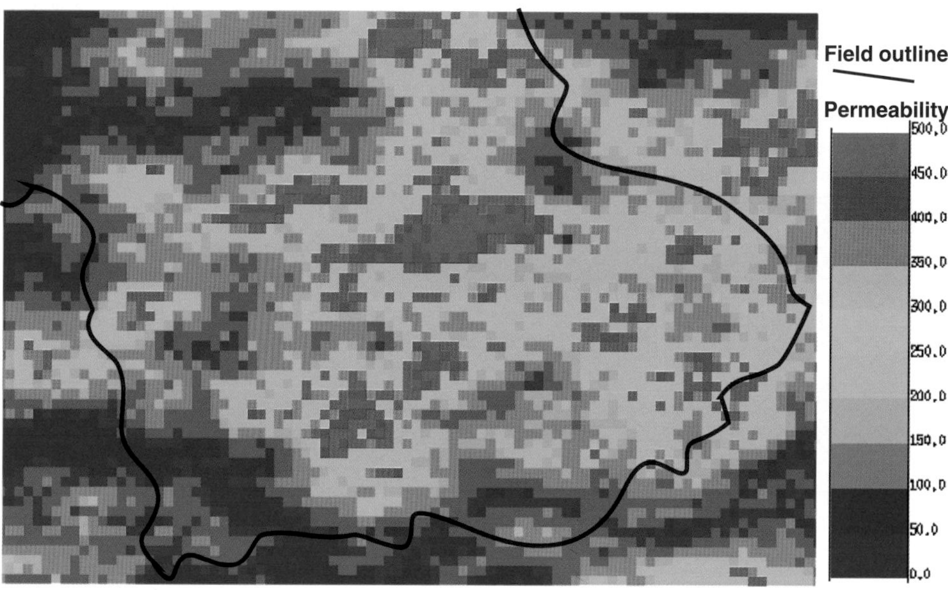

Fig. 10. Stochastic realization of permeability.

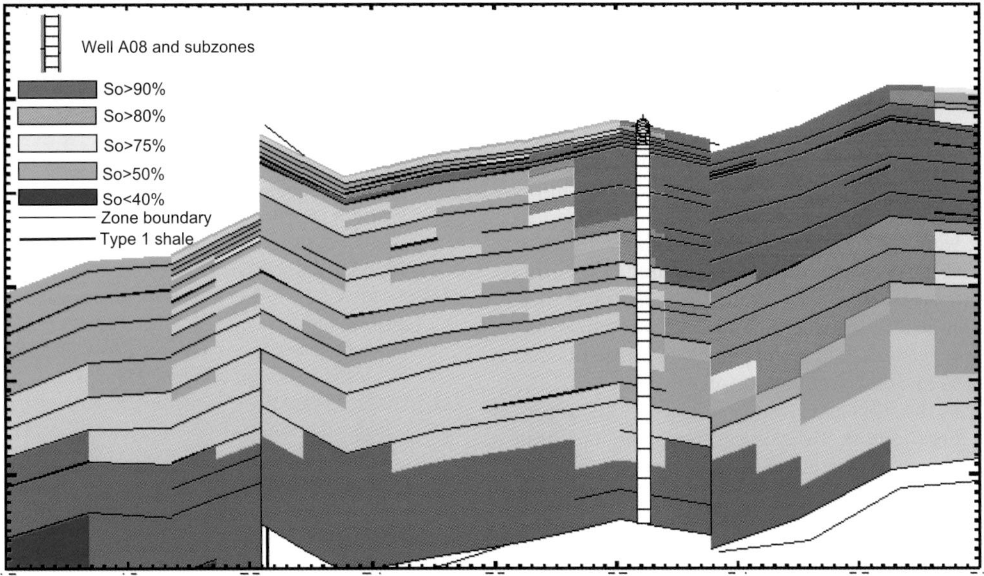

Fig. 11. Well cross-section with oil saturation, May 1997.

Type 3
Calcite-cemented sandstones. These were interpreted to be nodular in shape on geochemical grounds, from isotopic evidence and on the basis of their curved boundaries in core. Their estimated thickness to width ratios were *c.* 1:5. They are abundant in certain reservoir zones (e.g. M5.1) where they can reach 11 m thickness in core but there is no dynamic evidence to suggest that they form extensive barriers.

For each reservoir zone, input of estimates of the range in proportion and dimensions of each lithotype together with interpreted trends and the layer-by-layer well conditioning data was sufficient to populate the zone with its own characteristic distribution of shales. Numerous iterations were made to produce a series of different realizations some of which were selected for up-scaling into the dynamic model. Figure 9 shows one realization of the three types of shale in zone M1.

The key to preserving these mapped heterogeneities lay in the up-scaling which was programmed for each zone to reduce the detail of 30–80 layers into four subzones. During upscaling the type 1 shales were migrated to the new subzone boundaries to produce transmissibility barriers between each subzone whilst the smaller type 2 and type 3 heterogeneities were blended into the horizontal and vertical permeability description for each subzone.

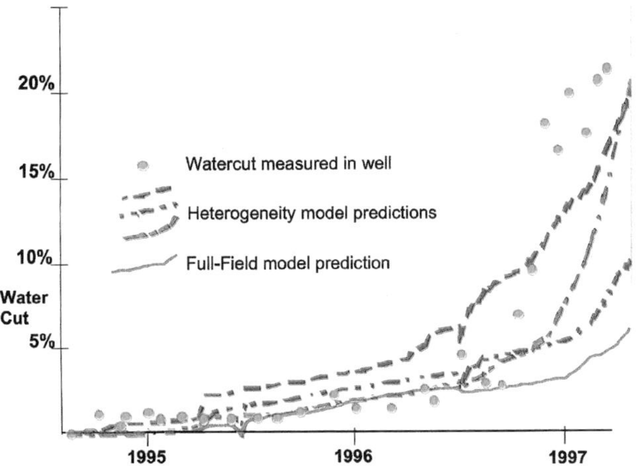

Fig. 12. A08 water-cut from well and models.

Permeable lithotypes

Although permeability has been shown clearly to be controlled by lithotype, the permeable reservoir section is dominated by massive and mottled sandstone with minor development of pebbly, dewatered, and stratified sandstones. Within these permeable lithotypes the over-riding control on permeability is the extent of quartz cement, interpreted to have been inhibited by early hydrocarbon migration and reservoir filling (Gluyas *et al.* 1998), with less cement occurring towards the top of the reservoir section where greater porosity and permeability are preserved. Even when permeability were treated on a zone by zone basis there were insufficient data from the less abundant lithotypes to justify using lithotype subsets: nor was there any obvious guidance from the depositional model as to how the different permeable lithotypes might be distributed in space. However, statistical analysis showed that each zone had a characteristic permeability distribution and it was decided to use a single combined permeable lithotype description in the model. This honoured the well data, captured the zonal permeability variation and reflected the impact of diagenetic overprinting.

Permeability variograms were used to explore the pattern of vertical permeability correlation. Ranges and periodicities showed that m-scale ranges were commonly developed, corresponding to the scale of bedding observed in core (see also Prosser *et al.* 1995 for details of probe permeameter profiles). Periodicities reflect bedding repetitions. Horizontal correlation scales were more difficult to constrain and were guided by qualitative input from outcrop analogues, for example Wagon Rock, California (Graham 1979). Bed lengths of the order of 500–1000 m with length–width ratios of 3:1 were adopted in the light of the good bed continuity in these exposures of high net : gross 'depositional' mode sandy fans. This also allowed for possible poor interwell permeability correlation (Prosser *et al.* 1995). A realization of the permeability distribution (Fig. 10) shows higher permeabilities extending laterally in lobe axes with subdued permeability in the southwest. Scope was identified for an improved database of field outcrop measurements, to obtain better dimensional data of lateral and vertical permeability variations.

Modelling results

Completion of the reservoir description in 1997 represented a timely milestone in field development because, as planned, it coincided with the end of the plateau period and the need to investigate possible infill targets and enhanced recovery options. Results from the detailed model were initially closer to reality in respect of fluid flow into wells than had been those from the coarser full-field model. For example, the heterogeneity model showed water breakthrough in Well A08 at the correct timing several months earlier than the full-field model had predicted. In the cross-section (Fig. 11) the 33 subzones are shown in the well with the shales retained at subzone boundaries shown as black lines. The water front is seen to be irregular with water held up over some of the shales and over-running oil-bearing subzones. Despite not being perforated, the uppermost subzone indicates significant over-ride with a risk that some oil may be bypassed unless action is taken. Such fine-scale over-ride has indeed been logged in other production wells.

An advantage of the stochastic simulator is its ability to produce numerous iterations of the description based on input parameters. These realizations are similar in that they contain the same statistical distribution of shale dimensions and rock permeability but they differ in the exact location of shales and high-permeability streaks. The realizations are thus a valuable tool in the investigation of uncertainty in the model since different realizations perform differently in dynamic mode (Fig. 12). The chart shows the actual water cut measurements taken in Well A08 (yellow dots). The full-field model trace (red) lies close to real water-cut in the early years of production but greatly under-estimates the rapid increase in water-cut produced by the well in 1997. Three of the new model realizations (blue) demonstrate this rapid increase, one of them coming close to actual well performance. The differences between the realizations indicate that analysis in dynamic mode of numerous realizations is necessary to cover a representative set of likely performance outcomes.

This insight into reservoir behaviour underlines the improvement in the model as a result of the detailed description. The model has been vital in generating production profiles for the recent gas injection scheme in which heterogeneity has an even more important effect on fluid flow. It will be the main tool for investigating other tertiary recovery options, such as depressurisation, in which gas is the most important phase. A work programme has been set up to address this by enabling more rapid dynamic simulation of the many static realizations that can be produced. The programme includes expanding the area of interest to the whole field and investigating the possibilities offered by other simulation tools.

Conclusions

The objective of the modelling work was achieved only after more than two years of effort during which the depositional architecture evolved together with the perception of the most effective means of incorporating the sedimentology in static and dynamic simulators. In the absence of good seismic resolution, a great reliance had to be placed on biostratigraphy for reservoir zonation and on deterministic mapping for the distribution of depositional elements. In such a high net : gross reservoir even very thin shales were shown to have a great importance to fluid flow, which necessitated the use of numerous very fine layers to capture sufficient heterogeneity in the static model. In its completed state the model has shown water over-riding shales indicating the possibility of the waterflood bypassing small oil accumulations. The model has also demonstrated gas under-running shales, thereby offering a realistic means of analysing the effectiveness of the gas injection scheme. The analysis of different realizations has shown that there still remains considerable uncertainty associated with model results. The advantages of capturing so much detail have been such that an expansion of the model is seen to be essential to fully analyse the potential that infill drilling and depressurization might offer to extend the life of the Miller Field.

The authors acknowledge the support of Badley-Ashton & Associates and of Miller Unit Partners Conoco UK Ltd, Enterprise Oil plc and Saga Petroleum Limited in publishing this work.

References

CHAPIN, M. A., DAVIES, P., GIBSON, J. L. & PETTINGHILL, H. S. 1994. Reservoir architecture of turbidite sheet sandstones in laterally extensive outcrops, Ross Formation, western Ireland. *In*: WEIMER, P., BOUMA, A. H. & PERKINS, B. F. *Submarine Fans and Turbidite Systems*. Gulf Coast Section SEPM Foundation 15th Annual Research Conference, 53–68.

GARLAND, C. R. 1993. Miller Field: reservoir stratigraphy and its impact on development. *In*: PARKER, J. R. (ed.) *Petroleum Geology of Northwest Europe, Proceedings of the 4th Conference*. Geological Society, London, 953–964.

GLUYAS, J., GARLAND, C., OXTOBY, N. & HOGG, A. J. C. 1998. Quartz cement: the Miller'sTale. *In*: WORDEN, R. H. & MORAD, S. (eds) *Quartz Cement: Quartz Cement in Sandstones*. Special Publication of the International Association of Sedimentologists.

GRAHAM, S. A. 1979. Tertiary stratigraphy and depositional environments near Indians Ranch, Monterey County, California. *In*: *Pacific Section*, SEPM Field Guide 4, 3–12.

HISCOTT, R. N. 1994. Loss of capacity, not competence, as the fundamental process governing deposition from turbidity currents. *Journal of Sedimentary Research*, **A64**, 209–214.

KNELLER, B. 1995. Beyond the turbidite paradigm: physical models for deposition of turbidites and their implications for reservoir prediction. *In*: HARTLEY, A. J. & PROSSER, D. J. (eds) *Characterization of Deep Marine Clastic Systems*. Geological Society, London, Special Publications, **94**, 201–219.

MAHAFFIE, M. 1994. Reservoir classification for turbidite intervals at the Mars Discovery, Mississippi Canyon 807, Gulf of Mexico. *In*: WEIMER, P., BOUMA, A. H. & PERKINS, B. F. (eds) *Submarine Fans and Turbidite Systems*. Gulf Coast Section SEPM Foundation 15th Annual Research Conference, 233–244.

MCCLURE, N. M. & BROWN, A. A. 1992. Miller Field, a subtle Upper Jurassic submarine fan trap in the South Viking Graben, United Kingdom Sector, North Sea. *In*: HALBOUTY, M. T. (ed.) *Giant Oil and Gas Fields of the Decade 1978–88*. AAPG Memoir 54.

MUTTI, E. 1985. Turbidite systems and their relation to depositional sequences. *In*: ZUFFA, G. G. (ed) *Provenance of Arenites*. NATO-ASI SERIES, D. Reidal Publishing Co., Amsterdam, 65–93.

—— & NORMARK, W. R. 1987. Comparing examples of modern and ancient turbidite systems: problems and concepts. *In*: LEGGETT, J. K. & ZUFFA, G. G. (eds) *Marine Clastic Sedimentology*. Graham & Trotman, London, 1–38.

—— & ——1991. An integrated approach to the study of turbidite systems. *In*: WEIMER, P. & LINK, H. (eds) *Seismic Facies and Sedimentary Processes of Submarine Fans and Turbidite Systems*. Springer-Verlag, New York, 75–106.

NORMARK, W. R. 1985. Local morphologic controls and effects of basin geometry on flow processes in deep marine basins. *In*: ZUFFA, G. G. (ed.) *Provenance of Arenites*. NATO-ASI SERIES, D. Reidal Publishing Co., Amsterdam, 47–63.

PROSSER, D. J., MCKEEVER, M., HOGG, A. J. C. & HURST, A. 1995. Permeability heterogeneity within massive Jurassic submarine fan sandstones from the Miller Field, northern North Sea, UK. *In*: HARTLEY, A. J. & PROSSER, D. J. (eds) *Characterization of Deep Marine Clastic Systems*. Geological Society, London, Special Publications, **94**, 201–219.

ROOKSBY, S. K. 1991. The Miller Field, Blocks 16/7b, 16/8b, UK North Sea. *In*: ABBOTTS, I. L. (ed.) *UK Oil & Gas Fields, 25 Years Commemorative Volume*. Geological Society Memoirs, **14**.

SHANMUGAM, G. 1996. High-density turbidity currents: are they sandy debris flows? *Journal of Sedimentary Research*, **66**, 2–10.

STOW, D. A. V., BISHOP, C. D. & MILLS, S. J. 1982. Sedimentology of the Brae Oilfield Area, North Sea: fan models and controls. *Journal of Petroleum Geology*, **5**, 129–148

TURNER, C. C., COHEN, J. M., CONNELL, J. R. & COOPER, D. M. 1987. A depositional model for the South Brae Oilfield. *In*: BROOKS, J. & GLENNIE, K. W. (eds) *Petroleum Geology of North West Europe*, **14**, 853–864.

Integrated reservoir characterization and uncertainty analysis, Heidrun Field, Norway

T. OLSEN,[1] K. J. ROSVOLL,[1] J. M. KJÆREFJORD,[1] D. M. ARNESEN,[1] C. SANDSDALEN,[1] S. H. JØRGENVÅG,[2] V. LANGLAIS[2] and K. E. SVELA[3]

[1] *Statoil, N-4035, Stavanger, Norway (e-mail: tod@statoil.no)*
[2] *Statoil, PO. Box 273, N-7501 Stjørdal, Norway*
[3] *Conoco Inc., Houston TX77079, USA*

Abstract: The Lower Jurassic Åre and Tilje Formations of the Heidrun Field contain some 350×10^6 Sm^3 (2160×10^6 BBL) of oil in place. The reservoirs are highly heterogeneous and represent deposition in a wide range of fluvial, tidal and marginal marine environments. This, together with a high level of faulting and a relatively viscous oil type, has led to low recovery estimates. To help improve recovery, an integrated reservoir description project including a thorough sedimentological analysis, stochastic modelling of genetic and diagenetic facies, and an associated uncertainty analysis also using stochastic modelling was initiated.

Facies architectures were modelled in 17 individual reservoir zones, each zone consisting of up to 10×10^6 grid blocks. The Åre Formation is characterized by alluvial plain and low energy deltaic systems, including incised valley fills, fluvial channels, crevasse splays, upward coarsening bayfills and large splay lobe deposits. The overlying Tilje Formation is characterized by mixed tidal and marginal marine depositional systems with tidal channels, tidal sand and mud flats, tidal shoals and shoreface and offshore sands. Several facies were modelled within each zone and the desired facies architecture was often achieved by merging several individual stochastic realizations. Input to the facies modelling was based on well data as well as information from outcrop analogues and modern depositional systems. Petrophysical attributes were distributed stochastically within each facies body type, using frequency distributions from the wells and interpreted variogram functions. The realizations were finally fitted to the structural maps and upscaled for flow simulation. This enabled the building of a 'best guess', or most likely, full-field geological and dynamic simulation model.

A subsequent uncertainty study integrated and evaluated the full spectrum of geological and petrophysical uncertainties related to the dynamic behaviour of the reservoir including facies geometries and facies volume fractions. Best, worst and intermediate case facies realizations with respect to fluid flow were first generated using stochastic modelling. These were combined with other major reservoir uncertainties (gross rock volume, petrophysical values) and 150 complete geological models were established. The hydrocarbon pore volume in each of these models was calculated, and the models were taken through a simplified flow simulation. The results from this process allowed a ranking of the models and a selection of representative models for further dynamic flow simulations. The uncertainty study shows that the uncertainty related to the gross rock volume is the most significant on a field-wide scale. Uncertainties in the facies input parameters (geometry, facies volume fraction) have relatively little impact at a field wide scale. However, their impact upon individual zones or segments (local scale) can be large.

The Heidrun Field is a large oil and gas field located in the Haltenbanken area, offshore mid-Norway (Fig. 1). Currently, recoverable reserves are estimated to 150×10^6 Sm^3 (950×10^6 BBL) of oil and 1.5×10^{12} SCF of gas. The field has at present (early 1998) been in production for more than two years and produces up to 250 000 barrels of oil a day (BOPD). The production facilities consist of a concrete tension leg platform with wells drilled from both the platform and from subsea templates. The water depth is approximately 350 m.

The field contains a viscous, 22–29°API, oil in Jurassic sandstone reservoirs that vary significantly in reservoir quality (Whitley 1992). The best reservoir quality is within the Middle Jurassic Fangst Group. However, the largest proportion of the oil occurs in the lower Jurassic Tilje and Åre Formations (Fig. 2) which are estimated to have a hydrocarbon pore volume (HCPV) of around 600×10^6 m^3 (approximately 3.8×10^9 BBL). Previous estimates of recovery are relatively low (18–25%).

A 'Tilje/Åre Reservoir Development Project' was initiated early 1995. Improved reservoir characterization using stochastic modelling techniques was identified as an important element. Therefore, the projects 'Stochastic Modelling Tilje/Åre' and an associated 'Uncertainty Study' were initialized. The two projects represent the conclusions of a complete re-evaluation of the field, including an update of seismic maps and the structural model, a full revision of all petrophysical data, and an update of the sedimentological model and the sequence stratigraphic driven reservoir zonation.

The objectives of the integrated project were: (i) to create a full-field stochastic reservoir model, containing a best possible description of the various reservoir heterogeneities; (ii) through an integrated uncertainty study, using stochastic modelling, establish a reliable 'base case' geological model; (iii) to provide a realistic description of the uncertainty related to hydrocarbon volumes. This paper describes the results of this project with a particular focus on the geological issues, in particular the use of stochastic facies modelling.

Geological setting

The Heidrun Field was discovered in 1985 by a Conoco-operated consortium (Koenig 1986). The discovery well (Well 6507/7-2) proved hydrocarbons both in the Fangst Group and in the underlying Tilje and Åre formations. Subsequent appraisal drilling confirmed the large volume and lateral extent of the accumulation and formed the basis for a development decision in 1991. The field is a large (37 km^2), fault-bounded, structural

OLSEN, T., ROSVOLL, K. J., KJÆREFJORD, J. M., ARNESEN, D. M., SANDSDALEN, C., JØRGENVÅG, S. H., LANGLAIS, V. & SVELA, K. E. 1999. Integrated reservoir characterization and uncertainty analysis, Heidrun Field, Norway. *In*: FLEET, A. J. & BOLDY, S. A. R. (eds) *Petroleum Geology of Northwest Europe: Proceedings of the 5th Conference*, 1209–1220.

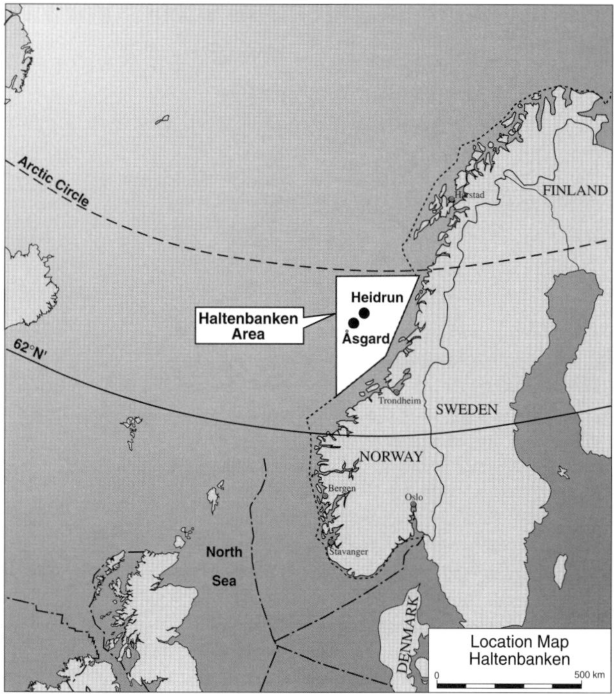

Fig. 1. Location map of the Haltenbanken area, offshore Mid-Norway.

closure dissected by numerous minor normal faults that occur in a conjugate pattern (Fig. 3) (Whitley 1992). The minor faults typically have throws of less than 50 m, but nevertheless serve to divide the field into a large number of fault-bounded segments that differ somewhat in oil–water contacts and oil types. The segments are typically elongate in a north to south direction and are usually 500–1000 m wide (Fig. 3). Several undrilled segments still exist, particularly in the northern part of the field. Diagenesis has had only a minor influence on the overall reservoir quality, hence, clean sandstones typically have porosity values of more than 30% and permeability values in the Darcy range. However, carbonate-cemented levels with virtually zero permeability exist and make up 2–10% of the rock volume within any given zone.

The Åre and Tilje formations together reach a thickness of approximately 700 m and form the main reservoir horizons in a number of large offshore fields in the Haltenbanken area such as the Åsgard and Heidrun fields (Fig. 1). The two formations were deposited within the north to south oriented Haltenbanken Basin (600 km long and up to 200 km wide). It developed as a part of the North Atlantic rift system and was infilled during latest Triassic to Cretaceous times. The basin may be regarded as a mirror image of the much better exposed Jameson Land Basin in East Greenland (e.g. Dam & Surlyk 1995). In the early Jurassic, both of these basins were fairly shallow without a deep marine basin centre.

Stratigraphy and sedimentological model

The Åre and Tilje formations comprise a large-scale transgressive systems tract (TST), with non-marine fluvial strata in the lower part of the Åre Formation (Rhaetian–Hettangian), marginal marine and non-marine strata in the upper Åre (Hettangian to Sinemurian), and marginal marine and marine strata in the Tilje Formation (Pliensbachian) (Fig. 2). The basin was flooded in Toarcian times resulting in deposition of marine shales of the Ror Formation. Within this large-scale TST, higher frequency sea-level changes resulted in abrupt changes in depositional environment and units of fairly similar thickness and lithology may be correlated across large areas creating an unusual 'layer cake' stacking pattern (Fig. 2).

In the Heidrun area, the Åre and Tilje reservoirs have been divided into 3 main parts, the Åre 1 Member, the Åre 2 Member and the Tilje Formation. These have further been subdivided into 17 reservoir zones that generally can be recognized field wide (over distances of more than 10 km).

The Åre 1 Member has a total thickness of approximately 500 m and was deposited in a fluvial to deltaic setting. Variations in sea-level, subsidence, and sediment supply controlled the distribution of the different sedimentary facies and their reservoir properties. Incised valley deposits and fluvial channels form the best reservoirs in this part of the succession.

The Åre 2 Member has a thickness of *c.* 100 m and consists of shallow marine deposits with an increasing tidal influence upward in the section. Sub-environments include: tidal flats, tidal channels, tidal shoals, and bay-fill facies. The reservoir quality of the tidal flat facies is relatively low because of its high clay content (20–80%) whereas the channel- and shoal facies have good reservoir properties (up to Darcy level permeability). The bay-fill facies units have a sandy upper part and presumably a large lateral continuity. However, their reservoir potential is limited, partly because the base of the individual, coarsening upwards, bay-fill sequences are shaly and will act as vertical permeability barriers, at least on a local scale.

The Tilje Formation has an average thickness of 125 m and was deposited in alternating tidal and shallow shelf settings. In general, tidal processes dominated often resulting in deposition of strongly heterolithic lithologies. Thin, argillaceous and often heterolithic units (3–5 m thick) are seen to influence fluid flow because vertical permeability is strongly restricted by clay drapes and lenticular bedding. Confirmation that such levels act as barriers is revealed by pressure data as well as by differences in the oil types above and below them.

Sedimentary facies and general facies modelling philosophy

In the Heidrun Field, there is a strong element of heterogeneity where permeability values range from several Darcy within fluvial and tidal channel sands down to approximately zero in adjacent types of mudrocks and carbonate cemented units (see also Fig. 4). In the fluvial-dominated reservoir zones (Åre 1), the distribution of highly permeable channels will, to a large degree, control the flow pattern. It is important to recognize that traditional deterministic modelling does not describe these highly permeable channels despite their indisputable importance on the flow behaviour. Within the tidal-dominated zones (Åre 2, Tilje), the distribution of reservoir facies is also very important for the flow processes. The main barriers to fluid flow will be the cemented intervals as well as intervals of mud-dominated facies.

In order to achieve a realistic dynamic reservoir model it is therefore crucial to describe the geometry of the various facies bodies before the associated petrophysical parameters can be distributed within the model. However, a deterministic description is impossible because of the well spacing that at present ranges from 700–5000 m, significantly greater than the expected size of most sedimentary bodies. Stochastic facies modelling is therefore applied in order to analyse the likely behaviour of the Åre and Tilje reservoirs. Well calibration was achieved by interpreting facies in all wells (cored and uncored) throughout the reservoir section. In total, approximately 6.6 km of well penetration (22 wells) through the reservoirs was interpreted of which 1.4 km was cored. About 3000 facies units were defined, each unit at least 30 cm thick, and listed as well files. The manual interpretations were based on gamma ray, calliper, neutron–porosity, density, and sonic logs as well as estimated permeability curves and existing core descriptions and core photographs.

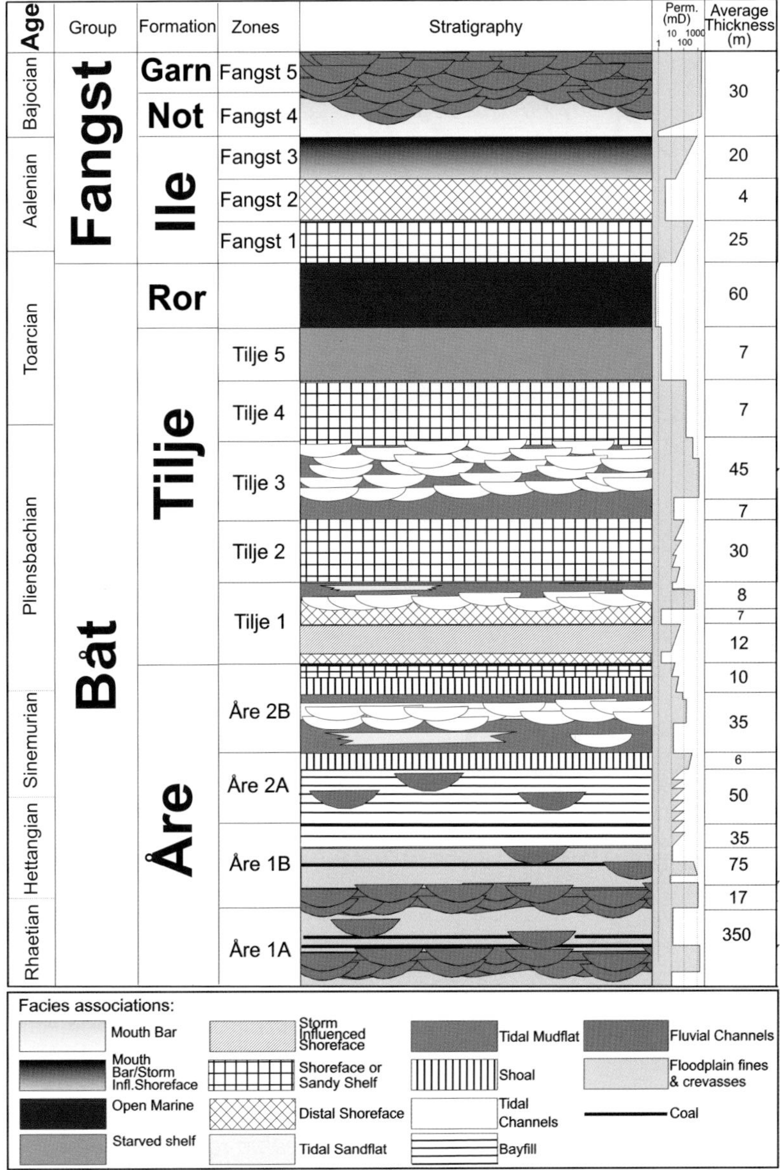

Fig. 2. Stratigraphic overview of the Lower and Middle Jurassic reservoirs of the Heidrun Field. The zones refer to a previously used subdivision. In this project, the Åre and Tilje reservoirs were divided into 17 zones. Note that the average permeability of each zone is indicated on the right hand side of the figure.

Eleven genetic and two diagenetic facies were defined and modelled geometrically: fluvial channel sand (FCS), crevasse splay sand (CSS), incised valley fill (IVF), bay-fill mud and sand (BMS), splay lobe sand (SLS), tidal channel sand (TCS), tidal mud flat (TMF), shoreface sand (SFS), storm dominated shoreface sand (HMS), open marine mud (OMM), calcite cementation (CEM), and dipping calcite cementations (CEMX) (Table 1). Usually, several facies were modelled within each zone. The above facies were modelled into a background consisting of one or several of four facies: floodplain fines (FLF), coal (COA), tidal shoal sand (SHS), and tidal sand flat (TSF). The 'facies' in reality represent facies associations (Reading 1986), and usually contain several types of sedimentary structures, lithologies and trace fossils (summarized in Table 1). Some further details on the facies are found in Rosvoll *et al.* (1997).

The choice of which facies to model as bodies or which to use as a background was determined by their importance for fluid flow. In high net:gross zones emphasis was put on the modelling of barriers whereas focus in low net:gross zones was put on the geometry of sandy facies and the barriers within them. The large size of the field restricted the level of detail possible to achieve, and the heterogeneity at the bedding and laminae scale has therefore not been addressed in this study although important heterogeneity also exist at this level (e.g. Fig. 5).

Stochastic modelling outline

A full-field scale, 3D stochastic model that describes the medium- to larger-scale genetic facies and associated diagenetic cement distribution within the Åre and Tilje reservoir zones, was generated by using integrated modelling package *STORM* of Geomatic (now Smedvig Technologies). This package utilizes several types of marked point processes in order to create different facies architectures. The program module FLUVIAL was used for modelling fluvial channels and incised valley fills whereas the module GMPP (General Marked Point Processes) was used for modelling the remaining facies types. The STORM modelling steps involved the treatment of up to 10×10^6 grid blocks per zone.

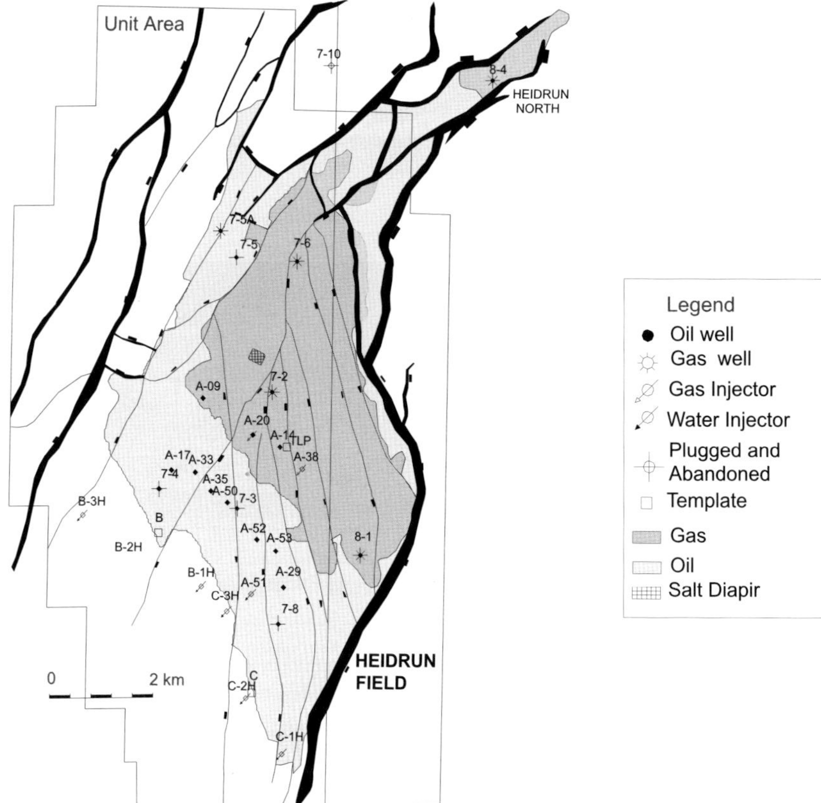

Fig. 3. Map of the Heidrun Field showing the numerous fault segments and the location of wells (per 01.07.96). Note that a large gas cap is present.

Once individual facies architecture was established, petrophysical parameters (porosity, permeability and water saturation) were distributed stochastically within the facies grids. Values were assigned to the individual grid cells within the facies bodies based on user-specified variogram functions and are 100% conditioned to well observations. The fine-scale petrophysical grids were fitted to the structural maps and up-scaled before flow simulations within the coarser-scale ECLIPSE dynamic flow simulator were undertaken.

In total, 17 reservoir zones were modelled. Underlining the multidisciplinary approach to the project, a data summary sheet containing key model input information and modelling

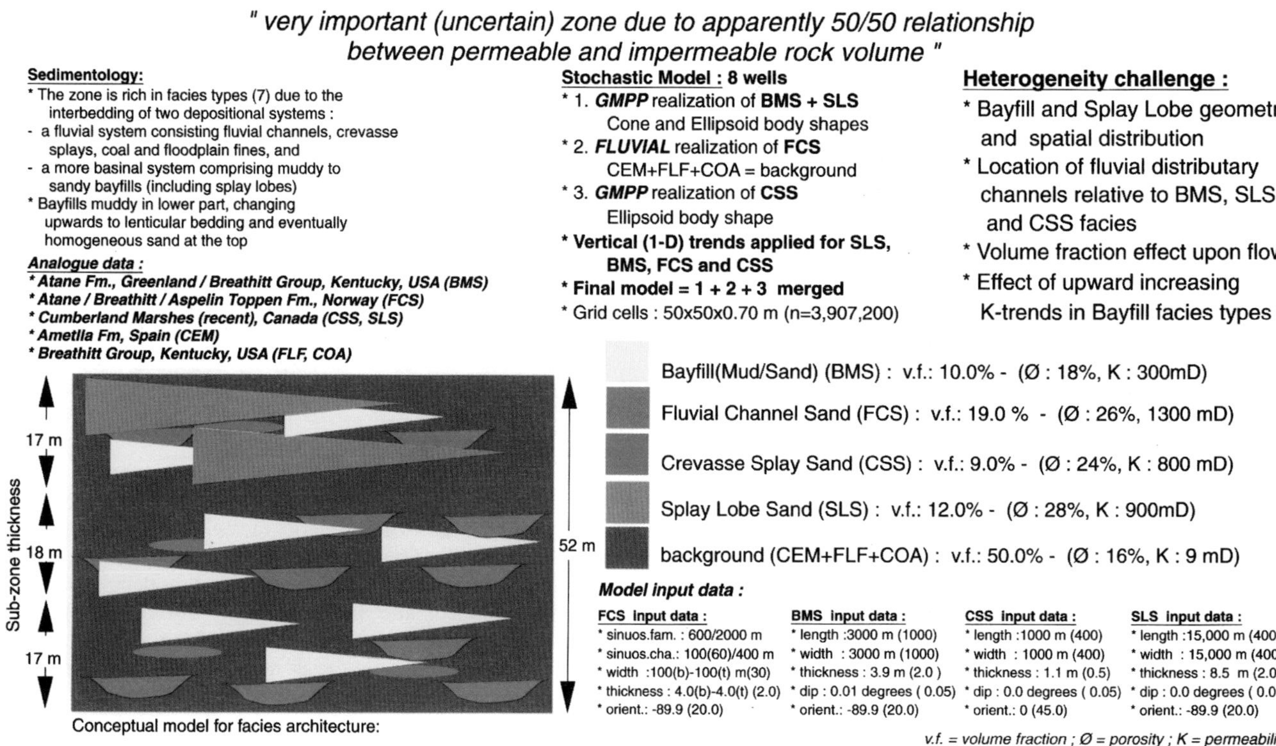

Fig. 4. Conceptual model and summary of the Årel B4-5 reservoir zone. The numbers in brackets following the facies codes refer to average well values. In the model input data part, standard deviation input is given in brackets.

Table 1. Summary of facies characteristics

Facies	Abbreviation	Unit thickness	Sedimentary structures	Grain size	Bioturbation	Perm.
Fluvial channel sand	FCS	4.0	Through cross-bedding Current ripple cross-lamination	silt–m	Absent	600 mD
Crevasse splay sand	CSS	1.0	Current ripple cross-lamination Trough cross-bedding	vf–f	Absent	80 mD
Incised valley fill	IVF	10.0	Through cross-bedding Current ripple cross-lamination	m	Absent	950 mD
Bayfill mud and sand	BMS	4.2	Wave ripple cross-lamination Hummocky cross-stratification Current ripple cross-lamination	vf–f	*Pl, Th, Sk, Di*	70 mD
Splay lobe sand	SLS	8.5	Current ripple cross-lamination	vf–f	Absent	380 mD
Tidal channel sand	TCS	6.0	Trough cross-bedding Current ripple cross-lamination Wave ripple cross-lamination	vf–c	*Pl, Th, large Di*	270 mD
Tidal mud flat	TMF	4.0	Current ripple cross-lamination Wave ripple cross-lamination Trough cross bedding	mud, silt, vf, f	*Di, Pi*	12 mD
Shoreface sand	SFS	3.3	Hummocky cross-stratification Wave ripple cross-lamination	mud, silt, vf, f	*Te, Sk, Mu,* *Pl, Th, Pa*	6 mD
Storm dominated delta	HMS	2.6	Hummocky cross-stratification	f	Rare	12 mD
Open marine mud	OMM	1.4	Starved wave ripple cross-lamination	mud	*Te, Di, Ch, Mu*	5 mD
Calcite cementation	CEM	0.7	–	–	–	0 mD
Dipping calcite cementation	CEMX	0.7	–	–	–	0 mD
Floodplain fines	FLF	4.0	Current ripple cross-lamination	mud, silt, vf	Absent	2 mD
Coal	COA	0.4	–	–	–	–
Shoal sand	SHS	7.0	Wave ripple cross-lamination Trough cross-bedding	f–c	*Sk, Pl*	100 mD
Tidal sand flat	TSF	2.0	Current ripple cross-lamination Wave ripple cross-lamination Trough cross-bedding	mud, silt vf–c	*Pl, Th, Sk,* *As, Di, Te*	80 mD

The unit thickness indicates the thickness of amalgamated beds. Trace fossils are *Pl – Planolites, Pa –Palaeophycus, Th – Thalassinoides, Sk – Skolithos, Di – Diplocraterion, Cy – Cylindrichnus, As – Asterosoma, Te – Teichichnus, Op – Ophiomorpha, Rh – Rhizocorallium, Ar – Arenicolites, Ta – Taenidium, Ch – Chondrites.*

approach, together with a conceptual sketch of the geological interpretation, was prepared for each zone (Fig. 4). Desired facies architectures were obtained by merging two or more realizations made by the different programme modules. The final models were thoroughly quality controlled to ensure that they were consistent with the conceptual model constraints and the well data.

Initially, a single 'most likely' or 'best guess' stochastic model of each reservoir zone was established and up-scaled. The term 'best guess' was used to differentiate it from the term 'base case', which, in the subsequent uncertainty study, was selected on the basis of dynamic and static 'ranking' of 150 different geological realizations.

The generation of stochastic models, being sedimentological facies or petrophysical, requires input of numerous different and invariably complex model parameters derived from well- and/or outcrop analogue databases. 'Best guess' estimates of the individual facies parameters were generated through simple averaging of well data (e.g. facies thicknesses), by using entire distributions or histograms from wells (e.g. poro–perm data), by extracting data from relevant outcrop analogue databases (e.g. length–width relationships of facies bodies) or, by simple guessing based on conceptual understanding (e.g. lateral correlation ranges). Obviously, the uncertainty related to the estimation of the latter two types of parameters is significantly greater than the uncertainty related to the estimation of the well data based parameters.

Input data

Input data to facies modelling are mostly 'intuitive' as the scale of the Åre and Tilje depositional systems invariably differs from known outcrop analogues and because the input data to the stochastic modelling routines are *a priori* input, which is modified in the final facies mosaic. Typically, the *a priori* specified extent of bodies are reduced due to 'erosion' of bodies into each other during the stochastic simulation. The input data was therefore 'tuned' and quality checked in order to obtain the appropriate conceptual facies pattern. One criterion for the acceptance of a given facies realization has been to check that the volume fractions of the various facies in the realization correspond to the targeted volume fractions given by the well data. Further, the spatial distribution of facies was carefully checked since the conditioning to well data can potentially cause unrealistic clustering in and adjacent to densely drilled areas. The tuning of volume fractions can be a time (and CPU) consuming process, especially in cases where a final realization consists of several merged GMPP and/or FLUVIAL realizations. Hence, a 1–2% discrepancy between the target fractions and the output volume fractions were accepted.

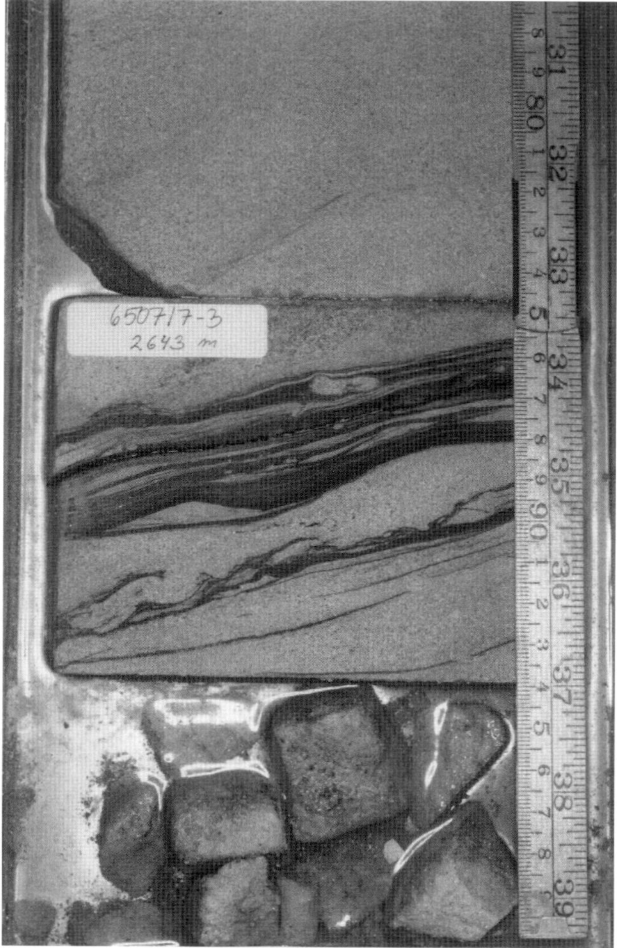

Fig. 5. Mud-drapes within tidal channel deposits from the Tilje Formation.

To guide the concepts behind the facies modelling, and to reduce some of the significant uncertainties related to the input data, outcrop analogues were studied. For the Åre Formation, the Pennsylvanian Breathitt Group of eastern Kentucky, USA. was visited and found to be a relevant analogue (Aitken & Flint 1994, 1995). Data from the Atane Formation in West Greenland (Olsen 1993) and Aspelintoppen Formation, Svalbard (Dreyer 1990) and the modern Cumberland Marshes, Canada (Smith *et al.* 1989) were also used. For the upper Åre and Tilje formations, data collected from the time-equivalent Neill Klinter Formation in Jameson Land, East Greenland were used (Dam & Surlyk 1995) in combination with data from the modern German Bight (Ehlers 1988). It should be noted that the terminology and definition of depositional geometry of such tidal and shallow marine strata is far less mature compared to the alluvial strata in the lower part of the section.

Reservoir zone modelling

In total, 17 zones were defined and modelled. Here, two zones are briefly described. One (Åre 1 B4-5) has an alluvial to delta plain architecture, whereas the other (Tilje 3C) represents a typical tidal zone.

Åre 1 B 4–5 (alluvial to delta plain). The conceptual facies model for this 52 m thick, relatively important, reservoir zone is shown in Fig. 4. Despite containing some 50% non-pay flood plain fines (FLF), coal seams (COA) and cemented beds (CEM) facies elements, it is among the more important Åre 1 member zones in terms of STOIIP (36–38% of the Åre 1 member oil). There are four facies types with reservoir potential, namely bay-fill mud and sand (BMS, 10% of total rock volume), fluvial channel sand (FCS, 19%), crevasse splay sand (CSS, 9%), and splay lobe sand (SLS, 12%), which, being part of a relatively complicated depositional system, have created a complex facies architecture. In fact, three different facies realizations (2 GMPP + 1 FLUVIAL) were merged to produce the desired facies distribution (Fig. 6). In addition to the complexity associated with conditioning the differently shaped and sized facies body types to 8 wells, vertical trend functions for guiding the facies distribution were also applied. The SLS body is correlative over a fairly large area (Fig. 6). This was achieved by specifying a length and a width that exceeded the length and width of the modelling area. Because of well conditioning constraints, the body would only appear in the proper areas with the remaining parts of the body outside the STORM modelling box.

When merging facies realizations, the order of 'erosion' between the reservoir facies specified was: 1. SLS; 2. BMS; 3. FCS; and 4. CSS. This means that no facies erodes into the SLS, whereas the SLS, BMS and FCS facies bodies all erode, or cut into, the CSS (note that all facies erode into the background). The BMS facies was modelled as cone shaped bodies, with their thinner, narrower part pointing in an upstream direction (N) reflecting the interpreted sediment transport direction and the inferred bayfill/subdelta geometry (Fig. 6). BMS erodes into the FCS, in an attempt to achieve the physical termination of individual distributaries into the bays. The connectivity across the field within this sub-zone should be fairly good, assuming the 50% net sand target is met.

The final, merged facies realization consists of 19.5% FCS, 10.1% CSS, 10.9% SLS, 11.3% BMS, and 48.2% FLF/COA/CEM. Because of the significant petrophysical contrast between the background (FLF/COA/CEM) facies association (average porosity and permeability of 15.8% and 9 mD, respectively) and the other, main reservoir quality facies types (average porosity and permeabilities ranging from 18.1–27.6% and 326–1315 mD, respectively), the facies heterogeneity can be seen to be fairly well preserved throughout the petrophysical modelling stage (Fig. 6). Note also the location and heterogeneity pattern of the good reservoir quality SLS facies (Fig. 6).

Tilje 3C (tidal dominated). This reservoir zone is 15 m thick and contains some 31% non-reservoir facies, these being tidal mud flat (TMF, 23%), dipping cementation (CEMX, 4%) and flat-lying cementation (CEM, 4%). As far as in-place hydrocarbons are concerned, this zone is relatively important, containing some 14% of the Tilje Formation STOIIP. The most important reservoir facies are tidal channel sand (TCS, 64%), but tidal sand flat (TSF, 5%) is also expected to contribute to production. Two GMPP realizations were merged to create the desired facies architecture (Fig. 7). First, a GMPP model of TCS, TMF and CEM was generated, each facies being modelled as ellipsoid shaped bodies within a background of TSF. A 1D vertical trend was applied to impose a correct vertical facies arrangement within the zone (as observed in wells), i.e. forcing the TMF towards the top and the TCS + TSF towards the lower part of the sub-zone (Fig. 7). Secondly, a GMPP model of the dipping CEMX was generated. When merging the two realizations, CEMX was specified to erode into the TCS facies only. As a result, CEMX facies bodies only occur within the TCS facies. The lateral connectivity across the TCS-dominated lower part of the sub-zone is believed to be excellent (Fig. 7). However, the total zone vertical permeability will be somewhat restricted because of the concentration of low-permeability TMF in the upper part of the zone.

Upscaling

The last step in the static description of the reservoir, is the upscaling of petrophysical parameters from the fine-scale

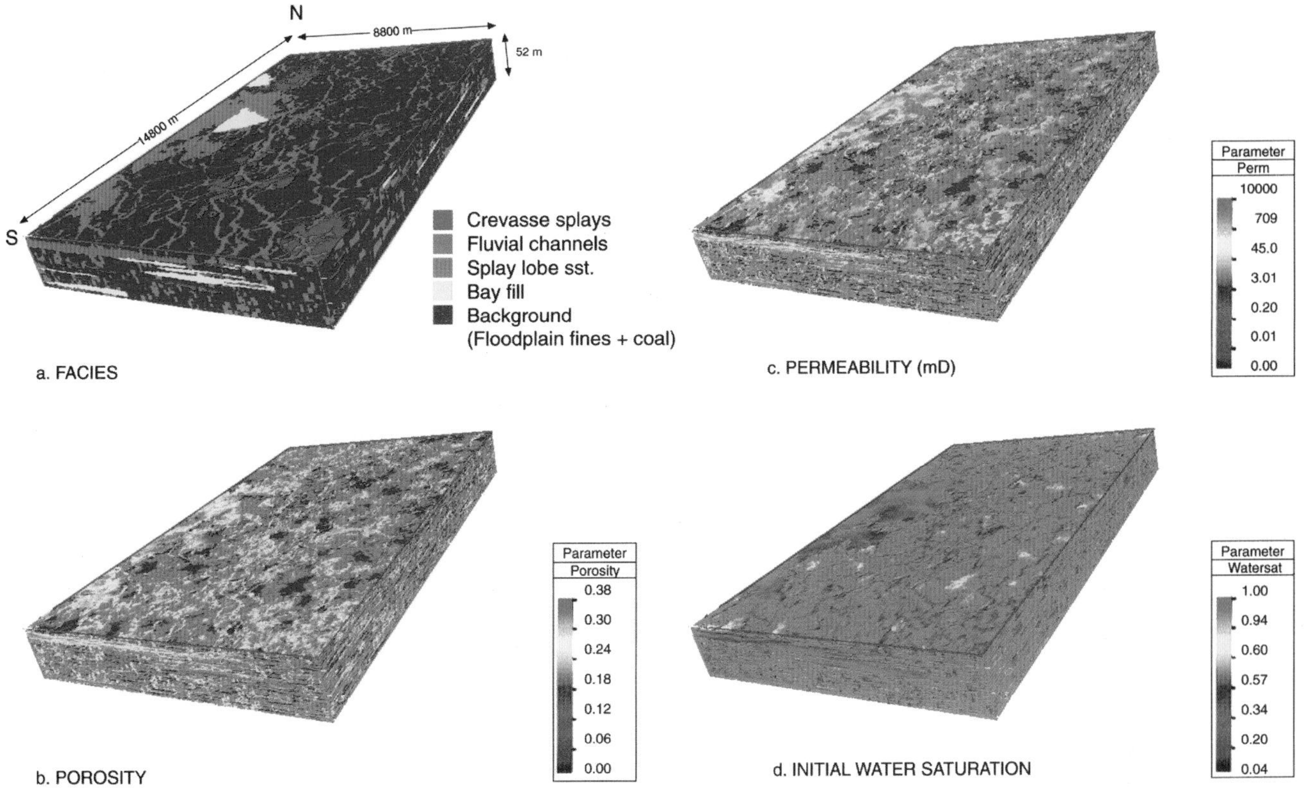

Fig. 6. Initial (unadjusted) facies, porosity, permeability and water saturation realizations of the Åre 1 B 4-5 zone.

geological model to the coarser-scale dynamic ECLIPSE simulation model. The stochastic simulation blocks are approximately $75 \times 75 \times 0.25\,m^3$, as compared to the ECLIPSE simulator blocks of approximately $100 \times 100 \times (5–100)\,m^3$. Therefore, the scale of the stochastic modelling and the full field dynamic simulation are similar laterally whereas the simulation scale is orders of magnitude coarser in the vertical direction.

In order to conserve the dynamic effects of the facies-scale heterogeneity, the performance of the upscaling is vital. The

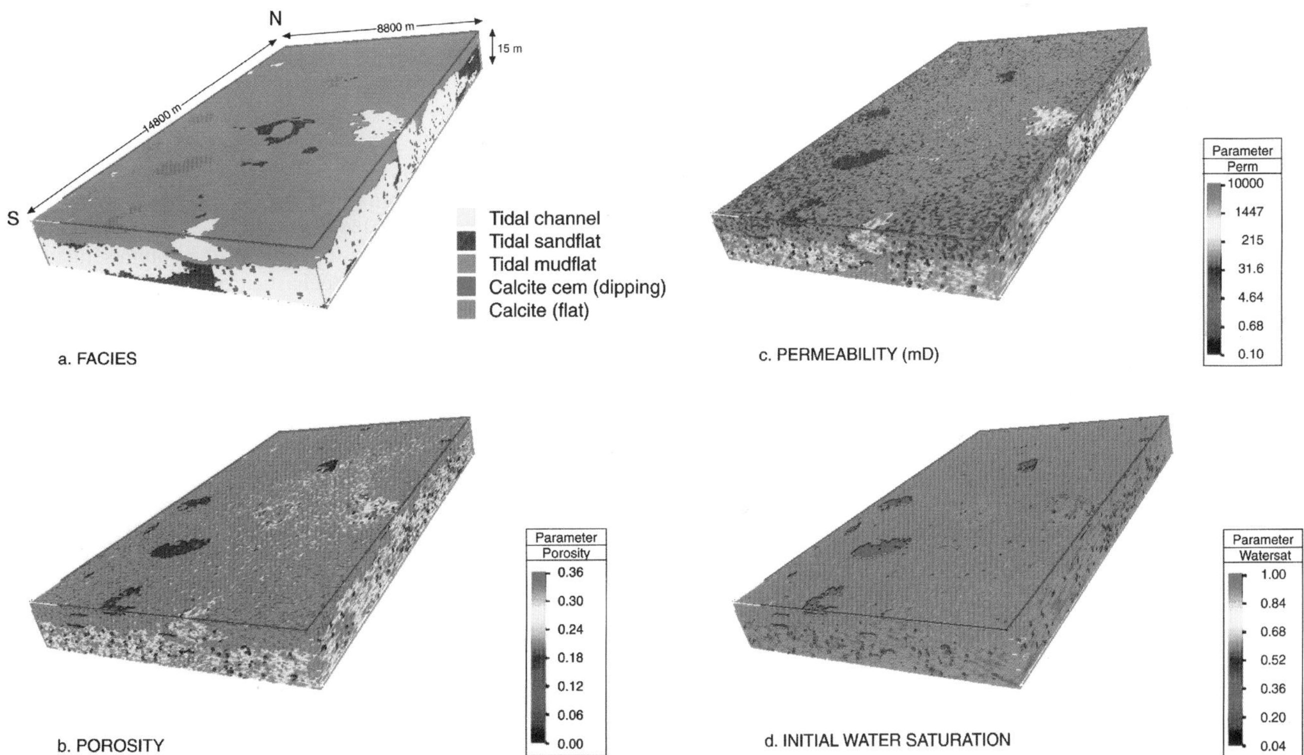

Fig. 7. Initial (unadjusted) facies, porosity, permeability and water saturation realizations of the Tilje 3C zone. Note the use of vertical trend functions that here serve to concentrate the good tidal channel and tidal sandflat facies in the lower and middle parts of the zone.

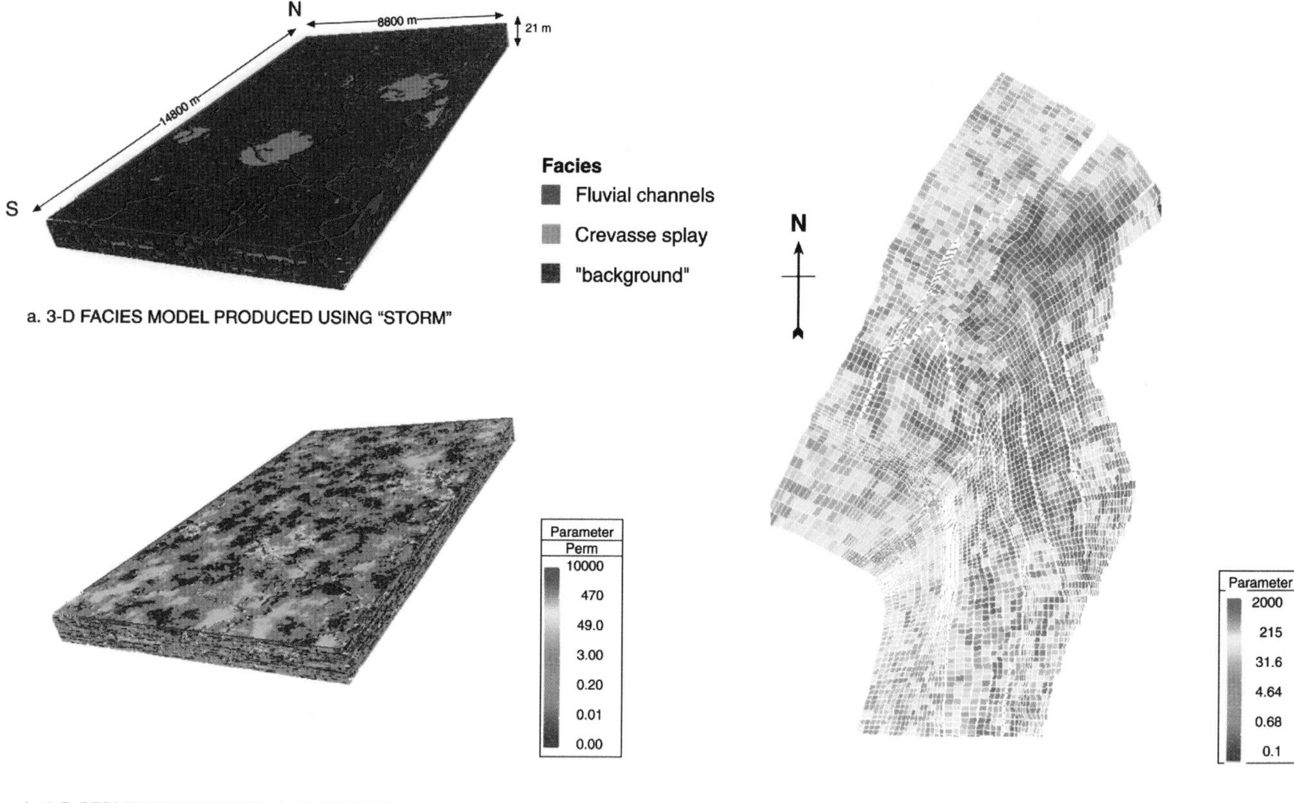

Fig. 8. Example of adjusted and upscaled zone (Åre 1 B 2-3). Original facies and permeability realizations are shown for comparison.

main challenge is to incorporate permeability in a realistic manner due to its directional dependency. Porosity and initial water saturation in contrast, are scalar quantities, and may be arithmetically averaged. The upscaling step is an integrated part of the STORM 3D modelling package. An example of an upscaled realization is shown in Fig. 8, and by visual inspection it can be seen that some heterogeneity is preserved after upscaling. However, a large amount of the fine-scale heterogeneity is smoothed and incorporated in the model as effective properties.

Results

The results of the upscaling procedure describe the static distribution of parameters for the dynamic flow simulation, and are therefore of great importance. Each of the 17 zones within the Tilje and Åre formations express different modelling challenges as far as facies geometry and architecture are concerned. The use of the relatively flexible GMPP program for modelling of ellipsoid and cone-shaped facies bodies (i.e. crevasse splays, cementations, bay-fill units), and the options for integrated use of FLUVIAL + GMPP and GMPP + GMPP through model merging routines, represent a major improvement. The possibility of imposing spatial trends in the facies distribution within individual zones by the implementation of simple trend functions also represents a significant improvement.

The main challenge within the Åre Formation has been to model the conceptually well understood architectural relationships between fluvial channels, crevasse splays, splay lobes and bay-fill units. By merging FLUVIAL and GMPP realizations a conceptually correct spatial relationship was achieved among these facies areally and vertically within given zones. Grouping together floodplain fines, cementation, and coal, as a single background facies within the Åre 1 member may be too simplistic, bearing in mind the possible differences in both geometrical and petrophysical properties of the three lithologies. However, this possible over-simplification is considered of little importance as most of the Åre 1 sub-zones contain relatively small amounts of hydrocarbons. Also, the contrast in permeability between any of the background facies and the associated reservoir facies (FCS, IVF, CSS, etc.) is always several orders of magnitude.

When this study was completed STORM did not give *a posteriori* statistics of facies geometry parameters, thus making it impossible to make a quantitative comparison with the *a priori* input data. Bearing in mind the uneven distribution of wells within the Heidrun area, and the potential consequences of the strict well conditioning option in STORM, it would have been advantageous to be able to tune in facies geometry parameters in a similar way to the tuning in of the volume fractions.

An important part of the stochastic petrophysical modelling stage, was a continuous evaluation and comparison of the output realization data against an ongoing, deterministic (kriging), mapping of properties. Applying similar cut-off criteria, the 3D stochastic porosity and water saturation realizations were re-scaled to 2D IRAP format (surface mapping and static volume calculation tool), such that calculated initial hydrocarbon pore volume (HCPV) could be compared from the two different methods of parameter mapping. Particularly important, was a correct implementation of depth trends documented as part of the deterministic mapping and eventually there was less than 5% difference in total HCPV (of oil) between the two mapping procedures (the stochastic approach gave the lowest result). The difference can be explained by the fact that (i) the application of petrophysical data is quite different; (ii) the effects of the stochastic distribution of facies bodies; (iii) shoulder effects, particularly related to cementations and coal seams resulting in net porosity within zero porosity facies; and (iv) the occasional inclusion of erroneous porosity values above 36% in the calculated averages used in the deterministic mapping.

Uncertainty analysis

By using stochastic modelling as a tool to integrate the various uncertainties of the reservoir description, an uncertainty evaluation of the hydrocarbons in place (HCPV) as well as producible reserves was undertaken. Simplified flow simulations and volumes-in-place were calculated for 150 different reservoir simulation runs, each run based on different structural models and geological and petrophysical realizations. By ranking the 150 simulation results, a risked-base case and alternative geological models for further, more detailed, dynamic uncertainty analysis were selected. The analysis included 3 groups of input: (1) uncertainties related to gross rock volume; (2) uncertainties related to facies architecture and facies volume; and (3) uncertainties related to the petrophysical evaluation. Some parameters were considered as global (field-scale) variables and 1 value was selected for each model. The remaining variables were considered as local (zone-scale) variables and 1 value was selected for each zone. 'Model breakdown', the uncertainty associated with the conceptual understanding of the sequence stratigraphic correlation between wells, and possible errors associated with the facies interpretation, were not included in this study.

Gross rock volume

The uncertainty in bulk reservoir volume was quantified in a separate study where the effects of seismic interpretation, the seismic velocity model, oil–water contacts, and probability of hydrocarbons in undrilled field segments had been evaluated. This was basically a Monte Carlo type of geostatistical analysis and an automatic process involving a total of 1200 simulations was run following the methods outlined in Tyler *et al.* (1996). The normal distribution of bulk rock volume from this study was converted into a discrete distribution with three levels and three complete structural models were then built in the ECLIPSE flow simulator. These models included top reservoir maps, top zone maps, and faults. For each simulation run 1 of these 3 models would be selected.

Facies geometry

The uncertainties related to facies are the geometries of reservoir and non-reservoir units, and the actual volume fractions of the different facies types. Facies geometry largely controls the connectivity within a given reservoir zone. These uncertainties were incorporated by constructing an 'optimistic' and a 'pessimistic' set of modelling parameters for each facies, as evaluated in terms of their expected impact upon fluid flow. These choices were based on instinct and previous experience rather than rigorous simulation and testing. The conceptual geological model parameters are not regarded as uncertain in this study (i.e. interpreted tidal zones are tidal, and were never considered as fluvial).

GMPP modelling

There are several input parameters required for the GMPP modelling. The shift in the different parameters within individual facies for the best and worst cases, depended largely on the reservoir properties of the particular facies and how they were expected to influence fluid flow.

Angle of dip of the poor reservoir quality facies bodies (CEM and CEMX) are reduced in the best case, minimizing restriction to fluid flow. In the worst case, the dip is increased for all facies bodies, independent of their reservoir quality.

Length and width were, in general, increased for good reservoir quality facies bodies and reduced for poor reservoir quality facies bodies in the best case. Because of modelling tool constraints however, the TCS and SFS bodies were not extended because of difficulties in conditioning to well data. In the worst case, the length and width of the good reservoir quality facies bodies were generally reduced, whereas the opposite was done for the poor reservoir quality facies bodies.

Thickness was generally increased for the poor reservoir quality facies bodies in the best case. This is because an increase in the thickness implies a decrease in the length and width in order to conserve the facies body volume fraction within a zone. The values of the good reservoir quality facies bodies were kept unchanged. In the worst case the thickness was reduced for the poor reservoir quality facies bodies. These changes in thickness were estimated based on the variations seen in the wells.

To reduce the probability of generating large, laterally extensive CEM bodies, the length/width correlation coefficient was decreased in the best case. The length/thickness and width/thickness correlation coefficients were increased in order to get the thickness of the CEM bodies more dependent on the lateral extension. In the worst case, the length/thickness and width/thickness correlation coefficient were decreased for the poor reservoir quality facies bodies such that relatively thin facies bodies could develop even if the length and width parameters of these bodies were large. In order to keep the volume fraction of the individual facies constant, an overall thinning of the poor reservoir quality facies bodies results in an increase in the total number of bodies within any realization. To reduce the probability of generating large, laterally extensive good reservoir quality facies bodies, the length/width correlation coefficients of these facies bodies were decreased in the worst case.

FLUVIAL Modelling

There are numerous input parameters for the FLUVIAL program, but only a few were considered to have substantial influence on fluid flow. These parameters relate to the ability of individual channels to erode into each other, and to the volume of individual channels. The parameters controlling the geometry of the channels are the family line (direction line of each channel), the amplitude and the wavelength of the family line (creating large bends in channels), the amplitude and wave-length of the channel line (creating small-scale bends superimposed on the bigger bends), the thickness, and the width. For each parameter, a standard deviation value also needs to be specified.

Family line direction in the best guess case is 89.9° (N–S). This parameter was considered insignificant for the communication between individual channels and was therefore not included in the analysis. The standard deviation, however, influences channel-to-channel communication significantly since it may increase or decrease the spread in channel orientations. Communication between individual channels improves if the standard deviation is increased, whereas the channels become more isolated if the standard deviation is reduced (channels oriented parallel). The standard deviation was therefore increased in the best case and decreased in the worst case models.

Amplitude of the family line controls the effective width of the channel belt, and could therefore improve communication if increased. Consequently, in the best case, the family line amplitude was increased and subsequently in the worst case, the amplitude was reduced to impose isolation of the channel bodies. For the same reasons, the channel line amplitude was reduced in the worst case and increased in the best cases (Fig. 9).

In order to achieve a higher density of channel bodies within the family belt, (i.e. improving communication) the wavelength of the family line was reduced in the best case. In contrast, in the worst case the wavelength is increased, resulting in relatively straight, more isolated channel bodies. Similarly, as for the family line wavelength, the channel line wavelength is decreased in the worst case, and increased in the best case (Fig. 9).

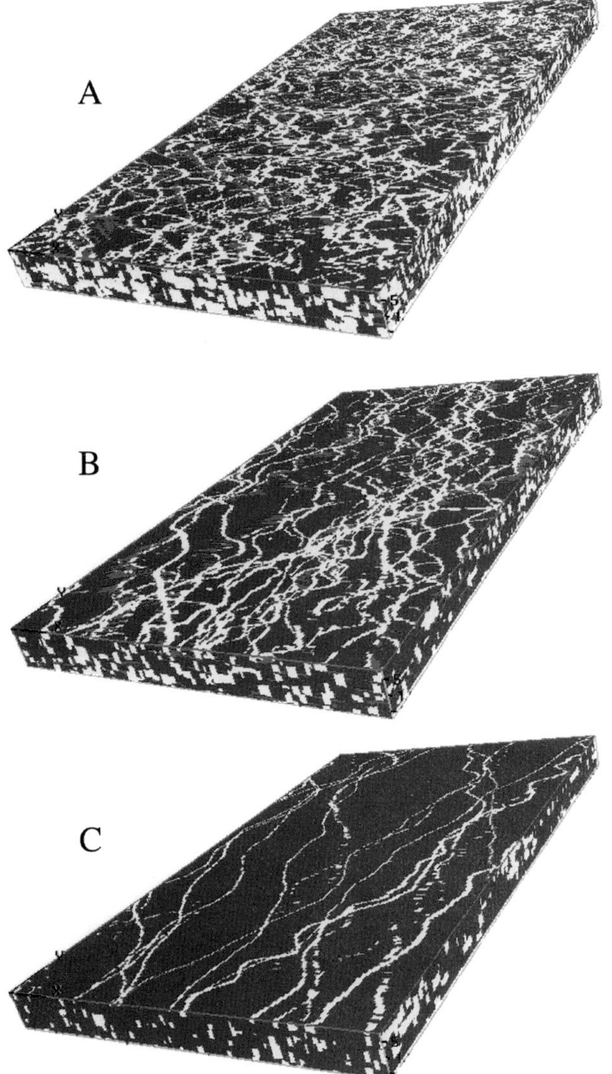

Fig. 9. Illustration of the uncertainty in the facies volume fraction and facies geometry parameters. Fluvial channel fills in yellow, sandy crevasse splays in red, non-reservoir facies in blue. (**A**) A high facies volume and favourable facies geometry realization. Channels are modelled as very sinuous and frequently cross thus establishing a fair degree of communication. (**B**) A best guess realization. (**C**) A low facies volume and unfavourable facies geometry realization. The few channels present are nearly straight and rarely cross. Very limited production can be expected from such zones. All three zones are conditioned to the wells penetrating this zone.

In the best case, the channel width is increased slightly to achieve more laterally extensive channel bodies. The reason for the rather marginal increase in channel widths is the effect of the conservation of the volume fraction, since an increase in channel width will imply fewer and likely more isolated channels. In the worst case, the channel width was reduced to generate smaller and more isolated channel bodies.

Facies volume fractions

The uncertainty in the facies volume fraction influences both the connectivity and HCPV present in the reservoir, and depends on several variables, such as the number of wells, the well configuration, the facies classification and aspect ratios, lateral facies distribution, etc. A quantification of this uncertainty by simply calculating the mean and standard deviation from the actual well observations is likely to be biased because of the uneven well pattern as well as random effects caused by the small number of wells, particularly in the lower zones of the Åre Formation. A solution to these problems was found assuming that the 'best guess' stochastic realization is representative for the facies body distribution within the given zone. In practice, 2D maps of the facies distributions were calculated from the 3D 'best guess' facies realizations simply by vertically averaging the fraction of each facies. These 2D maps were then sampled by the same number of wells as in the relevant zone, honouring the well configuration. The well configuration was then systematically moved through all possible positions in the model. The results of the 1000–20 000 samples for each zone were subsequently analysed and P10 and P90 estimates extracted.

Petrophysical model

Uncertainty in the petrophysical properties can be divided into two main groups; firstly, uncertainties caused by limited amounts of data or contradicting data that vary independently between the reservoir zones and, secondly, uncertainty in the petrophysical measurements caused by systematic errors in the equipment and method. In this uncertainty analysis the uncertainty related to the following parameters were studied: porosity, initial water saturation, permeability, petrophysical correlation range, the systematic uncertainty in the estimation of HCPV, and porosity cut-off (net sand definition). The last variable is of particular importance as many intervals consist of interbedded sandstone and mudstone where the definition of net sand and net sand porosity will be very uncertain when based on standard logging tools. During the simulation loop, the porosity cut-off was considered a global variable and one value for each model selected. All other petrophysical parameters were local and varied from zone to zone. These values were distributed stochastically within the selected facies models as part of the automated modelling loop.

Simulation and ranking

From the discrete distribution functions, the input variables were combined to a total of 150 simulation runs (geological models). Some of the input variables, such as the bulk reservoir volume and porosity cut-off (net sand definition), were considered 'global' variables. This means that only one value was chosen for one complete geological model, hence the same value was applied to all 17 zones. The remaining variables, i.e. facies model parameters (facies volume fractions and facies geometry), and petrophysical parameters, were considered local variables, (i.e. the values vary between the different reservoir zones in one geological model). Hence, if a favourable facies volume fraction was chosen in one particular zone, this did not affect the selected volume fraction of a reservoir facies in the neighbouring zones. In other words, the local variables are uncorrelated and independent.

For the facies geometry parameters, one 'high' and one 'low' case were estimated where all the individual facies geometries in each reservoir zone were defined (although some of these geometry parameters are believed to be independent). As an example, in the 'high' case, the geometry parameters for all facies were set favourable for fluid flow. The opposite was done for the low case. For the uncertainty in the facies volume fraction, the high and low cases were defined with respect to the volume fraction of reservoir facies versus non-reservoir facies. The result was three complete cases (low = L, 'best guess' = B, high = H) with facies geometry parameters, and additional three cases with different volume fractions. Out of the nine possible combinations, only five were chosen for simulations, being; best guess (BB), high volume fraction and facies geometries (HH), low volume fraction and facies geometries (LL),

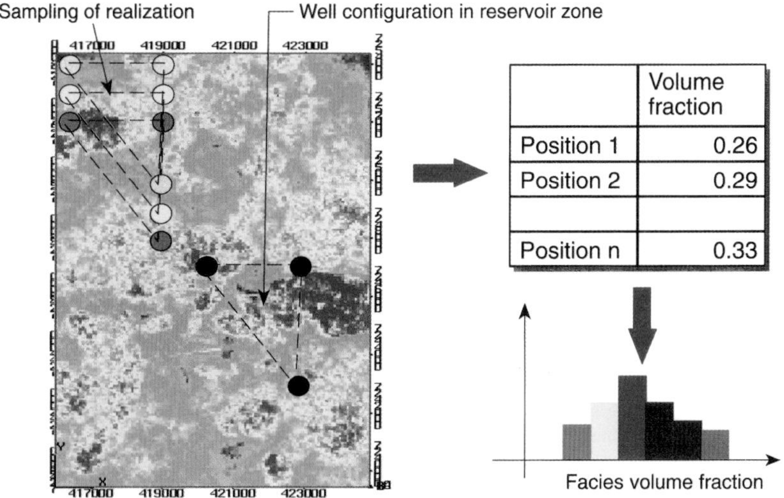

Fig. 10. Illustration of how the uncertainty in the facies volume fraction was handled (see text for further details).

high volume fraction and best guess facies geometries (HB), and low volume fraction and best guess facies geometries (LB). Three alternative facies realizations of the same zone are shown in Fig. 10.

The 150 geological models generated in the uncertainty study were established in the following way. Firstly, the global variables were drawn (one random selection for each complete model). This included choosing a bulk reservoir model (P_{10}, P_{50} or P_{90}) and a porosity cut-off value. Then, the local variables were selected (one random selection for each reservoir zone). This included choosing a facies model (LL, LB, BB, HB or HH) as well as petrophysical parameters.

After completion of each single geological model, the fine-scale realizations were immediately upscaled for HCPV calculation and simplified flow simulation. The fine-scale realizations were not saved after each run because of computer disk storage limitations. The only data saved after one single 'loop', were, the input data for the stochastic model (the model files), the HCPV calculations, and the simulation results. By saving the input data, the realizations could be re-generated and upscaled if selected for further dynamic analysis.

The 150 geological models were subsequently ranked with respect to key properties describing the static and dynamic behaviour of the reservoir. The ranking parameters were HCPV, oil pore volume (OPV), gas pore volume (GPV) and cumulative oil production from the simplified dynamic simulation. The HCPV and the cumulative oil production ranking parameters were plotted against each other in order to establish criteria for selection of models for further dynamic simulations. An additional outcome of the volume-calculation was uncertainty distributions of the HCPV, the OPV and GPV in Tilje and Åre, taking the uncertainty in the structural model, facies parameters and petrophysical properties thoroughly into account.

Results

The 'best guess' model showed a HCPV of approximately $650 \times 10^6\,m^3$ of which $450 \times 10^6\,m^3$ are oil and $200 \times 10^6\,m^3$ are gas. The uncertainty study indicates a P_{90}–P_{10} range of the HCPV between 515 and $690 \times 10^6\,m^3$ (3240–4340×10^6 BBL).

The uncertainty in global parameters (gross rock volume and porosity cut-off) has, not surprisingly, the largest impact on the total HCPV uncertainty. The local uncertainties, i.e. combined effects of the local facies and petrophysical variations, are not as significant at this scale. As these parameters vary from zone to zone, they tend to average each other out, making it very difficult to identify the effect of any individual parameter on the total HCPV. However, these local uncertainties do have an important effect on the local uncertainty, i.e. the uncertainty within individual zones and segments.

The porosity cut-off was treated as a global parameter in this project although, to a great extent, it depends on the heterogeneity at bed and laminae scale. If the porosity cut-off had been treated as facies dependent (i.e. a local parameter) the total uncertainty range would have been somewhat lower and the importance of the facies uncertainty increased.

Conclusions

A full-field scale 3D stochastic model that incorporates the medium- to large-scale facies heterogeneity within the Åre and Tilje formation reservoir zones has been established. It represents a major improvement of the geological reservoir description of the Heidrun Field. Although the process of upscaling from the fine-scale geological models to the coarser-scale dynamic simulator grid (ECLIPSE) inevitably smoothes out some of the finer-scale geological heterogeneities, significant features of the geological models are retained. This means that an improved foundation for detailed dynamic reservoir simulation has been generated.

A rigorous uncertainty analysis using stochastic modelling has allowed selection of alternative simulations models on which a more complete understanding of the dynamic behaviour of the field can be based. The uncertainty study shows that the largest uncertainty in field-scale production is oil in place. Uncertainty in facies parameters are only of minor full field importance. However, this uncertainty can be very important for specific zones or local areas and should be considered.

The project has shown that object-based stochastic modelling can be applied to large, complex fields. The methodology is robust and flexible and may also be applied to other types of deposits such as deep marine reservoirs. For small fields with few wells, uncertainty in facies geometry and reservoir facies volumes can be the most important factor and should not be under-estimated. Dynamic production forecast and history matching must pay attention to the fact that the geological model is uncertain

We wish to express our gratitude to the many people who have been involved in this project both within Statoil and among the licence partners (Conoco, Neste). We also acknowledge the sedimentological work done by J. Harms and later E. Clifton who in many ways have established the sedimentological framework of the Heidrun Field.

We thank the partners of the Heidrun licence for the permission to publish this paper. The paper benefited from reviews by A. Hurst, T. Reynolds and S. Currie.

References

AITKEN, J. F. & FLINT, S. S. 1994. High frequency sequences and the nature of incised valley fills in fluvial systems of the Breathitt group (Pennsylvanian), Appalachian foreland basin, eastern Kentucky. *In*: DALRYMPLE, R., BOYD, R. & ZAITLIN, B. (eds), *Incised Valley Systems: Origin and Sedimentary Sequences.* Society of Economic Paleontologists and Mineralogists, Special Publications, **51**, 353–368.

AITKEN, J. F. & FLINT, S. S. 1995. The application of sequence stratigraphy to fluvial systems: an example from the Late Carboniferous of the Appalachians. *Sedimentology*, **42**, 3–30.

DAM, G. & SURLYK, F. 1995. Sequence stratigraphic correlation of Lower Jurassic shallow marine and paralic successions across the Greenland–Norway seaway. *In:* STEEL, R. (ed.) *Sequence Stratigraphy of the Northwest European Margin.* Norwegian Petroleum Society, Special publications, **5**, 483–509.

DREYER, T. 1990. Sand body dimensions and infill sequences of stable humid-climate delta plain channels. *In*: BULLER, A. T., BERG, E., HJELMELAND, O., KLEPPE, J., TORSÆTER, O. & ÅSEN, J. O. (eds) *North Sea Oil and Gas Reservoirs II.* Graham & Trotman, London, 337–351.

EHLERS, J. 1988. *The Morphodynamics of the Wadden Sea.* A. A. Balkema, Rotterdam.

KOENIG, R. H. 1986. Oil discovery in 6507/7; an initial look at the Heidrun field. *In*: SPENCER, A. M. *et al.* (eds). *Habitat of Hydrocarbons on the Norwegian Continental Shelf.* Norwegian Petroleum Society. Graham & Trotman, London, 307–313.

OLSEN, T. 1993. Large fluvial systems: a fluvio–deltaic example from the Upper Cretaceous of central Vest Greenland. *Sedimentary Geology*, **85**, 457–473.

READING, H. G. 1986. Facies. *In*: READING, H. G. (ed.) *Sedimentary Environments and Facies*, Blackwell Science, Oxford, 4–19.

ROSVOLL, K. J., OLSEN, T., KJÆREFJORD, J. M., ARNESEN, D. M., SANDSDALEN, C., JØRGENVÅG, S. H., LANGLAIS, V. & SVELA, K. E. 1997. Paralic and tidal reservoirs of the Heidrun Field, offshore Mid-Norway – Integrated reservoir characterization and uncertainty analysis using stochastic modelling. *In*: SHANLEY, K. W. & PERKINS, B. F. (eds) *Shallow Marine and Nonmarine Reservoirs –Sequence Stratigraphy, Reservoir Architecture and Production Characteristics.* Gulf Coast Section SEPM, 259–282.

SMITH, N. D., CROSS, T. A., DUFFICY, J. P. & CLOUGH, S. R. 1989. Anatomy of an avulsion. *Sedimentology,* **36**, 1–23.

TYLER, K., SANDSDALEN, C., MAELAND, L., AASEN, J. O., SIRING, E. & BARBIERI, M. 1996. *Integrated stochastic modeling in reservoir evaluation for project evaluation and risk assesment.* Society of Petroleum Engineers, Paper 36706.

WHITLEY, P. K. 1992. The geology of Heidrun: a giant oil and gas field on the mid-Norwegian shelf. *In*: HALBOUTY, M. T. (ed.) *Giant Oil and Gas Fields of the Decade 1978–1988.* American Association of Petroleum Geologists, Memoirs, **54**, 383–406.

An integrated approach to hydrocarbon emplacement in chalk, Norwegian North Sea Central Graben

I. E. I. ØXNEVAD and M. S. G. TAYLOR

Amoco Norway Oil Company, P.O Box 8088, 400 Stavanger, Norway (e-mail: ioxnevad@amoco.com)

Abstract: North Sea Central Graben chalk reservoirs are unique in that they have exceptionally high porosities at several thousand metres depth. This is partly an effect of overpressure, but, equally important are the combination of diagenesis, fracturing, and the timing of hydrocarbon generation, migration and entrapment.

For chalk to serve as a reservoir, available porosity and permeability at the time of hydrocarbon migration are critical. Porosity in a normal chalk is reduced by early marine cementation, mechanical compaction and chemical compaction (i.e. dissolution and precipitation of calcite cement). To what extent these processes influence porosity evolution through time is related to the chalk's burial history, specifically the pressure history, thermal history and the partial pressure of CO_2 (P_{CO_2}).

This was demonstrated by modelling porosity evolution through time in a cross-section extending from crestal Valhall Field to basin areas. The modelling results show that at crestal Valhall the chalk is highly porous and only mechanically compacted. Thermal and pressure (P_{CO_2}) conditions were unfavourable for carbonate burial diagenetic cement to form prior to $\approx$20 Ma. At this point, oil emplacement prevented further porosity reduction, despite increasing temperatures and favourable P_{CO_2} conditions during continued burial. In basin areas, rapid burial and exposure to high temperatures combined with favourable P_{CO_2} conditions, from $\approx$40 Ma until present, resulted in more extensive porosity reduction by mechanical and chemical compaction.

Permeability in chalk is significantly enhanced by fracturing. Chalk fractures if total stress (pore pressure + bending moment) is equal to or exceeds fracture pressure. Providing that fractures are open while hydrocarbons are migrating, these will serve as migration pathways. As for the modelled basin areas, absence of tensional fractures at the time of hydrocarbon migration prevented filling of potential reservoirs. Instead, hydrocarbons were directed laterally towards crestal Valhall where pore space and permeability enhancing fractures were available.

By combining the results from the chalk diagenesis and fracture studies with hydrocarbon generation, migration and entrapment modelling, the distribution of known chalk fields and dry holes in the area was reproduced. The approach taken in the study emphasizes the necessity of a detailed understanding of the processes behind empirical observations such as porosity values in North Sea chalk reservoirs, a full evaluation of all factors having an impact on fracturing, and the integration of this understanding with basin-scale hydrocarbon migration models. Despite still unresolved questions concerning the chalk hydrocarbon system, the achievements so far are promising and encouraging for future prediction of hydrocarbon accumulations.

Recent chalk exploration in the North Sea Central Graben, focusing on off-structure areas, has challenged some established concepts in the petroleum industry. Among these are the necessity of maintaining hydrocarbon saturation to preserve high porosities in chalk at great depth, the impact of depositional processes on porosity preservation, and the effects of timing and magnitude of overpressure on chalk porosity. Also highlighted is the importance of integrated approaches to fully understand the chalk hydrocarbon system.

Having drilled the main structures (Fig. 1), explorationists began investigating the potential for new plays in the deeper areas off the structural highs. An overall understanding of chalk reservoirs derived from the producing fields, structural and stratigraphic trapping mechanisms, more advanced methods for identifying high porosity chalk from seismic data, and sedimentological and diagenetic models predicting preferential preservation of high porosities in redeposited chalk, were some of the reasons behind this off-flank interest. Encouraging results from the Saddle area between the Valhall and East Hod fields (Well 2/11-A8) in 1994, testing the stratigraphic trap concept (D'Angelo *et al.* 1997), added to the off-structure prospect optimism. However, despite the Saddle area discovery, off-structure successes remain elusive. High porosity chalk at great depths are found (e.g. Wells 2/7-30, 2/8-15), but little oil (Brasher & Vagle 1996).

Building on the success of the Saddle area well and the positive experience of integrating seismic data analysis with a detailed understanding of petrophysical properties and the geological history of the sediments, the Nøkken prospect (Well 2/8-15) was drilled by Amoco in early 1996. The prospect, located in basin areas east of Valhall Field (Fig. 1), was picked primarily by utilizing seismic analysis of amplitude anomalies. The model predicted relatively high porosity (28–33%), allochthonous, moderately fractured reservoir quality chalk at about 3200 m depth sub-sea. Vertical migration was assumed from an Upper Jurassic source to reservoir. Drilling however, revealed a somewhat different picture: the chalk had an average porosity of 29%, but contained no open fractures[1] and no traces of oil. Thus, the methods applied seemed sufficient for accurately identifying high porosity chalk, but they were inadequate for predicting economic hydrocarbons.

Given the scarcity of successful discoveries in these high porosity flank and basin chalks, the natural question to ask is

[1] In this paper fracture is used generically, including both joints and faults (Park 1983).

ØXNEVAD, I. E. I. & TAYLOR, M. S. G. 1999. An integrated approach to hydrocarbon emplacement in chalk, Norwegian North Sea Central Graben. *In*: FLEET, A. J. & BOLDY, S. A. R. (eds) *Petroleum Geology of Northwest Europe: Proceedings of the 5th Conference*, 1221–1230.

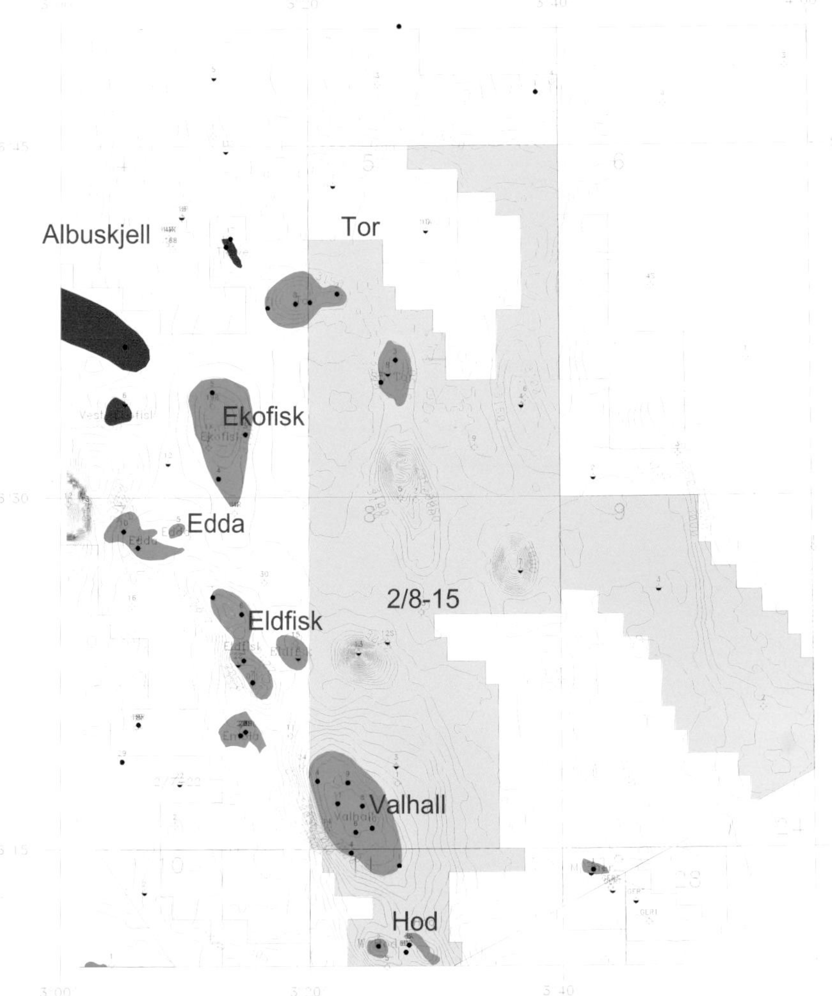

Fig. 1. Norwegian sector of the Southern North Sea Central Graben. The known chalk fields are shown in green and the Amoco acreage shown in yellow. The BP Amoco operated Valhall Field is located in the south, close to the Danish sector. Valhall Field contains 2.4×10^9 barrels oil in place (OIP). The Phillips operated Ekofisk Field, further north, contains 6×10^9 OIP.

what are we doing wrong? Assuming that the stratigraphic trap concept is valid, as is suggested by the Saddle area well, why are we unable to make discoveries? Is it a result of insufficiently sophisticated methods, or inability to capture the full picture of the chalk system and the complex interactions between sedimentology, structural evolution, diagenesis and hydrocarbon generation, migration and entrapment on basin to reservoir scales? Witnessed in the Nøkken prospect was the need for an integrated approach to a system where all components must be understood and appropriately timed to gain the necessary understanding required for chalk exploration success. Specifically, it was necessary to consider the methods for fracture prediction, the impact of pore fluid (hydrocarbons versus water) on chalk cementation and vertical versus lateral migration. This paper reviews the current status of a project that addresses these issues. The main goal of the project is to evaluate key risk elements in chalk reservoirs. This implies: (i) understanding key processes in chalk diagenesis, pressure, and fracture distribution; (ii) evaluating multiple layer migration as a concept for understanding mechanisms controlling hydrocarbon generation, migration and entrapment within the chalk; and (iii) validating modelling results and linking key learning to chalk exploration. In this paper the preliminary results of this work are reviewed. By combining results from chalk diagenesis and fracture studies with hydrocarbon generation, migration and entrapment modelling it has been possible to reproduce the distribution of known chalk fields in the area. The modelling also correctly reproduces dry holes which is an improvement from previous migration models. The approach taken in the study emphasizes the necessity of a detailed understanding of the processes behind empirical observations such as porosity values in North Sea chalk reservoirs. It illustrates the importance of evaluating all factors that may have an impact on fracturing, and finally, shows the need for integrating this understanding with basin-scale hydrocarbon migration models. There are refinements in the model and details that need to be taken further to clarify still unresolved questions concerning the chalk hydrocarbon system. However, the achievements so far are judged as promising and potentially leading to an approach that may improve the ability to predict future hydrocarbon accumulations in chalk.

Study area

The area studied in the project is the Norwegian sector of the Southern North Sea Central Graben (Fig. 1). The main known oil fields are the Ekofisk, Tor, SE Tor, Edda, Eldfisk, Valhall and Hod fields, the two latter being operated by BP Amoco Norway. Reservoir chalks are Late Cretaceous to Early Tertiary (Danian) in age. Reservoir porosity is up to 50% at 2500–3000 m depth whereas matrix permeability is merely a few mD (although significantly enhanced by fractures). The reservoir chalks are overpressured and highly fractured. The latter

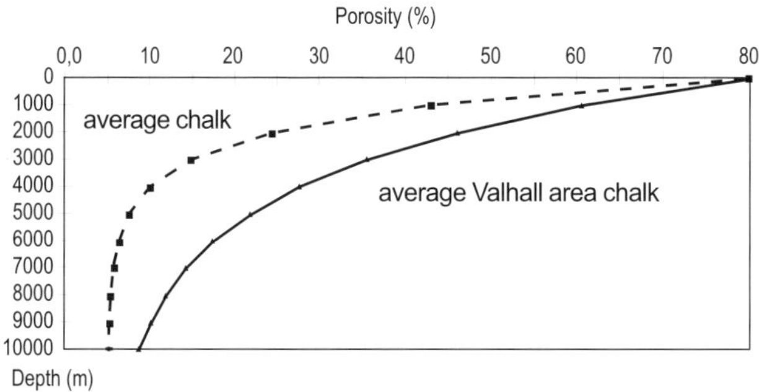

Fig. 2. Porosity versus depth for a normal and a Valhall area reservoir chalk. Note porosity difference at typical Valhall Field reservoir depths of about 2500 m.

is the key for migration into the reservoir and economic production whereas the high porosity provides the volume in which hydrocarbons are stored.

Chalk diagenesis

The Central Graben reservoir chalks have abnormally high porosities at depths where a normal chalk has lost up to 75% of its primary porosity. The rapid porosity loss seen in a normal chalk is caused by early marine cementation, mechanical compaction and chemical compaction (i.e. pressure solution and cementation) (Scholle 1977). These processes reduce porosity from initial values of 70–80% to about 20% at 2500 m depth (Fig. 2). In contrast, a typical Valhall reservoir chalk will, at the same depth, have a porosity of about 40–45% ≈20–25% higher than that of a normal chalk. This anomalous porosity observed in the North Sea chalk fields is generally explained as being a result of overpressure, hydrocarbon emplacement and depositional processes (Hardman 1982; Kennedy 1987). However, for predicting future chalk plays, the processes behind these observations need to be more fully understood. Such understanding requires a detailed evaluation of the effects of pressure and temperature on diagenesis, the impact of pore fluid content and availability of moveable ions in the pore fluid system, and the significance of depositional rate.

Diagenetic modelling

To assess the question of porosity loss in chalk, porosity evolution through time was modelled in crestal reservoir chalk (Valhall) and non-reservoir chalk east of Valhall (Nøkken). The chalk at Nøkken was deposited in a basinal low, east of the Valhall structure which already, in Turonian–Maastrichtian times was established as a high as a result of structural inversion along the Skrubbe fault (Farmer & Barkved, 1999). The chalks of both the crestal reservoir and the non-reservoir in the basin are primarily composed of redeposited material (i.e. slump, debris flow and mudflow deposits), but with some intervening crestal winnowed and pelagic platform facies, respectively, supporting the difference in structural setting (Sikora *et al.* in press). The high proportion of redeposited material implies fairly high rates of sedimentation and thus no significant loss of porosity by early cementation at the seafloor. During burial diagenesis the Valhall reservoir chalk was mechanically compacted, but not cemented (Matthews 1998). At Nøkken, however, the chalk is both mechanically and chemically compacted as is evident from stylolites and isotope analysis studies (Matthews 1998). Thus, diagenetically the two sites (crestal versus basin) differ although the depositional processes involved appear to be largely the same.

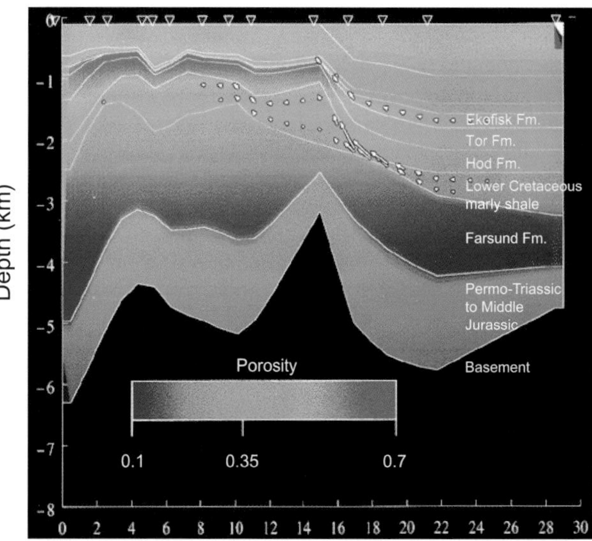

Fig. 3. Simulated porosity at 22.5 Ma. From time of deposition to 22.5 Ma a marked porosity contrast has developed between the Valhall crest and eastern basin areas. At crestal Valhall, top Tor Formation is at a burial depth of 500–800 m, below Paleocene shales. High porosities (around 60%) are maintained in both Hod and Tor Formations. At the flank, top Tor Formation is at 1700 m burial depth. Porosity is reduced to 45%. Top Hod Formation, at 2200 m burial depth, has a porosity of 30–40%.

The modelling of porosity evolution in the two chalks was done using a 2D basin modelling package, Integrated Basin Chemical Modelling (IBCM) (Meshri 1990). The modelling specifically aimed to: (i) evaluate differences in mechanisms that control porosity evolution in the chalk from crest to flank; (ii) determine timing of late carbonate cementation; and (iii) investigate the effect of oil emplacement on porosity evolution. An interpreted cross-section (extending from crestal Valhall to flank and basin areas to the east), layer subdivision with ages, lithologies and thicknesses, hiatuses and erosion, and heat flow data, served as input data. Log data, measured core porosities and isotope data were used for calibration.

The modelling results clearly illustrate a difference in porosity reduction through time between crest and basin area chalks. At 62 Ma, high porosity (70–80%) coccolithic ooze was deposited over the entire area. At 22.5 Ma, a marked porosity contrast had evolved between crest and basin areas (Fig. 3). In the crestal chalks, high porosities (50–60%) were maintained whereas in the basinal chalks porosities had been reduced to 30–45%. This is also largely the situation today. Importantly, both the crest and basin areas are overpressured and the chalk mechanically compacted. However, the basin chalks have experienced further porosity loss through burial cementation as is evident from stable isotope analysis (Matthews 1998). Similar evidence has not been found in the crestal chalk at Valhall.

Calcite cementation

The main chemical reaction controlling cementation in chalk is precipitation of calcite. This can be expressed in the form of the reaction (Morse & Mackenzie 1990)

$$Ca^{2+} + CO_3^{2-} \Leftrightarrow CACO_3.$$

In an ideal solution (i.e. Ca^{2+} and CO_3^{2-} in solution and stable pH and E_H conditions) the equilibrium position of this reaction is a function of temperature and the partial pressure of CO_2 (P_{CO_2}, derived from pore pressure after Oddo & Tomson 1982), and can be modelled by omega ($\Omega = \log IAP/K$) (IAP = ionic activity product, K = solubility product) (Berner 1980). When Ω is positive, equilibrium is to the right and precipitation will occur. When Ω is negative, equilibrium is to the left and ions will remain in solution (Berner 1980). By plotting temperature versus P_{CO_2} and Ω it can be shown that as the chalk is buried, P_{CO_2} and temperature will increase. Omega, however, changes from positive to negative to positive, allowing precipitation to occur at the seafloor (early marine cementation and formation of hardgrounds) and at depth (burial cementation). At depths in between, ions will remain in solution and no cementation will occur.

This understanding was taken back to the modelled section from crestal Valhall to eastern flank and basin areas. Temperature and Ω were plotted versus time (Figs 4 and 5). This shows that in the basin area, temperature increases rapidly from time of deposition until present whereas at the crest, the temperature increase is slower, and even today temperatures are lower than in the basin (Fig. 4). Omega varies from negative to positive in both crestal and basin area chalks (Fig. 5). At the flank and basin areas however, Ω becomes positive about 20 Ma earlier than at the crest. Chalk in these areas is thus likely to have undergone cementation over the last 40 Ma. At the crest, even though cementation could have taken place over the last 20 Ma, no evidence of burial cementation has been observed (Matthews 1998). This lack of burial cement, despite favourable conditions as expressed by Ω begs the question as to what factors may inhibit the process of calcite precipitation. Obvious factors to evaluate are overpressure and presence of hydrocarbons as these are known to be important elements in the area reviewed in this study (Spencer *et al.* 1996). Overpressure hinders mechanical compaction. It also inhibits the release of ions at grain contacts (pressure solution) and thereby has a negative affect on chemical diagenesis by hindering supply of ions from the sediment to the pore fluid (Scholle & Halley 1985). In the system modelled in this study, this is the situation at both the crest and in the basin and therefore cannot explain the observed differences in diagenetic evolution. Turning to the distribution of hydrocarbons and the timing of hydrocarbons migration into the system, hydrocarbon generation, migration and entrapment modelling indicate a marked difference between crest and basin. At the crest, hydrocarbons were present in the system when Ω became positive. Oil, in contrast with water, is not an electrolyte and will therefore hinder free movement of ions and inhibit precipitation of calcite cement in the pores. In the basin area the pore fluid is water. As water is an electrolyte, precipitation of ions already in solution could take place when Ω becomes positive. Thus, in this system, pore fluid content, timing of hydrocarbon emplacement and Ω were critical factors causing the differences in diagenetic evolution observed between crest and basin area chalks.

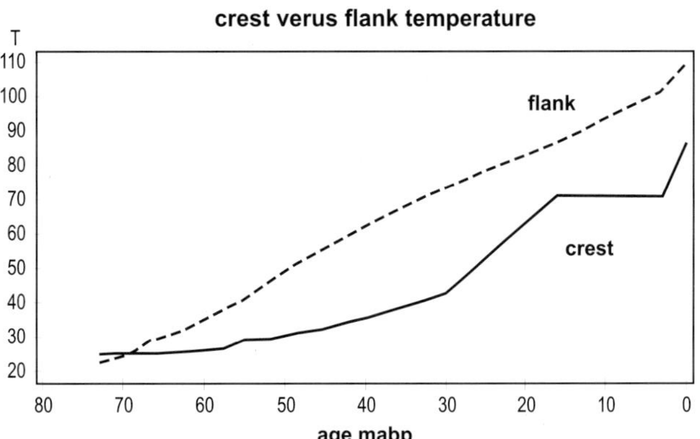

Fig. 4. Temperature plotted versus time for crest and flank to basin areas. Compared to the crest, the deeper flank and basin area shows a more rapid temperature increase, and even today, temperatures are higher in the basin than at the crest.

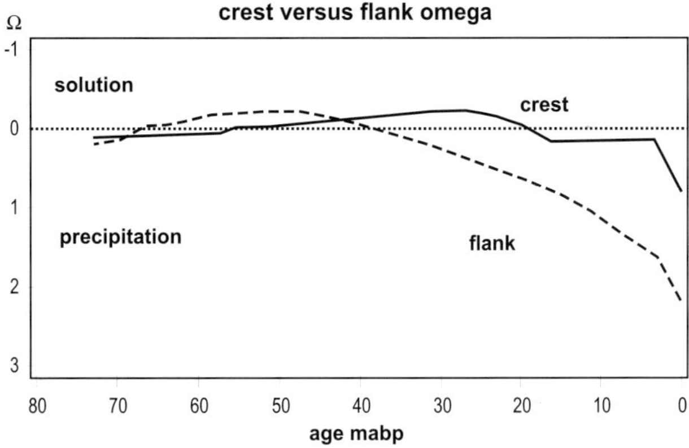

Fig. 5. Omega plotted versus time for crest and flank to basin areas. At the flank to basin, Ω becomes positive about 20 Ma earlier than at the crest, implying that flank to basin chalk is likely to have undergone cementation over the last 40 Ma.

Fractures

Productive reservoirs need fractures to fill and drain pore volumes and for economic production. Fractures increase permeability and are the reason why total permeability at the crest of Valhall is significantly higher than in the basin for a similar range of porosity (Fig. 6).

Fractures occur when applied stress on the rock is greater than the ultimate load or fracture pressure. Conventional models normally only consider pore pressure as the applied stress (Caillet *et al.* 1997). However, to get a full understanding of fracture distribution, the total stress acting on the rock needs to be taken into account. In addition to the pore pressure there are also mechanical forces acting on the rock surface and the total stress is the sum of body forces and surface forces. The body force is the pore pressure, and the surface forces are the sum of vertical (bending) and lateral shear moments. In this area the bending moment (F), derived from structure, isopach and rheology, is greater than lateral and regional tectonic stresses and, for the scope of this study, the total stress is defined as the sum of pore pressure and bending moment (Fig. 7).

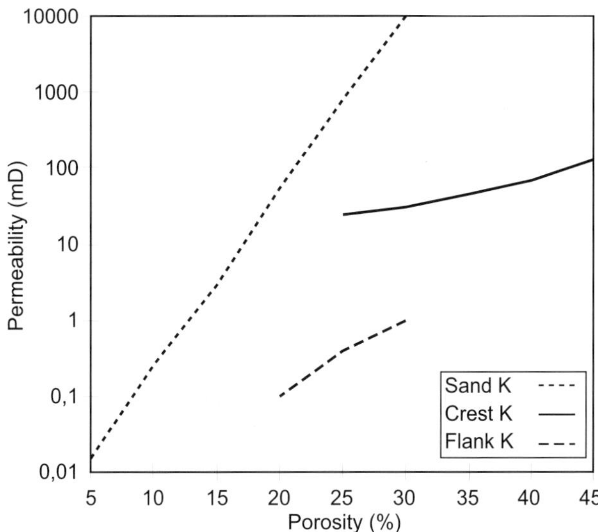

Fig. 6. Total permeability in crestal versus flank chalks. For the same porosity, total permeability in crestal chalk are orders of magnitude higher than at the flank because of fractures.

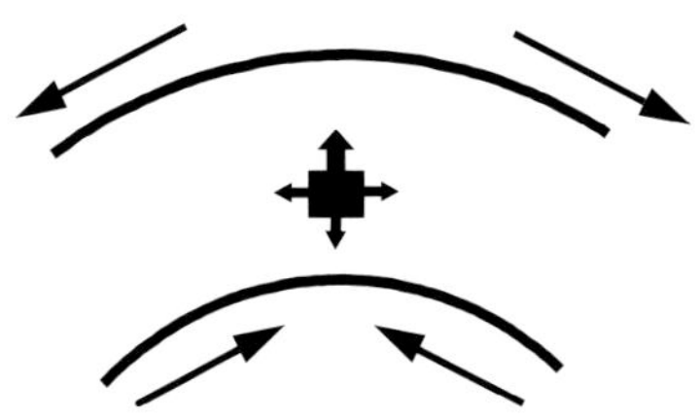

total stress = body forces + surface forces
= pore pressure + bending moment

Fig. 7. The total stress acting on a rock is the sum of body forces and surface forces or pore pressure and bending moment.

This implies that when the total stress exceeds fracture pressure, fracturing will occur. The distribution of open versus closed fractures at top chalk level (Fig. 8) can also be derived from the bending moment (F). Where F is positive the rock matrix is under tension and the fractures will be open. If F is negative then the rock matrix will be under compression and the fractures will be closed.

Hydrocarbon generation, migration and entrapment modelling

It is now necessary to incorporate the results of the diagenetic and fracture distribution studies with hydrocarbon generation, migration and entrapment modelling. For migration modelling a 2D horizontal plane program Finesse was used (Taylor *et al.* 1999).

In the study area, the main source rocks are the Jurassic Mandal and Farsund formations. The Upper Cretaceous chalks are the main reservoirs. Fluids migrate following paths of least resistance (i.e. along pressure gradients). Further, it is postulated that: (i) expelled hydrocarbons will remain in the Jurassic unless there is no seal or seal capacity failure, and (ii) hydrocarbons will migrate beneath the chalk until encountering chalks that are fractured under tension and uncemented (Fig. 9).

This posulate implies a need for understanding where the chalk (matrix and fractures) is likely to be cemented and thereby identifying where burial cement might be a hinderance to migration. This is done by comparing the timing of earliest migrated oil in the system and the onset of calcite cementation. The onset of cementation is determined by modelling Ω as a function of reservoir pressure and temperature through time (Fig. 10). The time of peak oil generation at the base of the source rock (Farsund Formation) is used as an indication of when hydrocarbons first entered the system (Fig. 11). If this was before the time when burial diagenesis could have occurred (Ω positive) fractures would have acted as conduits. If it was later, then matrix and fractures could have been cemented and the fractures would have acted as barriers.

Modelling primary migration from source gives an indication of where the most productive source areas are located (Fig. 12). In the modelled area, the richest areas are located west of the Eldfisk Field and southeast of the Valhall Field. Assuming this picture is correct, a migration model

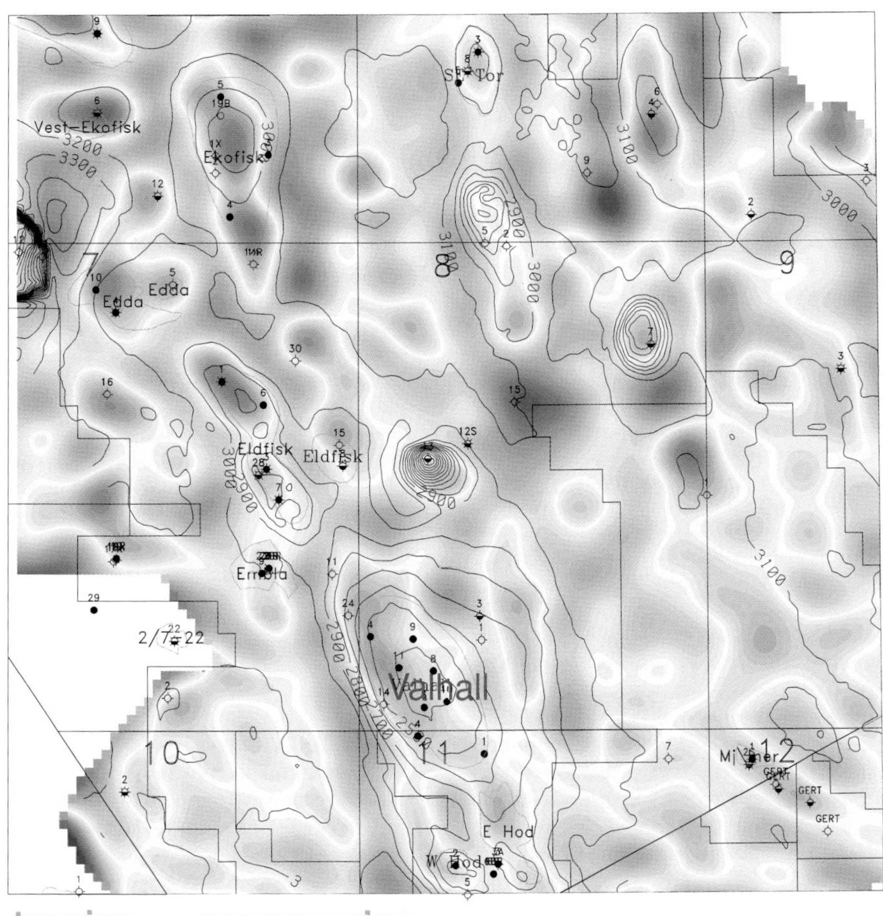

Fig. 8. Distribution of open (tensional) and closed (compressional) fractures at top chalk level. Red areas show where fractures are under compression. Blue areas show where fractures are under tension.

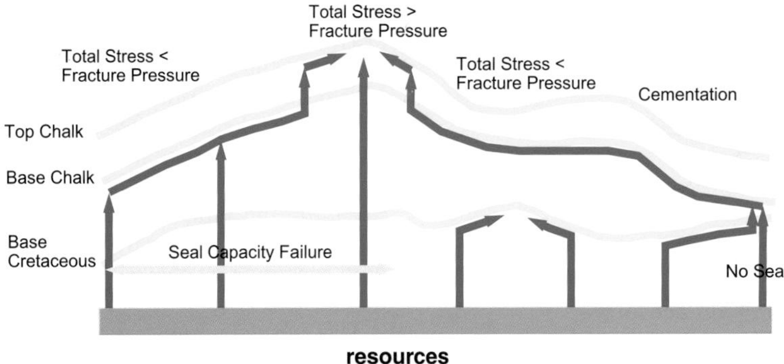

Fig. 9. Hydrocarbon generation, migration and entrapment modelling using 'Finesse'. In the model it is assumed that fluids will migrate following paths of least resistance, that expelled resources will remain in the Jurassic unless there is no seal or seal capacity failure occurs, and that hydrocarbons will migrate beneath the chalk until encountering chalk that is fractured under tension and uncemented.

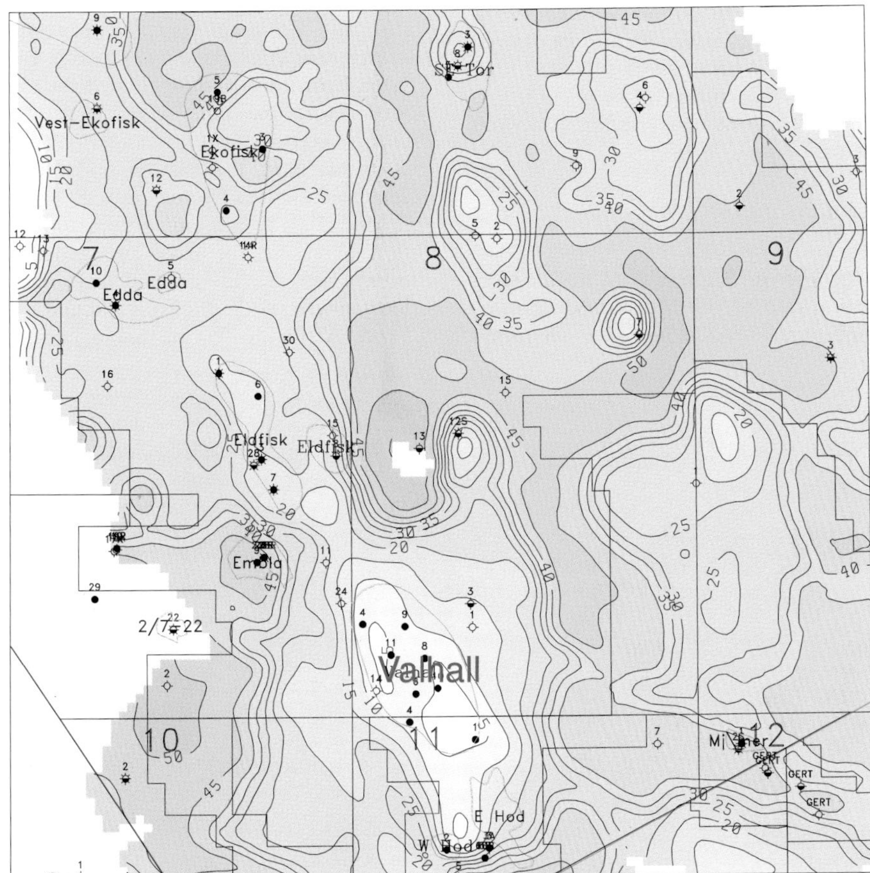

Fig. 10. Modelling Ω indicates an onset of burial cementation as early as 50 Ma in basin areas west and northeast of Valhall Field.

based on vertical migration only cannot reproduce the known exploration results, neither successes nor failures.

In the secondary migration model each of the layers from the Jurassic source to the Upper Cretaceous are modelled stepwise taking into account vertical versus lateral migration. At the first level, Base Cretaceous, moveable hydrocarbons and hydrocarbon flux (i.e. volume of hydrocarbons that has migrated through an individual grid cell) show where lateral migration has taken place beneath the Base Cretaceous level (Fig. 13). These hydrocarbons will either be trapped in the Jurassic or migrate vertically to layers above where Base Cretaceous seal capacity has been exceeded or there is no seal. At the next level, Base Chalk, hydrocarbons that migrated vertically from the Jurassic will be focused into areas where the chalk is fractured under tension and uncemented (Fig. 14). Finally, migration and entrapment within the chalk is modelled. Moveable hydrocarbons and hydrocarbon flux show where lateral migration has taken place within the chalk, filling the presently known structures (Fig. 15). If there is no seal, these hydrocarbons will be lost by continued vertical migration.

Summary and conclusions

The studies on diagenesis, fracturing and migration in overpressured chalks reviewed in this paper have raised questions concerning the relationships between depositional processes and diagenesis, fracture mechanisms, structural evolution and stress regimes, and diagenesis and hydrocarbon migration. These issues need to be investigated further and will be addressed in more detail in the future. Nevertheless, the investigations completed so far, and the integrated approach taken in this study, have helped us identify potential key risk elements when predicting the quality of chalk reservoirs (Fig. 16). Important however, are not only the key factors, but

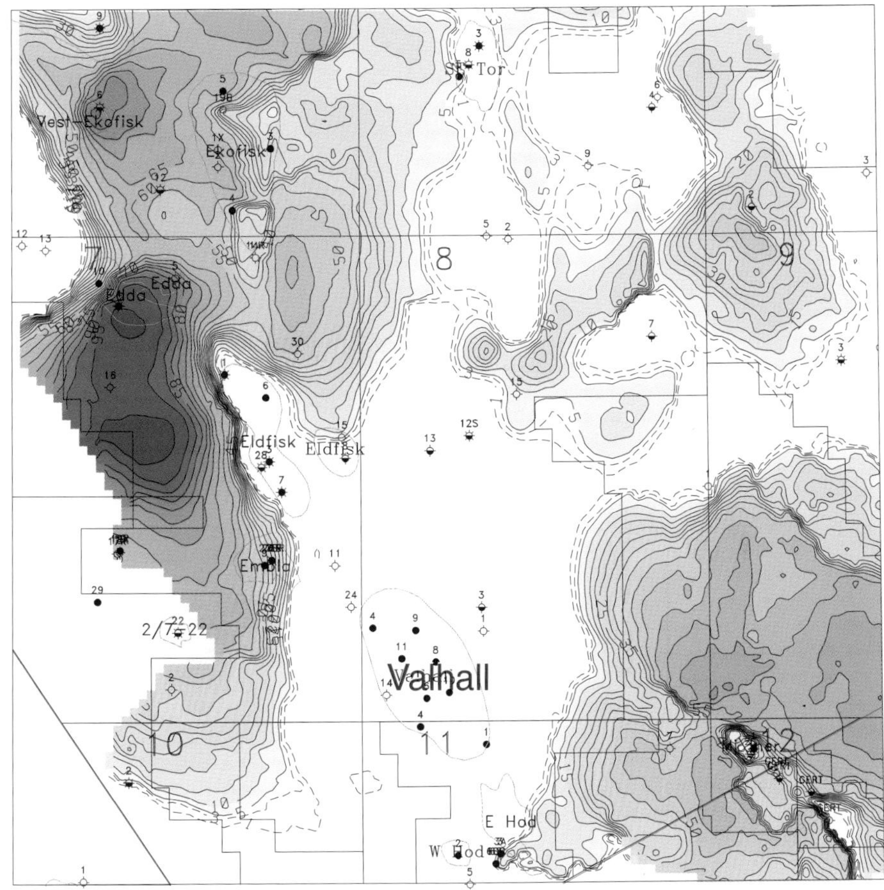

Fig. 11. Base Farsund time of peak oil generation indicates when hydrocarbons entered the system.

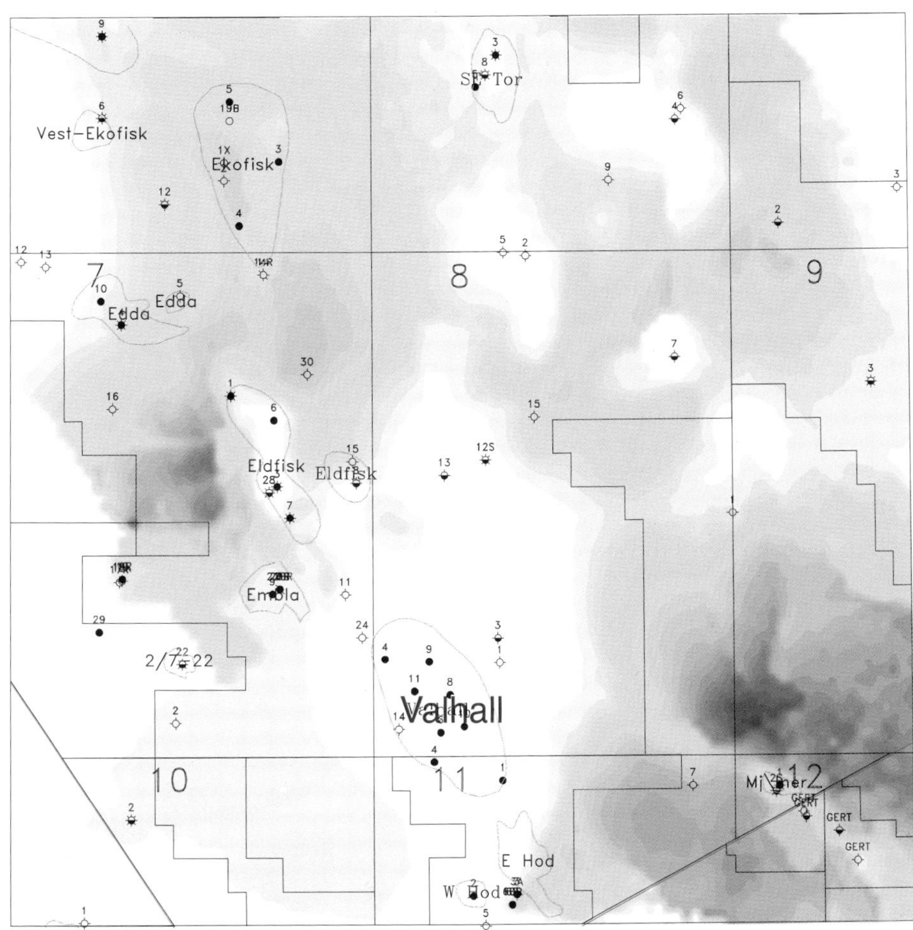

Fig 12. Map showing primary migration from Jurassic source. The most productive areas are west of the Eldfisk Field and southeast of the Valhall Field.

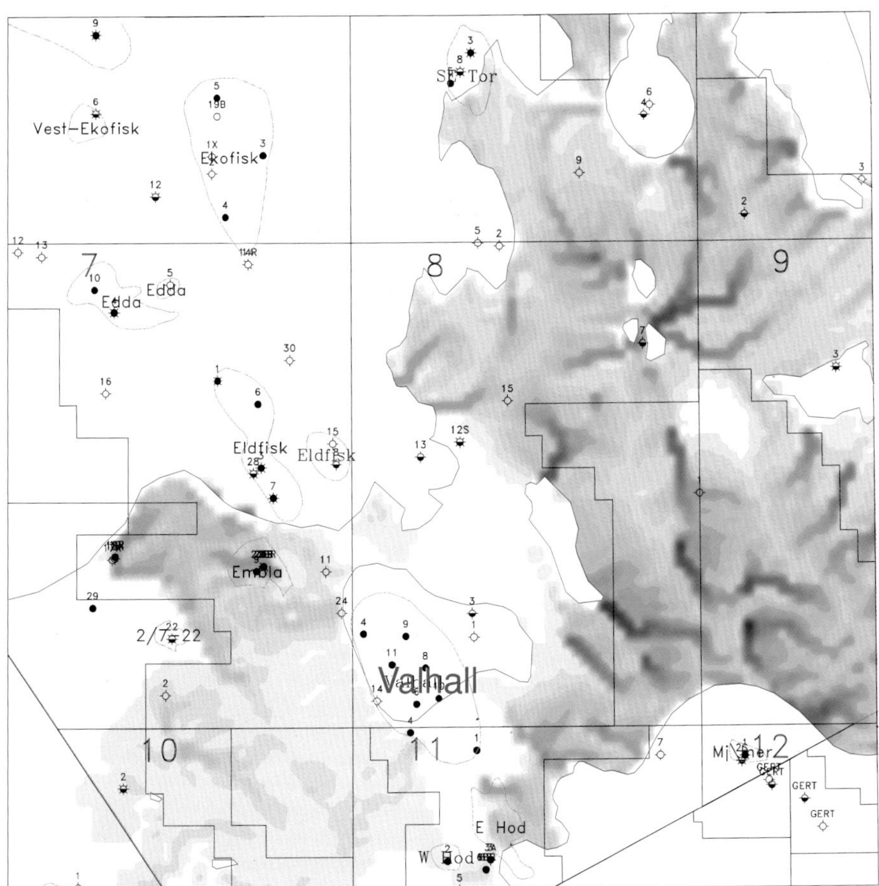

Fig. 13. The mapped surface shows the volume of hydrocarbons that have migrated through individual grid cells at the Base Cretaceous: dark green shows flow focusing, dead ends indicate traps. The red line shows a transition to areas with no seal or seal capacity failure: here, hydrocarbons can migrate vertically to layers above.

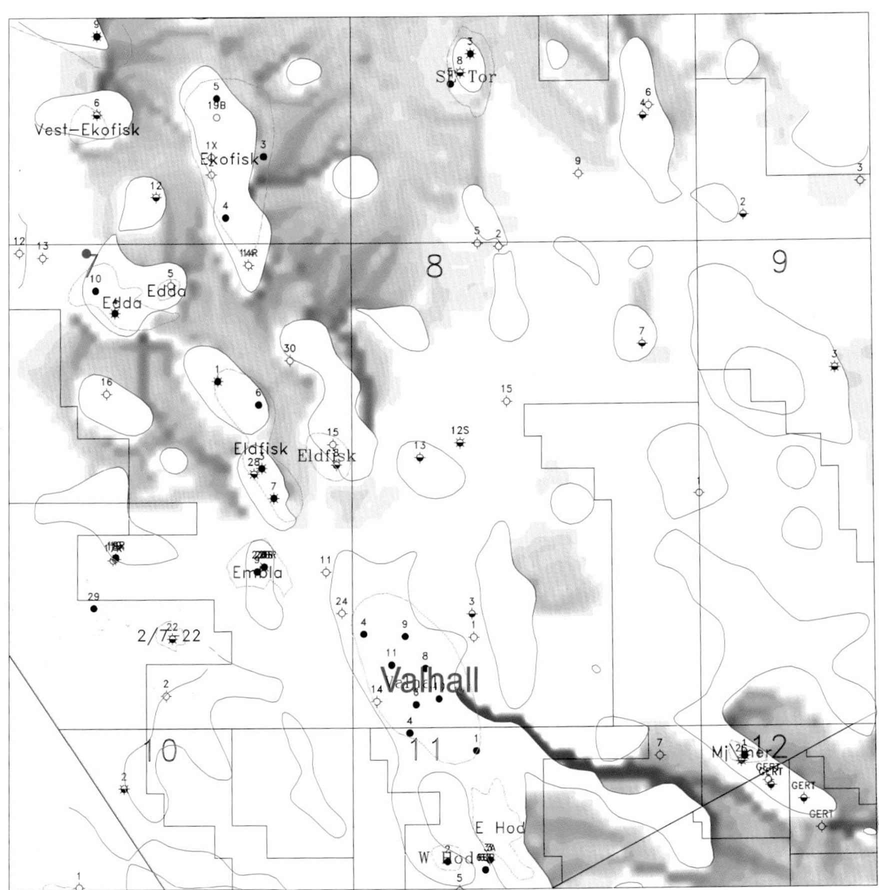

Fig. 14. Vertical migration from the Jurassic through seal failure or lack of seal in green areas to Base Chalk level. Hydrocarbon flow is then focused to areas where the chalk is fractured under tension and uncemented (transition zone is marked by red line).

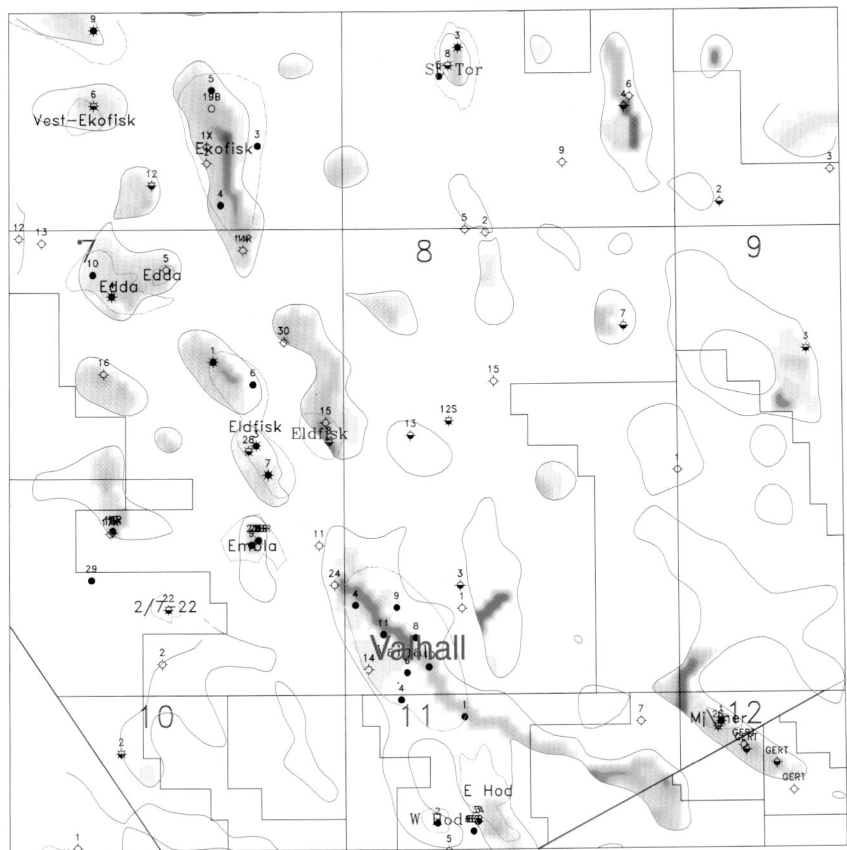

Fig. 15. Within-chalk migration and entrapment. Map shows how the generated hydrocarbons have entered all the known chalk fields in the area and also highlights areas of future potential.

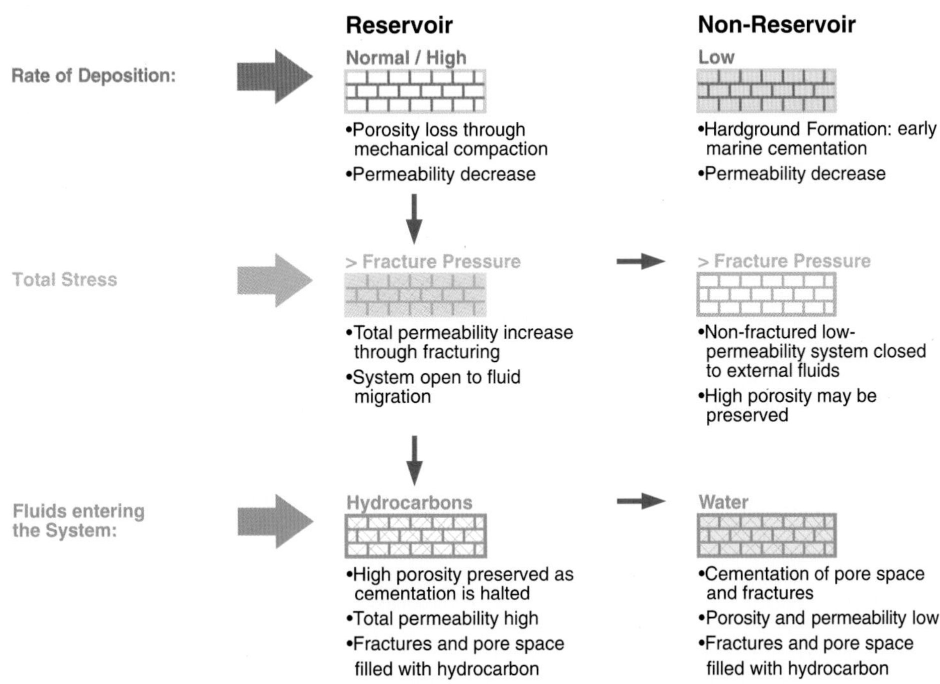

Fig. 16. Key risk elements in overpressured chalk reservoirs: rate of deposition, total stress and fluids entering the system.

also the order in which they occur. Timing is thus critical in controlling whether hydrocarbon accumulations have formed or not.

In addition to overpressure, we have singled out three main factors controlling chalk reservoir evolution.

(1) Rate of deposition; initial rates of deposition need to be relatively high to prevent porosity loss through calcite cementation at or close to the seafloor. This process may eventually result in the formation of hardgrounds and condensed zones. Notably, rate of porosity loss is the same for a chalk with extensive early cement as with minimal early cement (Hardman 1982) and these zones will therefore form low porosity zones in chalk reservoirs.
(2) Total stress; total stress needs to exceed fracture pressure. This causes a total increase in permeability so that the system will be more open to fluid migration. If total stress is less than fracture pressure, the chalk will remain a low permeability system more or less closed to external fluids. Under such conditions porosity may be preserved as the lack of fluid influx can limit the amount of ions available for the precipitation of calcite cement.
(3) Pore fluid; hydrocarbons need to enter the system before conditions become favourable for burial cement to form. This ensures a significant slowing down of calcite precipitation in both chalk matrix and fractures, the latter ensuring that a high total permeability is maintained. If the system is water filled when Ω becomes positive, cementation of pore space and fractures is likely to occur (providing ions are available in solution) causing reduction of pore volume and permeability.

To summarize, productive chalk reservoirs need porosity and fractures, assuming that there is a hydrocarbon source and a top seal. Porosity preservation is controlled by overpressure combined with Ω (temperature and PCO_2) and ionic supply. Fracture prediction needs to consider total stress, implying that when total stress exceeds fracture pressure, fracturing will occur. By integrating the above with basin modelling, the known results for the area have been matched. The model correctly simulates both known chalk fields and areas where no hydrocarbons have been found (e.g. Nøkken). It also indicates areas of future potential, suggesting sites that should be studied more closely. This leads to the conclusion that the integrated approach taken in this study, combining reservoir-specific problems with basin modelling, should have the potential to help future successful predictions of hydrocarbon accumulations.

We thank Amoco Norway Oil Company and partners Amerada Hess, Elf, and Enterprise for the permission to publish the results of this work. I. D. Meshri, ABCM Inc. (Advanced Basin Chemical Modelling, Inc.) USA is acknowledged for her important contribution in basin chemical modelling. M. Martines, Amoco Norway Oil Company, is thanked for valuable contributions on pressure. A. Matthews, Reading University, UK should be mentioned for her excellent support on isotope analysis and diagenetic studies on Valhall and adjacent area chalks. These data have served as valuable calibration data for our modelling. Finally, we thank A. Hurst for his support throughout, in completing this text. Likewise, the reviewers J. Ineson and J. Brewster, are acknowledged for their helpful comments.

References

BERNER, R. A. 1980. *Early Diagenesis. A Theoretical Approach.* Princeton University Press, Princeton NJ, USA.

BRASHER, J. E. & VAGLE, K. R. 1996. Influence of lithofacies and diagenesis on Norwegian North Sea chalk reservoirs. *American Association of Petroleum Geologists Bulletin*, **80**, 746–769.

D'ANGELO, R. M., BRANDAL, M. K. & RORVIK, K. O. 1997. Porosity detection and mapping in basinal carbonate setting: offshore Norway. *In*: PALEZ, I. & MARFURT, K. J. (eds) *Carbonate Seismology*, Geophysical Development Series, **6**, 321–336.

CAILLET, G., JUDGE, N. C., BRAMWELL, N. P., MECIANI, L., GREEN, M. & ADAM, P. 1997. Overpressure and hydrocarbon trapping in the chalk of the Norwegian Central Graben. *Petroleum Geoscience*, **3**, 33–42.

FARMER, C. L. & BARKVED, O. I. 1999. Influence of syn-depositional faulting and thickness variations in chalk reservoirs – Valhall and Hod fields. *In*: FLEET, A. J. & BOLDY, S. A. R. (eds) *Petroleum Geology of Northwest Europe: Proceedings of the 5th Conference*. Geological Society, London, 949–957.

HARDMAN, R. F. P. 1982. Chalk reservoirs of the North Sea. *Bulletin of the Geological Society, Denmark*, **30**, 119–137.

KENNEDY, W. J. 1987. Sedimentology of Late Cretaceous/Paleocene chalk reservoirs, North Sea Central Graben. *In*: BROOKS, J. & GLENNIE, K. (eds) *Petroleum Geology of North West Europe*. Graham & Trotman, London, 469–481.

MATTHEWS, A. 1998. *Depositional and Diagenetic Controls on Reservoir Heterogeneity in the Valhall and Hod Chalk Fields, Norwegian North Sea*. PhD thesis, Reading University.

MESHRI, I. D. 1990. An overview of chemical models and their relationship to porosity prediciton in the subsurface. *In*: MESHRI, I. D. & ORTOLEVA, P. J. (eds) *Prediciton of Reservoir Quality Through Chemical Modeling*, American Association Petroleum Geologists Memoirs, **49**, 45–53.

MORSE, J. W. & MACKENZIE, F. T. 1990. Geochemistry of Sedimentary Carbonates. *Developments in Sedimentology 48*, Elsevier.

ODDO, J. E. & TOMSON, M. B. 1982. Simplified calculation of $CaCO_3$ saturation at high temperatures and pressures in brine solutions. *Journal of Petroleum Technology*, **SPE 10352**, 1583–1590.

PARK, R. G. 1983. *Foundation of Structural Geology*. Blackie and Son Ltd.

SCHOLLE, P. A. 1977. Chalk diagenesis and its relation to petroleum exploration: oil from chalks, a modern miracle? *American Association of Petroleum Geologists Bulletin*, **61**, 982–1009.

—— & HALLEY, R. B. 1985. Burial diagenesis: out of sight out of mind. *In*: SCHNEIDERMAN, N. & HARRIS, P. M. (eds) *Carbonate Cements*. Society of Economic Paleontologists and Mineralogists Special Publications, **36**, 309–334.

SIKORA, P. J., BERGEN, J. A. & FARMER, C. L. in press. Chalk depositional model for the Valhall/Hod fields, Southern Norwegian Sea. *In*: *Biostratigraphy in Production and Development Geology*. Geological Society, London, Special Publications.

SPENCER, A. M., LECKIE, G. G. & CHEW, K. J. 1996. North Sea hydrocarbon plays and their resources. *In*: GLENNIE, K. & HURST, A. (eds) *NW Europe's Hydrocarbon Industry*. Geological Society, London, 25–41.

TAYLOR, M. S. G., LEROY, A. & FØRLAND, M. 1999. Hydrocarbon systems modelling of the Norwegian Central Graben fairway trend. *In*: FLEET, A. J. & BOLDY, S. A. R. (eds) *Petroleum Geology of Northwest Europe: Proceedings of the 5th Conference*. Geological Society, London, 1325–1338.

Applications of geophysical technology

Applications of geophysical technology

Introduction and review

J. W. MUNNS

Oil and Gas Division, Department of Trade and Industry, 1 Victoria Street, London SW1H 0ET (formerly Amoco (UK))

The application of geophysical technology in the exploration for, and appraisal of, hydrocarbon accumulations in the basins of northwest Europe is a fundamental part of the exploration process. As exploration in the North Sea matures and geoscientists are evaluating prospects of ever decreasing size, the ability to image both the geometry of the trap and the nature of the material contained within the trap is of paramount importance. Although exploration on the Atlantic margin is at a relatively immature phase, the recently discovered large fields are combination structural/stratigraphic traps and are therefore best illuminated with state-of-the-art geophysics. Appraisal and development drilling is also reliant on high quality seismic data to map both the distribution and quality of reservoirs across fields.

The complex nature of the exploration targets and the inhomogeneity of reservoirs continually challenge geophysicists to improve techniques from acquisition through processing to innovative interpretative analysis. The five years since the 4th Conference on the 'Petroleum Geology of Northwest Europe' (Parker 1993) have seen tremendous advances in seismic processing which has sustained exploration in areas where the prospects are relatively small. There are nine papers in this section of the Proceedings. Three relate to innovative seismic acquisition techniques. The paper by **Leach** describes the use of the vertical cable seismic technique on the Strathspey Field in the North Viking Graben. The technique deploys cables suspended vertically in the water column with hydrophones located along the cables. The processed data are significantly improved when compared to the pre-existing data on the field, with the additional benefit of providing a dataset that can be readily conditioned for 3D pre-stack depth migration. The final data have resulted in an improved understanding of the structural detail, particularly the presence of low angle gravity slides, on the eastern flank of the field.

White *et al.* and **Barton *et al.*** describe techniques that are potentially useful in areas where imaging the structural fabric is difficult because of the presence of high velocity volcanics above or within a sedimentary sequence. **White *et al.*** point out that much of the prospective northwest European continental margin from the Norwegian basins to the Rockall Trough contains significant quantities of basalt as flows or sills. They acquired continuous traverses using conventional vessels with long streamers to provide the large apertures that lead to improved velocity discrimination with the added long offset data from fixed seismometers on the Faeroese island of Suduroy. **Barton *et al.*** demonstrate, through velocity modelling, the value of wide-angle profiling using ocean bottom seismometers. Both techniques may assist in understanding the distribution of the volcanics in the subsurface and hence reduce the uncertainty in high grading prospective parts of the basins.

The importance of geophysical analysis in field delineation is discussed by **Neilsen *et al.*** from the Ekofisk Field example in the Norwegian Central Graben in which the crest of the field is masked by large volumes of gas in the overburden. Conventional surface seismic techniques are of limited use because of absorption of the surface generated signal. By using a 3D walkaway technique, improved images of the field have been obtained, although depth migration is still necessary to assist in mapping the structure of the field.

The remaining papers discuss various processing techniques that assist the seismic interpreter to extract more precise information from the data. Three papers are related to the application of inversion of seismic data in an attempt to map reservoir thickness and variation across a field. **Simm *et al.*** demonstrate the importance of an accurate well tie and discuss the processing that both the seismic and borehole data require prior to identifying the optimum dataset for advanced processing such as inversion and amplitude versus offset (AVO) analysis. **Buitjing and Bacon** illustrate the value of inversion using examples from three North Sea fields. They interpret the relationship of variation in acoustic impedance in the subsurface to variation in reservoir properties such as porosity and/or net to gross ratio. They make the important point that such analysis provides data that can be readily utilized by other earth science disciplines in the integrated analysis necessary to solve complex reservoir problems. **Wood *et al.*** present a case study integrating post stack seismic inversion into more conventional datasets to assist in building an improved geological model for the Callovian–Late Oxfordian in the Beryl Embayment of the Northern North Sea. They acknowledge that individual sandbody distribution and geometry are difficult to map because of resolution problems, but demonstrate that inversion processing has enhanced their knowledge of both sand presence and porosity variation near the well bores.

Isaacson and Neff document subtle AVO anomalies in the Norwegian Barents Sea and offshore west Greenland. They are able to refine their prospect analysis by using layer specific amplitude analysis and cross plot techniques. They conclude that the use of various cross plotting techniques has made AVO analysis a more reliable prediction tool for the explorationists. **Hughes *et al.*** describe the application of the coherency cube with three examples from the UKCS. The need for integration of coherency data with other forms of geological data is again emphasized to ensure consistency in the interpretation. Examples of sub-seismic features such as potential permeability barriers in the Leman Field and polygonal faults in the Arkwright Field are well illustrated. Finally the application on a more regional basis is also discussed by demonstrating the distribution of fault bounded rift–raft Mesozoic morphologies on the eastern margins of the Central Graben. This paper

MUNNS, J. W. 1999. Applications of geophysical technology. *In*: FLEET, A. J. & BOLDY, S. A. R. (eds) *Petroleum Geology of Northwest Europe: Proceedings of the 5th Conference*, 1233–1234.

demonstrates the broad application of the coherency cube technology to both the exploration and production problems.

Geoscientists in future years will need to apply geophysical techniques ever more rigorously as the problems encountered in exploring for smaller fields and depleting reservoirs become more complex. During presentation of the papers at the conference we saw early examples of techniques that are likely to be more frequently used by the time of the 6th conference. The use of ocean bottom seismometers and vertical cable seismic is almost certain to increase, given the significant improvements in imaging demonstrated. 4D seismic techniques and pre-stack depth migration are further techniques I expect to see given greater prominence by the next conference.

References

PARKER, J. R. (ed.) 1993. *Petroleum Geology of Northwest Europe: Proceedings of the 4th Conference*. Geological Society, London.

Strathspey vertical-cable seismic survey: a North Sea first

P. E. LEACH

Texaco EPTD, 3901 Briarpark, Houston, Texas, TX 77042, USA

Abstract: In 1995–96, the Strathspey Field Group (Texaco, Shell, Esso, and Oryx) acquired and processed the first vertical-cable seismic survey in the North Sea. Strathspey is a tilted, eroded fault block, and production is from the Brent and Statfjord reservoirs. The eastern flank of Strathspey is marked by low-angle footwall degradation complexes in both reservoirs. Historically, these features have been very difficult to image seismically, both on Strathspey and on neighbouring fields. Vertical-cable seismic, with its uniform distribution of azimuths and its economical 3D pre-stack depth migration, was judged to have the best potential to image these features. The survey was acquired in six swaths in the summers of 1995 and 1996. Processing of the pre-stack depth-migrated data volume was completed in October of 1996. The dataset shows remarkable improvement over the previous 3D dataset (vintage 1985), and compares favourably with the Brent Field dataset which was acquired immediately to the north of Strathspey in 1995. Improved data quality has allowed a more confident interpretation of the low-angle fault scarp features, as well as a more detailed structural model of both reservoirs. In addition, the superior data resulted in an improved assessment of the remaining exploration potential in the Strathspey area. The information gained from the interpretation of the vertical-cable seismic data has given the field partners more confidence in siting wells and in the reservoir simulation models.

The Strathspey Field is located in the East Shetland Basin in Block 3/4a of the UK sector of the North Sea, approximately 470 km northeast of Aberdeen (Fig. 1). The water depth is approximately 134 m. Geologically, the field is a tilted, eroded fault block producing from two reservoirs: the middle Jurassic Brent Group, which contains volatile oil, and the Upper Triassic–Lower Jurassic Banks Group (Statfjord and Nansen formations), which contains condensate-rich gas with an oil rim (Figs 2 & 3). These two reservoirs are separated by the Dunlin Group shale, which is approximately 800 ft thick in the Strathspey area. Expected ultimate recoverable hydrocarbons are 89×10^6 barrels of liquids, and 332×10^9 SCF of gas. The field is produced via a sub-sea manifold which is controlled remotely from the Ninian Central platform. Partners are Texaco (67% and operator), Shell (13.25%), Esso (13.25%), and Oryx (6.5%). First oil was produced in December of 1993.

The Brent Field, immediately to the north, is structurally analogous to Strathspey. By early 1993, extensive drilling on Brent had convinced the operator, Shell, that the erosional crest of the field was far more structurally complex than had been previously believed. In particular, a complex of en-echelon rotational slides (informally referred to as 'slumps'), formed as part of a low-angle footwall degradation complex, was found to feature heavily on the eastern flank of both the Brent reservoir and the Statfjord reservoir. By analogy, these features were highly likely to be present on Strathspey; however, in the absence of significant well control, they would have to be delineated using seismic data alone. Historically, this had been very difficult, both on the Strathspey Field and on the Brent Field, owing to several factors: (1) the low angle of the faults causes them to offset very few seismic reflectors; (2) the material within the slumps themselves is comprised of narrow pieces of strata which have been rotated into fairly steep bed dips (up to 40° in Brent Field); and (3) the slump complexes are partially overlain by a wedge of onlapping lower Cretaceous material of a high seismic velocity. These last two factors result in an invalidation of some of the assumptions which are made in conventional seismic data processing, and therefore, conventional processing results in mediocre data. The best processing technique for imaging geological cases such as these is 3D pre-stack depth migration (3DPSDM), but at the time, this process used tremendous amounts of computer time and was therefore very expensive to run on conventional marine seismic data.

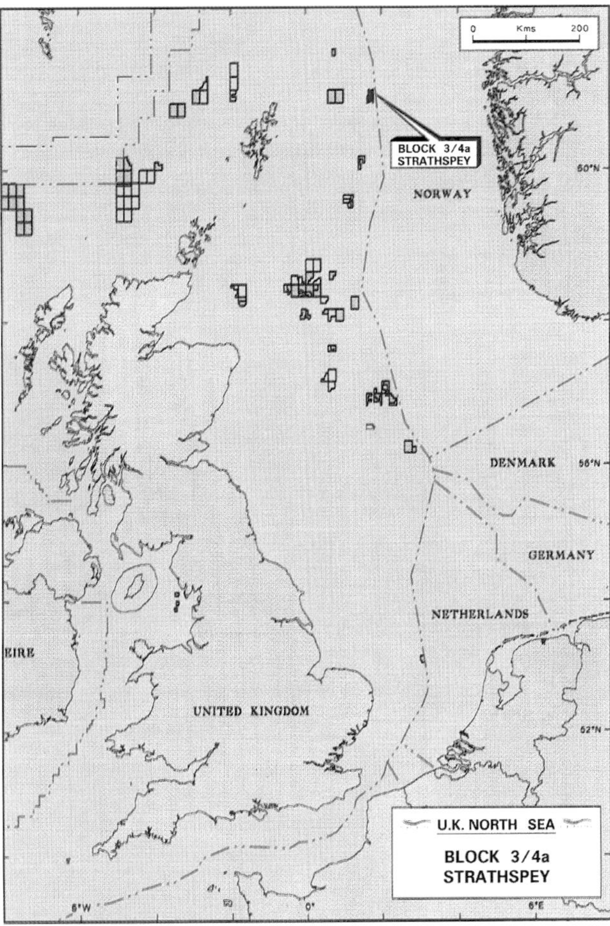

Fig. 1. Location of the Strathspey Field, Block 3/4a, East Shetland Basin, UK North Sea.

LEACH, P. E. 1999. Strathspey vertical-cable seismic survey: a North Sea first. *In*: FLEET, A. J. & BOLDY, S. A. R. (eds) *Petroleum Geology of Northwest Europe: Proceedings of the 5th Conference*, 1235–1242. © Petroleum Geology '86 Ltd. Published by the Geological Society, London.

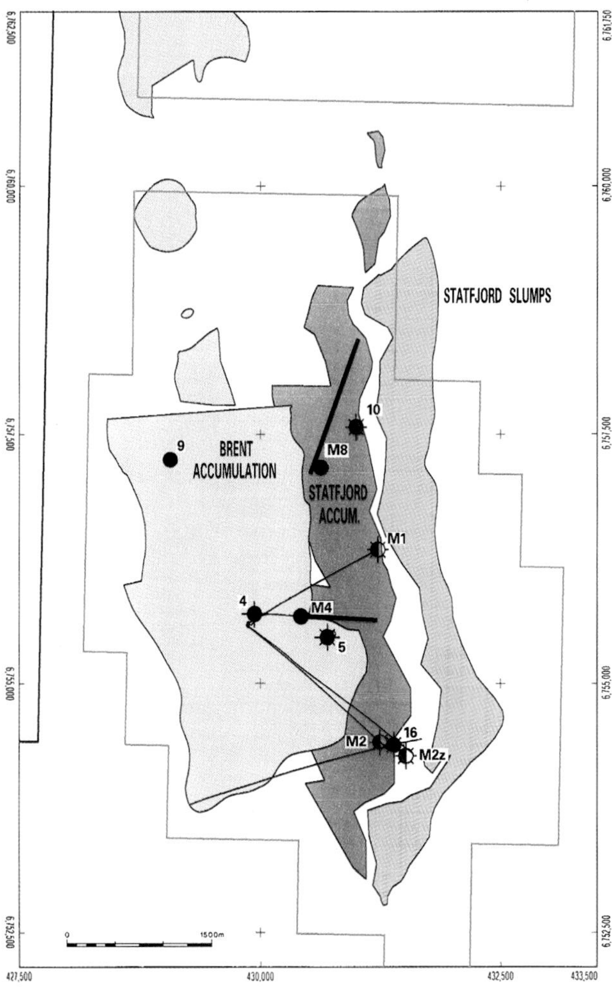

Fig. 2. Hydrocarbon accumulations of the Strathspey Field.

Vertical-cable seismic

Acquisition and processing technique

Throughout the 1980s and early 1990s, Paul Krail and Dwight Sukup of Texaco's Exploration and Production Technology Division (EPTD) had been developing a method of acquiring and processing marine seismic data using cables which are suspended vertically in the water column with an anchor at one end, a buoy at the other, and a recording buoy at the surface. Hydrophones are located along each of the cables. The shooting vessel, unencumbered by the usual recording streamer, fires a pattern of shots on the surface (typically 10 to 25 m spacings in both X and Y directions), covering the area around and between the cables (Fig. 4). Geometries are chosen with as much symmetry as possible in the X and Y directions, such that every hydrophone records a patch of data in the subsurface that is nearly square in shape. Once one swath of data is completed, the cables are moved to another location, and the process is repeated until the desired area of coverage is acquired. Alternatively, cables can be 'rolled' from the back of the swath to the front whilst shooting is ongoing, resulting in a nearly continuous acquisition technique. A trial survey of this type was acquired in the deep water Gulf of Mexico in 1992 using limited equipment (six cables, three of them live at any one time).

Vertical-cable seismic (VCS) traces are processed using Texaco proprietary software which performs 3D PSDM on all of the traces in a hydrophone gather simultaneously, rather than one trace at a time. This greatly reduces the cost of 3DPSDM, making it economical to run this process on every trace of the entire 3D survey. The key to this process is the inclusion of a wide range of azimuths and offsets in every hydrophone gather; thus, the importance of as much X–Y symmetry as possible in the acquisition geometry. This geometry also results in a more complete sampling of the 3D velocity field, which improves the accuracy of the depth migration. In this manner, the VCS acquisition technique was specifically developed to dovetail with an economical way to run a superior processing sequence.

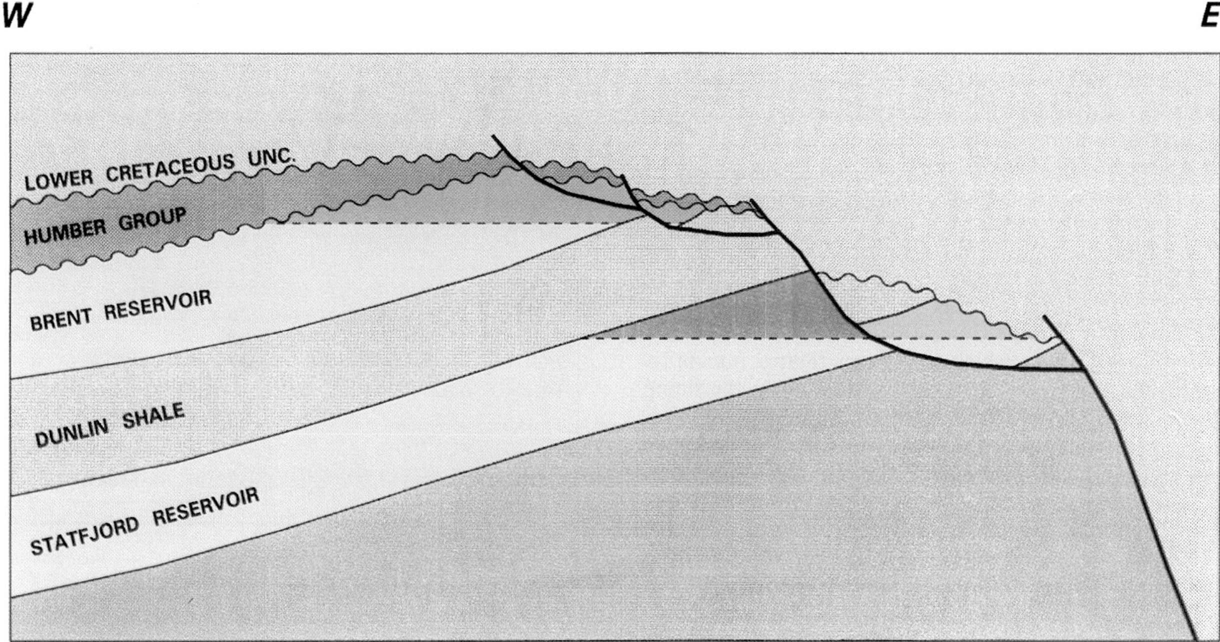

Fig. 3. Schematic cross-section of the Strathspey Field.

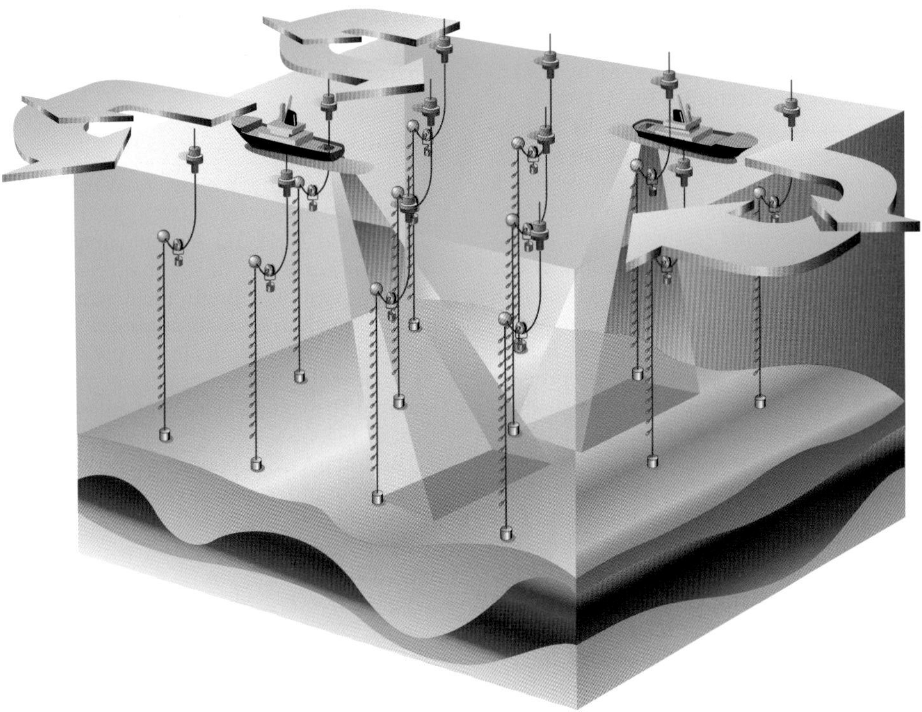

Fig. 4. Schematic diagram of the vertical-cable seismic acquisition technique. Cables, with hydrophones located along their lengths, are suspended vertically in the water, while the vessel fires an array of shots to cover the area around and between the cables.

Advantages

The most significant advantage of the VCS technique is the application of economical 3DPSDM processing, resulting in a superior image in areas with complex seismic velocities. There are, however, other advantages, including:

(1) Rough weather acquisition. When swells reach about 1.5 m, conventional marine streamer data begins to show significant wave-induced noise; VCS data can be acquired in seas of up to 3.5 m. This is a significant advantage in the North Sea.
(2) A broader effective frequency bandwidth. VCS hydrophones are deployed deep in the sea, in an environment far quieter than that of a conventional streamer, which is pulled along several metres below the waves. This results in a higher signal-to-noise ratio for VCS data, especially in the high frequencies, where the signal-to-noise ratio is usually a greater problem. The increase in useable high frequencies yields a broader bandwidth, which in turn results in finer vertical resolution.
(3) Using the water surface 'ghost.' In any marine seismic acquisition, the seismic signal reflected by the strata of interest arrives at the hydrophones not only via a direct route (the 'primary' signal), but also via a longer, indirect route in which the energy reflects off the sea surface, and comes back down to the hydrophones (the 'ghost' of the primary signal). In conventional streamer acquisition, this ghost interferes with the clarity of the primary signal. Because VCS acquisition uses vertical arrays of hydrophones, however, the up-coming primary signal can be separated from the down-going ghost, similarly to to the way that up-coming and down-going energies are separated in wellbore vertical-seismic profiles. Both the primary and the ghost can then be processed, and the two images stacked together, improving the signal-to-noise ratio still more.

All of these expected advantages convinced the Strathspey Field Group to acquire a VCS dataset over the field in order to get the best possible image of the crestal structural complexities, as well as the intra-reservoir structuring.

Strathspey VCS acquisition and processing

By the summer of 1995, fourteen cables were ready for use on the Strathspey VCS acquisition. Twelve were to be deployed in a three-by-four matrix for each swath, with two cables held as spares (Fig. 5 shows the acquisition parameters for a typical

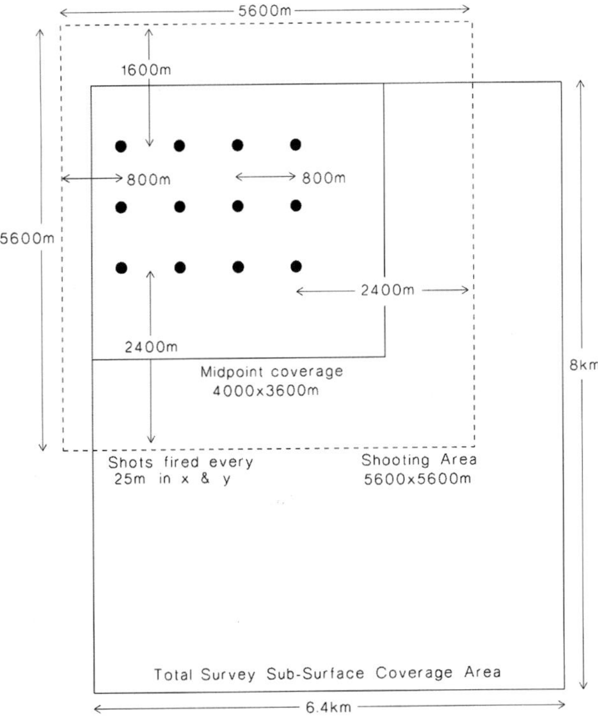

Fig. 5. Acquisition parameters for a single swath of data.

swath of data). Each cable held 16 hydrophones vertically, spaced 7.6 m apart. Six overlapping swaths were planned, giving a total subsurface coverage of 8 km (N–S) by 6.4 km (E–W), covering the whole of the Strathspey Field. Petroleum Geo-Services, to whom Texaco have licensed the VCS technique, were contracted for the acquisition phase of the project. Acquisition was begun on 27 July 1995, with two vessels: a shooting boat, and a boat to deploy and maintain the cables, recording buoys, and magnetic tapes. Progress was not as rapid as had been anticipated, largely because of considerable seismic acquisition activity in the area which resulted in significant time-sharing (this was alleviated somewhat whenever summer squalls forced the shut-down of the nearby streamer vessels, allowing the VCS acquisition to proceed unimpeded in the rougher seas). Other problems were encountered, too, including storms which moved cables and buoys as much as two hundred metres away from their initial sites. By the time very heavy weather forced the cessation of all activity on 11 October, only five of the six planned swaths had been acquired.

Processing of these swaths was begun by Texaco's EPTD in September of 1995, and the sixth and final swath was acquired in June of 1996. All swaths were migrated in depth using a velocity field designed to optimize the seismic image. These traces were then converted into the time domain, then re-converted to depth using a different velocity model – one which tied the well control and made use of regional geological knowledge. A final, 3D pre-stack depth migrated dataset was produced with a vertical scale in depth in October 1996. The cost of the entire processing sequence for the VCS dataset was approximately $700 000; it was estimated at the time that the cost of running 3DPSDM alone on a conventional dataset with the same number of recorded traces (60 000 000) would have been in the range of $8 to $10 million. Subsequent increases in computing power have reduced this estimate to approximately $1.5 million today, but that is still substantially higher than the cost of the VCS processing.

Results

Figures 6, 7, and 8 show E–W seismic lines from the 1985 Block 3/4a 3D seismic survey, the 1995–6 VCS survey, and the 1995 Brent Field 3D seismic survey, respectively, all from a location just north of the main accumulations in Strathspey. The conventional Brent Field streamer survey was acquired with a single source to minimize azimuthal striping, and its processing sequence included pre-stack time migration; thus, it is probably a near-optimum conventional marine seismic survey. The vertical scale is in milliseconds in Figs 6 and 8, and feet in Fig. 7.

Both the VCS survey and the 1995 Brent Field survey show marked improvement over the 1985 dataset. In particular, the resolution of the Statfjord reservoir degradation features (the faulted zone from 10 100–10 900 ft, between traces 270 and 380 in Fig. 7) is drastically improved. On the 1985 data (Fig. 6), events in this area are extremely difficult to interpret. On the VCS data and the 1995 Brent Field data, however, the rotated, steeply west-dipping event that marks the top of the Statfjord reservoir is apparent. The VCS appears to have imaged these events in the slumps marginally better than the conventional Brent Field data, and also shows a more continuous event at the base of the Brent reservoir in the western flank of the field. Conversely, the 1995 Brent Field data show slightly better continuity along the top of the Statfjord reservoir, and again along the strong event below the base of the Statfjord. Both datasets show better character within the reservoirs than was present in the 1985 dataset, allowing for a more confident interpretation of intra-reservoir events.

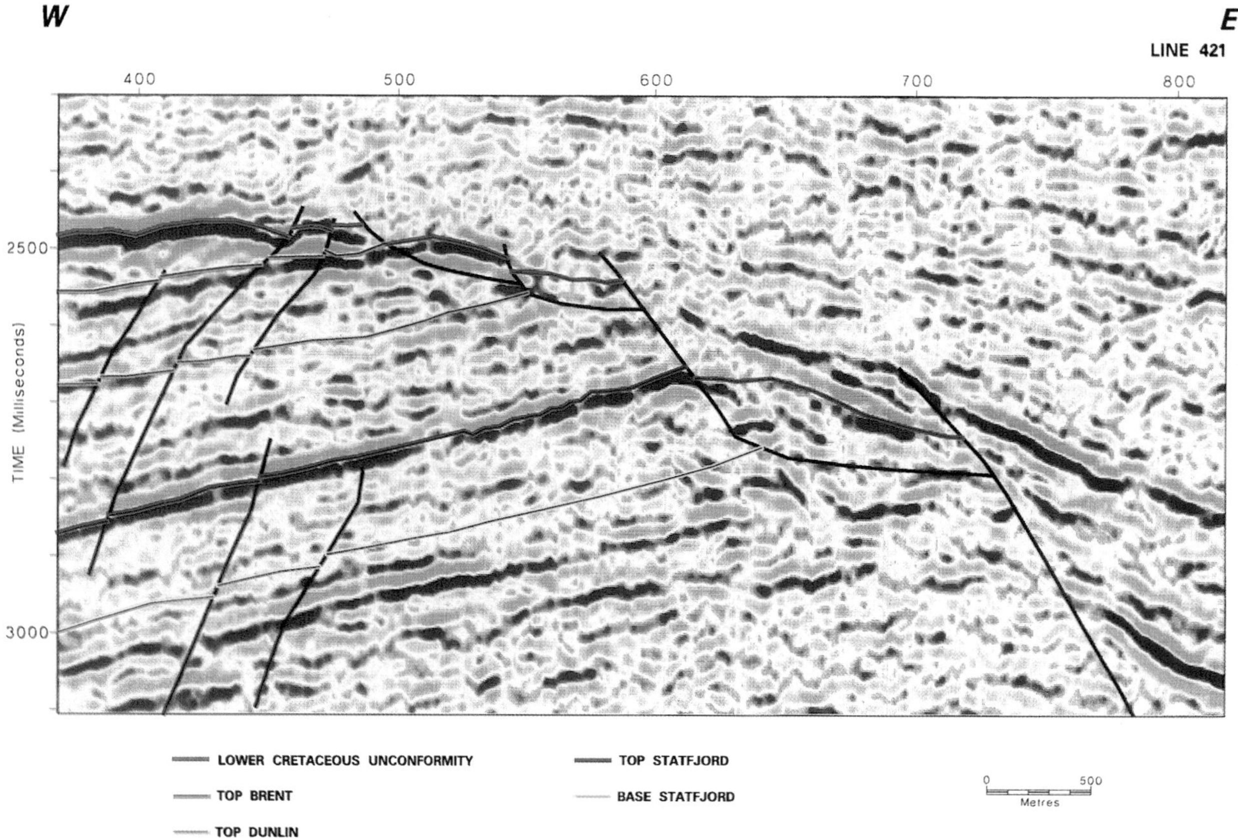

Fig. 6. East–west seismic line from the 1985 Block 3/4a 3D seismic survey.

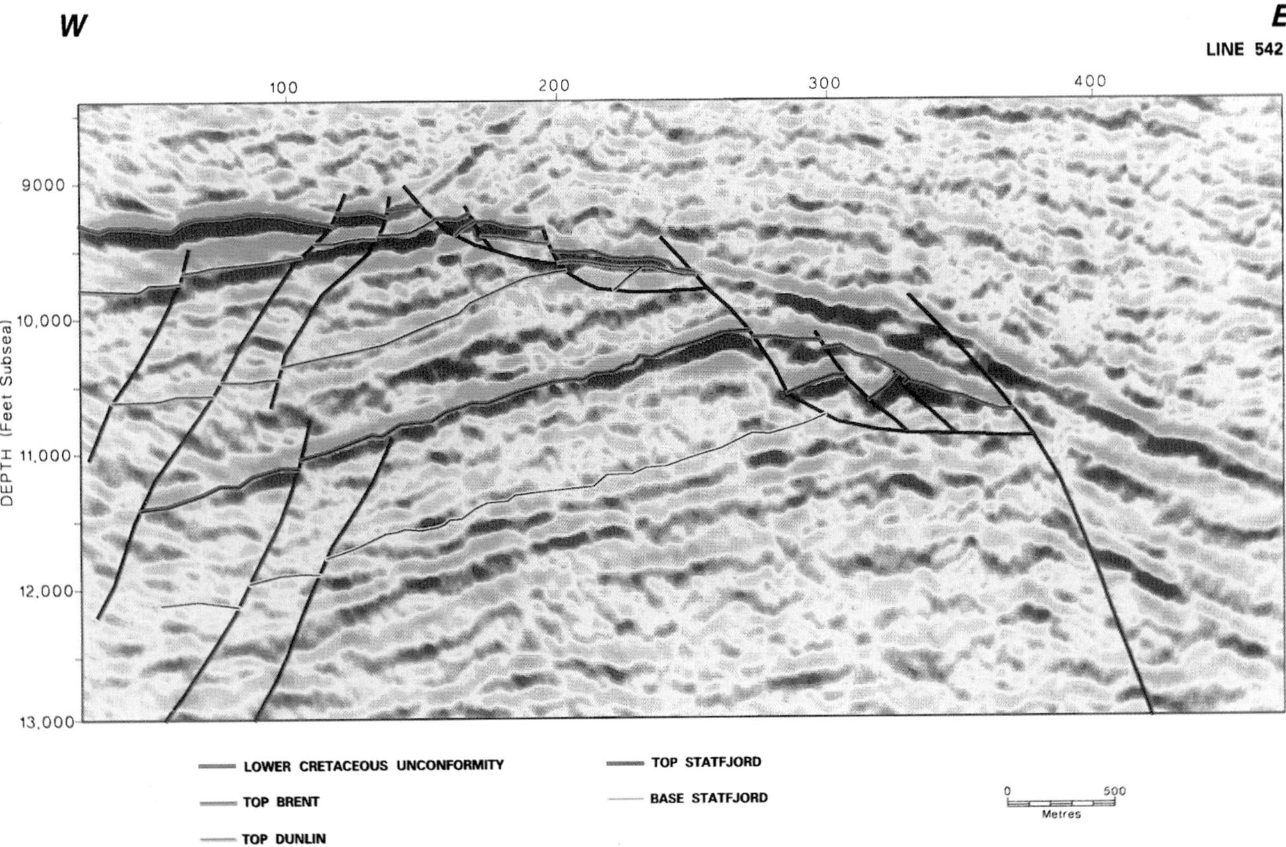

Fig. 7. East–west seismic line from the 1995–6 vertical-cable seismic (VCS) survey.

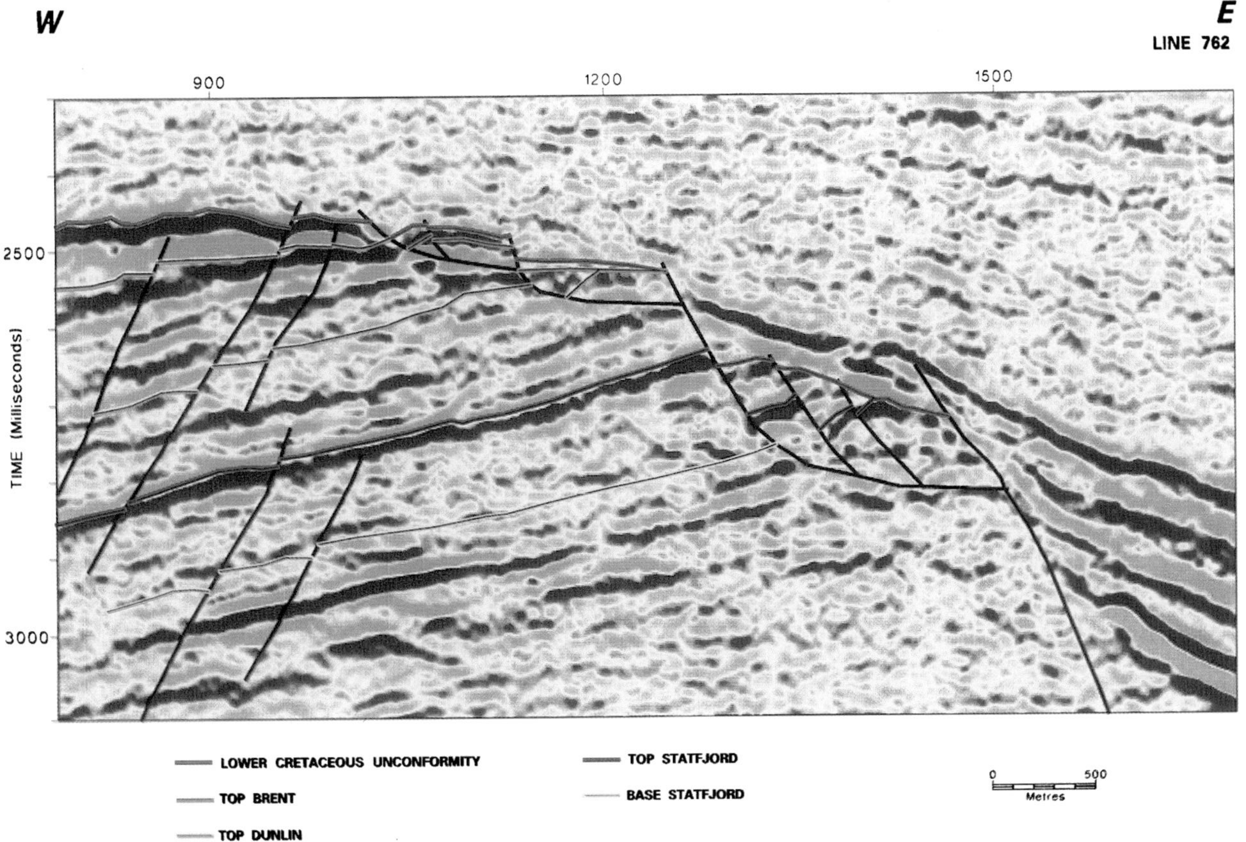

Fig. 8. East–west seismic line from the 1995 Brent Field 3D seismic survey.

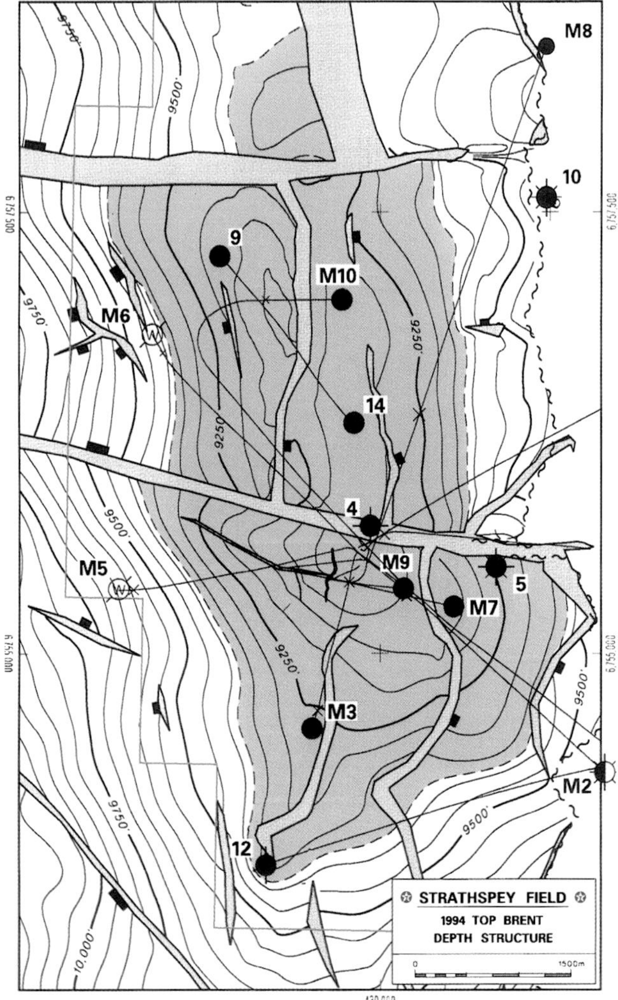

Fig. 9. Top Brent horizon structure map before interpretation of the VCS data.

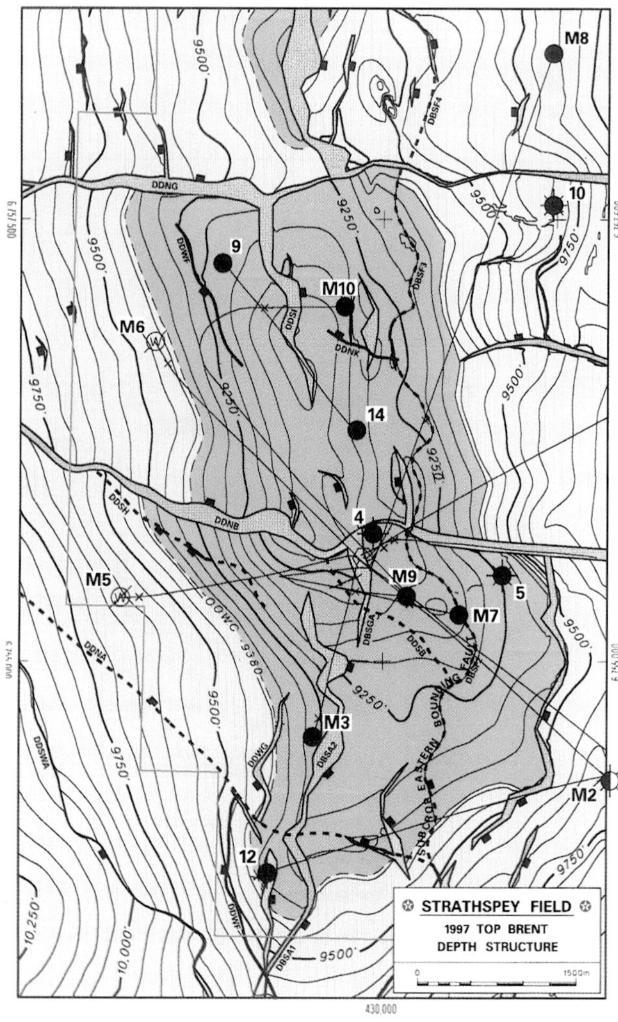

Fig. 10. Top Brent horizon structure map after interpretation of the VCS data.

Figures 9 and 10 show the structure map of the Top Brent horizon before and after interpretation of the VCS data (the 1995 Brent Field survey covered only a small portion of the northern part of Strathspey; thus, there are no Strathspey Field maps based upon this dataset). The increased detail that is visible on the VCS dataset has translated into a more detailed structure map, as well as a more accurate reservoir layering model to be incorporated into the reservoir simulation. The planned well trajectory of a £14.5 million producer/injector has been optimized, based on the interpretation of the new VCS survey.

Likewise, Figs 11 and 12 show the change in the structure map of the Top Statfjord horizon, highlighting the much greater detail which is visible in the VCS dataset, and the new interpretation of the slumped reservoir material. In the northern part of the block, the improved dataset indicates that much of the slumped reservoir material lies below the field oil–water contact. This will have a major effect on plans to drill and/or produce from the slumped Statfjord.

In addition to improvements within the Brent and Statfjord reservoirs, the improved data quality of the VCS has given the Strathspey partners a clearer picture of the remaining exploration potential on the block.

In summary, the Strathspey VCS dataset is a dramatic improvement over the 1985 3D dataset, and shows comparable data quality to the 1995 Brent Field 3D survey, which is an optimized, state-of-the-art 3D seismic survey.

The future of VCS technology

The results of the Strathspey VCS survey are very encouraging with regard to future applications of the technology. This was only the second attempt in the world at a large-area VCS survey, and the results are comparable to the best that conventional seismic methods could produce. As the VCS technology matures, more equipment is built, and additional software is written, data quality will surely improve, and costs will drop. Had four more cables been available for the Strathspey VCS survey, for instance, the acquisition could have been done in four swaths instead of six, significantly reducing the acquisition time.

PGS are already looking to improve the hardware involved, developing cables that are more resistant to movement by sea currents. Software will also be developed to improve the processing sequence. (For example, computer code to suppress the water-bottom multiple had to be written at the time of the processing of the Strathspey VCS dataset, since conventional multiple-suppression packages cannot be applied to VCS data. Such processing packages will surely be developed and refined for future VCS surveys).

Perhaps more importantly, the easy-to-find oil and gas fields in the world have largely been found. More and more, the industry finds itself forced to look in deeper water, and in areas of increasing geological complexity. These are ideal conditions for VCS surveys. VCS acquisition becomes more cost effective

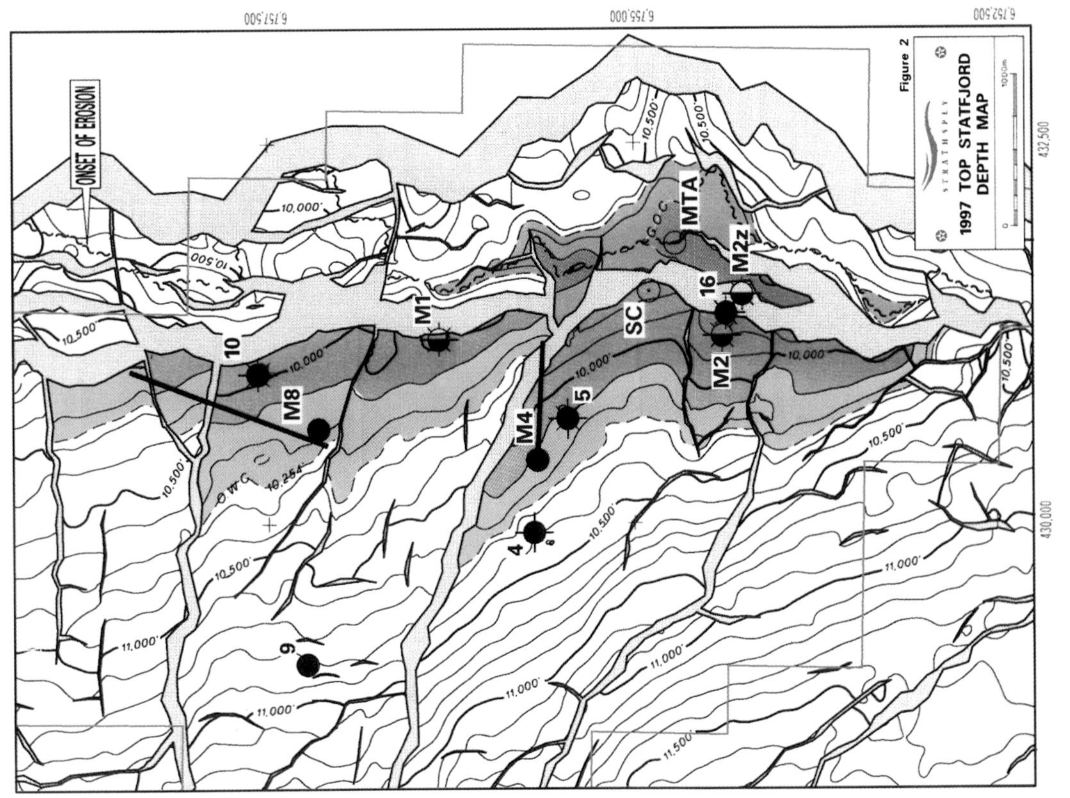

Fig. 12. Top Statfjord horizon structure map after interpretation of the VCS data.

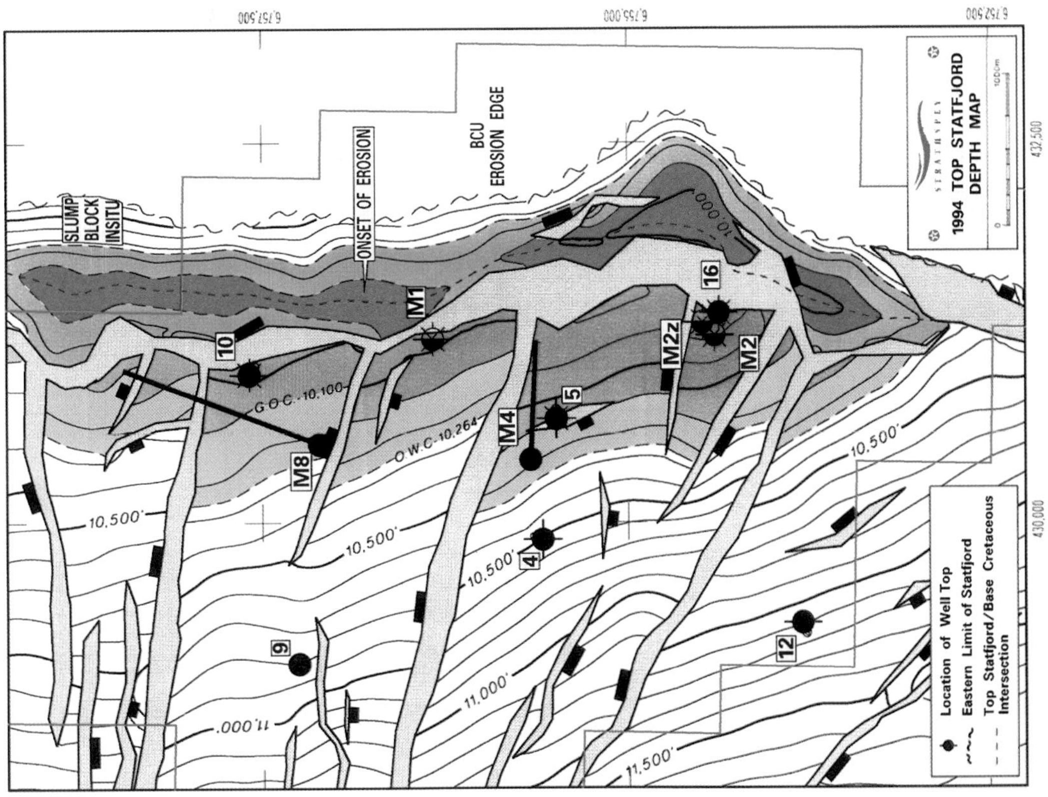

Fig. 11. Top Statfjord horizon structure map before interpretation of the VCS data.

in deep water, where the greater vertical spacing of the hydrophones allows for greater horizontal spacing of the cables, resulting in larger swaths and reduced acquisition time. VCS processing, with its economical 3D pre-stack depth migration, is the best method available for imaging complex geological structures, such as sub-salt, sub-volcanic, and overthrust areas. Thus, the VCS acquisition and processing technique is ideally suited for finding and developing the complex offshore oil fields of tomorrow.

The author would like to acknowledge D. Sukup and P. Krail of Texaco's EPTD for all of the information which they have provided over the past few years, and Shell, Esso, and Oryx, for granting permission for this paper to be presented and published.

Faeroes Large Aperture Research Experiment (FLARE): imaging through basalt

R. S. WHITE,[1] J. FRUEHN,[1] K. R. RICHARDSON.[1] E. CULLEN,[2] W. KIRK,[2]
J. R. SMALLWOOD[1,2] and C. LATKIEWICZ[2]

[1] *Bullard Laboratories, University of Cambridge, Madingley Road, Cambridge CB3 OEZ, UK*
[2] *Amerada Hess Ltd, 33 Grosvenor Place, London, SW1X 7HY, UK*

Abstract: The acquisition of high density, large aperture seismic data may allow the deep crustal structure to be studied in areas that have traditionally proven difficult to image using conventional seismic profiling techniques, such as those where high-velocity basalt flows or sills overlie sedimentary sections. This is because the amplitudes of reflections at wide angles are generally much larger than at near normal-incidence, and because large aperture seismic data carries much more velocity information than the limited aperture data recorded along conventional seismic profiles. We discuss the acquisition and processing of synthetic aperture seismic profiles, using two 2D seismic vessels to achieve continuous offsets to more than 38 000 m along profiles near the Faeroe Islands, shot as part of the Faeroes Large Aperture Research Experiment (FLARE).

The new technique shows the presence of lava flows extending away from the Faeroe Islands across a thick (up to 4 km), probably Mesozoic and early Tertiary underlying sedimentary section. Seismometers on the Faeroese island of Suduroy show that the sedimentary section pinches out beneath the island, and also provides control on the crustal thinning beneath the region southeast of the Faeroe Islands. Since Tertiary basalt flows and sills are such a pervasive feature of the geology of the highly prospective northwest European continental margins, synthetic aperture profiles are likely to be of considerable importance in the future in imaging sub-basalt structure in these areas.

The presence of layers of basalt, emplaced either as flows or as sills in a sedimentary section, creates a considerable barrier to imaging the underlying structure using conventional seismic profiling methods. This is because the high impedance contrast between sediments and basalts cause strong reflections which can easily mask deeper, weaker reflections and which often generate prominent inter-bed multiples, again obliterating underlying reflections. Since much of the highly prospective northwest European continental margin, stretching from the Norwegian basins, through the Faeroes–Shetland region to Rockall and Hatton troughs contains significant quantities of basalt as flows or sills (e.g. White & McKenzie 1989; Joppen & White 1990), there is considerable interest in developing new methods of imaging through basalts.

Marked enhancements to sub-basalt imaging can be gained if much larger offsets are considered than are normal for single-ship profiling. This is because the amplitudes of wide-angle reflections increase toward the critical point, so wide-angle reflections are generally of much higher amplitude than are near-normal incidence reflections. Thus sub-basalt reflections which are weak at normal incidence may be very strong at wide-angle.

A further advantage of using larger offsets is that the velocity control is much improved over that derived from single-ship data, which rarely extends to offsets of greater than 6000 m. In addition to wide-angle reflections, large offsets also enable diving waves (often called 'refractions') to be recorded. In conventional seismic processing, these diving waves are usually muted out, but they carry considerable additional information on the velocity structure. The improved seismic velocity control derived from very large offset data, using both reflections and diving waves, is of direct use in providing a tomographic image of the crustal structure, as we show later in this paper. Improved velocity control is also likely to lead to better migrations of the reflection data, particularly where deep reflectors are weak, and where the high amplitude wide-angle reflections can be migrated back to normal incidence.

Finally, the larger offsets, with their attendant large angles of incidence, may allow considerable compressional (P) to shear (S) wave conversion to occur. The velocity contrasts across sediment–basalt interfaces are almost perfect for mode conversion between P-waves and S-waves: when the P-wave velocity in the sediments is the same as the S-wave velocity in the basalt, then at wide angles of incidence almost all the energy may convert from P-wave in the sediments to S-wave in the basalt and vice-versa (White & Stephen 1980). Unconsolidated sediments directly overlying the basalts east of the Faeroes typically have P-wave velocities of $c. 2.2\,km\,s^{-1}$, almost identical to the S-wave velocities in the basalt flows, so strong mode conversion occurs in both down-going and up-coming waves. The presence of converted S-wave arrivals opens up the possibility of imaging using S-waves in addition to P-waves, and also of characterizing the physical properties of the crust in better detail than through using P-waves alone.

The acquisition of new two-ship data from the Faeroes Large Aperture Research Experiment (FLARE) to the east of the Faeroe Islands is described here (Fig. 1), and it is shown how these data can be used to assist in imaging problematic areas, such as those where basalt flows lie above sediments. Three separate profiles were acquired as part of FLARE (Fig. 2). In this paper we show results from Line 1, which extends from the region of thick basalt flows near the Faeroe Islands to the feather edge of the basalts 150 km to the southeast.

Acquisition of large offset data

There are two main methods of acquiring seismic data with offsets larger than the 6000–7000 m typically available from single ship 2D seismic vessels.

The first method is to deploy fixed seabed recorders, which enables the shooting ship to move to any desired offset. The

WHITE, R. S., FRUEHN, J., RICHARDSON, K. R., CULLEN, E., KIRK, W., SMALLWOOD, J. R. & LATKIEWICZ, C. 1999. Faeroes Large Aperture Research Experiment (FLARE): imaging through basalt. *In*: FLEET, A. J. & BOLDY, S. A. R. (eds) *Petroleum Geology of Northwest Europe: Proceedings of the 5th Conference*, 1243–1252.

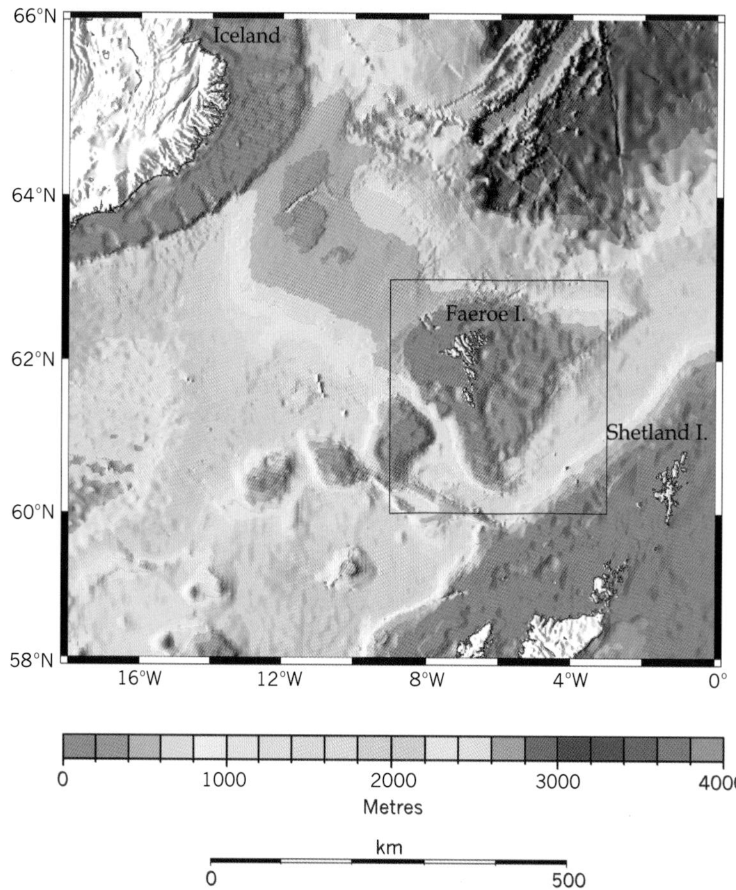

Fig. 1. Regional location map showing setting of Faeroe Islands on the continental margin of NW Europe.

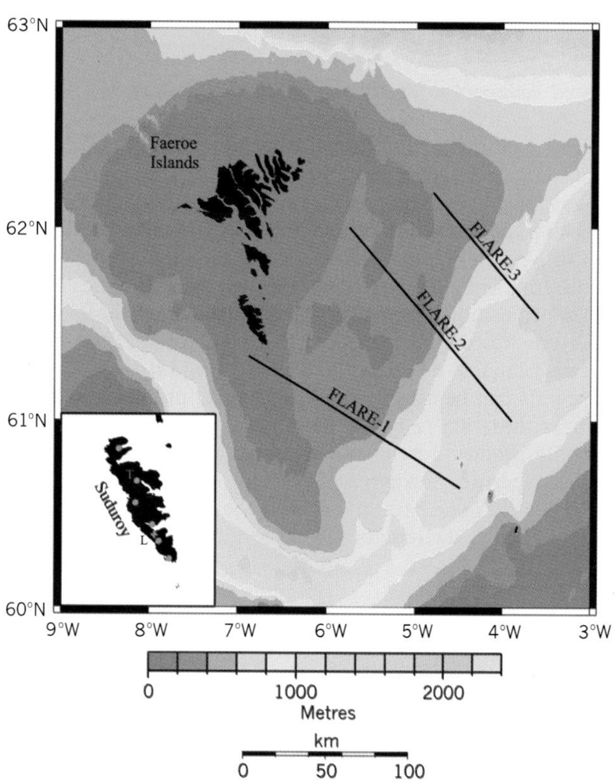

Fig. 2. Location map showing bathymetry around the Faeroe Islands, with the location of the FLARE profiles and (inset) land seismometer positions on Suduroy. T marks the location of the seismometer at Trongisvagur used to generate the seismic section shown in Fig. 8, and the cross marked L shows the position of the Lopra borehole.

maximum offset is limited only by the range to which useful seismic data can be recorded: in practice, in the Faeroe–Iceland region, seismic arrivals from an airgun array on a conventional seismic vessel have been recorded to ranges in excess of 400 km (White *et al.* 1996), so the main limit on the maximum offset is the required depth of penetration and the resolution: at larger offsets the diving waves penetrate deeper, but because the high frequencies are removed by absorption, they have lower dominant frequencies and therefore lower resolution. If the objective was to determine the crustal structure down to, say, the base of the crust, a maximum offset of *c.* 100 km would be required to record sub-crustal diving waves through the upper mantle to the east of the Faeroe Islands. Shallower crustal targets would require smaller maximum offsets.

Seabed seismometers may be either autonomous recording packages with their own internal time base, as are commonly used in ocean bottom seismometers, or may be seabed arrays (often called ocean bottom cables) with a direct link to a surface vessel equipped with a conventional digital acquisition system. In both cases, the main advantage is that three-component geophones can be deployed on the seabed, enabling the direct detection of shear-waves. With a conventional airgun array as a seismic source, there is still the requirement that mode conversion from P-wave to S-wave occurs at or beneath the seabed. But unlike conventional hydrophone streamers in the water column, seabed seismometers do not require a further conversion from S-waves back to P-waves before the converted waves can be detected. Another advantage of seabed seismometers is that it may be possible to detect, and to process out, water column multiples because they produce downward travelling waves at the seabed which can be distinguished, using geophones, from upward travelling sub-bottom arrivals.

The main disadvantage of seabed recorders, and particularly of ocean bottom seismometers, is that they produce more sparse data than do towed streamer acquisition systems. This makes seabed recorders less good than towed streamer systems for imaging sub-surface structure. Seabed systems are also more inflexible and expensive to operate than are methods which rely on towed streamer acquisition using seismic vessels.

The second method of recording large offset data is to use two conventional seismic acquisition ships sailing in line astern. By shooting alternately from the lead and the trail ships, and by recording data on both streamers, it is possible to synthesize arbitrarily long arrays (see Fig. 3 for a schematic representation of the multiple-pass 2-ship acquisition used in the FLARE profiles). This method was first described by Stoffa & Buhl (1979) and by Buhl *et al.* (1982): it has been called variously 'synthetic aperture profiling', 'constant offset profiling', 'wide aperture recording' and 'large aperture recording'. It has hitherto been used primarily in academic whole-crustal studies, but is increasingly seen as being useful in difficult data areas such as those involving high-velocity layers of salt or basalt overlying sedimentary sections. On the northwest European margin examples of two-ship synthetic aperture studies have been published from work on the Lewisian continental basement (Hughes *et al.* 1983), the Hatton Bank continental margin west of Rockall (Fowler *et al.* 1989; Morgan *et al.* 1989), and the Rockall Basin (Joppen & White 1990).

Two main technical advances in recent years have significantly enhanced the capabilities of synthetic aperture profiling. The first is the routine availability of long digital streamers: the use of two ships with 7000 m streamers, for example, would allow acquisition of data to offsets of more than 20 000 m with a single pass of the two ships. The second advance is in towed streamer positioning capabilities to within a few metres or better, using differential global positioning satellite techniques (DGPS): this means that shot positions can be re-occupied on successive passes of the two ships and that the precise locations both of the sources and of the streamers (through the use of DGPS in tail buoys) can be recorded for use in subsequent binning and processing.

The operational strengths of two-ship synthetic aperture profiling include the ability to record industry-standard seismic profiles rapidly and flexibly with normal 2D vessels. At the processing stage the additional velocity information from the wide-angle data can be incorporated seamlessly with conventional reflection profile processing of the same data to improve the imaging of difficult areas.

FLARE acquisition

In the acquisition of wide-angle data during FLARE, advantage was taken of the ability to deploy fixed seismometers on land in Suduroy, the southernmost Faeroese island (Fig. 2). This enabled us to record arrivals to offsets in excess of 100 km, thus providing control on the Moho depth and the crustal thickness southeast of the Faeroe Islands.

Six land stations were deployed, two of which straddled the Lopra borehole (inset, Fig. 2). Each contained a three-component geophone sensor, with a Reftek digital recording package powered by batteries that were recharged by solar panels. Since each station was self-contained, it was important to have an absolute time-base recorded on each: for this we used GPS clocks, and ensured that the shot instants from the seismic vessels were also recorded against GPS, to a precision of 1 ms.

The offshore acquisition was undertaken in August–September 1996 by Western Geophysical and the Amerada Hess Limited Partner Group (LASMO (ULX) Limited, Norsk Hydro a.s. and DOPAS) using the 2D seismic vessels *M/V Western Cove* and *I/S Thetis* (for acquisition parameters see Table 1). Ideally, the sources, streamers and acquisition systems on both vessels would be identical. In practice, the availability of ships for this work meant that one ship deployed a 6000 m streamer and the other a 4800 m streamer. Both streamers were run relatively deep, at 15 m depth, since we wished to enhance low-frequency arrivals from sub-basalt structure. The sources on the two vessels used TI sleeveguns, but were slightly different in overall size. The *Thetis* source was 83.1 l, compared to the 49.2 l Western Cove source. However,

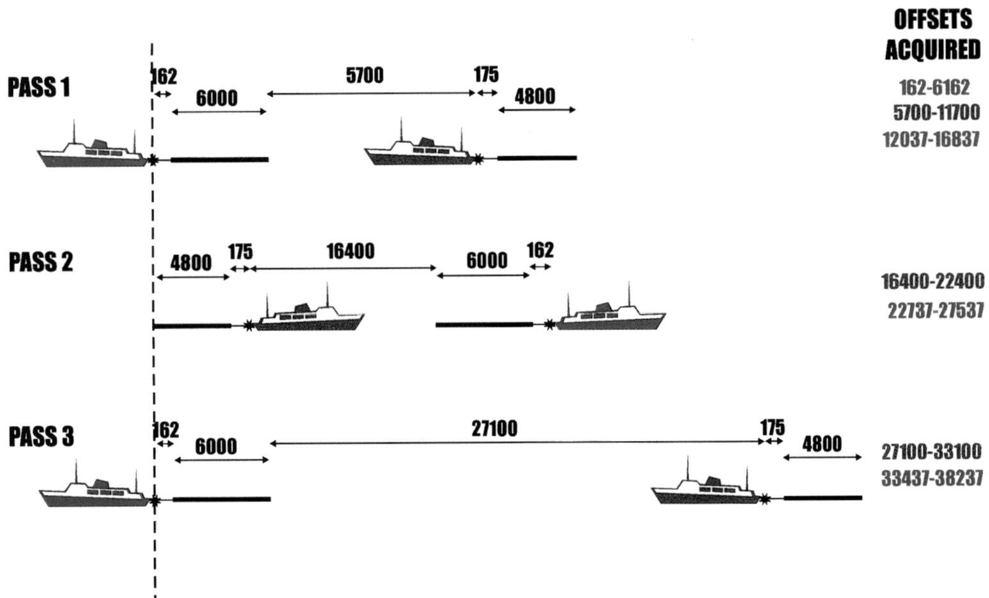

Fig. 3. Acquisition geometry used in acquiring FLARE data (not to scale) showing ship separations in metres required to construct a supergather from a shotpoint at the position of the vertical dashed line. The *M/V Western Cove* (coloured red) was the lead ship and the *I/S Thetis* (coloured blue) the trail ship. The offsets of seismic data acquired in each pass, assuming that there is no streamer feathering, are shown at the right-hand end. The colours of the numbers denote the ship from which the source was fired. Note the 337 m gap in offset coverage that occurs in each pass resulting from the gap between the guns and the nearest streamer channel on each ship.

Table 1. FLARE acquisition parameters

M/V Western Cove	*I/S Thetis*
Source	
49.21 (3000 in^3)	83.11 (5070 in^3)
TI sleevegun array	TI sleevegun array
4 gun strings	4 gun strings
32 guns	30 guns
Nominal 100 bar-m	Nominal 140 bar-m
(34–128 Hz)	(34–128 Hz)
100 m shot interval	100 m shot interval
Streamer	
6000 m Titan streamer	4800 Titan streamer
480 × 12.5 groups	384 × 12.5 groups
15 m depth	15 m depth
162 m gap from guns to channel 1	175 m gap from guns to channel 1
Recording system	
4 ms sampling	4 ms sampling
18 s record length	18 s record length
Low cut out (4 Hz)	Low cut out (4 Hz)

although the difference between the sources was discernible in the very long offset data recorded on the land stations (with the larger source producing arrivals above the noise level to greater ranges), there was little apparent difference in the offshore data synthesized from the two ships. This is, of course, important, because data from both sources contribute to the final supergathers and if there were significant uncorrected differences then the processing algorithms, such as stacking, deconvolution and migration, might produce artefacts.

The way in which the offsets were built up in successive passes is shown in Fig. 3. The separation between the two ships was chosen so as to provide approximately 400 m overlap in coverage wherever possible. Thus in pass 1, the lead ship source firing into its own streamer gave offsets from 162 to 6162 m: the separation between the guns and the first active section of the streamer controlled the minimum offset of 162 m. With the trail ship's source positioned 5700 m behind the end of the lead ship's streamer, arrivals in the offset range 5700 to 11 700 m were recorded by the trail ship's airguns firing into the lead ship's streamer. There are overlapping arrivals from the two sources in the range 5700–6162 m. This redundancy allows timing checks to be made in the construction of the supergathers to ensure that there is a seamless juxtaposition of the data at different offsets recorded by different combinations of sources and streamers. The overlap also provides a margin to allow for small variations in station-keeping between the two ships during data acquisition, and for range variations resulting from feathering of the streamers caused by wind and current effects.

The third offset range acquired in Pass 1 of the two ships is that generated by using the trail ship's streamer to record the lead ship's source. In the case of FLARE this produced arrivals at offsets between 12 037–16 837 m. We note that there is now an unavoidable gap with no offset coverage in the range 11 700–12 037 m (Fig. 3). This is caused by the sum of the gun-streamer offsets on the two ships. In our case the two gun-streamer offsets were 162 and 175 m (Table 1), thus giving a gap of 337 m in total. One such gap is produced at each successive pass. With the geometry on FLARE the gaps occur at 11 700–12 037 m (Pass 1), at 22 400–22 737 m (Pass 2) and at 33 100–33 437 m (Pass 3). Any streamer feathering slightly increases the size of the gaps. In the data gathers shown later in this paper, these gaps are visible as blank stripes across the shot supergathers.

There is no simple way to avoid the gaps in offset coverage with the geometry shown here. Operational difficulties limit how close the front of the streamer can be to the airgun array, but the smaller the offset between gun and streamer, the smaller the overall data gap. One alternative to avoid the data gaps would be to make twice as many passes, shooting from only one ship at a time and adjusting the ship separation between successive passes to remove the gun offset effect. A bonus from this style of acquisition would be that shot points could be spaced *c.* 50 m apart, rather than the 100 m shot spacing generated by our alternate firing strategy. The downside, of course, is that twice as many passes would be required in order to acquire the same overall offsets.

For FLARE, the maximum offsets acquired were a little over 38 000 m, using three separate passes of the two ships (Fig. 3). There is essentially no limit to the number of passes that can be used to build up the overall range of offsets required, although of course the signal to noise ratio decreases as the offset increases.

FLARE processing

The data acquisition stage of FLARE produced seven different source-streamer offset panels for each shotpoint. The seven panels resulting from a single shot on each ship are shown in Fig. 4. Each of these panels is the shot-gather from one streamer, so has a trace spacing of 12.5 m. The ground waves dip in opposite directions on alternate panels because of the flip-flop shooting. Note also the strong coherent noise from other seismic vessels, particularly on some of the panels from passes 2 and 3.

Prior to velocity analysis, the seismic data were resorted and binned into synthetic supergathers: a supergather is equivalent to the seismic section that would have been recorded by a single shot into a 38 000 m long streamer. The first and third panels are already in the correct format since they were recorded from the same shot. In order to use the data from the second panel in the supergather, we assume that reciprocity applies, i.e. we assume that the seismic path from a source to a receiver at any given offset would be identical if the source and the receiver were interchanged. Since the shot points from the trail ship are now taken by reciprocity to be equivalent receiver positions, it is immediately apparent that the minimum equivalent receiver spacing is 100 m, since this is the spacing at which shots were fired. The supergathers were therefore constructed with a 100 m trace spacing throughout and each trace in the supergather was constructed by binning an average of eight streamer traces (since the streamer groups were each 12.5 m long). To allow for streamer feathering, each supergather trace was constructed from the streamer traces that fell in 100 m bins extending perpendicularly across the line of the profile, using the streamer geometry reconstructed from DGPS positions and compass sections along the streamer.

An example of a raw supergather is shown in Fig. 5a. This shows clear continuity of crustal arrivals at wide-angles. The boundaries between adjacent panels are shown in three positions by the data gaps discussed earlier. In the remaining three positions, where different panels join with a small overlap (*c.* 6, 16.5 and 27.3 km), there is often a change in the character of the noise, although the crustal arrivals are continuous across the joins.

This illustrates one of the aspects that have to be addressed for noise reduction in the FLARE data. Since each panel may have been acquired at a different time, and possibly under different sea and wind conditions, the noise pattern on each panel may be quite different from that on its neighbour. In particular, coherent noise from other ships is likely to exhibit quite different apparent velocities on different panels, as is clear on Fig. 5a. Therefore it is important to pre-process

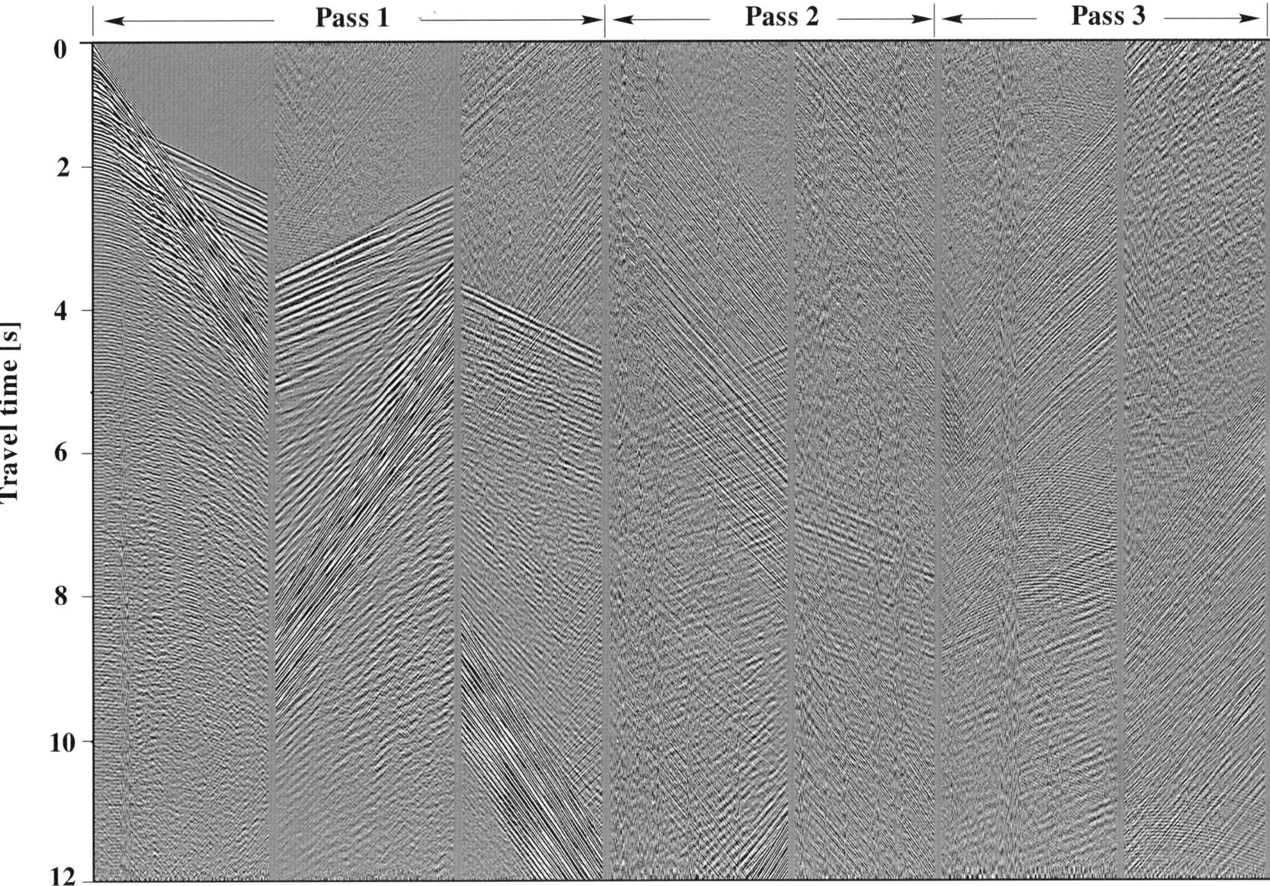

Fig. 4. Examples of the seven raw shot gathers recorded from the three passes of the two ships (see Fig. 3 for geometry). Trace spacing 12.5 m. Streamer on *M/V Western Cove* was 6000 m long, while that on *I/S Thetis* was only 4800 m long, thus generating panels of differing sizes.

each panel separately for noise reduction before constructing the supergathers. This has been done in Fig. 5b, which is the filtered version of Fig. 5a.

Synthetic aperture profiles are somewhat more susceptible to coherent noise from other vessels than are conventional seismic profiles. This is because at large offsets the moveout of the crustal arrivals of interest is almost linear, with generally little of the hyperbolic shape seen at near-offsets. However, distant seismic vessels also produce coherent noise with almost linear moveout. Where the apparent velocities of the seismic arrivals and the noise are very different, as is the case for the example in the panel between 16–22 km on Fig. 5a, it is straightforward to separate and to remove the noise (e.g. see same 16–22 km offset range in the filtered version shown in Fig. 5b). However, if the noise has a similar moveout to the data of interest it is, of course, much harder to separate them.

For the velocity modelling described later in this paper the data from supergathers were used. When the wide-angle data are used for direct imaging it is much better, however, to use the original shot gather data because they retain a trace spacing of 12.5 m, so the effects of spatial aliasing are reduced.

Effect of basalt layers on seismic sections

Although at near-normal incidence a high-velocity basalt layer may mask arrivals from deeper horizons, at wide angles the effect of an underlying low-velocity sediment layer may be easily detected. The synthetic seismogram shown in Fig. 6a is a representative supergather constructed from a simplified one-dimensional model of the velocity structure at the location of the supergather shown in Fig. 7a. It has a 1.5 km thick basalt layer overlying a 3.5 km thick sedimentary section, which itself sits above basement (see Table 2 for a full listing of the velocity model). For our purposes, two seismic phases are of interest, and are shown in the ray-traced model in Fig. 6b. The first is the diving wave through the basalt layer (red rays on Fig. 6b), which creates the strong wide-angle arrival labelled 'Basalt' on Figs 6a and 7. The second phase of importance is the one labelled 'Basement', which is a wide-angle reflection and diving wave from the basement underlying the deep sedimentary section (blue rays on Fig. 6b).

For the model used to construct the supergather shown in Fig. 6a, the basalt diving wave dies out at offsets above 15 km. This is because the diving wave that is turned back to the surface just above the base of the basalt emerges at the receiver at about 15 km offset (Fig. 6b). Rays penetrating deeper than this are refracted at the base of the basalt and propagate down to the basement before they are refracted or reflected back to the surface (blue rays in Fig. 6b). The low-velocity sediment beneath the basalt causes a 'step-back' of about 1 s in time before the wide-angle basement phase arrives. This is characteristic of the effect on wide-angle arrivals of a low-velocity (sediment) layer beneath a high-velocity (basalt) layer. The magnitude of the 'step-back' is controlled by the thickness and the velocity of the relatively low-velocity sedimentary layer, while the offset at which the basalt diving waves die out is controlled by the thickness of the basalt layer and by the vertical velocity gradient within it. Although the ray-theory approximation shows the basalt arrival terminating abruptly at *c.* 15 km (Fig. 6b), in reality the wavefield allows some energy to propagate beyond this ray-theoretical cut-off. Thus in the full wavefield synthetic seismogram shown in Fig. 6a, the basalt diving wave energy continues to *c.* 20 km, although with rapidly decreasing amplitudes beyond 15 km offset.

For comparison, Fig. 7a shows an example of a supergather from a region with a thicker basalt layer than that which

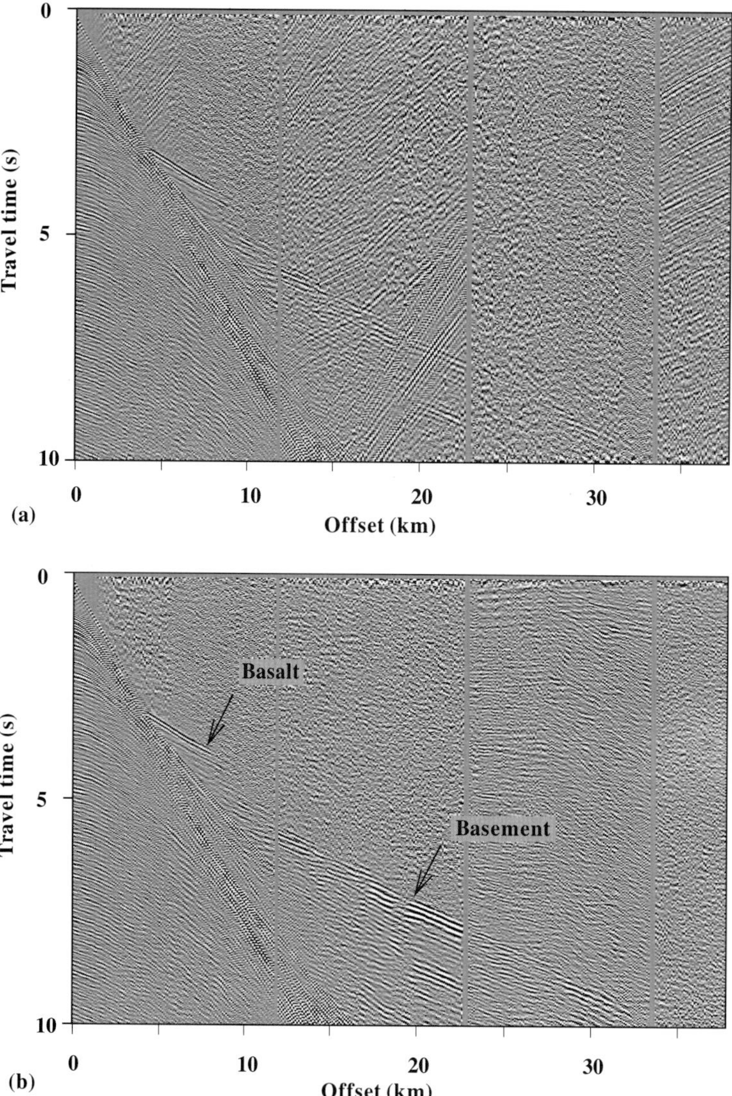

Fig. 5. Examples of supergathers synthesized with 100 m trace spacing. Blank traces are caused by unavoidable data gaps between offsets recorded using the trail ship's source and the lead ship's streamer, and those recorded using the lead ship's source and the trail ship's streamer (see Fig. 3 for explanation of geometry). Wide-angle arrivals from a 1.5 km thick basalt layer die out at *c.* 8 km offset, and are succeeded by a step-back of 1 s in the arrivals caused by the underlying 3.5 km thick sedimentary section with its lower velocities. (**a**) Supergather contaminated by noise from other ships. (**b**) Supergather after pre-bin filtering of raw data panels to reduce other ship noise.

produced the supergather in Fig. 5, although the sub-basalt sedimentary section which gives rise to the step-back is similar. By contrast, Fig. 7b shows a supergather from a region with a thick basalt layer where no underlying sediments are visible.

Velocity modelling along FLARE Line 1

Results are shown here from modelling the crustal velocity structure along one of the profiles, FLARE Line 1 (for location see Fig. 2), using both the offshore two-ship data and the onshore seismometers on Suduroy. The velocity model was constructed by working down from the surface, incorporating the previously determined shallow velocity structure as successively deeper structure was determined.

For the shallowest unconsolidated sedimentary section of post-basalt Tertiary sediments conventional semblance velocity analysis was used on the 6000 m offset single-ship reflection data. The top of the basalts is imaged clearly on conventional seismics, and a pre-stack depth migrated profile was used to define the intra-sediment and top-basement horizons along the line.

The velocity structure shown here for the deeper crust was determined by picking basalt and basement reflections and diving arrivals such as those annotated on Figs 5 and 7, and then modelling the arrival times using Zelt & Smith's (1992) forward and inverse ray-tracing computer program for two-dimensionally varying structure. The two-ship data provided control on the upper 10 km of the model, extending down to the basement, while the land data (Fig. 8), with its greater offsets, gave control down to the Moho. Strong wide-angle reflections from the Moho, such as those identified on the record section in Fig. 8, enabled the base of the crust to be modelled over a portion of the profile southeast of the Faeroes.

In Fig. 9b a representative section of the ray-paths used to constrain the crustal velocity structure along the profile is shown. The deep (orange coloured) raypaths recorded on the land stations show the crust thinning southeastward: along the remainder of the profile the crustal thickness was extrapolated by modelling the gravity field. Basalt phases identified on the two-ship data (red rays in Fig. 9b) show the basalt thinning away from the Faeroe Islands (Fig. 9a), while the phases that reflect off and travel through the basement (blue rays in Fig. 9b), provide information on the thickness of the relatively low-velocity sediments underlying the basalts.

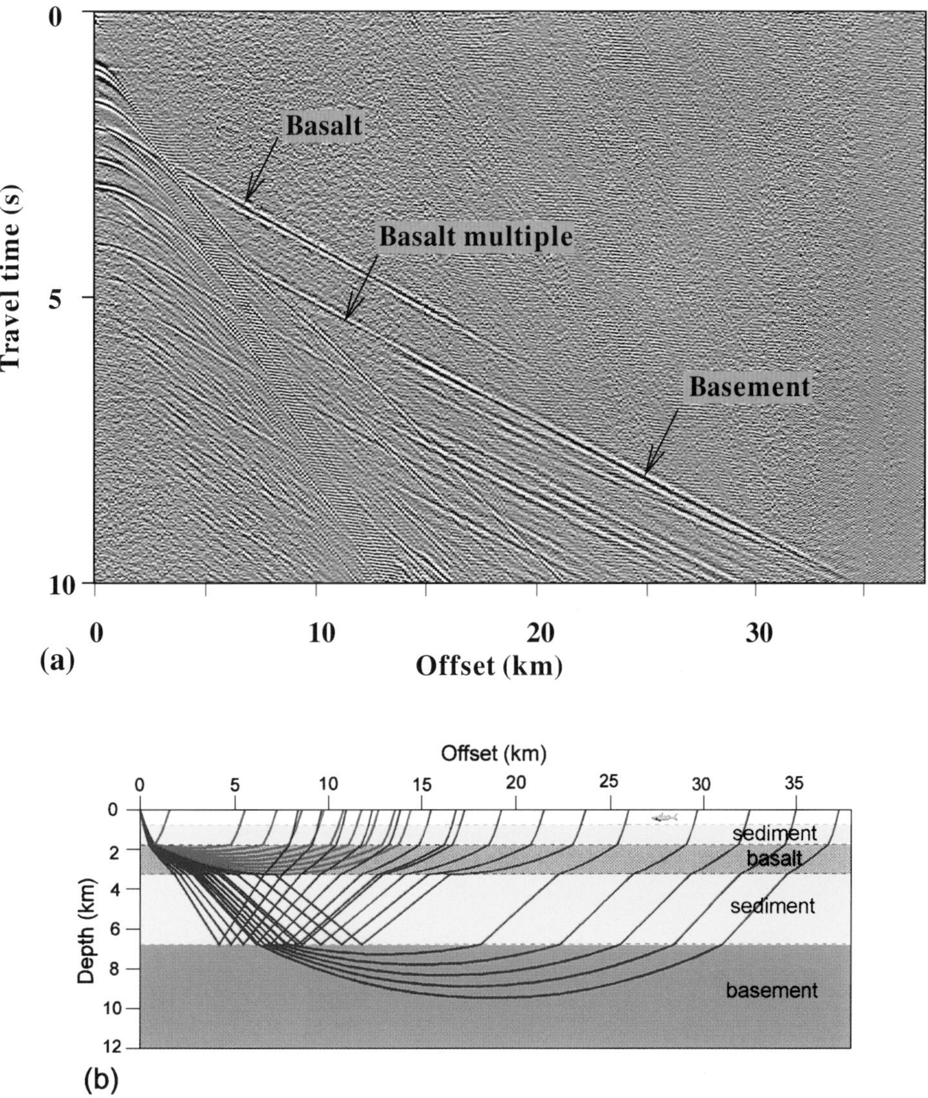

Fig. 6. (**a**) Example synthetic seismogram from a laterally uniform model calculated using the full waveform reflectivity method to show the effect on wide-angle arrivals of low-velocity sediments beneath high-velocity basalts; (**b**) examples of some of the ray-paths followed by wide-angle arrivals through the basalt (red rays), and reflected from or travelling through the basement (blue rays). Velocity model is listed in Table 2.

Geological interpretation

The region between the Faeroe and the Shetland Islands suffered several phases of lithospheric stretching between the Permo-Trias and the Late Cretaceous (Stoker *et al.* 1993). This led to thinning of the Archaean Lewisian crust and the deposition of thick sediments in the basins that were generated by the rifting. Previous seismic refraction work in the Faeroe–Shetland Trough has reported depths to the present Moho of 16–20 km, based on time-term analysis (Bott & Smith 1983; Bott 1984), and 18 ± 3 km, based on a wide-angle Moho reflection (Hughes *et al.* 1998). At the southeastern end of our profile the base of the crust deduced by extrapolation of our seismic control by gravity modelling is at 20 km depth (Fig. 9a), consistent with these earlier results. Since at least the upper 5 km of the crustal section on our FLARE profile in the Faeroe–Shetland Trough represents syn- and post-rift sediments deposited above the basement, and the unstretched Archaean crust beneath northwest Scotland and the Shetland Islands is *c.* 30 km thick, then the Faeroe–Shetland Trough region must have been stretched and thinned by a factor of at least 2 and possibly as much as 3.

The last phase of lithospheric stretching occurred in the early Tertiary when the North Atlantic finally opened. To the east of the Faeroe Islands there was limited Tertiary stretching, leading to the accumulation of up to 2 km of post-rift sediments with a present-day water depth reaching 1 km in the Faeroe–Shetland Basin (blue shading in Fig. 9a) (Mudge & Rashid 1987; Turner & Scrutton 1993). However, to the west of the Faeroe Islands, the continental break-up left a rifted continent–ocean boundary bordering the North Atlantic (White & McKenzie 1989; Richardson *et al.* 1998; Smallwood *et al.* in press).

The seismic velocity of the top of the basement of a little over 5 km s^{-1} is lower than velocities reported from samples of Lewisian basement from NW Scotland (Hall & Simmons 1979). This leads Hughes *et al.* (1997) to postulate that there may be significant volumes of basalt, which exhibit seismic velocities closer to 5 km s^{-1}, emplaced or intruded at the top of the Lewisian basement. An alternative explanation of the basement velocities is that the Lewisian gneissic basement is overlain by indurated Torridonian sandstone or by Permian sandstone, which could also produce velocities around 5 km s^{-1}.

The presence of the Iceland plume at the time of continental break-up caused the generation of huge volumes of basaltic melt, totalling as much as 10×10^6 km^3 along the rifted North Atlantic margins (White & McKenzie 1989; Eldholm & Grue 1994; White 1997; Barton & White 1997*b*). The Faeroe Islands were sitting above the hottest, central part of the mantle plume

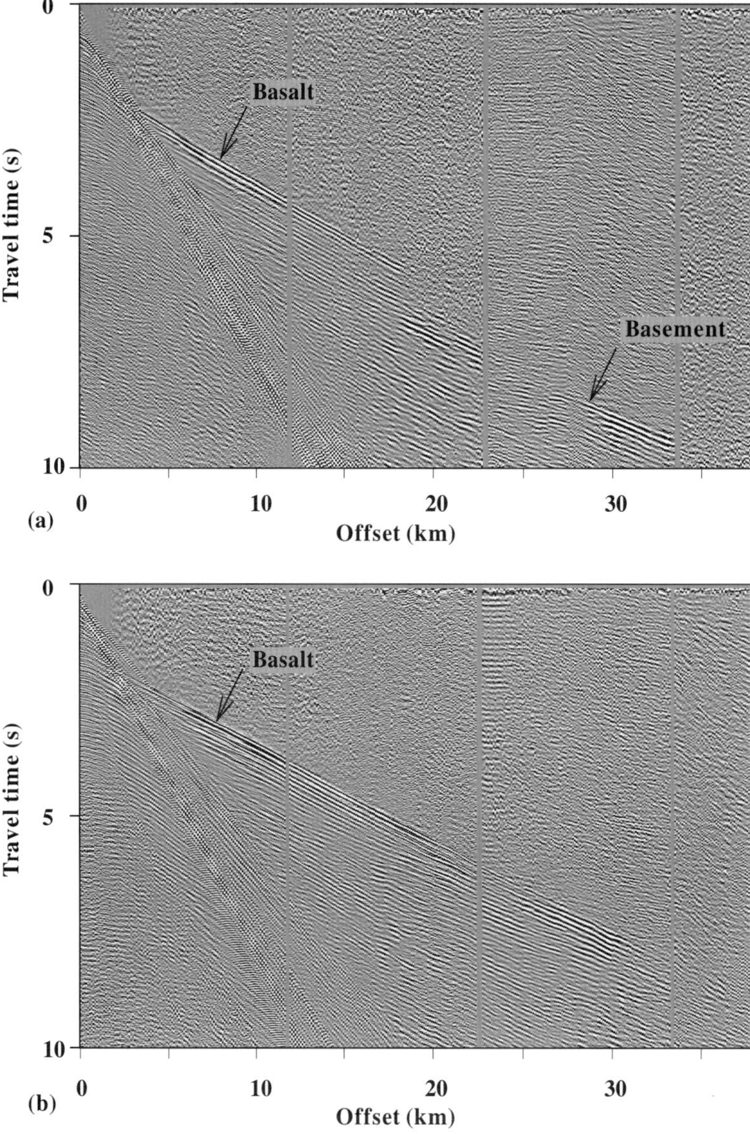

Fig. 7. Representative filtered supergathers from FLARE showing (**a**) the effect on wide-angle basalt and basement arrivals of the presence of a sedimentary section underlying a thicker basalt layer than that shown in Fig. 5; and (**b**) a very thick basalt layer with no underlying sediments visible.

(Barton & White 1997*a*), and more than 7 km of extrusive lavas were emplaced on the Faeroe Islands (Fig. 9a). There has probably been relatively little Tertiary lithospheric stretching beneath the Faeroe Islands themselves. The Faeroese lavas were erupted subaerially or close to sea-level, and include a coal seam between the Lower and Middle series of basalts (Waagstein 1988). Since the early Tertiary the Faeroe Islands have remained at much the same height, without the Tertiary subsidence that occurred both to the east and the west (Smallwood *et al.* in press).

The total crustal thickness beneath Suduroy is 35 km (Fig. 9a), consistent with the inference of Richardson *et al.* (1998) and Smallwood *et al.* (in press), of approximately 40 km thick crust under the northern Faeroe Islands. It is likely that the lower 10 km of the Faeroese crust contains high-velocity material (orange shading with velocities above 7.0 km s^{-1} in Fig. 9a), caused by igneous underplating or lower crustal intrusion at the time of continental break-up. Surface volcanism such as that seen on the Faeroe Islands is commonly accompanied by a similar or greater volume of intruded mafic rocks at the base of the crust elsewhere on the North Atlantic continental margins (Fowler *et al.* 1989; Morgan *et al.* 1989; Eldholm & Grue 1994; Barton & White 1997*a*).

Large basaltic flows similar to those found on the Faeroe Islands extend eastward into the Faeroe–Shetland Basin. They

Table 2. Model used to construct synthetic seismogram in Fig. 6

Depth, km	V_p, km s^{-1}	V_s, km s^{-1}	Density, kg m^{-3}	Lithology
0	1.48	0	1030	sea surface
0.75	1.48	0	1030	sea floor
0.75	1.75	0.45	1800	top sediment
1.25	1.75	0.45	1800	sediment
1.25	2.20	0.95	2000	sediment
1.75	2.20	0.95	2000	base sediment
1.75	4.50	2.50	2450	top basalt
3.25	5.00	2.80	2450	base basalt
3.25	4.00	2.10	2350	top sediment
6.75	4.00	2.10	2350	base sediment
6.75	5.20	3.10	2650	top basement
12.00	6.20	3.50	2650	base of model

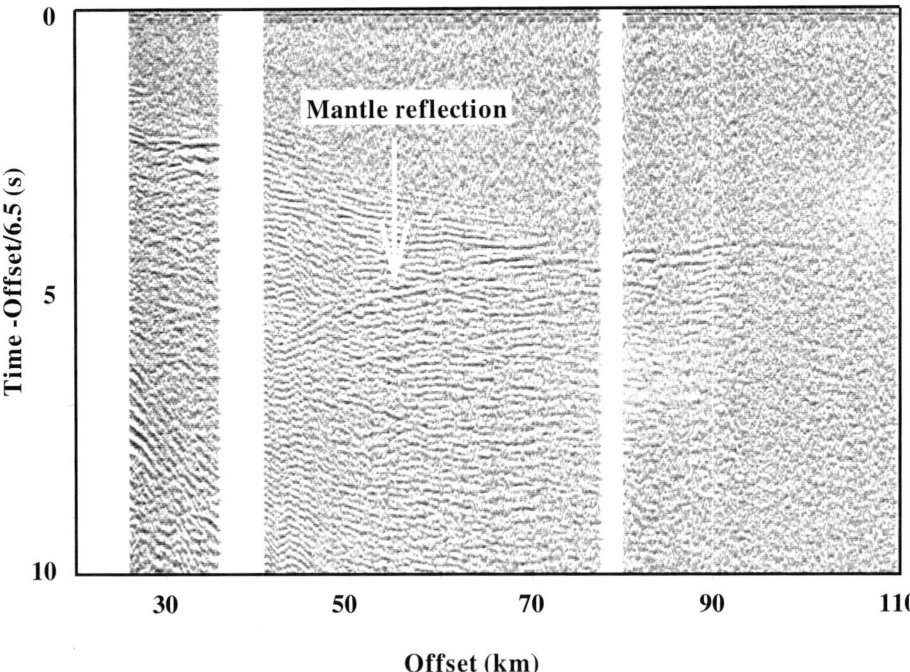

Fig. 8. Wide-angle seismic section recorded on the vertical geophone at the land station at Trongisvagur on Suduroy (see Fig. 2 for location). Zero offset is at the seismometer, and blank sections are a result of the recording disk becoming full on the remote station. Travel time is reduced at 6.5 km s^{-1}. The wide-angle reflection off the Moho is labelled.

thin away from the islands, eventually feathering out near the southeastern end of our profile (Fig. 9a). Beneath the flows, up to 4 km of Mesozoic and possibly early Tertiary sediments are trapped. The underlying sediments thin toward the Faeroe Islands, eventually decreasing to absent or thinner than we can resolve beneath the islands themselves (Fig. 9a). This is consistent with our inference of crustal thinning: the Archaean block beneath the Faeroe Islands cannot have been thinned greatly, since it is now 35–40 km thick, and so extensive Mesozoic sedimentary basins are not expected to have formed

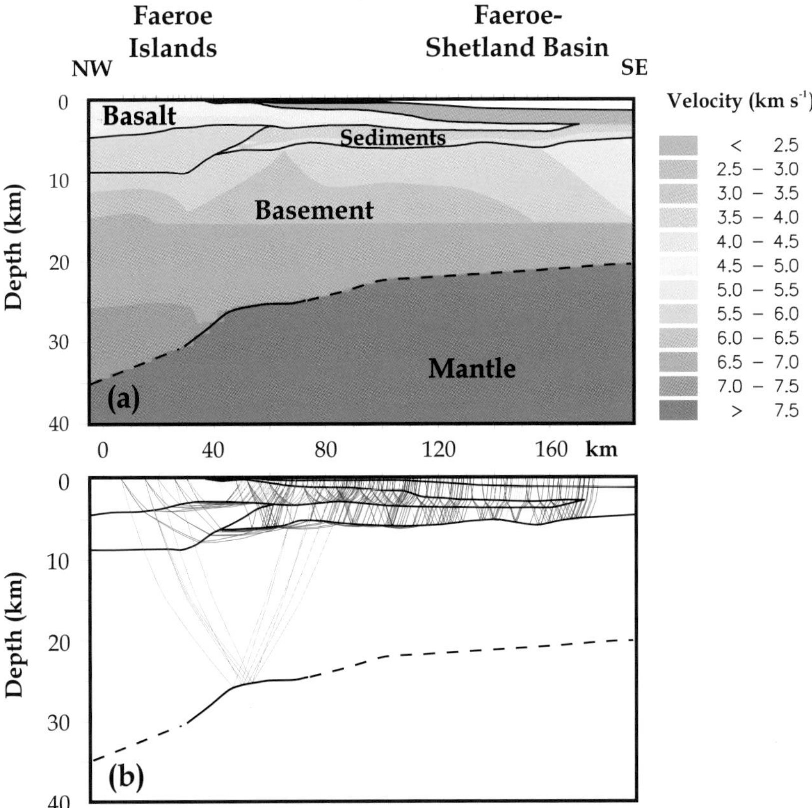

Fig. 9. (**a**) Seismic velocity model of the crust to the southeast of the Faeroe Islands, constrained by FLARE data recorded both offshore on the *M/V Western Cove* and *I/S Thetis*, and onshore at 6 stations on Suduroy (station locations shown by tick marks on upper axis). Vertical exaggeration 2.5:1. (**b**) Examples of some of the ray-paths through the basalt and basement traversed by the wide-angle arrivals used to construct the velocity model.

beneath the present location of the islands: this is in contrast to the area east of the Faeroe Islands, where the Archaean crust is thinned by a factor of 2–3, leading to the development of major Mesozoic sediment accumulations. The early Tertiary basalts flowed across the top of these Mesozoic sediments, creating the extensive basalt cap that is seen today (Fig. 9a).

Conclusions

The two-ship synthetic aperture technique used in FLARE has been highly successful in providing seismic data that are capable of imaging through the high-velocity basalt layers that lie throughout the western Faeroe–Shetland Basin. Results are reported here from wide-angle seismic data that show extensive and thick sedimentary sections lying beneath the basalts, and which provide crustal thickness information that enables the subsidence and tectonic history of the basin to be investigated.

As 7000 m streamers on 2D seismic vessels become routinely available, it will be feasible with a single pass to collect continuous seismic profile data to offsets in excess of 20 000 m using the two-ship technique developed in FLARE. This is likely to lead to significant advances in hydrocarbon prospecting in areas containing large basalt flows or sills, and will therefore be of importance throughout the northwest European frontier areas.

We thank Western Geophysical, Amerada Hess Limited and its partners LASMO (ULX) Limited, Norsk Hydro a.s. and DOPAS for permission to publish this article. Western Geophysical acquired the data and undertook the navigation corrections, preliminary processing including noise reduction in the shot-gather domain, and sorting into supergathers. P. Burton of the University of East Anglia kindly lent us five Reftek seismometers for land recording, and we are grateful to T. Madsen for helping KRR arrange the land work in Suduroy, Faeroe Islands. KRR and JRS acknowledge studentship support from the Natural Environment Research Council. Department of Earth Sciences contribution number 5044.

References

BARTON, A. J. & WHITE, R. S. 1997*a*. Crustal structure of the Edoras Bank continental margin and mantle thermal anomalies beneath the North Atlantic. *Journal of Geophysical Research*, **102**, 3109–3129.

—— & ——1997*b*. Volcanism on the Rockall continental margin. *Journal of the Geological Society of London*, **154**, 531–536.

BOTT, M. H. P. 1984. Deep structure and origin of the Faeroe–Shetland Channel. *In*: SPENCER, A. M. (ed.) *Petroleum Geology of the North European Margin*. Graham & Trotman, London, 314–347.

—— & SMITH, P. J. 1983. Crustal structure of the Faeroe–Shetland Channel. *Geophysical Journal of the Royal Astronomical Society*, **76**, 383–398.

BUHL, P., DIEBOLD, J. B. & STOFFA, P. L. 1982. Array length magnification through the use of multiple sources and receiving arrays. *Geophysics*, **47**, 311–315.

ELDHOLM, O. & GRUE, K. 1994. North Atlantic volcanic margins: Dimensions and production rates. *Journal of Geophysical Research*, **99**, 2955–2968.

FOWLER, S. R., WHITE, R. S., SPENCE, G. D. & WESTBROOK, G. K. 1989. The Hatton Bank continental margin – II. Deep structure from two-ship expanding spread seismic profiles. *Geophysical Journal*, **96**, 295–309.

HALL, J. & SIMMONS, G. 1979. Seismic velocities of Lewisian metamorphic rocks at pressures to 8 kbar: relationship to crustal layering in north Britain. *Geophysical Journal of the Royal Astronomical Society*, **58**, 337–347.

HUGHES, S., BARTON, P. J. & HARRISON, D. J. 1997. Characterizing the Mid-Faeroe Ridge using seismic velocity measurements. *Journal of Geophysical Research*, **102**, 7837–7847.

——, —— & ——1998. Exploration in the Shetland-Faeroe basin using densely spaced arrays of ocean bottom seismometers. *Geophysics*, **63**, 490–501.

HUGHES, V. J., WHITE, R. S., JONES, E. J. W., MATTHEWS, D. H., BREWER, J. A. & SMYTHE, D. K. 1983. A wide angle seismic profile. *In*: BALLY, A. W. (ed.) *Seismic Expression of Structural Styles*. American Association of Petroleum Geologists, Studies in Geology, No. 15, vol. 1, 1.5–6 to 1.5–11.

JOPPEN, M. & WHITE, R. S. 1990. The structure and subsidence of Rockall Trough from two-ship seismic experiments. *Journal of Geophysical Research*, **95**, 19 821–19 837.

MORGAN, J. V., BARTON, P. J. & WHITE, R. S. 1989. The Hatton Bank continental margin – III. Structure from wide-angle OBS and multichannel seismic refraction profiles. *Geophysical Journal International*, **98**, 367–384.

MUDGE, D. C. & RASHID, B. 1987. The Geology of the Faeroe Basin area. *In*: BROOKS, J. & GLENNIE, K. W. (eds) *Petroleum Geology of North West Europe*. Graham & Trotman, Norwell, Mass., 751–763.

RICHARDSON, K. R., SMALLWOOD, J. R., WHITE, R. S., SNYDER, D. & MAGUIRE, P. K. H. 1998. Crustal structure beneath the Faroe Islands and the Faroe-Iceland Ridge. *Tectonophysics*, **300**, 159–180.

SMALLWOOD, J. R., STAPLES, R. K., RICHARDSON, D. R., WHITE, R. S. & FIRE WORKING GROUP, in press. Crust generated above the Iceland mantle plume: from continental rift to oceanic spreading center. *Journal of Geophysical Research*.

STOFFA, P. L. & BUHL, P. 1979. Two-ship multichannel seismic experiments for deep crustal studies: Expanding spread and constant offset profiles. *Journal of Geophysical Research*, **84**, 7645–7660.

STOKER, M. S., HITCHEN, K. & GRAHAM, C. C. 1993. *The Geology of the Hebrides and west Shetland shelves and adjacent deep water areas*. United Kingdom offshore regional report. Her Majesty's Stationery Office, Norfolk, England.

TURNER, J. D. & SCRUTTON, R. A. 1993. Subsidence patterns in western margin basins: Evidence from the Faeroe–Shetland basin. *In*: PARKER, J. R. (ed.) *Petroleum Geology of Northwest Europe: Proceedings of the 4th Conference*. Geological Society, London, 975–983.

WAAGSTEIN, R. 1988. Structure, composition and age of the Faeroe basalt plateau. *In*: MORTON, A. C. & PARSON, L. M. (eds) *Early Tertiary Volcanism and the Opening of the NE Atlantic*. Geological Society, London, Special Publications, **39**, 225–238.

WHITE, R. S. 1997. Rift–plume interaction in the North Atlantic. *Philosophical Transactions of the Royal Society, London, Series A*, **355**, 319–339.

—— & MCKENZIE, D. 1989. Magmatism at rift zones: The generation of volcanic continental margins and flood basalts. *Journal of Geophysical Research*, **94**, 7685–7729.

—— & STEPHEN, R. A. 1980. Compressional to shear wave conversion in oceanic crust. *Geophysical Journal of the Royal Astronomical Society*, **63**, 547–566.

——, MCBRIDE, J. H., MAGUIRE, P. K. H., BRANDSDÓTTIR, B., MENKE, W. H., MINSHULL, T. A., RICHARDSON, K. R., SMALLWOOD, J. R., STAPLES, R. K. & THE FIRE WORKING GROUP 1996. Seismic images of crust beneath Iceland contribute to long-standing debate. *EOS*, **77**, 197 & 200–201.

ZELT, C. A. & SMITH, R. B. 1992. Seismic traveltime inversion for 2-D crustal velocity structure. *Geophysical Journal International*, **108**, 16–34.

Exploring the Shetland–Faeroes Basin using wide-angle seismic technology

P. J. BARTON,[1] S. HUGHES,[2] C. ZELT[3] and R. MASOTTI[2]

[1] *Bullard Laboratories, Department of Earth Sciences, University of Cambridge, UK*
[2] *Mobil North Sea Ltd, Aberdeen, UK*
[3] *Department of Geology and Geophysics, Rice University, Houston, USA*

Densely sampled wide-angle seismic profiles using ocean-bottom seismometers have been used to obtain detailed velocity models of the Shetland–Faeroes Basin in both two and three-dimensions. We demonstrate that the wide-angle (refraction) technique, which employs dense spatial sampling to long offsets, may be successful in areas such as the Atlantic margin, where deep water and/or volcanic horizons mitigate against successful profiling using conventional methods. We employ a series of ray-trace and tomographic inversion procedures on travel time data from profiles across the basin axis to give detailed *in situ* velocity models and accompanying resolution and uncertainty estimates. Comparison of the *in situ* velocity of the Mid-Faeroe Ridge with deterministic lithology–velocity data from nearby boreholes strongly implies that Cretaceous–Tertiary shale and sandstone sequences extend to depths of 4.5 km. The presence of pre-Cretaceous sedimentary lithologies at 4.5–8.0 km depth is supported by *in situ* velocities of 4.0–4.5 km s^{-1} which are best explained by well-consolidated sediments and are incompatible with likely constituents of the basement. The southeastern flank of the Mid-Faeroe Ridges is marked by a prominent fault marking a lateral velocity variation of about 0.5 km s^{-1}. A rapid increase in velocity at 8 km depth suggests transition into the basement, whose velocity is similar to high-pressure measurements of basalts from the Faeroe Islands. Data from an areal grid of shots and receivers centred over the Mid-Faeroe Ridge have been inverted to give a fully three-dimensional velocity model of a small volume to depths of 10+ km. Variations in the depth of isovelocity surfaces from this model correspond closely with the geometry of the Ridge, and the position of the flanking normal fault and its adjacent basin to the southeast.

Further details of aspects of this poster presentation may be found in the following papers:

HUGHES, S., BARTON, P. J. & HARRISON, D. J. 1997. Characterising the Mid-Faeroe Ridge using physical property measurements. *Journal of Geophysical Research*, **102**, 7837–7847.

——, —— & ——1998. Exploration in the Shetland–Faeroe Basin using densely spaced arrays of ocean-bottom seismometers. *Geophysics*, **63**, 490–501.

ZELT, C. & BARTON, P. J. 1998. 3D seismic refraction tomography: an application of two methods to data from the Faeroe Basin. *Journal of Geophysical Research*, **103**, 7187–7210.

BARTON, P. J., HUGHES, S., ZELT, C., & MASOTTI, R. 1999. Exploring the Shetland–Faeroes Basin using wide-angle seismic technology. *In*: FLEET, A. J. & BOLDY, S. A. R. (eds) *Petroleum Geology of Northwest Europe: Proceedings of the 5th Conference*, 1253. Published by the Geological Society, London.

Three-component 3D borehole profile imaging program on Ekofisk Field

H. H. NIELSEN,[1] J. DANGERFIELD,[2] S. C. KEY,[3] G. V. SØILAND[4] and L. BERG[5]

[1] *Phillips Petroleum Company Norway, Postboks 220, 4056 Tananger, Norway (e-mail: hhniels@bvemx.ppco.com)*
[2] *Phillips Petroleum Company Norway, Postboks 220, N-4056 Tananger, Norway (e-mail: jdanger@bvemx.ppco.com)*
[3] *Phillips Petroleum Company, 500 Plaza Office Building, Bartlesville, OK 74005, USA (e-mail: sckey@bvemx.ppco.com)*
[4] *Norwegian Petroleum Directorate, Postboks 600, N-4011 Stavanger, Norway (e-mail: gunnar.soiland@npd.no)*
[5] *Read Well Services a.s, Ravnsborgveien 56, Postboks 25, N-1364 Hvalstad, Norway (e-mail: lars@read-well.no)*

Abstract: A complete series of 3D walkaway borehole profiles have been collected for the Ekofisk Field that are expected to image most of the crestal area of the field. This area has gas present in the overburden which obscures the seismic imaging using conventional surface seismic data. Good compressional images are obtained by undershooting the gas zones and taking advantage of the small Fresnel zones using the 3D walkaway technique. Considerable compressional to shear wave conversion was observed at the reservoir level in these profiles. Shear waves may be particularly suitable for imaging because they are less affected by gas than the compressional waves. Several 3D walkaway borehole profile surveys have been used to derive a 3D up-going shear image. This paper describes the results of this shear wave work from one of these surveys.

The Ekofisk Field, located 240 km SW of Stavanger in the Norwegian North Sea, was discovered in 1969 and started production in 1971. The original in-place reserves amounted to 6.4×10^9 STB of oil and 9.8×10^{12}SCF of gas. Estimated recovery factors are 38% for oil and 70% for gas; 17% of the oil and 28% of the gas is still to be produced. The hydrocarbons are produced from Cretaceous chalk of the Tor and Ekofisk formations. New production facilities (Ekofisk II) were being installed on the field during 1996–97 which marks the beginning of a new development phase that includes drilling up to 50 new production wells during the coming years. The licence period has been extended to year 2028, with blowdown starting in year 2012.

The crestal area of the Ekofisk Field is obscured by gas in the overburden sediments that prevents surface seismic imaging of the reservoir (Fig. 1). The chalk reservoir models in this gas-affected area are solely based on well information, which makes the structural and stratigraphic interpretation of this complex field uncertain. A detailed structural and stratigraphic geological understanding of the gas-affected area is critical for maximizing the value of future development drilling and enhancement of ultimate recovery. Two three-component 3D borehole profile surveys were acquired in 1995 to solve the crestal imaging problems. This was made possible through the drilling of two highly deviated water injectors, well 2/4-K-3 (6585 m MD) and well 2/4-K-6 (5310 m MD). The positions of these two wells gave the opportunity to cover a significant portion of the gas-affected area with 3D borehole profile data (Fig. 1). The two surveys were designed to both undershoot and partly to shoot through the gas-obscured overburden by taking advantage of the 'nearly one way travelling' nature of the seismic signal in borehole profiles. Previous experience with 3D borehole profiling on Ekofisk (Dangerfield 1991) concluded that compressional (P) waves effectively improved seismic imaging beneath the gas obscured overburden.

Wavefield separation processing dealt with separation of up- and down-going compressional (P) and shear (S) wavefields, which are superimposed in the borehole profile recordings. Such processing had not previously been applied on Ekofisk 3D borehole profile data. The survey acquired in well 2/4-K-3 was selected to test the potential for shear wave imaging of the reservoir formations. It was expected that at the sea bottom, converted P- to S-waves would pass unaffected through the gas-disturbed overburden, and provide clear reservoir reflections. Both compressional and shear wave reflections are generated at every impedance boundary. It was anticipated that shear wave reservoir reflections generated from down-going P wavefields would also give an image where P down-going waves either passed through or undershot the gas-affected overburden.

In this paper, three-component 3D seismic borehole profile results acquired in well 2/4-K-3 are discussed. It is demonstrated that besides the P-wave reflections, converted P- to S-wave reservoir reflections are successfully identified in the data. Processing and analysis of the 2/4-K-3 survey shows the existence of a very high compressional and shear velocity (V_p/V_s) relationship in the overburden sediments which greatly impacts the resulting shear wave behaviour, (Dangerfield & Brown 1987). No S–S, i.e. downgoing and reflected shear waves, have been observed in the data. This understanding of the S wavefield behaviour travelling in the gas-affected overburden has damped the expectations on how successful any surface-acquired 'shear' seismic survey (ocean bottom cable) may be in crestal areas of the Ekofisk Field.

Acquisition

Borehole profile acquisition was carried out by Schlumberger Wireline, and Andrew Hydrographics Ltd acquired the source

NIELSEN, H. H., DANGERFIELD, J., KEY, S. C., SØILAND, G. V. & BERG, L 1999. Three component 3D borehole profile imaging program on Ekofisk Field. *In*: FLEET, A. J. & BOLDY, S. A. R. (eds) *Petroleum Geology of Northwest Europe: Proceedings of the 5th Conference*, 1255–1264.

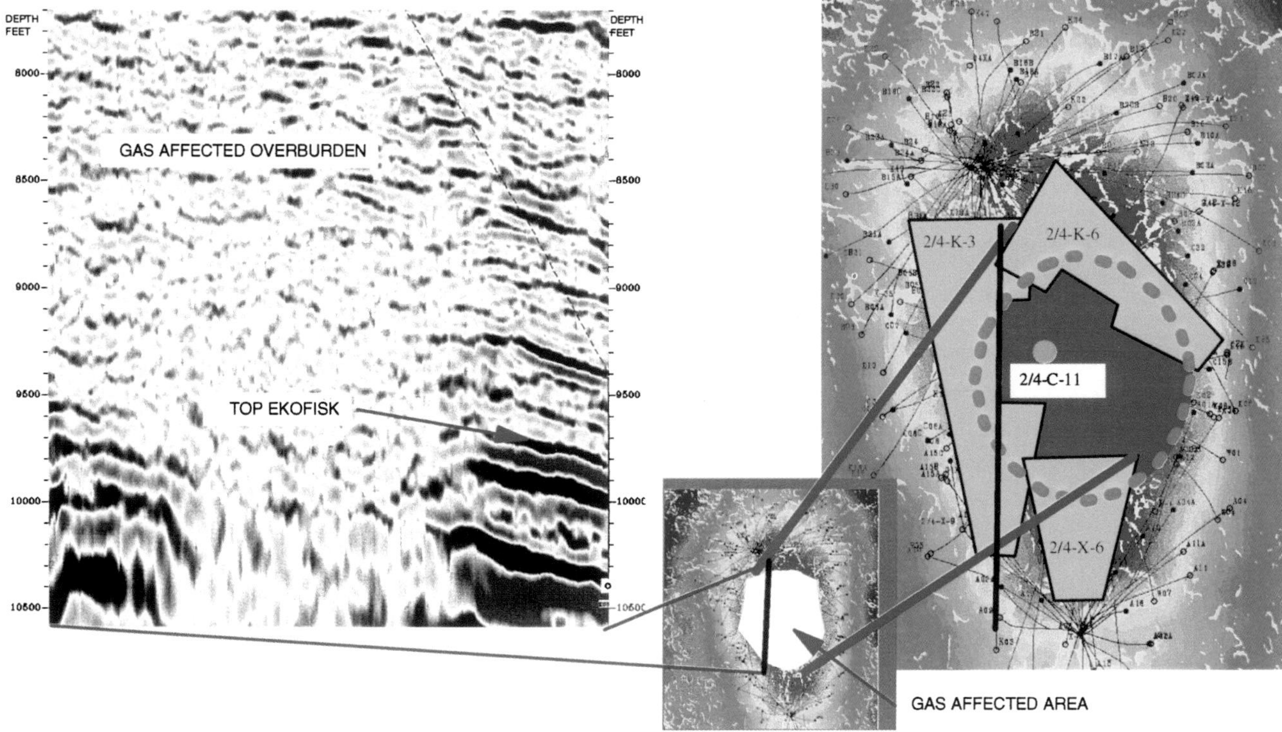

Fig. 1. Map of the Ekofisk Field showing the layout of the 3D borehole profile surveys and a surface seismic line along the 2/4-K-3 water injection well displaying the gas obscured zone.

ship navigation. The Schlumberger Array Seismic Imager was used for downhole data collection. It consisted of five shuttles, 15 m apart. Each shuttle contained x, y and z sensors operated as triaxial non-gimballed geophones. The source was a cluster array consisting of three 155 cubic inch Bolt airguns, which were fired at 2000 PSI pressure at 4 m depth. A total of 59 east–west lines were shot with a length of 6.2 km, 3.1 km on either side of the well, and the line spacing averaged 50 m on the sea surface. The Ekofisk production complex is situated in the middle of the survey, so 23 lines were restricted to the west of the 2/4-K-3 well path, as seen on Fig. 2.

Processing

Read Well Services a.s. did the pre-migration data processing. This part of the processing was directed to focus on 3D processing with the main objective being to separate the up- and down-going compressional and shear wavefields. Three-dimensional depth migration will be performed at a later stage when a tomographically derived update of the overburden gas velocity model is available. This will be based on first break time picks of direct arrivals and timing of reflected events from a series of three-component 3D borehole profile datasets.

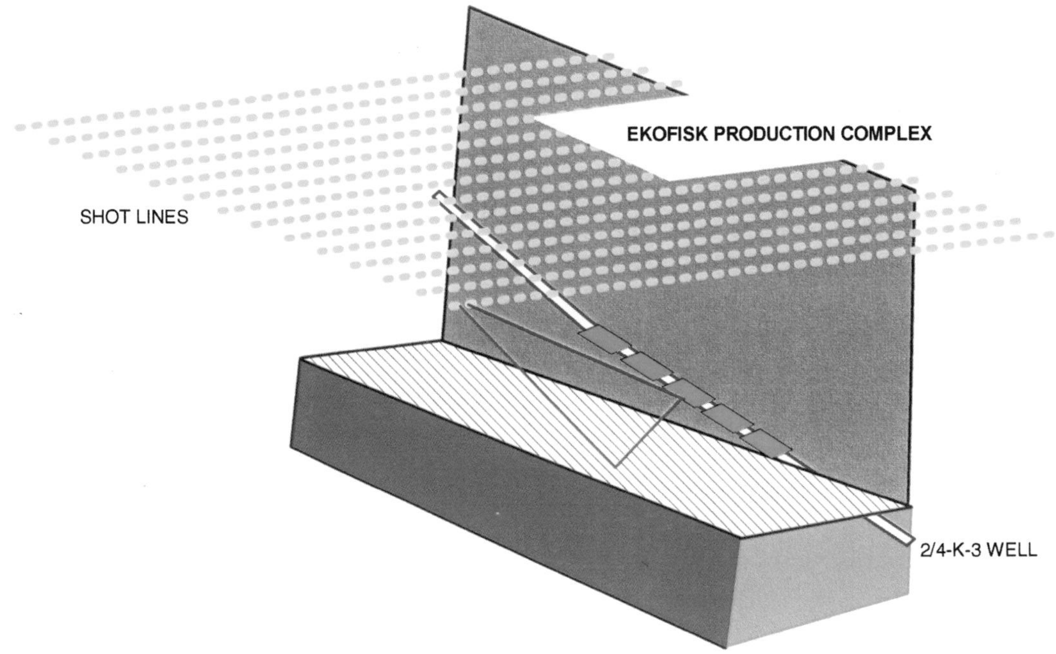

Fig. 2. Conceptual acquisition layout for the three-component 3D borehole profile programme acquired in well 2/4-K-3.

Pre-migration processing and results

Figure 3 summarizes the main steps in the processing of 3D borehole profiling. Simultaneous processing in the x–t and the τ–p domains was performed for the complete dataset acquired in well 2/4-K-3. This demonstrated the superiority of multiple removal in the τ–p domain (stationary conditions) compared to the x–t domain (non-stationary conditions). Forward and backward τ–p transformation stability was also verified by this test. The 3D processing in the two domains provided the possibility at every processing step to apply cross-line filtering and also to display cross-sections of the data volumes as common receiver gathers (CRG), common offset gathers (COG) and common slowness gathers (CSG) in the τ–p domain for quality control.

Identification and separation of wave modes

Up- and down-going P and S wavefields in the 2/4-K-3 data are clearly demonstrated in Figs 4 and 5. The up-going S wavefield can be seen to originate from P- to S-converted waves at the reflection boundaries. The plots demonstrates that shear waves are generated in the overburden, analysis has shown that S-waves are generated both at the sea bottom and

⋆ Correction For System Delay and Geometry Static
   – Time Integration of Accelerometer Data
⋆ Trace Editing
   – NMO (P-P Velocities)
⋆ Binning Single Fold
   – Rotation Into True X,Y,Z Components
⋆ Post - Binning Data Editing
   – Live Trace Construction in Empty Bin Cells
⋆ Reverse NMO
   – Scaling
⋆ Forward Tau-P Transformation
   – Rotation of Z and X Into Radial and Transverse Components
⋆ Extraction of downgoing P and S wavefields
   – Subtraction of Extracted S Wavefield from Total Wavefield
⋆ VSP Deconvolution Applied on Residual Wavefield
   – Wavefield Separation
⋆ Rotation of Upgoing Radial and Transverse Components to Z and X
   – Vector Wavefield Decomposition Into Scalar P- and -S Wavefields
⋆ Data Enhancement of Each Common Slowness Domain Gathered Across the Complete Data Set
   – Inverse Tau-P
⋆ Reverse Scaling and Divergence Correction
   – Data Enhancement of Common Offset Gathers
⋆ VSP/CMP Transformation or Depth Migration

Fig. 3. Three-component 3D borehole profile processing flow diagram.

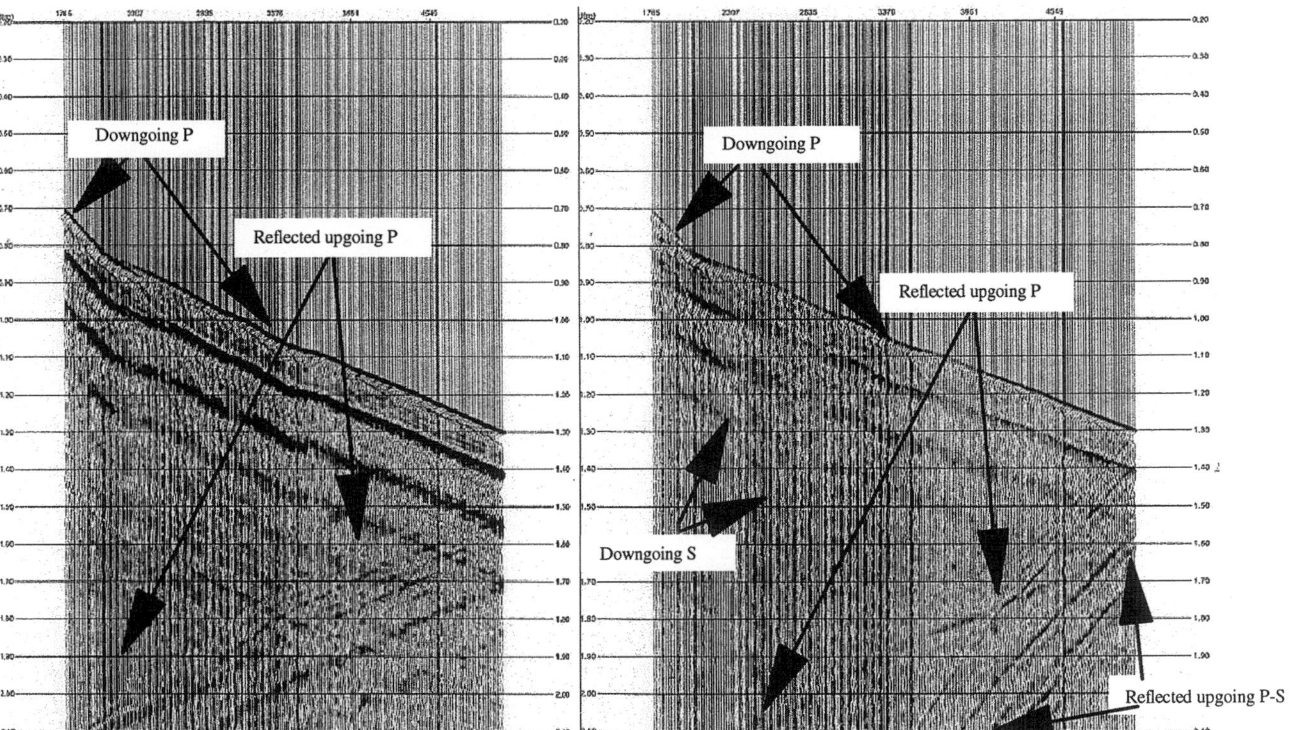

Fig. 4. Left: common slowness gather displaying the vertical component of the total wavefield. Right: common slowness gather displaying the horizontal component of the total wavefield.

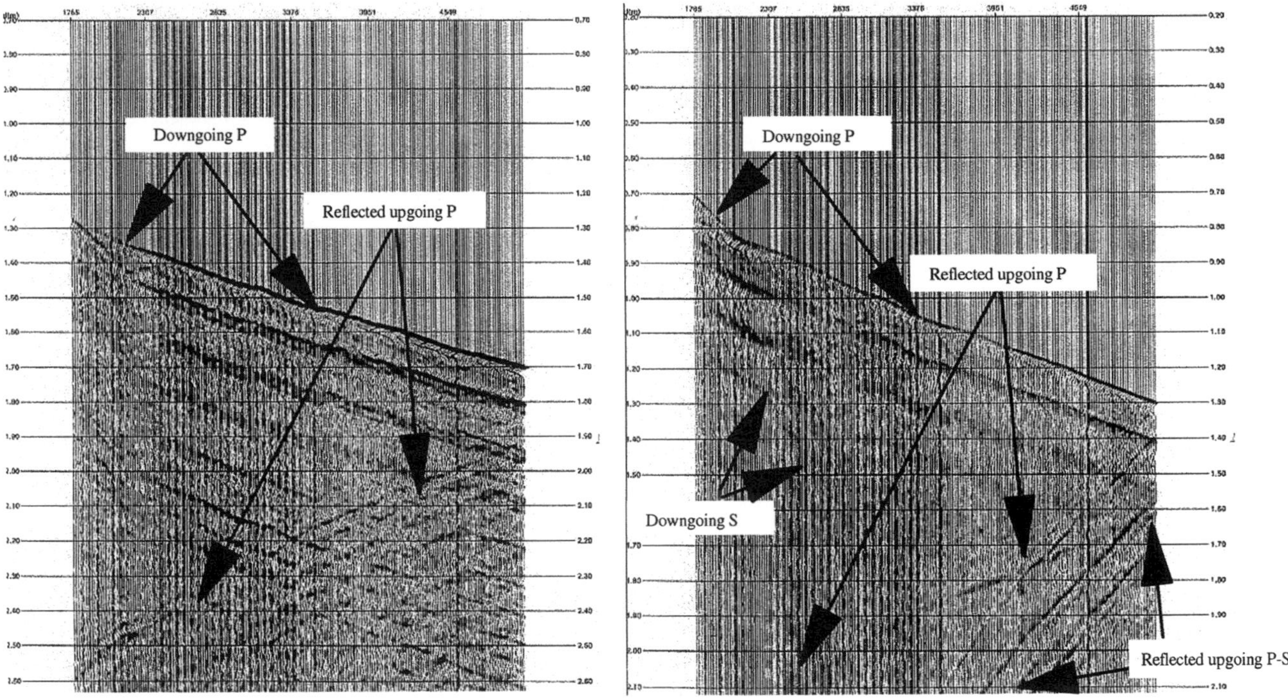

Fig. 5. Left: True Z-component displayed in a common offset gather after inserting live traces into empty cells. Right: true X-component displayed in a common offset gather after inserting live traces into empty cells.

deeper in the overburden sediments. In spite of that, S–S reflections from the reservoir horizons have not been observed in the up-going wavefields. Shear wave velocities in the overburden are as low as 600 m s^{-1} and a ratio of compressional to shear velocities (V_P/V_S) between three and four is shown in full wave form sonic measurements in well 2/4-K-3 (Fig. 6). Such low overburden velocities cause the shear wave travel time from sea bottom to top of reservoir to be greater than five seconds. Any S–S reflections from the reservoir layers arrive even later. The 2/4-K-3 three component 3D borehole profile was recorded to 7 s, which should have covered the S–S reflections. The reason for not seeing these reflections is likely to be found in the shear wave ray path geometry and the amplitude behaviour. Low shear velocities in the overburden

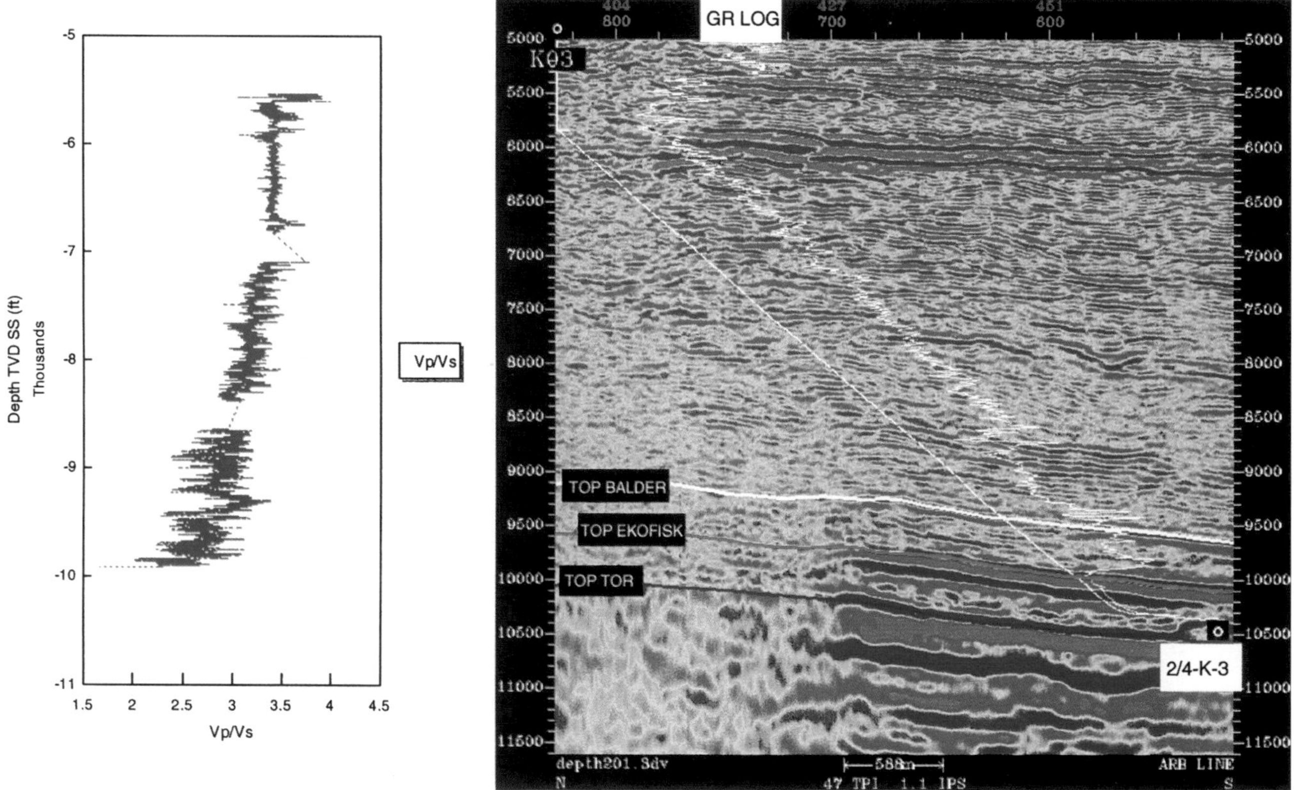

Fig. 6. Left: V_p/V_s ratio derived form full wave-form sonic logging in well 2/4-K-3. The logged depths range from −5000 ft in overburden down to top of the reservoir at −10 000 ft. Right: seismic depth section covering the logging interval with gamma ray log superimposed.

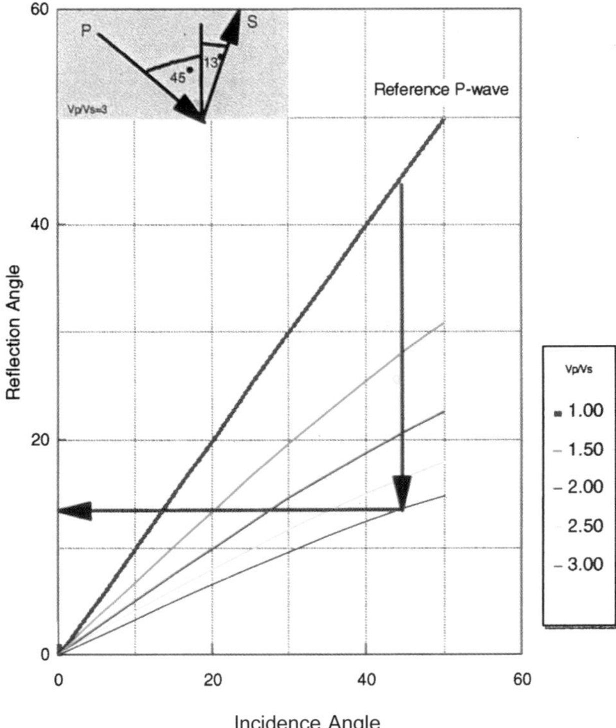

Fig. 7. Reflection and transmission angles as a function of V_p/V_s ratio. Constant ray parameter is used for every V_p/V_s value.

sediments cause the ray paths of P- to S-converted waves to be transmitted or reflected with angles close to vertical, following Snell's law. Figure 7 displays this relationship as a function of compressional and shear velocities (V_p/V_s). A compressional wave incident at an angle of 45° will, in a medium with V_p/V_s ratio of 3, generate a shear wave with reflection angle of 13°. Geometrically, that means only very short offsets will generate S–S reflections that can arrive at the wellbore geophones. In addition, S-waves generated by nearly vertically incident P angles have very low amplitude since the Zoepperitz equation has zero amplitude for converted S at zero offset and vertical incidence. Any recordable S–S signal will be weak and have limited reflection apertures around the wellbore.

Deconvolution

Significant signature variations were detected in the data (Fig. 8). A solution to this problem was provided by incorporating designature as a part of the VSP deconvolution processing. A downgoing P-wavefield with all signature variations maintained was separated from the dataset using a combination of long and short median filters and wave mode separation techniques. This vertical seismic profile (VSP) deconvolution design using the downgoing P-wavefield with all signature variations preserved is now applied by the processors as a standard VSP deconvolution procedure. Figure 9 displays the up-going P wavefield before and after VSP deconvolution. The sea bottom multiples have been removed effectively and the signature has been corrected

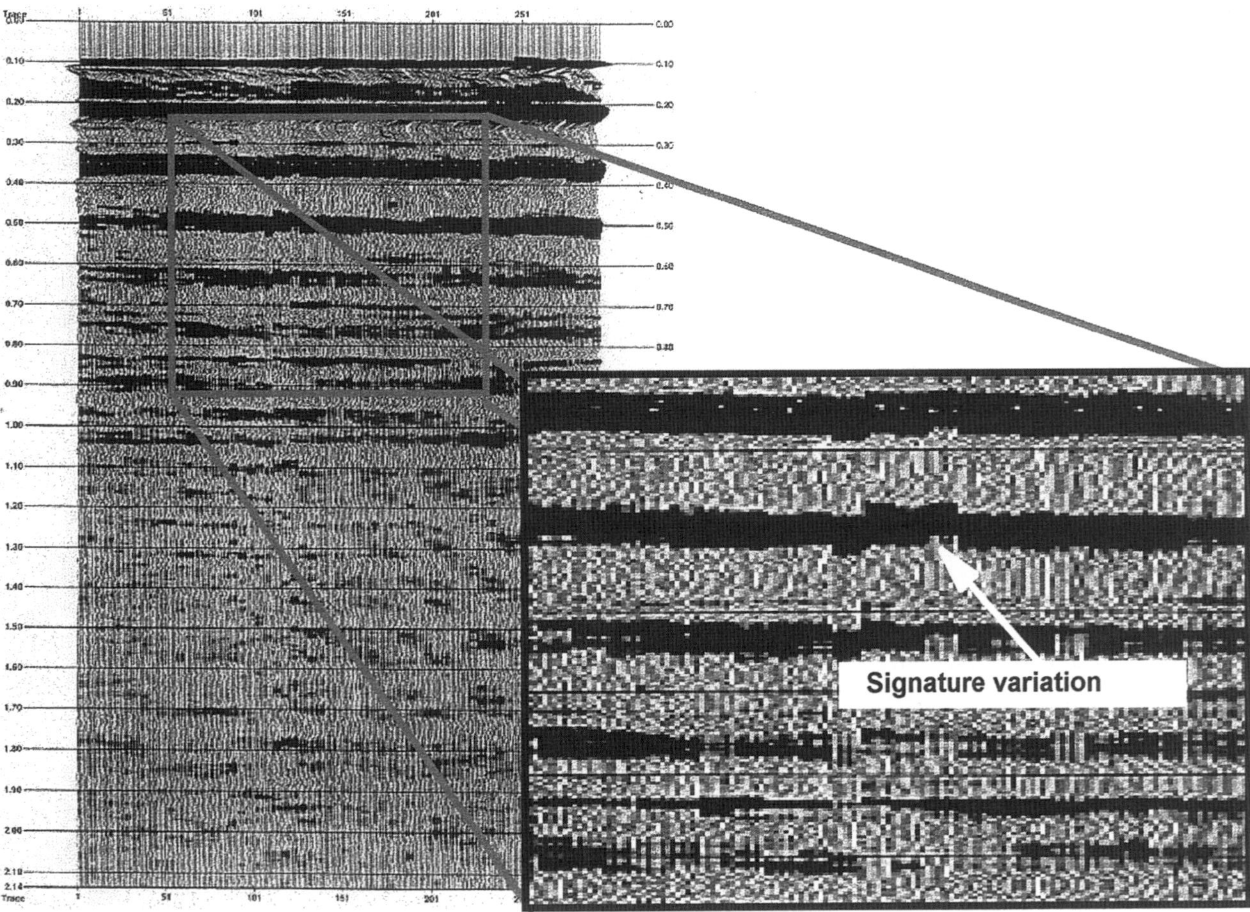

Fig. 8. Radial components of final unconvolved down-going wavefield in a common slowness gather display. Signature variability is clearly seen.

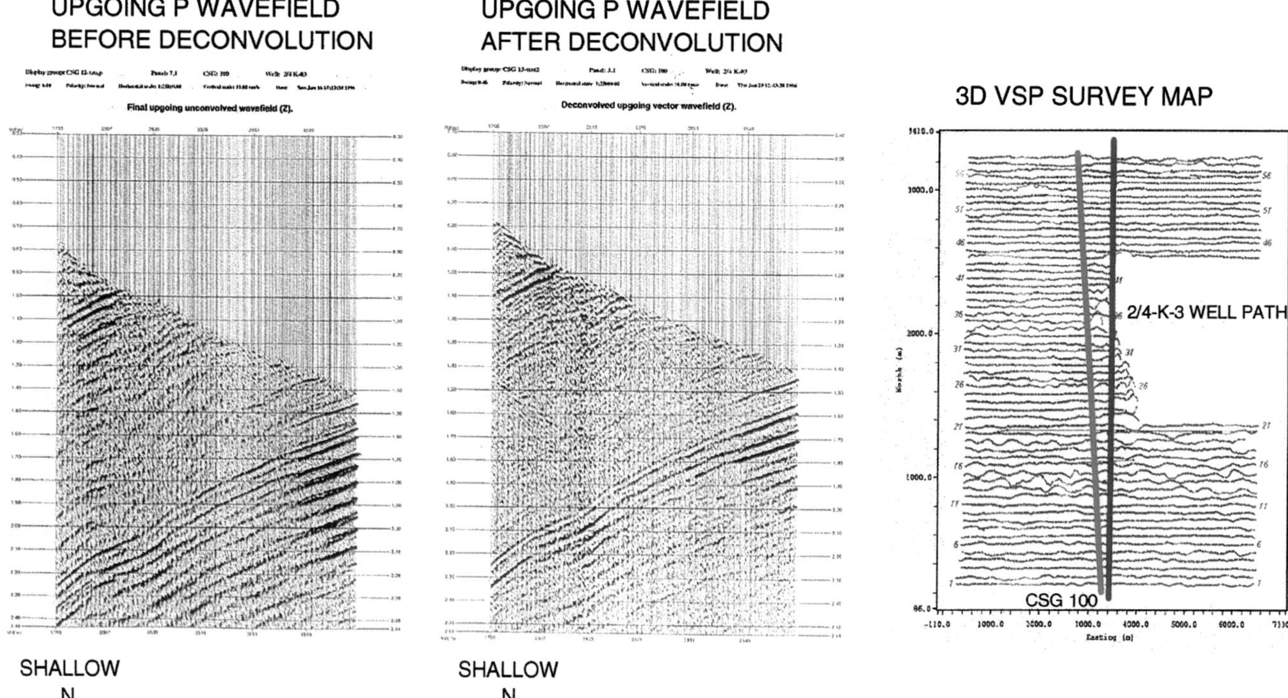

Fig. 9. Common slowness gathers displaying the up-going P wavefield before and after deconvolution. The map displays the shot lines in black, the projection of 2/4-K-3 well path in red. Since a common slowness gather cannot be displayed as a line, the blue line is only indicating where the data belongs.

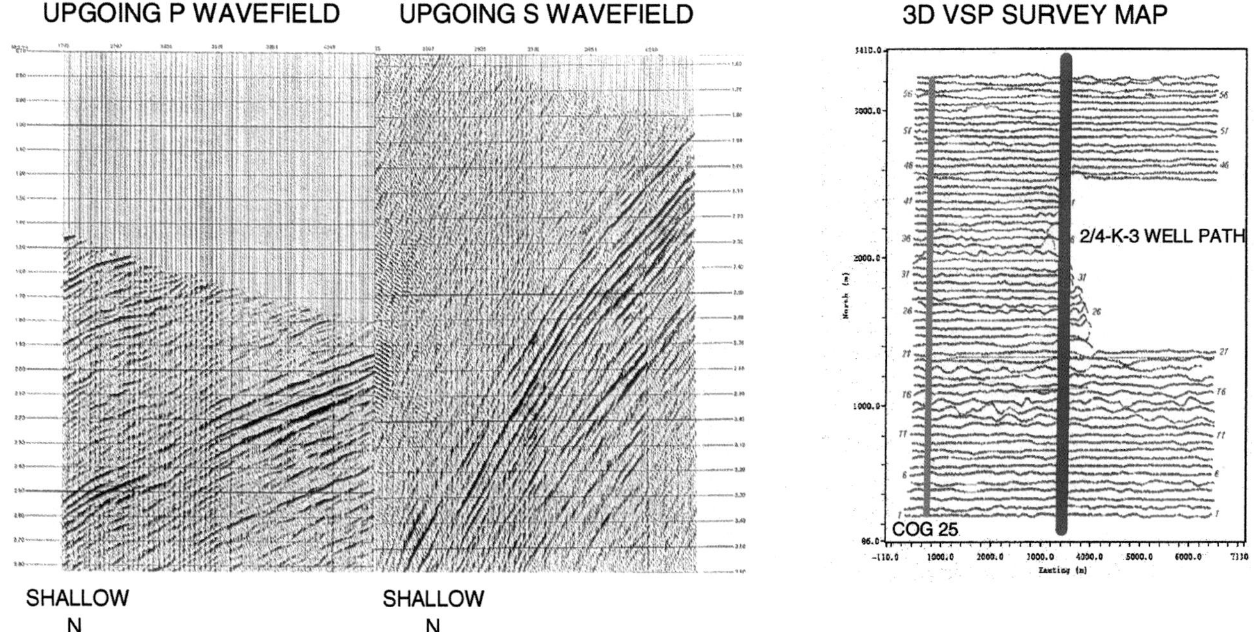

Fig. 10. Common offset gathers displaying the upgoing residual P and S wavefields after wavefield separation. The map displays the shot lines in black, the projection of 2/4-K-3 well path in red. The position of the common offset gather is a blue line.

properly. After deconvolution the data were separated in upgoing P- and S-wavefields (Fig. 10).

Preliminary imaging of the two wavefields was performed as a simple VSP/CMP (common midpoint) transformation. The resulting VSP/CMP transformed data are seen in Fig. 11. These compressional and shear wave reflections were recorded within the area obscured by gas effects in surface seismic data.

Modelling results

Two-dimensional modelling was conducted to evaluate the processing results. The results were complicated by the Tight Zone between the productive Tor and Ekofisk reservoirs. The Tight Zone has significantly higher velocities and densities than the surrounding reservoir zones. Such a high impedance tight layer further complicates the interpretation of the shear wave generated image.

Figure 12 displays the 2D model used for this modelling. Modelling results of the reflected P and the converted P–S are shown in Figs 13 through 21. The amplitude of S reflections as a function of offset (Amplitude versus offset; AVO) displays a low-amplitude non-linear behaviour and critical reflection angles occur at significantly smaller angles than for P reflections. AVO effects seem to have a severe impact on

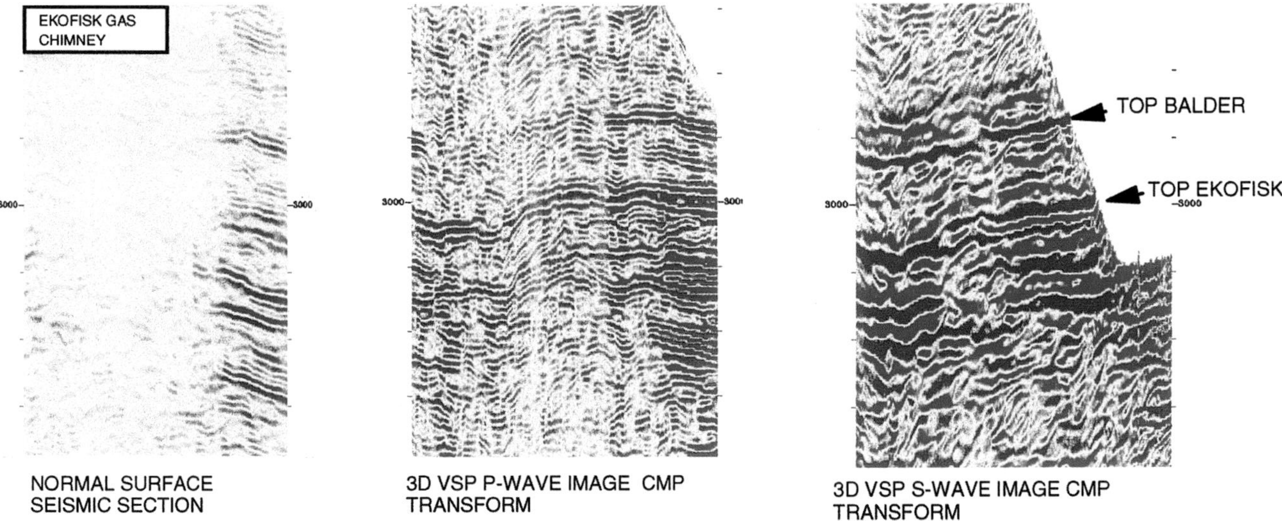

Fig. 11. Display of surface seismic, VSP/CMP transformed reflected P and S wavefields along the same profile.

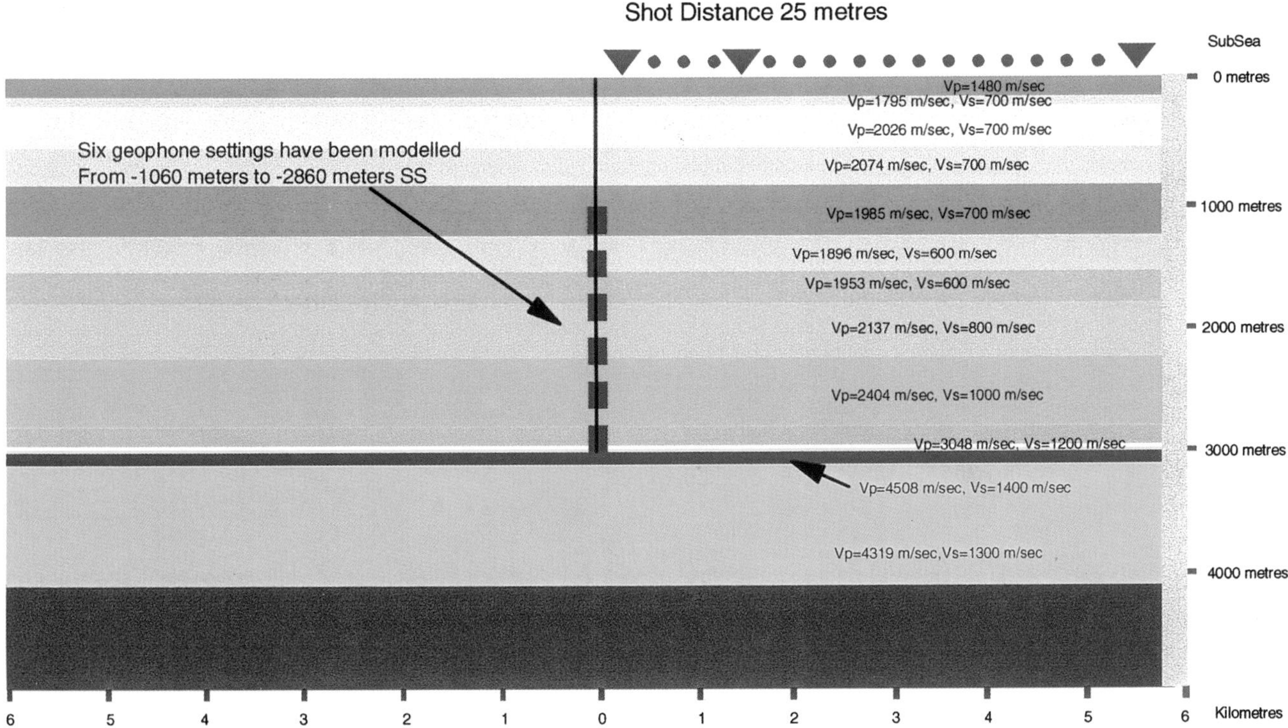

Fig. 12. Two-dimensional model used in the P- and S-wavefield modelling.

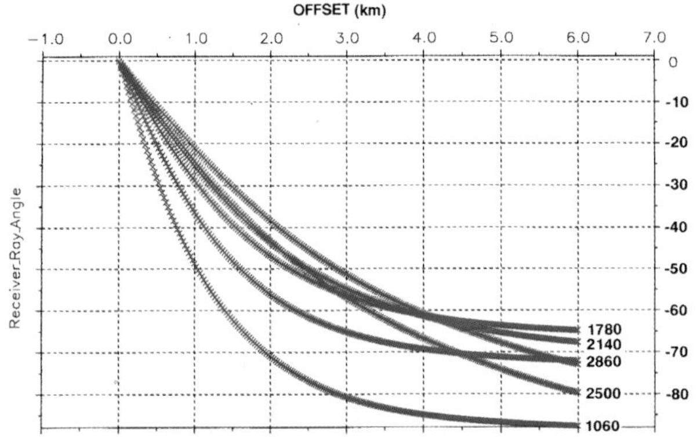

Fig. 13. Modelling results displaying the direct P receiver angles as a function of offset and receiver depth.

amplitudes throughout all offset ranges, which complicates any straightforward horizon interpretation of the shear reflection data. One way to minimize the shear wave modulation is to have a survey design which has constant incident angles. The most recent 3D borehole profile survey was designed as a circle survey around a vertical well in the centre of the Ekofisk Field. The angle of incidence is kept constant by increasing the offset every time the geophone array is moved up the well. S and P data will, as a result of this design, have nearly constant AVO effect, which should make shear wave interpretation of such a 3D dataset much easier.

Conclusions

Three-dimensional borehole profiling can be used to undershoot and shoot through gas-affected overburden in the Ekofisk Field. Three-dimensional processing of the three

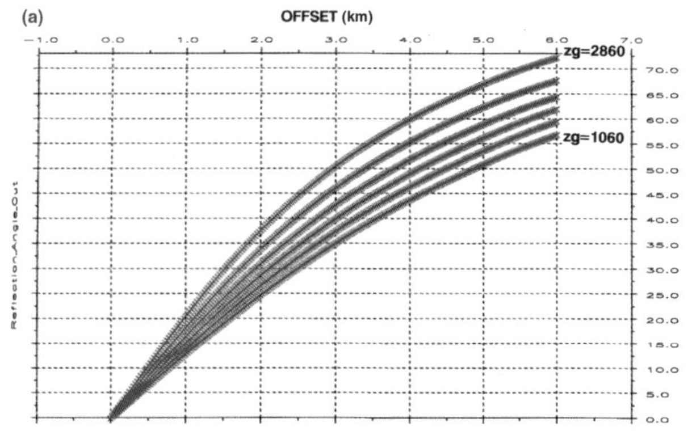

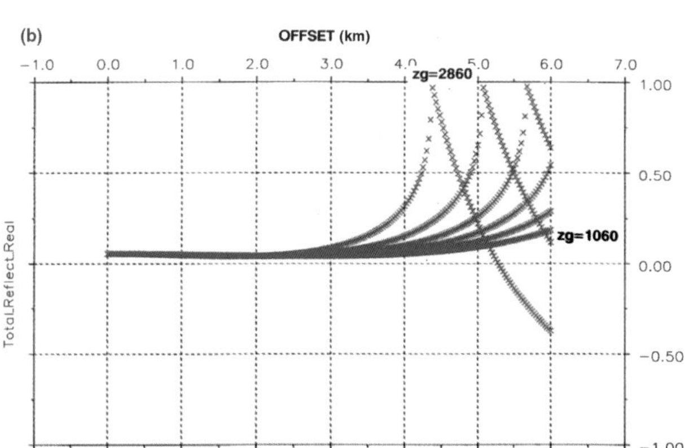

Fig. 14. Top: P–P reflection angle as function of source–receiver offset at Top Balder. Bottom: P–P reflection coefficient as function of source–receiver offset at Top Balder.

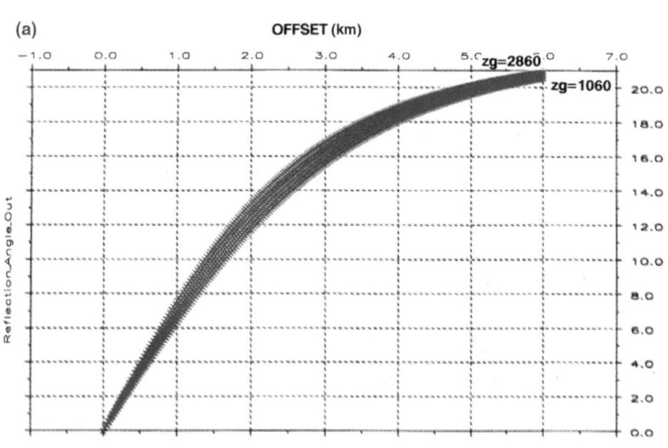

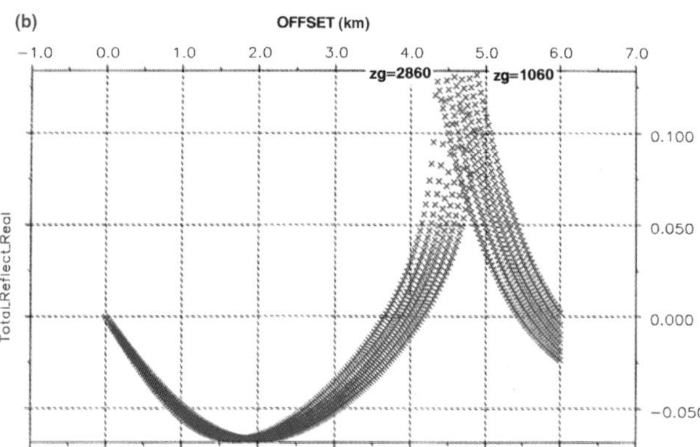

Fig. 15. Top: P–S reflection angle as function of source–receiver offset at Top Balder. Bottom: P–S reflection coefficient as function of source–receiver offset at Top Balder.

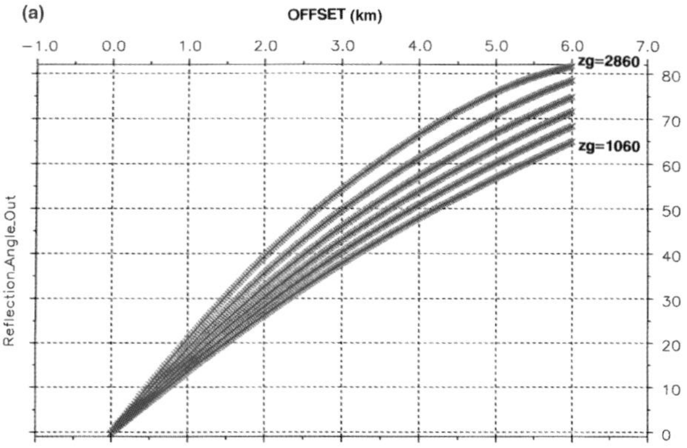

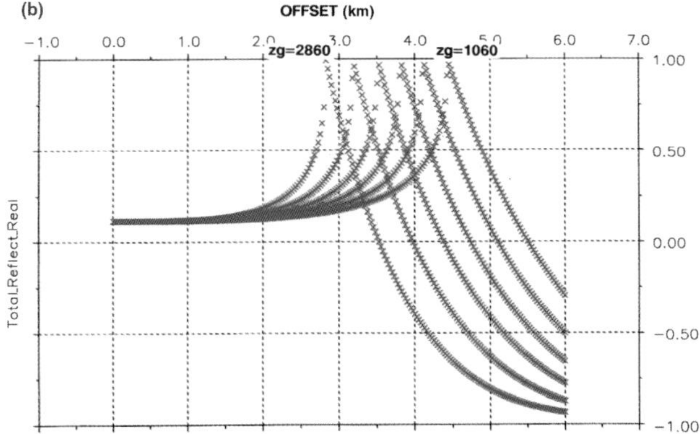

Fig. 16. Top: P–P reflection angle as function of source–receiver offset at Top Ekofisk. Bottom: P–P reflection coefficient as function of source–receiver offset at Top Ekofisk.

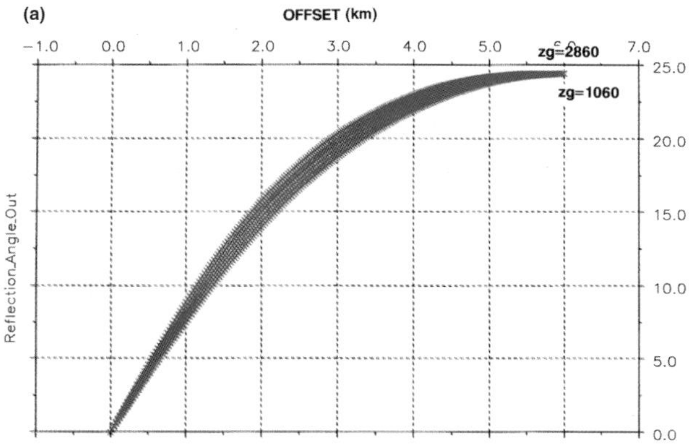

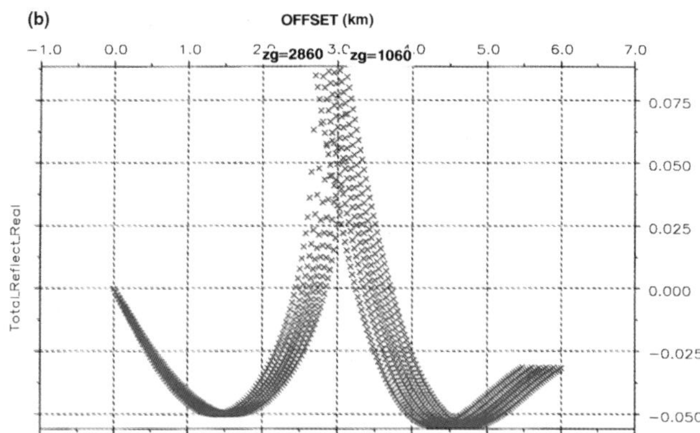

Fig. 17. Top: P–S reflection angle as function of source–receiver offset at Top Ekofisk. Bottom: P–S reflection coefficient as function of source–receiver offset at Top Ekofisk.

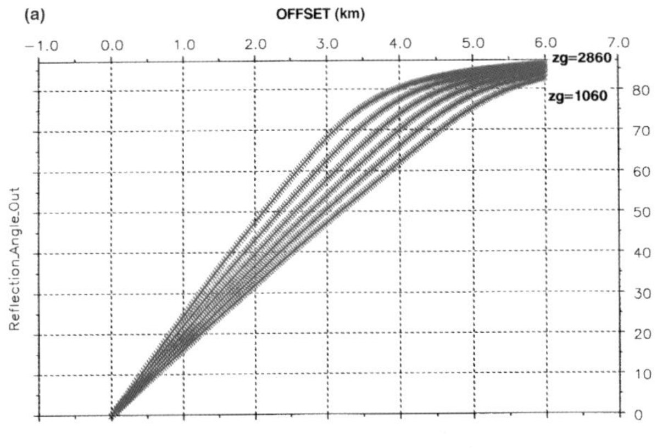

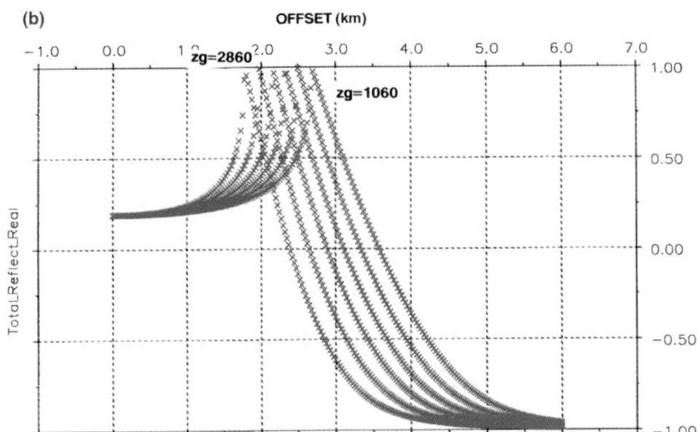

Fig. 18. Top: P–P reflection angle as function of source–receiver offset at Top of the Ekofisk Tight Zone. Bottom: P–P reflection coefficient as function of source–receiver offset at Top of the Ekofisk Tight Zone.

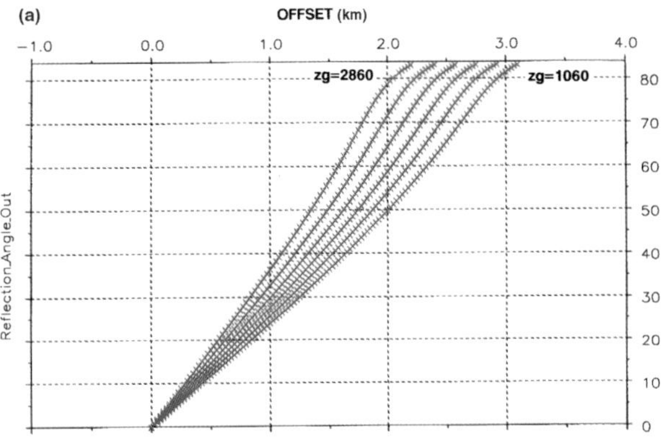

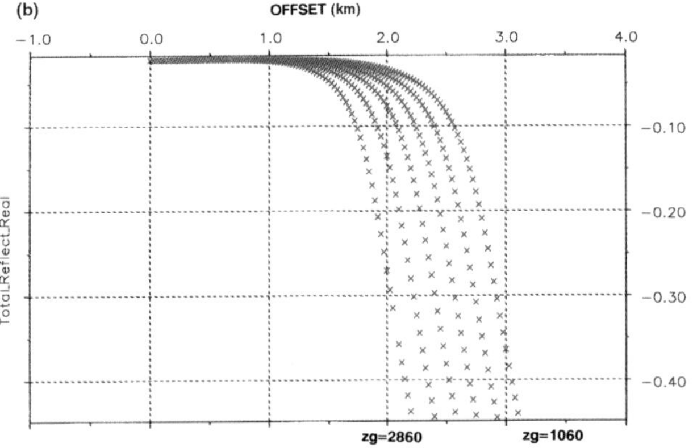

Fig. 20. Top: P–P reflection angle as function of source–receiver offset at Top Tor. Bottom: P–P reflection coefficient as function of source–receiver offset at Top Tor.

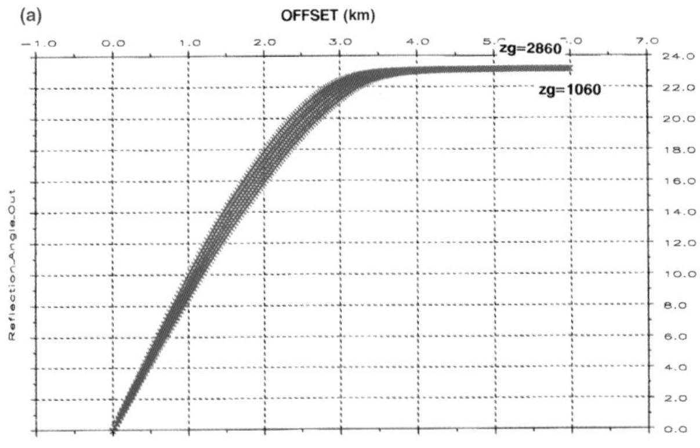

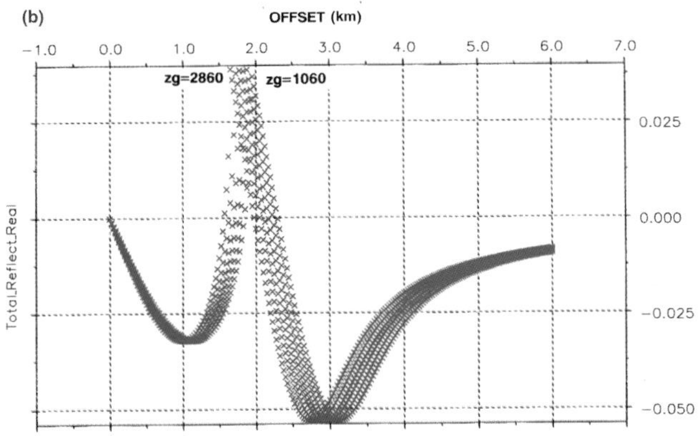

Fig. 19. Top: P–S reflection angle as function of source–receiver offset at Top of the Ekofisk Tight Zone. Bottom: P–S reflection coefficient as function of source–receiver offset at Top of the Ekofisk Tight Zone.

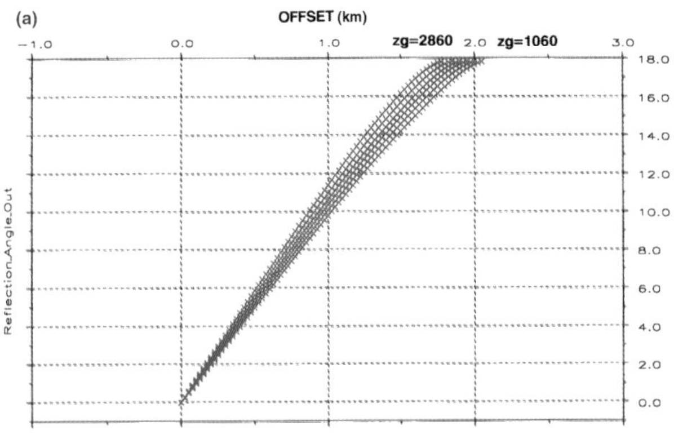

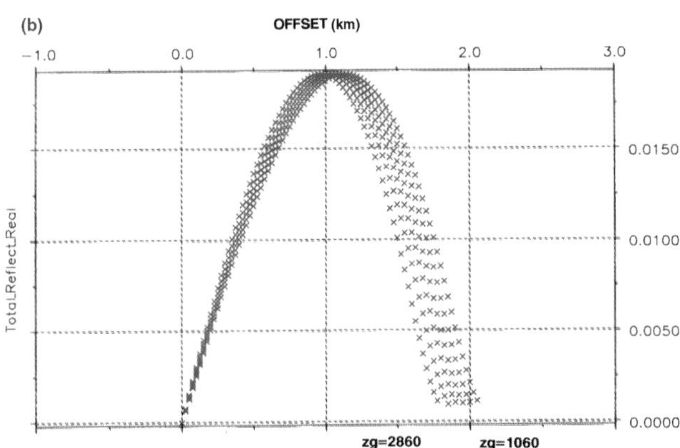

Fig. 21. Top: P–S reflection angle as function of source–receiver offset at Top Tor. Bottom: P–S reflection coefficient as function of source–receiver offset at Top Tor.

component 3D borehole profile acquired in well 2/4-K-3 has resulted in successful separation of both P and P–S up-going and down-going wavefields. These data have, together with full wave form sonic data and forward modelling, indicated that reflected P–S wavefields have associated amplitude modulations within nearly all offsets ranges, and have limited aperture around the well bore before critical reflections are reached. P-wave reflections have a much bigger offset range with stable amplitudes, which is the reason for the great success of conventional marine seismic streamer surveys. The absence of S–S wave generated reservoir reflections is most likely caused by the fact that S waves have close to vertical ray paths in the overburden with low shear velocities. Strong S amplitude modulations and the fact that shear amplitudes are an order or two lower than P reflection amplitudes may be another reason for not observing the S–S reflections.

There remains the challenge of properly depth migrating the acquired data. Successful migration demands a detailed overburden velocity model which reflects the variability in overburden gas content. Such a velocity estimation program is underway. First and reflected arrivals from the 3D borehole profiles are being used in tomographic inversion to build a detailed velocity model.

The author acknowledges permission to publish this paper from Phillips Petroleum Company Norway and Coventurers, including Fina Exploration Norway S.C.A., Norsk Agip A/S, Elf Petroleum Norges A.S, Det Norske Stats Oljeselskap a.s, Elf Rex Norge A/S and Saga Petroleum a.s.

References

DANGERFIELD, J. & BROWN, D. A. 1987. The Ekofisk Field. *In*: KLEPPE, J. *et al. North Sea Oil & Gas Reservoirs*. The Norwegian Institute of Technology. Graham & Trotman, London, 3–22.

DANGERFIELD, J. 1991. Shallow 3-D Borehole Profile at Ekofisk Field. *American Association of Petroleum Geologists*, Memoirs, **42**, 3rd Edition, 271–279.

Rock physics and quantitative wavelet estimation for seismic interpretation: Tertiary North Sea

R. W. SIMM,[1] S. XU[2] and R. E. WHITE[2]

[1] *Enterprise Oil plc, Grand Buildings, Trafalgar Square, London WC2N 5EJ, UK*
Present address: Rock Physics Associates Ltd, 3 Roundwood Gardens, Harpenden, Herts AL5 3AJ, UK (e-mail: rob.simm@rockphysassoc.demon.co.uk)
[2] *Birkbeck College, Malet Street, London WC1E, UK*

Abstract: A case study from the Tertiary of the North Sea is presented in which a well tie is improved through the application of zero offset processing and well log velocity prediction. The well ties are quantified using the techniques of White (1980, Partial coherence matching of synthetic seismograms with seismic traces. *Geophysical Prospecting*, **28**, 333–358) and Walden & White (1984, On the errors of fit and accuracy in matching synthetic seismograms and seismic traces. *Geophysical Prospecting*, **32**, 871–891) and log conditioning employs the Xu–White sand/clay velocity model (Xu, S. & White, R. E. 1995. A new velocity model for clay–sand mixtures. *Geophysical Prospecting*, **43**, 91–118; Xu, S. & White, R. E. 1996. A physical model for shear-wave velocity prediction. *Geophysical Prospecting*, **44**, 687–717). A well tie of a migrated stack section to a zero offset synthetic, produced with minimal data conditioning, gave a poor tie and event identification was in doubt. Additional data conditioning improved the tie dramatically (from 43% to 72% energy predicted and a reduction in phase error on the wavelet estimation from >20° to <10°). These enhancements in the well tie are important in justifying decisions to perform wavelet deconvolution, zero phasing or seismic trace inversion to acoustic impedance as well as correctly identifying the top reservoir reflection. This study also demonstrates that detailed log conditioning is crucial in this area to predict a diagnostic AVO (amplitude variation with offset) response related to the presence of hydrocarbons.

This study uses a Tertiary example from the North Sea to illustrate the importance of data conditioning (both log and seismic) not only to achieve good well ties which enhance the confidence in seismic interpretation but also to enable recognition of subtle hydrocarbon indicators.

It is common practice to perform well ties by visual matching of synthetics to seismic data. Traditionally, the synthetic has been created by convolving the log-derived reflection series with an idealized wavelet of similar bandwidth and phase to that posted on the seismic section side label. This technique has resulted in a large degree of ambiguity. It is often not possible to distinguish whether the best tie is made using normal polarity minimum phase synthetics with minimal time shift or time shifted reverse polarity zero phase synthetics. Without adequate quantitative measures of phase, polarity and timing of the seismic wavelet there will always be this ambiguity with an associated uncertainty in the seismic interpretation.

Two important factors impact the accuracy of well ties in this area of the Tertiary in the North Sea. The first is that the impedances of sands and shales are quite similar (particularly where the sand is saturated with medium grade oil and a reasonable component of dissolved gas) and the second is that zero offset synthetics are very sensitive to small changes in impedance. Log conditioning, not only in terms of applying the standard borehole and tool corrections but also corrections for invasion, is very important. The second factor is the effect of amplitude variation with offset (AVO). There is a subtle (Class II, Rutherford & Williams 1989) AVO effect which comprises a low amplitude intercept at zero offset and a phase reversal with offset. This has the effect of significantly reducing the amplitude on the migrated stack compared to the normal incidence trace. This study demonstrates that matching a normal incidence synthetic to the migrated stack data is, in this area, inappropriate. These subtle AVO effects are difficult to detect as they have a similar appearance to residual moveout on NMO (normal move out) corrected gathers. Reliable forward modelling evidence is crucial for their recognition.

Well tie methodology

This study tracks the accuracy of a well tie in a Tertiary sequence as different processes are applied to the data. The approach to quantifying well ties followed here is that published by White (1980) and Walden & White (1984), in which well logs are used together with a least squares fitting technique to derive a wavelet from seismic data and a statistical description of the goodness-of-fit and accuracy of the tie. The strength of this method is that it is pragmatic (requires no assumption concerning phase), quantitative (gives measures of accuracy that can be used to evaluate, for example, the basis of zero phasing or seismic inversion) and is interpretation-oriented (it makes sense of what is found in the borehole in terms of the seismic response). The working philosophy is one of starting simply with the primaries-only synthetic and adding other components (such as surface multiples) as needed to evaluate the effect on the tie.

Initial well ties

The data comprise a 2D sail line (from a 3D survey) through a well with a full suite of logs (including a shear wave log handpicked from monopole array sonic waveforms). Coherence analysis showed that both the seismic data have high signal to noise ratios (in excess of 10 dB) and a broad bandwidth (10–70 Hz). The data were initially processed through to migrated stack in the following sequence:

SIMM, R. W., XU, S. & WHITE, R. E. 1999. Rock physics and quantitative wavelet estimation for seismic interpretation: Tertiary North Sea. *In*: FLEET, A. J. & BOLDY, S. A. R. (eds) *Petroleum Geology of Northwest Europe: Proceedings of the 5th Conference*, 1265–1270.

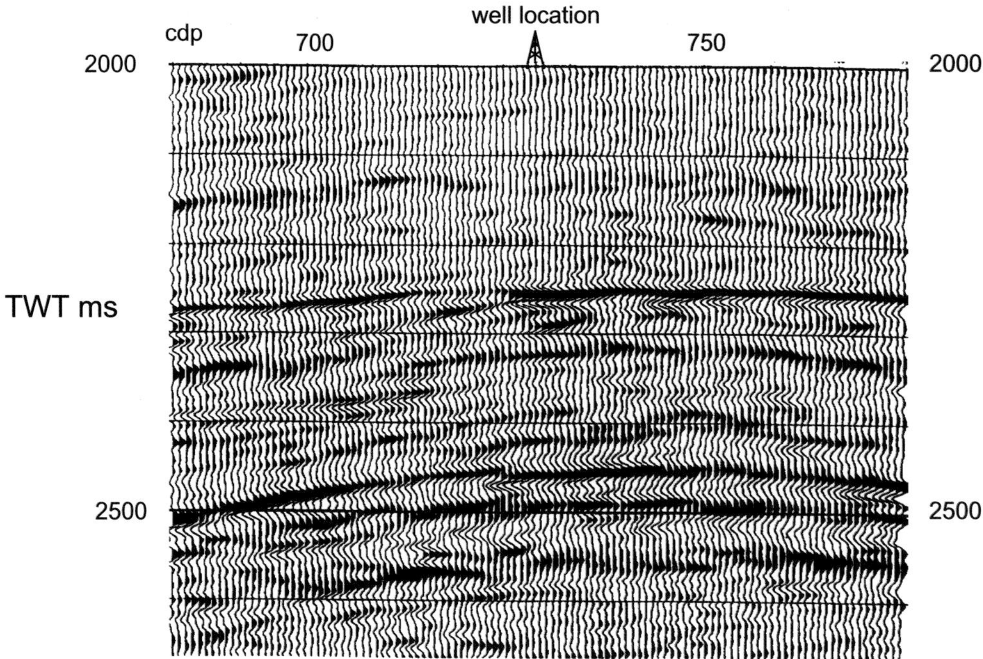

Fig. 1. Initial migrated stack section.

(1) Pre-processing (designature, edit, predictive deconvolution, mute);
(2) Velocity anlaysis;
(3) DMO (dip moveout);
(4) Pre stack time migration (with single velocity function);
(5) Multiple attenuation;
(6) Velocity analysis;
(7) NMO (normal moveout);
(8) Full offset stack;
(9) Inverse migration;
(10) Post stack migration (with laterally varying velocity function).

Figure 1 illustrates the initial migrated stack section through the well location. The top of the reservoir is around 2310 ms. Standard environmental corrections were applied to the logs. An erroneous portion of log (above the reservoir) was edited using straight line interpolation between good data segments. The sonic log was calibrated using a minimum number of linear drift lines with knee points located at major breaks in the sonic log.

Matching of the reflectivity series to the seismic data was done over two time gates; a shallow zone from 750 ms to 1250 ms and a deeper zone from 1850 to 2350 ms. Inputs to this process are the seismic data, a specified time gate (not less than 500 ms) and a wavelet length (ms TWT; two way time). A good tie is a compromise between the wavelet length (any synthetic can be matched to seismic by using unrealistically long wavelets), the frequency of the estimated wavelet and the goodness-of-fit and accuracy of the match. The data are scanned for the best match location. Outputs that describe the match include:

(1) B – statistical bandwidth (Hz) of the seismic data;
(2) b – analysis bandwidth (Hz) (a smoothing parameter, directly related to the wavelet length, which should be $<B/2$);
(3) T – data segment length (bT should be in the range of 5–12);
(4) PEP – percentage of energy predicted (a measure of goodness-of-fit) (where energy is calculated as the sum of squares);
(5) NMSE – normalized mean square error (a measure of accuracy) (NMSE relates to phase error in the wavelet estimation such that the standard error in phase = $(\mathrm{NMSE}/2)^{0.5}$ radians).

It was found that the initial tie at the shallow gate was good whereas the tie at the deep gate was poor. Well tie results are shown in Table 1. The shallow tie has a very low NMSE of 0.06 (equating to a phase error of $<10^\circ$) and 76% of the energy in the trace is predicted by the synthetic. In contrast, the deeper tie has an NMSE of 0.25 (equating to a phase error of $>15^\circ$) and only 43% of the seismic trace energy predicted by the synthetic (Table 1). Figure 2 shows the tie for the deep gate (tie 'deep 1' in Table 1). The figure shows the reflectivity series, the estimated wavelet, a comparison of the filtered synthetic with the seismic data from the best location, and the residual or difference trace. The time series representation of the wavelet illustrates a response to an increase in acoustic impedance. The wavelet is symmetrical with time zero located at the zero crossing between the trough and the peak. Thus, a positive reflection such as that from the top of the reservoir sands would be picked as a black peak. It was found in this study that all the estimated wavelets looked similar, yet the ties varied in their fit and accuracy. The prominent reflector at 2260 ms is the Top Balder. A comparison of the filtered synthetic trace and the seismic trace (labelled 'data segment') reveals a poor match at the top reservoir, with a prominent reflection, and on the synthetic, a low amplitude peak set in a generally low amplitude and apparently higher frequency zone of peaks and troughs on the seismic trace. Event identification on the basis of this tie is quite difficult.

Table 1. Well tie results

	Initial tie			Final tie
	Shallow	Deep 1	Deep 2	Deep
B	57.86	62.22	67	67.25
b	17.04	17.04		17.04
Bt	7.67	8.52		8.52
PEP	0.76	0.43	0.61	0.72
NMSE	0.04	0.16	0.11	0.05

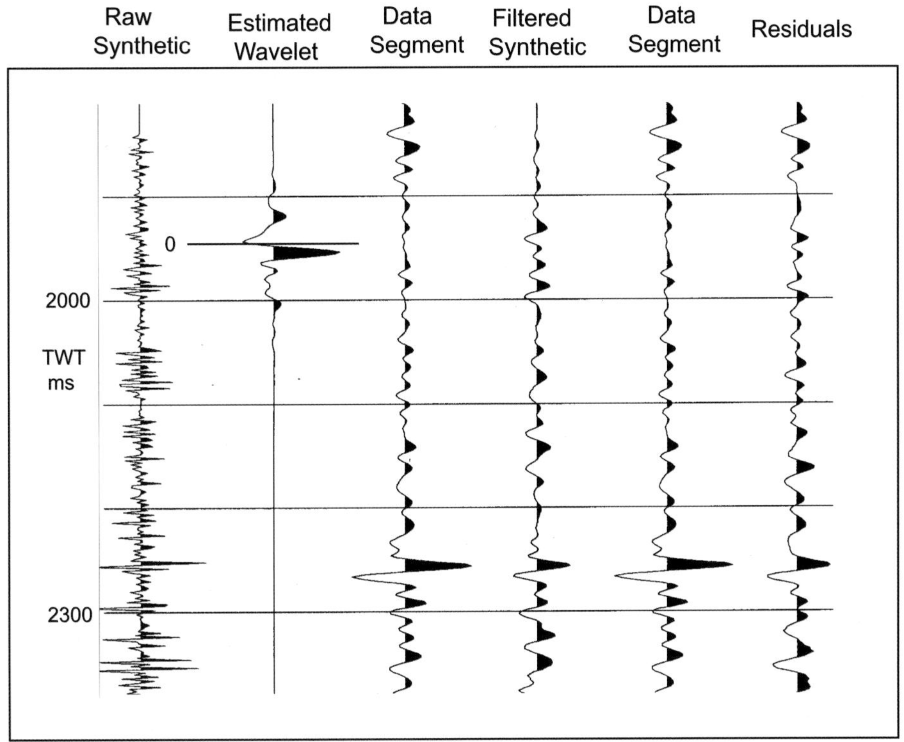

Fig. 2. Initial well tie ('deep 1') over the reservoir section, matching the zero offset synthetic to the migrated stack data. Wavelet time zero is at 1950 ms.

Improving the well tie

A first improvement to the tie was made by replacing the erroneous section above the reservoir with sonic velocities derived from a velocity model (the Xu–White sand/clay model, Xu & White 1995) (Fig. 3). This model uses petrophysical estimates of porosity, shale and water saturation, an implementation of Kuster–Toksoz theory, assumptions concerning the aspect ratios of sand-related and clay-related pores and their distributions, and Gassmans equation to predict the (low frequency) velocity over the whole continuum from sands to shales. As such it is a very useful tool for quality control of the sonic log in siliclastic sequences. The effect of replacing the erroneous sonic log above the reservoir on the well tie is to improve the tie to the migrated stack section by increasing the spectral bandwidth (B) of the estimated wavelet from

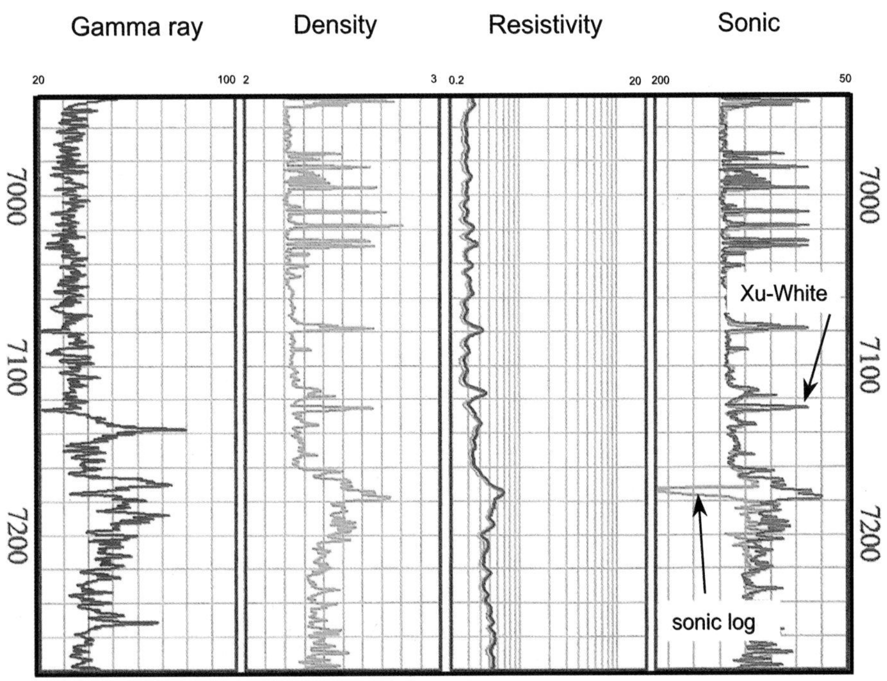

Fig. 3. An illustration of the use of the Xu–White model for sonic log QC. Note the erroneous log readings at around 7175 ft.

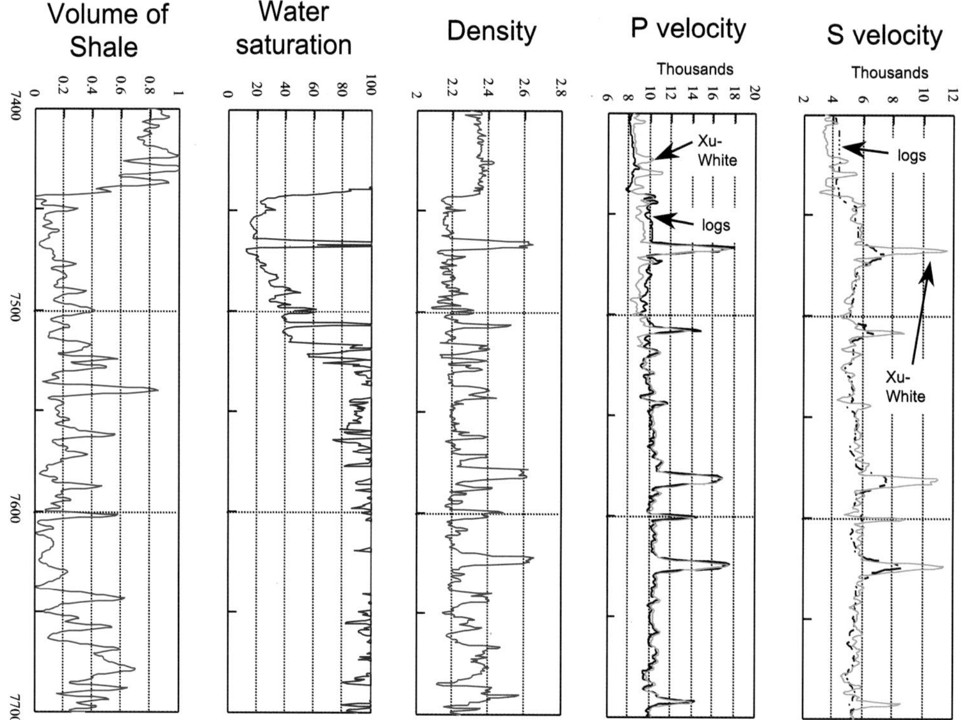

Fig. 4. Illustrating the effect of fluid substitution (using the Xu–White model) on the sonic velocity, together with the difference between predicted and log shear velocity.

62 to 67 Hz, decreasing the NMSE to 0.11 from 0.25, and increasing the proportion of predicted energy from 43% to 61% (tie 'deep 2' Table 1)

Further improvements in the tie were made by processing the seismic to zero offset and applying fluid substitution corrections to the sonic log to account for the effects of invasion. The zero offset processing was accompanied by closer attention to velocities, pre-stack migration and multiple attenuation. Fluid substitution was performed using a predicted shear velocity log and a trial and error approach to the problem of determining the 'log' fluid parameters. It is a common feature in hydrocarbon bearing zones that velocities derived from the sonic are too high, as a result of the replacement of compressible hydrocarbon with filtrate of lower compressibility. Invasion effects can also occur in the water zone, though the magnitude of the effect (sonic velocities too low) is generally less than in the hydrocarbon zone. Figure 4 illustrates that the correction for invasion is up to 10% of the measured velocity. The shear velocity prediction (using the Xu–White model, Xu & White 1996) highlights the fact that the shear wave velocities in the shales are erroneous, resulting from P-wave mud arrivals obscuring the (slower) S-wave velocity arrival of the shales

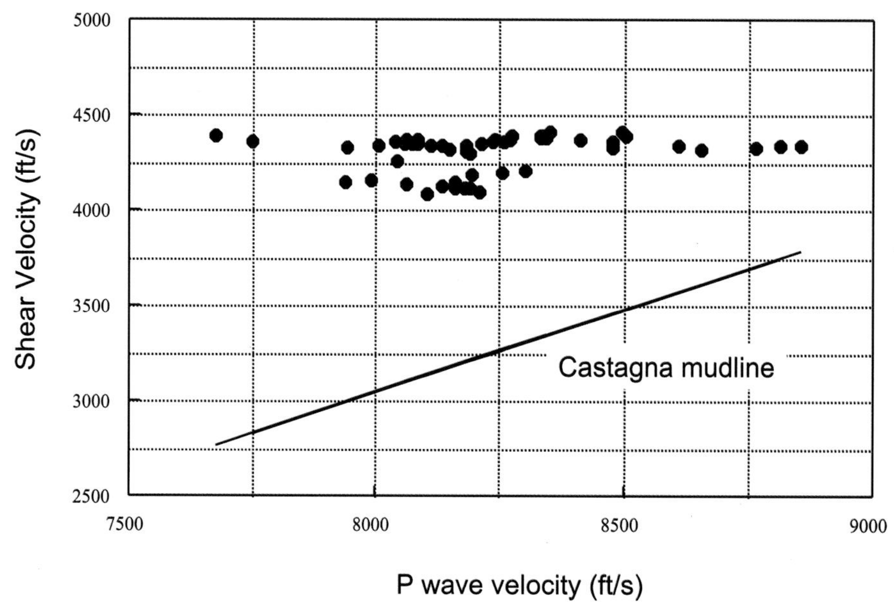

Fig. 5. V_p/V_s cross plot for shales, showing that where the shear velocity of the shales is lower than the mud wave, it is the mud wave, which is recorded by the monopole array sonic tool.

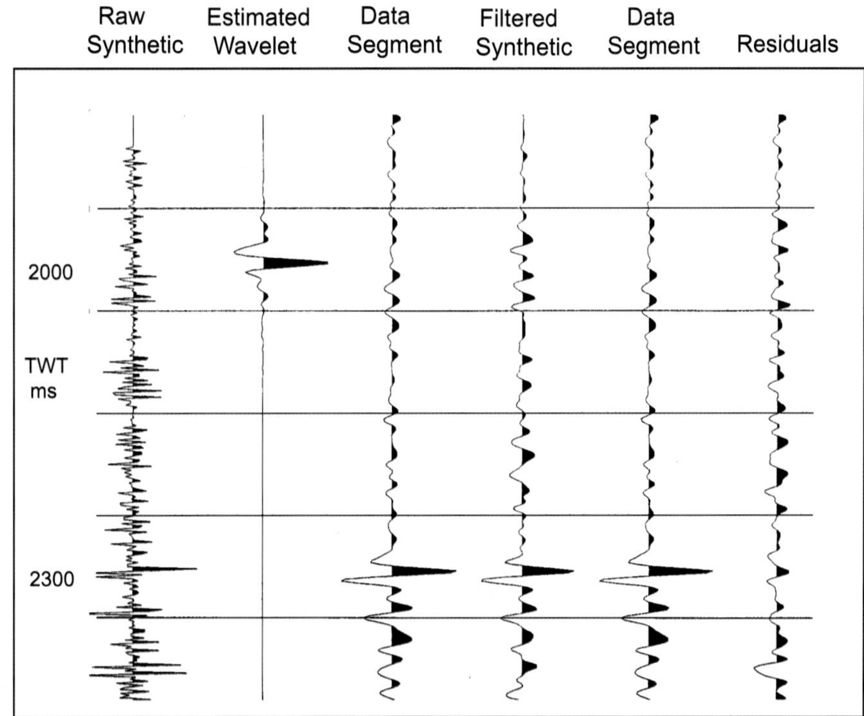

Fig. 6. Final well tie ('final deep') over the reservoir section, matching the zero offset synthetic to the zero offset seismic section. Wavelet time zero is at 1950 ms.

(Fig. 4). The effect is also illustrated in Fig. 5 where the shale velocities from the array sonic are cross-plotted, together with an empirical V_p/V_s relation for mudrocks taken from Castagna *et al.* (1985).

Table 1 shows the effect of all this data conditioning. The deep tie ('final deep' in Table 1) now has very good accuracy (an NMSE of 0.05) and a very good fit (a significant proportion (72%) of the energy is predicted by the synthetic model) and the bandwidth of the estimated wavelet is high (67 Hz). Figure 6 shows the 'final deep' well tie. The prominent reflection at 2320 ms on the synthetic, related to the top reservoir, is now matched clearly by a similar reflection, albeit with a slightly different amplitude, on the seismic trace. There is no mistaking the correct event identification in this case.

Recognizing and modelling the AVO effect

A gather from the reprocessed dataset is shown in Fig. 7. A Class II AVO effect is evident at 2320 ms, where a peak on the near traces (representing a compression) changes polarity

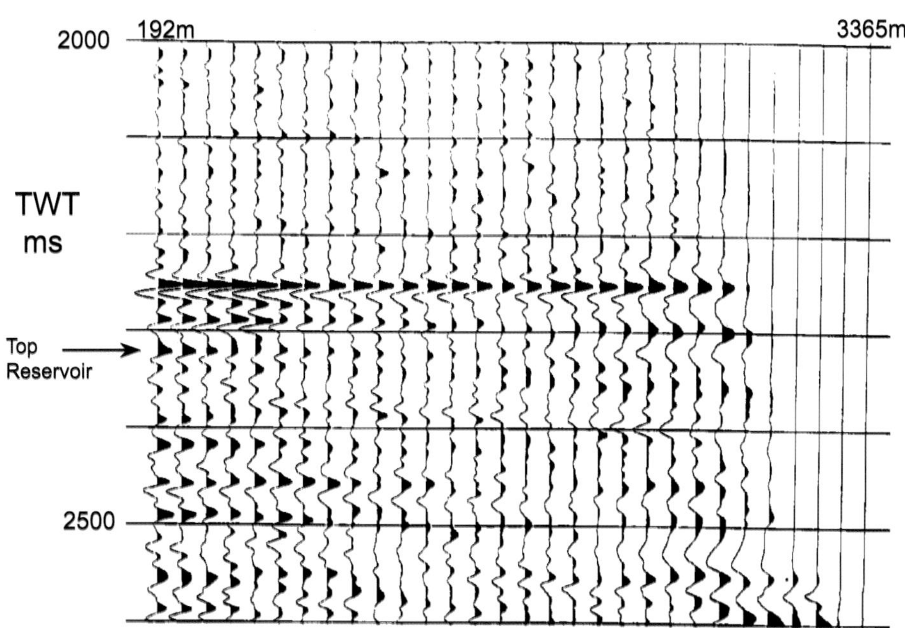

Fig. 7. Common ray point gather 735, showing a class II AVO effect at the top of the reservoir.

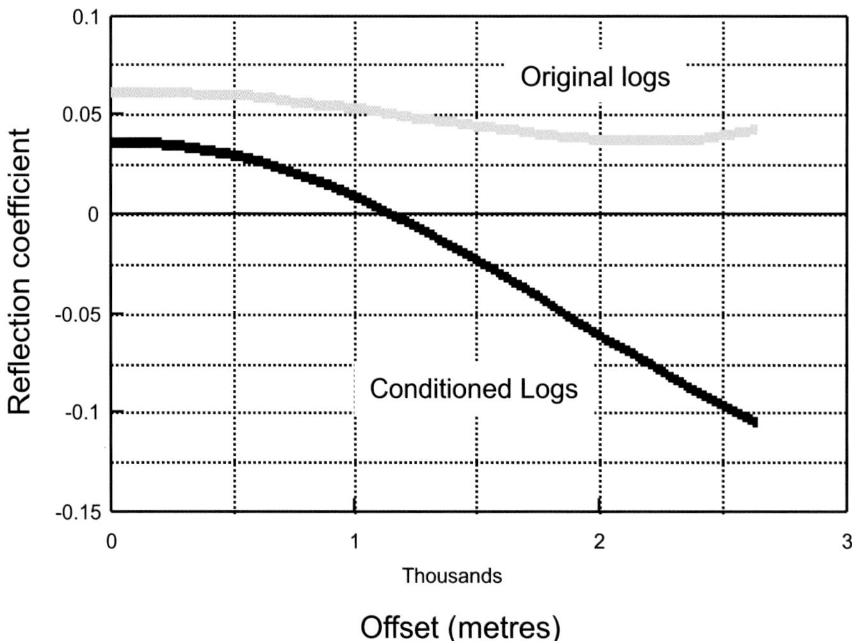

Fig. 8. AVO plot showing the effect of fluid substitution and shear wave prediction on the predicted AVO response.

with offset. This is a subtle effect and can easily be mistaken for residual NMO (normal moveout). The low amplitude normal incidence reflection is caused by the effect of hydrocarbon significantly lowering the impedance of the sands. The phase reversal occurs because there is a marked decrease in amplitude with offset, resulting from a significant contrast in Poissons ratio at the top of the reservoir. Figure 8 shows a comparison of single interface AVO models for the top reservoir reflection based on recorded velocities and density and those with corrections applied. The AVO response predicted using the raw log data is relatively flat and does not show a phase reversal with offset. In contrast, the response derived from the conditioned logs shows a lower zero offset amplitude and a steeper gradient, giving rise to a phase reversal with offset. It is quite clear that without the log conditioning, the AVO effect related to the presence of hydrocarbons would not be predicted.

Conclusions

This study has shown that the application of zero offset processing and log QC and conditioning (in the form of velocity prediction) can improve the accuracy of well ties. A tie of a migrated stack section to a zero offset synthetic, produced with minimal data conditioning, gave a poor tie, and event identification was in doubt. Additional data conditioning improved the tie dramatically (from 43% to 72% energy predicted and a reduction in phase error on the wavelet estimation from $>15°$ to $<10°$). This enhancement gives confidence in performing seismic inversion and the mapping of impedance changes related to changes in lithology and fluid. This study has also shown that detailed log conditioning is crucial in predicting a diagnostic AVO response related to the presence of hydrocarbons.

References

CASTAGNA, J. P., BATZLE, M. L. & EASTWOOD, R. L. 1985. Relationships between compressional-wave and shear-wave velocities in clastic silicate rocks. *Geophysics*, **50**, 571–581.

RUTHERFORD, S. R. & WILLIAMS, R. H. 1989. Amplitude versus offset variations in gas sands. *Geophysics*, **54**, 680–688.

WALDEN, A. T. & WHITE, R. E. 1984. On the errors of fit and accuracy in matching synthetic seismograms and seismic traces. *Geophysical Prospecting*, **32**, 871–891.

WHITE, R. E. 1980. Partial coherence matching of synthetic seismograms with seismic traces. *Geophysical Prospecting*, **28**, 333–358.

XU, S. & WHITE, R. E. 1995. A new velocity model for clay–sand mixtures. *Geophysical Prospecting*, **43**, 91–118.

—— & ——1996. A physical model for shear-wave velocity prediction. *Geophysical Prospecting*, **44**, 687–717.

Seismic inversion as a vehicle for integration of geophysical, geological and petrophysical information for reservoir characterization: some North Sea examples

J. J. M. BUITING and M. BACON

Shell UK Exploration and Production, Shell-Mex House, Strand, London WC2, UK

Abstract: Inversion of seismic trace data to acoustic impedance is an old technique which has become of greater value in the last few years as a consequence of improvements in seismic data quality. It can offer a useful pathway for inference of reservoir quality variation from seismic data, as is demonstrated by three examples from the Jurassic of the North Sea.

Seismic inversion aims to convert a reflection seismic dataset into a representation of acoustic impedance variation in the subsurface. This concept has been generally known for many years (Lindseth 1979). It has not found wide application, however, probably because it requires excellent input seismic data, with low noise levels and faithful representation of amplitudes. The general availability of high-quality modern 3D seismic data, coupled with the availability of easy-to-use commercial inversion software, has stimulated us to revisit the application of the technique to North Sea reservoirs.

Inversion has turned out to add significant value to the seismic data, for several reasons:

(1) Impedance displays are layer-oriented, unlike standard reflectivity displays which are interface oriented. This greatly simplifies interaction with geologists, petrophysicists and reservoir engineers. Although seismic interpreters are used to the mental conversion of lateral changes in reflection strength into estimates of lateral impedance changes within layers, other geoscientists often find that the need for this conversion obscures the significance of seismic information.

(2) Tuning effects are resolved, enhancing the resolution of thin beds; for example, pinch-outs can be more precisely mapped than on conventional reflectivity data.

(3) Impedance is often related to reservoir parameters such as porosity or net-to-gross ratio. The inverted dataset therefore offers a route by which seismic data can fairly directly be used to constrain reservoir models; to improve volumetric estimates, and to target wells more precisely.

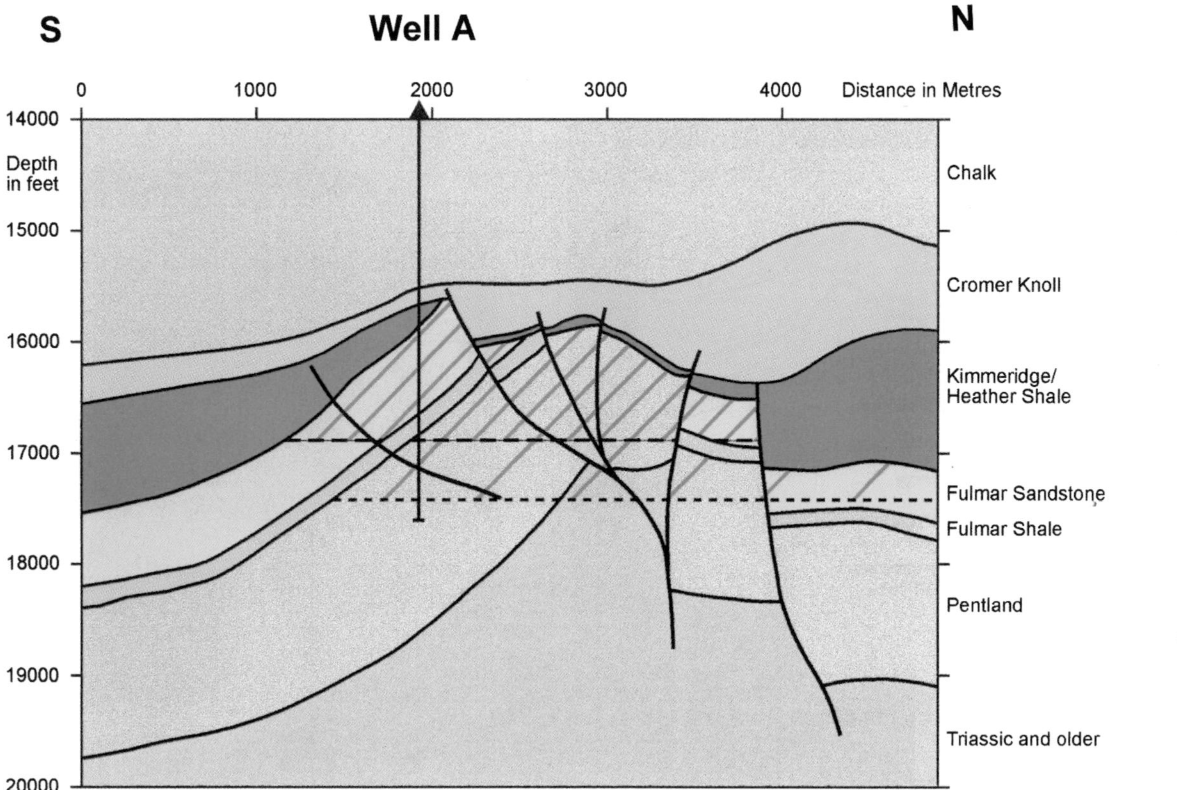

Fig. 1. Schematic cross-section through field.

BUITING, J. J. M. & BACON, M 1999. Seismic inversion as a vehicle for integration of geophysical, geological and petrophysical information for reservoir characterization: some North Sea examples. *In*: FLEET, A. J. & BOLDY, S. A. R. (eds) *Petroleum Geology of Northwest Europe: Proceedings of the 5th Conference*, 1271–1280.

(4) Inversion lends itself to stochastic approaches that allow exploration of the range of reservoir models that are consistent with the observed seismic data.

Before discussing three North Sea examples that illustrate some of these benefits, especially the two last, we briefly summarize the essential points of the inversion methodology employed.

Inversion method

A basic problem is that the seismic trace does not contain very low frequency information. The inversion process therefore has to include two steps: the reflectivity trace is transformed to a band-limited impedance trace, and the low-frequency information is then added in from another source.

The first part of this process is carried out by replacing the seismic wiggle trace by a number of reflectivity spikes; the idea is that when this train of spikes is convolved with the seismic wavelet, the wiggle trace is reconstituted. Various algorithms exist, which work by finding a train of spikes which is in some sense parsimonious (i.e. minimal number and/or size of spikes) while giving a satisfactory representation of the trace data (i.e. minimal error between actual trace and the result of convolving the spike sequence with the wavelet). Obviously, accurate estimation of the wavelet is critical; this may be estimated from the data by several means, including matching the seismic trace against well synthetics, which was the approach adopted in the following examples. The reflectivity spike series can then be integrated to give a band-limited impedance trace. In effect, this first stage has removed the effect of the wavelet present in the data, and so has performed a deconvolution. Because of this, the inverted data will have better resolution than the original trace data.

The second part of the process is to add the missing low-frequency information. In our case this was provided by a 3D 'earth model', constructed using key stratigraphic horizons and all available impedance information from well penetrations. Essentially, the well impedances were interpolated and extrapolated within macrolayers defined by a small number of interpreted horizons, which were picked on the reflectivity data using conventional manual and autotracking methods. To allow for unconformable relationships, thickness variations between and around wells could be accommodated by thickening or thinning of a layer from the base or top, as well as the obvious conformable stretching or squeezing. Model construction can be problematic if the distribution of wells is not random; since wells are drilled primarily for economic objectives, they tend to be found primarily on structural crests. To account for known changes of impedance with depth, it may then be necessary to introduce artificial wells in synclines.

Merging of the results of the two parts of the process is then carried out, using filters such that higher-frequency data (e.g. above 5 Hz) is derived from the first part, i.e. from the seismic traces, and lower-frequency data from the second part.

An additional refinement is to adopt a stochastic approach. The principles of this type of inversion have been discussed by Haas & Dubrule (1994). Briefly, the technique of cokriging allows the combination of seismic and well impedance estimates to produce a maximum-likelihood estimation of impedance variation in a subsurface volume, honouring the 3D statistical correlation properties of both datasets. However, the result is a smoothed model of the subsurface, which does not represent the likely spatial variability of impedance in the real

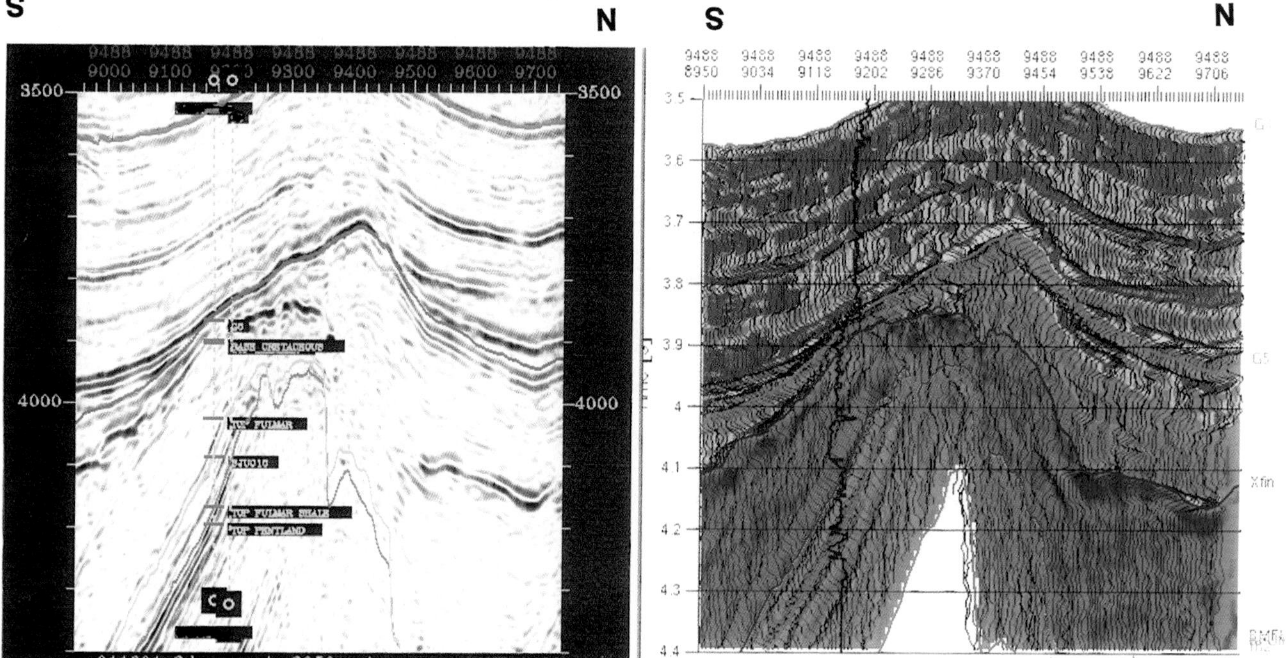

Fig. 2. Seismic reflectivity and corresponding acoustic impedance section. Here and in other figures, the polarity convention is as follows: for reflectivity, a red loop corresponds to an increase in acoustic impedance with depth, a blue loop to a decrease; for impedance, red is hard (high impedance) and blue is soft (low impedance). The picked horizon marked in purple on the impedance section is an event within the Fulmar sandstone reservoir, about 60 ms below its top; the horizon marked Xfin is the picked Base Cretaceous.

subsurface. This is an important issue for simulation of the flow of fluids within the reservoir, whose behaviour may be dominated by the very heterogeneities that are absent from the smoothed model. Therefore, it is useful to employ stochastic techniques, which construct a family of models of subsurface impedance; in essence, the idea is to assign an impedance value to successive subsurface points based on random selection from a probability distribution which is built up from the seismic and well information, together with values previously assigned to other subsurface points. The order in which subsurface points are selected for estimation (the path through the dataset) is itself random. In this way a large family of models can be constructed, allowing exploration of the range of subsurface models that are compatible with the seismic and well data.

To illustrate some of these points, there now follow three examples of the application of these techniques.

Example 1

Seismic and well data were used in an inversion study of a gas-condensate accumulation (Fig. 1) in the Upper Jurassic Fulmar sandstone in the Central North Sea. The objective was the prediction of lateral variations in reservoir quality. This is a geological setting in which conventional approaches through measurement of seismic amplitudes have had limited success, probably because of variability in the overlying shales. Data from four wells were used to build the low-frequency earth model, which was further constrained by artificial impedance profiles calculated from seismic velocities in the area remote from well control. Two cross-sections (Fig. 2) demonstrate the reflectivity data and the derived impedance dataset. On the impedance section the hard Chalk (red zone above the G5 marker) is well expressed, as is the very soft Kimmeridge Clay (dark blue zone below the Xfin marker). The top of the Fulmar reservoir is some 60 ms above the purple intra-Fulmar marker, and is quite easily picked on the impedance data.

Acoustic impedance values for the upper sandstone unit (above the purple marker) were extracted from the inverted dataset and converted to porosity using a linear relationship between core porosity and acoustic impedance, based on the four wells within the study area, as shown in Fig. 3. Note that the effect of porefill on impedance is in this case rather small;

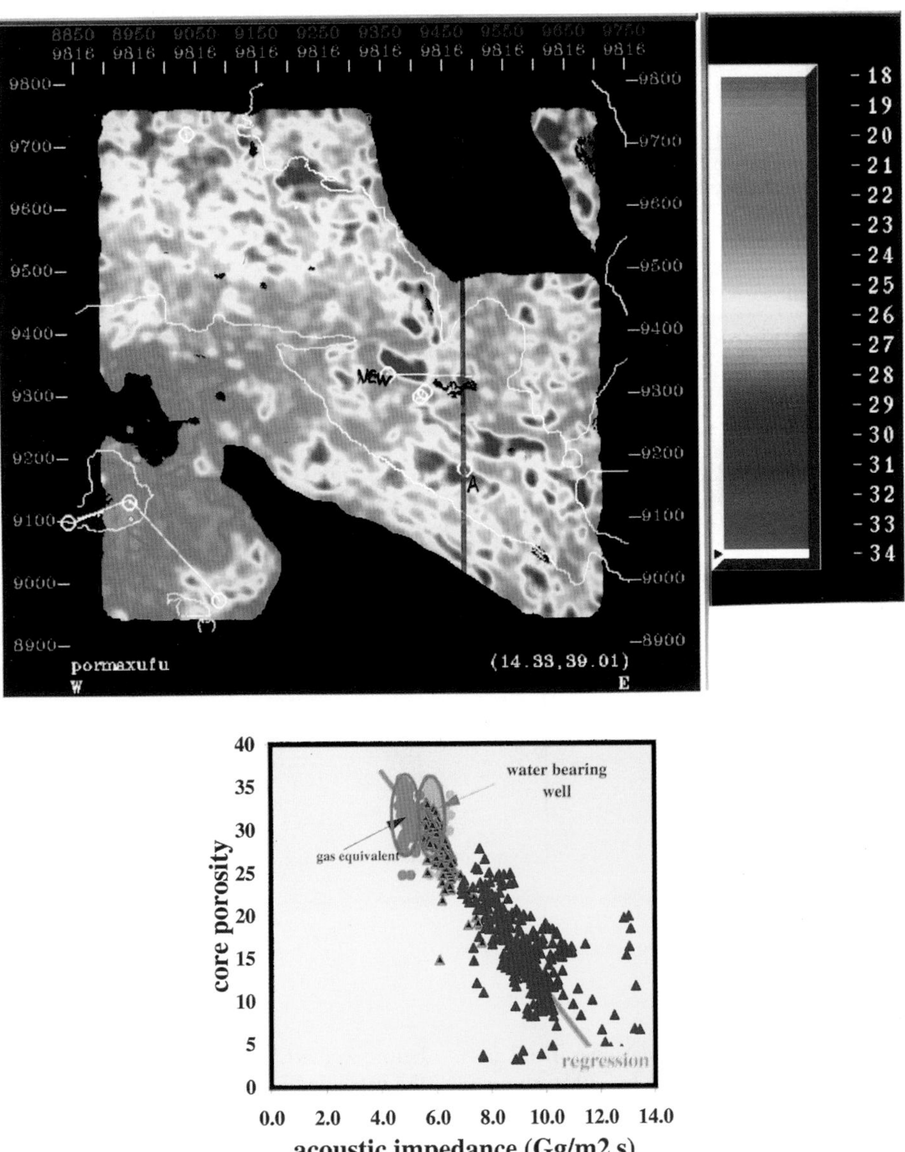

Fig. 3. Porosity of the Upper Fulmar sandstone, inferred from the acoustic impedance data using the well calibration shown in the lower part of the figure. Colour bar shows porosity in %. N–S line through well A shows location of section in Fig. 2.

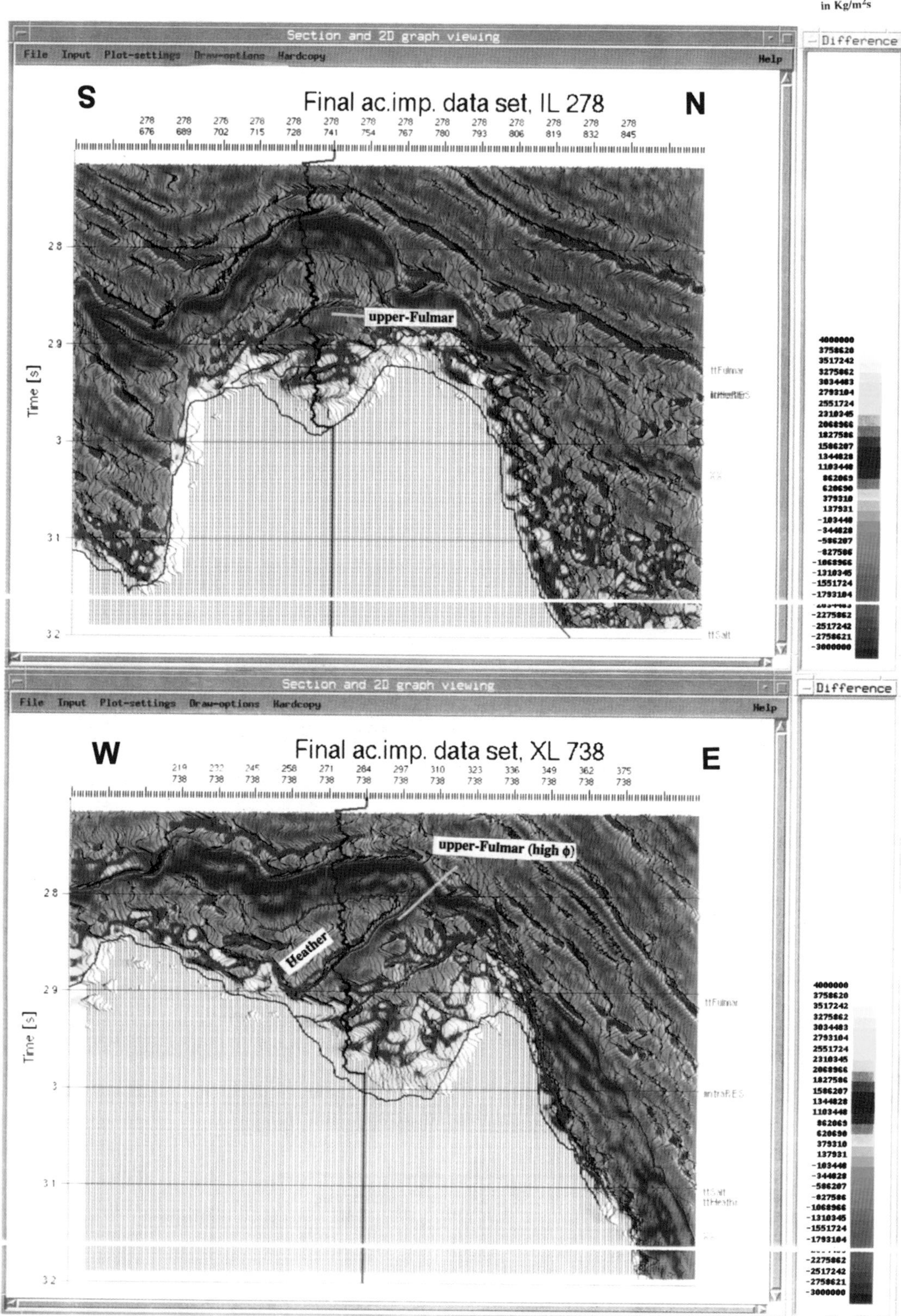

Fig. 4. Orthogonal acoustic impedance sections through the discovery well.

in Fig. 3 are shown a cluster of impedance values from a waterbearing well, and the values calculated by substituting gas for brine using Gassmann's equation. This means that the impedance-porosity trend can be used to a first approximation to predict porosity, without needing to know the porefill. The resulting porosity map shows higher porosities in the southeast of the field than in the northwest. This work was carried out before well NEW was drilled; the findings of this well agree with the predicted high porosity of the reservoir at this location.

Example 2

This is another example where the reservoir is the Fulmar sandstone of the Central North Sea. It is located in the

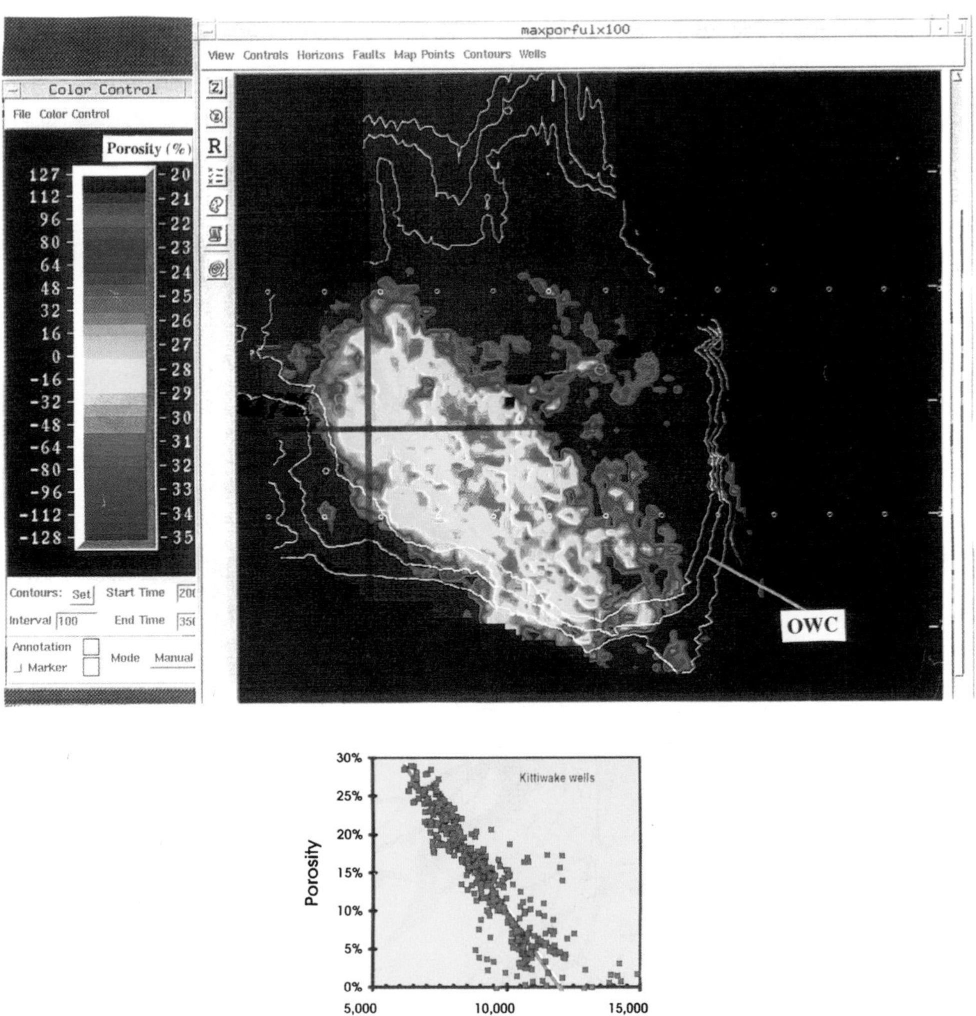

Fig. 5. Porosity of the Upper Fulmar sandstone, inferred from the acoustic impedance data using the calibration from adjacent wells shown in the lower part of the figure. N–S and E–W lines at left of map show location of the sections in Fig. 4.

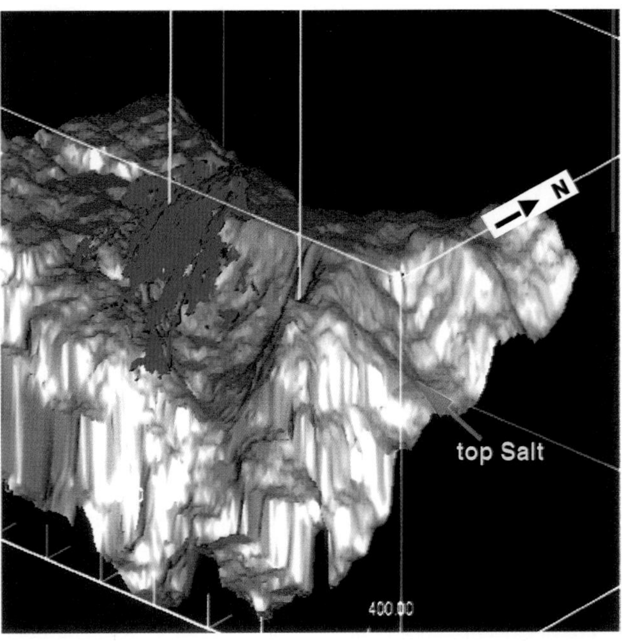

Fig. 6. Perspective view of reservoir body (in red) above grey Top Salt surface.

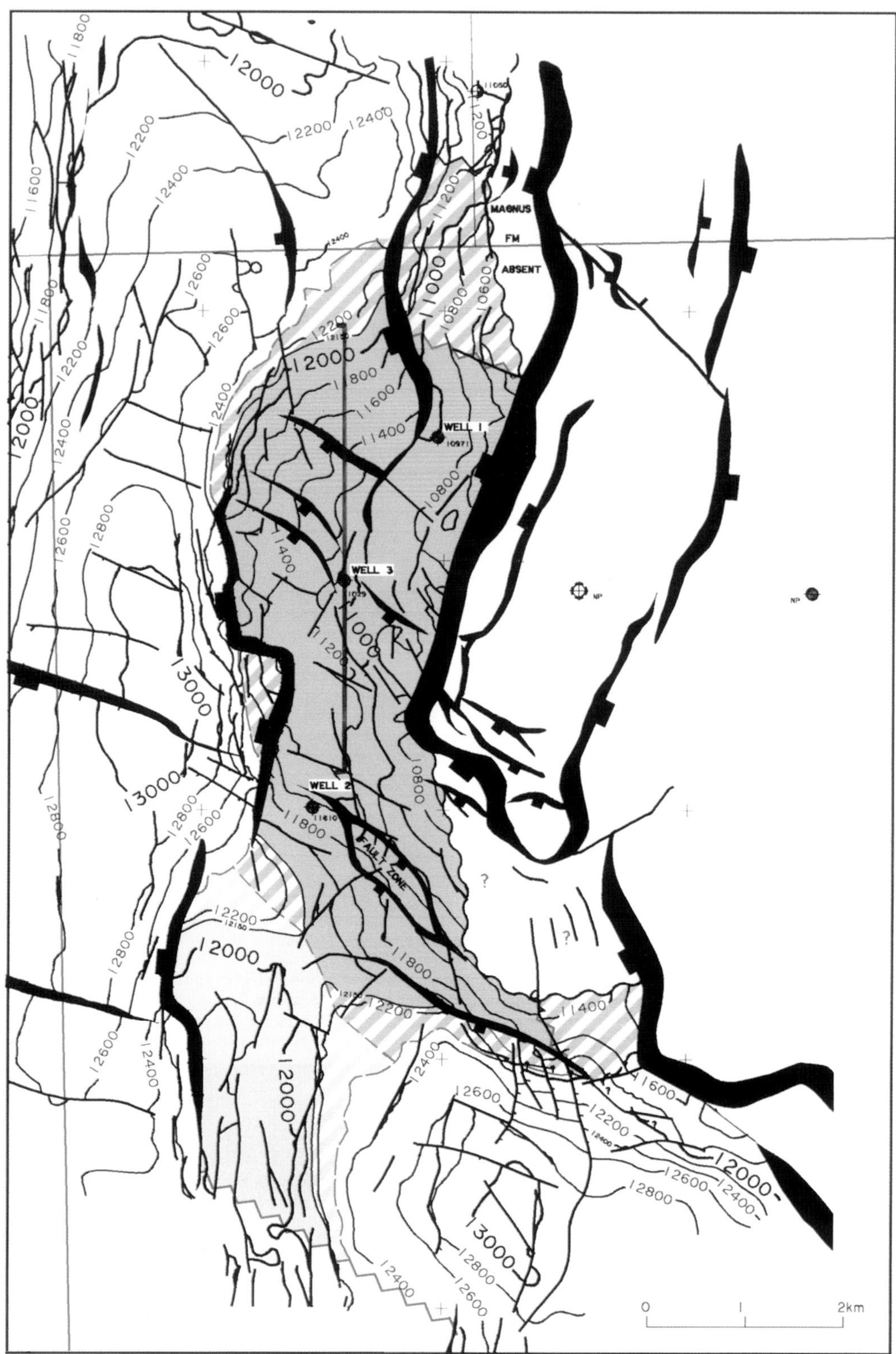

Fig. 7. Depth map (ft) of top reservoir. Pink and hatched pink shading show extent of proven and possible reserves, respectively; yellow shading denotes an undrilled prospect. N–S line through well 3 shows location of section in Figs 8, 10 and 11.

Kittiwake area and is an oil accumulation. The upper part of the reservoir is of much better quality than the lower. Inversion was carried out with the objective of mapping the distribution of good quality reservoir. Figure 4 shows orthogonal sections through the discovery well. The high-porosity Fulmar reservoir is acoustically soft, and is clearly indicated by the mid-dark blue zone indicated on the impedance sections. These impedance values were converted to porosity using a trend established for the wells drilled on the Kittiwake Field, as shown in Fig. 5. As in the previous example, there are considerable lateral variations of calculated reservoir porosity, and the variation occurs above the oil–water contact and is therefore a genuine lithological effect. The high-porosity band visible in the map has been confirmed by a recent production well. The information on reservoir quality has influenced the development plan for this accumulation; it has been determined that a single

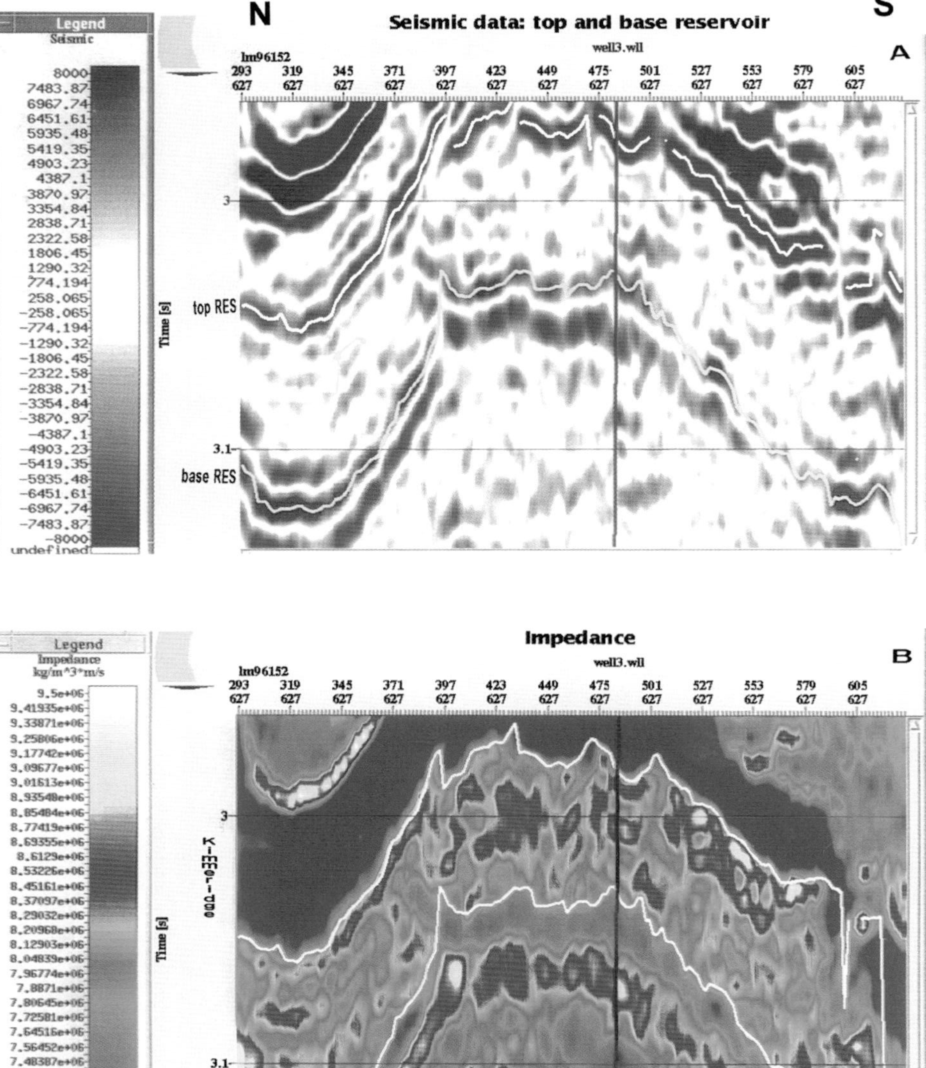

Fig. 8. Reflectivity and impedance versions of a seismic line approximately north–south through well 3. The picked top and base reservoir horizons are shown.

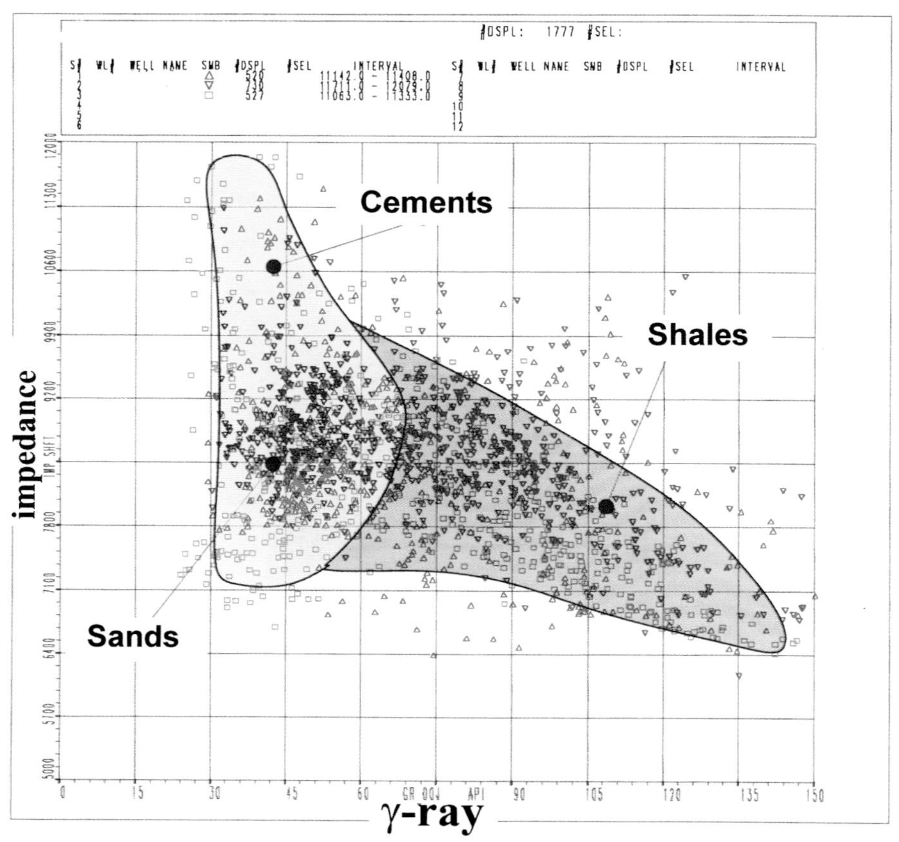

Fig. 9. Cross plot of well log impedance versus gamma ray reading, incorporating data from all three wells on the structure.

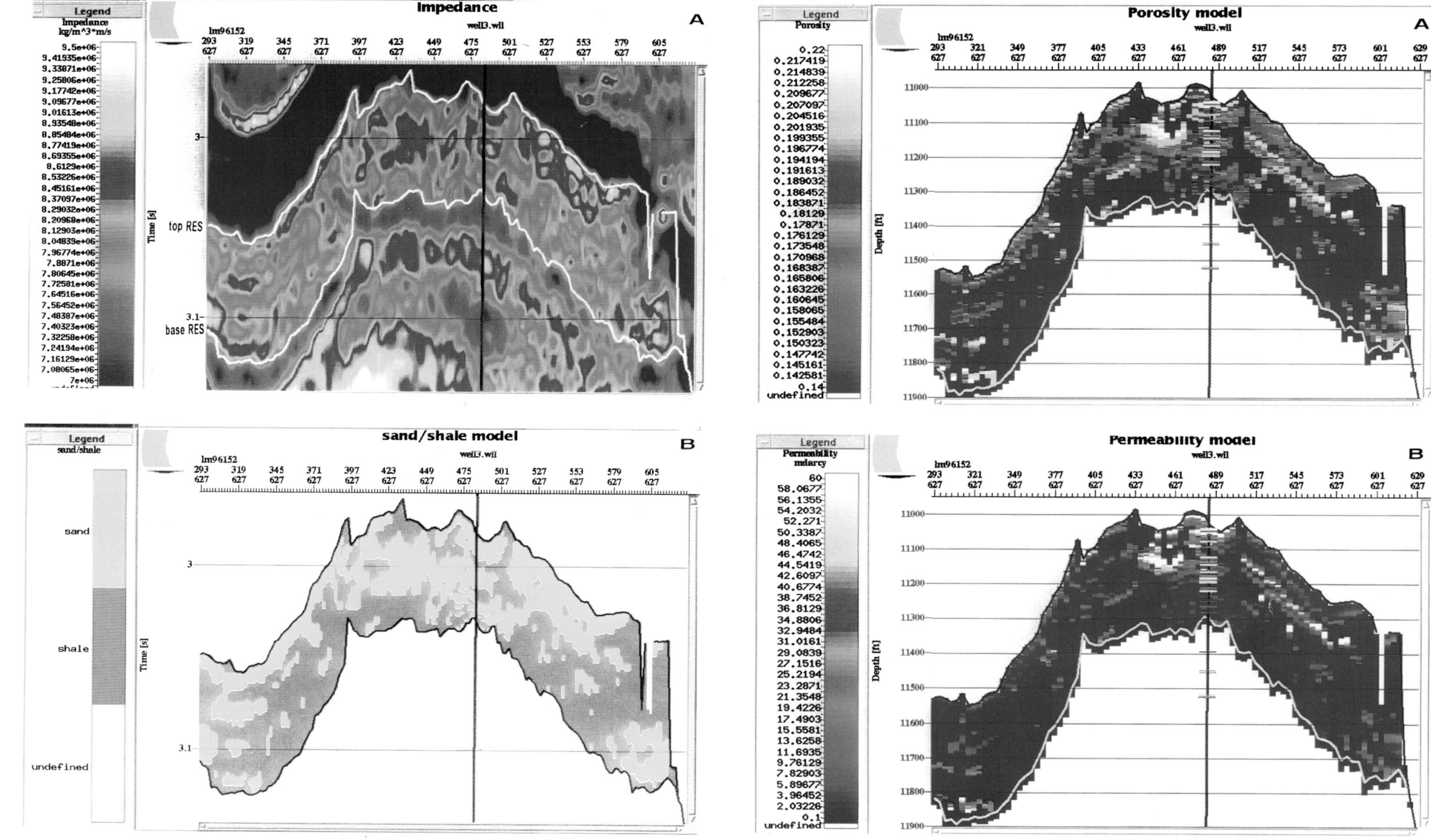

Fig. 10. Same line as Fig. 8, showing the use of an impedance threshold to separate sands from shales.

Fig. 11. Same line as Fig 8, showing a cross-section through one realization of the porosity and permeability volume. Well values are porosity in both A and B.

water injector will provide adequate drive, whereas previous planning without the benefit of the reservoir quality map had needed two water injectors, at significantly higher cost.

Imaging of the best reservoir unit was improved by delineating the connected low-impedance volume using Voxelgeo software (proprietary software of Paradigm Geophysics). As well as a comprehensive suite of applications for viewing data in 3D, this software has the ability to explore how anomalous impedance volumes are spatially connected. In this instance, a starting point was chosen within the low-impedance Fulmar, and the software explored the data volume away from this point, looking to connect together a region whose impedance value was less than a user-defined threshold. By careful selection of the threshold, it proved possible to isolate the good-quality Fulmar reservoir from its surroundings (Fig. 6). By displaying the reservoir in this way it is possible to appreciate its 3D geometry and to visualize, for example, its relationship to structure on the underlying Top Zechstein surface.

Example 3

This example is from the Northern North Sea. The reservoir consists of Upper Jurassic mass-flow sands within a north–south elongated fault-bounded structure (Fig. 7). Three wells have penetrated the reservoir; in all of these wells the same five depositional units were identified, leading to a possible inference of simple layer-cake stratigraphy. However, the seismic data (Fig. 8), though only of modest quality, suggested a lack of lateral continuity within the reservoir. Compartmentalization of the reservoir sands would have significant implications for the field development plan, so a study was carried out to investigate the meaning of the seismic response.

The seismic data were inverted, making use of the information from all three wells and picked top and base reservoir horizons. The main stratigraphic units can easily be identified on the impedance sections (Fig. 8): within the reservoir there is a complex variation between soft (blue) and hard (red) units, contrasting with the relative uniformity of the very soft (dark blue) Kimmeridge Clay above it, and of the soft shale (medium blue) below it. An aid to understanding the intra-reservoir impedance variation is the cross plot of impedance against gamma ray (combined data for all three wells) shown in Fig. 9. The softest units are the shales with the highest gamma ray reading. The hardest units are cemented sand-streaks with low gamma ray response. However, there is no clear separation between very good sands (i.e. high porosity and low impedance) and sandy shales. Still, there is an overall softening towards higher gamma-ray readings; lower impedance values are more likely to be caused by shales, and high impedance values are more likely to be caused by sands.

The impedance sections give a clear indication of lateral discontinuity in the reservoir sands. To evaluate its significance for reservoir behaviour, porosity and permeability data were derived from the inverted dataset for input into a reservoir simulator. This was carried out in several steps, as follows. First, sands were separated from shales by applying a threshold impedance cut-off (Fig. 10). Secondly, data were converted to the depth domain as this is required by the reservoir simulation software. Thirdly, porosity values were calculated within the sandbodies using a stochastic approach, in which the impedance data were given a heavy weighting so that they would be the most significant source of information in the parts of the dataset remote from the wells. In this way, several realizations of the 3D porosity field were generated, all of which honoured the well data exactly. A cross-section through one of these realizations is shown in Fig. 11.

By using core-derived porosity–permeability relations at the wells, a permeability cube was generated for each porosity realization (Fig. 11). Both porosity and permeability were input into a reservoir simulator. A simulation result shows the expected effect on reservoir pressure of production from a centrally placed well (Fig. 12). It clearly shows that production

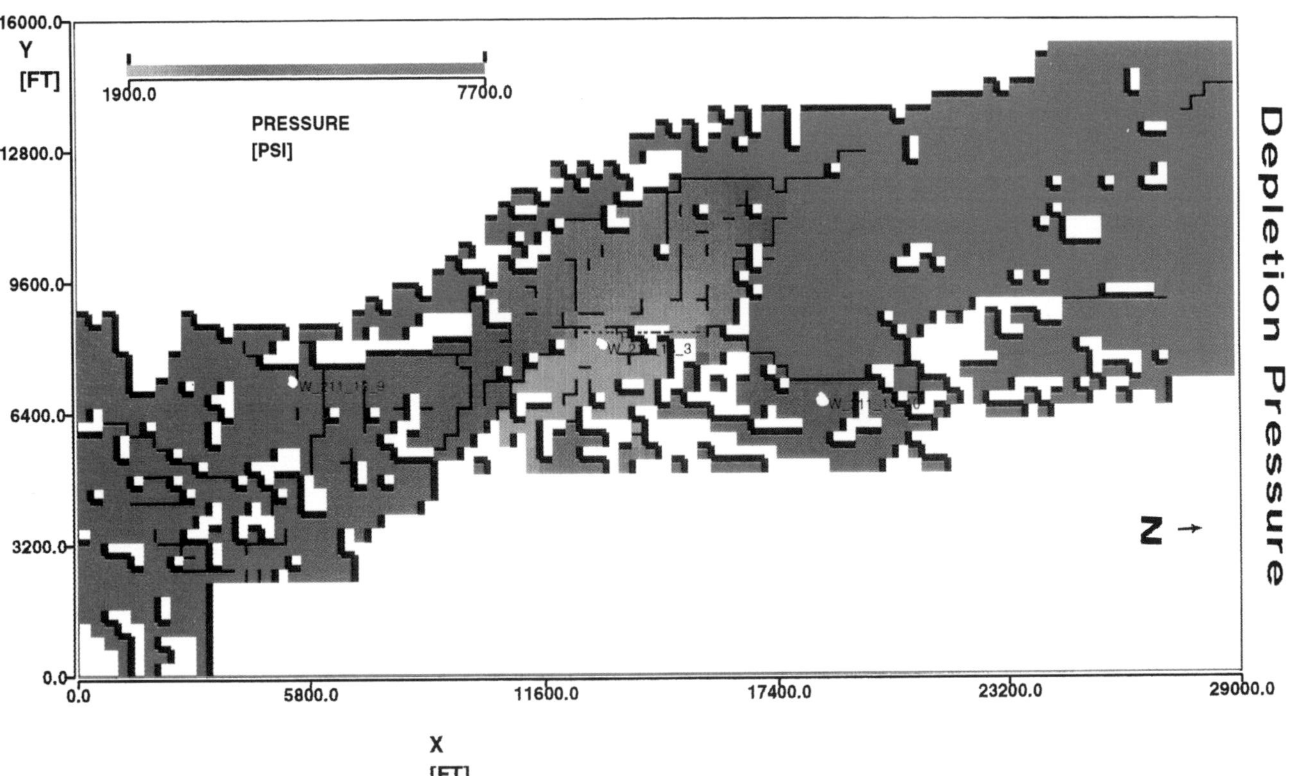

Fig. 12. Map of simulated pressure depletion.

would be from a limited area. This conclusion is a direct consequence of the intra-reservoir heterogeneity the presence of which is inferred from the seismic data.

Conclusions

The examples show that inversion is a useful tool to extract information about the reservoir from seismic data. The variation in acoustic impedance in the subsurface can be linked to important reservoir properties such as porosity or net/gross ratio. The data are well adapted to the use of geostatistical techniques to explore multiple realizations of the subsurface. This can all have significant impact on business decisions. In our experience, another important benefit is the availability of seismic data in a form that can be readily assimilated by experts in other disciplines, making it much easier to bring into being the integrated work practices that have been an objective for years past.

We should like to thank S. Dekker and R. Moon of Shell Expro and D. O'Leary of Jason Geosystems for their contributions to the inversion and reservoir modelling studies.

References

Haas, A. & Dubrule, O. 1994. Geostatistical inversion – a sequential method of stochastic reservoir modelling constrained by seismic data. *First Break*, **12**, 561–569.

Lindseth, R. O. 1979. Synthetic sonic logs – a process for stratigraphic interpretation. *Geophysics*, **44**, 3–26.

Predicting sandbody distribution and porosity for Callovian to late Oxfordian succession; Block 9/13 UKCS: an integrated approach

M. WOOD,[1] G. BINGHAM[1] and P. MITCHELL[2]

[1] *Mobil North Sea Limited, Grampian House, Union Row, Aberdeen, AB10 1SA, UK*
[2] *Mobil Exploration & Producing Technology Company, 13777, Midway Road, Farmers Branch, Texas 752444, USA*

Abstract: Middle to Upper Jurassic clastic deposits of the Block 9/13 area show an evolution in their sedimentary characteristics and depositional style, which are attributable to the interplay between rising relative sea-level, decreasing sediment supply and the development of an extensional fault framework. An understanding of the temporal and spatial relationship between fault activity and sediment supply is critical in determining reservoir distribution. Four evolutionary stages are identified: (a) Bajocian–Bathonian fluvio–tidal deposits: sedimentation occurred in a simple N–S trending extensional system, comprising discrete fault segments, coupled with high rates of sedimentation with a southerly provenance. (b) Callovian–Oxfordian submarine channel to pro-delta deposits: axially transported sediments are deposited in hanging wall lows of N–S orientated fault segments. Sediment supply is outstripped by the creation of accommodation space. (c) Mid–late Oxfordian submarine gravity flow deposits: axially transported sediments were deposited in closed synclinal lows created by the intersection of N–S and NW–SE, SW–NE fault trends, resulting from ramp-relay collapse. (d) Kimmeridgian–Volgian debris flow deposits derived from the footwalls of uplifted fault blocks.

A case study is presented, integrating post-stack seismic inversion with more conventional datasets, to provide increased confidence in the Callovian–late Oxfordian geological model. The gross stratigraphic package between the Callovian and late Oxfordian is easily distinguished using conventional seismic data. However, with conventionally processed seismic data individual sandbody distribution and geometry is difficult to determine because of a combination of non-unique seismic responses at sand–shale interfaces and resolution limitations. Recent success has been achieved using post-stack seismic inversion of a wavelet-processed volume, to distinguish sand within a particular porosity range from all other lithologies, to an acceptable level of confidence.

The Mobil operated Block 9/13 is located on the western margin of the Viking Graben in the UK sector of the Northern North Sea (Fig. 1). The block hosts the giant Beryl Field and several smaller satellite accumulations. Reserves and production are primarily associated with the prolific Bajocian to Bathonian age Beryl Formation sandstones. Secondary reservoirs exist in Lower Jurassic and Triassic formations (Robertson 1993). Upper Jurassic reservoirs have contributed, to date, a relatively minor volume of hydrocarbon.

To assess and exploit effectively the hydrocarbon potential of the Upper Jurassic sequence of the Beryl Embayment (Fig. 1), a thorough understanding of the interplay between sedimentation and structural development must be achieved. Further, potential drilling locations may be constrained by the use of specially processed seismic data (post-stack inversion).

This paper attempts to demonstrate how post-stack seismic inversion helped to support the pre-appraisal geological model, which was proven to be robust, and ultimately aided the placement of a successful production well.

Block 9/13 has full 3D seismic coverage and in excess of 170 Jurassic well penetrations. Within the specific study area of this paper (Fig. 2), control is provided by the following wells: 9/13-8, 9/13-18, 9/13a-27, 9/13a-39 & 9/13a-46 of which 9/13-18 & 9/13a-27 have core from Upper Jurassic intervals. While the broader structural interpretation was conducted on the full block 3D dataset (vintage 1992) a subset of these data (10 square km) was re-processed to extend the bandwidth (from 40 to 50 Hz) and to ensure the data were appropriately conditioned for inversion (zero phasing).

Stratigraphy and sedimentology

The stratigraphy of the Beryl Embayment has been documented by Robertson (1993). A graphical representation of the key elements of Middle and Upper Jurassic stratigraphy is summarized in Fig. 3.

The Humber Group was deposited from late Bathonian to Volgian times. Particular emphasis is placed on the most prospective, Upper Bathonian to Upper Oxfordian interval, known locally as the Heather Formation (Fig. 4)

There is a marked change in sedimentary character between the Bajocian to Bathonian Beryl Formation and overlying Heather Formation. The Beryl Formation is interpreted to have been deposited in a fluvio–tidal environment, with some shallow marine influence in the north. The sediments are dominantly clean, well sorted sands with net : gross ratios in the range 0.8–1.0. Occasional shale and coal horizons reflect overbank and/or interdeltaic deposition.

The Heather Formation by contrast is sand poor, dominated instead by shallow to deep marine silts and shales. Very fine- to fine-grained sand intervals are locally encountered and can be subdivided from biostratigraphic data into four main 'pulses' (Fig. 4). Individual sandbodies are typically finely interbedded at the base, becoming more massive towards the top. Core description suggests a pro-delta to submarine channel depositional environment. When encountered these sand intervals are often highly productive and laterally extensive with net to gross values of 0.5–0.8, and permeabilities of 100–200 mD. Thin highly interbedded intervals are often tightly cemented, with

WOOD, M., BINGHAM, G. & MITCHELL, P. 1999. Predicting sandbody distribution and porosity for Callovian to late Oxfordian succession; Block 9/13 UKCS: an integrated approach. *In*: FLEET, A. J. & BOLDY, S. A. R. (eds) *Petroleum Geology of Northwest Europe: Proceedings of the 5th Conference*, 1281–1287.

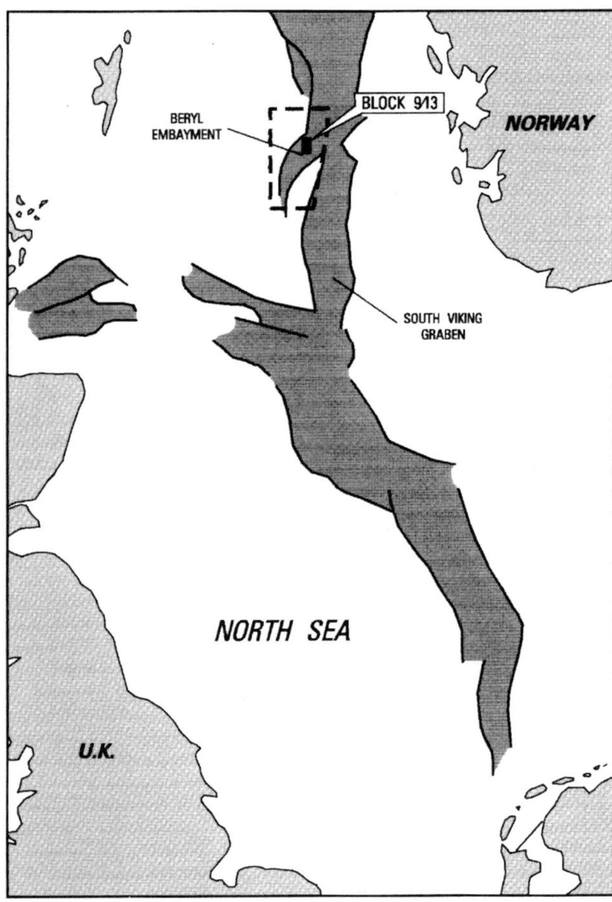

Fig. 1. Regional location of UKCS Block 9/13.

diagenetic fluids interpreted to have been derived during the de-watering of adjacent shales. These intervals constitute only a minor component of the gross reservoir.

Late Oxfordian to Volgian sands are occasionally encountered. These are of two types. Firstly, those that resemble sands of the Callovian to late Oxfordian (9/13-18, 9/13a-27); however, they are significantly thinner and not as laterally extensive, and are interpreted from core to reflect deposition from turbidity currents. Reservoir quality is poor, as they are often tightly cemented. Secondly, thick heterogeneous, debris flow deposits which are developed very locally and contain recognizable components of Triassic and Lower Jurassic formations are encountered (9/13a-45). Reservoir quality is typically poor as a result of the highly intermixed nature of the sediment.

Structure

The evolution of the controlling fault systems, from middle Jurassic times through to the end of the Jurassic, must be considered in order to understand the influence of structure on Upper Jurassic sediment distribution. The importance of interplay between clastic sediment supply and available accommodation space is evident throughout this time period but becomes critical in the Late Jurassic.

During Bajocian–Bathonian times, the area is dominated by a simple N–S orientated extensional fault system. Extension is accommodated by discrete fault segments (Fig. 5a) which display classic dip-slip fault displacement profiles (Walsh & Watterson 1991; Peacock & Sanderson 1994). Isochron thicks (Fig. 5) demonstrate that deposition is focused in the hanging wall lows of these faults. Sediment supply (from a southern provenance) keeps pace with the creation of accommodation space so that the dominantly, fluvio–tidal deposits (Beryl Formation) are widespread. Notably, evidence that the faults are separated by ramp-relays and remain essentially unconnected comes from onlap relationships observed on seismic data (Fig. 6).

The same pattern of N–S oriented faults separated by ramp-relays is interpreted to persist through Callovian and early Oxfordian times. While E–W extension continues to be accommodated by the established fault system, clastic sediment supply is no longer sufficient to occupy all the available accommodation space. Slightly deeper water conditions prevail and reservoir quality facies of the resultant pro-delta to submarine channel deposits are relatively restricted. These axially transported sediments are deposited in the deep hanging wall lows of the N–S faults.

During mid-late Oxfordian times, continued, and probably accelerated, E–W extension ultimately lead to the collapse of ramp-relays and the linkage of N–S faults into more continuous systems (Cartwright *et al.* 1996). Isochron thicks shift from hanging wall lows of N–S oriented faults (Fig. 5a) to hanging wall lows of longer, linked faults systems (Fig. 5b). Shifts in isochron patterns (Fig. 5), fault displacement profiles and geometries observed on seismic data (Fig. 6) provide evidence for this interpretation. Axial (S to N) turbidity currents locally deposited coarse clastics in closed synclinal lows, formed at the intersection of coalesced fault trends. Sediment supply was insufficient to match the creation of accommodation space and potential reservoir quality sands were restricted. Locally, uplifted and exposed footwalls may have provided an additional clastic sediment supply.

Thick deposits of Volgian conglomerates are developed locally (9/13a-45). These are interpreted to have been deposited as debris flows derived from a western provenance. They cannot be uniquely associated with a specific fault set. Consequently, they are interpreted to represent a separate sedimentary system to that dominant through much of the Middle and Late Jurassic.

Seismic inversion

The target reservoir cannot be uniquely imaged with conventionally processed seismic data. This is because of several factors: (i) sandbodies seldom reach a thickness greater than 60 ft whilst vertical resolution in the dataset is limited to approximately 50 ft (40 Hz); (ii) in general, the lithological interfaces at both the top and base of the gross sand package have small and spatially inconsistent reflection coefficients; (iii) intra-formational shales are thin (relative to seismic resolution limitations) and have similar acoustic properties to much of the sandstone they are associated with. Although the top and base of the sand-prone formation can be mapped with a reasonable degree of certainty, attempts to map internal sand distribution are limited to qualitative observations of 'seismic character'.

In an effort to extract more useful predictive stratigraphic information from the seismic dataset, post-stack amplitude inversion was attempted. For the five wells in the study area (9/13-8, 9/13-18, 9/13a-27, 9/13a-39 & 9/13a-46), integrated log analysis, using VSP and edited openhole logs, was performed to improve the synthetic to surface seismic tie in the zone of interest (2000–3200 ms). Analysis of wavelets extracted from the five wells demonstrated spatial stability of the wavelet within the study area (critical for the inversion to succeed). Seismic bandwidth and resolution were improved through application of proprietary (ENTEC Energy Consultants) post stack wavelet processing and the resultant zero phased data was inverted to relative acoustic impedance (RAI) using proprietary software of Entec Energy Consultants (a model based inversion approach). With spatial stability of the wavelet ensured, amplitudes preserved and a higher resolution dataset,

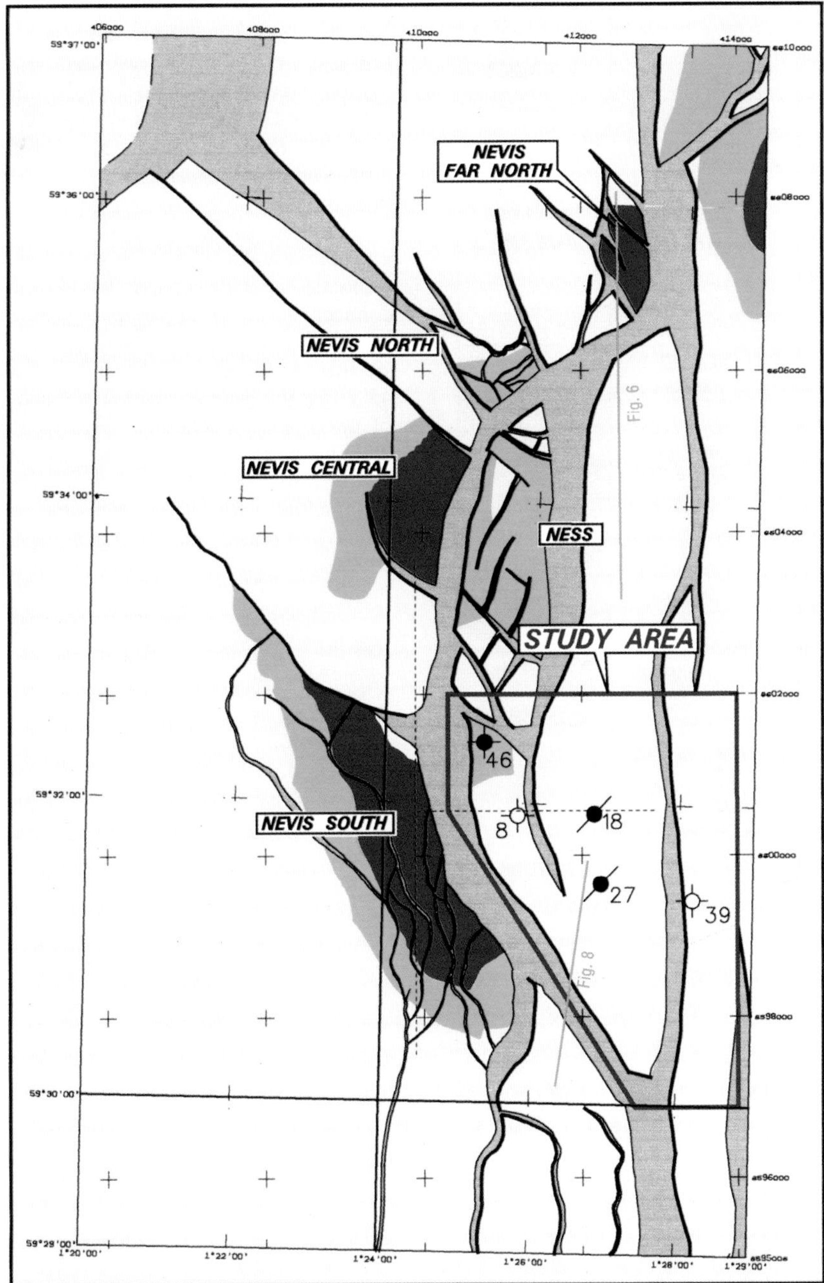

Fig. 2. Structural elements and detailed location of study area. Key wells and seismic sections of Figs 6 and 8 are located on the map.

the chances of obtaining a meaningful result from inversion were significantly enhanced.

To perform a quantitative analysis of the data, absolute acoustic impedance (AAI) is required. The relative acoustic impedance (RAI) dataset provided a measure of impedance relative to the zero mean of each trace for frequencies down to where the signal to noise ratio is one (approximately 4Hz). In order to derive the 0–4 Hz information, log acoustic impedance (for each of the five study wells) was mapped onto traces at the well locations. The log impedance was then summed with the RAI to derive AAI. Through this process, the amplitude distribution and spectral characteristics of the RAI were not altered. Five horizons were interpreted on the RAI datset and used to constrain the projection of AAI throughout the 3D volume.

Detailed petrophysical analysis of five wells (9/13-8, 9/13-18, 9/13a-27, 9/13a-39 & 9/13a-46) was conducted to establish a link between lithology and acoustic impedance for Middle and Upper Jurassic sediments. Six lithofacies were identified based upon the following criteria (Fig. 7): lithofacies 1 RQ Sand (very high), $\phi > 18\%$, $V_{\text{shale}} < 20\%$; lithofacies 2 RQ Sand (high), $14\% < \phi < 18\%$, $V_{\text{shale}} < 20\%$; lithofacies 3 RQ Sand (moderate), $10\% < \phi < 14\%$, $V_{\text{shale}} < 20\%$; lithofacies 4 RQ Sand (low), $\phi < 10\%$, $V_{\text{shale}} < 20\%$; lithofacies 5 Shaly sand, $20\% < V_{\text{shale}} < 60\%$; lithofacies 6 Shale, $V_{\text{shale}} > 60\%$;. Several critical relationships were established: (i) high porosity sand ($\phi > 18\%$) is acoustically indistinguishable from shale; (ii) sand in the moderate porosity range ($10\% < \phi < 18\%$) is distinguishable from all other lithologies to a confidence level of 70%; (iii) if lithology is known (i.e. sand) there is a strong relationship between and ϕ acoustic impedance. Though the target sands are not uniquely distinguishable, clearly the combination of this new dataset and our understanding of the geological model represents a significant step towards an acceptable lithological predictive capability.

The inverted data volume was transformed into a sand probability volume (for the porosity range $10\% < \phi < 18\%$)

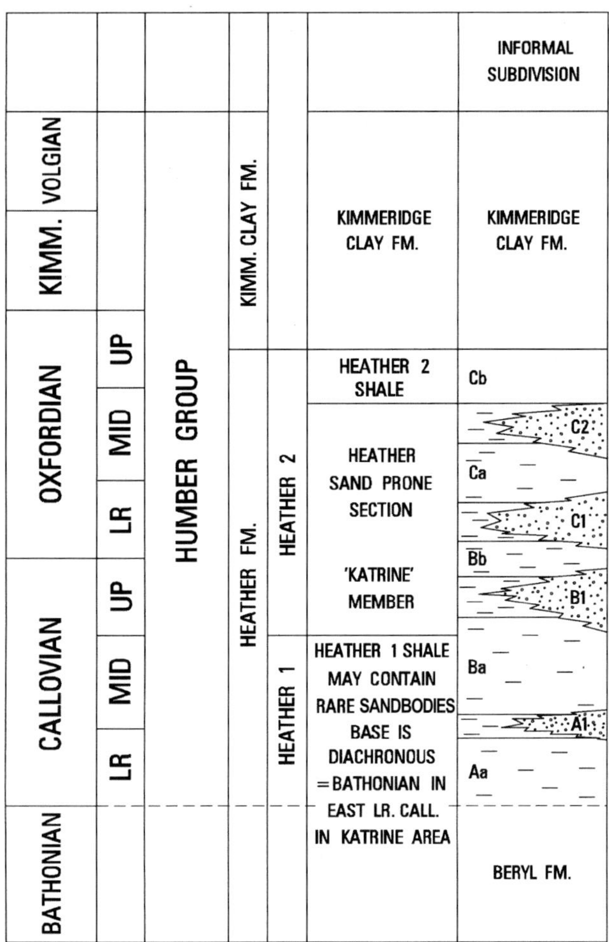

Fig. 3. Detail of Upper Jurassic stratigraphy.

using a probability density function (PDF) derived from acoustic impedance (AI) distributions identified by petrophysical analysis of the well data (Fig. 7). Each value of AI can be directly related to a probability of occurrence for the target sand. Figure 8 is a seismic section from the sand probability volume. Within the Oxfordian section, patches of high probability (green to red) were used to define target sand distribution.

To use the resultant probability volume in a predictive sense, a probability cut-off was chosen with reference to the existing well data, such that criteria based on the known thickness and connectivity of the upper sand were satisfied. Applying a cut-off of 45% these criteria were satisfied for all five wells in the study area. All AI values resulting in a probability of less than 45% (for the target sand) were considered to be representative of non-reservoir lithologies. Having chosen this cut-off, predictions of gross reservoir thickness and average porosity were made away from the well data. These maps were used in conjunction with depth structure maps, Oil–water contact (OWC) estimates and the structural/stratigraphic model to choose the optimal site for appraisal of the accumulation.

Results

A comparison of pre- and post-drill data interpretations for Well 9/13a-59 is the most useful and objective assessment of the validity of the approach adopted.

The top sand and gross reservoir thickness were encountered as prognosed. Also, the predicted porosity range within the target interval was as prognosed. However, the net : gross (N/G) (using $\phi < 10\%$ as a cut-off) was found to be significantly lower than in the offset wells. Additionally, water was encountered higher than expected.

A comparison of the appraisal well results and offset well control (Fig. 9) suggests three important conclusions: (i) sands

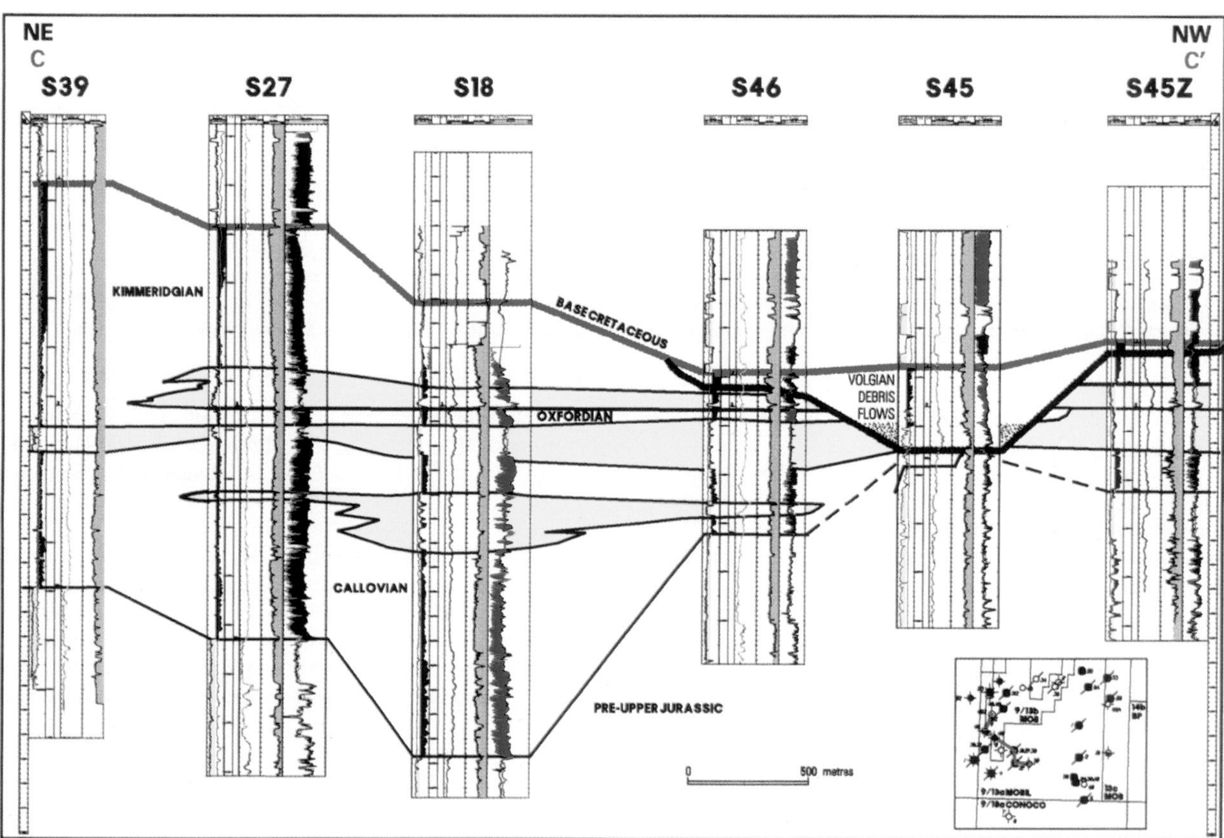

Fig. 4. Log cross-section through study area. N–S thickening of Oxfordian C2 sand is evident between 9/13-18 and 9/13a-27. Conversely, the C1 sand shows the inverse (N–S thinning) relationship.

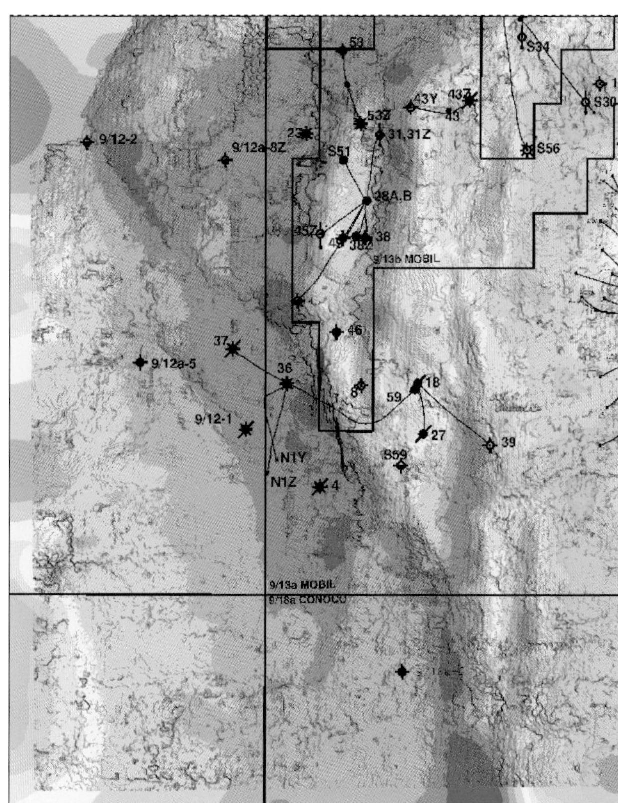

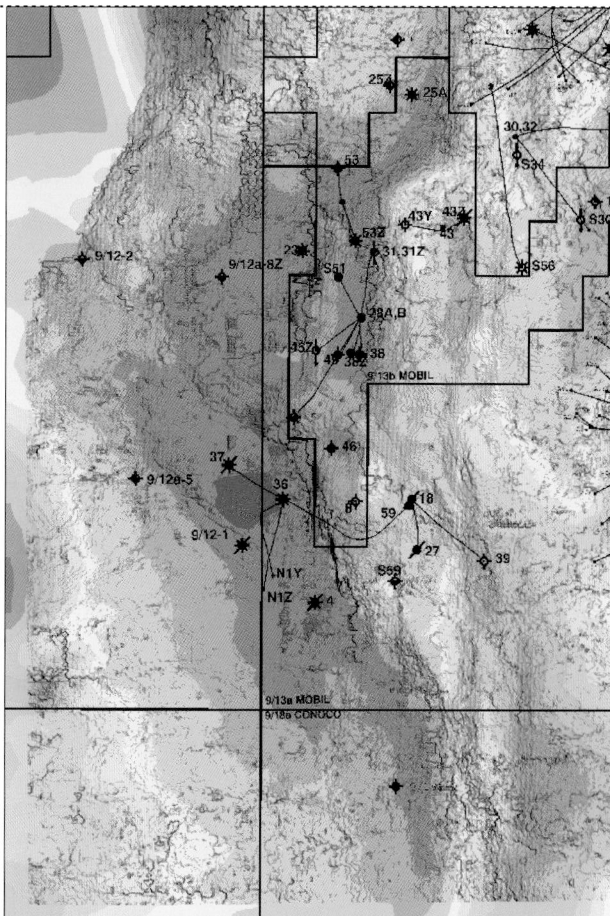

Fig. 5. Isochron relationships between key seismic markers. The displays are of gradational isochron thickness (red = thin; blue = thick) superimposed upon a shaded relief map of Base Cretaceous time structure: (**a**) Triassic–Callovian, isochron thicks are clearly associated with discrete linear N–S (fault) trends; (**b**) Isochron thicks have developed along connecting faults in response ramp relay collapse.

and shales in 9/13a-59 are more thinly interbedded than in 9/13a-27 (this variation is interpreted to result from 9/13a-27 being representative of a channelized facies while those of 9/13a-59 are more marginal relative to the main axis of the channelised system); (ii) reduction of primary permeability is the result of carbonate cements precipitated from fluids migrating up nearby faults or, more likely, derived from shales during compaction. Though permeability is degraded at their tops and bases, thicker sands are generally less susceptible to damage than thinner sands. Hence, permeabilities in the sands of 9/13a-59 are typically an order of magnitude lower than in the offset wells; (iii) water wet C1 sand at the 9/13a-59 location implies an OWC immediately below the oil down to (ODT) encountered in 9/13a-59x. Given that existing RFT data indicate a deeper contact, oil saturations at the ODT remain high (i.e. no evidence of a transition zone that would indicate proximity to a contact) and no water has been produced from 9/13a-59x (6 months @ 6 STBD), it appears likely that the C1 sands at the 9/13a-59 location are partially isolated from those at 9/13a-59x. This is most likely the result of sub-seismic faulting offsetting the C1 sands. A throw of less than 20 feet is required to offset the sands encountered in 9/13a-59.

To secure economic production rates, a decision was made to sidetrack to the north towards the 9/13a-18 location (proven C1 deliverability). Also, since the seismic inversion volumes indicated thickening C2 sand probability towards the western bounding fault of the accumulation, the planned sidetrack trajectory was likely to encounter a thicker C2 than that at the 9/13a-18 location. 9/13a-59x encountered both C1 and C2 sands as prognosed and is currently producing through existing infrastructure on an extended well test. Production data indicate reservoir boundaries at offsets corresponding to the mapped boundary faults. These data provide further evidence of the sand distribution as predicted from seismic inversion.

Conclusions

Several conclusions can be drawn from the various aspects of this work and from the results of Wells 9/13a-59 and 9/13a-59x:

(1) Present-day fault linkage and isochron distribution patterns can be explained within a simple model of E–W Jurassic extension and gradual transgression of the Beryl Embayment from N–S.
(2) Seismic based porosity prediction is possible if the target formation is well constrained (e.g. within the near ubiquitous Middle Jurassic Beryl Formation). Within the main Beryl Field, work is currently in progress utilizing this finding to enhance our predictive capability at both the reservoir simulator flow unit and well planning stages.
(3) Within the limitations of vertical seismic resolution, use of inverted seismic data allows accurate mapping (previously impossible) of moderate ($10\% < \phi < 18\%$) quality Upper Jurassic reservoir distribution.
(4) Seismic resolution constraints currently preclude the accurate risking of permeability distributions within the gross Upper Jurassic sand system.

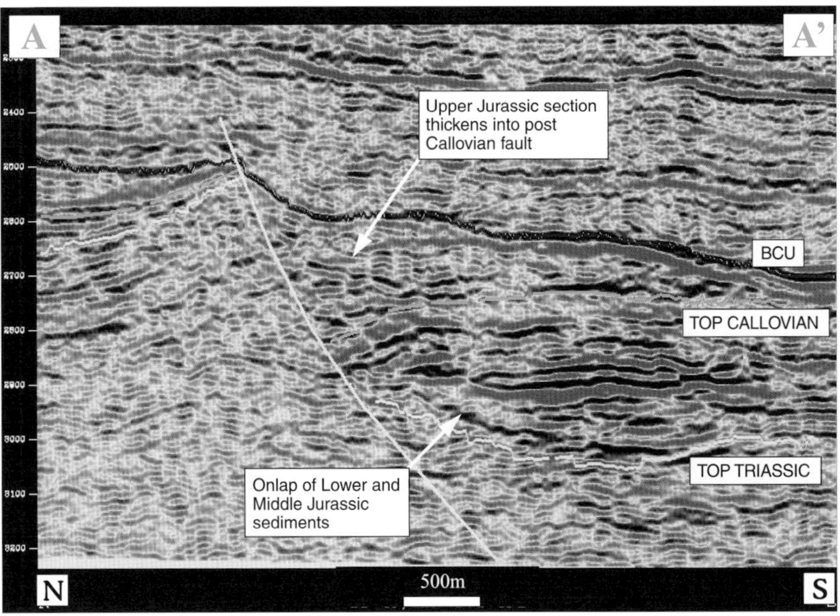

Fig. 6. Seismic section parallel to early fault trend and across the late trend of ramp-relay connecting faults. The Lower and Middle Jurassic sections thin towards the connecting fault, suggesting there was no significant displacement across it during this time period. In contrast, the Upper Jurassic section thickens significantly into the hanging wall of this fault. BCU: Base Cretaceous unconformity.

(5) The seismic inversion volumes contributed positively to target definition for the sidetrack production well. Despite mechanical problems forcing two further short sidetracks, 9/13a-59x was completed successfully and is currently producing through existing infrastructure. Future development plans for the accumulation include the drilling of a water injection well to support 9/13a-59x oil production. The seismic inversion volumes have played a pivotal role in the detailed trajectory planning for this well.

(6) The best quality target sands remain undetectable directly because of their acoustic similarity to Heather Formation shales. Gross thickness variations, in association with indications of moderate porosity sand, may be useful to infer the presence of better quality sands.

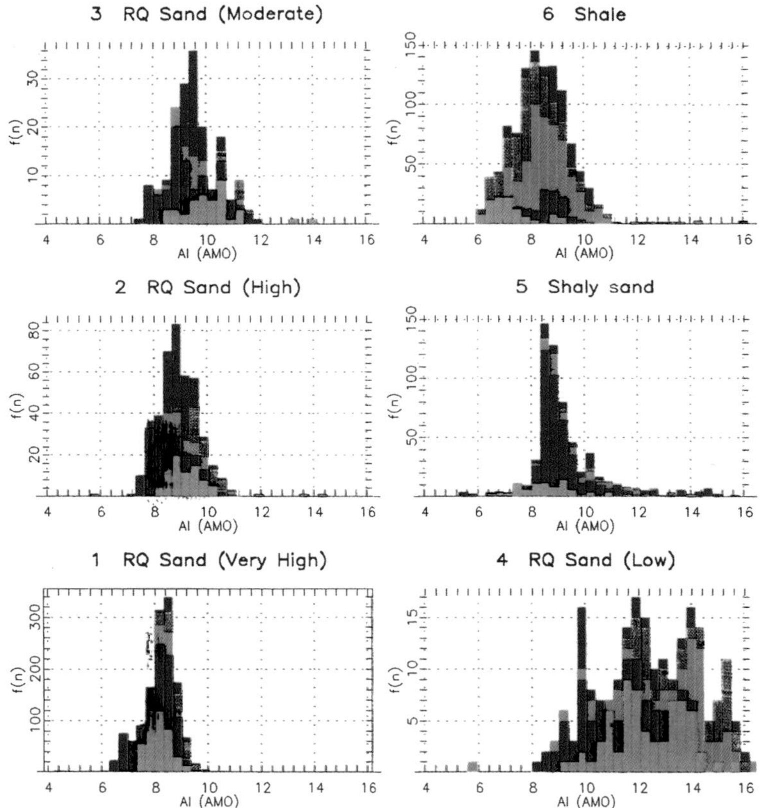

Fig. 7. Histograms of acoustic impedance (AI) for porosity lithofacies. The data are calculated at two samples/foot from openhole sonic and density logs of the five control wells. Six 'lithologies' are broken out using porosity ranges and shale cut-offs. The distributions for very high quality reservoir sand ($\phi > 18\%$) and shale effectively overlay. Hence, these sands cannot be distinguished from shale using AI. However, the distributions for high and moderate porosity sands (ϕ 10%–18%) show some separation from all other lithologies.

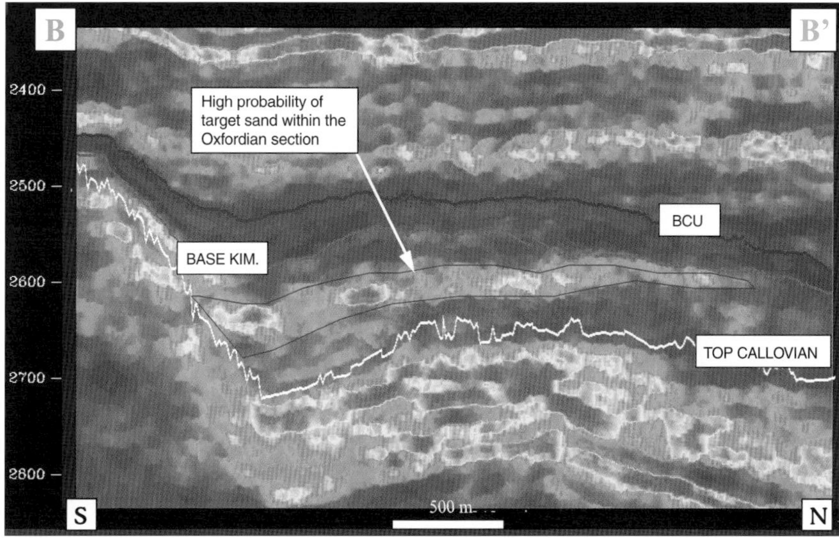

Fig. 8. Section of sand probability. The section shows a potential thickening of sand into the hangingwall of the main bounding fault. This evidence supports the geological model for C2 sand distribution. Kim: Kimmeridgian. BCU: Base Cretaceous unconformity.

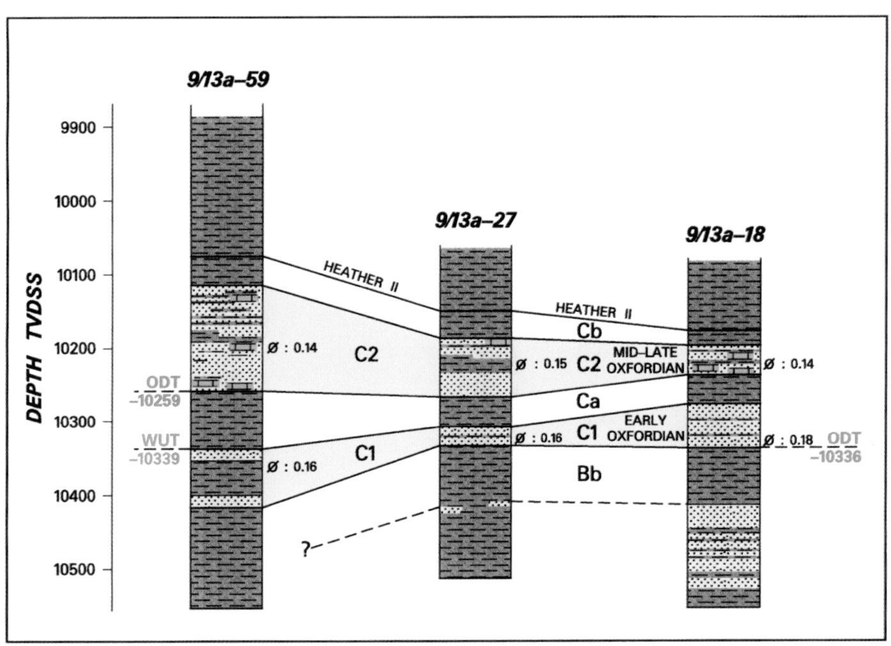

Fig. 9. Schematic cross-section through 9/13a-59 and offset control wells. The section demonstrates that the thickness of C2 sands at the 9/13a-59 location were as predicted by the model. ODT: oil down to; WUT: water up to.

The authors wish to acknowledge the contribution of staff at EnTec Energy Consultants for their valuable insights during many technical discussions and their tireless efforts in delivering the various datasets used in this study. The material in this discussion is published with the kind permission of our 9/13 partners: Amerada Hess, Enterprise Oil, OMV and BG.

References

Cartwright, J. A., Mansfield, C. & Trudgill, B. 1996. The growth of normal faults by segment linkage. *In*: Buchanan, P. G. & Nieuwland, D. A. (eds) *Modern Developments in Structural Interpretation, Validation and Modelling*. Geological Society, London, Special Publications, **99**, 163–177.

Peacock, D. C. P. & Sanderson, D. J. 1994. Geometry and development of relay ramps in normal fault systems. *American Association of Petroleum Geology Bulletin*, **78**, 147–165

Robertson, G. 1993. Beryl Field, geological evolution and reservoir behaviour. *In*: Parker, J. R. (ed.) *Petroleum Geology of Northwest Europe: Proceedings of the 4th Conference*. Geological Society, London.

Walsh, J. J. & Watterson, J. 1991. Geometric and kinematic coherence and scale effect in normal fault systems. *In*: Yielding, A. M & Freeman, G. (eds) *The Geometry of Normal Faults*. Geological Society, London, Special Publications, **56**, 193–203.

A, B AVO cross plotting and its application in Greenland and the Barents Sea

E. S. ISAACSON[1] and D. B. NEFF[2]

[1] *Phillips Petroleum Company Norway, P.O. Box 220, N-4056 Tananger, Norway, (e-mail: esisaac@bvemx.ppco.com)*
[2] *Phillips Petroleum Company, Bartlesville, Oklahoma 74004, USA*

Abstract: Recent amplitude versus offset (AVO) interpretations in the Norwegian Barents Sea and offshore West Greenland have identified subtle and complex anomalies which are best interpreted using a layer-specific, amplitude and gradient cross plot analysis scheme. The creation of AVO intercept (A) and gradient (B) seismic sections allows for a variety of stacks including A, B, A times B, and A plus B. Also, A versus B cross plots are easily generated to help define shale, wet sand and hydrocarbon trend lines that better differentiate the anomalies and provide information concerning the geological framework that created the AVO response.

Determination of the background trend on an A versus B cross plot is problematic in AVO analysis since variations in lithology and depth are interdependent, with both factors greatly influencing this trend. Also, the background trend is empirically defined by the AVO response of shale-on-shale boundaries or shale-on-silt reflectors, and this may not be indicative of the trend line for a shale-on-wet sand response. However, once the empirical background trend or wet trend is established, A and B data can be rescaled such that the shale line takes on a slope of −1. Potential hydrocarbon anomalies will then plot as data points with maximum scatter away from the normalized shale line. An A plus B section based upon a normalized shale line shows the potential hydrocarbon anomalies at maximum amplitude and the wet sands at minimum amplitude.

AVO analysis of A and B is generally performed together with forward modelling that generates theoretical responses for intercept amplitude (A) and gradient (B) parameters. The forward modelling helps validate the processing steps, give clues as to the non-uniqueness of various A and B responses, and integrates the geology into the study.

In the Fylla area, offshore West Greenland, an AVO analysis focused on large flat spots identified on the seismic data, as part of a licence application. A and B analysis was used to delineate trends in the data, to isolate three different classes of AVO anomalies which suggest the presence of hydrocarbons, and to provide insight as to the rock properties of the interbedded sandstones and shales.

An AVO analysis was also performed to help evaluate the prospectivity of an area in the Norwegian Hammerfest Basin. The purpose of the study was to establish the expected AVO response for the prospective interval from nearby gas discoveries and determine if similar anomalies exist within the prospect area. The AVO work consisted of forward modelling and A plus B analysis. Subtle AVO effects associated with gas in the Middle Jurassic section were identified.

Amplitude versus offset (AVO) as an exploration tool for risk analysis has been significantly advanced in the last several years through better data processing and AVO presentation schemes. Historically, AVO analysis has had mixed results in exploration. Success was generally associated with good quality data, soft rocks and gaseous or high gas : oil ratio (GOR) reservoirs. Failures were blamed on poor imaging or data processing, but often involved a misunderstanding of the rock physics for the prospect area or a misinterpretation of the data. Today, the industry has a better rock physics database and has employed new analytical techniques, such as AVO intercept (A) and gradient (B) displays that remove some of the ambiguity found in early AVO presentation formats. Research into AVO responses has yielded significant progress in the areas of: (1) cross plot analysis; (2) display of A and B attributes; and (3) insights into the petrophysical characteristics that create the various AVO responses. This paper summarizes and expands upon previous publications concerning A and B cross plotting and A plus B (A + B) displays, and presents the theory behind using a horizon-based interpretation scheme.

Two exploration problems are used to illustrate the A, B AVO technique and show how it is integrated with other exploration tools. Seismic data from West Greenland contain flat spots, bright spots and dim spots associated with large tilted fault blocks. In the Hammerfest Basin of northern Norway, several large gas fields have been discovered but no discernible change in the stacked seismic response across the reservoirs is observed. These cases illustrate two extremes of AVO analysis: the first is an integration of several types of responses, which together provide geological information on the potential reservoir; and the second is a very subtle AVO response that requires forward modelling to determine its characteristics.

Theory

Rutherford & Williams (1989) set forth a fundamental description of three sand types and how they vary in AVO response (Fig. 1, wiggle traces). Following Shuey (1985), a two-term approximation to the Zoeppritz Equations can be defined:

$$R(\theta) = A + B\sin^2(\theta) \qquad (1)$$

where

R = reflection coefficient; A = AVO intercept;
θ = angle of incidence; B = AVO gradient.

This provides a linear relationship between R (approximated by seismic amplitude) and the square of the sine of the angle of

ISAACSON, E. S. & NEFF, D. B. 1999. A, B AVO cross plotting and its application in Greenland and the Barents Sea. *In*: FLEET, A. J. & BOLDY, S. A. R. (eds) *Petroleum Geology of Northwest Europe: Proceedings of the 5th Conference*, 1289–1298.

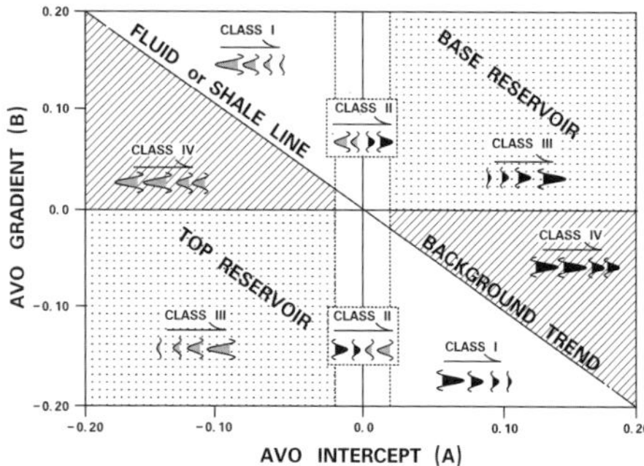

Fig. 1. AVO anomaly classification diagram based on an A versus B cross plot with the four different classes located for the top and base of a reservoir. The wiggle traces represent amplitude response with offset, with the arrow pointing towards increasing offset. An increase in impedance is a peak, shown as a deviation to the right.

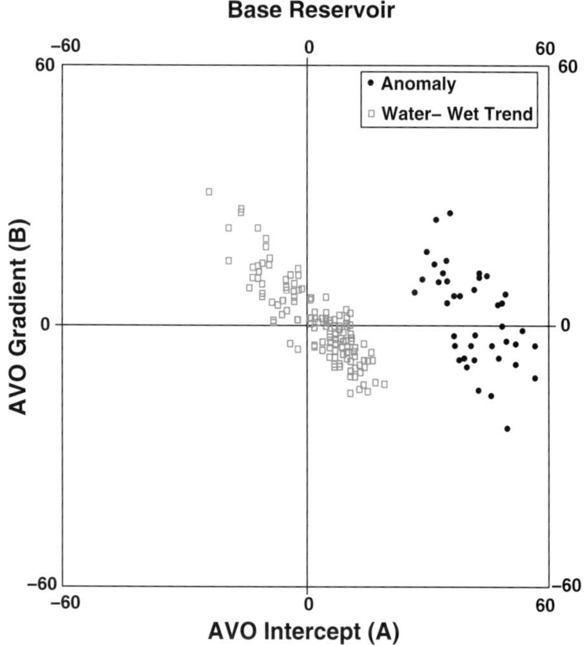

Fig. 2. An A versus B cross plot for the reflector defining the base reservoir in the Greenland example, point b in Fig. 7. The grey squares represent data from the down-dip water-wet portion and define an A, B trend through the origin.

incidence, and defines the AVO attributes A and B. With the enhancement of A versus B cross plotting, Castagna & Swan (1997) proposed that AVO responses be classified by the position of the reflector of interest on an A versus B cross plot, and that a fourth category, or class, be added (Fig. 1). Each of these classes defines a characteristic lithologic contrast between two horizons that is dependent upon a change in impedance and Poisson's ratio, where the Poisson's ratio is defined by:

$$\sigma = \frac{\left(\frac{V_\mathrm{P}}{V_\mathrm{S}}\right)^2 - 2}{2\left[\left(\frac{V_\mathrm{P}}{V_\mathrm{S}}\right)^2 - 1\right]} \tag{2}$$

where

V_P = P-wave velocity;
V_s = S-wave velocity.

The classes are summarized for top reservoir as follows:

(A) In Class I, the intercept amplitude (reflection coefficient) is large and positive in the brine filled case and reduces in amplitude as hydrocarbons are introduced, whilst the absolute gradient increases. A dim spot occurs in the hydrocarbon case relative to the brine case.
(B) In Class II, there may be a polarity reversal as the impedance of the reservoir is about the same as the surrounding layers, but may be higher or lower.
(C) In Class III and IV, the intercept amplitude (reflection coefficient) is large and negative in the brine filled case and increases in absolute amplitude as hydrocarbons are introduced. In Class III, the absolute amplitude increases with offset in the presence of hydrocarbons. In Class IV, the absolute amplitude decreases with offset in the presence of hydrocarbons. A bright spot occurs in the hydrocarbon case relative to the brine case.

Notably, Castagna & Swan's description of Class IV rocks was based upon an A versus B cross plot analysis where it has long been recognized that crossplotting of the A and B attributes from seismic data will show a 'background trend' that is often linear (Fig. 2, grey squares). Significantly, the Class I through IV sands are not coincident with the background trend line which was given lithological meaning by Smith & Gidlow (1987) and Fatti *et al.* (1994) when they presented the fluid factor concept. Mathematically the fluid factor is described by the following linear equation:

$$\Delta F = \frac{\Delta V_\mathrm{P}}{\bar{V}_\mathrm{P}} - k\left(\frac{\bar{V}_\mathrm{S}}{\bar{V}_\mathrm{P}}\right)\frac{\Delta V_\mathrm{S}}{\bar{V}_\mathrm{S}} \tag{3}$$

where

ΔF = fluid factor;
ΔV_P = change in P-wave velocity across the interface;
ΔV_s = change in S-wave velocity across the interface;
$\bar{V}_\mathrm{P}$ = average P-wave velocity across the interface;
$\bar{V}_\mathrm{s}$ = average S-wave velocity across the interface;
k = slope of the mudrock line of Castagna *et al.* (1985), or appropriate value for local lithology.

Swan (1993) later defined the fluid factor trend in terms of A and B assuming Gardner's relationship with the equation:

$$\Delta F = \frac{1}{5}\left[8 - k\left(\frac{\bar{V}_\mathrm{P}}{\bar{V}_\mathrm{S}}\right) + k\left(\frac{\bar{V}_\mathrm{S}}{\bar{V}_\mathrm{P}}\right)\right]A + \frac{1}{4}k\left(\frac{\bar{V}_\mathrm{P}}{\bar{V}_\mathrm{S}}\right)B. \tag{4}$$

By definition, the fluid factor should be close to zero for all water-bearing rocks, negative at the top of a gas-filled sand and positive at the base. However, this definition assumes that the layers above and below the boundary that produce the reflection share the same linear relationship between V_P and V_S, and have a constant $\bar{V}_\mathrm{P}/V_\mathrm{S}$. In practice this does not always happen and the assumptions used in defining the fluid factor trend line are often violated by the real Earth. The layers above and/or below the reservoir may not fit the 'mudrock line' defined by Castagna *et al.* (1985), or share any common linear relationship with respect to $\bar{V}_\mathrm{P}$ and $\bar{V}_\mathrm{S}$. The mudrock line defines an empirical linear relationship between P-wave velocity and S-wave velocity for water-bearing siliciclastic rocks of clay-sized or silt-sized particles. The introduction of lithologies other than sand and shale may invalidate this linear relationship or may produce a trend line which has a different slope and intercept.

Likewise, $V_\mathrm{P}/V_\mathrm{s}$ ratios usually decrease with depth owing to lithification. Shales are more variable and tend to have less stable $V_\mathrm{P}/V_\mathrm{s}$ ratios. If too large a time window is used to define the background trend line, there will naturally be a smearing of the data and possibly a bias in the trend line.

Methodology

Cross plot trends

The term fluid factor is somewhat ambiguous because the tight data clusters that control the variables in the trend line equation are not generated by fluid-filled sand versus shale interfaces, but rather come from shale–shale boundaries, silt–silt boundaries and shale–silt interfaces. As the sealing shale and high porosity reservoir rocks become more dissimilar in physical characteristics, the data points on an A versus B cross plot tend to migrate diagonally away from the fluid factor or shale line (Fig. 3, shale vectors). AVO analysis based upon a fluid factor trend line can work well for areas that consist of uniform sand–shale lithology and have well behaved $\bar{V}_p/\bar{V}_s$ ratios. In many instances, the layers creating the sand–shale interface do not share the same linear relationship between V_p and V_s or do not have a constant $\bar{V}_p/\bar{V}_s$ ratio. Subsequently, an A–B trend develops which does not pass through the origin as illustrated in Fig. 3. This graph was generated using the equations set forth in Castagna & Smith (1994), and porosity and shaliness were varied with respect to V_p using Wyllie's time average equation (Wyllie *et al.* 1958). The effects of increased hydrocarbon saturation were calculated using Gassmann's equation for fluid substitution. The upper and lower boundaries create two distinct 'sand trends' on the cross plot, which are radially symmetric with respect to the origin. The vectors show the relative movement of the trend lines as changes in lithology and pore fluid are introduced. As the saturation of gas increases, the greater contrast in Poisson's ratio causes the trend lines to move outward from the 'shale line' background trend. With increased shale volume in the sandstone, the two layers more closely share the same linear V_p, V_s relationship and the trend lines migrate toward the shale line. It is important to note that if the sand layer has a higher Poisson's ratio than the shale layer, the trend line for the shale over wet-sand interface may plot above the shale line, and the base-of-reservoir trend will fall below the shale line. Any gas effects would then move the data points toward the shale line and beyond with variable vector motions.

These models show the need to establish the trend of the shale versus wet-sand interface and to look for deviations from that trend in the area where hydrocarbons are expected. When a possible AVO anomaly is observed, it is best to analyse the down-dip equivalent reservoir interval to determine the true value for the background trend or possible 'wet-sand' trends that do not pass through the origin. Forward AVO modelling can provide information on what type of response to expect and how variations in lithology can affect the response. Predicting changes in lithology and the corresponding effects on the background or other trends is important for properly interpreting the A–B cross plots.

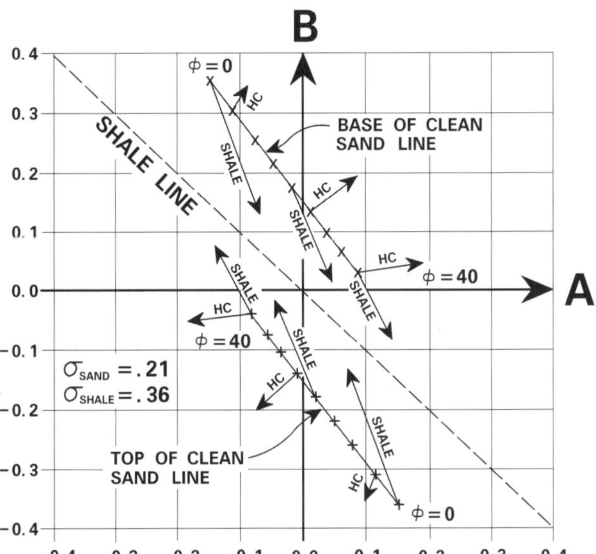

Fig. 3. This A versus B cross plot displays calculated values for a sandstone enclosed in a shale. The vectors represent the addition of shale and or hydrocarbons to the sandstone. Poisson's Ratios are displayed for the sand and shale.

A plus B sections

Once the best value for the background trend or shale line is established, the values of B can be scaled such that the local background trend or shale line takes on a slope of −1 (Fig. 3). When this occurs, A + B values tend toward zero for the shale line (positive A plus a negative B) and any hydrocarbon data are displayed as higher amplitude anomalies on the A + B section. Concurrently, an A + B section based upon a normalized shale line, when wet sand trends are present, will show the potential hydrocarbon anomalies at maximum absolute amplitudes and the wet sands at lower amplitudes, as displayed by the hydrocarbon arrows in Fig. 3. Figure 4 displays an unnormalized A + B attribute section and a normalized A + B attribute section with the distinct anomalies. Additionally, A + B plots concentrating on specific interfaces with wet-sand trends that do not pass through the origin can use a normalization of the slope and a shift in the B intercept to bring that trend through the origin. It must be understood that any resulting A + B section from such a procedure will be reflector specific and not valid for the rest of the section.

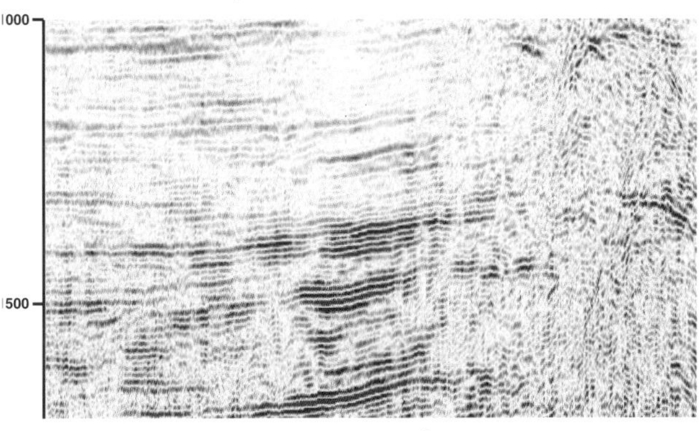

Fig. 4. These plots represent A + B sections in a sand–shale environment where gas is present. The top section displays an A + B section with no normalization of the A versus B cross plot, where as the bottom section are the same data after normalization.

Interpretation

The correlation of the seismic AVO response to empirical lithological data has greatly improved because of the growing rock physics database now available to geoscientists. In general, the more data that can be plotted and displayed in a horizon specific format, the better will be the understanding and predictive value of the AVO analysis. Much of this value is provided by the trend lines isolated on the A versus B cross plots which supply insight on the petrophysics of the layers.

The angle and offset from the origin of the trend line contain information about the difference in Poisson's ratio between the beds and the velocity contrast across the interface. In general, the A-axis provides information on impedance differences, while the B-axis provides information on Poisson's ratio differences. Reflections whose A and B values generate a trend which passes through the origin demonstrate layers which should have similar lithological/mineralogical compositions and $\bar{V}_p/\bar{V}_s$, while a trend with a non-zero B intercept shows dissimilar layers. When the interpreted information from the A versus B cross plot is combined with known geological information from wells, seismic interpretation, sequence stratigraphic analysis, etc., a more accurate picture of the detailed lithology can be developed. This information is helpful when interpreting stratigraphic events where a change in mineralogy is expected, such as at unconformities, in condensed sections, carbonate cemented sandstones or limestone stringers. The AVO cross plot information can go into building the geological models, and forward AVO modelling can be used to compare the AVO response to the predicted geological model. In this manner, a catalogue of AVO responses for possible geological variations can be built and the non-uniqueness of the AVO response can be established for the purpose of risk assessment.

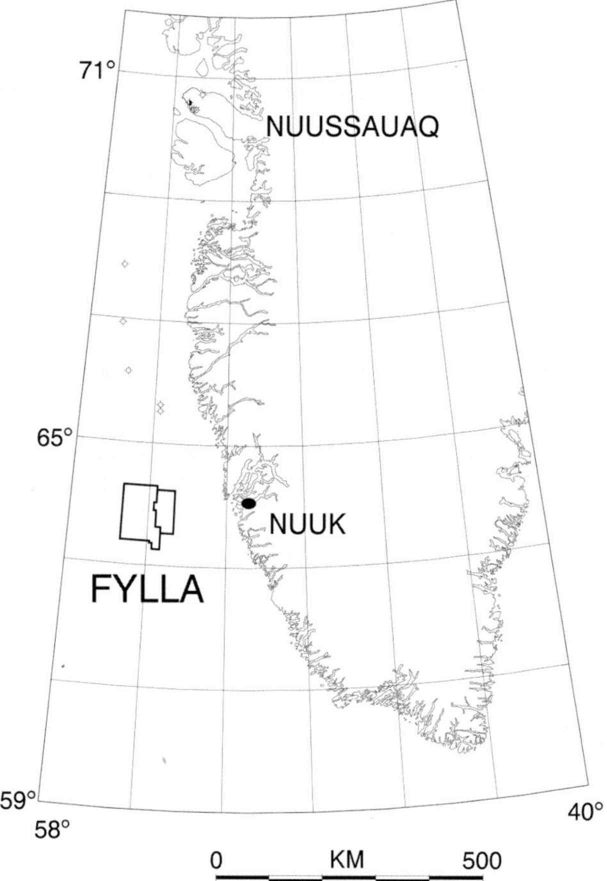

Fig. 5. Location map for West Greenland with Fylla License.

Case histories

Offshore West Greenland, Fylla area

Geological background. The Fylla area is located in the Labrador Sea–Davis Strait on the southwestern side of Greenland (Fig. 5). The structural setting is dominated by two Cretaceous age fault patterns. The older fault pattern is orientated NNW–SSE, and was created during early Cretaceous times when rifting was initiated between North America and Greenland. This rifting resulted in a series of half-graben, interpreted to be filled with coarse-grained, non-marine sediments. The remainder of the Cretaceous section is dominated by passive basin fill sediments, representing an overall transgression from fluvio–deltaic to marine depositional environments. During latest Cretaceous to earliest Eocene times, a second pulse of rifting created the second fault pattern which is oriented NNE–SSW in the Fylla area. This second pulse created large Cretaceous tilted fault blocks which were uplifted, eroded and subsequently covered by Palaeogene sediments consisting mainly of shales deposited during a period of passive subsidence.

Regional 2D seismic data acquired in 1992 generated interest in this area especially with the observation of flat events located within the seismic reflectors of large tilted fault blocks. The flat events are generated within an interval believed to be late Cretaceous in age and deltaic to marine in origin. The probable age equivalent unit that outcrops at Nuussauaq, West Greenland, is deltaic in origin with sand percentages ranging from almost 85% in proximal braided stream locations to 50% in distal deltaic sediments. The more distal marine, time equivalent section is not present in outcrop but is expected to contain sandy, pro-delta turbidites (Fig. 6). A comparative description of the play type is provide by Aram (1999).

AVO analysis. The AVO analysis provided significant information in the form of qualitative estimations of lithology types and sand amounts which were used to help develop the geological model for the potential reservoir. Flat seismic events are well developed on all lines for which structural closure was mapped. AVO analysis was performed on one particularly large structural closure depicted on the seismic line NUNA9401-203 (Fig. 7) where an increase in impedance is displayed as a peak (black). This line was chosen for the analysis because of its recent acquisition and high signal-to-noise ratio. The processing sequence was routine for AVO analysis and included a mild radon filter for water bottom multiple reduction, pre-stack time migration and a phase correction filter designed from the water bottom to achieve zero-phase data. True amplitude gain correction was thoroughly tested before application. This is a critical step as it affects the B values and the slope of the fluid line. The structure is located in 1200 m water depth so that the primary water bottom multiple occurs 300 ms below the flat spot, resulting in high quality data for the main area of interest. Every four CDPs (common depth points) were combined to create a super gather which was angle-limited from 0 to 30°. The analyses of the anomalies were performed with the use of interactive proprietary software that interfaced with a Landmark interpretation system. Figure 8 displays the regional A + B section based on a normalized trend line extracted from the reservoir interval down-dip of the flat spot.

Top reservoir. Analysis of the top reservoir (Fig. 7, location a disclosed a Class I AVO anomaly. The A versus B cross plot isolating the top reservoir reflector (Fig. 9) shows that the trend line for the reflector below the flat spot (water-wet trend,

Fig. 6. Exposed Cretaceous section on the north coast of Nuussauaq.

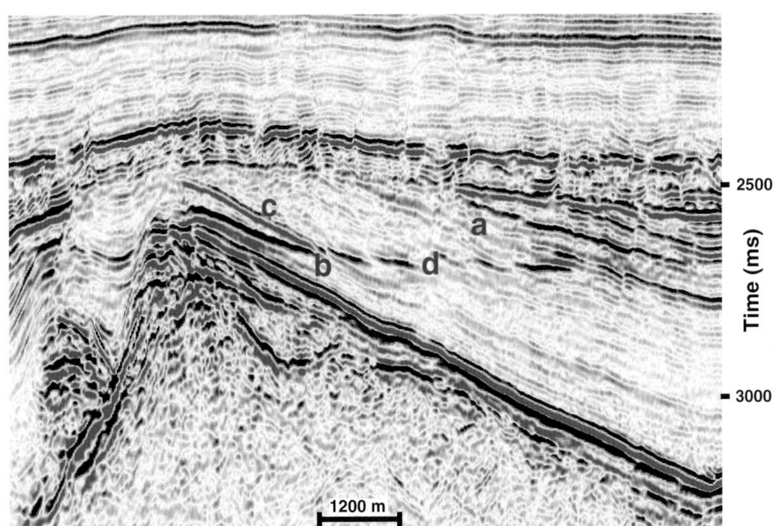

Fig. 7. Seismic line NUNA9401–203 displaying rotated fault block and flat spot where the data for the Greenland AVO example were extracted. locations **a**, **b**, **c** and **d** are anomalies analysed using A, B cross plotting.

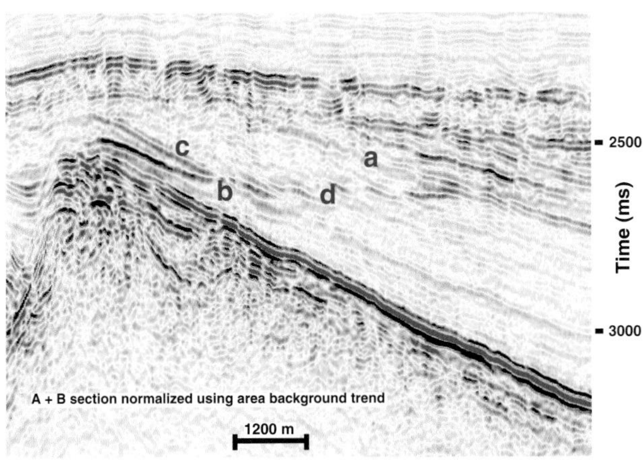

Fig. 8. A + B attribute section for seismic line NUNA9401-203 calculated using an average background trend for the area. Points **a**, **b**, **c** and **d** are anomalies analysed using A, B cross plotting.

grey squares) has a positive B-axis intercept. Significantly, the data points up-dip of the flat spot are displaced from this trend line (black points). This relationship describes a Class I AVO anomaly where the acoustic impedance of the brine and hydrocarbon-filled reservoir is higher than that of the overlying seal. The cross plot displays a wide spread in the x-axis intercept values which shows the variation in impedance differences along the upper reservoir interface. In places, the AVO anomaly could be Class II. The B-axis intercept for the water-wet trend line suggests that the reservoir unit and overlying seal are possibly of differing lithologic content and do not share the same linear relationship with respect to V_p and V_s. This conclusion supports the geological model which has this interface defined as a change in formations corresponding to an unconformity in the outcrops. The seismic stacking velocities and an inversion performed on the seismic data show the sealing formation to have consistently lower interval velocities than the reservoir formation. The crest of the structure is truncated by erosion and the stratified reservoir is here angularly unconformable. A younger sequence caps the

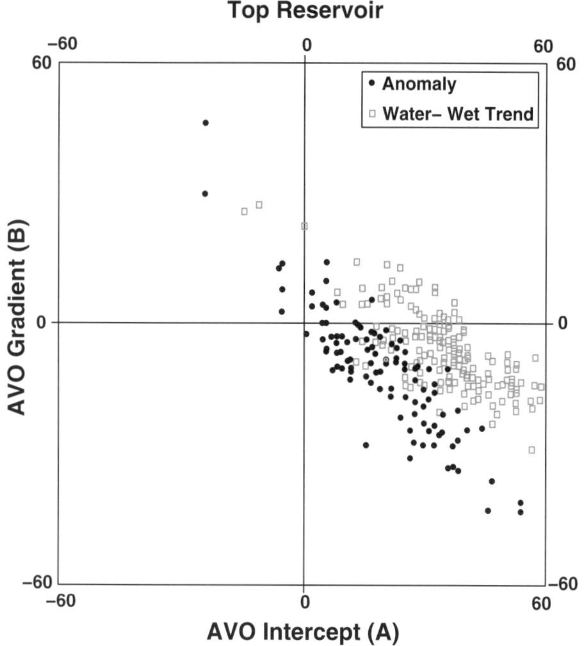

Fig. 9. An A versus B cross plot for the reflector defining the top reservoir, point a in Fig. 7. The grey squares represent data from the down-dip water-wet portion. The black points are data from within the potential gas interval but down-dip from the eroded crest.

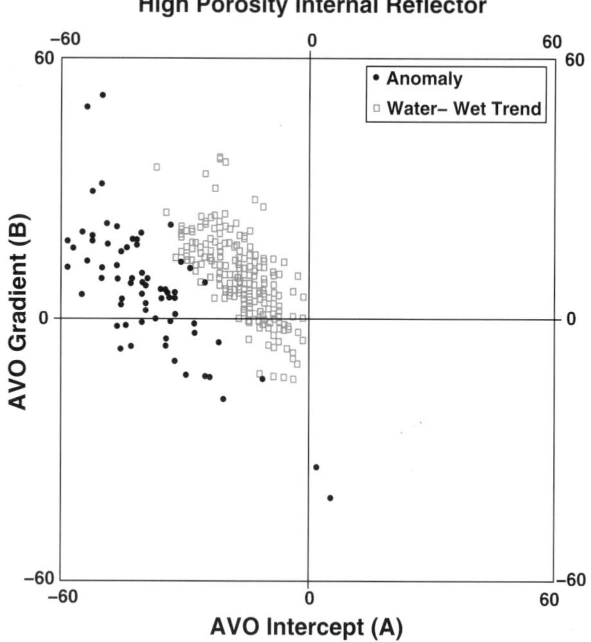

Fig. 10. An A versus B cross plot for the internal reflector labelled as point c in Fig. 7. The grey squares represent data from the down-dip water-wet extension of the reflector, while the black points are data from within the potential gas interval.

reservoir on the crest of the structure, while an older interval tops the anomaly on the flank (Fig. 7). Thus, it is not possible to determine a down-dip wet interface with A versus B trend analysis for the crestal anomaly and, without it, an AVO interpretation of the crestal area is less reliable.

Base reservoir. The stratigraphic base-of-reservoir is interpreted on the seismic data to be a strong peak above the flat spot changing to a weak peak in down-dip areas (Fig. 7, location b). The A versus B cross plot isolating this event (Fig. 2) shows very good development of the water-wet and potential hydrocarbon trends. This interface has a water-wet trend passing through the origin and an AVO anomaly showing both strong Class III and IV characteristics where the acoustic impedance of the underlying layer is higher than that of the potential hydrocarbon bearing layer. The geological model suggests that the stratigraphic base of the reservoir is represented by the transition of a silty/shaly section marking the end of the initial rift to an interval of increased sediment supply dominated by sandstones, siltstones and silty shales. These intervals would be dominated by sediments that closely follow the 'mudrock' V_p/V_s relationship, and would result in a water-wet or background trend line which passes roughly through the origin on an A versus B plot. The water-wet reflectivity amplitude is very weak, representing minor impedance changes between bottom seal and reservoir quality rock. The fluctuations from Class III to IV along the reflector are interpreted as minor lateral stratigraphic variations as porosity within the reservoir changes or the properties of the underlying shale or siltstone change. The interpretation of this anomaly added further support to the geological model and seismic interpretation.

Internal reflectors. The stratified nature of the potential reservoir unit allows for the development of AVO anomalies within the reservoir as varying lithology and porosity create tight and porous zones. Location c (Fig. 7) shows one such internal reflector on this structure. The A versus B cross plot isolating this event (Fig. 10) shows good development of the

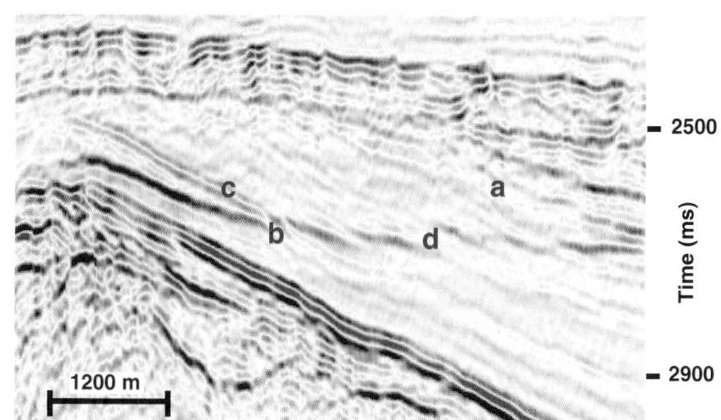

Fig. 11. Local A + B section of the internal reflector labelled as point c in Fig. 7, which was normalized using the water-wet trend established on the cross plot in Fig. 10.

water-wet and potential hydrocarbon trends which define this anomaly as Class IV. This internal reflector is interpreted as the interface between an overlying tight, fast layer, and an underlying sandstone with good porosity. The water-wet trend passes below the origin and is possibly caused by the high porosity sand or a lithologic difference in the overlying tight zone. Figure 11 is a detailed A + B section based on the normalized and shifted wet trend line. The trough (Fig. 11, c) shows higher amplitudes than the overlying peak defining the top of the tight zone (Fig. 7), suggesting that this might be an upward coarsening sequence or that the porosity of the underlying layer is quite high. These interpretations are highly dependent on data quality and geological understanding, and represent one of many possible scenarios.

Flat spot. Other internal AVO anomalies were identified, but are areally limited and do not represent such a consistent widespread stratigraphic event. These events are mostly associated with the shingled nature of the flat spot (Fig. 7, location d). The A versus B cross plot isolating this event

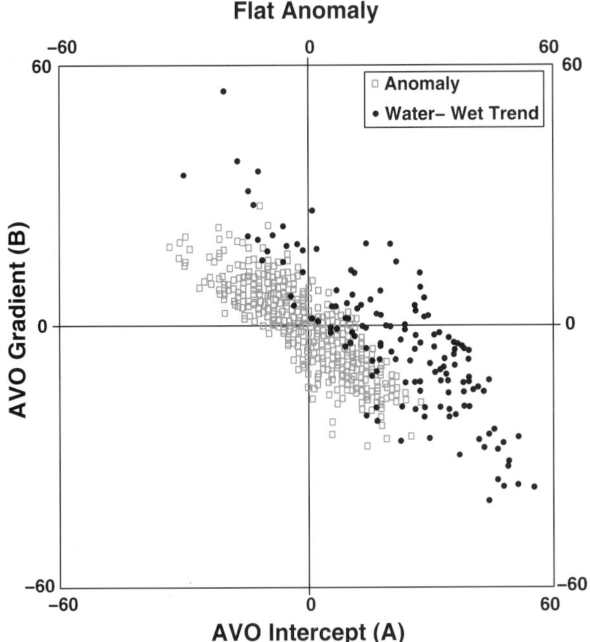

Fig. 12. An A versus B cross plot for the flat anomaly, point d in Fig. 7. The grey squares are from data within a 150 ms window, 50 ms below the flat spot. The black points are from data within the flat event.

(Fig. 12) has a background trend established from a 150 ms long window located 50 ms below the flat spot. The flat spot values plot as a scattering of points defining Class II, III and IV anomalies, which is expected because of the lithologically stratified nature of the reservoir unit. The shingled nature of the flat spot may be a result of seismic wavelet tuning, capillary effects from relative permeability changes caused by porosity variations, or some combination of the two. Figure 13 represents the quality of the data used and shows a NMO corrected gather extracted from a location where local Class III anomalies exist.

These combined interpretations complement the geological model and strongly suggest the presence of gas in the structure.

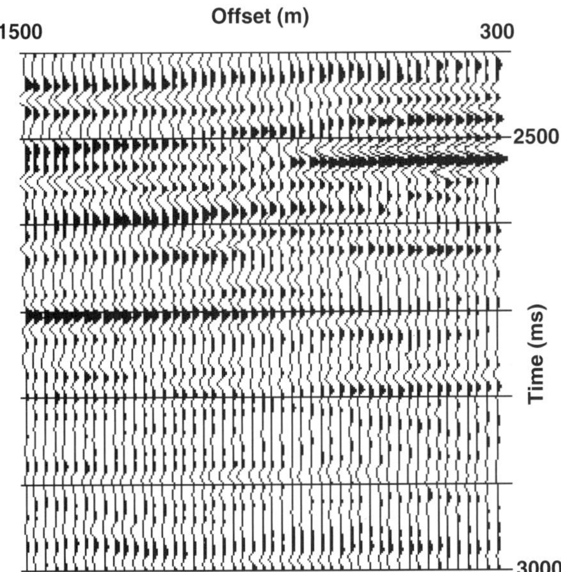

Fig. 13. An amplitude versus offset gather from the flat spot. Offset increases from right to left. A distinct increase in amplitude with offset is noted for the flat spot at 2700 ms.

The top reservoir shows a distinct Class I anomaly above the flat spot, with its characteristic decrease in amplitude. Below the flat spot, distinct dipping reflections within the reservoir interval are well-imaged, fairly uniform in amplitude and sub-parallel. In and above the flat spot, the reflection character of these same beds changes significantly, with both local increases and decreases in reflection amplitude representing AVO anomalies of Class II, III and IV. A more chaotic appearance in the reservoir unit is noted near the crest of the structure which may be associated with weathering from the overlying unconformity. The stratigraphic base of the reservoir also shows strong Class III and IV anomalies above the flat spot. The interpretation made is only possible because the seismic data are of very high quality and the magnitude of the structure and potential accumulation allows the development of widespread anomalies. There are many solutions possible, but the geological model developed for the area narrowed the selection.

Hammerfest Basin, Barents Sea

Geological background. The Hammerfest Basin is located in the southwestern portion of the Norwegian Barents Sea (Fig. 14). The dominant tectonic patterns resulted from the Caledonian Orogeny in Late Silurian–Early Devonian times, and today are expressed by a major northeast–southwest trending fault system bounding the basin to the south; a north–south fault system expanding the basin to the west; and an east–west trending system which dominates the structural orientation in the interior of the basin and bounds it to the north. The Hammerfest Basin began forming during the Late Jurassic and is predominantly a Cretaceous age extensional basin. The existing fields all have Middle Jurassic sandstone reservoirs and are sealed by the Upper Jurassic Hekkingen Formation which also serves as the source rock for the area. The fields discovered to date contain gas reservoirs with the exception of the Snøhvit Field which has a 14 m oil leg. Geochemical work has identified palaeo-oil legs in several fields.

An AVO study was performed with the goal of identifying any possible AVO anomalies present within a prospective area

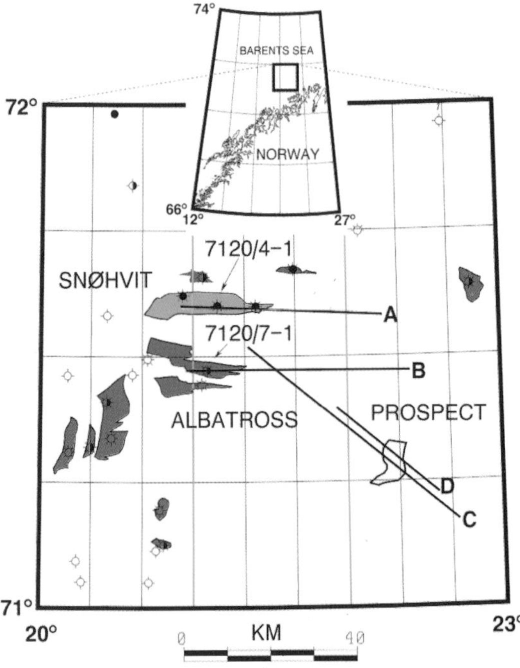

Fig. 14. Map of Hammerfest Basin with field, well and seismic line locations.

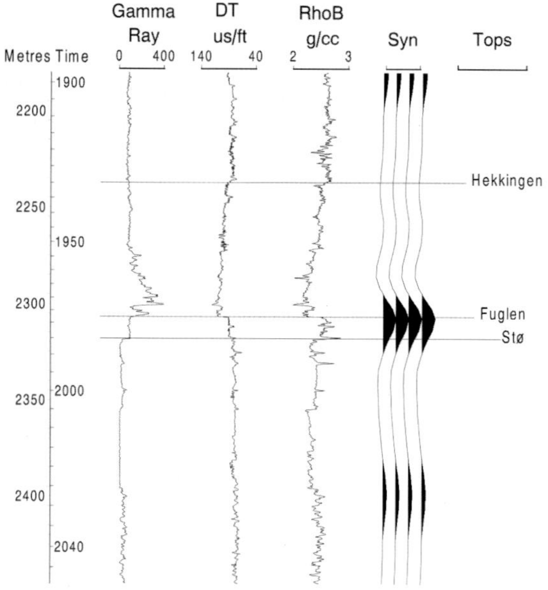

Fig. 15. Zero offset synthetic for well 7121/4-1.

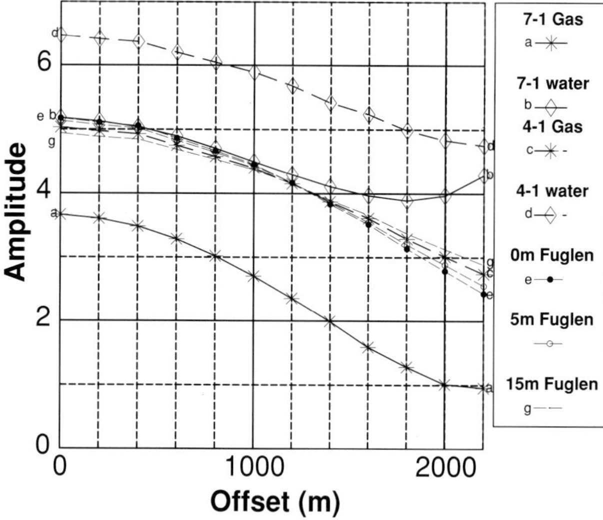

Fig. 17. Amplitude versus offset plot for top reservoir modelling of wells 7121/4-1 and 7121/7-1. The picks were derived from the peak for the Top Fuglen/Stø formations on the synthetic offset gathers generated during the forward modelling; Fig. 16 displays an example. The curves with Fuglen Formation thickness variations used the 4-1 well gas model as their base model.

available for application in the Barents Sea Project. The work consisted of forward AVO modelling of two wells in the central Hammerfest Basin, AVO processing of seismic data and analyses thereof. Wells 7120/4-1 and 7120/7-1 were modelled for the AVO responses of gas and water within the Stø Formation and for varying lithology overlying it. The four lines reprocessed for AVO analyses covered the prospective area and the modelled wells. The AVO models together with the geological model were used to analyse the seismic data in greater detail. In this case history of a subtle anomaly, forward modelling and A ,B analysis played a key role in understanding the prospect and interpreting the seismic data.

AVO forward modelling. AVO modelling using the Hampson–Russell software package was performed for well 7121/4-1 well on the Snøhvit Field, and well 7121/7-1 on the Albatross Field (Fig. 14). Shear wave velocity information was not available, thus V_p/V_s values were calculated using V_p versus V_s relationships from an empirical sampling of sandstones (Castagna *et al.* 1985, 1993) and V_p values from these and other area wells. Both wells were initially evaluated using Biot–Gassmann calculations to derive Poisson's ratios for the gas-filled and water-wet reservoirs. A dry rock Poisson's ratio of 0.16 gave a water-wet ratio of 0.245 and a 0.17 ratio for a gas reservoir with 15% water saturation. The wavelet used in the modelling was an average of the wavelets extracted at both well locations during the processing of the 2D seismic data.

The wells were modelled for the AVO responses of gas and water within the Top Middle Jurassic reservoir, Stø Formation. Also, seismic and geological mapping in the prospect area indicated that thickness and lithology fluctuations in the overlying shale horizons, the Fuglen and Hekkingen formations, were expected, and these variations were included in the modelling. Figure 15 displays a zero-offset synthetic for well 7121/4-1, while Fig. 16 displays the synthetic offset gather for the original gas filled case for this well. This gather displays a class I AVO anomaly at top reservoir, and a class III AVO anomaly at the base of the pay. The results of the modelling for the peak defining top Fulglen/Stø Formations are displayed in Fig. 17. Analysis of the forward modelling resulted in the following conclusions:

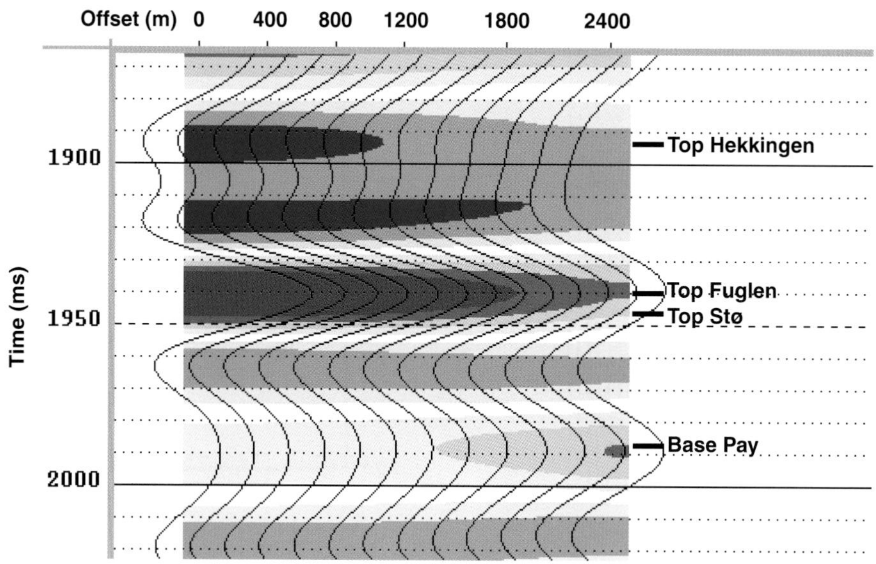

Fig. 16. Synthetic offset gather for the gas case of well 7121/4-1, generated using Hampson-Russell AVO package.

(1) The top of the Fuglen Formation is represented by a rise in acoustic impedance, represented by a peak. A subtle gas AVO response is noted at the top of the Stø Formation, characterized by a decrease in intercept amplitude caused by a loss in impedance, and an increasingly negative gradient caused by the change in Poisson's ratio (curves a, b, c and d on Fig. 17).
(2) Hydrocarbon fill history and the nature of capillary action have caused a long gas–water transition zone consisting of deeper residual low gas saturated intervals. AVO responses from these intervals may destructively interfere to effectively mask the AVO response for the base pay.
(3) The presence of the Fuglen Formation, not more than 20 m thick in this portion of the Hammerfest Basin, has a minor influence on the AVO intercept amplitude, but the gradient response is noticeably reduced as its thickness increases (Figs 15–17 curves e, f, and g).
(4) The two wells studied show that lithology and thickness changes in the overlying Hekkingen Formation affect the amplitude of the top Stø Formation peak. Impedance contrasts within the Hekkingen Formation, Fig. 15, create tuned reflection events with the top Fuglen Formation. Thus, any thickness variations result in amplitude variations related to a tuning curve defined by the seismic wavelet. These changes can completely mask the intercept AVO response. For example, the reduction in amplitude caused by gas could be offset by thickening the Hekkingen interval, but the gas could still be detected by observing the change in gradient response.
(5) Figure 17 shows similar gradients for all the models with the exception of the two water-wet cases which have the lowest absolute gradients.

The modelling has shown that the AVO response is subtle and that insight into possible lithology and thickness variations in the overlying units is required to properly interpret the AVO displays.

AVO analysis. The four seismic lines reprocessed for AVO analyses were speculative data and included two lines intersecting the modelled wells over the Snøhvit and Albatross fields, and two lines that crossed the main prospect in the application area (Fig. 14). The three longer lines A, B and C are of the same vintage and allow coverage from the existing fields into the prospect area. The processing sequence was routine and similar to that described in the Greenland example. Noisy data on one line and residual multiple energy in all the data make the AVO analyses difficult, and possibly obscure many of the subtle AVO effects.

Seismic line A tying well 7121/4-1 and extending the length of the Snøhvit Field showed no AVO anomalies during the A versus B cross plotting. The thick Fuglen Formation present in this area, up to 20 m thick, reduced most of the gradient response. Also, seismic mapping indicated that the Hekkingen Formation thickened off structure. As discussed earlier, this thickening may have partially compensated for the expected change in the intercept amplitude by wavelet tuning. Residual gas saturations may also have minimized the AVO response for the base reservoir across the field, as discussed in the modelling conclusions. The weak AVO response predicted by forward modelling for the Snøhvit Field was easily masked by geological variations.

A slight AVO response is indicated over the Albatross Field on seismic line B which ties well 7121/7-1 and is located on the eastern flank of the field. Figure 18 shows an A versus B cross plot of the peak that defines the top-of-reservoir. The red points are in the field area and the blue points are from an area down-dip of the zones noted for residual hydrocarbon saturation in the well. For a given intercept amplitude, the zone over the field has a higher absolute gradient.

Seismic line D, located over the crest of the prospect has generally noisy data with good underlying structural resolution. On the east side of the prospect, the Top Middle Jurassic is not faulted and dips from the crest of the field into the Troms–Finnmark Fault (Fig. 19). At this location, there are no shallow anomalies affecting the data, but offsets were limited to 1100 m and did not allow for the development of a strong AVO response at the far-offset traces. A gradient anomaly is observed over the crest of the prospect (Fig. 21). The intercept (Fig. 20) also shows a slight increase in amplitude over the crest which could indicate changes in the overlying Hekkingen Formation. The relatively strong gradient is consistent with the modelled result where gas is present and the Fuglen Formation is very thin or absent. Regional mapping of the Fuglen Formation suggests that regional thinning is to be expected to the southeast and over structural highs. The A + B section (Fig. 22) was normalized using the water-wet trend from this line. One interpretation of this anomaly is that a small gas cap in the crest of the prospect has caused an AVO effect. However, the limited offset range and noise in the data lower the confidence in any interpretation.

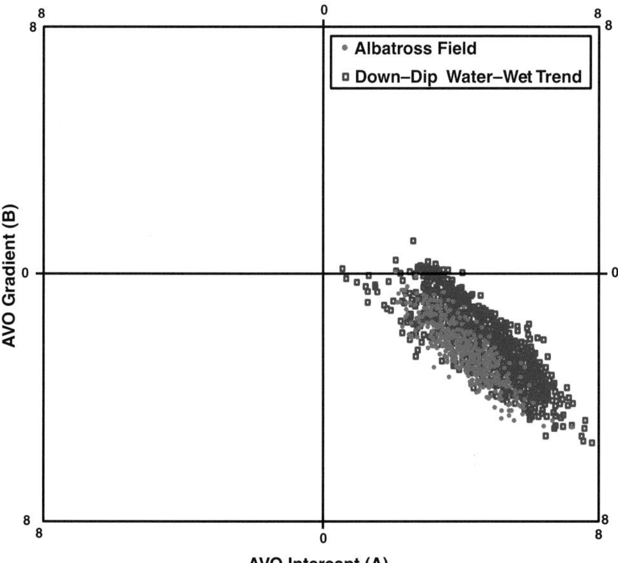

Fig. 18. An A versus B cross plot for the reflector defining top reservoir, seismic line B displayed in Fig. 14.

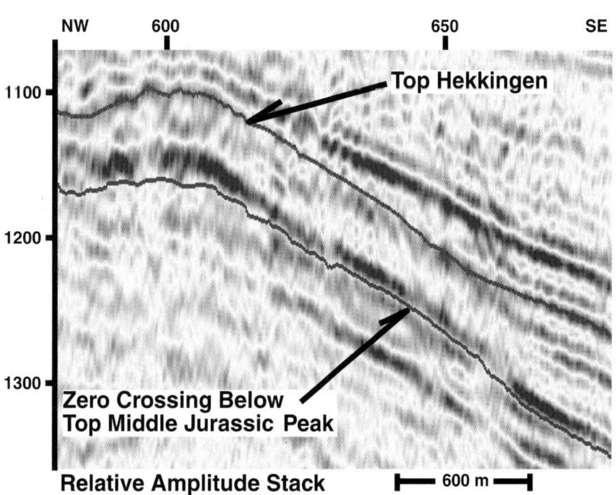

Fig. 19. Relative amplitude stack of seismic line D displaying prospect crest and eastern flank.

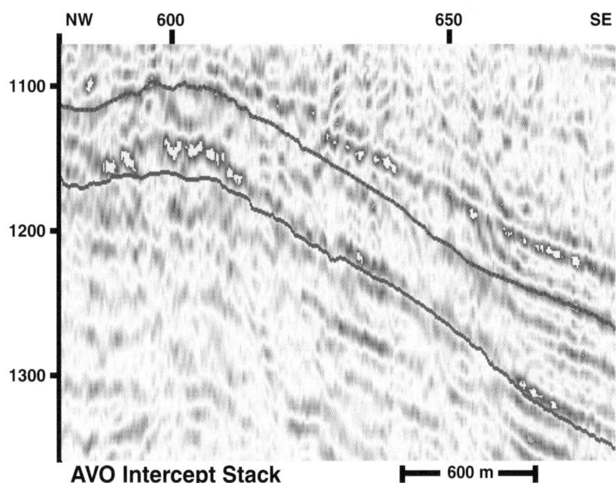

Fig. 20. AVO Intercept attribute section of seismic line D.

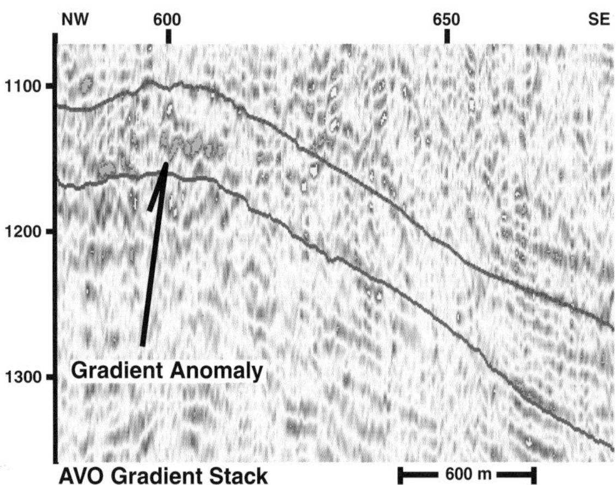

Fig. 21. AVO Gradient attribute section of seismic line D.

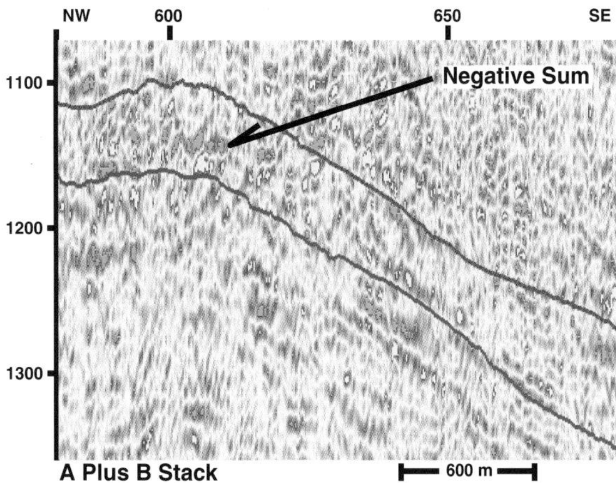

Fig. 22. A + B attribute section of seismic line D.

Summary

The use of A and B attributes combined with forward modelling has made AVO analysis a more useful and more reliable prediction tool for explorationists. Cross plotting A and B values to determine trends has allowed for a new classification scheme and a fast technique for relating measured AVO attributes to the petrophysical properties which create them.

The two examples presented in this paper represent two extremes in AVO analysis. The West Greenland area displays very complex geology with strong, conflicting AVO anomalies which required A, B cross plotting to adequately separate and classify the various anomalies. Analyses of the stratigraphic top, stratigraphic bottom, internal reflectors and the flat spot have resulted in the identification of all classes of AVO anomalies. The investigation resulted in strong evidence for the presence of gaseous hydrocarbons and provided information to develop and strongly support the current geological model.

The Hammerfest Basin example showed a very subtle AVO anomaly where forward modelling was used to determine the expected AVO response and A , B cross plotting was used to analyse the data. Expected changes in the geology were incorporated into the forward modelling to aid in the interpretation. This work identified a possible small gas cap on a fairly large prospect which when combined with the exploration model of remigrated oil and gas, helped address one critical risk factor. The factors common to both examples were the need for a good geological model to interpret properly, and extract information from the AVO analysis, and a good understanding of the limitations of the seismic data and forward AVO models.

We wish to acknowledge our partners in the Fylla License (Statoil, DOPAS, and Nunaoil) and thank them for permission to publish this paper. We thank the Danish Ministry of Resource Administration and Nunaoil for allowing the publication of the West Greenland seismic data. Thanks also to GECO for allowing the publication of the data in the Hammerfest Basin. B. Barrett and D. Burge of Phillips Petroleum are to be commended for their work on the AVO processing.

References

ARAM, R. B. 1999. West Greenland versus Vøring Basin: comparison of the deepwater frontier exploration plays. *In*: FLEET, A. J. & BOLDY, S. A. R. (eds) *Petroleum Geology of Northwest Europe: Proceedings of the 5th Conference*. Geological Society, London, 315–324.

CASTAGNA, J. P. & SMITH, S. W. 1994. Comparison of AVO indicators: A modelling study. *Geophysics*, **59**(12), 1849–1855.

—— & SWAN, H. W. 1997. Principles of AVO crossplotting. *The Leading Edge*, **16**(4), 337–342.

——, BATZLE, M. L. & EASTWOOD, R. L. 1985. Relationship between compressional-wave and shear-wave velocity in clastic silicate rocks. *Geophysics*, **50**, 571–581.

——, —— & KAN, T. K. 1993. Rock Physics – The link between rock properties and AVO response. *In*: CASTAGNA, J. P. & BACKUS, M. M. (eds) *Offset-Dependent Reflectivity – Theory and Practice of AVO Analysis. SEG*, 135–171.

FATTI, J. L., SMITH, G. C., VAIL, P. J., STRAUSS, P. J. & LEVITT, P. R. 1994. Detection of gas in sandstone reservoirs using AVO analysis: A 3-D seismic case history using the Geostack technique. *Geophysics*, **59**(9), 1362–1376.

RUTHERFORD, S. R. & WILLIAMS, R. H. 1989. Amplitude-versus-offset variations in gas sands. *Geophysics*, **54**(6), 680–688.

SHUEY, S. T. 1985. A simplification of the Zoeppritz equations. *Geophysics*, **50**, 609–614.

SMITH, G. C. & GIDLOW, P. M. 1987. Weighted stacking for rock property estimation and detection of gas. *Geophysical Prospecting*, **55**, 993–1014.

SWAN, H. W. 1993. Properties of direct AVO hydrocarbon indicators. *In*: CASTAGNA, J. P. & BACKUS, M. M. (eds) *Offset-Dependent Reflectivity – Theory and Practice of AVO Analysis. SEG*, 78–92.

WYLLIE, M. R. J., GREGORY, A. R., GARDNER, G. H. F. 1958. An experimental investigation of factors affecting elastic wave velocities in porous media. *Geophysics*, **23**, 680–688.

Applications of the coherency cube in the UKCS

M. J. HUGHES, S. DHANANI, R. K. FRIMPONG, M. GAINSKI, N. L. HASKELL, R. P. HEATH, J. D. KANTOROWICZ, P. M. MAGUIRE and S. E. NISSEN

Amoco (U.K.) Exploration Company, Amoco House, West Gate, Ealing, London, W5 1XL, UK

Abstract: Seismic coherency is a measure of the similarity between seismic traces. Coherency data play an important role in the delineation of structural and stratigraphic features by enhancing the images seen on conventional 3D seismic data. Through integration of coherency data with other technologies and calibration to well data, new applications are emerging. This paper discusses three examples from the UKCS.

Partial permeability barriers in the Leman Field were known to exist from well pressure data. A coherency cube revealed several lineations that separated the wells. These lineations can be correlated to a previously unmapped fault trend with very small throws on the vertical seismic lines. The coherency cube therefore provided additional information to improve confidence in the interpretation and enabled significant time-savings in the fault pattern interpretation.

Coherency data were used to assist in the well planning for the Arkwright Field development programme. Coherency slices through high pressure zones were characterized by polygonal faulting, whilst less faulting was observed in areas of lower pore pressure. These pressure zones were calibrated to pore pressures predicted from the original discovery well. The development trajectories were optimized with respect to the fault patterns interpreted from the coherency data. Model predictions were confirmed by drilling results.

A coherency cube was utilized to enable a quick interpretation of the structural framework of an area of the Central Graben. In particular the distribution of faulted Triassic rafts and Jurassic rifts is easily observed because the relatively coherent Jurassic reflectors contrast well with the relatively incoherent Triassic seismic reflectivity.

These three examples illustrate how coherency data can be used in production, development and exploration settings to improve the imaging of geological features ranging in scale from reservoir barriers to major faults.

Coherency is a measure of the similarity between a number of adjacent seismic traces. The degree of similarity between the traces can be measured by a variety of methods including cross correlation, semblance and eigenstructure (Bahorich & Farmer 1994; Marfurt *et al.* 1995; Gersztenkorn & Marfurt 1996). High coherency values represent areas where seismic traces are similar, whereas low coherency values occur where the adjacent seismic traces show more variation. Coherency algorithms are typically applied to 3D seismic data which have been loaded onto workstations creating a second volume of data called a coherency cube. Areas of discontinuity within the 3D seismic volume such as channel margins or faults appear greatly enhanced in the corresponding coherency cube data.

Over the last few years coherency data have been increasingly used in conjunction with conventional seismic data. Coherency is commonly generated at the start of a 3D interpretation project. This allows both faster interpretation and improved confidence in fault patterns (especially fault linkages) and large-scale stratigraphic features (Roberts *et al.* 1996). Coherency data has been of most benefit in complex geological settings and areas with poor quality seismic data.

Integration of coherency data with information from other technologies can provide additional insights. This paper discusses three case histories illustrating some innovative uses of coherency data.

Case history 1: partial permeability barriers in the Leman Field

The Leman Field is a giant gas field centred on UK Blocks 49/26 and 49/27 in the Southern North Sea (Fig. 1). The field is a faulted anticline that stretches for 50 km in an elongate NW–SE direction. Reservoir production is from Permian Rotliegend Group sandstones (Cameron *et al.* 1992) which are mainly aeolian in origin. These are vertically sealed by the overlying Zechstein Group which is predominantly carbonate

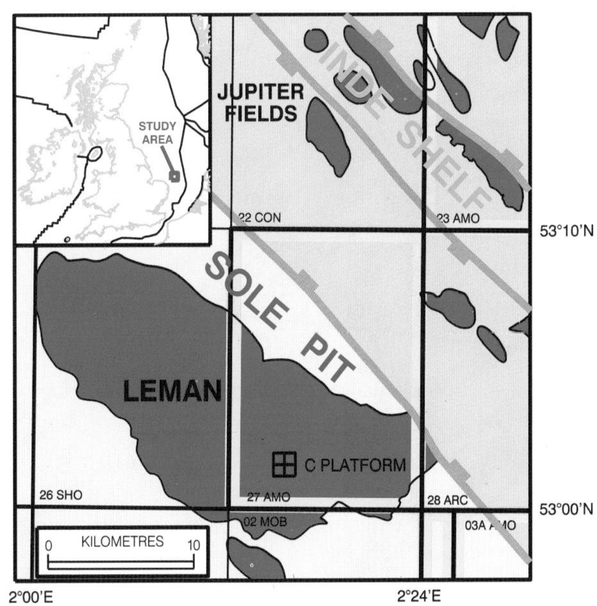

Fig. 1. Location map of the Leman Field.

HUGHES, M. J., DHANANI, S., FRIMPONG, R. K., GAINSKI, M., HASKELL, N. L., HEATH, R. P., KANTOROWICZ, J. D., MAGUIRE, P. M. & NISSEN, S. E. 1999. Applications of the coherency cube in the UKCS. *In*: FLEET, A. J. & BOLDY, S. A. R. (eds) *Petroleum Geology of Northwest Europe: Proceedings of the 5th Conference*, 1299–1305.

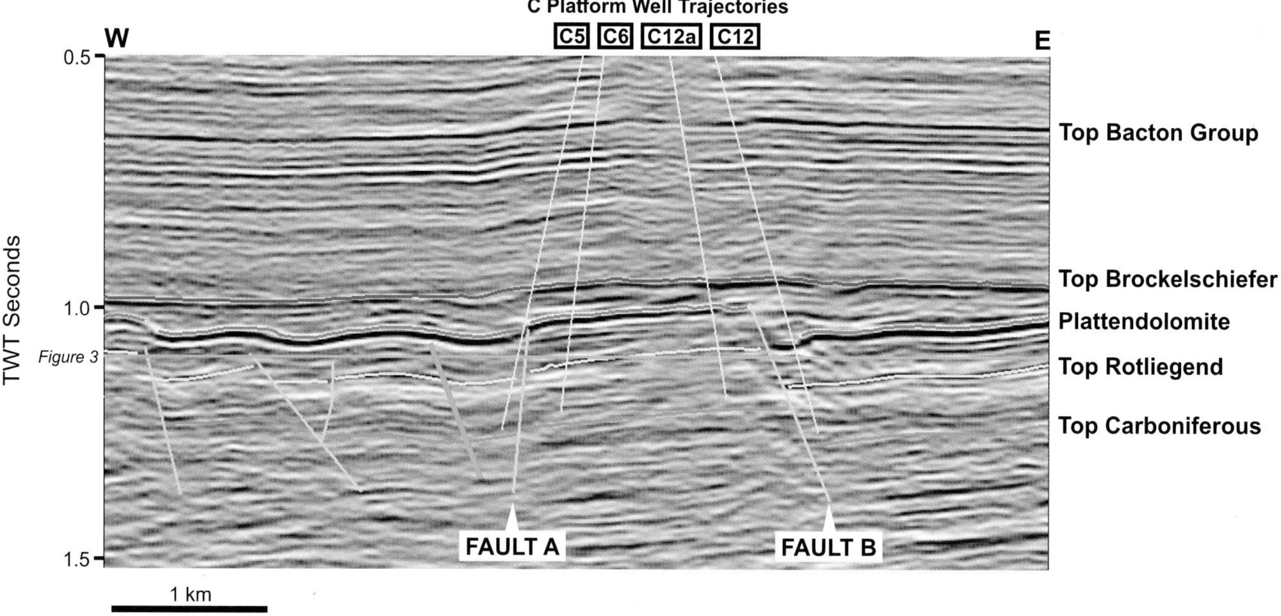

Fig. 2. Seismic line through the Leman C Platform area. (Location shown in Fig. 3.)

and anhydrite below the Plattendolomit whilst being halite rich above. The mobile salts have undergone plastic deformation to accommodate the underlying fault movement (Fig. 2). The Triassic sequence commences with a thin Brockelschiefer interval followed by the Bacton Group.

This case history focuses on the area around the C platform in the southern part of the Leman field (Fig. 1). Reservoir pressure data indicate that this area of the field contains several pressure regimes, interpreted as being the result of partial permeability barriers within the reservoir. The C8 and C12 wells were known to lie in a separate fault block which had been mapped using 2D seismic data. However, the cause of the pressure anomaly at the C5 well had not been identified.

Following the acquisition of a 3D seismic survey in 1995 a coherency cube was generated. A coherency slice at 1100 ms (through the Rotliegend and lower Zechstein intervals) is shown in Fig. 3. The encircled numbers on the figure indicate C platform well locations at Top Rotliegend. Immediately

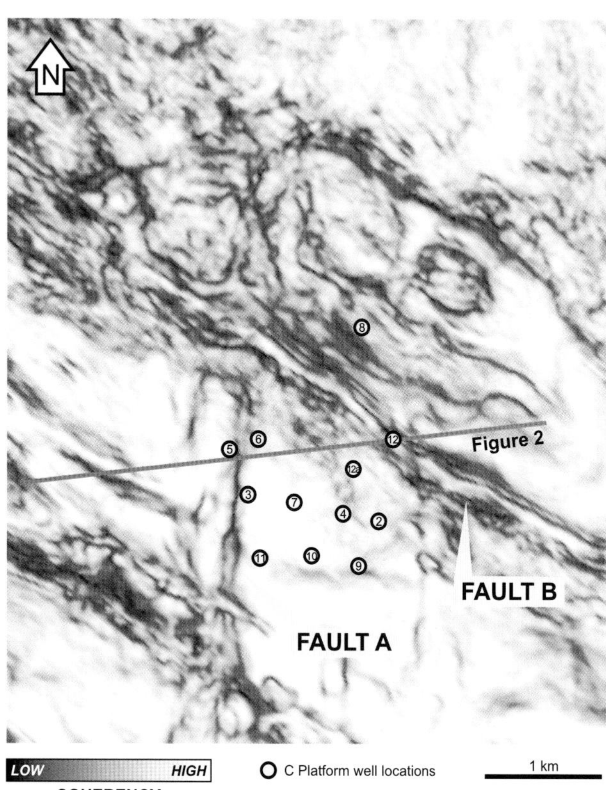

Fig. 3. Coherency slice at 1100 ms from the Leman C Platform area showing the position of a N–S low coherency lineation (Fault A) that isolates the C5 well.

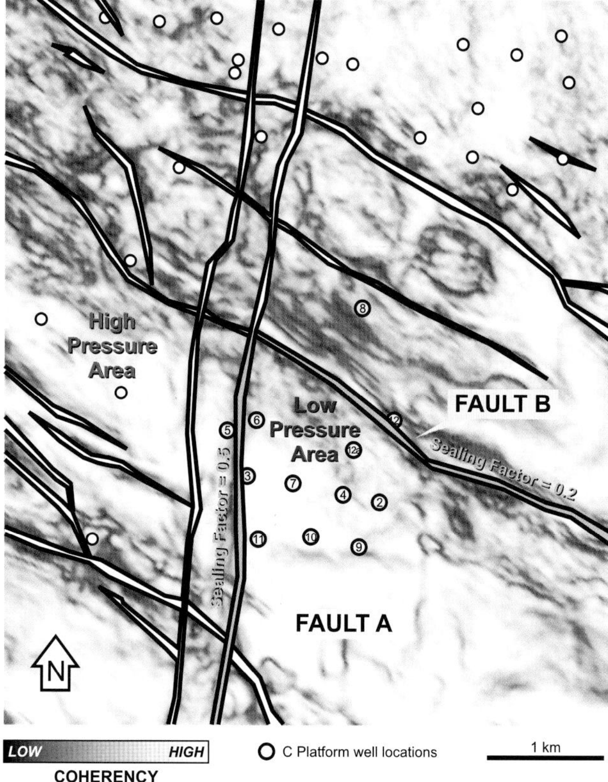

Fig. 4. Coherency slice at 1100 ms with fault interpretation at Top Rotliegend and fault seal data around the C platform from a reservoir simulation run.

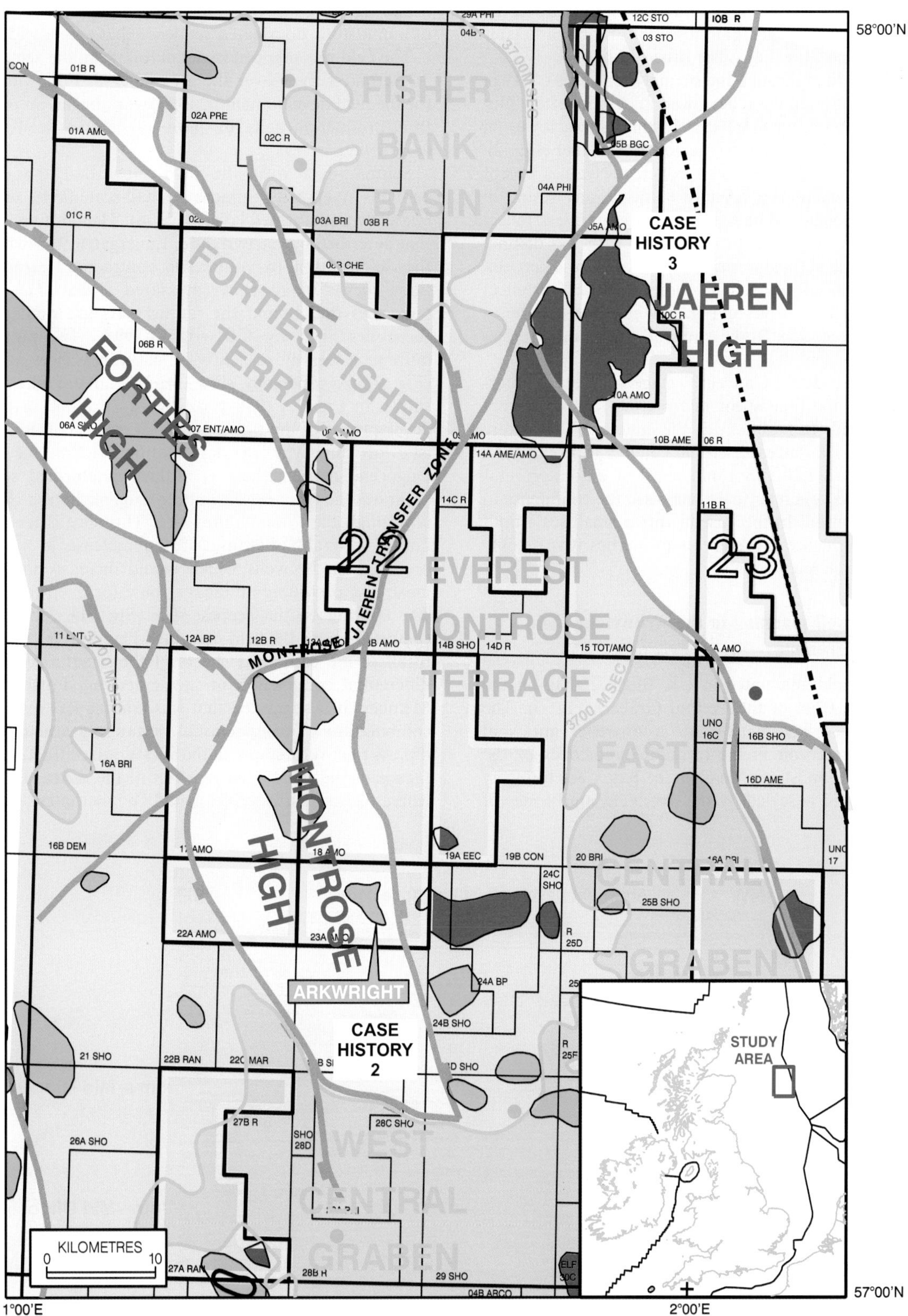

Fig. 5. Location map of the East Central Graben.

evident is a N–S trending low coherency lineation separating C5 from the remaining C platform wells (Fault A in Fig. 3). This lineation can be correlated to a fault with a small offset on the vertical seismic (Fault A in Fig. 2).

Reservoir simulation work has shown that a pressure barrier is required to separate the low reservoir pressure area around the C platform from a higher pressure area to the west. The faults identified were assigned a sealing factor between 0 (completely sealing) and 1 (no impact on reservoir flow). Fault A was assigned a sealing factor of 0.5 indicating that it forms a partially sealing reservoir barrier (Fig. 4).

Leveille *et al.* (1997) describe similar N–S trending faults in the Jupiter Fields area (25 km north) where, despite the small throws, the faults have a greater sealing potential when compared to other fault trends. This is explained by the high lateral continuity of these faults and their damage zones (when viewed regionally), the presence of halite and anhydrite in the fault rock cement and the fact that these faults represent a later phase of deformation (as they offset other faults).

The coherency slices through the strongly reflective package from the Top Rotliegend to the lower Zechstein often illuminate the fault patterns more clearly than slices lower in the Rotliegend Group where the reflectors are weaker (Fig. 2). The strong reflectors generate high coherency values except in faulted areas where the reflector terminations result in pronounced low coherency lineations. The deeper, less reflective data have a lower signal to noise ratio with less distinct terminations on the vertical seismic and less contrast between the faulted and unfaulted areas on coherency data. This effect is seen in the northern edge of Fig. 3 where the coherency slice cuts the base of the Rotliegend and the faults are less well defined.

Using coherency data at an early stage in the 3D interpretation project, the time spent interpreting faults was significantly decreased. In addition, as the coherency data were generated from an un-flattened seismic volume, it provided an image of the faulting that is not influenced by any interpretation. As a result the coherency data increased the confidence in the fault interpretation. In this case history a small-scale fault with important influence on reservoir properties was quickly mapped using the coherency data.

Case history 2: well planning in the Arkwright Field development programme

The Arkwright Field is situated in UK Block 22/23a on the Forties–Montrose High of the Central Graben (Fig. 5). The discovery well was drilled in 1990 into a low-relief, anticlinal closure with the reservoir in the turbidite sandstones of the Paleocene Forties Sandstone Member (of Knox & Holloway 1992). The structure is sealed by the overlying mudstones of the Sele Formation. The remainder of the overburden consists of a mudstone dominated sequence that exceeds 2500 m thick.

The field was mapped in detail following the acquisition of a 3D seismic survey over the area in 1993. Following approval for the field development in 1995, work began on planning for three production wells (for more information see Kantorowicz *et al.* 1999).

Seismic data over the field show that the overburden contains layers with numerous small-scale faults separated by relatively undeformed layers (Fig. 6). The faulting is similar to that described by Cartwright & Lonergan (1996) who attribute the deformation to volumetric contraction during compactional dewatering of overpressured shales. The condensed sequences that bound the faulted tiers are similar in age to those described by Cartwright (1994). The nature of the faulting is seen more clearly on coherency slices over the field (Fig. 7). A coherency slice through an unfaulted section is shown in Fig. 7A (952 ms). Figure 7B (1560 ms) shows the development of the polygonal fault trace geometry characteristic of this type of deformation. Below the Intra-Mid Oligocene marker there is a thin undeformed section that separates the two tiers of faulting (Fig. 6). Figure 7C (2100 ms) is through the lower faulted tier. This slice is less intensively faulted probably because of the increase in sand content observed in the wells which would increase horizontal permeability, providing an escape route for overpressured fluids. The faulting on the deepest slice (Fig. 7D, 2556 ms) is concentrated above the field margins where the dip is steepest as a result of the combined effects of the structural anticline and differential compaction in the underlying Forties Sandstone Member. It is suggested that this faulting has resulted from a combination of compactional dewatering and the effects of dip. As the overpressure in the shales neared fracture levels, the failure would have occurred first in the areas of steepest dip where the local stress field would be most intense.

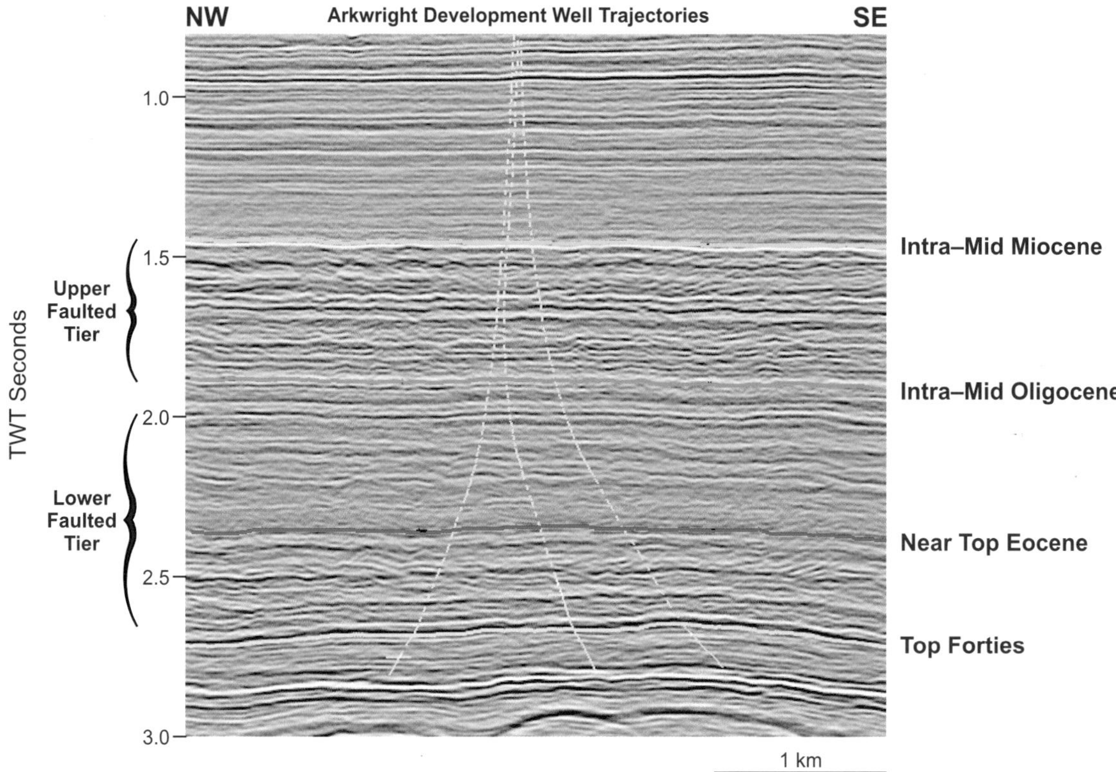

Fig. 6. Seismic line through the Arkwright Field (courtesy of PGS) showing proposed development well locations. Note the pervasive faulting in the upper and lower faulted tiers.

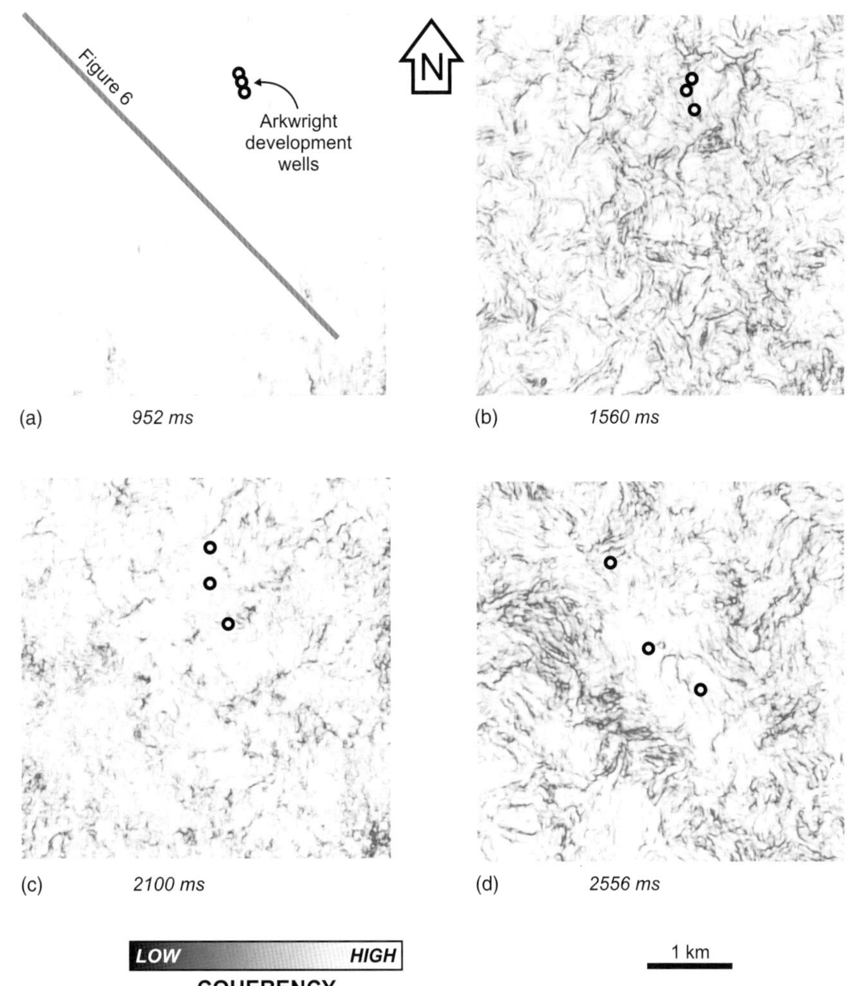

Fig. 7. Coherency slices above the Arkwright Field through undeformed and faulted levels.

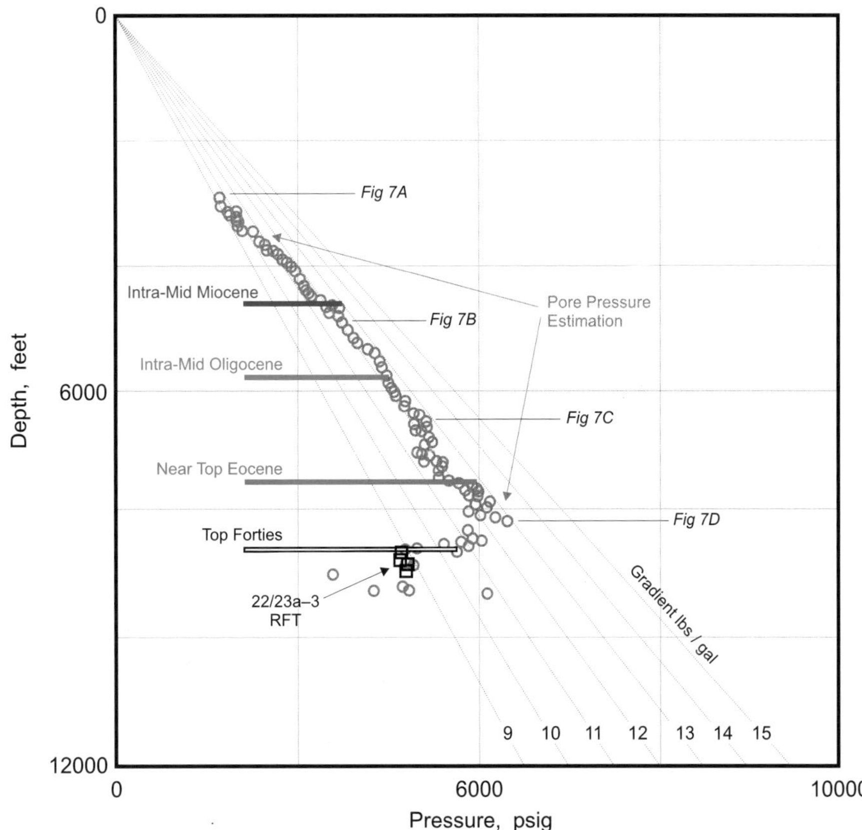

Fig. 8. Pore pressure estimation from the Arkwright discovery well. The seismic markers from Fig. 6 are shown along with the positions of the slices from Fig. 7.

Figure 8 shows a plot of a pore pressure estimation based on the sonic log data of the discovery well. Normal (hydrostatic) pressure is approximated by the 9 lbs/gal^{-1} line. It can be seen that the faulted slices occur in areas of marked overpressure which are probably close to fracture pressure. The faults may be acting as bleed valves (as described by Sibson *et al.* 1975) whereby pore fluids which have become highly pressured during burial are intermittently released through the faults in such a manner that overpressure remains at depth.

From the earlier discussion, it can be seen that within these shales, areas with low coherency values (highly faulted) can be inferred as being of relatively high pressure whereas high coherency levels (unfaulted) have lower pressure. This information was used to impact the calculation of appropriate mud weights, and to facilitate the design of the casing scheme. Drilling through these faults with an excessive mud weight may cause the pore pressure to exceed the fracture gradient, with a consequent loss of drilling fluid into the fault. Casing was set above and below the faulted zone thus isolating the hydrostatically pressured Forties Sandstone Member.

A further use of the coherency cube was to ensure that the proposed well paths were designed to avoid drilling along faults planes. The progressively deeper positions of the well paths from a drilling centre offset to the northeast of the field are shown on Fig. 7. The intensely faulted areas were avoided in a potentially unstable zone above the reservoir (Fig. 7D). However, some of the small-scale faults are unavoidable, thus the strategy utilized was to anticipate the type of instability that might occur and plan the drilling mud weight response accordingly.

All three development wells were drilled through the overburden without significant drilling problems. However, difficulties in accurately setting casing above the reservoir in two wells created a number of minor problems which confirmed the instability of the overpressured zones when exposed to the lower mud weights needed for the reservoir section.

Case history 3: structural interpretation of the Jaeren High

The Jaeren High lies on the eastern margin of the Fisher Bank Basin and the East Central Graben (Fig. 5). The structural evolution of the area has been described by Penge *et al.* (1993, 1999). During the main period of regional extension (late Triassic to Early Cretaceous) large fault blocks of Triassic sediments were translated and rotated on the Permian Zechstein salt substrate forming relatively undeformed, discrete blocks called rafts. The rafts are separated by rifts that have been filled by the reactive and active rise of the Zechstein salt and the deposition of a thicker Jurassic/Cretaceous section.

Figure 9 shows a typical seismic line through a series of rifts and rafts. The structural highs at the Base Cretaceous event define the position of the rafts which consist of a thick, acoustically quiet, sequence of Triassic sediments overlying a thin Zechstein layer. The lows in the Base Cretaceous show the position of the rifts which contain a more reflective sediment infill above the chaotic seismic character of the Zechstein salt. The spatial distribution of the rifts (lows) and rafts (highs) can be seen in the 3D illumination of the Base Cretaceous TWT surface in Fig. 10A.

Coherency data can be used as a complimentary method of imaging the structural fabric. The rifts contain bright, continuous reflectors (above top Zechstein) that result in high coherency values whereas the rafts consist of a lower amplitude, more disordered sequence with lower coherency values. Figure 10B shows a 3D image of the Base Cretaceous coloured by coherency values at Base Cretaceous that clearly illustrate the position of the rifts. The coherency data also allow the detailed mapping of faults in both the rifted and rafted areas.

Figure 10C contains only the high coherency data in a window stretching 100 ms below Base Cretaceous. The low coherency data have been made transparent using voxel rendering software. The high coherency areas in the rifts are visible through the semi-transparent Base Cretaceous TWT surface.

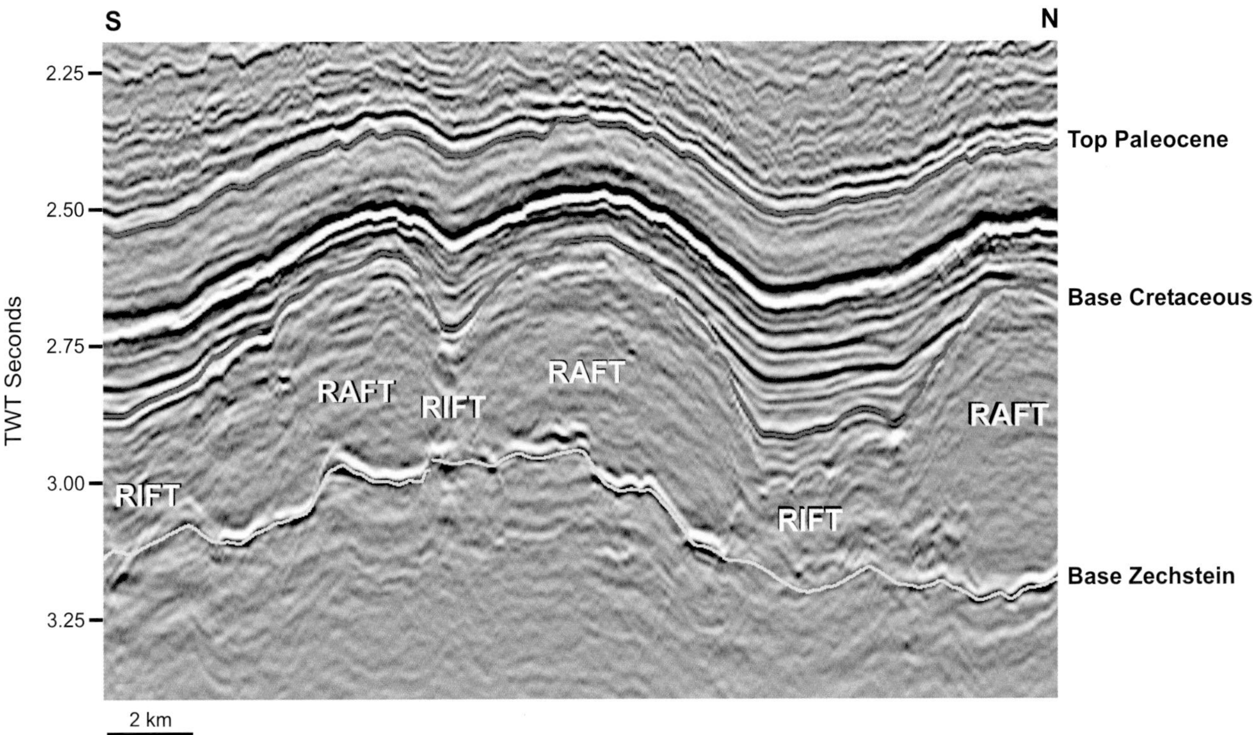

Fig. 9. Seismic line from the Jaeren High showing rift–raft tectonism (courtesy of PGS).

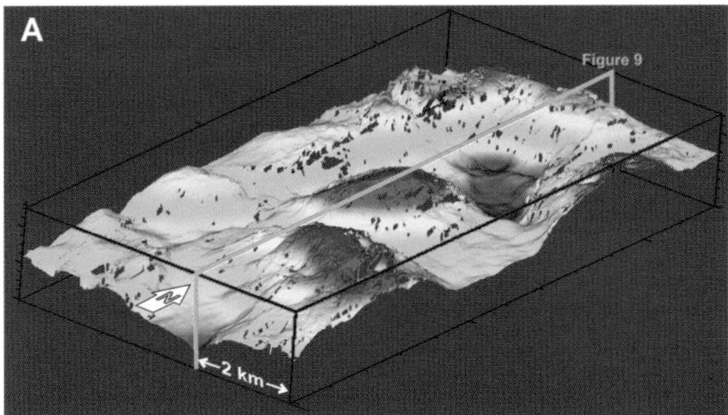

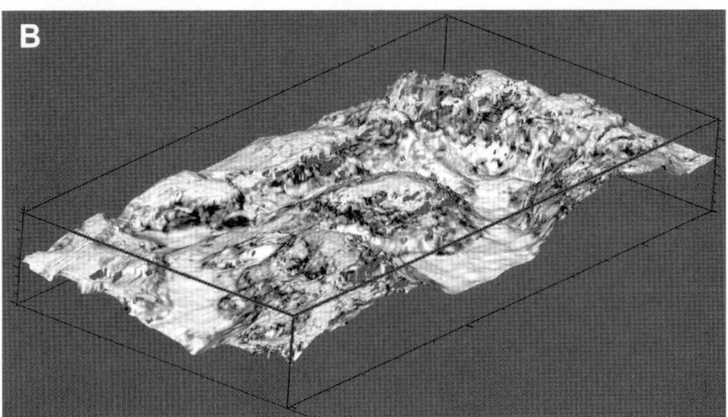

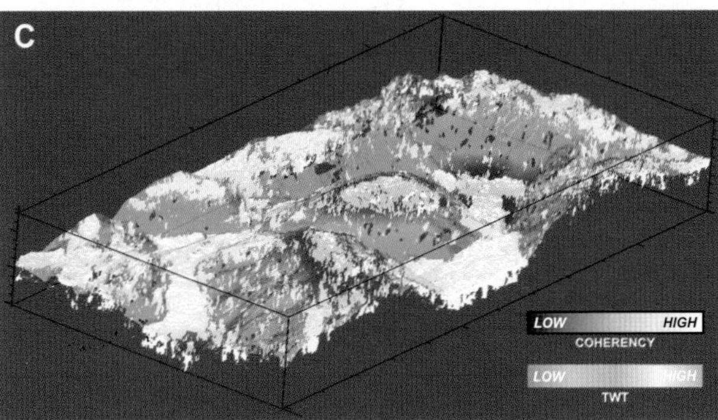

Fig. 10. 3D views of the Base Cretaceous horizon coloured by TWT (**A**), coherency (**B**), and partially transparent TWT (**C**). The high coherency values in a window stretching 100 ms below the Base Cretaceous are visible in Fig. 10C.

Analysis of coherency data has enabled the rapid interpretation of this structural fabric by clearly illuminating the positions of the rifts and rafts. The coherency data have been used to great effect in structurally complex areas where the rifts cannot be distinguished using Base Cretaceous topography alone and in areas deeper in the basin where seismic quality deteriorates.

Conclusions

Over the last few years coherency has played an increasingly important role in improving the cycle time and confidence of 3D seismic interpretations by improving the imaging of structural fabric and stratigraphic features. Coherency, being a relatively new application, is beginning to be integrated with other technologies to provide additional insights. Three examples have been discussed showing the integration of coherency data in production, development and exploration settings to improve the imaging of geological features ranging in scale from reservoir barriers to major faults, and to provide information for applications as diverse as calculating drilling mud weights to scoping the potential for infill well placement. As coherency technology matures it is likely that numerous other applications will emerge.

The authors would like to thank the following people at Amoco: P. Izienicki and J. Munns for reviewing the paper; C. McCrone for discussions on SNS stratigraphy; A. Cushing for drafting the diagrams; T. Walsgrove for work on the pressure prediction over the Arkwright Field; J. Penge for discussions on rift/raft tectonism. We are grateful to Dr J. Cosgrove of Imperial College for useful discussions on the relationship between overpressure and faulting. C. Hawkes of Texaco is thanked for work over Leman while employed at Amoco. We would like to thank the following partners for their co-operation in publishing this work: Amerada Hess Ltd, British Gas Exploration and Production Ltd and Enterprise Oil PLC. We are grateful to PGS for permission to show seismic data over the Arwright Field and the Jaeren High.

References

BAHORICH, M. S. & FARMER, S. L. 1994. 3-D Seismic discontinuity: the coherency cube for faults and stratigraphic features. *64th Annual International Meeting, Society Exploration Geophysics, Expanded Abstracts*.

CAMERON, T. D. J., CROSBY, A., BALSON, P. S., JEFFERY, D. H., LOTT, G. K., BULAT, J. & HARRISON, D. J. 1992. *United Kingdom offshore regional report: the geology of the southern North Sea*. London: HMSO for the British Geological Survey.

CARTWRIGHT, J. A. 1994. Episodic basin-wide hydrofracturing of overpressured Early Cenozoic mudrock sequences in the North Sea Basin. *Marine and Petroleum Geology*, **11**, 587–607.

—— & LONERGAN, L. 1996. Volumetric contraction during the compaction of mudrocks: a mechanism for the development of regional-scale polygonal fault systems. *Basin Research*, **8**, 183–193.

GERSZTENKORN, A. & MARFURT, K. J. 1996. Coherence computations with Eigenstructure. *58th EAGE Conference, Geophysical Division, Expanded Abstracts, X031*.

KANTOROWICZ, J. D., ANDREWS, I. J., DHANANI, S., GILLIS, M., JENNINGS, C., LUMSDEN, P. J., ORR, G., SIMM, R. W. & WILLIAMS, J. 1999. Innovation and risk management in a small subsea-tieback: Arkwright Field, Central North Sea, UK. *In*: FLEET, A. J. & BOLDY, S. A. R. (eds) *Petroleum Geology of Northwest Europe: Proceedings of the 5th Conference*. Geological Society, London, 1125–1134.

KNOX, R. W. O'B. & HOLLOWAY, S. 1992. Paleogene of the Central and Northern North Sea. *In*: KNOX, R. W. O'B. & CORDEY, W. G. (eds) *Lithostratigraphic Nomenclature of the UK North Sea*. British Geological Survey, Nottingham.

LEVEILLE, G. P., KNIPE, R., MORE, C., ELLIS, D., DUDLEY, G., JONES, G., FISHER, Q. J. & ALLINSON, G. 1997. Compartmentalisation of Rotliegendes gas reservoirs by sealing faults, Jupiter Fields area, Southern North Sea. *In*: ZIEGLER, K., TURNER, P. & DAINES, S. R. (eds) *Petroleum Geology of the Southern North Sea: Future Potential*. Geological Society, London, Special Publications, **123**, 87–104.

MARFURT, K. J., KIRLIN, R. L., FARMER, S. L. & BAHORICH, M. S. 1995. 3-D seismic attributes using a running window multitrace coherency algorithm. *65th Annual International Meeting, Society Exploration Geophysics, Expanded Abstracts*.

PENGE, J., TAYLOR, B., HUCKERBY, J. A., & MUNNS, J. W. 1993. *Extension and salt tectonics in the East Central Graben*. *In*: PARKER, J. R. (ed.) *Petroleum Geology of Northwest Europe: Proceedings of the 4th Conference*. Geological Society, London, 1197–1209.

——, ——, MUNNS, J. W. & WINDLE, T. M. F. 1999. Rift-raft tectonics: examples of gravitational tectonics from the Zechstein basins of Northwest Europe. *In*: FLEET, A. J. & BOLDY, S. A. R. (eds) *Petroleum Geology of Northwest Europe: Proceedings of the 5th Conference*. Geology Society, London, 201–214.

ROBERTS, G. A., ROBERTS, R. E., HUGHES, M. J. & MARFURT, K. J. 1996. Structural imaging using the Coherency Cube: A SNS Example. *PETEX 96 Conference Proceedings, A4*.

SIBSON, R. H., MOORE, M. C. M. & RANKIN, A. H. 1975. Seismic pumping – a hydrothermal fluid transport mechanism. *Journal of the Geolgical Society, London*, **131**, 653–659.

Basin modelling applications in reducing risk and maximizing reserves

Basin modelling applications in reducing risk and maximizing reserves

Introduction and review

S. D. BURLEY[1,2] and I. C. SCOTCHMAN[3]

[1] *BG Technology, Gas Research Centre, Ashby Road, Loughborough, LE11 3GR, UK (e-mail: stuart.burley@bgtech.co.uk)*
[2] *Basin Dynamics Group, Department of Earth Sciences, University of Keele, Keele, Staffordshire ST5 5BG, UK (e-mail: gga40@keele.ac.uk)*
[3] *Statoil (UK) Ltd, Statoil House, 11a Regent Street, London, SW1Y 4ST, UK (e-mail: iain.scotchman@statoil.com)*

The conference session was originally planned to address aspects of regional and reservoir diagenesis. However, at an early planning stage we decided that basin modelling was going to be the explorationists' technique of the future and that a theme in the 'Advances in Technology' section incorporating basin modelling – but not excluding diagenesis – was more appropriate.

How prophetic: some 10 presentations were initially offered for the session, two of which were given in other sessions and two of which had to be withdrawn for reasons of commerciality. Of the six papers presented at the conference and included here, four use 3D migration modelling (all of them integrated with 1D and 2D), one is based on 2D generation and migration modelling and one integrates diagenesis, pressure prediction

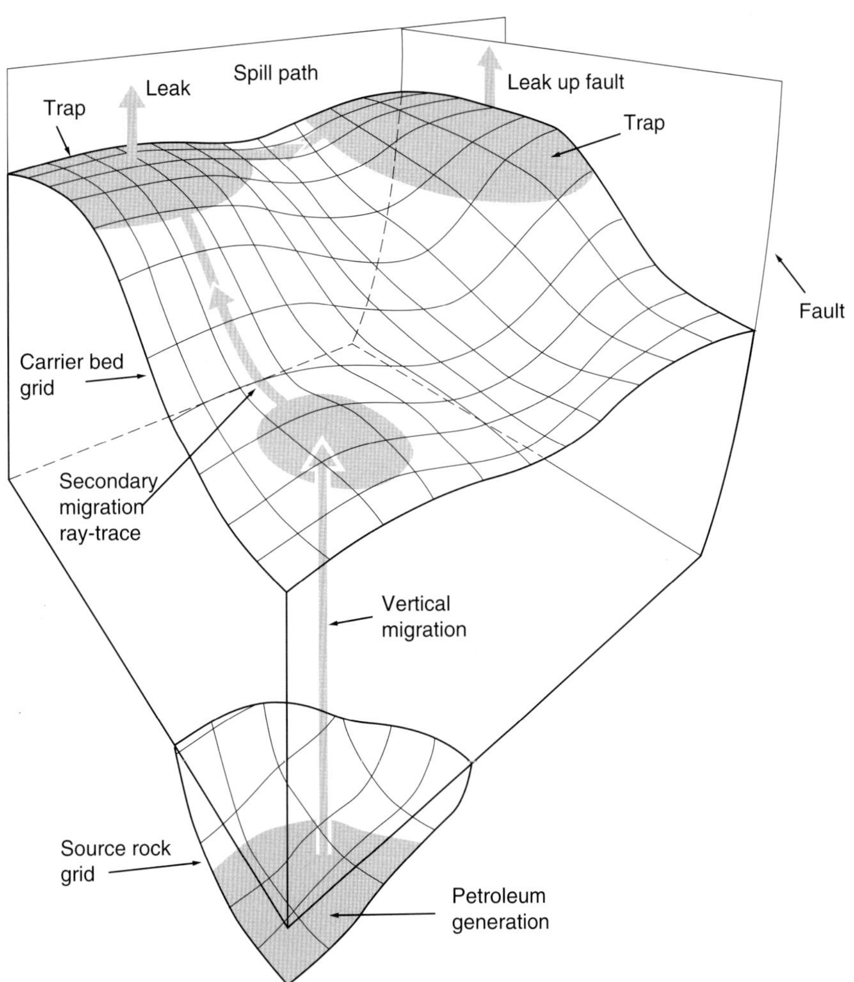

Fig. 1. The concept of ray-trace migration modelling. Petroleum generated in a source rock grid is expelled vertically into a carrier grid through which it migrates under buoyancy. Traps fill with hydrocarbons which then spills to adjacent traps. Vertical leakage takes place through top structure or up faults.

BURLEY, S. D. & SCOTCHMAN, I. C. 1999. Basin modelling applications in reducing risk and maximizing reserves. *In*: FLEET, A. J. & BOLDY, S. A. R. (eds) *Petroleum Geology of Northwest Europe: Proceedings of the 5th Conference*, 1309–1311. © Petroleum Geology '86 Ltd. Published by the Geological Society, London.

and fluid migration. The papers encompass frontier exploration on the North Atlantic margin and hydrocarbon systems/diagenetic modelling in the mature exploration areas of the East Irish Sea and the UK and Norwegian Central North Sea.

The 3D modelling papers all employ variations of ray-trace (or ray-path) modelling. From the efforts of our trawling and the resulting responses from oil companies and software vendors it would appear that no one has yet applied a full physics, gridded 3D cellular basin model to case studies based in the NW European Shelf – or if they have it is too confidential to be presented. No doubt that dawn is not far away.

Ray-trace modelling provides a simple, computationally fast approach to modelling petroleum migration. The technique assumes that petroleum migration is driven by bouyancy, and it is the dip of the petroleum surface that dictates the migration pathway (Fig. 1). The result of this approach is that petroleum migration is very rapid and highly focussed – in effect the models produce inverted rivers of migrating petroleum. Given that geochemists tell us that petroleum migration is focussed into thin stringers of relatively high (>30%?) saturation and that only <5% of the sedimentary basin is ever exposed to hydrocarbon migration (England *et al.* 1987; Larter *et al.* 1996; Schowalter 1979), then this approach appears to mimic our current prejudice of how hydrocarbons move in the subsurface. Thus the key parameter in this modelling approach is having an accurate structure contour map that reproduces the top surface of the carrier system (or the base of the regional seal). However, this fundamental pre-requisite appears to limit the usefulness of the technique to the more mature petroleum basins of the world such as the North Sea where the subsurface structure is seismically well defined. Frontier areas such as the Atlantic margin where the source horizons and migration routes are sub-basalt and cannot be seen on seismic, let alone structurally mapped, will remain the domain of 1D and 2D modelling until either technological developments allow these problems to be overcome or surfaces can be extrapolated mathematically. Also, the existing models use only the present-day structure contour surfaces and perform only 1D vertical decompaction – there is no structural restoration, although expect this capability to appear in the near future. With current developments, ray-trace migration modelling will soon be integrated with 3D petroleum and pressure generation engines (as CAULDRON now is), and will incorporate multi-carrier layer models, structural restoration and fault properties (Fig. 2).

Giles *et al.* provide a glimpse on the workings and output from CAULDRON, the in house SHELL 4D (3 dimensions plus time) simulator. This simulator has a linked 3D generation and migration engine, with the secondary migration based on ray-tracing. These authors show that heat flow is a true 3D process and significant errors can be introduced if only 1D approaches are employed. **Jowitt *et al.*** present one of two papers on the Atlantic Frontier, using PATHWAYS (Hindle 1997) to predict charge distribution and vertical migration. **Holmes *et al.*** show how geochemistry can effectively be used to

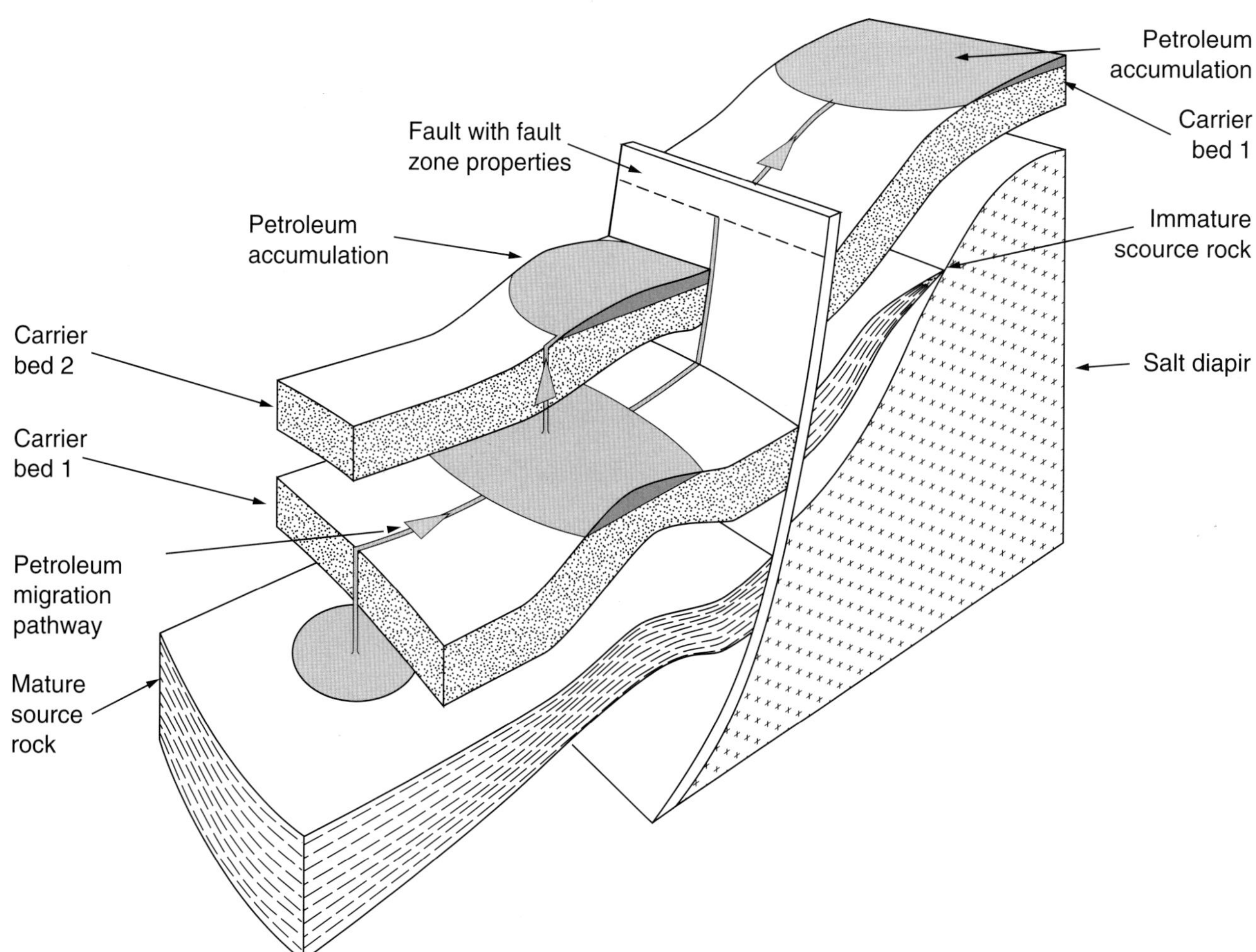

Fig. 2. Multi-layer ray-path modelling of petroleum generation and migration in structurally restored volumes. The generation engine includes a pressure calculation. Bed geometries evolve through time. Migration takes place within and between carrier beds that change geometry through time as the basin develops. Faults are restored with inclined

constrain 2D models of petroleum migration in an example from the North Atlantic margin. **Taylor *et al.*** provide a regional study of the Central North Sea Graben Fairway trend using FINESSE, the *in house* Amoco ray-trace simulator, and demonstrate the importance of seal integrity in controlling hydrocarbon accumulations. **Cowan *et al.*** demonstrate how SEMI (Sylta 1993) can be used in a mature exploration province to reconstruct filling history through time and predict hydrocarbon phase type, in a model calibrated to known discoveries and the regional seal distribution. Effectively then, the papers capture a comparison of CAULDRON, PATHWAYS, FINESSE and SEMI.

Haszeldine *et al.* collate many of their ideas on basin scale diagenesis together to propose an integrated model of pressure development and diagenesis for the North Sea, employing 1D and 2D basin models to predict overpressure and fluid migration pathways. This approach is innovative, opening-up new avenues in the integration of diagenesis into basin models. Here the challenge is to provide both a spatial framework for process and diagenetic product distribution and for predicting porosity and diagenesis in unexplored parts of basins. Perhaps this type of approach will promote a renaissance in studies of sediment diagenesis.

The next advance for basin modelling will be towards quantitatively reducing risk in prospect evaluation – what is referred to as play modelling – incorporating statistical ranking of prospects and leads. With the rapid simulation times of ray-trace approaches the sensitivity of the petroleum system to any geological parameter – source-rock properties, carrier bed properties, seal integrity and petroleum phase type – can all be quantitatively assessed. No longer are we restrained by deterministic models. The explorationist can now ask 'What if?' questions. Indeed, Monte Carlo approaches to investigating sensitivities and volumetrics are already possible (Krokstad & Sylta 1996). Perhaps this probablistic approach will herald a revolution in exploration and prospect evaluation.

References

ENGLAND, W. A., MACKENZIE, A. S., MANN, D. M. & QUIGLEY, T. M. 1987. The movement and entrapment of hydrocarbons in the subsurface. *Journal of the Geological Society of London*, **44**, 327–347.

HINDLE, A. 1997. Petroleum migration pathways and charge concentration: a three dimensional model. *American Association of Petroleum Geologists Bulletin*, **81**, 1451–1481.

KROKSTAD, W. & SYLTA, O. 1996 Risk assessment using volumetrics from secondary migration modelling: assessing uncertainties in source rock yields and trapped hydrocarbons. *In*: DORÉ, A. G. & LARSEN, R. (eds) *Quantification and Prediction of Petroleum Resources*. NPF Special Publication, Elsevier, Amsterdam, 219–235.

LARTER, S., TAYLOR, P., CHEN, M., BOWLER, B., RINGROSE, P. & HORSTAD, I. 1996. Secondary migration – visualising the invisible – what can geochemistry potentially do? *In*: GLENNIE, K. & HURST, A. (eds) *AD1995: NW Europes' Hydrocarbon Industry*. Geological Society, London, 137–143.

SCHOWALTER, T. T. 1979. The mechanics of secondary migration and entrapment. *American Association of Petroleum Geologists Bulletin*, **63**, 723–760.

SYLTA, O. 1993. New techniques and their applications in the analysis of secondary migration. *In*: DORÉ, A. G. *et al.* (eds) *Basin Modelling: Advances and Applications*. NPF Special Publication, **3**, Elsevier, 385–398.

Charge and overpressure modelling in the North Sea: multi-dimensional modelling and uncertainty analysis

M. R. GILES,[1] S. L. INDRELID,[1] N. J. KUSZNIR,[2] A. LOOPIK,[1] J. A. MEIJERINK,[1] J. MCNUTT,[1,3] P. DIJKSTRA,[1] W. HEIDUG,[1] J. TOTH,[1] M. WILLIS,[1,4] K. RUTTEN,[1,5] B. ELSINGA,[1] P. HUYSSE,[1] P. RIVIERE,[1] H. BÜRGISSER[1,6] and E. ROWLEY[7]

[1] *Shell International Exploration and Production B.V., Research and Technical Services, PO Box 60, 2280 AB Rijswijk, The Netherlands (e-mail: m.r.giles@siep.shell.com)*
[2] *Department of Earth Sciences, University of Liverpool, Jane Herdman Laboratories, Brownlow Street, Liverpool, UK*
[3] *Present address: Woodside Offshore Petroleum, No. 1 Adelaide Terrace, Perth, Western Australia, 6000, Australia*
[4] *Present address: Shell Exploration Pakistan B.V., 80 Khayaban-e-Iqbal, F-6/2, PO Box 3031, Islamabad, Pakistan*
[5] *Present address: Nederlandse Aardolie Maatschappij B.V., P.O. Box 28000, 9400 HH, Assen, The Netherlands*
[6] *Present address: Shell Gabon, B.P. 146, port Gentil, Republic of Gabon*
[7] *Department of Earth Sciences, Bullard Laboratories, University of Cambridge, Madingley Road, Cambridge, UK*

Abstract: Over the past one and a half decades developments in our understanding of earth physics and the increase in computer power have enabled quantitative modelling of subsurface temperature, hydrocarbon charge, migration, overpressures and palinspastics. The North Sea has provided the test bed for many of these efforts. Initial developments focused on one dimensional models of temperature and charge as these were computationally possible at that time, and by the late 80s such models were widely available.

Despite the current availability of 2D charge modelling tools, most modelling carried out at present is still 1D. Hydrocarbon generation is driven by the temperature field which depends on the heat flow, which is only truly vertical in exceptional circumstances. In principle, a whole lithosphere 1D model will only agree with a 3D model for a horizontally layered section. Thermal conductivity anisotropy (lateral/vertical conductivity) of mudstones can reach three. Lateral differences in geology also promote changes in geothermal gradients and therefore lateral heat movement. At the lithosphere scale, differences in the depth to the convecting asthenosphere, and the distribution of hot spots may also cause lateral heat flow. In the North Sea, the complex geology particularly within the syn-rift section makes heat flow strongly 3D. In the Inner Moray Firth and Halten Terrace there are considerable differences between the predictions of fully transient 1D and 3D models for the temperature and hydrocarbon expulsion flux histories of the kitchen areas. Differences can exceed 15°C close to major faults: kitchen areas in the hanging walls are typically cooler than would be expected from 1D models, whereas basement cored highs are typically hotter than might be expected. The differences between the predictions of 1D and 3D models are driven by structural effects and are thus temporally variant.

The importance of 3D effects in charge modelling is compounded in hydrocarbon migration models. Temporal changes in carrier bed interconnectivity, fault seal properties and basin structure influence migration, re-migration and even refilling of breached traps. For instance, hydrocarbons found in the Tertiary of the Central North Sea are derived from underlying Jurassic reservoirs where high overpressures have lead to hydrofracturing and hence leakage.

Numerical models of overpressure generation, including rapid sedimentation (under-compaction), thermal expansion (aquathermal pressuring), smectite to illite transition (water generation), etc., tell only part of the story: in order for pressures to rise the fluids have to be contained by rocks with sufficiently low permeability. Furthermore, overpressures are transient and gradually diminish when generation ceases. These processes can be described by a relatively simple differential equation, which can be solved to predict overpressures in one or more dimensions. However, in the North Sea, widespread aquifers (e.g. the Fulmar Formation sands) allow pressure transmission out of synclines. Thus, simple 1D models are of limited use, and pressure modelling requires prediction of the stratigraphy and temporal variations in aquifer connectivity resulting from structural movement. Palinspastic restoration is thus a prerequisite. In areas such as the Central North Sea, where there is good pressure calibration and relatively simple stratigraphy, modelling enables prediction of overpressure, trap integrity and reservoir continuity.

One problem with physical models discussed above has been their inability to incorporate uncertainties. New models are capable of taking into account uncertainties in both model parameters (e.g. compaction

GILES, M. R., INDRELID, S. L., KUSZNIR, N. J., LOOPIK, A., MEIJERINK, J. A., MCNUTT, J., DIJKSTRA, P., HEIDUG, W., TOTH, J., WILLIS, M., RUTTEN, K., ELSINGA, B., HUYSSE, P., RIVIERE, P., BÜRGISSER, H. & ROWLEY, E. 1999. Charge and overpressure modelling in the North Sea: multi-dimensional modelling and uncertainty analysis. *In*: FLEET, A. J. & BOLDY, S. A. R. (eds) *Petroleum Geology of Northwest Europe: Proceedings of the 5th Conference*, 1313–1324.

coefficients) and input data (e.g. stratigraphic age) to calculate the uncertainty in the modelled variable (e.g. hydrocarbon flux history). Such models provide a much more realistic evaluation of wildcat prospects.

The potential of basin models for prospect evaluation and field development is still in its infancy. From a commercial view point, in areas such as the North Sea where data are readily available to most competitors there is little advantage in having the same models as everybody else. The advantage lies in being able to evaluate acreage faster and with greater accuracy, both in the prediction and the uncertainties.

The science of basin modelling is essentially the physical description of the evolution of a sedimentary basin and its component parts in space and time. From a petroleum industry perspective this impacts prospect appraisal in a number of areas including:

(1) prediction of the temperature and hydrocarbon generation/expulsion histories;
(2) secondary migration of hydrocarbons;
(3) sediment infill and reservoir distribution;
(4) evolution of fluid pressures and trap integrity;
(5) evaluation of the volumes and composition of hydrocarbons in place.

The roots of basin modelling go back to the 1920s (e.g. compaction – Terzaghi 1923). However, as a coherent science

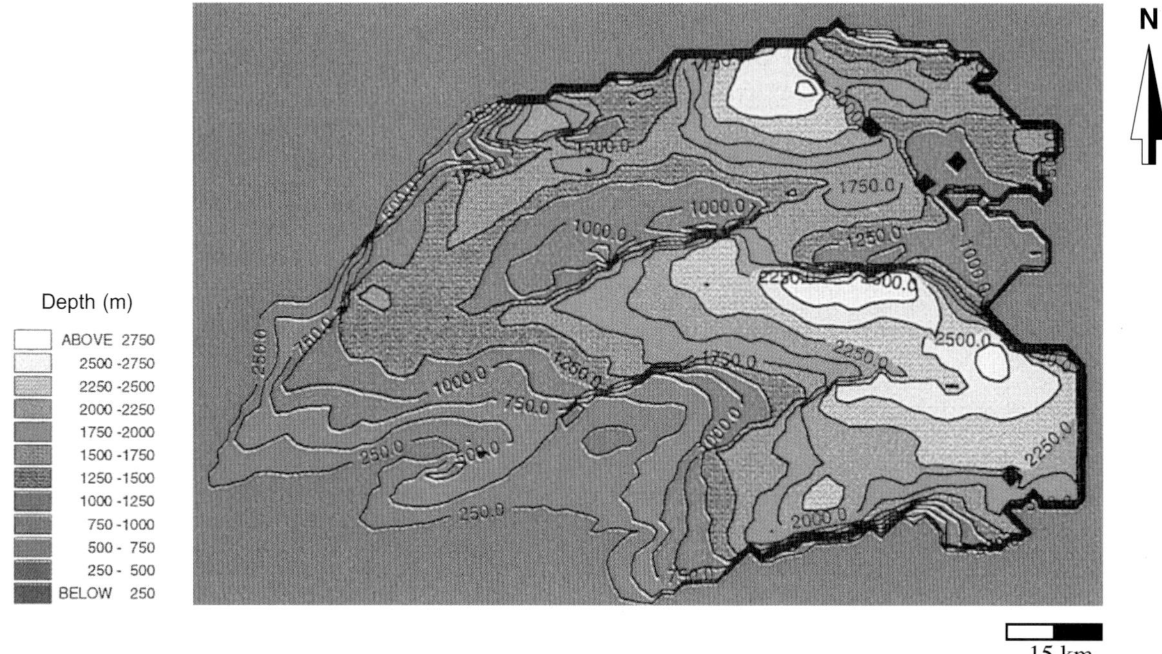

Fig. 1. Depth to the top of the Kimmeridge source rock in the inner Moray Firth at the present day – note the location of highs and grabens.

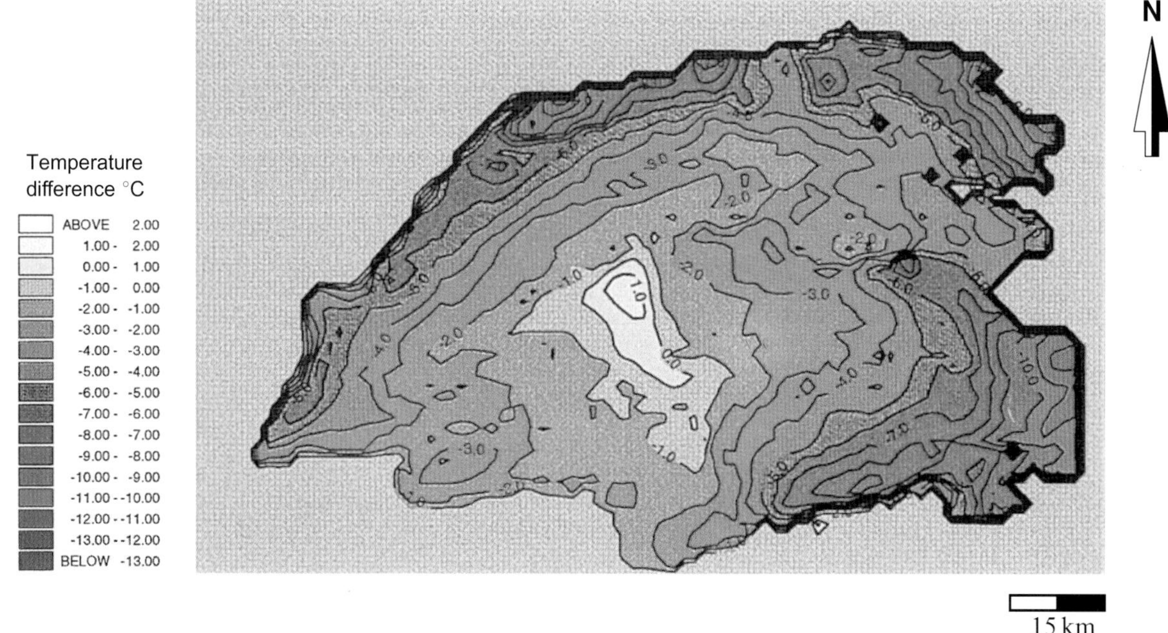

Fig. 2. Difference between the 3D and 1D models for the temperatures of the Kimmeridge source rock at the present day. In general the area is cooler by 1–8°C in the 3D model. The deep graben in the centre of the area is slightly warmer due to its position between two basement highs.

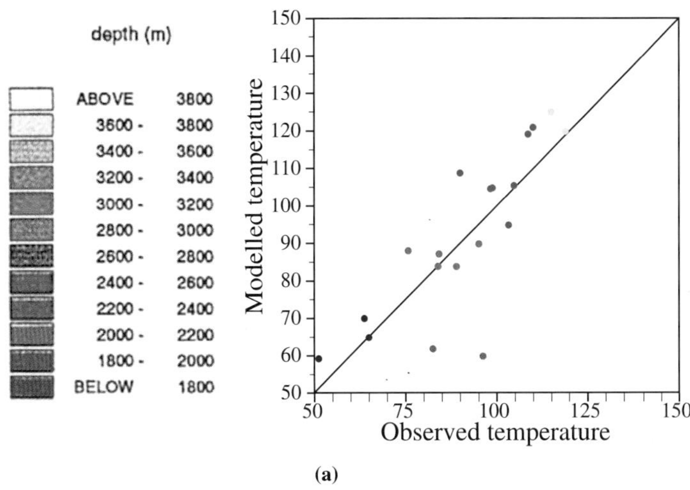

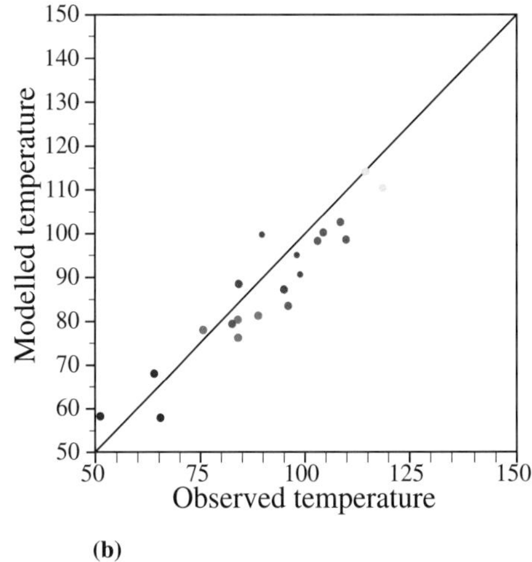

Fig 3. Fit of modelled and corrected measured bottom hole temperatures measurements for (**a**) the 1D model and (**b**) the 3D model. The 3D model provides a significantly better fit to the data for the same assumed heat flow.

it emerged from six developments which occurred in the mid to late 1970s:

(1) understanding of temperature control on source rock maturity (Lopatin 1971; Tissot & Espitalié 1975);
(2) development of the concept of geohistory analysis as expounded by van Hinte (1978);
(3) understanding and mathematical formulation of back-stripping (Perrier & Quiblier 1974; Watts & Ryan 1976; Sclater & Christie 1980);
(4) major breakthroughs in geodynamics, e.g. the rift model of McKenzie (1978);
(5) widespread availability of computers;
(6) growth of the petroleum industry in areas outside the Middle East, where the need to understand charge as a basic control on hydrocarbon distribution was widely recognized.

Within Shell Research, basin modelling technology has been continuously developed since the late 1970s (see Acknowledgements for an overview of developments by Shell), often using the North Sea as a test bed.

Why use multi-dimensional models?

The petroleum industry has employed basin models as a quantitative tool for the prediction of the distribution and

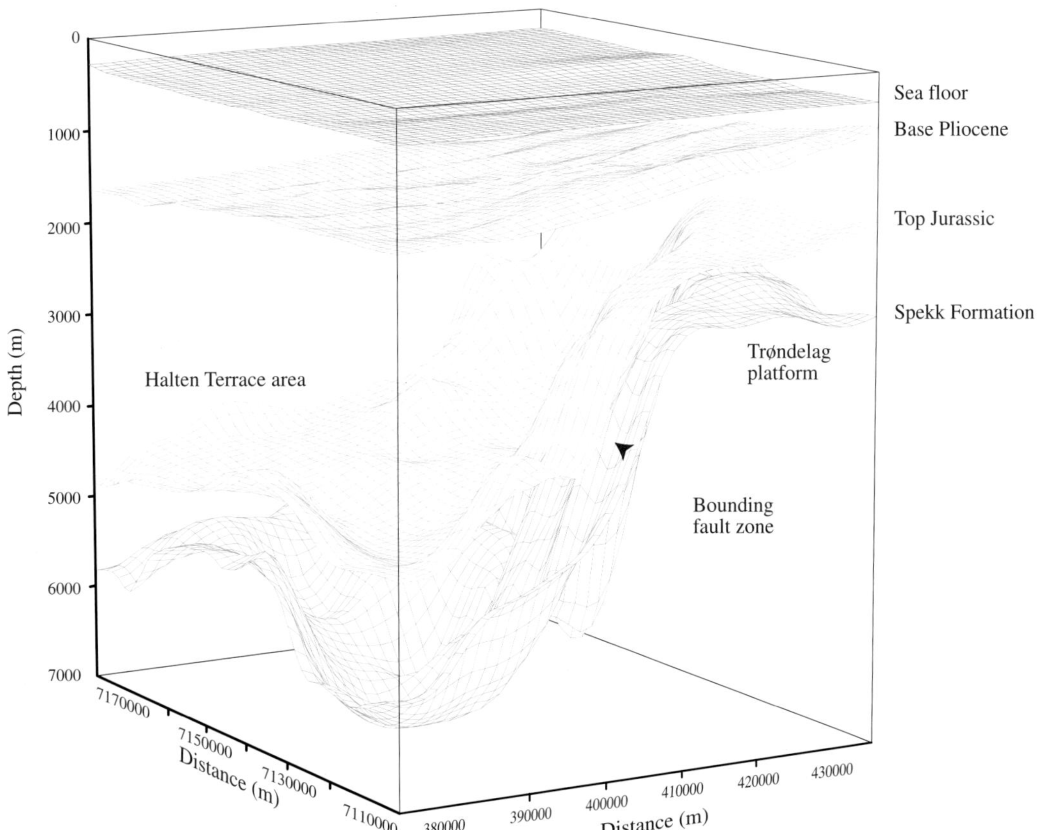

Fig. 4. Halten Terrace study area: a major fault zone separates the Trøndelag platform (right hand side) from the down-thrown Halten Terrace (left hand side). The Spekk Formation source rock is shown as the pink grid.

Temperature correlation plot

Measured Temperature (C)

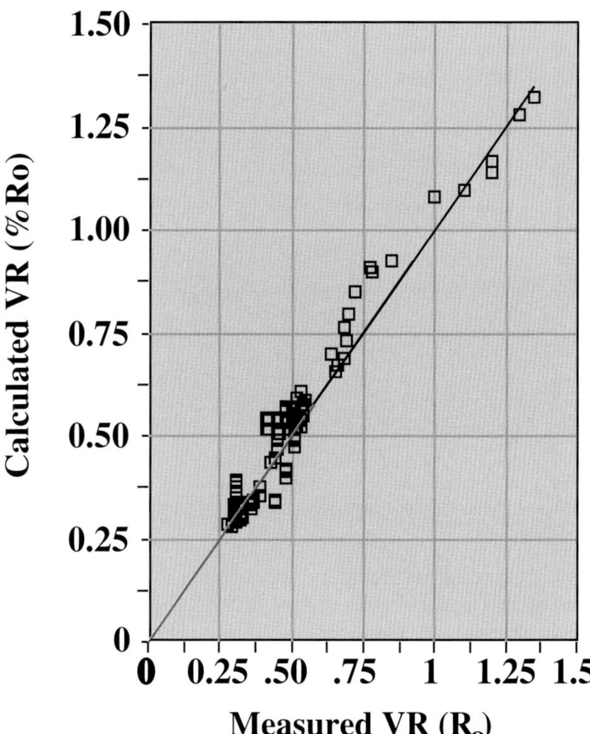

Fig. 5. Comparison of measured and predicted present-day temperature and vitrinite reflectance for the Halten Terrace study area using a 3D model. A consistently good fit is obtained.

volumes of hydrocarbons, and more recently the prediction of overpressures for well planning and trap integrity estimation. The full impact of basin modelling on exploration has only recently been appreciated, in part because of past data scarcity (multi-dimensional models require a great deal of information, particularly in basinal areas), lack of computing power, and the problem of data uncertainties in the models. The latter problem is not approached by conventional basin models which in contrast to the users' view, treat the input data as error-free and subsequently calculate a single result.

In many exploration areas the abundance of 3D seismic data has largely eliminated the data scarcity issue, and also reduced data uncertainties. Desk-top computing power has recently become sufficient to allow 4D models (here meaning 3 dimensions plus time) to be run. Finally, inherent uncertainties in the input data are being addressed by new techniques that are capable of providing probability distributions rather than single answers.

The need for multi-dimensional models can be appreciated by considering the heat flow equation. The full heat flow equation (Phillips 1991; Giles 1997) can be written simply in words as:

> Rate of addition of heat = Rate at which heat is conducted into the unit + Rate at which heat is moved (to a unit of porous rock) into unit by movement of the fluid and rock + Rate at which heat is generated by internal processes such as radioactive decay.

As the gross heat flow through the lithosphere is controlled by the temperature at the surface of the Earth and the base of the lithosphere it has often been assumed that 1D thermal models will provide an adequate description of the sediment pile. However, 3D effects arise from structural and stratigraphic geometry, because the movement of heat is controlled by the thermal conductivity of the rocks (a measure of how good an insulator the rock is). The presence of highly conductive lithologies such as salt or basement cause focusing of heat flow, drawing heat out of the surrounding basins and conducting it into the overlying sediments. Hence thermal anomalies occur above salt domes or basement highs. Similar effects can arise due to thermal conductivity contrasts across major faults. At a larger scale, differences in the depth to the base of the lithosphere) (e.g. due to rifting) will also cause lateral heat flow. In addition, thermal conductivity is an anisotropic property (i.e. directionally dependent). The average lateral thermal conductivity of a shale is around 1.5 times the vertical conductivity. Thus, for basins in which shale beds are not horizontal, the heat flow will not be vertical. Where fluid flow is an important heat transfer mechanism (Giles 1997) then the distribution of aquifers becomes the gross control, together with the fluid potential gradient. On a smaller scale, flow focusing resulting from the interplay of the fluid potential gradient and permeability contrasts within the aquifers can generate local effects. Similarly, as studies of hydrocarbon migration have shown (e.g. Sylta 1993) migration is a highly focused process.

Thus, given the 3D nature of geology, as exemplified by the North Sea rift system, the assumption of vertical heat flow inherent in the 1D thermal models, is fundamentally flawed. Two dimensional models will also be in error depending on the extent to which the geometry changes along strike.

Multi-dimensional thermal and charge modelling: North Sea examples

Shell proprietary full lithosphere models have been used to assess the differences between 1D and 3D models of temperature and hydrocarbon charge. The models use surface and base

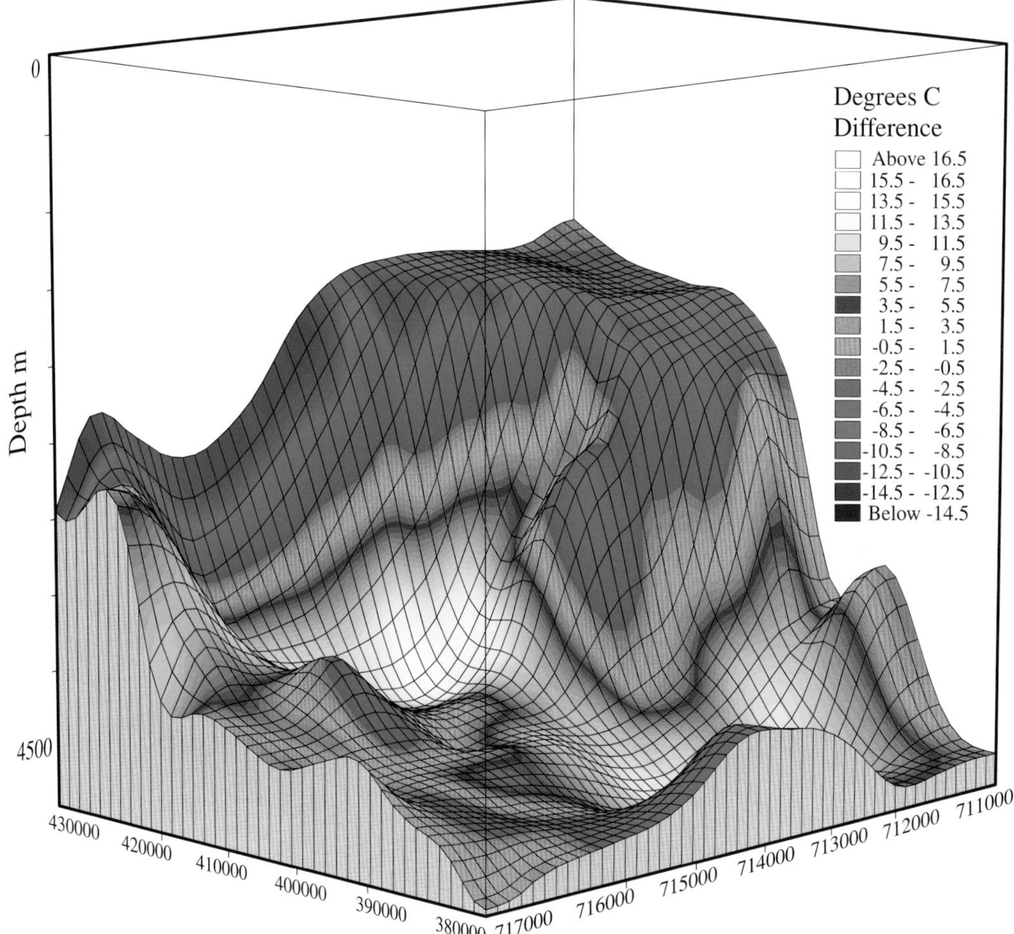

Fig. 6. Difference between 1D and 3D models of the temperature at the top Spekk in the Halten Terrace area, expressed as 1D predicted temperature minus 3D predicted temperature. Differences of as much as 20°C are observed in the hanging-wall close to the fault. The figure shows a rotated view of the Spekk Formation grid from Fig. 4, with the Trøndelag platform lying away from the reader, and the Halten Terrace at the front.

lithosphere temperature boundary conditions and lateral no-flow boundaries. Full lithosphere models are necessary to account for heat storage in the lithosphere which arises during rapid sedimentation or uplift (so-called transient effects). Models which do not account for heat storage in the lithosphere greatly under-estimate the thermal transient effect (Vik & Hermanrud 1993; Giles 1997).

Input to the models is provided by depth converted seismic horizon maps, with the properties between the horizons specified by the user in table or map form. The thermal conductivities of end member lithologies with zero porosity may be specified by the user, or employ data from an extensive quality controlled database of default lateral and vertical thermal conductivities. The thermal conductivity employed in the model at any time step is calculated from the porosity, the end member thermal conductivity and the temperature. In other words, the thermal conductivities are corrected for temperature and porosity effects. Porosities are calculated employing a model linking them to vertical effective stress (Giles 1997).

Inner Moray Firth

The Inner Moray Firth (IMF) was chosen as an example to quantify the differences between 1D and 3D thermal models in a typical North Sea setting. The study was based on a regional evaluation of the IMF carried out in 1990 by Shell Expro in support of the 12th UK Offshore Round. Nine seismic markers (e.g. Fig. 1) were mapped across the area. Missing section due to Tertiary uplift and inversion was estimated using regional seismic, apatite fission track (AFTA) and vitrinite reflectance (VR) data. This indicated that up to 1000 m of section had been removed largely in the western half of the area. A regional pseudo 3D model of hydrocarbon generation and expulsion, and map based modelling of hydrocarbon migration, was then carried out.

These data were used as input to Shell proprietary full 3D charge model. Calibration data in the form of bottom hole temperature (BHT) and VR data were available from 15 wells. For comparison, the results of a pseudo 3D model (i.e. multiple 1D models on the same grid) were recomputed, using the same top and bottom boundary conditions i.e. time variant surface temperature and base lithosphere temperature.

The results show that present-day burial depth controls present-day temperatures, whereas source rock maturity (calculated VR) mirrors the maximum burial depth prior to Tertiary inversion. The differences between the present-day temperatures modelled in 1D and 3D are shown in Fig. 2. Interestingly, the comparison of the BHT data with the temperatures calculated by the pseudo 3D and full 3D demonstrates that the full 3D provides a better overall fit (Fig. 3), but is cooler than the 1D prediction in the basinal areas by up to 12°C. Consequently, the predicted maturity (estimated vitrinite maturity or VRE for short, unit %Ro) of the basinal areas is also lower by up to 0.1. Although the fit provided by the 1D calculations can be improved by varying lithosphere thickness or radiogenic heat production locally, such an approach does not facilitate the development of a regionally consistent interpretation, and does not provide a tool with which to determine

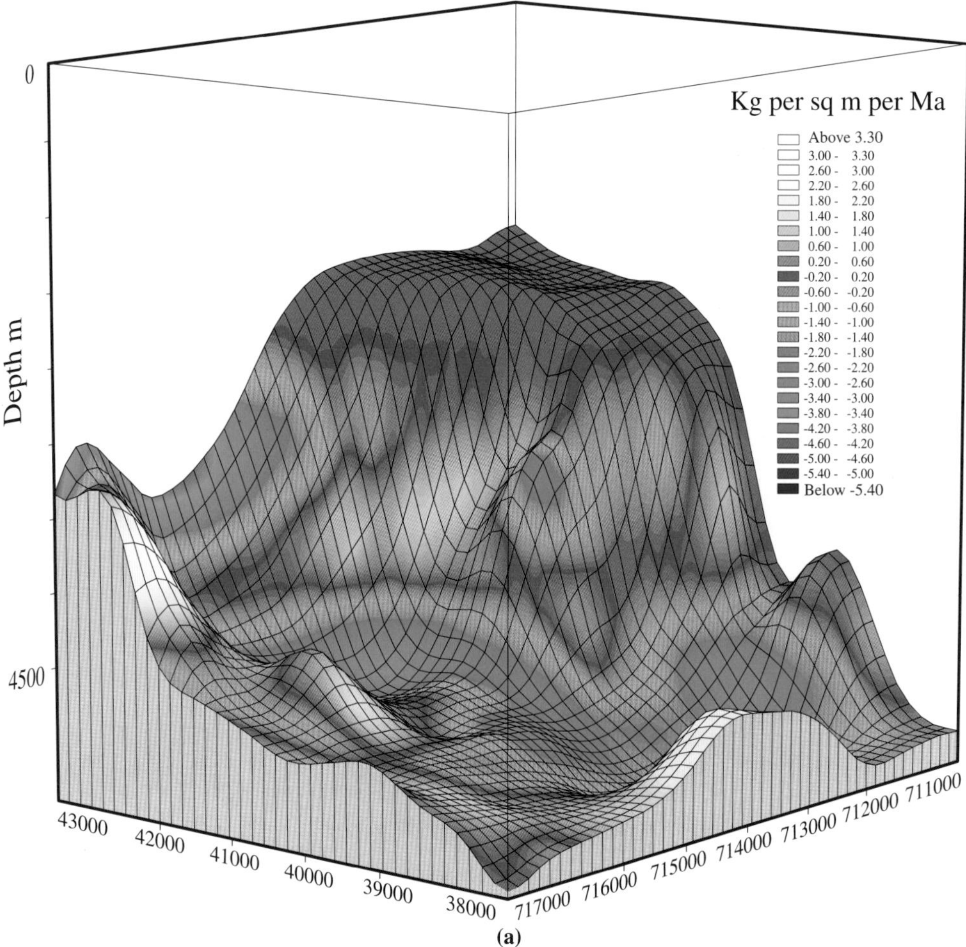

(a)

Fig. 7. Difference between 1D and 3D models of: (**a**) the rate of oil expulsion and; (**b**) the cumulative volumes of oil expelled from the Spekk source rock in the Halten Terrace area. Again, expressed as 1D–3D. The most pronounced differences are close to the fault. View as in Fig. 6.

the heat flow in the kitchen areas. The temperature differences between 1D and 3D models in basinal areas is largely a result of conduction of heat out of the basin into the adjacent more conductive basement. True 3D models automatically account for for these processes and are thus useful in modelling both the shallow locations and the kitchen areas well locations.

Temperature differences of 12°C between the 1D and 3D models can produce major differences in the predicted expulsion history of the kitchen area, and are explored in the Halten Terrace example discussed next.

Halten Terrace

The study area is offshore Norway. Late Jurassic/early Cretaceous rifting resulted in a major SW–NE fault zone separating the stable Trøndelag Platform (which includes the Draugen Field) from the more heavily structured Halten Terrace (Fig. 4) which forms the main kitchen area. The main source rock is the Upper Jurassic Spekk Formation. A deeper gas-prone source rock (the coal-bearing Triassic Åre Formation) is also present. The study used six horizons aged from 1.5 to 213 Ma mapped over an area 82.5 by 72 km.

Calibration data (VR and corrected BHT measurements) were available from five wells in the study area. The overall fit to the data obtained by the Shell proprietary modelling program Cauldron is shown in Fig. 5. As with the Inner Moray Firth example, the fitting procedure produces a regional calibration which automatically takes care of the problem of extrapolating heat flow into the graben. Figure 6 shows the difference between predictions made with 1D and 3D models at the level of the Spekk Formation. The maximum temperature difference is in excess of 20°C, and occurs in the hanging-wall of the major fault separating the Halten Terrace from the Trøndelag Platform, where the 1D model consistently over-estimates the temperatures in the kitchen by up to 16°C. (Fig. 6). This effect is due to the presence of conductive basement in the footwall of the major fault resulting in a lower overall temperature gradient compared to the hanging-wall. The lateral change in temperature gradient across the fault drives heat out of the basinal area resulting in a relative cooling. This translates into differences in the predicted timing, composition and volumes of hydrocarbons expelled. Figure 7(a) is a comparison of the difference in the rate of oil expulsion for 1D and 3D models (based on the model of Stainforth & Reinders 1990) at the present day, while Fig. 7(b) shows the difference in the cumulative volume of hydrocarbons expelled.

Figures 6 and 7 clearly show that 3D effects are important particularly when the intention is to predict the volume or composition of hydrocarbons in place, or in areas of marginal maturity.

Multi-dimensional pressure modelling

In the exploration of the Jurassic of the Central and Northern North Sea, overpressures provide a drilling hazard and also a primary control on trap integrity (Gaarenstroom *et al.* 1993). Overpressures are generated by a variety of mechanisms including: (1) under-compaction (rapid burial and failure of mudstone sections to effectively dewater; Dickinson 1953); (2) aquathermal pressuring (temperature induced increase in

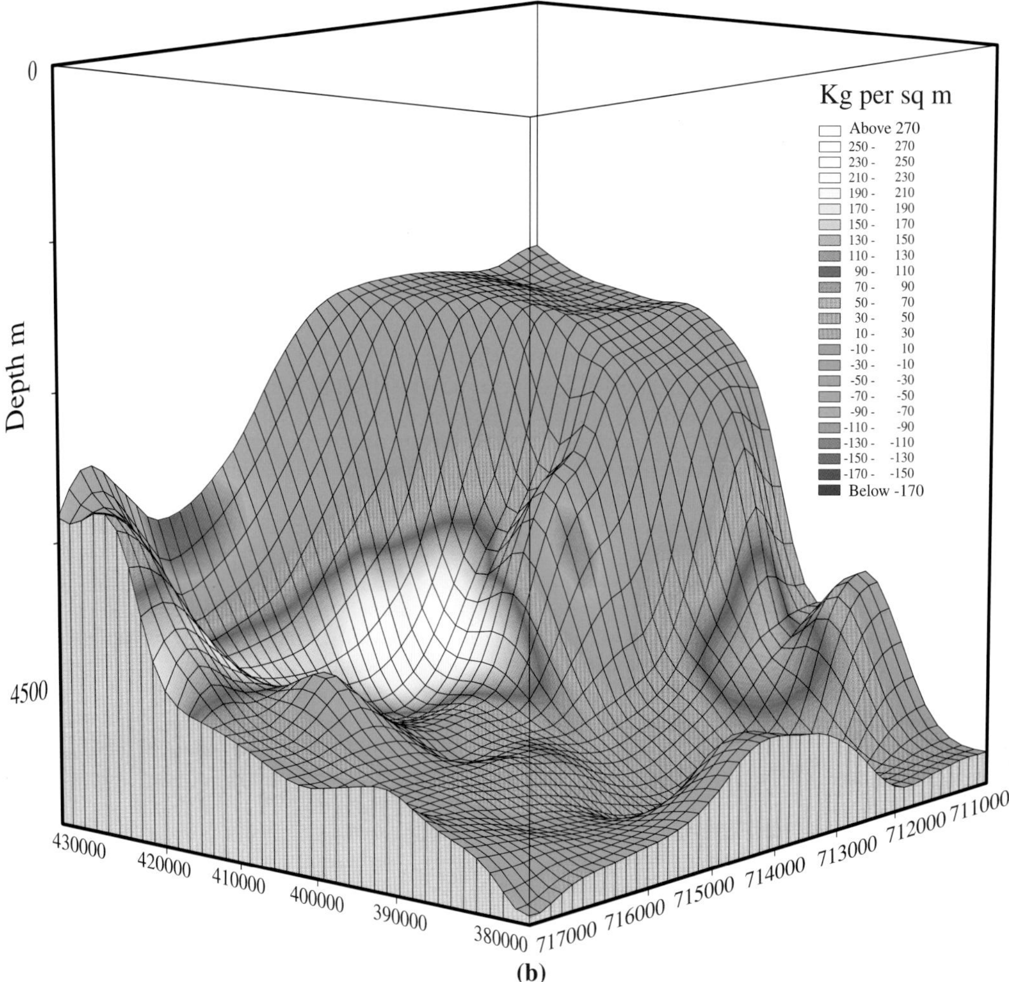

Fig. 7. (*continued*).

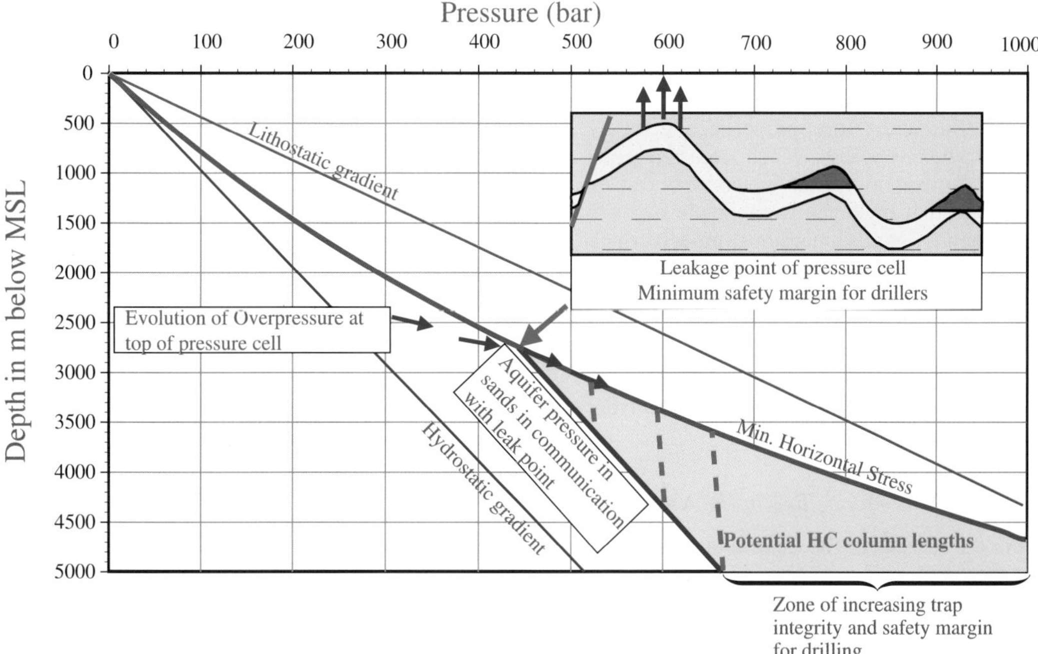

Fig. 8. Pressure cell evolution: as long as high overpressures are maintained, pressure in the pressure cell will be controlled by the fracture strength at the leak point, with all other points in the aquifer lying on a common hydrostatic gradient with the leak-point. As burial progresses, the pressure at the leak-point remains constrained by the fracture strength.

fluid pressure at constant fluid mass; Barker 1972); and (3) hydrocarbon generation and expulsion (Law & Dickinson 1985). Other mechanisms have also been proposed, ranging from smectite dehydration to compressive tectonic stress. The overpressure generation mechanism is, however, only part of the equation: the rate at which the excess pressures leak away through the seal is equally important (Giles 1997).

In addition, the overpressure at a given point in the subsurface reflects the aquifer continuity and temporal changes in connectivity resulting from tectonic activity or fault seal breakdown. The principal engines for overpressure generation are located in the depocentres where more rapid burial and/or hydrocarbon expulsion have occurred. Pressures generated in synclinal areas can then be transmitted up-dip via aquifers into structural highs. In such cases the pressure at a given point in a reservoir is determined not by the burial history at that point, but by the burial history of the depocentre, and the history of aquifer continuity into the syncline. Where pressure transmission has been temporally continuous such overpressures might be termed 'hypergeopressures'. Where overpressures are generated late in the burial history or a fault seal breaks down enabling pressure communication between previously isolated compartments, then there is an increase in the fluid pressure. This is termed 'inflationary overpressure'. Inflation can occur in all overpressured settings from Tertiary deltas to ancient rift settings such as the North Sea. In order to predict overpressures, a 2D or 3D model which reflects the history of aquifer connectivity is thus needed. This requires knowledge of both the tectonic evolution and aquifer distribution. The resolution (in terms of the number of grid blocks to adequately represent the reservoir) necessary to obtain good pressure estimates make true 3D modelling an emerging technology, but given the increase in computing power such models will become available over the coming years. Nevertheless, with good calibration data much can be achieved in 2D as shown by the Central North Sea example discussed later.

Changes in rock properties such as porosity are caused by compaction and cementation, both of which are largely driven by increasing vertical effective stress (Giles 1997), i.e. the difference between the vertical stress and the fluid pressure (Terzaghi 1923). Generally, pressures will have varied in a systematic way with burial history, and hence the evolution of rock properties will reflect the current vertical effective stress. Thus for instance, overpressured reservoirs in undercompacted areas can be expected to have higher porosities than would be predicted based on their depth alone. Whereas, in the case of inflationary overpressures, the rock properties are set by the maximum vertical effective stress, which occurred prior to late overpressuring. In this case, reservoir porosity can be expected to be similar to that predicted from simple porosity depth graphs. Consequently, multi-dimensional models which include rock property calculations based on a maximum effective stress model may also be used to predict reservoir properties for volumetric evaluations. The influence of vertical effective stress history on rock properties also influences the reliability of geophysical techniques for the prediction of overpressures. For example, prediction of overpressures from logs may fail where inflationary pressures occur.

Geological context of pressure modelling in the North Sea

Overpressures within the Jurassic of the Central and Northern North Sea reflect the interplay of a number of causes including rapid sedimentation and hydrocarbon generation which occurred during the Tertiary. The mechanisms for the generation and leakage of overpressures can be incorporated into one relatively simple equation which can be solved in 1D to 3D (Giles 1997). However, one of the features of the present-day pressure field within the Central North Sea is that it is constrained by the minimum horizontal stress. When the fluid pressure within a hydraulically continuous but finite region (so-called pressure cell) reaches the minimum horizontal stress, the weakest point in the cell will fail. This is generally close to the highest point in the pressure cell (Fig. 8) (Gaarenstroom *et al.* 1993). The pressures within any aquifer connected to the leak point may then be estimated from the failure pressure, and the depth difference from the leak point and the hydrostatic pressure gradient. With further burial and pressure build-up, the pressure at the leak point will be constrained to move along the minimum horizontal stress–depth curve, and the leak point will continue to 'weep'. Lateral boundaries to pressure cells are typically formed by major sealing faults or shale-outs, although not all faults form boundaries to the pressure cells. Vertical stacking of pressure cells is also possible: in the North Sea, for instance, isolated Upper Jurassic turbidite sands may form a separate pressure cell from the underlying more continuous sands of the Fulmar Formation or equivalent.

Central North Sea example

Pressure modelling within the North Sea is possible using 2D models, providing that the fault movement and fault sealing history are accounted for. Within the Central North Sea the extent of the Upper Jurassic Fulmar Formation sands is the principle stratigraphic uncertainty in pressure modelling.

The pressure modelling study described here was carried out to estimate the overpressure and trap integrity for a prospect in the Heron area of the Central North Sea. Trap integrity, the difference between the minimum horizontal stress and fluid pressure, were required to calculate potential hydrocarbon column height and drilling margin (difference between the formation breakdown pressure and the mud pressure). The input data consisted of a 2D depth converted cross-section extracted from a Landmark 3D project, running from well A through the prospect into the syncline. The section was palinspastically restored using the Shell proprietary minimum strain energy restoration program MESH. The restored sections and interpreted lithologies formed the input to the proprietary 2D pressure modelling program VESMESH. This is a 2D forward modelling program based on a finite element solution to a general model of overpressure generation and retention which includes fault and top seal leakage, and laterally variable lithologies and overpressure generation by a variety of mechanisms. Properties such as lithology may be assigned for each element of the model. Temporally variant properties such as porosity and permeability are calculated from an initial i.e. depositional value, and the vertical effective stress history.

Calibration to the model is provided by the present-day stratigraphic geometries and fluid pressure data (RFT) from a number of fields. Initial simplified model runs demonstrated that there are two primary controls on the pressure distribution: (1) the permeability of the Kimmeridge and Lower Cretaceous section; and (2) the lateral continuity of the Fulmar sands.

A present-day permeability of 2.5 nD is required in the model for the Kimmeridge, Lower Cretaceous and Lower Chalk to fit the pressure data. Doubling the permeability gives results which are 1000 psi too low, whereas halving the permeability raises the pressures to almost 1000 psi beyond their observed values. Acceptable present-day permeability therefore falls into a very narrow range. The top Chalk permeability was set at 10 nD to ensure that the overpressures in the Hod Formation were of the expected order of magnitude. These requirements on the permeabilities along with the relatively simple sand distributions are a significant constraint on the models.

The Fulmar Formation sands are the major conduit by which pressures generated in the deep portions of the graben are

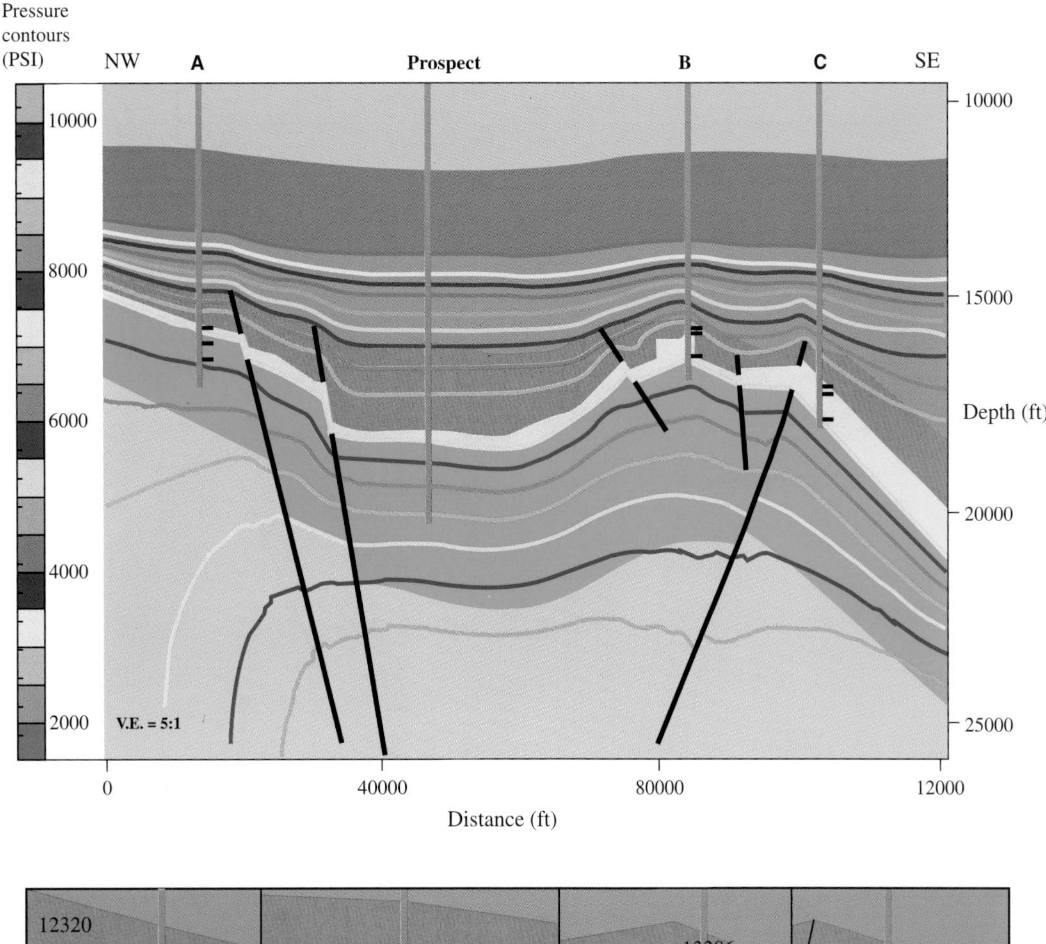

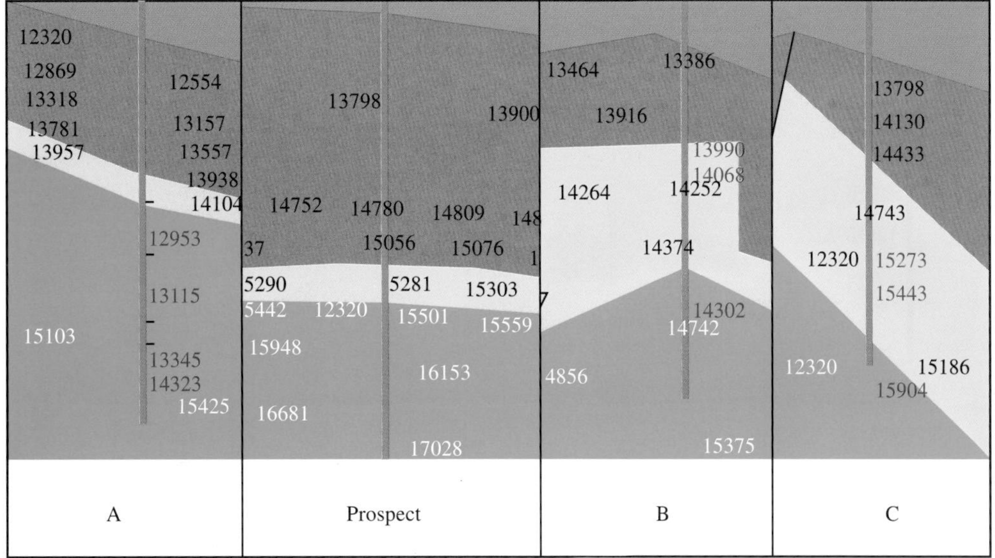

Fig. 9. 2D pressure model for the Fulmar sands in the Central Graben, Heron area, for the scenario where the Fulmar sands are connected across the whole area. In this case the pressures at A and B are over-predicted. Background colours are formations used in the model, contour colours are predicted pressure in PSI. Fulmar Formation shown in yellow.

transmitted into the structural highs. Thus, the pressure within a given field reflects the continuity of the sands into the adjacent synclines. By varying the lateral continuity of the sands and the cross-fault pressure communication it is possible to determine the most likely present-day geometry. For instance, if the Fulmar Formation sands were in pressure communication across the whole area (Fig. 9) then predicted pressures at A and C would be higher than observed. In fact few scenarios will adequately fit the pressure data, allowing a number of important conclusions:

(1) For instance, the A area forms a pressure cell which extends southeastwards into the syncline separating it from the B. The leak point of the A pressure cell lies somewhere further up-dip, and permeable beds must also extend up-dip to the leak point. Permeable sands must extend down-dip all or most of the way across the syncline separating the A and B pressure cells.
(2) The C area is a separate pressure cell from the B area and in order to explain the pressures observed in well C, permeable beds, most likely the Fulmar Formation sands must

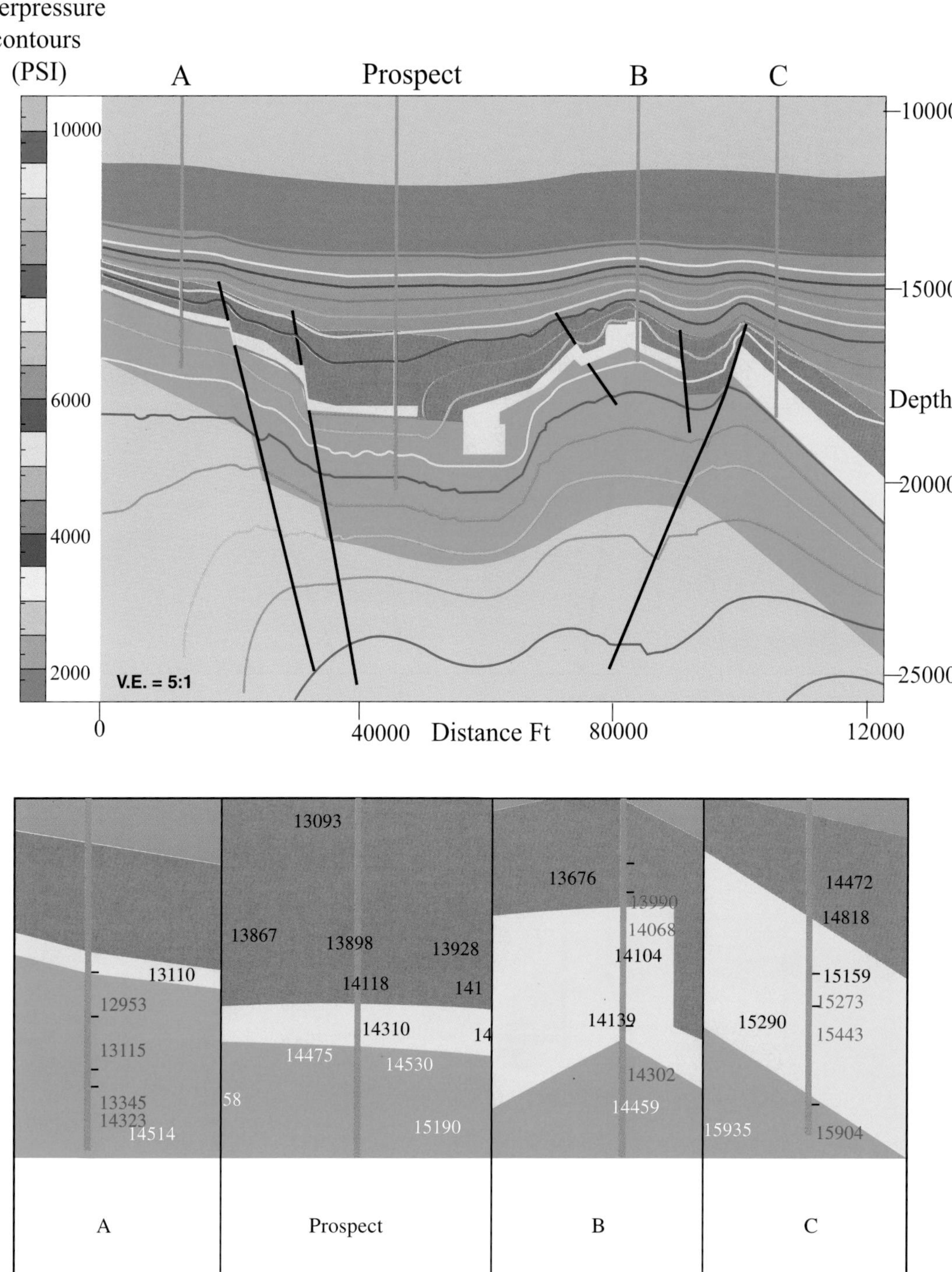

Fig. 10. Best fit model for pressures in the Central Graben, Heron area. The best fit model requires that pressures are not continuous across the area – either due to a shale-out or a pressure-sealing fault. Red numbers show measured pressures in the well (in psi) and other numbers are predicted by the model. Background colours are formations used in the model. Fulmar Formation shown in yellow.

extend down-dip into the syncline to the south/southwest of the field.

(3) Modelling does not enable discrimination between Fulmar and Skagarrak Formation sands as the conduit for pressure communication between well B and the adjacent syncline, although the former is more likely because of the variable nature of the Triassic in the Central Graben and its typically poor lateral permeability.

(4) The 'best fit' model (Fig. 10) suggests a reservoir discontinuity caused either by a shale-out to the east of the prospect (Fig. 10a) or by a pressure sealing fault to the west (Fig. 10b). The pre-drill pressure, trap integrity and reservoir distributions predictions were all confirmed when the prospect was drilled in 1996.

Quantifying uncertainties in basin modelling and their use in prospect appraisal

Forward, deterministic basin models, which are typically applied to charge and pressure modelling, provide one answer

Table 1. Source-rock parameters and associated uncertainties

Present-day net thickness	30 m	20–40 m
Initial total organic carbon	7%	5–9%
Initial H/C	1.13	1.06–1.20
Initial O/C	0.08	–
Characteristic length (measure of the primary migration distance)	0.2 m	0.1–0.3 m
Biot number of lithology above (measure of the efficiency of the secondary carrier network)	0.001 (perfect seal)	–
Biot number of lithology below	1000 (perfect carrier)	–
Activation energy start asphalthene cracking	208 kJ mol^{-1}	206–210 kJ mol^{-1}
Activation energy end asphalthene cracking	226 kJ mol^{-1}	224–228 kJ mol^{-1}

from a suite of possible solutions. At best, the impact which different scenarios have on the outcome may be investigated as in the pressure modelling example above (so-called sensitivity analysis). Ideally, the complete distribution of possible answers is required to analyse the likely economic value of a prospect.

The sources of errors within basin models arise from two principle areas: (1) physical variables such as compaction coefficients; and (2) geological uncertainties such as the age of a formation, or the depth (where no well data are available). In 1D models, Monte Carlo methods (Rubinstein 1981) can be used to assess the total uncertainty by running the model a large number of times, each time resampling the distributions assigned to the physical and geological variables. In multiple dimensions, alternative strategies are needed for the problem to be computationally solved in a reasonable time with the computing power available today.

Central North Sea example

Quantitative analysis of the uncertainties in the volumes and composition of hydrocarbons expelled has been attempted for a prospect in Block 22/23. The prospect is in the Central Graben and consists of Jurassic and Triassic sandstones in a structural/stratigraphic trap. Throughout the area the rocks are at their maximum burial depth at present. Hydrocarbon charge is a primary risk.

A geodynamic model was calibrated against the stratigraphy, VR and BHT data from the nearby well 22/24b-8. These results, together with the prognosed stratigraphy for the kitchen area, formed the input for charge modelling of the 22/23 prospect.

The greatest uncertainties in a continuously buried section with nearby well control reside in the generation and expulsion models. Thus uncertainty analysis concentrated on the parameters of the proprietary GENEX (Stainforth & Reinders 1990) hydrocarbon generation and expulsion model, including source-rock thickness, TOC, H/C, O/C, and cracking energies. The values and uncertainties (based on an evaluation of other Central Graben wells) are given in Table 1.

By running the Shell proprietary charge modelling program Cauldron in 1D Monte Carlo mode the uncertainties in the predicted hydrocarbon volume and composition can be assessed. The results of this analysis (Table 2) provided a primary input to prospect risking. Interestingly, the prognosed range of expulsion GOR (780–975 SCF BBL^{-1}) is close to the actual GOR of the nearby Skua Field (790 SCF BBL^{-1}).

Although in this example the availability of well data close to the prospect precluded the need to extend the uncertainty analysis beyond the source-rock properties, the method is not restricted to these variables. Figure 11 illustrates another example from the Central North Sea, in which uncertainties in depth of the kitchen, compaction parameters etc. were also taken into account.

Conclusions

Three-dimensional basin modelling is capable of providing key input into prospect evaluation. Indeed 3D has many advantages over the earlier 1D and 2D methods – notably the ability to obtain a regional calibration. In addition, basin models can start to address the uncertainties in the modelled results, another key requirement for quantitative prospect evaluation.

The examples given above demonstrate what can be done now with multi-dimensional basin modelling. Future developments will ensure that basin modelling will evolve into the primary vehicle for integrating all available data for prospect evaluation and risking.

The results shown in this paper are built on a continuous history of proprietary basin modelling technology development by Shell research laboratories. Far too many people have been involved to mention them all; however, significant developments on the road to the models shown here, and the staff involved include:

(1) Full lithosphere 1D thermal model in 1979 by P. Wells, A. van Kuyk, and J. Houbolt;
(2) 1D full lithosphere rift model in 1988 by M. Doyle, A. van Kuyk and P. Featherstone;
(3) map based thermal modelling (pseudo 3D i.e. multi 1D) in 1987, by P. Featherstone;
(4) hydrocarbon generation and expulsion modelling in 1988 by J. Stainforth;
(5) hydrocarbon migration modelling in 1986 by F. Lehner and L. Hermans;

Table 2. Expelled hydrocarbon volumes and uncertainties

	99% Percentile	Mean	1% Percentile
Oil generated	1230 kg m^{-2}	1991 kg m^{-2}	2765 kg m^{-2}
Volume generated from kitchen area (16.5 km^2)	159 × 10^6 BBL/16.5 km^2	258 × 10^6 BBL/16.5 km^2	358 × 10^6 BBL/16.5 km^2
Oil expelled	750 kg m^2	1408 kg m^{-2}	2279 kg m^2
Oil expelled from kitchen area (16.5 km^2)	97 × 10^6 BBL/16.5 km^2	182 × 10^6 BBL/16.5 km^2	295 × 10^6 BBL/16.5 km^2
Oil expelled : generated	61%	71%	82%
Gas generated = gas expelled	130 kg m^{-2}	218 kg m^{-2}	316 kg m^2
Gas expelled from kitchen area (16.5 km^2)	95 × 10^9 SCF/16.5 km^2	159 × 10^9 SCF/16.5 km^2	230 × 10^9 SCF/16.5 km^2
Expulsion GOR	975 SCF BBL^{-1}	871 SCF BBL^{-1}	780 SCF BBL^{-1}
Oil + gas generated	1360 kg m^{-2}	2209 kg m^{-2}	3081 kg m^{-2}
Oil + gas expelled	880 kg m^{-2}	1626 kg m^{-2}	2595 kg m^{-2}
HC expelled : generated	65%	74%	84%

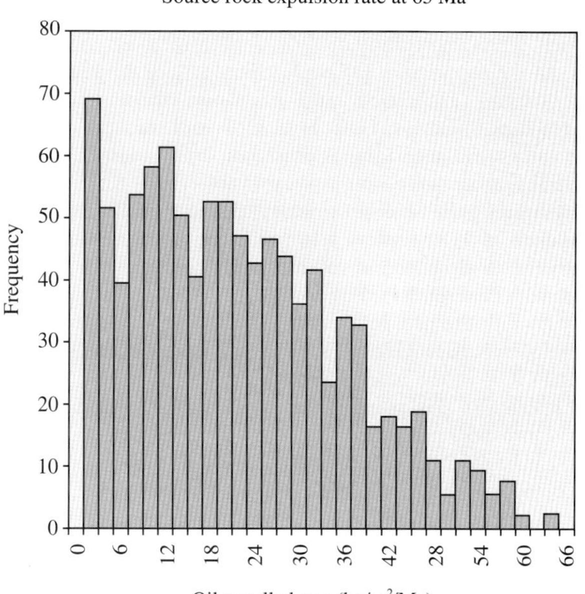

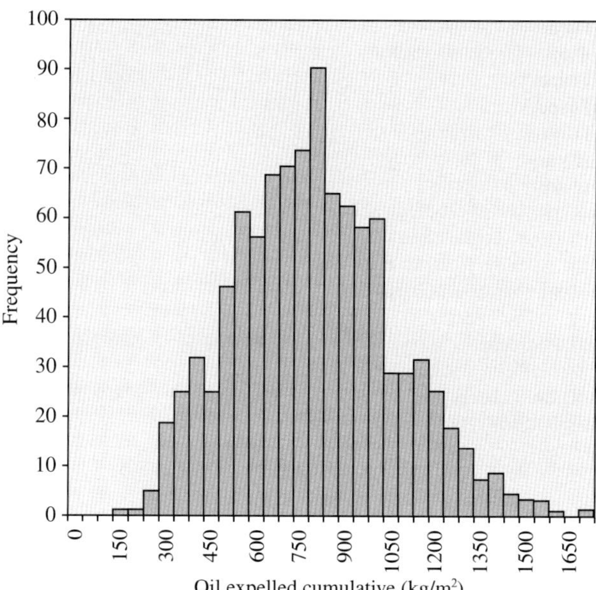

Fig. 11. Uncertainty in source rock expulsion rate (at 65 Ma) and cumulative amount of hydrocarbons expelled by the present day for a Central North Sea well. Cumulative expulsion shows a broad distribution of possible values, around a most likely volume of 800 kg m^{-2}. The most likely rate of expulsion is zero, but there is a good probability that expulsion was occurring at 65 Ma. These other possibilities would be overlooked by a single-answer deterministic model.

(6) 2D pressure modelling in 1992 by C. Harvie and J. McNutt of the Bellaire Research Centre, Houston;
(7) inclusion of uncertainty analysis in 1D charge models in 1993 by G. Marsden.

These models and other models have been in use by Shell operating units since the late 1980s.

The authors wish to thank Shell Exploration and Productions Research and Technical Services for permission to publish this paper, and Wouter de Koning and Kees van Ommeren for their help in preparing the figures.

References

BARKER, C. 1972. Aquathermal pressuring: Role of temperature in development of abnormal pressure zones. *Bulletin of the American Association of Petroleum Geologists*, **56**, 2068–2078.

DICKINSON, G. 1953. Geological aspects of abnormal reservoir pressures in Gulf Coast Louisiana. *Bulletin of the American Association of Petroleum Geologists*, **37**, 410–432.

GAARENSTROOM, L., TROMP, R. A. J., DE JONG, M. C. & BRANDENBURG, A. M. 1993. Overpressures in the Central North Sea: Implications for trap integrity and drilling safety. *In*: PARKER, J. R. (ed.) *Petroleum Geology of Northwest Europe: Proceedings of the 4th Conference*. Geological Society, London, 1305–1313.

GILES, M. R. 1997. *Diagenesis: A Quantitative Perspective*. Kluwer.

HERMANS, L. K., A. D. VAN, LEHNER, F. K. & FEATHERSTONE, P. S. 1992. Modelling secondary hydrocarbon migration in Haltenbanken, Norway. *In*: LARSEN, R. M., BREKKE, H. & LARSEN, B. T. (eds) *Structural and Tectonic Modelling and its Application to Petroleum Geology*. Elsevier Science, 305–323.

HINTE, J. E. VAN 1978. Geohistory analysis – applications of micropaleontology in exploration geology. *Bulletin of the American Association of Petroleum Geologists*, **72**, 758–764

LAW, B. & DICKINSON, W. 1985. Conceptual model for origin of abnormally pressure and hydrocarbon migration. *Bulletin of the American Association of Petroleum Geologists*, **69**, 1295–1304.

LOPATIN, N. V. 1971. Temperature and geologic time as factors in coalification. Akade. Nauk SSSR, *Izve. Ser. Geol.*, **3**, 95–106.

MCKENZIE, D. 1978. Some remarks on the development of sedimentary basins. *Earth and Planetary Science Letters*, **40**, 25–32.

PERRIER, R. & QUIBLIER, J. 1974. Thickness changes in sedimentary layers during compaction history. *Bulletin of the American Association of Petroleum Geologists*, **52**, 57–65.

PHILLIPS, O. M. 1991. *Flow and Reactions in Permeable Rocks*. Cambridge University Press.

RUBINSTEIN, R. Y. 1981. *Simulation and the Monte Carlo Method*. John Wiley and Sons, New York.

SCLATER, J. G. & CHRISTIE, P. A. F. 1980. Continental stretching: An explanation of the post Mid-Cretaceous subsidence of the Central North Sea Basin. *Journal of Geophysical Research*, **85**(B7), 3711–3739.

STAINFORTH, J. G. & REINDERS, J. E. A. 1990. Primary migration of hydrocarbons by diffusion through organic matter networks, and its effects on oil and gas generation. *Advances in Organic Geochemistry*, **16**, 61–74.

SYLTA, Ø. 1993. New techniques and their application in the analysis of secondary migration. *In*: DORÉ, A. G. *et al.* (eds) *Basin Modelling: Advances and Applications*. Norwegian Petroleum Society (NPF) Special Publication **3**, 385–398.

TERZAGHI, K. 1923. Die Berechnung der Durchlässigkeitsziffer des Tones aus dem verlauf der hydronamischen Spannungserscheinungen, *Sitzungen der Akademie der Wissenschaften Wien Mathematisch-naturwissenschaftliche. Klasse*. **132**, 105–124.

TISSOT, B. & ESPITALIÉ, 1975. L'evolution thermique de la matiére organique des sediments: application d'one simulation mathématique. *Revue de l'Institut Francois de Petrole*, **30**, 743–777.

VIK, E. & HERMANRUD, H. C. 1993. Transient thermal effects of rapid subsidence in the Haltenbanken area. *In*: DØRÉ, A. G. *et al.* (eds) *Basin Modelling: Advances and Applications*. Norwegian Petroleum Society (NPF) Special Publication **3**, 107–117.

WATTS, A. B. & RYAN, W. B. F. 1976. Flexure of the lithosphere and continental margin basins. *Tectonophysics*, **36**, 25–44.

Hydrocarbon systems modelling of the Norwegian Central Graben fairway trend

M. S. G. TAYLOR, A. LEROY and M. FØRLAND

BP Amoco Norway, Norge HS Forusheen 35, PO Box 197 4065 Stavanger, Norway (e-mail: taylormsg@bp.com)

Abstract: The known hydrocarbon accumulations in the Norwegian Central Graben Fairway trend are forward modelled in this study. Particular attention is paid to the petroleum phase in the reservoirs as commercial and economic models of Central Graben prospects are closely linked to hydrocarbon type, especially in the less explored downdip areas.

Detailed seismic structure grids and well data are utilized in Finesse, an integrated 2D horizontal plane modelling program to simulate the maturation of source rocks and the expulsion, migration, and entrapment of generated hydrocarbons through time. All known Jurassic, Cretaceous, and Paleocene fields and discoveries were used to calibrate the model.

The study focused on migration through multiple layers defining vertical conduits between layers based on modelling seal capacity failure and fracturing rather than using faults as conduits. The maturity indicator used was the total transformation ratio (TTR) (the sum of the oil and oil to gas cracking transformation ratios) rather than vitrinite reflectance (R_o). TTR is an accurate reflection of the state of source maturity whereas Ro is an indication of the thermal stress applied to the source.

The results show that 2D horizontal plane models can be used to predict known hydrocarbon accumulations over large regions and highlight areas of future prospectivity. This allows the explorationist to effectively focus on specific areas where more detailed 2D or 3D modelling can be applied.

Basin modelling is used to quantify the risks associated with exploring for new hydrocarbon accumulations. The economics of these are closely linked to hydrocarbon type: oil, gas or condensate. In this respect it is important to model and match migration pathways not only to highlight future prospectivity, especially in unexplored downdip areas, but also to show where migration has not occurred. This type of modelling should be used to rank prospects and so enable explorationists to focus their efforts on factors such as seal integrity and reservoir properties. Just because hydrocarbons have migrated to a prospect does not mean they will be in economic volumes or still be present.

The aim of any basin modelling study is to forward model known hydrocarbon accumulations and to predict the location of future prospects. This process can be divided into three steps: hydrocarbon generation and expulsion; hydrocarbon migration; and history matching. To model hydrocarbon generation and expulsion the following source-rock characteristics are required: volume, kinetics, richness and thermal history. These determine the volume, type and timing of hydrocarbons expelled. In this study buoyancy is considered to be the primary drive for migration (Sylta 1993) and thus the carrier bed geometries delimit where the hydrocarbons migrated and accumulated through time. By comparing the known to modelled hydrocarbon accumulations (so-called history matching) the validity of the model can be assessed. If the model cannot match the known fields and migration pathways then further work is needed before the model can be used to predict the future prospectivity of an area.

Study area

The Norwegian Central Graben Fairway Trend (Fig. 1) is defined as much by commercial and geographical criteria as by geological criteria. It is that part of the Norwegian sector of the Central Graben which contains prospectivity that is likely to be economic through existing and potential future infrastructure. The study covered the area 56°20′ to 57°20′N and 2° to 3°20′E.

Methodology and input data

Source-rock characteristics

(1) Thickness and total organic carbon contents. The Mandal Formation is the richest oil source in the study area; however, the Farsund and Haugesund formations are also viable and proven oil-source intervals. Because the Mandal and Farsund formations are in general more organic rich and are present more often than the Haugesund, the combined Mandal + Farsund interval was used as the gross source interval for hydrocarbon generation and expulsion modelling. Net producing source thickness and total organic carbon (TOC) contents (%) of the Mandal + Farsund interval were derived mainly from calibrated delta log R calculations from well log data (Passey *et al.* 1990).

(2) Kinetics. The kinetics used in the study were derived from proprietary analyses of Kimmeridge Clay kerogen from the North Viking Graben.

(3) Burial history. Depth grids covering the entire study area were used to simulate the burial history. Grids were decompacted after Sclater & Christie's (1980) equation

$$\phi = \alpha e^{-\beta z} + \chi,$$

where

ϕ = porosity (decimal) of formation at depth z (m);
α = depth dependent porosity;
β = lithology dependent constant;
χ = minimum porosity.

Table 1 details the units that were decompacted based on 1D modelling and the depth surfaces available.

(4) Thermal history. The program 'Finesse' is capable of modelling temperature through time using thermal conductivity (as a function of mineralogy and compaction) and heat flow. However, present-day temperature gradient data were used as primary input for thermal modelling in this study for the following reasons:

(i) present-day temperatures represent the maximum thermal stress that rocks have been exposed to within this system;

TAYLOR, M. S. G., LEROY, A. & FØRLAND, M. 1999. Hydrocarbon systems modelling of the Norwegian Central Graben fairway trend. *In*: FLEET, A. J. & BOLDY, S. A. R. (eds) *Petroleum Geology of Northwest Europe: Proceedings of the 5th Conference*, 1325–1338. © Petroleum Geology '86 Ltd. Published by the Geological Society, London.

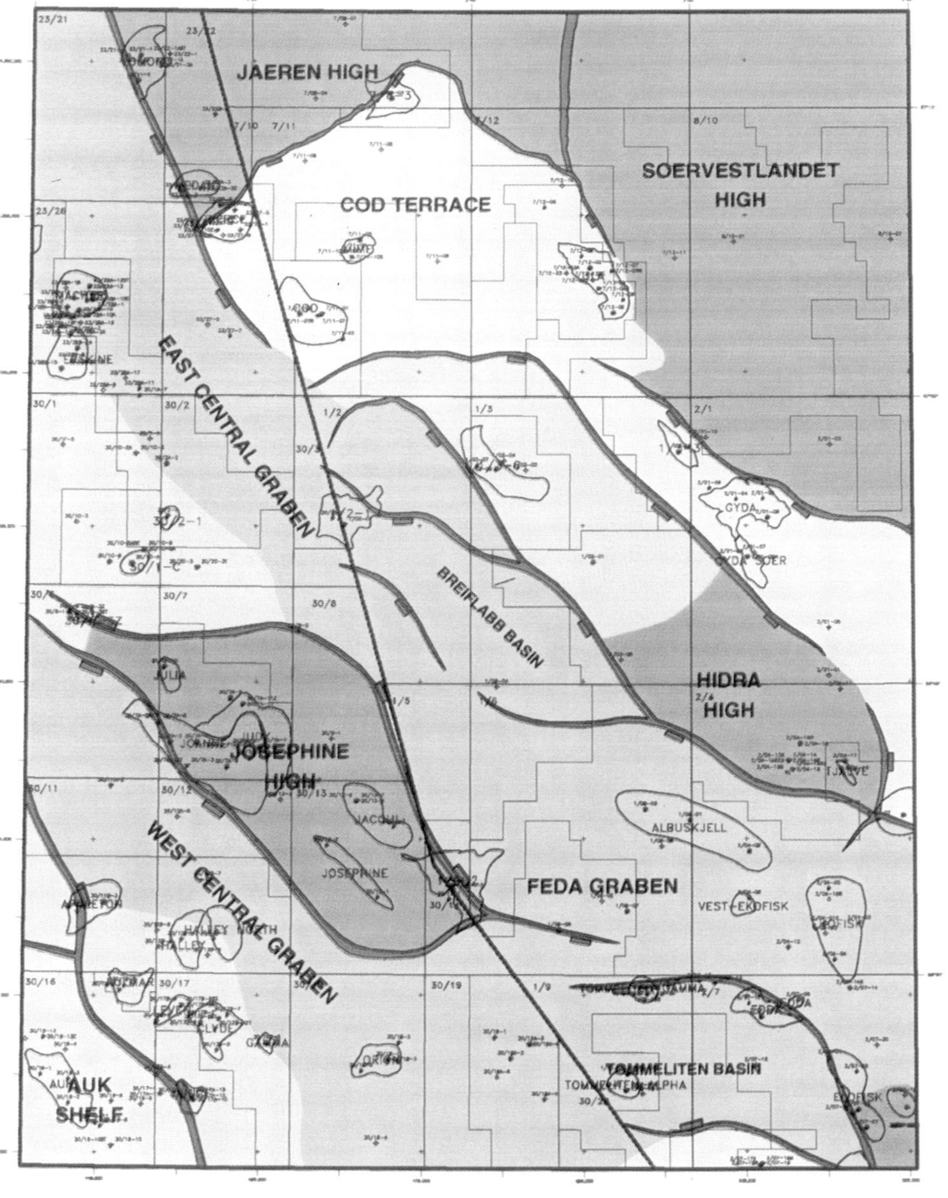

Fig. 1. Study area of interest.

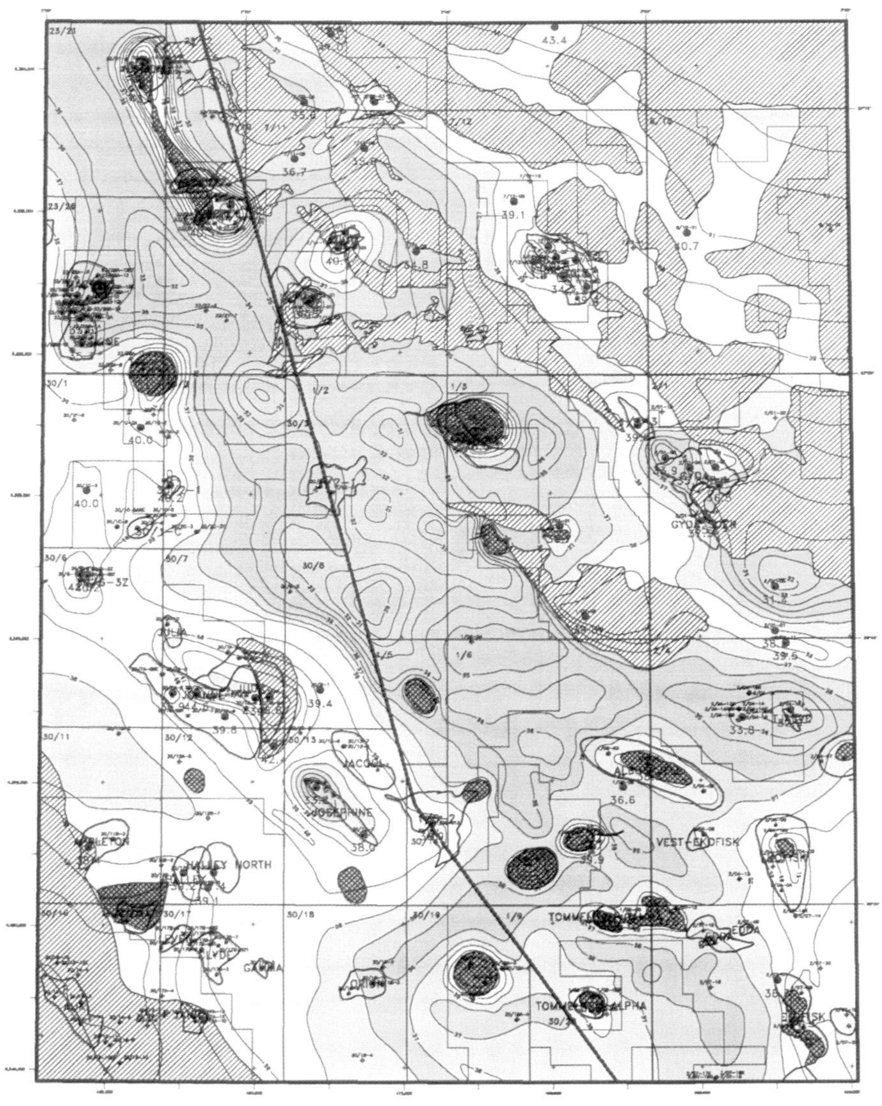

Fig. 2. Geothermal gradient (°F/1000 ft) to Base Cretaceous unconformity.

Table 1. Decompaction surfaces and parameters

Age	Surface	Lithology	α	β	χ
0	Seafloor	Sand shale	0.47	0.39	0.05
2	Base Pleistocene	Limy Shale	0.55	0.48	0.05
23	Base Lower Miocene	Shale	0.58	0.51	0.02
57	Top Balder	Sandy shale	0.52	0.46	0.05
66	Top U. Cretaceous	Limestone/chalk	0.57	0.22	0.03
97	Base U. Cretaceous	Limy shale	0.55	0.48	0.05
141	Base Cretaceous	Shale	0.58	0.51	0.05
144	Base source				

(ii) present-day temperature data are readily available for gridding and calibration;
(iii) thermal models of present conditions are more deterministic than those of earlier time periods when assessing liquid hydrocarbon generation and stability windows.

Temperature input consisted of average temperature gradients from the seafloor to the Base Cretaceous unconformity (BCU) for each well. In most wells, the BCU represents the top of the source-rock interval. The gradients were derived from present-day corrected bottom hole temperature (BHT) and drill stem test (DST) temperature data. The temperature gradients were then geographically interpolated based on integrating the depth of the BCU with the depth vs gradient relationship to generate a geothermal gradient grid that could be used in the model (Fig. 2).

The seafloor to BCU temperature gradients tend to decrease as the depths to the BCU increase. This is a critical trend to recognize and incorporate when extrapolating gradients into the deeper parts of the basin, where there are no BCU penetrations. The trend has not been recognized in many earlier published and proprietary studies (e.g. Robertson Research 1997) because these studies generally do not consider the stratigraphic-specific signature of the gradients.

Failure to incorporate geology/thermal conductivity/temperature gradient relationships will generally result in the following pitfalls in the deeper parts of the basin: over-estimation of temperature gradients; over-estimation of source rock maturity; and under-estimation of liquid hydrocarbon generation and preservation potential.

Hydrocarbon generation and expulsion

Hydrocarbon generation can be modelled in a simplistic manner by two equations (Tissot & Welte 1978):

$$k = \mathrm{A}\,\mathrm{e}^{Ea/\mathrm{R}T(t)}$$

expresses the variation in the rate of oil generation (k) with temperature, and

$$\mathrm{d}x/\mathrm{d}t = -kx$$

expresses the fact that the rate of conversion of the kerogen into oil depends on the fractional amount (x) of the original (convertible) kerogen remaining.

Where
k = reaction rate (e.g. grams oil/gram kerogen Ma^{-1})
A = Arrhenius constant (frequency factor) (e.g. Ma)
Ea = activation energy (e.g. calories mol^{-1})
R = universal gas constant (e.g. calories mol-degree^{-1})
T = temperature (Kelvin degrees)
t = time (e.g. Ma)
x = fractional amount of convertible kerogen remaining
Ma = million years

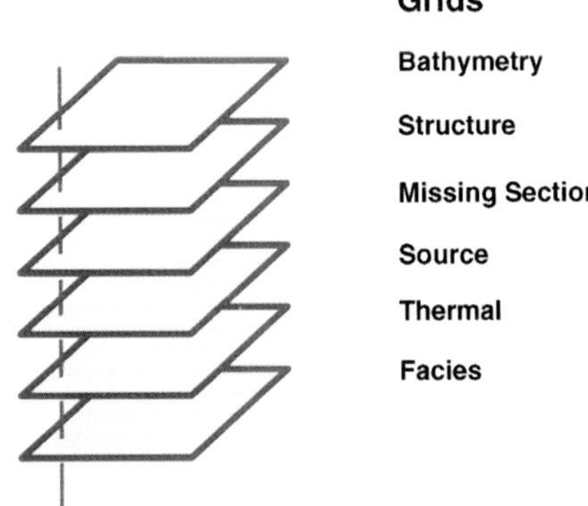

Fig. 3. Grid node: each node in a series of stacked grids can be treated as an ID point.

Calculation of the fractional amount of kerogen remaining (x) and the rate of oil generation (kx) at any time requires the evaluation of:

$$\int_{t_1}^{t_2} k(t)\,\mathrm{d}t$$

In this study, A and Ea were constant, thus to model x the only variable is temperature through time.

Rather than modelling individual points and integrating the results over the basin an alternative method used in Finesse is to model the complete basin in one run. This can be done with a grid approach where surfaces instead of individual data values are input. The grids have identical dimensions thus each grid node location can be treated as a 1D point (Fig. 3). In this study there were approx. 60 000 nodes. The input grids (horizons, TOC and geothermal gradients) and results were calibrated against well control.

Total transformation ratio

The transformation ratio (TR) ($1 - x$) is a measure of how much kerogen has been converted to hydrocarbons. As this is a

Table 2. Total transformation ratio and corresponding generation state

Total TR	State
0.1–0.5	Early oil
0.5–0.7	Peak oil
0.7–0.9	End oil
0.9–1.1	Quiescence
1.1–1.5	Early gas
1.7–1.7	Peak gas
1.7–1.9	End gas
>1.9	Inert

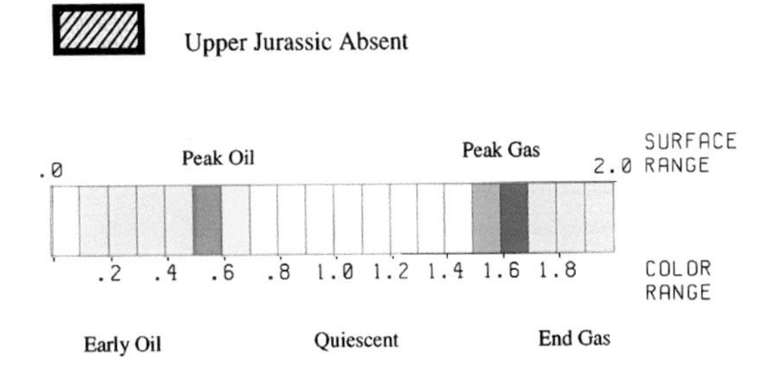

Key to Fig. 4 overleaf

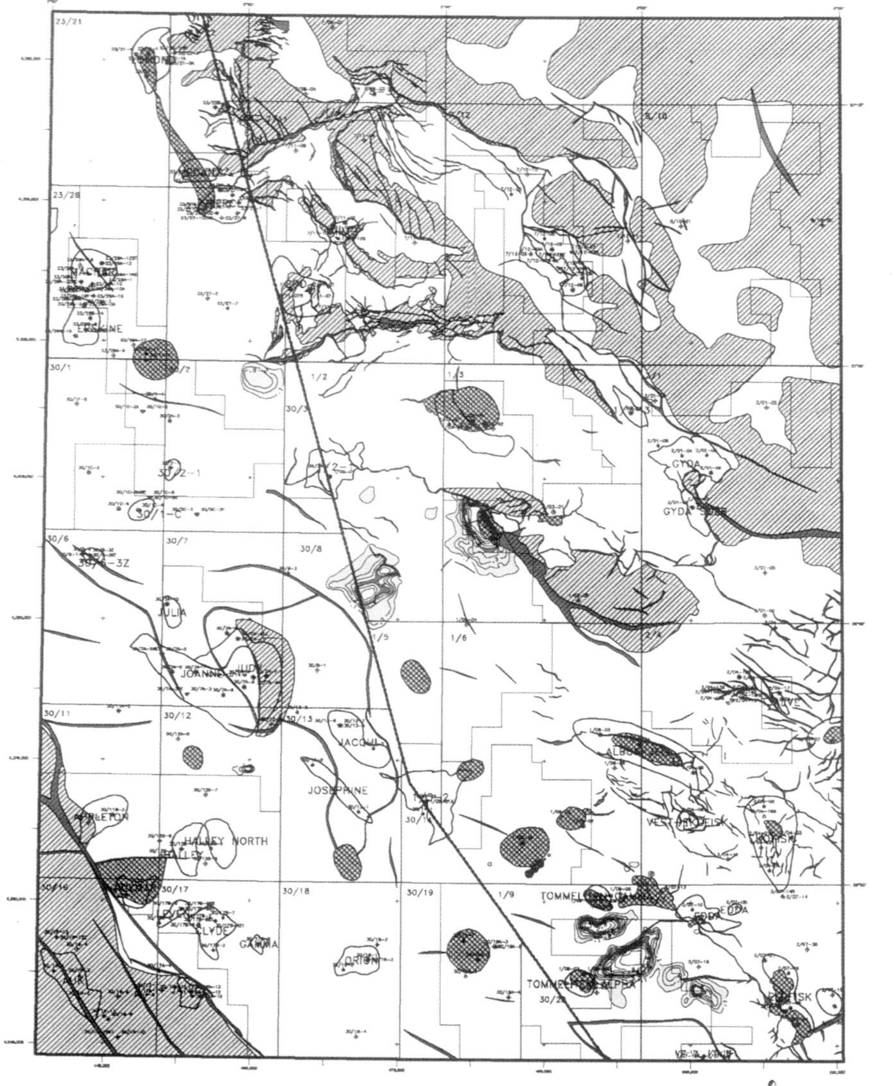

Fig. 4. Total transformation ratio, 50 Ma. Start of liquid hydrocarbon generation in Tommeliten and Brieflabb Basins.

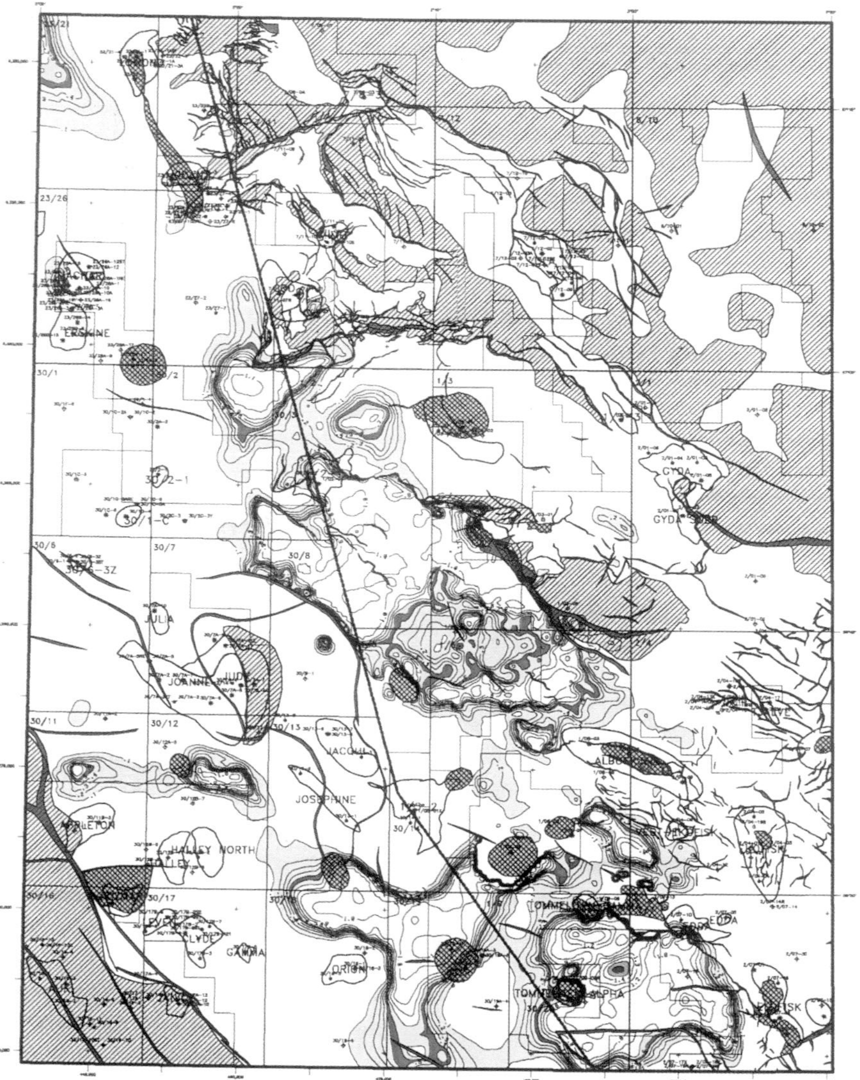

Fig. 5. Total transformation ratio, 23 Ma. Tommeliten and Brieflabb basins quiescent, liquid hydrocarbon generation moving up the sides of the depocentres and subsidence continues.

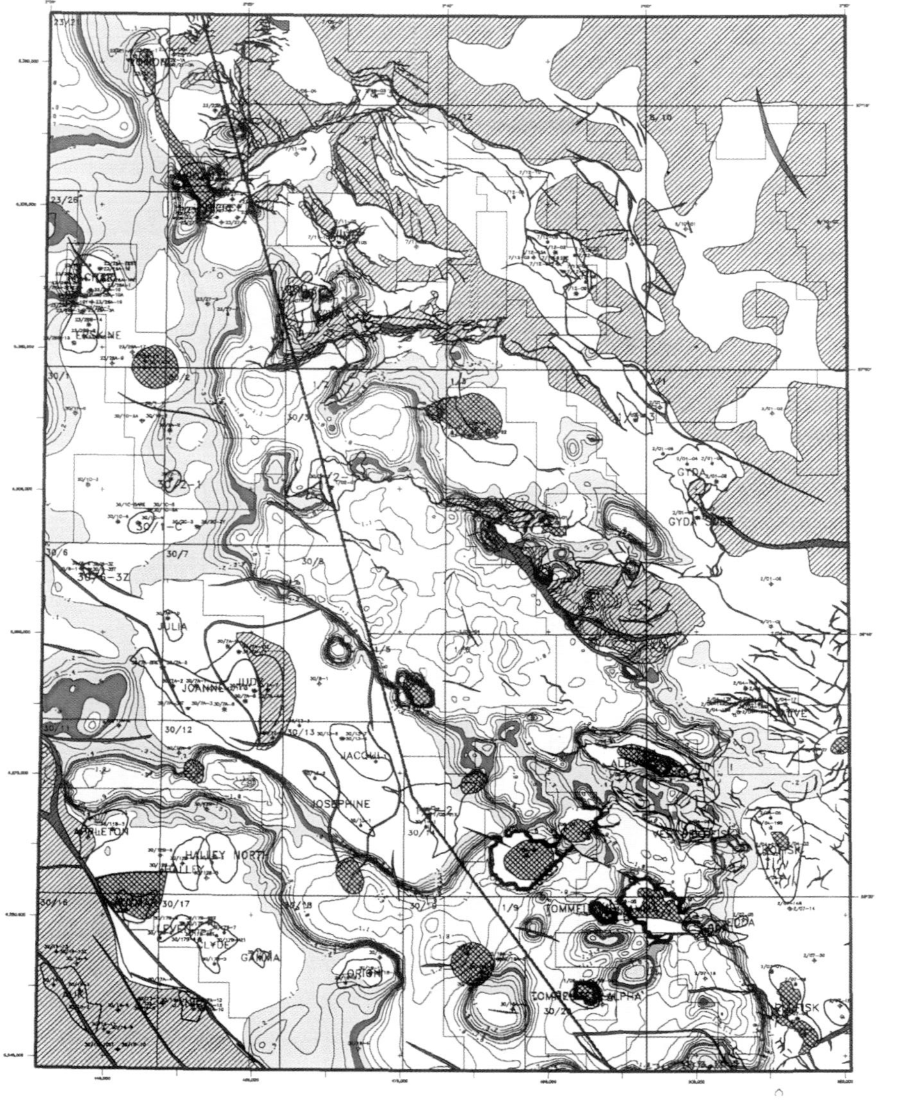

Fig. 6. Total transformation ratio, 16 Ma. Tommeliten Basin at peak gas generation. Brieflab Basin still quiescent. Liquid hydrocarbon generation continues to move up-dip.

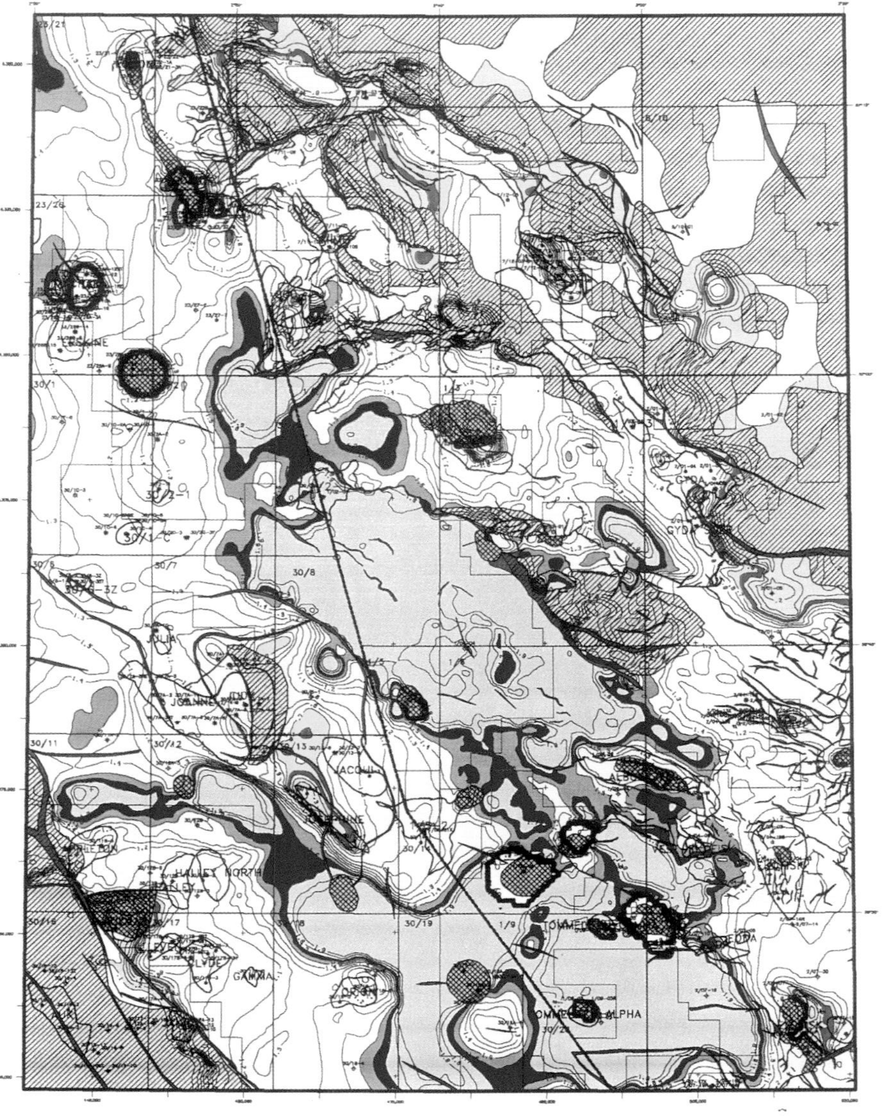

Fig. 7. Total transformation ratio, present day. Tommeliten and Breiflabb basins and Feda and West central grabens all past peak gas generation. Liquid hydrocarbon generation confines to Cod Terrace, Josephine High and Auk Shelf.

function of actual kerogen kinetics, it is a better indicator of conversion than $\%R_o$, which is merely a reflection of maximum thermal stress.

In addition to the oil TR, an oil to gas cracking TR was also calculated using kinetics derived from proprietary analyses of various reservoir oils. This TR refers to the ratio of gas to original oil. The source of the oil can be either residual or migrated. The residual oil is oil that has not been expelled from the source and remains *in situ*. Migrated oil is that which has been expelled and has migrated to a trap. Further burial of the traps can result in increased thermal stress.

Total TR (TTR) is the sum of the oil TR and average oil to gas cracking TR. The values range from 0 to 2 (Table 2).

TTR maps were constructed at several time steps to illustrate the evolution of source-rock kitchens from the pre-oil generation stage through to the post-oil to gas cracking stage (Figs 4 to 7).

Oil expulsion

The method used to calculate the volume of hydrocarbons that have been expelled from the source is based on a proprietary forward mass balance method of oil expulsion (after Cooles *et al.* 1986).

As the kerogen is heated and buried it is transformed into a fluid with consequent loss of part of the rock matrix (kerogen). This change in rock matrix volume has the effect of squeezing the fluid into the carrier. In this study, an initial hydrogen index (HI_0) value of 500 was used. From proprietary modelling this results in a petroleum expulsion efficiency of 80% when the oil TR has reached 1. Expulsion begins when the transformation ratio reaches 0.3. Peak Oil generation is defined in this model as the time when the oil transformation ratio reaches a value of 0.6.

The output from this method includes the total hydrocarbons generated and moveable hydrocarbons expelled. The moveable hydrocarbons expelled grid was used for oil migration. The difference between the moveable hydrocarbons generated and moveable hydrocarbons expelled was used to compute the residual oil (oil left behind in the source).

For TOC, the observed and initial values were assumed to be the same. This is not a true reflection of the system, and initial TOC values will be used in future studies.

Gas generation and expulsion

Gas is generated by three distinct processes: (1) biogenic; (2) during oil generation; and (3) oil to gas cracking. In this instance, gas generated by processes (2) and (3) was considered.

For a typical Type II kerogen, proprietary hydrous pyrolysis results indicate that 16% by weight of gas is expelled in addition to the oil expelled (i.e. if 100 g of oil was expelled, then 16 g of gas would have been expelled too). This gas volume is one component of the total gas volume simulated.

With continued heating, oil eventually cracks to gas. For this study, the kinetics for the gas to oil cracking of a low sulphur oil from a Type II source were assumed. The oil being cracked can be either migrated or remain as residual. Migrated oil is that which has been expelled and resides in a trap that is heated further (normally through burial). Residual oil has not been expelled and remains in the source. This oil is converted directly to gas. It is assumed that all this gas will be expelled and thus available for migration.

To convert these weights into volumes, an oil density of $0.8\,g\,cm^{-3}$ and gas density of $0.35\,g\,cm^{-3}$ were used. As an example of how gas volumes were calculated, if the source has passed the end of the oil to gas cracking window and expelled 80% of the generated oil, then for one barrel of oil expelled, the following volumes of gas would be expelled:

Through the oil window

$$0.16 \times (0.8\,g\,cm^{-3})/(0.35\,g\,cm^{-3}) = 0.37\,\text{BBL gas expelled}$$

Through oil to gas cracking

$$[(1/0.8) - 1)] \times (0.8\,g\,cm^{-3})/(0.35\,g\,cm^{-3}) = 0.57\,\text{BBL gas expelled}$$

Total $= 0.94\,\text{BBL or } 5.26\,ft^3$

Hydrocarbon migration

Single layer

The simplest method to simulate paths along which hydrocarbons have migrated is to assume vertical (up or down) migration of hydrocarbons from the source to a carrier bed and up-dip migration thereafter. The limitations of this method are that no assumptions are made about the phase or density of the product migrating or about the properties of the carrier bed. Barriers to migration such as faults or pinch-outs are, however, considered. The volume of hydrocarbons expelled in each grid cell is calculated and allowed to migrate up-dip (secondary migration). The migration pathway from each cell is shown as a raypath. The raypaths are colour coded according to the volume of hydrocarbons associated with the raypath. Once the raypaths have reached a trap, the volume of hydrocarbons in that trap is calculated by summing the volumes associated with each raypath. The volume of available pore space is then calculated (using top and, optionally, base carrier), and if this is less than the volume of hydrocarbons that has reached the trap, a spill point is found and the excess hydrocarbons are allowed to migrate further up-dip (tertiary migration). Secondary and tertiary migration, in their simplest forms, are represented in Figs 8 and 9.

Dynamic migration through time

Carrier-bed geometry changes through time occur either through catastrophic events, such as faulting, or by more subtle processes such as changing depositional rates or bathymetry across the basin. These changes can have a profound effect on the migration of hydrocarbons, especially if hydrocarbons were generated prior to these events. It is, therefore, important to include evolving carrier-bed geometries into the migration model through time.

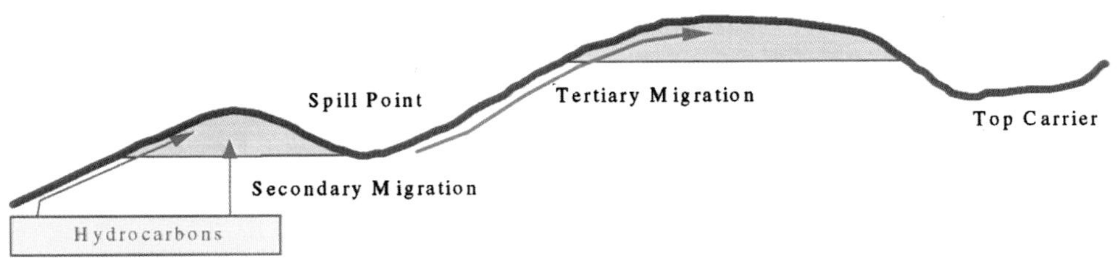

Fig. 8. Single layer migration.

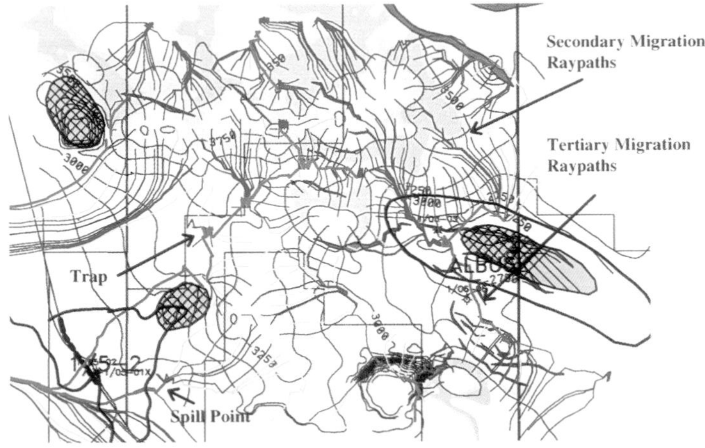

Fig. 9. Hydrocarbon generation and structure drive raypaths showing secondary and tertiary migration, traps and spill points.

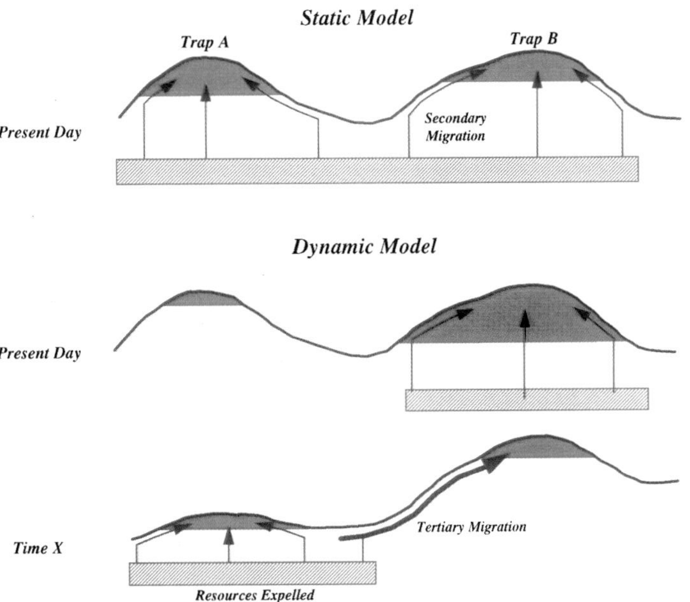

Fig. 10. Dynamic migration through time.

For example in Fig. 10, moveable hydrocarbons have been expelled over the whole basin with the earliest generation having occurred to the west. Using the present-day geometry only (Static Model), Traps A and B have both been filled with the same volume of hydrocarbons. However, there has been a change in basin geometry between the time of earliest hydrocarbon generation and present-day. At X Ma, the moveable hydrocarbons were being generated towards the west of the section. These moveable hydrocarbons filled Trap A and then spilled up to Trap B. At X Ma the volume of Trap A is less than the present-day static volume. Between X Ma and present-day, hydrocarbon generation shifted from west to east of the section. These incremental (generated between X Ma and present-day) moveable hydrocarbons migrate only into Trap B. The result from the dynamic model shows significantly greater volumes in Trap B.

Multiple layer migration

Vertical leakage. The single layer migration model works well when the seal above the carrier system remains competent. In the Central Graben, as in most areas, seals leak, and leaky seals act as migration conduits to shallower units. In this study, vertical fractures and some faults were identified as major conduits. Whereas faults are commonly identifiable on seismic data, fractures are not; therefore, a reliable means of predicting fractures is necessary in order to assess their impact on hydrocarbon migration. Two methods were utilized: (1) the difference between fracture pressure and pore pressure; and (2) flexural strain to determine where fracturing was likely to have occurred.

Migration through pressure-induced fractures

Drilling, core, fluid inclusion and seismic (gas clouds and shallow gas amplitudes) data indicate that seals over North Sea Jurassic reservoirs commonly leak. This is true for small fields as wells as giant fields. One of the key factors responsible for leakage is seal failure caused by excessive overpressure. By mapping the difference between fracture pressure and pore pressure, we can assess the theoretical probability and relative likelihood of this occurring.

Overpressure mapping is commonly used to identify fluid compartments, as differences in overpressure are independent of depth (pore pressures in hydraulically communicative sections may be different because of depth differences, but overpressures in hydraulically communicative sections with similar fluid densities should be the same regardless of depth). The entire study area is overpressured (pore pressure > hydrostatic pressure) at the BCU. The highest modelled overpressure (>10,000 psi) occurs in the deepest parts of the basin. The highest measured overpressure below the BCU is 8285 psi (well 1/6-6).

Seal capacity (fracture–pore pressure) was one of two parameters used in this study to determine where vertical leakage was likely to have occurred. The smaller the seal capacity, the greater the risk of seal failure. From proprietary studies in the Northern Viking Graben and the Moray Firth area and from published studies (e.g. Gaarenstroom *et al.* 1993), leakage is known to have occurred where seal capacity is 1000 psi or less, and this relationship appears valid within the Fairway Trend study area.

Seal capacity results

The 1000 psi contour interval is highlighted on the BCU seal capacity map in Fig. 11. Values of 1000 psi and less occur in the deeper parts of the basin, but along somewhat different trends than the highest pore pressure and overpressure values. These values virtually all occur where there is shallower pay above the BCU. The 1000 psi contour interval at the BCU underlies parts of almost all Chalk discoveries in the Ekofisk area to the southeast. The 1000 psi contours also underlie parts of the Josephine, Joanne, Julia, UK30/2-1, Machar, Lomond, Medan, Pierce, and Cod Chalk and Paleocene discoveries. There is a striking correlation between these low seal capacities at the BCU and shallower discoveries; this correlation is the result of vertical migration associated with hydraulic fracture related seal failure.

By understanding this relationship and mapping seal capacity, we are able to predict where vertical migration conduits to shallower reservoirs are likely to exist. These vertical conduits were used in the multiple layer migration model to simulate the filling of the Chalk and Paleocene reservoirs.

Migration through tectonic-induced fractures

A few of the Chalk and Paleocene discoveries in Fig. 1 do not overlie areas where the seal capacity at the BCU is less than 1000 psi. However, there is an alternative mechanism for charging these discoveries; this mechanism consists of fracture conduits caused by flexural strain.

In this model it is assumed that the rock matrix will fracture when the total stress exceeds the fracture pressure. The total

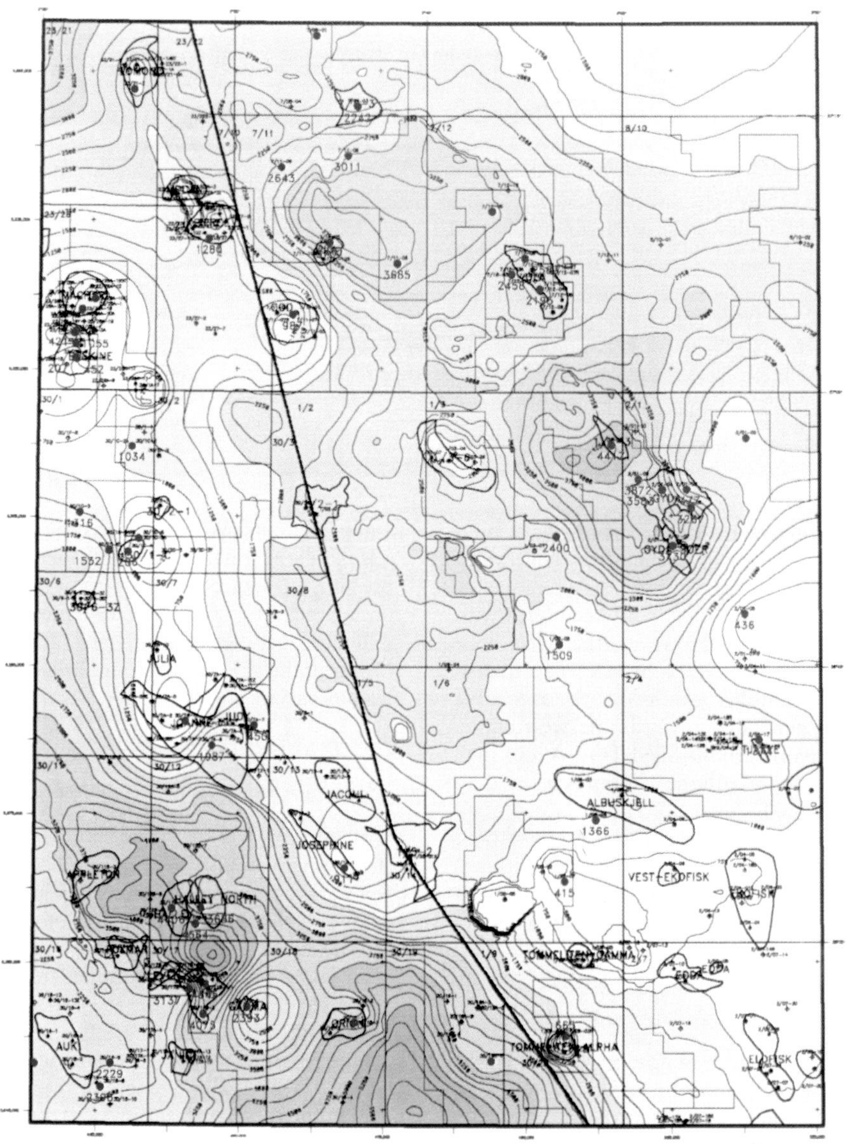

Fig. 11. Seal capacity at Base Cretaceous (psi). Seal capacity failure <1000 psi.

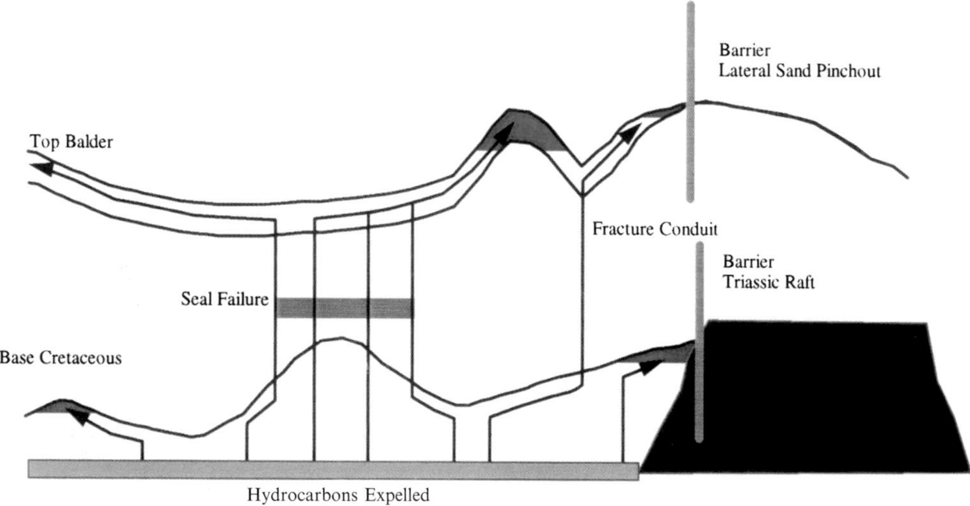

Fig. 12. Multiple layer migration.

stress is a combination of both surface and body forces. The body force is measured by the pore pressure and the surface force by the bending moment (Øxnevad & Taylor 1999).

A simplified method of representing this moment is the second derivative or curvature of a surface. Anticlinal areas have a positive curvature, and synclines are negative. This method was used on the Top Balder grid. In areas of negative curvature the horizons below the Balder are under tension. It is assumed that in highly negative areas the rock matrix below the Balder will fracture and these fractures will propagate through the Lower Cretaceous causing seal failure at the BCU.

Once conduits are identified, hydrocarbon migration along a deep carrier, up a vertical conduit, and along a shallower carrier can be simulated using a multiple layer migration model. In this case, the BCU is used as the top of the deep carrier system, vertical fracture systems are used as the vertical conduits, and the Top Balder surface is used as the top of the shallow carrier system. This integrated model was necessary in order to explain the emplacement of hydrocarbon in Paleocene reservoirs (Fig. 12).

Moveable hydrocarbons generated will initially migrate along the Base Cretaceous carrier. These moveable hydrocarbons will either be trapped, lost from the system, or will migrate vertically to the next carrier. The top chalk and top Balder are viable carrier surfaces. For this simulation, the top Balder was used as a carrier surface.

Dynamic multiple layer migration

In the simulation, the multiple layer migration model was run at 50, 40, 30, 23, 16, 2 and 0 Ma. Any moveable hydrocarbons that migrated into the Balder system before 30 Ma or where the top Balder was less than 500 m were removed from the system based on the assumption that the top Balder seal would be inadequate.

History matching

Generation and expulsion history

Incremental generated oil resource surfaces were constructed for various time periods in order to illustrate the generation history of the Mandal/Farsund source-rock interval (Figs 13 to 16).

Oil was first generated from the Mandal/Farsund source rocks during the Eocene, in the deepest parts of the Central Graben sub-basins. From the Eocene through to the Miocene, the generation kitchens shifted from the deep sub-basins to the terrace areas as source rocks became thermally overmature in the deep sub-basins and thermally mature in the terraces.

Generation began in the shallowest terraces (e.g. Ula–Gyda trend of the Cod Terrace) in late Neogene, and most of that did not occur until the Pliocene. In the last 2 Ma, oil generation was limited to the up-dip Cod Terrace area, the Josephine High, the Clyde–Fulmar area, and the Eldfisk area. Basinal areas had stopped generating (Fig. 16).

Expelled gas simulated in this study is a combination of gas expelled during oil generation and during cracking of oil to gas. Incremental generated gas maps were constructed for various time steps in order to illustrate the gas expulsion history of the Mandal/Farsund source-rock interval. Gas, in association with oil, was first generated from the Mandal/Farsund source rocks during the Eocene, in the deepest parts of the Central Graben sub-basins. From the Eocene through the Early Miocene, the gas generation kitchens were essentially the same as the oil generation kitchens, as expelled gas volumes were those mainly associated with oil generation.

Near the end of the Neogene, two things happened. Gas expulsion associated with oil generation shifted from the deep sub-basins to the terrace areas as source rocks became thermally overmature in the deep sub-basins and thermally mature in the terraces. More significantly, in terms of gas volumes, the deeper areas reached thermal conditions that caused extensive cracking of oil to gas.

During the last 2 Ma, continued cracking of oil to gas occurred in the basinal areas, although at lower rates, as the 'peak' stage of cracking had already occurred throughout most of the area. Up-dip terrace areas continue to expel some gas in association with oil generation.

As indicated earlier, the first significant oil and associated gas generation occurred during the Early Eocene in the deepest parts of the Central Graben sub-basins. With continued burial and heating, these kitchens expanded geographically, with peak oil generation (TTR = 0.6) 'windows' moving to the peripheries of these kitchens as the axial areas became overmature for oil. These overmature, or 'quiescent', areas also expanded geographically with time.

It was not until the very late Neogene that these broad quiescent areas evolved thermally into areas where significant oil to gas cracking occurred within the Mandal/Farsund interval. The highest rates of cracking are indicated by the red and orange areas (TTR = 1.5–1.7) (Fig. 7). The latest Neogene was also the time that oil (and associated gas generation) was occurring in the up-dip terrace areas.

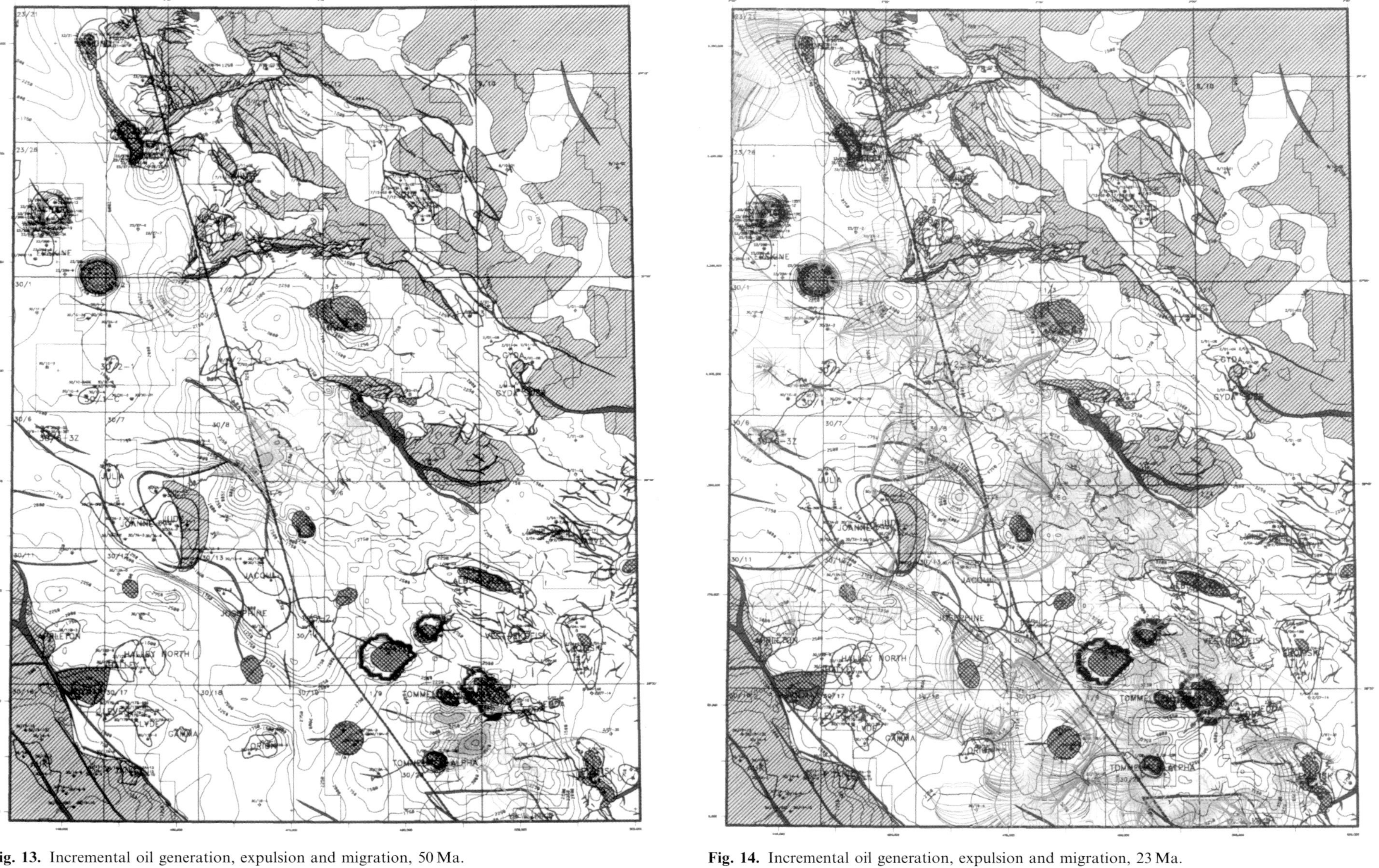

Fig. 13. Incremental oil generation, expulsion and migration, 50 Ma.

Fig. 14. Incremental oil generation, expulsion and migration, 23 Ma.

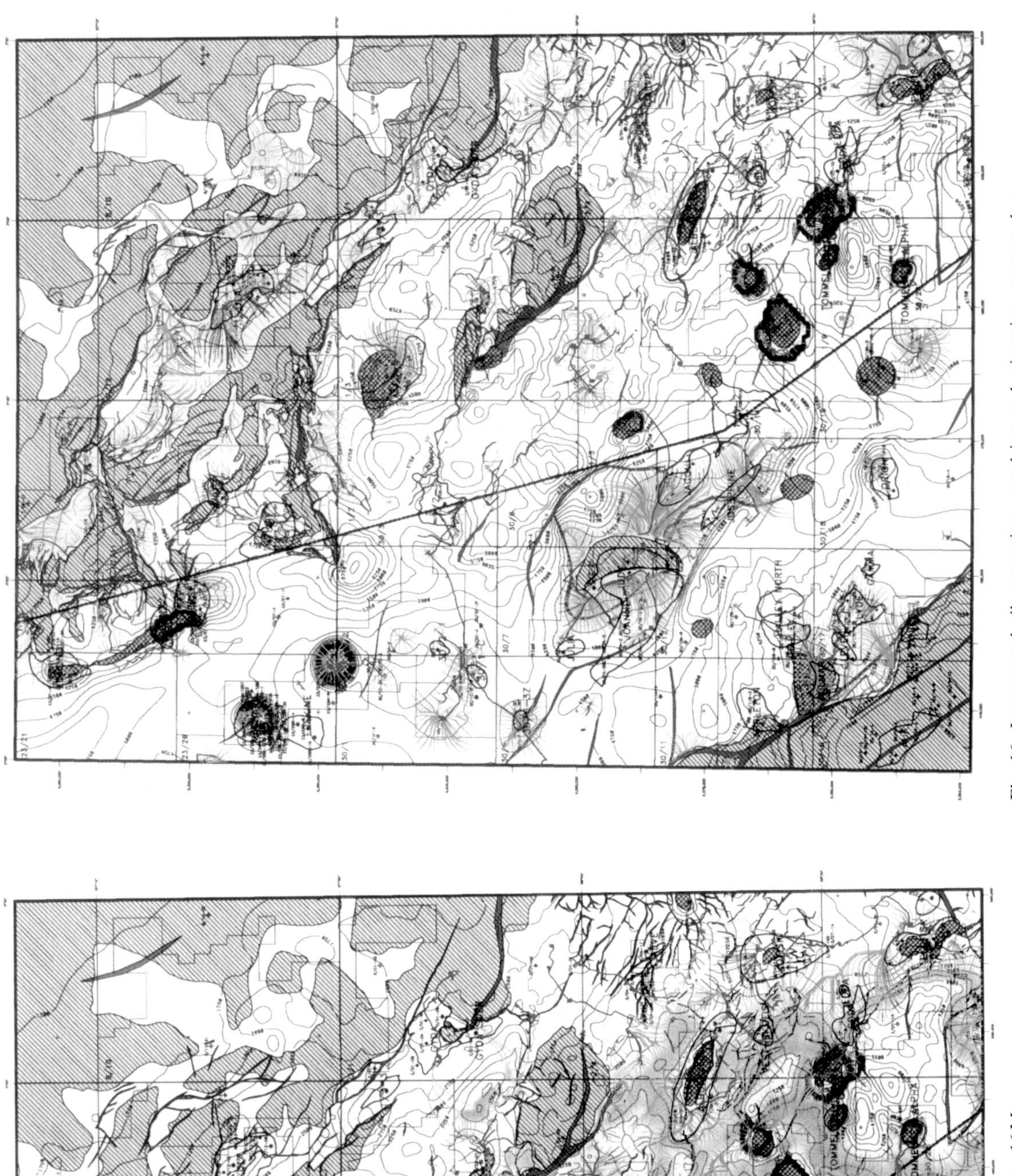

Fig. 16. Incremental oil generation, expulsion and migration, present day.

Fig. 15. Incremental oil generation, expulsion and migration, 16 Ma.

Migration history

Jurassic

Carrier systems and conduits. The qualitative distribution of hydrocarbons in the Jurassic can be modelled quite successfully using single layer dynamic migration modelling through time. This is possible because both the hydrocarbon source rocks and the carrier system underlie the BCU, and the BCU is a reliable mapping horizon throughout most of the area. Accordingly, the BCU was used as both the top of the source interval and the top of the carrier system in this study.

While the BCU is a reliable mapping horizon, Upper Jurassic reservoirs and carrier beds are time transgressive and commonly not resolvable seismically; therefore, it is not possible to map specific carrier beds. Even though these carrier beds rarely subcrop at the BCU, the shallowest ones are generally within 200 m of the BCU; therefore, it is reasonable to treat the BCU as the shallowest and most regionally extensive Jurassic carrier surface in the study area.

Barriers. Hydrocarbons migrate in a carrier system until a trapping mechanism causes them to accumulate. The most common cause of these accumulations is a four-way closure. Another cause is a lateral permeability barrier.

Within the study area, Triassic rafts commonly border Jurassic depocenters, and the interfaces between Jurassic reservoir sands and Triassic non-reservoir sediments have been effective barriers to migrating hydrocarbons through time. This is substantiated by general differences in overpressure across these interfaces, poor permeability and porosity in even sandy Triassic rocks, and the lack of hydrocarbons in structurally trapped Triassic 'reservoirs' (the 7/12-6 well is the only well in the Norwegian sector of the study area that is productive from the Triassic). It is possible, with extensive 3D coverage, to map these Triassic rafts; they are depicted by the grey hatched areas in Figs 13–16. Most of the major faults in the Norwegian sector border these Triassic rafts. These faults are, therefore, also treated as migration barriers.

Migration and entrapment history. All of the Upper Jurassic oil and gas discoveries in the study area have a structural trapping component; most have four-way closure. This enables us to closely match simulated entrapment of hydrocarbons with known accumulations using Finesse.

Oil migration and entrapment. Initial oil generation and migration occurred in the Eocene and was confined to the deep sub-basins of the Central Graben (Fig. 3).

By Late Eocene times, a significant amount of migration had occurred into the Josephine High, as the Judy, Jacqui, and Josephine fields became charged (Fig. 9). Deep Jurassic structures in the Tommeliten sub-basin were filled; however, subsequent seal failure associated with later overpressuring fed the Cretaceous chalk reservoirs and depleted the Jurassic reservoirs. Tertiary (fill and spill) migration probably resulted in the initial filling of the Mime (7/11), Jade (UK30/2C) and UK30/1C structures. Oil did not migrate up to the shallower terraces at this time.

As the source kitchens expanded and the cumulative generated volumes increased, the down-dip traps became full, and migration progressed to more up-dip areas. In the Oligocene, initial generation from the Kamskjell (east margin of Block 1/3) and Cod kitchens occurred and migration into the Cod structure began. Initial charging of Gyda Field also possibly occurred. In the UK sector, filling and spilling from down-dip traps allowed oil to reach the Clyde–Fulmar terrace area, whereas Appleton was probably charged via secondary migration from its adjacent kitchen to the north (Fig. 10). Initial charging of the Erskine structure (UK23/26) probably began at this time.

By the early Miocene, up-dip expansion of the source kitchens had occurred, and the Tjalve (Block 2/4) and Gyda South (Block 2/1) structures became charged. The Gyda Field continued to receive hydrocarbons, but the Ula Field and 7/8-3 structures remained in the migration shadows of the Triassic horsts and were not charged.

In the late Neogene, the up-dip Cod Kitchen areas became mature and provided the local charge for the Ula Field, 7/8-3, and 1/3-3 traps. Much of the deeper parts of the Central Graben were no longer generating oil, but the Josephine High continued to receive a huge amount of oil from the peripheral kitchens.

During the last 2 Ma, Upper Jurassic oil generation has been confined to the up-dip Cod Terrace, the Josephine High, the Fulmar–Clyde area, and the Eldfisk area. All other kitchen areas, with the exception of the salt-cored rifts of the Sœrvestlandet High in the northeast, had matured beyond the oil generation phase.

Gas migration and entrapment. Gas generation and migration was simulated for the last 50 Ma. From the Eocene through the Oligocene, gas generation occurred mainly in association with oil generation, and gas migration was constrained by the same dynamic migration parameters through time as oil migration; therefore, oil and gas generation and migration patterns were similar during this period.

By the Early Miocene, however, some of the deeper kitchen areas that had stopped generating oil had reached a level of maturity where residual oil in the Mandal/Farsund interval began to crack to gas. Accordingly, gas generation and migration but no oil generation and migration is indicated in these deep kitchen areas.

Gas generation from the cracking of oil became volumetrically more significant in the late Neogene, as the deeper areas reached thermal conditions that caused extensive cracking of oil to gas. Regionally, this caused an overall increase in the GOR (gas : oil ratio) of hydrocarbons in the system. At the reservoir scale, it resulted in one or more of the following: dissolution of gas in undersaturated oil; accumulation of gas caps in gas-saturated reservoirs; and fill and spill displacement by gas of the heavier hydrocarbons into updip reservoirs. Reservoirs that were open to this late gas charge were affected. Reservoirs in migration shadows (e.g. 7/8-3, Ula, and 1/3-3) were not. Because of this, these 'protected' reservoirs retained lower GORs.

This late gas charge had the effect of increasing hydrocarbon column heights and lowering average hydrocarbon densities, both of which caused crestal reservoir pressures to increase. For reservoir seals that were already close to seal capacity (i.e. fracture pressure–pore pressure), seal failure ensued, which preferentially allowed the lighter hydrocarbons to migrate vertically into shallower (e.g. Cretaceous and Paleocene) reservoirs.

During the last 2 Ma, continued cracking of oil to gas and migration occurred in the basinal areas, although at lower rates, as the 'peak' stage of cracking had already occurred throughout most of the area (Fig. 7). Up-dip terrace areas continue to expel some gas in association with oil generation.

Cretaceous and Paleocene

Carrier systems and conduits. The distribution of Tertiary (Paleocene) discoveries in the study area is ultimately controlled by the distribution of reservoir sands. Where the sands are well developed, in the northwest part of the area, they provide not only the reservoirs, but also a component of the carrier system to the reservoirs from the chalk. Northwest of the study area, this trend is even more apparent, as both the Paleocene and the chalk are normally pressured and in obvious hydraulic communication. As the Paleocene sands become thinner, more argillaceous, and more discontinuous to the southeast, they lose their ability to transmit fluids to the normally pressured up-dip area; therefore, both the Paleocene and the Chalk become progressively more overpressured to the southeast. An effect of this is a regional hydrodynamic drive from the southeast to the northwest for both units. This hydrodynamic component is reflected by tilted oil–water contacts in some of the UK Paleocene reservoirs e.g. Montrose and Arbroath.

A dynamic multiple layer migration model was built to simulate migration into Paleocene reservoirs. Conduits from the BCU up to the Paleocene were defined by: (1) the 1000 psi seal capacity contour; and (2) flexural strain axes. The designated carrier surface in the Paleocene is the Top Balder. (Fig. 17).

Barriers. For the dynamic multiple migration model, the down-dip limit of the Paleocene sand system was used as a lateral migration barrier; however, the barrier was not used in the southeast, where the sands are absent, in order that migration into the intermediate chalk system could be simulated. West of the indicated migration barrier, no additional lateral migration barriers were assumed.

Migration and entrapment history. All Paleocene discoveries in the study area are on highs with structural closure. This, along with the assumption of no lateral barriers west of the Paleocene sand system migration barrier, enables a rather straightforward simulation of hydrocarbon migration within the Paleocene.

In the Late Oligocene, most of the structures associated with Paleocene discoveries were in place, but not all of them were being charged. Jurassic source rocks underlying the chalk fields in the southeast part of the study area were mature, and oil migration into the chalk had probably begun. Jurassic source rocks beneath the Judy/Joanne–Machar conduit system were immature; therefore, charging of the Tertiary reservoirs over this area had not occurred.

By the Early Miocene, however, oil migration into most of the Paleocene structures was occurring from the Upper Jurassic through vertical fractures and subsequent secondary and tertiary migration within the Paleocene; this has continued through to the present-day (Fig. 17)

Gas associated with oil generation migrated into the Paleocene along with the oil; however, the migration of gas associated with the cracking of oil was not significant until the Late Neogene.

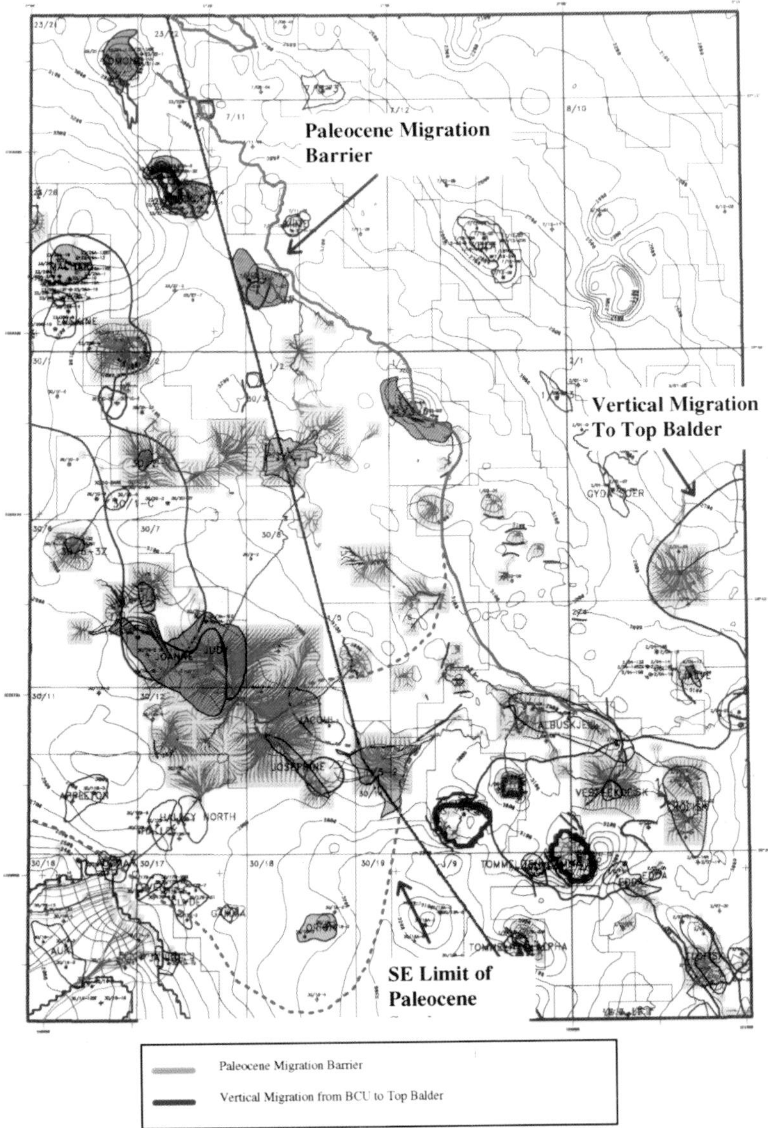

Fig. 17. Paleocene conduits and traps, present day.

These models simulate the filling of virtually all Paleocene discoveries in the area; however, they do not explain the differences in hydrocarbon types within the reservoirs. For example, the Blane (Block 1/2) and Flyndre (Block 1/5) reservoirs contain oil, but they are located above some of the deeper and gas mature Upper Jurassic source-rock fetch areas.

Hydrocarbon characteristics in Paleocene reservoirs are largely a function of charge mechanisms and timing. There are two main classes. Class one examples (e.g. 1/3-6 discovery and Cod Field) have the following attributes in common:

(i) high GOR (mainly gas) reservoirs;
(ii) reservoirs overlie high relief salt diapirs;
(iii) thin section of rock between reservoir and salt; and
(iv) faults (and probable fractures) associated with the salt diapirs.

Class two examples (e.g. Flyndre and Blane fields) are quite different from class one. They have the following characteristics:

(i) low GOR (oil) reservoirs;
(ii) reservoirs do not overlie high relief salt diapirs;
(iii) thick section of rock beneath reservoir; and
(iv) no obvious conduits from BCU to reservoir.

All of the structures were in place in time to receive the main oil charge; modelling and trapping assumptions indicate that oil and associated gas was trapped as early as 30 Ma in all cases. The salt diapirs at 1/3-6 and Cod were also in place, and probably provided migration conduits from the BCU, either along the mobile sediment–salt interfaces or along faults and fractures associated with the mobile salt.

This type of conduit system did not exist at Flyndre and Blane. Lateral migration within the Paleocene can be invoked from down-dip BCU-Paleocene leak points; however, sand/carrier systems are poorly developed down-dip, at least at Flyndre. At least some amount of vertical migration from the BCU to the reservoirs at Flyndre and Blane probably occurred, and this could have been via matrix permeability (albeit low) of the comparatively shallow sediments and also through fractures associated with the bending or folding of the BCU-Paleocene section.

Subsequent burial of the area elevated the maturities of the underlying Upper Jurassic source kitchens to the point at which oil was no longer being generated, but significant amounts of gas were being generated as residual and migrated oil was cracked. By this time, salt inversion had increased at 1/3-6 and Cod; this had the effect of: (1) focusing the movement of fluids from the adjacent down-dip kitchens; and (2) creating additional pathways to the Paleocene by the additional faulting and fracturing associated with the continued salt movement. In Cod, pore pressures at and below the BCU increased to within 1000 psi the horizontal minimum stress which resulted in hydraulic fracturing and the creation of additional vertical migration pathways and hydrodynamic drive. The same may have been true at 1/3-6, but there are no BCU penetrations or associated pressure data to document it. The late gas flux moved into the 1/3-6 and Cod reservoirs, diluting and/or displacing the original oil charge, hence the higher GORs at both.

At Blane and Flyndre, this late gas flux did not reach the reservoirs, at least not to the extent that it did at 1/3-6 and Cod. This may have been because: (1) matrix permeabilities that allowed initial vertical migration into the reservoirs had been reduced by subsequent burial, compaction, and diagenesis; (2) entry pressures for gas in a water wet capillary system are higher than those for oil; and/or (3) original faults or fractures (if present) had healed.

Regardless of the specific cause, reservoirs above high relief salt diapirs generally have higher GORs than those that are not; this relationship is undoubtedly a function of the communication from deep source rocks and carriers to shallow reservoirs that these salt diapirs directly or indirectly provide. By understanding the generation and expulsion history of these source rocks and the structural development of these salt diapirs, it is quite possible to predict hydrocarbon types in Tertiary reservoirs within this trend e.g. Cod, Albuskjell.

Conclusions

The aim of the study was to model known hydrocarbon accumulations, matching known and predicted hydrocarbon phases (oil, gas, condensate), in order to assess the future prospectivity of an area. This was successfully done using a 2D horizontial plane approach. This enables the explorationist to highlight areas where more detailed studies can be undertaken and, equally as important, areas where no further work is required.

The study also shows that it is possible to model migration from the source to shallower reservoirs without using faults as conduits, rather concentrating on modelling areas of seal capacity failure and fracturing.

Thanks to Amoco Norway Oil Company for allowing publication and to Christian Zwach and Niall Hoey who reviewed this paper. Special thanks to Stuart Burley for his patience in editing this paper.

References

Cooles, G. P., Mackenzie, A. S. & Quigley, T. M. 1986. Calculation of petroleum masses generated and expelled from source rocks. *Advances in Organic Geochemistry*, **10**, 235–245.

Gaarenstroom, L., Tromp, R. A. J., de Jong & Brandenburg, A. M. 1993. Overpressures in the Central North Sea: implications for trap integrity and drilling safety. *In*: Parker, J. R. (ed.) *Petroleum Geology of Northwest Europe: Proceedings of the 4th Conference*. Geological Society, London, 1305–1313.

Passey, Q. R., Creaney, S., Kulla, J. B., Moretti, F. J. & Stroud, J. D. 1990. A practical model for organic richness from porosity and resistivity logs. *American Association of Petroleum Geologists Bulletin*, **74**(12), 1777–1794.

Robertson Research 1997. Geothermal Database Onshore Northwest Europe, Phase V.

Sclater, J. G. & Christie, P. A. F. 1980. Continental stretching: an explanation of the post-mid-Cretaceous subsidence of the Central North Sea basin. *Journal of Geophysical Research*, **85**, 3711–3739.

Sylta, Ø. 1993. New techniques and their applications in the analysis of secondary migration. *In*: Dore, A. G. *et al.* (eds) *Basin Modelling: Advances and Applications*. NPF Special Publications **3**, Elsevier, Amsterdam, 385–398.

Tissot, B. & Welte, D. 1978. *Petroleum Formation and Occurrence*. Springer-Verlag, Berlin.

Øxnevad, I. E. I. & Taylor, M. S. G. 1999. An integrated approach to hydrocarbon emplacement in chalk, Norwegian North Sea Central Graben. *In*: Fleet, A. J. & Boldy, S. A. R. (eds) *Petroleum Geology of Northwest Europe: Proceedings of the 5th Conference*. Geological Society, London, 1221–1230.

Diagenetic porosity creation in an overpressured graben

R. S. HASZELDINE,[1] M. WILKINSON,[1] D. DARBY,[1,3] C. I. MACAULAY,[2] G. D. COUPLES,[1,4] A. E. FALLICK,[2] C. G. FLEMING,[1] R. N. T. STEWART[1] and G. McAULAY[1]

[1] *University of Edinburgh, Dept Geology and Geophysics, Edinburgh EH9 3JW, UK (e-mail: s.haszeldine@glg.ed.ac.uk)*

[2] *Isotope Geology Unit, East Kilbride, G75 0QF, UK*

[3] *Present address: British Gas Research, Loughborough, LE11 3GR, UK*

[4] *Present address: Dept Petroleum Engineering, Heriot-Watt University, Edinburgh EH14 4AS, UK*

Abstract: The Central Graben of the North Sea is an actively subsiding, highly overpressured, basin. At the present day, hydrocarbons are migrating both vertically and laterally through the stratigraphy to fill reservoirs from Permian through to Eocene. The late Jurassic Fulmar Sandstone approaches rock fracture pressure in many Central Graben areas. Petrographic studies show that sandstones originally contained as much as 35–40% potassium feldspar. This has dissolved rapidly below 3 km, so that by 4.5 km sandstones may contain only 5% feldspar. This loss is not matched by growth of authigenic clays or feldspars; aluminium is interpreted to have been exported from the sandstones by an unknown mechanism. In some cases, excess kaolin may form in overlying Palaeogene sandstones. Improved stratabound secondary porosity (an additional 5–15%) is created along the top of reservoir sandstones and at structurally high leak-off points. Leak-off points maintain high porosities, partly because overpressure reduces the effective compactional stress. This secondary porosity forms zones of good reservoir quality in predictable positions.

Oils migrating vertically and laterally into Palaeogene sandstones have been bacterially oxidized, to form calcites with distinctive carbon isotope signatures. The distribution of such cements can be a guide to deeper leak-off positions. Modelling of modern temperatures across the graben shows that spikes of elevated temperature occur above leak-off positions, demonstrating that vertical fluid-flow is still active.

The Central Graben, and any actively subsiding deep basin, can be viewed as one interconnected system, where localized deep porosity is created, and shallow porosity is destroyed. The organic, inorganic, temperature and overpressure fluid systems are all interactive.

Not all processes of sandstone diagenesis result in a decrease in reservoir quality. During deep burial some processes can resurrect the original primary porosity, and others may produce genuine additional secondary porosity (Wilkinson *et al.* 1997). Both these can result in improved quality of reservoir, in both porosity and permeability, at depths to 6 km. It is the aim of this paper to show that such improvements in porosity may be predictable. The locations of high-quality sandstones can be broadly predicted by synthesizing data on stratigraphic and structural setting, together with a knowledge of computer-modelled basin subsidence, and overpressure history. The predictions may be tested and improved by drilling boreholes, and analysing the petrographic and isotopic evidence preserved in diagenetic mineral cements.

Two basins are examined here. Firstly, the Central Graben of the North Sea: this is an active basin, which is experiencing continued rapid subsidence, with rocks at their maximum burial depths at present day. Overpressure, hydrocarbon migration, cementation and dissolution are all active today. This basin is out of equilibrium. By examining this basin we can look at geological processes within hydrocarbon systems occurring at the present day. Secondly, the Viking Graben of the North Sea: this is an old basin, which has not suffered subsidence or additional heating for between 2 and 20 Ma. Similar processes to those of the Central Graben may have occurred, but mainly in the past. This basin is re-approaching equilibrium.

This paper proposes that changes in reservoir quality of sandstones are produced by the effects of geochemical reactions in subsiding sediment, together with fluid flow focused by stratigraphy and structure. These changes to reservoir quality may be detrimental, but in some cases may be very beneficial. Our hypotheses draw from several independent lines of approach. Amongst these are:

(1) the systematic decrease in feldspar with burial in sandstones, and implied export of aluminium;
(2) inferred vertical leak-off of overpressured fluid at geologically determined positions, replenished by lateral flow of porefluid through aquifers;
(3) present-day warm temperature anomalies, which are best explained by vertical fluid flow;
(4) steep-dipping mineralized veins, which provide evidence for vertical fluid flow in the geological past;
(5) ranges of measured age dates from diagenetic illite clay, which combine with computer basin model predictions to date past periods of fluid flow;
(6) seismic reflection visualization of porosity changes on a large scale, which agree with those deduced on a small scale;
(7) theoretical predictions of high porosity in reservoir sandstones, which agree with high porosities observed today.

It is necessary to point out that many hypotheses in this paper are inductive, and attempt to link obervations in terms of geological or physical processes. There are still many problems to be considered, in particular the export of aluminium from sandstones has no simple explanation in current equilibrium geochemistry. However, this incomplete mechanism should not discourage us from proposing new theories, in the same way as the observations and explanation of continental drift became accepted, before the wider theories of plate tectonics were suggested, which themselves still lack a quantified driving mechanism.

HASZELDINE, R. S., WILKINSON, M., DARBY, D., MACAULAY, C. I., COUPLES, G. D., FALLICK, A. E., FLEMING, C. G., STEWART, R. N. T. & McAULAY, G. 1999. Diagenetic porosity creation in an overpressured graben. *In*: FLEET, A. J. & BOLDY, S. A. R. (eds) *Petroleum Geology of Northwest Europe: Proceedings of the 5th Conference*, 1339–1350.

Upper Jurassic sandstones: geological setting

The Central North Sea contains a widespread sandstone reservoir, known as the Fulmar Sandstone Formation of the Humber Group (Price *et al.* 1993). We have studied these sediments from borehole records, and from core material in the western part of the Central Graben (Fig. 1). The Humber Group also contains the Kimmeridge Clay Formation, which is the major hydrocarbon source rock for the region. This mudrock is currently mature for gas generation over much of the Central Graben. Sedimentology of the Fulmar Sandstone is summarized by Howell *et al.* (1996). The Fulmar Sandstone forms the principal hydrocarbon reservoir target in pre-Cretaceous strata of the Central Graben. In this paper, the Puffin and Ula formations are embraced within this term. The Fulmar Sandstone was deposited on a shallow marine shelf, as prograding shoreface deposits and storm produced sandsheets, during active rift subsidence and overall relative rise of sea-level. Depth of water during deposition appears to have varied, becoming generally deeper out to the graben areas. The sandstone appears to be diachronous, formed as lenses related to faulting or to salt tectonics (Howell *et al.* 1996). The Fulmar Formation is characterized by:

(1) large thickness and massive nature;
(2) restricted nature of the basin;
(3) localized occurrence, passing laterally and basinward into mudrocks;
(4) mineralogical immaturity.

The sandstone lenses are only semi-continuous or discontinuous regionally and no good aquifer connection need have existed to a coastline or to fluvial facies. At the present day, these sandstones are buried to depths of 3.5 to 6 km. Up to 3.0 km of Tertiary mudrocks have been deposited, of which 1.0 km may have been deposited in the past 5 Ma. As a consequence of rapid subsidence and lack of fluid escape, these sandstones are very highly overpressured, often to the point of rock fracture.

Petrography and cementation

The bulk compositions and volumes of both detrital grains and of cementing minerals has been examined by thin-section and scanning electron microscope (SEM) petrography and by point-counting. Versions of the paragenetic sequence have been presented by Stewart (1986), Clelland *et al.* (1993) and Wilkinson *et al* (1997). The Fulmar sandstones are feldspar-rich, and are thought to have contained 35–40% potassium feldspar upon deposition (Wilkinson & Haszeldine 1996, 1997). We infer the composition of these sandstones to have been geographically uniform upon deposition in the UK Central Graben (Wilkinson & Haszeldine 1996). The cementation sequence appears to be similar throughout the Central Graben, but can vary in abundance. Important cements are: dolomite, quartz overgrowth, illite, ankerite, albite and bitumen. Many grains are coated by microquartz, but this is not an abundant or pore-filling cement except locally, for example within the Fulmar oilfield. Dissolution of dolomite and potassium feldspar is observed in thin-section and SEM samples and forms obvious secondary porosity. Plots of detrital and authigenic mineral abundance against present-day burial depth (Fig. 2) clearly show that potassium feldspar is consumed, illite clay is formed, but only minor quartz cement is formed.

Aluminium loss with burial: porosity enhancement

The Fulmar Sandstones contain potassium feldspar, which can be seen to have at least partly dissolved, and the clay content of these sandstones is large. However, a mass-balance approach suggests that there is too little clay in these sandstones to contain all the aluminium produced by feldspar dissolution (Fig. 2). This is discussed by Wilkinson & Haszeldine (1996, 1997).

This calculation is made by considering average sandstone compositions (based on many point count data) over the depth range 3.2–5.7 km. The amount of feldspar preserved at any depth is measured, and the amount of illite clay + all other aluminium-bearing phases at the same depth is measured. The chemical equation of feldspar transformation into illite clay enables us to predict the quantity of clay which should have grown from a given volume of feldspar dissolution. This can be compared with the volume of clay measured by point-counting. Note that the calculated volume of illite assumes a 50% microporosity, and also the entire amount of clay in the sandstones was assumed to be authigenic (i.e. any detrital clay was considered as authigenic). Both of these are conservative assumptions in that they tend to overestimate the volume of authigenic illite.

In spite of conservative assumptions, we find that these sandstones are short of aluminium by a factor of two. This means that feldspar has dissolved, and some of the aluminium, and maybe other dissolution products too, have not been

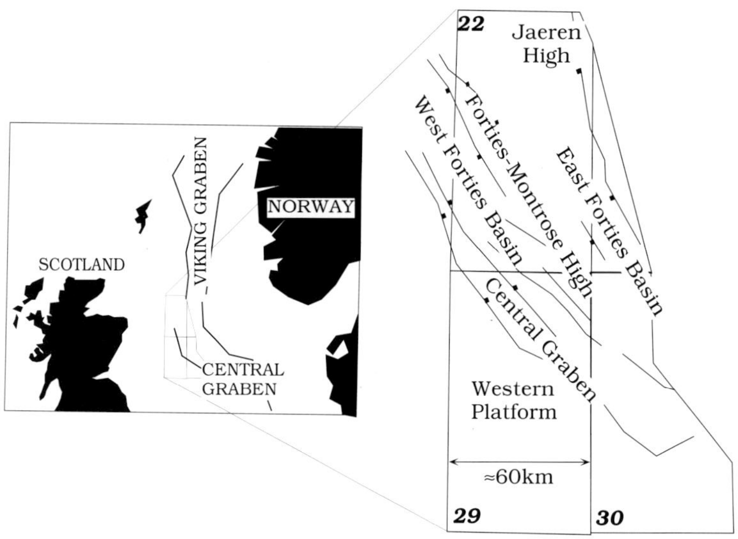

Fig. 1. Location map of the Central Graben, showing the area most intensively studied for overpressure and diagenesis.

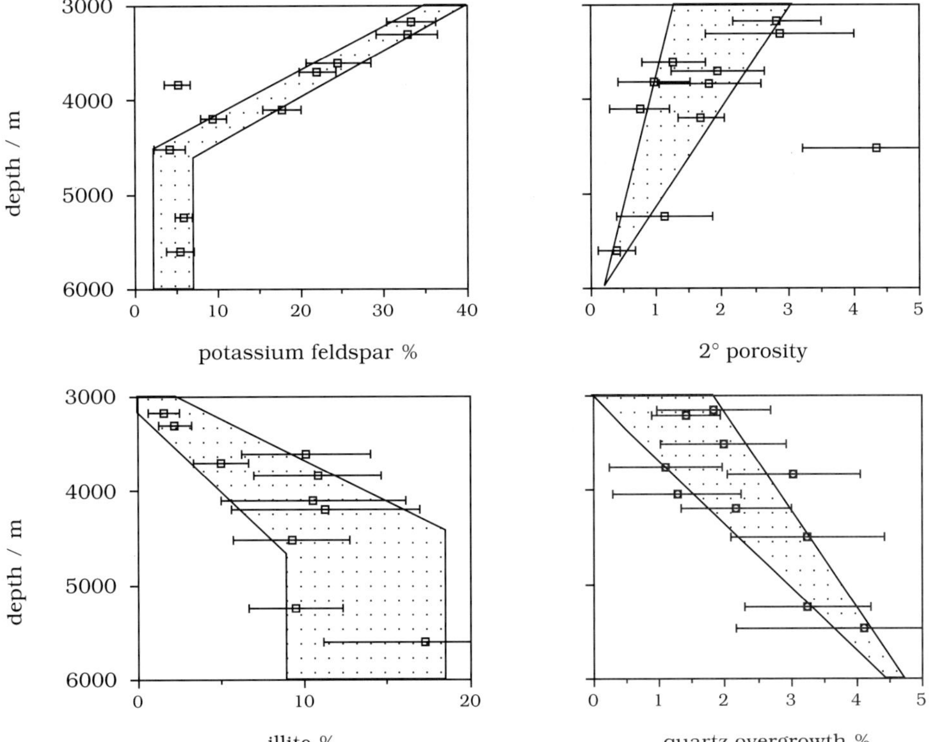

Fig. 2. Plots derived from point count data, with 2σ error bars. Each point represents the mean of 3–15 different thin-sections from a single borehole, hence 750–3750 counts. Feldspar decreases; illite (including detrital clay and microporosity) increases; secondary porosity is uniformly low; quartz overgrowth is low and increases slowly.

retained within the sandstone. Export of aluminium is a likely answer, though this has been disputed, for example by Giles *et al.* (1994). Where the aluminium is exported to remains a mystery, as does the mechanism of transport. It is possible that illitization reactions in adjacent mudrocks consume aluminium. Alternatively, aluminium may be exported to higher levels of the basin; anecdotal evidence of kaolin mineralized fractures in the overlying Chalk, and petrographic evidence of local excesses of kaolin in some Palaeogene sandstones (McLaughlin *et al.* 1996*a*) support this concept.

Aluminium export is of great importance for reservoir quality for the following reasons. Feldspar can dissolve, and usually forms clay in a closed system without any export of aluminium. This is simply redistributing the porosity in the sandstone, changing the quality of the porosity, but without increasing the total amount (Giles & de Boer 1990). By contrast, in the Fulmar Sandstone, feldspar has been dissolved and the products have been removed; the bulk composition of the rock has changed. Thus secondary porosity can result from feldspar dissolution which is not counteracted by growth of clay. Here the diagenesis has resulted in the evolution of a porous quartzitic rock (Haszeldine *et al.* 1996).

We have inferred that the process of aluminium loss occurs regionally throughout the Fulmar Sandstone (Wilkinson & Haszeldine 1996, 1997). A similar loss of aluminium with increased burial has also been inferred by McBride (1987), Sullivan & McBride (1991) and Gluyas & Coleman (1992). In contradiction to this evidence for aluminium loss and generation of secondary porosity, is the observation in thin-section that secondary porosity forms only 2–4% of the rock (Fig. 2). We consider that such textural estimates of secondary porosity are unreliable, and these greatly underestimate the true quantity of secondary porosity generated during burial. Similar information of the unreliability of textures is expressed by Harris (1992) in the Brent Group, and Milliken *et al.* (1989) in the Frio Formation of the USA Gulf. It is remarkable in all these cases that secondary porosity remains constant at around 2–4% irrespective of the depth of burial, or the quantity of feldspar dissolved. We infer that compaction continues after secondary porosity reaches a threshold value of around 4%. The exception to this being in positions of extreme overpressure (see later section).

We have identified a process which can improve sandstone reservoir quality. To apply this process in a predictive sense, we need to understand how this process varies with depth, with structural position, and with overpressure. These factors are examined in the next section.

Overpressure in the Central Graben

Many hydrocarbon basins worldwide are overpressured (Bradley 1975). This physical disequilibrium can influence many aspects of subsurface geology, including reservoir quality, cementation, and hydrocarbon generation. The Central Graben is divided into an upper hydropressured regime, generally occurring above 3.0 km and including the Palaeogene sandstone reservoirs, and a lower overpressured regime including Upper Jurassic, mid-Jurassic and Triassic reservoirs. This lower part of the Central Graben of the North Sea is highly overpressured in world terms, up to 40 MPa above hydrostatic pressure. The overpressure encountered varies with depth and stratigraphy. Previous work has delineated the distribution of overpressure within Jurassic sandstones (Cayley 1987). Overpressures were proposed to be caused by rapid basin subsidence and restriction of vertical fluid flow through the Cromer Knoll and Chalk aquitard (Mudford *et al.* 1991). Overpressure leaks off by hydraulic fracturing of the top seal in pressure cells (Gaarenstroom *et al.* 1993).

Pressure seals and distribution controls

In the highly overpressured stratigraphy below the Chalk and Lower Cretaceous Cromer Knoll Group, the distribution of pressure is complex. Darby *et al.* (1996, 1998) used RFT, mudweight, sonic log data and basin modelling to delineate the controls on pressure distribution. Pressure seals are generally stratigraphically controlled by mudrock lithologies, and not by layer-cake cementation or temperature boundaries as suggested by Hunt (1990). A general concentric pattern of overpressure is evident, with normal pressures on the shallow western platform, increasing towards the Graben centre. Unexpectedly, the most extreme overpressures are encountered on the axial Forties–Montrose High and its adjacent terraces (Fig. 3). At a more detailed scale, individual pressure cells of a 10–20 km size can be identified, separated by NW–SE structural and NE–SW stratigraphic boundaries. Mapping the potentiometric surface of the Jurassic sandstone gives a measure of potential energy to drive fluid flow (Darby *et al.* 1996). It is clear that a regional scale hydraulic connection exists from the highly overpressured western Central Graben (4.0 km potential) to the normally pressured western platform (zero potential), and also to the less-overpressured Forties–Montrose High (3.5 km potential). Thus potential energy exists to drive fluid flow from the deep graben laterally outwards to the surrounding platforms and

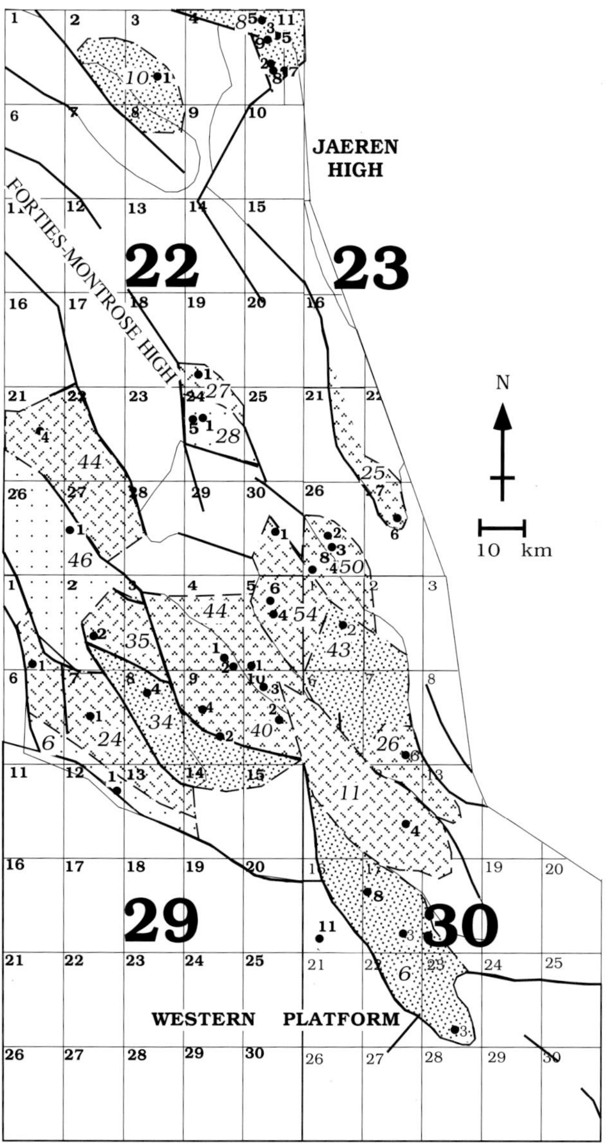

Fig. 3. Distribution of overpressure and pressure cells in the Central Graben at sub-Cretaceous level (from Darby *et al.* 1996). Italics show overpressure in each cell (MPa), black dots are released borehole locations. Note high pressure in graben axis, and especially on Forties–Montrose High axial horst.

to the axial highs (Darby *et al.* 1996). In worldwide terms the situation in the Central Graben is unusual: the regional distribution of pressure does not relate directly to the thickness and permeability of the lithological seal to vertical leak-off (Darby *et al.* 1998).

Controlled fluid leak-off

On the axial Forties–Montrose High 'potentiometric low points' form 'bullseyes' which have a lower fluid energy potential than their surroundings. These locations, such as 22/30a-1 and 30/1c-2, or 20/10–2 on the Puffin High, have structural dip closures. Thus the only way for overpressured fluid to leak off and reduce potential energy, is to move vertically through matrix permeability or through a fractured seal. Thus we infer that fluid escapes through the pressure seal at structurally controlled leak points (Dahlberg 1982). Consequently the basin fluid system is not static, but dynamic and moving over short and long geological timescales (Bredehoeft *et al.* 1994; Neuzil 1995). It is by such flow that the basin re-equilibrates through time to an equilibrium pressure state. Two types of flow must exist: (1) slow flows through pressure barriers between cells and lithological seals to vertical leak-off; and (2) more rapid vertical flows through hydraulically fractured lithological seals. The concept of a pressure 'seal' is too simplistic, and we could perhaps gain a better understanding by considering such features as permeability restrictions, rather than impermeable barriers on a geological time-scale.

The effects of such three-dimensionally-driven fluid connectivity, lateral and vertical leak-off within the Central Graben means that using 1-dimensional modelling of overpressure at any location can do no more than give a guide to the prediction of overpressuring. Darby *et al.* (1998) show that such modelling consistently predicts pressures in the deep subsurface which are less than observed overpressures. Any predictive model must be at least 2-dimensional.

The effects of these different leak-off positions can be seen by means of the observed pressure–depth plots in different locations (Darby *et al.* 1996). Where relatively shallow-buried sandstones are connected to deeper, more overpressured regions, then pressure transfer occurs. This results in higher than expected pressures in shallow sandstones with wide pressure transition zones (Fig. 4A). Deeply buried sandstones with a Kimmeridge Clay lithological pressure seal have lower than expected pressures, with a thin pressure transition zone (Fig. 4B).

The leak-off of pressure must physically transport aqueous pore-fluid, and consequently may result in the transport of solutes, so facilitating diagenetic cementation and dissolution (see later). As hydrocarbons are buoyant, the vertical migration of hydrocarbons is even more probable from these leak points. Support for this is inferred from the occurrence of bitumen in structures such as 22/30a-1, showing that hydrocarbons have formerly been present, even though the sandstones are today water-bearing. Drilling on too high a structure thus carries a risk that hydrocarbons may have leaked off. Such vertical leakage is inferred to be a mechanism by which Palaeogene reservoirs have charged with oils derived from the Upper Jurassic Kimmeridge Clay (Fig. 5, Darby *et al.* 1998).

Independent evidence for vertical fluid leak-off at present day: temperature

Lateral fluid transfer and vertical leak-off are inferred from indirect sources, such as pressure profiles and basin modelling. Is there a more direct way of confirming that vertical leak-off has occurred?

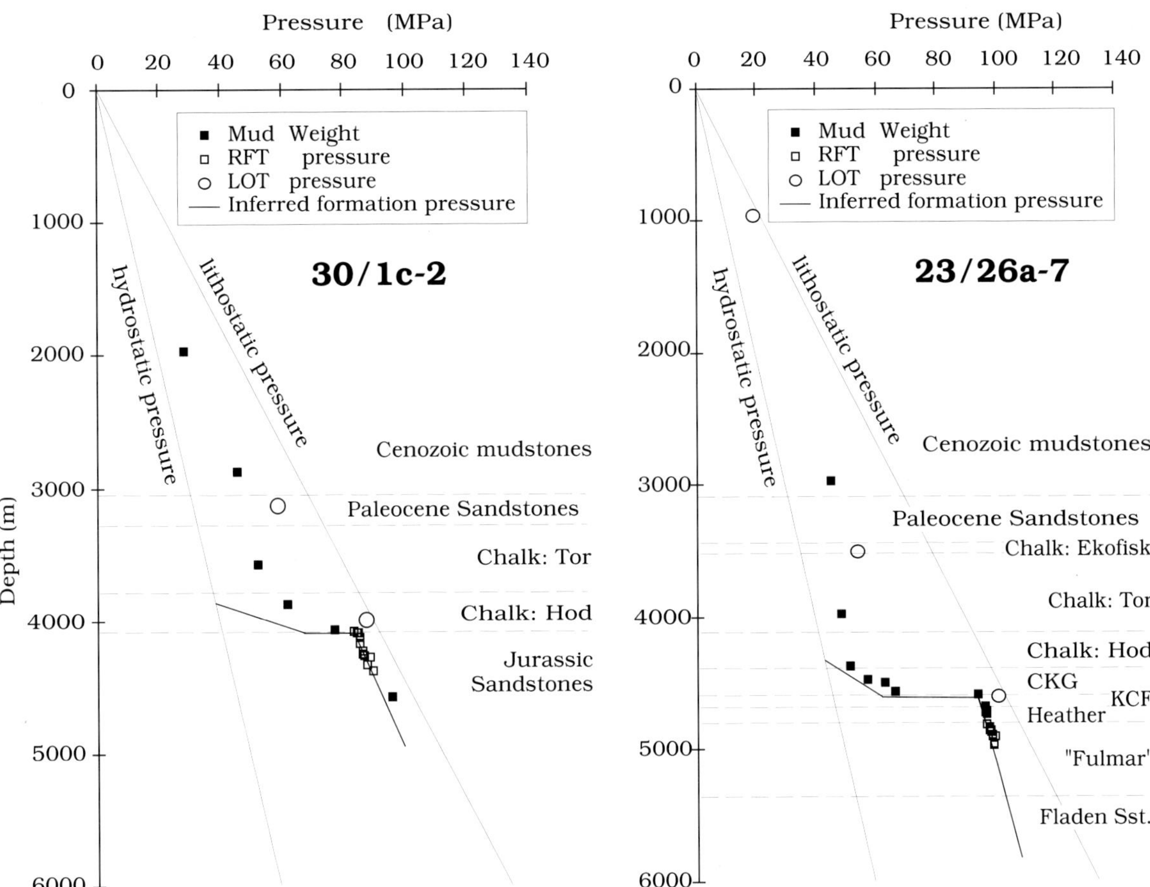

Fig. 4. Pressures in boreholes from the Central Graben (cf. also Darby *et al.* 1996). Well 30/1c-2 is on the axial high of the Central Graben. There is no Kimmeridge Clay Formation (KCF) or other mudrock seal, but pressure connection laterally into the graben means that the reservoir target sandstones (Triassic in this case) are highly overpressured. Pressure begins to rise within the partial seal at the muddy base of the Chalk Group. Well 23/26a-2 is on a terrace east of the axial horst. Jurassic Fulmar sandstones show intra-formational pressure seals, and are at a similar pressure to the immediately overlying Heather mudrock. The Kimmeridge Clay Formation partially seals, but pressure still begins to rise within the muddy Hod Formation of the Chalk (CKG = Cromer Knoll Group).

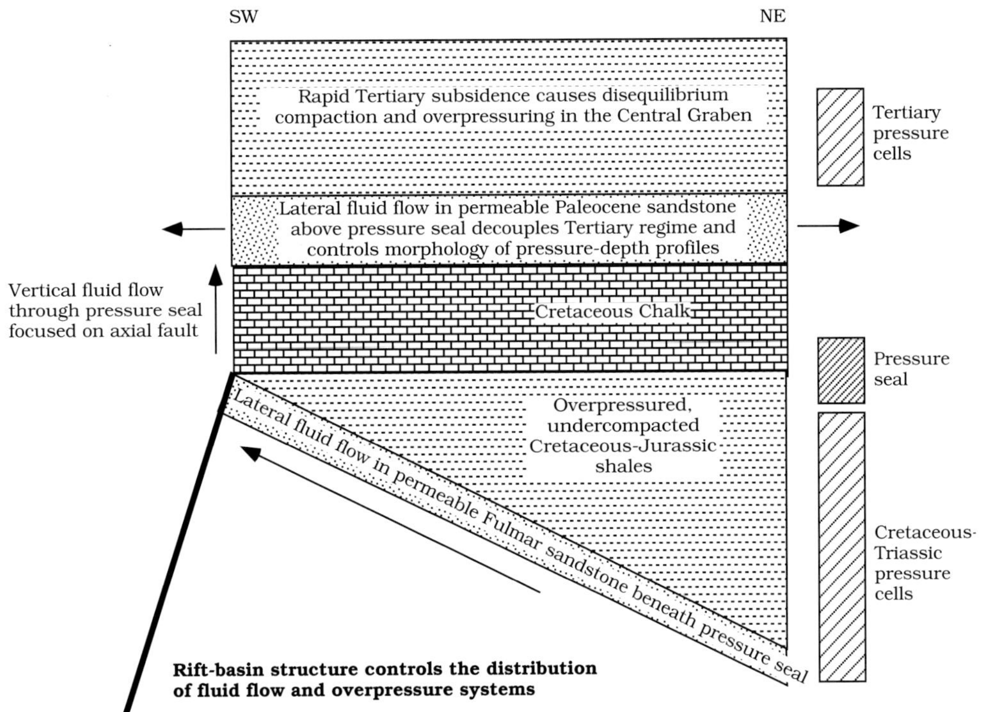

Fig. 5. Cartoon illustrating our concept of how lateral and vertical flows in the Central Graben are controlled by overpressure, from Darby *et al.* (1998).

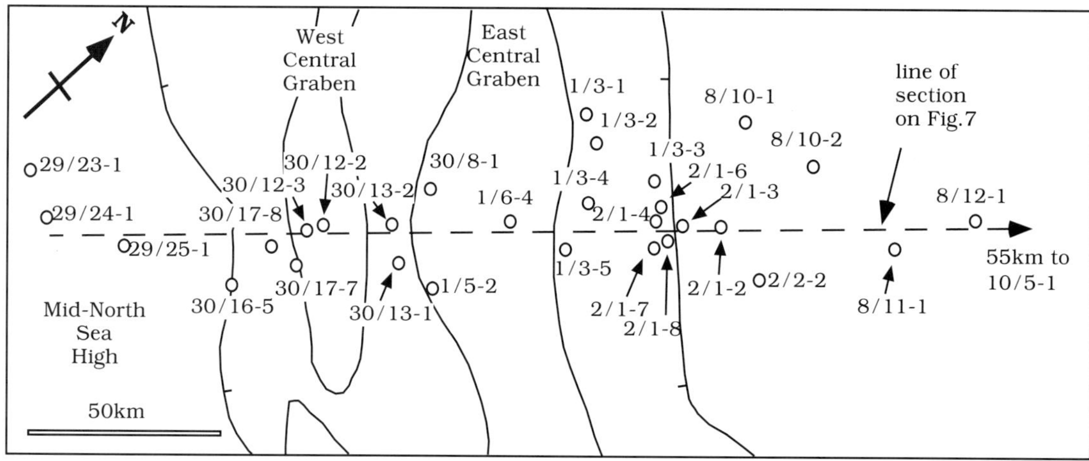

Fig. 6. Enlarged portion of line of 800 km straight cross-section used by Fleming *et al.* (1998) to image and model modern temperature profile (see Fig. 7) across the Central Graben. Line runs from near Skipton in English Pennines, to NE of Egersund, Norway.

When a fluid moves from a deep to a shallow position in the basin, it moves from a warm temperature to a cooler temperature. Thus we can search for temperature anomalies to track the vertical motion of fluids carrying heat from the deeper basin. Such anomalies are manifestations of disequilibrium, for warm fluid at shallow depth will tend to cool rapidly by conduction or mixing. Such temperature anomalies are expected to have only a geologically short lifetime of 1000 to 100 000 years after fluid flow has ceased (Fleming *et al.* 1998). Thus if any such anomalies can be detected in the present-day temperature field, they may signify geologically recent movement of hot fluids.

Andrews-Speed *et al.* (1984) examined temperatures in the Central Graben, using bottom-hole temperatures from exploration boreholes. They detected excess heat-flow anomalies of up to 20 m Wm^{-2} within the Chalk above axial horsts. This was explained by suggesting advection of fluid to these positions at the present day or in the geologically recent past. We suggest that these heat flow anomalies are caused by vertical flow of porefluid through the thin or absent pressure seals at leak-off points of the Forties–Montrose High.

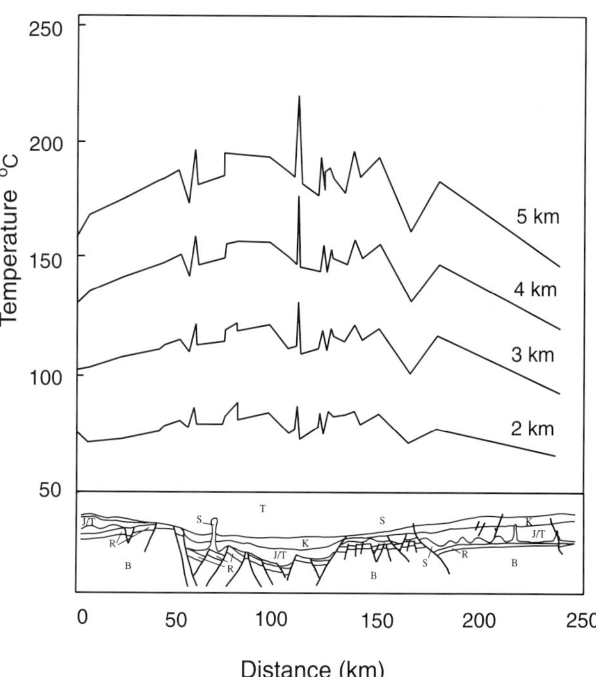

Fig. 7. Modern temperature profiles across the Central Graben, SW to NE from Fleming *et al.* (1998). Data are from corrected bottom-hole temperatures. Interpolation has been made, by hand and by computer, to depths of 2, 3, 4 and 5 km, with identical results. A long wavelength positive anomaly across the whole graben is complicated by many short wavelength positive anomalies. The short wavelength anomalies persist vertically. Distances start from zero, which is Well 29/23-1 (projected on Fig. 6).

Fleming *et al.* (1998) have made a different type of analysis of the present-day temperature field. They have made a cross-section SW to NE from England to Norway, through the Fulmar oilfield (Fig. 6). In detail, this passes slightly south of the area studied by Darby *et al.* (1996), but the geological setting is similar. Down-hole temperatures were compiled from a dataset of corrected bottom-hole temperatures, and interpolated sections at depths of 2, 3, 4 and 5 km were drawn (Fig. 7). A broad wavelength positive temperature anomaly is visible above the sedimentary fill of the Central Graben. Superimposed on this are short wavelength (<10 km) positive spikes of temperature anomalies, which may exceed local temperatures by 40°C. These anomalies persist for more than 4 km with depth, and are robust to errors of measurement in the original downhole data. Most significantly, these anomalies are positioned above major basement faults, and above the centres of horst blocks. These are exactly analogous to the structural positions deduced for vertical leak-off points from the pressure analysis of Darby *et al.* (1996).

A two-dimensional hydrogeological model of this cross-section permits the hydrogeological impact of vertical flow at such positions to be evaluated (Fleming *et al.* 1998). These simulations model vertical flow within faults and their associated 300 m wide damage zones. Results of these simulations show that temperature anomalies, of 15–40°C with wavelengths less than 10 km, are robustly reproduced within and around fault planes which have vertical permeabilities (k_v) 100 × horizontal permeabilities (k_h). Fault zone k_v need be only 50 mD, with pre-Cretaceous sediments k_h 10 mD. These are very similar to the natural faults, temperature anomalies and rock permeabilities in the Central Graben. To achieve temperature anomalies exceeding 15°C at the fault tip, it is required that the fault geometry is arranged so that the fluid updraft discharges into an asymmetric permeable 'outlet zone' at its upper tip. This model geometry is remarkably similar to the dilatent damage zone described from real faults by Knipe (1997). The stratigraphic location of such outlet zones in the Fleming *et al.* (1998) model is within and above the Palaeogene sandstones.

Modelling of the modern temperature data provides strong further support for the concepts derived from overpressure studies. Vertical leak-off focused above basement structures, can rapidly transport porewater and hydrocarbons into the Palaeogene stratigraphy, and is still occurring at the present day.

Independent evidence for ancient vertical fluid leak-off: mineralization

If vertical leak-off has occurred, is there any evidence for this in ancient times? The Fulmar oil field lies at the faulted edge of the Central Graben. Reservoir sandstones in this oil field occur from the structural shelf to the basin edge and contain many soft sediment deformation structures. Some of these Fulmar Formation sandstones are unusual in preserving steeply angled veins which show brittle deformation. The veins are filled with chalcedony, quartz containing anhydrite inclusions, and dolomite (Macaulay *et al.* 1997). The veins contain fluid inclusions formed around 120°C, from highly saline fluids, with oxygen isotope signatures indicating pore-water derived from a deep basin. These fluids are thought to have migrated vertically up basin margin faults, 600–2000 m through the Zechstein and Fulmar Sandstone, carrying deep basin water and dissolved ions to form anhydrite and dolomite. Silica cements may have been derived locally from siliceous sponge debris in the Upper Jurassic.

Extensive veining is unusual in North Sea sandstones. In this specific structural setting at the margin of the Central Graben, these veins, formed from deep-derived warm fluids, provide very good evidence of rapid vertical fluid movement being structurally controlled.

Links between diagenesis, overpressure, and fluid movement

Can any connections be made between the loss of aluminium demonstrated in Fulmar Formation sandstones as they are buried, the overpressure energy available to drive fluid flow, and the lateral and vertical fluid flows inferred from overpressure distribution and the temperature field? In this section we examine links to timing of fluid motion, to effects generating additional porosity in sandstones, and the preservation of such porosity. Lastly we examine effects of such links to diagenesis at stratigraphically higher levels of the basin.

Illite growth: Jurassic

Illite clay is commonly recognized in sandstone reservoirs, especially in the deeply buried Fulmar Sandstone (Wilkinson *et al.* 1994). This clay has a fibrous 'hairy' growth habit, and is detrimental to permeability. Illite can be dated by the radiometric K–Ar method, to yield an absolute age. Swarbrick (1994) made a link between the time of illite growth and variations in overpressure history; does such a relationship hold in the Fulmar Sandstone? Darby *et al.* (1997) dated illite from the Fulmar Sandstone in three boreholes forming a cross-section across the Central Graben. On the two graben margins, illites have ages 84–58 Ma; on the central horst illites have ages 33–30 Ma. Two-dimensional basin modelling (BasinMod-2D^{TM}) of a section through these wells was calibrated to reproduce present-day observed overpressures. This model was then used to reconstruct palaeopressure, palaeotemperature and palaeofluid movement.

The measured illite ages (84–58 Ma) are coincident with the start of rapid basin subsidence (Darby *et al.* 1997). This drove porewater laterally through the Fulmar Sandstone at the graben flanks, driven by compaction of sediments in the deep graben centre. This illite was not linked to charging of hydrocarbon, as is commonly inferred (Liewig *et al.* 1987), because oil had not yet been generated or migrated at that time (Cornford 1994). The most likely explanation is that illite growth records the 26 Ma duration of increased flow rate of basin-derived compactional water.

By contrast, illite on the graben axial horst grew at temperatures of 83–90°C, in overpressured porefluids. This was at a similar time to the 35 Ma 'critical moment' for hydrocarbon maturation and migration in this system (Cornford 1994). We infer that, at this time, porewater and hydrocarbons moved from the Kimmeridge Clay Formation (KCF) source rock to the underlying Fulmar Sandstone. The downward stratigraphic movement of fluids could have been driven by the pressure potential difference between highly overpressured KCF and less overpressured Fulmar Sandstone, which was able to release pressure laterally and by vertical leak-off.

Thus, illite growth records the commencement of fluid movement in each case, but is driven by two very different mechanisms (Fig. 8), which can be distinguished by basin modelling.

Maximum potential porosity: Fulmar Sandstone

As discussed earlier, the Fulmar Sandstone systematically loses feldspar with increasing burial. This loss is not counterbalanced by clay precipitation, so that export of aluminium and possibly of other ions has been inferred. Upon more detailed inspection of the dataset, it is apparent that a wide scatter of mean porosity values exists around 4 km in this dataset (Wilkinson *et al.* 1997). Sandstones in some boreholes are less porous than the hydropressured compaction curve. Some sandstones are much more porous than suggested by the hydropressured compaction curve. We must again assume that this sandstone was uniform across the study area when it was deposited (Howell *et al.* 1996; Wilkinson & Haszeldine 1997). This assumption is made stronger in this case, by taking poroperm data over a depth interval in these wells and averaging the porosity values.

By examining the porosity data from a geographical perspective, it can be seen that the sandstones which have high porosities tend to lie on or close to the vertical leak-off points inferred from mapping the overpressure potentiometric surface. This is important. We can hypothesize that lateral fluid movement has enabled more feldspar to be dissolved from sandstones which are further along the fluid expulsion flow path. Also a greater volume of moving fluid would enable export of feldspar dissolution products from the sandstone by physical transport of dissolved ionic complexes. Inspection of the bulk composition of these sandstones shows that 22/30a-1 (lying close to a leak-off point) is significantly more quartzitic than 23/27-6 (which does not lie close to a leak-off point). Thus a high ratio of fluid–rock in the 4–6 km deep subsurface may enhance the generation of secondary porosity by feldspar dissolution and removal of the reaction products.

It is also necessary to hold this porosity open. The present-day overpressure is important for this, as it reduces the effective vertical stress between the sand grains, and so reduces the forces of compaction. Using the basin modeling program BasinMod-2D^{TM}, we can simulate the burial history, and hence overpressure history of these individual boreholes in a two-dimensional section (Wilkinson *et al.* 1997). From this we can calculate the effective vertical stress between the grains, and hence an equilibrium porosity which a sandstone could support at those particular burial-pressure conditions. Thus a hydrostatically pressured sandstone at 4 km could only support about 16.5% porosity, whereas a highly overpressured sandstone (22 MPa) at the same burial depth would experience vertical stress equivalent to about 1.3 km of hydrostatic overburden, and support a maximum porosity of 32%. We call the result

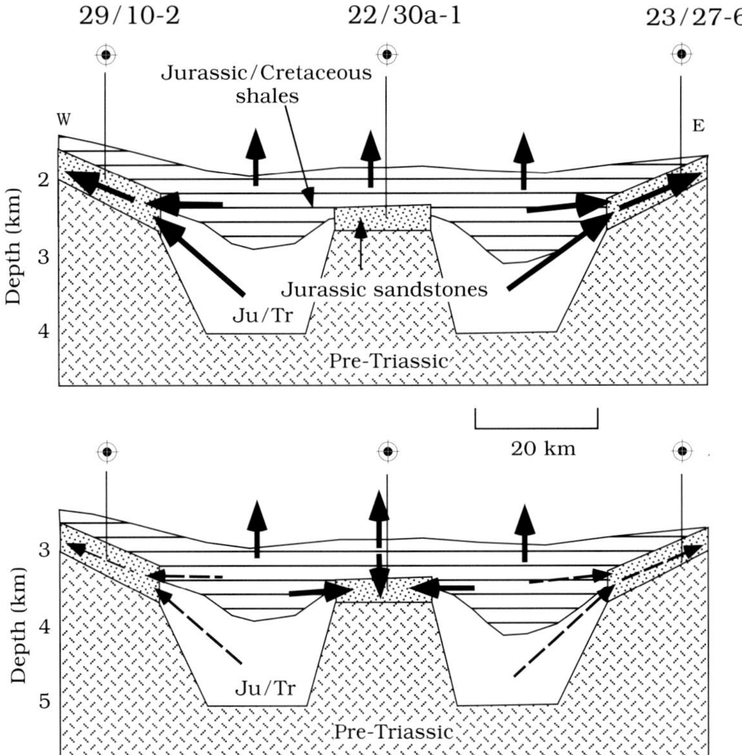

Fig. 8. Cartoon illustrating timing of illite growth, linked to different episodes of fluid movement at the margins of (top, 80 Ma), and the axis of (bottom, 30 Ma), the Central Graben. From Darby *et al.* (1997).

of this calculation the maximum potential porosity (MPP) (Wilkinson *et al.* 1997).

In our study set, Well 22/30a-1 lies near an interpreted leak-off point, and also has an exceptionally high porosity of 31%. By contrast, Well 23/27-6 is more representative of the majority of boreholes in our study set, with 21% porosity. Basin modelling of the porosity evolution of 23/27-6 shows that no additional porosity has been preserved. By contrast, basin modelling of 22/30a-1 shows that 10% extra porosity has been formed and has been preserved in the past 30 Ma of overpressure history (Wilkinson *et al.* 1997). It is not possible to preserve these high porosities from shallow burial simply by overpressure. This would necessitate hard overpressure generation at 65 Ma, whereas overpressure is not modelled to commence until 40 Ma (Fig. 9).

We consider that secondary porosity is forming by feldspar dissolution at the present day in Well 22/30a-1 and at similar sites in the Central Graben. Components such as silicon, aluminium and potassium are removed from the sandstone, into surrounding mudrocks and by vertical leak-off of fluids. The pore spaces are kept open by high overpressure, and porosity increases towards the MPP.

Seismic reflection evidence for enhanced porosity

In several oil field structures, operated by different companies, it is observed from conventional core laboratory data that the average porosity of the Upper Fulmar Sandstone (25–30%) is significantly greater than the Lower Fulmar Sandstone (10–15%). This can be explained in two ways: either a systematic facies change occurs, so that the Upper Fulmar was more porous at the time of deposition, or this is a diagenetic effect, selectively modifying a relatively uniform sandstone.

Proponents of the depositional facies explanation would perhaps suggest that porosity is held open by microquartz cement, derived from dissolution of siliceous sponge spicule debris (Aase *et al.* 1996). They would suggest that the Upper Fulmar is consistently an upper shoreface deposit, where sponge spicules were hydraulically concentrated, by contrast the Lower Fulmar is a lower shoreface deposit, with less sponge spicules. Against these arguments, we counter that our SEM

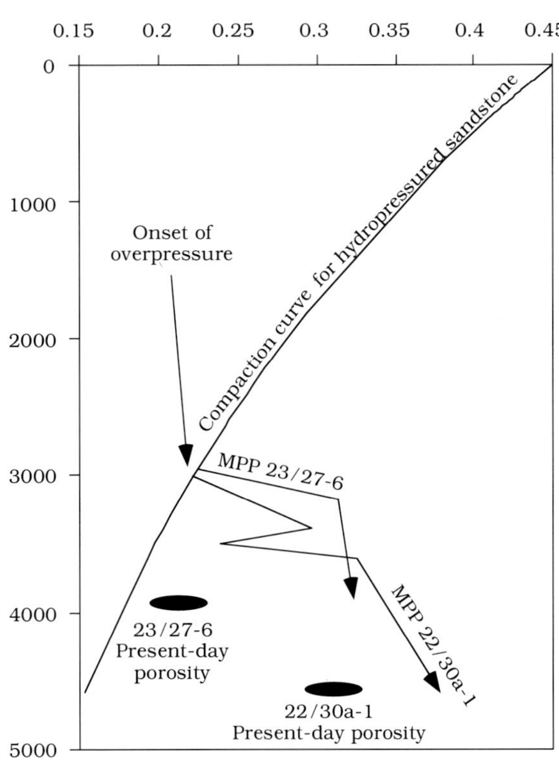

Fig. 9. Plot of burial and maximum potential porosity (MPP) for two Central Graben Wells (22/30a-1 and 23/27-6). From Wilkinson *et al.* (1997).

petrography shows microquartz cement to be common in sandstones with low porosity and those with high porosity – so no difference in cement sequence exists to selectively preserve porosity. Similarly, the geographically wide-ranging sedimentological analysis by Howell *et al.* (1996) failed to discern any systematic differences of depositional grain size, or facies between the Upper and Lower Fulmar.

Proponents of a diagenetic origin for this porosity difference would need to suggest that greater dissolution and secondary porosity development had occurred in the Upper Fulmar. This would be caused by preferentially focused movement of basinal fluids laterally through the Upper Fulmar, so enhancing dissolution.

Several companies have indicated that the porosity differences between the Upper and Lower Fulmar can be weakly imaged by seismic reflection. This reflector is said to be parallel to the stratigraphical layering deduced from wireline correlations of boreholes and core within the individual fields. Thus this is a potentially useful observation in mapping reservoir architecture, but does not help to determine the origin of the porosity differences.

However, in at least one case, the seismic reflection quality is such that the intra-Fulmar reflector can be well imaged towards the structural crest (Fig. 10). In this case, the reflector turns concave-down on a dip line, and the interpretation can be validated by ties into several boreholes. There is no fluid boundary within this section to produce such a reflector, so that an origin from changes in rock property is highly probable. The concave-down geometry of this reflector is very difficult to envisage from a facies progradation or from antithetic faulting. This geometry is easy to envisage from lateral flow of fluid along the Upper Fulmar Sandstone, spreading at the crest of the structure, before vertical leak-off. This is similar to the additional porosity at structural crests proposed by Burley (1993). Porosity resulting from feldspar dissolution is preserved from extensive compaction by present-day overpressure.

Effects at higher stratigraphic levels

We have inferred that hydrocarbons, porewater, and possibly solutes including aluminium are exported from the Upper Jurassic sandstones. Can these components be identified at higher stratigraphic levels in the Central Graben?

Excess kaolin. The Brae oil fields are at the southern limit of the Viking Graben, at its western faulted edge. Their Upper Jurassic reservoir sandstones are intimately interbedded with the KCF source rock, and form an aquifer beneath it. This is similar, though not identical, to the geometrical arrangement of the Fulmar Sandstone. It is possible that similar processes occurred here during burial diagenesis, leading to porosity enhancement of up to 10%. McLaughlin *et al.* (1994) studied diagenesis of the Brae reservoir, and discovered that it contains very little detrital or authigenic clay. Comparison of feldspar contents inside calcite concretions that grew at shallow burial with feldspar contents outside such calcite concretions suggests that about 5% of the rock has dissolved, leaving no diagenetic clay product. Porosity within the upper layers of the reservoir has been still further enhanced by warm basinal pore fluids moving upwards and outwards from the basin beneath the KCF aquitard (McLaughlin *et al.* 1996*b*).

Pore-waters and hydrocarbons from these Jurassic sandstones have migrated 2 km vertically up bounding faults of the Viking Graben. These fluids have migrated into the Palaeogene reservoir sandstones, including those in the West Brae oil field. These West Brae sandstones have excess quantities of authigenic kaolin cement (up to 19%) close to the geographical position identified as the entry point for hydrocarbon charging of the Palaeogene. This quantity of kaolin cannot have been supplied by local feldspar dissolution (Fig. 11), which could typically provide 3% kaolin cement (McLaughlin *et al.* 1996*a*). We consider it possible that some aluminium has been transported as organic complexes in migrating pore-water and

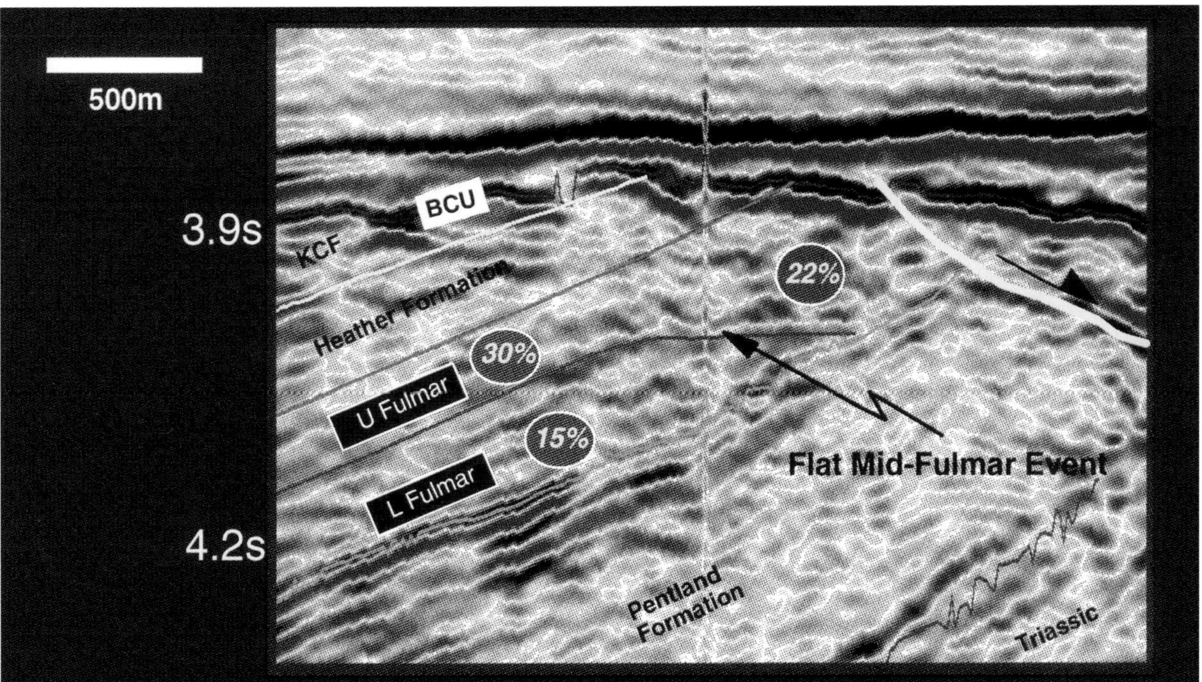

Fig. 10. Seismic reflection section across the Shearwater high pressure/high temperature oil field in the Central Graben. Picks show top and base of Fulmar Sandstone reservoir. Pick within Fulmar Sandstone is the division between low porosity sandstone (below) and high porosity sandstone (above). This boundary turns to form a concave-down surface at the field crest. Such a boundary is difficult to envisage from a depositional facies change or faulting, but could originate by leak-off of fluid from the crest. Pick within Fulmar Sandstone, and porosity values, are calibrated to Well data. BCU = Basal Cretaceous unconformity, KCF = Kimmeridge Clay Formation.

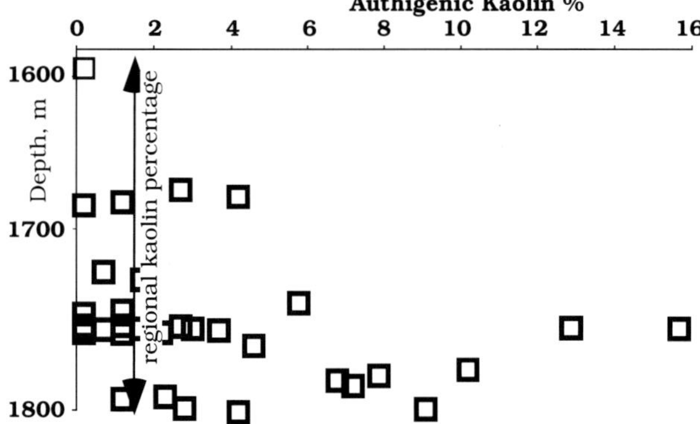

Fig. 11. Plot of authigenic kaolin in West Brae sandstones, derived from thin-section point count data.

hydrocarbons. Upon entering the shallower sandstones, the changed physical conditions enabled precipitation of this aluminium as authigenic kaolin. This small quantity of kaolin in no way mass-balances the quantity of aluminium exported from the deeper sandstones, but it may represent a partial record of past fluid movements and ion transfer on the scale of the Central Graben.

Carbonate cements. Vertical migration of hydrocarbons from the KCF into Palaeogene reservoirs (Cayley 1987) has resulted in abundant carbonate cementation. This is dominated by calcite produced by bacterially-mediated oxidation of hydrocarbons in crude oils. Studies by Watson *et al.* (1995) and Stewart (1995) have shown that such calcite cements in Paleocene and Eocene sandstones formed at very shallow burial depths. These cements are locally abundant, and contain unusual carbon isotope signatures. Macaulay *et al.* (1999) have compiled all published carbon isotope data from North Sea Tertiary sandstones. They find that three modes exist, at around $\delta^{13}C + 12‰$, 0‰ and −25‰ PDB. The most negative is characteristic of cements originating from bacterially oxidized oils. This evidence confirms the origin of the carbon in calcite

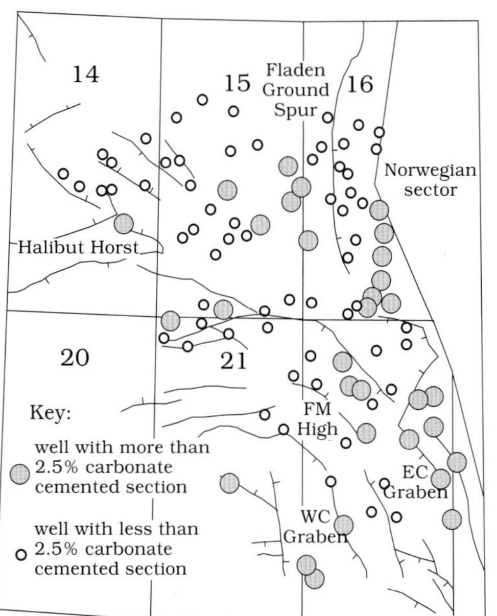

Fig. 12. Map compiled from well log information, of carbonate cement percentages in Paleocene sandstones of the Montrose Group (Stewart 1995). Dark circles around well locations indicate where carbonate exceeds 2.5% of drilled thickness within Montrose Group. FM High = Forties–Montrose High, EC Graben = East Central Graben and WC Graben = West Central Graben.

cements in the Palaeogene sandstones to be from re-migrated hydrocarbons more than 2 km below.

Stewart (1995) used geophysical log information across the Central and Southern Viking Graben to compile a map of the abundance of carbonate cements (Fig. 12). He also made isotopic analyses of selected cements. These findings indicate that carbonate cements are most abundant above basement-controlled faults at the margin of the Central Graben, on structural highs immediately adjacent to the Central Graben, and above the axial parts of the Central Graben where thick mudrocks occur. Many of these cements show carbon isotope signatures characteristic of oxidized oil. A similar correlation between cements and underlying structure has been observed offshore of NW Australia by O'Brien & Woods (1994).

Thus the cementation of Palaeogene sandstones mirrors and records the effects of leak-off processes and leak-off positions 2 or 3 km deeper in the Graben. Hydrocarbons and pore fluids leak-off from structurally controlled positions in the Upper Jurassic, and move upwards by buoyancy. In a process remarkably similar to that modelled by Fleming *et al.* (1998), the vertical transfer of fluids can be preferentially located up fault planes or fractured damage zones, which are most efficient when discharging into porous and permeable outlet zones within the normally pressured Palaeogene regional aquifer.

Conclusions (Fig. 13)

(1) Within the highly overpressured Central Graben of the North Sea, lateral pressure communication exists on a basin scale. 1D modelling cannot reliably predict overpressure. Pore fluids leak off laterally and vertically through faults and fractures at structurally controlled leak-points.
(2) Evidence of structurally controlled vertical leak-off within the geological past is recorded by deep saline porewaters which formed mineralized veins. Evidence of modern leak-off is provided by 10–40°C temperature anomalies (<10 km wavelength) at 2–5 km depth. Hydrogeological modelling shows that these can be generated up faults of 50 mD permeability discharging into porous and permeable outlet zones such as a Palaeogene regional aquifer
(3) Sandstones show a systematic loss of feldspar with increased depth, which is not matched by an increase in authigenic clay abundance. Up to 30% bulk volume additional porosity must be created. The mechanism of aluminium transport and the final destination remain obscure. Continued compaction destroys the petrographic textural evidence for the formation of more than 2–4% secondary porosity unless halted by extreme overpressure.
(4) Computer modelling in 2D shows that growth of illite clay records the onset of compactional outflux at the margins of the Central Graben, and the onset of vertical leak-off in the axial horst.
(5) Enhanced sandstone porosities are preferentially located at leak-off points, and where fluid flows preferentially along the upper part of the reservoir sandstone. These enhanced porosities can sometimes be imaged by seismic reflection. Computer modelling can predict the maximum porosity achievable at any depth–pressure condition. Secondary porosity from feldspar dissolution can increase porosity, by 10% at 4–6 km, towards this maximum value.
(6) The products of vertical leak-off form enhanced kaolin or carbonate cement concentrations in Palaeogene sandstones 2–3 km higher. The carbonates form preferentially above structurally-controlled leak-off positions, and have diagnostic negative carbon isotope signatures. Shallow cementation anomalies could act as exploration guides to deeper leak-off targets. The Central Graben is interconnected both within the overpressured aquifers, and between the overpressured and normally pressured reservoirs.

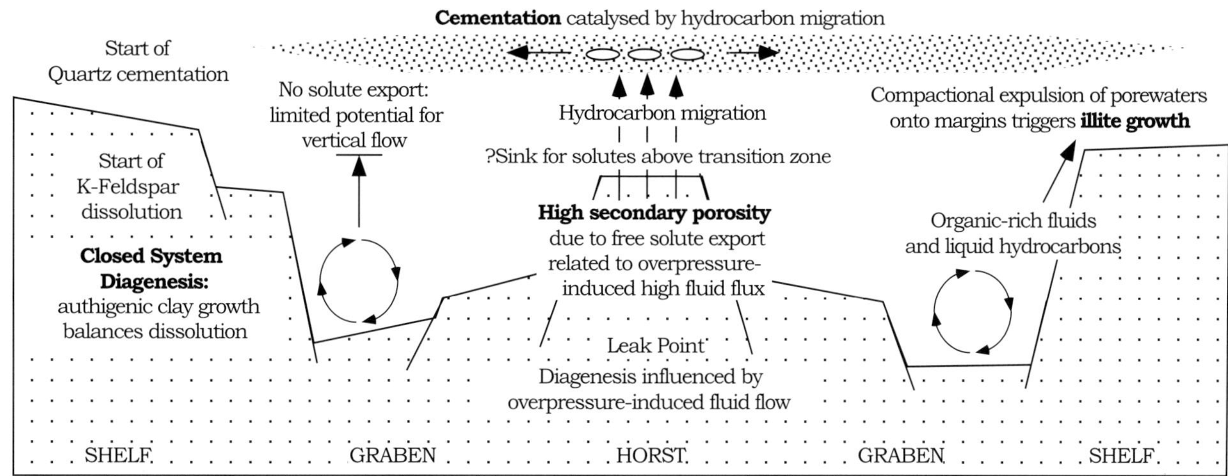

Fig. 13. Cartoon illustrating the principles outlined in this paper. Overpressure drives fluid flow laterally through the Fulmar reservoir sandstones, and vertically from structurally-located leak-off points. Porosity is improved in positions of fluid flow, by dissolution of feldspar and export of ions. The resultant secondary porosity slowly compacts and is texturally unrecognizable. In overpressured settings, porosity may be held open as a result of lowered effective stress; thus porosity may increase in such positions. Vertical leak-off forms anomalous kaolin and carbonate cements in overlying Palaeogene reservoirs.

We thank the many companies and research organizations who have funded this work, or supplied information, data or samples. These include Elf UK, Shell Oil, British Petroleum, Marathon Oil UK, Robertson Group, Platte River Associates, Amoco, and The Natural Environment Research Council. Mobil provided Fig. 10 including the seismic interpretation therein. SURRC is partly funded by a consortium of Scottish Universities. Thanks to referees F. Kreiger (Philips, UK) and R. Worden (Queens University of Belfast) who helped us to improve our explanations, and to S. Burley (BG plc) for his editorial assistance.

References

AASE, N. E., BJORKUM, P. A. & NADEAU, P. H. 1996. The effect of grain coating microquartz on preservation of reservoir microporosity. *American Association of Petroleum Geologists Bulletin*, **80**, 1654–1673.

ANDREWS-SPEED, C. P., OXBURGH E. R. & COOPER, B. A. 1984. Temperatures and depth dependent heat-flow in the western North Sea. *American Association of Petroleum Geologists Bulletin*, **68**, 1764–1781.

BRADLEY, J. S. 1975. Abnormal formation pressure. *American Association of Petroleum Geologists Bulletin*, **59**, 957–973.

BREDEHOEFT J., WESLEY, J. & FOUCH, T. 1994. Simulations of the origin of fluid pressure, fracture generation and the movement of fluids in the Uinta Basin, Utah. *American Association of Petroleum Geologists Bulletin*, **78**, 1729–1747.

BURLEY, S. 1993. Models of burial diagenesis for deep exploration plays in Jurassic fault traps of the Central and Northern North Sea. *In*: PARKER, J. R. (ed.) *Petroleum Geology of Northwest Europe: Proceedings of the 4th Conference*. Geological Society, London, 1353–1375.

CAYLEY, G. T. 1987. Hydrocarbon migration in the central North Sea. *In*: BROOKS, J. & GLENNIE, K. W. (eds) *Petroleum Geology of North West Europe*. Graham & Trotman, London, 549–555.

CLELLAND, W. D., KANTOROWICZ, J. D. & FENS, T. W. 1993. Quantitative analysis of pore structure and its effects on reservoir behaviour: upper Jurassic Ribble Member sandstones, Fulmar Field, UK North Sea. *In*: ASHTON, M. (ed.) *Advances in Reservoir Geology*. Geological Society, London, Special Publications, **69**, 57–79.

CORNFORD C. 1994. The Mandal–Ekofisk(!) petroleum system in the Central Graben of the North Sea. *In*: MAGOON, L. & DOW, W. (eds) *The Petroleum System – from Source to Trap*. American Association of Petroleum Geologists, Memoirs, **60**, 537–571.

DAHLBERG, E. C. 1982. *Applied Hydrodynamics in Petroleum Exploration*. Springer-Verlag, New York.

DARBY, D., HASZELDINE, R. S. & COUPLES, G. D. 1996 Pressure cells and pressure seals in the UK Central Graben. *Marine and Petroleum Geology*, **13**, 865–878.

——, WILKINSON, M., FALLICK, A. E. & HASZELDINE, R. S. 1997. Illite dates record deep fluid movements in petroleum basins. *Petroleum Geoscience*, **3**, 133–140.

——, HASZELDINE, R. S. & COUPLES, G. D. 1998. Central North Sea overpressures: insights into fluid flow from 1- and 2-D basin modelling. *In*: ILIFFE, J. & DUPPENBECKER, S. (eds) *Basin Modelling: Practice and Progress*. Geological Society, London, Special Publications, **141**, 95–107.

FLEMING, C. G., COUPLES, G. D. & HASZELDINE, R. S. 1998. Thermal effects of fluid flow in steep fault zones. *In*: JONES, G., FISHER, Q. J. & KNIPE, R. J. (eds) *Faulting, Fault Sealing and Fluid Flow in Hydrocarbon Reservoirs*. Geological Society, London, Special Publications, **147**, 217–229.

GAARENSTROOM, L., TROMP, R., DE JONG, M. & BRANDENBURG, A. 1993. Overpressures in the Central North Sea: implications for trap integrity and drilling safety. *In*: PARKER, J. R. (ed.) *Petroleum Geology of Northwest Europe: Proceedings of the 4th Conference*. Geological Society, London, 1305–1313.

GILES, M. R. & DE BOER, R. B. 1990. Origin and significance of redistributional secondary porosity. *Marine and Petroleum Geology*, **7**, 378–397.

——, —— & MARSHALL, J. D. 1994. How important are organic acids in generating secondary porosity in the subsurface? *In*: PITTMAN, E. D. & LEWAN, M. D. (eds) *Organic Acids in Geological Processes*. Springer-Verlag, Berlin, 449–470.

GLUYAS J. & COLEMAN, M. 1992. Material flux and porosity changes during sediment diagenesis. *Nature*, **356**, 52–54.

HARRIS, N. B. 1992 Burial diagenesis of Brent Sandstones: a study of Statfjord, Hutton and Lyell fields. *In*: MORTON, A. C., HASZELDINE, R. S., GILES, M. R. & BROWN, S. (eds) *Geology of the Brent Group*. Geological Society, London, Special Publications, **61**, 351–376.

HASZELDINE, R. S., WILKINSON, M., DARBY, D., MCLAUGHLIN, Ó. M., STEWART, R. N. T., MCAULAY, G., COUPLES, G. D. & FALLICK, A. E. 1996. The secondary porosity trick: arkose to quartzite in the North Sea. *Abstracts, Ann Convention American Association of Petroleum Geologists, Tulsa*, A62.

HOWELL, J. A., FLINT, S. S. & HUNT, C. 1996. Sedimentological aspects of the Humber Group (Upper Jurassic) of the South Central Graben, UK North Sea. *Sedimentology*, **43**, 89–114.

HUNT, J. M. 1990. Generation and migration of petroleum from abnormally pressured fluid compartments. *Bulletin of the American Association of Petroleum Geologists*, **74,** 1–12.

KNIPE, R. J. 1997. Juxtaposition and seal diagrams to help analyze fault seals in hydrocarbon reservoirs, *Bulletin of the American Association of Petroleum Geologists*, **81**, 187–195.

LIEWIG, N., CLAUER, N. & SOMMER, F. 1987. Rb–Sr and K–Ar dating of clay diagenesis in Jurassic Sandstone Oil Reservoirs, North Sea. *Bulletin of the American Association of Petroleum Geologists*, **71**, 1467–1474.

MACAULAY, C. I., BOYCE, A. J., FALLICK, A. E. & HASZELDINE, R. S. 1997. Quartz veins record vertical flow at a Graben edge: Fulmar oilfield, central North Sea. *Bulletin of the American Association of Petroleum Geologists*, **81**, 2024–2035.

——, FALLICK, A. E., MCAULAY, G. E. & HASZELDINE, R. S. 1999. Oil migration makes the difference: regional distribution of carbonate cement $\delta^{13}C$ in northern North Sea Tertiary sandstones. *Clay Minerals*, **34**, in press.

MCBRIDE, E. F. 1987. Diagenesis of the Maxon Formation Sandstone, (Early Cretaceous), Marathon Region, Texas: a diagenetic quartzarenite. *Journal of Sedimentary Petrology*, **57**, 98–107.

MCLAUGHLIN, Ó. M., HASZELDINE, R. S., FALLICK, A. E. & ROGERS, G. 1994. The case of the missing clay, aluminium loss and secondary porosity, South Brae Oilfield, North Sea. *Clay Minerals*, **29**, 651–664.

——, MCAULAY, G. E., HASZELDINE, R. S. & ROGERS, G. 1996*a*. Deep to shallow kaolinite relocation generates porosity. *Abstract, American Association of Petroleum Geologists Ann Convention*, A96.

——, HASZELDINE, R. S. & FALLICK, A. E. 1996*b*. Quartz diagenesis in layered fluids in the South Brae Oilfield, North Sea. *In*: CROSSEY, L. J., LOUCKS, R. & TOTTEN, M. W. (eds) *Siliclastic Diagenesis and Fluid Flow: Concepts and Applications*. SEPM Special Publications, **55**, 103–113.

MILLIKEN, K. L., MCBRIDE, E. F. & LAND, L. S. 1989. Numerical assessment of dissolution versus replacement in the subsurface destruction of detrital feldspars, Frio Formation, South Texas. *Journal of Sedimentary Petrology*, **59**, 740–757.

MUDFORD, B. S., GRADSTEIN, F. M., KATSUBE, T. J. and BEST, M. E. 1991. Modelling 1-D compaction driven flow in sedimentary basins: a comparison of the Scotian Shelf, North Sea and Gulf Coast. *In*: ENGLAND, W. A. & FLEET, A. J. (eds) *Petroleum Migration*. Geological Society, London, Special Publications, **59**, 65–85.

NEUZIL, C. E. 1995. Abnormal pressures as hydrodynamic phenomena. *American Journal of Science*, **295**, 742–786.

O'BRIEN, W. O. & WOODS, P. 1994. Vulcan sub-basin, Timor Sea. Clues to the structural reactivation and migration history from the recognition of hydrocarbon seepage indicators. *Australian Geological Survey Organization Newsletter*, **21**, 8–11.

PRICE J., DYER, R., GOODALL, I., MCKIE, T., WATSON, P. & WILLIAMS, G. 1993 Effective stratigraphic subdivision of the Humber Group and the late Jurassic evolution of the UK Central Graben. *In*: PARKER, J. R. (ed.) *Petroleum Geology of Northwest Europe: Proceedings of the 4th Conference*. Geological Society, London, 443–458.

STEWART, D. J. 1986. Diagenesis of the shallow marine Fulmar Formation in the Central North Sea. *Clay Minerals*, **21**, 537–564.

STEWART, R. N. T. 1995. *Regional Diagenetic Porosity Changes in Palaeocene Oilfield Sandstones: UK North Sea*. PhD Thesis, University of Glasgow, UK.

SULLIVAN, K. B. & MCBRIDE, E. F. 1991 Diagenesis of sandstone at shale contacts and diagenetic heterogeneity, Frio Formation, Texas. *Bulletin of the American Association of Petroleum Geologists*, **75**, 121–138.

SWARBRICK, R. E. 1994. Reservoir diagenesis and hydrocarbon migration under hydrostatic paleopressure conditions. *Clay Minerals*, **29**, 463–473.

WATSON, R. S., TREWIN, N. H. & FALLICK, A. E. 1995. The formation of carbonate cements in the Forth and Balmoral fields, northern North Sea: a case for biodegradation, carbonate cementation and oil leakage during early burial. *In*: HARTLEY, A. J. & PROSSER, D. J. (eds) *Characterisation of Deep Marine Clastic Systems*. Geological Society, London, Special Publications, **94**, 177–200.

WILKINSON M. & HASZELDINE, R. S. 1996. Aluminium loss during sandstone diagenesis. *Journal of the Geological Society, London*, **153**, 657–660.

—— & ——1997. Discussion on: Aluminium loss during sandstone diagenesis. *Journal of the Geological Society, London*, **154**, 747–751.

——, DARBY, D., HASZELDINE, R. S. & COUPLES, G. D. 1997. Secondary porosity generation during deep burial associated with overpressure leak-off: Fulmar Formation UKCS. *American Association of Petroleum Geologists Bulletin*, **81**, 803–813.

——, FALLICK, A. E., KEARNEY, G. M., HASZELDINE, R. S. & MCHARDY, W. 1994. Stable isotopes in illite: the case for meteoric water flushing within the Upper Jurassic Fulmar Sandstone. *Clay Minerals*, **29**, 567–574.

The Jurassic petroleum system of the West of Britain Atlantic margin – an integration of tectonics, geochemistry and basin modelling

A. J. HOLMES,[1] C. E. GRIFFITH[1] and I. C. SCOTCHMAN[2]

[1] *Mobil North Sea Ltd, Mobil Court, 3 Clements Inn, London WC2A 2EB, UK (e-mail: andrew_j_holmes@email.mobil.com)*
[2] *Statoil (UK) Ltd, Statoil House, 11 Regent St, London SW1Y 4ST, UK*

Abstract: A re-appraisal of the Mesozoic and Cenozoic evolution of the Atlantic margin basins has been integrated with new data on source-rock kinetics, oil-source geochemistry and fluid inclusion studies to calibrate the petroleum systems of the study area and model these systems utilizing 2D modelling software.

The high β factors that are reported from these basins are cumulative estimates. Superposition of rifting events and evidence of prolonged rifting until the early Paleocene demonstrate that heat flow patterns associated with a 'cool' rift model are most appropriate.

New kinetic models for 'Kimmeridge Clay' and Middle Jurassic source-rock samples from released wells and BGS shallow boreholes allow more precise maturation modelling. Prolific oil-prone, Type I and Type I/II Middle Jurassic source rocks, together with fast-reacting Type IIS Upper Jurassic–Lower Cretaceous source rocks have been identified and indicate the range of kinetic models that must be considered during sensitivity analysis.

In the Faeroe–Shetland area, complex mixing of both 'fresh' and biodegraded oils from different source rocks as well as different facies of the same source-rock formation are recognized. Gas chromatography–mass spectrometry (GC–MS) and compound specific isotope analysis (CSIA) of oil samples and petroleum fluid inclusions are used to differentiate between oil families and also to separate oils within a sample.

A number of regional seismic sections were utilized for 2D modelling which was calibrated from well or pseudo-well models and incorporated new heat flow and kinetic data. These results and regional mapping indicate that the respective location of Lower Tertiary versus Upper Cretaceous depocentres is critical in determining the timing of maturation. Peak oil maturation occurs from mid Cretaceous to the present-day. Migration pathways initially focus hydrocarbons to Mesozoic (or older) highs. Early Tertiary faulting, mid Tertiary uplift and gas flushing then control re-distribution of hydrocarbons.

The petroleum system approach to exploration in the Atlantic margin basins requires, as a starting point, that the generation of hydrocarbons and the subsequent migration and accumulation history be defined. The pre-requisites for best defining this history are a thorough understanding of:

(1) the tectonic evolution of the area;
(2) the character and nature of the source rock(s);
(3) the distribution and nature of the carrier systems;
(4) the presence and availability of reservoir rocks; and
(5) the presence of effective seals.

This paper reflects the integration of tectonics, geochemistry and field data to provide the input for qualitative 2D modelling along the NE Atlantic margin. Use of BasinMod™ 2D modelling software allows qualitative analysis of the petroleum system and provides a means of testing the modelled data against observation. Additionally, uncertainties in interpretation can be modelled and sensitivity analysis of the more critical input parameters can be performed.

Tectonic evolution

Principal tectonic elements of the region are shown in Fig. 1. Numerous authors (e.g. Knott *et al.* 1993; Musgrove & Mitchener 1996; Lundin & Doré 1997; Doré *et al.* 1997; Dean *et al.* 1999) have described the tectonic evolution of various areas along the NE Atlantic margin. Figure 2 summarizes the tectonic history relating the timing of events along the Atlantic margin to the resultant hydrocarbon plays. The principal contributing components are superposition of successive rift events from the Permo-Triassic to the early Tertiary; Paleocene magmatic events are associated with continental break-up and late Tertiary compressional events.

Deep-crustal modelling (including subsidence history analysis and cross-section balancing) across the Faeroe–Shetland Basin (FSB) and Northern Rockall Trough (RT) suggest the UK Atlantic margin basins have been highly attenuated ($\beta = 3$–5) with β factor decreasing away from the basin axes. At this level of extension, it is to be expected that rift systems would likely attain oceanic status. However, the β-factors quoted provide a cumulative estimate of the total extension and do not equate to the β-factor associated with a single rift event. They are the result of major rift events during the Permo-Trias, Cretaceous and early Paleocene (and possibly limited Jurassic rifting). Although the duration of the heating effects is longer, heat flow increase is negligible in long duration, low β-factor rifts (Jarvis & McKenzie 1980; Fig. 3). This provides a mechanism to explain the low geothermal gradients observed in these areas of repeated rift episodes. Dean *et al.* 1999, provide a more detailed description of these processes and effects.

In the UK Atlantic margin basins, syn-rift growth suggests Permo-Triassic rifting, although these 'wedges' have been strongly modified by major erosion in intra-Jurassic, early Paleocene and Recent times. Lower and Middle Jurassic sediments are found as isolated erosional remnants in the FSB and in the flanking basins e.g. the West Lewis Basin. This suggests a more widespread distribution as seen in the extensive sequences reported from the Slyne–Erris troughs to the south (Scotchman & Thomas 1995). Fault block rotation and erosion in ?Callovian times may reflect the extension seen in the Sea of

Holmes, A. J., Griffith, C. E. & Scotchman, I. C. 1999. The Jurassic petroleum system of the West of Britain Atlantic margin – an integration of tectonics, geochemistry and basin modelling. *In*: Fleet, A. J. & Boldy, S. A. R. (eds) *Petroleum Geology of Northwest Europe: Proceedings of the 5th Conference*, 1351–1365.

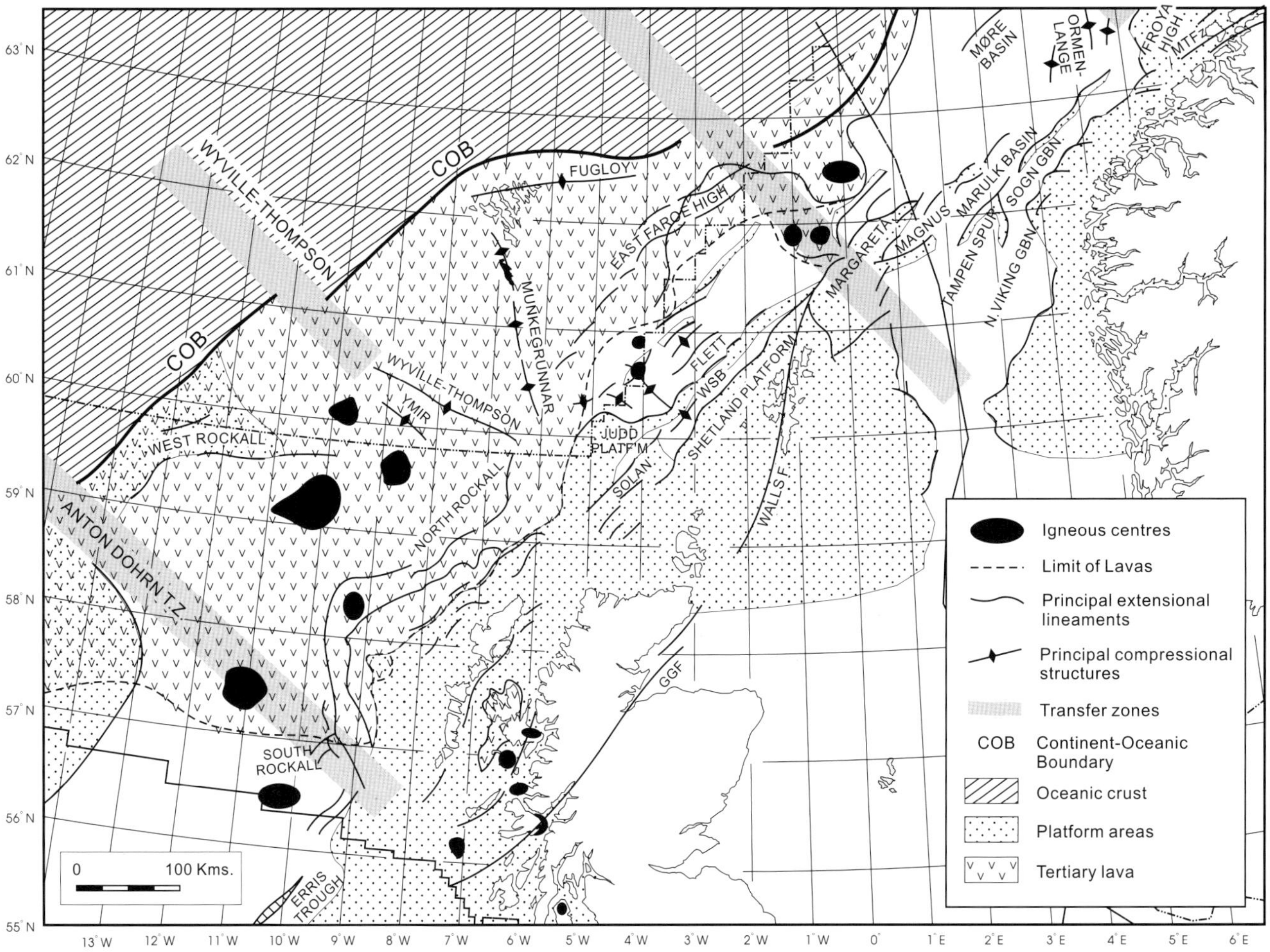

Fig. 1. Principal tectonic elements of the West of Britain Atlantic margin.

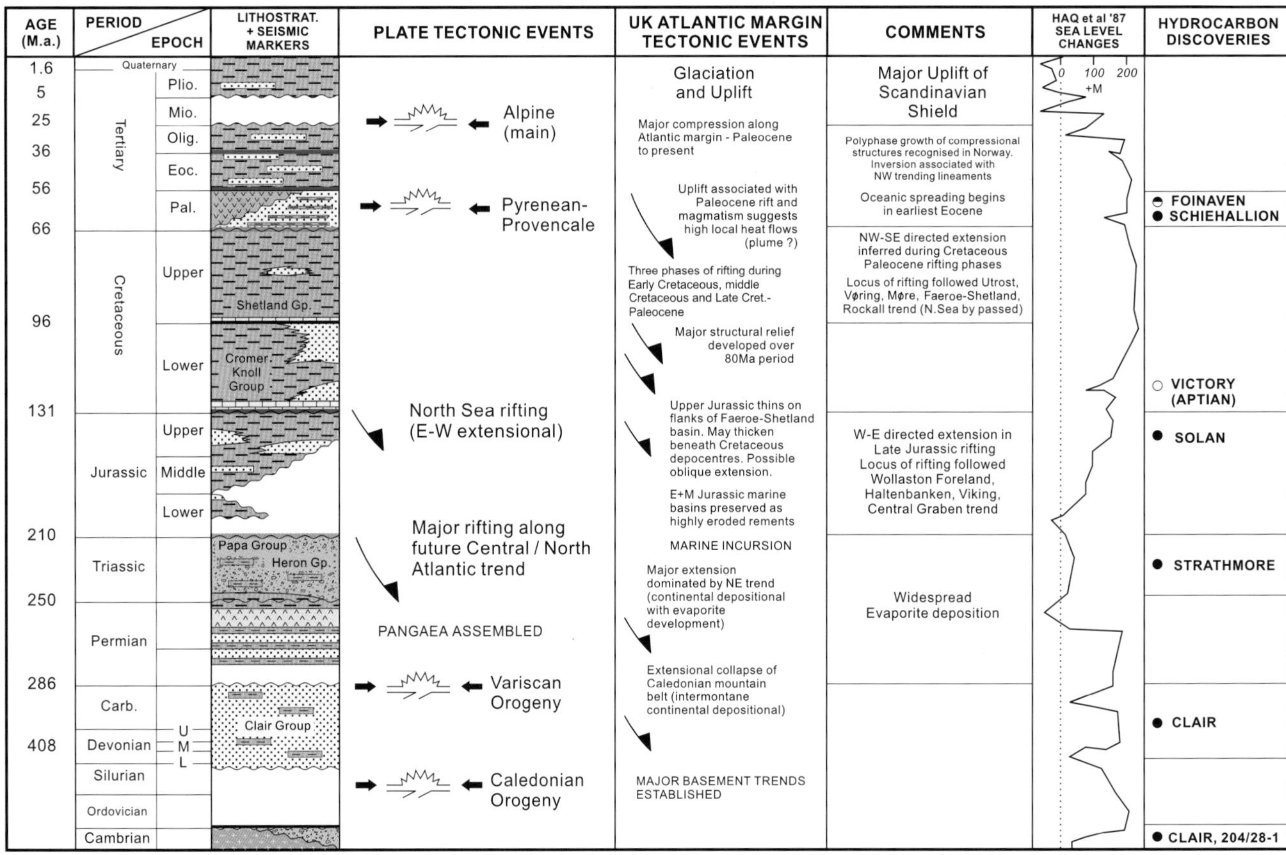

Fig. 2. Summary of the tectonic history of the Atlantic margin basins, West of Britain.

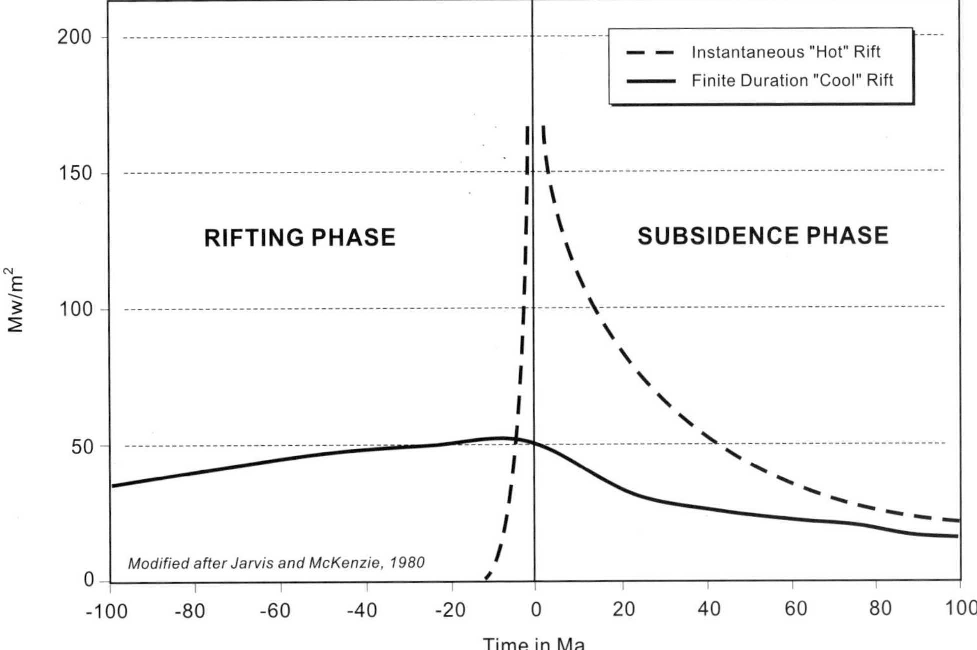

Fig. 3. Surface heat flow as a function of time for 'hot' and 'cool' rifts. For a constant stretching factor, the duration of rifting markedly affects the magnitude of the heat flow anomaly. For the 'cool' rift model, the heat flow anomaly is significantly lower at the end of the rifting phase as a result of partial thermal re-equilibration prior to the cessation of rifting.

Hebrides and Slyne–Erris troughs to the southwest and south. These basins may have developed in response to sinistral oblique extension along the proto-North Atlantic at this time. Small isolated basins developed, which in the FSB and flanking areas, are the site of shallow marine and lacustrine deposits (Knott *et al.* 1993), including Type I and Type I/II source rocks.

During the late Jurassic, the area underwent renewed subsidence but with none of the major extension recorded from the North Sea northwards to Haltenbanken. Major Upper Jurassic thickness variations are generally absent in the UK part of the NE Atlantic margin. Seismic reconstructions and well data indicate regional flooding of a peneplaned erosion surface (Verstralen *et al.* 1995; Musgrove & Mitchener 1996). Subsequent transgression with restricted marine circulation led to anoxic conditions and deposition of Kimmeridge Clay Formation (KCF) source rocks and their equivalents. The presence of well-developed organic-rich source-rock facies, in areas marginal to any Upper Jurassic rift has implications in the RT. The transgressive nature of Upper Jurassic source facies development is not dependent on the presence of a rifted basin.

Major structural relief was produced along the entire margin caused by to northwest–southeast directed early–mid Cretaceous extension. Structural analysis demonstrates that Cretaceous rifting was not a single discrete event (Dean *et al.* 1999). Fault activity persisted throughout the Cretaceous. Coarse clastic influx characterizes the Lower Cretaceous while thick mud-prone sediments suggesting tectonic quiescence dominate the Upper Cretaceous which was a period of global first-order sea-level highstand (Haq *et al.* 1987) sufficient to overwhelm footwall uplift or rift shoulder uplift.

The model of prolonged and progressive rifting fits the data from the FSB and more accurately describes the Vøring, Møre and, by analogy, the Rockall basins. Three individual rifting episodes are recognized: (1) Valanginian–Apto/Albian; (2) Cenomanian? (Vøring Basin)–Turonian, and (3) Maastrichtian–Paleocene. Cumulatively these contribute to an overall large stretching factor but as explained earlier, may be associated with small increases in heat flow. Superposition of rifting episodes and depocentre shifting can be well demonstrated in the southwestern part of the FSB. Similar variations in fault timing can be inferred across the basin and in the RT. This switching of depocentres during the Cretaceous and early Paleocene leads to the variability in timing of hydrocarbon generation in different areas along the margin.

Rifting continued into the early Paleocene as a precursor to break-up in the early Eocene (Skogseid 1994). Significant rift flank uplift occurred with the Scottish Massif and adjacent platforms supplying coarse clastics into the basin. Evidence for Paleocene extension in the FSB and RT is widespread with angular discordance between top and base Paleocene reflectors, extensional offsets at base Tertiary level (e.g. Fig. 4), and depocentre switching between the late Cretaceous and Paleocene. The northwestward shifting of rift axes is noted throughout the NE Atlantic margin (Lundin & Doré 1997). It may be that the axis of Paleocene rifting lies beneath the depocentre of the Faeroes plateau basalts. Explanations for uplift on the margins and major subsidence, range from mantle phase changes (Hall & White 1994) to dynamic plume related uplift (Turner & Scrutton 1993; Nadin & Kuznir 1995). These fail to explain the seismic geometries or depocentre switching.

The extensive igneous activity associated with the development of the Iceland mantle plume (Richie & Hitchen 1996) appears to have had little regional impact on palaeotemperature data (Turner & Scrutton 1993). There are, however, localized effects seen in wells penetrating intrusives and a relatively narrow thermal aureole is to be expected around igneous centres. Overall heat flow in the NE Atlantic margin appears to have been little affected.

Compressional events, climaxing during late Tertiary times, interrupted post-rift thermal subsidence and are partly responsible for facilitating hydrocarbon migration and complicating the fill history of hydrocarbon accumulations. These features are exhibited throughout the Atlantic margin from the Barents Sea to offshore western Ireland (Boldreel & Andersen 1993). The compressional stress field is a result of oblique interaction between Alpine compression and ridge-perpendicular

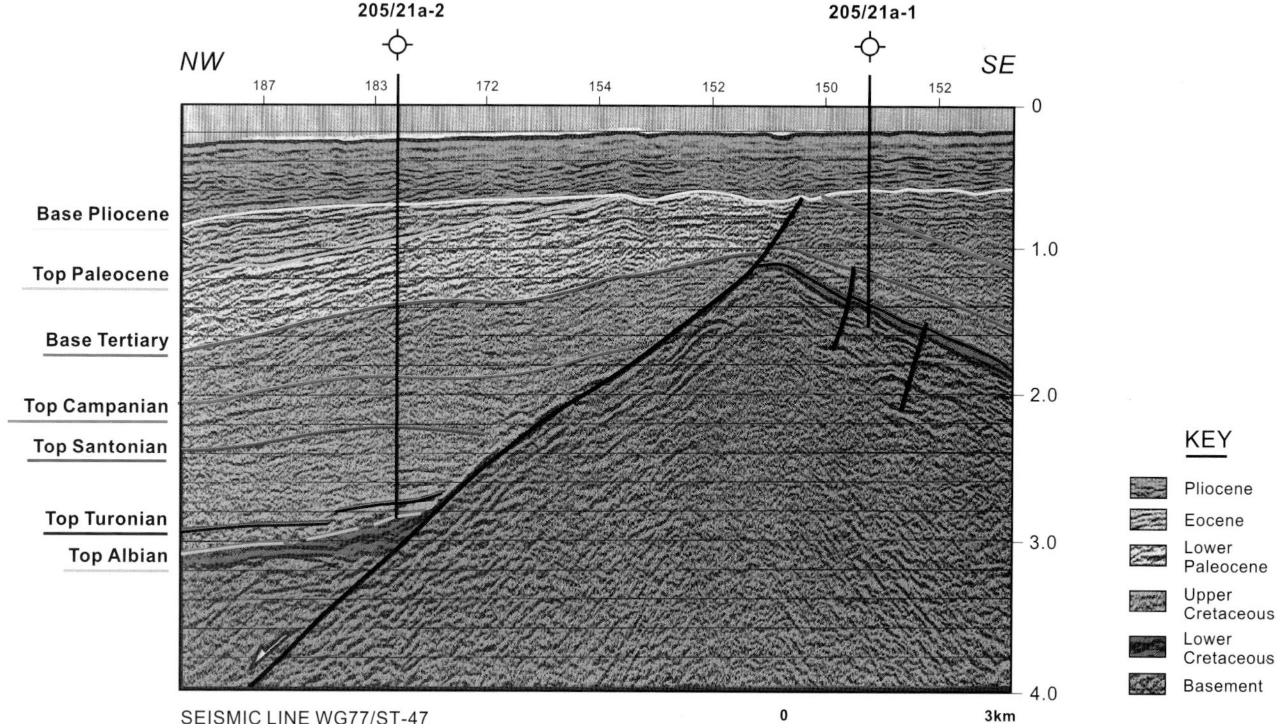

Fig. 4. Seismic evidence for extensional displacement at base Tertiary level. (Data courtesy of Western Geophysical).

compression ('ridge-push') from early Eocene times to the present-day (Doré & Lundin 1996). Many of the compressional structures are interpreted as reflecting this northwest–southeast directed compression. However, several features, such as the north–south trending Munkegrunnar Ridge and Ormen Lange Dome (Fig. 1) deviate from this direction. It is possible these structures originate from strike-slip motion on major northwest–southeast trending transfer zones in late Oligocene–early Miocene times as a result of a change in spreading direction.

These events have resulted in the re-focusing of late stage hydrocarbon migration and re-migration, and erosion of the basin margins. In themselves, the resultant structures may represent attractive exploration targets either as periclinal domes or as a significant component in structural–stratigraphic traps.

Source rocks – type and distribution

Nine potential source-rock horizons are identified in the Atlantic margin area and have been described by Scotchman & Doré (1995). All geochemical and well data indicate that Jurassic source horizons are the most relevant to the NE Atlantic margin area.

Early Jurassic transgressive black shales are more important to the Slyne/Erris Trough area (Scotchman & Thomas 1995) possibly extending into the Irish sector of the RT and the Porcupine Basin.

Middle Jurassic source intervals, when encountered, are highly oil-prone and potentially very rich. Their contribution to the hydrocarbon accumulations found to date has not yet been established. The interval has been sampled in the West Lewis and West Flannan basins and is encountered in a small number of wells in the FSB. Distribution of these marginal marine/lacustrine facies source rocks is not widespread (Fig. 5a). These environments appear in small pockets of embayments and lagoons along the basin margins, preserved during the mid Jurassic regression.

Upper Jurassic/Lower Cretaceous source rocks (Kimmeridgian–Ryazanian) are the most effective source rocks in the FSB and are likely to be so in other NE Atlantic basins (Fig. 5b). Variable source facies result in variable oil composition, as outlined later. Variability in source-rock quality is shown in Fig. 6. Well 205/26a-2 was examined using sonic/resistivity overlays (adapted from Passey *et al.* 1990) correlated to measured total organic carbon (TOC) data. An excellent match was obtained (TOCs from 4–8%). Extrapolating this relationship to Well 205/26a-3 (5 km basinward) reveals TOCs in excess of 15%, demonstrating the excellent source potential of this KCF equivalent.

Six oil families have been recognized in the NE Atlantic margin basins west of Britain and Ireland (Fig. 7; Scotchman & Griffith pers. comm. 1996). In the FSB and adjacent areas, these oils are predominantly derived from various facies of the KCF or its equivalents. Figure 8 is a statistical analysis of some of the oil samples and source rocks in the area. Clair Field and Strathmore area oils, though different, are most closely associated with KCF samples. In Well 204/22-1, Middle Jurassic source rocks display no affinity to the oil extracted from immediately underlying basement core.

Many of the oils found (e.g. the 'Clair Family') demonstrate mixing, with both biodegraded and 'fresh' oils, originating from different source facies. Geochemical analysis of oils (Rooney *et al.* 1998), including gas chromatography-mass spectrometry (GC-MS), biomarker, compound specific isotope analysis (CSIA) and petroleum fluid inclusion data demonstrate the complexity of hydrocarbon charging. Oils with clear biomarker distributions, characteristic of heavy biodegradation also contain abundant alkanes and hopanes indicating a later 'fresh' oil charge. New fluid inclusion data indicate that petroleum was first present at formation temperatures experienced during early late Cretaceous time (Scotchman *et al.* 1998).

Figure 9 compares 'Clair Family' and Strathmore area ('Northern North Sea Family') oils using CSIA profiles of the light hydrocarbons. There is a clear shift to the isotopically

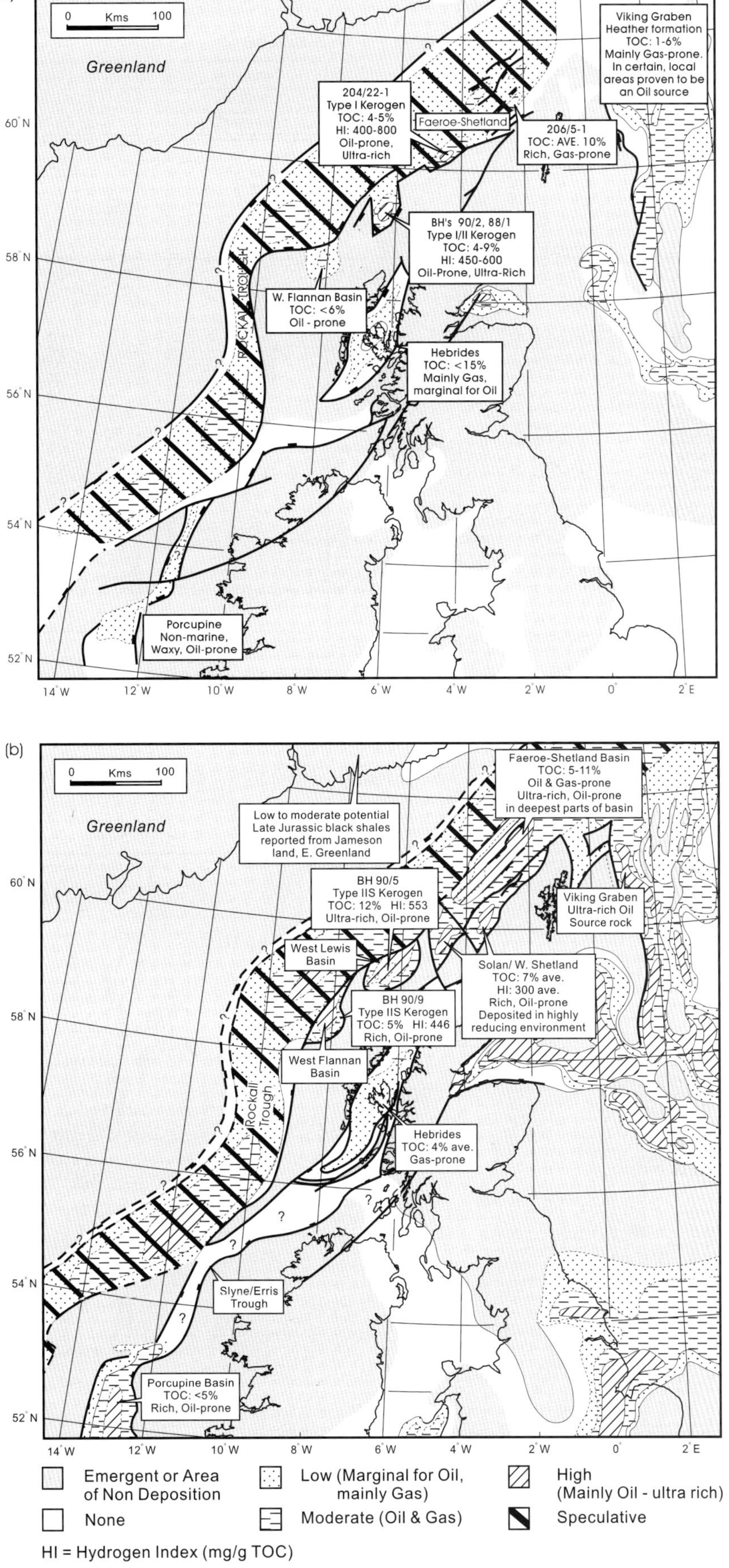

Fig. 5. (**a**) Estimated original generative potential of mid Jurassic source rocks. Highly oil-prone mid Jurassic source rocks are encountered in areally restricted lagoon or lacustrine embayments. (**b**) Estimated original generative potential of late Jurassic source rocks. Widespread distribution of rich to ultra-rich highly oil-prone source rocks along the Atlantic margin basins.

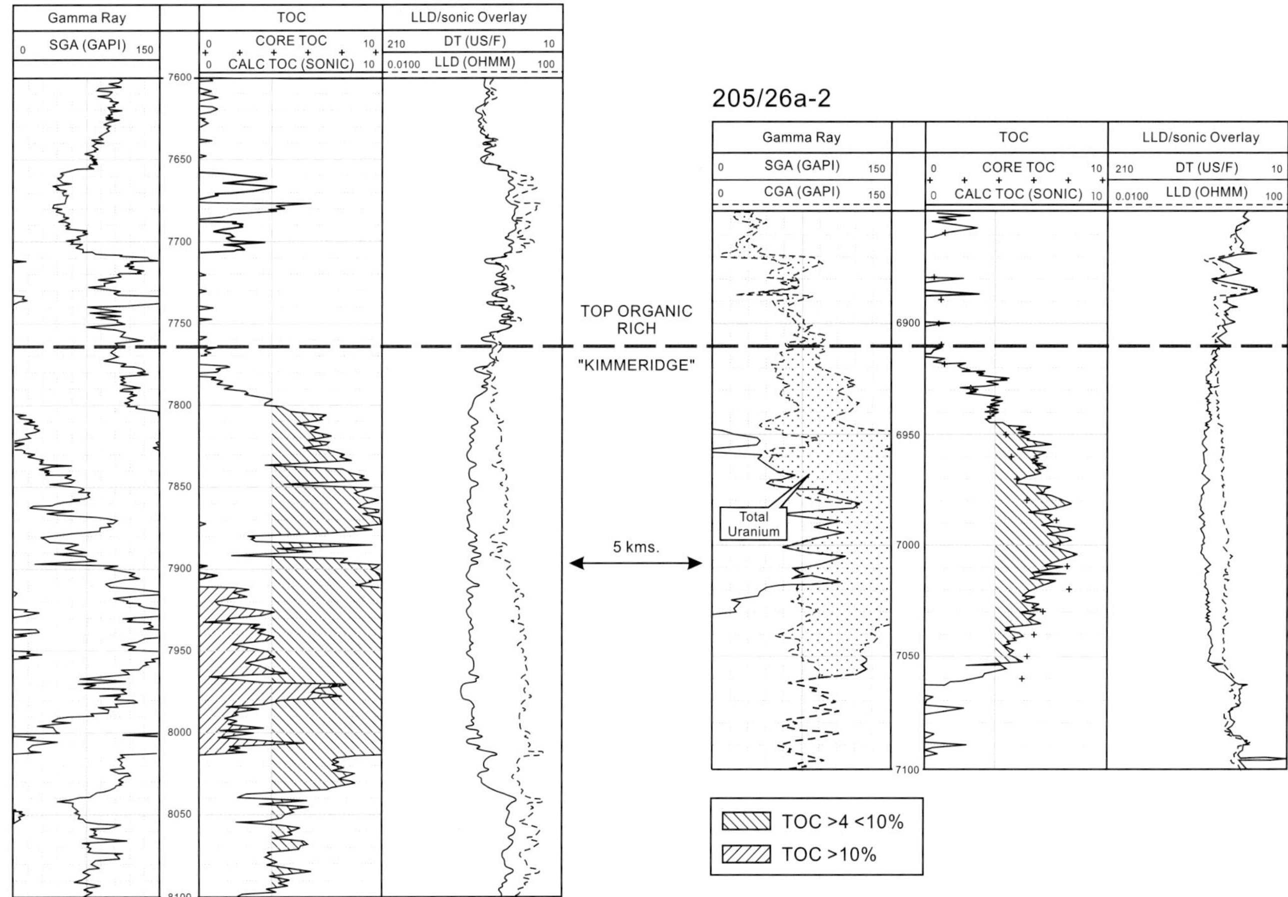

Fig. 6. Estimation of total organic carbon from wireline logs. Note the increase in source-rock quality over a short distance basinward.

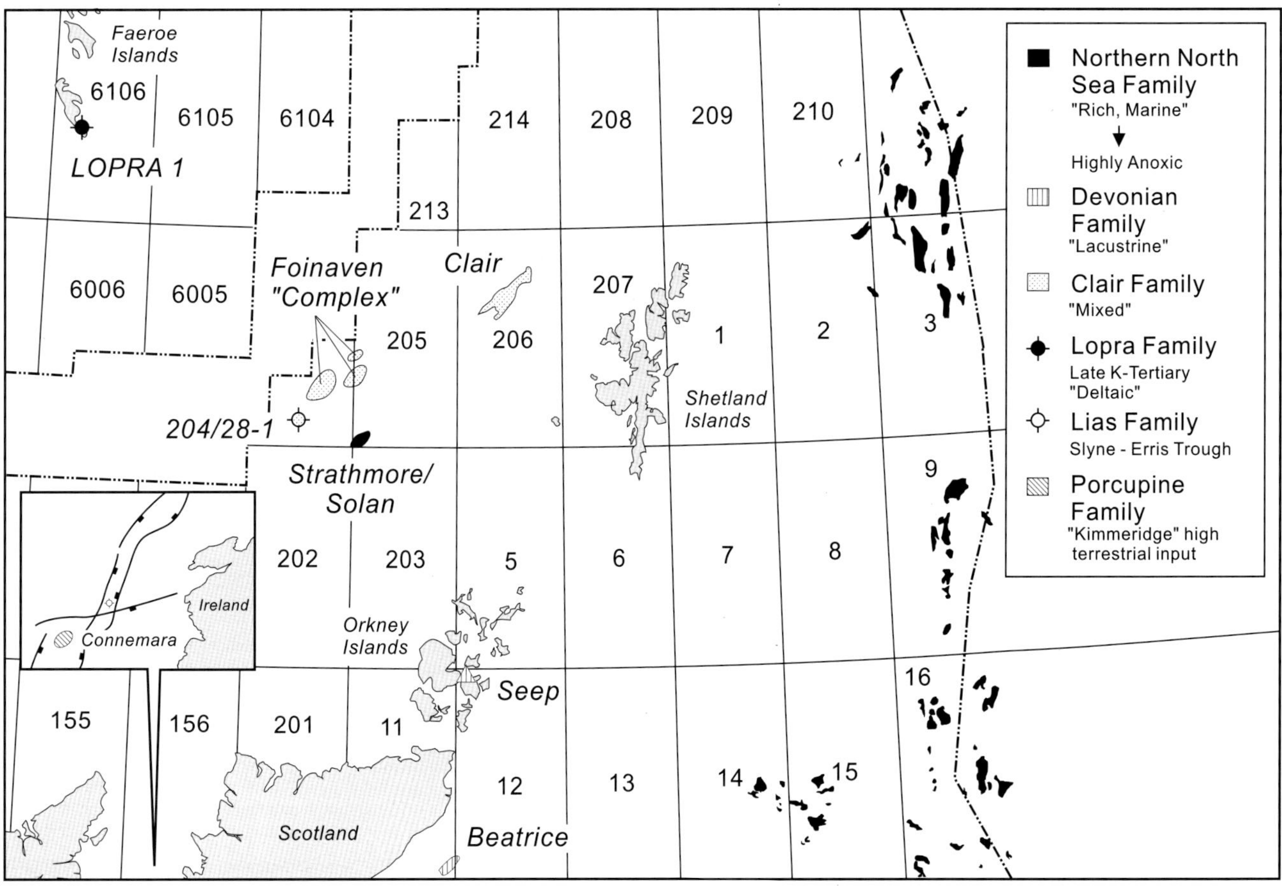

Fig. 7. Known distribution of distinct oil 'families', north and west of Britain and Ireland.

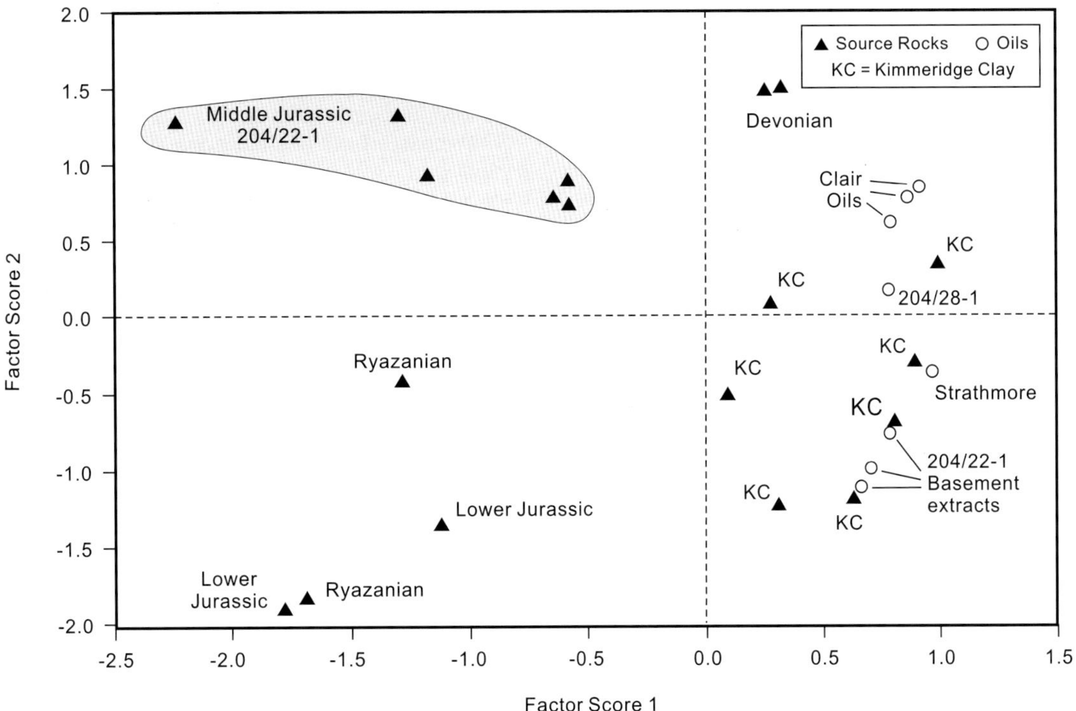

Fig. 8. Oil to source rock correlation relationships. Correlation of oils and source rocks was performed using multivariate factor analysis on molecular and isotope data. This plot is constructed by removing aromatic hydrocarbon data (a maturity indicator).

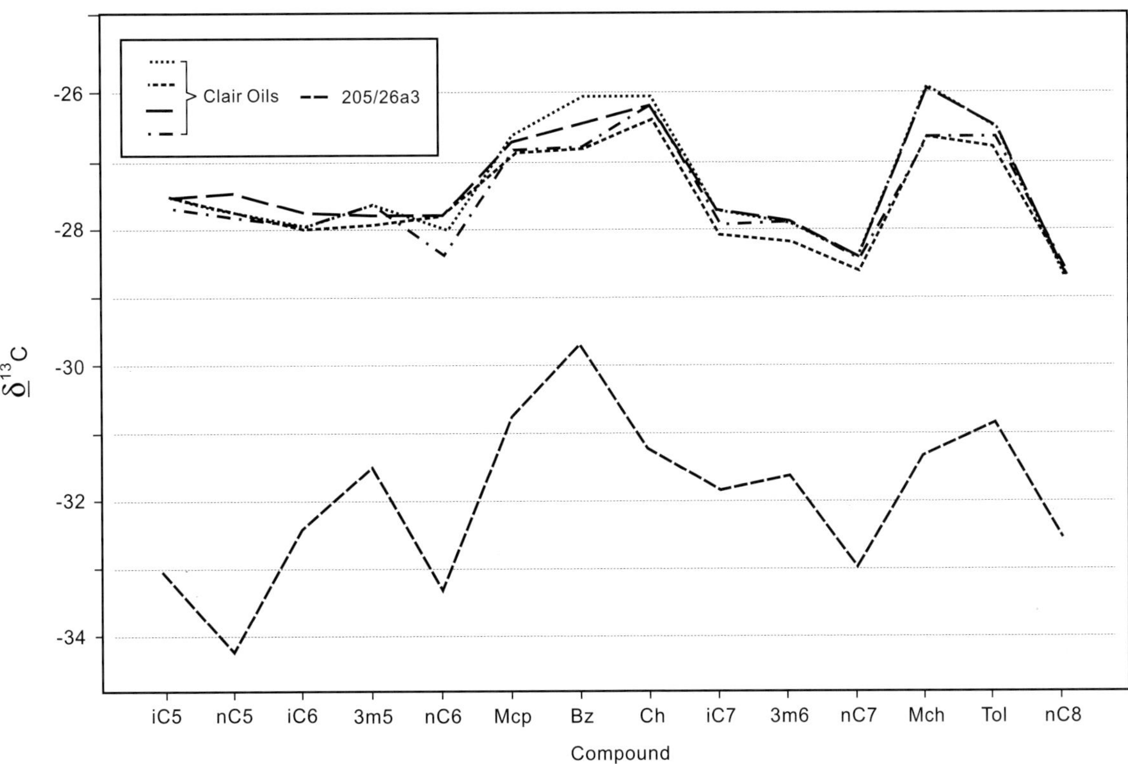

Fig. 9. Gasoline range CSIA (compound specific isotope analysis) for oil samples from the Faeroes–Shetland Basin. The Clair samples are nearly identical while the Strathmore oil (205/26a-3) is very different. Similar analysis of the light hydrocarbons extracted from pyrolysis of the Clair oil asphaltenes show a different pattern, indicating a different source (Rooney *et al.* 1998).

lighter profile of the 205/26a-3 sample (Solan/Strathmore area). The 205/26a-3 sample shows no evidence of biodegradation and is considered to be early mature oil, derived from the West Shetland Basin and generated at low thermal conditions. It has been generated from a Type IIS kerogen and deposited under highly anoxic conditions, similar to that sampled in the West Lewis Basin.

Basin modelling

Using BasinMod™ 1D software, all available wells in the NE Atlantic margin basins were calibrated to vitrinite reflectance, apatite fission track and temperature data, where these data were available. New fluid inclusion data were also incorporated into the models as a further check.

Kinetics

Customized kinetic models were derived (Mobil Technical Centre) from samples in the FSB and the West Lewis and West Flannan basins. Middle Jurassic Type I and Type I/II and KCF facies Type IIS source rocks were identified. Figure 10 compares the rate of reaction of these versus standard kinetic models under the same temperature history. Note how the Type IIS kerogen reacts with earliest generating oil at the lowest thermal conditions. Understanding the uncertainty in kinetic models is important to sensitivity analysis.

Temperature calibration

The most sensitive input to modelling simulation is temperature, yet it is the most poorly constrained. Temperature data, obtained from corrected bottom-hole temperatures in wells, is generally confined to the basin margins and structural highs. These data do not have a high degree of accuracy. However, there is a broad trend of increasing temperature gradients to the northwest. Control on this trend is extremely limited to the south with few control points in the RT and the northern limits of the Erris Trough. The impact of temperature errors in modelling can be very large. A $\pm 10\%$ error in heat flow can produce a significant variation in timing and amounts of hydrocarbons generated. The errors are similar in magnitude to those introduced if the wrong kinetic model is selected.

Sensitivity analysis, using 1D burial history modelling, examined the effects of uncertainties in temperature input to the basin models. Figure 11 shows the outcome of sensitivity analysis on five burial history cases derived from a 'pseudo-well'. Each output is in terms of oil generation timing and shows end member results. These cases represent the most influential factors in the basin modelling performed. Cases 4 and 5 are considered to be extreme and least likely to occur. Case 1 is the geological best estimate where it is assumed that depth and heat flow input have been calibrated to a nearby well. Introducing error bars of increasing complexity shows the sensitivity of the timing of oil generation. Compounded errors are shown in Cases 4 and 5.

The impact of the late Paleocene magmatic event affecting a large part of the study area, is neither uniform nor well understood. Wells such as 214/28-1 (Fig. 12) show the result of local, low impact contact metamorphism and possible hot fluid circulation. However, palaeotemperature indicators such as apatite fission track and vitrinite reflectance, show little evidence of elevated regional heat flow. For sub-regional 2D modelling, the local effects of the magmatic event together with the negligible effects occasioned by rift associated heat flow anomalies (as discussed earlier) have been ignored.

Two-dimensional modelling

2D modelling using BasinMod™ was performed along a number of regional seismic lines across the UK Atlantic margin. Qualitative assessment of the timing, maturation, migration and accumulation of hydrocarbons can be made with this method of modelling. The technique integrates available data (e.g. maturity, temperature and source-rock kinetics) with interpretation (e.g. depth conversion, uplift history, and lithology distribution). Source, timing and migration risks within the petroleum system can then be assessed and evaluated during prospect generation.

Two cross-sections are presented. Section A–A′ (Fig. 13) lies across the southwest end of the FSB from the Rona Ridge, crossing the Westray Ridge into the 'White Zone'. Section B–B′ (Fig. 14) lies in the North Rockall Trough from the West Lewis Ridge towards the Darwin igneous centre.

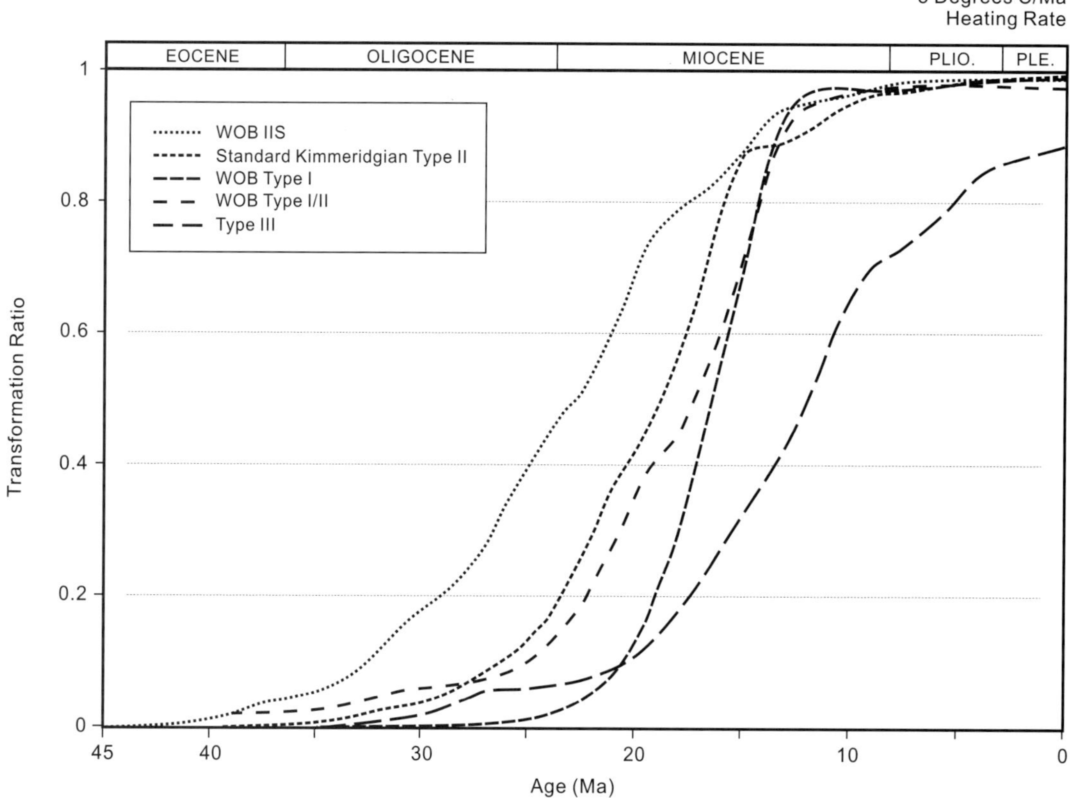

Fig. 10. Rates of reaction for different kinetic models. Using a standard burial rate and a constant heating rate, there is a significant difference between 'standard' kinetic models and customized kinetic models derived from sampled source rocks in the area.

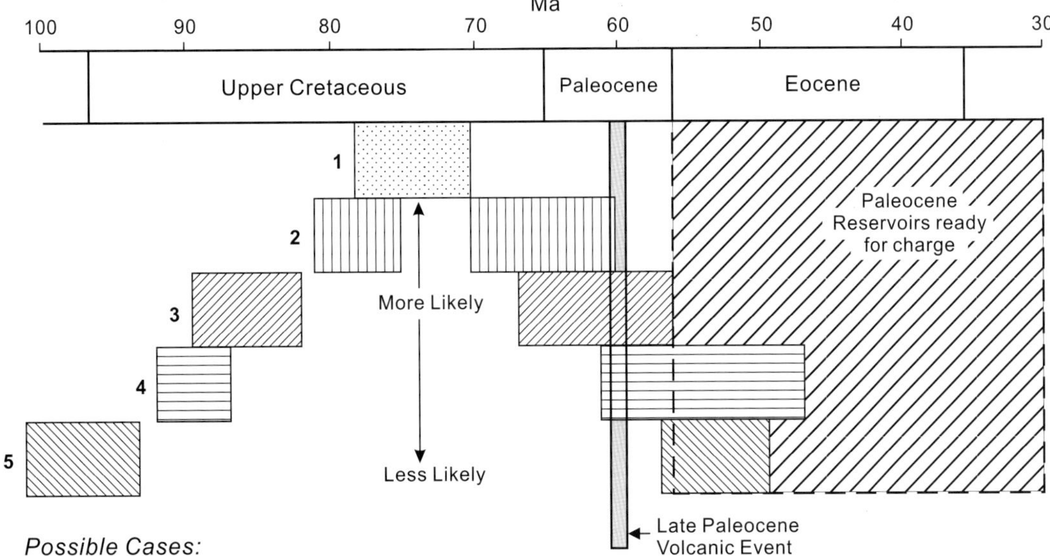

Fig. 11. Sensitivity analysis. Timing of oil generation differs according to different burial and thermal histories as shown in this matrix.

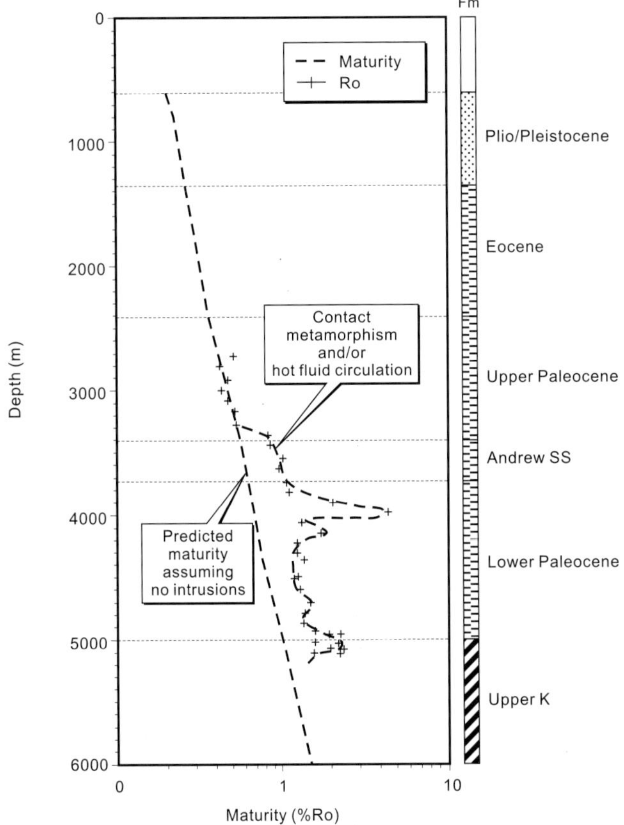

Fig. 12. Impact of an igneous intrusion on thermal maturity. Well 214/28-1 displays the localized low impact of a thin intrusive unit plus associated hot fluids, on thermal maturity (as expressed by R_0).

Model parameters

Section A–A′ has a small number of 1D calibration wells close by, while Section B–B′ only has a single nearby well located on the basin margin. This well is not considered to be a true reflection of the section believed to be present in the basin and the input stratigraphy to the model is thus based on regional mapping.

Calibration from the 1D models suggests that a constant heat flow model is appropriate in both cases. Section A–A′ is modelled with a heat flow of $48\,\mathrm{mW\,m^{-2}}$ while $50\,\mathrm{mW\,m^{-2}}$ is modelled in Section B–B′.

Palaeobathymetry data were derived from structural cross-section balancing and palaeontological evidence. Lithological input was based on well data and depositional models, whilst thermal conductivity values for each lithology were generally derived from BasinMod^{TM} defaults checked against additional measurements.

Three unconformities were defined in the models: at 'Base Cretaceous', 'Base Tertiary' and 'Miocene' levels. 1D modelling showed that from a maturation perspective, the amounts of missing section represented by these unconformities has no impact. 'Base Cretaceous' uplift occurs too early. In the kitchen areas, 'Base Tertiary' and Miocene uplift is generally <500 m and is insufficient to significantly affect thermal maturity of Jurassic source rocks. The 2D models reflect the variation in uplift from basin margins to basin centres.

On Section A–A′, a Type II kinetic model (Espitalié *et al.* 1988) was used for the Upper Jurassic. The Middle Jurassic source rocks were modelled using custom kinetics generated from well samples in the area most closely resembling a Type I kerogen. Only Upper Jurassic source rocks were modelled on Section B–B′ (Fig. 14). Again, the Upper Jurassic kinetic model was for a Type II kerogen.

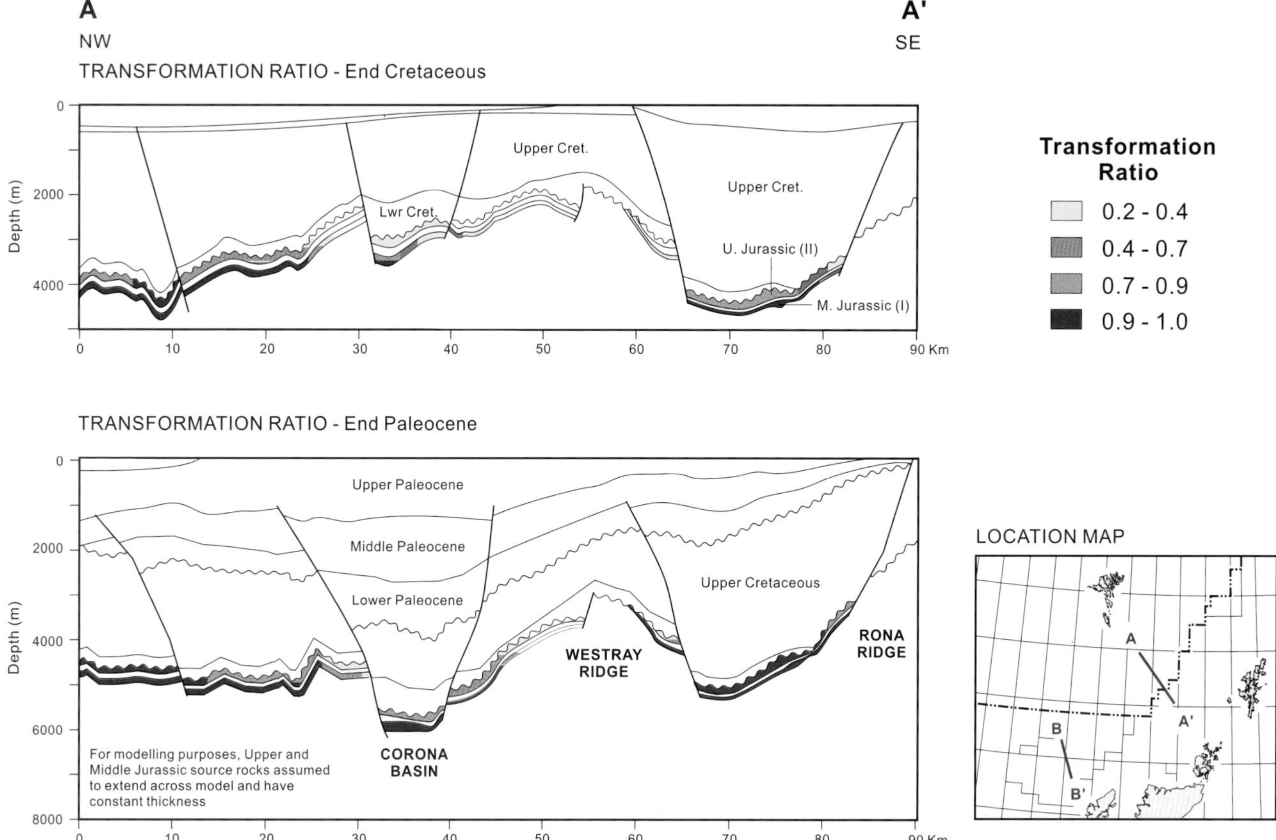

Fig. 13. Transformation ratio through time along a regional seismic line in the southwest Faeroes–Shetland Basin.

Maturation

Figures 13 and 14 display maturation levels as transformation ratio of the original kerogen to hydrocarbon. On Section A–A′, beneath Cretaceous depocentres, local early oil generation from the Upper Jurassic began during the mid Cretaceous. Oil generation peaked by the late Cretaceous and gas was being generated during the Paleocene. The less reactive Middle Jurassic source rock began generating during the early part of the late Cretaceous but then rapidly became post-mature by Paleocene times. Beneath Paleocene depocentres such as the Corona Basin, oil generation began from the Upper Jurassic source rock during the late Cretaceous, peaking during mid–late Paleocene times. Middle Jurassic source rocks are post-mature by mid–late Paleocene times in the basins but were generating oil on the up-dip flanks of the Corona Basin.

The modelled source rock on Section B–B′ lies at significantly shallower depths than on Section A–A′, resulting in much later generation. Early oil generation commenced in basinal areas and in the hanging walls of major Cretaceous faults during late Cretaceous–early Paleocene times.

The peak period for oil generation was during the late Paleocene–early Eocene. By the end of the Eocene, most of the basin passed through the oil window and progressed rapidly to a post-mature stage. In the deeper parts of the basin, gas generation began by mid–late Eocene times. At present, the intrabasinal Mesozoic highs, and the flanks of the West Lewis Ridge are modelled to be still generating oil and gas.

Expulsion and migration

BasinMod^{TM} 2D performs a coupled, three-phase fluid flow calculation. Expulsion from the source rock is modelled using the pressure–fracture expulsion model (Düppenbecker *et al.* 1991). Migration of hydrocarbons from source to reservoir intervals is a complex and non-specific process, reflected in the complex oil charging history discussed earlier. Using Section A–A′ and fluid flow modelling (BasinMod^{TM} 2D), Fig. 15 illustrates the variation of oil saturation through time, and how oil and gas migration vectors might charge reservoirs at various stratigraphic levels.

In the late Paleocene time slice, Upper Cretaceous depocentres such as between the Westray and Rona ridges, generated hydrocarbons first (Fig. 15). Buoyancy drive moved hydrocarbons up-dip through carrier systems towards the basin margins. Additionally, the high sedimentation rates in these areas lead to overpressure and fracturing. Vertical expulsion then slowly moved hydrocarbons through thick, lower permeability Cretaceous sequences, or more rapidly via Cretaceous deep water or shallow marine sandstones. Oil reservoired in shallow middle Paleocene sandstones could then be subject to biodegradation.

In the Paleocene depocentres such as the Corona Basin, again, very high sedimentation rates lead to overpressure in both Lower Paleocene and Upper Cretaceous mudstones, possibly resulting in vertical migration through pressure-fracturing. In this model, migration is primarily via fault conduits to the west and east; flank oil migration is focused along Jurassic and Lower Cretaceous carrier beds to the old highs (e.g. Westray Ridge). Paleocene faulting could result in rapid vertical migration into Lower Paleocene reservoirs while vertical pressure-fracture controlled migration continues at a slower rate. Later cracking to gas, (if any oil remains in the source rock or in Jurassic–Lower Cretaceous reservoirs), or primary gas generated from the source rock, may have flushed some oil, up-dip to the basin flanks.

The relative rates of migration via these different processes would result in different pulses of hydrocarbon charge to

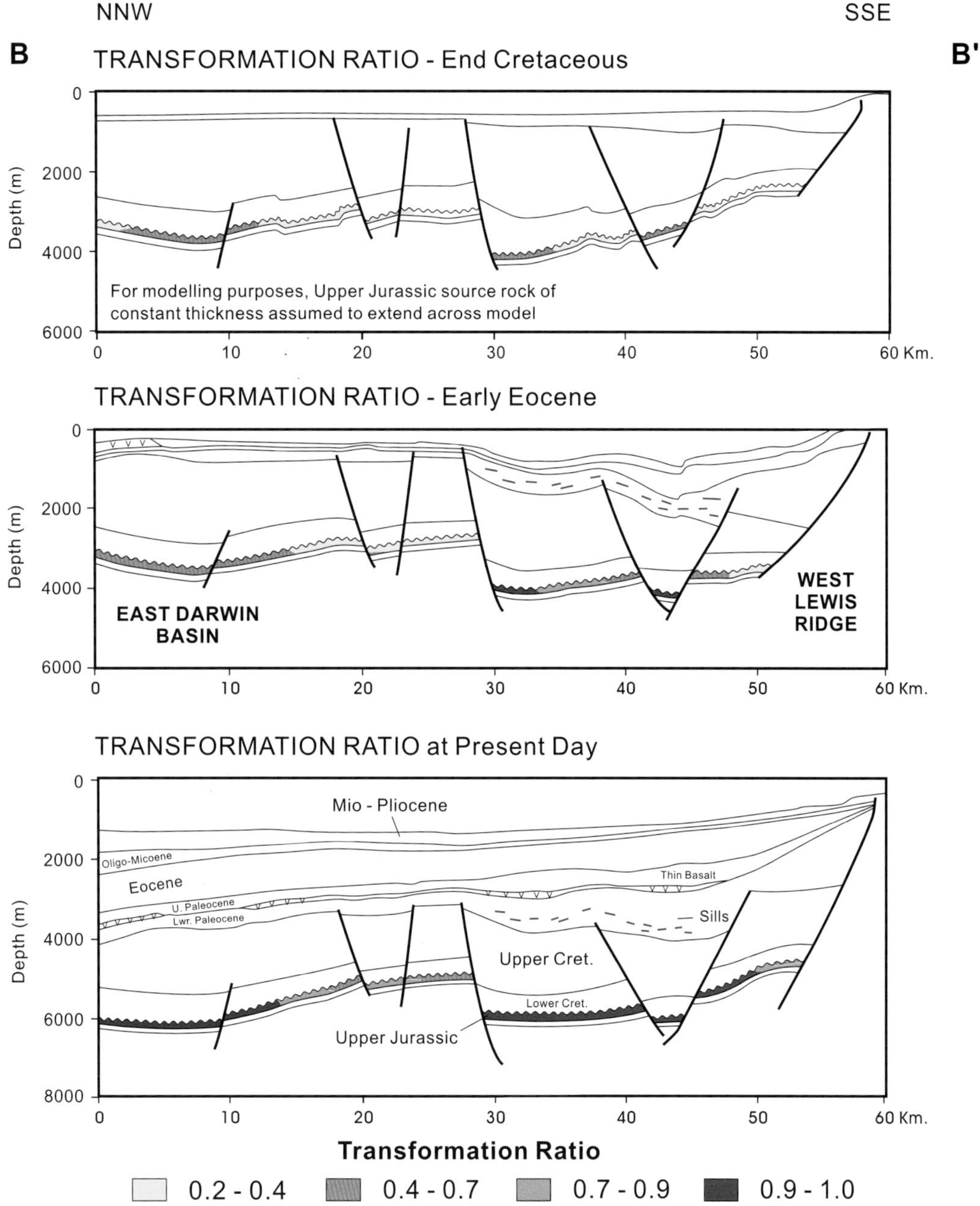

Fig. 14. Transformation ratio through time along a regional seismic line in the northern Rockall Trough.

reservoirs ranging from latest Paleocene through to the Oligo–Miocene. Conventional GC-MS, biomarker, fluid inclusions and CSIA studies support this hypothesis of multiple phases of hydrocarbon charging.

Migration pathways

Back-stripped and orthocontoured regional structure maps at Base Cretaceous level over the FSB are shown in Fig. 16a and b, for end Cretaceous and end Paleocene times. They indicate migration routes for essentially buoyancy-driven migration pathways. These maps only display orthocontours from areas of Cretaceous and Paleocene depocentres. These areas are considered to be regions of predominantly late Cretaceous/early Tertiary and late Paleocene/post Paleocene generation and expulsion. This display allows risk associated with timing of migration into various stratigraphic levels to be evaluated. Vertical migration routes are primarily via fault conduits and pressure fracturing. Once hydrocarbons have migrated away from the source rock by these methods, sand fairway overlay maps can then high-grade prospective areas. Similar maps can be generated in areas where Eocene (or later) depocentres delay maturation and migration longer and thus increase oil prospectivity.

The orthocontours in Fig. 16a illustrate how the Clair Field and the accumulations in southern Quadrant 204 drain Cretaceous depocentres during late Cretaceous times and could receive a hydrocarbon charge. Figure 16b shows how the Paleocene depocentres have shifted to the west at the southwest end of the FSB and that southern Quadrant 204 receives a significant charge from the north. In the central FSB, the Paleocene depocentre has shifted northwest of the Flett Ridge. Later charging of the Clair Field from this area is unlikely. The later charge is probably from more terrestrially dominated KCF on the basin flanks and not from the main depocentres to the northwest.

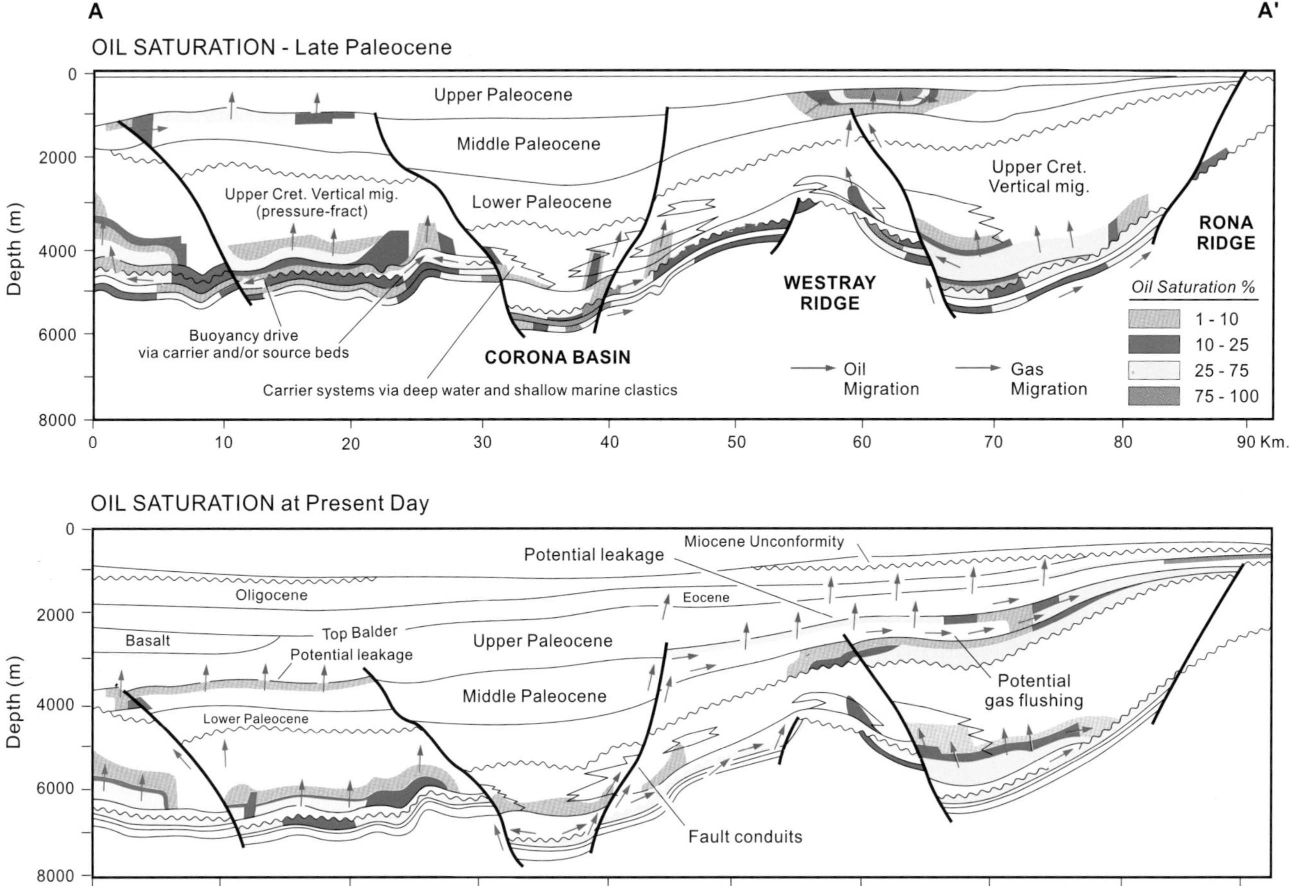

Fig. 15. Oil saturation during the late Paleocene and at present-day along section A–A′ (Fig. 19). The model demonstrates migration concepts and highlights the importance of buoyancy drive and vertical migration via both pressure-fracturing and fault conduits.

Play assessment

The timing chart in Fig. 17 illustrates the components of the petroleum system in a number of sub-basins along the UK Atlantic margin. This chart allows a rapid comparison of these areas and the plays within them. Play assessment maps combine modelled source maturation (with appropriate timing) and migration risk with the presence and effectiveness of reservoir and vertical seal. An example play assessment map for the pre-Jurassic play is shown in Fig. 18. These maps illustrate the play risk within the play fairway i.e. the chance of finding one hydrocarbon accumulation in that play. Numeric values are assigned to these areas for incorporation into overall prospect chance of success.

Individual prospect assessment requires that the influence of mid–late Tertiary compression and subsequent re-configuration of traps and hydrocarbon accumulations be taken into account during risk analysis.

Conclusions

There is prolonged and progressive rifting from the Permo-Triassic to the Paleocene along the NE Atlantic margin. This observation leads directly to a 'cool' rift model, low increases in heat flow and depocentre shifting with resultant effects on the modelled generation and migration history. Mid–late Tertiary compression generally has a more prospect-specific effect, re-distributing hydrocarbons and locally 'freezing' generating kitchens.

Upper and (to a lesser extent) Middle Jurassic intervals are the most important and effective source rocks encountered to date in the Atlantic margin basins, West of Britain. Geochemical analyses on both source rocks and oils indicates variable source-rock facies are present. Analysis of some of the oils discovered to date shows that they commonly contain biodegraded and 'fresher' components. This indicates a complex and varied charging history. To develop a greater understanding of these fill histories, new kinetic models were generated and multi-dimensional models were constructed. Integration of data and interpretations into the models, allowed qualitative assessment of the timing, maturation and accumulation of hydrocarbons in this petroleum system. The results of the geochemical analyses are supported by the 2D modelling and the migration pathway analysis.

Heat flow variations are relatively poorly constrained. However, increases in heat flow associated with Tertiary and Cretaceous rifting are not significant. Similarly, at a basin-wide level, additional heat introduced by Paleocene–Eocene magmatic activity is not a major factor.

Modelling has demonstrated the importance of Cretaceous and Paleocene depocentre shifting on the timing of maturation. Many areas were generating oil during late Cretaceous times with migration being focussed towards Mesozoic structures and the basin margins. For these areas to charge Tertiary reservoirs, re-migration, focussed through faulting and compressional events, is a requirement. In areas where rapid Paleocene subsidence has taken place, more favourable timing for Tertiary traps occurs.

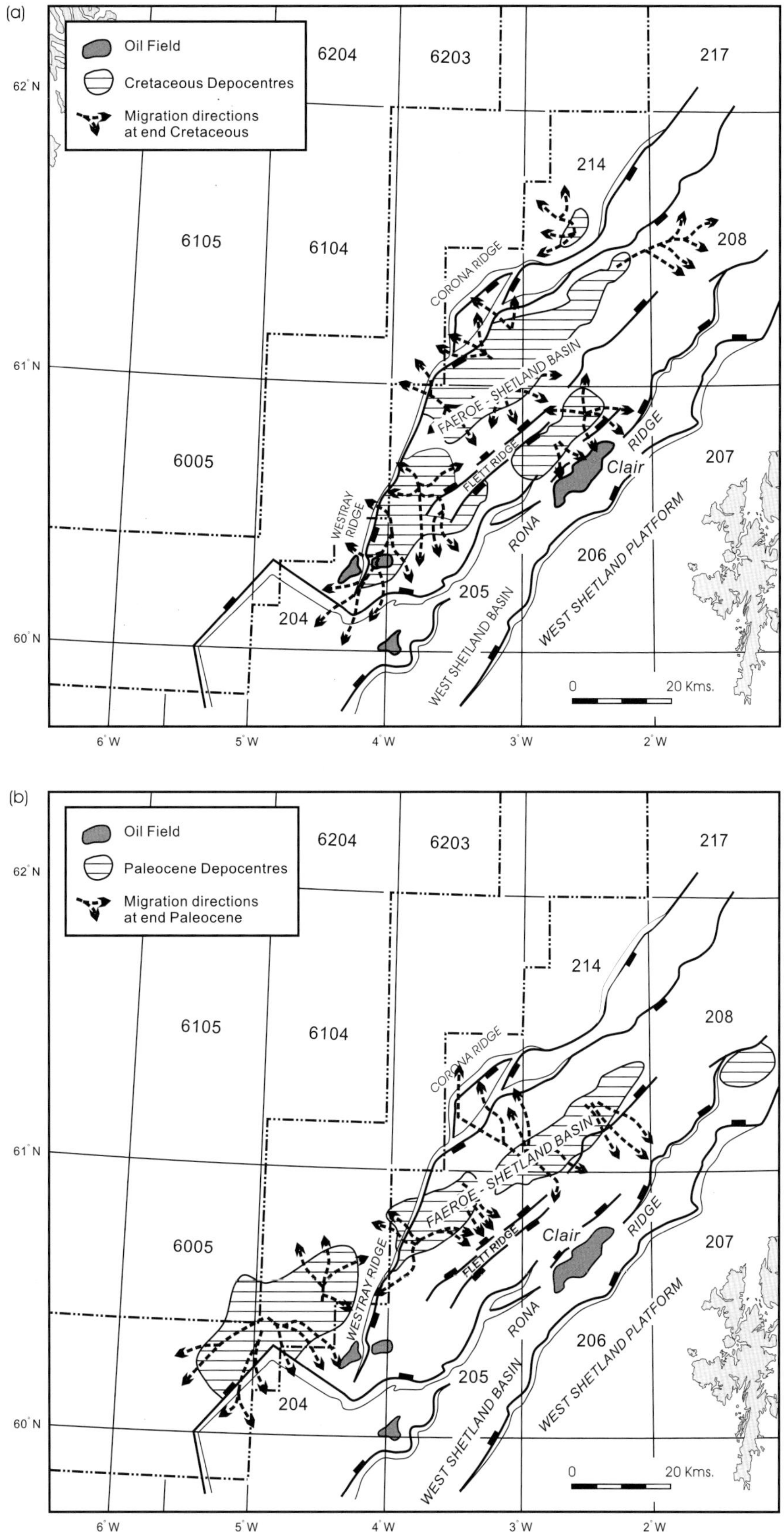

Fig. 16. (**a**) Migration directions out of Cretaceous depocentres from an Upper Jurassic source rock, back-stripped to end Cretaceous times. (**b**) Migration directions out of Paleocene depocentres from an Upper Jurassic source rock, back-stripped to end Paleocene times.

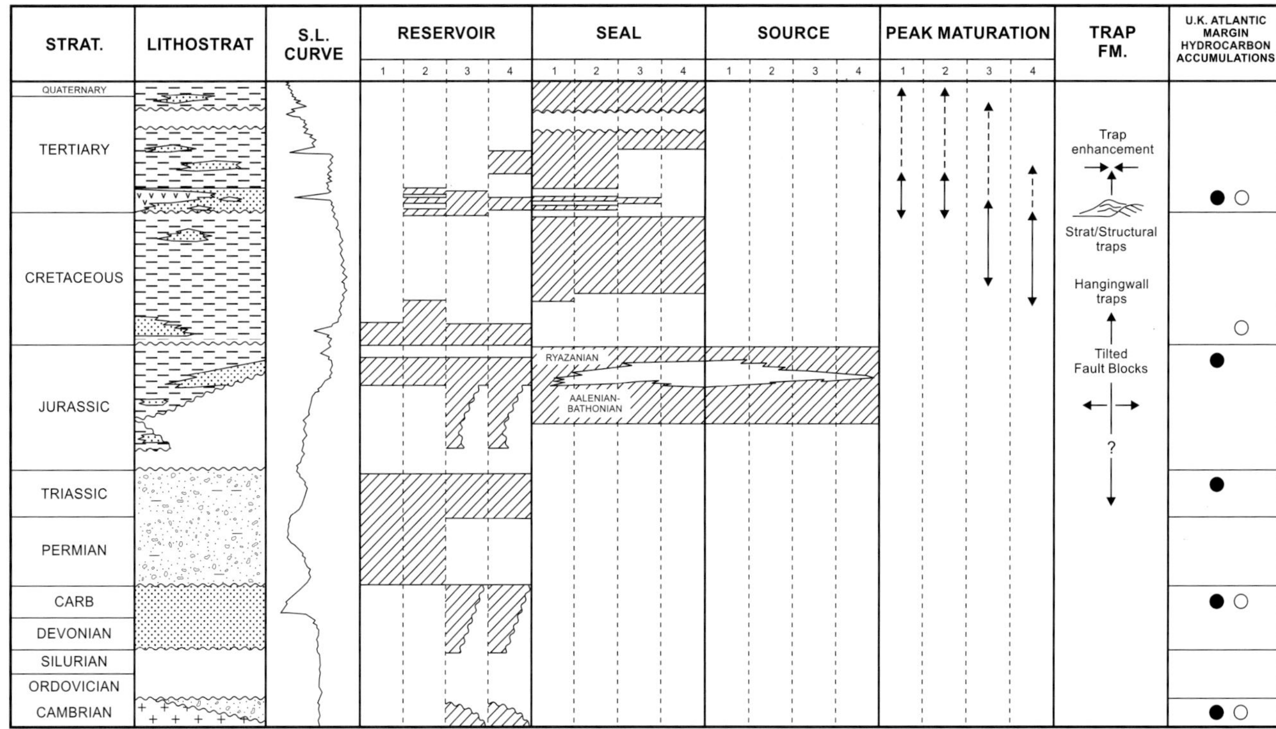

Fig. 17. Petroleum system events chart. The chart illustrates the relative timing of reservoir, seal and source-rock deposition, maturation and principal trap formation in 4 areas along the Atlantic margin. 1. South Rockall Trough; 2. North Rockall Trough; 3. Faeroes–Shetland area; 4. North Shetlands area. • = oil, ○ = gas.

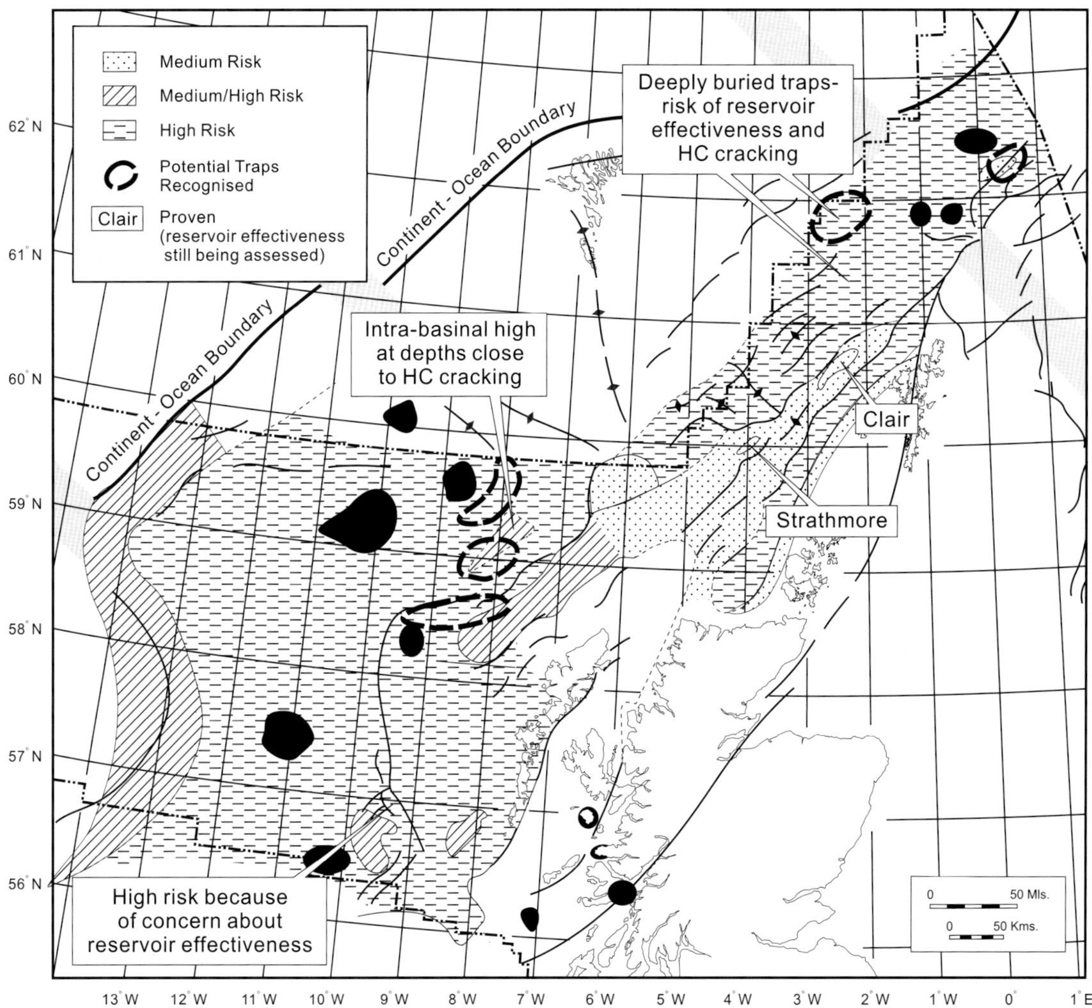

Fig. 18. Pre-Jurassic play assessment. The map incorporates the risk of effective reservoir and seal presence, source presence, level of maturation and timing. Areas of combined risk are then outlined. Black patches indicate igneous centres (see also Fig. 1).

The authors would like to thank the exploration management of Mobil North Sea Ltd, Enterprise Oil plc and Statoil (UK) for permission to publish this paper. Many of the concepts outlined in this paper result from the efforts of our co-explorationists. Special thanks are owed to A. Chambers and T. Doré for their vital input on the tectonic evolution of the study area and to Helen Naylor for her work on play/risk assessment. Editorial comments from M. Giles, J. McQuilken and S. Burley were greatly appreciated.

References

BOLDREEL, L. O. & ANDERSEN, M. S. 1993. Late Paleocene to Miocene compression in the Faeroe–Rockall area. *In*: PARKER, J. R. (ed.) *Petroleum Geology of Northwest Europe: Proceedings of the 4th Conference*. Geological Society, London, 1025–1034.

DEAN, K. P., MCLACHLAN, K. & CHAMBERS, A. 1999. Rifting and the Development of the Faeroe–Shetland Basin. *In*: FLEET, A. J. & BOLDY, S. A. R. (eds) *Petroleum Geology of Northwest Europe: Proceedings of the 5th Conference*. Geological Society, London, 533–544.

DORÉ, A. G. & LUNDIN, E. R. 1996. Cenozoic compressional structures on the NE Atlantic margin: nature, origin and potential significance for hydrocarbon exploration. *Petroleum Geoscience*, **2**, 299–311.

——, ——, FICHLER, C. & OLESEN, O. 1997. Patterns of basement structure and reactivation along the NE Atlantic margin. *Journal of the Geological Society, London*, **154**, 85–92.

DÜPPENBECKER, S. J., DOHMEN, L. & WELTE, D. H. 1991. Numerical modelling of petroleum expulsion in two areas of the Lower Saxony Basin, Northern Germany. *In*: ENGLAND, W. A. & FLEET, A. J. (eds) *Petroleum Migration*. Geological Society, London, Special Publications, **59**, 47–64.

ESPITALIÉ, J., UNGERER, P., IRWIN, I. & MARQUIS, F. 1988. Primary cracking of kerogens. Experimenting and modelling C_1, C_2-C_5, C_6-C_{15}, and $C_{15}+$ classes of hydrocarbons. *In*: MATAVELI, L. & NOVELLI, L. (eds) *Advances in Organic Geochemistry* 1987, Venice, *Organic Geochemistry*, **13**, 893–899.

HALL, B. D. & WHITE, N. 1994. Origin of anomalous Tertiary subsidence adjacent to North Atlantic continental margins. *Marine and Petroleum Geology*, **11**, 702–714.

HAQ, B. U., HARDENBOL, J. & VAIL, P. R. 1987. Chronology of fluctuating sea levels since the Triassic (250 Myr ago to present). *Science*, **235,** 1156–1167.

JARVIS, G. T. & MCKENZIE, D. P. 1980. Sedimentary basin formation with finite extension rates. *Earth and Planetary Science Letters*, **48**, 42–52.

KNOTT, S. D., BURCHELL, M. T., JOLLEY, E. J. & FRASER, A. J. 1993. Mesozoic to Cenozoic plate reconstructions of the North Atlantic and hydrocarbon plays of the Atlantic margins. *In*: PARKER, J. R. (ed.) *Petroleum Geology of Northwest Europe: Proceedings of the 4th Conference*. Geological Society, London, 953–974.

LUNDIN, E. R. & DORÉ, A. G. 1997. A tectonic model for the Norwegian passive margin with implications for the NE Atlantic: Early Cretaceous to break-up. *Journal of the Geological Society, London*, **154**, 545–550.

MUSGROVE, F. W. & MITCHENER, B. 1996. Analysis of the pre-Tertiary rifting history of the Rockall Trough. *Petroleum Geoscience*, **2**, 353–360

NADIN, P. A. & KUSZNIR, N. J. 1995. Paleocene uplift and Eocene subsidence in the northern North Sea Basin from 2D forward and reverse stratigraphic modelling. *Journal of the Geological Society, London*, **152**, 833–848.

PASSEY, Q. R., CREANEY, S., KULLA, J. B., MORETTI, F. J. & STOUD, J. D. 1990. A practical model for organic richness from porosity and resistivity logs. *American Association of Petroleum Geologists Bulletin*, **74**, 1777–1794.

RITCHIE, J. D. & HITCHEN, K. 1996. Early Paleogene offshore igneous activity to the northwest of the UK and its relationship to the North Atlantic Igneous Province. *In*: KNOX, R. W. O'B., CORFIELD, R. M. & DUNAY, R. E. (eds) *Correlation of the Early Paleogene in Northwest Europe*. Geological Society, London, Special Publications, **101**, 63–78.

ROONEY, M. A., VULETICH, A. K. & GRIFFITH, C. E. 1998. Compound specific isotope analysis as a tool for characterising mixed oils: an example from West of Shetland Islands. *Organic Geochemistry*, **29**, 241–254.

SCOTCHMAN, I. C. & DORÉ, A. G. 1995. A regional appraisal of source rocks north and west of Britain (Abstract) *American Association of Petroleum Geologists Bulletin*, **79**, 1247.

—— & THOMAS, J. R. W. 1995. Maturity and hydrocarbon generation in the Slyne Trough, Northwest Ireland. *In*: CROKER, P. F. & SHANNON, P. M. (eds) *The Petroleum Geology of Ireland's Offshore Basins*. Geological Society, London, Special Publications, **93**, 385–411.

——, GRIFFITH, C. E. & HOLMES, A. J. 1998. The Jurassic petroleum system north and west of Britain: a geochemical oil–source correlation study. *Organic Geochemistry*, **29**, 671–700.

SKOGSEID, J. 1994. Dimensions of the Late Cretaceous–Paleocene Northeast Atlantic rift derived from Cenozoic subsidence. *Tectonophysics*, **240**, 225–247.

TURNER, J. D. & SCRUTTON, R. A. 1993. Subsidence patterns in western margin basins: evidence from the Faeroe–Shetland Basin. *In*: PARKER, J. R. (ed.) *Petroleum Geology of Northwest Europe: Proceedings of the 4th Conference*, Geological Society, London, 975–983.

VERSTRALEN, I., HARTLEY, A. J. & HURST, A. 1995. The sedimentological record of a late Jurassic transgression: Rona Member (Kimmeridge Clay Formation equivalent), West Shetland Basin, UKCS. *In*: HARTLEY, A. J. & PROSSER, D. J. (eds) *Characterization of Deep Marine Clastic Systems*. Geological Society London, Special Publications, **94**, 155–176.

Petroleum systems analysis of the Paleocene play in the West of Shetland area

R. JOWITT,[1] A. HINDLE,[1,3] D. JONES[2] and P. ROSE[2]

[1] *Texaco Limited, 1, Westferry Circus, Canary Wharf, Texaco Limited, London E14 4HA, UK (e-mail: jowitrj@texaco.com)*

[2] *Texaco Limited, Langlands House, Huntly Street, Aberdeen AB10 1SH, UK (e-mail: jonesdj2@texaco.com, rosept@texaco.com)*

[3] *Present address: Egdon Resources (UK) Limited, Hallams Court, Littleford Lane, Blackheath, Guildford, Surrey GU4 8QZ, UK (e-mail: adh@globalnet.co.uk)*

Abstract: The Lower Tertiary petroleum system in the West of Shetland area has been reconstructed by integrating sequence stratigraphical interpretation, pressure data analysis and basin modelling with hydrocarbon migration pathways prediction.

Twelve sequences in the Paleocene–Early Eocene section can be grouped into three sequence sets. The lower two sequence sets are dominated by deep marine turbidite fan reservoir sandstones encased within hemipelagic shales. The youngest sequence set is dominated by a series of prograding delta facies rocks. A regionally extensive shale, deposited during a marine flooding event sits at the top of the oldest sequence set. This shale is an effective regional seal and pressure barrier. A study of well pressure data and sedimentary facies variations within the oldest sequence set has led to the identification of three pressure cells.

Structural modelling, heat flow mapping, vitrinite reflectance and apatite fission track analysis were used to reconstruct the thermal history West of Shetland. From this dataset, the Kimmeridge Clay Formation source-rock maturity and hydrocarbon generation history were modelled for several time periods. These results were used to generate migration pathways at the Base Tertiary unconformity which sits stratigraphically below the reservoirs in the oldest Paleocene to Eocene sequence set. The resulting model predicts an oil-prone southern province and gas-prone central province which accords with the Foinaven and Schiehallion oil fields in Quadrant 204 and the gas discoveries in Quadrants 206 and 214. The model also suggests the possibility of further oil potential in Quadrant 208.

The Paleocene play in the West of Shetlands area has been actively explored since the early 1980s. Although early results were disappointing with the discovery of gas in the northern and central parts of the basin, exploration interest was increased in the early 1990s with the discovery of BP's Foinaven and Schiehallion fields in Quadrant 204 (Cooper *et al.* 1999; Leach *et al.* 1999). Within the Paleocene section the trapping style is a combination of stratigraphical pinch-out with structural dip closure. Exploration of this play within the area requires integration of the structure, sedimentology and stratigraphical architecture of the principal reservoir horizons, with an understanding of the petroleum system.

In this paper, Texaco's sequence stratigraphical framework for the Paleocene is described and the distribution of fluids and formation pressures are reviewed. From this review the principal reservoir and seal horizons are established. The second half of the paper presents a map-based empirical model for the generation and migration of hydrocarbons within the Faeroes Basin, derived from the integration of structural, stratigraphical and geochemical interpretation.

Regional stratigraphical and structural context

The structural history of the West of Shetland area has been complex (Duindam & van Hoorn 1987; Earle *et al.* 1989; Stoker *et al.* 1993; Rumph *et al.* 1993) with Phanerozoic reactivation of inherited structural grains. The principal structural elements that define the many Mesozoic and Cenozoic depocentres are shown in Fig. 1. The area is divided at the base Cretaceous stratigraphical level into a number of sub-basins defined by four principal structural grains; NW–SE, NNE–SSW, E–W and NE–SW.

The post-Precambrian Basement stratigraphy of the area ranges from the Devonian to the Recent (Fig. 2). The Upper Carboniferous to Lower/Middle Jurassic intervals are not penetrated except in the Sula Sgier and Papa Basins where a thick Lower Jurassic to Triassic sequence has been encountered (Booth *et al.* 1993; Verstalen *et al.* 1995). Devonian to Lower Carboniferous red-bed sandstones and shales are present on many of the Lewisian Basement Highs; however, the main basin-fill consists of a variable thickness of Jurassic to Lower Cretaceous syn-rift rocks, including significant reservoir sandstones in the Upper Jurassic and Lower Cretaceous (Booth *et al.* 1993; Goodchild *et al.* 1999). Lundin & Doré (1997) indicate that the dominant basin axial trend switched from NNE–SSW in the Jurassic to a NE–SW direction in the Cretaceous, which has been confirmed by regional isopach maps for these intervals.

Post-rift sedimentation commenced during the Upper Cretaceous with marls, shales and thin limestones (with some sandstones at the base of the sequence) onlapping the syn-rift sequence. As a result of both sea-level rise and post-rift thermal subsidence, the old basins and basement ridges were buried beneath an argillaceous Upper Cretaceous section that is now up to 10 000 ft thick. An unconformity at the end Cretaceous/early Paleocene is identified by uplift and erosion on the basin margins and some structural highs.

An increase in subsidence related to thermal uplift and faulting occurred during the Paleocene to Lower Eocene. This was coincident with extensive volcanic activity; north of Quadrant 205, sills were intruded (Hitchen & Ritchie 1993) while volcanics were extruded over a large area to the northwest of the Corona Ridge and along the northeast margin of the West Shetland Platform.

JOWITT, R., HINDLE, A., JONES, D. & ROSE, P. 1999. Petroleum systems analysis of the Paleocene play in the West of Shetland area. *In*: FLEET, A. J. & BOLDY, S. A. R. (eds) *Petroleum Geology of Northwest Europe: Proceedings of the 5th Conference*, 1367–1381. Published by the Geological Society, London.

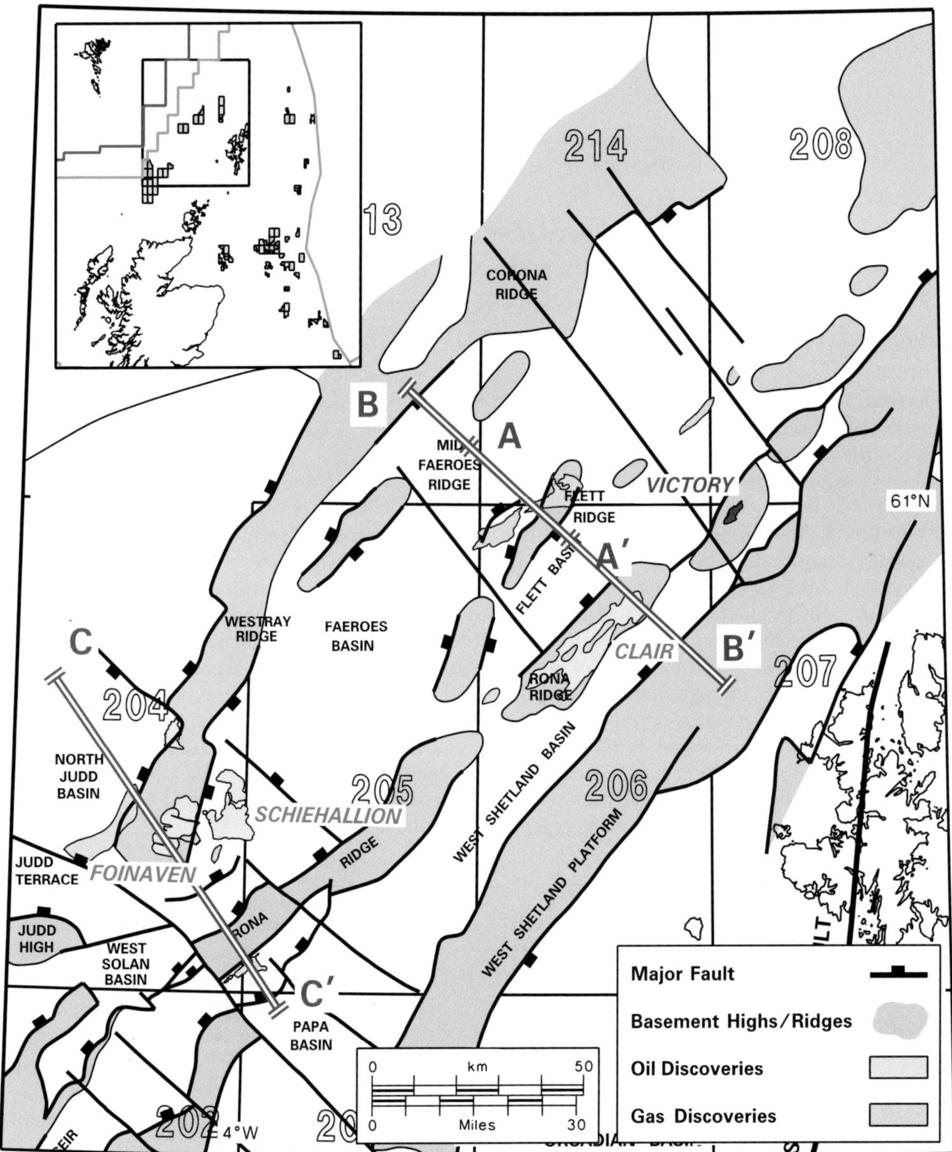

Fig. 1. Location map showing the main basement structural elements and the location of cross sections A–A′ (Fig. 4), B–B′ (Fig. 14a) and C–C′ (Fig. 14b).

Sedimentation during the Paleocene to Lower Eocene occurred within a pronounced NE–SW trough developed between the Flett and Corona Ridges. Upper Paleocene sediments consist of deep marine turbidites made up of interbedded reservoir quality sandstones and shales, overlain by a Lower Eocene deltaic system. This deltaic system was terminated by a major marine transgression.

During the Eocene to recent, a regressive sequence of north-westerly prograding shelf sands developed. Deposition was broken up by a period of uplift and erosion in the Oligocene–Miocene.

Lower Tertiary sequence stratigraphy

The importance of the Lower Tertiary of the West Shetland area as an exploration target was highlighted by a series of major gas and oil discoveries made in the late 1980s and early–mid 1990s. This interval comprises a series of clastic sedimentary rocks that were deposited in environments ranging from basinal marine to deltaic and alluvial plain. The complex lateral and vertical facies variations within this section create a significant stratigraphical-trapping component to most of the Tertiary oil and gas accumulations. Therefore an understanding of the Tertiary stratigraphical framework is fundamental to petroleum systems analysis in this area.

The Tertiary succession West of the Shetlands has been subdivided into sequence stratigraphical units by several companies (e.g. Mitchell *et al.* 1993, Ebdon *et al.* 1995) with low-stand (LST), transgressive (TST) and high-stand (HST) systems tracts all being identified. Texaco has interpreted 12 third-order sequences (Vail *et al.* 1977) in the Paleocene and Lower Eocene (Figs 3 and 4). The sequences boundaries picked in this framework are seismically defined surfaces that formed in response to relative sea-level fall. In wells the sequence boundaries are picked, in basinal settings, at the bottom of sharp based fan sands (Fig. 5). Condensed sections and maximum flooding surfaces (sensu. Galloway 1989) have also been picked on gamma ray maxima (Fig. 5), and biostratigraphically.

The oldest sequences, sequences 80 and 90 (Figs 3 and 5), consist of predominantly unprospective deep marine mudstones of Early Paleocene age intruded by basic sills. They are equivalent to the Sullom Formation of Knox *et al.* (1996) and

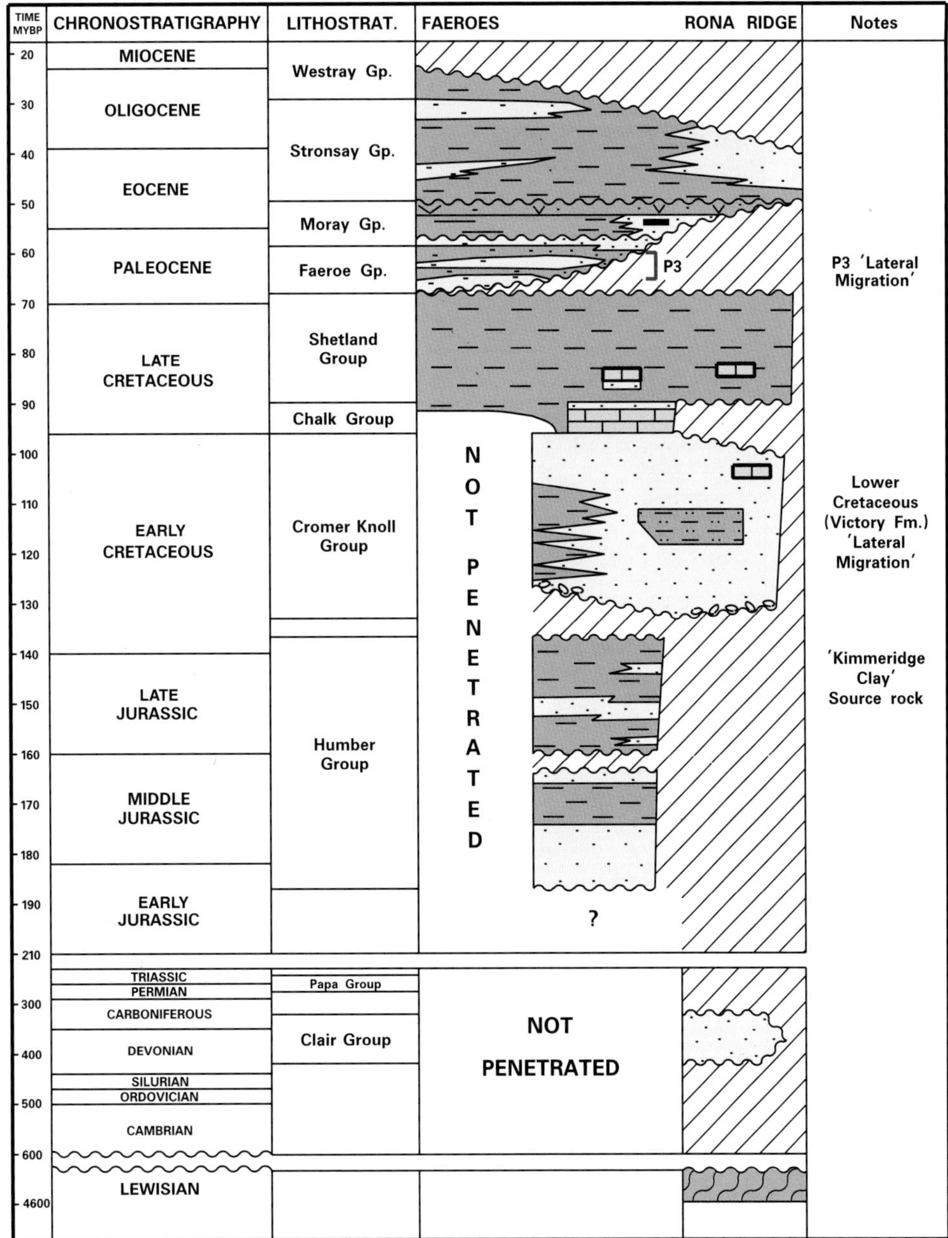

Fig. 2. General stratigraphy based on well penetrations in the Faeroes Basin to Rona Ridge area, West of Shetland.

are preserved in the central portion of the Faeroes Basin (e.g Quadrants 206 and 214). These mudstones were deposited in a fully marine basin with access to open oceanic circulation (as indicated by the occurrence of planktonic foraminifera).

Sequences 70 to 15 can be grouped into three sequence sets. The oldest sequence set, P3 (discussed in detail below), consists of three sequences 70, 62 and 60 which are equivalent to the Vaila Formation of the Faeroe Group (Knox *et al.* 1996). Sequence set P3 comprises a series of stacked turbidite sandstones that are important reservoirs. These are overlain by and separated by siltstones and hemipelagic shales which act as effective seals. Trap geometries consist of stratigraphic pinch-out combined with structural dip closure. Most hydrocarbon shows identified to date within the Paleocene to Lower Eocene have been from sequence set P3, probably as a result of a regional seal at the top of the sequence set (Fig. 3).

Sedimentologically sequence set P2 is similar to P3 but sandstones are more extensive. It consists of sequences 50 and 55 and is equivalent to the Lamba formation of Knox *et al.* (1996). P2 and P3 are separated by a change in basin geometry which will be discussed with sequence set P3 in the next section.

Sequence set P1 is dominated by a series of vertically stacked, low-stand deltas equivalent to the Flett Formation of Knox *et al.* (1996). The range of facies identified varies from alluvial plain in the SSE part of the area to pro-delta turbidites/mass flow sediments in the basinal area to the NNW (Well 214/28-1). Reservoir sands for both P2 and P1 sit stratigraphically above the regional seal interpreted in P3 and are therefore not considered to be highly prospective.

A major marine transgression coincident with deposition of the Balder Formation of Knox *et al.* (1996) terminated the P1 sequence set.

Sequence set P3

This Late Paleocene sequence set is dominated volumetrically by rocks deposited within low-stand and transgressive systems tracts. Collectively, they have a thickness of up to 6000 ft and

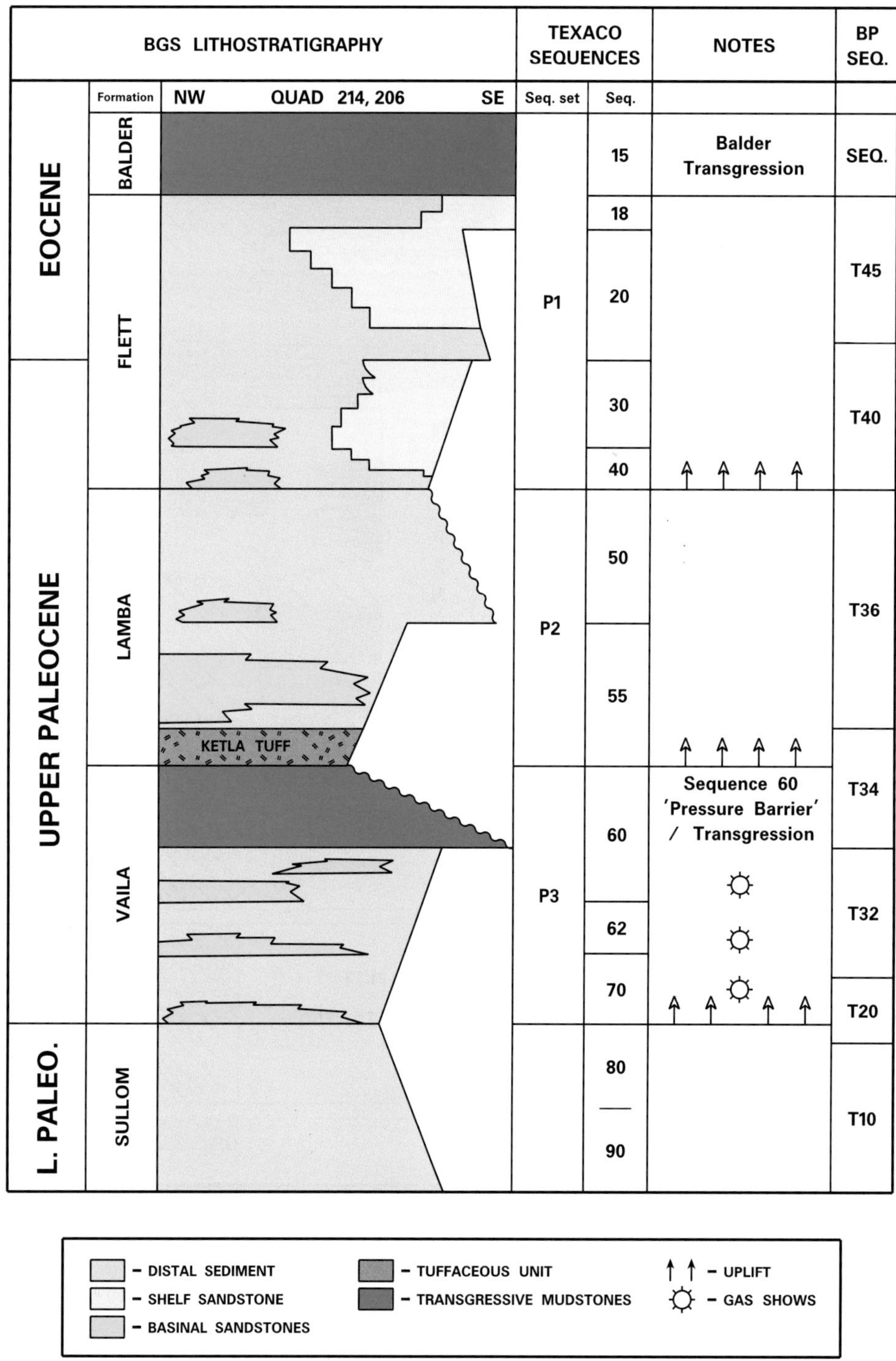

Fig. 3. Paleocene to Lower Eocene stratigraphy based on biostratigraphy and well log interpretation combined with seismic interpretation in Quadrants 214 and 206, West of Shetland. Lithostratigraphy based on Knox *et al.* 1997; BP scheme extrapolated from the Westray Ridge area taken from Ebdon *et al.* 1995.

are developed in the NE–SW trending Faeroe Basin located between the Flett and Corona Ridges/Mid Faeroes Ridge (Figs 1 and 4). They tend to be thin to absent on the shelf area to the southeast and to the west over the Corona Ridge/ Mid Faeroes Ridge (Fig. 4). Shelfal facies associated with low-stand and high-stand prograding complexes have not been definitively identified across much of the area because of subsequent erosion.

Sedimentary facies within sequence set P3 in the Faeroes Basin are composed of stacked turbidite sandstones. These are overlain by and separated laterally by siltstones and hemipelagic shales which act as effective seals. Individual turbidite fan complexes have been constrained by NNW–SSE and E–W structural lineaments. Movement along these lineaments creates intra-basin ridges which break up the overall NE–SW trending trough. This has resulted in a series of vertically and laterally isolated reservoir sandstone bodies separated by hemipelagic shales. Three major sub-troughs have been identified within the Faeroes Basin which are illustrated on Fig. 6 as low-stand fan thicks/low-stand fan areas.

The top of sequence set P3 is marked by a thick shale unit. It is suggested that the shale was deposited within the transgres-

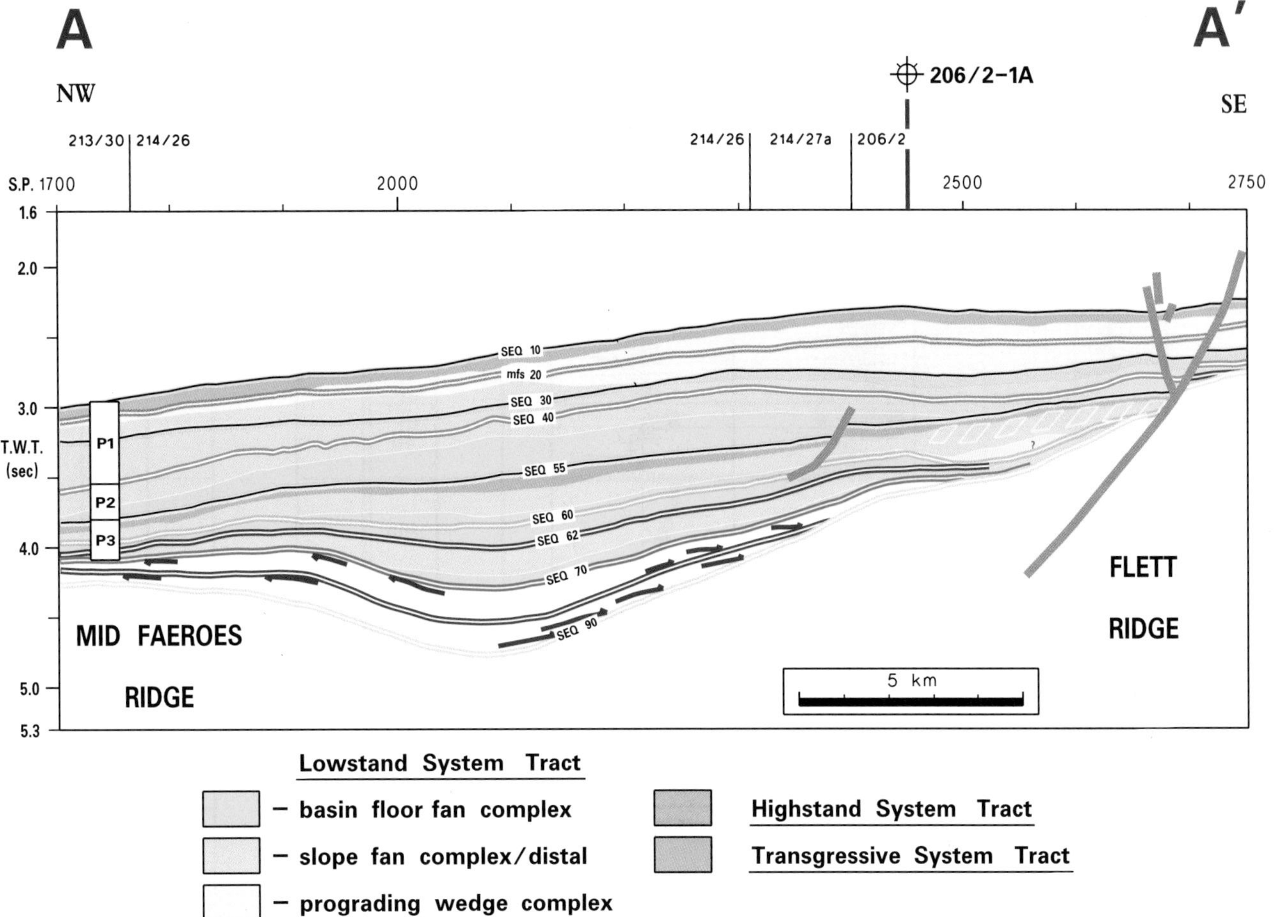

Fig. 4. NW to SE two-way time cross-section through the Faroes Basin illustrating Paleocene to Lower Eocene sequence distribution based on seismic interpretation, located on figure 1.

sive systems tract during a change in the tectonic style from rapid localized subsidence within the Faeroes Basin to a more regional and slower phase of subsidence. This resulted in a change in basin geometry from a deep NE–SW orientated trough to a more open, 'saucer-shaped' basin. This transition is coincident with the onset of volcanic activity over the Faeroes shelf associated with the extrusion of the Lower Faeroes Lava Series (Rasmussen & Noe-Nygaard 1970). It is marked in the area of study by the presence of volcaniclastic fragments in the basal turbidite fan of the subsequent sequence set P2 (Well 205/9-1 core) and is equivalent to the Ketla Member of Knox *et al.* (1996).

The change in basin geometry is important in allowing deposition of the sequence 60 shale across most of the Faeroes Basin, which, in the centre of the basin acts as an extensive top-seal for hydrocarbon migration. The study of the areal extent of such seals is critical to basin analysis (Downey 1984). Beneath the transgressive mudstone, oil and gas-condensate accumulations are reservoired within the stacked turbidite fan sandstones that are sealed laterally and vertically by deep marine shales, siltstones and mudstones.

Formation pressures and Paleocene formation water salinity

RFT pressure data for released wells has been plotted for the Paleocene sandstone reservoirs (Fig. 7). These data demonstrate the development of overpressure in sequence set P3, whereas the overlying sequences lie on a normal hydrostatic pressure gradient, indicating that the sequence 60 transgressive shale forms an effective regional seal in the northern and central parts of the Faeroes Basin. Indeed all significant hydrocarbon shows have been recorded from sequence set P3 or deeper in this area. Sequence set P3 can be divided into three principal pressure cells (Figs 7a and 8): a normally pressured cell in the south; an intermediate pressure cell centred on Quadrant 205; and an extensive pressure cell at approximately 600 psi above the normal hydrostatic gradient in the north of the basin.

Pressure data from the pre-Paleocene sequences demonstrate that reservoirs (8000 ft) on the shallowly buried Rona Ridge are at hydrostatic pressure but in the centre of the basin significant overpressure can be developed. In Well 204/19-1, drilled on the flanks of the Westray Ridge, the Lower Cretaceous section is 3800 psi overpressure; the overall pressure is close to the rock fracture gradient (0.8–1.0 psi ft^{-1}, Fig. 7b). Such elevated pressures confirm the sealing capacity of the Upper Cretaceous Shetland Group shales. Therefore it is speculated that elevated pressure may be present in deeply buried Mesozoic reservoirs on other undrilled basement ridges, for example the Flett Ridge.

Formation water salinity data are available from analysis of rare RFT samples (e.g. Well 208/19-1) and has been calculated from wireline logs for key wells. These data indicate that in the deeper parts of the basin, formation water salinities are notably fresh, the freshest waters being encountered in sequence set P3 (in the Flett Ridge area averaging at 8000 ppm total

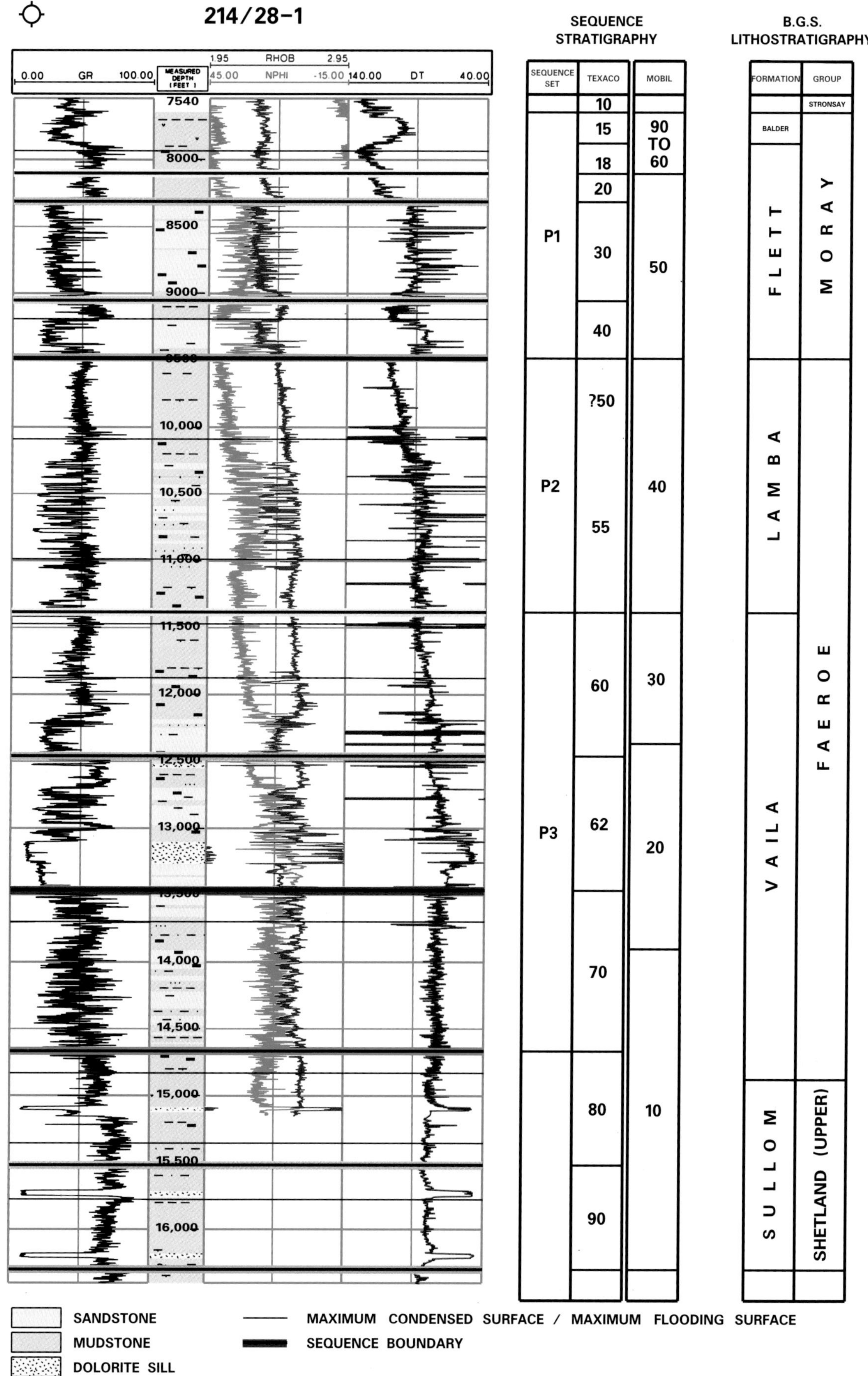

Fig. 5. Interpretation of the Paleocene to Lower Eocene in Well 214/28-1. BGS Lithostratigraphy based on Knox *et al.* 1996; Mobil sequence stratigraphy based on Mitchell *et al.* 1993.

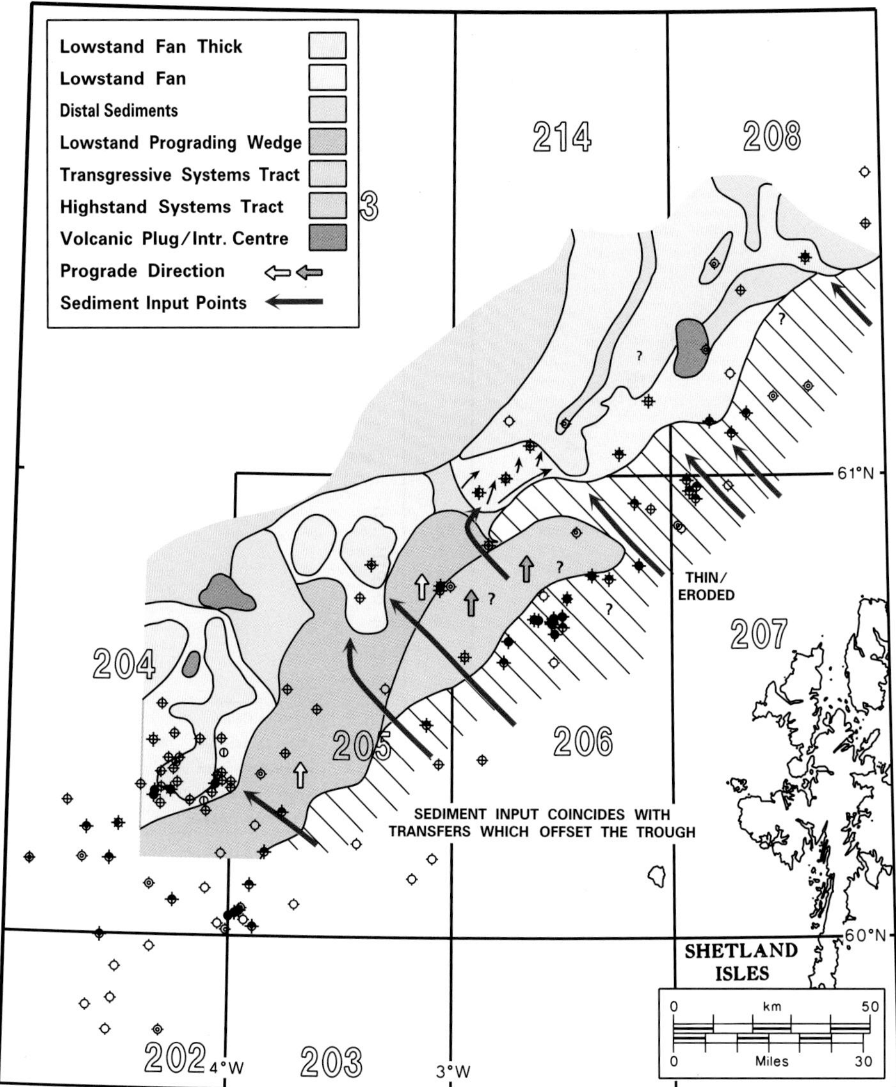

Fig. 6. Sequence set P3 stratigraphical palaeogeography, West of Shetland.

dissolved solids (TDS); (Well 208/19-1 with 2600 ppm TDS). More saline waters are encountered in the higher sequences. P1 reservoirs and P2 and P3 reservoirs at the margins of the basin have formation waters with normal seawater salinities (e.g. Well 214/29-1 with 33 000 ppm TDS).

Biostratigraphical analysis indicates that the sequence set P3 sandstones were deposited under normal marine conditions, therefore the fresh waters must have been introduced post-deposition. The simplest way in which this could have been achieved is flushing by meteoric water. It is proposed that this would have occurred during the establishment of deltaic environments across the whole basin in P1 times, with fresh water flushing the P3 reservoirs before the development of overpressure. This implies that the P3 transgressive shale did not become a regional seal until it was sufficiently compacted after the deposition of sequence P1 in the Eocene. Meteoric water influx into the basin may have been responsible for the biodegradation of an early oil charge in the Clair Field (Scotchman & Griffith 1996; Holmes *et al.* 1999). Subaerial exposure of parts of the basin also occurred during later periods, for example during the Oligo–Miocene inversion, which provided other opportunities for meteoric water influx.

Basin modelling inputs and methodology

Methodology

The modelling approach used in this evaluation is a technique based on gridded map inputs. The model reconstructs the basin structure back through time by using a simple vertical decompaction model which takes into account erosion. The source rock and generation model are empirical, with generated hydrocarbon volumes derived by the combination of calibrated thermal history and source rock isopach and source rock richness maps with experimental data on hydrocarbon transformation from similar source rocks.

Inputs consisted of present-day structure maps, palaeo-erosion maps, source rock isopach and richness maps and heat flow maps over time. The modelling was performed using an in-house program in conjunction with ZMAP software (Landmark Corporation). Outputs were maturity maps for the top and bottom of the source rock interval, generated hydrocarbons for five time intervals and palaeo-structure maps. Additionally, hydrocarbon migration pathways were predicted using the software programme PATHWAYS of Geofocus Limited.

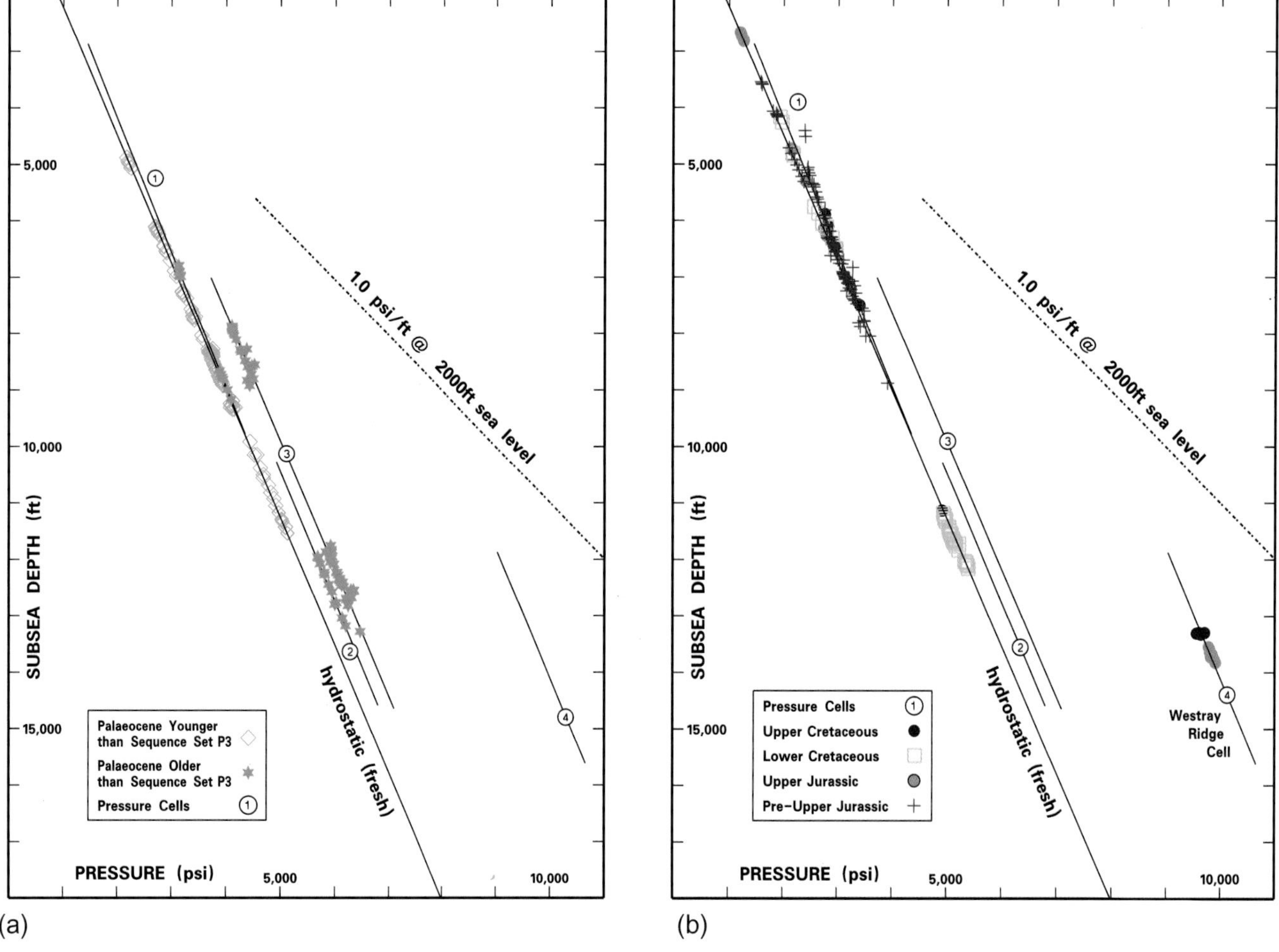

Fig. 7. (**a**) RFT pressure versus depth graph, Paleocene to Lower Eocene section, West of Shetland. (**b**) RFT pressure versus depth graph, Mesozoic section, West of Shetland.

Structure map and Palaeo-erosion inputs

Five present-day structure maps were derived from regional seismic mapping in the West of Shetlands area at the following stratigraphic levels: Miocene Unconformity, Top sequence set P1 (Top Balder Formation), Base Tertiary Unconformity, Top Lower Cretaceous and Base Cretaceous Unconformity. These maps were vertically decompacted to produce palaeo-structure maps which were used to constrain the time intervals modelled (Lower Cretaceous, Upper Cretaceous, Paleocene to Lower Eocene, Lower Eocene to Oligocene and the Miocene to Recent).

Two principal erosional events were modelled at base Paleocene and in the Oligo–Miocene; with the magnitude of these events estimated from shale velocity studies, vitrinite reflectance profiles, apatite fission track analysis and observation of truncation on structural cross-sections. These were used to constrain maturation and palaeo-structural development.

Source rock inputs

In this study the only source rock modelled is the Kimmeridge Clay Formation (Bailey *et al.* 1987; Scotchman & Griffith 1996). The results of in-house geochemical analysis indicate that the Kimmeridge Clay Formation contains an average TOC (total organic carbon) of 7% (maximum 15%), and pyrolysis data indicate hydrocarbon generation potential. Also, a comparison of the C_{27}, C_{28} and C_{29} sterane distribution indicates a good correlation between the Kimmeridge Clay Formation source rocks and the West of Shetland oils.

Two key input maps, source rock thickness and source rock richness (genetic potential, S1 plus S2 from pyrolysis data), were generated from well control and from a geological model for the Upper Jurassic basin configuration dominated by NNE–SSW faults. Both of these parameters are assumed to increase towards the Mesozoic basin centre, away from the well control.

Thermal history

Heat-flow maps were generated for each time interval to be modelled (listed earlier). For the Miocene to Recent time interval, the present-day surface heat flow across the basin was used. Present-day heat flow was estimated from well bottom hole temperatures using Platt River Associate's BASINMOD software and contoured to conform to the present-day structure. Values along the Rona Ridge trend ($65\,mW\,m^{-2}$) are higher than those observed in the basin centre ($45\,mW\,m^{-2}$). Heat flow maps for the other intervals were derived using heat flow ranges typical of rift basins, calibrated so that the final predicted maturity map at Base Cretaceous (Fig. 9) tied extrapolated well vitrinite reflectance profiles.

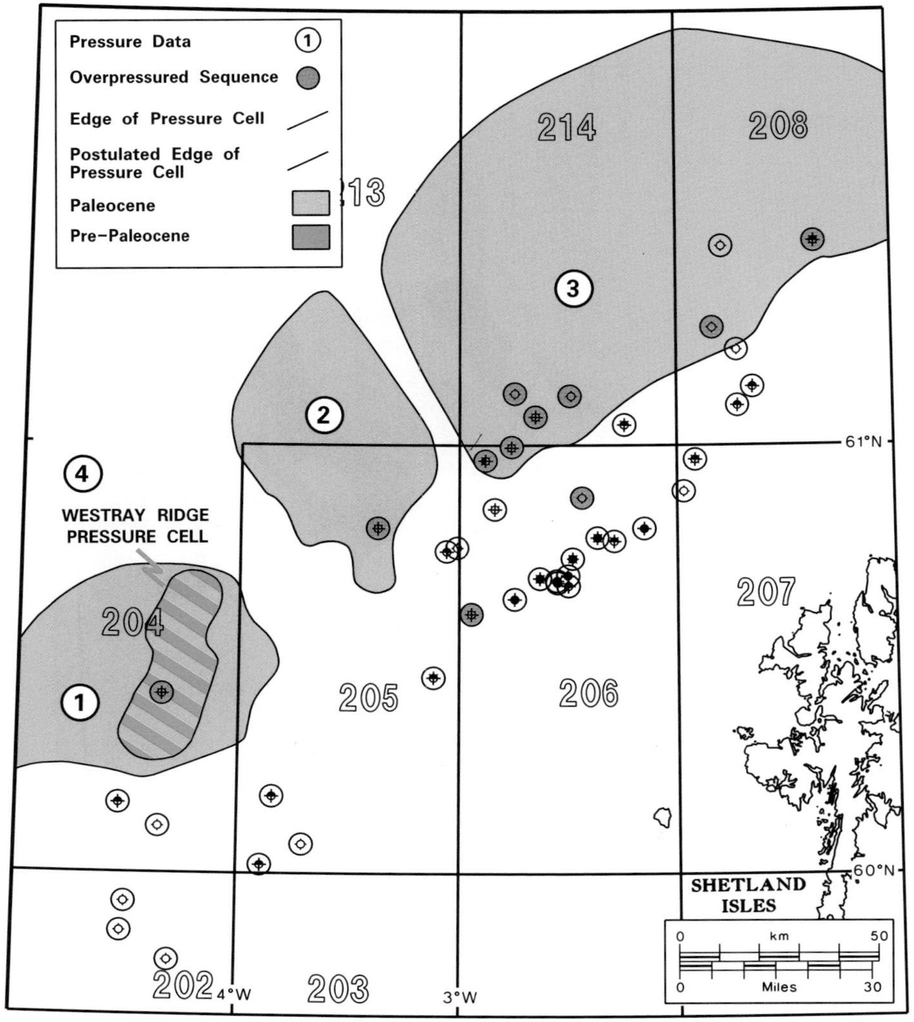

Fig. 8. Areal distribution of abnormal pressure cells highlighted in Fig. 7a and b, West of Shetland.

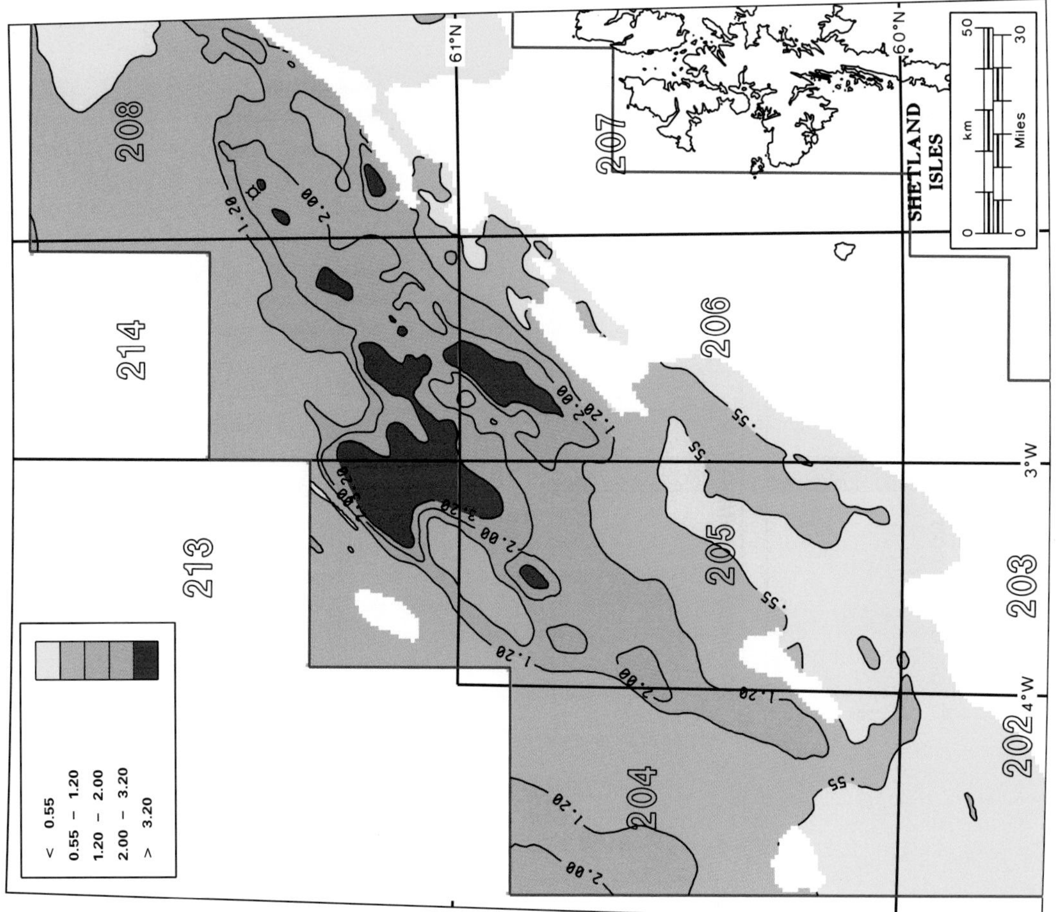

Fig. 9. Present-day predicted vitrinite reflectance at Top Kimmeridge Clay Formation. Map ties extrapolated from actual well data.

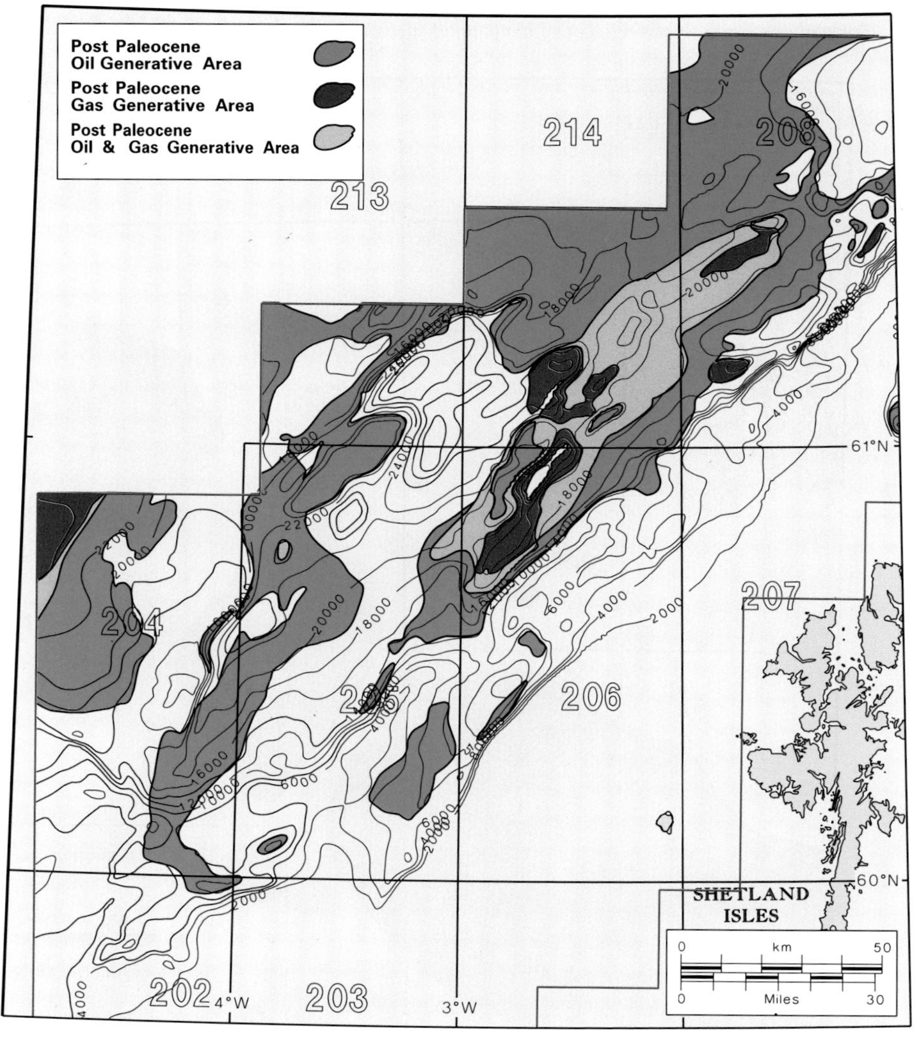

Fig. 10. Base Cretaceous unconformity, structure map in feet, contour interval equals 2000 ft. The post Paleocene generative areas of the underlying Kimmeridge Clay Formation are outlined.

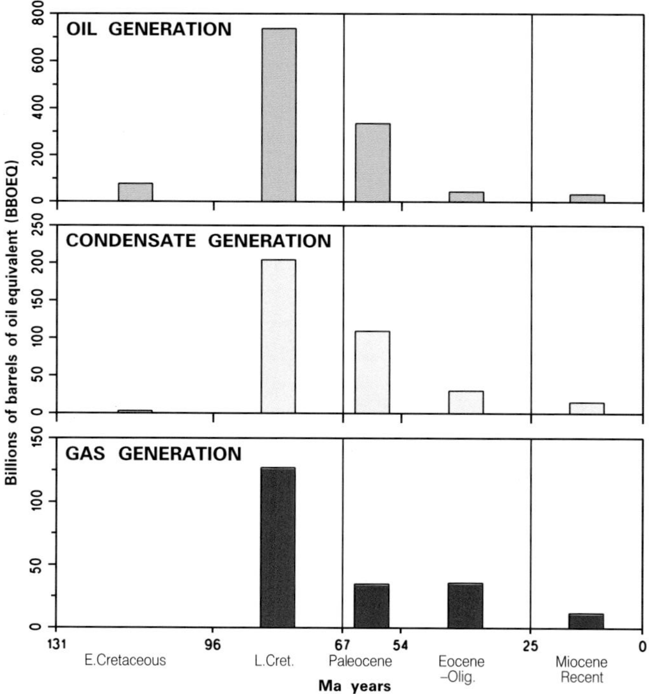

Fig. 11. Graph of hydrocarbon generation from the Early Cretaceous to the present-day, assuming a Kimmeridge Clay Formation source rock. Hydrocarbon volumes are derived by the combination of calibrated thermal history, source rock isopachs and source rock richness maps with experimental data on hydrocarbon transformation from similar source rocks.

Migration pathway methodology

Hydrocarbon migration pathways were predicted using the software programme PATHWAYS (Geofocus Limited) which assumes that the principal migration route is determined by buoyancy effects beneath a given sealing surface (Hindle 1997).

To model migration pathways, carrier beds and seal horizons must be identified. The stratigraphic analysis documented above indicates that there are extensive reservoirs at the Paleocene level with reservoirs also occuring at Upper Jurassic, e.g. Solan (Booth *et al.* 1993) and the Lower Cretaceous levels, e.g. Victory (Goodchild *et al.* 1999). The Upper Cretaceous provides a thick sequence of sealing shales. In the Paleocene, as discussed, pressure data demonstrate that the transgressive shale at the top of the Paleocene sequence set P3 provides a regional seal and in the northern and central parts of the basin, all significant Paleocene hydrocarbon shows occur in the stacked basin floor fans below this horizon.

Consequently, migration in the West of Shetlands was modelled as occurring at two horizons: base Cretaceous, to account for migration in pre-Upper Cretaceous reservoirs; and base Tertiary, to account for migration in sequence set P3. Figure 10 outlines the post-Paleocene generative area for the Kimmeridge Clay Formation superimposed on the base Cretaceous structure map (i.e. the top of the Kimmeridge Clay Formation). These outlines are the starting points for oil and gas migration pathways. Migration pathways were first predicted for the base Cretaceous level. Migration through the Upper Cretaceous into the Lower Paleocene (P3) occurred where either the Upper Cretaceous is absent, allowing the Paleocene to be in direct contact with Lower Cretaceous and Upper Jurassic reservoir, or by vertical migration associated with faults. The latter may occur by juxtaposition of Paleocene reservoirs with Lower Cretaceous/Upper Jurassic reservoirs or through fault-induced fracture conduits, during periods of structural displacement, located above intra-basinal highs where the Upper Cretaceous has a reduced thicknes. The potential for open fracture propagation from Upper Jurassic and Lower Cretaceous reservoirs through the Upper Cretaceous Shetland Group shales to the Lower Paleocene is suggested by the extreme overpressure (close to the fracture gradient) recorded in the Jurassic of Well 204/19-1 (Fig. 7b) on the Westray Ridge. The build-up of formation pressure may cause the faults to dilate and expel fluids as a result of 'seismic valving' (Sibson 1981; Burley *et al.* 1989; Burley & MacQuaker 1992). The zones of potential vertical migration into the Tertiary reservoirs were noted on the base Cretaceous structure map. The locations where the migration pathways, calculated at the base Cretaceous unconformity, intersected these zones subsequently became the starting points for migration of oil and gas at the base Tertiary unconformity.

Petroleum systems analysis

Results from the modelling indicate that continuous generation of hydrocarbons from the Kimmeridge Clay Formation, punctuated by periods of uplift and erosion during the Paleocene and Miocene, has occurred in shifting generative areas since the Lower Cretaceous. The majority of the hydrocarbons had been generated by the end of the Cretaceous (Fig. 11) with much of this charge lost through seepage from the flanks of the basin at this time or through the uplift and erosion that occurred during the early Paleocene. The Cretaceous sequence is thin to absent on the margins of the basin where the bulk of these early-generated hydrocarbons would have migrated. While it is likely that Cretaceous charge may account for some of the oil seen in the area (e.g. the Clair Field, Scotchman & Griffith 1996; Holmes *et al.* 1999), it is thought that little or none of this charge currently remains in the basin in an un-biodegraded state.

Significant hydrocarbons continued to be generated through the Tertiary (Fig. 11) and post-Paleocene generative areas are shown on the base Cretaceous unconformity structure map (Fig. 10). Note that the Kimmeridge Clay Formation in the deepest parts of the basin is post-mature by this time and the central Flett Ridge area is dominated by gas generation. The map also indicates significant oil potential in the south of the basin, as proven by the recent discoveries in Quadrant 204, and predicts further zones of oil potential along the Corona Ridge, on the flanks of the Rona Ridge and in the northern part of the basin. Tertiary migration caused by trap leakage or displacement of oil by a lighter charge has also been locally important.

Eocene to present charge maps are required to explain the hydrocarbon distribution in the Paleocene play. Figure 12 shows the predicted oil and gas migration maps for pathways at the base Tertiary structural horizon (Fig. 13) during the Paleocene to recent time period. The migration pathways for the base Tertiary section commence at intra-basinal highs where vertical migration from the Lower Cretaceous and Upper Jurassic was possible, as discussed. This is illustrated on Fig. 14, which is a schematic representation of the 3D model on NW–SE trending cross-sections over the Flett Ridge and Westray Ridge. The reservoir sands of sequence set P3 sit stratigraphically above the base Tertiary unconformity and comparison of the base Tertiary migration pathways (Fig. 12) with lowstand fan sand distribution (Fig. 6) predict areas of possible hydrocarbon focusing. Pinch-out of sandstones controlled by NW–SE transfers act as lateral barriers to migration that separate the pressure compartments described above. These are largely parallel to the migration direction (Figs 6 and 12) therefore allowing hydrocarbons to migrate up-dip until they reach the NE–SW-trending pinch-out line where the hydrocarbons are trapped. Prospectivity could theoretically occurs in reservoirs above sequence set P3 if hydrocarbons could migrate through the regional seal. This is most likely in the south of the West of Shetlands where the P3 transgressive shale is poorly developed or on the faulted margins of the Corona Ridge, where sequence set P3 is thin to absent.

Summary

The area has been divided into seven charge provinces by combining the results of the basin modelling for the Early Cretaceous to present-day with simplified migration pathways for both the base Cretaceous and base Tertiary unconformities (Fig. 15):

(1) Solan Basin; oil-prone with generation from areally restricted kitchens;
(2) Westray Ridge Area; very prolific oil and gas province; focused migration to the Westray Ridge and Judd High from the North Judd Basin and the eastern flank of the Westray Ridge;
(3) South Faeroes Basin; an oil-prone area, sourced from the Mid-Faeroes Ridge, Corona Ridge and West Shetland Basin;
(4) Central Faeroes Province; considered not prospective since it overlies a deeply buried overmature Kimmeridge Clay section and the hydrocarbons generated in surrounding areas do not migrate into this area;
(5) Flett Basin; prolific oil and gas province; considered largely prospective for gas, with the exception of the Rona Ridge; and
(6) and (7) N. Faeroes Basin and Corona Ridge; predominantly oil province with gas in places. These areas are structurally complex with extrusive and intrusive igneous centres.

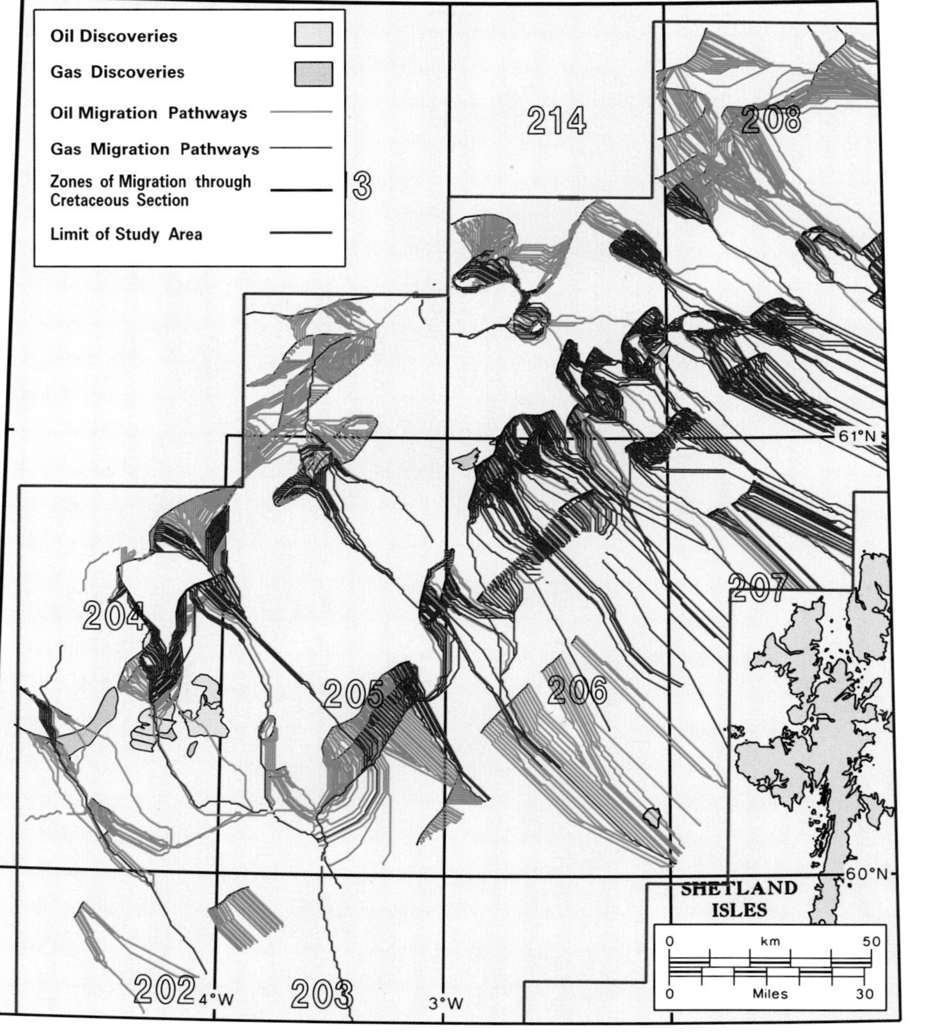

Fig. 12. Post Paleocene oil and gas migration pathways at the base Tertiary. Migration pathways are calculated assuming buoyancy driven migration, taking the structurally most advantageous routes using the base Tertiary structure map.

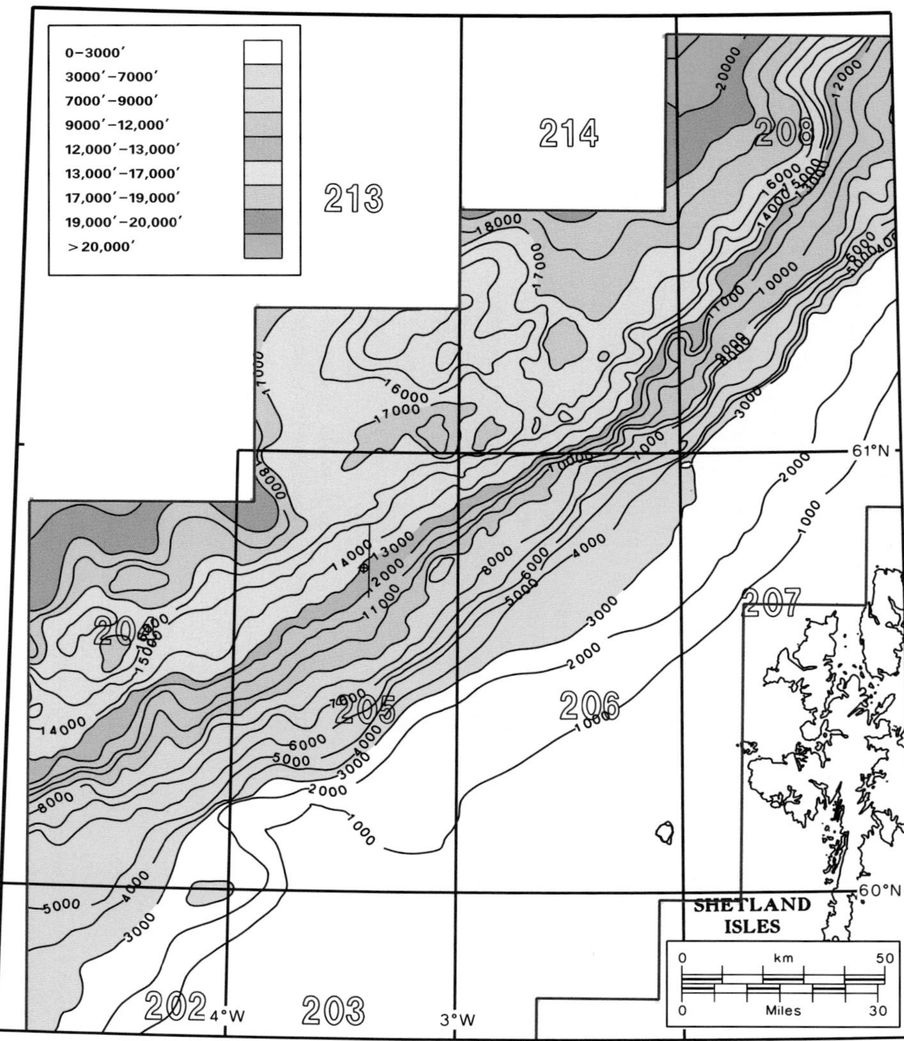

Fig. 13. Base Tertiary unconformity structure map.

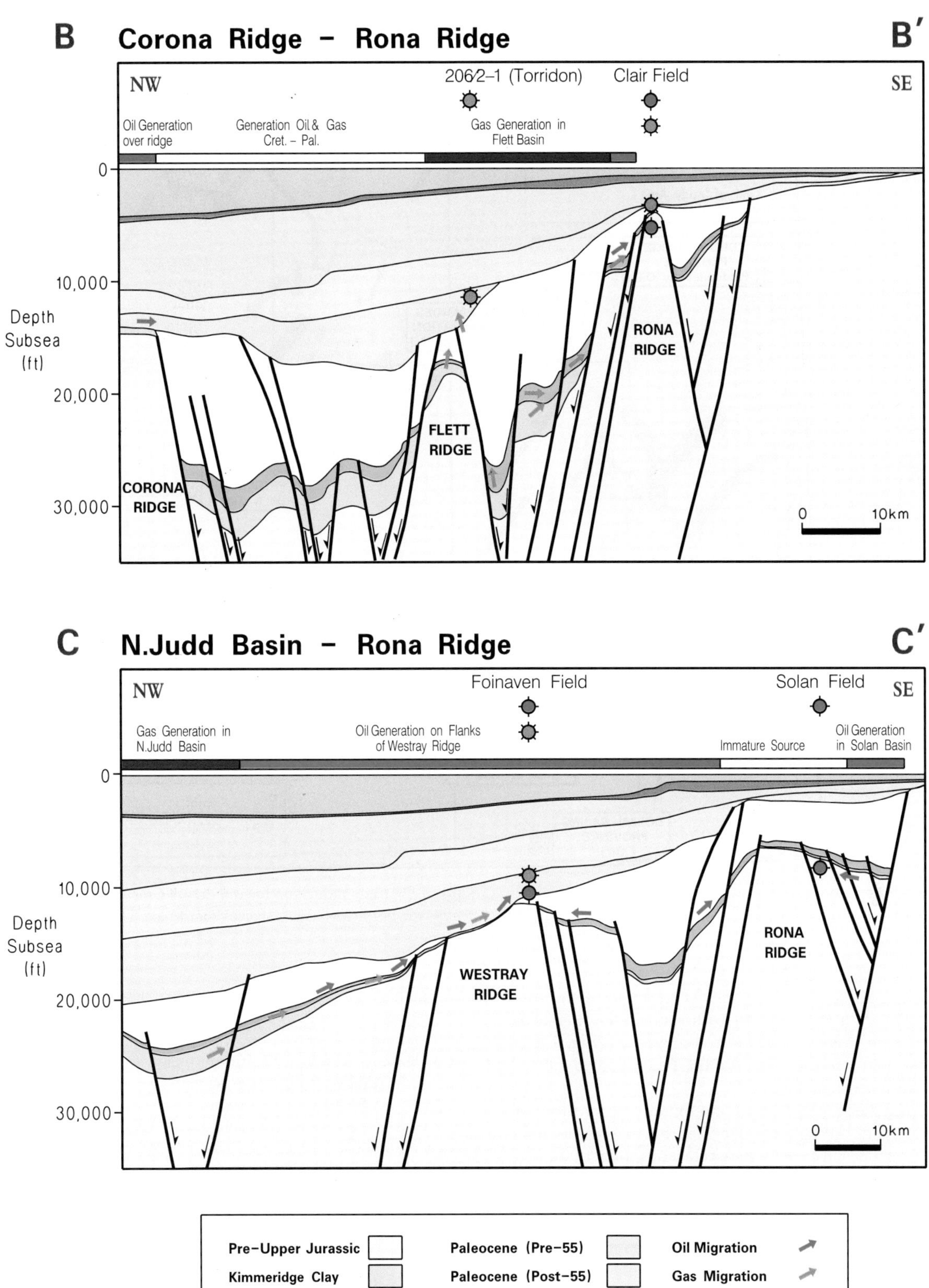

Fig. 14. (**a**) NW to SE line in the Corona Ridge to Rona Ridge area showing the migration model schematically in 2D for the post-Paleocene, located on Fig. 1. (**b**) NW to SE line in the North Judd Basin to Rona Ridge area showing migration model schematically in 2D for the post-Paleocene, located on Fig. 1. Note that hydrocarbons migrate vertically into the sequence set P3 where the Cretaceous section is thin/absent.

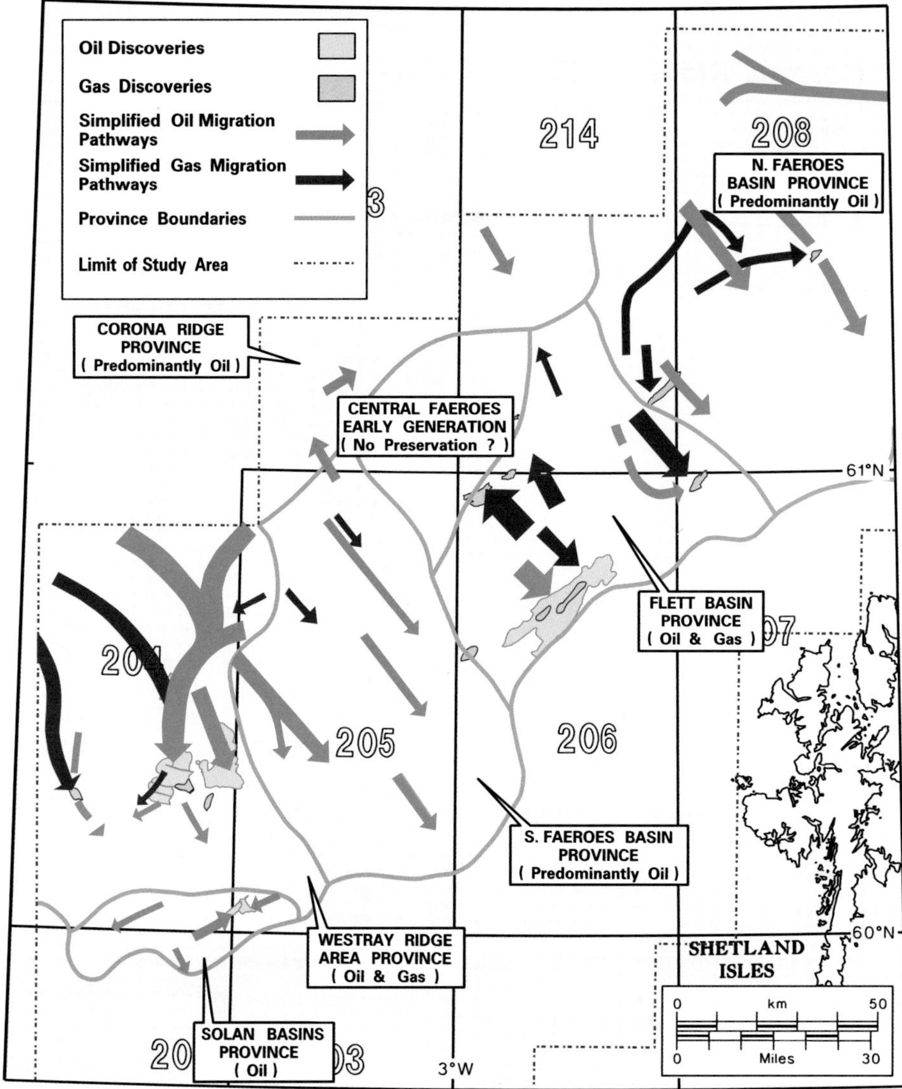

Fig. 15. Hydrocarbon charge provinces, West of Shetland. Combines the results of the basin modelling for the Lower Cretaceous to present day of the Kimmeridge Clay Formation source rock with simplified migration pathways for both the base Cretaceous and base Tertiary unconformities.

By integrating sequence stratigraphy (Figs 3 and 6) and formation pressure data (Fig. 7a, 7b) with the results of hydrocarbon generation (Figs 10 and 11) and migration (Fig. 12), a model for the petroleum system for the Paleocene to Lower Eocene has been created.

The charging history is one of continuous generation of hydrocarbons from the Kimmeridge Clay Formation in shifting generative areas since the Early Cretaceous, punctuated by periods of uplift and erosion during the early Paleocene and Miocene.

Migration into sequence set P3 reservoirs has occurred over the intra-basinal highs where the intervening Cretaceous interval is thin and disturbed by faulting. The development of a laterally extensive regional seal overlying reservoir sandstones which both extend over NNE–SSW and NE–SW intrabasinal highs have enabled the drainage of significant quantities of oil and gas into stratigraphic traps in the West of Shetlands area.

This model is in accordance with the observed oil province in the Westray Ridge area (Foinaven and Schiehallion fields) and the gas province in the Flett Basin (Fig. 15). This 'best fit' model predicts oil potential in the North and South Faeroes Basins and Corona Ridge, whilst the Central Faeroes Basin is considered less prospective due to a high charge risk.

The authors would like to acknowledge the many geoscientists at Texaco who have contributed to the interpretation of the West of Shetland area, in particular, the UK 16th Round co-ordinator D. O'Driscoll. The Texaco drawing office are also thanked for the figures. In addition, the authors would like to acknowledge the management of Texaco and Amerada Hess for permission to publish this work. The manuscript benefited greatly from reviews by the following, who are also acknowledged: S. Pinnock, M. Goodchild and R. Phair; and conference paper reviewers I. Scotchman, M. Houchen, J. McQuilken and S. D. Burley.

References

Bailey, N. J. L., Walko, P. & Sauer, M. J. 1987. Geochemistry and source rock potential of the west of Shetlands. *In*: Brooks, J. & Glennie, K. W. (eds) *Petroleum Geology of North West Europe*. Graham & Trotman, London, 711–721.

Booth, J., Swiecicki, T. & Wilcockson, P. 1993. The tectono-stratigraphy of the Solan Basin, west of Shetland. *In*: Parker, J. R. (ed.) *Petroleum Geology of Northwest Europe: Proceedings of the 4th Conference*. Geological Society, London, 987–999.

Burley, S. D. & Macquaker, J. H. S. 1992. Authigenic clays, diagenetic sequences and conceptual diagenetic models in contrasting basin-margin and basin-center North Sea Jurassic sandstones and mudstones. *In*: Houseknecht, D. W. & Pittman, E. D. (eds)

Origin, diagenesis and petrophysic of clay minerals in sandstones. *SEPM Special Publication*, **47**, 81–110.

——, MULLIS, J. & MATTER, A. 1989. Timing diagenesis in the Tartan reservoir (UK North Sea): Constraints from combined cathodoluminescence microscopy and fluid inclusion studies. *Marine and Petroleum Geology*, **6**, 98–120.

COOPER, M. M., EVANS, A. C., LYNCH, D. J., NEVILLE, G. & NEWLEY, T. 1999. The Foinaven Field: managing reservoir development uncertainty prior to start-up. *In*: FLEET, A. J. & BOLDY, S. A. R. (eds) *Petroleum Geology of Northwest Europe: Proceedings of the 5th Conference*. Geological Society, London, 675–682.

DOWNEY, M. W. 1984. Evaluating seals for hydrocarbon accumulations. *Bulletin of American Association of Petroleum Geologists*, **68**, 1752–1763.

DUINDAM, P. & VAN HOORN, B. 1987. Structural evolution of the West Shetland continental margin. *In*: BROOKS, J. & GLENNIE, K. W. (eds) *Petroleum Geology of North West Europe*. Graham & Trotman, London, 765–775.

EBDON, C. C., GRANGER, P. J., JOHNSON, H. D. & EVANS, A. M. 1995. Early Tertiary evolution and sequence stratigraphy of the Faeroe–Shetland Basin: implications for hydrocarbon prospectivity. *In*: SCRUTTON, G. B. & TUDHOPE, A. W. (eds) *The Tectonics, Sedimentation and Palaeoceanography of the North Atlantic Region*. Geological Society, London, Special Publications, **90**, 51–69.

EARLE, M. M., JANKOWSKI, E. J. & VANN, I. R. 1989. Structural and stratigraphical evolution of the Faeroe–Shetland Channel and Northern Rockall Trough. *In*: TANKARD, A. J. & BALKWILL, H. R. (ed.) *Extensional Tectonics and Stratigraphy of the North Atlantic Margins*. Memoirs of the American Association of Petroleum Geologists, **46**, 461–469

GALLOWAY, W. B. 1989. Genetic sequences in basin analysis I: architecture and genesis of flooding-surface bounded depositional units. *Bulletin of American Association of Petroleum Geologists*, **73**, 125–142.

GOODCHILD, M. W., HENRY, K. L., HINKLEY, R. J. & IMBUS, S. W. 1998. The Victory Gas Field, West of Shetland. *In*: FLEET, A. J. & BOLDY, S. A. R. (eds) *Petroleum Geology of Northwest Europe: Proceedings of the 5th Conference*. Geological Society, London, 713–724.

HINDLE, A. D. 1997. Petroleum migration pathways and charge concentration; a three dimensional model. *Bulletin of American Association of Petroleum Geologists*, **81**, 1451–1481.

HITCHEN, K., & RITCHIE, J. D. 1993. New K–Ar ages, and a provisional chronology, for the offshore parts of the British Tertiary Igneous Province. *Scottish Journal of Geology*, **29**, 73–86.

HOLMES, A. J., GRIFFITH, C. E. & SCOTCHMAN, I. C. 1998. The Jurassic petroleum system of the west of Britain Atlantic Margin – an integration of tectonics, geochemistry and basin modelling. *In*: FLEET, A. J. & BOLDY, S. A. R. (eds) *Petroleum Geology of Northwest Europe: Proceedings of the 5th Conference*. Geological Society, London, 1351–1366.

KNOX, R. W. O'B., HOLLOWAY, S. & BAILEY, H. E. 1997. *Stratigraphic Nomenclature of the UK Northwest Margin, 2. Early Paleogene Lithostratigraphy and Sequence Stratigraphy*. British Geological Survey, Nottingham.

LEACH, H. M., HERBERT, N., LOS, A. & SMITH, R. L. 1997. The Schiehallion development. *In*: FLEET, A. J. & BOLDY, S. A. R. (eds) *Petroleum Geology of Northwest Europe: Proceedings of the 5th Conbference*, Geological Society, London, 683–692.

LUNDIN, E. R. & DORÉ, A. G. 1997. A tectonic model for the passive margin between the Rockall Trough and the Lofotens: Early Cretaceous break-up. *Journal of the Geological Society, London*, **154**, 545–550.

MITCHELL, S. M., BEAMISH, G. W. J., WOOD, M. V., MALACEK, S. J., ARMENTROUT, J. A., DAMUTH, J. E. & OLSON, H. C. 1993. Paleogene sequence stratigraphical framework of the Faeroe Basin. *In*: PARKER, J. R. (ed.) *Petroleum Geology of Northwest Europe: Proceedings of the 4th Conference*. Geological Society, London, 1011–1025.

RASMUSSEN, J. & NOE-NYGAARD, A. 1970. Geology of the Faeroe Islands. *Danmarks Geologiske Undersogelse* 1 Series, no **25**.

RUMPH, B., REAVES, C. M., ORANGE, V, G. & ROBINSON, D. L. 1993. Structuring and transfer zones in the Faeroe Basin in a regional tectonic context. *In*: PARKER, J. R. (ed.) *Petroleum Geology of Northwest Europe: Proceedings of the 4th Conference*. Geological Society, London, 999–1010.

SCOTCHMAN, I. C. & GRIFFITH, C. E. 1996. The late Jurassic petroleum system, UK west of Shetlands – A geochemical and basin modelling study. *Abstract, EAGE 58th Conference and Technical* Exhibition – Amsterdam, The Netherlands, 3–7 June 1996 – Petroleum Division Paper L003.

SIBSON, R. H. 1981. Controls on low-stress hydro-fracture dilatancy in thrust, wrench and normal fault terrains. *Nature*, **289**, 5799, 665–667

STOKER, M. S., HITCHEN, K. & GRAHAM, C. C. 1993. *The geology of the Hebrides and West Shetland shelves, and adjacent deep-water areas*. British Geological Survey. United Kingdom Offshore Regional Report.

VAIL, P. R., MITCHEM, R. M. JR & THOMPSON, S. III, 1977. Seismic stratigraphy and global changes of sea level, part 3: relative changes of sea level from coastal onlap. *In*: PAYTON, C. E. (ed.) *Seismic Stratigraphy – Applications to Hydrocarbon Exploration*. Memoirs of the American Association of Petroleum Geologists, **26**, 63–81.

VERSTALEN, I., HARTLEY, A. & HURST, A. 1995. The sedimentological record of a late Jurassic transgression: Rona Member (Kimmeridge Clay Formation equivalent), West Shetland Basin, UKCS. *In*: HARTLEY, A. J. & PROSSER, D. J. (eds) *Characterization of Deep Marine Clastic Systems*, Geological Society, London, Special Publications, **94**, 155–176.

Oil and gas migration in the Sherwood Sandstone of the East Irish Sea Basin

G. COWAN,[1] S. D. BURLEY,[2,4] N. HOEY,[1] P. HOLLOWAY,[1] P. BERMINGHAM,[1] N. BEVERIDGE,[2,5] M. HAMBORG[3] and Ø. SYLTA[3]

[1] *BG E&P, Thames Valley Park, Reading, Berkshire, UK*
[2] *BG Technology, Gas Research Centre, Ashby Road, Loughborough LE11 3GR, UK*
[3] *Sintef Petroleum Research, N-7034, Trondheim, Norway*
[4] *Basin Dynamics Group, Department of Earth Sciences, University of Keele, Staffordshire ST5 5BG, UK*
[5] *Present address: BP Petroleum Development, Farburn Industrial Estate, Dyce, Aberdeen AB2 0PB, UK*

Abstract: The East Irish Sea Basin is a simple petroleum system with a complex geological history. The petroleum play comprises a Namurian source with a Sherwood Sandstone Group carrier and reservoir sequence, sealed by shales and salts of the Mercia Mudstone Group. The source underwent rapid burial during the Triassic and Jurassic, reaching a maximum burial depth of 5 km by the end-Cretaceous. Uplift by as much as 2 km took place between 60 and 20 Ma across the basin.

One-dimensional modelling predicts that oil generation took place over a temperature range of 70–120°C. Primary gas generation began contemporaneously with oil generation but continued to temperatures >180°C. Pseudo-3D ray tracing modelling of the volume and distribution of hydrocarbons in the Sherwood Sandstone Group, matched to known hydrocarbon discoveries in the East Irish Sea Basin, indicates that before 180 Ma, traps were mainly gas filled. Continuous burial to 144 Ma resulted in an oil leg developing in most traps, with significant oil accumulations present in the south of the basin. Thermogenic gas generation in the Keys Basin displaced oil in the northern traps during the period leading to maximum burial at 65 Ma, by which time the basin was characterized by a distinct northern gas province and a southern oil province. Subsequent uplift from 60 Ma caused trapped gas to expand and further displace oil from most of the remaining traps in the southern part of the basin. Hydrocarbon flow rates were greatest between 65–60 Ma during maximum burial. Subsequently, hydrocarbon flow rates decreased dramatically, although gas generation continued until 20 Ma.

The discovery of the North and South Morecambe fields in 1974 and their subsequent development led to the widely-held industry view that the East Irish Sea Basin (EISB) is a 'gas basin' (Colter 1978), despite the fact that the Calder Field discovery well (110/7-3), drilled in 1976, encountered a 7 m (20 ft) live oil column (Blow & Hardman 1997). Subsequently, wells 110/12a-1 and 110/14-1 (wells X and Y of Hardman *et al.* 1993), drilled in the late 80s by BG (then British Gas) penetrated a live oil column with no gas cap. With the discovery of the commercial Douglas and Lennox oil fields by Hamilton Oil (now BHP) in 1990 and 1991, respectively (Yaliz 1997; Haig *et al.* 1997), the industry began to consider the southern EISB as distinctly 'oil prone'. However, the presence of under-saturated oil juxtaposed with dry gas – the Hamilton, Lambda and Asland gas accumulations lie between the Douglas and Lennox oil fields (Fig. 1) – is difficult to reconcile assuming a uniform single hydrocarbon source rock and comparable burial histories for these structures using only conventional 1D basin modelling techniques.

The present study sets out to predict the hydrocarbon phase likely to be encountered in the smaller structures in the Sherwood Sandstone reservoir now being drilled as the basin approaches a mature period of exploration. A secondary migration model was constructed to test the hypothesis that a late phase of gas generation originating from the Keys Basin displaced an earlier phase of oil from traps in the north of basin (Cowan & Bradney 1997) and resulted in the present heterogeneous distribution of oil and gas in the basin.

Structural framework of the EISB

Three dominant structural trends, NE–SW Caledonoid, NW–SE Charnoid and N–S Malvernoid, are present in the basin, and are related to Permo-Triassic rifting in the proto-North Atlantic. The margins of the basin are well defined by a series of bounding faults (Lagman Fault, Keys Fault, Formby Point Fault and the Lake District Boundary Fault) which crudely define a rhomb-shaped grabenal area (Fig. 1). Within the EISB, two distinct structural provinces are recognized (Jackson *et al.* 1995). Firstly, a southern area, comprising the Godred Croven and West and East Deemster basins, is dominated by linear N–S trending half graben connected by subordinate E–W trending normal faults. Secondly, a northern area, is dominated by three westerly tilted half graben, defining the Eubonia, Keys and Tynwald basins, that were major syn-sedimentary depocentres.

Extensional faults trending NW–SE such as the Keys fault and the NE–SW trending faults such as the Lagman fault were certainly active by Permian times, and continued to be so through the Triassic, and may represent faults that were active during Carboniferous basin formation. The long history of fault activity during basin development is reflected in displacements that exceed 1 km on the major faults. Seismic profiles across the basin document that the Permo-Triassic sediments thicken in the hangingwalls of these major faults (e.g. Jackson *et al.* 1987, 1995).

Subsequent late Cretaceous and Tertiary inversion of the EISB did not produce significant reactivation of these faults

COWAN, G., BURLEY, S. D., HOEY, N., HOLLOWAY, P., BERMINGHAM, P., BEVERIDGE, N., HAMBORG, M. & SYLTA, Ø. 1999. Oil and gas migration in the Sherwood Sandstone of the East Irish Sea Basin. *In*: FLEET, A. J. & BOLDY, S. A. R. (eds) *Petroleum Geology of Northwest Europe: Proceedings of the 5th Conference*, 1383–1398.

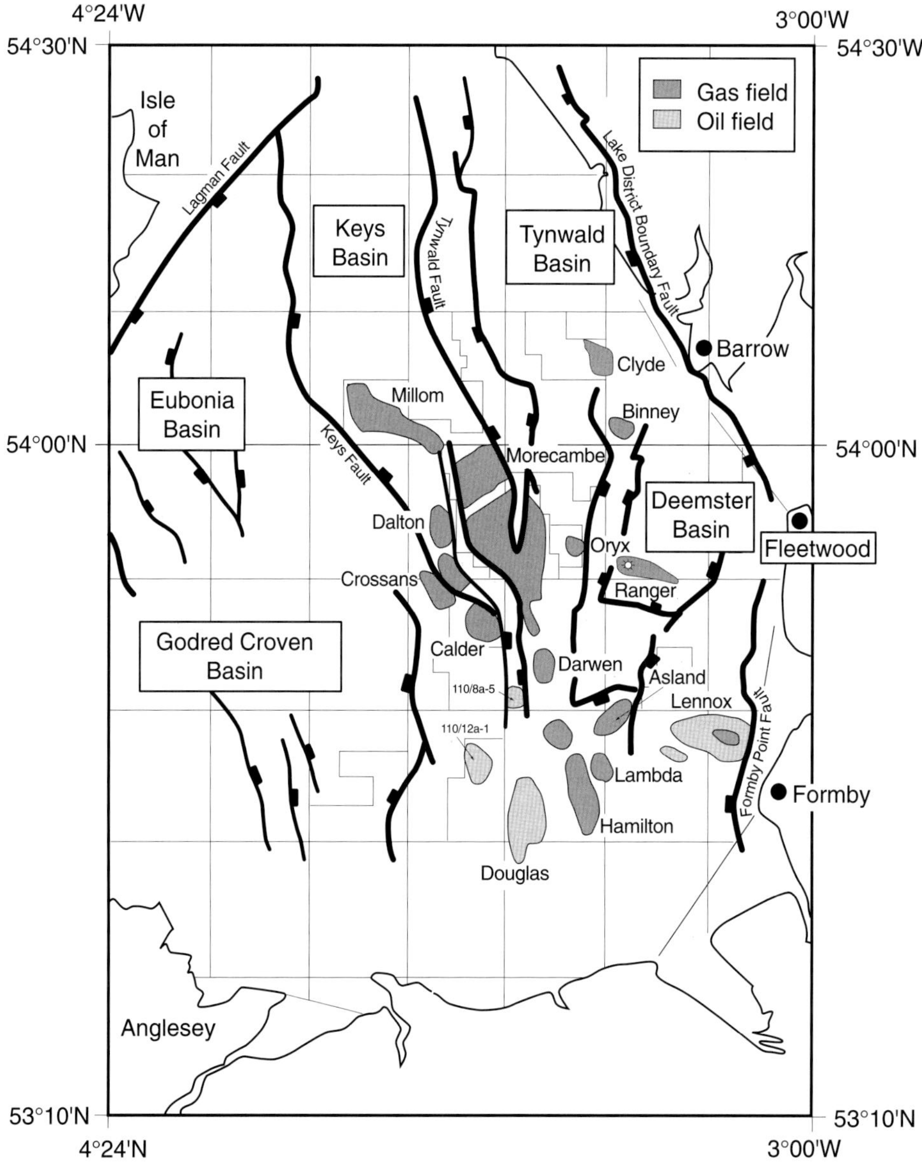

Fig. 1. Location map of the East Irish Sea Basin showing the major structural elements, depositional basins and distribution of oil and gas fields.

and reverse faults are not generally observed. This suggests that displacement related to inversion on individual faults is always less than normal fault displacement. Small NE–SW trending folds observed by Knipe *et al.* (1993) may be related to early Tertiary inversion and compression in the basin, but generally, inversion has not been accommodated by the faults that define the graben and horst structural grain of the basin.

The hydrocarbon system in the EISB

The hydrocarbon system of the EISB can be considered in terms of a very simple stratigraphy, comprising a Carboniferous source, a combined Sherwood Sandstone Group carrier system and reservoir horizon, and a Mercia Mudstone Group seal (Fig. 2). The Permian, which lies between the source and reservoir, was the primary exploration target in the basin during the 1970s (Colter & Barr 1975; Colter 1978; Ebbern 1981) as it was thought that the equivalents of the Southern North Sea Rotliegend reservoir and Zechstein salt seal would be present in the EISB. However, the expected Permian reservoir–seal couplet was not encountered, and although Permian mudstones and halite are developed in parts of the basin (Jackson & Johnson 1997; Jackson *et al.* 1995), these do not constitute an effective seal and migrating hydrocarbons have by-passed the Permian to be trapped in the Triassic. Major gas accumulations are now found reservoired in the upper part of the Triassic Sherwood Sandstone Group in the northern part of the basin (Millom, N and S Morecambe, Dalton, Hodder, Crossans, Calder, Clyde, Binney Oryx and Ranger discoveries) whilst in the southern part, two oil fields (Douglas and Lennox) are associated with gas accumulations (Hamilton, Asland and Darwen discoveries; Fig. 1).

Source rocks

Oils in the basin have been correlated with the Sabden and Holywell shales (Hardman *et al.* 1993; Armstrong *et al.* 1997). These shales were deposited on the pro-delta slopes of the Namurian depositional system during the Arnsbergian to Sabdenian. The Namurian delta system prograded from east to west over the East Midlands shelf (Fraser & Gawthorpe 1993), although the coarse clastic facies of the Kinderscoutian delta front and Marsdenian fluvio–deltaic delta top did not prograde as far west as the East Irish Sea Basin. A Yoredale-type cyclothem sequence advanced from the northeast to onlap onto the Manx–Whitehaven Ridge (Smith 1985). Namurian

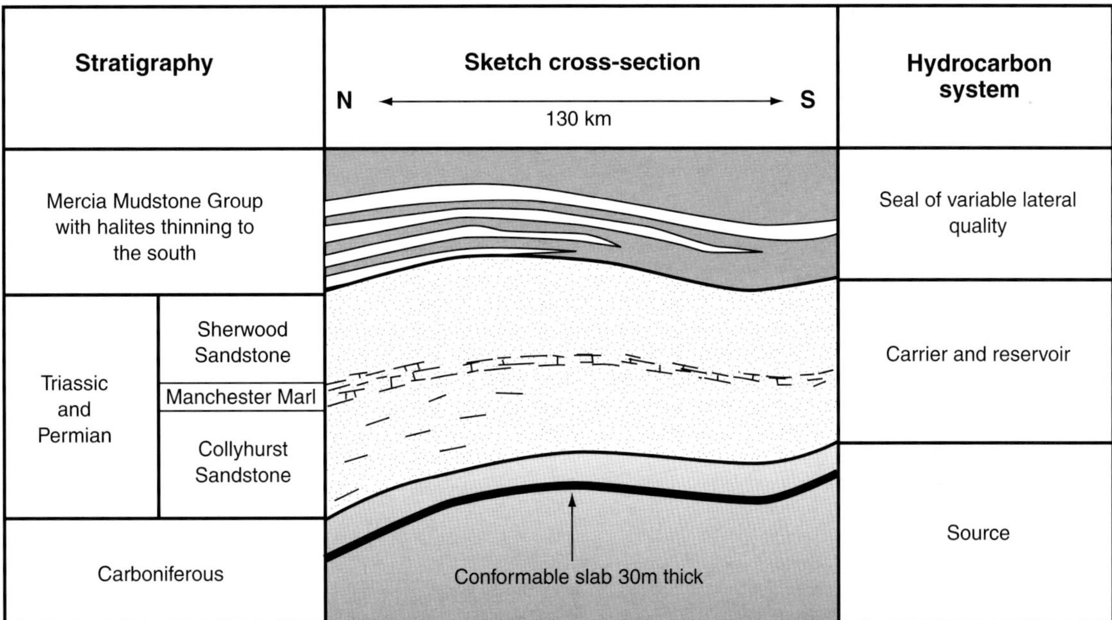

Fig. 2. Schematic stratigraphy of the East Irish Sea Basin capturing the main elements of the hydrocarbon system incorporated into the 3D model.

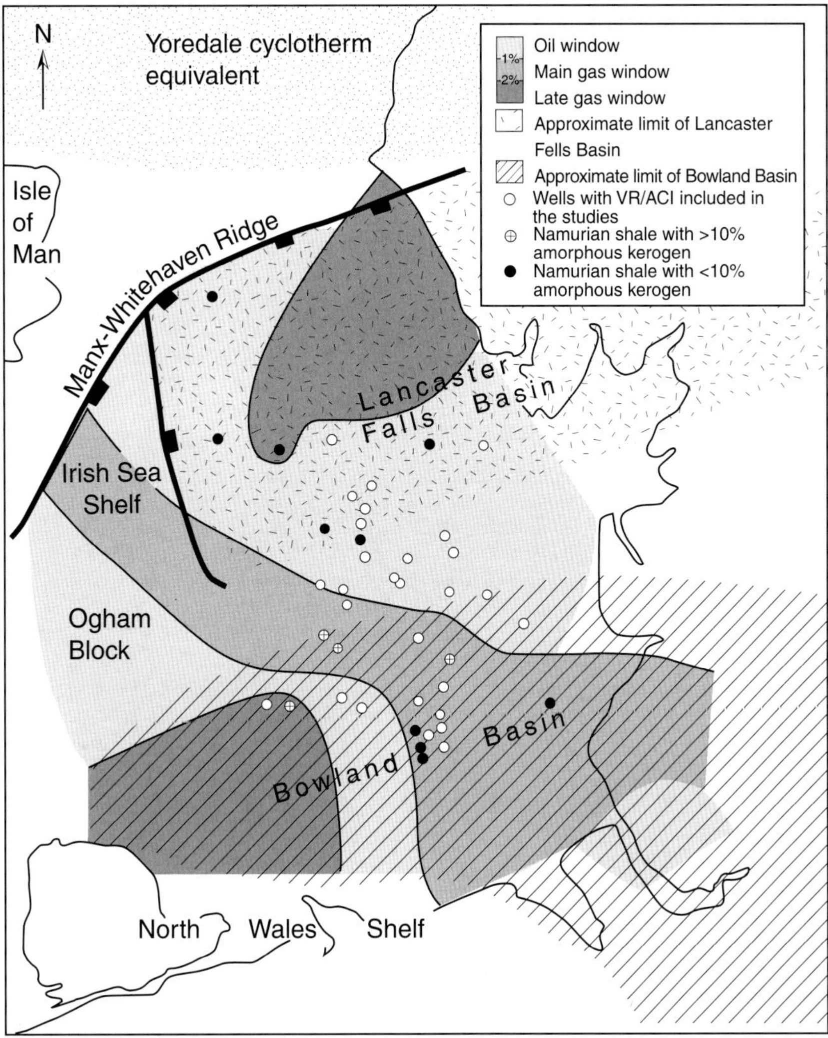

Fig. 3. The Namurian basins of the East Irish Sea Basin (based partly on Corfield *et al.* 1996) and the measured vitrinite reflectance (VR) values for Carboniferous samples projected to the top Namurian surface. No attempt is made to discriminate between position in the Carboniferous section since variation in VR within each well is much less than between wells.

well penetrations are sparse, but regional palaeogeographical data suggests that source facies should be present throughout the entire basin (Fig. 3) with two sub-basins, the Bowland Basin to the south and the Lancaster Fells Basin to the north, in existence during Dinantian and Namurian times. The limited well data suggest that the Namurian of the Bowland Basin is characterized by >10% amorphous type II kerogen and is more oil prone than the Namurian source rocks of the Lancaster Fells Basin which contain <10% amorphous kerogen and are dominated by type III kerogens (Fig. 3). Westphalian coals provide an additional potential gas-prone source and are present around the basin margins as well as in parts of the basin centre. However, these coals have an high inertinite content and would not have made a significant contribution to the overall petroleum budget of the basin.

Carrier beds and reservoir

In total, the Sherwood Sandstone Group carrier system and reservoir horizon comprise over 1800 m (4000 ft) of predominantly fine- to coarse-grained sandstones which were deposited in a semi-arid, mixed fluvial and aeolian setting. The sequence is sand-dominated and has a sandstone : shale ratio of around 10 : 1. The basal aeolian sandstones are of Permian age and comprise the lateral equivalents of the Collyhurst Sandstone (Smith *et al.* 1974). These are overlain by an interbedded sequence of Upper Permian limestones, anhydritic mudstones and halite, equivalent to the St Bees Evaporites and Manchester Marls, which in the centre of the basin attain a total thickness of 300 m (1000 ft) (Jackson *et al.* 1987, 1995). Around the basin margins and across much of the south of the basin, the St Bees Evaporite equivalents are absent and reservoir quality Collyhurst Sandstone rocks are developed. Only where halites are present in the St Bees Evaporites (mainly in the north of basin) is the Collyhurst Sandstone represented by mixed red mudstones and sheet sandstones, although an effective Permian seal–reservoir couplet has not been encountered.

The reservoir for all the EISB fields is the uppermost Sherwood Sandstone Group sediments of Triassic age. In the EISB these are known locally as the Ormskirk Sandstone Formation (Jackson *et al.* 1987) and are equivalent to the Helsby Sandstone Formation of northern Cheshire (Warrington *et al.* 1980). Only in the North and South Morecambe fields does the hydrocarbon column extend into the underlying St Bees Sandstone Formation. Generally, the reservoir sandstones have excellent reservoir properties (Bushell 1986; Meadows & Beach 1993) with arithmetic average porosities in excess of 15% and permeabilities in the 100 mD to 1 D range. Thin aeolian units, which form laterally extensive sheets, can have porosities of up to 30% and permeabilities of up to 10 D. Both porosity and permeability decline systematically with depth (Fig. 4). Shales are rare in the reservoir sequence and do not form widespread barriers to vertical migration (see Thompson & Meadows 1997; Herries & Cowan 1997, for an up to date summary of EISB sedimentology).

Permeabilities in the Sherwood Sandstone are reduced by authigenic platy illite which precipitated in the basin between 120 and 180 Ma (Burley 1987; Bushell 1986). Illite precipitated below a palaeo-hydrocarbon contact in the North and South Morecambe fields (Colter & Barr 1975) and its distribution is limited to the Keys Basin between the Tynwald and Keys faults and the southern and eastern margins of the South Morecambe Field. This led Cowan & Bradney (1997) to propose that this illite distribution recorded the southward migration pathway of a basinal, aqueous fluid from the deeply buried Keys Basin which may have carried organic acids capable of dissolving feldspar as a source of potassium for illite precipitation.

Seal

The Mercia Mudstone Group provides a regional seal across the EISB (Jackson *et al.* 1987; Wilson 1990), and reaches a thickness of up to 3.2 km (10 500 ft) in the deepest part of the Keys Basin, although here the sequence is complicated by low-angle faulting and halokinesis. The Mercia Mudstone Group comprises alternating red mudstones and halites, together with subordinate anhydrite and dolomite, organized into 5 cycles (Jackson *et al.* 1987) which extend southwards across the basin into northern Cheshire (Arthurton 1980).

There is considerable lateral variability in the lithologies of the Mercia Mudstone Group across the basin, particularly

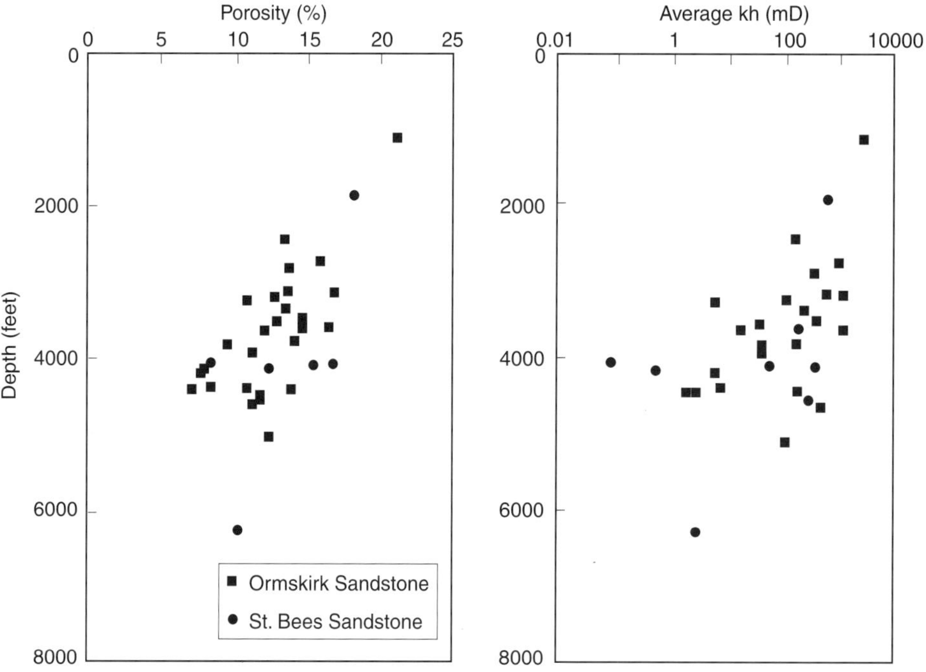

Fig. 4. Porosity and permeability–depth relationships for representative Sherwood Sandstone samples in the East Irish Sea Basin.

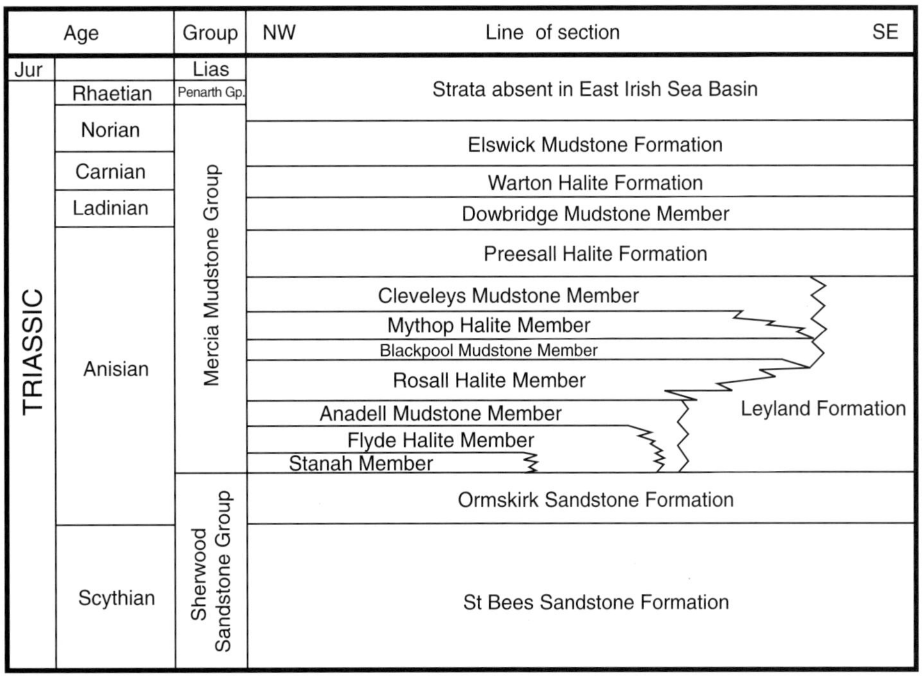

	Age	Group	NW Line of section SE
Jur		Lias	Strata absent in East Irish Sea Basin
TRIASSIC	Rhaetian	Penarth Gp.	Strata absent in East Irish Sea Basin
	Norian	Mercia Mudstone Group	Elswick Mudstone Formation
	Carnian		Warton Halite Formation
	Ladinian		Dowbridge Mudstone Member
	Anisian		Preesall Halite Formation
			Cleveleys Mudstone Member
			Mythop Halite Member
			Blackpool Mudstone Member
			Rosall Halite Member
			Anadell Mudstone Member / Leyland Formation
			Flyde Halite Member
			Stanah Member
		Sherwood Sandstone Group	Ormskirk Sandstone Formation
	Scythian		St Bees Sandstone Formation

Fig. 5. Regional stratigraphy of Mercia Mudstone Group across the East Irish Sea Basin in a north–south section illustrating the lateral variation in the distribution of halite and mudstone members.

in the lower part of the sequence (Seedhouse & Racey 1997; Fig. 5). Only in the northern part of the EISB does the basal halite form a continuous cap rock; to the south the three lowermost halites of the Mercia Mudstone Group are replaced by the Leyland Formation which comprises an interbedded sequence of playa mudstones and sheet sandstones that constitutes a poor quality reservoir. Halite directly overlies the Sherwood Sandstone carrier bed/reservoir sequence in only in a few areas of the basin. This variation in halite distribution has a strong effect on the sealing capacity across the basin and controls the performance of traps throughout geological time.

This effect is most pronounced with the basal halite, the Fylde Halite Member, which is restricted in its occurrence to the north and centre of the basin (Fig. 6). Wells drilled on shallow structures (<450 m, 1500 ft) outside the areal extent of the Fylde Halite Member are dry whilst prospects within the limits of the Fylde Halite Member (such as the Ranger accumulation 110/4-1 and the Clyde accumulation 113/8-2) document that it is possible for commercial accumulations of gas to be present at shallow depths beneath a coherent halite cap rock. Indeed, where Fylde Halite Member directly overlies the Sherwood Sandstone as in the South Morecambe Field, the gas column supported by this seal is an anomalous 410 m (1350 ft). These simple relationships indicate that the Flyde Halite Member is an excellent seal in the north of the basin but in the south of the basin, where it is replaced by the Leyland Mudstone Formation, hydrocarbon leakage readily occurs through the cap rock over geological time. The lateral distribution of the Fylde Halite accounts for almost all of the dry wells drilled within the EISB on valid structures as a consequence of tertiary leakage.

Previous burial and thermal models

The timing, quantity and composition of hydrocarbon generation throughout the EISB is critically dependent upon the thermal history of the source rocks, which is in turn a function of the depth of burial and variations in palaeo-heat flow. However, defining the thermal and burial history of the East Irish Sea Basin is complicated by the lack of post-Triassic cover and by the fact that there are no absolute dates for the Permian and Triassic sediments. It is now recognized that the EISB has undergone a complex burial and thermal history that involves several kilometres of uplift and probable circulation of convective warm fluids (Hardman *et al.* 1993; Green *et al.* 1993*a*; Cowan & Bradney 1997).

Figure 7(a) summarizes present-day temperature data obtained throughout the EISB from drill string tests (DSTs) and from the Robertson Research database, plotted against depth. The average temperature–depth trend corresponds to a present day geothermal gradient of 27.9°C throughout the basin, given an average surface temperature of 7°C. At shallower depths within the basin (<2 km, 6600 ft) the temperature gradient is slightly higher. The average heat flow (q_i) for the basin is estimated from the equation:

$$q_i = \lambda_i \delta T$$

(where λ_i is the average thermal conductivity and T is the observed temperature) to be in the order of 50 mW m^{-2} (=1.2 HFU). If this value is used to compute expected vitrinite reflectance (VR) maturity assuming the heat flow has remained constant through time and that there has not been uplift in the basin, there is a significant mismatch between predicted and observed vitrinite values, with observed values being significantly higher than predicted from the simple model (Fig. 7b). Thus, either heat flow must have varied through geological time or considerable amounts of uplift have taken place in the basin.

The fact that the East Irish Sea Basin has been inverted was recognized by the earliest workers in the basin, although estimates of uplift range from 0.7 to 3 km (Fig. 8). Colter (1978) used the shale velocity curve of Marie (1975) to estimate about 2 km uplift for the Mercia Mudstone in well 11/2-1, which on regional considerations was thought to have occurred during the Tertiary. Bushell (1986) derived a burial curve for the South Morecambe Field which included 1.5 km of Cimmerian and Tertiary uplift. Since these early estimates, there are now data from several geochemical techniques which can be used to calibrate the thermal and burial history of the basin, although they provide non-unique solutions to constraining palaeo-heat flow and burial history. Fitting the thermal history to a burial

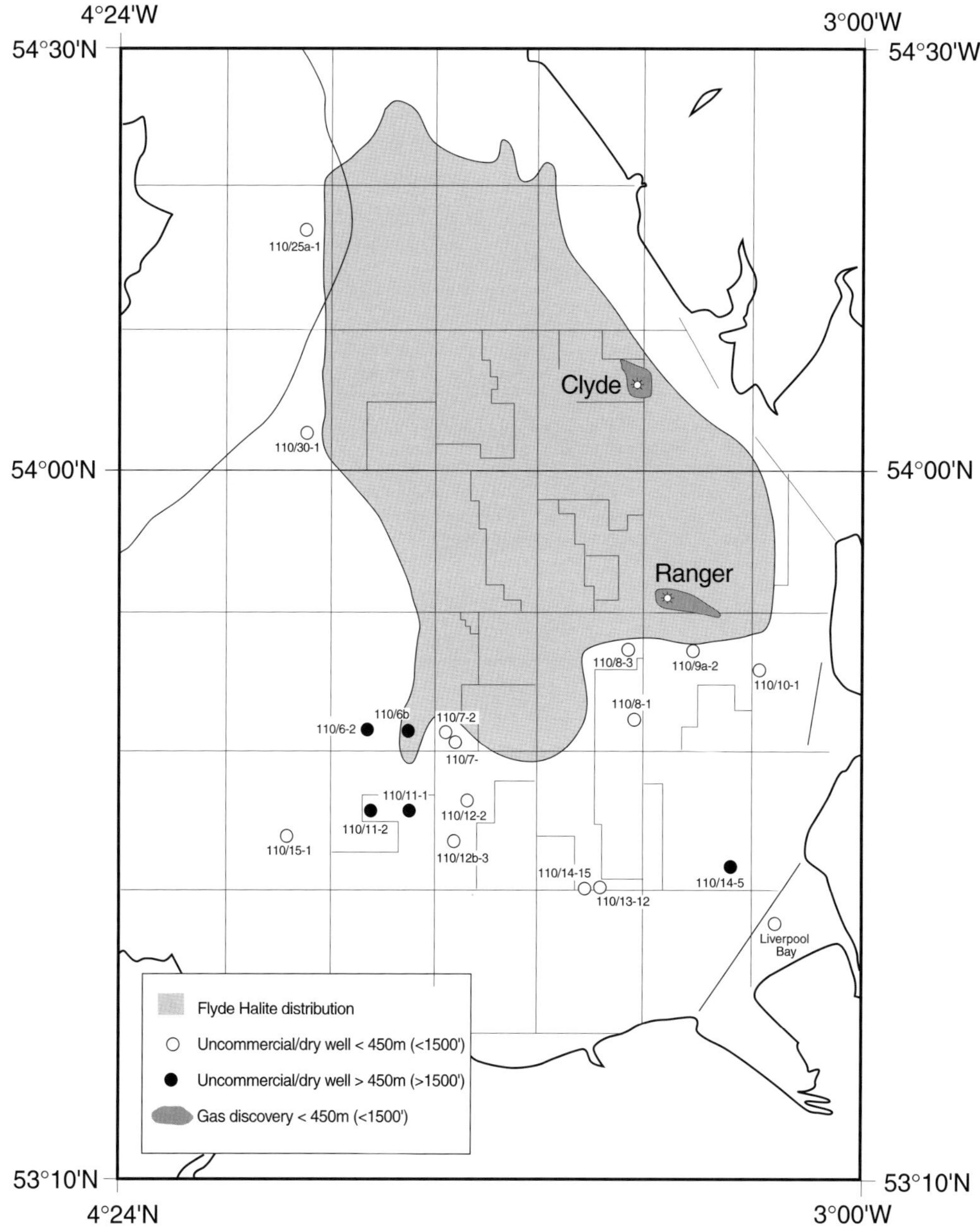

Fig. 6. Map of the extent of the Fylde Halite (based on wireline log interpretation) across the East Irish Sea Basin in relation to the distribution of dry and uncommercial wells and gas discoveries on structures with crestal depths shallower than 450 m (<1500 ft).

model for the EISB has provided much entertainment for geologists for 20 years, and has resulted in thermal- and burial-dominated extremes of interpretation. Fission track workers (Lewis *et al.* 1992; Green *et al.* 1993*a*) postulated a constant geothermal gradient with 3 km inversion to explain the apatite fission track analysis (AFTA) data, although Green *et al.* (1993*b*, 1997) later suggested that AFTA data from the EISB are best explained by a combination of some 2 km uplift together with transient elevated temperatures in the Tertiary as a result of hot fluid flow. Similarly, Stuart & Cowan (1993) considered that the AFTA data could be accounted for by uplift accompanied by a period of high heat flow around 65 Ma. Hardman *et al.* (1993) presented a model of hydrocarbon generation based on 1D geochemical modelling, and superimposed this on an interpretation of the EISB burial history using a detailed analysis of two wells in the southern part of the basin, 110/12-a1 and 110/14-1. These authors were unable to find any evidence for Cimmerian uplift but could not rule out the existence of such uplift since the apatite fission tracks had been reset at temperatures in excess of 125°C during the Tertiary. Utilizing AFTA, fluid inclusion studies and VR data they postulated that a Tertiary heating event was responsible for causing H_2S generation by thermal sulphate reduction (TSR), and suggested that T_h data from fluid inclusions in quartz and carbonate cements preserved evidence of at least two periods of mineral precipitation.

Reconstructing the burial history is complicated by the almost complete lack of post-Triassic cover in the basin, with only remnants of early Jurassic sediments being preserved in the centre of the Keys Basin (Jackson & Mulholland 1993), and in the adjacent onshore Carlisle (Ivimey-Cook *et al.* 1995) and Cheshire (Poole & Whiteman 1966) basins. As a result, the burial history younger than the Liasssic is largely conjectural, defined only by regional knowledge of the Mesozoic and Tertiary stratigraphy, together with constraints provided by VR and AFTA data. Further complications arise from the fact that there are no absolute ages for the Permo-Triassic sequence. Early workers that attempted to reconstruct the burial history of the basin assumed that the Sherwood Sandstone was Scythian (242 Ma) in age (e.g. Bushell 1986). Most

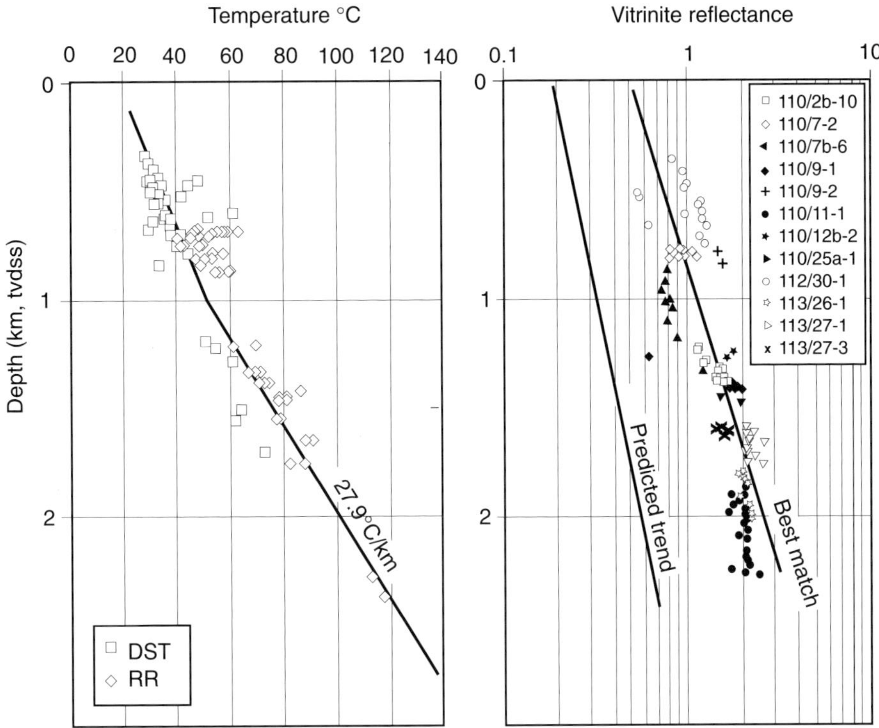

Fig. 7. Temperature and VR data for all wells in the EISB. (**a**) Compiles drill stem test (DST) and the Robertson Research (RR) databases and extrapolates the best fit thermal gradient through the data. (**b**) Shows the predicted VR trend from a constant 27.9°C geothermal gradient and best fit match to the VR data incorporating 1 km of Tertiary uplift and a 60% increased heat flow to 80 mW m^{-2} during the early Tertiary.

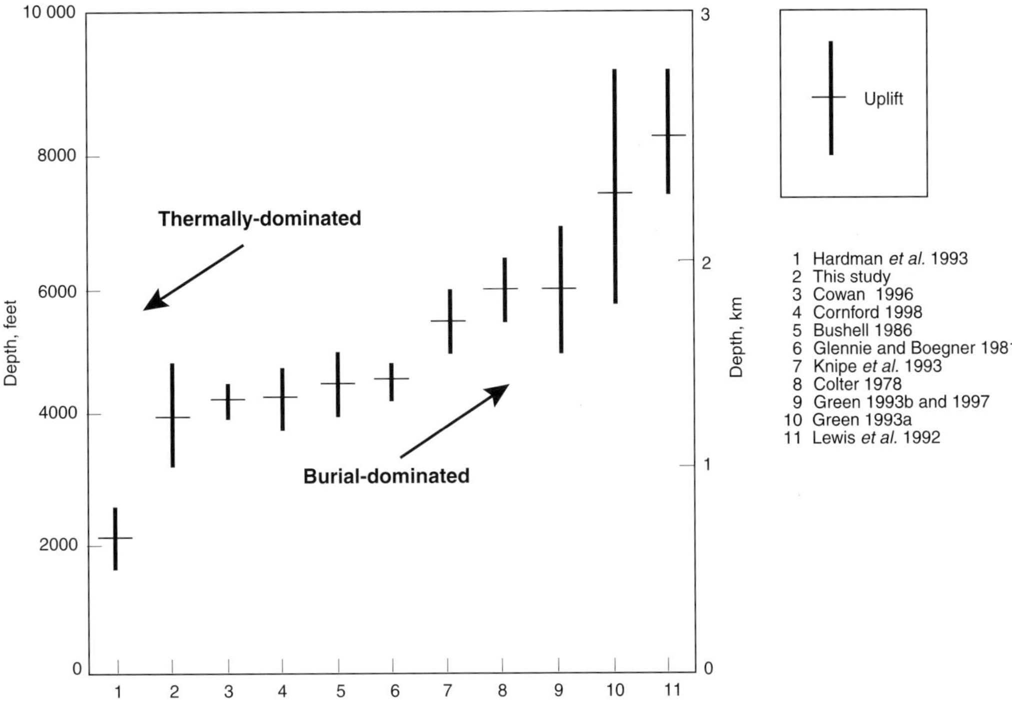

Fig. 8. Compilation of estimates of Tertiary uplift in the EISB from published literature employing shale velocities, maturity modelling and AFTA.

recently, Jackson & Johnson (1997) propose that the Sherwood Sandstone is more probably Anisian (234 Ma) in age. Whilst these age differences may appear small, they highlight the lack of precision in the dataset. Moreover, since the Carboniferous structure and stratigraphy are poorly understood, the pre-Variscan burial history is equally difficult to interpret. Trueblood (pers. comm.) postulates that up to 5 km of burial may have occurred during the Carboniferous in some sub-basins of the EISB. Burial to such depth would remove all post-Varisan hydrocarbon potential from the source rocks. Clearly, this is not the case throughout the basin (as there would be no hydrocarbon accumulations at all at the present-day).

Taken together, the geological and geochemical data indicate that a combination of uplift and higher transient heat flows (above a McKenzie-type (1978) rifting heat flow model) are both likely to have occurred in the EISB. The current

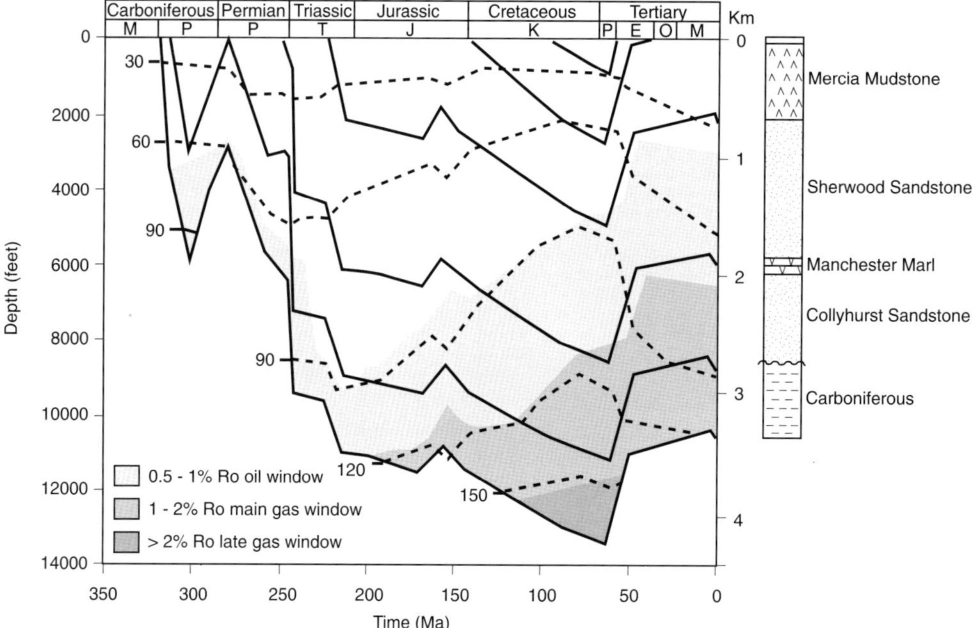

Fig. 9. General 1D burial and thermal history for the EISB (compiled from 1D BasinMod simulations) showing a late Carboniferous burial cycle prior to the main Permo-Triassic extensional subsidence. Isotherms are calculated from a Mckenzie-type (1978) heat flow upon which a transient Tertiary heating event is superimposed.

understanding of the burial history of the EISB is summarized in Fig. 9, which includes a best fit to the VR data of Fig. 7(b) incorporating an elevated heat flow of 80 mW m^{-2} in the early Tertiary and around 1 km of Tertiary uplift. In this model, 1.8 km (6000 ft) of burial in the late Carboniferous is inferred from regional considerations. Variscan uplift of around 0.3 km (1000 ft) is included, which is of the order of magnitude to that observed in the better constrained East Midlands Shelf (Corfield *et al.* 1996). The key issue here for the hydrocarbon generation modelling being that the Upper Caroniferous Namurian shales did not generate significant hydrocarbons prior to Variscan up-lift. Rapid burial in the Permian and Tertiary coincides with extensional rift faulting and a high heat flow, taking the top of the Carboniferous source rocks into the oil generation window by the early Triassic and the gas window in the late Jurassic–Early Cretaceous. K–Ar dates of the timing of illite precipitation (180 Ma max.) coincide with the time at which the top of the Carboniferous source rocks entered the oil window and constrains the palaeo-hydrocarbon–water contact in the North and South Morecambe fields. This inference on hydrocarbon accumulation in the Morecambe fields is the last piece of 'hard' data in the burial model until un-reset fission track data provide a detailed account of the thermal history from *c.* 60 Ma to the present-day. The thermal history (AFTA and VR) can be matched by either a constant geothermal gradient of *c.* 29°C km^{-1} and uplift of up to 3 km (Lewis *et al.* 1992) or, as in the model in Fig. 9, a combination 1 km of uplift and early Tertiary transient elevated heat flow (Hardman *et al.* 1993; Cornford 1998).

Hydrocarbon migration modelling in the Sherwood Sandstone

Prediction of hydrocarbon phase type and distribution in the Sherwood Sandstone carrier sequence across the EISB basin was modelled by means of a ray-tracing technique called SEMI (SEcondary MIgration). This program models buoyancy-driven oil and gas migration within a single layer in three dimensions (Sylta 1993). Secondary migration of hydrocarbons is considered to occur as a local steady state process (Selle *et al.* 1993) so the oil and gas flow down-dip from points in the migration path are not influenced by processes taking place in the shallower areas (Sylta *et al.* 1998). The pressure potential field is not modelled with this technique so no account of hydrodynamic flow is considered. Decompacted maps are constructed in sequential forward simulations enabling palaeomigration to be studied quantitatively, although no structural restoration is performed in the surface reconstructions. The single most important input to the model is the regional high resolution seismic grid for the top of the EISB Sherwood Sandstone Group carrier bed constructed by BG from 1250 km of 3D and 20 000 km of 2D seismic data (covering an area of 80 × 130 km^2) shown in 3D view in Fig. 10. As hydrocarbon flow rates, distribution and spill in the migration model are a function of buoyancy and the dip of the carrier bed, such a high resolution grid is essential to accurately model migration. The volume of oil and gas within prospects is computed through time and the model predictions are matched to hydrocarbon discoveries in the basin.

Modelling methodology

The initial phase of modelling involved simulating the subsidence and thermal history of the source-rock and carrier system. A total of 65 1D *BasinMod*™ and 4 2D *PetroMod*™ models of the subsidence and maturation history were undertaken to provide rigorous, calibrated input to the 3D modelling. A map-based thermal calibration of the maturity of the source rock was compiled from measured vitrinite reflectance data taken from wells which penetrated the Carboniferous (as shown in Fig. 3). Two heat flow models were tested to match modelled and measured vitrinite reflectance to the thermal model. Initially, a schematic vitrinite reflectance gradient diagram was used to estimate the equivalent ambient geothermal gradient zones across the EISB. The resulting palaeo-gradients estimated ranged from 100°C km^{-1} to less than 25°C km^{-1}. This map was digitized and used as input into the maturity model, assuming a constant gradient through time. The resulting modelled vitrinite reflectance distribution was completely incompatible with the observed distribution, thereby invalidating this approach. A much simpler model using a single regional temperature

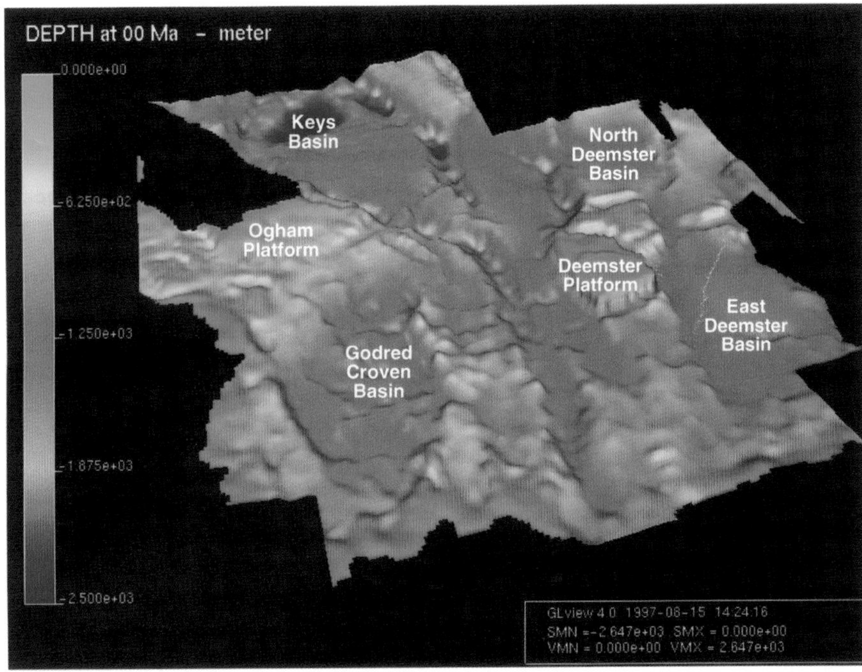

Fig. 10. The regional top Sherwood Sandstone surface, viewed in GLview, dipping to the S, and looking towards the NE. Colour graded for depth: warm colours shallow, blue colours deep. The main basins and the Deemster Platform are clearly visible, and the lineaments that define the Keys and Tynwald faults can be identified. Compare with Fig. 1.

gradient of 29°C km^{-1}, comparable to the calculated present day gradient, was then tested. In order to match the average observed vitrinite reflectance, the burial history of the basin had to be increased by approximately 1 km, reaching a maximum burial depth around 65 Ma. Because this thermal model matched the observed vitrinite reflectance and the burial model was consistent with that calibrated in 1D models, it was used in the 3D migration modelling. It was assumed that the entire basin underwent uniform burial and uplift; the effects of differential burial and uplift within the EISB are not considered in the 3D migration modelling.

Next, the history of hydrocarbon generation within the basin was reconstructed in order to produce a grid of the amounts of oil and gas generated in each time step included in the modelling. This model incorporated the thermal history of the basin and geochemical parameters for the source rock interval. A mixed Type II/III kerogen with an intitial TOC of 3%, an HI of 250 mg HC per g TOC and a yield of 7.5 kg ton^{-1} was initially used for the hydrocarbon generation modelling. This source rock was assumed to be present and 33 m (100 ft) thick across the whole basin and was projected from a top Carboniferous structure map datum covering the same area as the top Sherwood Sandstone grid. IKU-modified Sweeny & Burnham (1990) kinetic parameters were used to describe the conversion of organic matter to oil and gas. Oil to gas cracking in the source rock was not modelled, and constant gas and oil expulsion efficiencies were used.

Hydrocarbons were injected vertically into the carrier bed from the Carboniferous source, where they are able to migrate in the 3D model according to buoyancy and capillary pressure forces. The Permian sequence was assumed to be completely by-passed by vertical migration, although a permeability reduction in northern part of the basin was included to account for the presence of halite at the level of the St Bees Evaporites (Fig. 3). Pressure data indicate that hydrodynamic flow within the basin is unimportant at the present day and it is assumed to have been negligible in the past. The regional hydrocarbon migration model was developed for the whole of the EISB with a 400 m grid cell size. Trap volumetrics, gas density changes, gas dissolved in oil, gas leakage and oil migration losses during migration were all computed during subsidence for each time step (Sylta 1993).

Hydrocarbon losses during secondary migration were modelled using a constant relative permeability of 0.5. Oil was also modelled to be trapped in microtraps along the migration pathways with lost volumes corresponding to 0.25 Sm^3 per m^2. Even with these losses, the yields and maturities assigned to the source rocks generated sufficient oil to migrate and fill the available traps in the basin.

Cap rock leakage model

A depth-dependent, rate-driven cap-rock leakage model based upon membrane leakage (Watts 1987) was included in the model in accordance with the observation in the EISB that seal capacity is directly related to depth of burial. The Fylde Halite Member was treated as a perfect seal in accordance with the present-day distribution of hydrocarbon accumulations in the EISB and the leakage model was only applied to the Leyland Formation outside the limit of the Fylde Halite Member in the southern part of the basin (Fig. 6). In this model, once the hydrocarbon column capacity is exceeded, traps leak through the cap rock until the column height is restored to the trap capacity. During increasing burial, maximum hydrocarbon column heights increase according to the relationship:

$$\text{column height/carrier depth}$$

where the carrier depth is the depth from the seabed to the top of the carrier bed. In the model, the calibrated maximum column height was 0.2, which means that a carrier bed at 3000 m (10 000 ft) is able to seal a maximum gas or oil column height of 600 m (2000 ft). For single-phase reservoirs the same relationship is used for both oil and gas. For two-phase reservoirs the maximum gas column height is given by:

$$\text{total column} = (\text{gas column} + \text{oil column}) \times (\text{oil density/gas density})$$

Thus, if a trap contains oil and gas the maximum hydrocarbon column height is larger than if the trap contains only gas. The liquid oil phase is assumed to leak at the contact between the cap rock and the gas–oil interface so separate oil column height calculations are performed independent of the gas phase.

Spatial variation in cap rock seal efficiency was implemented in the model by means of a 'mask grid' in which the Fylde Halite Member is interpreted to be present on the basis of its known distribution in wells (Fig. 6), reducing the effective permeability within the grid (and thus leakage) to zero.

Model calibration

The temperature and maturity data available for many wells across the basin (Fig. 3) was used to construct 1D BasinMod and 2D PetroMod models which were then utilized for initial calibration of the 3D model. Subsequent simulations were made to incorporate lateral variation in source-rock quality and seal properties. The initial model parameters contained the assumption that source rocks were of uniform quality across the basin and early model runs generated more oil than is observed at present. Later simulations incorporated the palaeogeographical distribution of the Namurian source rock basins with >10% amorphous kerogen in the Lancaster Fells Basin and <10% amorphous kerogen in the Bowland Basin, and were therefore more gas prone. The lateral change in oil and gas generation potential was accounted for by the use of 'effective yield anomaly' grids which provide considerable freedom in adjusting the model to the observed field data. Such freedom is not used arbitrarily to change the source-rock yield to fit the observed volumes of oil and gas accumulations but rather refinements made during calibration simulations are considered to indicate misrepresentations in the geological model. It is acceptable to increase the gas-proneness of a source-rock area when the model results support such a modification and other geological data indicate that this may be the case. Thus, the modelling provided increased confidence to include a more sophisticated interpretation of the source rock distribution than was initially thought possible with the sparse dataset, placing more Type II kerogen in the south of the basin and a higher percentage of Type III kerogen in the north.

The early model runs also indicated the control on hydrocarbon accumulation in the EISB exerted by seal capacity. Since the South Morecambe Field (crest 730 m, 2400 ft) supports a 410 m (1350 ft) hydrocarbon column, seal capacity was initially interpreted to be excellent throughout the basin. However, the early runs showed hydrocarbon fills in a number of known dry structures. Re-examination of the data showed that of 16 dry holes drilled on apparently valid structures, 10 have crests of <450 m (1500 ft). Using the well database an empirical relationship between column height and depth-to-crest of partially filled structures was used to derive a capillary entry pressure–depth relationship (Fig. 11) based on the equations described by Schowalter (1979) and assuming that traps are in present-day steady state equilibrium. The resulting estimated capillary entry pressures increase with depth, reflecting greater compaction of the cap rock, and mean that it is possible to relate the porosity of the cap rock to capillary entry pressures in order to modify simulations of hydrocarbon leakage in the 3D model.

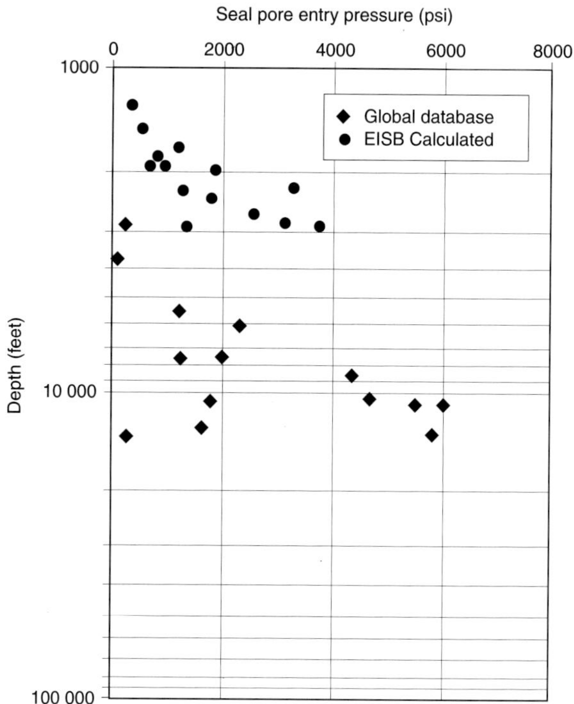

Fig. 11. Calculated capilliary entry pressures (based on Schowalter 1979) for partially filled structures in the EISB plotted against depth, assuming that traps are in present-day steady state equilibrium. Also plotted are capilliary entry pressure measurements of shales from a global database (PetroTech Associates 1994). Although these samples are not direct analogues for the Mercia Mudstone, they exhibit much lower capillary entry pressures than for an equivalent depth in the EISB, consistent with deeper burial of 1–2 km prior to Tertiary inversion.

Migration modelling results

Hydrocarbon (oil and gas) flow rate maps were simulated across the basin in the time steps 180, 144, 97, 65, 60, 2 and 0 Ma using the input data together with petrophysical properties of the carrier bed. These maps provide an aid to understanding the patterns of hydrocarbon migration and accumulation through time. Hydrocarbon flow rate maps of critical time periods in the evolution of the basin are included here to illustrate the history of hydrocarbon migration and accumulation. Interpretation of the relationship between hydrocarbon flow rates and hydrocarbon phase distribution with burial history reveal information on the processes influencing migration and on the mechanisms that provide the driving force for migration. On the hydrocarbon flow rate maps, warmer colours (orange and red) represent areas of high hydrocarbon flow rate, whereas cooler colours (green and blue) depict areas of low migration rates. A $\log_{10}$ scaling is used for the maps, and the units are $\log_{10}(\mathrm{Sm^3\,m^2\,Ma^{-1}})$ for oil and $1000\log_{10}(\mathrm{Sm^3\,m^2\,Ma^{-1}})$ for gas. The actual values plotted in the flow-rate maps are averages of the hydrocarbon flow at that point in the carrier over the time step modelled. Traps are plotted with a bright red colour for the gas cap, and dark blue for the oil leg. Areas of zero flow are shown with a light blue colour. The oil and gas flow rate map time steps included as figures in this paper were chosen to correspond to rapid burial into the oil generation window (180 Ma; Fig. 12), maximum burial (65 Ma; Fig. 13), post-uplift (2 Ma; Fig. 14) and the present-day (Fig. 15), the latter to provide a match with known discoveries. The hydrocarbon phase type and volumetrics through time for the North and South Morecambe fields and the Lennox Field are shown in Fig. 16.

In the flow rate maps it is not possible to separate distinct oil and gas generation windows because, in the modified Sweeny & Burnham (1990) kinetic scheme used to model hydrocarbon generation, these intervals overlap in both depth and time. Gas generation is modelled to start at shallower depths than that

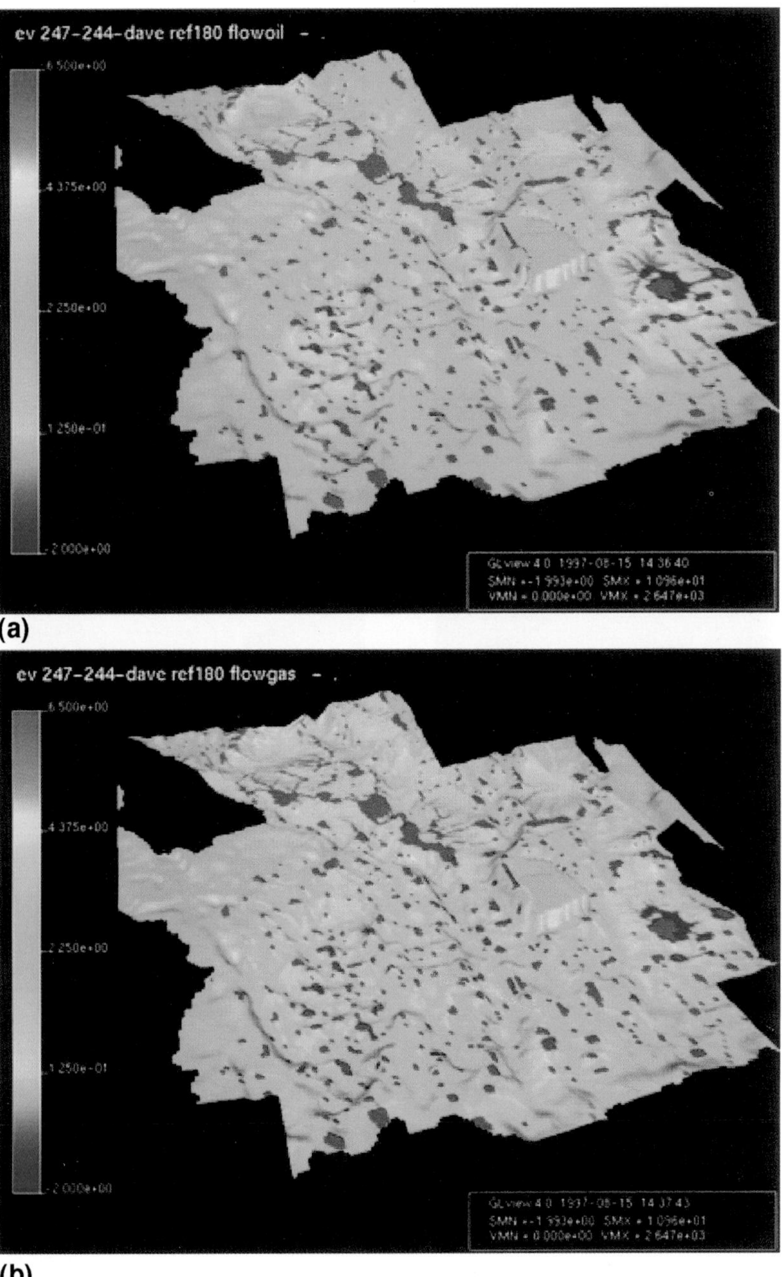

Fig. 12. Hydrocarbon flow rate maps; (**a**) for oil; (**b**) for gas; for the time step 180 Ma. Warmer colours (orange and red) represent areas of high hydrocarbon flow rate, whereas cooler colours (green and blue) depict ares of low migration rates. Flow rate units are $\log_{10}(\mathrm{Sm^3\,m^{-2}\,Ma^{-1}})$ for oil and $1000\log_{10}(\mathrm{Sm^3\,m^{-2}\,Ma^{-1}})$ for gas. See text for description.

which is normally considered to be the depth of the onset of gas generation, while the base of the oil generation window occurs at temperatures usually considered to be within the gas generation window.

Oil flow rates in the period leading up to 180 Ma (Fig. 12a) are high in all the main depocentres but the Keys Basin has already been exhausted of its oil potential and is generating abundant gas (Fig. 12b). The flanks of the basin (Ogham Platform, Lancashire and Cumbrian margins, and the Deemster High) have not yet entered the oil window. Oil and gas migration is already focused, with gas stringers charging many of the traps and feeding structures on the northern margins of the basin, whilst oil stringers are more restricted, but feed structures in the southern part of the basin. Most traps throughout the basin are gas filled at this time, with structures in the northern part of the basin already spilling to the south. The North Morecambe Field is only a small gas accumulation with a discrete oil leg, and oil columns are present in many of the small structures to the south of the South Morecambe Field, in the Godred Croven Basin and in the Lennox Field (Fig. 16). Although not apparent in Fig. 12, because it only depicts the hydrocarbon flows and accumulations at one particular time, by 180 Ma the two phase traps were initially charged with a small oil accumulation before receiving gas from the deeper kitchens, thereby pushing the oil leg deeper. Filling in this manner leaves residual oil saturation in the pore space as the early oil is displaced by gas migrating into the structures.

With further burial, continued hydrocarbon generation is expressed through high oil and gas flow rates in the Sherwood Sandstone. Gas flows remain high as burial continues, but oil flow rates decrease significantly in the northern part of the EISB as large parts of the source rock become exhausted. The time period approaching 65 Ma was characterized by con-

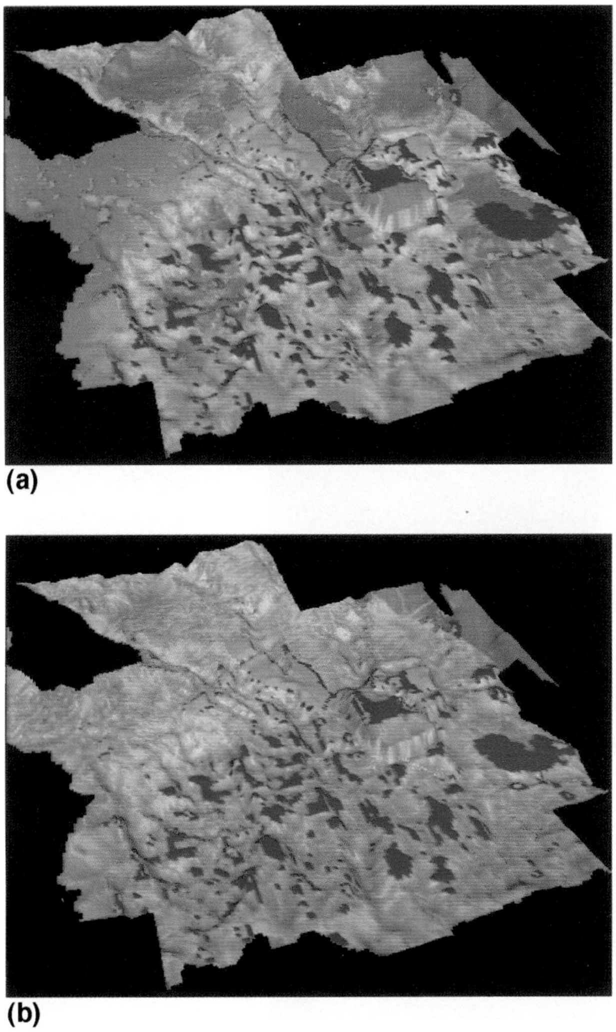

Fig. 13. Hydrocarbon flow rate maps; (**a**) for oil; (**b**) for gas; for the time step 65 Ma. Colours and flow rate units as for Fig. 12. See text for description.

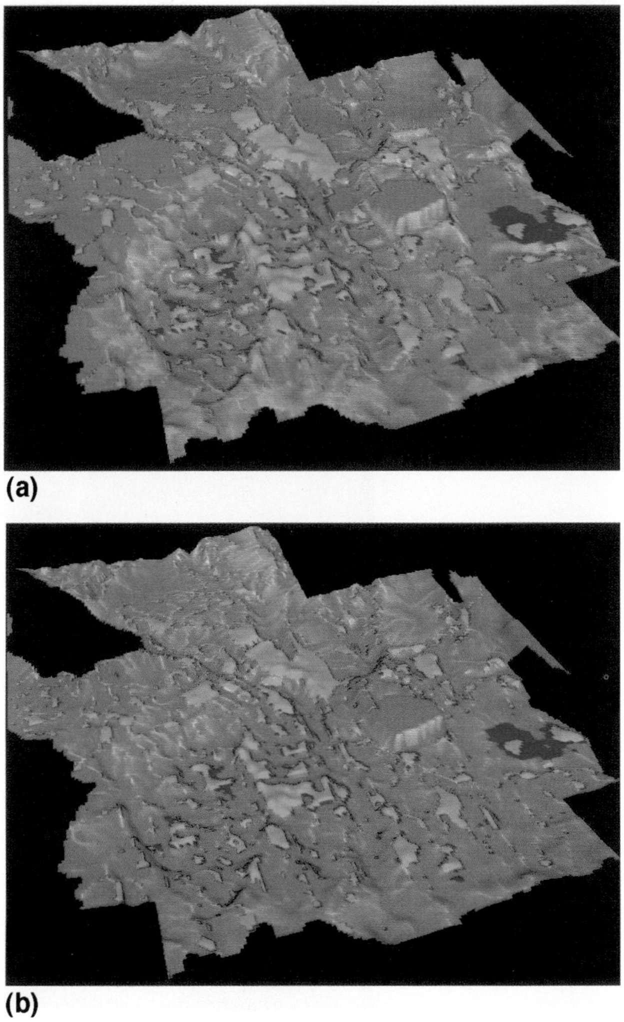

Fig. 14. Hydrocarbon flow rate maps; (**a**) for oil; (**b**) for gas; for the time step 2 Ma. Colours and flow rate units as for Fig. 12. See text for description.

tinued subsidence and overall increased gas generation. While gas generation is primarily modelled to occur in the deeper kitchen areas at 180 Ma (Keys, Eubonia, Godred Croven and Deemster basins), large non-basinal areas have started to generate gas in the period leading up to 65 Ma, when the source rocks were buried to their maximum. There is also significant gas migration as a result of focusing of earlier generated gas on many of the flanks to the deep source kitchens, while migration in the Keys Basin is approaching exhaustion (low flow rates are shown with green colours in Fig. 13b). Comparison of the gas and oil flow rate maps shows that the areas of active oil migration are much smaller than those of active gas migration. This is a result of using a narrower kinetic scheme for modelling oil than gas generation. There is a clear separation into a gas-prone northern basin and an oil-prone southern basin at 65 Ma, with most of the structures in the southern part of the basin containing an oil charge. The North Morecambe Field at this time is gas filled but South Morecambe has an oil leg whilst the Lennox Field has only a small free-gas cap (Fig. 16).

Migration flow rates decrease rapidly during the period of uplift from 60 to 2 Ma (Fig. 14) because of the combined effect of the source rock becoming exhausted of its hydrocarbon potential and because of the lowering of the source-rock temperature (see Fig. 9). Oil and gas flow-rates in this time step are a result of hydrocarbon generation early in the time step, but are averaged over the time interval in the figures. At maximum uplift, 2 Ma, the rates of migration are low across the basin, with highest oil flow rates around the periphery of the basin and highest gas flow rates concentrated around the structural highs. The most important migration

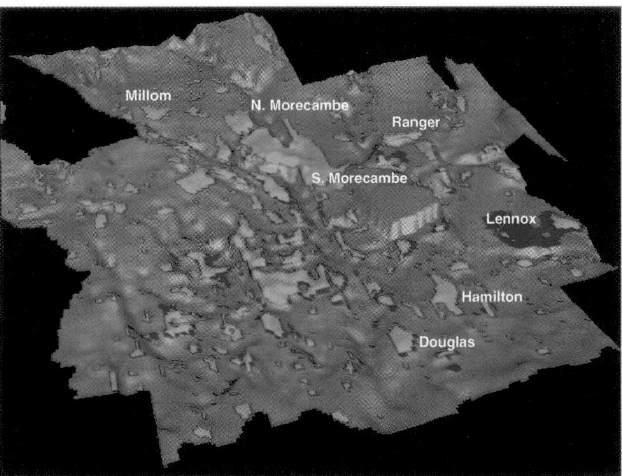

Fig. 15. Present-day distribution of hydrocarbon accumulations. Light blue colour of the carrier indicates no hydrocarbon flow. Traps are plotted with a bright red colour for the gas cap, and dark blue for the oil leg. See text for description.

Erratum

From COWAN, G., BURLEY, S. D., HOEY, N., HOLLOWAY, P., BERMINGHAM, P., BEVERIDGE, N., HAMBORG, M. & SYLTA, Ø. 1999. Oil and gas migration in the Sherwood Sandstone of the East Irish Sea Basin. *In*: FLEET, A. J. & BOLDY, S. A. R. (eds) *Petroleum Geology of Northwest Europe: Proceedings of the 5th Conference*, 1383–1398. Published by the Geological Society, London.

During printing of these two volumes, Figs 10 (p. 1391) and 13–15 (p. 1394) of this paper underwent significant colour change. We apologize for this corruption to the digital files and any embarrassment caused to the authors.

Figure 10 (below) and Figs 13–15 (overleaf) are here printed in their original colours to aid correct interpretation of the hydrocarbon migration rates and hydrocarbon accumulations.

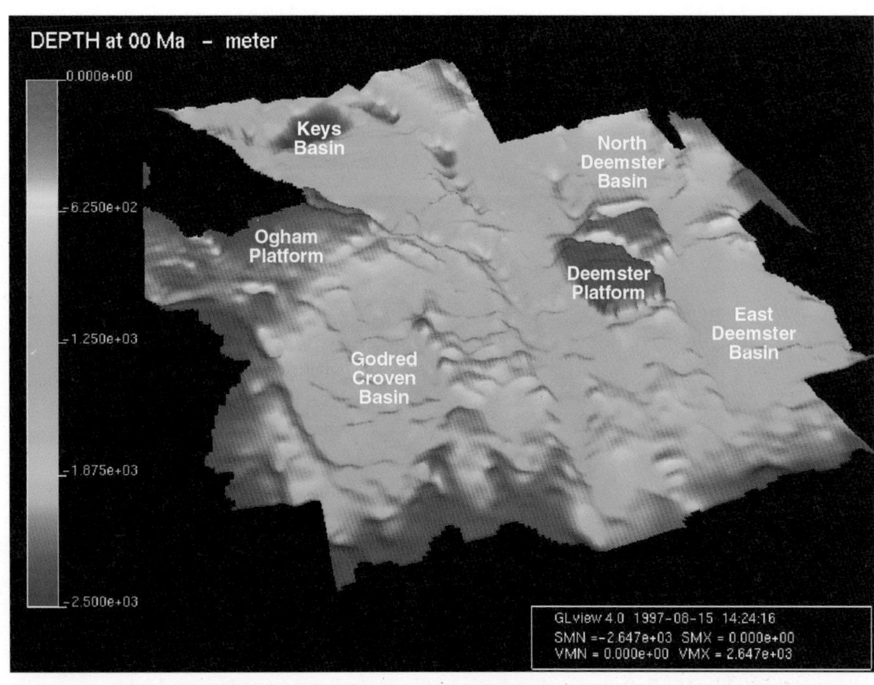

Fig. 10. The regional top Sherwood Sandstone surface, viewed in GLview, dipping to the S, and looking towards the NE. Colour graded for depth: warm colours shallow, blue colours deep. The main basins and the Deemster Platform are clearly visible, and the lineaments that define the Keys and Tynwald faults can be identified. Compare with Fig. 1.

(a)

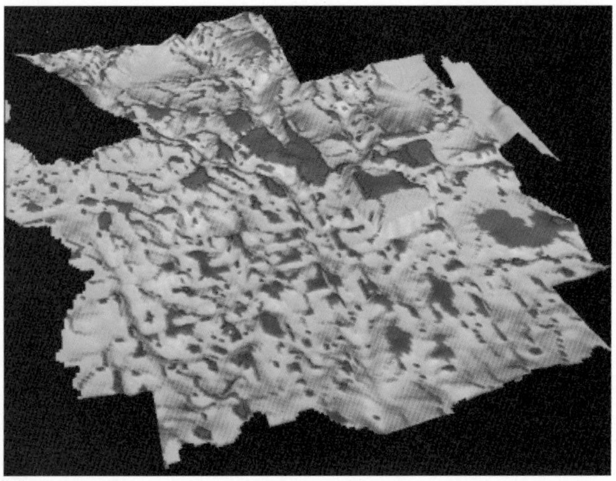

(b)

Fig. 13. Hydrocarbon flow rate maps; (**a**) for oil; (**b**) for gas; for the time step 65 Ma. Colours and flow rate units as for Fig. 12. See text for description.

(a)

(b)

Fig. 14. Hydrocarbon flow rate maps; (**a**) for oil; (**b**) for gas; for the time step 2 Ma. Colours and flow rate units as for Fig. 12. See text for description.

Fig. 15. Present-day distribution of hydrocarbon accumulations. Light blue colour of the carrier indicates no hydrocarbon flow. Traps are plotted with a bright red colour for the gas cap, and dark blue for the oil leg. See text for description.

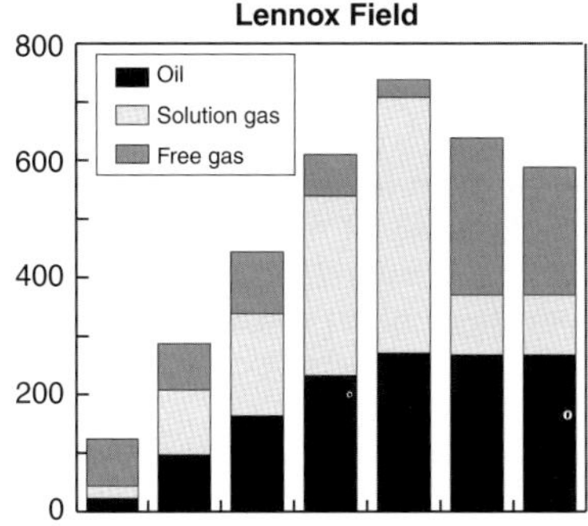

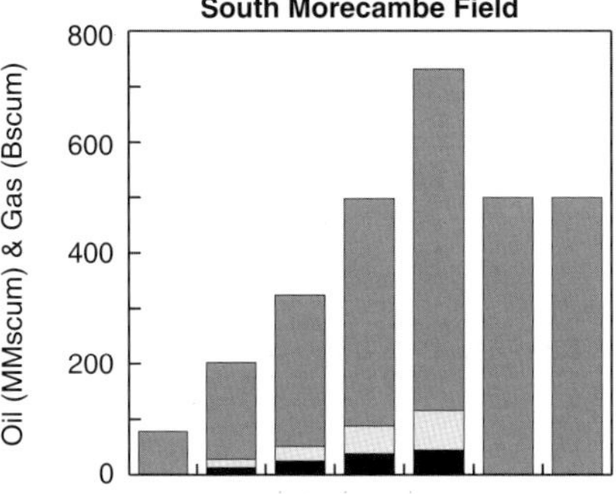

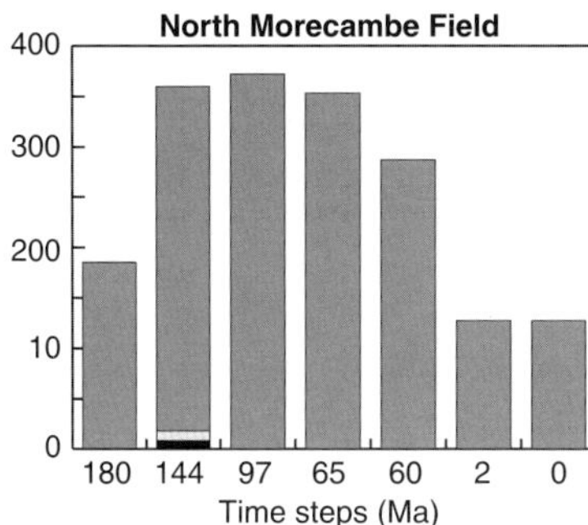

Fig. 16. Histograms of phase type for the North and South Morecambe and Lennox structures showing the evolution of hydrocarbon volumetrics through time. Oil volumetrics in million scum; gas volumetrics in billion scum. Lennox volumetrics shown for the eastern-most of the Lennox structures.

process during these later stages of uplift is the spill of oil and gas out of traps that experience a rapid pressure decrease. The liberation of a gas phase from liquid oil during pressure decrease, and the associated decrease in gas density, causes significant amounts of oil to spill out of the traps. The migrating oil spilled out of the traps over a relatively short time interval because of the rapid expansion of gas during uplift. At this time North and South Morecambe were both completely gas-filled structures, and the expansion of the gas cap is clearly apparent in the Lennox structure (Fig. 16). A direct consequence of the transition from mostly oil trapped at 65 Ma (Fig. 13) to gas trapped at 2 Ma (Fig. 14) would be large volumes of oil migrating laterally out of the EISB towards the west, south and east. Natural oil seeps would have resulted from this process (such as the relic seeps still active in the northern Cheshire Basin and at Formby in Lancashire; Binney & Talbot 1869; Cope 1939; Kent 1947).

During the period from 2 Ma to the present-day, no migration is modelled (Fig. 15), so present-day accumulations are modelled to be virtually identical to those predicted at 2 Ma. Burial beneath a thin uaternary sequence during the last 2 Ma may have resulted in some traps becoming slightly under-filled due to an increase in pressure and thus gas density. The modelled prediction of hydrocarbon phase distribution matches extremely well with present-day distributions of hydro-carbons, with the exception of the Douglas Field, which is modelled as a gas accumulation with an oil leg. However, the general phase distribution is consistent with large gas accumulations in the north of the basin, and mixed oil and gas accumulations in the southern part of the basin.

iscuss ion

Effects of burial history on hydrocarbon migration

One of the striking results of the hydrocarbon migration modelling is the strong influence the burial history exerts on flow rates and resulting hydrocarbon distribution. There are two main components of the burial history in the EISB pertinent to the hydrocarbon system in the Sherwood Sandstone; post-rifting subsidence to maximum burial depths; and uplift in the Tertiary. These two components have driven the secondary and tertiary migration of hydrocarbons throughout the basin.

Rapid burial during the Triassic is required to allow the generation and migration of hydrocarbons into the proto-EISB traps. In the time step leading up to 180 Ma, high flow rates are modelled in the deepest basins. Remarkably, the 3D migration model predicts that all the major proto-structures were charged with hydrocarbons by 180 Ma, including an oil leg in the proto-Morecambe structures, consistent with K–Ar age dating of illites in the Morecambe fields which are interpreted to have formed beneath a palaeo-oil–water contact. It is therefore the rapid burial during the Triassic that initiated the hydrocarbon migration system. Overall maximum flow rates in the basin are, however, modelled during the time step ending at 65 Ma, coinciding with maximum burial, when the basin was separated into two distinct hydrocarbon provinces; mostly gas-filled structures in the north, contrasting with predominantly oil-filled structures in the south.

There is a dramatic decrease in overall hydrocarbon flow rates during Tertiary uplift as source-rock temperatures fall and generation of hydrocarbons slows. Undoubtedly, many of the source-rock kitchens were additionally by now exhausted of their hydrocarbon potential. Secondary migration of hydrocarbons thus declines in importance during the rapid Tertiary uplift. However, the resulting pressure decrease provides a different drive for further migration. During uplift, gas volumes expand because of lower densities and lower gas–oil ratios (GORs) as a consequence of pressure decrease and exsolution. Although minor contraction of gas and liquids is likely to have occurred during uplift and cooling from approximately 90°C to 30°C, this effect will have been more than offset by the pressure drop caused by 1 km of uplift. As an indication of the scale of the gas expansion, PVT (pressure, volume, temperature) analysis of a gas of composition representative of the EISB indicates that the gas would have expanded in volume by 200–300% given an uplift of 2 km, depending on the pre-uplift temperature (Fig. 17). Gas expansion is thus the major driving force for re-migration in the Tertiary and is responsible for displacing most of the oil that was formerly present in the southern province prior to uplift.

Thus the 3D migration modelling approach employed here clearly demonstrates the dynamic nature of the hydrocarbon migration system through time, and the strong influence of temperature and pressure (as reflected in the burial history) on

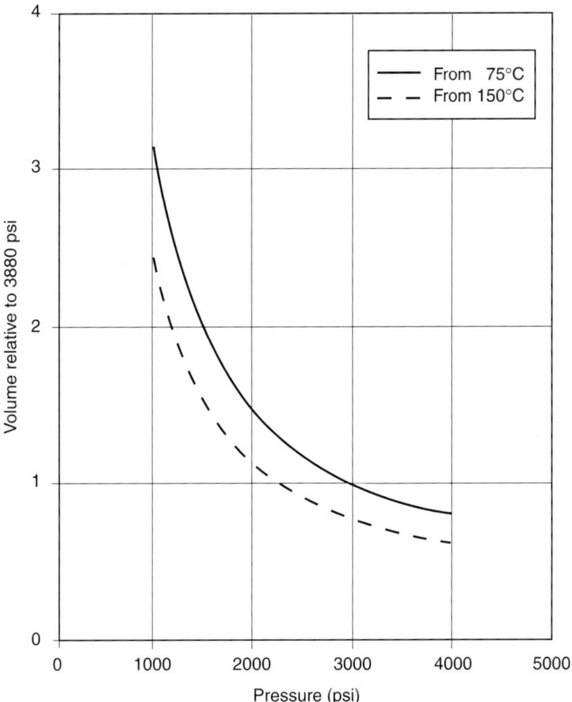

Fig. 17. Change in volume of a representative South Morecambe Field gas sample resulting from uplift from depths equivalent to 75 and 150°C, based on a PVT calculation of the gas expansion factor (in-house BG software). Compressibility factors estimated using standard correlations.

flow rates and migration processes. Remarkably, the hydrocarbon migration system in the EISB has remained active over a 180 Ma history.

Influence of seal

The distribution of shallow dry wells and their relationship to the Fylde Halite Member (Fig. 6) document the importance of the properties of the regional seal on the trapped hydrocarbon phases in the EISB. Wells drilled on shallow structures outside the extent of the Fylde Halite have a high risk of being dry. Additionally, sequential simulations in the 3D migration model with varying seal properties support this inference. A reasonable migration model match to present-day accumulations could not be made without incorporating the northern 'perfect' Fylde Halite seal into the models but at the same time allowing accumulations outside the limits of the halite to leak.

Figure 18 shows the observed empirical relationship between hydrocarbon column height and the minimal crestal depth of structures across the basin. Most of the dry structures occur at depths of <450 m (1500 ft). Structures that are filled to spill show no relationship between depth and hydrocarbon column height as these are limited in terms of their geometry and not the cap rock effectiveness. However, there is a strong relationship between the minimum depth of the structure and and the hydrocarbon column height for partially filled structures. The thickness of the hydrocarbon column in these structures increases in parallel with burial depth, suggesting that the competency of the seal is related to compaction of the Mercia Mudstone. Shallow structures, <450 m (1500 ft) simply lose their hydrocarbon accumulations through tertiary leakage over geological time. The anomalous 410 m (1350 ft) gas column in the South Morecambe Field is an exception to this general trend as this is the only trap in the basin that is directly overlain by salt.

A consequence of this seal model is that gas, in particular, is modelled to leak out of shallower structures where no salt is present. This gas leakage creates space for trapping oil, if there is any oil to trap. Two-phase traps that experience uplift during the period from 60 to 2 Ma are modelled with a strong gas expansion because of the reduced pressures. This gas expansion will be accommodated in some traps by gas leakage from the trap, instead of oil spillage. This is clearly evident in the south of the basin, where two-phase traps are maintained during uplift (Fig. 14).

Most of the structures in the southern part of the basin are single phase oil filled structures at 65 Ma. During uplift the capacity for holding gas in solution decreases as a result of the decreasing pressures. When the GOR decreases, many traps change from single phase oil to 2-phase gas and oil. If too much gas is modelled to come out of solution, it fills the entire structure and causes oil to be spilled into the neighbouring trap or to the basin margins. It is quite important to note that when gas is modelled to exsolve during uplift of single phase oil filled traps from 60 to 2 Ma, some of this gas is also modelled to be lost in the southern part of the basin margins. Therefore, some of the structures maintain their capacity for preserving at least some oil at 2 Ma.

Whilst gas expansion provides a mechanism for expulsion of oil from traps which are now filled to spill with gas, the Morecambe fields are not full and have no oil rims preserved, although they do exhibit indications of a former oil leg in the form of oil staining (Stuart & Cowan 1993; Cowan 1996). Evidence of a previously greater hydrocarbon column is additionally preserved in residual gas saturations of up to 35% below the free water level (FWL) of both fields. Knipe *et al.* (1993) and Stuart & Cowan (1993) have also shown that the Morecambe structures were in existence at the time of illite precipitation at 180 Ma, but were of lower relief than the present-day structures. In this context, the hydrocarbon migration model constructed for this study did not enable palinspastic structural restoration during burial and uplift. As seal leakage during uplift is not a valid mechanism for gas loss in the Morecambe fields which are overlain by salt, another mechanism must have been operative. There is evidence revealed by 3D seismic of gas chimneys and salt movement above the Morecambe structures. Salt movement may have occurred either during Tertiary uplift or may be even more recent. Over 1.5 km of ice was present across the EISB during the Pleistocene, and halokinesis and gas leakage may have occurred during glacial unloading. Whatever the cause, the seismic evidence suggests a local halokinetic contribution in partial seal failure.

Conclusions

The East Irish Sea Basin has a complex burial history which is now well constrained by BHT, shale velocity, VR and AFTA data all best matched with 1 km of uplift in the Tertiary and an increase in heat flow by 60%, some 65–60 Ma. This burial history is paramount in driving secondary hydrocarbon migration through the Sherwood Sandstone of the EISB. Rapid burial provides the driving force for initial oil and gas migration, reaching maximum flow rates coincident with maximum burial. Gas expansion during uplift provides a further drive for oil spillage in the southern part of the basin, indicating that tertiary migration of hydrocarbons had a significant impact on the present-day distribution of hydrocarbons throughout the basin. Much of this re-migration took place during the early Tertiary as fluids and gases expanded due to depressurization. In contrast to the influence of burial history, incorporating lateral variation in the modelled heat flows did not result in an improved match of the migration model to the existing fields in

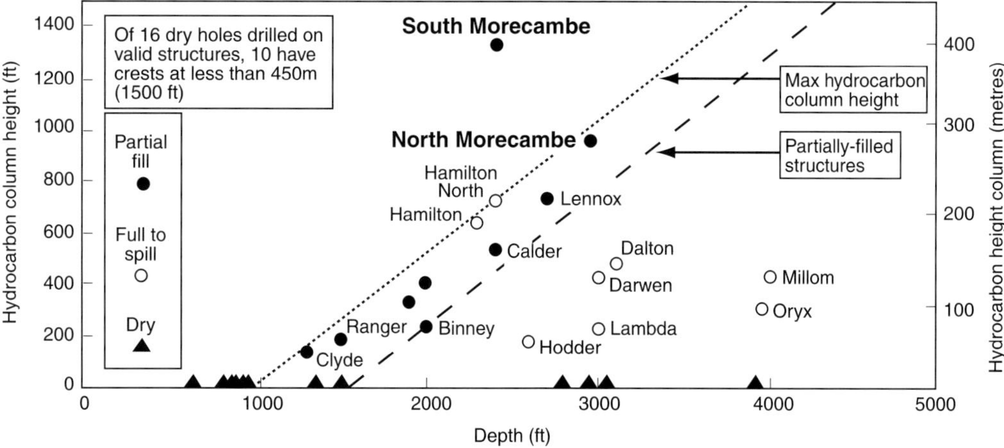

Fig. 18. The relationship between hydrocarbon column height and the minimal crestal depth of structures across the EISB. Note that South Morecambe supports an anomalous hydrocarbon column height because the Fylde Halite directly overlies the reservoir in this structure.

the area. The model was just as easily matched with a simple constant gradient heat flow model using 29°C/km^{-1}.

Source and seal properties are also critical in explaining the present distribution of hydrocarbons. The present day distribution of trapped hydrocarbons (both oil and gas) can only be matched by employing a mixed Type II and III source rock and a laterally varying seal model. This meant incorporating a better quality oil source rock to the south and a very good salt seal to the north. The dividing line between the two areas is inferred to be just south of the Morecambe Field.

The initial hypothesis of a late stage of gas generation, originating in the Keys Basin kitchen, which displaced oil in the Morecambe structures (Cowan & Bradney 1997) may thus be consistent with the secondary hydrocarbon modelling results and remains a useful working hypothesis for the evolution of hydrocarbon generation and accumulation in the north of the EISB. The southern part of the basin is, however, more complex and the earlier oil charge has been displaced southwards as a result of gas expansion during Tertiary uplift. Together, secondary hydrocarbon migration during rapid burial and gas displacement (tertiary migration) during uplift goes a long way to explaining the present-day distribution of hydrocarbons around the EISB. Moreover, the present-day model matched to known hydrocarbon discoveries highlights the potential for finding small accumulations in the largely unexplored south-western part of the basin.

BG Exploration & Production and BG Technology are thanked for permission to publish. Colleagues in BG and IKU Sintef are thanked for helpful discussions over many years on the geology of the EISB and development of SEMI. In particular, the 1996 version of the top Sherwood Sandstone structure map has relied on much work by BG geophysicists. C. Cornford of IGI compiled much of the source-rock geochemical data whilst U. Ritter of IKU helped with the maturity assessments and selection of appropriate kinetics for the 3D migration study. C. Zwach and C. Cornford provided constructive reviews of early drafts of the manuscript for which we are grateful. A. Newsome skillfully turned our sketches into the publication standard figures included here.

eference s

ARMSTRONG, J. P., SMITH, J., D'ELIA, V. A. A. & TRUEBLOOD, S. F. 1997. The occurrence and correlation of oils and Namurian source rocks in the Liverpool Bay–North Wales area. *In*: MEADOWS, N. S., TRUEBLOOD, S. P., HARDMAN, M. & COWAN, G. (eds) *Petroleum Geology of the Irish Sea and Adacent Areas*. Geological Society, London, Special Publications, **124**, 195–212.

ARTHURTON, R. S. 1980. Rhythmic sedimentary sequences in the Triassic Keuper Marl (Mercia Mudstone Group) of Cheshire, northwest England. *Geological ournal* , **15**, 43–58.

BINNEY, E. S. & TALBOT, J. H. 1869. On the petroleum in the Downholland Moss near Ormskirk. *Transactions of Manchester Geological Society*, **8**, 41–46.

BLOW, R. A. & HARDMAN, M. 1997. Calder Field appraisal well, 110/7a-8, East Irish Sea Basin. *In*: MEADOWS, N. S., TRUEBLOOD, S. P., HARDMAN, M. & COWAN, G. (eds) *Petroleum Geology of the Irish Sea and adacent areas*. Geological Society, London, Special Publications, **124**, 387–398.

BURLEY, S. D. 1987. *Diagenetic Modelling in the Sherwood Sandstone of England and its offshore equivalents, UKCS*. PhD Thesis, University of Hull.

BUSHELL, T. P. 1986. Reservoir Geology of the Morecambe Field. *In*: BROOKS, J., GOFF, G. & VAN HOORN, B. (eds) *abitat of Palaeooi c Gas in Europe*. Geological Society, London, Special Publications, **23**, 189–208.

COLTER, V. S. 1978. Exploration for gas in the Irish Sea. *In*: VAN LOON, A. J (ed.) *Key Notes of the MEGS. Geologie en Minbouw* , **57**, 503–516

& BARR, K. W. 1975. Recent developments in the geology of the Irish Sea and Cheshire Basins. *In*: WOODLAND, A. W. (ed.) *Petroleum and the Continental Shelf of North-est Europe*, vol. 1, Applied Science, London, 61–75.

COPE, F. W. 1939. Oil occurrences in south-west Lancashire. *Bulletin of Geological Survey, GB.*, **2**, p. 18.

CORFIELD, S. M., GAWTHORPE, R. L., GAGE, M., FRASER, A. J. & BESLEY, B. M. 1996. Inversion tectonics of the Variscan foreland of the British Isles. *ournal of the Geological Society, London*, **153**, 17–32.

CORNFORD, C. 1998. Source rocks and hydrocarbons of the UKCS. *In*: GLENNIE, K. W. (ed.) *Introduction to the Petroleum Geology of the North Sea* (4th edn). Blackwell, Oxford.

COWAN, G. 1996. The development of the North Morecambe Gas Field, East Irish Sea Basin, UK. *Petroleum Geoscience*, **2**, 43–52.

& BRADNEY, J. 1997. Regional diagenetic controls on reservoir properties in the Millom accumulation: implications for field development. *In*: MEADOWS, N. S., TRUEBLOOD, S. P., HARDMAN, M. & COWAN, G. (eds) *Petroleum Geology of the Irish Sea and Adacen t Areas*. Geological Society, London, Special Publications, **124**, 373–386.

EBBERN, J. 1981. The Geology of the Morecambe Gas Field. *In*: ILLING, L. V. & HOBSON, G. D. (eds) *Petroleum Geology of the Continental Shelf of North-e st Europe*. Heydon, London, 458–493.

FRASER, A. J. & GAWTHORPE, R. L. 1993. Tectono-stratigraphic development and hydrocarbon habitat of the Carboniferous in northern England. *In*: HARDMAN, R. F. P. & BROOKS, J. (eds) *Tectonic Events Responsible for Britains il and Gas Reserves*. Geological Society, London, Special Publications, **55**, 49–86.

Glennie, K. W. & Boegner, P. 1981. Sole Pit inversion tectonics. *In*: Illing, L. V. & Hobson, G. D. (eds) *The Petroleum Geology of the Continental Shelf of North-west Europe*. Hayden, London, London, 110–120.

Green, P. F., Duddy, I. R. & Bray, R. J. 1993*a*. Early Tertiary heating in Northwest England: Fluids or burial (or both) *In*: Parnell *et al.* (eds) *Geofluids 3, Etended Abstracts*, 199–124.

, , & Lewis, C. L. E. 1993*b*. Elevated palaeotemperatures prior to Early Tertiary cooling throughout the UK region: implications for hydrocarbon generation. *In*: Parker, J. R. (ed.) *Petroleum Geology of Northwest Europe: Proceedings of the 4th Conference*. Geological Society, London, 1067–1074.

, & 199 7. Variation in thermal history styles around the Irish Sea and adjacent areas: implications for hydrocarbon occurrence and tectonic evolution. *In*: Meadows, N. S., Trueblood, S. P., Hardman, M. & Cowan, G. (eds) *Petroleum Geology of the Irish Sea and Adacent Areas*. Geological Society, London, Special Publications, **124**, 73–93

Haig, D. B., Pickering, S. C. & Probert, R. 1997. The Lennox oil and gas field. *In*: Meadows, N. S., Trueblood, S. P., Hardman, M. & Cowan, G. (eds) *Petroleum Geology of the Irish Sea and Adacent Areas*. Geological Society, London, Special Publications, **124**, 417–437.

Hardman, M., Buchanan, J., Herrington, P. & Carr, A. D. 1993. Geochemicl modelling of the East Irish Sea Basin: its influence on predicting hydrocarbon type and quality. *In*: Parker, J. R. (ed.) *Petroleum Geology of Northwest Europe: Proceedings of the 4th Conference*. Geological Society, London, 809–822.

Herries, R. D. & Cowan, G. 1997. Challenging the sheet flood myth: the role of water-table-controlled sabkha deposits in redefining the depositional model for for the Ormskirk Sandstone Formation (Lower Triassic), East Irish Sea Basin. *In*: Meadows, N. S., Trueblood, S. P., Hardman, M. & Cowan, G. (eds) *Petroleum Geology of the Irish Sea and Adacent Areas*. Geological Society, London, Special Publications, **124**, 253–276.

Ivimey-Cook, H. C., Warrington, G., Worley, N. E., Holloway, S. & Young, B. 1995. Rocks of Late Triassic and Early Jurassic age in the Carlisle Basin, Cumbria (north west England). *Proceedings of the orkshire Geological Society*, **50**, 305–316.

Jackson, D. I. & Johnson, H. 1997. Lithostratigraphic nomenclature of the Triassic, Permian and Carboniferous of the UK offshore East Irish Sea Basin. *British Geological Survey*, 1–161.

, Mulholland, P. 1993. Tectonic and stratigraphic aspects of the East Irish Sea Basin and adjacent areas: contrasts in their post-Carboniferous structural styles. *In*: Parker, J. R. (ed.) *Petroleum Geology of Northwest Europe: Proceedings of the 4th Conference*. Geological Society, London, 791–808.

, , Jones, S. M. & Warrington, G. 1987. The geological framework of the East Irish Sea Basin. *In*: Brooks, J. & Glennie, K. (eds) *Petroleum Geology of Northwest Europe*. Graham & Trotman, London, 191–203.

, Jackson, A. A., Evans, D., Wingfield, R. T. R., Barnes, R. P. & Arthur, M. J. 1995. *The Geology of the Irish Sea*. BGS UK Offshore Regional Report. HMSO.

Kent, P. E. 1947. Oilfields of Great Britain. *Geography*, **34**, 103–113.

Knipe, R. J., Cowan, G. & Balendran, V. S. 1993. The tectonic history of the East Irish Sea Basin with reference to the Morecambe Fields. *In*: Brooks, J. & Glennie, K. (eds) *Petroleum Geology of North-est Europe: Proceedings of the 4th Conference*. Geological Society, London, 191–203.

Lewis, C. L. E., Green, P. F., Carter, A. & Hurford, A. J. 1992. Elevated K/T palaeotemperatures throughout north-west England: three kilometres of Tertiary erosion *Earth and Planetry Science Letters*, **112**, 131–145.

Marie, J. P. P. 1975. Rotliegendes stratigraphy and diagenesis. *In*: Woodland, A. W. (ed.) *Petroleum and the Continental Shelf of North est Europe*, Vol. 1. Applied Science, Barking, 205–210.

McKenzie, D. P. 1978. Some remarks on the development of sedimentary basins. *Earth and Planetry Science Letters*, **40**, 25–32.

Meadows, N. S. & Beach, A. 1993. Controls on reservoir quality in the Triassic Sherwood Sandstone of the Irish Sea. *In*: Parker, J. R. (ed.) *Petroleum Geology of Northwest Europe: Proceedings of the 4th Conference*. Geological Society, London, 823–833.

PetroTech Associates 1994. A catologue of seal and flow barrier rock types – A multi- company participation project. PetroTech, Houston.

Poole, E. G. & Whiteman, A. J. 1966. *Geology of the Country around Nantwich and hitchurc h*. Geological Survey of Great Britain Memoir, England and Wales, Sheet 122.

Schowalter, T. T. 1979. Mechanisms of secondary hydrocarbon migration and entrapment. *American Association of Petroleum Geologists Bulletin*, **63**, 723–760.

Seedhouse, J. & Racey, A. 1997. Seal characteristics of the Mercia Mudstone Group in the East Irish Sea Basin. *ournal of Petroleum Geology*, **20**, 261–286.

Selle, O. M., Jensen, J. L., Sylta, O., Andersen, T., Nyland, B. & Broks, T. M. 1993. Experimental verification of low-dip, low rate two-phase (secondary) migration by means of gamma-ray absorption. *In*: Parnell, J. *et al.* (eds) *Geofluids 13: Proc. Int. Conference on fluid evolution, migration and interaction in rocks*, 72–75.

Smith, D. B, Brunstrom, R. G. W., Manning, P. I., Simpson, S. & Shotton, F. W. 1974. A correlation of Permian Rocks in the British Isles. *Geological Society, London, Special Report*, **5**.

Smith, N. J. P. 1985. (Compiler) *Pre-Permian Geology of the United Kingdom south.* British Geological Survey 150th Anniversary Publication. Keyworth, BGS.

Stuart, I. A. & Cowan, G. 1993. The South Morecambe Field. *In*: Abbotts, I. L. 1991. *United Kingdom il and Gas elds, 25 ear Commemorative volume*. Geological Society of London Memoir, **14**, 527–541.

Sweeny, J. J. & Burnham, A. K. 1990. Evaluation of a simple model of vitrinite reflectance based on chemical kinetics. *American Association of Petroleum Geologists Bulletin*, **74**, 1559–1570.

Sylta, O. 1993. New techniques and their applications in the analysis of secondary migration. *In*: Dore, A. G. *et al.* (eds) *Basin Modelling: Advances and Applications*. NPF Special Publications, **3**, 385–398.

, Pedersen, J. I. & Hamborg, M. 1998. On the vertical and lateral distribution of hydrocarbon migration velocities during secondary migration. *In*: Parnell, J. (ed.) *Dating and Duration of Fluid Flow and Fluid Rock Interaction*, Geological Society, London, Special Publications, **144**, 221–232.

Thompson, D. B. & Meadows, N. S. 1997. Clastic sabkhas and diachroneity at the top of the Sherwood Sandstone Group, East Irish Sea Basin. *In*: Meadows, N. S., Trueblood, S. P., Hardman, M. & Cowan, G. (eds) *Petroleum Geology of the Irish Sea and Adacent Areas*. Geological Society, London, Special Publications, **124**, 237–252.

Warrington, G. Audley-Charles, M. G., Elliott, R. E., Evans, W. B., Ivimy-Cook, H. C., Kent, P. E., Robinson, P. L., Shotton, F. W. & Taylor, F. M. 1980. *A Correlation of Triassic Rocks in the British Isles*. Geological Society, London, Special Report, **13**.

Watts, N. L. 1987. Theoretical aspects of cap-rock and fault seals for single- and two-phase hydrocarbon columns. *Marine and Petroleum Geology*, **4**, 274–307.

Wilson, A. A. 1990. The Mercia Mudstone Group (Trias) of the East Irish Sea Basin. *Proceedings of orkshire Geological Society*, **48**, 1–22.

Yaliz, A. M. 1997. The Douglas Oil Field. *In*: Meadows, N. S., Trueblood, S. P., Hardman, M. & Cowan, G. (eds) *Petroleum Geology of the Irish Sea and Adacent Areas*. Geological Society, London, Special Publications, **124**, 399–416.

Appendix: A list of common abbreviations

Abbreviation	Meaning
AAI	Absolute acoustic impedance
AI	Acoustic impedance
°API	Oil gravity, American Petroleum Institute degrees
AFTA	Apatite fission track analysis
AST	Aggradational system tract
AVO	Amplitude versus offset (amplitude variation with offset)
BBL	Barrel
BCPD	Barrels of condensate per day
BGS	British Geological Survey
BHT	Bottom hole temperature
BIRPS	British Institutions Reflection Profiling Syndicate
BKB	Below Kelly bushing
BMSL	Below mean sea-level
BOPD	Barrels of oil per day
BOE	Barrels of oil equivalent
BRT	Below rotary table
BWPD	Barrels of water per day
CDR	Common depth ratio
CMP	Common mid point
CNS	Central North Sea
COG	Common offset gather
CRG	Common receiver gather
CSG	Common slowness gather
CSIA	Compound specific isotope analysis
$\delta^{13}C$	Ratio of carbon-13 isotope to carbon-12 isotope measured in a sample relative to a standard
$\delta^{15}N$	Ratio of nitrogen-15 isotope to nitrogen-14 isotope measured in a sample relative to a standard
$\delta^{18}O$	Ratio of oxygen-18 isotope to oxyge-16 isotope measured in a sample relative to a standard
DHI	Direct hydrocarbon indicator
DMO	Dip move out
DSDP	Deep Sea Drilling Project
DST	Drill stem test
DTI	UK Department of Trade and industry
ERD	Extended reach drilling
EWT	Extended well test
FIT	Formation interval test
FSB	Faeroe–Shetland Basin
FT SS	Feet, subsea
GC	Gas chromatography
GC–MS	Gas chromatography–mass spectrometry
GEUS	Geological Survey of Denmark and Greenland
GIIP	Gas initially in place
GOC	Gas–oil contact
GOR	Gas–oil ratio
GRV	Gross rock volume
GWC	Gas–water contact
HDIL	High definition induction log
HI	Hydrogen index
HP/HT	High pressure/high temperature
HST	Highstand system tract
HWC	Hydrocarbon–water contact
IMF	Inner Moray Firth
IOR	Improved oil recovery
KCF	Kimmeridge Clay Formation
Kh	Horizontal permeability
Kv	Vertical permeability
LPG	Liquified petroleum gas
LST	Lowstand system tract
LWD	Logging while drilling
LSW	Lowstand wedge
Ma	million years
mBRT	Metres below rotary table
mD	millidarcies
mfs	maximum flooding surface
MORB	Mid-ocean ridge basalt
MRIL	Magnetic resonance imaging log
ms	milliseconds
N:G (NG)	Net to gross
NGL	Natural gas liquids
NMO	Normal move out
NMR	Nuclear magnetic resonance
NOCS	Norwegian Continental Shelf
NPD	Norwegian Petroleum Directorate
NNS	Northern North Sea
OBC	Ocean bottom cable
OBS	Ocean bottom seismograph
ODP	Ocean Drilling Program
ODT	Oil-down-to
OMF	Outer Moray Firth
OWC	Oil–water contact
PCA	Principal component analysis
PBU	Pressure build-up
PSDM	Pre-stack depth migration
psi	Pounds per square inch
PVT	Pressure, volume, temperature
RFT	Repeat formation test
R_o	Vitrinite reflectance measured using oil immersion objectives
r_o	Resistivity (oil)
RSA	Residual salt analysis
R_W	Resistivity (water)
S_1	Yield during (RockEval) pyrolysis of petroleum-like material contained in sample
S_2	Maximum petroleum yield from kerogen of sample released during (RockEval) pyrolysis of petroleum
SB	Sequence boundary
SCF	Standard cubic feet
SEM	Scanning electron microscope
Sm^3	Standard cubic metres
SNS	Southern North Sea
SrRSA	Strontium isotope residual salt analysis
ss	Subsea
STB	Stock tank barrel
STOIIP	Oil initially in place
S_w	Water saturation
S_{wirr}	Irreducible water saturation
TD	Total depth
TDS	Total dissolved solids
TOC	Total organic carbon
TSR	Thermal sulphate reduction
TST	Transgressive system tract
TVD	True vertical depth
TVDSS	True vertical depth, subsea
TWT	two-way time
UKCS	United Kingdom Continental Shelf
VCS	Vertical cable seismic
V_p	P-(compressional) wave velocity

VR	Vitrinite reflectance
V_s	S-(shear) wave velocity
VSP	Vertical seismic profile
WAG	Water-alternating-gas (oil recovery technique)
WUT	Water-up-to
XRD	X-ray diffraction

Index

Page numbers in **bold** refer to tables and page numbers in *italics* refer to figures

Acadian orogeny 512
acoustic impedance (AI) 1047–1048
Adolphus Field **474**
Aegean Sea, as structural model *147*, 148
Aegir Ridge **42**
aeromagnetic data *see* magnetic data
AFTA *see* apatite fission track analysis
Aghardfjellet Formation 252
AI (acoustic impedance) 1047–1048
Albuskjell Field 912, 913
Alder fan 854
Alexis Formation 510
Alleghenian orogeny 512, 513
Alpha Field 912
Alpha Ridge *172*, *174*, 250
Alpine orogeny 137, 146, 915
aluminium
  export 1345–1347
  mobilization 1340–1341
amplitude studies, seismic resolution enhancement 1047
amplitude *versus* offset *see* AVO
Amroth, sediment log *776*
analogue modelling
  strike-slip fault system
    method 216–217
    results 217–220
    results discussed 221–224
Andrew tuff 651, 655
Anguille Group 513
Anticosti Basin 511–513
Anton Dohrn Lineament 408
Anton Dohrn Seamount **42**, *392*, 401, 579, 586
Anton Dohrn Transfer **42**, 46
apatite fission track analysis (AFTA) 349–350
  Faeroe-Shetland Basin 588
  method 614–615
  North Atlantic margin studies 351–354
  results 616–619
Appalachian Basin, Namurian stratigraphy 760–763
Arbroath Field 1125, 1128, 1129
Åre Formation 1209, 1210, **1213**
  facies analysis 1214
  reservoir geometry modelling 1211–1216
Arenicolites 1034
Argo Formation 504, 520
Argyll Field **474**
Arkwright Field
  coherency study 1302–1304
  development 1128–1133
  discovery 1125–1126
  reservoir characteristics 1126
  volumetric predictions 1126–1128
  well testing 1126
Asterosoma 1191, **1213**
Atlantic margin
  basin modelling 1357–1359
  hydrocarbon expulsion and migration 1360–1361
  hydrocarbon maturation 1360
  large igneous province (LIP)
    flood basalts 574–578
    Iceland plume 573
    sediment sill complexes 578–579
    source rocks 1354–1357
    tectonic evolution 1351–1354
    volcaniclastics 581
    volcano complexes 579–581
  post-Triassic development 231–232
  prospectivity 227–228
  tectonic events
    Caledonian 42–46
    Cretaceous extension 49–51
    Eocene inversion 52–53
    Jurassic uplift 47–49
    Neogene rifting 53–56
    Paleocene magmatism 51–52
    Permo-Triassic extension 46–47
  thermal history reconstruction
    methods 349–350
    results 351–354
Atlantic Ocean (North) 1250
  Caledonian setting 8–11
  Carboniferous setting 15–18
  Cretaceous setting 31–33
  Devonian setting 12–15
  Jurassic setting 20–29
  Permian setting 19–20
  seafloor spreading 8
  Tertiary setting 33–35
Auk Field **474**
Auk Horst 75
Avalon Formation 504, 506, 518
Avalon Uplift 492
AVO
  A + B sections 1291
  A *v.* B crossplot 1291
  case studies
    Barents Sea 1295–1297
    Brent Field 1047
    chalk 928, 943–944
    Greenland West 1292–1295
    Tor Formation 945–947
    West Shetland modelling
      anisotropy 639–641
      conventional model compared 641
      pre-drill model 635–636
      walkaway vertical seismic profile 638–639
      well data 636–638
  effect on well ties 1265, 1270
  theory 1289–1290
Aylesbeare Group 1157

back basin problem *see* Strathmore Field *also* Solan Field
Bacton Group 203, 1300
Baikalian orogeny 248
Bakevellia Basin 204
Balder Formation 1369, *1370*
Balder Graben 386
Balder tuff 650
Banff Field 975
  reservoir properties
    characterization 980–982
    development 979–980
    fracturing 984–985
    lithofacies 984
    modelling development 986–987
    performance 980
    stratigraphy 982
  seismic image 978–979
  structural development 977–978
Banks Group 93, 103, 1235
Barachois Group 513
Barents Sea (Norwegian Sector) 247
  margin areas
    reservoirs and traps 256–257
    source rocks 255–256
    structure 254–255
  platform areas
    evolution 249–250
    reservoirs and traps 252–254
    source rocks 250–252
    structure 248–249
  see also Hammerfest Basin
Barra Fan **42**
Barra Volcanic Complex 579
Barra Volcanic Ridge **42**
basalt
  seismic imaging problems 1243
    relation to Iceland plume 1250–1251
    wide angle data
      acquisition 1245–1246
      interpretation 1247–1248
      processing 1246–1247
Base Cretaceous Event (BCE) 829, *830*, *831*
Base Cretaceous unconformity (BCU) 1014
basement
  gravity anomaly 602
  highs and heat flow 1316
basin modelling
  charge model 1323–1324
  history of 1314–1315
  pressure model 1320–1323
  Rockall Trough 428–430
  thermal model 1317–1318
basinal facies, NE Greenland 331, 333
Bean Basin 410–411
Beatrice Field **474**
Ben Nevis Formation 504, 506, 518
Beothuk Field **474**, **475**
Bernard parameter 802
Beryl Embayment 127
  seismic inversion
    method 1282–1284
    results 1284–1285
    results discussed 1285–1287
  stratigraphy 1281–1282
  structure 1282
Beryl Field 1187
  Beryl Formation reservoir 1188–1189
    cross Field correlation 1192–1195
    depositional model 1195–1197
    engineering properties 1192
    facies analysis 1191–1192
    sedimentology 1189–1191
Beryl Formation 1053, 1054, 1281
Beta North East Terrace 868
beta stretching
  Atlantic margin 1351
  Rockall Trough 429
Billefjorden Fault Zone **42**
biomarkers, marine *v.* non-marine 480–483
biostratigraphy, chalk 916–917
BIRPS Westline 374, *410*
Biscay, Bay of 8
Bivrost Lineament **42**
Bjarni Formation 510
Bjørnøya Basin **42**
Bjørnøya Fan **42**
Black Cove Formation 512
Blackstones 581
Blodøks Formation 915, 919
Boat Harbour Formation 513
Bosies Bank Formation 179
Boss Point Formation 765
Bothnian Senja Shear Zone **42**
Bothnian-Kvaenangen Fault Complex **42**
Bothnian-Senja Shear Zone 46
Bouguer gravity
  Erris Trough 458
  Faeroe–Shetland Basin 601–602
  Intra-Basin 602–603
  Slyne Trough *450*, 451
  see also gravity
Bowland Shale Formation *813*
Brae Field 1347
Brae Formation 855, 1200
Brendan Complex 579

Brent Field 92–93, 1039–1040, 1235
  development 1040–1041
  fault scarp case study
    degradation products 97–102
    external geometry 95–96
    internal structure 96–97
    reservoir potential 103–104
    scarp evolution 102–103
    slope failure 102
  full field simulation model
    applications 1043–1045
    inputs 1041–1043
  hydrocarbon potential 94
  reservoir characterisation 1048–1049
  reservoirs 93
  seismic survey 1045–1047
    resolution enhancement 1047–1048
  structure 93–94
Brent Group 93, **474**, *830*, 1039, 1040, 1063, 1064–1066, 1177, 1235
  reservoir model 1043
Bridport Sandstone Formation **474**
Britannia Field
  history 1115
  modelling
    facies heterogeneity 1120–1122
    well type impact 1122–1123
  reservoir properties 1115–1116
    facies analysis 1116–1117
    stratigraphy 1117–1119
Broadford Beds Formation 446
Brockelschiefer 1300
Brønnøysund Basin **42**
Broom Formation 93, 103, 1043, **1064**, 1177
Buchan fans 855
Buchan Field **474**

^{13}C *see* carbon isotopes
Caister Coal Formation 809, 811, *813*, 816
Caister Field 725, 800
calcite
  cementation in chalk 1223–1224
  in fluid inclusion analysis 620–621, 622–623
Calder Field 1383
Caledonian orogeny and structures 248, 601
  Atlantic margin 8–11, 42–46
  Central North Sea Trough 68, 79
  Irish Rockall Trough 434, 438
  Witch Ground Graben 135
Cambro-Ordovician seeps, Anticosti basin 511
Canada *see* Maritime Basin
Captain Field
  depositional environment 1110–1111
  development problems 1101–1102
  facies analysis 1105–1107
  history 1101
  horizontal drilling 1111–1112
  reservoir architecture 1107–1109
  reservoir stratigraphy 1104
  seismic survey 1104–1105
  structural setting 1102–1104
Captain Ridge 1102, 1104
carbon dioxide in gas 800–802
carbon isotopes 803, 917
carbonate cements 1348
  see also calcite
Carboniferous
  depositional model for Trent Field 816–820
  incised valley fill
    reservoir properties 785
    valley connectivity 777–779
    valley extent 775–777
    valley fill 779–784
  plays
    case study by ribbon interpretation 795–797
    Irish Rockall Trough 441–442
  reservoir rocks
    Barents Sea 252
    Caister Field 725
    Faeroe–Shetland Basin 661
    Newfoundland West 514
    Southern Permian Basin 800
  sediments
    Irish Rockall Trough 434–435
    Slyne Trough 447
  source rocks
    Barents Sea 250
    East Irish Sea Basin 1384
    Erris Trough 463–464
    Newfoundland West 513
    Southern Permian Basin 798–800
  tectonics and palaeogeography
    North Atlantic *12*, 15–18
    West of Shetland 647
  see also Dinantian; Namurian; Westphalian
Carson-Bonnition Basin 501
Cartwright Formation 510, 511
Catoche Formation 513
cementation 1223–1224
Central Graben **42**, **474**, **475**
  gravity gliding 201
  chalk study 1222–1223
    diagenesis and cementation 1223–1224
    fractures 1224–1225
    hydrocarbon emplacement 1225–1226
  overpressure 1341–1342
  pop-up and pull-apart structures 223
  structure 207–210
  see also Arkwright Field; Banff Field; chalk exploration project; Eastern Trough Area Project (ETAP); Elgin Field; Frankin Field; Fulmar Field; Greater Shearwater area; Norwegian Central Graben; Shearwater prospect
Central North Sea Trough 64–66
  Caledonian features 68
  evolution model 75–80
  Jurassic facies 68–75
  salt tectonics 66–68
  structures 66
chalk
  Central Graben study 1222–1223
    diagenesis and cementation 1223–1224
    fractures 1224–1225
    hydrocarbon emplacement 1225–1226
  exploration risks 1221–1222, 1226–1230
  first drilled in North Sea 907
  fluid effects on rock physics 944–945
  petrology 940
  porosity characteristics
    AVO analysis 943–944
    seismic attributes 940–942
    seismic inversion effects 942–943
  reservoir properties, Banff Field 980–987
  seal properties 1093
  sedimentary properties **952**
  seismic inversion 1273
  stratigraphic play concept 912, *915*
  Tor Formation study 945–947
Chalk Exploration project 911–912
  Greater Ekofisk area
    basin evolution 931–934
    chalk stratigraphic plays 912, *915*
    exploration history 912
    exploration model 934
    palaeoenvironment analysis 917–921
    reservoir evaluation 921–929
    sedimentology 921
    source rocks 931
    stratigraphy 915–917
    trap/seal evaluation 929–931
Chalk Group 814, 965, 969, 970, 1015, *1369*
  Fife Field 1138
  hydrocarbon system 932–934
  Mid North Sea High
    erosion 175–177
    seismic analysis 171–175
  Slyne Trough 445
  top chalk surface *176*, *177*
Chanter Field 854, 865
charge modelling 1323–1324
Charlie Gibbs Fracture Zone *392*
Cheshire Basin **475**
Chondrites 966, 968, 1142, 1191, **1213**
chromatograms, Jurassic oils *651*
chronostratigraphy *v.* lithostratigraphy 156–157
Cimmerian unconformity 136
Cimmerian uplift, East Irish Sea Basin 1387–1390
Clair Basin *602*
Clair Field 645, 693, 722
Clair Group 661, *1369*
Clair Ridge *602*
Clare Basin 765, *778*
Claymore Fan 852–853
Claymore Field 851
Clyde Sands 1094
Codroy Group 513
Coffee-Soil Fault 897
coherency
  case studies
    Arkwright Field 1302–1304
    Jaeren High 1304–1305
    Leman Field 1299–1302
  as a tool 1299
coiled tubing side tracking 1070
Commodore Formation 664, 671
concurrency 1070
Connemara Field 242, **474**, **475**
Conona Ridge *602*
constant offset profiling 1245
Conybeare Group *817*
Cook Formation 1177
Cormorant Group 1053, 1063, 1066
Corona Ridge 533, 543, 1377
Cow Head Formation 512
Cretaceous
  compression, Witch Ground Graben 137
  facies analysis
    Kangerlussuaq Basin *339*, 340–342
    NE Greenland 329–333
  migration, Norwegian Central Graben 1336–1338
  palaeogeography
    Irish Rockall Trough *436*
    Norwegian Sea 267–268
  palaeotemperature analysis, Rona Ridge *619*
  plate tectonic modelling, Rockall Trough 361, *364*, *365*
  plays
    Irish Rockall Trough 443
    Norwegian Sea 269
  reservoir rocks
    Barents Sea 254, 256
    Britannia Field 1115–1119
    Captain Field 1104
    Central Graben 1225
    Eastern Trough Area Project 993, 1000
    Foula Sub-basin 664–669
    Greenland (West) 321–323
    Newfoundland Grand Banks 518
    North Sea (North) 232
    Norwegian Sea 278, 279–280
    Porcupine Basin 242
    Vøring Basin 282, 323
  rifting
    Faeroe–Shetland Basin 536–538
    NE Greenland 327–329
  sea-level evidence 334–335
  seal rocks
    Fife Field 1138
    Fulmar Field 1093
  sediments
    Faeroe Shetland White Zone 603
    Rockall Trough 415, 425–427, 436–437
    Slyne Trough 445
  source rocks
    Barents Sea 256

Labrador Shelf 510, 511
Newfoundland Grand Banks 503–504, 506, 507, 508
Vøring Basin 236
stratigraphy
Atlantic margin (North) 231
Banff Field 982
Central North Sea 190
Elgin/Franklin Fields 1014–1015
Foula Sub-basin 664
Trent Field 814
tectonics
Atlantic margin *23*, *25*, 31–33, 1353
Banff Field 977–978
Nordland Ridge 89
North Atlantic margin 49–51
West of Shetland 647–649
volcanics, Northeast Rockall Basin 401
volcano complexes of North Atlantic 579
Cromer Knoll Group 103, *174*, 814, 829, 880, *1369*
Cruiser Formation 664
crustal structure, Rockall Trough 422–424
Cullaidh Shale Formation **475**, 482, 484
Cylindrichnus 1141, 1191, **1213**

Dalle Nacree Formation **474**
Danish Central Graben 897, *898*
see also Gertrud Graben
Darwin Complex 580–581, 586
Darwin Igneous Centre *392*, *396*, 401
Dauntless Field 883, 884–886
debris flow 984
deconvolution processing 1259–1260
Deer Lake Group 513
deltaic facies 1190–1191
deltaic sandstone 343–344
density calculations 602, *603*, **604**
Devonian
reservoir rocks
Barents Sea 252
Faeroe–Shetland Basin 661
sediments, Irish Rockall Trough 434
source rocks, Barents Sea 250
tectonics and palaeogeography
North Atlantic *11*, 12–15
West of Shetland 647
diagenesis
chalk 921, 1223
Fulmar Formation 1018, 1345
diffusivity, Piper Formation 1081
Dinantian stratigraphy *see under* North Sea (South)
Diplocraterion 1141, 1142, 1191, **1213**
Donegal Basin *404*, 409
Dønna Terrace 83, 263, 264
Doon Rock Fault 438
Douglas Field 1383, *1384*
Downing Formation 504
Draupne Formation 827, 829, *830*, *831*, 836
seismic nature 833–835
stratigraphic architecture 829–832
drilling technology, Tern Field 1069–1074
Dun Caan Shale **475**
Dunlin Group 93, 103, 1039, 1040, 1235
Durward Field 883, 884–886
Dyroey Formation **474**

Eakring Field **474**
East Central Graben, salt tectonics 185
East Faeroes High **42**, *602*
East Greenland Rift **42**
East Hatton–Rockall Basin Centre 579
East Irish Sea Basin
burial history 1387–1390
hydrocarbon migration model
method 1390–1392
results 1392–1395
results discussed 1395–1397
rift-raft morphology *208*
reservoir rocks 1386
seal rocks 1386–1387
source rocks 1384–1386
structure 206–207, 1383–1384
Triassic lithostratigraphy 206
East Jan Mayen Fracture Zone **42**
East Midlands oilField 748–754
East Midlands Shelf *774*
East Piper High 856
East Shetland Basin *see* Brent Field; Strathspey Field
East Shetland Platform 232
East Solan Basin *694*, 701
Eastern Graben *1030*
Eastern Interior Basin 764
Eastern Shoals Formation 518
Eastern Trough Area Project (ETAP)
development 993–994, 1004–1005
reservoir behaviour 994–1004
Edale Gulf *778*, *781*
Edda Field 912, 913, 940–941
Edgeøya Platform 248
Egmanton Field **474**
Egret Field
development 993–994
reservoir **994**, 1002
Egret Formation **475**
Eider Field 1066–1067
Eiriksson Formation 1053
Ekofisk Field **474**, 912, 913, 915, *941*, 945, 1147, 1255
3D borehole profile
acquisition 1255–1256
processing 1256–1260
results 1260–1261
results discussed 1261–1264
Reservoir Characterization Project
3D model 1153–1154
anisotropy 1152–1153
architecture 1148
description 1147–1148
facies analysis 1150
fault analysis 1150
permeability 1151–1152
porosity 1150
seismic monitoring 1154–1155
upscaling 1154
water saturation 1150–1151
see also Chalk Exploration Project
Ekofisk Formation 177, **474**, 915, 917, 920–921, *923*, *928*, *929*, 967, *972*, 973, 975, 982
Eldfisk Field 912, 913, 941, 945
Elgin Field
geophysics 1015
history 1007–1008
reservoir rocks 1018
source rocks 1018–1019
stratigraphy 1008–1015
trap type 1015–1018
England (Northern)
Tertiary Volcanic Province 354
thermal history reconstruction 354–355
Eocene
generation of oil, Norwegian Central Graben 1333
inversion, North Atlantic margin 52
sediments
Faeroe Shetland White Zone 604
Irish Rockall Trough 437
North Sea (Central) 1348
Northeast Rockall Basin 400
Norwegian Sea 295–296, 298
Rockall Trough 417
tectonics and palaeogeography
North Atlantic *33*
West of Shetland 650
volcanics, Slyne Trough 445
Eqalulik type oil 311–312
Erlend Complex **42**, 580, 586
Erlend Platform 261
Erlend Transfer **42**
Erris Ridge 438
Erris Trough **42**, *404*, 410, *411*, 455–456
burial history model
inputs 464–466
results 466–468
evolution 461–463
hydrocarbon potential 463–464
morphology 456
prospectivity **227**
stratigraphy 457–459
structural evolution 240–242
structure 459–461
Etive Formation 93, 103, 1043, **1064**, 1065–1066, 1177
Ettrick fans 855
Euramerican Carboniferous basins *758*, *761*
European Basin, Namurian stratigraphy 764–765
Eurydice Formation 504, 520
Evvia 108
expulsion of hydrocarbons, modelling characteristics 1330
extended reach drilling 1070

facies analysis
Beryl Formation 1191–1192
Carboniferous
Pennines 748–754
Southern Permian Basin *799*
chalk 921
Cretaceous
Captain sandstone 1105–1107
NE Greenland 329–333
high density turbidite 1116
Jeanne d'Arc Basin 498
Jurassic
Central North Sea Trough 68–75, 79–80
Fife Field 1140
Fulmar sands 1093–1094
Kangerlussuaq Basin *339*, 340–344
Porcupine Basin 496
slurry flow 1116–1117
Tilje/Åre Formations 1210–1211
facies modelling, Brent Field 1044
Faeroe Basalt Plateau 559
development interpreted 561–564
seismic resolution 560–561
stratigraphy 565–567
Faeroe Basin *602*, **647**, *694*
Paleocene
geophysical properties 631–633
petrology 630–631
reservoir properties 628
sedimentology 628–629
stratigraphy 627–628
Faeroe Channel Basin *602*
Faeroe Channel Knoll 579, *602*
Faeroe Group *1369*
Faeroe Islands, basalt stratigraphy 565
Faeroe Plateau Lava Group 574–578
Faeroe Shelf
prospectivity **227**
structural evolution 237
Faeroe-Shetland Basin 8, **42**, *56*, 237, *392*, 560, 585–586, *602*, 661–662
compression event 541–542
development of rifting
basement 533
Cretaceous 536–538
Jurassic 535–536
Paleocene 538–541
Permo-Triassic 533–535
gravity modelling 601–602, 604–605
heat flow modelling 541
method 588–589
results 589–591

Faeroe–Shetland Basin (*continued*)
igneous rocks
central complexes 550–551
dyke swarms 548
lavas (central volcanoes) 551–553
lavas (regional) 546–548
sills 550
prospectivity **227**
sequence stratigraphy 564
underplating 586–588
see also Foula Sub-basin
Faeroe–Shetland Channel Sub-basin **647**
Faeroe–Shetland Escarpment 561, 563–564, *602*
Faeroe–Shetland Intrusive Complex 578–579, 586
Faeroe–Shetland White Zone 601
maturity 607
migration model 608–610
overpressure 607–608
sedimentary history 603–605
source rocks 605
structural elements 601–603
tectonic episodes 601
thermal model 605–607
Faeroes Dome **42**
Faeroes Large Aperture Research Experiment (FLARE)
seismic section interpretation
effect of basalt 1247–1248
geological significance 1249–1251
velocity model 1248–1249
wide angle data
acquisition 1245–1246
processing 1246–1247
Fairhead-Clewbay Fault 438
fan sandstone 342–343
Fangst Group 1209
Farewell Rock sediment log *776*
Farsund Formation 897, *898*, 899, 902, 1225, 1325, 1333
fault analysis
Brent Field 1044, 1046
Hibernia Field
genesis 523–525
trends 519–523
ribbon interpretation 795–796
fault scarp degradation 91
Brent Field case study
degradation products 97–102
external geometry 95–96
internal structure 96–97
reservoir potential 103–104
scarp evolution 102–103
slope failure 102
slope instability 91–92
fault seal analysis 1177–1179
methods 1179–1180
results 1180–1184
Feda Graben *898*, *1030*
feldspar 620, 622, 1340–1341
Fell Sandstone Formation 800
depositional model 740–742
reservoir potential 735–736
Feni Ridge 412
Fife Field
development history 1135–1136
reservoir characterisation
facies analysis 1140–1142
modelling behaviour 1143–1145
sedimentology 1138–1140
sequence stratigraphy 1142–1143
stratigraphy 1138
structure 1138
well database 1136–1138
Fisher Bank Basin 120–123, *124*, 204, *1030*
Fladen Ground Spur 119–120, *122*, 844, 855
Palaeozoic sequences 138
seismic line *139*, *146*
Fladen Group 1014, 1078
FLARE *see* Faeroes Large Aperture Research Experiment
flaser bedding 1191
Flemish Pass Basin *505*, 507–509
Fles Fault Zone **42**, 263, 264
Flett Formation 1369, *1370*
Flett Ridge *602*, 604, 672
Flett Sub-basin 645, *646*, **647**, *694*, 1377
fault trends 650
petroleum systems analysis 657
reservoir rocks 654–656
seal rocks 656
seismic analysis 657
source rocks 652–653
Tertiary stratigraphy *649*
trap structure 656
flood basalts, North Atlantic LIP 574–578
fluid flow, Central Graben 1342–1345
fluid inclusion analysis
method 615–616
results 619–623
fluvial complexes, multistorey 773–775
fluvial facies 748–752
fluvial sandstone 343–344
fluvio-deltaic facies 329
fluvio-estuarine sandstone 340–342
Foinaven Field 693
appraisal 677–678
pressure build-ups 681–682
reservoir management 679–681
reservoir properties 678–679
structure 676–677
Foinaven Sub-basin 645, *646*, **647**
fault trends 650
petroleum systems analysis 657
reservoir rocks 653–654, 654–656, 657
seal rocks 656
seismic analysis 657
source rocks 651–652
Tertiary stratigraphy *649*
trap structure 656
footwall degradation *see* fault scarp degradation
Forth Approaches Basin, salt tectonics 184
Forth Formation 865
Forties Field **474**
Forties Sandstone Formation **474**, 1126, 1302
Forties–Montrose High 1342
Fortune Bay Formation 493
fossils, role in correlation 155, *339*
see also trace fossils
Foula Group 661, **695**, 700–704
Foula Sub-basin **647**
reservoir properties 664–669
stratigraphy 664
structure 662
Turonian palaeogeography 670–672
fractures
chalk 984–986, 1224–1225
modelling behaviour in migration 1331, 1332–1333
fragmentograms, West Greenland seepages *309*, *310*, *311*, *312*
Franklin Basin *120*
Franklin Field
geophysics 1015
history 1007–1008
reservoir 1018
source rocks 1018–1019
stratigraphy 1008–1015
trap type 1015–1018
Frigate Formation 157
Froan Basin **42**
full field simulation model (FFSM)
Brent Field 1041
application 1043–1045
inputs 1041–1043
Fulmar Field 211
by-passed oil potential 1098–1099
history 1089–1090
performance 1090–1091
reservoir facies 1093–1094
reservoir modelling 1091
sediment architecture 1096–1098
stratal stacking 1094–1096
structural setting 1092–1093
Fulmar Formation 153, 157, 1014, 1021, 1090–1091, 1340
illite growth 1345
petrography 1340
porosity 1340–1341
pressure model 1320–1323
seismic character 1346–1347
seismic inversion studies 1273–1274, 1274–1279
West Central Shelf distribution 880
depositional environment 880
provenance 889
Fulmar Terrace 211
Fylla 1292
AVO analysis 1292
reservoir interpretation 1292–1295

Gainsborough Field **474**
Galicia Bank Basin **42**
Galley Central High 846
Galley Fan 854
Galley Field 874
Galway Graben 410–411
Gamma Field 912, 913
gamma ray logs, Brent Field *97*, *98*
Gamma structure 863
Gardarbanken High 249
Garn Formation 265
gas chromatography, West Greenland seepages **308**, *309*, *310*, *311*, *312*
gas composition, Southern Permian Basin 800–803
gas generation modelling 1330
Geike Centre 579
Geike margin **42**
genetic stratigraphy 154
geochemistry applied to source rocks
methods 476–477
results 477–484
result discussed 484–485
Gertrud Graben 897–899
lithological setting 903–904
sedimentology 902–903
seismic facies 899
seismic inversion 899–902
Gjallar Ridge **42**, 263, 264, 269, 279, 323
glacioeustasy, Carboniferous 752, 757, 766
Glen Ridge 845
Glenworth Field **474**
Goban Spur *404*
Goose Tickle Group 513
Grand Banks *see* Newfoundland Grand Banks
gravity
NE Rockall Basin 379–382
Rockall Trough 427–428
West of Shetland *694*
gravity slides 113
Great Glen Fault 10, **42**
Greater Ekofisk area *see* Chalk Exploration Project
Greater Shearwater area
Jurassic sequence stratigraphy
Kimmeridgian 164–167
Oxfordian 157–163
Green Point Formation 512
Greenland (East) *404*
lava correlations 567–569
see also Kangerlussuaq Basin
Greenland (NE)
controls on sedimentation 333–335
Cretaceous facies analysis 329–333
Cretaceous rift events 326–329
structure 325–326

Greenland (West) 1292
  AVO analysis 1292
  exploration history 315–317
    geological evolution 318–319
    reservoir rocks 321–323
    trap types 323
  reservoir interpretation 1292–1295
  see also Nuussuaq Basin
Griesbachian Shale **695**
Gudrid Formation 510
Gullfaks Field
  fault seal study 1177–1179
    methods 1179–1180
    results 1180–1184
  reservoir properties 1177
  structure 1177

Haisborough Group 203
Halibut Horst 844–845, 855, 856–857
Halibut Platform 863
Halibut Shelf *122*
Halten Terrace **42**, 83, 263, 264
  geophysical properties 284–285, *286*
  structural evolution *56*, 232–233
  thermal model 1318
Haltenbanken *see* Heidrun Field
Hammerfest Basin **42**, 1295–1296
  AVO analysis 1296–1297
Hampshire Basin **474**
Hardangerfjord Shear Zone **42**
Hardegsen unconformity 203, 213
Hatton Basin 414
Hatton Trough **42**
Hauptdolomite **474**
heat flow equations 1316
heat flow modelling
  method 588–589
  results 589–591
  study areas
    East Irish Sea Basin 1387
    Faeroe–Shetland Basin 541
    Faeroe–Shetland White Zone 605–607
Heather Formation 93, 102, 157, 605, 827, 829, *830*, *831*, 836, 1014, 1021, 1281, *1284*
heavy mineralogy 177
  Cretaceous, Norwegian Sea 279–280
  Helland Hansen 282
Hebrides Basin *404*, **475**, 476
  source rocks *480*, *481*
Hebrides Terrace Seamount 581
Hebron Field **474**
Heidrun Field **474**, 1209–1211
  facies analysis 1210–1211
  reservoir modelling
    data 1211–1216
    results 1216
    uncertainty analysis 1217–1219
  stratigraphy 1210
Hekkingen Formation 252
Hel Graben **42**
Helland Hansen licence
  depositional model 291
  geophysical modelling 284–286
  lithologies 286–291
  reservoir properties 282
  seismic characterization 282–284
  structural setting 282
Helland-Hansen Arch **42**, 264
Helminthopsis 1189, 1190, 1191
Heno Formation 897, *898*
Heno Plateau *898*
Hercynian unconformity 447
Heron Field
  development 993–994
  reservoir **994**, 1001–1002
Hibernia Field **474**, 517–518
  lithostratigraphy 518–519
  reservoir character 525–526
  structural patterns
    fault genesis 523–525
    fault trends 519–523
Hibernia Formation **474**, 493, 504, 506
Hidra Formation 915, 917, 919, *922*
high pressure/high temperature plays defined 989
Highland Boundary Fault 10, **42**
Highlander-Piper High 846
Hod Field 912, 913, 949
  chalk core details 952
  cross section 955
  stratal thicknesses 952–953
  stratigraphy 949–951
  structure 951–952
Hod Formation 915, 917, 919–920, *922*, *929*, 950, 952
Hold with Hope Group 325
  facies analysis 329–333
Holywell Shale **475**, 1384
Home Forland Formation 325
Hopedale Basin 509
Horda Platform 232
horizontal drilling 1111–1112
  see also Nevis Field
Hornsund Fault Zone **42**
Horseshoe Basin 501
Hospital Ground Formation 800
Hot Lens 867
Hot Sand 867
Howley Formation 513
Humber Group 93, 102, 157, *174*, 1014, 1054, 1281, *1284*, 1340, *1369*
  Outer Moray Firth study
    biozones *841*
    depositional history *844*, *845*, 846
    lithostratigraphy *841*
    origins 855–858
    sequence stratigraphy *841*
      sequence description 847–855
      terminology 842–843
  see also Fulmar Formation; Kimmeridge Clay
hydrocarbon generation modelling
  inputs 1327, 1330
  outputs 1333–1336

Iapetus Suture **42**
Iceland plume 573–574, 650, 1250–1251
ichnofabric and icnofacies
  Fife Field 1141
  Fulmar sands 1093–1094
  West Central Shelf 880
igneous activity *see* magmatism
Ile Formation 265
illite 1345
incised valley fill (IVF) 766
  recognition 775
  Trent Field 817–818
  Upper Carboniferous examples
    reservoir properties 785
    valley connectivity 777–779
    valley extent 775–777
    valley fill 779–784
Inner Moray Firth 64, *65*, 120–123, *124*, **474**, **475**
  pull-apart basin 222
  thermal model 1317–1318
Inner Snørre Fault 107, 108–109
Innuitian orogeny 248
intrusive igneous rocks *see* sill complexes
inversion events
  Central North Sea 193–195
  Tertiary 35
    Rockall 452
Iona Field 865
Irish Rockall Trough *see* Rockall Trough (Irish sector)
Irish Sea *see* East Irish Sea Basin
Iroquois Formation 504, 520
Itilli type oil 310–311

J Ridge 154
Jackfork Sandstone 764
Jacqui Graben 75
Jaeren High
  coherency study 1304–1305
  salt tectonics 184–185
Jan Mayen Lineament **42**, 46, *262*, 263
Jeanne d'Arc Basin **42**, 473, **474**, **475**, 476, 504–507
  facies analysis 498
  sedimentation 491, 492–494
  source-rock correlations 477–485
  tectonic history 488–491
  see also Hibernia Field
Jeanne d'Arc Formation **475**, 483–485, 492, 496, 498, 504, 506, 518
Joggins Formation 766
Judd Basin *694*
Judd Fault Complex *602*, *694*
Judd High **647**, *694*
Judd Platform *602*
Judd Transfer **42**
Jurassic
  facies analysis, Fife Field 1140
  migration, Norwegian Central Graben 1336
  palaeogeography 1205
    Grand Banks 490
    Irish Rockall Trough *436*
    Norwegian Sea 265–267
  plate setting, Slyne Trough *452*
  plays, Irish Rockall Trough 442
  reservoir rocks
    Barents Sea 254, 256
    Beryl Formation 1054
    Brae Formation 1200
    Brent Field 93
    Brent Group 1039, 1063, **1064**, 1235
    Elgin/Franklin Fields 1018
    Faeroe–Shetland Basin 661
    Fife Field 1138
    Fulmar Formation 1089, 1090
    Fulmar Sandstone 1340
    North Sea (North) 232
    Solan Field 705–706
    Tilje/Are formations 1211–1216
  rifting, Faeroe–Shetland Basin 535–536
  seal rocks 93, 1093, 1138
  sediments
    Central North Sea Trough 68–75
    Faeroe Shetland White Zone 603
    Gertrud Graben 902–903
    Irish Rockall Trough 435–436
    Jeanne d'Arc Basin 491, 492–494
    Northeast Rockall Basin 399
    Porcupine Basin 491–492, 494–496
    Rockall Trough 415, 427
    Slyne Trough 445–446
    see also Humber Group
  sequence stratigraphy
    Fife Field 1142–1143
    Greater Shearwater 157–167
    Telford Field 1078–1080
    West Central Shelf 881–886
  source rocks
    Atlantic margin 1354
    Barents Sea 252, 255
    Central Graben 1225
    Erris Trough 464
    Faeroe–Shetland Basin 237
    Halten Terrace 233
    Hebrides Basin 476, *480*
    Irish Rockall Trough 440
    Jeanne d'Arc Basin 473, *480*
    Kimmeridge Clay 1340
    Minches Basin 476, *480*
    Newfoundland Grand Banks 502, 505, 507, 509

Jurassic, source rocks (*continued*)
North Sea (North) 232
Norwegian Central Graben 1325, 1333
Porcupine Basin 242, 472, *480*
Rockall Trough 240
Slyne Trough 476, *480*
Solan Field 711
West of Shetland 651
West Shetland 1377
stratigraphy
Atlantic margin (North) 231
Central North Sea 187–190, 1032–1033
Elgin/Franklin Fields 1014
Tampen Spur 827–828, 829–832
Trent Field 814
Witch Ground Graben 140–141
tectonics
Banff Field 977
Nordland Ridge 87–88
North Atlantic margin 47–49
North Sea 117
West of Shetland 647
Witch Ground Graben 141–143
tectonics and palaeogeography *18*, 20–29, 1353
thermal doming, Witch Ground Graben 136, 138–139
unconformities, North Sea 117–118

Kangerlussuaq Basin 337
basin evolution 339
petroleum potential 344–345
sandstone wedges 340–344
stratigraphy 337–339
kaolin, role in diagenesis 1347
Kenamu Formation 510, 511
Ketch Field 800
Keys Fault *208*
Kimmeridge Clay Formation 93, 157, 388, **474**, **475**, 483–485, 535, 603, 605, *607*, *608*, 650, **695**, 704–706, 711, 827, 851, 880, 1014, 1080, 1089, 1093, *1284*, 1340
Fife Field 1138
seismic inversion 1273, 1279
vitrinite reflectance data *1375*
West Shetland 1377, 1380
Kinderscout Grit *778*, *781*
Kingfisher Field 1200
Kittiwake Field 879, 880–881
sequence stratigraphy *881*, 882–883, 886
Knipovitch Ridge **42**, 254
Kolbeinsey Ridge **42**
Kong Karls Land Platform 248
Kraka Field 912
Kuugannguaq type oil 310

Labrador Sea 8
Labrador Shelf *505*, 509–511
lacustrine facies *749*
Lamba Formation 1369, *1370*
Lange Formation 268, 282
Laramide events 177
large aperture recording 1245
Lealt Formation 484
Leman Field 1299–1302
Lennox Field 1383, *1384*
Leyland Formation 1387
Lindesnes Ridge 913, 941
Lista Formation 177
lithofacies analysis 984
lithostratigraphy *v.* chronostratigraphy 156–157
Little Minch Trough, thermal history reconstruction 353
Loch Lomond Prospect 669
Lofoten Line **42**
Lofoten Ridge 263
Logan Canyon Formation 503
Lola Formation *898*
Loppa-Ringvassoy Fault Complex **42**

Lowlander Field 868, *872*
Loyal Field 683–684
development 691
gas management 691–692
history 684
reservoir properties 686–691
seal rocks 686
seismic data 684–685
structure 685–686
trap type 686
Luva structure 275, *276*
reservoir/play behaviour 278–280
seismic evaluation 275–278
Lysing Formation 268, 278, 282

Machar Field
development 993–994
reservoir **994**, 999–1001
Madgard Field **474**
magmatism
Norwegian Sea 272
Palaeogene, Faeroe–Shetland Basin 546–553
West of Shetland 650
see also Atlantic margin large igneous province (LIP)
magnetic data, NE Rockall Basin 382
magnetic resonance imaging log (MRIL) 632
Magnus Field **474**
Mammal Centre 579
Mandal Formation 931, 1225, 1325, 1333
Mandal High 897
marine shelf facies, NE Greenland 330–331
Maritimes Basin 513–514, 765–766
Markland Formation 510, 511
Marnock Field
development 993–994
reservoir 994–996
Marnock Sands 185–186
Marraat type oil 309–310
Marulk Basin 107
maturity
Barents Sea 257
modelling in Faeroe Shetland White Zone 607
Southern Permian Basin 800
Maureen Formation 177
maximum flooding surfaces (mfs)
Greater Shearwater area
Aemula 158–160
Compat 167
Crystallinum 163
Jurapannosum 165–166
Pannosum 166–167
Polonicum 162
Redcliffense 163
Jeanne d'Arc Basin 493
Telford Field 1084
West Central Shelf 881–882
see also TEMFS
Median Volcanic Ridge **42**
Mercia Mudstone Group 203, 207, 447, 1157, 1384, 1386
Mexborough Rock 748–752
micropalaeontology, role in correlation 155
Mid North Sea Dome 136
Mid North Sea High 171
Chalk Group
erosion 175–177
seismic analysis 171–175
Mid-Cimmerian unconformity 117
Mid-Faeroe Ridge 1253
migration of hydrocarbons 1225, *1308*
modelling characteristics
inputs 1330–1333
outputs 1336–1338
regions modelled
Atlantic margin 1360–1361
Faeroe Shetland White Zone 608–610
NE Rockall Basin 387–388
Rona Sandstone 623–624
West Shetland 1377
Miller Field 1199–1200
depositional setting 1203–1204
heterogeneity evaluation 1205–1207
palaeogeography 1205
reservoir modelling 1200
architecture 1201–1202
lithology 1202
Millstone Grit Formation **474**, 800, 809, 811, *813*, 816
Minches Basin **475**, 476
source rocks *480*
mineralogy
Carboniferous sediment provenance 783–784, 785
chalk 926
Kangerlussuaq Basin sandstones *344*
see also heavy mineralogy
minibasins 886–887, 1008
Miocene
inversion, North Atlantic margin 52–53
sediments
Faeroe Shetland White Zone 604–605
Norwegian Sea 296, 300
Rockall Trough 418
Slyne Trough 445
Mississauga Formation 503
Mjød prospect 956
Modgunn Arch **42**, 264
Mohns Ridge **42**
Moine Thrust 10, **42**
Mokami Formation 510, 511
Monan Field
development 993–994
reservoir **994**, 999
Montrose Field 1125, 1128, 1129
Montrose Group *172*, 176, 177
Moray Firth *65*, *71*, 1093
see also Captain Field; Inner Moray Firth; Outer Moray Firth
Moray Group *172*, 176, 177, *1369*
Møre Basin 8, *10*, 21, 34, **42**
Cenozoic development
sedimentary breaks 295–298
sedimentary units 298–300
sequence stratigraphy 300–302
structural setting 293–294
tectonic history 302–303
hydrocarbon prospectivity 269–270
magmatism 272
palaeogeography
Cretaceous 267–268
Jurassic 265–267
Tertiary 268–269
prospectivity **227**
stratigraphy 262–263
structural evolution *56*, 236–237, 263–265
tectonic setting 261–262
thermal history 270–271
Møre-Trøndelag Fault Zone 10, **42**, 46
Morecambe Fields 207
Motel Model 652
multi-layer generation and migration modelling *1308*
multilateral drilling 1070
Mungo Field
development 993–994
reservoir **994**, 996–999
Munkegrunnur Ridge *392*, *559*, *602*
Murdoch Field *793*, *794*, 800
ribbon interpretation 796–797
Murre East Fault 519–520, 523
Murre Fault 519–520, 523

Naglfar Dome **42**, 264–265, 323
Namurian stratigraphy
palaeovalley systems 766
regional basins
Appalachian Basin 760, 763

Eastern Interior Basin 764
Euramerican basins *758*, *761*
European Basin 764–765
Maritimes Basin 765–766
Ouachita Basin 764
Southern North Sea Basin *772*
sandbody classification *760*
Trent Field 811, *813*, 816
Nansen Formation 1235
Nautilus Fault 521, 525
Neogene rifting and uplift 53–56
Neptune Formation 672
Ness Fault Zone 383
Ness Formation 93, 102, 1043, **1064**, 1065–1066, 1070, 1177
Ness Lineament 392
net : gross ratio **1130**
Netherlands
pop-up structure 222–223
pull-apart basin 221–222
Nevis Field 1051
horizontal well project
application of VSP 1055
evaluation 1060
perforating 1059–1060
pilot result 1055–1057
reservoir simulation 1054
well planning
method 1054–1055
results 1058–1059
stratigraphy 1053–1054
structure 1051–1052
Newfoundland Grand Banks 501
basin structure and potential 501–509
Jurassic palaeogeography *490*
see also Hibernia Field
Newfoundland 511–514
see also Labrador Shelf
Niaqornaariuk type oil 312–313
Nise Formation 278, 282
nitrogen in gas 800, 804–805
Nokken prospect 1221
Nordfjord-Sogn Detachment **42**
Nordkapp Basin **42**
Nordland Ridge **42**, 83–86, 671
salt tectonic effects 86–89
North Anatolian Fault 147
North Brook Formation 513
North Buchan Graben 856
North Claymore Field 873
North Halibut Basin *862*, 863–865
North Halibut Graben 853, 856
North Mayo Basin 409
North Minch Basin *404*
North Morecambe Field 1383
North Permian Basin *see* North Sea (Central)
North Porcupine Basin *404*
North Rona Basin *602*
North Sea 293
charge models 1323–1324
pressure models 1320–1323
Tertiary sequence well ties 1268–1270
thermal models 1317–1318
triple junction area
thermal doming 117–118
unconformities 117–118
North Sea (Central)
major graben *1030*
salt tectonic control on inversion 191–195
salt tectonic control on sedimentation
Cretaceous 191
Jurassic 187–190
Tertiary 181
Triassic 182–185
seismic sections *1030–1033*
stratigraphy
Jurassic 186
Permian 179–181
Tertiary 190–191
Triassic 181
structural development 1030–1033
experimental analogue 1033
see also Arkwright Field; Britannia Field Central Graben;
Fife Field; Fulmar Formation
North Sea (Danish Sector) 897, *898*
see also South Arne Field; Gertrud Graben
North Sea (North)
structural evolution 232
see also Beryl Embayment; Brent Field; Tampen Spur; Tern Field; Viking Graben
North Sea (Norwegian) *see* Edda Field; Ekofisk Field; Norwegian Central Graben
North Sea Rift
evolution model 75
regional setting 63–64
sub-basins *65*
North Sea (South) 772–773, 796–797
Dinantian stratigraphy 729–730, *731*, *732*, *735*, *736*, *738*
basin structure 730–733, *734*
depositional model 740–742
reservoirs 735–740
sand body geometry 743–744
sedimentary history 733–735
Upper Carboniferous
incised valley fill reservoir properties 785
lithostratigraphy *773*
Westphalian sand bodies 754–755
see also Leman Field
North Westray Ridge *602*
Northeast Rockall Basin (NERB) 391
chronostratigraphy 404
crustal structure 401
gravity modelling 379–382
magnetic modelling 382
modelling hydrocarbon potential 387–389
stratigraphy 398–401
structure 382–383, 386, 392–398
tectonic evolution 402
Tertiary sequence stratigraphy 387
volcanism 401
Northwest European Gas Atlas project 798
Norwegian Central Graben *898*, *1326*
modelling characteristics
inputs
hydrocarbon expulsion 1330
hydrocarbon generation 1327, 1330
hydrocarbon migration 1330–1333
source rocks 1325–1327
outputs 1333–1338
Norwegian Central Trough 71
Norwegian Continental margin *84*
see also Vøring Basin *also* Møre Basin
Norwegian Sea *see* Nyk High
Nuussuaq Basin 305–306
exploration history 306
seepage studies
analysis 308
characterization of oil 309–313
recognition 306–308
Nyk High 263, 264, 323
reservoir/play behaviour 278–280
seismic evaluation 275–278
structural setting 275

Olga Basin 248–249
Oligocene
inversion, North Atlantic margin 52
sediments
Irish Rockall Trough 437
Northeast Rockall Basin 400
Norwegian Sea 296, 298
Rockall Trough 418
Slyne Trough 445
opal reflector 270–271
Ophiomorpha 880, 1093, 1094, 1190, 1191, **1213**
Orcadian Basin **647**
Ordovician reservoir rocks 513
Ormen Lange Dome **42**
Orphan Basin **42**
Oslo Graben **42**
Otter Bank Fault *694*, *695*
Otter Bank Sandstone **695**, 701–704, **710**
Otter Bank Shale **695**
Ouachita Basin 764
Outer Hebrides Fault Zone **42**
Outer Isles Thrust 8
Outer Moray Firth *65*, *124*
fault seals 863
Jurassic tectonics 858
Paleocene uplift 175
reservoir geology 862
stratigraphy *862*
structural setting 843–846
trap geometry and integrity 875–877
Lowlander area 868, *872*
North Halibut Basin 863–865
Scott area 870, 873, *874*
South Piper area 865
Tartan area 865–868, *869*, *871*
see also Humber Group; Telford Field
Outer Ridge Complex *505*, 507
overpressure 1318–1319
Central Graben 1341–1342
exploration risk 1226–1230
Faeroe Shetland White Zone 607–608
modelling 1320–1323

P waves *see* seismic waves
Pabba Shale **475**
Pabba Shale Formation 446, 482
palaeogeography
Carboniferous *733*, *737*, *799*
Cretaceous 267–268, 670–672
Jurassic 1205
Central North Sea Trough *74*
Grand Banks *490*
Norwegian Sea 265–267
Porcupine Basin *477*
Slyne Trough *452*
Mesozoic, Irish Rockall Trough *436*
Tertiary 268–269, *552*
Palaeophycus 1191, **1213**
palaeotemperature analysis *619*
palaeovalley systems *see* incised valley fill
Paleocene
compression, Faeroe–Shetland Basin 541–542
facies analysis, Kangerlussuaq Basin *339*, 342–344
igneous activity, West of Shetland 650
inversion tectonics 175
magmatism, North Atlantic margin 51–52
migration, Norwegian Central Graben 1336–1338
palaeogeography, Irish Rockall Trough *436*
reservoir rocks 693, 993, 996, 999
Arkwright Field 1125, 1302
Faeroe–Shetland Basin 237, 556, 628
Greenland (West) 321–323
Labrador Shelf 511
Schiehallion Field 683
West of Shetland 653–656
rifting, Faeroe–Shetland Basin 538–541
seal rocks, West of Shetland 656
sediments
Faeroe Shetland White Zone 603–604
Irish Rockall Trough 437
North Sea (Central) 1348
Northeast Rockall Basin 400
Norwegian Sea 295, 298
Rockall Trough 415–417
sequence stratigraphy, West Shetland 1368–1371
source rocks, Vøring Basin 236

Paleocene (*continued*)
  stratigraphy
    Atlantic margin (North) 231
    Banff Field 982
    Faeroe Basin 627–628
    Foula Sub-basin 664–665
    West of Shetland 649
  tectonics
    Banff Field 977–978
    North Atlantic *25*, *32*
    West of Shetland 650
palynology, role in correlation 155
Papa Basin *602*, **647**, *694*, 701
Papa Group *1369*
Papa High *602*
Paris Basin **474**
Pennine Basin 764–765, *778*, 817
Pennine coalfield 748–754
Pentland Formation 119, *121*, *126*, 153, 156, 1002, 1014, 1021–1022, 1030, *1031*, 1078
permeability
  Arkwright reservoir **1130**
  Brae Formation 1207
  chalk 926
  Ekofisk Formation 1150
  fault gouge 1179
  Piper Formation 1081
  Tilje/Åre formations *1215*
  see also porosity *v*. permeability
Permian
  reservoir rocks
    Barents Sea 252–254
    Leman Field 1299
  seal rocks, Leman Field 1299
  sediments, Slyne Trough 447
  source rocks, Barents Sea 250
  stratigraphy
    Central North Sea 179–181
    Elgin/Franklin Fields 1008
    Trent Field 812, *813*
  tectonics and palaeogeography
    North Atlantic *13*, 19–20
    West of Shetland 647
Permo-Triassic
  extension and rifting
    Faeroe–Shetland Basin 533–535
    North Atlantic margin 46–47
    North Sea 63–64
    Witch Ground Graben 136
  plays, Irish Rockall Trough 442
  sediments
    Rockall Trough and NE Basin 399, 415, 427, 435
Perth Field 863
petrography, Paleocene sandstone 689
petroleum systems 231
  Atlantic margin (North) 242–243
  success/failure analysis 657–658
petrophysical analysis, Arkwright reservoir **1130**
Phoebichnus 1191
Phycosiphon 1141, 1142, 1189
phyllosilicates in fault gouge 1179
Pijnacker Field 222, *223*
Piper Field 149, 847, 851, 865
Piper Shelf 119–120
Planolites 966, 968, 1141, 1191, **1213**
plate tectonic reconstructions
  North Atlantic margin 48
  Northeast Rockall Basin 402, *403*
  Rockall Trough 361–362
    modelling 368–369
    plate boundaries 362–364
    poles of rotation 364
    rigid plate method 364
    stretching data 366–368
plateau basalts, West of Shetland 650
Pleistocene of Norwegian Sea 296–298, 302
Plio-Pleistocene of NE Rockall Basin 401
Pliocene sediments
  Faeroe Shetland White Zone 605
  Norwegian Sea 296, 302
pods *see* minibasins
Poisson's ratio 1290
pop-up structures 215, 222–223
  modelling behaviour 216–221
Porcupine Bank 411
Porcupine Basin **42**, *404*, 472–473, **474**, **475**
  facies analysis 496
  oil geochemistry 477–479
  palaeogeography *477*
  prospectivity **227**
  sedimentation 491–492, 494–496
  source rock correlations 477–485
  structural evolution *56*, 242
  tectonic history 488–491
  tectonostratigraphy *476*
Porcupine Seabight Basin *392*
porosity
  Arkwright reservoir **1130**
  chalk 924–925
  Chalk Group *973*
  depth relationship, chalk 1223
  Ekofisk Formation 1150
  Fulmar Sandstone 1340–1341
    diagenetic effects 1345–1346
  Piper Formation 1081
  relation to seismic response of chalk 939, 940–943
    effect of fluid 944–945
    Tor Formation study 945–947
  Tilje/Åre formations *1215*
porosity depth cube 956
porosity *v*. permeability *719*, *742*, *970*, *972*
Portree Shale Formation 446, **475**, 482
Präsident Sandstone *779*, *782*
pressure models 1320–1323
principal displacement zones (PDZ) 215
pristane/phytane ratio 309, 310, 311, 312
Protogine Zone **42**
pseudo-acoustic impedance 1067
Puffin High 123, *126*
pull-apart basins 215, 221–222
  modelling behaviour 216–217
Pyrenean phase 915
pyroclastics, West of Shetland 650–651

quartz in fluid inclusion analysis 620, 621–622
Quaternary of Captain Ridge 1104

Rankin Fault 521, 525
Rankin Field **475**
Rankin Formation 484, 491, 492, 505–506, 507
Rannoch Formation 93, 103, 1043, **1064**, 1066, 1070, 1177
RAPIDS 422
Rås Basin 263, 264
Rattray Volcanics Formation *121*, 1078
Raude Formation 1053
Rauen-Witten Quarry *774*
ray-trace (path) migration modelling *1307*, 1308
Redshin Quarry (Northumberland) 739–740, *743*
releasing/restraining step-over *216*
reservoir properties 921–929, 1025
  see also porosity *also* permeability
reservoir rocks
  Carboniferous 785
    Caister Field 725
    Newfoundland West 514
    North Sea (South) 735–740
    Southern Permian Basin 800
    Trent Field 816
  Cretaceous 993
    Britannia Field 1115–1119
    Captain Field 1104
    Central Graben 1225
    Helland Hansen licence 282–284
    Labrador Shelf 510, 511
    Newfoundland Grand Banks 503–504, 506, 507, 508, 518
    North Sea (North) 232
    Norwegian Sea 278, 279–280
    Vøring Basin 323
  Cretaceous/Paleocene, Greenland (West) 321–323
  Devonian/Carboniferous, Faeroe–Shetland Basin 661
  Jurassic
    Beryl Formation 1054
    Brae Formation 1200
    Brent Field 93
    Elgin/Franklin Field 1008
    Faeroe–Shetland Basin 661
    Fife Field 1138
    Fulmar Formation 1089, 1090, 1340
    North Sea (North) 232
    Solan Field 705–706
    Telford Field 1080–1086
    Tern Field 1063, 1064, 1065–1066
    Tilje/Åre formations 1211–1216
  Jurassic/Cretaceous, Barents Sea 252–254
  Ordovician, Newfoundland West 513
  Paleocene 993
    Arkwright Field 1125, 1302
    Faeroe Basin 628
    Faeroe–Shetland Basin 556
    Machar/Monan/Mungo fields 996, 999
    Schiehallion Field 683
    Vøring Basin 236
    West of Shetland 653–656, 693
  Permian, Leman Field 1299
  Triassic 993
    East Irish Sea Basin 1384, 1386, *1387*
    Faeroe–Shetland Basin 661
    Marnock Field 994
    Strathmore Field 700–704
    Tern Field 1066
    Wytch Farm Field 1157
residual salt analysis 1129
resistivity *632*, *633*
Revfallet fault 83, *88*
Rhizocorallium 1191, **1213**
Ribban Basin 263
ribbon interpretation 792–795
rift-raft tectonics 201, *202*, *203*
rifting events 53–56
  Faeroe–Shetland Basin 536–538
  NE Greenland 327–329
  North Sea 63–64
Roan Sandstone **695**, 704–705
Rockall Centre 581
Rockall Trough 8, **42**, 359–360, 371, 391, 585–586
  basin model 428–430
  Caledonian Front 9
  chronostratigraphy *404*
  crustal structure 422–424
  forward modelling basin geometry
    method 373–375
    results 375–377
  gravity survey 427–428
  heat flow modelling
    method 588–589
    results 589–591
  Jurassic tectonics 21
  plate tectonic reconstructions 361–362
    modelling 368–369
    plate boundaries 362–364
    poles of rotation 364
    rigid plate method 364
    stretching data 366–368
  prospectivity **227**
  rifting history
    crustal structure 372, *374*
    gravity anomalies 373
    stratigraphy 373
  sediment sequence 424–427

seismic survey 422
structural evolution *56*, 239–240
underplating 586–588
Rockall Trough Intrusive Complex 579
Rockall Trough (Irish sector) 433
crust 434
crustal features 412–414
modelling evolution 439–439
palaeogeography *436*
perched basins 409–412
petroleum potential 440–444
stratigraphy 434–437
stretching factor 414
structure 407–409, 437–439
tectonostratigraphy 415–418
Rona Fault 536
Rona Ridge 538, *602*, 613–614, 670, 672, *694*, *695*, 719
thermal history reconstruction
methodology 614–616
results 616–623
use in migration studies 623–624
Rona Sandstone Formation 535, 661
thermal history reconstruction
methodology 614–616
results 616–623
use in migration studies 623–624
Ror Formation 1210
Rosemary Bank **42**, *392*, 401
Rosemary Bank seamount 579, 586
Rossan Basin and Ridge 411
Rosselia 1191
Rost Basin **42**
Rotliegendes Group 812, 1008, *1031*, 1138, 1299, 1384
Rough Rock Group 765, 766, *774*
Ruhr District 773, *779*, *780*

S waves *see* seismic waves
Sabden shale 1384
Saglek Basin 509
Saglek Formation 510
St George Group 513
St Kilda Centre 580
salt, role in rift-raft tectonics 201, 205
salt chimneys 886
salt domes, effect on heat flow 1316
salt minibasins 886–887
salt tectonics
Banff Field 977
Central North Sea 63–64, 66–68, 79, 182–191, 1033
Nordland Ridge 86–89
North Sea Rift 63–64
Saltire Field 854, 865
sandbox modelling 1033
Scalpa Sandstone Formation 446
Scandian trend 135
Scapa Field 873
Schaubcylindrichnus 1189
Schiehallion Field 645, 683–684, 693
development 691
gas management 691–692
history 684
reservoir properties 686–691
reservoirs 657
seal rocks 686
seismic data 684–685
structure 685–686
trap type 686
Scott Field 870, 873, *874*
Scremerston Coal Formation **475**, 736–740
Sea of the Hebrides Basin **42**, 353
sea-level change
Carboniferous 752, 757, 766
Cretaceous 334–335
seal rocks 148, 863, 1129, 1331, 1332
Cretaceous 929, 931
Fife Field 1138
Fulmar Field 1093
Jurassic
Brent Field 93
Fife Field 1138
Fulmar Formation 1089, 1090
Labrador Shelf 511
Nevis Field 1054
Paleocene
Arkwright Field 1302
West of Shetland 656
Permian, Leman Field 1299
Schiehallion Field 686
Triassic
East Irish Sea Basin 1384, 1386–1387
Wytch Farm Field 1157
seaward dipping reflector sequences (SDRS) 578
seepage studies
Anticosti Basin 511
Nuussuaq Basin 308–313
seismic imaging
acquisition 1255–1256
processing 1256–1260
results 1260–1261
results discussed 1261–1264
seismic interpretation 795–797, 1243–1245
facies 899
ribbon correlation 792–795
workflow 790–792
seismic inversion 928–929, 1271–1280
Beryl Embayment 1282–1287
Brent Field 1047–1048
Tern Field 1067–1068
seismic properties of chalk 940–943
effect of fluid 944–945
Tor Formation study 945–947
seismic sections
Arkwright Field *1128*, *1302*
Brent Field 95, *1239*
Central North Sea *1031*
East Midlands oilField *753*
Elgin Field *1010*
Erris Trough *459*
Faeroe–Shetland Basin *550*, *551*
Fladen Ground Spur *139*, *146*
Franklin Field *1011*
Fulmar Field *1093*
Gertrud Graben *899*
Greater Shearwater *161*
Helland Hansen licence *287*
Jaeren High *1304*
Leman Field *1300*
Murdoch Field *793*
Nevis Field *1053*
Northeast Rockall Basin *395*
Revfallet fault *88*
Rockall Trough *425*, *426*, *427*
Shetland–Faeroes Basin *1253*
Slyne Trough *449*, *450*
Snorre-H Basin *833*, *834*, *835*
Solan Field *699*
South Arne Field *969*, *972*
Southern North Sea *180*
Strathmore Field *697*
Strathspey Field *1238*, *1239*
Telford Field *1077*
Trent gasfield *815*
Victory Field *716*
West Central Shelf *180*
Witch Ground Graben *139*, *143*, *147*
seismic sections Keys Fault *208*
Central Graben *212*
Fisher Bank Basin *212*
seismic waves
conversion 1243, 1257–1259
velocity crossplots *1268*
velocity ratio 1290
Sele Formation 1302
s.e.m., Paleocene sandstone *631*
Senja Fracture Zone **42**, 46
Senja Ridge **42**
Sentralbanken High 250
sequence boundary defined 1084
sequence seismostratigraphy 284
sequence stratigraphy 154
Carboniferous, Trent Field *819*
Jurassic
Fife Field 1142–1143
Greater Shearwater 157–167
Telford Field 1078–1080
West Central Shelf 881–886
Tertiary
NE Rockall Basin 387
Norwegian Sea 300–302
West Shetland 1368–1371
Seymore Field 210
Sgiath Formation 127
shale gouge ratio 1179, *1182*
Shallow Bay Formation 512
Shearwater prospect
appraisal 1021–1022
development 1024–1026
feasibility study 1022–1024
Sherwood Sandstone Group 447, **474**, 1157
age 1388–1389
hydrocarbon migration modelling
method 1390–1392
results 1392–1395
results discussed 1395–1397
reservoir properties 1384, 1386, *1387*
Shetland Group 915, 916, 917, *1369*
hydrocarbon system 931–932
palaeoenvironment analysis 917–921
porosity/permeability analysis *928*
Shetland Spine fault 536, *602*
Shetland, West 613–614
amplitude *versus* offset (AVO) case study
anisotropy 639–641
conventional model compared 641
pre-drill model 635–636
walkaway vertical seismic profile 638–639
well data 636–638
evolution 647–650
exploration history 645–646
reservoir rocks 653–656
seal rocks 656
source rocks 651–653
thermal history reconstruction
methodology 614–616
results 616–623
use in migration studies 623–624
trap structure 656
see also Foinaven Field
Shetland–Faeroes Basin 1253
shoreface sediments 1093
Sigmundur Centre 579
sill complexes, North Atlantic LIP 578–579
Siphonichnus 1191
Skagerrak Formation 185–186, 203, 1002, 1008
reservoir model 1002–1004
Skolithos 1141, 1191, **1213**
Skua Field 1324
development 993–994
reservoir **994**, 1002
Sleipner Formation 119
slurry flow 1116–1117
Slyne Trough **42**, *404*, 410, 476
plate tectonic setting 451–452
prospectivity **227**
section restoration 448–451
source rocks *480*, *481*
stratigraphy 445–447
structural evolution 240–242
structure 448
smear-gouge ratios 526
Smith Bank Formation 203, 880, 886, 1008, 1138
Snakes Bight Formation 513
Snoevit Field **474**
Snorre fault block and horst 109

Sola Formation 1117
Solan Basin *602*, **647**, 1377
Solan Field
appraisal 696
discovery 696
maturation history 711
reservoir rocks 705–706
source rocks 711
trap structure 696–699
Solan Sandstone **695**, 704–706, **710**
Sorvestlandet High 897
Sorvestnaget Basin **42**
source rocks 355–356, 476–485, 1325–1327
Cambro-Ordovician, Newfoundland West 512–513
Carboniferous
East Irish Sea Basin 1384
Erris Trough 463–464
Newfoundland West 513
Southern Permian Basin 798–800
Trent Field 814
Cretaceous, Labrador Shelf 511
Jurassic
Atlantic margin 1354
Central Graben 931, 1225
Erris Trough 464
Hebrides Basin 476, *480*
Irish Rockall Trough 440
Jeanne d'Arc Basin 473, *480*
Kimmeridge Clay 1340
Minches Basin 476, *480*
NE Rockall Basin 387
Newfoundland Grand Banks 502, 505, 507, 509
Norwegian Central Graben 1325, 1333
Porcupine Basin 242, 472, *480*
Slyne Trough 476, *480*
West of Shetland 651–653
West Shetland 1377
Jurassic/Cretaceous
Barents Sea 250–252
Faeroe–Shetland Basin 237
Halten terrace 233
North Sea (North) 232
Rockall Trough 240
South Arne Field
appraisal 961–964
exploration 959–961
reservoir character 965–968
reservoir fracturing 968–969
reservoir prediction 969–974
seismic section *969*
structural setting 964–965
trap mechanism 974–975
South Brae Field 1200
South Halibut Trough 123, *125*
South Morecambe Field 1383, 1387
South Scott Field 149
South Solan Basin *694*
South Viking Graben 119–120, *122*
South Wales Basin lithostratigraphy *778*
South Whale Sub-basin 501–504, *505*
Southern Permian Basin
Carboniferous rocks 798–800
gases 800–805
Spekk Formation 267
Staffin Bay Formation **475**
Stappen High 249
Statfjord East *see* Tampen Spur
Statfjord East Fault *837*
Statfjord Formation 1039, 1040, 1177, 1235
reservoir model 1043
Steensby Bjerg Formation 325
steranes **308**
Storegga Slide 237
Strathmore Field
appraisal 696
depositional environment 701
discovery 695–696
maturation history 711
reservoir rocks 700–704
fluid properties 706–711
source rocks 711
stratigraphy 700
trap structure 696–699
Strathspey Field 1039, 1235
vertical-cable seismic
method 1237–1238
results 1238–1240
stratigraphic geocellular model (SGM)
Brent Field
evaluation 1043–1045
inputs 1041, 1042, 1043
stretching factor (beta) 541
Faeroe–Shetland Basin 587
Irish Rockall Trough 414, 440
NE Greenland 326, 328
NE Rockall Basin 401
Rockall Trough 366–368, 373, 374, 375
strike-slip faults analogue modelling
method 216–217
results 217–220
results discussed 221–224
Stronsay Group *172*, 176, *1369*
strontium isotope analysis 1129
strontium residual salt analysis *632*
Suilen Field 693
Sula Sgeir Fault 536
Sula Sgeir High *602*
Sullom Formation 1368, *1370*
Surt Lineament **42**, 263, 264
Svalbard margin *404*
Svalbardian orogeny 250
Sverdrup Basin **42**
synthetic aperture profiling 1245

Table Head Group 513
Taconic orogeny 512
Taenidium **1213**
Tail End Graben *65*, *898*, *1030*
Tampen Spur 827
evolution 835–836
faulting 836–837
stratigraphy 827–828
Draupne Formation 829–835
structural framework 828–829
see also Zeta Structure
Tarbert Formation 93, 829, 1043, **1064**, 1177
Tartan Field 849, 865–868, *869*, *871*
tectonically enhanced maximum flooding surfaces (TEMFS) 857–858
Teichichnus 1141, 1142, 1191, **1213**
Telford Field 1075–1077
history of development 1077
reservoir engineering properties 1084–1086
reservoir geophysics 1081
reservoir zonation 1080–1081
sequence stratigraphy 1078–1080
stratal surfaces 1084
Telford Ridge 846
TEMFS (tectonically enhanced maximum flooding surfaces) 857–858
Terebellina 1189, 1190, 1191
Tern Field 1063–1064
reservoir rocks 1064–1066
seismic evaluation 1067–1068
well technology 1069–1074
terpanes **308**
Terra Nova Field **474**
Tertiary
lithospheric stretching 1250
palaeogeography, Norwegian Sea 268–269
plays
Irish Rockall Trough 443–444
Norwegian Sea 270
reservoirs, Barents Sea 256
sediments, Rockall Trough 424
stratigraphy, Central North Sea 190–191
tectonic history
Atlantic margin 1353–1354
West Central Shelf 892
Witch Ground Graben 137, 146
thermal history, Rona Ridge 616–618
uplift
East Irish Sea Basin 1387–1390
Faeroe–Shetland Basin 601
volcano complexes, North Atlantic 579–581
well ties, North Sea 1268–1270
Thalassinoides 1141, 1191, **1213**
thermal history reconstruction
methodology 349–350, 614–616
results 616–623
North Atlantic margin 351–354
Northern England 354–355
West Shetland 1374
results discussed 355–357
use in migration studies 623–624
thermal models 1317–1318
see also heat flow model
Theta Graben 845, 847, 853, 856
Thistle Field **474**
tidal facies 1191
Tiffany Field **474**
Tilje Formation 1209, 1210, **1213**
facies analysis 1214
reservoir geometry modelling 1211–1216
Tomma Formation **474**
Tommeliten Field 912, 913
Tor Field 912, 913
Tor Formation **474**, 915, 917, 920, *923*, *928*, *929*, 941, 975, 980
depositional model 952
fault controls on 952–953
porosity 1000
porosity depth cube 956
seismic response 945–947
South Arne Field 966–967, 969–970, *972*, 973
thickness 949, 950, 952
Tornquist Line 10, 135
trace fossils
Beryl Formation 1189–1268
South Arne Field 966, 968
Tilje/Åre formations **1213**
West Central Shelf 880
Trans-European Fault Zone 135
transformation ratio 1327–1330
transgressive systems tract (TST) 1210
trap structures 148, 875–877, 929–931
Barents Sea 252–254, 257
Elgin Field 1015
Faeroe–Shetland Basin 556–557
Franklin Field 1015–1018
Greenland (West) 323
Lowlander area 868, *872*
Machar Field 999
Marnock Field 994
Monan Field 999
Mungo Field 996
Newfoundland Grand Banks 507
North Halibut Basin 863–865
Scott area 870, 873, *874*
Solan Field 696–699
South Arne Field 974–975
South Piper area 865
Tartan area 865–868, *869*, *870*
Trent Field 814–816
Victory Field 715
Vøring Basin 323
West of Shetland 656
Trent gasfield 800, 809, *810*
depositional model 816–820
development drilling 809, 811
exploration history 809
geophysical data 814
reservoir rocks 816
seismic section *815*
source rocks 814
stratigraphy 811–814
trap structure 814

Triassic
lithostratigraphy
Irish Sea *206*
North Sea *206*
minibasins, West Central Shelf 886–887
reservoir rocks 993, 994
Banks Group 1235
Barents Sea 254, 256
East Irish Sea Basin 1384, 1386, *1387*
Faeroe–Shetland Basin 661
Statfjord Formation 1039
Strathmore Field 700–704
Tern Field 1066
Wytch Farm Field 1157
seal rocks, Wytch Farm Field 1157
sediments
North Sea 202–204
Slyne Trough 446–447
source rocks, Barents Sea 250
stratigraphy
Atlantic margin (North) 231
Central North Sea 181
Elgin/Franklin Fields 1008
Trent Field 814
tectonics and palaeogeography 212–213
Banff Field 977
North Atlantic *15*, *16*, 19–20
West of Shetland 647
Trichichnus 1141
tritium tracers 1166–1167
Troena Basin 263, 264
Trømso Basin **42**
Trøndelag Platform 83, 261, 263
tuffs of West of Shetland 650–651
turbidites 902–903, 1093, 1116

unconformities
Base Cretaceous 1014
Cimmerian 117, 136
Hardegsen 203, 213
Hercynian 447
North Sea Jurassic 117–118
areal extent 119–123
causal mechanisms 127–129
stratigraphic resolution 118–119
underplating, Rockall–Faeroe–Shetland area 586–588
Unst Basin **42**
upscaling problems 1044–1045
Uralian orogeny 250
USA *see* Appalachian basin; Eastern Interior Basin; Ouachita Basin
Utgard High 264
Utrost Ridge 263
Utsira Formation 302
Utsira High *122*

Vaila Formation 1369, *1370*
Valhall Field 912, 913, 914, 941, 949
chalk core details 952
cross section *954*
stratal thicknesses 952–953
stratigraphy 949–951
structure 951–952
Valhall Formation 1104, *1105*, 1117
Van Mijenforden Group 256
Variscan Foreland 773, *779*, *780*
Variscan Front **42**
Vema Dome **42**, 265, 323
Verril Canyon Formation 502
vertical seismic profile 1055
vertical-cable seismic 1236–1237
future potential 1240–1242
use in Strathspey Field
method 1237–1238
results 1238–1240
Veslemøy High **42**
Vestbakken Volcanic Province **42**
Vestfjorden Basin **42**, 263
Victory Field 645, 661
exploration history 713
reservoir properties
charge model 722–723
depositional environment 719
hydrocarbons 721
lithology 715–719
quality 720–721
stratigraphy 713–714
structure 714–715
Victory Formation 715, *717*, *718*, **720**
Victory Ridge *602*
Victory Transfer **42**, *602*
Viking Graben *10*, **42**, *65*, 232, **474**, 1347–1348
see also Beryl Embayment; Miller Field; Nevis Field; Tampen Spur
Villeperdue Field **474**
vitrinite reflectance (VR) 349–350, 614–617
Kimmeridge Clay of West Shetland *1375*
North Atlantic margin studies 351–354
Norwegian Sea *270*
Southern Permian Basin 800
volcaniclastics 581
volcano complexes 579–581
Vøring Basin **42**
exploration history 317–318
geological evolution 319–320
hydrocarbon prospectivity 269–270
magmatism 272
palaeogeography
Cretaceous 267–268
Jurassic 265–267
Tertiary 268–269
prospectivity **227**
reservoir rocks 323
stratigraphy 262–263
structural evolution *56*, 233–236, 263–265
tectonic setting 261–262
thermal history 270–271
trap types 323
see also Helland Hansen licence; Nyk High
Vøring Marginal High **42**
Vøring Plateau 8
Voyager Formation **475**

Walls Boundary Fault *602*
Watts Bight Formation 513
Weald inversion 176
well technology development 1069–1074
methodology 1265
results 1268–1270
Wessex Basin 176
West Central Graben 123, *125*
salt tectonics 185
West Central Shelf 880
effects of salt 890–892
Jurassic provenance study 889–890
seismic analysis 886–889
sequence stratigraphy 881–886
stratigraphy 880–881
Tertiary folding 892
West Ekofisk 912, 913
West Fladen Basin 847, 848, 849
West Flannan Basin 386
West Halibut Basin 1102
West Jan Mayen Fracture Zone **42**
West Lewis Basin 384–385, *396*, 399
West Lewis High 386
West Lewis Ridge *396*, 397–398
West Orkney Basin 351–352
West of Shetland
basin modelling
method 1373–1374
results 1374–1377
formation pressures 1371–1373
structural setting 1367–1368
Tertiary sequence stratigraphy 1368–1371
West Shetland Basin **42**, *602*, **647**, *694*
chronostratigraphy *404*
thermal history reconstruction 352–353
West Shetland Platform *694*
West Solan Basin *694*
West Spitzbergen orogen **42**
West Suduroy 580
Western Graben *1030*
Western Platform 75
Westphalian
North Sea (South) 754–755, *772*
Pennine/East Midlands 748–754
Westray Field 854
Westray Group *1369*
Westray Ridge **42**, 536, *602*, *646*, 647, 651, 653, 672, *694*, 1377
Westray Transfer Zone **42**, *602*
Whale Basin 501
Whitehurst Group *817*
Wick Sandstone Formation 1104, 1105
wide aperture recording 1245
Witch Ground Graben *120*, *122*, **475**, 856, *1030*
Base Cretaceous mapping 137–138
modelling structural evolution
Cretaceous 143–146
Jurassic 138–143
Tertiary 146
models discussed 147–149
petroleum potential 133, 148–149
seismic studies *139*, *143*, *146*, *147*
stratigraphy 133–135
structure 135–137
see also Britannia Field
Wytch Farm Field **474**
discovery 1157–1158
infill drilling 1169–1170
reservoir characterization 1159–1160
formation evaluation 1163–1165
miscible gas injection 1170–1171
petrophysics 1163
pressure 1165
production logging 1165–1166
structure 1160–1161
tritium tracing 1166–1167
use of deviated wells 1167–1169
Wyville-Thompson Ridge **42**, 384, 392–395, *602*
evolution 395–397, 399

XRD *339*, 916

Yermak Plateau 255
Ymir Ridge **42**, *392*, 397

Zechstein basins of Europe *205*
Zechstein Group 174, **695**, 1008, 1138, 1299, 1384
salt tectonics 1032, 1033
Trent Field 812
Zeta Fault and Ridge 111–113
Zeta Structure
footwall uplift 109–111
tectonic setting 107–108
Zoepritz equation 1289
Zoophycus 968